Henry Gray

HENRY GRAY, F.R.S., F.R.C.S.

As the readers of Gray's *Anatomy* may be interested to learn something of its original author, Henry Gray, the following information as to his career has been extracted from an article which appeared in the *St. George's Hospital Gazette* of May 21, 1908.

Gray, whose father was private messenger to George IV, and also to William IV, was born in 1827, but of his childhood and early education nothing is known.

On May 6, 1845, he entered as a perpetual student at St. George's Hospital, London, and he is described by those who knew him as "a most painstaking and methodical worker, and one who learned his anatomy by the slow but invaluable method of making dissections for himself."

While still a student he secured, in 1848, the triennial prize of the Royal College of Surgeons for an essay entitled, "The Origin, Connections and Distribution of the Nerves to the Human Eye and Its Appendages, Illustrated by Comparative Dissections of the Eye in Other Vertebrate Animals."

At the early age of twenty-five he was, in 1852, elected a Fellow of the Royal Society, and in the following year he obtained the Astley Cooper prize of three hundred guineas for a dissertation, "On the Structure and Use of the Spleen."

He held successively the posts of demonstrator of anatomy, curator of the museum, and lecturer on anatomy at St. George's Hospital, and was in 1861, a candidate for the post of assistant surgeon. Unfortunately he was struck down by an attack of confluent smallpox, which he contracted while looking after a nephew who was suffering from that disease, and died at the early age of thirty-four. A career of great promise was thus untimely cut short. Writing on June 15, 1861, Sir Benjamin Brodie (to whom the first edition of this work was dedicated) said, "His death, just as he was on the point of obtaining the reward of his labors . . . is a great loss to the Hospital and School."

In 1858 Gray published the first edition of his *Anatomy* which covered 750 pages and contained 363 figures. He had the good fortune to secure the help of his friend, Dr. H. Vandyke Carter, a skilled draughtsman and formerly a demonstrator of anatomy at St. George's Hospital. Carter made the drawings from which the engravings were executed, and the success of the book was, in the first instance, undoubtedly due in no small measure to the excellence of its illustrations. A second edition was prepared by Gray and published in 1860.

The frontispiece of Gray is a reproduction of one which appeared in the *St. George's Hospital Gazette* of May 21, 1908, where the original is described as being "a very faded photograph taken by Mr. Henry Pollock, second son of the late Lord Chief Baron Sir Frederick Pollock, and one of the earliest members of the Photographic Society of London."

ANATOMY

OF

THE HUMAN BODY

BY

HENRY GRAY, F.R.S.

*Late Fellow of the Royal College of Surgeons; Lecturer on Anatomy at St. George's
Hospital Medical School, London*

TWENTY-FIFTH EDITION, EDITED BY

CHARLES MAYO GOSS, M.D.

*Managing Editor of the Anatomical Record; Professor of Anatomy,
Louisiana State University School of Medicine,
New Orleans, Louisiana*

Illustrated with 1263 Engravings

LEA & FEBIGER

PHILADELPHIA

PRINTED IN U. S. A.

PREFACE TO THE TWENTY-FIFTH EDITION.

THE familiar aspect of Gray's Anatomy, known to generations of medical students and practicing physicians, has been retained in this edition. The text has been revised and illustrations replaced or added where research in the expanding science of anatomy has offered new material or new points of view. In addition to this, certain changes have been made which, it is hoped, will increase the acknowledged value of the book as a practical working text for students and teachers of anatomy.

Although there has been a return to the policy of entrusting the new edition to a single editor, the publishers and the editor wish to acknowledge with gratitude the contributions of the Associate Editors of the last edition: Earl T. Engle, The Ductless Glands; Joseph C. Hinsey, The Peripheral Nervous System, The Autonomic Nervous System; Normand L. Hoerr, Blood Vascular System; Karl E. Mason, Respiratory and Digestive Systems; David McK. Rioch, The Central Nervous System; Roy G. Williams, The Urogenital System. Their work has been left almost intact and it is with pleasure and confidence that the editor has relied upon their expert accomplishment. This applies also to the former editor in chief, Warren H. Lewis, and refers particularly to his work on Embryology.

The chapter on Muscles and Fasciae has received major attention. The arrangement of the muscles in regional sequence has been retained. The action and nerve supply are given for each muscle separately instead of in groups, and after each functional group a new paragraph has been added to point out the coordinated actions within the group. The muscle actions have been made very brief and include only carefully authenticated actions; they have been placed immediately after the descriptions of the muscles because of their intimate association with the position and attachments of the muscle.

The short preliminary general account of the fascia follows the plan of Bern B. Gallaudet, a former editor (1896 Edition). A terminology has been adopted which could be applied consistently to all parts of the body. This has caused occasional divergence from accepted nomenclature but confusion has been avoided by including synonyms in parentheses. Many of the descriptions are based upon the unpublished original research of the editor, and as much as possible of the contribution of recent investigators, especially Anson, Tobin and Benjamin, and Grodinsky and Holyoke has been included.

The lists of references at the ends of the chapters are much more extensive than in previous editions and are designed to stimulate the interest of the student in further reading. Many references may be used to expand and authenticate statements in the text, but many more are of value as collateral reading in fields other than anatomy. These lists are not intended to be comprehensive. The choice of references was governed, first, by a desire to have a recent article with a bibliography which would be an introduction to the field, and second, by a desire to introduce the names of as many contemporary anatomists as possible. It is hoped that this will make easier that important task of the teacher, to stimulate interest in original research and independent reading, since a student is drawn, almost invariably, toward bibliographies and independent reading after he finds the research of his teacher mentioned in his textbook.

The table of contents has been shortened because most of it seemed superfluous and especial care has been taken with the index to make it compensate for this omission.

It is a pleasure to thank the many friends and colleagues who have assisted the editor in his work of revision by pointing out errors or omissions and by sending reprints of articles which contain appropriate new material. Grateful acknowledgement is made to the artists: Joseph G. Cowell for the new illustrations of the sympathetic nervous system and William B. Stewart for drawings of the fasciæ made from photographs of dissections by the editor. Gratitude is also due John F. Huber for an illustration of the bronchopulmonary segments, to Charles E. Tobin for illustrations of the renal fascia, and to Martin Nordland for an illustration of the thyroid gland.

The editor is grateful for this opportunity to thank Dean Vernon W. Lippard for his friendly encouragement and the publishers for their generosity and confidence.

NEW ORLEANS   C. M. G.
JULY, 1948.

CONTENTS.

EMBRYOLOGY.

The Animal Cell
  Cytoplasm 17
  Nucleus 18
The Ovum 20
The Spermatozoön 22
Fertilization of the Ovum 24
Segmentation of the Fertilized Ovum . . 25
Implantation or Imbedding of Ovum . . 26
Fetal Membranes and Placenta 27

Development of Embryo from Inner Cell-
  mass 37
The Neural Groove and Tube 42
The Primitive Segments or Somites . . . 43
The Early Growth of the Embryo . . . 44
The Branchial Region. 45
Development of the Body Cavities . . . 52
Development of the Cerebrospinal Spaces . 55
The Growth of the Embryo 56

OSTEOLOGY.

Development of the Skeleton 59

BONE.
Structure and Physical Properties . . . 66
Ossification 70

THE VERTEBRAL COLUMN.
General Characteristics of a Vertebra. . . 75
  The Cervical Vertebræ 76
  The Thoracic Vertebræ 81
  The Lumbar Vertebræ 83
  The Sacral and Coccygeal Vertebræ . 85
Ossification of the Vertebral Column. . . 90
The Vertebral Column as a Whole . . . 93

THE THORAX.
The Sternum 97
The Ribs 101
The Costal Cartilages 105

THE SKULL.
The Exterior of the Skull 106
The Interior of the Skull 119
  Differences in the Skull Due to Age . 125
  Sex Differences, Function and Cleft
    Palate 127
The Mandible (Lower Jaw) 127
The Hyoid Bone 133
The Cranial Bones.
  The Occipital Bone 134
  The Parietal Bone 138
  The Frontal Bone 141
  The Temporal Bone 143
  The Sphenoid Bone 152
  Ethmoid Bone 157
  Sutural Bones 160

The Facial Bones.
  The Nasal Bones 160
  The Maxillæ (Upper Jaw) 162
  The Lacrimal Bone 168
  The Zygomatic Bone 168
  The Palatine Bone 170
  The Inferior Nasal Concha . . . 173
  The Vomer 174

THE EXTREMITIES.
The Bones of the Upper Extremity.
  The Clavicle 175
  The Scapula 178
  The Humerus 183
  The Ulna 189
  The Radius 194
The Hand. 196
  The Carpus 196
  The Metacarpus 202
  The Phalanges of the Hand . . . 205
The Bones of the Lower Extremity.
  The Hip Bone 206
  The Ilium 206
  The Ischium 209
  The Pubis 211
  The Acetabulum 212
  The Pelvis 213
  The Femur 217
  The Patella 230
  The Tibia 231
  The Fibula 235
The Foot. 237
  The Tarsus 237
  The Metatarsus 247
  The Phalanges of the Foot . . . 250
  Comparison of the Bones of the Hand
    and Foot 251
The Sesamoid Bones 252

JOINTS AND LIGAMENTS.

Development of the Joints 255
Classification of Joints 260
The Kinds of Movement Admitted in Joints 262

ARTICULATIONS OF THE TRUNK.
Articulations of the Vertebral Column . 263
  Articulations of Vertebral Bodies . 263
  Articulations of Vertebral Arches . 266
Articulation of the Atlas with the Epistro-
  pheus or Axis 268
Articulations of the Vertebral Column with
  the Cranium 272
Articulation of the Mandible 273

Costovertebral Articulations 275
  Articulations of the Heads of the Ribs . 275
  Costotransverse Articulations . . . 277
Sternocostal Articulations 278
Articulation of the Sternum 280
Mechanism of the Thorax 281
Articulation of the Vertebral Column with
  the Pelvis 282
Articulations of the Pelvis 282
Mechanism of the Pelvis 287

ARTICULATIONS OF THE UPPER EXTREMITY.
Sternoclavicular Articulation 289

Acromioclavicular or Scapuloclavicular
   Articulation, ... 291
The Ligaments of the Scapula . . . 292
Humeral Articulation or Shoulder-joint . . 293
Elbow-joint 297
Radioulnar Articulations 301
Radiocarpal Articulation or Wrist-joint . 303
Intercarpal Articulations 306
   Articulations of the Proximal Row of
     Carpal Bones 306
   Articulations of the Distal Row of
     Carpal Bones 306
   Articulations of the Two Rows of Carpal
     Bones with Each Other 307
Carpometacarpal Articulations 308

Intermetacarpal Articulations 309
Metacarpophalangeal Articulations . . . 309
Articulations of the Digits 311

THE ARTICULATIONS OF THE LOWER EXTREMITY.

Coxal Articulation or Hip-joint 311
The Knee-joint 317
Articulations between the Tibia and Fibula 325
Talocrural Articulation or Ankle-joint . . 327
Intertarsal Articulations 330
Tarsometatarsal Articulations 336
Intermetatarsal Articulations 336
Metatarsophalangeal Articulations . . . 337
Articulations of the Digits 338
Arches of the Foot 338

MUSCLES and FASCIÆ

Development of the Muscles 341
Structure of Muscle 343
Connective Tissues. 345
Tendons, Aponeuroses, ... 346
Fasciae 347
Muscle Action 351

THE MUSCLES AND FASCIÆ OF THE HEAD.

The Facial Muscles 352
The Muscles of Mastication 361

THE MUSCLES AND FASCIÆ OF THE ANTERO-
LATERAL REGION OF THE NECK.

The Superficial Cervical Muscle . . . 364
The Cervical Fasciæ 365
The Lateral Cervical Muscles 371
The Suprahyoid Muscles 371
The Infrahyoid Muscles 374
The Anterior Vertebral Muscles . . . 375
The Lateral Vertebral Muscles . . . 376

THE MUSCLES AND FASCIÆ OF THE TRUNK.

The Deep Muscles of the Back . . . 377
The Suboccipital Muscles 384
The Muscles of the Thorax 386
The Muscles and Fasciæ of the Abdomen. . 392
   The Antero-lateral Muscles of the Abdo-
     men 392
   The Posterior Muscles of the Abdomen 406
The Muscles and Fasciæ of the Pelvis . . 407
The Muscles and Fasciæ of the Perineum . 411
   The Muscles of the Urogenital Region
     in the Male 417
   The Muscles of the Urogenital Region in
     the Female 419
   Muscles of the Anal Region 421

THE MUSCLES AND FASCIÆ OF THE UPPER
EXTREMITY.

The Muscles Connecting the Upper Extrem-
   ity to the Vertebral Column . . . 422
The Muscles Connecting the Upper Extrem-
   ity to the Anterior and Lateral Thoracic
   Walls 426
The Muscles and Fasciæ of the Shoulder . 431
The Muscles and Fasciæ of the Arm . . 434
The Muscles and Fasciæ of the Forearm.
   The Volar Antibrachial Muscles . . 438
   The Dorsal Antibrachial Muscles . . 444
The Muscles and Fasciæ of the Hand . . 449
   The Thenar Muscles 459
   The Hypothenar Muscles 461
   The Intermediate Muscles 462

THE MUSCLES AND FASCIÆ OF THE LOWER
EXTREMITY.

The Muscles and Fasciæ of the Iliac Region 464
The Muscles and Fasciæ of the Thigh . . 466
   The Anterior Femoral Muscles . . 469
   The Medial Femoral Muscles . . . 471
   The Muscles of the Gluteal Region . . 473
   The Posterior Femoral Muscles . . 479
The Muscles and Fasciæ of the Leg. . . 480
   The Anterior Crural Muscles . . 480
   The Posterior Crural Muscles . . 483
   The Lateral Crural Muscles . . . 487
The Fasciæ Around the Ankle 489
The Muscles and Fasciæ of the Foot.
   The Dorsal Muscle of the Foot . . 491
   The Plantar Muscles of the Foot . . 491

THE BLOOD–VASCULAR SYSTEM.

DEVELOPMENT OF THE VASCULAR SYSTEM 502
The Development of the Heart . . . 504
Further Development of the Arteries . . 509
Further Development of the Veins . . . 515

STRUCTURE OF BLOOD VESSELS.

Structure of Arteries 521
Capillaries 522
Structure of Veins 524
The Blood 525
Red Corpuscles or Erythrocytes . . . 525
White Corpuscles or Leucocytes . . . 525

THE HEART

The Thoracic Cavity 527
The Pericardium. 528
   Structure of the Pericardium . . . 528
The Heart 530
   Component Parts 531
   Cardiac Muscular Tissue 544
Peculiarities in the Vascular System of the
   Fetus.
   Fetal Circulation 546
   Changes in the Vascular System at Birth 548

THE ARTERIES.

The Pulmonary Artery 553
The Aorta 553

THE ARTERIES OF THE HEAD AND NECK.

The Common Carotid Artery . . . 557
   The External Carotid Artery . . 559
   The Internal Carotid Artery . . . 570
The Arteries of the Brain 579

THE ARTERIES OF THE UPPER EXTREMITY.

The Subclavian Artery 580
The Axillary Artery 590
The Brachial Artery 595
The Radial Artery 598
The Ulnar Artery 602

THE ARTERIES OF THE TRUNK.

The Descending Aorta.
The Thoracic Aorta 605

The Abdominal Aorta 608
The Common Iliac Arteries 619
  The Hypogastric Artery 620
  The External Iliac Artery . . . 628
THE ARTERIES OF THE LOWER EXTREMITY.
The Femoral Artery 630

The Popliteal Artery 638
The Anterior Tibial Artery 641
The Arteria Dorsalis Pedis 642
The Posterior Tibial Artery 643

THE VEINS.

THE PULMONARY VEINS . . 650
THE SYSTEMIC VEINS
The Veins of the Heart 650
The Veins of the Head and Neck.
  The Veins of the Exterior of the Head
    and Face 652
  The Veins of the Neck 654
  The Diploic Veins 659
  The Veins of the Brain 660
  The Sinuses of the Dura Mater . . . 661
    The Emissary Veins 668
THE VEINS OF THE UPPER EXTREMITY
AND THORAX
The Superficial Veins of the Upper
  Extremity 668

The Veins of the Upper Extremity and
  Thorax—
    The Deep Veins of the Upper Extremity 671
    The Veins of the Thorax 673
  The Superior Vena Cava 674
  The Veins of the Vertebral Column . . 676
The Veins of the Lower Extremity, Abdomen,
  and Pelvis. 678
    The Superficial Veins of the Lower Ex-
      tremity 678
    The Deep Veins of the Lower Extremity 681
    The Veins of the Abdomen and Pelvis . 682
  The Inferior Vena Cava 685
THE PORTAL SYSTEM OF VEINS.
The Portal Vein 688

THE LYMPHATIC SYSTEM.

The Development of the Lymphatic Vessels 693
Lymphatic Capillary Plexuses . . . 694
Lymphatic Vessels 697
  Structure of Lymphatic Vessels . . 698
The Lymph Nodes 698
THE THORACIC DUCT . . . 700
The Right Lymphatic Duct 702
THE LYMPHATICS OF THE HEAD, FACE, AND
NECK.
The Lymph Nodes of the Head . . . 702
The Lymphatic Vessels of the Head . . 704
The Lymph Nodes of the Neck . . . 707
The Lymphatic Vessels of the Neck . . 709
THE LYMPHATICS OF THE UPPER EXTREMITY.
The Lymph Nodes of the Upper Extremity 710
The Lymphatic Vessels of the Upper Ex-
  tremity 711
THE LYMPHATICS OF THE LOWER EXTREMITY.
The Lymph Nodes of the Lower Extremity 712
The Lymphatic Vessels of the Lower Extrem-
  ity 713

THE LYMPHATICS OF THE ABDOMEN AND PELVIS.
The Lymph Nodes of the Abdomen and
  Pelvis 714
The Lymphatic Vessels of the Abdomen and
  Pelvis 717
The Lymphatic Nodes of the Abdominal and
  Pelvic Viscera 717
The Lymphatic Vessels of the Abdominal
  and Pelvic Viscera 721
THE LYMPHATICS OF THE THORAX.
The Parietal Lymph Nodes 726
The Lymphatic Vessels of the Thoracic Wall 728
The Lymphatic Vessels of the Thoracic
  Viscera 730
THE SPLEEN 730
Development 731
Structure 732
THE THYMUS
Development of the Thymus 734
Structure of the Thymus 735

NEUROLOGY.

Development of the Nervous System . . . 737
Histology of the Nervous System . . . 755
THE CENTRAL NERVOUS SYSTEM
The Medulla Spinalis or Spinal Cord . . . 767
  Enlargements - Fissures and Sulci . . 769
  The Internal Structure of the Medulla
    Spinalis 770
  Roots of the Spinal Nerves 782
THE ENCEPHALON OR BRAIN. 784
The Medulla Oblongata 785
The Pons 803
The Cerebellum 807
The Fourth Ventricle 814
The Mid-brain or Mesencephalon . . 817
The Fore-brain or Prosencephalon.
  The Diencephalon 825
  The Telencephalon 840
  The Cerebral Hemispheres . . . 840
  The Rhinencephalon 854
  Basal Ganglia 859
Structure of Cerebral Cortex . . . 868

Composition and Central Connections of the
  Spinal Nerves 876
Composition and Central Connections of the
  Cranial Nerves 881
Pathways from the Brain to the Spinal Cord.
  The Motor Tract 898
Meninges of the Brain and Medulla Spinalis.
  The Dura Mater 901
  The Arachnoid 903
  The Pia Mater 906
  The Cerebrospinal Fluid 907
THE PERIPHERAL NERVOUS SYSTEM.
THE CRANIAL NERVES.
The Olfactory Nerve 911
The Optic Nerve 912
The Oculomotor Nerve 913
The Trochlear Nerve 914
The Trigeminal Nerve.
  The Semilunar Ganglion 915
  The Ophthalmic Nerve 916
  The Maxillary Nerve 918
  The Mandibular Nerve 923
The Abducent Nerve 929

The Facial Nerve 930
The Acoustic Nerve 935
The Glossopharyngeal Nerve 936
The Vagus Nerve 938
The Accessory Nerve 942
The Hypoglossal Nerve 943

THE SPINAL NERVES   946

Nerve Roots 948
Divisions of the Spinal Nerves . . . 950
    Posterior Rami of the Spinal Nerves 950
    Anterior Rami of the Spinal Nerves 954
The Cervical Nerves 954
    The Cervical Plexus 954
    The Brachial Plexus 959
The Thoracic Nerves 973
The Lumbosacral Plexus 977
    The Lumbar Nerves 977
        The Lumbar Plexus 978
    The Sacral and Coccygeal Nerves . 986
        The Sacral Plexus . . 986

THE AUTONOMIC NERVOUS SYSTEM.   997
The Cranial Outflow 1001
The Sacral Outflow 1004
The Thoracolumbar Outflow 1004
    Connections with the Spinal Nerves . 1006

THE SYMPATHETIC SYSTEM

The Cephalic Portion 1008
The Cervical Portion 1009
The Thoracic Portion 1012
The Abdominal Portion 1013
The Pelvic Portion 1013
The Great Plexuses 1014
    The Cardiac Plexus 1015
    The Celiac Plexus 1016
    The Hypogastric Plexus 1019

THE ORGANS OF THE SENSES.

THE PERIPHERAL ORGANS OF THE SPECIAL
            SENSES.
The Organ of Taste.
    Structure 1023
    Nerves of Taste 1024
The Organ of Smell.
    The External Nose 1024
    The Nasal Cavity 1026
The Accessory Sinuses of the Nose . 1030
The Organ of Sight. 1032
    Development 1033
    The Tunics of the Eye 1037
        The Fibrous Tunic 1037
        The Vascular Tunic . . . 1040
        The Retina 1045
    The Refracting Media 1049
    The Accessory Organs of the Eye . 1051

The Organ of Sight—
    The Accessory Organs of the Eye—
        The Ocular Muscles 1051
        The Eyebrows 1055
        The Eyelids 1055
        The Tarsal Glands . . . 1056
        The Conjunctiva 1056
        The Lacrimal Apparatus . . . 1058
The Organ of Hearing.
    The Development of the Ear . . . 1060
    The External Ear 1064
    The Middle Ear or Tympanic Cavity . 1068
    The Auditory Ossicles 1074
    The Internal Ear or Labyrinth . . . 1078
        The Osseous Labyrinth . . . 1078
        The Membranous Labyrinth . . 1082
    PERIPHERAL   TERMINATIONS   OF
    NERVES OF GENERAL SENSATIONS 1090

THE COMMON INTEGUMENT.

Development 1096
Structure 1096
    The Epidermis. 1096
    The Corium 1098
    Cleavage Lines (Langer's) . . . 1100

The Appendages of the Skin.
    The Nails 1101
    Hairs 1102
    The Sebaceous Glands 1104
    The Sudoriferous or Sweat Glands . 1104

THE RESPIRATORY APPARATUS.

Development 1107
The Larynx 1108
    The Cartilages of the Larynx . . 1109
    The Ligaments of the Larynx . . 1112
    Interior of the Larynx 1114
    Muscles of the Larynx 1118

The Trachea and Bronchi 1121
The Pleuræ 1124
The Mediastinum 1127
The Lungs 1129
    Bronchopulmonary Segments . . . 1133
    Structure of the Lungs 1136

THE DIGESTIVE APPARATUS.

The Development of the Digestive Tube . . 1141
The Mouth.
    The Mouth Cavity Proper . . . 1151
    The Teeth 1156
    The Tongue 1165
    The Salivary Glands 1172
        The Parotid Gland . . 1172
        The Submaxillary Gland . . 1175
        The Sublingual Gland . . 1175
The Fauces 1177
    The Palatine Tonsils 1177
    The Muscles of the Palate . . . 1180
The Pharynx 1182
    The Muscles of the Pharynx . . 1184

The Esophagus 1187
The Abdomen 1189
    The Peritoneum 1194
        Main Peritoneal Cavity . . 1200
        Omental Bursa . . . 1200
        The Omenta 1202
        The Mesenteries 1202
        The Peritoneal Recesses or Fossæ . 1204
The Stomach 1207
The Small Intestine.
    The Duodenum 1213
    Jejunum and Ileum 1216

The Large Intestine.
The Cecum 1222
The Vermiform Process or Appendix . . 1224
The Colon 1225
The Rectum 1227

THE LIVER
Anatomy 1233
Development 1238
Structure 1239
Excretory Apparatus of the Liver . . 1242

The Liver—
Excretory Apparatus of the Liver—
The Hepatic Duct 1242
The Gall-bladder 1243
The Cystic Duct 1243
The Common Bile Duct . . 1244

THE PANCREAS
Anatomy. 1244
The Pancreatic Duct 1247
Development 1248
Structure 1248

THE UROGENITAL SYSTEM.

DEVELOPMENT OF THE URINARY AND GEN-
ERATIVE ORGANS.
The Pronephros and Wolffian Duct . . 1253
The Mesonephros, Müllerian Duct, and
Genital Gland 1254
The Ovary 1257
The Testis 1258
Descent of the Testes . . . 1258
The Metanephros and the Permanent
Kidney 1260
The Urinary Bladder 1261
The External Organs of Generation . . 1262

THE URINARY ORGANS.
The Kidneys 1264
Anatomy 1264
General Structure of the Kidney . 1270
Minute Anatomy 1272
The Ureters 1275
The Urinary Bladder 1277
Structure 1282
The Male Urethra 1284
The Female Urethra 1286

THE MALE GENITAL ORGANS.
The Testes and their Coverings . . . 1286
Structure 1293
The Ductus Deferens 1296
The Vesiculæ Seminales 1297
The Ejaculatory Ducts 1298
The Penis 1298
Structure 1302
The Prostate 1303
The Bulbourethral Glands 1305

THE FEMALE GENITAL ORGANS.
The Ovaries 1305
Structure 1307
The Uterine Tube 1308
The Uterus 1310
Supports 1313
Structure 1314
The Vagina 1316
The External Genital Organs . . . 1317
The Mammæ 1319

THE DUCTLESS GLANDS.

The Thyroid Gland 1327
The Parathyroid Glands 1330
The Hypophysis Cerebri 1331
The Pineal Body 1335

The Chromaphil and Cortical Systems.
Development 1335
The Suprarenal Glands 1336
Glomus Coccygeum 1339

SURFACE AND TOPOGRAPHICAL ANATOMY.

The Head and Neck 1343
The Cranium 1348
The Face 1353
The Eye 1357
The Ear 1357
The Neck 1360
The Triangles of the Neck . . 1362

The Back 1365
The Thorax 1369
The Abdomen 1379
The Perineum 1392
The Upper Extremity 1394
The Lower Extremity 1410

INDEX TO BIBLIOGRAPHIES . . . 1428   SUBJECT INDEX . . . 1431

ANATOMICAL BIBLIOGRAPHY.

INDEXES.

Anatomical Bibliography of the Councilium Bibliographicum.
Bibliographic Service; Wistar Institute of Anatomy, 1917–
Index Catalogue, Library of the Surgeon-General's Office, U. S. Army, 1880–
Index Medicus, 1879–1927, combined with the
Quarterly Cumulative Index, 1916–1927, and continued as
Quarterly Cumulative Index Medicus, 1927–

JOURNALS, REVIEWS AND ABSTRACTS.

The Anatomical Record, 1906–
The American Journal of Anatomy, 1901–
The American Journal of Physical Anthropology, 1918–
American Anatomical Memoirs, Wistar Institute, 1911–
Anatomischer Bericht, 1923–
Anat. Hefte, Abt. I., 1892–1921, continued as Zeit. f. d. Ges. Anat., Abt. I., 1921–
Anat. Hefte, Abt. II., Ergeb. d. Anat. u. Entwchlngsch., 1892–1914, continued as
    Zeit. f. d. Ges. Anat., Abt. III., 1921–
Anatomischer Anzeiger, 1886–
Archives d'Anatomie, d'Histologie, et d'Embryologie, 1922–
Archives d'Anatomie Microscopique, 1897–
Archiv für Anatomie und Physiologie, 1795–1920, continued as Zeit. f. d. Ges. Anat.,
    Abt. I., 1921.
Archiv für Entwicklungsmechanik der Organismen, 1894–1923 united with
Archiv für Mikroskopische Anatomie, 1865–1923 and continued as
Archiv für Mikr. Anat. u. Entwcklngsmech. d. Organ., 1923–
Archivio de Anatomia e Anthropologia, 1912–
Archivo Italiano di Anatomia e di Embriologia, 1902–
Biological Abstracts, 1926–
Contributions to Embryology, Carnegie Institution of Washington, 1914–
Competes Rendus de l'Association des Anatomistes, 1899–
Folia Anatomica Japonica, 1923–
Gegenbaur's Morphologisches Jahrbuch, 1876–
Growth, 1937–
The Journal of Anatomy and Physiology, 1867–1916, continued as
Journal of Anatomy, 1917–
Journal of Comparative Neurology, 1891–
Journal de l'Anatomie et de Physiologie, etc., 1864–
Journal of Experimental Zoölogy, 1904–
Journal of Morphology, 1887–
Proceedings of the Royal Society, Series B., 1905–
Quarterly Journal of Microscopical Science, 1853–
Zeitschrift für Morphologie und Anthropologie, 1899–
Zeitschrift für Wissenschaftliche Mikroskopie, 1884–
Zeitschrift für die Gesamte Anatomie, Abt. I., Zeitschrift für Anatomie und Entwick-
    lungsgeschichte, 1921–. Abt. III., Ergebnisse der Anatomie u. Entwicklungs-
    geschichte, 1921–

ANATOMY OF THE HUMAN BODY.

INTRODUCTION.

THE term *human anatomy* comprises a consideration of the various structures which make up the human body. In a restricted sense it deals merely with the parts which form the fully developed individual and which can be rendered evident to the naked eye by various methods of dissection. Regarded from such a standpoint it may be studied by two methods: (1) the various structures may be separately considered—**systemic anatomy;** or (2) the organs and tissues may be studied in relation to one another—**topographical** or **regional anatomy.**

It is, however, of much advantage to add to the facts ascertained by naked-eye dissection those obtained by the use of the microscope. This introduces two fields of investigation, viz., the study of the minute structure of the various component parts of the body—**microscopic anatomy** or **histology**—and the study of the human organism in its immature condition, *i. e.*, the various stages of its intrauterine development from the fertilized ovum up to the period when it assumes an independent existence—**developmental anatomy** or **embryology.** Owing to the difficulty of obtaining material illustrating all the stages of this early development, gaps must be filled up by observations on the development of lower forms—**comparative embryology,** or by a consideration of adult forms in the line of human ancestry—**comparative anatomy.** The direct application of the facts of human anatomy to medicine, surgery and pathology constitutes the subject of **applied anatomy.** The appreciation of structures on or immediately underlying the surface of the body is frequently made the subject of special study—**surface anatomy.** Finally, **physiological anatomy,** which is concerned with the function of every part of the body both gross and microscopic should always be considered, since the final aim of anatomy is the understanding of the living organism.

SYSTEMATIC ANATOMY.—After a short account of the animal cell and the early development of the body, the various systems of organs which compose the human body are treated under their respective heads as indicated by the table of contents. These great systems are functional systems as well as anatomical ones. The skeletal system supports and protects the soft parts and supplies the levers for movements. The joints provide for but limit the movements. The skeletal or voluntary muscular system consists of the organs, muscles, which by contraction produce the movements of the skeleton. All the organs and tissues of the body perform work, they metabolize. The blood-vascular system pumps and distributes the blood which carries food and oxygen for energy to every part of the body, to every organ. The blood also conveys away from these organs the waste products of metabolism. The lymphatic system drains the tissue spaces and conveys certain food products from the digestive system to the blood. The respiratory system brings oxygen to the blood and eliminates the waste product CO_2. The digestive system converts the raw food into substances which can be utilized by the organs for energy. The urinary system eliminates certain waste products from the body. The reproductive system, as its name indicates, is for the perpetuation of the species. The nervous system is the great correlating and controlling system of the body. It is intimately connected with all the other systems and through the organs of the senses with the outside world. The ductless glands through their internal secretions, the hormones, subserve additional regulatory functions. Most of the systems have additional functions either in whole or in part. All the systems are functionally interrelated and coördinated.

Topographical Anatomy.—The final section of this book is concerned with the location and relations of the various organs and parts of the body to one another and to the surface of the body. The form of the body is dependent upon the structures which lie beneath the skin. The visualization of these structures with reference to the surface, especially in the living should be constantly exercised during the study of systematic anatomy. The great development of roentgenography has added much to this subject.

Terms of Position and Direction.—For descriptive purposes the body is supposed to be in the erect posture, with the arms hanging by the sides, and the head, the eyes and the palms of the hands directed forward. The *median plane* is a vertical antero-posterior plane, passing through the center of the trunk. This plane will pass approximately through the sagittal suture of the skull, and hence any plane parallel to it is termed a *sagittal plane*. A vertical plane at right angles to the median plane passes, roughly speaking, through the central part of the coronal suture or through a line parallel to it; such a plane is known as a *frontal plane* or sometimes as a *coronal plane*. A plane at right angles to both the median and frontal planes is termed a *transverse plane*.

The terms *anterior* or *ventral*, and *posterior* or *dorsal*, are employed to indicate the relation of parts to the front or back of the body or limbs, and the terms *superior* or *cephalic*, and *inferior* or *caudal*, to indicate the relative levels of different structures; structures nearer to or farther from the median plane are referred to as *medial* or *lateral*, respectively.

The terms *superficial* and *deep* are strictly confined to descriptions of the relative depth from the surface of the various structures; *external* and *internal* are reserved almost entirely for describing the walls of cavities or of hollow viscera. In the case of the limbs the words *proximal* and *distal* refer to the relative distance from the attached end of the limb.

EMBRYOLOGY.

THE ANIMAL CELL.

THE human body is composed of several hundred trillion cells, comprising hundreds of types, and a large amount of intercellular material (bone and cartilage, collagenous, elastic, and reticular fibers, intercellular ground substance, blood plasma, and lymph, etc.) produced by the metabolism of the cells. About 45 generations of cells would be sufficient to produce this enormous number. Cell division, cell growth, cell differentiation and cell metabolism are the fundamental processes involved in building the body from the fertilized egg.

Most animal cells consist of a soft jelly-like **cytoplasm** surrounding a more viscous **nucleus** and a centrally located **central body** or **centrosome**. Resting cells have a definite structure or architecture. At the center is the central body. The intracellular bodies, such as mitochondria, granules, and fat globules, tend to be radially arranged about the central body in zones in the above order, except where this is interrupted by the more or less eccentrically located nucleus, and some scattering

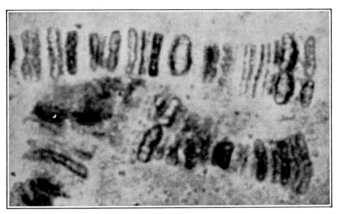

Fig. 1.—The two ends, about one-fifth, of a giant chromosome from the parotid gland of the fungus fly. The maternal and paternal chromosomes are not completely united at one end. The bands or chromomeres are constant for each chromosome. × 2500. (Metz.)

of the intracellular bodies. It is the central body, not the nucleus, about which the intracellular bodies are oriented. A thin superficial layer of the cytoplasm, the gel layer or **ectoplasm,** is more viscous than the deeper **endoplasm** which contains most of the intracellular bodies. This superficial gel layer (plasmagel) plays an important rôle in changes of cell form, in cell locomotion, and in cell cleavage, by virtue of the fact that protoplasm, which is a colloid, automatically exerts contractile tension when it gels or becomes more viscous. The surface of the cell has an invisible semipermeable surface membrane which controls the osmotic phenomena.

Cytoplasm of living cells is optically homogeneous and structureless. Its viscosity differs in different types of cells, and in different regions of the same cell. It is often subject to rapid changes and may vary from a fluid condition, either local or general, to a semisolid gel. A local fluid condition may be revealed by Brownian movements of intracellular bodies and a semisolid condition by refractile striæ.

The **central body** or **centrosome** is a minute mass of specialized material at the center of the cell. It plays an important rôle in cell division and in certain activities

2

of the resting cell. In fixed material, two minute granules (centrioles) can frequently be seen at its center. It has been called the "dynamic center" of the cell by Boveri.

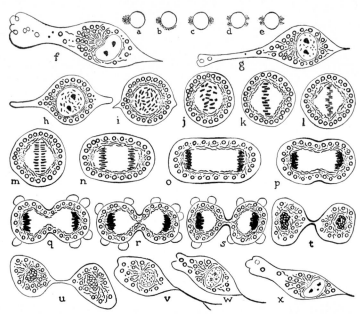

Fig. 2.—Cell division. **a-e.** From motion picture of a living monkey egg. Part of the finely granular centrosome material spreads around the nucleus to the opposite pole and there forms a second centrosome. Each centrosome divides and then unites to form a duplex centrosome. The process begins three and one-half and ends one and one-half hours before cell cleavage. **f-x.** From a living fibroblast dividing in a tissue culture. **f.** Resting stage. The centrally located centrosome is surrounded by a radial zone of mitochondria, a granular zone and a radial zone of fat globules except where interrupted by the somewhat eccentrically located nucleus and some intermingling of these intracellular bodies. A few bodies are scattered in the homogeneous ectoplasm. Ruffle pseudopodia at the tip of the advancing cell process are engulfing globules of fluid (pinocytosis). The nucleus has a thin membrane, a homogeneous nucleoplasm and two nucleoli. **g.** Beginning prophase. Chromosomes are beginning to appear as granules. Cell processes are retracting. **h.** Mid-prophase. Chromosomes are more evident in the otherwise homogeneous nucleoplasm. Cell processes are more retracted. The nucleus has become centrally located. **i.** Late prophase. Chromosomes nearly fill the nucleus. They now exhibit movements, probably passive ones. Nucleoli have split into their chromosomal elements The nuclear membrane has disappeared. The cell has become nearly spherical. The nucleus is surrounded by an endoplasmic zone with mitochondria, granules, and fat globules and this in turn by a homogeneous zone, the ectoplasm or superficial gel layer. **j.** Transition from prophase to metaphase. The chromosomes are being pulled into the metaphase plate, presumably by invisible spindle fibers. **k.** Metaphase. The nucleus has become spindle-shaped. The chromosomes are in the equatorial plane where they slowly oscillate in short paths, presumably due to variations of the contractile tension of the spindle fibers. The clear interchromosomal material shows a relative increase over the chromosomes. **l.** Late metaphase. Each chromosome has split longitudinally into two equal parts. **m.** Early anaphase. Each group of chromosomes has begun to move toward the poles of the spindle. **n.** Late anaphase. The chromosomes have nearly reached the poles. Between the two groups of chromosomes is the homogeneous interchromosomal material, or exnuclear sap. The cell has been flattened in the equatorial region and elongated in the polar direction by the contraction of a broad thickened band of the superficial gel layer. **o.** End of anaphase. Chromosomes form small compact daughter nuclei. The cell is more flattened and elongated by the automatic contraction of a broad equatorial band of the ectoplasm or gel layer. **p.** Beginning telophase. The cleavage furrow has begun to appear due to the automatic constriction of an equatorial band of the gel layer. The endoplasmic zone is bent inward and indents the softer interchromosomal material. **q.** Early telophase. The cleavage furrow has deepened and bent the endoplasm with its intracellular bodies still farther inward. The relatively soft interchromosomal material is partially divided. The intracellular bodies retain their spacial relations in the relatively firm endoplasm. A few blebs have appeared on the surface of the cell. **r.** Mid-telophase. The constricting gel layer has bent the endoplasm inward until it meets and fuses in the equatorial region and divides the interchromosomal material into two parts. **s.** Late telophase. Continued contraction of the superficial equatorial band of the gel layer has nearly divided the endoplasm. Fat globules, granules and mitochondria that were in the equatorial region have been pressed into one or the other daughter cell. **t.** End of telophase. The daughter cells are connected by the ectoplasmic stalk. The endoplasm has been completely divided by the constriction of the equatorial band. It has mixed with the interchromosomal (exnuclear) material. The compact daughter nuclei have begun to show clear areas and to enlarge. **u.** The daughter cells have moved in opposite directions and stretched the connecting stalk. The nuclei have larger clear areas and less visible chromosome material. **v.** The connecting stalk has been pulled into a thin strand by the migration of the daughter cells in opposite directions. The visible chromosome material has been reduced to granules in the clear nucleoplasm. A nuclear membrane has developed. **w.** Some of the chromosomal granules have begun to agglutinate to form the nucleoli; the others have begun to disappear. The connecting stalk is broken. **x.** All the chromosomal granules except those which have agglutinated to form the nucleoli have disappeared into homogeneous nucleoplasm.

Nuclei are usually oval or round. The resting nucleus of living cells has a thin nuclear membrane, a translucent homogeneous nucleoplasm, and one to several nucleoli. The nucleoplasm probably consists of optically invisible **chromosomes.** They become visible during cell division. These complicated structures play **an** important rôle in inheritance (Fig. 1). **Nucleoli** are specialized parts of chromosomes.

Intracellular Bodies.—All cells have mitochondria, in the form of threads, rods, or granules. Their function is unknown. Most cells have granules of one sort or another, such as secretion granules, pigment granules, ingested material, small globules of fluid (vacuoles), and fat globules. Golgi bodies can not be seen in living cells. They are probably artifacts, as are many other coagulation products seen in dead cells.

Cell Division, Mitosis or **Karyokinesis.**—An hour or two before prophase begins, part of the centrosome material moves or is moved to the opposite pole of the nucleus. Each polar mass divides and then agglutinates.

The following series of events can be observed in living fibroblasts of tissue cultures (Fig. 2).

During **prophase**, chromosomes become visible, cell processes retract and the cell tends to become spherical. The nucleus becomes centrally located and surrounded by a zone of endoplasm filled with mitochondria, fat globules, and intracellular bodies. This in turn is surrounded by a thin layer of ectoplasm, the gel layer. Near the end of prophase, which takes about an hour, the nuclear membrane disappears, the chromosomes begin to move, and the nucleoli split into their chromosomal elements. Chromosome movements, which are probably passive, result in their rearrangement in the equatorial plane of the nucleus which has become spindle-shaped. The cell is now approximately bilateral.

During **metaphase**, the chromosomes oscillate back and forth in short paths in the equatorial region as though they were pulled first toward one pole and then toward the other by invisible spindle fibers. Slight changes in the viscosity of the latter would account for the alterations of their contractile tension. Each chromosome splits longitudinally into two equal and similar chromosomes.

During **anaphase**, one set of chromosomes moves to each pole of the spindle or is pulled there by contraction of invisible spindle fibers. There they clump together into small compact daughter nuclei. A homogeneous material, the interchromosomal mass, is left behind between the two daughter nuclei. As the chromosomes approach the poles, the cell flattens in the equatorial region and elongates. This is due to the contractile tension of a thickened broad equatorial band of the superficial gel layer. Increased gelation of the equatorial part of this band results in increased contractile tension and the formation of a groove around the equator of the cell.

During **telophase**, contraction of this equatorial band bends the endoplasm inward until it divides the less viscous interchromosomal mass. Continued contraction of the equatorial band deepens the groove and divides the endoplasmic layer. The two daughter cells remain connected for a short time by a slender stalk of the gel layer. The interchromosomal material (ex-nuclear sap) mixes with the endoplasm of each daughter cell. Approximately one-half of the mitochondria go to each daughter cell. The segregation of fat globules is more haphazard.

Metaphase takes about six minutes, anaphase and telophase each about three minutes.

The compact daughter nuclei slowly increase in size as clear areas appear and split the compact mass into granules. A nuclear membrane forms. As the nucleus enlarges, the clear areas increase and most of the chromosomal granules disappear from view. A few remain. They are the nucleoli. They usually agglutinate and form one to several nucleoli. It takes several hours for the nucleus to attain the adult resting condition.

Amitosis or direct cell division probably does not occur under normal conditions. Degenerating cells may show nuclear fragmentation without division of the cytoplasm or the centrosome.

Mitotic division of the nucleus and division of the centrosome without division of the cytoplasm frequently occurs and produces binucleate cells.

THE OVUM.

When the ovum is discharged into the uterine tube it is surrounded by several layers of radially arranged cells, the **corona radiata**, derived from cells of the follicle. These cells disappear during the first twenty-four hours in the upper part of the tube. They are probably rubbed off by the mechanical action of the tube from their attachment to the zona pellucida.

The **zona pellucida** is a tough transparent membrane, about 12μ in thickness, surrounding the vitellus or the living part of the egg. It is somewhat radially striated and protects the delicate vitellus during segmentation and early blastocyst formation. The origin of the zona is uncertain. In the ovary and at the time of ovulation the zona is in contact with the vitellus. Shortly after ovulation, however, the zona enlarges and the vitellus shrinks and there develops a perivitelline space filled with a clear fluid. The perivitelline space persists during cleavage but disappears during the blastocyst stage. The vitellus then enlarges, comes into contact with the zona pellucida and gradually stretches the latter into an exceedingly thin membrane which ultimately disappears.

The **vitellus** is the living part of the ovum and consists of cytoplasm, nucleus and centrosome.

The **cytoplasm** (Fig. 3) is crowded with many granular mitochondria and many yolk globules that supply nourishment to the egg until it becomes implanted in the wall of the uterus.

The **nucleus** or germinal vesicle lies near the center of the cell. In the living resting condition, it shows a thin nuclear membrane, a homogeneous nucleoplasm, and one or two nucleoli.

A **centrosome** with two centrioles lies close to the nucleus. It consists of specialized material unlike that of the surrounding cytoplasm.

Size of the Ovum.—The outside diameter of the zona of the human egg measures about 175μ and the vitellus after the formation of the perivitelline space 104μ. The dimensions of some other mammalian eggs are given in the following table:

COMPARATIVE SIZE OF LIVING ONE-CELL TUBAL EGGS AFTER THE FORMATION OF THE PERIVITELLINE SPACE (LEWIS AND WRIGHT).

Volume and surface area of vitellus in cubic and square microns estimated by authors. ODZ: outside diameter of zona. IDZ: inside diameter of zona. DV: Diameter of vitellus in microns.

Animal.	Eggs.	Author.	ODZ.	IDZ.	DV.	Volume.*	Surface.*
Mouse	26	Lewis and Wright	113.0	87.8	71.6	192000	16100
Guinea-pig	1	Squier	121.3	96.8	84.3	314000	22300
Macaque I	1	Corner		109.0*	86.0	333000	23400
Macaque two-cell	1	Lewis and Hartman	150.0	125.0	103.0*	562000	
Macaque IV	1	Allen	178.5	138.5*	104.0	589000	34000
Human	1	Allen et al.	176.0*	139.0*	104.0*	589000	34000
Human (abnormal)	1	Lewis	148.0	136.0			
Rabbit	2	Gregory	174.0	126.0*			
Rabbit	9	Lewis	174.2	126.5	111.0	718000	38700
Pig	4	Heuser and Streeter	160.0	130.0	111.0	718000	38700
Cow (non-fertile)	1	Hartman and Lewis	170.0	143.0	120.0	907000	45300
Cow two-cell	1	Miller and Swett	162.5	135.0		740000	
Dog	3	Hartman	172.0	141.0	120.0	907000	45300
Sheep	6	Clark	178.0*	150.0*	133.0*	1232000	55700

* Determined or estimated from illustrations and data in articles quoted.

Maturation of the Ovum.—Before an ovum can be fertilized it must undergo a process of **maturation** or **meiosis**. This takes place previous to or immediately after its escape from the follicle into the uterine tube. The primary ovum or

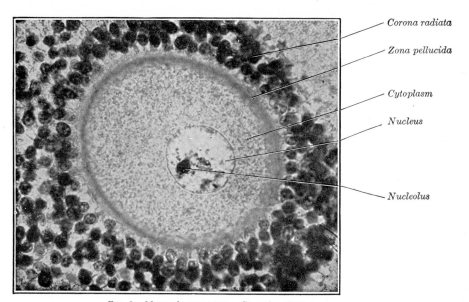

Corona radiata

Zona pellucida

Cytoplasm

Nucleus

Nucleolus

FIG. 3.—Mature human ovum. Carnegie collection.

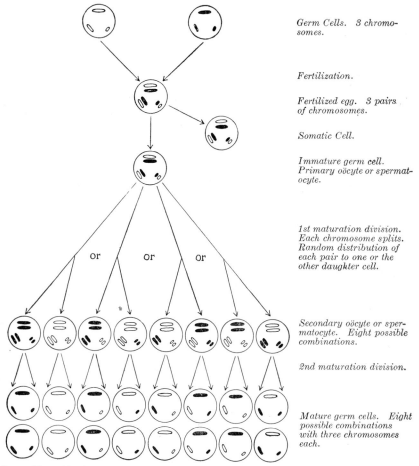

Germ Cells. 3 chromosomes.

Fertilization.

Fertilized egg. 3 pairs of chromosomes.

Somatic Cell.

Immature germ cell. Primary oöcyte or spermatocyte.

1st maturation division. Each chromosome splits. Random distribution of each pair to one or the other daughter cell.

Secondary oöcyte or spermatocyte. Eight possible combinations.

2nd maturation division.

Mature germ cells. Eight possible combinations with three chromosomes each.

FIG. 4.—Equally possible combinations of independent segregation during maturation with three pairs of chromosomes.

oöcyte divides into a large cell the secondary oöcyte and a small one, the first polar body. This is followed by another division of the ovum into the large mature ovum and a small cell the second polar body (Fig. 6). The first polar body may or may not divide into two smaller polar bodies. The most important part of maturation is the distribution of the chromosomes which play such an important rôle in inheritance. The human primary ovum has 24 pairs or 48 chromosomes, each pair consists of a maternal and a paternal chromosome. During the first maturation division each chromosome splits into a pair. There is a random distribution of maternal and paternal pairs of homologous chromosomes to the daughter cells. Thus each of these daughter cells has 24 pairs or 48 chromosomes. As a result there are over 16,000,000 equally possible combinations for the daughter cells. During the second division each pair splits apart and each daughter cell receives 24 chromosomes. If crossing over occurs in the first division the number of equally possible combinations is almost infinitely great. With 3 pairs of chromosomes there are eight equally possible combinations as in Fig. 4.

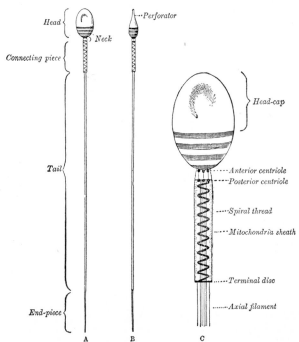

FIG. 5.—Human spermatozoön. Diagrammatic. *A*. Surface view. *B*. Profile view. **In *C* the head, neck,** and connecting piece are more highly magnified.

THE SPERMATOZOÖN.

The **spermatozoa** or **male germ cells** are developed in the testes and are present in enormous numbers in the seminal fluid. Each consists of a small but greatly modified cell. The human spermatozoön possesses a **head**, a **neck**, a **connecting piece** or **body**, and a **tail** (Fig. 5).

The **head** is oval or elliptical, but flattened, so that when viewed in profile it is pear-shaped. Its anterior two-thirds are covered by a layer of modified protoplasm, which is named the **head-cap**. This, in some animals, *e. g.*, the salamander, is prolonged into a barbed spear-like process or **perforator**, which probably facilitates the entrance of the spermatozoön into the ovum. The posterior part of the head exhibits an affinity for certain reagents, and presents a transversely striated appearance, being crossed by three or four dark bands. In some animals a central rod-like filament extends forward for about two-thirds of the length of the head, while in others a rounded body is seen near its center. The head contains a mass of chromatin, and is generally regarded as the nucleus of the cell surrounded by a thin envelope.

The **neck** is less constricted in the human spermatozoön than in those of some of the lower animals. The **anterior centriole**, represented by two or three rounded particles, is situated at the junction of the head and neck, and behind it is a band of homogeneous substance.

The **connecting piece** or **body** is rod-like, and is limited behind by a *terminal disk*. The **posterior centriole** is placed at the junction of the body and neck and, like the anterior, consists of two or three rounded particles. From this centriole an **axial filament**, surrounded by a sheath, runs backward through the body and tail. In the body the sheath of the axial filament is encircled by a **spiral thread**, around which is an envelope containing mitochondria granules, and termed the **mitochondria sheath**.

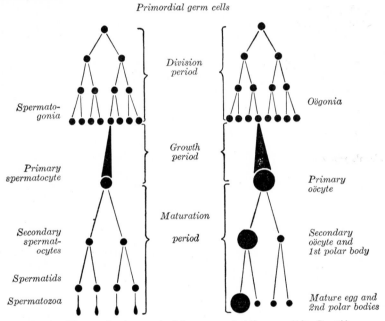

FIG. 6.—Diagram showing genesis of the sperm and of the egg. (After Boveri.)

The **tail** is of great length, and consists of the axial thread or filament, surrounded by its sheath, which may contain a spiral thread or may present a striated appearance. The terminal portion or **end-piece** of the tail consists of the axial filament only.

Krause gives the length of the human spermatozoön as between 52μ and 62μ. the head measuring 4 to 5μ, the connecting piece 6μ, and the tail from 41μ to 52μ.

By virtue of their tails, which act as propellers, the spermatozoa are capable of free movement, and if placed in favorable surroundings, *e. g.*, in the female passages, will retain their vitality and power of fertilizing for a day or two. In certain animals, *e. g.*, bats, it has been proved that spermatozoa retained in the female passages for several months are capable of fertilizing.

The spermatozoa are developed from the primitive germ cells which have become imbedded in the testes, and the stages of their maturation are very similar to those of the maturation of the ovum. The primary germ cells undergo division and produce a number of cells termed **spermatogonia**, and from these the **primary**

spermatocytes are derived. Each primary spermatocyte divides into two **secondary spermatocytes**, and each secondary spermatocyte into two **spermatids** or young spermatozoa; from this it will be seen that a primary spermatocyte gives rise to *four* spermatozoa (Fig. 6). Each one is capable of fertilizing a mature ovum.

During the first maturation division there is the same random distribution of the chromosomes to the secondary spermatocytes as to the secondary oöcytes and consequently the same number of equally possible combinations of the chromosomes. Since the primary spermatocyte contains, as does the primary oöcyte, 24 pairs or 48 chromosomes, there are also over 16,000,000 equally possible combinations for the daughter spermatozoa. During the second maturation division there is a similar reduction in the number of chromosomes in the spermatids as in the mature egg and polar bodies (Fig. 4). The spermatozoa thus have 24 chromosomes.

According to the work of Painter and of Evans and Swezy the spermatogonia of both white and negroes show forty-eight chromosomes. The male somatic cells have forty-eight chromosomes, one of which is the small Y-chromosome. The human female somatic cells also have forty-eight chromosomes, the X-chromosome being the female determiner.

FERTILIZATION OF THE OVUM.

Fertilization consists in the union of the spermatozoön with the mature ovum (Fig. 7). Nothing is known regarding the fertilization of the human ovum, but

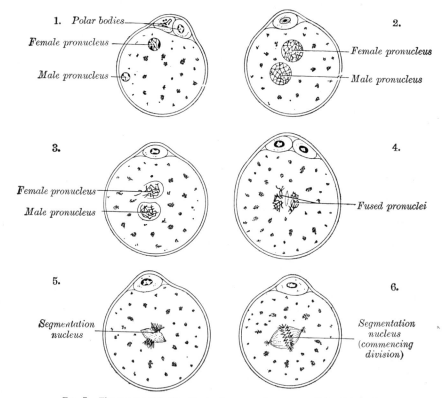

Fig. 7.—The process of fertilization in the ovum of a mouse. (After Sobotta.)

the various stages of the process have been studied in other mammals, and from the knowledge so obtained it is believed that fertilization of the human ovum takes place in the lateral or ampullary part of the uterine tube, and the ovum is then conveyed along the tube to the cavity of the uterus—a journey probably occupying three days and during which the ovum loses its corona radiata and undergoes segmentation. Unless the egg is fertilized within about six hours after ovulation it becomes impotent or incapable of being fertilized. Sometimes the fertilized ovum is arrested in the uterine tube, and there undergoes development, giving rise to a *tubal pregnancy;* or it may fall into the abdominal cavity and produce an *abdominal pregnancy.* Occasionally the ovum is not expelled from the follicle when the latter ruptures, but is fertilized within the follicle and produces what is known as an *ovarian pregnancy.* Under normal conditions only one spermatozoön enters the ovum and takes part in the process of fertilization. As soon as the spermatozoön has entered the yolk, the peripheral portion of the latter is transformed into a membrane, the **vitelline membrane** which prevents the passage of additional spermatozoa. Having pierced the yolk, the spermatozoön loses its tail, while its head and connecting piece assume the form of a nucleus containing a cluster of chromosomes. This constitutes the **male pronucleus,** and associated with it there are a centriole and centrosome. The male pronucleus passes more deeply into the yolk, and coincidently with this the granules of the cytoplasm surrounding it become radially arranged. The male and female pronuclei migrate toward each other, and, meeting near the center of the yolk, fuse to form a new nucleus, the **segmentation nucleus.**

In man, there are 24 male and 24 female, or 48 chromosomes. Some animals have more, some fewer. All somatic cells are derived from the fertilized egg and are supposed to have the same number of chromosomes.

Cell division, cell growth, cell differentiation, and the formation of various intercellular substances by cells play rôles in the development of the human body. An average of 45 to 50 generations of cell divisions would be sufficient to produce the several hundred trillion cells of the body.

SEGMENTATION OF THE FERTILIZED OVUM.

The segmentation of the human egg has not been observed. The first cleavage of the monkey egg occurs about twenty-four hours after ovulation. The two cells are about equal in size. About twelve hours later each cell divides to give the four-cell stage. The eight-cell stage is attained before the egg is seventy-two hours old at about which time it passes into the uterus. The process of division is repeated again and again until a mass of small cells, the morula, results. The mouse morula has about thirty-two cells, the rabbit one hundred and twenty-eight cells, the exact number in man is unknown. Divisions are not always simultaneous and mammalian eggs frequently have three, five, seven and other odd numbers of cells. Before each cleavage the nucleus undergoes the usual mitotic division. During segmentation the egg does not increase in size. The morula is about the same size as the one-cell stage. During cleavage there is probably an incomplete segregation of different protoplasmic stuffs into different groups of cells.

The Morula.—During the morula stage this segregation becomes visible and there develops an outer cuboidal layer of cells, the trophoblast and an inner cell-mass (Fig. 8E). These two sorts of cells have very different potencies. From the trophoblast develop the membranes which nourish and protect the embryo and which attach it to the mother. The inner cell-mass produces the embryo. The trophoblast soon secretes fluid into the interior of the morula and the blastocyst stages begins (Fig. 8F).

The Blastocyst.—The trophoblast cells secrete fluid under pressure into the interior of the morula which is slowly expanded into a large vesicle, the blastocyst.

The trophoblast cells multiply and become flattened against the zona pellucida which is stretched into a thin membrane and disappears. The inner cell-mass remains attached to one pole of the blastocyst (Figs. 8*F*, 9*A*, 9*B*). The blastocyst cavity is later obliterated by the expansion of the amnion.

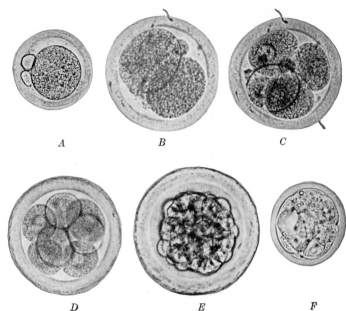

A *B* *C*

D *E* *F*

Fig. 8.—Photographs of living eggs, × 200. (*A*) Fertile one-cell mouse egg showing the zona pellucida, perivitelline space, vitellus, first and second polar bodies (Lewis and Wright). (*B*) Two-cell monkey egg. (*C*) Four-cell stage of same egg, extra sperm in zona (Lewis and Hartman). (*D*) Eight-cell rabbit egg. (*E*) Rabbit morula (Gregory). (*F*) Early blastocyst, seventy-six-hour mouse egg with a small amount of fluid.

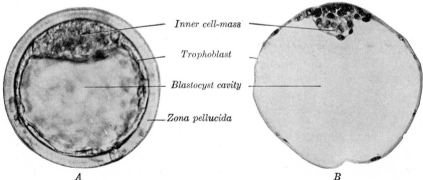

Inner cell-mass

Trophoblast

Blastocyst cavity

Zona pellucida

A *B*

Fig. 9.—(*A*) Blastocyst, ninety-two-hour rabbit egg. Trophoblast and inner cell-mass. × 200. (Gregory.) (*B*) Blastocyst, nine-day monkey egg. Stained section. The zona has disappeared, the trophoblast is thin and the inner cell-mass small. × 200. (Carnegie collection.)

IMPLANTATION.

Implantation or Imbedding of the Ovum.—The blastocyst, when it attains a diameter of about 0.5 mm., becomes adherent by its embryonic pole to the epithelial lining of the uterus. There it flattens out somewhat and erodes and digests the underlying surface of the uterus. The surrounding uterine epithelium, however, soon covers over the blastocyst, which now lies implanted or imbedded in the endometrium beneath the epithelium of the uterus (Fig. 10). In the ovum described by Bryce and Teacher the point of entrance was visible as a small gap closed by a mass of fibrin and leucocytes; in the ovum described by Peters the opening was covered by a mushroom-shaped mass of fibrin and blood-clot, the narrow stalk of which plugged the aperture in the mucous membrane.

In the youngest known human ovum, ten to eleven days old, the trophoblast is actively invading the uterine tissues (Fig. 10). The trophoblast proliferates rapidly, forms a network of branching processes which cover the entire ovum, invade the maternal tissues and open into the maternal bloodvessels, with the result that the spaces in the trophoblastic network are filled with maternal blood; these spaces communicate freely with one another and become greatly distended and form the **intervillous space.**

The implanted ovum or blastocyst consists of two very distinct parts, the trophoblast and the inner cell-mass.

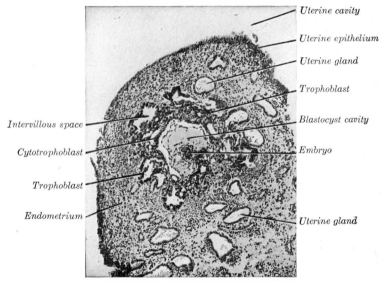

Fig. 10.—Section through the youngest-known human ovum, about eleven days old, imbedded in the uterine endometrium. The blastocyst cavity is surrounded by trophoblast. The dark staining syncytiotrophoblast is invading the maternal tissue. In the trophoblast are cavities which will become intervillous spaces. In the endometrium are large uterine glands. The inner cell-mass is attached to the inner wall of the trophoblast. × 40. (Streeter.)

FETAL MEMBRANES AND PLACENTA.

Development of the Fetal Membranes and the Placenta.—The **trophoblast** consists at first of a single layer of cells. They soon give rise to an outer syncytial layer, the **syncytiotrophoblast**, a layer rich in nuclei but without cell boundaries. On the inner surface over the embryonic disk they early give rise to the amnion. Mesoderm and angioblasts are given off from the cellular layer to form an inner layer. The cellular layer is known as the **cytotrophoblast** or layer of Langhans. The trophoblast proliferates, invades and digests the maternal tissues. This proliferating and invading mass of syncytiotrophoblast and cytotrophoblast becomes converted into a thick-walled sponge-like structure by the development of communicating cavities lined by syncytiotrophoblast which invests the thick cellular anastomosing cytotrophoblast strands. Maternal bloodvessels are eroded and blood pours into the cavities which soon become the intervillous space. The strands become anchored to the wall of the uterus and develop into the chorionic villi and the trophoblast then becomes known as the chorion and its cavity the chorionic cavity.

The Chorion (Fig. 11).—The chorion steadily increases in size by the multiplication of its cells and the accumulation of fluid in its cavity. Later the amnion

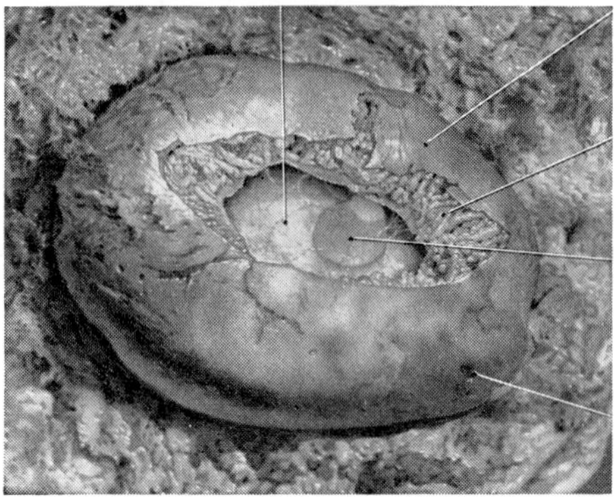

Chorionic cavity

Decidua capsularis

Villi

Embryo

Uterine gland

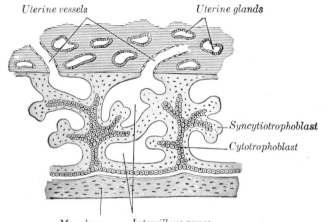

FIG. 11.—Human ovum, about fourteen days old, imbedded in the wall of the uterus. A window has been cut through the decidua capsularis (reflexa) and the chorion to show the embryo with its large yolk-sac and amnion. × 4.5 diameter. (Carnegie collection.)

Uterine vessels   *Uterine glands*

Syncytiotrophoblast

Cytotrophoblast

Mesoderm   Intervillous space
FIG. 12.—Primary chorionic villi. Diagrammatic. (Modified from Bryce.)

Uterine vessels

Uterine glands

Syncytiotrophoblast

Cytotrophoblast
Core of mesoderm
with bloodvessels

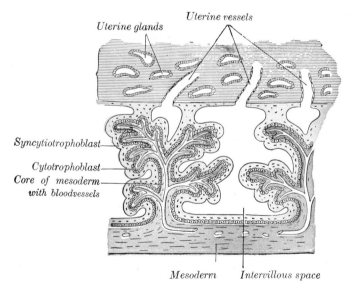

Mesoderm   Intervillous space
FIG. 13.—Secondary chorionic villi. Diagrammatic. (Modified from Bryce.)

expands, comes into contact with the inner wall of the chorion and obliterates the chorionic cavity (Figs. 19 to 22). The two membranes can usually be separated even at birth. As the chorion increases in size the decidua capsularis which covers it is brought into contact with the decidua vera and all traces of the uterine cavity are obliterated (Fig. 17).

The Chorionic Villi.—The primary villi develop from the solid strands of trophoblast which, as already noted, extend from the chorion to the uterine wall and consist of an outer layer of syncytiotrophoblast and an inner mass of cytotrophoblast cells (Fig. 12 and 13). According to Hertig the cytotrophoblast cells give off mesoderm and angioblasts to form a central core. As the villi increase in size

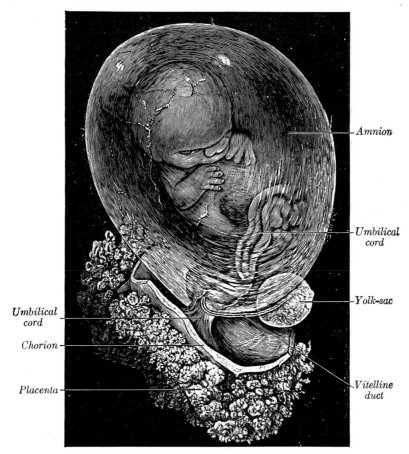

FIG. 14.—Fetus of about eight weeks, enclosed in the amnion. Magnified a little over two diameters. (Drawn from stereoscopic photographs lent by Prof. A. Thomson, Oxford.)

and ramify, this process stops and the mesenchymal core grows in from the primary ones to keep pace with the increase in size and complexity of the secondary villi. As the chorion increases in size many secondary villi grow out from its wall. As they grow and branch chorionic mesoderm and angioblasts extend into them and multiply to keep pace with their growth. The isolated angioblasts in the villi and in the chorion multiply and develop isolated vascular channels which soon connect to form vascular plexuses that unite to form the vascular tree which finally connects with the bloodvessels of the embryo.

The Decidua.—Before the fertilized ovum reaches the uterus, the mucous membrane or endometrium of the body of the uterus undergoes the usual premenstrual changes. About the eleventh day of pregnancy **decidual cells** begin to appear in the interglandular tissue and increase in number. The thickness and vascularity of the mucous membrane are greatly increased; its glands are elongated and open on its free surface by funnel-shaped orifices, while their deeper portions are tortuous and dilated into irregular spaces. These changes are well advanced by the second month of pregnancy, when the mucous membrane is crowded with

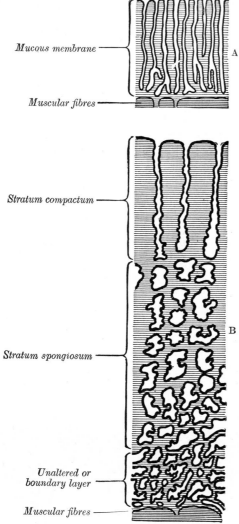

Mucous membrane

Muscular fibres

Stratum compactum

Stratum spongiosum

Unaltered or boundary layer

Muscular fibres

Fig. 15.—Diagrammatic sections of the uterine mucous membrane: *A.* The non-pregnant uterus. *B.* The pregnant uterus, showing the thickened mucous membrane and the altered condition of the uterine glands. (Kundrat and Engelmann.)

decidua cells. It consists of the following strata (Fig. 15): (1) **stratum compactum**, next the free surface; in this the uterine glands are only slightly expanded, and are lined by columnar cells; (2) **stratum spongiosum**, in which the gland tubes are greatly dilated and very tortuous, and are ultimately separated from one another by only a small amount of interglandular tissue, while their lining cells are flattened or cubical; (3) a thin **unaltered** or **boundary layer**, next the uterine muscular fibers, containing the deepest parts of the uterine glands, which are not dilated, and are lined with columnar epithelium; it is from this epithelium that the epithelial lining of the uterus is regenerated after pregnancy. Distinctive names are applied to different portions of the decidua. The part which covers in the ovum is named the **decidua capsularis**; the portion which intervenes between the ovum and the uterine wall is named the **decidua basalis** or **decidua placentalis**; it is here that the placenta is subsequently developed. The part of the decidua which lines the remainder of the body of the uterus is known as the **decidua vera** or **decidua parietalis**.

Coincidentally with the growth of the embryo, the decidua capsularis is thinned and extended (Fig. 16) and the space between it and the decidua vera is gradually obliterated, so that by the third month of pregnancy the two are in contact. By the fifth month of pregnancy the decidua capsularis has practically disappeared, while during the succeeding months the decidua vera also undergoes atrophy, owing to the increased pressure. The glands of the stratum compactum are obliterated, and their epithelium is lost. In the stratum spongiosum the glands are compressed and appear as slit-like fissures, while their epithelium undergoes degeneration. In the unaltered or boundary layer, however, the glandular epithelium retains a columnar or cubical form.

Until about the end of the second month of pregnancy the villi cover the entire chorion, and are almost uniform in size, but after this they develop unequally.

The greater part of the chorion is in contact with the decidua capsularis (Fig. 16), and over this portion the villi, with their contained vessels, undergo atrophy, so that by the fourth month scarcely a trace of them is left, and hence this part of the chorion becomes smooth, and is named the **chorion læve**; as it takes no share in the formation of the placenta, it is also named the non-placental part of the chorion. On the other hand, the villi on that part of the chorion which is in contact with the decidua basalis increase greatly in size and complexity, and hence this part is named the **chorion frondosum** (Fig. 22).

The Placenta.—The placenta connects the fetus to the uterine wall, and is the organ by means of which the nutritive, respiratory, and excretory functions of the fetus are carried on. It is composed of **fetal** and **maternal** portions.

Fetal Portion.—The fetal portion of the placenta consists of the villi of the chorion frondosum; these branch repeatedly, and increase enormously in size. These greatly ramified villi are suspended in the intervillous space, and are bathed in maternal blood, which is conveyed to the space by the uterine arteries and

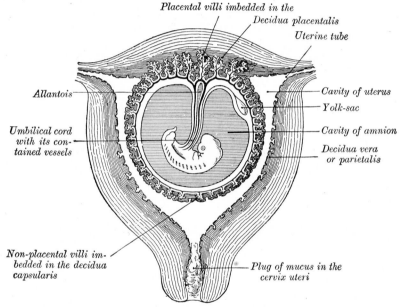

Placental villi imbedded in the
Decidua placentalis
Uterine tube

Allantois

Umbilical cord with its con-tained vessels

Cavity of uterus
Yolk-sac
Cavity of amnion
Decidua vera or parietalis

Non-placental villi im-bedded in the decidua capsularis

Plug of mucus in the cervix uteri

FIG. 16.—Sectional plan of the gravid uterus in the third and fourth month. (Modified from Wagner.)

carried away by the uterine veins. A branch of an umbilical artery enters each villus and ends in a capillary plexus from which the blood is drained by a tributary of the umbilical vein. The vessels of the villus are surrounded by a thin layer of mesoderm consisting of gelatinous connective tissue, which is covered by two strata of ectodermal cells derived from the trophoblast: the deeper stratum, next the mesodermic tissue, represents the cytotrophoblast or layer of Langhans; the superficial, in contact with the maternal blood, the syncytiotrophoblast (Figs. 12 and 13). After the fifth month the two strata of cells are condensed to a single layer of somewhat flattened cells.

Maternal Portion.—The maternal portion of the placenta is formed by the decidua placentalis. The changes involve the disappearance of the greater por-tion of the stratum compactum, but the deeper part of this layer persists and is condensed to form what is known as the **basal plate**. Between this plate and the uterine muscular fibres are the stratum spongiosum and the boundary layer; through these and the basal plate the uterine arteries and veins pass to and from the intervillous space. The endothelial lining of the uterine vessels ceases at the point where they terminate in the intervillous space which is lined by the syncytio-trophoblast. Portions of the stratum compactum persist and are condensed to form a series of septa, which extend from the basal plate through the thickness

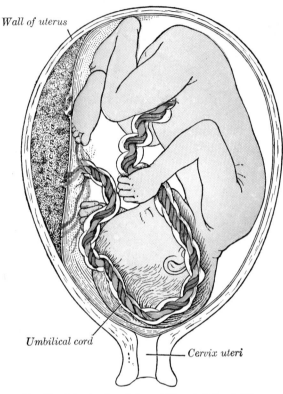

Wall of uterus

Umbilical cord

Cervix uteri

Fig. 17.—Fetus in utero, between fifth and sixth months.

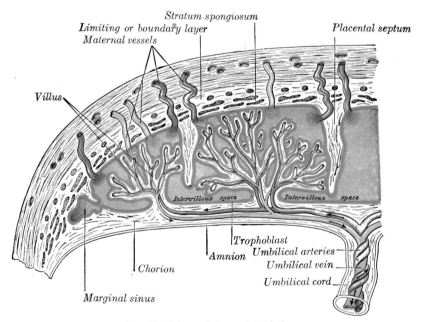

Stratum spongiosum
Limiting or boundary layer
Maternal vessels
Placental septum
Villus
Intervillous space
Intervillous space
Trophoblast
Amnion *Umbilical arteries*
Chorion *Umbilical vein*
Umbilical cord
Marginal sinus

Fig. 18.—Scheme of placental circulation.

of the placenta and subdivide it into the lobules or **cotyledons** seen on the uterine surface of the detached placenta.

The fetal and maternal blood currents traverse the placenta, the former passing through the bloodvessels of the placental villi and the latter through the inter-villous space (Fig. 18). The two currents do not intermingle, being separated from each other by the delicate walls of the villi. Nevertheless, the fetal blood is able

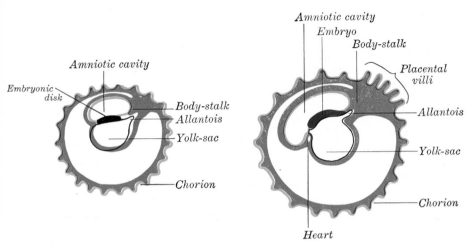

FIG. 19.—Diagram illustrating early formation of allantois and differentiation of body-stalk.

FIG. 20.—Diagram showing later stage of allantoic development with commencing constriction of the yolk-sac.

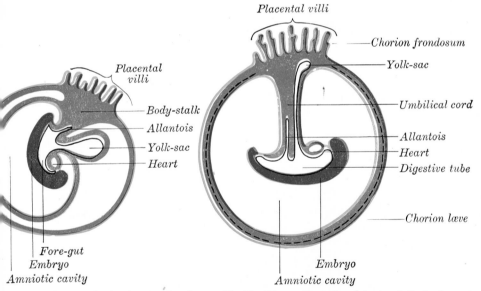

FIG. 21.—Diagram showing the expansion of amnion and constriction of the yolk-sac.

FIG. 22.—Diagram illustrating a later stage in the development of the umbilical cord.

to absorb, through the walls of the villi, oxygen and nutritive materials from the maternal blood, and give up to the latter its waste products. The blood, so purified, is carried back to the fetus by the umbilical vein. It will thus be seen that the placenta not only establishes a mechanical connection between the mother and the fetus, but subserves for the latter the purposes of nutrition, respiration, and ex-cretion. In favor of the view that the placenta possesses certain selective powers

3

may be mentioned the fact that glucose is more plentiful in the maternal than in the fetal blood. It is interesting to note also that the proportion of iron, and of lime and potash, in the fetus is increased during the last months of pregnancy.

The placenta is usually attached near the fundus uteri, and more frequently on the posterior than on the anterior wall of the uterus. It may, however, occupy a lower position and, in rare cases, its site is close to the internal os of the uterus, which it may occlude, thus giving rise to the condition known as *placenta previa*.

Separation of the Placenta.—After the child is born, the placenta and membranes are expelled from the uterus as the **after-birth**. The separation of the placenta from the uterine wall takes place through the stratum spongiosum, and necessarily causes rupture of the uterine vessels. The orifices of the torn vessels are, however, closed by the firm contraction of the uterine muscular fibers, and thus *postpartum hemorrhage* is controlled. The epithelial lining of the uterus is regenerated by the proliferation and extension of the epithelium which lines the persistent portions of the uterine glands in the unaltered layer of the decidua.

The expelled placenta appears as a discoid mass which weighs about 450 gm. and has a diameter of from 15 to 20 cm. Its average thickness is about 3 cm., but this diminishes rapidly toward the circumference of the disk, which is continuous with the membranes. Its uterine surface is divided by a series of fissures into lobules or **cotyledons**, the fissures containing the remains of the septa which extended between the maternal and fetal portions. Most of these septa end in irregular or pointed processes; others, especially those near the edge of the placenta, pass through its thickness and are attached to the chorion. In the early months these septa convey branches of the uterine arteries which open into the intervillous space on the surfaces of the septa. The fetal surface of the placenta is smooth, being closely invested by the amnion. Seen through the latter, the chorion presents a mottled appearance, consisting of gray, purple, or yellowish areas. The umbilical cord is usually attached near the center of the placenta, but may be inserted anywhere between the center and the margin; in some cases it is inserted into the membranes, *i. e.*, the **velamentous insertion.** From the attachment of the cord the larger branches of the umbilical vessels radiate under the amnion, the veins being deeper and larger than the arteries. The remains of the vitelline duct and yolk-sac may be sometimes observed beneath the amnion, close to the cord, the former as an attenuated thread, the latter as a minute sac.

On section, the placenta presents a soft, spongy appearance, caused by the greatly branched villi; surrounding them is a varying amount of maternal blood giving the dark red color to the placenta. Many of the larger villi extend from the chorionic to the decidual surface, while others are attached to the septa which separate the cotyledons; but the great majority of the villi hang free in the intervillous space.

The Amnion.—The exact mode of origin of the amnion in man is unknown. In the monkey it arises from a group of trophoblast cells over the inner cell-mass. As the latter flattens out into the embryonic disk these amniotic cells form a membrane of cuboidal cells attached to the edge of the disk. Fluid is secreted between the amnion and embryonic disk and forms the amniotic cavity (Fig. 27). As the amnion increases in size its cells become flat and mesenchyme separates it from the cytotrophoblast (Fig. 28). The outer surface of the amnion becomes covered by a layer of mesoderm. About the fourth week fluid (liquor amnii) accumulates and expands it until it comes into contact with the inner wall of the chorionic sac and obliterates the primitive blastocyst cavity. It also grows around the body-stalk and yolk-sac and thus forms the covering of the umbilical cord (Figs. 19 to 22).

The liquor amnii increases in quantity up to the sixth or seventh month of pregnancy, after which it diminishes somewhat; at the end of pregnancy it amounts to about 1 liter. It allows of the free movements of the fetus during the later stages of pregnancy, and also protects it by diminishing the risk of injury from without. It contains less than 2 per cent. of solids, consisting of urea and other extractives, inorganic salts, a small amount of protein, and frequently a trace of sugar. That some of the liquor amnii is swallowed by the fetus is proved by the fact that epidermal débris and hairs have been found among the contents of the fetal alimentary canal.

The Body-stalk and Umbilical Cord.—The body-stalk connects the embryonic disk with the trophoblast or chorion. The inner cell-mass is at first directly in contact with the trophoblast. After the development of the amnion on one side of the embryonic disk and the yolk-sac on the other they become surrounded by chorionic mesoderm which anchors the embryo to the inner wall of the chorion (Fig. 28). As the embryo and the chorion increase in size this attachment becomes relatively reduced and extends from the posterior end of the embryo to the chorion (Figs. 19 to 24). When the posterior end of the embryo elongates, its attachment to the embryo becomes ventral (Figs. 25 and 26). The allantois, a tubular diverticulum of the posterior part of the yolk-sac, grows into the body-stalk. In its mesenchymal wall are developed the large umbilical bloodvessels. They join the chorionic vessels and thus provide the vascular pathway from the embryo to the chorion. With the development of the embryo and the expansion of the amnion around the body-stalk and yolk-sac the umbilical cord is formed. The mesoderm of the body-stalk blends with that of the yolk-sac and its elongated vitelline duct. The mesoderm of the cord develops into a gelatinous tissue, **jelly of Wharton.** The vitelline vessels and duct, together with the right umbilical vein, undergo atrophy and disappear; and thus the cord, at birth, contains a pair of umbilical arteries and one (the left) umbilical vein. It attains a length of about 50 cm.

THE YOLK–SAC AND ALLANTOIS.

Endodermal cells arise from the inner cell mass. Two distinct layers are evident. One consists of cuboidal cells and lies against the embryonic disk. It gives rise to the gut endoderm. The second layer separated by a cleft from the gut endoderm consists of flattened cells. It gives rise to the yolk sac endoderm (Fig. 27). The cleft rapidly enlarges into a dual yolk-sac. Later, the expansion of the amnion constricts the connection between the two parts, namely, the gut or primitive alimentary canal and the extra-embryonic part, the vitelline duct, and yolk-sac (Figs. 19 to 22).

The yolk-sac is filled with fluid, the **vitelline fluid,** which possibly may be utilized for the nourishment of the embryo during the earlier stages of its existence. Blood is conveyed to the wall of the sac by the primitive aortæ, and after circulating through a wide-meshed capillary plexus, is returned by the vitelline veins to the tubular heart of the embryo. This constitutes the **vitelline circulation,** and by means of it nutritive material is absorbed from the yolk-sac and conveyed to the embryo. At the end of the fourth week the yolk-sac presents the appearance of a small pear-shaped vesicle (umbilical vesicle) opening into the digestive tube by the long narrow **vitelline duct.** As the amnion spreads around the body-stalk and over the inner surface of the chorion, the proximal part of the vitelline duct becomes enclosed in the umbilical cord, the distal part extends to the placenta and ends in the yolk-sac vesicle which lies between amnion and chorion either on the placenta or a short distance from it. The vesicle can be seen in the after-birth as a small, somewhat oval-shaped body whose diameter varies from 1 mm. to 5 mm. As a rule the duct undergoes complete obliteration during the seventh week, but in about 3 per cent. of cases a continuation of it within the embryo persists as a diverticulum from the small intestine, **Meckel's diverticulum,** which is situated about 3 or 4 feet above the ileocolic junction, and may be attached by a fibrous cord to the abdominal wall at the umbilicus.

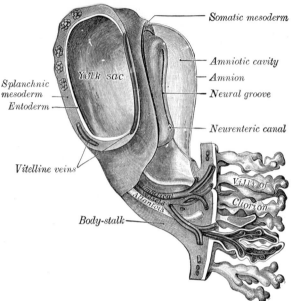

Fig. 23.—Model of human embryo 1.3 mm. long.   (After Eternod.)

The Allantois (Figs. 19 to 22) arises as a tubular diverticulum of the posterior part of the yolk-sac; when the hind-gut is developed the allantois is carried back-

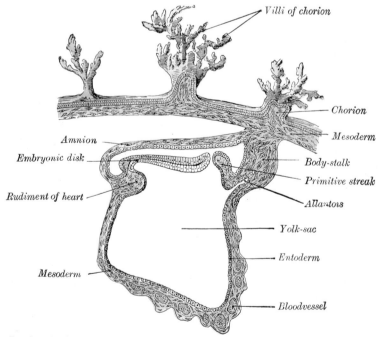

Fig. 24.—Section through the embryo which is represented in Fig. 16.   (After Graf Spee.)

ward with it and then opens into the cloaca or terminal part of the hind-gut; it grows out into the body-stalk, a mass of mesoderm which lies below and around the tail end of the embryo. The diverticulum is lined by entoderm and covered by mesoderm, and in the latter are carried the allantoic or umbilical vessels.

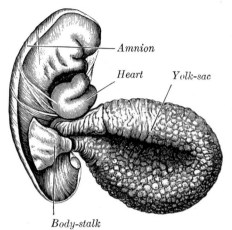

Fig. 25.—Human embryo of 2.6 mm. (His.)

In reptiles, birds, and many mammals the allantois expands into a large sac, acquires an elaborate blood supply and plays an important role in the early nutrition of the embryo. In man and other primates it remains rudimentary. Its blood-vessels, however, become functionally significant as the umbilical vessels.

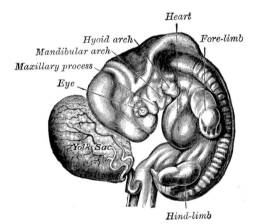

Fig. 26.—Human embryo from thirty-one to thirty-four days. (His.)

THE DEVELOPMENT OF THE EMBRYO FROM THE INNER CELL–MASS.

The Inner Cell-mass becomes distinguishable in the late morula stage. As fluid accumulates in the blastocyst cavity the inner cell-mass remains adherent to the animal pole. After the formation of the amnion from the trophoblast the inner cell-mass becomes known as the embryonic disk (Fig. 27).

The Embryonic Disk now consists of a layer of columnar cells somewhat higher in the center than at the periphery to which is attached the amnion (Fig. 28). The amnion does not contribute cells to the embryo. On the ventral side of the disk the yolk-sac develops from the inner cell-mass. The amnion, embryonic disk and yolk-sac are anchored to the chorion by chorionic mesoderm (Fig. 28). The yolk-sac is in contact by a considerable area with the ventral surface of the disk. Along the midline of the posterior part of the disk the **primitive streak** is produced by multiplication of cells in the axial line. Its location is marked by the **primitive groove** (Figs. 29 and 30). The disk is at first nearly round but it soon lengthens in the anterior-posterior direction.

In front of the primitive streak the embryonic disk cells multiply to form the **primitive node** (Hensen's knot) (Fig. 30). From the anterior end of the primitive

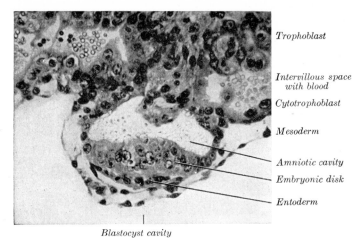

Trophoblast

Intervillous space with blood

Cytotrophoblast

Mesoderm

Amniotic cavity

Embryonic disk

Entoderm

Blastocyst cavity

FIG.—27. Section through a twelve-day monkey embryo showing embryonic disk, amnion, amniotic sac, chorion, chorionic mesoderm and beginning yolk-sac and blastocyst or chorionic cavity. The chorion is imbedded in the uterine wall in this region. The chorionic sac at this magnification would be about a foot in diameter. × 300. (Carnegie collection.)

groove a canal, the neurenteric canal or "blastopore," passes through the primitive node to the yolk-sac. On the dorsal surface the medullary folds grow upward. The lateral regions of the disk form the ectoderm of the body wall. Posterior to the primitive streak is the cloacal membrane.

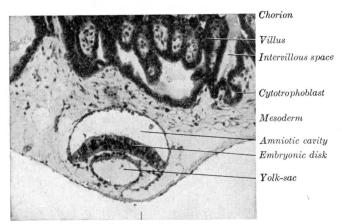

Chorion

Villus

Intervillous space

Cytotrophoblast

Mesoderm

Amniotic cavity

Embryonic disk

Yolk-sac

Blastocyst or chorionic cavity

FIG. 28.—Section through a seventeen-day monkey embryo showing embryonic disk, amnion and yolk-sac surrounded by chorionic mesoderm. This part of the chorion has large villi. × 100. (Carnegie collection.)

The Primitive Streak (Figs. 29, 30 and 31) is clearly derived from the embryonic disk. From it many cells migrate laterally and multiply to form the primitive mesoderm, a layer between the embryonic disk and the yolk-sac. The angioblasts, the primitive blood-vascular cells of the embryo, probably arise from the primitive streak, posterior to the region which gives origin to the mesoderm. The primitive streak is a temporary structure.

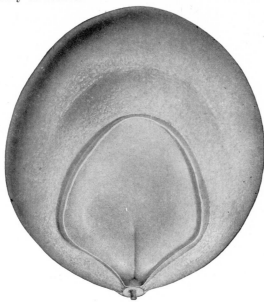

FIG. 29.—Dorsal view, human embryo of the presomite stage. The embryonic disk surrounded by the cut edge of the amnion rests on the large yolk-sac. The primitive groove extends forward from the body-stalk. × 50. (Streeter.)

The Primitive Node (Figs. 30 and 31*C*) is continuous with the anterior end of the primitive streak but appears to subserve an entirely different function. According to Heuser it probably does not give off mesoderm but seems to be intimately concerned with the formation of the notochord which is continuous with its anterior end. As the notochord elongates, the primitive node with its neurenteric canal remains at the caudal end of the notochord which grows in a caudal direction.

The Notochord.—The notochord begins to develop at the anterior end of the primitive node before the neural folds appear (Fig. 31*B*). It is usually described as developing from a furrow-like thickening of the entoderm in the axial line beneath the neural groove. The chordal furrow extends forward from the primitive node. Its margins come into contact ventrally to form a rod of cells in which traces of a canal can be detected for a time. The neurenteric canal opens into the posterior end of the chordal furrow. The exact rôles of the primitive node, entoderm and neurenteric canal in the formation of the notochord are yet to be completely worked out. The notochord separates completely from the entoderm and lies between it and the neural tube. It constitutes the foundation of the axial skeleton, since around it the segments of the vertebral column are formed.

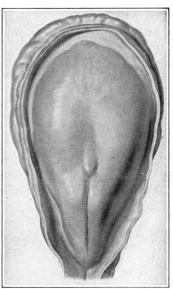

FIG. 30.—Embryonic disk of sixteen-day-old human embryo surrounded by cut edge of amnion. Body-stalk cut off at posterior end. Primitive groove overlies primitive streak. Primitive node at anterior end of primitive groove. × 50. (Heuser.)

They arise from mesoderm which migrates around the notochord but do not arise from it. It extends throughout the entire length of the future vertebral column, and reaches as far as the anterior end of the mid-brain, where it ends in a hook-like extremity in the region of the future dorsum sellæ of the sphenoid bone. It lies at first between the neural tube and the entoderm of the yolk-sac, but soon

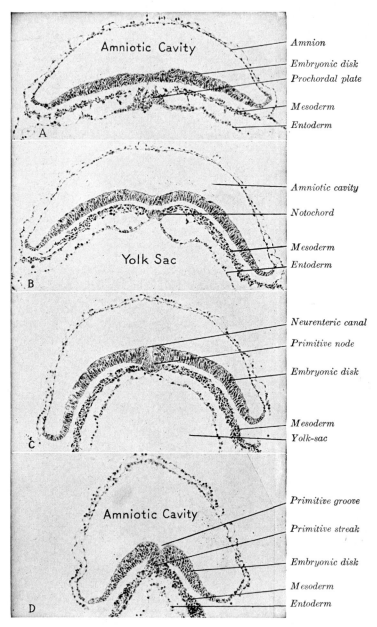

Fig. 31.—Transverse sections through presomite embryo shown in Fig. 30. (*A*) Prochordal region. (*B*) Notochordal region. (*C*) Primitive node region. (*D*) Primitive streak region. × 100. (Heuser.)

becomes separated from them by the mesoderm, which grows medialward and surrounds it. From the mesoderm surrounding the neural tube and notochord, the skull and vertebral column, and the membranes of the brain and medulla spinalis are developed.

The prochordal plate extends forward from the notochord with which it is continuous. It is intimately associated with the entoderm. It appears to give off mesoderm (Fig. 31*A*).

The Mesoderm.—It has already been noted that the cytotrophoblast gives rise to extra-embryonic mesoderm which lines the inner wall of the chorion and extends from there around the embryonic rudiment with its amnion and yolk-sac and anchors or suspends this complex to the chorion. The anchoring mesoderm becomes the body-stalk.

The embryonic mesoderm grows out from the primitive streak and probably also from the prochordal plate between the embryonic disk and the entoderm. It extends throughout the region between the embryonic disk and the entoderm, except in certain regions. One of these is immediately in front of the neural tube. Here the mesoderm extends forward in the form of two crescentic masses, which meet in the middle line so as to enclose behind them an area which is devoid of mesoderm. Over this area the ectoderm and entoderm come into direct contact with each other and constitute a thin membrane, the **buccopharyngeal membrane**, which forms a septum between the primitive mouth and pharynx. In front of the buccopharyngeal area, where the lateral crescents of mesoderm fuse in the middle line, the pericardium is afterward developed, and this region is therefore designated the **pericardial area**. A second region where the mesoderm is absent at least for a time, is that immediately in front of the pericardial area. A third region is at the hind end of the embryo where the ectoderm and entoderm come into apposition and form the **cloacal membrane.**

The blastoderm now consists of three layers, named from without inward: ectoderm, mesoderm, and entoderm; each has distinctive characteristics and gives rise to certain tissues of the body.

Ectoderm.—The ectoderm consists of columnar cells, which are, however, somewhat flattened or cubical toward the margin of the embryonic disk. It forms the whole of the nervous system, the epidermis of the skin, the lining cells of the sebaceous, sudoriferous, and mammary glands, the hairs and nails, the epithelium of the nose and adjacent air sinuses, and that of the cheeks and roof of the mouth. From it also are derived the enamel of the teeth, and the anterior lobe of the hypophysis cerebri, the epithelium of the cornea, conjunctiva, and lacrimal glands, and the neuro-epithelium of the sense organs.

Entoderm.—The entoderm consists at first of cuboidal cells, which subsequently become columnar. It forms the epithelial lining of the whole of the digestive tube excepting part of the mouth and pharynx and the terminal part of the rectum (which are lined by involutions of the ectoderm), the lining cells of all the glands which open into the digestive tube, including those of the liver and pancreas, the epithelium of the auditory tube and tympanic cavity, of the trachea, bronchi, and air cells of the lungs, of the urinary bladder and part of the urethra, the follicles of the thyroid gland, the thymus and the parathyroids.

Mesoderm.—The mesoderm consists of loosely arranged branched cells surrounded by a considerable amount of intercellular fluid. From it the remaining tissues of the body are developed. The endothelial lining of the heart and blood-vessels and the blood corpuscles are, however, probably derived directly from the primitive streak.

As the mesoderm develops between the ectoderm and entoderm it is separated into lateral halves by the notochord and neural tube, presently to be described. A longitudinal groove appears on the dorsal surface of either half and divides it into a medial column, the **paraxial mesoderm**, lying on the side of the neural tube, and a lateral portion, the **lateral mesoderm**. The mesoderm in the floor of the groove connects the paraxial with the lateral mesoderm and is known as the **intermediate cell-mass**; in it the genito-urinary organs are developed. The lateral mesoderm splits into two layers, an outer or **somatic**, which becomes applied to the inner surface of the ectoderm, and with it forms the **somatopleure**; and an inner or **splanchnic**, which adheres to the entoderm, and with it forms the **splanchnopleure** (Fig. 33). The space between the two layers of the lateral mesoderm is termed the **celom**.

The Angioblast, a term used by His, is probably an independent rudiment for the vascular endothelium and the blood cells. The angioblasts of the embryo probably arise from the primitive streak. As already pointed out it seems highly probable that the extra-embryonic angioblasts of the chorion, chorionic villi and body-stalk arise directly from the cytotrophoblast. They become connected with those of the embryo. They form an independent self-perpetuating tissue which spreads through the body as endothelial capillary plexuses. From these plexuses all subsequent vessels develop.

THE NEURAL GROOVE AND TUBE.

In front of the primitive streak two longitudinal ridges, caused by a folding up of the ectoderm, make their appearance, one on either side of the middle line. These are named the **neural folds**; they commence some little distance behind

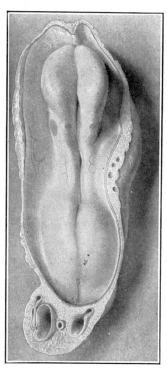

Fig. 32.—Dorsal view human embryo 1.38 mm. in length, medullary groove open, about eighteen days old. X 52.5. (Ingalls.)

the anterior end of the embryonic disk, where they are continuous with each other, and from there gradually extend backward, one on either side of the anterior end of the primitive streak. Between these folds is a shallow median groove, the **neural groove**. The groove gradually deepens as the neural folds become elevated, and ultimately the folds meet and coalesce in the middle line and convert the groove into a closed tube, the **neural tube** or **canal** (Figs. 32 and 34), the ectodermal wall of which forms the rudiment of the nervous system. After the coalescence of the neural folds over the anterior end of the primitive streak, the "blastopore" no longer opens on the surface but into the closed canal of the neural tube, and thus a transitory communication, the **neurenteric canal**, is established between the neural tube and the primitive digestive tube. The coalescence of the neural folds occurs first in the region of the hind-brain, and from there extends forward and backward; toward the end of the third week the front opening (anterior neuropore) of the tube finally closes at the anterior end of the future brain, and forms a recess which is in contact, for a time, with the overlying ectoderm; the hinder part of the neural groove presents for a time a rhomboidal shape, and to this expanded portion the term **sinus rhomboidalis** has been applied. Before the neural groove is closed a ridge of ectodermal cells appears along the prominent margin of each neural fold; this is termed the **neural crest** or **ganglion ridge**, and from it the spinal and cranial nerve ganglia and the ganglia of the sympathetic nervous system are developed. By the upward growth of the mesoderm the neural tube is ultimately separated from the overlying ectoderm.

The cephalic end of the neural groove is expanded and the large vesicle formed corresponds to the future **fore-brain** (*prosencephalon*), **mid-brain** (*mesencephalon*), and **hind-brain** (*rhombencephalon*) (Fig. 38). The walls develop into the nervous tissue and neuroglia of the brain, and the cavity is modified to form its ventricles.

The remainder of the tube forms the **medulla spinalis** or **spinal cord**; from its ectodermal wall the nervous and neuroglial elements of the medulla spinalis are developed while the cavity persists as the central canal.

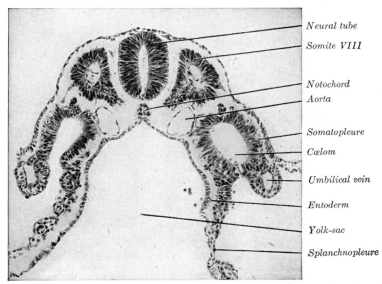

Neural tube

Somite VIII

Notochord

Aorta

Somatopleure

Cœlom

Umbilical vein

Entoderm

Yolk-sac

Splanchnopleure

Fig. 33.—Transverse section through somites VIII (primitive segments) of the 14-somite human embryo shown in Fig. 37. × 150. (Heuser.)

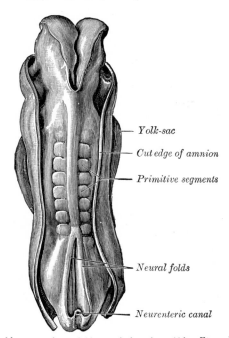

Yolk-sac

Cut edge of amnion

Primitive segments

Neural folds

Neurenteric canal

Fig. 34.—Dorsum of human embryo, 2.11 mm. in length. (After Eternod.)

THE PRIMITIVE SEGMENTS OR SOMITES.

Toward the end of the second week a progressive caudal transverse segmentation of the paraxial mesoderm begins, and it is converted into a series of well-defined, more or less cubical masses, the **primitive segments** (*somites*) (Figs. 33, 34, 37), which occupy the entire length of the trunk on either side of the middle line from the occipital region of the head. Each segment contains a central cavity—**myocœl**—which, however, is soon filled with angular and spindle-shaped cells.

The primitive segments (somites) lie immediately under the ectoderm on the

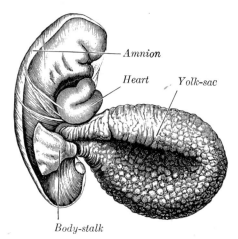

Fig. 35.—Human embryo of 2.6 mm. (His.)

lateral aspect of the neural tube and notochord, and are connected to the lateral mesoderm by the **intermediate cell-mass.** There are 3 occipital, 8 cervical, 12 thoracic, 5 lumbar, and 5 to 8 coccygeal somites. The first occipital somite disappears at an early stage.

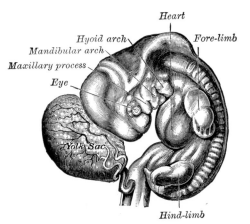

Fig. 36.—Human embryo from thirty-one to thirty-four days. (His.)

THE EARLY GROWTH OF THE EMBRYO.

The embryo increases rapidly in size, but the circumference of the embryonic disk, or line of meeting of the embryonic and amniotic parts of the ectoderm, is of relatively slow growth and gradually comes to form a constriction between the embryo and the greater part of the yolk-sac. By means of this constriction, which corresponds to the future umbilicus, a small part of the yolk-sac is enclosed within the embryo and constitutes the primitive digestive tube.

The embryo increases more rapidly in length than in width, and its cephalic and caudal ends soon extend beyond the corresponding parts of the circumference of the embryonic disk and are bent in a ventral direction to form the **cephalic** and **caudal folds** respectively (Figs. 21, 22, 24). The cephalic fold is first formed, and carries with it the posterior end of the pericardial area, so that this area and the buccopharyngeal membrane are folded back under the head of the embryo which now encloses a diverticulum of the yolk-sac named the **fore-gut**. The caudal end of the embryo is at first connected to the chorion by a band of mesoderm called the **body-stalk**, but with the formation of the caudal fold the body-stalk assumes a ventral position; a diverticulum of the yolk-sac extends into the tail fold and is

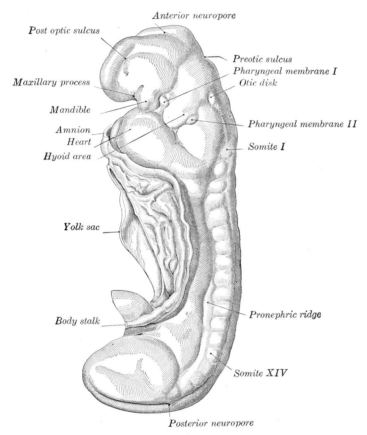

Fig. 37.—Lateral view of a 14-somite human embryo. × 50. (Heuser.)

termed the **hind-gut**. Between the fore-gut and the hind-gut there exists for a time a wide opening into the yolk-sac, but the latter is gradually reduced to a small pear-shaped sac (sometimes termed the **umbilical vesicle**), and the channel of communication is at the same time narrowed and elongated to form a tube called the **vitelline duct**.

THE BRANCHIAL REGION.

The Branchial or Visceral Arches and Pharyngeal Pouches.—In the lateral walls of the anterior part of the fore-gut five *pharyngeal pouches* appear (Fig. 40); each of the upper four pouches is prolonged into a dorsal and a ventral diverticulum. Over these pouches corresponding indentations of the ectoderm occur, forming what are known as the **branchial** or **outer pharyngeal grooves**. The intervening mesoderm is pressed aside and the ectoderm comes for a time into contact with the entodermal lining of the fore-gut, and the two layers unite along the floors of the grooves to form thin **closing membranes** between the fore-gut and the exterior. Later the mesoderm again penetrates between the entoderm and the ectoderm. In gill-bearing animals the closing membranes disappear, and the grooves become

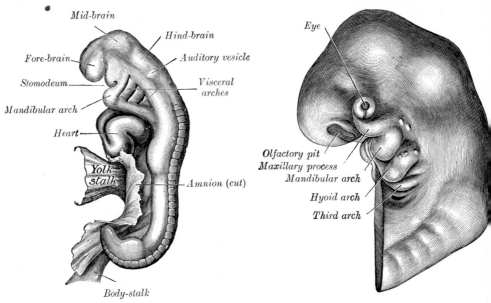

FIG. 38.—Embryo of the fourth week. (His.)

FIG. 39.—Head end of human embryo, about the end of the fourth week. (From model by Peter.)

complete clefts, the **gill-clefts**, opening from the pharynx on to the exterior; perforation, however, does not occur in birds or mammals. The grooves separate a series of rounded bars or arches, the **branchial** or **visceral arches**, in which thickening of the mesoderm takes place (Figs. 38 and 39). The dorsal ends of these arches are attached to the sides of the head, while the ventral extremities ultimately meet in the middle line of the neck. In all, six arches make their appearance, but of these only the first four are visible externally. The first arch is named the

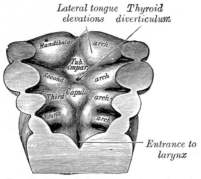

FIG. 40.—Floor of pharynx of embryo shown in Fig. 38.

mandibular, and the second the hyoid; the others have no distinctive names. The mandibular and hyoid arches are the first ones to appear and are recognizable in the 14-somite stage (Fig. 37). In each arch a cartilaginous bar, consisting of right and left halves, is developed, and with each of these there is one of the primitive aortic arches.

The **mandibular arch** lies between the first branchial groove and the stomodeum; from it are developed the lower lip, the mandible, the muscles of mastication, and the anterior part of the tongue. Its cartilaginous bar is formed by what are known as **Meckel's cartilages** (right and left) (Fig. 41); above this the incus is developed. The dorsal end of each cartilage is connected with the ear-capsule and is ossified to form the malleus; the ventral ends meet each other in the region of the symphysis menti, and are usually regarded as undergoing ossification to form that portion of the mandible which contains the incisor teeth. The intervening part of the cartilage disappears; the portion immediately adjacent to the malleus is replaced by fibrous membrane, which constitutes the spheno-mandibular ligament, while from the connective tissue covering the remainder of the cartilage the greater part of the mandible is ossified. From the dorsal ends of the mandibular arch a triangular process, the **maxillary process**, grows forward on either side and forms the cheek and lateral part of the upper lip. The **second** or **hyoid arch** assists in forming the side and front of the neck. From its cartilage are developed the styloid process, stylohyoid ligament, and lesser cornu of the hyoid bone. The stapes probably arises in the upper part of this arch. The cartilage of the **third arch** gives origin to the greater cornu of the hyoid bone. The ventral ends of the second and third arches unite with those of the opposite side, and form a transverse band, from which the body of the hyoid bone and the posterior part of the tongue are developed. The ventral portions of the cartilages of the **fourth** and **fifth arches** unite to form the thyroid cartilage; from the cartilages of the **sixth arch** the cricoid and arytenoid cartilages and the cartilages of the trachea are developed. The mandibular and hyoid arches grow more rapidly than those behind them, with the result that the latter become, to a certain extent, telescoped within the former, and a deep depression, the **sinus cervicalis**, is formed on either side of the neck. This sinus is bounded in front by the hyoid arch, and behind by the thoracic wall; it is ultimately obliterated by the fusion of its walls.

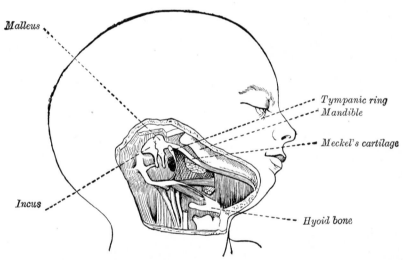

Fig. 41.—Head and neck of a human embryo eighteen weeks old, with Meckel's cartilage and hyoid bar exposed. (After Kölliker.)

From the first branchial groove the concha auriculæ and external acoustic meatus are developed, while around the groove there appear, on the mandibular and hyoid arches, a number of swellings from which the auricula or pinna is formed. The first pharyngeal pouch is prolonged dorsally to form the auditory tube and the tympanic cavity; the closing membrane between the mandibular and hyoid arches is invaded by mesoderm, and forms the tympanic membrane. No traces of the second, third, and fourth branchial grooves persist. The inner part of the second pharyngeal pouch is named the **sinus tonsillaris**; in it the tonsil is developed, above which a trace of the sinus persists as the supratonsillar fossa. The fossa of Rosenmüller or lateral recess of the pharynx is by some regarded as a persistent part of the second pharyngeal pouch, but it is probably developed as a secondary formation. From the third pharyngeal pouch the thymus arises as an entodermal diverticulum on either side, and from the fourth pouches small diverticula project and become incorporated with the thymus, but in man these diverticula probably never form true thymus tissue. The parathyroids also arise as diverticula from the third and fourth pouches. From the fifth pouches the ultimobranchial bodies

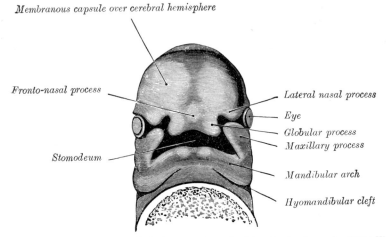

FIG. 42.—Under surface of the head of a human embryo about twenty-nine days old. (After His.)

originate and are enveloped by the lateral prolongations of the median thyroid rudiment; they do not, however, form true thyroid tissue, nor are any traces of them found in the human adult.

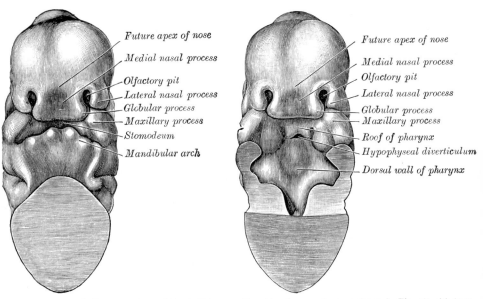

FIG. 43.—Head end of human embryo of about thirty to thirty-one days. (From model by Peters.)

FIG. 44.—Same embryo as shown in Fig. 43, with front wall of pharynx removed.

The Nose and Face.—During the third week two areas of thickened ectoderm, the **olfactory areas**, appear immediately under the fore-brain in the anterior wall of the stomodeum, one on either side of a region termed the **fronto-nasal process** (Fig. 42). By the upgrowth of the surrounding parts these areas are converted into pits. the **olfactory pits**, which indent the fronto-nasal process and divide it into a

medial and two **lateral nasal processes** (Fig. 43). The rounded lateral angles of the medial process constitute the **globular processes** of His. The olfactory pits form the rudiments of the nasal cavities, and from their ectodermal lining the epithelium of the nasal cavities, with the exception of that of the inferior meatuses, is

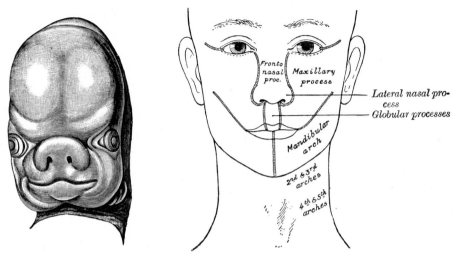

FIG. 45.—Head of a human embryo of about eight weeks, in which the nose and mouth are formed. (His.)

FIG. 46.—Diagram showing the regions of the adult face and neck related to the fronto-nasal process and the branchial arches.

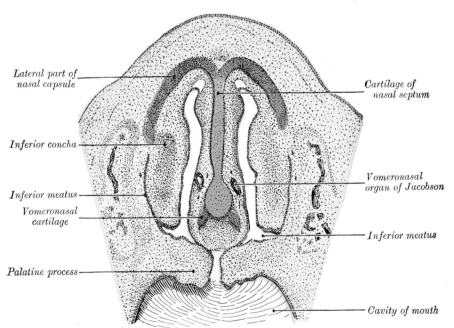

FIG. 47.—Frontal section of nasal cavities of a human embryo 28 mm. long. (Kollmann.)

derived. The globular processes are prolonged backward as plates, termed the **nasal laminæ**: these laminæ are at first some distance apart, but, gradually approaching, they ultimately fuse and form the nasal septum; the processes themselves meet in the middle line, and form the premaxillæ and the philtrum or central part of the upper lip (Fig. 46). The depressed part of the medial nasal process

4

between the globular processes forms the lower part of the nasal septum or **columella**; while above this is seen a prominent angle, which becomes the future apex (Figs. 43, 44), and still higher a flat area, the future bridge, of the nose. The lateral nasal processes form the alæ of the nose.

Continuous with the dorsal end of the mandibular arch, and growing forward from its cephalic border, is a triangular process, the **maxillary process**, the ventral extremity of which is separated from the mandibular arch by a > shaped notch (Fig. 42). The maxillary process forms the lateral wall and floor of the orbit, and in it are ossified the zygomatic bone and the greater part of the maxilla; it meets with the lateral nasal process, from which, however, it is separated for a time by a groove, the **naso-optic furrow,** that extends from the furrow encircling the eyeball to the olfactory pit. The maxillary processes ultimately fuse with the lateral nasal and globular processes, and form the lateral parts of the upper lip and the posterior boundaries of the nares (Figs. 45, 46). From the third to the fifth month the nares are filled by masses of epithelium, on the breaking down and disappearance of which the permanent openings are produced. The maxillary process also gives rise to the lower portion of the lateral wall of the nasal cavity. The roof of the nose and the remaining parts of the lateral wall, viz., the ethmoidal

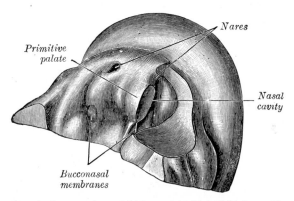

Primitive palate

Nares

Nasal cavity

Bucconasal membranes

FIG. 48.—Primitive palate of a human embryo of thirty-seven to thirty-eight days. (From model by Peters.) On the left side the lateral wall of the nasal cavity has been removed.

labyrinth, the inferior nasal concha, the lateral cartilage, and the lateral crus of the alar cartilage, are developed in the lateral nasal process. By the fusion of the maxillary and nasal processes in the roof of the stomodeum the **primitive palate** (Fig. 49) is formed, and the olfactory pits extend backward above it. The posterior end of each pit is closed by an epithelial membrane, the **bucco-nasal membrane,** formed by the apposition of the nasal and stomodeal epithelium. By the rupture of these membranes the **primitive choanæ** or openings between the olfactory pits and the stomodeum are established. The floor of the nasal cavity is completed by the development of a pair of shelf-like **palatine processes** which extend medial-ward from the maxillary processes (Figs. 47 and 48); these coalesce with each other in the middle line, and constitute the entire palate, except a small part in front which is formed by the premaxillary bones. Two apertures persist for a time between the palatine processes and the premaxillæ and represent the permanent channels which in the lower animals connect the nose and mouth. The union of the parts which form the palate commences in front, the premaxillary and palatine processes joining in the eighth week, while the region of the future hard palate is completed by the ninth, and that of the soft palate by the eleventh week. By the completion of the palate the **permanent choanæ** are formed and are situated a considerable distance behind the primitive choanæ. The deformity known as cleft palate results from a non-union of the palatine processes, and that of hare-lip through a non-union of the maxillary and globular processes (see page 127). The nasal cavity becomes divided by a vertical septum, which extends downward and backward from the medial nasal process and nasal laminæ, and unites below with the palatine processes. Into this septum a plate of cartilage extends from the under aspect of the ethmoid plate of the chondrocranium. The anterior part of this cartilaginous plate persists as the septal cartilage of the nose and the medial crus of the alar cartilage, but the posterior and upper parts are replaced by the vomer and perpendicular plate of the ethmoid. On either side of the nasal septum, at its lower and anterior part, the ectoderm is invaginated to form a blind pouch or diverticulum, which extends backward and upward into the nasal septum and is supported by a curved plate of cartilage. These pouches form the rudiments of the **vomero-nasal organs** of Jacobson, which open below, close to the junction of the premaxillary and maxillary bones.

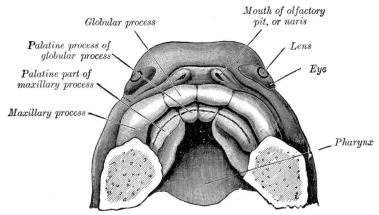

FIG. 49.—The roof of the mouth of a human embryo, aged about two and a half months, showing the mode of formation of the palate. (His.)

The Limbs.—The limbs begin to make their appearance in the fourth week as small elevations or buds at the side of the trunk. Unsegmented somatic meso-derm pushes into the limb buds and multiplies by division of its cells into closely packed cellular masses. The intrinsic muscles of the limbs differentiate *in situ* from the peripheral portions of this unsegmented mesoderm. The upper limb begins its differentiation in the neck region and receives its nerve supply from the fourth cervical to the second thoracic before it migrates caudally. The lower limb arises in the region from the twelfth thoracic to the fourth sacral inclu-sive receiving nerves from these segments before its caudal migration. The axial part of the mesoderm of the limb-bud becomes condensed and converted into its cartilaginous skeleton, and by the ossification of this the bones of the limbs are formed. By the sixth week the three chief divisions of the limbs are marked off by furrows—the upper into arm, forearm, and hand; the lower into thigh, leg, and foot (Fig. 50). The limbs are at first directed backward nearly parallel to the long axis of the trunk, and each presents two surfaces and two borders. Of the surfaces, one — the future *flexor* surface of the limb—is directed ventrally; the other, the *extensor* surface, dorsally; one border, the *preaxial*, looks forward toward the cephalic end of the embryo, and the other, the *postaxial*, backward toward the caudal end. The lateral epicondyle of the humerus, the radius, and the thumb lie along the preaxial border of the upper limb; and the medial epicondyle of the femur, the tibia, and the great toe along the corresponding border of the lower limb. The preaxial part is derived from the anterior segments, the postaxial from the posterior segments of the limb-bud; and this explains, to a large extent, the innervation of the adult limb, the nerves of the more anterior segments being distributed along the preaxial (radial or tibial), and those of the more posterior along the postaxial (ulnar or fibular) border of the limb. The limbs next undergo a rotation through an angle of 90° around their long axes the rotation being effected almost entirely at the limb girdles. In the upper limb the rotation is outward and forward; in the lower limb, inward and backward. As a consequence of this rotation the preaxial (radial) border of the fore-limb is directed lateralward, and the preaxial (tibial) border of the hind-limb is directed medialward; thus the flexor surface of the fore-limb is turned forward, and that of the hind-limb backward.

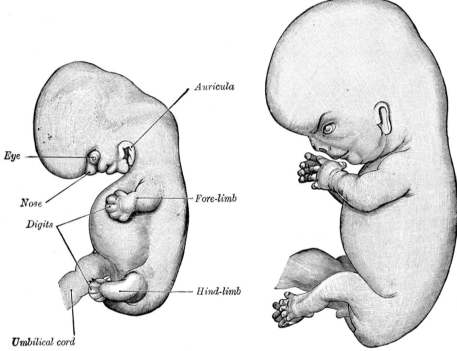

FIG. 50.—Embryo of about six weeks. (His.)   FIG. 51.—Human embryo about eight and a half weeks old. (His.)

DEVELOPMENT OF THE BODY CAVITIES.

In the human embryo described by Peters the mesoderm outside the embryonic disk is split into two layers enclosing an extra-embryonic cœlom; there is no trace of an intra-embryonic cœlom. At a later stage four cavities are formed within the embryo, viz., one on either side within the mesoderm of the pericardial area, and one in either lateral mass of the general mesoderm. All these are at first independent of each other and of the extra-embryonic celom, but later they become continuous. The two cavities in the general mesoderm unite on the ventral aspect of the gut and form the pleuro-peritoneal cavity, which becomes continuous with the remains of the extra-embryonic celom around the umbilicus; the two cavities in the pericardial area rapidly join to form a single pericardial cavity, and from this two lateral diverticula extend caudalward to open into the pleuro-peritoneal cavity (Fig. 52). Between the two latter diverticula is a mass of mesoderm containing the ducts of Cuvier, and this is continuous ventrally with the mesoderm in which the umbilical veins are passing to the sinus venosus. A septum of mesoderm thus extends across the body of the embryo. It is attached in front to the body-wall between the pericardium and umbilicus; behind to the body-wall at the level of the second cervical segment; laterally it is deficient where the pericardial and pleuro-peritoneal cavities communicate, while it is perforated in the middle line by the fore-gut. This partition is termed the **septum transversum**, and is at first a bulky plate

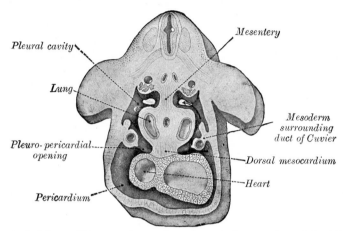

FIG. 52.—Figure obtained by combining several successive sections of a human embryo of about the fourth **week.** (From Kollmann.)   The upper arrow is in the pleuroperitoneal opening, the lower in the pleuropericardial.

of tissue. As development proceeds the dorsal end of the septum is carried grad-ually caudalward, and when it reaches the fifth cervical segment muscular tissue with the phrenic nerve grows into it. It continues to recede, however, until it

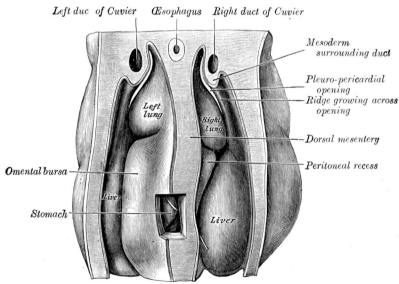

FIG. 53.—Upper part of celom of human embryo of 6.8 mm., seen from behind.   (From model by Piper.)

reaches the position of the adult diaphragm on the bodies of the upper lumbar vertebræ. The liver buds grow into the septum transversum and undergo development there.

The lung buds meantime have grown out from the fore-gut, and project laterally into the forepart of the pleuro-peritoneal cavity; the developing stomach and liver are imbedded in the septum transversum; caudal to this the intestines project into the back part of the pleuro-peritoneal cavity (Fig. 53). Owing to the descent of the dorsal end of the septum transversum the lung buds come to lie above the septum and thus pleural and peritoneal portions of the pleuro-peritoneal cavity (still, however, in free communication with one another) may be recognized; the pericardial cavity opens into the pleural part.

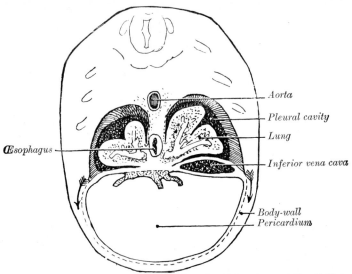

FIG. 54.—Diagram of transverse section through rabbit embryo. (After Keith.)

The ultimate separation of the permanent cavities from one another is effected by the growth of a ridge of tissue on either side from the mesoderm surrounding the duct of Cuvier (Figs. 52, 53). The front part of this ridge grows across and obliterates the pleuro-pericardial opening; the hinder part grows across the pleuro-peritoneal opening.

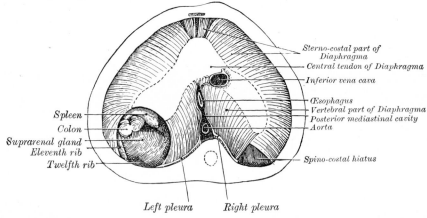

FIG. 55.—The thoracic aspect of the diaphragm of a newly born child in which the communication between the peritoneum and pleura has not been closed on the left side; the position of the opening is marked on the right side by the spinocostal hiatus. (After Keith.)

With the continued growth of the lungs the pleural cavities are pushed forward in the body-wall toward the ventral median line, thus separating the pericardium from the lateral thoracic walls (Fig. 50). The further development of the peritoneal cavity has been described with the development of the digestive tube.

Development of the Cerebrospinal Spaces.—The dura mater, arachnoid and pia mater develop from a thick layer of primitive mesenchyme surrounding the nervous system. In the outer region of this layer there early occurs a condensation of the mesenchyme for the bone, periosteum and part of the dura. This is separated from the nervous system by a layer of loose mesenchyme containing in its meshes albuminous tissue fluid. The pia begins early as a condensation of mesenchymal cells on the surface of the nervous system except in two small areas in the roof of the fourth ventricle. With the beginning of the development of the chorioid plexus in the roof of the fourth ventricle the cerebrospinal fluid is secreted faster than the ventricles expand. The excess fluid is supposed to pass through the above areas, the area membranacea inferior and superior, into tissue spaces and converts them into the subarachnoid spaces. Many cellular connections are forced apart but some remain as the arachnoid trabeculæ which run from the pia to a peripheral condensation for the arachnoid membrane and the inner surface of the dura. This process begins in embryos of 14 mm. and is well established at 26 mm. The process proceeds rapidly in all directions from the future cisterna magna, parallel with the increase in the size of the chorioid plexuses and their increased secretion of fluid. The subdural space is formed by a split in the dura-arachnoid condensation and the differentiation of mesothelial cells on the inner surface of the dura and the outer surface of the arachnoid. A capillary layer of fluid quite separate from the subarachnoid fluid collects between the two layers. This begins in embryos about 50 mm. in length.

MENSTRUAL AGE WITH MEAN SITTING HEIGHT AND WEIGHT OF FETUS. (STREETER.)

Menstrual age, weeks.	Sitting height at end of week, mm.	Increment in height.		Formalin weight, grams.	Increment in weight.	
		mm.	per cent.		grams.	per cent.
8	23	...	...	1.1		
9	31	8	26.0	2.7	1.6	59.3
10	40	9	22.5	4.6	1.9	41.3
11	50	10	20.0	7.9	3.3	41.8
12	61	11	18.0	14.2	6.3	44.4
13	74	13	17.6	26.0	11.8	45.4
14	87	13	15.0	45.0	19.0	42.2
15	101	14	14.0	72.0	27.0	37.5
16	116	15	13.0	108.0	36.0	33.3
17	130	14	10.8	150.0	42.0	28.0
18	142	12	8.4	198.0	48.0	24.2
19	153	11	7.2	253.0	55.0	21.7
20	164	11	6.7	316.0	63.0	20.0
21	175	11	6.3	385.0	69.0	18.0
22	186	11	6.0	460.0	75.0	16.3
23	197	11	5.6	542.0	82.0	15.0
24	208	11	5.3	630.0	88.0	14.0
25	218	10	4.6	723.0	93.0	13.0
26	228	10	4.4	823.0	100.0	12.2
27	238	10	4.2	930.0	107.0	11.5
28	247	9	3.6	1045.0	115.0	11.0
29	256	9	3.5	1174.0	129.0	11.0
30	265	9	3.4	1323.0	149.0	11.3
31	274	9	3.3	1492.0	169.0	11.3
32	283	9	3.1	1680.0	188.0	11.2
33	293	10	3.4	1876.0	196.0	10.4
34	302	9	3.0	2074.0	198.0	9.5
35	311	9	3.0	2274.0	200.0	8.8
36	321	10	3.1	2478.0	204.0	8.2
37	331	10	3.0	2690.0	212.0	8.0
38	341	10	3.0	2914.0	224.0	7.7
39	352	11	3.1	3150.0	236.0	7.5
40	362	10	2.8	3405.0	255.0	7.5

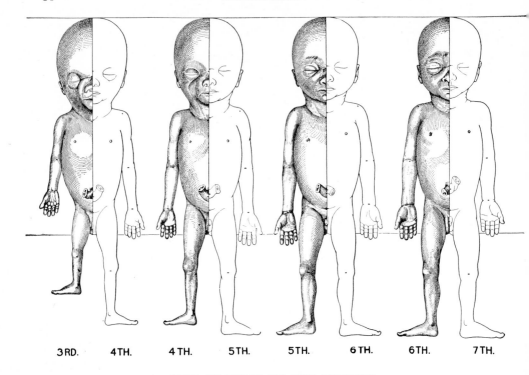

3RD.   4TH.   4TH.   5TH.   5TH.   6TH.   6TH.   7TH.

THE GROWTH OF THE EMBRYO.

First Week.—No fertile human ova of the first week have been examined. From what we know of the monkey and other mammals it seems probable that the egg is fertilized in the upper end of the uterine tube and segments into about eight cells before it passes into the uterus at the end of the third day. In the uterus it continues to segment and develop into a blastocyst with a trophoblast and an inner cell-mass.

Second Week.—The blastocyst enlarges, loses its zona pellucida and becomes implanted in the uterine wall. By the eleventh day the age of the youngest known human embryo, the trophoblast, has developed into actively invading syntiotrophoblast and cytotrophoblast. Primitive villi develop and chorionic mesoderm and angioblasts arise from the cytotrophoblast. The amnion develops from the cytotrophoblast, the inner cell-mass becomes the embryonic disk and the yolk sac begins to form. The primitive streak forms and gives off mesoderm. The notochord begins to form.

Third Week.—During the first part of the third week the neural folds appear (Figs. 13, 23, 24), the allantoic duct begins to develop, the yolk-sac enlarges and bloodvessels begin to form. Before the end of the week the neural folds begin to unite (Fig. 16). The neurenteric canal opens. The primitive segments begin to form. The changes during this week occur with great rapidity.

Fourth Week.—During the fourth week (Figs. 20, 38, 39) the neural folds close, the primitive segments increase in number, the branchial arches appear and the connection of the yolk-sac with the embryo becomes considerably narrowed so that the embryo assumes a more definite form. The limb-buds begin to show and the heart increases greatly in size, producing a prominent bulge in the branchial region.

Fifth Week.—The embryo becomes markedly curved, the head increases greatly in size and the limb-buds show segments (Fig. 21). The branchial arches undergo profound changes and partly disappear. The superficial nose, eye and ear rudiments become prominent.

Sixth Week.—The curvature of the embryo is further diminished. The branchial grooves—except the first—have disappeared, and the rudiments of the fingers and toes can be recognized (Fig. 50).

Seventh and Eighth Weeks.—The flexure of the head is gradually reduced and the neck is somewhat lengthened. The upper lip is completed and the nose is more prominent. The nostrils are directed forward and the palate is not completely developed. The eyelids are present in the shape of folds above and below the eye, and the different parts of the auricula are distinguishable. By the end of the second month the fetus measures from 28 to 30 mm. in length (Fig. 51).

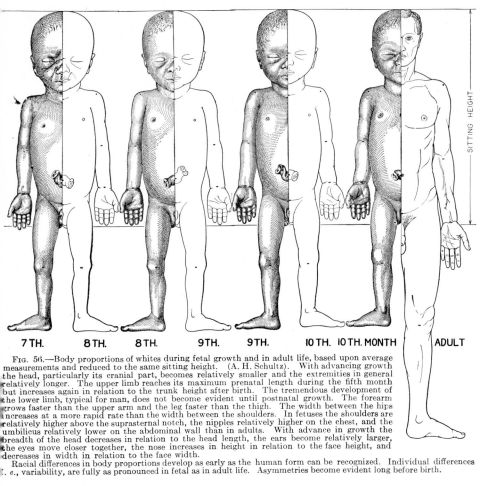

7TH.   8TH.   8TH.   9TH.   9TH.   10TH. 10TH. MONTH   ADULT

SITTING HEIGHT

Fig. 56.—Body proportions of whites during fetal growth and in adult life, based upon average measurements and reduced to the same sitting height. (A. H. Schultz). With advancing growth the head, particularly its cranial part, becomes relatively smaller and the extremities in general relatively longer. The upper limb reaches its maximum prenatal length during the fifth month but increases again in relation to the trunk height after birth. The tremendous development of the lower limb, typical for man, does not become evident until postnatal growth. The forearm grows faster than the upper arm and the leg faster than the thigh. The width between the hips increases at a more rapid rate than the width between the shoulders. In fetuses the shoulders are relatively higher above the suprasternal notch, the nipples relatively higher on the chest, and the umbilicus relatively lower on the abdominal wall than in adults. With advance in growth the breadth of the head decreases in relation to the head length, the ears become relatively larger, the eyes move closer together, the nose increases in height in relation to the face height, and decreases in width in relation to the face width.

Racial differences in body proportions develop as early as the human form can be recognized. Individual differences *i. e.*, variability, are fully as pronounced in fetal as in adult life. Asymmetries become evident long before birth.

Third Month.—The head is extended and the neck is lengthened. The eyelids meet and fuse, remaining closed until the end of the sixth month. The limbs are well-developed and nails appear on the digits. The external generative organs are so far differentiated that it is possible to distinguish the sex. By the end of this month the length of the fetus is about 7 cm., but if the legs be included it is from 9 to 10 cm.

Fourth Month.—The loop of gut which projected into the umbilical cord is withdrawn within the fetus. The hairs begin to make their appearance. There is a general increase in size so that by the end of the fourth month the fetus is from 12 to 13 cm. in length, but if the legs be included it is from 16 to 20 cm.

Fifth Month.—It is during this month that the first movements of the fetus are usually observed The eruption of hair on the head commences, and the *vernix caseosa* begins to be deposited. By the end of this month the total length of the fetus, including the legs, is from 25 to 27 cm.

Sixth Month.—The body is covered by fine hairs (*lanugo*) and the deposit of vernix caseosa is considerable. The papillæ of the skin are developed and the free border of the nail projects from the corium of the dermis. Measured from vertex to heels, the total length of the fetus at the end of this month is from 30 to 32 cm.

Seventh Month.—The pupillary membrane atrophies and the eyelids are open. The testis descends with the vaginal sac of the peritoneum. From vertex to heels the total length at the end of the seventh month is from 35 to 36 cm. The weight is a little over three pounds.

Eighth Month.—The skin assumes a pink color and is now entirely coated with vernix caseosa, and the lanugo begins to disappear. Subcutaneous fat has been developed to a considerable extent, and the fetus presents a plump appearance. The total length, *i. e.*, from head to heels at the end of the eighth month is about 40 cm., and the weight varies between four and one-half and five and one-half pounds.

Ninth Month.—The lanugo has largely disappeared from the trunk. The umbilicus is almost in the middle of the body and the testes are in the scrotum. At full time the fetus weighs from six and one-half to eight pounds, and measures from head to heels about 50 cm.

BIBLIOGRAPHY

EARLY HUMAN EMBRYOS

A well-preserved human embryo of 10 somites. CORNER, G. W.: 1929. Carnegie Cont. to Emb., Vol. 20, pp. 81–102.

A presomite human embryo with chorda canal and prochordal plate. GEORGE, W. C.: 1942. Carnegie Cont. to Emb., Vol. 30, pp. 1–7.

Two human ova of the pre-villous stage, having a developmental age of about seven and nine days respectively. HERTIG, A. T., and J. ROCK: 1945. Carnegie Cont. to Emb., Vol. 31, pp. 65–84.

Two human embryos showing early stages of the definitive yolk sac. HEUSER, C. H., J. ROCK, and A. T. HERTIG: 1945. Carnegie Cont. to Emb., Vol. 31, pp. 85–100.

A human embryo of the presomite period from the uterine tube. KINDRED, J. E.: 1933. Am. J. Anat., Vol. 53, pp. 221–241.

A human embryo of two to three pairs of somites. SHANER, R. F.: 1945. Canadian J. Research, E, Vol. 23, pp. 235–243.

EARLY MAMMALIAN EMBRYOS

The blastocyst of the fisher. ENDERS, R. K., and O. P. PEARSON: 1943. Anat. Rec., Vol. 85, pp. 285–287.

Development of the macaque embryo. HEUSER, C. H., and G. L. STREETER: 1941. Carnegie Cont. to Emb., Vol. 29, pp. 15–55.

Early cleavage stages of the egg of the monkey (Macacus rhesus). LEWIS, W. H., and C. G. HARTMAN: 1933. Carnegie Cont. to Emb., Vol. 24, pp. 187–201.

The embryology of the opossum. McCRADY, E.: 1938. Am. Anat. Mem. No. 16. Wistar Inst., Phila., 233 pp.

PLACENTA, FETAL MEMBRANES AND IMPLANTATION

Delayed implantation and discontinuous development in the mammals. HAMLETT, G. W. D.: 1935. Quart. Rev. of Biol., Vol. 10, pp. 432–447.

The histology and cytology of the human and monkey placenta, with special reference to the trophoblast. WISLOCKI, G. B., and H. S. BENNETT: 1943. Am. J. Anat., Vol. 73, pp. 335–449.

DEVELOPMENTAL PHYSIOLOGY

Fetal behavior. HOOKER, D.: 1939. Res. Publ. Assn. Nerv. Ment. Dis., Vol. 19, pp. 237–243.

Developmental physiology. MOSSMAN, H. W.: 1940. Ann. Rev. Physiol., Vol. 2, pp. 1–20.

Physiology of the Fetus. WINDLE, W. F.: 1940. Saunders, Phila., 249 pp.

EXPERIMENTAL EMBRYOLOGY

The development of limb primordia within the anterior chamber of the eye. EASTLICK, H. L., and R. H. ANDERSON: 1944. J. Morph., Vol. 75, pp. 1–9.

Double hearts produced experimentally in rat embryos. GOSS, C. M.: 1935. J. Exp. Zool., Vol. 72, pp. 33–49.

The effect of male hormone substances upon birth and prenatal development in the rat. HAMILTON, J. B., and J. M. WOLFE: 1938. Anat. Rec., Vol. 70, pp. 433–440.

Heteroplastic grafting in embryology. HARRISON, R. G.: 1934. Harvey Lecture, pp. 116–157.

An attempt at an x-ray analysis of embryonic processes. HARRISON, R. G., W. T. ASTBURY, and K. M. RUDALI: 1940. J. Exp. Zool., Vol. 85, pp. 339–363.

Homotransplantation of embryonic and adult gastro-intestinal tract mucosa of the rat to the anterior chamber of the eye. KAMMERAAD, A.: 1942. J. Exp. Zool., Vol. 91, pp. 45–63.

Experiments on developing rats. II. The development of isolated blastomeres and fused eggs. NICHOLAS, J. S., and B. V. HALL: 1942. J. Exp. Zool., Vol. 90, pp. 441–459.

In vitro fertilization and cleavage of human ovarian eggs. ROCK, J., and M. F. MENKIN: 1944. Science, Vol. 100, pp. 105–107.

Embryonic Development and Induction. SPEMANN, H.: 1938. Yale Univ. Press, New Haven, xii + 401 pp.

Formation of the primitive streak in the explanted chick blastoderm marked with carbon particles. SPRATT, N. T., JR.: 1946. J. Exp. Zool., Vol. 103, pp. 259–304.

ANOMALIES AND MULTIPLE BIRTHS

Multiple congenital anomalies in a stillborn infant. ASHLEY, L. M., and G. E. RICHARDSON: 1943. Anat. Rec., Vol. 86, pp. 457–471.

The survival of the Dionne quintuplets. DAFOE, A. R.: 1940. Am. J. of Obs. and Gyn., Vol. 39, pp. 159–164.

Spontaneous twinning in the amphibia. SCHWIND, J. L.: 1942. Am. J. Anat., Vol. 71, 117–151.

Report of a newborn human presenting sympus dipus, anomalous umbilical vein, transposition of the viscera and other anomalies. SHRYOCK, E. H., J. JANZEN, and M. C. BARNARD: 1942. Anat. Rec., Vol. 82, pp. 347–360.

TEXTBOOKS

Developmental Anatomy. AREY, L. B.: 1946. Saunders, Phila., 5th Ed., ix + 616 pp.

Human Embryology. HAMILTON, W. J., J. D. BOYD, and H. W. MOSSMAN: 1945. Williams & Wilkins, Baltimore, viii + 366 pp.

A Textbook of Embryology. JORDAN, H. E., and J. E. KINDRED: 1942. Appleton-Century, New York, 4th Ed., xiv + 613 pp.

Human Embryology. PATTEN, B. M.: 1946. Blakiston, Phila., xv + 776 pp.

OSTEOLOGY.

THE general framework of the body is built up mainly of a series of bones supplemented, however, in certain regions by pieces of cartilage; the bony part of the framework constitutes the **skeleton.**

In the skeleton of the adult there are 206 distinct bones, as follows:—

Axial Skeleton	Vertebral column	26	
	Skull	22	
	Hyoid bone	1	
	Ribs and sternum	25	
		—	74
Appendicular Skeleton	Upper extremities	64	
	Lower extremities	62	
		—	126
Auditory ossicles	. . . .		6
	Total		206

The patellæ are included in this enumeration, but the smaller sesamoid bones are not reckoned.

DEVELOPMENT OF THE SKELETON.

The **skeleton** is of mesodermal origin. The first indications usually appear as condensations of the mesenchyme into the membranous or blastemal rudiments in which cartilage and bone differentiate. With the exception of certain of the cranial bones the membranous rudiments are converted into cartilage which is in turn replaced by bone.

The Vertebral Column.—The notochord (Fig. 33) is a temporary structure and forms a central axis, around which the segments of the vertebral column are developed. It is derived from the entoderm, and consists of a rod of cells, which lies on the ventral aspect of the neural tube and reaches from the anterior end of the mid-brain to the extremity of the tail. On either side of it is a column of paraxial mesoderm which becomes subdivided into a number of more or less cubical segments, the **primitive segments** (Figs. 31 and 33). These are separated from one another by **intersegmental septa** and are arranged symmetrically on either side of the neural tube and notochord: to every segment a spinal nerve is distributed. At first each segment contains a central cavity, the **myocœl,** but this is soon filled with a core of angular and spindle-shaped cells. The cells of the segment become differentiated into three groups, which form respectively the cutis-plate or dermatome, the muscle-plate or myotome, and the sclerotome (Fig. 33). The **cutis-plate** is placed on the lateral and dorsal aspect of the myocœl, and from it the true skin of the corresponding segment is derived; the **muscle-plate** is situated on the medial side of the cutis-plate and furnishes the muscles of the segment. The cells of the **sclerotome** are largely derived from those forming the core of the myocœl, and lie next the notochord. Fusion of the individual sclerotomes in an antero-posterior direction soon takes place, and thus a continuous strand of cells, the **sclerotogenous layer,** is formed along the ventro-lateral aspects of the neural tube. The cells of this layer proliferate rapidly, and extending medialward surround the notochord; at the same time they grow backward on the lateral aspects of the neural tube and eventually surround it, and thus the notochord and neural tube are enveloped by a continuous sheath of mesoderm, which is termed the **membranous vertebral column**. In this mesoderm the original segments are still distinguishable, but each is now differentiated into two portions, an anterior, consisting of loosely arranged cells, and a posterior, of more condensed tissue (Fig. 57, *A* and *B*). Between the two portions the rudiment of the intervertebral fibrocartilage is laid down (Fig. 57, *C*). Cells from the posterior mass grow into the intervals between the myotomes (Fig. 57, *B* and *C*) of the corresponding and succeeding segments, and extend both dorsally and ventrally; the dorsal extensions surround the neural tube and represent the future neural arch, while the ventral extend into the body-wall as the costal processes. The hinder part of the posterior mass joins the anterior mass of the succeeding segment to form the vertebral body. Each vertebral body is therefore a composite of two segments, being formed from the posterior portion of one segment and the anterior part of that immediately behind it. The vertebral and costal arches are derivatives of the posterior part of the segment in front of the intersegmental septum with which they are associated.

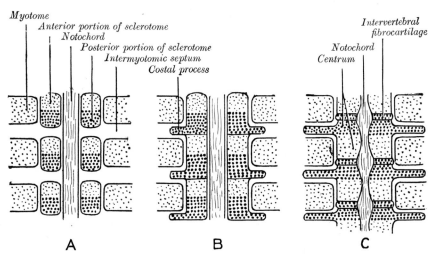

FIG. 57.—Scheme showing the manner in which each vertebral centrum is developed from portions of two adjacent segments.

This stage is succeeded by that of the **cartilaginous vertebral column**. In the fourth week two cartilaginous centers make their appearance, one on either side of the notochord; these extend around the notochord and form the body of the cartilaginous vertebra. A second pair of cartilaginous foci appear in the lateral parts of the vertebral bow, and grow backward on either side of the neural tube to form the cartilaginous vertebral arch, and a separate cartilaginous center appears for each costal process. By the eighth week the cartilaginous arch has fused with the body, and in the fourth month the two halves of the arch are joined on the dorsal aspect of the neural tube. The spinous process is developed from the junction of the two halves of the neural or vertebral arch. The transverse process grows out from the vertebral arch behind the costal process.

In the upper cervical vertebræ a band of mesodermal tissue connects the ends of the vertebral arches across the ventral surfaces of the intervertebral fibrocartilages. This is termed the **hypochordal bar** or **brace**; in all except the first it is transitory and disappears by fusing with the fibrocartilages. In the atlas, however, the entire bow persists and undergoes chondrification; it develops into the anterior arch of the bone, while the cartilage representing the body of the atlas forms the dens or odontoid process which fuses with the body of the second cervical vertebra.

The portions of the notochord which are surrounded by the bodies of the vertebræ atrophy, and ultimately disappear, while those which lie in the centers of the intervertebral fibrocartilages undergo enlargement, and persist throughout life as the central **nucleus pulposus** of the fibrocartilages (Fig. 58).

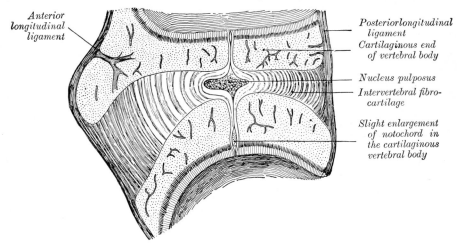

FIG. 58.—Sagittal section through an intervertebral fibrocartilage and adjacent parts of two vertebræ of an advanced sheep's embryo. (Kölliker.)

The Ribs.—The ribs are formed from the ventral or costal processes of the primitive vertebral bows, the processes extending between the muscle-plates. In the *thoracic region* of the vertebral column the costal processes grow lateralward to form a series of arches, the **primitive costal arches.** As already described, the

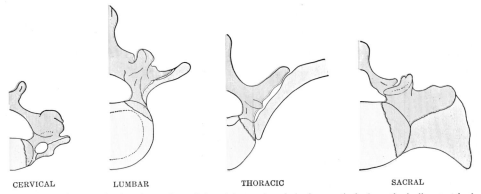

CERVICAL   LUMBAR   THORACIC   SACRAL

FIG. 59.—Diagrams showing the portions of the adult vertebræ derived respectively from the bodies, vertebral arches, and costal processes of the embryonic vertebræ. The bodies are represented in yellow, the vertebral arches in red, and the costal processes in blue.

transverse process grows out behind the vertebral end of each arch. It is at first connected to the costal process by continuous mesoderm, but this becomes differentiated later to form the costotransverse ligament; between the costal process and the tip of the transverse process the costotransverse joint is formed by absorption. The costal process becomes separated from the vertebral bow by the development of the costocentral joint. In the *cervical vertebræ* (Fig. 59) the transverse process forms the posterior boundary of the foramen transversarium, while the costal process corresponding to the head and neck of the rib fuses with the body of the vertebra, and forms the antero-lateral boundary of the foramen. The distal portions of the primitive costal arches remain undeveloped; occasionally

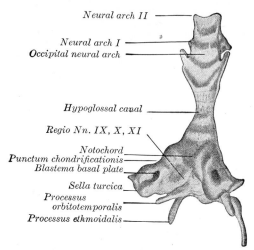

Fig. 60.—Membranous skull of a human embryo 13 mm. long. (Levi.)

the arch of the seventh cervical vertebra undergoes greater development, and by the formation of costovertebral joints is separated off as a rib. In the *lumbar region* the distal portions of the primitive costal arches fail; the proximal portions fuse with the transverse processes to form the transverse processes of descriptive

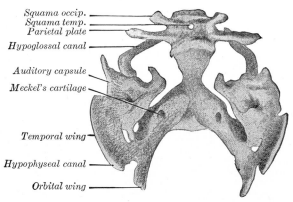

Fig. 61.—Membranous and cartilaginous skull of a human embryo 14 mm. long. (Levi.)

anatomy. Occasionally a movable rib is developed in connection with the first lumbar vertebra. In the *sacral region* costal processes are developed only in connection with the upper three, or it may be four, vertebræ; the processes of adjacent segments fuse with one another to form the lateral parts of the sacrum. The *coccygeal vertebræ* are devoid of costal processes.

The Sternum.—The ventral ends of the ribs become united to one another by a longitudinal bar termed the **sternal plate,** and opposite the first seven pairs of ribs these sternal plates fuse in the middle line to form the manubrium and body of the sternum. The xiphoid process is formed by a backward extension of the sternal plates.

The Skull.—The first indications of the membranous skull are found in the basi-occipital and basisphenoid and about the auditory vesicles. The condensation of the mesoderm gradually extends from these areas around the brain until the latter is enclosed by the **membranous cranium.** This is incomplete in the region where the large nerves and vessels pass into or out of the cranium. Before the membranous cranium is complete, chondrification begins to show in the basioccipital. Two centers (Fig. 60) appear one on either side of the notochord near where it enters the occipital blastema or condensed mesoderm. Chondrification gradually spreads from these centers, medially around the notochord, laterally about the roots of the hypoglossal nerve, and anteriorly to unite with the spreading cartilaginous center of the basisphenoid to form an elongated basal plate of cartilage extending from the foramen magnum to the anterior end of the sphenoid where it continues

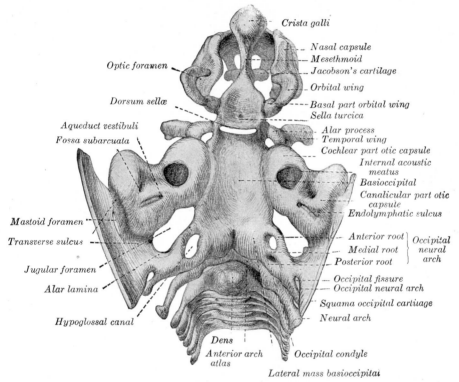

FIG. 62.—Cartilaginous skull of 21 mm. human embryo. (Lewis.)

into the blastema of the ethmoid region which later becomes chondrified. When the auditory capsules begin to chondrify they are quite widely separated from the basal plate (Fig. 61). By the time the embryo is 20 mm. in length the cochlear portion of the auditory or otic capsule is fused to the widened basal plate and the jugular foramen has become separated from the foramen lacerum (Fig. 62). From the lateral region of the occipital cartilage a broad thin plate of cartilage (tectum posterius or nuchal plate) extends around the caudal region of the brain in a complete ring (Fig. 63) forming the primitive foramen magnum. The complete chondrocranium is shown in Figs. 64 and 65. There are other minor cartilaginous centers which unite with main continuous mass. The chondrocranium forms only a small part of the future ossified skull. Various centers of ossification develop in the cartilage and give rise to all of the occipital bone, except the upper part of the squama, to the petrous and mastoid portions of the temporal, to the sphenoid,

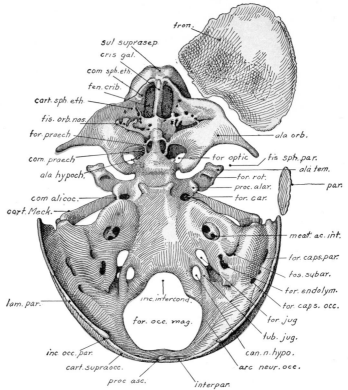

Fig. 63.—Cartilaginous skull of a 43 mm. human embryo. (Macklin).

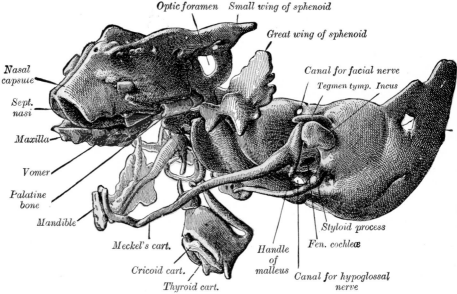

Fig. 64.—Model of the chondrocranium of a human embryo, 8 cm. long. (The same model as shown in Fig. 65 from the left side. Certain of the membrane bones of the right side are represented in yellow. (Hertwig.)

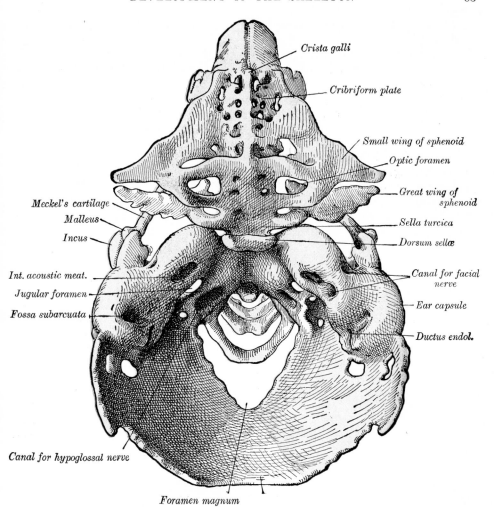

Crista galli

Cribriform plate

Small wing of sphenoid

Optic foramen

Great wing of sphenoid

Meckel's cartilage

Malleus

Incus

Sella turcica

Dorsum sellæ

Int. acoustic meat.

Jugular foramen

Fossa subarcuata

Canal for facial nerve

Ear capsule

Ductus endol.

Canal for hypoglossal nerve

Foramen magnum

Fig. 65.—Model of the chondrocranium of a human embryo, 8 cm. long.   (Hertwig.)   The membrane bones are not represented.

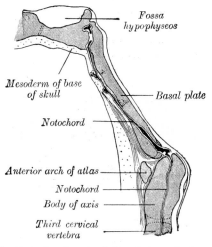

Fossa hypophyseos

Mesoderm of base of skull

Basal plate

Notochord

Anterior arch of atlas

Notochord

Body of axis

Third cervical vertebra

Fig. 66.—Sagittal section of cephalic end of notochord.   (Kiebel.)

except its medial pterygoid plates and part of the temporal wings, and to the ethmoid.

The **membrane bones** of the cranial vault and face ossify directly in the mesoderm of the membraneous cranium. They comprise the upper part of the occipital squama (interparietal), the squamæ and tympanic parts of the temporals, the parietals, the frontal, the vomer, the medial pterygoid plates, and the bones of the face. Some of them remain distinct throughout life, e. g., parietal and frontal, while others join with the bones of the chondrocranium, e. g., interparietal, squamæ of temporals, and medial pterygoid plates.

The anterior and posterior thirds of the cranial notochord become surrounded by the cartilage of the basal plate, its middle part lies between the middle part of the basal plate and the wall of the pharynx (Fig. 66). The anterior end is embedded in the basisphenoid. There are very distinct indications of an occipital vertebra at the caudal end of the occipital cartilage in embryos about 20 mm. in length.

BONE

Structure and Physical Properties.—Bone is one of the hardest structures of the animal body; it possesses also a certain degree of toughness and elasticity. Its color, in a fresh state, is pinkish-white externally, and deep red within. If one examines a section cut through a dried bone, one sees that it is composed of two kinds of osseous tissue. One is dense in texture, like ivory, and is termed compact tissue; the other consists of slender spicules, trabeculæ, and lamellæ, joined into a spongey structure which is called, from its resemblance to latticework, cancellous tissue. The compact tissue is always placed on the exterior of the bone, the cancellous in the interior. The relative quantity of these two kinds of tissue varies in different bones, and in different parts of the same bone, according as strength or lightness is requisite. Close examination of the compact tissue shows it to be extremely porous, so that the difference in structure between it and the cancellous tissue depends merely upon the different amount of solid matter, and the size and number of spaces in each; the cavities are small in the compact tissue and the solid matter between them abundant, while in the cancellous tissue the spaces are large and the solid matter is in smaller quantity.

Bone during life is permeated by vessels, and is enclosed, except where it is coated with articular cartilage, in a fibrous membrane, the **periosteum**, by means of which many of these vessels reach the hard tissue. If the periosteum be stripped from the surface of the living bone, small bleeding points are seen which mark the entrance of the periosteal vessels; and on section during life every part of the bone exudes blood from the minute vessels which ramify in it. The interior of each of the long bones of the limbs presents a cylindrical cavity filled with marrow and lined by a highly vascular areolar structure, called the **medullary membrane.**

THE STRENGTH OF BONE COMPARED WITH OTHER MATERIALS

Substance.	Weight in pounds per cubic foot.	Ultimate strength. Pounds per square inch.		
		Tension.	Compression.	Shear.
Medium steel	490	65,000	60,000	40,000
Granite	170	1,500	15,000	2,000
Oak, white	46	12,500[1]	7,000[1]	4,000[2]
Compact bone (low)	119	13,200[1]	18,000[1]	11,800[2]
Compact bone (high)	. . . . . .	17,700[1]	24,000[1]	7,150[1]

[1] Indicates stresses with the grain, i. e., when the load is parallel to the long axis of the material, or parallel to the direction of the fibers of the material.
[2] Indicates unit-stresses across the grain, i. e., at right angles to the direction of the fibers of the material.

Periosteum.—The periosteum adheres to the surface of each of the bones in nearly every part, but not to cartilaginous extremities. When strong tendons or ligaments are attached to a bone, the periosteum is incorporated with them. It consists of two layers closely united together, the outer one formed chiefly of collagenous tissue, containing occasionally a few fat cells; the inner one, of elastic fibers of the finer kind, forming dense membranous networks, which again can be separated into several layers. In young bones the periosteum is thick and very vascular, and is intimately connected at either end of the bone with the epiphysial cartilage, but less closely with the body of the bone, from which it is separated by a layer of soft tissue, containing a number of **granular corpuscles** or **osteoblasts,** by which ossification proceeds on the exterior of the young bone. Later in life the periosteum is thinner and less vascular, and the osteoblasts are converted into an epithelioid layer on the deep surface of the periosteum. The periosteum serves as a nidus for the ramification of the vessels previous to their distribution in the bone; hence the liability of bone to exfoliation or necrosis when denuded of this membrane by injury or disease. Fine nerves and lymphatics, which generally accompany the arteries, may also be demonstrated in the periosteum.

Bone Marrow.—Bone marrow fills the cavities of the bones. **Yellow marrow** is found in the large cavities of the long bones. It consists for the most part of fat cells and a few primitive blood cells. It may be replaced by red marrow in anemia. **Red marrow** is the site for the production of the granular leucocytes (neutrophil, eosinophil, and basophil leucocytes) and the red blood cells (erythrocytes). It is found in the flat and short bones, the articular ends of the long bones, the bodies of the vertebræ, the cranial diploe, and the sternum and ribs. It consists, for the most part, of myeloid cells, namely, primitive blood cells, immature stages and many mature ones. Macrophages, fat cells and megakaryocytes (giant cells) are always present. Both types of marrow have a supporting connective tissue and numerous bloodvessels. Thin-walled sinusoids are supposed to connect the terminal arterioles with the veins in the red bone marrow. Great numbers of mature blood cells (both red and white) pass into the blood stream. The mechanism whereby the mature cells escape into the blood stream and immature ones are held back is not known. *Osteoclasts* large, multinucleated, protoplasmic masses, are to be found in both sorts of adult marrow, but more particularly in red marrow. They were believed to be concerned in the absorption of bone matrix, and to excavate in the bone small shallow pits or cavities, **Howship's lacunæ,** in which they are often located.

Vessels and Nerves of Bone.—The **bloodvessels** of bone are very numerous. Those of the compact tissue are derived from a close and dense network of vessels ramifying in the periosteum. From this membrane vessels pass into the minute orifices in the compact tissue, and run through the canals which traverse its substance. The cancellous tissue is supplied in a similar way, but by less numerous and larger vessels, which, perforating the outer compact tissue, are distributed to the cavities of the spongy portion of the bone. In the long bones, numerous apertures may be seen at the ends near the articular surfaces; some of these give passage to the arteries of the larger set of vessels referred to; but the most numerous and largest apertures are for some of the veins of the cancellous tissue, which emerge apart from the arteries. The marrow in the body of a long bone is supplied by one large artery (or sometimes more), which enters the bone at the nutrient foramen (situated in most cases near the center of the body), and perforates obliquely the compact structure. The *medullary* or *nutrient* artery, usually accompanied by one or two veins, sends branches upward and downward, which ramify in the marrow and give twigs to the adjoining canals. The ramifications of this vessel anastomose with the arteries of the cancellous and compact tissues. In most of the flat, and in many of the short spongy bones, one or more large apertures are observed, which transmit to the central parts of the bone vessels corresponding to the nutrient arteries and veins. The **veins** emerge from the long bones in three places (Kölliker): (1) one or two large veins accompany the artery; (2) numerous large and small veins emerge at the articular extremities; (3) many small veins pass out of the compact substance. In the flat cranial bones the veins are large, very numerous, and run in tortuous canals in the diploic tissue, the sides of the canals being formed by thin lamellæ of bone, perforated here and there for the passage of branches from the adjacent cancelli. The same condition is also found in all cancellous tissue, the veins being enclosed and supported by osseous material, and having exceedingly thin coats. When a bone is divided, the vessels remain patulous, and do not contract in the canals in which they are contained. **Lymphatic vessels,** in addition to those found in the periosteum, have been traced by Cruikshank into the substance of bone, and Klein describes them as running in the Haversian canals. **Nerves** are distributed freely to the periosteum, and accompany the nutrient arteries into the interior of the bone. They are said by Kölliker to be most numerous in the articular extremities of the long bones, in the vertebræ, and in the larger flat bones.

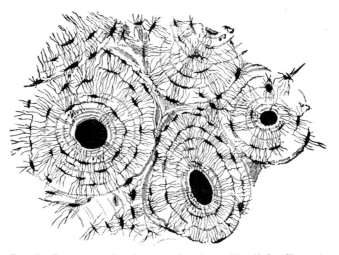

Fig. 67.—Transverse section of compact tissue bone. Magnified. (Sharpey.)

Minute Anatomy.—A transverse section of dense bone may be cut with a saw and ground down until it is sufficiently thin.

If this be examined with a rather low power the bone will be seen to be mapped out into a number of circular districts each consisting of a central hole surrounded by a number of concentric rings. These districts are termed **Haversian systems;** the central hole is an **Haversian canal,** and the rings are layers of bony tissue arranged concentrically around the central canal, and termed **lamellæ.** Moreover, on closer examination it will be found that between these lamellæ, and therefore also arranged concentrically around the central canal, are a number of little dark spots, the **lacunæ,** and that these lacunæ are connected with each other and with the central Haversian canal by a number of fine dark lines, which radiate like the spokes of a wheel and are called **canaliculi.** Filling in the irregular intervals which are left between these circular systems are other lamellæ, with their lacunæ and canaliculi running in various directions, but more or less curved (Fig. 67); they are termed **interstitial lamellæ.** Again, other lamellæ, found on the surface of the bone, are arranged parallel to its circumference; they are termed **circumferential,** or by some authors **primary** or **fundamental lamellæ,** to distinguish them from those laid down around the axes of the Haversian canals, which are then termed **secondary** or **special lamellæ.**

The **Haversian canals,** seen in a transverse section of bone as round holes at or about the center of each Haversian system, may be demonstrated to be true canals if a longitudinal section be made (Fig. 68). It will then be seen that the canals run parallel with the longitudinal axis of the bone for a short distance and then branch and communicate. They vary considerably in size, some being as much as 0.12 mm. in diameter; the average size is, however, about 0.05 mm. Near the medullary cavity the canals are larger than those near the surface of the bone. Each canal contains one or two bloodvessels, with a small quantity of delicate connective tissue and some nerve filaments. In the larger ones there are also lymphatic vessels, and cells with branching processes which communicate, through the canaliculi, with the branched processes of certain bone cells in the substance of the bone. Those canals near the surface of the bone open upon it by minute orifices, and those near the medullary cavity open in the same way into this space, so that the whole of the bone is permeated by a system of bloodvessels running through the bony canals in the centers of the Haversian systems.

The **lamellæ** are thin plates of bony tissue encircling the central canal, and may be compared, for the sake of illustration, to a number of sheets of paper pasted one over another around a central hollow cylinder. After macerating a piece of bone in dilute mineral acid, these lamellæ may be stripped off in a

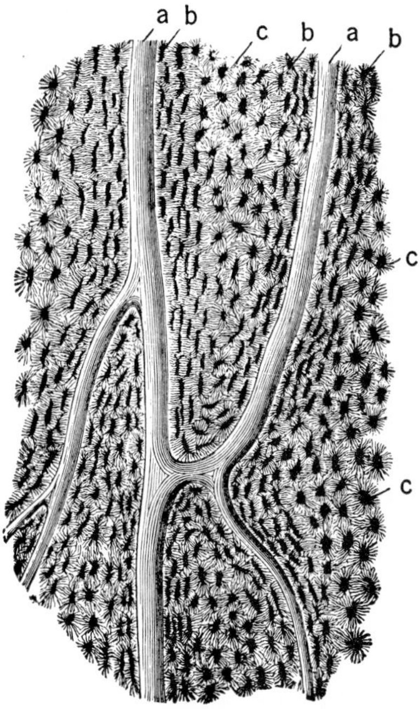

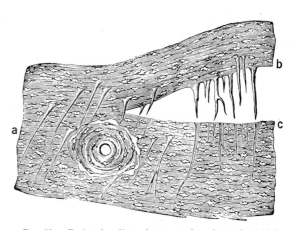

Fig. 68.—Section parallel to the surface from the body of the femur. × 100. *a,* Haversian canals; *b,* lacunæ seen from the side; *c,* others seen from the surface in lamellæ, which are cut horizontally.

Fig. 69. — Perforating fibers, human parieta bone, decalcified (H. Müller.) *a,* perforating fibers *in situ; b,* fibres drawn out of their sockets; *c,* sockets.

longitudinal direction as thin films. If one of these be examined with a high power of the microscope, it will be found to be composed of a finely reticular structure, made up of very slender transparent fibers, decussating obliquely; and coalescing at the points of intersection; these fibers are composed of fine fibrils identical with those of white connective tissue. The intercellular matrix between the fibers is impregnated by calcareous deposit which the acid dissolves. In many places the various lamellæ may be seen to be held together by tapering fibers, which run obliquely through them, pinning or bolting them together; they were first described by Sharpey, and were named by him **perforating fibers** (Fig. 69).

The **Lacunæ** are situated between the lamellæ, and consist of a number of oblong spaces. In an ordinary microscopic section, viewed by transmitted light, they appear as fusiform opaque spots. Each lacuna is occupied during life by a branched cell, termed a **bone-cell** or **bone-corpuscle**, the processes from which extend into the canaliculi (Fig. 70).

The **Canaliculi** are exceedingly minute channels, crossing the lamellæ and connecting the lacunæ with neighboring lacunæ and also with the Haversian canal. From the Haversian canal a number of canaliculi are given off, which radiate from it, and open into the first set of lacunæ between the first and second lamellæ. From these lacunæ a second set of canaliculi is given off; these run outward to the next series of lacunæ, and so on until the periphery of the Haversian system is reached; here the canaliculi given off from the last series of lacunæ do not as a rule communicate with the lacunæ of neighboring Haversian systems, but after passing outward for a short distance form loops and return to their own lacunæ. Thus every part of an Haversian system is supplied with nutrient fluids derived from the vessels in the Haversian canal and distributed through the canaliculi and lacunæ.

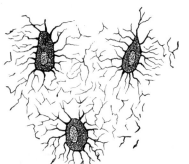

The **bone cells** are contained in the lacunæ, which, however, they do not completely fill. They are flattened nucleated branched cells, homologous with those of connective tissue; the branches, especially in young bones, pass into the canaliculi from the lacunæ.

In thin plates of bone (as in the walls of the spaces of cancellous tissue) the Haversian canals are absent, and the canaliculi open into the spaces of the cancellous tissue (medullary spaces), which thus have the same function as the Haversian canals.

Fig. 70.—Nucleated bone cells and their processes, contained in the bone lacunæ and their canaliculi respectively. From a section through the vertebra of an adult mouse. (Klein and Noble Smith.)

Chemical Composition.—Bone consists of an animal and an earthy part intimately combined together.

The animal part may be obtained by immersing a bone for a considerable time in dilute mineral acid, after which process the bone comes out exactly the same shape as before, but perfectly flexible, so that a long bone (one of the ribs, for example) can easily be tied in a knot. If now a transverse section is made the same general arrangement of the Haversian canals, lamellæ, lacunæ, and canaliculi is seen.

The earthy part may be separately obtained by calcination, by which the animal matter is completely burnt out. The bone will still retain its original form, but it will be white and brittle, will have lost about one-third of its original weight, and will crumble down with the slightest force. The earthy matter is composed chiefly of calcium phosphate, about 58 per cent. of the weight of the bone, calcium carbonate about 7 per cent., calcium fluoride and magnesium phosphate from 1 to 2 per cent. each and sodium chloride less than 1 per cent.; they confer on bone its hardness and rigidity, while the animal matter (*ossein*) determines its tenacity.

Ossification.—Some bones are preceded by membrane, such as those forming the roof and sides of the skull; others, such as the bones of the limbs, are preceded by rods of cartilage. Hence two kinds of ossification are described: the **intramembranous** and the **intracartilaginous**.

INTRAMEMBRANOUS OSSIFICATION.—In the case of bones which are developed in membrane, no cartilaginous mould precedes the appearance of the bony tissue. The membrane which occupies the place of the future bone is of the nature of connective tissue, and ultimately forms the periosteum; it is composed of fibers and granular cells in a matrix. The peripheral portion is more fibrous, while, in the interior the cells or *osteoblasts* predominate; the whole tissue is richly supplied with bloodvessels. At the outset of the process of bone formation a little network of spicules is noticed radiating from the point or center of ossification. These rays consist at their growing points of a network of fine clear fibers and granular corpuscles with an intervening ground substance. The fibers are termed **osteogenetic fibers**, and are made up of fine fibrils differing little from those of white fibrous tissue. The membrane soon assumes a dark and granular appearance from the deposition of calcareous granules in the fibers and in the intervening matrix, and in the calcified material some of the granular corpuscles or osteoblasts are enclosed. By the fusion of the calcareous granules the tissue again assumes a more transparent appearance, but the fibers are no longer so distinctly seen.

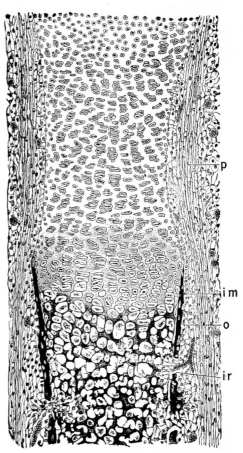

FIG. 71.—Section of fetal bone of cat. *ir.* Irruption of the subperiosteal tissue. *p.* Fibrous layer of the periosteum. *o.* Layer of osteoblasts. *im.* Subperiosteal bony deposit. (From Quain's "Anatomy," E. A. Schäfer.)

The involved osteoblasts form the corpuscles of the future bone, the spaces in which they are enclosed constituting the lacunæ. As the osteogenetic fibers grow out to the periphery they continue to ossify, and give rise to fresh bone spicules. Thus a network of bone is formed, the meshes of which contain the bloodvessels and a delicate connective tissue crowded with osteoblasts. The bony trabeculæ thicken by the addition of fresh layers of bone formed by the osteoblasts on their surface, and the meshes are correspondingly encroached upon. Subsequently successive layers of bony tissue are deposited under the periosteum and around the larger vascular channels which become the Haversian canals, so that the bone increases much in thickness.

INTERCARTILAGINOUS OSSIFICATION. —Just before ossification begins the mass is entirely cartilaginous, and in a long bone, which may be taken as an example, the process commences in the center and proceeds toward the extremities, which for some time remain cartilaginous. Subsequently a similar process commences in one or more places in those extremities and gradually extends through them. The extremities do not, however, become joined to the body of the bone by bony tissue until growth has ceased; between the body and either extremity a layer of cartilaginous tissue termed the **epiphysial cartilage** persists for a definite period.

The first step in the ossification of the cartilage is that the cartilage cells, at the point where ossification is commencing and which is termed a **center of ossification**, enlarge and arrange themselves in rows (Fig. 71). The matrix in which they are imbedded increases in quantity, so that the cells become further separated from each other. A deposit of calcareous material now takes place in this matrix, between the rows of cells, so that they become separated from each other by longitudinal columns of calcified matrix, presenting a granular and opaque appearance. Here and there the matrix between two cells of the same row also becomes calcified, and transverse bars of calcified substance stretch across from one calcareous column to another. Thus there are longitudinal groups of the cartilage cells enclosed in oblong cavities, the walls of which are formed of calcified matrix which cuts off all nutrition from the cells; the cells, in consequence, atrophy, leaving spaces called the **primary areolæ.**

SUBPERIOSTEAL OSSIFICATION.—At the same time that this process is going on in the center of the solid bar of cartilage, certain changes are taking place on its surface. This is covered by a very vascular membrane, the **perichondrium,** entirely similar to the embryonic connective tissue already described as constituting the basis of membrane bone; on the inner surface of this—that is to say, on the

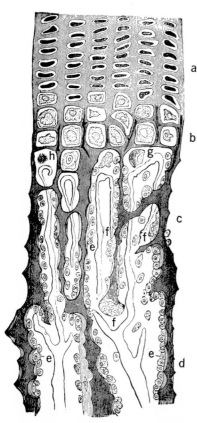

surface in contact with the cartilage—are gathered the formative cells, the **osteoblasts.** By the agency of these cells a thin layer of bony tissue is formed between the perichondrium and the cartilage, by the *intramembranous* mode of ossification just described. There are then, in this first stage of ossification, two processes going on simultaneously: in the center of the cartilage the formation of a number of oblong spaces, formed of calcified matrix and containing the withered cartilage cells, and on the surface of the cartilage the formation of a layer of true membrane bone.

The second stage of the intercartilagenous ossification consists in the prolongation into the cartilage of processes of the deeper or osteogenetic layer of the perichondrium, which has now become periosteum (Fig. 71, *ir*). The processes consist of bloodvessels and cells —**osteoblasts,** or **bone-formers,** and **osteoclasts,** or **bone-destroyers.** The latter are similar to

FIG. 72.—Part of a longitudinal section of the developing femur of a rabbit. *a.* Flattened cartilage cells. *b.* Enlarged cartilage cells. *c, d.* Newly formed bone. *e.* Osteoblasts. *f.* Giant cells or osteoclasts. *g, h.* Shrunken cartilage cells. (From "Atlas of Histology," Klein and Noble Smith.)

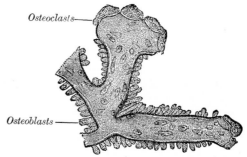

FIG. 73.—Osteoblasts and osteoclasts on trabecula of lower jaw of calf embryo. (Kölliker.)

the giant cells (myeloplaxes) found in marrow, and they excavate passages through the new-formed bony layer by absorption, and pass through it into the calcified matrix (Fig. 72). Wherever these processes come in contact with the calcified walls of the primary areolæ they absorb them, and thus cause a fusion of the original cavities and the formation of larger spaces, which are termed the **secondary areolæ** or **medullary spaces.** These secondary spaces become filled with embryonic marrow, consisting of osteoblasts and vessels, derived, in the manner described above, from the osteogenetic layer of the periosteum (Fig. 72).

Thus far there has been traced the formation of enlarged spaces (secondary areolæ), the perforated walls of which are still formed by calcified cartilage matrix, containing an embryonic marrow derived from the processes sent in from the osteogenetic layer of the periosteum, and consisting of bloodvessels and osteo-blasts. The walls of these secondary areolæ are at this time of only inconsiderable thickness, but they become thickened by the deposition of layers of true bone on their surface. This process takes place in the following manner: Some of the osteoblasts of the embryonic marrow, after undergoing rapid division, arrange themselves as an epithelioid layer on the surface of the wall of the space (Fig. 73). This layer of osteoblasts forms a bony stratum, and thus the wall of the space becomes gradually covered with a layer of true osseous substance in which some of the bone-forming cells are included as bone corpuscles. The next stage in the process consists in the removal of these primary bone spicules by the osteoclasts. One of these giant cells may be found lying in a Howship's foveola at the free end of each spicule. The removal of the primary spicules goes on *pari passu* with the formation of permanent bone by the periosteum, and in this way the medullary cavity of the body of the bone is formed.

This series of changes has been gradually proceeding toward the end of the body of the bone, so that in the ossifying bone all the changes described above may be seen in different parts, from the true bone at the center of the body to the hyaline cartilage at the extremities.

While the ossification of the cartilaginous body is extending toward the articular ends, the cartilage immediately in advance of the osseous tissue continues to grow until the length of the adult bone is reached.

During the period of growth the articular end, or epiphysis, remains for some time entirely cartilaginous, then a bony center appears, and initiates in it the process of intracartilaginous ossification; but this process never extends to any great distance. The epiphysis remains separated from the body by a narrow cartilaginous layer for a definite time. This layer ultimately ossifies, the distinction between body and epiphysis is obliterated, and the bone assumes its completed form and shape. The same remarks also apply to such processes of bone as are separately ossified, *e. g.*, the trochanters of the femur. The bones therefore continue to grow until the body has acquired its full stature. They increase in length by ossification continuing to extend behind the epiphysial cartilage, which goes on growing in advance of the ossifying process. They increase in circumference by deposition of new bone, from the deeper layer of the periosteum, on their external surface, and at the same time an absorption takes place from within, by which the medullary cavities are increased.

The permanent bone formed by the periosteum when first laid down is cancellous in structure. Later the osteoblasts contained in its spaces become arranged in the concentric layers characteristic of the Haversian systems, and are included as bone corpuscles.

The number of ossific centers varies in different bones. In most of the short bones ossification commences at a single point near the center, and proceeds toward the surface. In the long bones there is a central point of ossification for the body or diaphysis: and one or more for each extremity, the epiphysis. That for the body is the first to appear. The times of union of the epiphyses with the body vary inversely with the dates at which their ossifications began (with the exception of the fibula) and regulate the direction of the nutrient arteries of the bones. Thus, the nutrient arteries of the bones of the arm and forearm are directed toward the elbow, since the epiphyses at this joint become united to the bodies before those at the opposite extremities. In the lower limb, on the other hand, the nutrient arteries are directed away from the knee: that is, upward in the femur, downward in the tibia and fibula; and in them it is observed that the upper epiphysis of the femur, and the lower epiphyses of the tibia and fibula, unite first with the

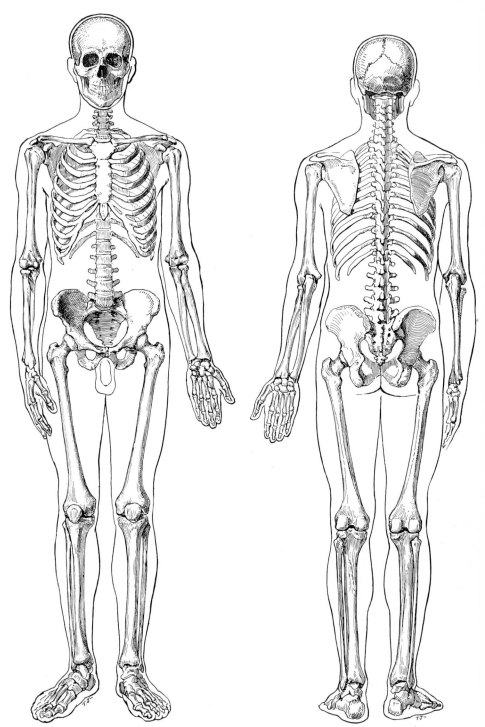

Fig. 74.—The skeleton as projected on the surface of the body viewed from in front and from behind. (Eycleshymer and Jones.)

bodies. Where there is only one epiphysis, the nutrient artery is directed toward the other end of the bone; as toward the acromial end of the clavicle, toward the distal ends of the metacarpal bone of the thumb and the metatarsal bone of the great toe, and toward the proximal ends of the other metacarpal and metatarsal bones.

THE VERTEBRAL COLUMN (COLUMNA VERTEBRALIS; SPINAL COLUMN).

The **vertebral column** is a flexuous and flexible column, formed of a series of bones called **vertebræ**.

The vertebræ are thirty-three in number, and are grouped under the names **cervical, thoracic, lumbar, sacral,** and **coccygeal,** according to the regions they occupy; there are seven in the cervical region, twelve in the thoracic, five in the lumbar, five in the sacral, and four in the coccygeal.

This number is sometimes increased by an additional vertebra in one region, or it may be diminished in one region, the deficiency often being supplied by an additional vertebra in another. The number of cervical vertebræ is, however, very rarely increased or diminished.

The vertebræ in the upper three regions of the column remain distinct throughout life, and are known as **true** or **movable** vertebræ; those of the sacral and coccygeal regions, on the other hand, are termed **false** or **fixed** vertebræ, because they are united with one another in the adult to form two bones—five forming the upper bone or **sacrum,** and four the terminal bone or **coccyx.**

With the exception of the first and second cervical, the true or movable vertebræ present certain common characteristics which are best studied by examining one from the middle of the thoracic region.

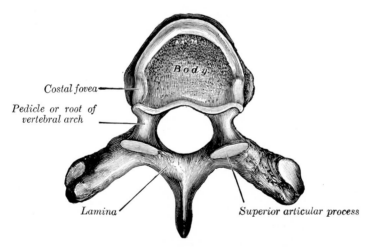

Body

Costal fovea

Pedicle or root of vertebral arch

Lamina

Superior articular process

Fig. 75.—A typical thoracic vertebra, viewed from above.

GENERAL CHARACTERISTICS OF A VERTEBRA.

A **typical vertebra** consists of two essential parts—viz., an anterior segment, the **body,** and a posterior part, the **vertebral** or **neural arch**; these enclose a foramen, the **vertebral foramen.** The vertebral arch consists of a pair of **pedicles** and a pair of **laminæ** and supports **seven processes**—viz., four **articular,** two **transverse,** and one **spinous.**

When the vertebræ are articulated with each other the bodies form a strong pillar for the support of the head and trunk, and the vertebral foramina constitute a canal for the protection of the medulla spinalis (*spinal cord*), while between every pair of vertebræ are two apertures, the **intervertebral foramina**, one on either side, for the transmission of the spinal nerves and vessels.

Body (*corpus vertebræ*).—The body is the largest part of a vertebra, and is more or less cylindrical in shape. Its upper and lower surfaces are flattened and rough, and give attachment to the intervertebral fibrocartilages, and each presents a rim around its circumference. In front, the body is convex from side to side and concave from above downward. Behind, it is flat from above downward and slightly concave from side to side. Its anterior surface presents a few small apertures, for the passage of nutrient vessels; on the posterior surface is a single large, irregular aperture, or occasionally more than one, for the exit of the basivertebral veins from the body of the vertebra.

Pedicles (*radices arci vertebræ*).—The pedicles are two short, thick processes, which project backward, one on either side, from the upper part of the body, at the junction of its posterior and lateral surfaces. The concavities above and below the pedicles are named the **vertebral notches**; and when the vertebræ are articulated, the notches of each contiguous pair of bones form the intervertebral foramina, already referred to.

Laminæ.—The laminæ are two broad plates directed backward and medialward from the pedicles. They fuse in the middle line posteriorly, and so complete the posterior boundary of the vertebral foramen. Their upper borders and the lower parts of their anterior surfaces are rough for the attachment of the ligamenta flava.

Processes.—**Spinous Process** (*processus spinosus*).—The spinous process is directed backward and downward from the junction of the laminæ, and serves for the attachment of muscles and ligaments.

Articular Processes.—The articular processes, two superior and two inferior, spring from the junctions of the pedicles and laminæ. The superior project upward, and their articular surfaces are directed more or less backward; the inferior project downward, and their surfaces look more or less forward. The articular surfaces are coated with hyaline cartilage.

Transverse Processes (*processus transversi*).—The transverse processes, two in number, project one at either side from the point where the lamina joins the pedicle, between the superior and inferior articular processes. They serve for the attachment of muscles and ligaments.

Structure of a Vertebra (Fig. 76).—The body is composed of cancellous tissue, covered by a thin coating of compact bone; the latter is perforated by numerous orifices, some of large size for the passage of vessels; the interior of the bone is traversed by one or two large canals, for the reception of veins, which converge toward a single large, irregular aperture, or several small apertures, at the posterior part of the body. The thin bony lamellæ of the cancellous tissue are more pronounced in lines perpendicular to the upper and lower surfaces and are developed in response to greater pressure in this direction (Fig. 76). The arch and processes projecting from it have thick coverings of compact tissue.

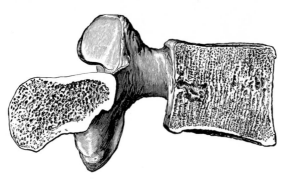

Fig. 76.—Sagittal section of a lumbar vertebra.

The Cervical Vertebræ (Vertebræ Cervicales).

The **cervical vertebræ** (Fig. 77) are the smallest of the true vertebræ, and can be readily distinguished from those of the thoracic or lumbar regions by the presence of a foramen in each transverse process. The first, second, and seventh present exceptional features and must be separately described; the following characteristics are common to the remaining four.

The **body** is small, and broader from side to side than from before backward The **anterior and posterior surfaces** are flattened and of equal depth; the former is placed on a lower level than the latter, and its inferior border is prolonged downward, so as to overlap the upper and forepart of the vertebra below. The **upper surface** is concave transversely, and presents a projecting lip on either side; the **lower surface** is concave from before backward, convex from side to side, and

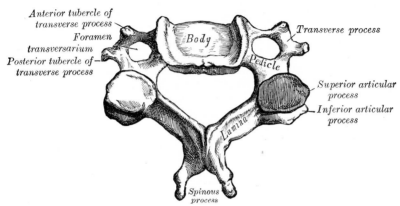

FIG. 77.—A cervical vertebra.

presents laterally shallow concavities which receive the corresponding projecting lips of the subjacent vertebra. The **pedicles** are directed lateralward and backward, and are attached to the body midway between its upper and lower borders, so that the superior vertebral notch is as deep as the inferior, but it is, at the same time, narrower. The **laminæ** are narrow, and thinner above than below; the **vertebral foramen** is large, and of a triangular form. The **spinous process** is short and bifid, the two divisions being often of unequal size. The **superior** and **inferior articular processes** on either side are fused to form an articular pillar, which projects lateralward from the junction of the pedicle and lamina. The articular facets are flat and of an oval form: the superior look backward, upward, and slightly medial-

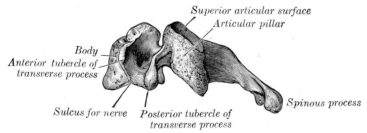

FIG. 78.—Side view of a typical cervical vertebra.

ward: the inferior forward, downward, and slightly lateralward. The **transverse processes** are each pierced by the **foramen transversarium**, which, in the upper six vertebræ, gives passage to the vertebral artery and vein and a plexus of sympathetic nerves. Each process consists of an anterior and a posterior part. The **anterior** portion is the homologue of the rib in the thoracic region, and is therefore named the **costal process** or **costal element**: it arises from the side of the body, is directed lateralward in front of the foramen, and ends in a tubercle, the **anterior tubercle**. The **posterior** part, the true transverse process, springs from the vertebral arch behind the foramen, and is directed forward and lateralward; it ends in a flattened vertical tubercle, the **posterior tubercle.** These two parts are joined, outside the foramen, by a bar of bone which exhibits a deep sulcus on its upper surface for the passage of the corresponding spinal nerve.[1]

First Cervical Vertebra.—The first cervical vertebra (Fig. 79) is named the **atlas** because it supports the globe of the head. Its chief peculiarity is that it has no body, and this is due to the fact that the body of the atlas has fused with that of the next vertebra. Its other peculiarities are that it has no spinous process, is ring-like, and consists of an anterior and a posterior arch and two lateral masses. The **anterior arch** forms about one-fifth of the ring: its anterior surface is convex, and presents at its center the **anterior tubercle** for the attachment of the Longus colli muscles; posteriorly it is concave, and marked by a smooth, oval or circular facet (*fovea dentis*), for articulation with the odontoid process (*dens*) of the axis. The upper and lower borders respectively give attachment to the anterior atlanto-occipital membrane and the anterior atlantoaxial ligament; the former connects it with the occipital bone above, and the latter with the axis below. The **posterior arch** forms about two-fifths of the circumference of the ring: it ends behind in the **posterior tubercle,** which is the rudiment of a spinous process and gives origin to the Recti capitis posteriores minores. The diminutive size of this process pre-

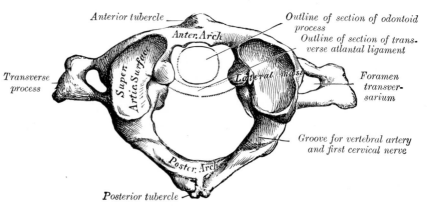

Anterior tubercle

Outline of section of odontoid process

Outline of section of transverse atlantal ligament

Transverse process

Foramen transversarium

Groove for vertebral artery and first cervical nerve

Posterior tubercle

FIG. 79.—First cervical vertebra, or atlas.

vents any interference with the movements between the atlas and the skull. The posterior part of the arch presents above and behind a rounded edge for the attachment of the posterior atlantoöccipital membrane, while immediately behind each superior articular process is a groove (*sulcus arteriæ vertebralis*), sometimes converted into a foramen by a delicate bony spiculum which arches backward from the posterior end of the superior articular process. This groove represents the superior vertebral notch, and serves for the transmission of the vertebral artery, which, after ascending through the foramen in the transverse process, winds around the lateral mass in a direction backward and medialward; it also transmits the suboccipital (first spinal) nerve. On the under surface of the posterior arch, behind the articular facets, are two shallow grooves, the **inferior vertebral notches.** The lower border gives attachment to the posterior atlantoaxial ligament, which connects it with the axis. The **lateral masses** are the most bulky and solid parts of the atlas, in order to support the weight of the head. Each carries two articular facets, a superior and an inferior. The **superior facets** are of large size, oval, concave, and approach each other in front, but diverge behind: they are directed upward, medialward, and a little backward, each forming

[1] The *costal element* of a cervical vertebra not only includes the portion which springs from the side of the body, but the anterior and posterior tubercles and the bar of bone which connects them (Fig. 59).

a cup for the corresponding condyle of the occipital bone, and are admirably adapted to the nodding movements of the head. Not infrequently they are partially subdivided by indentations which encroach upon their margins. The **inferior articular facets** are circular in form, flattened or slightly convex and directed downward and medialward, articulating with the axis, and permitting the rotatory movements of the head. Just below the medial margin of each superior facet is a small tubercle, for the attachment of the transverse atlantal ligament which stretches across the ring of the atlas and divides the vertebral foramen into two unequal parts—the anterior or smaller receiving the odontoid process of the axis, the posterior transmitting the medulla spinalis and its membranes. This part of the vertebral canal is of considerable size, much greater than is required for the accommodation of the medulla spinalis, and hence lateral displacement of the atlas may occur without compression of this structure. The **transverse processes** are large; they project lateralward and downward from the lateral masses, and serve for the attachment of muscles which assist in rotating the head. They are long, and their anterior and posterior tubercles are fused into one mass; the foramen transversarium is directed from below, upward and backward.

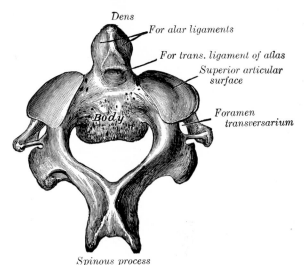

Fig. 80.—Second cervical vertebra, or epistropheus, from above.

Second Cervical Vertebra.—The second cervical vertebra (Figs. 80 and 81) is named the **epistropheus** or **axis** because it forms the pivot upon which the first vertebra, carrying the head, rotates. The most distinctive characteristic of this bone is the strong odontoid process which rises perpendicularly from the upper surface of the body. The **body** is deeper in front than behind, and prolonged downward anteriorly so as to overlap the upper and fore part of the third vertebra. It presents in front a median longitudinal ridge, separating two lateral depressions for the attachment of the Longus colli muscles. Its under surface is concave from before backward and convex from side to side. The **dens** or **odontoid process** exhibits a slight constriction or neck, where it joins the body. On its anterior surface is an oval or nearly circular facet for articulation with that on the anterior arch of the atlas. On the back of the neck, and frequently extending on to its lateral surfaces, is a shallow groove for the transverse atlantal ligament which retains the process in position. The **apex** is pointed, and gives attachment to the apical odontoid ligament; below the apex the process is somewhat enlarged, and presents on either side a rough impression for the attachment of the alar ligaments these ligaments connect the process to the occipital bone. The internal str' of the odontoid process is more compact than that of the body. The **pedicles** are broad and strong, especially in front, where they coalesce with the sides of the body and the root of the odontoid process. They are covered above by the superior articular surfaces. The **laminæ** are thick and strong, and the vertebral

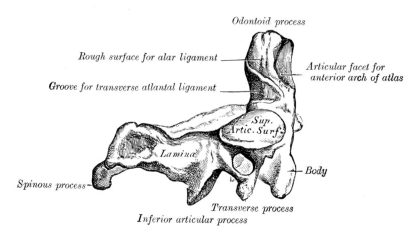

Odontoid process

Rough surface for alar ligament

Articular facet for anterior arch of atlas

Groove for transverse atlantal ligament

Sup. Artic. Surf.

Lamina

Body

Spinous process

Transverse process

Inferior articular process

FIG. 81.—Second cervical vertebra, epistropheus, or axis, from the side.

foramen large, but smaller than that of the atlas. The **transverse processes** are very small, and each ends in a single tubercle; each is perforated by the foramen transversarium, which is directed obliquely upward and lateralward. The **superior articular surfaces** are round, slightly convex, directed upward and lateralward, and are supported on the body, pedicles, and transverse processes. The **inferior articular surfaces** have the same direction as those of the other cervical vertebræ. The **superior vertebral notches** are very shallow, and lie behind the articular processes; the **inferior** lie in front of the articular processes, as in the other cervical vertebræ. The **spinous process** is large, very strong, deeply channelled on its under surface, and presents a bifid, tuberculated extremity.

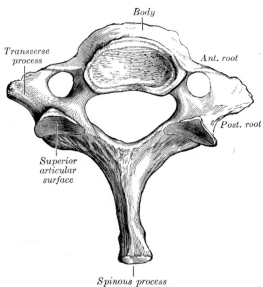

Body

Transverse process

Ant. root

Post. root

Superior articular surface

Spinous process

FIG. 82.—Seventh cervical vertebra.

The Seventh Cervical Vertebra (Fig. 82).—The most distinctive characteristic of this vertebra is the existence of a long and prominent spinous process, hence the name **vertebra prominens**. This process is thick, nearly horizontal in direction, not bifurcated, but terminating in a tubercle to which the lower end of the ligamentum nuchæ is attached. The **transverse processes** are of considerable size, their posterior roots are large and prominent, while the anterior are small and faintly marked. The foramen transversarium may be as large as that in the other cervical vertebræ, but is generally smaller on one or both sides; occasionally it is double, sometimes it is absent. On the left side it occasionally gives passage to the vertebral artery; more frequently the vertebral vein traverses it on both sides; but the usual arrangement is for both artery and vein to pass in front of the transverse process, and not through the foramen. Sometimes the anterior root of the transverse process attains a large size and exists as a separate bone, which is known as a **cervical rib**.

The Thoracic Vertebræ (Vertebræ Thoracales).

The **thoracic vertebræ** (Fig. 83) are intermediate in size between those of the cervical and lumbar regions; they increase in size from above downward, the upper vertebræ being much smaller than those in the lower part of the region. They are distinguished by the presence of facets on the sides of the bodies for articulation with the heads of the ribs, and facets on the transverse processes of all, except the eleventh and twelfth, for articulation with the tubercles of the ribs.

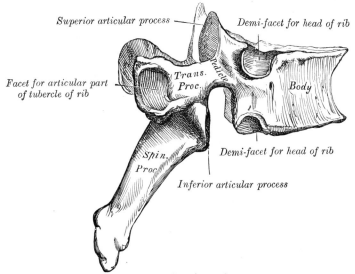

Fig. 83.—A thoracic vertebra.

The **bodies** in the middle of the thoracic region are heart-shaped, and as broad in the antero-posterior as in the transverse direction. At the ends of the thoracic region they resemble respectively those of the cervical and lumbar vertebræ. They are slightly thicker behind than in front, flat above and below, convex from side to side in front, deeply concave behind, and slightly constricted laterally and in front. They present, on either side, two costal demi-facets, one above, near the root of the pedicle, the other below, in front of the inferior vertebral notch; these are covered with cartilage in the fresh state, and, when the vertebræ are articulated with one another, form, with the intervening intervertebral fibrocartilages, oval surfaces for the reception of the heads of the ribs. The **pedicles** are directed backward and slightly upward, and the inferior vertebral notches are of large size, and deeper than in any other region of the vertebral column. The **laminæ** are broad, thick, and imbricated—that is to say, they overlap those of subjacent vertebræ like tiles on a roof. The **vertebral foramen** is small, and of a circular form. The **spinous process** is long, triangular on coronal section, directed obliquely downward, and ends in a tuberculated extremity. These processes overlap from the fifth to the eighth, but are less oblique in direction above and

6

below. The **superior articular processes** are thin plates of bone projecting upward from the junctions of the pedicles and laminæ; their articular facets are practically flat, and are directed backward and a little lateralward and upward. The **inferior articular processes** are fused to a considerable extent with the laminæ, and project but slightly beyond their lower borders; their facets are directed

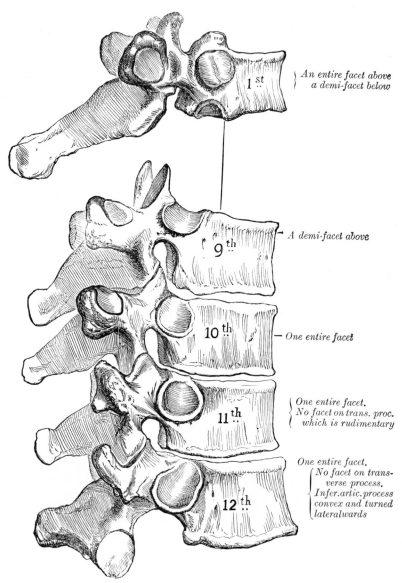

An entire facet above a demi-facet below

A demi-facet above

One entire facet

One entire facet. No facet on trans. proc. which is rudimentary

One entire facet. No facet on transverse process. Infer.artic.process convex and turned lateralwards

Fig. 84.—Peculiar thoracic vertebræ

forward and a little medialward and downward. The **transverse processes** arise from the arch behind the superior articular processes and pedicles; they are thick, strong, and of considerable length, directed obliquely backward and lateralward, and each ends in a clubbed extremity, on the front of which is a small, concave surface, for articulation with the tubercle of a rib.

The *first*, *ninth*, *tenth*, *eleventh*, and *twelfth* thoracic vertebræ present certain peculiarities, and must be specially considered (Fig. 84).

The **First Thoracic Vertebra** has, on either side of the **body,** an entire articular facet for the head of the first rib, and a demi-facet for the upper half of the head of the second rib. The body is like that of a cervical vertebra, being broad transversely; its upper surface is concave, and lipped on either side. The **superior articular surfaces** are directed upward and backward; the **spinous process** is thick, long, and almost horizontal. The **transverse processes** are long, and the upper vertebral notches are deeper than those of the other thoracic vertebræ.

The **Ninth Thoracic Vertebra** may have no demi-facets below. In some subjects however, it has two demi-facets on either side; when this occurs the tenth has only demi-facets at the upper part.

The **Tenth Thoracic Vertebra** has (except in the cases just mentioned) an entire articular facet on either side, which is placed partly on the lateral surface of the pedicle.

In the **Eleventh Thoracic Vertebra** the **body** approaches in its form and size to that of the lumbar vertebræ. The articular facets for the heads of the ribs are of large size, and placed chiefly on the pedicles, which are thicker and stronger in this and the next vertebra than in any other part of the thoracic region. The **spinous process** is short, and nearly horizontal in direction. The **transverse processes** are very short, tuberculated at their extremities, and have no articular facets.

The **Twelfth Thoracic Vertebra** has the same general characteristics as the eleventh, but may be distinguished from it by its inferior articular surfaces being convex and directed lateralward, like those of the lumbar vertebræ; by the general form of the body, laminæ, and spinous process, in which it resembles the lumbar vertebræ; and by each transverse process being subdivided into three elevations, the superior, inferior, and lateral tubercles: the superior and inferior correspond to the mammillary and accessory processes of the lumbar vertebræ. Traces of similar elevations are found on the transverse processes of the tenth and eleventh thoracic vertebræ.

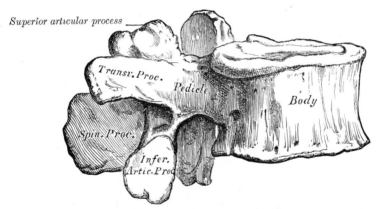

Fig. 85.—A lumbar vertebra seen from the side.

The Lumbar Vertebræ (Vertebræ Lumbales).

The **lumbar vertebræ** (Figs. 85 and 86) are the largest segments of the movable part of the vertebral column, and can be distinguished by the absence of a foramen in the transverse process, and by the absence of facets on the sides of the body.

The **body** is large, wider from side to side than from before backward, and a little thicker in front than behind. It is flattened or slightly concave above and below, concave behind, and deeply constricted in front and at the sides. The **pedicles** are very strong, directed backward from the upper part of the body;

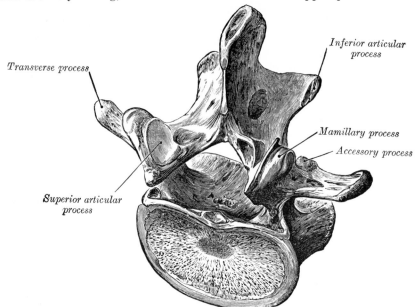

Inferior articular process

Transverse process

Mamillary process

Accessory process

Superior articular process

FIG. 86.—A lumbar vertebra from above and behind.

consequently, the inferior vertebral notches are of considerable depth. The **laminæ** are broad, short, and strong; the **vertebral foramen** is triangular, larger than in the thoracic, but smaller than in the cervical region. The **spinous process**

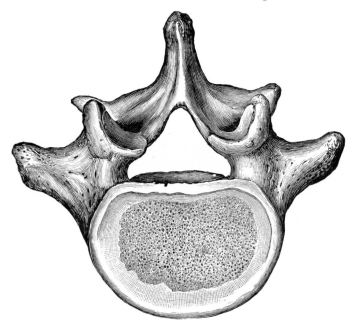

FIG. 87.—Fifth lumbar vertebra, from above.

is thick, broad, and somewhat quadrilateral; it projects backward and ends in a rough, uneven border, thickest below where it is occasionally notched. The **superior** and **inferior articular processes** are well-defined, projecting respectively upward and downward from the junctions of pedicles and laminæ. The facets on the superior processes are concave, and look backward and medialward; those on the inferior are convex, and are directed forward and lateralward. The former are wider apart than the latter, since in the articulated column the inferior articular processes are embraced by the superior processes of the subjacent vertebra. The **transverse processes** are long, slender, and horizontal in the upper three lumbar vertebræ; they incline a little upward in the lower two. In the upper three vertebræ they arise from the junctions of the pedicles and laminæ, but in the lower two they are set farther forward and spring from the pedicles and posterior parts of the bodies. They are situated in front of the articular processes instead of behind them as in the thoracic vertebræ, and are homologous with the ribs. Of the three tubercles noticed in connection with the transverse processes of the lower thoracic vertebræ, the superior one is connected in the lumbar region with the back part of the superior articular process, and is named the **mammillary process**; the inferior is situated at the back part of the base of the transverse process, and is called the **accessory process** (Fig. 86).

The **Fifth Lumbar Vertebra** (Fig. 87) is characterized by its body being much deeper in front than behind, which accords with the prominence of the sacro-vertebral articulation; by the smaller size of its spinous process; by the wide interval between the inferior articular processes; and by the thickness of its transverse processes, which spring from the body as well as from the pedicles.

Variations.—The last **lumbar vertebra** is subject to certain defects described as bifid and separate neural arches, the latter occurring three times as frequently as the former. Both defects result in weakness of the column; the bifid arch by impairing ligamentous attachments; the separate arch through loss of bony anchorage of the column to its base.

The Sacral and Coccygeal Vertebræ.

The **sacral and coccygeal vertebræ** consist at an early period of life of nine separate segments which are united in the adult, so as to form two bones, five entering into the formation of the sacrum, four into that of the coccyx. Sometimes the coccyx consists of five bones; occasionally the number is reduced to three.

The Sacrum (*os sacrum*).—The sacrum is a large, triangular bone, situated in the lower part of the vertebral column and at the upper and back part of the pelvic cavity, where it is inserted like a wedge between the two hip bones; its upper part or base articulates with the last lumbar vertebra, its apex with the coccyx. It is curved upon itself and placed very obliquely, its base projecting forward and forming the **prominent sacrovertebral angle** when articulated with the last lumbar vertebra; its central part is projected backward, so as to give increased capacity to the pelvic cavity.

Pelvic Surface (*facies pelvina*).—The pelvic surface (Fig. 88) is concave from above downward, and slightly so from side to side. Its middle part is crossed by four **transverse ridges**, the positions of which correspond with the original planes of separation between the five segments of the bone. The portions of bone intervening between the ridges are the bodies of the sacral vertebræ. The body of the first segment is of large size, and in form resembles that of a lumbar vertebra; the succeeding ones diminish from above downward, are flattened from before backward, and curved so as to accommodate themselves to the form of the sacrum, being concave in front, convex behind. At the ends of the ridges are seen the **anterior sacral foramina**, four in number on either side, somewhat rounded in form, diminishing in size from above downward, and directed lateralward and forward; they give exit to the anterior divisions of the sacral nerves and entrance to the lateral sacral arteries. Lateral to these foramina are the **lateral parts of the sacrum,** each consisting of five separate segments at an early period of life; in the adult, these are blended with the bodies and with each other. Each lateral part is traversed by four broad, shallow grooves, which lodge the anterior divisions of the sacral nerves, and are separated by prominent ridges of bone which give origin to the Piriformis muscle.

If a sagittal section be made through the center of the sacrum (Fig. 92), the bodies are seen to be united at their circumferences by bone, wide intervals being left centrally, which, in the fresh state, are filled by the intervertebral fibrocartilages. In some bones this union is more complete between the lower than the upper segments.

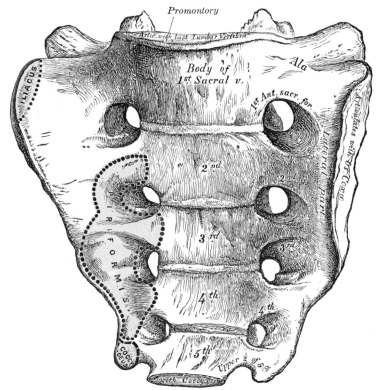

FIG. 88.—Sacrum, pelvic surface.

Dorsal Surface (*facies dorsalis*).—The dorsal surface (Fig. 89) is convex and narrower than the pelvic. In the middle line it displays a crest, the **middle sacral crest**, surmounted by three or four tubercles, the rudimentary spinous processes of the upper three or four sacral vertebræ. On either side of the middle sacral crest is a shallow groove, the **sacral groove**, which gives origin to the Multifidus, the floor of the groove being formed by the united laminæ of the corresponding vertebræ. The Sacrospinalis arises partly from the medial and lateral crests and the Latissimus dorsi partly from the medial crest. The laminæ of the fifth sacral vertebra, and sometimes those of the fourth, fail to meet behind, and thus a hiatus or deficiency occurs in the posterior wall of the sacral canal. On the lateral aspect of the sacral groove is a linear series of tubercles produced by the fusion of the articular processes which together form the indistinct **sacral articular crests**. The articular processes of the first sacral vertebra are large and oval in shape; their facets are concave from side to side, look backward and medialward, and articulate with the facets on the inferior processes of the fifth lumbar vertebra. The tubercles which represent the inferior articular processes of the fifth sacral vertebra are prolonged downward as rounded processes, which are named the **sacral cornua**, and are connected to the cornua of the coccyx. Lateral to the articular processes are the four **posterior sacral foramina**; they are smaller in size and less regular in form than the anterior, and transmit the posterior divisions of the sacral nerves. On the lateral side of the posterior sacral foramina is a series of tubercles, which represent the transverse processes of the sacral vertebræ, and form the **lateral crests** of the sacrum. The transverse tubercles of the first sacral vertebra are large and very distinct; they, together with the transverse tubercles of the second vertebra, give attachment to the horizontal parts of the posterior sacroiliac ligaments; those of the third vertebra give attachment to the oblique fasciculi of the posterior sacroiliac ligaments; and those of the fourth and fifth to the sacrotuberous ligaments.

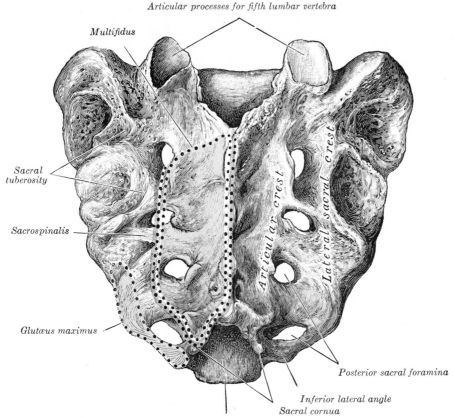

Fig. 89.—The sacrum, dorsal aspect.

Lateral Surface.—The lateral surface is broad above, but narrowed into a thin edge below. The upper half presents in front an ear-shaped surface, the **auricular surface**, covered with cartilage in the fresh state, for articulation with the ilium. Behind it is a rough surface, the **sacral tuberosity**, on which are three deep and uneven impressions, for the attachment of the posterior sacroiliac ligament. The lower half is thin, and ends in a projection called the **inferior lateral angle**; medial to this angle is a notch, which is converted into a foramen by the transverse process of the first piece of the coccyx, and transmits the anterior division of the fifth sacral nerve. The thin lower half of the lateral surface gives attachment to the sacrotuberous and sacrospinous ligaments, to some fibers of the Glutæus maximus behind, and to the Coccygeus in front (Fig. 89.)

Base (*basis oss. sacri*).—The base of the sacrum, which is broad and expanded, is directed upward and forward. In the middle is a large oval articular surface, the upper surface of the body of the first sacral vertebra, which is connected with

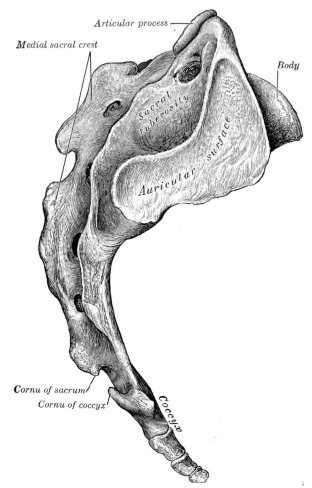

FIG. 90.—Lateral surfaces of sacrum and coccyx.

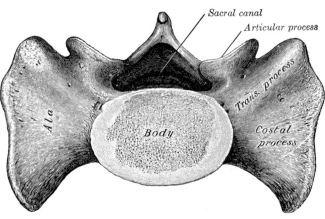

FIG. 91.—Base of sacrum

the under surface of the body of the last lumbar vertebra by an intervertebral fibrocartilage. Behind this is the large triangular orifice of the sacral canal, which is completed by the laminæ and spinous process of the first sacral vertebra. The superior articular processes project from it on either side; they are oval, concave, directed backward and medialward, like the superior articular processes of a lumbar vertebra. They are attached to the body of the first sacral vertebra and to the alæ by short thick pedicles; on the upper surface of each pedicle is a vertebral notch, which forms the lower part of the foramen between the last lumbar and first sacral vertebræ. On either side of the body is a large triangular surface, which supports the Psoas major and the lumbosacral trunk, and in the articulated pelvis is continuous with the iliac fossa. This is called the **ala**; it is slightly concave from side to side, convex from before backward, and gives attachment to a few of the fibers of the Iliacus. The posterior fourth of the ala represents the transverse process, and its anterior three-fourths the costal process of the first sacral segment.

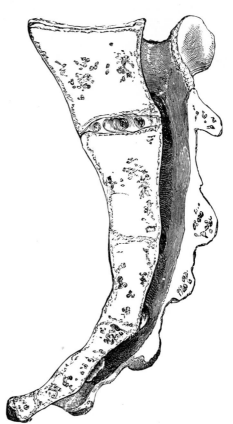

FIG. 92.—Median sagittal section of the sacrum.

Apex (*apex oss. sacri*).—The apex is directed downward, and presents an oval facet for articulation with the coccyx.

Vertebral Canal (*canalis sacralis; sacral canal*).—The vertebral canal (Fig. 92) runs throughout the greater part of the bone; above, it is triangular in form; below, its posterior wall is incomplete, from the non-development of the laminæ and spinous processes. It lodges the sacral nerves, and its walls are perforated by the anterior and posterior sacral foramina through which these nerves pass out.

Structure.—The sacrum consists of cancellous tissue enveloped by a thin layer of compact bone.

Articulations.—The sacrum articulates with *four* bones; the last lumbar vertebra above, the coccyx below, and the hip bone on either side.

Differences in the Sacrum of the Male and Female.—In the female the sacrum is shorter and wider than in the male; the lower half forms a greater angle with the upper; the upper half is nearly straight, the lower half presenting the greatest amount of curvature. The bone is also directed more obliquely backward; this increases the size of the pelvic cavity and renders the sacrovertebral angle more prominent. In the male the curvature is more evenly distributed over the whole length of the bone, and is altogether greater than in the female.

Variations.—The sacrum, in some cases, consists of six pieces; occasionally the number is reduced to four. The bodies of the first and second vertebræ may fail to unite. Sometimes the uppermost transverse tubercles are not joined to the rest of the ala on one or both sides, or the sacral canal may be open throughout a considerable part of its length, in consequence of the imperfect development of the laminæ and spinous processes. The sacrum, also, varies considerably with respect to its degree of curvature.

The Coccyx (*os coccygis*).—The coccyx (Figs. 93 and 94) is usually formed of four rudimentary vertebræ; the number may however be increased to five or diminished to three. In each of the first three segments may be traced a rudimentary body and articular and transverse processes; the last piece (sometimes the third) is a mere nodule of bone. All the segments are destitute of pedicles, laminæ, and spinous processes. The first is the largest; it resembles the lowest sacral vertebra, and often exists as a separate piece; the last three diminish in size from above downward, and are usually fused with one another.

Surfaces.—The **anterior surface** is slightly concave, and marked with three transverse grooves which indicate the junctions of the different segments. It gives attachment to the anterior sacrococcygeal ligament and the Levatores ani, and supports part of the rectum. The **posterior surface** is convex, marked by transverse grooves similar to those on the anterior surface, and presents on either side a linear row of tubercles, the rudimentary articular processes of the coccygeal vertebræ. Of these, the superior pair are large, and are called the **coccygeal cornua;** they project upward, and articulate with the cornua of the sacrum, and on either side complete the foramen for the transmission of the posterior division of the fifth sacral nerve.

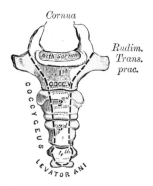

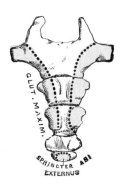

Fig. 93.—Coccyx anterior surface.　　　　　Fig. 94.—Coccyx posterior surface.

Borders.—The **lateral borders** are thin, and exhibit a series of small eminences, which represent the transverse processes of the coccygeal vertebræ. Of these, the first is the largest; it is flattened from before backward, and often ascends to join the lower part of the thin lateral edge of the sacrum, thus completing the foramen for the transmission of the anterior division of the fifth sacral nerve; the others diminish in size from above downward, and are often wanting. The borders of the coccyx are narrow, and give attachment on either side to the sacrotuberous and sacrospinous ligaments, to the Coccygeus in front of the ligaments, and to the Glutæus maximus behind them.

Base.—The base presents an oval surface for articulation with the sacrum.

Apex.—The apex is rounded, and has attached to it the tendon of the Sphincter ani externus. It may be bifid, and is sometimes deflected to one or other side.

Ossification of the Vertebral Column.—Each cartilaginous vertebra is ossified from three primary centers (Fig. 95), two for the vertebral arch and one for the body.[1] Ossification of the vertebral arches begins in the upper cervical vertebræ about the seventh or eighth week of fetal life, and gradually extends down the column. The ossific granules first appear in the situations where the transverse processes afterward project, and spread backward to the spinous process forward into the pedicles, and lateralward into the transverse and articular processes. Ossification of the bodies begins about the eighth week in the lower thoracic region, and subsequently extends upward and downward along the column. The center for the body does not give rise to the whole of the body of the adult vertebra, the postero-lateral portions of which are ossified by extensions from the vertebral arch centers. The body of the vertebra during the first few years of life shows, therefore, two synchondroses, **neurocentral synchondroses,** traversing it along the planes of junction of the three centers (Fig. 96). In the thoracic region, the facets for the heads of the ribs lie behind the neurocentral synchondroses and are ossified from the centers for the vertebral arch. At birth the vertebra consists of three pieces, the body and the halves of the vertebral arch. During the

---

[1] A vertebra is occasionally found in which the body consists of two lateral portions—a condition which proves that the body is sometimes ossified from *two* primary centers, one on either side of the middle line.

first year the halves of the arch unite behind, union taking place first in the lumbar region and then extending upward through the thoracic and cervical regions. About the third year the bodies of the upper cervical vertebræ are joined to the arches on either side; in the lower lumbar vertebræ the union is not completed until the sixth year. Before puberty, no other changes occur, excepting a gradual increase of these primary centers, the upper and under surfaces of the bodies and the ends of the transverse and spinous processes being cartilaginous. About the sixteenth year (Fig. 96), five secondary centers appear, one for the tip of each transverse process, one for the extremity of the spinous process, one for the upper and one for the lower surface of the body (Fig. 97). These fuse with the rest of the bone about the age of twenty-five.

Exceptions to this mode of development occur in the first, second and seventh cervical vertebræ, and in the lumbar vertebræ.

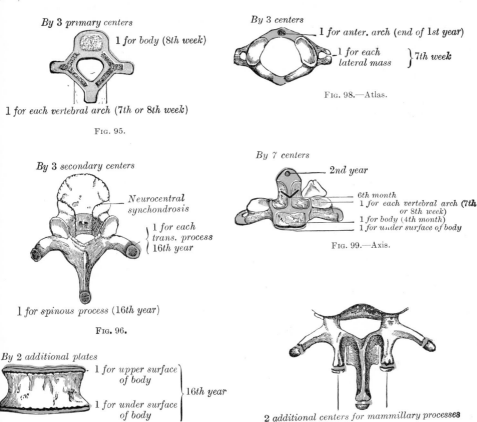

By 3 primary centers

1 for body (8th week)

1 for each vertebral arch (7th or 8th week)

FIG. 95.

By 3 centers

1 for anter. arch (end of 1st year)

1 for each lateral mass } 7th week

FIG. 98.—Atlas.

By 3 secondary centers

Neurocentral synchondrosis

1 for each trans. process 16th year

1 for spinous process (16th year)

FIG. 96.

By 7 centers

2nd year

6th month
1 for each vertebral arch (7th or 8th week)
1 for body (4th month)
1 for under surface of body

FIG. 99.—Axis.

By 2 additional plates

1 for upper surface of body

1 for under surface of body

16th year

FIG. 97.

FIGS. 95–97.—Ossification of a vertebra.

2 additional centers for mammillary processes

FIG. 100.—Lumbar vertebra.

FIGS. 98–100.—Individual peculiarities.

Atlas.—The atlas is usually ossified from *three* centers (Fig. 98). Of these, one appears in each lateral mass about the seventh week of fetal life, and extends backward; at birth, these portions of bone are separated from one another behind by a narrow interval filled with cartilage. Between the third and fourth years they unite either directly or through the medium of a separate center developed in the cartilage. At birth, the anterior arch consists of cartilage; in this a separate center appears about the end of the first year after birth, and joins the lateral masses from the sixth to the eighth year—the lines of union extending across the anterior portions of the superior articular facets. Occasionally there is no separate center, the anterior arch being formed by the forward extension and ultimate junction of the two lateral masses; sometimes this arch is ossified from two centers, one on either side of the middle line.

Epistropheus or Axis.—The axis is ossified from *five* primary and *two* secondary centers (Fig. 99). The body and vertebral arch are ossified in the same manner as the corresponding parts in the other vertebræ, viz., one center for the body, and two for the vertebral arch. The centers for the arch appear about the seventh or eighth week of fetal life, that for the body about the fourth or fifth month. The dens or odontoid process consists originally of a continuation upward of the cartilaginous mass, in which the lower part of the body is formed. About the sixth month of fetal life, two centers make their appearance in the base of this process: they are placed laterally, and join before birth to form a conical bilobed mass deeply cleft above; the interval between the sides of the cleft and the summit of the process is formed by a wedge-shaped piece of cartilage. The base of the process is separated from the body by a cartilaginous disk, which gradually becomes ossified at its circumference, but remains cartilaginous in its center until advanced age. In this cartilage, rudiments of the lower epiphysial lamella of the atlas and the upper epiphysial lamella of the axis may sometimes be found. The apex of the odontoid process has a separate center which appears in the second and joins about the twelfth year; this is the upper epiphysial lamella of the atlas. In addition to these there is a secondary center for a thin epiphysial plate on the under surface of the body of the bone.

The Seventh Cervical Vertebra.—The anterior or costal part of the transverse process of this vertebra is sometimes ossified from a separate center which appears about the sixth month of fetal life and joins the body and posterior part of the transverse process between the fifth and sixth years. Occasionally the costal part persists as a separate piece, and, becoming lengthened lateralward and forward, constitutes what is known as a *cervical rib*. Separate ossific centers have also been found in the costal processes of the fourth, fifth, and sixth cervical vertebræ.

Lumbar Vertebræ.—The lumbar vertebræ (Fig. 100) have each *two* additional centers, for the mammillary processes. The transverse process of the first lumbar is sometimes developed as a separate piece, which may remain permanently ununited with the rest of the bone, thus forming a lumbar rib—a peculiarity, however, rarely met with.

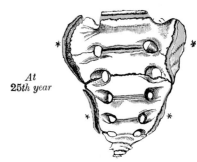

At birth

At
25th year

At 4½ yrs.

Fig. 101.—(*) Additional centers for costal elements.

Fig. 103.—(*) Two epiphysial plates for each lateral surfa[ce]

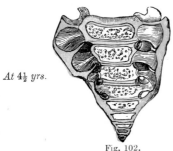

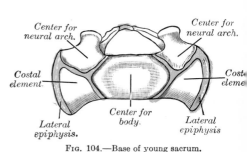

Center for
neural arch.

Center for
neural arch.

Costal
element

Cost[al]
eleme[nt]

Center for
body.

Lateral
epiphysis.

Lateral
epiphysis

Fig. 102.

Fig. 104.—Base of young sacrum.

Figs. 101–104.—Ossification of the sacrum.

Sacrum (Figs. 101 to 104).—The *body* of each sacral vertebra is ossified from a primary center and *two* epiphysial plates, one for its upper and another for its under surface, while each vertebral arch is ossified from two centers.

The anterior portions of the *lateral parts* have *six* additional centers, two for each of the three vertebræ; these represent the costal elements, and make their appearance above and lateral to the anterior sacral foramina (Figs. 101, 102).

On each *lateral surface* two epiphysial plates are developed (Figs. 103, 104): one for the auricular surface, and another for the remaining part of the thin lateral edge of the bone.

PERIODS OF OSSIFICATION.—About the eighth or ninth week of fetal life, ossification of the central part of the body of the first sacral vertebra commences, and is rapidly followed by deposit of ossific matter in the second and third: ossification does not commence in the bodies of the lower two segments until between the fifth and eighth months of fetal life. Between the sixth and eighth months ossification of the vertebral arches takes place; and about the same time the costal centers for the lateral parts make their appearance. The junctions of the vertebral arches with the bodies take place in the lower vertebræ as early as the second year, but are not effected in the uppermost until the fifth or sixth year. About the sixteenth year the epiphysial plates for the upper and under surfaces of the bodies are formed; and between the eighteenth and twentieth years, those for the lateral surfaces make their appearance. The bodies of the sacral vertebræ are, during early life, separated from each other by intervertebral fibrocartilages, but about the eighteenth year the two lowest segments become united by bone, and the process of bony union gradually extends upward, with the result that between the twenty-fifth and thirtieth years of life all the segments are united. On examining a sagittal section of the sacrum, the situations of the intervertebral fibrocartilages are indicated by a series of oval cavities (Fig. 92).

Coccyx.—The coccyx is ossified from *four* centers, one for each segment. The ossific nuclei make their appearance in the following order: in the first segment between the first and fourth years; in the second between the fifth and tenth years; in the third between the tenth and fifteenth years; in the fourth between the fourteenth and twentieth years. As age advances, the segments unite with one another, the union between the first and second segments being frequently delayed until after the age of twenty-five or thirty. At a late period of life, especially in females, the coccyx often fuses with the sacrum.

THE VERTEBRAL COLUMN AS A WHOLE.

The vertebral column is situated in the median line, as the posterior part of the trunk; its average length in the male is about 71 cm. Of this length the cervical part measures 12.5 cm., the thoracic about 28 cm., the lumbar 18 cm., and the sacrum and coccyx 12.5 cm. The female column is about 61 cm. in length.

Curves.—Viewed laterally (Fig. 105), the vertebral column presents several curves, which correspond to the different regions of the column, and are called cervical, thoracic, lumbar, and pelvic. The **cervical** curve, convex forward, begins at the apex of the odontoid process, and ends at the middle of the second thoracic vertebra; it is the least marked of all the curves. The **thoracic** curve, concave forward, begins at the middle of the second and ends at the middle of the twelfth thoracic vertebra. Its most prominent point behind corresponds to the spinous process of the seventh thoracic vertebra. The **lumbar** curve is more marked in the female than in the male; it begins at the middle of the last thoracic vertebra, and ends at the sacrovertebral angle. It is convex anteriorly, the convexity of the lower three vertebræ being much greater than that of the upper two. The **pelvic** curve begins at the sacrovertebral articulation, and ends at the point of the coccyx; its concavity is directed downward and forward. The thoracic and pelvic curves are termed primary curves, because they alone are present during fetal life. The cervical and lumbar curves are compensatory or secondary, and are developed after birth, the former when the child is able to hold up its head (at three or four months), and to sit upright (at nine months), the latter at twelve or eighteen months, when the child begins to walk.

The vertebral column has also a slight **lateral** curvature, the convexity of which is directed toward the right side. This may be produced by muscular action, most persons using the right arm in preference to the left, especially in making long-continued efforts, when the body is curved to the right side. In support of this explanation it has been found that in one or two individuals who were left-handed, the convexity was to the left side. By others this curvature is regarded as being produced by the aortic arch and upper part of the descending thoracic aorta—a view which is supported by the fact that in cases where the viscera are transposed and the aorta is on the right side, the convexity of the curve is directed to the left side.

Surfaces.—**Anterior Surface.**—When viewed from in front, the width of the bodies of the vertebræ is seen to increase from the second cervical to the first thoracic; there is then a slight diminution in the next three vertebræ; below this there is again a gradual and progressive increase in width as low as the sacrovertebral angle. From this point there is a rapid diminution, to the apex of the coccyx.

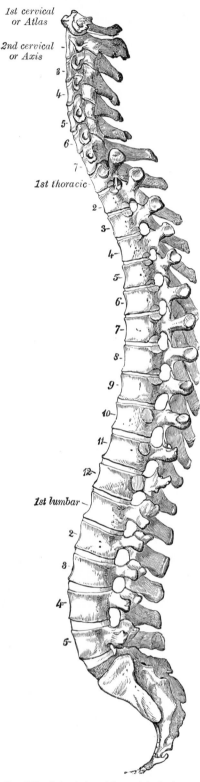

1st cervical or Atlas

2nd cervical or Axis

3-

4-

5-

6-

7-

1st thoracic

2-

3-

4-

5-

6-

7-

8-

9-

10-

11-

12-

1st lumbar

2-

3-

4-

5-

F̲ɪɢ. 105.—Lateral view of the vertebral column.

Posterior Surface.—The posterior surface of the vertebral column presents in the median line the spinous processes. In the cervical region (with the exception of the second and seventh vertebræ) these are short and horizontal, with bifid extremities. In the upper part of the thoracic region they are directed obliquely downward; in the middle they are almost vertical, and in the lower part they are nearly horizontal. In the lumbar region they are nearly horizontal. The spinous processes are separated by considerable intervals in the lumbar region, by narrower intervals in the neck, and are closely approximated in the middle of the thoracic region. Occasionally one of these processes deviates a little from the median line—a fact to be remembered in practice, as irregularities of this sort are attendant also on fractures or displacements of the vertebral column. On either side of the spinous processes is the **vertebral groove** formed by the laminæ in the cervical and lumbar regions, where it is shallow, and by the laminæ and transverse processes in the thoracic region, where it is deep and broad; these grooves lodge the deep muscles of the back. Lateral to the vertebral grooves are the articular processes, and still more laterally the transverse processes. In the thoracic region, the transverse processes stand backward, on a plane considerably behind that of the same processes in the cervical and lumbar regions. In the cervical region, the transverse processes are placed in front of the articular processes, lateral to the pedicles and between the intervertebral foramina. In the thoracic region they are posterior to the pedicles, intervertebral foramina, and articular processes. In the lumbar region they are in front of the articular processes, but behind the intervertebral foramina.

Lateral Surfaces.—The lateral surfaces are separated from the posterior surface by the articular processes in the cervical and lumbar regions, and by the transverse processes in the thoracic region. They present, in front, the sides of the bodies of the vertebræ, marked in the thoracic region by the facets for articulation with the heads of the ribs. More posteriorly are the intervertebral foramina, formed by the juxtaposition of the vertebral notches, oval in shape, smallest in the cervical and upper part of the thoracic regions, and gradually increasing in size to the last lumbar. They transmit the spinal nerves and are situated between the transverse processes in the cervical region, and in front of them in the thoracic and lumbar regions.

Vertebral Canal.—The vertebral canal follows the different curves of the column; it is large and triangular in those parts of the column which enjoy the greatest freedom of movement, viz., the cervical and lumbar regions; and is small and rounded in the thoracic region, where motion is more limited.

Abnormalities.—Occasionally the coalescence of the laminæ is not completed, and consequently a cleft is left in the arches of the vertebræ, through which a protrusion of the spinal membranes (dura mater and arachnoid), and generally of the medulla spinalis itself, takes place, constituting the malformation known as *spina bifida.* This condition is most common in the lumbosacral region, but it may occur in the thoracic or cervical region, or the arches throughout the whole length of the canal may remain incomplete.

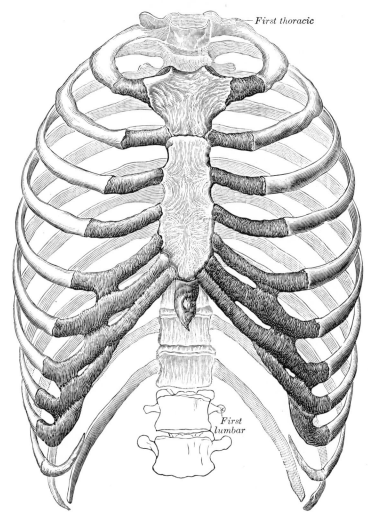

First thoracic

First lumbar

Fig. 106.—The thorax from in front. (Spalteholz.)

THE THORAX.

The skeleton of the **thorax** or **chest** (Figs. 106, 107, 108) is an osseo-cartilaginous cage, containing and protecting the principal organs of respiration and circulation.

It is conical in shape, being narrow above and broad below, flattened from before backward, and longer behind than in front. It is somewhat reniform on transverse section on account of the projection of the vertebral bodies into the cavity.

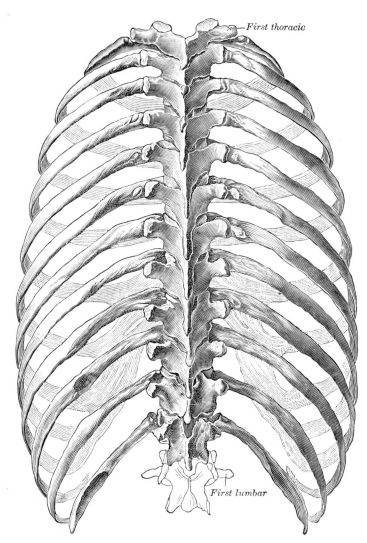

First thoracic

First lumbar

Fig. 107.—The thorax from behind. (Spalteholz.)

Boundaries.—The **posterior surface** is formed by the twelve thoracic vertebræ and the posterior parts of the ribs. It is convex from above downward, and presents on either side of the middle line a deep groove, in consequence of the lateral and backward direction which the ribs take from their vertebral extremities to their angles. The **anterior surface**, formed by the sternum and costal cartilages, is flattened or slightly convex, and inclined from above downward and forward. The **lateral surfaces** are convex; they are formed by the ribs, separated from each other by the intercostal spaces, eleven in number, which are occupied by the Intercostal muscles and membranes.

The **upper opening** of the thorax is reniform in shape, being broader from side to side than from before backward. It is formed by the first thoracic vertebra behind, the upper margin of the sternum in front, and the first rib on either side. It slopes downward and forward, so that the anterior part of the opening is on a lower level than the posterior. Its antero-posterior diameter is about 5 cm., and its transverse diameter about 10 cm. The **lower opening** is formed by the twelfth thoracic vertebra behind, by the eleventh and twelfth ribs at the sides, and in front by the cartilages of the tenth, ninth, eighth, and seventh ribs, which ascend on either side and form an angle, the **subcostal angle,** into the apex of which the xiphoid process projects. The lower opening is wider transversely than from before backward, and slopes obliquely downward and backward, it is closed by the diaphragm which forms the floor of the thorax.

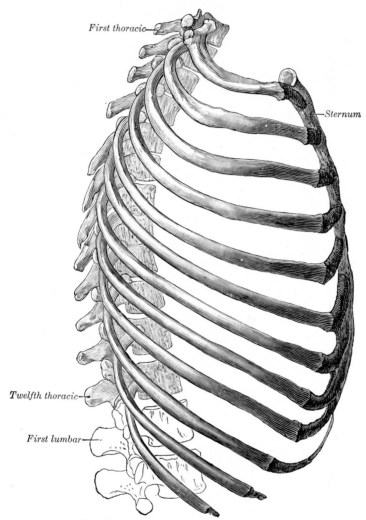

First thoracic

—Sternum

Twelfth thoracic—

First lumbar—

Fig. 108.—The thorax from the right. (Spalteholz.)

The thorax of the female differs from that of the male as follows: 1. Its capacity is less. 2. The sternum is shorter. 3. The upper margin of the sternum is on a level with the lower part of the body of the third thoracic vertebra, whereas in the male it is on a level with the lower part of the body of the second. 4. The upper ribs are more movable, and so allow a greater enlargement of the upper part of the thorax.

The Sternum (Breast Bone).

The **sternum** (Figs. 109 to 111) is an elongated, flattened bone, forming the middle portion of the anterior wall of the thorax. Its upper end supports the clavicles, and its margins articulate with the cartilages of the first seven pairs

7

of ribs. It consists of three parts, named from above downward, the **manubrium**, the **body** or **gladiolus**, and the **xiphoid process**; in early life the body consists of four segments or *sternebræ*. In its natural position the inclination of the bone is oblique from above, downward and forward. It is slightly convex in front and concave

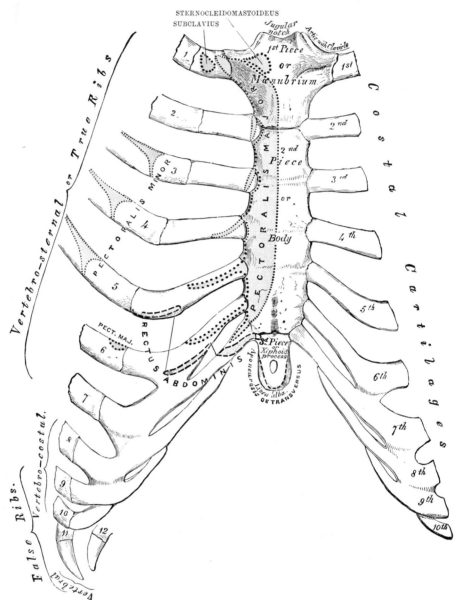

Fig. 109.—Anterior surface of sternum and costal cartilages.

behind; broad above, becoming narrowed at the point where the manubrium joins the body, after which it again widens a little to below the middle of the body, and then narrows to its lower extremity. Its average length in the adult is about 17 cm., and is rather greater in the male than in the female.

Manubrium (*manubrium sterni*).—The manubrium is of a somewhat quadrangular form, broad and thick above, narrow below at its junction with the body.

Surfaces.—Its **anterior surface**, convex from side to side, concave from above downward, is smooth, and affords attachment on either side to the sternal origins of the Pectoralis major and Sternocleidomastoideus. Sometimes the ridges limiting the attachments of these muscles are very distinct. Its **posterior surface,** concave and smooth, affords attachment on either side to the Sterno-hyoideus and Sternothyreoideus.

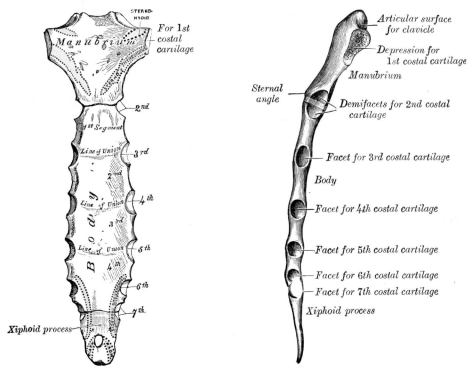

Fig. 110.—Posterior surface of sternum.　　　Fig. 111.—Lateral border of sternum.

Borders.—The **superior border** is the thickest and presents at its center the **jugular or presternal notch;** on either side of the notch is an oval articular surface, directed upward, backward, and lateralward, for articulation with the sternal end of the clavicle. The **inferior border,** oval and rough, is covered in a fresh state with a thin layer of cartilage, for articulation with the body. The **lateral borders** are each marked above by a depression for the first costal cartilage, and below by a small facet, which, with a similar facet on the upper angle of the body, forms a notch for the reception of the costal cartilage of the second rib. Between the depression for the first costal cartilage and the demi-facet for the second is a narrow, curved edge, which slopes from above downward and medialward.

Body (*corpus sterni; gladiolus*).—The body, considerably longer, narrower, and thinner than the manubrium, attains its greatest breadth close to the lower end.

Surfaces.—Its **anterior surface** is nearly flat, directed upward and forward, and marked by three transverse ridges which cross the bone opposite the third, fourth, and fifth articular depressions. It affords attachment on either side to the sternal origin of the Pectoralis major. At the junction of the third and fourth pieces of the body is occasionally seen an orifice, the **sternal foramen,** of varying size and form. The **posterior surface,** slightly concave, is also marked by three transverse lines, less distinct, however, than those in front; from its lower part, on either side, the Transversus thoracis takes origin.

Borders.—The **superior border** is oval and articulates with the manubrium, the junction of the two forming the **sternal angle.** The **inferior border** is narrow, and articulates with the xiphoid process. Each **lateral border** (Fig. 110), at its superior angle, has a small facet, which with a similar facet on the manubrium, forms a cavity for the cartilage of the second rib; below this are four angular depressions which receive the cartilages of the third, fourth, fifth, and sixth ribs, while the inferior angle has a small facet, which, with a corresponding one on the xiphoid process, forms a notch for the cartilage of the seventh rib. These articular depressions are separated by a series of curved interarticular intervals, which diminish in length from above downward, and correspond to the intercostal spaces. Most of the cartilages belonging to the true ribs, as will be seen from the foregoing description, articulate with the sternum at the lines of junction of its primitive component segments. This is well seen in many of the lower animals, where the parts of the bone remain ununited longer than in man.

Xiphoid Process (*processus xiphoideus; ensiform or xiphoid appendix*).—The xiphoid process is the smallest of the three pieces: it is thin and elongated, cartilaginous in structure in youth, but more or less ossified at its upper part in the adult.

Surfaces.—Its **anterior surface** affords attachment on either side to the anterior costoxiphoid ligament and a small part of the Rectus abdominis; its **posterior surface,** to the posterior costoxiphoid ligament and to some of the fibers of the diaphragm and Transversus thoracis, its **lateral borders,** to the aponeuroses of the abdominal muscles. Above, it articulates with the lower end of the body, and on the front of each superior angle presents a facet for part of the cartilage of the seventh rib; below, by its pointed extremity, it gives attachment to the linea alba. The xiphoid process varies much in form; it may be broad and thin, pointed, bifid, perforated, curved, or deflected considerably to one or other side.

Structure.—The sternum is composed of highly vascular cancellous tissue, covered by a thin layer of compact bone which is thickest in the manubrium between the articular facets for the clavicles.

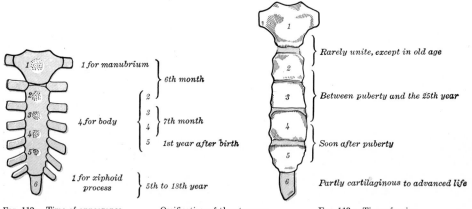

FIG. 112.—Time of appearance.   Ossification of the sternum.   FIG. 113.—Time of union.

Ossification.—The sternum originally consists of two cartilaginous bars, situated one on either side of the median plane and connected with the cartilages of the upper nine ribs of its own side. These two bars fuse with each other along the middle line to form the cartilaginous sternum which is ossified from *six* centers: one for the manubrium, four for the body, and one for the xiphoid process (Fig. 112). The ossific centers appear in the intervals between the articular depressions for the costal cartilages, in the following order: in the manubrium and first piece of the body, during the sixth month; in the second and third pieces of the body, during the seventh month of fetal life; in its fourth piece, during the first year after birth; and in the xiphoid process, between the fifth and eighteenth years. The centers make their appearance at the upper parts of the segments, and proceed gradually downward. To these may be added the occasional existence of two small episternal centers, which make their appearance one on either side of the jugular notch; they are probably vestiges of the episternal bone of the monotremata and lizards. Occasionally some of the segments are formed from more than one center, the number and position of which vary. Thus, the first piece may have two, three, or even six centers. When two are present, they are generally situated one above the other, the upper being the larger; the second piece has seldom more than one; the third, fourth, and fifth pieces are often formed from two centers placed laterally, the irregular union of which explains the rare occurrence of the sternal foramen, or of the vertical fissure which occasionally intersects this part of the bone constituting the malformation known as *fissura sterni;* these conditions are further explained by the manner in which the cartilaginous sternum is formed. More rarely still the upper end of the sternum may be divided by a fissure. Union of the various centers of the body begins about puberty, and proceeds from below upward (Fig. 113); by the age of twenty-five they are all united. The xiphoid process may become joined to the body before the age of thirty, but this occurs more frequently after forty; on the other hand, it sometimes remains ununited in old age. In advanced life the manubrium is occasionally joined to the body by bone. When this takes place, however, the bony tissue is generally only superficial, the central portion of the intervening cartilage remaining unossified.

Articulations.—The sternum articulates on either side with the clavicle and upper seven costal cartilages.

The Ribs (Costæ).

The **ribs** are elastic arches of bone, which form a large part of the thoracic skeleton. They are twelve in number on either side; but this number may be increased by the development of a cervical or lumbar rib, or may be diminished to eleven. The first seven are connected behind with the vertebral column, and in front, through the intervention of the costal cartilages, with the sternum (Fig. 109); they are called **true** or **vertebro-sternal ribs**.[1] The remaining five are **false ribs**; of these, the first three have their cartilages attached to the cartilage of the rib above (**vertebro-chondral**): the last two are free at their anterior extremities and are termed **floating** or **vertebral ribs**. The ribs vary in their direction, the upper ones being less oblique than the lower; the obliquity reaches its maximum at the ninth rib, and gradually decreases from that rib to the twelfth. The ribs are situated one below the other in such a manner that spaces called **intercostal spaces** are left between them. The length of each space corresponds to that of the adjacent ribs and their cartilages; the breadth is greater in front than behind, and between the upper than the lower ribs. The ribs increase in length from the first to the seventh, below which they diminish to the twelfth. In breadth they decrease from above downward; in the upper ten the greatest breadth is at the sternal extremity.

Common Characteristics of the Ribs (Figs. 114, 115).—A rib from the middle of the series should be taken in order to study the common characteristics of these bones.

Each rib has two extremities, a **posterior** or **vertebral**, and an **anterior** or **sternal**, and an intervening portion—the **body** or **shaft**.

Posterior Extremity.—The **posterior** or **vertebral extremity** presents for examination a head, neck, and tubercle.

The **head** is marked by a kidney-shaped articular surface, divided by a horizontal crest into two facets for articulation with the depression formed on the bodies of two adjacent thoracic vertebræ; the upper facet is the smaller; to the crest is attached the interarticular ligament.

The **neck** is the flattened portion which extends lateralward from the head; it is about 2.5 cm. long, and is placed in front of the transverse process of the lower of the two vertebræ with which the head articulates. Its **anterior surface** is flat and smooth, its **posterior** rough for the attachment of the ligament of the neck, and perforated by numerous foramina. Of its two borders the **superior** presents a rough crest (*crista colli costæ*) for the attachment of the anterior costotransverse ligament; its **inferior border** is rounded. On the posterior surface at the junction of the neck and body, and nearer the lower than the upper border, is an eminence

---

[1] Sometimes the eighth rib cartilage articulates with the sternum; this condition occurs more frequently on the right than on the left side.

—the **tubercle**; it consists of an articular and a non-articular portion. The *articular portion*, the lower and more medial of the two, presents a small, oval surface for

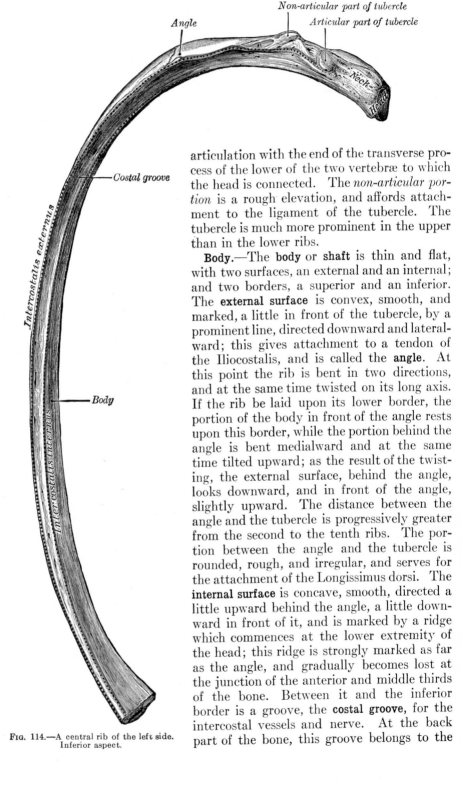

Non-articular part of tubercle

Articular part of tubercle

Angle

Neck

Head

Costal groove

Intercostalis externus

Body

Intercostalis internus

FIG. 114.—A central rib of the left side. Inferior aspect.

articulation with the end of the transverse process of the lower of the two vertebræ to which the head is connected. The *non-articular portion* is a rough elevation, and affords attachment to the ligament of the tubercle. The tubercle is much more prominent in the upper than in the lower ribs.

Body.—The **body** or **shaft** is thin and flat, with two surfaces, an external and an internal; and two borders, a superior and an inferior. The **external surface** is convex, smooth, and marked, a little in front of the tubercle, by a prominent line, directed downward and lateralward; this gives attachment to a tendon of the Iliocostalis, and is called the **angle**. At this point the rib is bent in two directions, and at the same time twisted on its long axis. If the rib be laid upon its lower border, the portion of the body in front of the angle rests upon this border, while the portion behind the angle is bent medialward and at the same time tilted upward; as the result of the twisting, the external surface, behind the angle, looks downward, and in front of the angle, slightly upward. The distance between the angle and the tubercle is progressively greater from the second to the tenth ribs. The portion between the angle and the tubercle is rounded, rough, and irregular, and serves for the attachment of the Longissimus dorsi. The **internal surface** is concave, smooth, directed a little upward behind the angle, a little downward in front of it, and is marked by a ridge which commences at the lower extremity of the head; this ridge is strongly marked as far as the angle, and gradually becomes lost at the junction of the anterior and middle thirds of the bone. Between it and the inferior border is a groove, the **costal groove**, for the intercostal vessels and nerve. At the back part of the bone, this groove belongs to the inferior border, but just in front of the angle, where it is deepest and broadest, it is on the internal surface. The superior edge of the groove is rounded and serves for the attachment of an Intercostalis internus; the inferior edge corresponds to the lower margin of the rib, and gives attachment to an Intercostalis externus. Within the groove are seen the orifices of numerous small foramina for nutrient vessels which traverse the shaft obliquely from before backward. The **superior**

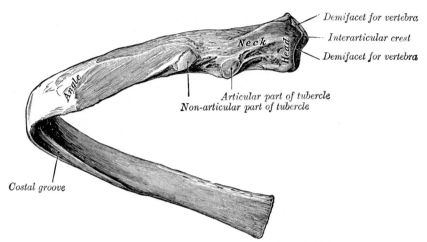

FIG. 115.—A central rib of the left side, viewed from behind.

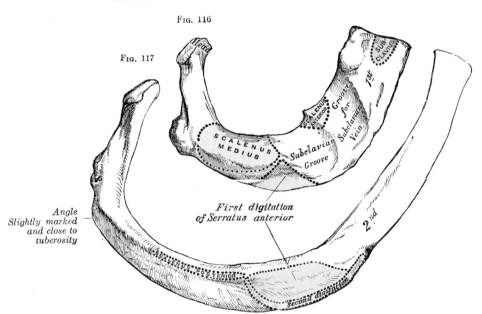

FIGS. 116 and 117.—Peculiar ribs.

border, thick and rounded, is marked by an external and an internal lip, more distinct behind than in front, which serve for the attachment of Intercostales externus and internus. The **inferior border** is thin, and has attached to it an Intercostalis externus.

Anterior Extremity.—The **anterior** or **sternal extremity** is flattened, and presents a porous, oval, concave depression, into which the costal cartilage is received.

Peculiar Ribs.—The first, second, tenth, eleventh, and twelfth ribs present certain variations from the common characteristics described above, and require special consideration.

First Rib.—The first rib (Fig. 116) is the most curved and usually the shortest of all the ribs; it is broad and flat, its surfaces looking upward and downward, and its borders inward and outward. The **head** is small, rounded, and possesses only a single articular facet, for articulation with the body of the first thoracic vertebra. The **neck** is narrow and rounded. The **tubercle**, thick and prominent, is placed on the outer border. There is *no angle*, but at the tubercle the rib is slightly bent, with the convexity upward, so that the head of the bone is directed downward. The **upper surface** of the body is marked by two shallow grooves, separated from each other by a slight ridge prolonged internally into a tubercle, the **scalene tubercle**, for the attachment of the Scalenus anterior; the anterior groove transmits the subclavian vein, the posterior the subclavian artery and the lowest trunk of the brachial plexus. Behind the posterior groove is a rough area for the attachment of the Scalenus medius. The **under surface** is smooth, and destitute of a costal groove. The **outer border** is convex, thick, and rounded, and at its posterior part gives attachment to the first digitation of the Serratus anterior; the **inner border** is concave, thin, and sharp, and marked about its center by the scalene tubercle. The **anterior extremity** is larger and thicker than that of any of the other ribs and gives attachment to the Subclavius muscle.

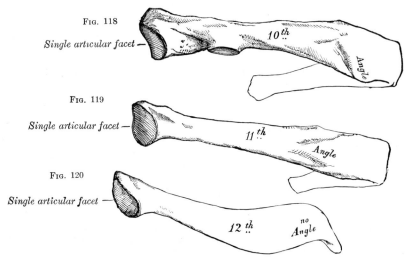

Fig. 118

Single articular facet — 10th

Fig. 119

Single articular facet — 11th

Fig. 120

Single articular facet — 12th

Figs. 118 to 120.—Peculiar ribs.

Second Rib.—The second rib (Fig. 117) is much longer than the first, but has a very similar curvature. The non-articular portion of the **tubercle** is occasionally only feebly marked. The **angle** is slight, and situated close to the tubercle. The **body** is not twisted, so that both ends touch any plane surface upon which it may be laid; but there is a bend, with its convexity upward, similar to, though smaller than that found in the first rib. The body is not flattened horizontally like that of the first rib. Its **external surface** is convex, and looks upward and a little outward; near the middle of it is a rough eminence for the origin of the lower part of the first and the whole of the second digitation of the Serratus anterior; behind and above this is attached the Scalenus posterior. The **internal surface**, smooth, and concave, is directed downward and a little inward: on its posterior part there is a short costal groove.

Tenth Rib.—The tenth rib (Fig. 118) has only a single articular facet on its head.

Eleventh and Twelfth Ribs.—The eleventh and twelfth ribs (Figs. 119 and 120) have each a single articular facet on the head, which is of rather large size; they have *no necks or tubercles*, and are pointed at their anterior ends. The eleventh has a slight angle and a shallow costal groove. The twelfth has neither; it is much shorter than the eleventh, and its head is inclined slightly downward. Sometimes the twelfth rib is even shorter than the first.

Structure.—The ribs consist of highly vascular cancellous tissue, enclosed in a thin layer of compact bone.

Ossification.—Each rib, with the exception of the last two, is ossified from *four* centers; a primary center for the body, and three epiphysial centers, one for the head and one each for the articular and non-articular parts of the tubercle. The eleventh and twelfth ribs have each only *two* centers, those for the tubercles being wanting. Ossification begins near the angle toward the end of the second month of fetal life, and is seen first in the sixth and seventh ribs. The epiphyses for the head and tubercle make their appearance between the sixteenth and twentieth years, and are united to the body about the twenty-fifth year.

The Costal Cartilages (Cartilagines Costales).

The **costal cartilages** (Fig. 109) are bars of hyaline cartilage which serve to prolong the ribs forward and contribute very materially to the elasticity of the walls of the thorax. The first seven pairs are connected with the sternum; the next three are each articulated with the lower border of the cartilage of the preceding rib; the last two have pointed extremities, which end in the wall of the abdomen. Like the ribs, the costal cartilages vary in their length, breadth, and direction. They increase in length from the first to the seventh, then gradually decrease to the twelfth. Their breadth, as well as that of the intervals between them, diminishes from the first to the last. They are broad at their attachments to the ribs, and taper toward their sternal extremities, excepting the first two, which are of the same breadth throughout, and the sixth, seventh, and eighth, which are enlarged where their margins are in contact. They also vary in direction: the first descends a little, the second is horizontal, the third ascends slightly, while the others are angular, following the course of the ribs for a short distance, and then ascending to the sternum or preceding cartilage. Each costal cartilage presents two surfaces, two borders, and two extremities.

Surfaces.—The **anterior surface** is convex, and looks forward and upward: that of the first gives attachment to the costoclavicular ligament and the Subclavius muscle; those of the first six or seven at their sternal ends, to the Pectoralis major. The others are covered by, and give partial attachment to, some of the flat muscles of the abdomen. The **posterior surface** is concave, and directed backward and downward; that of the first gives attachment to the Sternothyroideus, those of the third to the sixth inclusive to the Transversus thoracis, and the six or seven inferior ones to the Transversus abdominis and the diaphragm.

Borders.—Of the two borders the **superior** is concave, the **inferior** convex; they afford attachment to the Intercostales interni: the upper border of the sixth gives attachment also to the Pectoralis major. The inferior borders of the sixth, seventh, eighth, and ninth cartilages present heel-like projections at the points of greatest convexity. These projections carry smooth oblong facets which articulate respectively with facets on slight projections from the upper borders of the seventh, eighth, ninth, and tenth cartilages.

Extremities.—The **lateral end** of each cartilage is continuous with the osseous tissue of the rib to which it belongs. The **medial end** of the first is continuous with the sternum; the medial ends of the six succeeding ones are rounded and are received into shallow concavities on the lateral margins of the sternum. The medial ends of the eighth, ninth, and tenth costal cartilages are pointed, and are connected each with the cartilage immediately above. Those of the eleventh and twelfth are pointed and free. In old age the costal cartilages are prone to undergo superficial ossification.

Cervical ribs derived from the seventh cervical vertebra (page 63) are of not infrequent occurrence, and are important clinically because they may give rise to obscure nervous or vascular symptoms. The cervical rib may be a mere epiphysis articulating only with the transverse process of the vertebra, but more commonly it consists of a defined head, neck, and tubercle, with or without a body. It extends lateralward, or forward and lateralward, into the posterior triangle of the neck, where it may terminate in a free end or may join the first thoracic rib, the first costal cartilage, or the sternum. It varies much in shape, size, direction, and mobility. If it reach far enough forward, part of the brachial plexus and the subclavian artery and vein cross over it, and are apt to suffer compression in so doing. Pressure on the artery may obstruct the circulation so much that arterial thrombosis results, causing gangrene of the finger tips. Pressure on the nerves is commoner, and affects the eighth cervical and first thoracic nerves, causing paralysis of the muscles they supply, and neuralgic pains and paresthesia in the area of skin to which they are distributed: no oculopupillary changes are to be found.

The *thorax* is frequently found to be altered in shape in certain diseases.

In *rickets*, the ends of the ribs, where they join the costal cartilages, become enlarged, giving rise to the so-called "rickety rosary," which in mild cases is only found on the internal surface of the thorax. Lateral to these enlargements the softened ribs sink in, so as to present a groove passing downward and lateralward on either side of the sternum. This bone is forced forward by the bending of the ribs, and the antero-posterior diameter of the chest is increased. The ribs affected are the second to the eighth, the lower ones being prevented from falling in by the presence of the liver, stomach, and spleen; and when the abdomen is distended, as it often is in rickets, the lower ribs may be pushed outward, causing a transverse groove (Harrison's sulcus) just above the costal arch. This deformity or forward projection of the sternum, often asymmetrical, is known as *pigeon breast*, and may be taken as evidence of active or old rickets except in cases of primary spinal curvature. In many instances it is associated in children with obstruction in the upper air passages, due to enlarged tonsils or adenoid growths. In some rickety children or adults, and also in others who give no history or further evidence of having had rickets, an opposite condition obtains. The lower part of the sternum and often the xiphoid process as well are deeply depressed backward, producing an oval hollow in the lower sternal and upper epigastric regions. This is known as *funnel breast* (German, *Trichterbrust*); it never appears to produce the least disturbance of any of the vital functions. The *phthisical chest* is often long and narrow, and with great obliquity of the ribs and projection of the scapulæ In *pulmonary emphysema* the chest is enlarged in all its diameters, and presents on section an almost circular outline. It has received the name of the *barrel-shaped chest*. In severe cases of *lateral curvature of the vertebral column* the thorax becomes much distorted. In consequence of the rotation of the bodies of the vertebræ which takes place in this disease, the ribs opposite the convexity of the dorsal curve become extremely convex behind, being thrown out and bulging, and at the same time flattened in front, so that the two ends of the same rib are almost parallel. Coincidently with this the ribs on the opposite side, on the concavity of the curve, are sunk and depressed behind, and bulging and convex in front.

THE SKULL.

The **skull** is supported on the summit of the vertebral column, and is of an oval shape, wider behind than in front. It is composed of a series of flattened or irregular bones which, with one exception (the mandible), are immovably jointed together. It is divisible into two parts: (1) the **cranium**, which lodges and protects the brain, consists of eight bones, and (2) the **skeleton of the face**, of fourteen.

THE EXTERIOR OF THE SKULL.

Norma Verticalis.—When viewed from above the outline presented varies greatly in different skulls; in some it is more or less oval, in others more nearly circular. The surface is traversed by three sutures, viz.: (1) the **coronal sutures,** nearly transverse in direction, between the frontal and parietals; (2) the **sagittal sutures,** medially placed, between the parietal bones, and deeply serrated in its anterior two-thirds; and (3) the upper part of the **lambdoidal suture,** between the parietals and the occipital. The point of junction of the sagittal and coronal suture is named the **bregma,** that of the sagittal and lambdoid sutures, the **lambda;** they indicate respectively the positions of the anterior and posterior fontanelles in the fetal skull. On either side of the sagittal suture are the **parietal eminence** and **parietal foramen**—the latter, however, is frequently absent on one or both sides. The skull is often somewhat flattened in the neighborhood of the parietal foramina, and the term **obelion** is applied to that point of the sagittal suture which is on a level with the foramina. In front is the **glabella**, and on its lateral aspects are the **superciliary arches**, and above these the **frontal eminences**. Immediately above the glabella may be seen the remains of the **frontal suture**; in a small percentage of skulls this suture persists and extends along the middle line to the bregma. Passing backward and upward from the zygomatic processes of the frontal bone are the **temporal lines**, which mark the upper limits of the temporal fossæ. The zygomatic arches may or may not be seen projecting beyond the anterior portions of these lines.

Norma Basalis (Fig. 121).—The inferior surface of the base of the skull, exclusive of the mandible, is bounded in front by the incisor teeth in the maxillæ; behind, by the superior nuchal lines of the occipital; and laterally by the alveolar arch, the lower border of the zygomatic bone, the zygomatic arch and an imaginary line extending from it to the mastoid process and extremity of the superior nuchal line of the occipital. It is formed by the palatine processes of the maxillæ and palatine bones, the vomer, the pterygoid processes, the under surfaces of the great wings, spinous processes, and part of the body of the sphenoid, the under surfaces of the squamæ and mastoid and petrous portions of the temporals, and the under surface of the occipital bone. The anterior part or hard palate projects below the level of the rest of the surface, and is bounded in front and laterally by the alveolar arch containing the sixteen teeth of the maxillæ. Immediately behind the incisor teeth is the **incisive foramen**. In this foramen are two lateral apertures, the openings of the **incisive canals** (*foramina of Stenson*) which transmit the anterior branches of the descending palatine vessels, and the nasopalatine nerves. Occasionally two additional canals are present in the incisive foramen; they are termed the **foramina of Scarpa** and are situated in the middle line; when present they transmit the nasopalatine nerves. The vault of the hard palate is concave, uneven, perforated by numerous foramina, marked by depressions for the palatine glands, and traversed by a crucial suture formed by the junction of the four bones of which it is composed. In the young skull a suture may be seen extending on either side from the incisive foramen to the interval between the lateral incisor and canine teeth, and marking off the os incisivum or premaxillary bone. At either posterior angle of the hard palate is the **greater palatine foramen**, for the transmission of the descending palatine vessels and anterior palatine nerve; and running forward and medialward from it a groove, for the same vessels and nerve. Behind the posterior palatine foramen is the **pyramidal process of the palatine bone**, perforated by one or more **lesser palatine foramina**, and marked by the commencement of a transverse ridge, for the attachment of the tendinous expansion of the Tensor veli palatini. Projecting backward from the center of the posterior border of the hard palate is the **posterior nasal spine**, for the attachment of the Musculus uvulæ. Behind and above the hard palate are the **choanæ**, measuring about 2.5 cm. in their vertical and 1.25 cm. in their transverse diameters. They are separated from one another by the vomer, and each is bounded above by the body of the sphenoid, below by the horizontal part of the palatine bone, and laterally by the medial pterygoid plate of the sphenoid. At the superior border of the vomer may be seen the expanded alæ of this bone, receiving between them the rostrum of the sphenoid. Near the lateral margins of the alæ of the vomer, at the roots of the pterygoid processes, are the **pharyngeal canals**. The pterygoid process presents near its base the **pterygoid canal**, for the transmission of a nerve and artery. The medial pterygoid plate is long and narrow; on the lateral side of its base is the **scaphoid fossa**, for the origin of the Tensor veli palatini, and at its lower extremity the **hamulus**, around which the tendon of this muscle turns. The lateral pterygoid plate is broad; its lateral surface forms the medial boundary of the infratemporal fossa, and affords attachment to the Pterygoideus externus.

Behind the nasal cavities is the basilar portion of the occipital bone, presenting near its center the **pharyngeal tubercle** for the attachment of the fibrous raphé of the pharynx, with depressions on either side for the insertions of the Rectus capitis anterior and Longus capitis. At the base of the lateral pterygoid plate is the **foramen ovale,** for the transmission of the mandibular nerve, the accessory

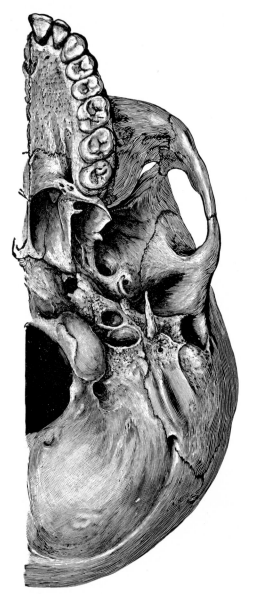

FIG. 121.—The external surface of the left half of the base of the skull. (Norma basalis.)

meningeal artery, and sometimes the lesser superficial petrosal nerve; behind this are the **foramen spinosum** which transmits the middle meningeal vessels, and the prominent **spina angularis** (*sphenoidal spine*), which gives attachment to the spheno-mandibular ligament and the Tensor veli palatini.   Lateral to the spina angularis is the **mandibular fossa,** divided into two parts by the **petrotympanic fissure;** the anterior portion, concave, smooth, bounded in front by the **articular tubercle,** serves for the articulation of the condyle of the mandible; the posterior portion, rough and bounded behind by the tympanic part of the temporal, is sometimes occupied by a part of the parotid gland. Emerging from between the laminæ of the vaginal process of the tympanic part is the **styloid process**; and at the base of this process is the **stylomastoid foramen**, for the exit of the facial nerve, and

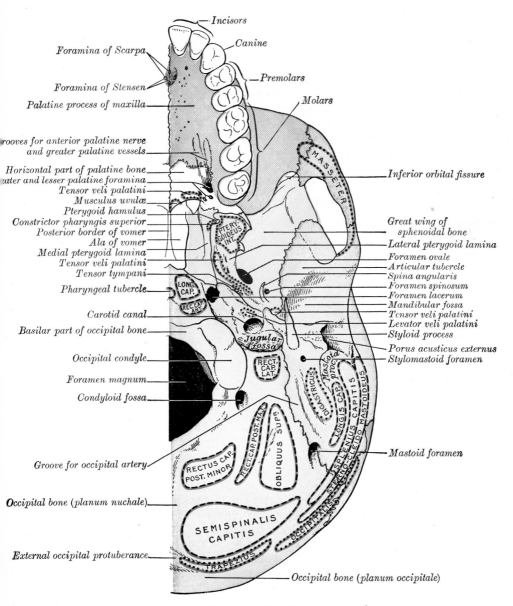

Incisors
Canine
Foramina of Scarpa
Foramina of Stensen
Premolars
Palatine process of maxilla
Molars
Grooves for anterior palatine nerve and greater palatine vessels
Inferior orbital fissure
Horizontal part of palatine bone
Greater and lesser palatine foramina
Tensor veli palatini
Musculus uvulæ
Pterygoid hamulus
Constrictor pharyngis superior
Posterior border of vomer
Ala of vomer
Medial pterygoid lamina
Tensor veli palatini
Tensor tympani
Pharyngeal tubercle
Carotid canal
Basilar part of occipital bone
Occipital condyle
Foramen magnum
Condyloid fossa
Great wing of sphenoidal bone
Lateral pterygoid lamina
Foramen ovale
Articular tubercle
Spina angularis
Foramen spinosum
Foramen lacerum
Mandibular fossa
Tensor veli palatini
Levator veli palatini
Styloid process
Porus acusticus externus
Stylomastoid foramen
Groove for occipital artery
Mastoid foramen
Occipital bone (planum nuchale)
External occipital protuberance
Occipital bone (planum occipitale)

FIG. 122.—Key to Fig. 121.

entrance of the stylomastoid artery. Lateral to the stylomastoid foramen, between the tympanic part and the mastoid process, is the **tympanomastoid fissure,** for the auricular branch of the vagus. Upon the medial side of the mastoid process is the **mastoid notch** for the posterior belly of the Digastricus, and medial to the notch, the **occipital groove** for the occipital artery. At the base of the medial pterygoid

plate is a large and somewhat triangular aperture, the **foramen lacerum,** bounded
in front by the great wing of the sphenoid, behind by the apex of the petrous
portion of the temporal bone, and medially by the body of the sphenoid and basilar
portion of the occipital bone; it presents in front the posterior orifice of the **pterygoid canal;** behind, the aperture of the **carotid canal.** The lower part of this opening
is filled up in the fresh state by a fibrocartilaginous plate, across the upper or
cerebral surface of which the internal carotid artery passes. Lateral to this aperture
is a groove, the **sulcus tubæ auditivæ,** between the petrous part of the temporal and
the great wing of the sphenoid. This sulcus is directed lateralward and backward
from the root of the medial pterygoid plate and lodges the cartilaginous part of the
auditory tube; it is continuous behind with the canal in the temporal bone which
forms the bony part of the same tube. At the bottom of this sulcus is a narrow
cleft, the **petrosphenoidal fissure,** which is occupied, in the fresh condition, by a
plate of cartilage. Behind this fissure is the under surface of the petrous portion
of the temporal bone, presenting, near its apex, the quadrilateral rough surface,
part of which affords attachment to the Levator veli palatini; lateral to this surface
is the orifice of the **carotid canal,** and medial to it, the depression leading to the
aquæductus cochleæ, the former transmitting the internal carotid artery and the
carotid plexus of the sympathetic, the latter serving for the passage of a vein from
the cochlea. Behind the carotid canal is the **jugular foramen,** a large aperture,
formed in front by the petrous portion of the temporal, and behind by the occipital;
it is generally larger on the right than on the left side, and may be subdivided
into three compartments. The anterior compartment transmits the inferior
petrosal sinus; the intermediate, the glossopharyngeal, vagus, and accessory
nerves; the posterior, the transverse sinus and some meningeal branches from the
occipital and ascending pharyngeal arteries. On the ridge of bone dividing the
carotid canal from the jugular foramen is the **inferior tympanic canaliculus** for
the transmission of the tympanic branch of the glossopharyngeal nerve; and on the
wall of the jugular foramen, near the root of the styloid process, is the **mastoid
canaliculus** for the passage of the auricular branch of the vagus nerve. Extending
forward from the jugular foramen to the foramen lacerum is the **petroöccipital fissure**
occupied, in the fresh state, by a plate of cartilage. Behind the basilar portion
of the occipital bone is the **foramen magnum,** bounded laterally by the occipital
condyles, the medial sides of which are rough for the attachment of the alar
ligaments. Lateral to each condyle is the **jugular process** which gives attachment
to the Rectus capitis lateralis muscle and the lateral atlantoöccipital ligament.
The foramen magnum transmits the medulla oblongata and its membranes, the
accessory nerves, the vertebral arteries, the anterior and posterior spinal arteries,
and the ligaments connecting the occipital bone with the axis. The mid-points
on the anterior and posterior margins of the foramen magnum are respectively
termed the **basion** and the **opisthion.** In the front of each condyle is the canal for
the passage of the hypoglossal nerve and a meningeal artery. Behind each condyle
is the **condyloid fossa,** perforated on one or both sides by the condyloid canal, for
the transmission of a vein from the transverse sinus. Behind the foramen magnum
is the **median nuchal line** ending above at the **external occipital protuberance,** while
on either side are the **superior** and **inferior nuchal lines;** these, as well as the surfaces
of bone between them, are rough for the attachment of the muscles which are
enumerated on Figs. 122 and 144.

Norma Lateralis (Fig. 123).—When viewed from the side the skull is seen to
consist of the cranium above and behind, and of the face below and in front. The
cranium is somewhat ovoid in shape, but its contour varies in different cases and
depends largely on the length and height of the skull and on the degree of prominence of the superciliary arches and frontal eminences. Entering into its formation
are the frontal, the parietal, the occipital, the temporal, and the great wing of the

sphenoid. These bones are joined to one another and to the zygomatic by the following **sutures**: the **zygomaticotemporal** between the zygomatic process of the temporal and the temporal process of the zygomatic; the **zygomaticofrontal** uniting the zygomatic bone with the zygomatic process of the frontal; the sutures surrounding the great wing of the sphenoid, viz., the **sphenozygomatic** in front, the **sphenofrontal** and **sphenoparietal** above, and the **sphenosquamosal** behind. The sphenoparietal suture varies in length in different skulls, and is absent in those cases where the frontal articulates with the temporal squama. The point corresponding with the posterior end of the sphenoparietal suture is named the **pterion**; it is situated about 3 cm. behind, and a little above the level of the zygomatic process of the frontal bone.

The **squamosal suture** arches backward from the pterion and connects the temporal squama with the lower border of the parietal: this suture is continuous behind with the short, nearly horizontal **parietomastoid suture**, which unites the mastoid process of the temporal with the region of the mastoid angle of the parietal. Extending from above downward and forward across the cranium are the **coronal** and **lambdoidal sutures**; the former connects the parietals with the frontal, the latter, the parietals with the occipital. The lambdoidal suture is continuous below with the **occipitomastoid suture** between the occipital and the mastoid portion of the temporal. In or near the last suture is the **mastoid foramen**, for the transmission of an emissary vein. The point of meeting of the parietomastoid, occipitomastoid, and lambdoidal sutures is known as the **asterion**. Immediately above the orbital margin is the **superciliary arch**, and, at a higher level, the **frontal eminence**. Near the center of the parietal bone is the **parietal eminence**. Posteriorly is the **external occipital protuberance**, from which the superior nuchal line may be followed forward to the mastoid process. Arching across the side of the cranium are the **temporal lines**, which mark the upper limit of the temporal fossa.

The Temporal Fossa (*fossa temporalis*).—The temporal fossa is bounded above and behind by the temporal lines, which extend from the zygomatic process of the frontal bone upward and backward across the frontal and parietal bones, and then curve downward and forward to become continuous with the supramastoid crest and the posterior root of the zygomatic arch. The point where the upper temporal line cuts the coronal suture is named the **stephanion**. The temporal fossa is bounded in *front* by the frontal and zygomatic bones, and opening on the back of the latter is the **zygomaticotemporal foramen**. *Laterally* the fossa is limited by the zygomatic arch, formed by the zygomatic and temporal bones; *below*, it is separated from the infratemporal fossa by the **infratemporal crest** on the great wing of the sphenoid, and by a ridge, continuous with this crest, which is carried backward across the temporal squama to the anterior root of the zygomatic process. In front and below, the fossa communicates with the orbital cavity through the **inferior orbital** or **sphenomaxillary fissure**. The floor of the fossa is deeply concave in front and convex behind, and is formed by the zygomatic, frontal, parietal, sphenoid, and temporal bones. It is traversed by vascular furrows; one, usually well-marked, runs upward above and in front of the external acoustic meatus, and lodges the middle temporal artery. Two others, frequently indistinct, may be observed on the anterior part of the floor, and are for the anterior and posterior deep temporal arteries. The temporal fossa contains the Temporalis muscle and its vessels and nerves, together with the zygomaticotemporal nerve.

The **zygomatic arch** is formed by the zygomatic process of the temporal and the temporal process of the zygomatic, the two being united by an oblique suture; the tendon of the Temporalis passes medial to the arch to gain insertion into the coronoid process of the mandible. The zygomatic process of the temporal arises by two roots, an anterior, directed inward in front of the mandibular fossa, where it expands to form the articular tubercle, and a posterior, which runs backward above the external acoustic meatus and is continuous with the supramastoid crest. The upper border of the arch gives attachment to the temporal fascia; the lower border and medial surface give origin to the Masseter.

Below the posterior root of the zygomatic arch is the elliptical orifice of the **external acoustic meatus,** bounded in front, below, and behind by the tympanic part of the temporal bone; to its outer margin the cartilaginous segment of the external acoustic meatus is attached. The small triangular area between the posterior root of the zygomatic arch and the postero-superior part of the orifice is termed the **suprameatal triangle,** on the anterior border of which a small spinous process, the **suprameatal spine,** is sometimes seen. Between the tympanic part and the articular tubercle is the **mandibular fossa,** divided into two parts by the

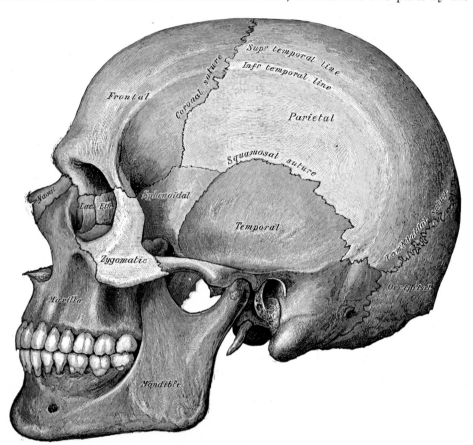

Fig. 123.—Side view of the skull.

petrotympanic fissure. The anterior and larger part of the fossa articulates with the condyle of the mandible and is limited behind by the external acoustic meatus: the posterior part sometimes lodges a portion of the parotid gland. The styloid process extends downward and forward for a variable distance from the lower part of the tympanic part, and gives attachment to the Styloglossus, Stylohyoideus, and Stylopharyngeus, and to the stylohyoid and stylomandibular ligaments. Projecting downward behind the external acoustic meatus is the mastoid process, to the outer surface of which the Sternocleidomastoideus, Splenius capitis, and Longissimus capitis are attached.

The Infratemporal Fossa (*fossa infratemporalis; zygomatic fossa*) (Fig. 124).—The infratemporal fossa is an irregularly shaped cavity, situated below and medial to the

:ygomatic arch. It is bounded, in *front*, by the infratemporal surface of the maxilla and the ridge which descends from its zygomatic process; *behind*, by the articular :ubercle of the temporal and the spina angularis of the sphenoid; *above*, by the great ving of the sphenoid below the infratemporal crest, and by the under surface of .he temporal squama; *below*, by the alveolar border of the maxilla; *medially*, by .he lateral pterygoid plate. It contains the lower part of the Temporalis, the ?terygoidei internus and externus, the internal maxillary vessels, and the man- libular and maxillary nerves. The **foramen ovale** and **foramen spinosum** open on ts roof, and the **alveolar canals** on its anterior wall. At its upper and medial)art are two fissures, which meet at right angles, the horizontal limb being named .he inferior orbital, and the vertical one the pterygomaxillary.

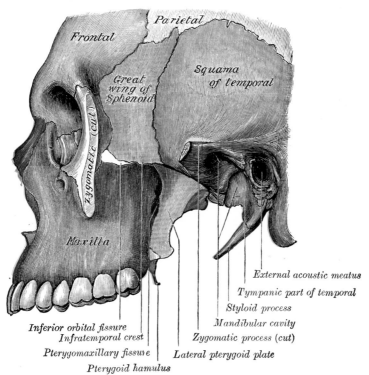

Fig. 124.—Left infratemporal fossa.

The **inferior orbital fissure** (*fissura orbitalis inferior; sphenomaxillary fissure*), horizontal in direction, opens into the lateral and back part of the orbit. It is bounded *above* by the lower border of the orbital surface of the great wing of the sphenoid; *below*, by the lateral border of the orbital surface of the maxilla and the orbital process of the palatine bone; *laterally*, by a small part of the zygomatic bone:[1] *medially*, it joins at right angles with the pterygomaxillary fissure. Through the inferior orbital fissure the orbit communicates with the temporal, infratem- poral, and pterygopalatine fossæ; the fissure transmits the maxillary nerve and its zygomatic branch, the infraorbital vessels, the ascending branches from the sphenopalatine ganglion, and a vein which connects the inferior ophthalmic vein with the pterygoid venous plexus.

The **pterygomaxillary fissure** is vertical, and descends at right angles from the medial end of the preceding; it is a triangular interval, formed by the diver-

---

[1] Occasionally the maxilla and the sphenoid articulate with each other at the anterior extremity of this fissure; the zygomatic is then excluded from it.

8

gence of the maxilla from the pterygoid process of the sphenoid. It connects the infratemporal with the pterygopalatine fossa, and transmits the terminal part of the internal maxillary artery and veins.

The **Pterygopalatine Fossa** (*fossa pterygopalatina; sphenomaxillary fossa*).—The pterygopalatine fossa is a small, triangular space at the angle of junction of the inferior orbital and pterygomaxillary fissures, and placed beneath the apex of the orbit. It is bounded *above* by the under surface of the body of the sphenoid and by the orbital process of the palatine bone; in *front*, by the infratemporal surface of the maxilla; *behind*, by the base of the pterygoid process and lower part of the anterior surface of the great wing of the sphenoid; *medially*, by the vertical part of the palatine bone with its orbital and sphenoidal processes. This fossa communicates with the orbit by the inferior orbital fissure, with the nasal cavity by the sphenopalatine foramen, and with the infratemporal fossa by the pterygo-maxillary fissure. Five foramina open into it. Of these, three are on the posterior wall, viz., the **foramen rotundum**, the **pterygoid canal**, and the **pharyngeal canal**, in this order downward and medialward. On the medial wall is the **sphenopalatine foramen**, and below is the superior orifice of the **pterygopalatine canal**. The fossa contains the maxillary nerve, the sphenopalatine ganglion, and the terminal part of the internal maxillary artery.

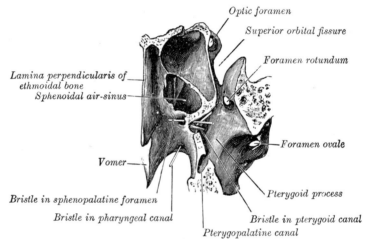

Optic foramen

Superior orbital fissure

Foramen rotundum

Lamina perpendicularis of ethmoidal bone

Sphenoidal air-sinus

Foramen ovale

Vomer

Pterygoid process

Bristle in sphenopalatine foramen

Bristle in pharyngeal canal

Bristle in pterygoid canal

Pterygopalatine canal

Fig. 125.—A section showing the posterior wall of the pterygopalatine fossa.

Norma Occipitalis.—When viewed from behind the cranium presents a more or less circular outline. In the middle line is the posterior part of the **sagittal suture** connecting the parietal bones; extending downward and lateralward from the hinder end of the sagittal suture is the deeply serrated **lambdoidal suture** joining the parietals to the occipital and continuous below with the **parietomastoid and occipitomastoid sutures**; it frequently contains one or more sutural bones. Near the middle of the occipital squama is the **external occipital protuberance** or **inion**, and extending lateralward from it on either side is the superior nuchal line, and above this the faintly marked highest nuchal line. The part of the squama above the inion and highest lines is named the **planum occipitale**, and is covered by the Occipitalis muscle; the part below is termed the **planum nuchale**, and is divided by the median nuchal line which runs downward and forward from the inion to the foramen magnum; this ridge gives attachment to the ligamentum nuchæ. The muscles attached to the planum nuchale are enumerated on p. 134. Below and in front are the mastoid processes, convex laterally and grooved medially by the mastoid notches. In or near the occipitomastoid suture is the **mastoid foramen** for the passage of the mastoid emissary vein.

Norma Frontalis (Fig. 126).—When viewed from the front the skull exhibits a somewhat oval outline, limited *above* by the frontal bone, *below* by the body of the mandible, and *laterally* by the zygomatic bones and the mandibular rami. The upper part, formed by the frontal squama, is smooth and convex. The lower part, made up of the bones of the face, is irregular; it is excavated laterally by the orbital cavities, and presents in the middle line the **anterior nasal aperture** leading to the nasal cavities, and below this the transverse slit between the upper and lower dental arcades. *Above*, the **frontal eminences** stand out more or less prominently, and beneath these are the **superciliary arches**, joined to one another in the middle by the **glabella**. On and above the glabella a trace of the **frontal suture** sometimes

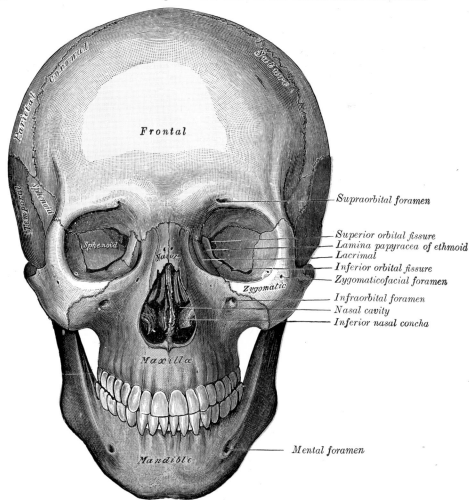

FIG. 126.—The skull from the front.

persists; beneath it is the frontonasal suture, the mid-point of which is termed the **nasion.** Behind and below the frontonasal suture the frontal articulates with the frontal process of the maxilla and with the lacrimal. Arching transversely below the superciliary arches is the upper part of the margin of the orbit, thin and prominent in its lateral two-thirds, rounded in its medial third, and presenting, at the junction of these two portions, the **supraorbital notch** or **foramen** for the supra-orbital nerve and vessels. The supraorbital margin ends laterally in the zygomatic process which articulates with the zygomatic bone, and from it the temporal line extends upward and backward. Below the frontonasal suture is the bridge of the nose, convex from side to side, concavo-convex from above downward, and formed by the two nasal bones supported in the middle line by the perpendicular plate of the ethmoid, and laterally by the frontal processes of the maxillæ which are prolonged upward between the nasal and lacrimal bones and form the lower and medial part of the circumference of each orbit. Below the nasal bones and between the maxillæ is the anterior aperture of the nose, pyriform in shape, with the narrow end directed upward. Laterally this opening is bounded by sharp margins, to which the lateral and alar cartilages of the nose are attached; *below*, the margins are thicker and curve medialward and forward to end in the **anterior nasal spine**. On looking into the nasal cavity, the bony septum which separates the nasal cavities presents, in front, a large triangular deficiency; this, in the fresh state, is filled up by the cartilage of the nasal septum; on the lateral wall of each nasal cavity the anterior part of the inferior nasal concha is visible. Below and lateral to the anterior nasal aperture are the anterior surfaces of the maxillæ, each perforated, near the lower margin of the orbit, by the **infraorbital foramen** for the passage of the infraorbital nerve and vessels. Below and medial to this foramen is the canine eminence separating the incisive from the canine fossa. Beneath these fossæ are the alveolar processes of the maxillæ containing the upper teeth, which overlap the teeth of the mandible in front. The zygomatic bone on either side forms the prominence of the cheek, the lower and lateral portion of the orbital

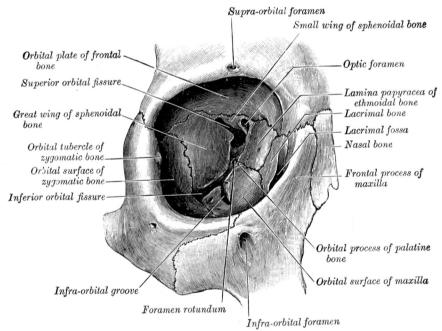

FIG. 127.—The right orbital cavity, anterior aspect.

cavity, and the anterior part of the zygomatic arch. It articulates medially with the maxilla, behind with the zygomatic process of the temporal, and above with the great wing of the sphenoid and the zygomatic process of the frontal; it is perforated by the **zygomaticofacial foramen** for the passage of the zygomaticofacial nerve. On the body of the mandible is a median ridge, indicating the position of the symphysis; this ridge divides below to enclose the mental protuberance, the lateral angles of which constitute the mental tubercles. Below the incisor teeth is the **incisive fossa,** and beneath the second premolar tooth the **mental foramen** which transmits the mental nerve and vessels. The oblique line runs upward from the mental tubercle and is continuous behind with the anterior border of the ramus. The posterior border of the ramus runs downward and forward from the condyle to the angle, which is frequently more or less everted.

The Orbits (*orbitæ*) (Fig. 127).—The orbits are two quadrilateral pyramidal cavities, situated at the upper and anterior part of the face, their bases being directed forward and lateralward, and their apices backward and medialward, so that their long axes, if continued backward, would meet over the body of the sphenoid. Each presents for examination a **roof,** a **floor,** a **medial** and a **lateral wall,** a **base,** and an **apex.**

The **roof** is concave, directed downward, and slightly forward, and formed in *front* by the orbital plate of the frontal; *behind* by the small wing of the sphenoid. It presents *medially* the **trochlear fovea** for the attachment of the cartilaginous pulley of the Obliquus oculi superior; *laterally,* the **lacrimal fossa** for the lacrimal gland; and *posteriorly,* the suture between the frontal bone and the small wing of the sphenoid.

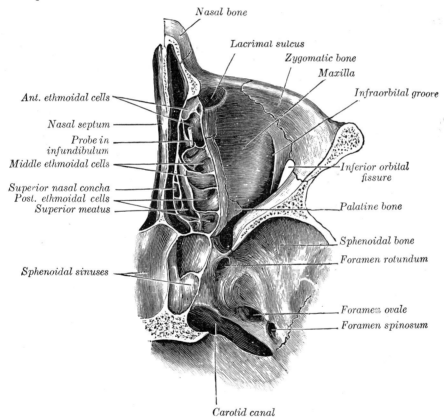

FIG. 128.—A horizontal section through the nasal and orbital cavities. Superior aspect.

The **floor** is directed upward and lateralward, and is of less extent than the roof; it is formed chiefly by the orbital surface of the maxilla; in *front* and *laterally,* by the orbital process of the zygomatic bone, and *behind* and *medially,* to a small extent, by the orbital process of the palatine. At its medial angle is the upper opening of the nasolacrimal canal, immediately to the lateral side of which is a depression for the origin of the Obliquus oculi inferior. On its lateral part is the suture between the maxilla and zygomatic bone, and at its posterior part that between the maxilla and the orbital process of the palatine. Running forward near the middle of the floor is the **infraorbital groove**, ending in front in the infraorbital canal and transmitting the infraorbital nerve and vessels.

The **medial wall** (Fig. 129) is nearly vertical, and is formed from before backward by the frontal process of the maxilla, the lacrimal, the lamina papyracea of the ethmoid, and a small part of the body of the sphenoid in front of the optic foramen. Sometimes the sphenoidal concha forms a small part of this wall (see page 156). It exhibits three vertical sutures, viz., the lacrimomaxillary, lacrimoethmoidal, and sphenoethmoidal. In front is seen the **lacrimal groove**, which lodges the lacrimal sac, and behind the groove is the **posterior lacrimal crest**, from which

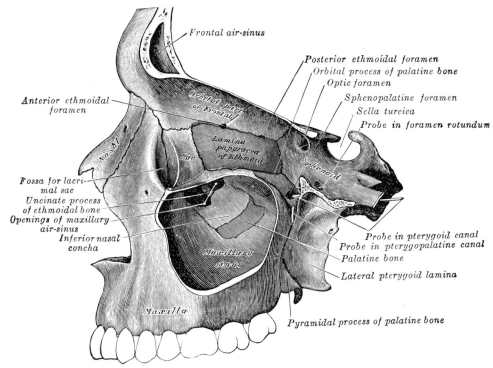

FIG. 129.—Medial wall of left orbit.

the lacrimal part of the Orbicularis oculi arises. At the junction of the medial wall and the roof are the frontomaxillary, frontolacrimal, frontoethmoidal, and sphenofrontal sutures. The point of junction of the anterior border of the lacrimal with the frontal is named the **dacryon**. In the frontoethmoidal suture are the **anterior** and **posterior ethmoidal foramina,** the former transmitting the nasociliary nerve and anterior ethmoidal vessels, the latter the posterior ethmoidal nerve and vessels.

The **lateral wall,** directed medialward and forward, is formed by the orbital process of the zygomatic and the orbital surface of the great wing of the sphenoid; these are united by the sphenozygomatic suture which terminates below at the front end of the inferior orbital fissure. On the orbital process of the zygomatic bone are the orbital tubercle (Whitnall) and the orifices of one or two canals which transmit the branches of the zygomatic nerve. Between the roof and the lateral wall, near the apex of the orbit, is the **superior orbital fissure.** Through this fissure the oculomotor, the trochlear, the ophthalmic division of the trigeminal, and the abducent nerves enter the orbital cavity, also some filaments from the cavernous plexus of the sympathetic and the orbital branches of the middle meningeal artery. Passing backward through the fissure are the ophthalmic vein and the recurrent branch from the lacrimal artery to the dura mater. The lateral wall and the floor are separated posteriorly by the **inferior orbital fissure** which transmits the maxillary nerve and its zygomatic branch, the infraorbital vessels, and the ascending branches from the sphenopalatine ganglion.

The **base** of the orbit, quadrilateral in shape, is formed *above* by the supraorbital arch of the frontal bone, in which is the **supraorbital notch or foramen** for the passage of the supraorbital vessels and nerve; *below* by the zygomatic bone and maxilla, united by the zygomaticomaxillary suture; laterally by the zygomatic bone and the zygomatic process of the frontal joined by the zygomaticofrontal suture; medially by the frontal bone and the frontal process of the maxilla united by the frontomaxillary suture.

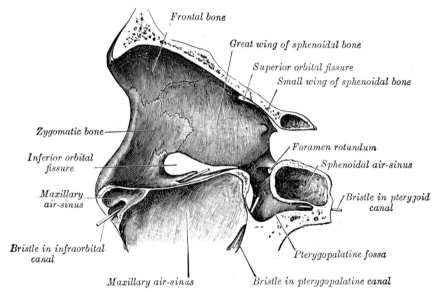

Fig. 130.—The lateral wall of the right orbit.

The **apex**, situated at the back of the orbit, corresponds to the optic foramen a short, cylindrical canal, which transmits the optic nerve and ophthalmic artery.

It will thus be seen that there are nine openings communicating with each orbit, viz., the optic foramen, superior and inferior orbital fissures, supraorbital foramen, infraorbital canal, anterior and posterior ethmoidal foramina, zygomatic foramen, and the canal for the nasolacrimal duct.

THE INTERIOR OF THE SKULL.

Inner Surface of the Skull-cap.—The inner surface of the skull-cap is concave and presents depressions for the convolutions of the cerebrum, together with numerous furrows for the lodgement of branches of the meningeal vessels. Along the middle line is a longitudinal groove, narrow in front, where it commences at the frontal crest, but broader behind; it lodges the superior sagittal sinus, and its margins afford attachment to the falx cerebri. On either side of it are several depressions for the arachnoid granulations, and at its back part, the openings of the **parietal foramina** when these are present. It is crossed, in front, by the **coronal suture,** and behind by the **lambdoidal,** while the **sagittal** lies in the medial plane between the parietal bones.

Upper Surface of the Base of the Skull (Fig. 131).—The upper surface of the base of the skull or floor of the cranial cavity presents three fossæ, called the **anterior, middle,** and **posterior cranial fossæ.**

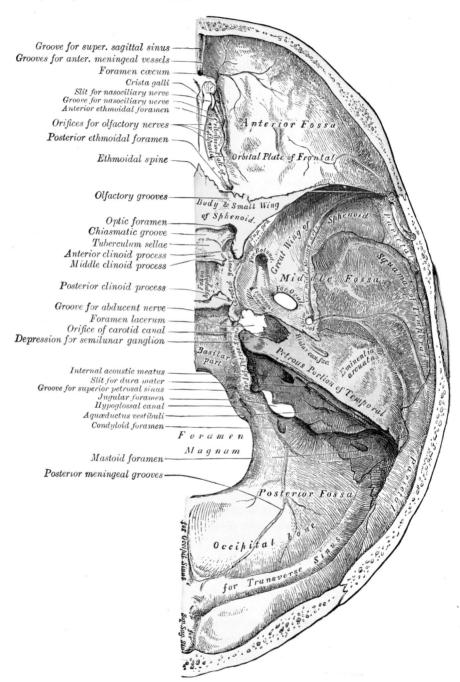

Groove for super. sagittal sinus
Grooves for anter. meningeal vessels
Foramen cœcum
Crista galli
Slit for nasociliary nerve
Groove for nasociliary nerve
Anterior ethmoidal foramen
Orifices for olfactory nerves
Posterior ethmoidal foramen
Ethmoidal spine
Olfactory grooves
Optic foramen
Chiasmatic groove
Tuberculum sellae
Anterior clinoid process
Middle clinoid process
Posterior clinoid process
Groove for abducent nerve
Foramen lacerum
Orifice of carotid canal
Depression for semilunar ganglion
Internal acoustic meatus
Slit for dura mater
Groove for superior petrosal sinus
Jugular foramen
Hypoglossal canal
Aquæductus vestibuli
Condyloid foramen
Mastoid foramen
Posterior meningeal grooves

Anterior Fossa
Orbital Plate of Frontal
Body & Small Wing of Sphenoid
Sphenoid
Great Wing of Sphenoid
Squama of Temporal
Middle Fossa
Basilar Part
Petrous Portion of Temporal
Eminentia arcuata
Foramen Magnum
Posterior Fossa
Occipital bone
for Transverse Sinus

FIG. 131.—Base of the skull. Upper surface.

Anterior Fossa (*fossa cranii anterior*).—The floor of the anterior fossa is formed by the orbital plates of the frontal, the cribriform plate of the ethmoid, and the small wings and front part of the body of the sphenoid; it is limited behind by the posterior borders of the small wings of the sphenoid and by the anterior margin of the chiasmatic groove. It is traversed by the **frontoethmoidal, sphenoethmoidal,** and **sphenofrontal sutures.** Its lateral portions roof in the orbital cavities and support the frontal lobes of the cerebrum; they are convex and marked by depressions for the brain convolutions, and grooves for branches of the meningeal vessels. The central portion corresponds with the roof of the nasal cavity, and is markedly depressed on either side of the crista galli. It presents, in and near the median line, from before backward, the commencement of the **frontal crest** for the attachment of the falx cerebri; the **foramen cecum,** between the frontal bone and the crista galli of the ethmoid, which usually transmits a small vein from the nasal cavity to the superior sagittal sinus; behind the foramen cecum, the **crista galli,** the free margin of which affords attachment to the falx cerebri; on either side of the crista galli, the **olfactory groove** formed by the cribriform plate, which supports the olfactory bulb and presents foramina for the transmission of the olfactory

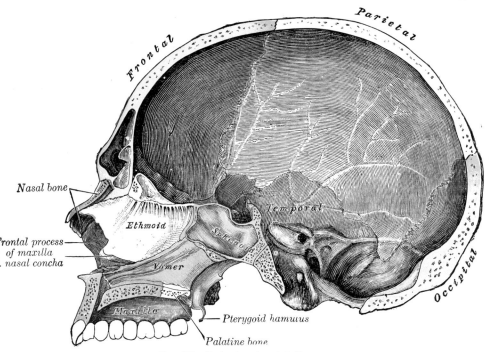

Fig. 132.—Sagittal section of skull.

nerves, and in front a slit-like opening for the nasociliary nerve. Lateral to either olfactory groove are the internal openings of the **anterior** and **posterior ethmoidal foramina;** the anterior, situated about the middle of the lateral margin of the olfactory groove, transmits the anterior ethmoidal vessels and the nasociliary nerve; the nerve runs in a groove along the lateral edge of the cribriform plate to the slit-like opening above mentioned; the posterior ethmoidal foramen opens at the back part of this margin under cover of the projecting lamina of the sphenoid, and transmits the posterior ethmoidal vessels and nerve. Farther back in the middle line is the **ethmoidal spine,** bounded behind by a slight elevation separating two shallow longitudinal grooves which support the olfactory lobes. Behind this is the anterior margin of the chiasmatic groove, running lateralward on either side to the upper margin of the optic foramen.

The Middle Fossa (*fossa cranii media*).—The middle fossa, deeper than the preceding, is narrow in the middle, and wide at the sides of the skull. It is bounded in *front* by the posterior margins of the small wings of the sphenoid, the anterior clinoid processes, and the ridge forming the anterior margin of the chiasmatic groove; *behind*, by the superior angles of the petrous portions of the temporals and the dorsum sellæ; *laterally* by the temporal squamæ, sphenoidal angles of the parietals, and great wings of the sphenoid. It is traversed by the **squamosals, sphenoparietal, sphenosquamosal,** and **sphenopetrosal sutures.**

The middle part of the fossa presents, in *front*, the **chiasmatic groove** and **tuberculum sellæ**; the chiasmatic groove ends on either side at the **optic foramen**, which, transmits the optic nerve and ophthalmic artery to the orbital cavity. Behind the optic foramen the **anterior clinoid process** is directed backward and medialward and gives attachment to the tentorium cerebelli. Behind the tuberculum sellæ is a deep depression, the **sella turcica**, containing the **fossa hypophyseos**, which lodges the hypophysis, and presents on its anterior wall the **middle clinoid processes.** The sella turcica is bounded posteriorly by a quadrilateral plate of bone, the **dorsum sellæ**, the upper angles of which are surmounted by the **posterior clinoid processes:** these afford attachment to the tentorium cerebelli, and below each is a notch for the abducent nerve. On either side of the sella turcica is the **carotid groove**, which is broad, shallow, and curved somewhat like the italic letter *f*. It begins behind at the foramen lacerum, and ends on the medial side of the anterior clinoid process, where it is sometimes converted into a foramen (*carotico-clinoid*) by the union of the anterior with the middle clinoid process; posteriorly, it is bounded laterally by the **lingula.** This groove lodges the cavernous sinus and the internal carotid artery, the latter being surrounded by a plexus of sympathetic nerves.

The lateral parts of the middle fossa are of considerable depth, and support the temporal lobes of the brain. They are marked by depressions for the brain convolutions and traversed by furrows for the anterior and posterior branches of the middle meningeal vessels. These furrows begin near the foramen spinosum, and the anterior runs forward and upward to the sphenoidal angle of the parietal, where it is sometimes converted into a bony canal; the posterior runs lateralward and backward across the temporal squama and passes on to the parietal near the middle of its lower border. The following apertures are also to be seen. In front is the **superior orbital fissure,** bounded above by the small wing, below, by the great wing, and medially, by the body of the sphenoid; it is usually completed laterally by the orbital plate of the frontal bone. It transmits to the orbital cavity the oculomotor, the trochlear, the ophthalmic division of the trigeminal, and the abducent nerves, some filaments from the cavernous plexus of the sympathetic, and the orbital branch of the middle meningeal artery; and from the orbital cavity a recurrent branch from the lacrimal artery to the dura mater, and the ophthalmic veins. Behind the medial end of the superior orbital fissure is the **foramen rotundum,** for the passage of the maxillary nerve. Behind and lateral to the foramen rotundum is the **foramen ovale,** which transmits the mandibular nerve, the accessory meningeal artery, and the lesser superficial petrosal nerve. Medial to the foramen ovale is the **foramen Vesalii,** which varies in size in different individuals, and is often absent; when present, it opens below at the lateral side of the scaphoid fossa, and transmits a small vein. Lateral to the foramen ovale is the **foramen spinosum,** for the passage of the middle meningeal vessels, and a recurrent branch from the mandibular nerve. Medial to the foramen ovale is the **foramen lacerum;** in the fresh state the lower part of this aperture is filled up by a layer of fibrocartilage, while its upper and inner parts transmit the internal carotid artery surrounded by a plexus of sympathetic nerves. The nerve of the pterygoid canal and a meningeal branch from the ascending pharyngeal artery pierce the layer of fibrocartilage. On the anterior surface of the petrous portion of the temporal bone are seen the eminence caused by the projection of the superior semicircular canal; in front of and a little lateral to this a depression corresponding to the roof of the tympanic cavity; the groove leading to the **hiatus of the facial canal,** for the transmission of the greater superficial petrosal nerve and the petrosal branch of the middle meningeal artery; beneath it, the smaller groove, for the passage of the lesser superficial petrosal nerve; and, near the apex of the bone, the depression for the semilunar ganglion and the orifice of the carotid canal.

The Posterior Fossa (*fossa cranii posterior*).—The posterior fossa is the largest and deepest of the three. It is formed by the dorsum sellæ and clivus of the sphenoid, the occipital, the petrous and mastoid portions of the temporals, and the mastoid angles of the parietal bones; it is crossed by the **occipitomastoid** and the **parietomastoid sutures,** and lodges the cerebellum, pons, and medulla oblongata. It is separated from the middle fossa in and near the median line by the dorsum sellæ of the sphenoid and on either side by the superior angle of the petrous portion of the temporal bone. This angle gives attachment to the tentorum cerebelli, is grooved for the superior petrosal sinus, and presents at its medial end a notch upon which the trigeminal nerve rests. The fossa is limited behind by the grooves for the transverse sinuses. In its center is the **foramen magnum,** on either side of which is a rough tubercle for the attachment of the alar ligaments; a little above this tubercle is the canal, which transmits the hypoglossal nerve and a meningeal branch from the ascending pharyngeal artery. In front of the foramen magnum the basilar portion of the occipital and the posterior part of the body of the sphenoid form a grooved surface which supports the medulla oblongata and pons; in the young skull these bones are joined by a synchondrosis. This grooved surface is separated on either side from the petrous portion of the temporal by the **petro-occipital fissure,** which is occupied in the fresh state by a plate of cartilage; the fissure is continuous behind with the jugular foramen, and its margins are grooved for the inferior petrosal sinus. The **jugular foramen** is situated between the lateral part of the occipital and the petrous part of the temporal. The anterior portion of this foramen transmits the inferior petrosal sinus; the posterior portion, the transverse sinus and some meningeal branches from the occipital and ascending pharyngeal arteries; and the intermediate portion, the glossopharyngeal, vagus, and accessory nerves. Above the jugular foramen is the **internal acoustic meatus,** for the facial and acoustic nerves and internal auditory artery; behind and lateral to this is the slit-like opening leading into the aquæductus vestibuli, which lodges the ductus endolymphaticus; while between these, and near the superior angle of the petrous portion, is a small triangular depression, the remains of the fossa subarcuata, which lodges a process of the dura mater and occasionally transmits a small vein. Behind the foramen magnum are the **inferior occipital fossæ,** which support the hemispheres of the cerebellum, separated from one another by the **internal occipital crest,** which serves for the attachment of the falx cerebelli, and lodges the occipital sinus. The posterior fossæ are surmounted by the deep grooves for the **transverse sinuses.** Each of these channels, in its passage to the jugular foramen, grooves the occipital, the mastoid angle of the parietal, the mastoid portion of the temporal, and the jugular process of the occipital, and ends at the back part of the jugular foramen. Where this sinus grooves the mastoid portion of the temporal, the orifice of the **mastoid foramen** may be seen; and, just previous to its termination, the **condyloid canal** opens into it; neither opening is constant.

The Nasal Cavity (*cavum nasi; nasal fossa*).—The nasal cavities are two irregular spaces, situated one on either side of the middle line of the face, extending from the base of the cranium to the roof of the mouth, and separated from each other by a thin vertical septum. They open on the face through the pear-shaped **anterior nasal aperture,** and their posterior openings or **choanæ** communicate, in the fresh state, with the nasal part of the pharynx. They are much narrower above than below, and in the middle than at their anterior or posterior openings: their depth, which is considerable, is greatest in the middle. They communicate with the frontal, ethmoidal, sphenoidal, and maxillary sinuses. Each cavity is bounded by a **roof**, a **floor**, a **medial** and a **lateral wall**.

The **roof** (Figs. 133, 187) is horizontal in its central part, but slopes downward in front and behind; it is formed in *front* by the nasal bone and the spine of the frontal; in the *middle*, by the cribriform plate of the ethmoid; and *behind*, by the body of the sphenoid, the sphenoidal concha, the ala of the vomer and the sphenoidal process of the palatine bone. In the cribriform plate of the ethmoid are the foramina for the olfactory nerves, and on the posterior part of the roof is the opening into the sphenoidal sinus.

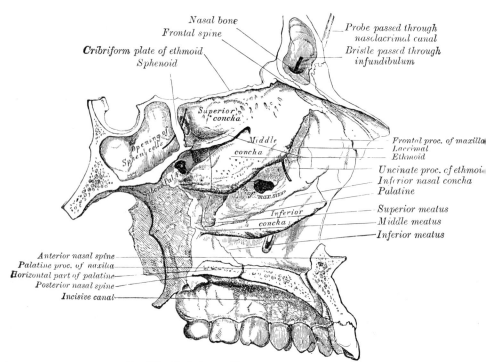

Fig. 133.—Roof, floor, and lateral wall of left nasal cavity.

The **floor** is flattened from before backward and concave from side to side. It is formed by the palatine process of the maxilla and the horizontal part of the palatine bone; near its anterior end is the opening of the incisive canal.

The **medial wall** (*septum nasi*) (Fig. 187), is frequently deflected to one or other side, more often to the left than to the right. It is formed, in *front*, by the crest of the nasal bones and frontal spine; in the *middle*, by the perpendicular plate of the ethmoid; *behind*, by the vomer and the rostrum of the sphenoid; *below*, by the crest of the maxillæ and palatine bones. It presents, in front, a large, triangular notch, which receives the cartilage of the septum; and behind, the free edge of the vomer. Its surface is marked by numerous furrows for vessels and nerves and by the grooves for the nasopalatine nerve, and is traversed by sutures connecting the bones of which it is formed.

The **lateral wall** (Fig. 133) is formed, in front, by the frontal process of the maxilla and by the lacrimal bone; in the middle, by the ethmoid, maxilla, and inferior nasal concha; behind, by the vertical plate of the palatine bone, and the medial pterygoid plate of the sphenoid. On this wall are three irregular antero-posterior passages, termed the superior, middle, and inferior meatuses of the nose. The **superior meatus,** the smallest of the three, occupies the middle third of the lateral wall. It lies between the superior and middle nasal conchæ; the **spheno-palatine foramen** opens into it behind, and the **posterior ethmoidal cells** in front. The sphenoidal sinus opens into a recess, the **sphenoethmoidal recess,** which is placed above and behind the superior concha. The **middle meatus** is situated between the middle and inferior conchæ, and extends from the anterior to the posterior end of the latter. The lateral wall of this meatus can be satisfactorily studied only after the removal of the middle concha. On it is a curved fissure, the **hiatus semilunaris,** limited below by the edge of the uncinate process of the ethmoid and above by an elevation named the **bulla ethmoidalis;** the middle ethmoidal cells are contained within this bulla and open on or near to it. Through the hiatus semilunaris the meatus communicates with a curved passage termed the **infundibulum,** which communicates in front with the anterior ethmoidal cells and in rather more than fifty per cent of skulls is continued upward as the **frontonasal duct** into the frontal air-sinus; when this continuity fails, the frontonasal duct opens directly into the anterior part of the meatus. Below the bulla ethmoidalis and hidden by the uncinate process of the ethmoid is the opening of the maxillary sinus (**ostium maxillare**); an accessory opening is frequently present above the posterior part of the inferior nasal concha. The **inferior meatus,** the largest of the three, is the space between the inferior concha and the floor of the nasal cavity. It extends almost the entire length of the lateral wall of the nose, is broader in front than behind, and presents anteriorly the lower **orifice of the nasolacrimal canal.**

The **Anterior Nasal Aperture** (Fig. 126) is a heart-shaped or pyriform opening, whose long axis is vertical, and narrow end upward; in the recent state it is much contracted by the lateral and alar cartilages of the nose. It is bounded *above* by the inferior borders of the nasal bones; *laterally* by the thin, sharp margins which separate the anterior from the nasal surfaces of the maxillæ; and *below* by the same borders, where they curve medialward to join each other at the anterior nasal spine.

The **choanæ** are each bounded *above* by the under surface of the body of the sphenoid and ala of the vomer; *below*, by the posterior border of the horizontal part of the palatine bone; *laterally*, by the medial pterygoid plate; they are separated from each other by the posterior border of the vomer.

DIFFERENCES IN THE SKULL DUE TO AGE.

At birth the skull is large in proportion to the other parts of the skeleton, but its facial portion is small, and equals only about one-eighth of the bulk of the cranium as compared with one-half in the adult. The frontal and parietal eminences are prominent, and the greatest width of the skull is at the level of the latter; on the other hand, the glabella, superciliary arches, and mastoid processes are not developed. Ossification of the skull bones is not completed, and many of them, *e. g.,* the occipital, temporals, sphenoid, frontal, and mandible, consist of more than one piece. Unossified membranous intervals, termed *fontanelles,* are seen at the angles of the parietal bones; these fontanelles are six in number: two, an anterior and a posterior, are situated in the middle line, and two, an antero-lateral and a postero-lateral, on either side.

The *anterior* or *bregmatic fontanelle* (Fig. 134) is the largest, and is placed at the junction of the sagittal, coronal, and frontal sutures; it is lozenge-shaped, and measures about 4 cm. in its antero-posterior and 2.5 cm. in its transverse diameter. The *posterior fontanelle* is triangular in form and is situated at the junction of the sagittal and lambdoidal sutures. The *lateral fontanelles* (Fig. 135) are small, irregular in shape, and correspond respectively with the sphenoidal and mastoid angles of the parietal bones. An additional fontanelle is sometimes seen in the sagittal suture at the region of the obelion. The fontanelles are usually closed by the growth and extension of the bones which surround them, but sometimes they are the sites of separate ossific centers which develop into sutural bones. The posterior and lateral fontanelles are obliterated within a month or two after birth, but the anterior is not completely closed until about the middle of the second year.

The smallness of the face at birth is mainly accounted for by the rudimentary condition of the maxillæ and mandible, the non-eruption of the teeth, and the small size of the maxillary air sinuses and nasal cavities. At birth the nasal cavities lie almost entirely between the orbits, and the lower border of the anterior nasal aperture is only a little below the level of the orbital floor. With the eruption of the deciduous teeth there is an enlargement of the face and jaws, and these changes are still more marked after the second dentition.

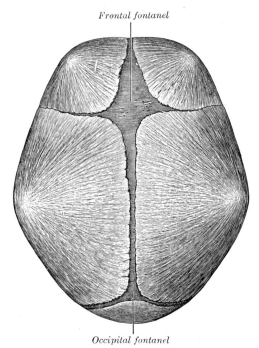

Frontal fontanel

Occipital fontanel

FIG. 134.—Skull at birth, showing frontal and occipital fontanelles.

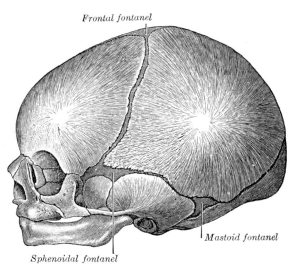

Frontal fontanel

Mastoid fontanel

Sphenoidal fontanel

FIG. 135.—Skull at birth, showing sphenoidal and mastoid fontanelles.

The skull grows rapidly from birth to the seventh year, by which time the foramen magnum and petrous parts of the temporals have reached their full size and the orbital cavities are only a little smaller than those of the adult. Growth is slow from the seventh year until the approach of puberty, when a second period of activity occurs: this results in an increase in all directions, but it is especially marked in the frontal and facial regions, where it is associated with the development of the air sinuses.

Suture closure begins at twenty-two years in the sagittal and sphenofrontal, at twenty-four years in the coronal and at twenty-six years in the lambdoid and masto-occipital. The process is most rapid from twenty-six to thirty years then slows down and may not be complete until old age. The sphenoparietal, sphenotemporal, parietomastoid and squamous begin to close at twenty-nine, thirty, thirty-seven and thirty-seven years. Closure progresses very slowly with a final burst of activity in old age. There is considerable individual variation.

The most striking feature of the old skull is the diminution in the size of the maxillæ and mandible consequent on the loss of the teeth and the absorption of the alveolar processes. This is associated with a marked reduction in the vertical measurement of the face and with an alteration in the angles of the mandible.

SEX DIFFERENCES, FUNCTION AND CLEFT PALATE.

Until the age of puberty there is little difference between the skull of the female and that of the male. The skull of an adult female is, as a rule, lighter and smaller, and its cranial capacity about 10 per cent. less, than that of the male. Its walls are thinner and its muscular ridges less strongly marked; the glabella, superciliary arches, and mastoid processes are less prominent, and the corresponding air sinuses are small or rudimentary. The upper margin of the orbit is sharp, the forehead vertical, the frontal and parietal eminences prominent, and the vault some-what flattened. The contour of the face is more rounded, the facial bones are smoother, and the maxillæ and mandible and their contained teeth smaller. From what has been said it will be seen that more of the infantile characteristics are retained in the skull of the adult female than in that of the adult male. A well-marked male or female skull can easily be recognized as such, but in some cases the respective characteristics are so indistinct that the determination of the sex may be difficult or impossible.

The chief function of the skull is to protect the brain, and therefore those portions of the skull which are most exposed to external violence are thicker than those which are shielded from injury by overlying muscles. Thus, the skull-cap is thick and dense, whereas the temporal squamæ, being protected by the temporales muscles, and the inferior occipital fossæ, being shielded by the muscles at the back of the neck, are thin and fragile. Fracture of the skull is further prevented by its elasticity, its rounded shape, and its construction of a number of secondary elastic arches, each made up of a single bone. The manner in which vibrations are transmitted through the bones of the skull is also of importance as regards its protective mechanism, at all events as far as the base is concerned. In the vault, the bones being of a fairly equal thickness and density, vibrations are transmitted in a uniform manner in all directions, but in the base, owing to the varying thickness and density of the bones, this is not so; and therefore in this situation there are special buttresses which serve to carry the vibrations in certain definite directions. At the front of the skull, on either side, is the ridge which separates the anterior from the middle fossa of the base; and behind, the ridge or buttress which separates the middle from the posterior fossa; and if any violence is applied to the vault, the vibrations would be carried along these buttresses to the sella turcica, where they meet. This part has been termed the "center of resistance," and here there is a special protective mechanism to guard the brain. The subarachnoid cavity at the base of the brain is dilated, and the cerebrospinal fluid which fills it acts as a water cushion to shield the brain from injury. In like manner, when violence is applied to the base of the skull, as in falls upon the feet, the vibrations are carried backward through the occipital crest, and forward through the basilar part of the occipital and body of the sphenoid to the vault of the skull.

In connection with the bones of the face a common malformation is *cleft palate.* The cleft usually starts posteriorly, and its most elementary form is a bifid uvula; or the cleft may extend through the soft palate; or the posterior part or the whole of the hard palate may be involved, the cleft extending as far forward as the incisive foramen. In the severest forms, the cleft extends through the alveolus and passes between the incisive or premaxillary bone and the rest of the maxilla; that is to say, between the lateral incisor and canine teeth. In some instances, the cleft runs between the central and lateral incisor teeth; and this has induced some anatomists to believe that the premaxillary bone is developed from two centers and not from one, as stated on p. 167. The cleft may affect one or both sides; if the latter, the central part is frequently displaced forward and remains united to the septum of the nose, the deficiency in the alveolus being complicated with a cleft in the lip (hare-lip).

The Mandible (Mandibula; Inferior Maxillary Bone; Lower Jaw).

The **mandible,** the largest and strongest bone of the face, serves for the reception of the lower teeth. It consists of a curved, horizontal portion, the **body,** and two perpendicular portions, the **rami,** which unite with the ends of the body nearly at right angles.

The Body (*corpus mandibulæ*).—The body is curved somewhat like a horseshoe, and has two surfaces and two borders.

Surfaces.—The **external surface** (Fig. 136) is marked in the median line by a faint ridge, indicating the **symphysis** or line of junction of the two pieces of which the bone is composed at an early period of life. This ridge divides below and encloses a triangular eminence, the **mental protuberance**, the base of which is depressed in the center but raised on either side to form the **mental tubercle.** On either side of the symphysis, just below the incisor teeth, is a depression, the **incisive fossa,** which gives origin to the Mentalis and a small portion of the Orbicularis oris. Below the second premolar tooth, on either side, midway between the upper and lower borders of the body, is the **mental foramen,** for the passage of the mental vessels and nerve. Running backward and upward from each mental tubercle is a faint ridge, the **oblique line,** which is continuous with the anterior border of the ramus; it affords attachment to the Quadratus labii inferioris and Triangularis; the Platysma is attached below it.

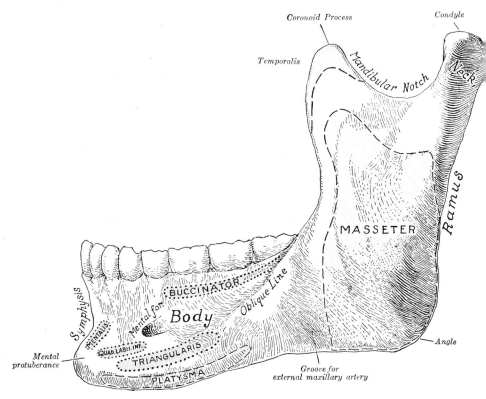

Fig. 136.—The left half of the mandible. Lateral aspect.

The **internal surface** (Fig. 137) is concave from side to side. Near the lower part of the symphysis is a pair of laterally placed spines, termed the **mental spines,** which give origin to the Genioglossi. Immediately below these is a second pair of spines, or more frequently a median ridge or impression, for the origin of the Geniohyoidei. In some cases the mental spines are fused to form a single eminence, in others they are absent and their position is indicated merely by an irregularity of the surface. Above the mental spines a median foramen and furrow are sometimes seen; they mark the line of union of the halves of the bone. Below the mental spines, on either side of the middle line, is an oval depression for the attachment of the anterior belly of the Digastricus. Extending upward and backward on either side from the lower part of the symphysis is the **mylohyoid line,** which gives origin to the Mylohyoideus; the posterior part of this line, near the alveolar margin, gives attachment to a small part of the Constrictor pharyngis superior, and to the pterygomandibular raphé. Above the anterior part of this line is a smooth triangular area against which the sublingual gland rests, and below the hinder part, an oval fossa for the submaxillary gland.

Borders.—The **superior** or **alveolar border**, wider behind than in front, is hollowed into cavities, for the reception of the teeth; these cavities are sixteen in number, and vary in depth and size according to the teeth which they contain. To the outer lip of the superior border, on either side, the Buccinator is attached as far forward as the first molar tooth. The **inferior border** is rounded, longer than the superior, and thicker in front than behind; at the point where it joins the lower border of the ramus a shallow groove; for the external maxillary artery, may be present.

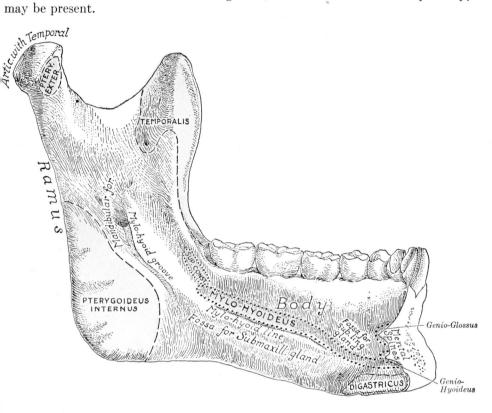

Fig. 137.—The left half of the mandible. Medial aspect.

The Ramus (*ramus mandibulæ; perpendicular portion*).—The ramus is quadrilateral in shape, and has two surfaces, four borders, and two processes.

Surfaces.—The **lateral surface** (Fig. 136) is flat and marked by oblique ridges at its lower part; it gives attachment throughout nearly the whole of its extent to the Masseter. The **medial surface** (Fig. 137) presents about its center the oblique **mandibular foramen**, for the entrance of the inferior alveolar vessels and nerve. The margin of this opening is irregular; it presents in front a prominent ridge, surmounted by a sharp spine, the **lingula mandibulæ**, which gives attachment to the sphenomandibular ligament; at its lower and back part is a notch from which the **mylohyoid groove** runs obliquely downward and forward, and lodges the mylohyoid vessels and nerve. Behind this groove is a rough surface, for the insertion of the Pterygoideus internus. The **mandibular canal** runs obliquely downward

9

and forward in the ramus, and then horizontally forward in the body, where it is placed under the alveoli and communicates with them by small openings. On arriving at the incisor teeth, it turns back to communicate with the mental foramen, giving off two small canals which run to the cavities containing the incisor teeth. In the posterior two-thirds of the bone the canal is situated nearer the internal surface of the mandible; and in the anterior third, nearer its external surface. It contains the inferior alveolar vessels and nerve, from which branches are distributed to the teeth. The **lower border** of the ramus is thick, straight, and continuous with the inferior border of the body of the bone. At its junction with the posterior border is the **angle of the mandible**, which may be either inverted or everted and is marked by rough, oblique ridges on each side, for the attachment of the Masseter laterally, and the Pterygoideus internus medially; the stylomandibular ligament is attached to the angle between these muscles. The **anterior border** is thin above, thicker below, and continuous with the oblique line. The **posterior border** is thick, smooth, rounded, and covered by the parotid gland. The **upper border** is thin, and is surmounted by two processes, the **coronoid** in front and the **condyloid** behind, separated by a deep concavity, the **mandibular notch**.

The **Coronoid Process** (*processus coronoideus*) is a thin, triangular eminence, which is flattened from side to side and varies in shape and size. Its *anterior border* is convex and is continuous below with the anterior border of the ramus; its *posterior border* is concave and forms the anterior boundary of the mandibular notch. Its *lateral surface* is smooth, and affords insertion to the Temporalis and Masseter. Its *medial surface* gives insertion to the Temporalis, and presents a ridge which begins near the apex of the process and runs downward and forward to the inner side of the last molar tooth. Between this ridge and the anterior border is a grooved triangular area, the upper part of which gives attachment to the Temporalis, the lower part to some fibers of the Buccinator.

The **Condyloid Process** (*processus condyloideus*) is thicker than the coronoid, and consists of two portions: the **condyle**, and the constricted portion which supports it, the **neck**. The **condyle** presents an articular surface for articulation with the articular disk of the temporomandibular joint; it is convex from before backward and from side to side, and extends farther on the posterior than on the anterior surface. Its long axis is directed medialward and slightly backward, and if prolonged to the middle line will meet that of the opposite condyle near the anterior margin of the foramen magnum. At the lateral extremity of the condyle is a small tubercle for the attachment of the temporomandibular ligament. The **neck** is flattened from before backward, and strengthened by ridges which descend from the forepart and sides of the condyle. Its posterior surface is convex; its anterior presents a depression for the attachment of the Pterygoideus externus.

The **mandibular notch**, separating the two processes, is a deep semilunar depression, and is crossed by the masseteric vessels and nerve.

Ossification.—The mandible is ossified in the fibrous membrane covering the outer surface of Meckel's cartilages. These cartilages form the cartilaginous bar of the mandibular arch (see p. 46), and are two in number, a right and a left. Their proximal or cranial ends are connected with the ear capsules, and their distal extremities are joined to one another at the symphysis by mesodermal tissue. They run forward immediately below the condyles and then, bending downward, lie in a groove near the lower border of the bone; in front of the canine tooth they incline upward to the symphysis. From the proximal end of each cartilage the malleus and incus, two of the bones of the middle ear, are developed; the next succeeding portion, as far as the lingula, is replaced by fibrous tissue, which persists to form the sphenomandibular ligament. Between the lingula and the canine tooth the cartilage disappears, while the portion of it below and behind the incisor teeth becomes ossified and incorporated with this part of the mandible.

Ossification takes place in the membrane covering the outer surface of the ventral end of Meckel's cartilage (Figs. 138 to 141), and each half of the bone is formed from a single center which appears, near the mental foramen, about the sixth week of fetal life By the tenth week the portion of Meckel's cartilage which lies below and behind the incisor teeth is surrounded and invaded by the membrane bone. Somewhat later, accessory nuclei of cartilage make their appearance, viz., a wedge-shaped nucleus in the condyloid process and extending downward through the ramus; a small strip along the anterior border of the coronoid process; and smaller nuclei in the front part of both alveolar walls and along the front of the lower border of the bone. These accessory nuclei possess no separate ossific centers, but are invaded by the surrounding membrane bone and undergo absorption. The inner alveolar border, usually described as arising from a

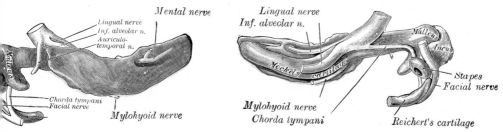

Fig. 138.—Mandible of human embryo, 24 mm. long. Outer aspect. (From model by Low.)

Fig. 139.—Mandible of human embryo 24 mm. long. Inner aspect. (From model by Low.)

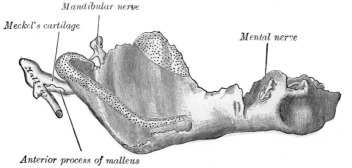

Fig. 140.—Mandible of human embryo 95 mm. long. Outer aspect. Nuclei of cartilage stippled. (From model by Low.)

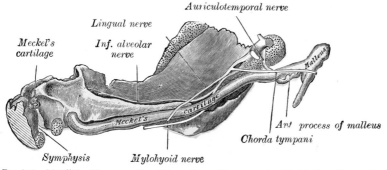

Fig 141.—Mandible of human embryo 95 mm. long. Inner aspect. Nuclei of cartilage strippled. (From model by Low.)

separate ossific center (*splenial center*), is formed in the human mandible by an ingrowth from the main mass of the bone. At birth the bone consists of two parts, united by a fibrous symphysis, in which ossification takes place during the first year.

The foregoing description of the ossification of the mandible is based on the researches of Low[1] and Fawcett,[2] and differs somewhat from that usually given.

Articulations.—The mandible articulates with the *two* temporal bones.

CHANGES PRODUCED IN THE MANDIBLE BY AGE.

At birth (Fig. 142 *A*) the body of the bone is a mere shell, containing the sockets of the two ncisor, the canine, and the two deciduous molar teeth, imperfectly partitioned off from one

[1] Proceedings of the Anatomical and Anthropological Society af the University of Aberdeen, 1905, and Journal of Anatomy and Physiology, vol. **44**.
[2] Journal of the American Medical Association, September 2, 1905.

another. The mandibular canal is of large size, and runs near the lower border of the bone; the mental foramen opens beneath the socket of the first deciduous molar tooth. The angle is obtuse (175°), and the condyloid portion is nearly in line with the body. The coronoid process is of comparatively large size, and projects above the level of the condyle.

After birth (Fig. 142, A and B) the two segments of the bone become joined at the symphysis, from below upward, in the first year; but a trace of separation may be visible in the beginning of the second year, near the alveolar margin. The body becomes elongated in its whole length, but more especially behind the mental foramen, to provide space for the three additional teeth developed in this part. The depth of the body increases owing to increased growth of the alveolar part, to afford room for the roots of the teeth, and by thickening of the subdental portion which

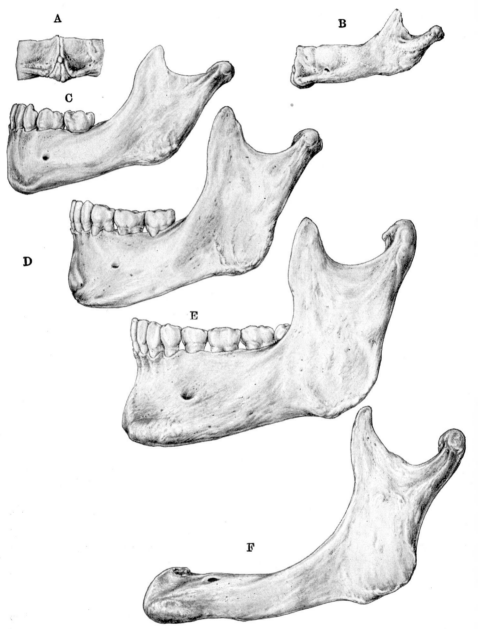

Fig. 142.—The mandible at different periods of life. A, at birth. Anterior aspect, showing the ossicula mentalia B, at birth. Left lateral aspect. C, at four years. Full milk dentition. D, at eight years. The permanent incisor and first molar teeth have erupted; the milk molars are in process of being shed. E, adult. F, old age.

enables the jaw to withstand the powerful action of the masticatory muscles; but the alveolar portion is the deeper of the two, and, consequently, the chief part of the body lies above the oblique line. The mandibular canal, after the second dentition, is situated just above the level of the mylohyoid line; and the mental foramen occupies the position usual to it in the adult. The angle becomes less obtuse, owing to the separation of the jaws by the teeth; about the fourth year it is 140 degrees.

In the adult (Fig. 142 *E*) the alveolar and subdental portions of the body are usually of equal depth. The mental foramen opens midway between the upper and lower borders of the bone, and the mandibular canal runs nearly parallel with the mylohyoid line. The ramus is almost vertical in direction, the angle measuring from 110° to 120°.

In old age (Fig. 142 *F*) the bone becomes greatly reduced in size, for with the loss of the teeth the alveolar process is absorbed, and, consequently, the chief part of the bone is below the oblique line. The mandibular canal, with the mental foramen opening from it, is close to the alveolar border. The ramus is oblique in direction, the angle measures about 140°, and the neck of the condyle is more or less bent backward.

The Hyoid Bone (Os Hyoideum; Lingual Bone).

The **hyoid bone** is shaped like a horseshoe, and is suspended from the tips of the styloid processes of the temporal bones by the stylohyoid ligaments. It consists of five segments, viz., a **body**, two **greater cornua**, and two **lesser cornua**.

The Body or Basihyal (*corpus oss. hyoidei*).—The body or central part is of a quadrilateral form. Its **anterior surface** (Fig. 143) is convex and directed forward and upward. It is crossed in its upper half by a well-marked transverse ridge with a slight downward convexity, and in many cases a vertical median ridge divides it into two lateral halves. The portion of the vertical ridge above the transverse line is present in a majority of speci-mens, but the lower portion is

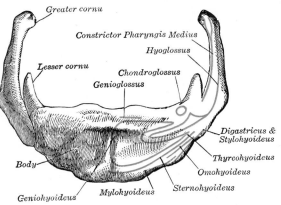

Fig. 143.—Hyoid bone. Anterior surface. Enlarged.

evident only in rare cases. The anterior surface gives insertion to the Genio-hyoideus in the greater part of its extent both above and below the transverse ridge; a portion of the origin of the Hyoglossus notches the lateral margin of the Geniohyoideus attachment. Below the transverse ridge the Mylohyoideus, Sternohyoideus, and Omohyoideus are inserted. The **posterior surface** is smooth, concave, directed backward and downward, and separated from the epiglottis by the hyothyroid membrane and a quantity of loose areolar tissue; a bursa intervenes between it and the hyothyroid membrane. The **superior border** is rounded, and gives attachment to the hyothyroid membrane and some aponeurotic fibers of the Genioglossus. The **inferior border** affords insertion medially to the Sternohyoideus and laterally to the Omohyoideus and occasionally a portion of the Thyreohyoideus. It also gives attachment to the Levator glandulæ thyreoideæ, when this muscle is present. In early life the **lateral borders** are connected to the greater cornua by synchondroses; after middle life usually by bony union.

The Greater Cornua or Thyrohyals (*cornua majora*).—The greater cornua pro-ject backward from the lateral borders of the body; they are flattened from above downward and diminish in size from before backward; each ends in a tuber-cle to which is fixed the lateral hyothyroid ligament. The **upper surface** is rough close to its lateral border, for muscular attachments: the largest of these are the origins of the Hyoglossus and Constrictor pharyngis medius which extend along the whole length of the cornu; the Digastricus and Stylohyoideus have small insertions in front of these near the junction of the body with the cornu. To the **medial border** the hyothyroid membrane is attached, while the anterior half of the **lateral border** gives insertion to the Thyreohyoideus.

The Lesser Cornua or Ceratohyals (*cornua minora*).—The lesser cornua are two small, conical eminences, attached by their bases to the angles of junction between the body and greater cornua. They are connected to the body of the bone by fibrous tissue, and occasionally to the greater cornua by distinct diarthrodial joints, which usually persist throughout life, but occasionally become ankylosed.

The lesser cornua are situated in the line of the transverse ridge on the body and appear to be morphological continuations of it. The apex of each cornua gives attachment to the stylohyoid ligament; the Chondroglossus rises from the medial side of the base.

Ossification.—The hyoid is ossified from *six* centers: two for the body, and one for each cornu. Ossification commences in the greater cornua toward the end of fetal life, in the body shortly afterward, and in the lesser cornua during the first or second year after birth.

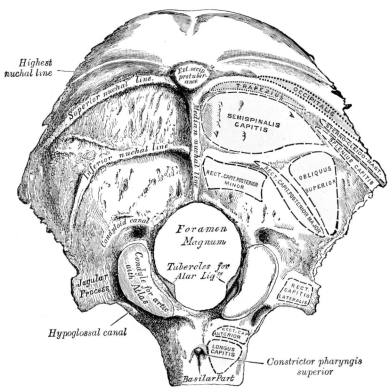

Fig. 144.—Occipital bone. Outer surface.

THE CRANIAL BONES (OSSA CRANII).

The Occipital Bone (Os Occipitale).

The **occipital bone** (Figs. 144, 145), situated at the back and lower part of the cranium, is trapezoid in shape and curved on itself. It is pierced by a large oval aperture, the **foramen magnum**, through which the cranial cavity communicates with the vertebral canal.

The curved, expanded plate behind the foramen magnum is named the **squama**;

the thick, somewhat quadrilateral piece in front of the foramen is called the **basilar part**, whilst on either side of the foramen is the **lateral portion**.

The Squama (*squama occipitalis*).—The squama, situated above and behind the foramen magnum, is curved from above downward and from side to side.

Surfaces.—The **external surface** is convex and presents midway between the summit of the bone and the foramen magnum a prominence, the **external occipital protuberance.** Extending lateralward from this on either side are two curved lines, one a little above the other. The upper, often faintly marked, is named the **highest nuchal line,** and to it the galea aponeurotica is attached. The lower is termed the **superior nuchal line.** That part of the squama which lies above the

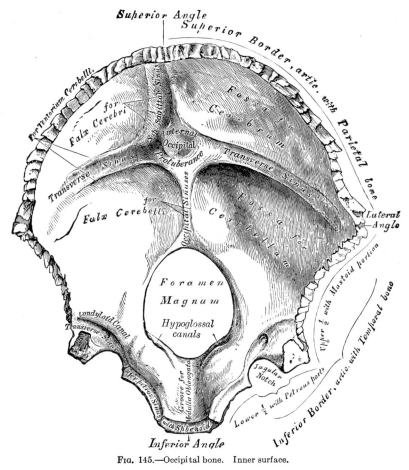

Fig. 145.—Occipital bone. Inner surface.

highest nuchal lines is named the **planum occipitale,** and is covered by the Occipitalis muscle; that below, termed the **planum nuchale,** is rough and irregular for the attachment of several muscles. From the external occipital protuberance a ridge or crest, the **median nuchal line,** often faintly marked, descends to the foramen magnum, and affords attachment to the ligamentum nuchæ; running from the middle of this line across either half of the nuchal plane is the **inferior nuchal line.** Several muscles are attached to the outer surface of the squama, thus: the superior nuchal line gives origin to the Occipitalis and Trapezius, and insertion to the Sternocleidomastoideus and Splenius capitis: into the surface between the superior and inferior nuchal lines the Semispinalis capitis and the Obliquus capitis superior are inserted, while the inferior nuchal line and the area below it receive the insertions of the Recti capitis posteriores major and minor. The posterior atlantoöccipital membrane is attached around the postero-lateral part of the foramen magnum, just outside the margin of the foramen.

The **internal surface** is deeply concave and divided into four fossæ by a **cruciate eminence.** The upper two fossæ are triangular and lodge the occipital lobes of the cerebrum; the lower two are quadrilateral and accommodate the hemispheres of the cerebellum. At the point of intersection of the four divisions of the cruciate eminence is the **internal occipital protuberance.** From this protuberance the upper division of the cruciate eminence runs to the superior angle of the bone, and on one side of it (generally the right) is a deep groove, the **sagittal sulcus,** which lodges the hinder part of the superior sagittal sinus; to the margins of this sulcus the falx cerebri is attached. The lower division of the cruciate eminence is prominent, and is named the **internal occipital crest;** it bifurcates near the foramen magnum and gives attachment to the falx cerebelli; in the attached margin of this falx is the occipital sinus, which is sometimes duplicated. In the upper part of the internal occipital crest, a small depression is sometimes distinguishable; it is termed the **vermian fossa** since it is occupied by part of the vermis of the cerebellum. Transverse grooves, one on either side, extend from the internal occipital protuberance to the lateral angles of the bone; those grooves accommodate the transverse sinuses, and their prominent margins give attachment to the tentorium cerebelli. The groove on the right side is usually larger than that on the left, and is continuous with that for the superior sagittal sinus. Exceptions to this condition are, however, not infrequent; the left may be larger than the right or the two may be almost equal in size. The angle of union of the superior sagittal and transverse sinuses is named the **confluence of the sinuses** (*torcular Herophili*[1]), and its position is indicated by a depression situated on one or other side of the protuberance.

Lateral Parts (*pars lateralis*).—The lateral parts are situated at the sides of the foramen magnum; on their under surfaces are the **condyles** for articulation with the superior facets of the atlas. The condyles are oval or reniform in shape, and their anterior extremities, directed forward and medialward, are closer together than their posterior, and encroach on the basilar portion of the bone; the posterior extremities extend back to the level of the middle of the foramen magnum. The articular surfaces of the condyles are convex from before backward and from side to side, and look downward and lateralward. To their margins are attached the capsules of the atlantoöccipital articulations, and on the medial side of each is a rough impression or tubercle for the alar ligament. At the base of either condyle the bone is tunnelled by a short canal, the **hypoglossal canal** (*anterior condyloid foramen*). This begins on the cranial surface of the bone immediately above the foramen magnum, and is directed lateralward and forward above the condyle. It may be partially or completely divided into two by a spicule of bone; it gives exit to the hypoglossal or twelfth cerebral nerve, and entrance to a meningeal branch of the ascending pharyngeal artery. Behind either condyle is a depression, the **condyloid fossa,** which receives the posterior margin of the superior facet of the atlas when the head is bent backward; the floor of this fossa is sometimes perforated by the **condyloid canal,** through which an emissary vein passes from the transverse sinus. Extending lateralward from the posterior half of the condyle is a quadrilateral plate of bone, the **jugular process,** excavated in front by the **jugular notch,** which, in the articulated skull, forms the posterior part of the jugular foramen. The jugular notch may be divided into two by a bony spicule, the **intrajugular process,** which projects lateralward above the hypoglossal canal. The

---

[1] The columns of blood coming in different directions were supposed to be pressed together at this point (*torcular*, a wine press).

under surface of the jugular process is rough, and gives attachment to the Rectus capitis lateralis muscle and the lateral atlantoöccipital ligament; from this surface an eminence, the **paramastoid process**, sometimes projects downward, and may be of sufficient length to reach, and articulate with, the transverse process of the atlas. Laterally the jugular process presents a rough quadrilateral or triangular area which is joined to the jugular surface of the temporal bone by a plate of cartilage; after the age of twenty-five this plate tends to ossify.

The **upper surface** of the lateral part presents an oval eminence, the **jugular tubercle**, which overlies the hypoglossal canal and is sometimes crossed by an oblique groove for the glossopharyngeal, vagus, and accessory nerves. On the upper surface of the jugular process is a deep groove which curves medialward and forward and is continuous with the jugular notch. This groove lodges the terminal part of the transverse sinus, and opening into it, close to its medial margin, is the orifice of the condyloid canal.

Basilar Part (*pars basilaris*).—The basilar part extends forward and upward from the foramen magnum, and presents *in front* an area more or less quadrilateral in outline. In the young skull this area is rough and uneven, and is joined to the body of the sphenoid by a plate of cartilage. By the twenty-fifth year this cartilaginous plate is ossified, and the occipital and sphenoid form a continuous bone.

Surfaces.—On its **lower surface**, about 1 cm. in front of the foramen magnum, is the **pharyngeal tubercle** which gives attachment to the fibrous raphé of the pharynx. On either side of the middle line the Longus capitis and Rectus capitis anterior are inserted, and immediately in front of the foramen magnum the anterior atlantoöccipital membrane is attached.

The **upper surface** presents a broad, shallow groove which inclines upward and forward from the foramen magnum; it supports the medulla oblongata, and near the margin of the foramen magnum gives attachment to the membrana tectoria. On the lateral margins of this surface are faint grooves for the inferior petrosal sinuses.

Foramen Magnum.—The foramen magnum is a large oval aperture with its long diameter antero-posterior; it is wider behind than in front where it is encroached

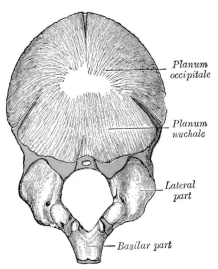

FIG. 146.—Occipital bone at birth.

Planum occipitale

Planum nuchale

Lateral part

Basilar part

upon by the condyles. It transmits the medulla oblongata and its membranes, the accessory nerves, the vertebral arteries, the anterior and posterior spinal arteries, and the membrana tectoria and alar ligaments.

Angles.—The **superior angle** of the occipital bone articulates with the occipital angles of the parietal bones and, in the fetal skull, corresponds in position with the **posterior fontanelle**. The **inferior angle** is fused with the body of the sphenoid. The **lateral angles** are situated at the extremities of the grooves for the transverse sinuses: each is received into the interval between the mastoid angle of the parietal and the mastoid part of the temporal.

Borders.—The **superior borders** extend from the superior to the lateral angles: they are deeply serrated for articulation with the occipital borders of the parietals, and form by this union the **lambdoidal suture**. The **inferior borders** extend from the lateral angles to the inferior angle; the upper half of each articulates with the mastoid portion of the corresponding temporal, the lower half with the petrous part of the same bone. These two portions of the inferior border are separated from one another by the jugular process, the notch on the anterior surface of which forms the posterior part of the jugular foramen.

Structure.—The occipital, like the other cranial bones, consists of two compact lamellæ, called the *outer* and *inner tables*, between which is the cancellous tissue or diploë; the bone is especially thick at the ridges, protuberances, condyles, and anterior part of the basilar part; in the inferior fossæ it is thin, semitransparent, and destitute of diploë.

Ossification (Fig. 146).—The planum occipitale of the squama is developed in membrane, and may remain separate throughout life when it constitutes the *interparietal* bone; the rest of the bone is developed in cartilage. The number of nuclei for the planum occipitale is usually given as four, two appearing near the middle line about the second month, and two some little distance from the middle line about the third month of fetal life. The planum nuchale of the squama is ossified from two centers, which appear about the seventh week of fetal life and soon unite to form a single piece. Union of the upper and lower portions of the squama takes place in the third month of fetal life. Each of the lateral parts begins to ossify from a single center during the eighth week of the fetal life. The basilar portion is ossified from one or two centers, these appear about the sixth week of fetal life. About the fourth year the squama and the two lateral portions unite, and about the sixth year the bone consists of a single piece. Between the eighteenth and twenty-fifth years the occipital and sphenoid become united, forming a single bone.

Articulations.—The occipital articulates with *six* bones: the two parietals, the two temporals, the sphenoid, and the atlas.

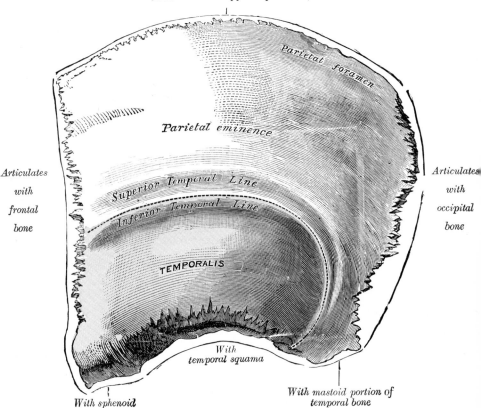

Articulates with opposite parietal bone

Articulates with frontal bone

Parietal foramen

Parietal eminence

Superior Temporal Line

Inferior Temporal Line

Articulates with occipital bone

TEMPORALIS

With temporal squama

With sphenoid

With mastoid portion of temporal bone

Fig. 147.—Left parietal bone.   Outer surface

The Parietal Bone (Os Parietale).

The **parietal bones** form, by their union, the sides and roof of the cranium. Each bone is irregularly quadrilateral in form, and has two surfaces, four borders, and four angles.

Surfaces.—The **external surface** (Fig. 147) is convex, smooth, and marked near the center by an eminence, the **parietal eminence** (*tuber parietale*), which indicates the point where ossification commenced. Crossing the middle of the bone in an arched direction are two curved lines, the **superior** and **inferior temporal lines**; the former gives attachment to the temporal fascia, and the latter indicates the upper limit of the muscular origin of the Temporalis. Above these lines the bone is covered by the galea aponeurotica; below them it forms part of the temporal fossa, and affords attachment to the Temporalis muscle. At the back part and close to the upper or sagittal border is the **parietal foramen**, which transmits a vein to the superior sagittal sinus, and sometimes a small branch of the occipital artery; it is not constantly present, and its size varies considerably.

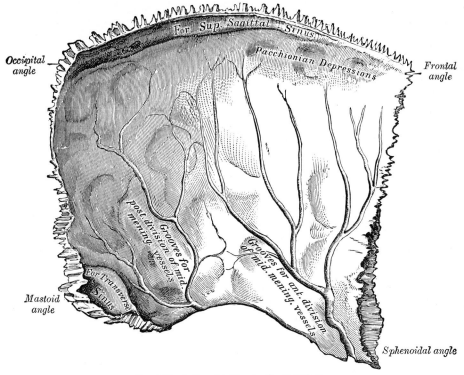

Fig. 148.—Left parietal bone. Inner surface.

The **internal surface** (Fig. 148) is concave; it presents depressions corresponding to the cerebral convolutions, and numerous furrows for the ramifications of the middle meningeal vessels; the latter run upward and backward from the sphenoidal angle, and from the central and posterior part of the squamous border. Along the upper margin is a shallow groove, which, together with that on the opposite parietal, forms a channel, the **sagittal sulcus**, for the superior sagittal sinus; the edges of the sulcus afford attachment to the falx cerebri. Near the groove are several depressions, best marked in the skulls of old persons, for the **arachnoid granulations** (*Pacchionian bodies*). In the groove is the internal opening of the parietal foramen when that aperture exists.

Borders.—The **sagittal border**, the longest and thickest, is dentated and articulates with its fellow of the opposite side, forming the sagittal suture. The **squamous border** is divided into three parts: of these, the anterior is thin and pointed, bevelled at the expense of the outer surface, and overlapped by the tip of the great wing of the sphenoid; the middle portion is arched, bevelled at the expense of the outer surface, and overlapped by the squama of the temporal; the posterior part is thick and serrated for articulation with the mastoid portion of the temporal. The **frontal border** is deeply serrated, and bevelled at the expense of the outer surface above and of the inner below; it articulates with the frontal bone, forming one-half of the **coronal suture**. The **occipital border**, deeply denticulated, articulates with the occipital, forming one-half of the **lambdoidal suture**.

Angles.—The **frontal angle** is practically a right angle, and corresponds with the point of meeting of the sagittal and coronal sutures; this point is named the **bregma**; in the fetal skull and for about a year and a half after birth this region is membranous, and is called the **anterior fontanelle**. The **sphenoidal angle**, thin and acute, is received into the interval between the frontal bone and the great wing of the sphenoid. Its inner surface is marked by a deep groove, sometimes a canal, for the anterior divisions of the middle meningeal artery. The **occipital angle** is rounded and corresponds with the point of meeting of the sagittal and lambdoidal sutures—a point which is termed the **lambda**; in the fetus this part of the skull is membranous, and is called the **posterior fontanelle**. The **mastoid angle** is truncated; it articulates with the occipital bone and with the mastoid portion of the temporal, and presents on its inner surface a broad, shallow groove which lodges part of the transverse sinus. The point of meeting of this angle with the occipital and the mastoid part of the temporal is named the **asterion**.

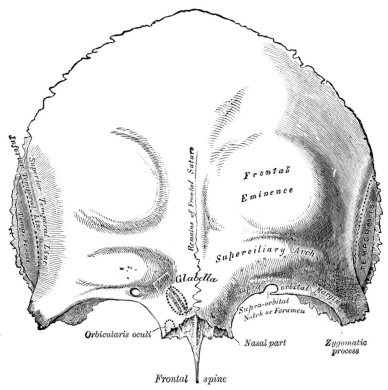

F̲ɪɢ. 149.—Frontal bone. Outer surface.

Ossification.—The parietal bone is ossified in membrane from a single center, which appears at the parietal eminence about the eighth week of fetal life. Ossification gradually extends in a radial manner from the center toward the margins of the bone; the angles are consequently the parts last formed, and it is here that the fontanelles exist. Occasionally the parietal bone is divided into two parts, upper and lower, by an antero-posterior suture.

Articulations.—The parietal articulates with *five* bones: the opposite parietal, the occipital, frontal, temporal, and sphenoid.

The Frontal Bone (Os Frontale).

The **frontal bone** resembles a cockle-shell in form, and consists of two portions —a **vertical** portion, the **squama**, corresponding with the region of the forehead; and an **orbital** or **horizontal** portion, which enters into the formation of the roofs of the orbital and nasal cavities.

Squama (*squama frontalis*).—**Surfaces.**—The **external surface** (Fig. 149) of this portion is convex and usually exhibits, in the lower part of the middle line, the remains of the **frontal** or **metopic suture;** in infancy this suture divides the bone into two, a condition which may persist throughout life. On either side of this suture, about 3 cm. above the supraorbital margin, is a rounded elevation, the **frontal eminence** (*tuber frontale*). These eminences vary in size in different individuals, are

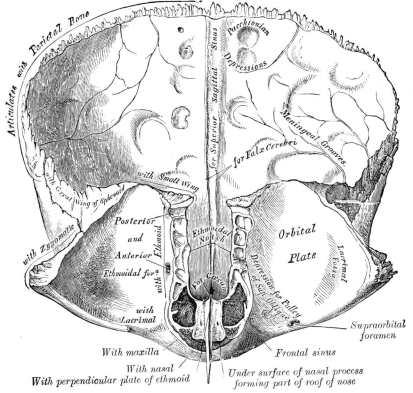

FIG. 150.—Frontal bone. Inner surface.

occasionally unsymmetrical, and are especially prominent in young skulls; the surface of the bone above them is smooth, and covered by the galea aponeurotica. Below the frontal eminences, and separated from them by a shallow groove, are two arched elevations, the **superciliary arches;** these are prominent medially, and are joined to one another by a smooth elevation named the **glabella.** They are larger in the male than in the female, and their degree of prominence depends to some extent on the size of the frontal air sinuses; prominent ridges are, however, occasionally associated with small air sinuses. Beneath each superciliary arch is a curved and prominent margin, the **supraorbital margin,** which forms the upper boundary of the base of the orbit, and separates the squama from the orbital portion of the bone. The lateral part of this margin is sharp and prominent, affording to the eye, in that situation, considerable protection from injury; the medial part is rounded. At the junction of its medial and intermediate thirds is a notch, sometimes converted into a foramen, the **supraorbital notch** or **foramen,** which transmits the supraorbital vessels and nerve. A small aperture in the upper part of the notch transmits a vein from the diploë to join the supraorbital vein. The supraorbital margin ends laterally in the **zygomatic process,** which is strong and prominent, and articulates with the zygomatic bone. Running upward and backward from this process is a well-marked line, the **temporal line,** which divides into the **upper** and **lower temporal lines,** continuous, in the articulated skull, with the corresponding lines on the parietal bone. The area below and behind the temporal line forms the anterior part of the temporal fossa, and gives origin to the Temporalis muscle. Between the supraorbital margins the squama projects downward to a level below that of the zygomatic processes; this portion is known as the **nasal part** and presents a rough, uneven interval, the **nasal notch,** which articulates on either side of the middle line with the nasal bone, and laterally with the frontal process of the maxilla and with the lacrimal. The term **nasion** is applied to the middle of the frontonasal suture. From the center of the notch the **nasal process** projects downward and forward beneath the nasal bones and frontal processes of the maxillæ, and supports the bridge of the nose. The nasal process ends below in a sharp **spine,** and on either side of this is a small grooved surface which enters into the formation of the roof of the corresponding nasal cavity. The spine forms part of the septum of the nose, articulating in front with the crest of the nasal bones and behind with the perpendicular plate of the ethmoid.

The **internal surface** (Fig. 150) of the squama is concave and presents in the upper part of the middle line a vertical groove, the **sagittal sulcus,** the edges of which unite below to form a ridge, the **frontal crest;** the sulcus lodges the superior sagittal sinus, while its margins and the crest afford attachment to the falx cerebri. The crest ends below in a small notch which is converted into a foramen, the **foramen cecum,** by articulation with the ethmoid. This foramen varies in size in different subjects, and is frequently impervious; when open, it transmits a vein from the nose to the superior sagittal sinus. On either side of the middle line the bone presents depressions for the convolutions of the brain, and numerous small furrows for the anterior branches of the middle meningeal vessels. Several small, irregular fossæ may also be seen on either side of the sagittal sulcus, for the reception of the arachnoid granulations.

Orbital or **Horizontal Part** (*pars orbitalis*).—This portion consists of two thin triangular plates, the **orbital plates,** which form the vaults of the orbits, and are separated from one another by a median gap, the **ethmoidal notch.**

Surfaces.—The **inferior surface** (Fig. 150) of each orbital plate is smooth and concave, and presents, laterally, under cover of the zygomatic process, a shallow depression, the **lacrimal fossa,** for the lacrimal gland; near the nasal part is a depression, the **fovea trochlearis,** or occasionally a small **trochlear spine,** for the attachment of the cartilaginous pulley of the Obliquus oculi superior. The **superior surface** is convex, and marked by depressions for the convolutions of the frontal lobes of the brain, and faint grooves for the meningeal branches of the ethmoidal vessels.

The **ethmoidal notch** separates the two orbital plates; it is quadrilateral, and filled, in the articulated skull, by the cribriform plate of the ethmoid. The margins of the notch present several half-cells which, when united with corresponding half-cells on the upper surface of the ethmoid, complete the ethmoidal air cells. Two grooves cross these edges transversely; they are converted into the **anterior** and **posterior ethmoidal canals** by the ethmoid, and open on the medial wall of the orbit. The anterior canal transmits the nasociliary nerve and anterior ethmoidal vessels, the posterior, the posterior ethmoidal nerve and vessels. In front of the ethmoidal notch, on either side of the frontal spine, are the openings of the **frontal**

air sinuses. These are two irregular cavities, which extend backward, upward, and lateralward for a variable distance between the two tables of the skull; they are separated from one another by a thin bony septum, which often deviates to one or other side, with the result that the sinuses are rarely symmetrical. Absent at birth, they are usually fairly well-developed between the seventh and eighth years, but only reach their full size after puberty. They vary in size in different persons, and are larger in men than in women. They are lined by mucous membrane, and each communicates with the corresponding nasal cavity by means of a passage called the **frontonasal duct.**

Borders.—The **border of the squama** is thick, strongly serrated, bevelled at the expense of the inner table above, where it rests upon the parietal bones, and at the expense of the outer table on either side, where it receives the lateral pressure of those bones; this border is continued below into a triangular, rough surface, which articulates with the great wing of the sphenoid. The **posterior borders of the orbital plates** are thin and serrated, and articulate with the small wings of the sphenoid.

Structure.—The squama and the zygomatic processes are very thick, consisting of diploic tissue contained between two compact laminæ; the diploic tissue is absent in the regions occupied by the frontal air sinuses. The orbital portion is thin, translucent, and composed entirely of compact bone; hence the facility with which instruments can penetrate the cranium through this part of the orbit; when the frontal sinuses are exceptionally large they may extend backward for a considerable distance into the orbital portion, which in such cases also consists of only two tables.

Ossification (Fig. 151).—The frontal bone is ossified in membrane from *two primary* centers, one for each half, which appear toward the end of the second month of fetal life, one above each supraorbital margin. From each of these centers ossification extends upward to form the corresponding half of the squama, and backward to form the orbital plate. The spine is ossified from a pair of *secondary* centers, on either side of the middle line; similar centers appear in the nasal part and zygomatic processes. At birth the bone consists of two pieces, separated by the frontal suture, which is usually obliterated, except at its lower part, by the eighth year, but occasionally persists throughout life. It is generally maintained that the development of the frontal sinuses begins at the end of the first or beginning of the second year, but Onodi's researches indicate that development begins at birth. The sinuses are of considerable size by the seventh or eighth year, but do not attain their full proportions until after puberty.

Articulations. — The frontal articulates with *twelve* bones: the sphenoid, the ethmoid, the two parietals, the two nasals, the two maxillæ, the two lacrimals, and the two zygomatics.

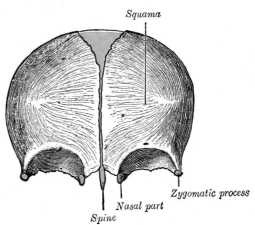

Fig. 151.—Frontal bone at birth.

The Temporal Bone (Os Temporale).

The **temporal bones** are situated at the sides and base of the skull. Each consists of five parts, viz., the **squama,** the **petrous, mastoid,** and **tympanic parts,** and the **styloid process.**

The **Squama** (*squama temporalis*).—The squama forms the anterior and upper part of the bone, and is scale-like, thin, and translucent.

Surfaces.—Its **outer surface** (Fig. 152) is smooth and convex; it affords attachment to the Temporalis muscle, and forms part of the temporal fossa; on its hinder part is a vertical groove for the middle temporal artery. A curved line, the **tem-**

poral line, or supramastoid crest, runs backward and upward across its posterior part; it serves for the attachment of the temporal fascia, and limits the origin of the Temporalis muscle. The boundary between the squama and the mastoid portion of the bone, as indicated by traces of the original suture, lies about 1 cm. below this line. Projecting from the lower part of the squama is a long, arched process, the zygomatic process. This process is at first directed lateralward, its two surfaces looking upward and downward; it then appears as if twisted inward upon itself, and runs forward, its surfaces now looking medialward and lateralward. The superior border is long, thin, and sharp, and serves for the attachment of the temporal fascia; the inferior, short, thick, and arched, has attached to it some fibers of the Masseter. The lateral surface is convex and subcutaneous; the medial is concave, and affords attachment to the Masseter. The anterior end is deeply

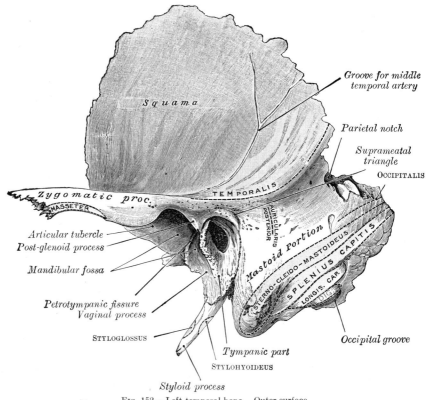

Fig. 152.—Left temporal bone. Outer surface.

serrated and articulates with the zygomatic bone. The posterior end is connected to the squama by two roots, the anterior and posterior roots. The posterior root, a prolongation of the upper border, is strongly marked; it runs backward above the external acoustic meatus, and is continuous with the temporal line. The anterior root, continuous with the lower border, is short but broad and strong; it is directed medialward and ends in a rounded eminence, the articular tubercle (eminentia articularis). This tubercle forms the front boundary of the mandibular fossa, and in the fresh state is covered with cartilage. In front of the articular tubercle is a small triangular area which assists in forming the infratemporal fossa; this area is separated from the outer surface of the squama by a ridge which is continuous behind with the anterior root of the zygomatic process, and in front, in the articulated skull, with the infratemporal crest on the great wing of the sphenoid.

Between the posterior wall of the external acoustic meatus and the posterior root of the zygomatic process is the area called the **suprameatal triangle** (Macewen), or **mastoid fossa**, through which an instrument may be pushed into the tympanic antrum. At the junction of the anterior root with the zygomatic process is a projection for the attachment of the temporomandibular ligament; and behind the anterior root is an oval depression, forming part of the mandibular fossa, for the reception of the condyle of the mandible. The **mandibular fossa** (*glenoid fossa*) is bounded, in front, by the articular tubercle; behind, by the tympanic part of the bone, which separates it from the external acoustic meatus; it is divided into two parts by a narrow slit, the **petrotympanic fissure** (*Glaserian fissure*). The anterior part, formed by the squama, is smooth, covered in the fresh state with cartilage, and articulates with the condyle of the mandible. Behind this part

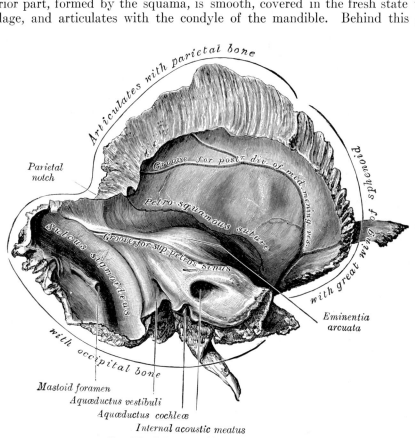

FIG. 153.—Left temporal bone. Inner surface.

of the fossa is a small conical eminence; this is the representative of a prominent tubercle which, in some mammals, descends behind the condyle of the mandible, and prevents its backward displacement. The posterior part of the mandibular fossa, formed by the tympanic part of the bone, is non-articular, and sometimes lodges a portion of the parotid gland. The petrotympanic fissure leads into the middle ear or tympanic cavity; it lodges the anterior process of the malleus, and transmits the tympanic branch of the internal maxillary artery. The chorda tympani nerve passes through a canal (*canal of Huguier*), separated from the anterior edge of the petrotympanic fissure by a thin scale of bone and situated on the lateral side of the auditory tube, in the retiring angle between the squama and the petrous portion of the temporal.

The **internal surface** of the squama (Fig. 153) is concave; it presents depressions

10

corresponding to the convolutions of the temporal lobe of the brain, and grooves for the branches of the middle meningeal vessels.

Borders.—The **superior border** is thin, and bevelled at the expense of the internal table, so as to overlap the squamous border of the parietal bone, forming with it the squamosal suture. Posteriorly, the superior border forms an angle, the **parietal notch**, with the mastoid portion of the bone. The **antero-inferior border** is thick, serrated, and bevelled at the expense of the inner table above and of the outer below, for articulation with the great wing of the sphenoid.

Mastoid Portion (*pars mastoidea*).—The mastoid portion forms the posterior part of the bone.

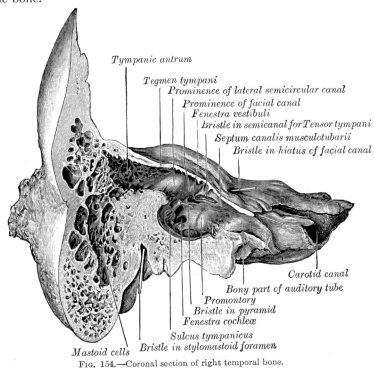

Tympanic antrum

Tegmen tympani
Prominence of lateral semicircular canal
Prominence of facial canal
Fenestra vestibuli
Bristle in semicanal for Tensor tympani
Septum canalis musculotubarii
Bristle in hiatus of facial canal

Carotid canal
Bony part of auditory tube
Promontory
Bristle in pyramid
Fenestra cochleæ
Sulcus tympanicus
Mastoid cells *Bristle in stylomastoid foramen*

Fɪɢ. 154.—Coronal section of right temporal bone.

Surfaces.—Its **outer surface** (Fig. 152) is rough, and gives attachment to the Occipitalis and Auricularis posterior. It is perforated by numerous foramina; one of these, of large size, situated near the posterior border, is termed the **mastoid foramen**; it transmits a vein to the transverse sinus and a small branch of the occipital artery to the dura mater. The position and size of this foramen are very variable; it is not always present; sometimes it is situated in the occipital bone, or in the suture between the temporal and the occipital. The mastoid portion is continued below into a conical projection, the **mastoid process**, the size and form of which vary somewhat; it is larger in the male than in the female. This process serves for the attachment of the Sternocleidomastoideus, Splenius capitis, and Longissimus capitis. On the medial side of the process is a deep groove, the **mastoid notch** (*digastric fossa*), for the attachment of the Digastricus; medial to this is a shallow furrow, the **occipital groove**, which lodges the occipital artery.

The **inner surface** of the mastoid portion presents a deep, curved groove, the **sigmoid sulcus**, which lodges part of the transverse sinus; in it may be seen the opening of the mastoid foramen. The groove for the transverse sinus is separated from the innermost of the mastoid air cells by a very thin lamina of bone, and even this may be partly deficient.

Borders.—The **superior border** of the mastoid portion is broad and serrated, for articulation with the mastoid angle of the parietal. The **posterior border,** also serrated, articulates with the inferior border of the occipital between the lateral angle and jugular process. Anteriorly the mastoid portion is fused with the descending process of the squama above; below it enters into the formation of the external acoustic meatus and the tympanic cavity.

A section of the mastoid process (Fig. 154) shows it to be hollowed out into a number of spaces, the **mastoid cells,** which exhibit the greatest possible variety as to their size and number. At the upper and front part of the process they are large and irregular and contain air, but toward the lower part they diminish in size, while those at the apex of the process are frequently quite small and contain marrow; occasionally they are entirely absent, and the mastoid is then solid throughout. In addition to these a large irregular cavity is situated at the upper and front part of the bone. It is called the **tympanic antrum,** and must be distinguished from the mastoid cells, though it communicates with them. Like the mastoid cells it is filled with air and lined by a pro'ongation of the mucous membrane of the tympanic cavity, with which it communicates. The tympanic antrum is bounded above by a thin plate of bone, the **tegmen tympani,** which separates it from the middle fossa of the base of the skull; below by the mastoid process; laterally by the squama just below the temporal line, and medially by the lateral semicircular canal of the internal ear which projects into its cavity. It opens in front into that portion of the tympanic cavity which is known as the **attic** or **epitympanic recess.** The tympanic antrum is a cavity of some considerable size at the time of birth; the mastoid air cells may be regarded as diverticula from the antrum, and begin to appear at or before birth; by the fifth year they are well-marked, but their development is not completed until toward puberty.

Petrous Portion (*pars petrosa* [*pyramis*]).—The petrous portion or **pyramid** is pyramidal and is wedged in at the base of the skull between the sphenoid and occipital. Directed medialward, forward, and a little upward, it presents for examination a base, an apex, three surfaces, and three angles, and contains, in its interior, the essential parts of the organ of hearing.

Base.—The base is fused with the internal surfaces of the squama and mastoid portion.

Apex.—The apex, rough and uneven, is received into the angular interval between the posterior border of the great wing of the sphenoid and the basilar part of the occipital and sphenoid; it presents the anterior or internal orifice of the carotid canal, and forms the postero-lateral boundary of the foramen lacerum.

Surfaces.—The **anterior surface** forms the posterior part of the middle fossa of the base of the skull, and is continuous with the inner surface of the squamous portion, to which it is united by the **petrosquamous suture,** remains of which are distinct even at a late period of life. It is marked by depressions for the convolutions of the brain, and presents six points for examination: (1) near the center, an **eminence** (*eminentia arcuata*) which indicates the situation of the superior semicircular canal; (2) in front of and a little lateral to this eminence, a depression indicating the position of the tympanic cavity: here the layer of bone which separates the tympanic from the cranial cavity is extremely thin, and is known as the **tegmen tympani;** (3) a shallow groove, sometimes double, leading lateralward and backward to an oblique opening, the **hiatus of the facial canal,** for the passage of the greater superficial petrosal nerve and the petrosal branch of the middle meningeal artery; (4) lateral to the hiatus, a smaller opening, occasionally seen, for the passage of the lesser superficial petrosal nerve; (5) near the apex of the bone, the termination of the carotid canal, the wall of which in this situation is deficient in front; (6) above this canal the shallow **trigeminal impression** for the reception of the semilunar ganglion.

The **posterior surface** (Fig. 153) forms the front part of the posterior fossa of the base of the skull, and is continuous with the inner surface of the mastoid portion. Near the center is a large orifice, the **internal acoustic meatus**, the size of which varies considerably; its margins are smooth and rounded, and it leads into a short canal, about 1 cm. in length, which runs lateralward. It transmits the facial and acoustic nerves, the nervus intermedius and the internal auditory branch of the basilar artery. The lateral end of the canal is closed by a vertical plate, which is divided by a horizontal crest, the **crista falciformis**, into two unequal portions (Fig. 155). Each portion is further subdivided by a vertical ridge into an anterior and a posterior part. In the portion beneath the crista falciformis are three sets of foramina; one group, just below the posterior part of the crest, situated in the **area cribrosa media**, consists of several small openings for the nerves to the saccule; below and behind this area is the **foramen singulare**, or opening for the nerve to the posterior semicircular duct; in front of and below the first is the **tractus spiralis foraminosus**, consisting of a number of small spirally arranged openings, which encircle the **canalis centralis cochleæ**; these openings together with this central canal transmit the nerves to the cochlea. The portion above the crista falciformis presents behind, the **area cribrosa superior**, pierced by a series of small openings, for the passage of the nerves to the utricle and the superior and lateral semicircular ducts, and, in front, the **area facialis**, with one large opening, the com-

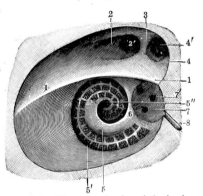

mencement of the canal for the facial nerve (**aquæductus Fallopii**). Behind the internal acoustic meatus is a small slit almost hidden by a thin plate of bone, leading to a canal, the **aquæductus vestibuli**, which transmits the ductus endolymphaticus together with a small artery and vein. Above and between these two openings is an irregular depression which lodges a process of the dura mater and transmits a small vein; in the infant this depression is represented by a large fossa, the **subarcuate fossa**, which extends backward as a blind tunnel under the superior semicircular canal.

Fig. 155.—Diagrammatic view of the fundus of the right internal acoustic meatus. (Testut.) 1 Crista falciformis. 2. Area facialis, with (2′) internal opening of the facial canal. 3. Ridge separating the area facialis from the area cribrosa superior. 4. Area cribrosa superior, with (4′) openings for nerve filaments. 5. Anterior inferior cribriform area, with (5′) the tractus spiralis foraminosus, and (5″) the canalis centralis of the cochlea. 6. Ridge separating the tractus spiralis foraminosus from the area cribrosa media. 7. Area cribrosa media, with (7′) orifices for nerves to saccule. 8. Foramen singulare.

The **inferior surface** (Fig. 156) is rough and irregular, and forms part of the exterior of the base of the skull. It presents eleven points for examination: (1) near the apex is a rough surface, quadrilateral in form, which serves partly for the attachment of the Levator veli palatini and the cartilaginous portion of the auditory tube, and partly for connection with the basilar part of the occipital bone through the intervention of some dense fibrous tissue; (2) behind this is the large circular aperture of the **carotid canal**, which ascends at first vertically, and then, making a bend, runs horizontally forward and medialward; it transmits into the cranium the internal carotid artery, and the carotid plexus of nerves; (3) medial to the opening for the carotid canal and close to its posterior border, in front of the jugular fossa, is a triangular depression; at the apex of this is a small opening, the **aquæductus cochleæ**, which lodges a tubular prolongation of the dura mater establishing a communication between the perilymphatic space and the subarachnoid space, and transmits a vein from the cochlea to join the internal jugular; (4) behind these openings is a deep depression, the **jugular fossa**, of variable depth and size in different skulls; it lodges the bulb of the internal jugular vein; (5) in the bony ridge dividing the carotid canal from the jugular fossa is the small **inferior tympanic canaliculus** for the passage of the tympanic branch of the glossopharyngeal nerve; (6) in the lateral part of the jugular fossa is the **mastoid canaliculus** for the entrance of the auricular branch of the vagus nerve; (7) behind the jugular fossa is a quadrilateral area, the **jugular surface**, covered with cartilage in the fresh state, and articulating with the jugular process of the occipital bone; (8) extending backward from the carotid canal is the **vaginal process**, a sheath-like plate of bone, which divides behind into two laminæ; the lateral lamina is continuous with the tympanic part of the bone, the medial with the lateral margin of the jugular surface; (9) between these laminæ is the **styloid process**, a sharp spine, about 2.5 cm. in length; (10) between the styloid and mastoid processes is the **stylomastoid foramen;** it is the termination of the facial canal, and transmits the facial nerve and stylomastoid artery; (11) situated between the tympanic portion and the mastoid process is the tympanomastoid fissure, for the exit of the auricular branch of the vagus nerve.

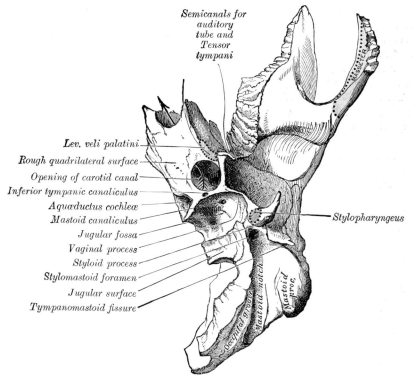

FIG. 156.—Left temporal bone. Inferior surface.

Angles.—The **superior angle,** the longest, is grooved for the superior petrosal sinus, and gives attachment to the tentorium cerebelli; at its medial extremity is a notch, in which the trigeminal nerve lies. The **posterior angle** is intermediate in length between the superior and the anterior. Its medial half is marked by a sulcus, which forms, with a corresponding sulcus on the occipital bone, the channel for the inferior petrosal sinus. Its lateral half presents an excavation —the **jugular fossa**—which, with the jugular notch on the occipital, forms the **jugular foramen;** an eminence occasionally projects from the center of the fossa, and divides the foramen into two. The **anterior angle** is joined to the squama by a suture (*petrosquamous*), the remains of which are more or less distinct; it also articulates with the sphenoid. At the angle of junction of the petrous part and the squama are two canals, one above the other, and separated by a thin plate of bone, the **septum canalis musculotubarii** (*processus cochleariformis*); both canals lead into the tympanic cavity. The upper one (*semicanalis m. tensoris tympani*) transmits the Tensor tympani, the lower one (*semicanalis tubæ auditivæ*) forms the bony part of the auditory tube.

The tympanic cavity, auditory ossicles, and internal ear, are described with the organ of hearing.

Tympanic Part (*pars tympanica*).—The tympanic part is a curved plate of bone lying below the squama and in front of the mastoid process.

Surfaces.—Its **postero-superior surface** is concave, and forms the anterior wall, the floor, and part of the posterior wall of the bony external acoustic meatus. Medially, it presents a narrow furrow, the **tympanic sulcus**, for the attachment of the tympanic membrane. Its **antero-inferior surface** is quadrilateral and slightly concave; it constitutes the posterior boundary of the mandibular fossa, and is in contact with the retromandibular part of the parotid gland

Borders.—Its **lateral border** is free and rough, and gives attachment to the cartilaginous part of the external acoustic meatus. Internally, the tympanic part is fused with the petrous portion, and appears in the retreating angle between it and the squama, where it lies below and lateral to the orifice of the auditory tube. Posteriorly, it blends with the squama and mastoid part, and forms the anterior boundary of the tympanomastoid fissure. Its **upper border** fuses laterally with the back of the postglenoid process, while medially it bounds the petrotympanic fissure. The medial part of the **lower border** is thin and sharp; its lateral part splits to enclose the root of the styloid process, and is therefore named the **vaginal process.** The central portion of the tympanic part is thin, and in a considerable percentage of skulls is perforated by a hole, the **foramen of Huschke.**

The **external acoustic meatus** is nearly 2 cm. long and is directed inward and slightly forward: at the same time it forms a slight curve, so that the floor of the canal is convex upward. In sagittal section it presents an oval or elliptical shape with the long axis directed downward and slightly backward. Its anterior wall and floor and the lower part of its posterior wall are formed by the tympanic part; the roof and upper part of the posterior wall by the squama. Its inner end is closed, in the recent state, by the tympanic membrane; the upper limit of its outer orifice is formed by the posterior root of the zygomatic process, immediately below which there is sometimes seen a small spine, the **suprameatal spine,** situated at the upper and posterior part of the orifice.

Styloid Process (*processus styloideus*).—The styloid process is slender, pointed, and of varying length; it projects downward and forward, from the under surface of the temporal bone. Its proximal part (*tympanohyal*) is ensheathed by the vaginal process of the tympanic portion, while its distal part (*stylohyal*) gives attachment to the stylohyoid and stylomandibular ligaments, and to the Styloglossus, Stylohyoideus, and Stylopharyngeus muscles. The stylohyoid ligament extends from the apex of the process to the lesser cornu of the hyoid bone, and in some instances is partially, in others completely, ossified.

Structure.—The structure of the squama is like that of the other cranial bones: the mastoid portion is spongy, and the petrous portion dense and hard.

Ossification.—The temporal bone is ossified from *eight* centers, exclusive of those for the internal ear and the tympanic ossicles, viz., one for the squama including the zygomatic process, one for the tympanic part, four for the petrous and mastoid parts, and two for the styloid process. Just before the close of fetal life (Fig. 157) the temporal bone consists of three principal parts: 1. The *squama* is ossified in membrane from a single nucleus, which appears near the root of the zygomatic process about the second month. 2. The *petromastoid* part is developed from four centers, which make their appearance in the cartilaginous ear capsule about the fifth or sixth month. One (*proötic*) appears in the neighborhood of the eminentia arcuata, spreads in front and above the internal acoustic meatus and extends to the apex of the bone; it forms part of the cochlea, vestibule, superior semicircular canal, and medial wall of the tympanic cavity. A second (*opisthotic*) appears at the promontory on the medial wall of the tympanic cavity and surrounds the fenestra cochleæ; it forms the floor of the tympanic cavity and vestibule, surrounds the carotid canal, invests the lateral and lower part of the cochlea, and spreads medially below the internal acoustic meatus. A third (*pterotic*) roofs in the tympanic cavity and antrum; while the fourth (*epiotic*) appears near the posterior semicircular canal and extends to form the mastoid process (Vrolik). 3. The *tympanic ring* is an incomplete circle, in the concavity of which is a groove, the tympanic sulcus, for the attachment of the circumference of the tympanic membrane. This ring expands to form the tympanic part, and is ossified in membrane from a single center which appears about the third month. The *styloid process* is developed from the proximal part of the cartilage of the second branchial or hyoid arch by two centers: one for the proximal part, the *tympanohyal*, appears before birth; the other, comprising the rest of the process, is named the *stylohyal*, and does not appear until after birth. The tympanic ring unites with the squama shortly before birth; the petromastoid part and squama join during the first year, and the tympanohyal portion of the styloid process about the same time (Figs. 158, 159). The stylohyal does not unite with the rest of the bone until after puberty, and in some skulls never at all.

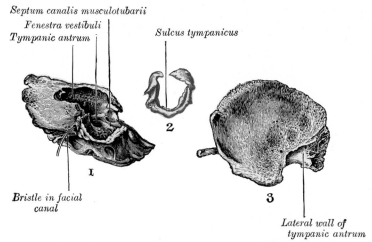

Septum canalis musculotubarii
Fenestra vestibuli
Tympanic antrum

Sulcus tympanicus

2

1

Bristle in facial canal

3

Lateral wall of tympanic antrum

Fig. 157.—The three principal parts of the temporal bone at birth. 1. Outer surface of petromastoid part. 2. Outer surface of tympanic ring. 3. Inner surface of squama.

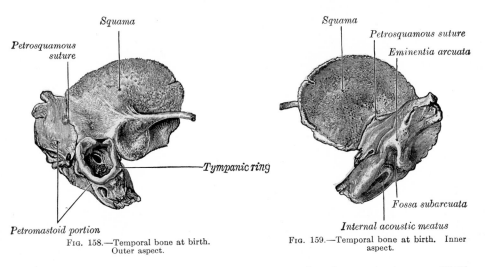

Squama

Petrosquamous suture

Squama

Petrosquamous suture

Eminentia arcuata

Tympanic ring

Fossa subarcuata

Petromastoid portion

Fig. 158.—Temporal bone at birth. Outer aspect.

Internal acoustic meatus

Fig. 159.—Temporal bone at birth. Inner aspect.

The chief subsequent changes in the temporal bone apart from increase in size are: (1) The tympanic ring extends outward and backward to form the tympanic part. This extension does not, however, take place at an equal rate all around the circumference of the ring, but occurs most rapidly on its anterior and posterior portions, and these outgrowths meet and blend, and thus, for a time, there exists in the floor of the meatus a foramen, the *foramen of Huschke;* this foramen is usually closed about the fifth year, but may persist throughout life. (2) The mandibular fossa is at first extremely shallow, and looks lateralward as well as downward; it becomes deeper and is ultimately directed downward. Its change in direction is accounted for as follows. The part of the squama which forms the fossa lies at first below the level of the zygomatic process. As, however, the base of the skull increases in width, this lower part of the squama is directed hori-zontally inward to contribute to the middle fossa of the skull, and its surfaces therefore come to look upward and downward; the attached portion of the zygomatic process also becomes everted, and projects like a shelf at right angles to the squama. (3) The mastoid portion is at first quite flat, and the stylomastoid foramen and rudimentary styloid process lie immediately behind the tympanic ring. With the development of the air cells the outer part of the mastoid portion grows downward and forward to form the mastoid process, and the styloid process and stylomastoid foramen now come to lie on the under surface. The descent of the foramen is necessarily accompanied by a corresponding lengthening of the facial canal. (4) The downward and forward growth of the mastoid process also pushes forward the tympanic part, so that the portion of it which formed the original floor of the meatus and contained the foramen of Huschke is ultimately found in the anterior wall. (5) The fossa subarcuata becomes filled up and almost obliterated.

Articulations.—The temporal articulates with *five* bones: occipital, parietal, sphenoid, mandible, and zygomatic.

The Sphenoid Bone (Os Sphenoidale).

The **sphenoid bone** is situated at the base of the skull in front of the temporals and basilar part of the occipital. It somewhat resembles a bat with its wings extended, and is divided into a median portion or body, two great and two small wings extending outward from the sides of the body, and two pterygoid processes which project from it below.

Body (*corpus sphenoidale*).—The body, more or less cubical in shape, is hollowed out in its interior to form two large cavities, the **sphenoidal air sinuses**, which are separated from each other by a septum.

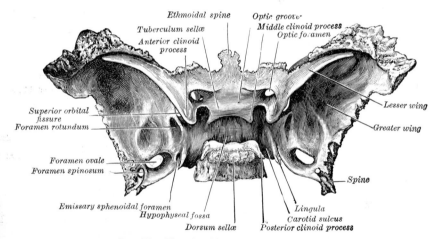

Fig. 160.—The sphenoid bone. Superior aspect.

Surfaces.—The **superior surface** of the body (Fig. 160) presents in front a promi-nent spine, the **ethmoidal spine**, for articulation with the cribriform plate of the ethmoid; behind this is a smooth surface slightly raised in the middle line, and grooved on either side for the olfactory lobes of the brain. This surface is bounded behind by a ridge, which forms the anterior border of a narrow, transverse groove, the **chiasmatic groove** (*optic groove*), above and behind which lies the optic chiasma; the groove ends on either side in the **optic foramen**, which transmits the optic nerve and ophthalmic artery into the orbital cavity. Behind the chiasmatic groove is an elevation, the **tuberculum sellæ**; and still more posteriorly, a deep depression, the **sella turcica**, the deepest part of which lodges the hypophysis cerebri and is known as the **fossa hypophyseos**. The anterior boundary of the sella turcica is completed by two small eminences, one on either side, called the **middle clinoid processes**, while the posterior boundary is formed by a square-shaped plate of bone, the **dorsum sellæ**, ending at its superior angles in two tubercles, the **posterior clinoid processes**, the size and form of which vary considerably in different individuals. The posterior clinoid processes deepen the sella turcica, and give attachment to the tentorium cerebelli. On either side of the dorsum sellæ is a notch for the passage of the abducent nerve, and below the notch a sharp process, the **petrosal process**, which articulates with the apex of the petrous portion of the temporal bone, and forms the medial boundary of the foramen lacerum. Behind the dorsum sellæ is a shallow depression, the **clivus**, which slopes obliquely backward, and is continuous with the groove on the basilar portion of the occipital bone; it supports the upper part of the pons.

The **lateral surfaces** of the body are united with the great wings and the medial pterygoid plates. Above the attachment of each great wing is a broad groove, curved something like the italic letter *f;* it lodges the internal carotid artery and the cavernous sinus, and is named the **carotid groove**. Along the posterior part of the lateral margin of this groove, in the angle between the body and great wing, is a ridge of bone, called the **lingula**.

The **posterior surface**, quadrilateral in form (Fig. 161), is joined, during infancy and adolescence, to the basilar part of the occipital bone by a plate of cartilage. Between the eighteenth and twenty-fifth years this becomes ossified, ossification commencing above and extending downward.

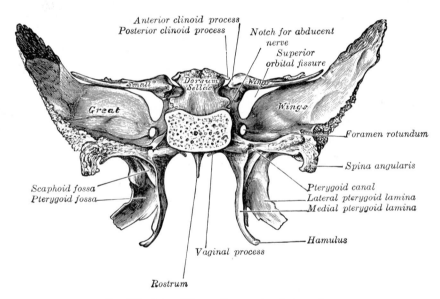

Fig. 161.—Sphenoid bone. Upper and posterior surfaces.

The **anterior surface** of the body (Fig. 162) presents, in the middle line, a vertical crest, the **sphenoidal crest**, which articulates with the perpendicular plate of the ethmoid, and forms part of the septum of the nose. On either side of the crest is an irregular opening leading into the corresponding **sphenoidal air sinus**. These sinuses are two large, irregular cavities hollowed out of the interior of the body of the bone, and separated from one another by a bony septum, which is commonly bent to one or the other side. They vary considerably in form and size, are seldom symmetrical, and are often partially subdivided by irregular bony laminæ. Occasionally, they extend into the basilar part of the occipital nearly as far as the foramen magnum. They begin to be developed before birth, and are of a considerable size by the age of six. They are partially closed, in front and below, by two thin, curved plates of bone, the **sphenoidal conchæ** (see page 156), leaving in the articulated skull a round opening at the upper part of each sinus by which it communicates with the upper and back part of the nasal cavity and occasionally with the posterior ethmoidal air cells. The lateral margin of the anterior surface is serrated, and articulates with the lamina papyracea of the ethmoid, completing the posterior ethmoidal cells; the lower margin articulates with the orbital process of the palatine bone, and the upper with the orbital plate of the frontal bone.

The **inferior surface** presents, in the middle line, a triangular spine, the **sphenoidal rostrum**, which is continuous with the sphenoidal crest on the anterior surface, and is received in a deep fissure between the alæ of the vomer. On either side of the rostrum is a projecting lamina, the **vaginal process**, directed medialward from the base of the medial pterygoid plate, with which it will be described.

The Great Wings (*alæ magnæ*).—The great wings, or **ali-sphenoids**, are two strong processes of bone, which arise from the sides of the body, and are curved upward, lateralward, and backward; the posterior part of each projects as a triangular process which fits into the angle between the squama and the petrous portion of the temporal and presents at its apex a downwardly directed process, the **spina angularis** (*sphenoidal spine*).

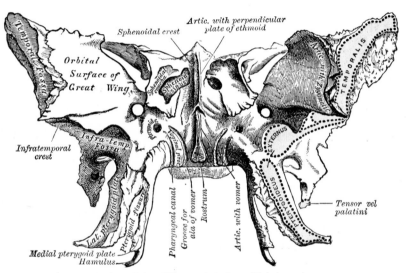

F<small>IG</small>. 162.—Sphenoid bone. Anterior and inferior surfaces.

Surfaces.—The **superior** or **cerebral surface** of each great wing (Fig. 160) forms part of the middle fossa of the skull; it is deeply concave, and presents depressions for the convolutions of the temporal lobe of the brain. At its anterior and medial part is a circular aperture, the **foramen rotundum**, for the transmission of the maxillary nerve. Behind and lateral to this is the **foramen ovale**, for the transmission of the mandibular nerve, the accessory meningeal artery, and sometimes the lesser superficial petrosal nerve. Medial to the foramen ovale, a small aperture, the **foramen Vesalii**, may occasionally be seen opposite the root of the pterygoid process; it opens below near the scaphoid fossa, and transmits a small vein from the cavernous sinus. Lastly, in the posterior angle, near to and in front of the spine, is a short canal, sometimes double, the **foramen spinosum**, which transmits the middle meningeal vessels and a recurrent branch from the mandibular nerve. The lesser superficial petrosal nerve sometimes passes through a special canal (*canaliculus innominatus* of Arnold) situated medial to the foramen spinosum.

The **lateral surface** (Fig. 124) is convex, and divided by a transverse ridge, the **infratemporal crest**, into two portions. The superior or temporal portion, convex from above downward, concave from before backward, forms a part of the temporal fossa, and gives attachment to the Temporalis; the inferior or infratemporal, smaller in size and concave, enters into the formation of the infratemporal fossa, and, together with the infratemporal crest, affords attachment to the Pterygoideus externus. It is pierced by the foramen ovale and foramen spinosum, and at its posterior part is the spina angularis, which is frequently grooved on its medial surface for the chorda tympani nerve. To the spina angularis are attached the sphenomandibular ligament and the Tensor veli palatini. Medial to the anterior extremity of the infratemporal crest is a triangular process which serves to increase the attachment of the Pterygoideus externus; extending downward and medialward from this process on to the front part of the lateral pterygoid plate is a ridge which forms the anterior limit of the infratemporal surface, and, in the articulated skull, the posterior boundary of the pterygomaxillary fissure.

The **orbital surface** of the great wing (Fig. 162), smooth, and quadrilateral in shape, is directed forward and medialward and forms the posterior part of the lateral wall of the orbit. Its upper serrated edge articulates with the orbital plate of the frontal. Its inferior rounded border forms the postero-lateral boundary of the inferior orbital fissure. Its medial sharp margin forms the lower boundary of the superior orbital fissure and has projecting from about its center a little tubercle which gives attachment to the inferior head of the Rectus lateralis oculi; at the upper part of this margin is a notch for the transmission of a recurrent branch of the lacrimal artery. Its lateral margin is serrated and articulates with the zygomatic bone. Below the medial end of the superior orbital fissure is a grooved surface, which forms the posterior wall of the pterygopalatine fossa, and is pierced by the foramen rotundum.

Margin (Fig. 160).—Commencing from behind, that portion of the circumference of the great wing which extends from the body to the spine is irregular. Its medial half forms the anterior boundary of the foramen lacerum, and presents the posterior aperture of the pterygoid canal for the passage of the corresponding nerve and artery. Its lateral half articulates, by means of a synchondrosis, with the petrous portion of the temporal, and between the two bones on the under surface of the skull, is a furrow, the **sulcus tubæ**, for the lodgement of the cartilaginous part of the auditory tube. In front of the spine the circumference presents a concave, serrated edge, bevelled at the expense of the inner table below, and of the outer table above, for articulation with the temporal squama. At the tip of the great wing is a triangular portion, bevelled at the expense of the internal surface, for articulation with the sphenoidal angle of the parietal bone; this region is named the **pterion**. Medial to this is a triangular, serrated surface, for articulation with the frontal bone; this surface is continuous medially with the sharp edge, which forms the lower boundary of the superior orbital fissure, and laterally with the serrated margin for articulation with the zygomatic bone.

The Small Wings (*alæ parvæ*).—The small wings or **orbito-sphenoids** are two thin triangular plates, which arise from the upper and anterior parts of the body, and, projecting lateralward, end in sharp points (Fig. 160).

Surfaces.—The **superior surface** of each is flat, and supports part of the frontal lobe of the brain. The **inferior surface** forms the back part of the roof of the orbit, and the upper boundary of the **superior orbital fissure.** This fissure is of a triangular form, and leads from the cavity of the cranium into that of the orbit: it is bounded *medially* by the body; *above*, by the small wing; *below*, by the medial margin of the orbital surface of the great wing; and is completed *laterally* by the frontal bone. It transmits the oculomotor, trochlear, and abducent nerves, the three branches of the ophthalmic division of the trigeminal nerve, some filaments from the cavernous plexus of the sympathetic, the orbital branch of the middle meningeal artery, a recurrent branch from the lacrimal artery to the dura mater, and the ophthalmic vein.

Borders.—The **anterior border** is serrated for articulation with the frontal bone. The **posterior border,** smooth and rounded, is received into the lateral fissure of the brain; the medial end of this border forms the **anterior clinoid process,** which gives attachment to the tentorium cerebelli; it is sometimes joined to the middle clinoid process by a spicule of bone, and when this occurs the termination of the groove for the internal carotid artery is converted into a foramen (*carotico-clinoid*). The small wing is connected to the body by two roots, the upper thin and flat, the lower thick and triangular; between the two roots is the **optic foramen,** for the transmission of the optic nerve and ophthalmic artery.

Pterygoid Processes (*processus pterygoidei*).—The pterygoid processes, one on either side, descend perpendicularly from the regions where the body and great wings unite. Each process consists of a medial and a lateral plate, the upper parts of which are fused anteriorly; a vertical sulcus, the **pterygopalatine groove,** descends on the front of the line of fusion. The plates are separated below by an angular cleft, the **pterygoid fissure,** the margins of which are rough for articulation with the pyramidal process of the palatine bone. The two plates diverge behind and enclose between them a V-shaped fossa, the **pterygoid fossa,** which contains the Pterygoideus internus and Tensor veli palatini. Above this fossa is a small, oval, shallow depression, the **scaphoid fossa,** which gives origin to the Tensor veli palatini. The anterior surface of the pterygoid process is broad and triangular near its root, where it forms the posterior wall of the pterygopalatine fossa and presents the anterior orifice of the pterygoid canal.

Lateral Pterygoid Plate.—The **lateral pterygoid plate** is broad, thin, and everted; its **lateral surface** forms part of the medial wall of the infratemporal fossa, and gives attachment to the Pterygoideus externus; its **medial surface** forms part of the pterygoid fossa, and gives attachment to the Pterygoideus internus.

Medial Pterygoid Plate.—The medial pterygoid plate is narrower and longer than the lateral; it curves lateralward at its lower extremity into a hook-like process, the **pterygoid hamulus,** around which the tendon of the Tensor veli palatini glides. The **lateral surface** of this plate forms part of the pterygoid fossa, the **medial surface** constitutes the lateral boundary of the choana or posterior aperture of the corresponding nasal cavity. Superiorly the medial plate is prolonged on to the under surface of the body as a thin lamina, named the **vaginal process,** which articulates in front with the sphenoidal process of the palatine and behind this with the ala of the vomer. The angular prominence between the posterior margin of the vaginal process and the medial border of the scaphoid fossa is named the **pterygoid tubercle,** and immediately above this is the posterior opening of the pterygoid canal. On the under surface of the vaginal process is a furrow, which is converted into a canal by the sphenoidal process of the palatine bone, for the transmission of the pharyngeal branch of the internal maxillary artery and the pharyngeal nerve from the sphenopalatine ganglion. The pharyngeal aponeurosis is attached to the entire length of the posterior edge of the medial plate, and the Constrictor pharyngis superior takes origin from its lower third. Projecting backward from near the middle of the posterior edge of this plate is an angular process, the **processus tubarius,** which supports the pharyngeal end of the auditory tube. The anterior margin of the plate articulates with the posterior border of the vertical part of the palatine bone.

The Sphenoidal Conchæ (*conchæ sphenoidales; sphenoidal turbinated processes*) —The sphenoidal conchæ are two thin, curved plates, situated at the anterior and lower part of the body of the sphenoid. An aperture of variable size exists in the anterior wall of each, and through this the sphenoidal sinus opens into the nasal cavity. Each is irregular in form, and tapers to a point behind, being broader and thinner in front. Its upper surface is concave, and looks toward the cavity of the sinus; its under surface is convex, and forms part of the roof of the corresponding nasal cavity. Each bone articulates in front with the ethmoid, laterally with the palatine; its pointed posterior extremity is placed above the vomer, and is received between the root of the pterygoid process laterally and the rostrum of the sphenoid medially. A small portion of the sphenoidal concha sometimes enters into the formation of the medial wall of the orbit, between the lamina papyracea of the ethmoid in front, the orbital plate of the palatine below, and the frontal bone above.

Ossification.—Until the seventh or eighth month of fetal life the body of the sphenoid consists of two parts, viz., one in front of the tuberculum sellæ, the *presphenoid*, with which the small wings are continuous; the other, comprising the sella turcica and dorsum sellæ, the *postsphenoid*, with which are associated the great wings, and pterygoid processes. The greater part of the bone is ossified in cartilage. There are fourteen centers in all, *six* for the presphenoid and *eight* for the postsphenoid.

Presphenoid.—About the ninth week of fetal life an ossific center appears for each of the small wings (orbitosphenoids) just lateral to the optic foramen; shortly afterward two nuclei appear in the presphenoid part of the body. The sphenoidal conchæ are each developed from

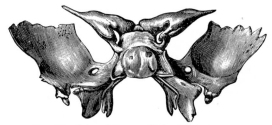

Fig. 163.—Sphenoid bone at birth. Posterior aspect.

four centers which make their appearance about the fifth month; at birth they consist of small triangular laminæ, and it is not until the third year that they become hollowed out and cone-shaped; about the fourth year they fuse with the labyrinths of the ethmoid, and between the ninth and twelfth years they unite with the sphenoid.

Postsphenoid.—The first ossific nuclei are those for the great wings (ali-sphenoids). One makes its appearance in each wing between the foramen rotundum and foramen ovale about the eighth week. The orbital plate and that part of the sphenoid which is found in the temporal fossa, as well as the lateral pterygoid plate, are ossified in membrane (Fawcett). Soon after, the centers for the postsphenoid part of the body appear, one on either side of the sella turcica, and become blended together about the middle of fetal life. Each medial pterygoid plate (with the exception of its hamulus) is ossified in membrane, and its center probably appears about the ninth or tenth week; the hamulus becomes chondrified during the third month, and almost at once undergoes ossification. The medial joins the lateral pterygoid plate about the six month. About the fourth month a center appears for each lingula and speedily joins the rest of the bone.

The presphenoid is united to the postsphenoid about the eighth month, and at birth the bone is in three pieces (Fig. 163): a central, consisting of the body and small wings, and two lateral, each comprising a great wing and pterygoid process. In the first year after birth the great wings and body unite, and the small wings extend inward above the anterior part of the body, and, meeting with each other in the middle line, form an elevated smooth surface, termed the *jugum sphenoidale*. By the twenty-fifth year the sphenoid and occipital are completely fused. Between the pre- and postsphenoid there are occasionally seen the remains of a canal, the *canalis craniopharyngeus*, through which, in early fetal life, the hypophyseal diverticulum of the buccal ectoderm is transmitted.

The sphenoidal sinuses are present as minute cavities at the time of birth, but do not attain their full size until after puberty.

Intrinsic Ligaments of the Sphenoid.—The more important of these are: the *pterygospinous*, stretching between the spina angularis and the lateral pterygoid plate (see *cervical fascia*); the *interclinoid*, a fibrous process joining the anterior to the posterior clinoid process; and the *caroticoclinoid*, connecting the anterior to the middle clinoid process. These ligaments occasionally ossify.

Articulations.—The sphenoid articulates with *twelve* bones: four single, the vomer, ethmoid, frontal, and occipital; and four paired, the parietal, temporal, zygomatic, and palatine. It also sometimes articulates with the tuberosity of the maxilla.

The Ethmoid Bone (Os Ethmoidale).

The **ethmoid bone** is exceedingly light and spongy, and cubical in shape; it is situated at the anterior part of the base of the cranium, between the two orbits, at the roof of the nose, and contributes to each of these cavities. It consists of four parts: a **horizontal** or **cribriform plate**, forming part of the base of the cranium; a **perpendicular plate**, constituting part of the nasal septum; and two **lateral masses** or **labyrinths**.

Cribriform Plate (*lamina cribrosa; horizontal lamina*).—The cribriform plate (Fig. 164) is received into the ethmoidal notch of the frontal bone and roofs in the nasal cavities. Projecting upward from the middle line of this plate is a thick, smooth, triangular process, the **crista galli,** so called from its resemblance to a cock's comb. The long thin posterior border of the crista galli serves for the attachment of the falx cerebri.

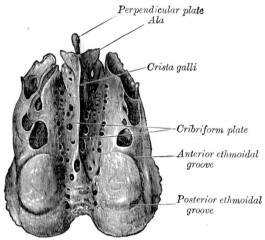

FIG. 164.—Ethmoid bone from above.

Its anterior border, short and thick, articulates with the frontal bone, and presents two small projecting **alæ**, which are received into corresponding depressions in the frontal bone and complete the foramen cecum. Its sides are smooth, and sometimes bulging from the presence of a small air sinus in the interior. On either side of the crista galli, the cribriform plate is narrow and deeply grooved; it supports the olfactory bulb and is perforated by foramina for the passage of the olfactory nerves. The foramina in the middle of the groove are small and transmit the nerves to the roof of the nasal cavity; those at the medial and lateral parts of the groove are larger—the former transmit the nerves to the upper part of the nasal septum, the latter those to the superior nasal concha. At the front part of the cribriform

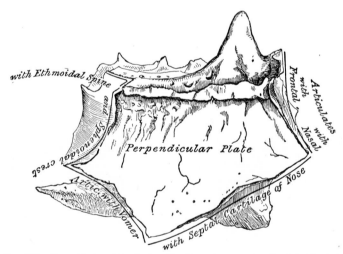

FIG. 165.—Perpendicular plate of ethmoid. Shown by removing the right labyrinth.

plate, on either side of the crista galli, is a small fissure which is occupied by a process of dura mater. Lateral to this fissure is a notch or foramen which transmits the nasociliary nerve; from this notch a groove extends backward to the anterior ethmoidal foramen.

Perpendicular Plate (*lamina perpendicularis; vertical plate*).—The perpendicular plate (Figs. 165, 166) is a thin, flattened lamina, polygonal in form, which descends from the under surface of the cribriform plate, and assists in forming the septum of the nose; it is generally deflected a little to one or other side. The **anterior border**

articulates with the spine of the frontal bone and the crest of the nasal bones. The **posterior border** articulates by its upper half with the sphenoidal crest, by its lower with the vomer. The **inferior border** is thicker than the posterior, and serves for the attachment of the septal cartilage of the nose. The surfaces of the plate are smooth, except above, where numerous grooves and canals are seen; these lead from the medial foramina on the cribriform plate and lodge filaments of the olfactory nerves.

The **Labyrinth** or **Lateral Mass** (*labyrinthus ethmoidalis*) consists of a number of thin-walled cellular cavities, the **ethmoidal cells**, arranged in three groups, *anterior*, *middle*, and *posterior*, and inter-

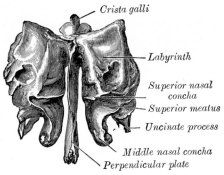

posed between two vertical plates of bone; the lateral plate forms part of the orbit, the medial, part of the corresponding nasal cavity. In the disarticulated bone many of these cells are opened into, but when the bones are articulated, they are closed in at every part, except where they open into the nasal cavity.

Surfaces.—The **upper surface** of the labyrinth (Fig. 164) presents a number of half-broken cells, the walls of which are completed, in the articulated skull, by the edges of the ethmoidal notch of the frontal bone. Crossing this surface are

Fig. 166.—Ethmoid bone from behind.

two grooves, converted into canals by articulation with the frontal; they are the **anterior** and **posterior ethmoidal canals**, and open on the inner wall of the orbit. The **posterior surface** presents large irregular cellular cavities, which are closed in by articulation with the sphenoidal concha and orbital process of the palatine. The **lateral surface** (Fig. 167) is formed of a thin, smooth, oblong plate, the **lamina papyracea** (*os planum*), which covers in the middle and posterior ethmoidal cells

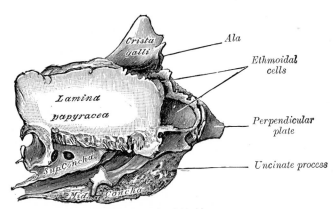

Fig. 167.—Ethmoid bone from the right side.

and forms a large part of the medial wall of the orbit; it articulates above with the orbital plate of the frontal bone, below with the maxilla and orbital process of the palatine, in front with the lacrimal, and behind with the sphenoid.

In front of the lamina papyracea are some broken air cells which are overlapped and completed by the lacrimal bone and the frontal process of the maxilla. A curved lamina, the **uncinate process**, projects downward and backward from this part of the labyrinth; it forms a small part of the medial wall of the maxillary sinus, and articulates with the ethmoidal process of the inferior nasal concha.

The **medial surface** of the labyrinth (Fig. 168) forms part of the lateral wall of the corresponding nasal cavity. It consists of a thin lamella, which descends from the under surface of the cribriform plate, and ends below in a free, convoluted margin, the **middle nasal concha.** It is rough, and marked above by numerous grooves, directed nearly vertically downward from the cribriform plate; they lodge branches of the olfactory nerves, which are distributed to the mucous membrane covering the superior nasal concha. The back part of the surface is subdivided by a narrow oblique fissure, the **superior meatus** of the nose, bounded above by a thin, curved plate, the **superior nasal concha;** the posterior ethmoidal cells open into this meatus. Below, and in front of the superior meatus, is the convex surface of the middle nasal concha; it extends along the whole length of the medial surface of the labyrinth, and its lower margin is free and thick. The lateral surface of the middle concha is concave, and assists in forming the **middle meatus** of the nose. The middle ethmoidal cells open into the central part of this meatus, and a sinuous passage, termed the **infundibulum,** extends upward and forward through the labyrinth and communicates with the anterior ethmoidal cells, and in about 50 per cent. of skulls is continued upward as the frontonasal duct into the frontal sinus.

Ossification.—The ethmoid is ossified in the cartilage of the nasal capsule by *three* centers: one for the perpendicular plate, and one for each labyrinth.

The labyrinths are first developed, ossific granules making their appearance in the region of the lamina papyracea between the fourth and fifth months of fetal life, and extending into the conchæ. At birth, the bone consists of the two labyrinths, which are small and ill-developed. During the first year after birth, the perpendicular plate and crista galli begin to ossify from a single center, and are joined to the labyrinths about the beginning of the second year. The cribriform plate is ossified partly from the perpendicular plate and partly from the labyrinths. The development of the ethmoidal cells begins during fetal life.

Articulations.—The ethmoid articulates with *fifteen* bones: four of the cranium—the frontal, the sphenoid, and the two sphenoidal conchæ; and eleven of the face—the two nasals, two maxillæ, two lacrimals, two palatines, two inferior nasal conchæ, and the vomer.

Sutural Bones.—In addition to the usual centers of ossification of the cranium, others may occur in the course of the sutures, giving rise to irregular, isolated bones, termed *sutural* or *Wormian bones.* They occur most frequently in the course of the lambdoidal suture, but are occasionally seen at the fontanelles, especially the posterior. One, the *pterion ossicle,* sometimes exists between the sphenoidal angle of the parietal and the great wing of the sphenoid. They have a tendency to be more or less symmetrical on the two sides of the skull, and vary much in size. Their number is generally limited to two or three; but more than a hundred have been found in the skull of an adult hydrocephalic subject.

THE FACIAL BONES (OSSA FACIEI).

The Nasal Bones (Ossa Nasalia).

The **nasal bones** are two small oblong bones, varying in size and form in different individuals; they are placed side by side at the middle and upper part of the face, and form, by their junction, "the bridge" of the nose (Fig. 169). Each has two surfaces and four borders.

Surfaces.—The **outer surface** (Fig. 170) is concavoconvex from above downward, convex from side to side; it is covered by the Procerus and Nasalis, and perforated about its center by a foramen, for the transmission of a small vein. The **inner surface** (Fig. 171) is concave from side to side, and is traversed from above downward, by a groove for the passage of a branch of the nasociliary nerve.

Borders.—The **superior border** is narrow, thick, and serrated for articulation with the nasal notch of the frontal bone. The **inferior border** is thin, and gives attachment to the lateral cartilage of the nose; near its middle is a notch which marks the end of the groove just referred to. The **lateral border** is serrated, bevelled at the expense of the inner surface above, and of the outer below, to articulate with the frontal process of the maxilla. The **medial border**, thicker above than below, articulates with its fellow of the opposite side, and is prolonged behind into

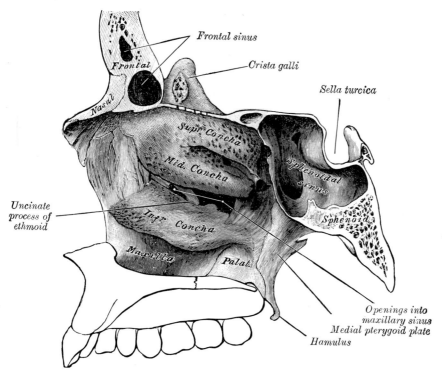

FIG. 168.—Lateral wall of nasal cavity, showing ethmoid bone in position.

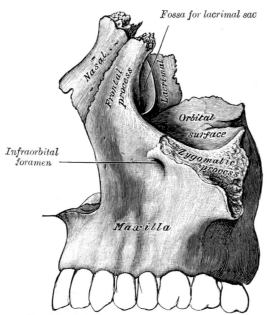

FIG. 169.—Articulation of nasal and lacrimal bones with maxilla.

a vertical crest, which forms part of the nasal septum: this crest articulates, from above downward, with the spine of the frontal, the perpendicular plate of the ethmoid, and the septal cartilage of the nose.

Ossification.—Each bone is ossified from *one* center, which appears at the beginning of the third month of fetal life in the membrane overlying the front part of the cartilaginous nasal capsule.

Articulations.—The nasal articulates with four bones: two of the cranium, the frontal and ethmoid, and two of the face, the opposite nasal and the maxilla.

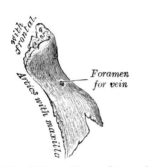

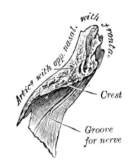

FIG. 170.—Right nasal bone. Outer surface.   FIG. 171.—Right nasal bone. Inner surface.

The Maxillæ (Upper Jaw).

The **maxillæ** are the largest bones of the face, excepting the mandible, and form, by their union, the whole of the upper jaw. Each assists in forming the boundaries of three cavities, viz., the roof of the mouth, the floor and lateral wall of the nose and the floor of the orbit; it also enters into the formation of two fossæ, the infratemporal and pterygopalatine, and two fissures, the inferior orbital and pterygomaxillary.

Each bone consists of a body and four processes—zygomatic, frontal, alveolar, and palatine.

The Body (*corpus maxillæ*).—The body is somewhat pyramidal in shape, and contains a large cavity, the **maxillary sinus** (*antrum of Highmore*). It has four surfaces—an anterior, a posterior or infratemporal, a superior or orbital, and a medial or nasal.

Surfaces.—The **anterior** or **facial surface** (Fig. 172) is directed forward and lateralward. It presents at its lower part a series of eminences corresponding to the positions of the roots of the teeth. Just above those of the incisor teeth is a depression, the **incisive fossa**, which gives origin to the Depressor alæ nasi; to the alveolar border below the fossa is attached a slip of the Orbicularis oris; above and a little lateral to it, the Nasalis arises. Lateral to the incisive fossa is another depression, the **canine fossa**; it is larger and deeper than the incisive fossa, and is separated from it by a vertical ridge, the **canine eminence**, corresponding to the socket of the canine tooth; the canine fossa gives origin to the Caninus. Above the fossa is the **infraorbital foramen**, the end of the infraorbital canal; it transmits the infraorbital vessels and nerve. Above the foramen is the margin of the orbit, which affords attachment to part of the Quadratus labii superioris. Medially, the anterior surface is limited by a deep concavity, the **nasal notch**, the margin of which gives attachment to the Dilatator naris posterior and ends below in a pointed process, which with its fellow of the opposite side forms the **anterior nasal spine**.

The **infratemporal surface** (Fig. 172) is convex, directed backward and lateralward, and forms part of the infratemporal fossa. It is separated from the anterior surface by the zygomatic process and by a strong ridge, extending upward from the socket of the first molar tooth. It is pierced about its center by the apertures of the **alveolar canals**, which transmit the posterior superior alveolar vessels and nerves. At the lower part of this surface is a rounded eminence, the **maxillary tuberosity**, especially prominent after the growth of the wisdom tooth; it is rough on its medial side for articulation with the pyramidal process of the palatine bone and in some cases articulates with the lateral pterygoid plate of the sphenoid. It gives origin to a few fibers of the Pterygoideus internus. Immediately above this is a smooth surface, which forms the anterior boundary of the pterygopalatine fossa, and presents a groove, for the maxillary nerve; this groove is directed lateralward and slightly upward, and is continuous with the infraorbital groove on the orbital surface.

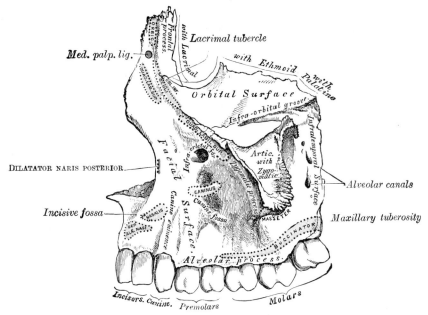

Fig. 172.—Left maxilla. Outer surface.

The **orbital surface** (Fig. 172) is smooth and triangular, and forms the greater part of the floor of the orbit. It is bounded *medially* by an irregular margin which in front presents a notch, the **lacrimal notch**; behind this notch the margin articulates with the lacrimal, the lamina papyracea of the ethmoid and the orbital process of the palatine. It is bounded *behind* by a smooth rounded edge which forms the anterior margin of the inferior orbital fissure, and sometimes articulates at its lateral extremity with the orbital surface of the great wing of the sphenoid. It is limited *in front* by part of the circumference of the orbit, which is continuous medially with the frontal process, and laterally with the zyogmatic process. Near the middle of the posterior part of the orbital surface is the **infraorbital groove**, for the passage of the infraorbital vessels and nerve. The groove begins at the middle of the posterior border, where it is continuous with that near the upper edge of the infratemporal surface, and, passing forward, ends in a canal, which subdivides into two branches. One of the canals, the **infraorbital canal**, opens just below the margin of the orbit; the other, which is smaller, runs downward in the substance of the anterior wall of the maxillary sinus, and transmits the anterior superior alveolar vessels and nerve to the front teeth of the maxilla. From the back part of the infraorbital canal, a second small canal is sometimes given off; it runs downward in the lateral wall of the sinus, and conveys the middle alveolar nerve to the premolar teeth. At the medial and forepart of the orbital surface, just lateral to the lacrimal groove, is a depression, which gives origin to the Obliquus oculi inferior.

The **nasal surface** (Fig. 173) presents a large, irregular opening leading into the maxillary sinus. At the upper border of this aperture are some broken air cel's, which, in the articulated skull, are closed in by the ethmoid and lacrimal bones. Below the aperture is a smooth concavity which forms part of the inferior meatus of the nasal cavity, and behind it is a rough surface for articulation with the perpendicular part of the palatine bone; this surface is traversed by a groove, commencing near the middle of the posterior border and running obliquely downward and forward; the groove is converted into a canal, the **pterygopalatine canal,** by the palatine bone. In front of the opening of the sinus is a deep groove, the **lacrimal groove,** which is converted into the nasolacrimal canal, by the lacrimal bone and inferior nasal concha; this canal opens into the inferior meatus of the nose and transmits the nasolacrimal duct. More anteriorly is an oblique ridge, the **conchal crest,** for articulation with the inferior nasal concha. The shallow concavity above this ridge forms part of the atrium of the middle meatus of the nose, and that below it, part of the inferior meatus.

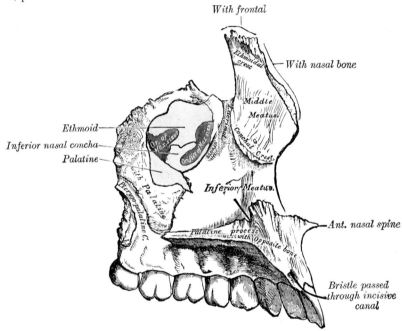

Fig. 173.—Left maxilla. Nasal surface.

The Maxillary Sinus or Antrum of Highmore (*sinus maxillaris*).—The maxillary sinus is a large pyramidal cavity, within the body of the maxilla. Its walls are thin, and correspond to the nasal, orbital, anterior and infratemporal surfaces of the body of the bone. Its **nasal wall,** presents, in the disarticulated bone, a large, irregular aperture, communicating with the nasal cavity. In the articulated skull this aperture is much reduced in size by the following bones: the uncinate process of the ethmoid above, the ethmoidal process of the inferior nasal concha below, the vertical part of the palatine behind, and a small part of the lacrimal above and in front (Figs. 173, 174); the sinus communicates with the middle meatus of the nose, generally by two small apertures left between the above-mentioned bones. In the fresh state, usually only one small opening exists, near the upper part of the cavity; the other is closed by mucous membrane. On the **posterior wall** are the **alveolar**

canals, transmitting the posterior superior alveolar vessels and nerves to the molar teeth. The floor is formed by the alveolar process of the maxilla, and, if the sinus be of an average size, is on a level with the floor of the nose; if the sinus be large it reaches below this level.

Projecting into the floor of the antrum are several conical processes, corresponding to the roots of the teeth; in some cases the floor is perforated by the fangs of the teeth. The infraorbital canal usually projects into the cavity as a well-marked ridge extending from the roof to the anterior wall; additional ridges are sometimes seen in the posterior wall of the cavity, and are caused by the alveolar canals. The size of the cavity varies in different skulls, and even on the two sides of the same skull.

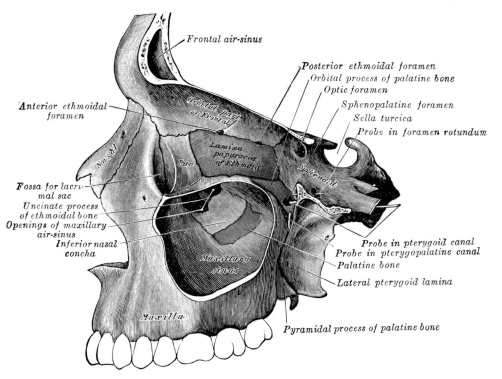

FIG. 174.—The left maxillary air-sinus. Opened from the lateral side.

The Zygomatic Process (*processus zygomaticus; malar process*).—The zygomatic process is a rough triangular eminence, situated at the angle of separation of the anterior, infratemporal and orbital surfaces. *In front* it forms part of the anterior surface; *behind,* it is concave, and forms part of the infratemporal fossa; *above,* it is rough and serrated for articulation with the zygomatic bone; while *below,* it presents the prominent arched border which marks the division between the anterior and infratemporal surfaces.

The Frontal Process (*processus frontalis; nasal process*).—The frontal process is a strong plate, which projects upward, medialward, and backward, by the side of the nose, forming part of its lateral boundary. Its *lateral surface* is smooth, continuous with the anterior surface of the body, and gives attachment to the Quadratus labii superioris, the Orbicularis oculi, and the medial palpebral ligament. Its *medial surface* forms part of the lateral wall of the nasal cavity; at its upper part is a rough, uneven area, which articulates with the ethmoid, closing in the anterior ethmoidal cells; below this is an oblique ridge, the **ethmoidal crest,** the posterior end of which articulates with the middle nasal concha, while the anterior part is termed the **agger nasi**; the crest forms the upper limit of the atrium of the middle meatus. The *upper border* articulates with the frontal bone and the *anterior* with the nasal; the *posterior border* is thick, and hollowed into a groove, which is continuous below with the lacrimal groove on the nasal surface of the body: by the articulation of the medial margin of the groove with the anterior border of the lacrimal a corresponding groove on the lacrimal is brought into continuity, and together they form the **lacrimal fossa** for the lodgement of the lacrimal sac. The lateral margin of the groove is named the **anterior lacrimal crest**, and is continuous below with the orbital margin; at its junction with the orbital surface is a small tubercle, the **lacrimal tubercle**, which serves as a guide to the position of the lacrimal sac.

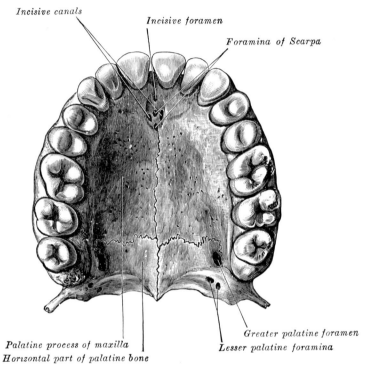

Incisive canals

Incisive foramen

Foramina of Scarpa

Greater palatine foramen
Lesser palatine foramina

Palatine process of maxilla
Horizontal part of palatine bone

Fig. 175.—The bony palate and the alveolar arch.   Inferior aspect.

The Alveolar Process (*processus alveolaris*).—The alveolar process is the thickest and most spongy part of the bone. It is broader behind than in front, and excavated into deep cavities for the reception of the teeth. These cavities are eight in number, and vary in size and depth according to the teeth they contain. That for the canine tooth is the deepest; those for the molars are the widest, and are subdivided into minor cavities by septa; those for the incisors are single, but deep and narrow. The Buccinator arises from the outer surface of this process, as far forward as the first molar tooth. When the maxillæ are articulated with each other, their alveolar processes together form the **alveolar arch;** the center of the anterior margin of this arch is named the **alveolar point.**

The Palatine Process (*processus palatinus; palatal process*).—The palatine process, thick and strong, is horizontal and projects medialward from the nasal surface of the bone. It forms a considerable part of the floor of the nose and the roof of the mouth and is much thicker in front than behind. Its *inferior surface* (Fig. 175) is concave, rough and uneven, and forms, with the palatine process of the opposite bone, the anterior three-fourths of the hard plate. It is perforated by numerous foramina for the passage of the nutrient vessels; is channelled at the back part of its lateral border by a groove, sometimes a canal, for the transmission of the descending palatine vessels and the anterior palatine nerve from the spheno-palatine ganglion; and presents little depressions for the lodgement of the palatine glands. When the two maxillæ are articulated, a funnel-shaped opening, the **incisive foramen**, is seen in the middle line, immediately behind the incisor teeth. In this opening the orifices of two lateral canals are visible; they are named the **incisive canals** or **foramina of Stenson**; through each of them passes the terminal branch of the descending palatine artery and the nasopalatine nerve. Occasionally two additional canals are present in the middle line; they are termed the **foramina of Scarpa**, and when present transmit the nasopalatine nerves, the left passing through the anterior, and the right through the posterior canal. On the under surface of the palatine process, a delicate linear suture, well seen in young skulls, may sometimes be noticed extending lateralward and forward on either side from the incisive foramen to the interval between the lateral incisor and the canine tooth. The small part in front of this suture constitutes the **premaxilla** (*os incisivum*), which in most vertebrates forms an independent bone; it includes the whole thickness of the alveolus, the corresponding part of the floor of the nose and the anterior nasal spine, and contains the sockets of the incisor teeth. The *upper surface* of the palatine process is concave from side to side, smooth, and forms the greater part of the floor of the nasal cavity. It presents, close to its medial margin, the upper orifice of the incisive canal. The *lateral border* of the process is incorporated with the rest of the bone. The *medial border* is thicker in front than behind, and is raised above into a ridge, the **nasal crest**, which, with the corresponding ridge of the opposite bone, forms a groove for the reception of the vomer. The front part of this ridge rises to a considerable height, and is named the **incisor crest**; it is prolonged forward into a sharp process, which forms, together with a similar process of the opposite bone, the **anterior nasal spine**. The *posterior border* is serrated for articulation with the horizontal part of the palatine bone.

Ossification.—The maxilla is ossified in membrane. Mall[1] and Fawcett[2] maintain that it is ossified from *two* centers only, one for the maxilla proper and one for the premaxilla. These centers appear during the sixth week of fetal life and unite in the beginning of the third month, but the suture between the two portions persists on the palate until nearly middle life. Mall states that the frontal process is developed from both centers. The maxillary sinus appears as a shallow groove on the nasal surface of the bone about the fourth month of fetal life, but does not reach its full size until after the second dentition.

FIG. 176.—Anterior surface of maxilla at birth.

FIG. 177.—Inferior surface of maxilla at birth.

Articulations.—The maxilla articulates with *nine* bones: two of the cranium, the frontal and ethmoid, and seven of the face, viz., the nasal, zygomatic, lacrimal, inferior nasal concha, palatine, vomer, and its fellow of the opposite side. Sometimes it articulates with the orbital surface, and sometimes with the lateral pterygoid plate of the sphenoid.

CHANGES PRODUCED IN THE MAXILLA BY AGE.

At birth the transverse and antero-posterior diameters of the bone are each greater than the vertical. The frontal process is well-marked and the body of the bone consists of little more than

[1] American Journal of Anatomy, 1906, vol. v.
[2] Journal of Anatomy and Physiology, 1911, vol. xlv.

the alveolar process, the teeth sockets reaching almost to the floor of the orbit. The maxillary sinus presents the appearance of a furrow on the lateral wall of the nose. In the adult the vertical diameter is the greatest, owing to the development of the alveolar process and the increase in size of the sinus. In old age the bone reverts in some measure to the infantile condition; its height is diminished, and after the loss of the teeth the alveolar process is absorbed, and the lower part of the bone contracted and reduced in thickness.

The Lacrimal Bone (Os Lacrimale).

The **lacrimal bone**, the smallest and most fragile bone of the face, is situated at the front part of the medial wall of the orbit (Fig. 179). It has two surfaces and four borders.

Surfaces.—The **lateral** or **orbital surface** (Fig. 178) is divided by a vertical ridge, the **posterior lacrimal crest**, into two parts. In front of this crest is a longitudinal groove, the **lacrimal sulcus** (*sulcus lacrimalis*), the inner margin of which unites with the frontal process of the maxilla, and the lacrimal fossa is thus completed. The upper part of this fossa lodges the lacrimal sac, the lower part, the naso-lacrimal duct. The portion behind the crest is smooth, and forms part of the medial wall of the orbit. The crest, with a part of the orbital surface immediately behind it, gives origin to the lacrimal part of the Orbicularis oculi and ends below in a small, hook-like projection, the **lacrimal hamulus**, which articulates with the lacrimal tubercle of the maxilla, and completes the upper orifice of the lacrimal canal; it sometimes exists as a separate piece, and is then called the **lesser lacrimal bone**.

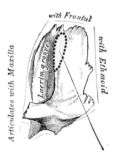

With inferior   Lacrimal part of
nasal concha   Orbicularis oculi

Fig. 178.—The left lacrimal bone.
Lateral aspect. (Enlarged.)

The **medial** or **nasal surface** presents a longitudinal furrow, corresponding to the crest on the lateral surface. The area in front of this furrow forms part of the middle meatus of the nose; that behind it articulates with the ethmoid, and completes some of the anterior ethmoidal cells.

Borders.—Of the *four borders* the **anterior** articulates with the frontal process of the maxilla; the **posterior** with the lamina papyracea of the ethmoid; the **superior** with the frontal bone. The **inferior** is divided by the lower edge of the posterior lacrimal crest into two parts: the posterior part articulates with the orbital plate of the maxilla; the anterior is prolonged downward as the **descending process**, which articulates with the lacrimal process of the inferior nasal concha, and assists in forming the canal for the nasolacrimal duct.

Ossification.—The lacrimal is ossified from a single center, which appears about the twelfth week in the membrane covering the cartilaginous nasal capsule.

Articulations.—The lacrimal articulates with *four* bones: two of the cranium, the frontal and ethmoid, and two of the face, the maxilla and the inferior nasal concha.

The Zygomatic Bone (Os Zygomaticum; Malar Bone).

The **zygomatic bone** is small and quadrangular, and is situated at the upper and lateral part of the face: it forms the prominence of the cheek, part of the lateral wall and floor of the orbit, and parts of the temporal and infratemporal fossæ (Fig. 179). It presents a malar and a temporal surface; four processes, the frontosphenoidal, orbital, maxillary, and temporal; and four borders.

Surfaces.—The **malar surface** (Fig. 180) is convex and perforated near its center by a small aperture, the **zygomaticofacial foramen**, for the passage of the zygomatico-facial nerve and vessels; below this foramen is a slight elevation, which gives origin to the Zygomaticus and the Quadratus labii superioris.

The **temporal surface** (Fig. 181), directed backward and medialward, is concave, presenting medially a rough, triangular area, for articulation with the maxilla, and laterally a smooth, concave surface, the upper part of which forms the anterior boundary of the temporal fossa, the lower a part of the infratemporal fossa. Near the center of this surface is the **zygomaticotemporal foramen** for the transmission of the zygomaticotemporal nerve.

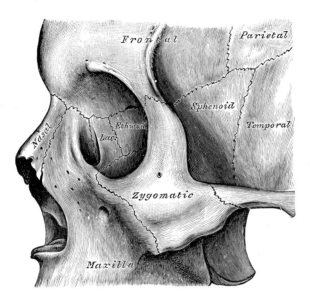

Fig. 179.—Left zygomatic bone *in situ.*

Processes.—The **frontosphenoidal process** is thick and serrated, and articulates with the zygomatic process of the frontal bone. On its orbital surface, just within the orbital margin and about 11 mm. below the zygomaticofrontal suture is a tubercle of varying size and form, but present in 95 per cent. of skulls (Whitnall[1]).

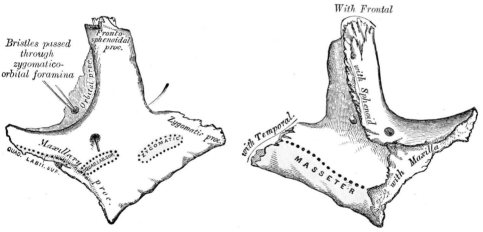

Fig. 180.—Left zygomatic bone. Malar surface.   Fig. 181.—Left zygomatic bone. Temporal surface.

The **orbital process** is a thick, strong plate, projecting backward and medialward from the orbital margin. Its *antero-medial surface* forms, by its junction with the orbital surface of the maxilla and with the great wing of the sphenoid, part of the floor and lateral wall of the orbit. On it are usually the orifices of two canals,

[1] Journal of Anatomy and Physiology, vol. **45**. The structures attached to this tubercle are: (1) the check ligament of the Rectus lateralis; (2) the lateral end of the aponeurosis of the Levator palpebræ superioris; (3) the suspensory ligament of the eye (Lockwood); and (4) the lateral extremities of the superior and inferior tarsi.

the **zygomaticoörbital foramina;** one of these canals opens into the temporal fossa, the other on the malar surface of the bone; the former transmits the zygomatico- temporal, the latter the zygomaticofacial nerve. Its *postero-lateral surface*, smooth and convex, forms parts of the temporal and infratemporal fossæ. Its *anterior margin*, smooth and rounded, is part of the circumference of the orbit. Its *superior margin*, rough, and directed horizontally, articulates with the frontal bone behind the zygomatic process Its *posterior margin* is serrated for articulation, with the great wing of the sphenoid and the orbital surface of the maxilla. At the angle of junction of the sphenoidal and maxillary portions, a short, concave, non-articular part is generally seen; this forms the anterior boundary of the inferior orbital fissure: occasionally, this non-articular part is absent, the fissure then being completed by the junction of the maxilla and sphenoid, or by the interposition of a small sutural bone in the angular interval between them. The **maxillary process** presents a rough, triangular surface which articulates with the maxilla. The **temporal process**, long, narrow, and serrated, articulates with the zygomatic process of the temporal.

Borders.—The **antero-superior** or **orbital border** is smooth, concave, and forms a considerable part of the circumference of the orbit. The **antero-inferior** or **maxillary border** is rough, and bevelled at the expense of its inner table, to articulate with the maxilla; near the orbital margin it gives origin to the Quadratus labii superioris. The **postero-superior** or **temporal border**, curved like an italic letter *f*, is continuous above with the commencement of the temporal line, and below with the upper border of the zygomatic arch; the temporal fascia is attached to it. The **postero-inferior** or **zygomatic border** affords attachment by its rough edge to the Masseter.

Ossification.—The zygomatic bone is generally described as ossifying from three centers— one for the malar and two for the orbital portion; these appear about the eighth week and fuse about the fifth month of fetal life. Mall describes it as being ossified from one center which appears just beneath and to the lateral side of the orbit. After birth, the bone is sometimes divided by a horizontal suture into an upper larger, and a lower smaller division. In some quad- rumana the zygomatic bone consists of two parts, an orbital and a malar.

Articulations.—The zygomatic articulates with *four* bones: the frontal, sphenoidal, temporal, and maxilla.

The Palatine Bone (Os Palatinum; Palate Bone).

The **palatine bone** is situated at the back part of the nasal cavity between the maxilla and the pterygoid process of the sphenoid (Fig. 182). It contributes to the walls of three cavities: the floor and lateral wall of the nasal cavity, the roof of the mouth, and the floor of the orbit; it enters into the formation of three fossæ, the **pterygopalatine, pterygoid,** and **infratemporal fossæ;** and one fissure, the **inferior orbital fissure.** The palatine bone somewhat resembles the letter L, and consists of a horizontal and a vertical part and three outstanding processes—viz., the pyramidal process, which is directed backward and lateralward from the junction of the two parts, and the orbital and sphenoidal processes, which surmount the vertical part, and are separated by a deep notch, the sphenopalatine notch.

The Horizontal Part (*pars horizontalis; horizontal plate*) (Figs. 183, 184).—The horizontal part is quadrilateral, and has two surfaces and four borders.

Surfaces.—The **superior surface**, concave from side to side, forms the back part of the floor of the nasal cavity. The **inferior surface**, slightly concave and rough, forms, with the corresponding surface of the opposite bone, the posterior fourth of the hard palate. Near its posterior margin may be seen a more or less marked transverse ridge for the attachment of part of the aponeurosis of the Tensor veli palatini.

Borders.—The **anterior border** is serrated, and articulates with the palatine process of the maxilla. The **posterior border** is concave, free. and serves for the attachment of the soft palate. Its medial end is sharp and pointed, and, when united with that of the opposite bone, forms a projecting process, the **posterior nasal spine**

for the attachment of the Musculus uvulæ. The **lateral border** is united with the lower margin of the perpendicular part, and is grooved by the lower end of the pterygopalatine canal. The **medial border**, the thickest, is serrated for articulation with its fellow of the opposite side; its superior edge is raised into a ridge,

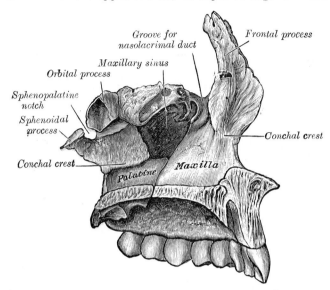

Fig. 182.—Articulation of left palatine bone with maxilla.

which, united with the ridge of the opposite bone, forms the **nasal crest** for articulation with the posterior part of the lower edge of the vomer.

The Vertical Part (*pars perpendicularis; perpendicular plate*) (Figs. 183, 184).— The vertical part is thin, of an oblong form, and presents two surfaces and four borders.

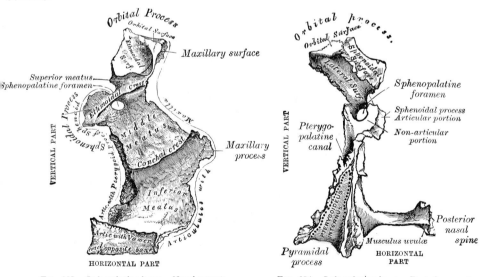

Fig. 183.—Left palatine bone. Nasal aspect. Enlarged.

Fig. 184.—Left palatine bone. Posterior aspect. Enlarged.

Surfaces.—The **nasal surface** exhibits at its lower part a broad, shallow depression, which forms part of the inferior meatus of the nose. Immediately above this is a well-marked horizontal ridge, the **conchal crest**, for articulation with the inferior nasal concha; still higher is a second broad, shallow depression, which forms part of the middle meatus, and is limited above by a horizontal crest less prominent than the inferior, the **ethmoidal crest,** for articulation with the middle nasal concha. Above the ethmoidal crest is a narrow, horizontal groove, which forms part of the superior meatus.

The **maxillary surface** is rough and irregular throughout the greater part of its extent, for articulation with the nasal surface of the maxilla; its upper and back part is smooth where it enters into the formation of the pterygopalatine fossa; it is also smooth in front, where it forms the posterior part of the medial wall of the maxillary sinus. On the posterior part of this surface is a deep vertical groove, converted into the **pterygopalatine canal,** by articulation with the maxilla; this canal transmits the descending palatine vessels, and the anterior palatine nerve.

Borders.—The **anterior border** is thin and irregular; opposite the conchal crest is a pointed, projecting lamina, the **maxillary process,** which is directed forward, and closes in the lower and back part of the opening of the maxillary sinus. The **posterior border** (Fig. 184) presents a deep groove, the edges of which are serrated for articulation with the medial pterygoid plate of the sphenoid. This border is continuous above with the sphenoidal process; below it expands into the pyramidal process. The **superior border** supports the orbital process in front and the sphenoidal process behind. These processes are separated by the **sphenopalatine notch,** which is converted into the **sphenopalatine foramen** by the under surface of the body of the sphenoid. In the articulated skull this foramen leads from the pterygopalatine fossa into the posterior part of the superior meatus of the nose, and transmits the sphenopalatine vessels and the superior nasal and nasopalatine nerves. The **inferior border** is fused with the lateral edge of the horizontal part, and immediately in front of the pyramidal process is grooved by the lower end of the pterygopalatine canal.

The Pyramidal Process or Tuberosity (*processus pyramidalis*).—The pyramidal process projects backward and lateralward from the junction of the horizontal and vertical parts, and is received into the angular interval between the lower extremities of the pterygoid plates. On its **posterior surface** is a smooth, grooved, triangular area, limited on either side by a rough articular furrow. The furrows articulate with the pterygoid plates, while the grooved intermediate area completes the lower part of the pterygoid fossa and gives origin to a few fibers of the Pterygoideus internus. The anterior part of the **lateral surface** is rough, for articulation with the tuberosity of the maxilla; its posterior part consists of a smooth triangular area which appears, in the articulated skull, between the tuberosity of the maxilla and the lower part of the lateral pterygoid plate, and completes the lower part of the infratemporal fossa. On the **base** of the pyramidal process, close to its union with the horizontal part, are the lesser palatine foramina for the transmission of the posterior and middle palatine nerves.

The Orbital Process (*processus orbitalis*).—The orbital process is placed on a higher level than the sphenoidal, and is directed upward and lateralward from the front of the vertical part, to which it is connected by a constricted neck. It presents five surfaces, which enclose an air cell. Of these surfaces, three are articular and two non-articular. The articular surfaces are: (1) the **anterior** or **maxillary,** directed forward, lateralward, and downward, of an oblong form, and rough for articulation with the maxilla; (2) the **posterior** or **sphenoidal,** directed backward, upward, and medialward; it presents the opening of the air cell, which usually communicates with the sphenoidal sinus; the margins of the opening are serrated for articulation with the sphenoidal concha; (3) the **medial** or **ethmoidal,** directed forward, articulates with the labyrinth of the ethmoid. In some cases the air cell opens on this surface of the bone and then communicates with the posterior ethmoidal cells. More rarely it opens on both surfaces, and then communicates with the posterior ethmoidal cells and the sphenoidal sinus. The non-articular surfaces are: (1) the **superior or orbital**, directed upward and lateralward; it is triangular in shape, and forms the back part of the floor of the orbit; and (2) the **lateral**, of an oblong form, directed toward the pterygopalatine fossa; it is separated from the orbital surface by a rounded border, which enters into the formation of the inferior orbital fissure.

The Sphenoidal Process (*processus sphenoidalis*).—The sphenoidal process is a thin, compressed plate, much smaller than the orbital, and directed upward and medialward. It presents three surfaces and two borders. The **superior surface** articulates with the root of the pterygoid process and the under surface of the sphenoidal concha, its medial border reaching as far as the ala of the vomer; it presents a groove which contributes to the formation of the pharyngeal canal. The **medial surface** is concave, and forms part of the lateral wall of the nasal cavity. The **lateral surface** is divided into an articular and a non-articular portion: the former is rough, for articulation with the medial pterygoid plate; the latter is smooth, and forms part of the pterygopalatine fossa. The **anterior border** forms the posterior boundary of the sphenopalatine notch. The **posterior border**, serrated at the expense of the outer table, articulates with the medial pterygoid plate.

The orbital and sphenoidal processes are separated from one another by the **sphenopalatine notch.** Sometimes the two processes are united above, and form between them a complete foramen (Fig. 183), or the notch may be crossed by one or more spicules of bone, giving rise to two or more foramina.

Ossification.—The palatine bone is ossified in membrane from a single center, which makes its appearance about the sixth or eighth week of fetal life at the angle of junction of the two parts of the bone. From this point ossification spreads medialward to the horizontal part, downward into the pyramidal process, and upward into the vertical part. Some authorities describe the bone as ossifying from four centers: one for the pyramidal process and portion of the vertical part behind the pterygopalatine groove; a second for the rest of the vertical and the horizontal parts; a third for the orbital, and a fourth for the sphenoidal process. At the time of birth the height of the vertical part is about equal to the transverse width of the horizontal part, whereas in the adult the former measures about twice as much as the latter.

Articulations.—The palatine articulates with *six* bones: the sphenoid, ethmoid, maxilla, inferior nasal concha, vomer, and opposite palatine.

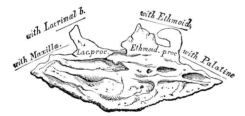

FIG. 185.—Right inferior nasal concha. Medial surface.

FIG. 186.—Right inferior nasal concha. Lateral surface.

The Inferior Nasal Concha (Concha Nasalis Inferior; Inferior Turbinated Bone).

The **inferior nasal concha** extends horizontally along the lateral wall of the nasal cavity (Fig. 168) and consists of a lamina of spongy bone, curled upon itself like a scroll. It has two surfaces, two borders, and two extremities.

The **medial surface** (Fig. 185) is convex, perforated by numerous apertures, and traversed by longitudinal grooves for the lodgement of vessels. The **lateral surface** is concave (Fig. 186), and forms part of the inferior meatus. Its **upper border** is thin, irregular, and connected to various bones along the lateral wall of the nasal cavity. It may be divided into three portions: of these, the anterior articulates with the conchal crest of the maxilla; the posterior with the conchal crest of the palatine; the middle portion presents three well-marked processes, which vary much in their size and form. Of these, the anterior or **lacrimal process** is small and pointed and is situated at the junction of the anterior fourth with the posterior three-fourths of the bone: it articulates, by its apex, with the descending process of the lacrimal bone, and, by its margins, with the groove on the back of the frontal process of the maxilla, and thus assists in forming the canal for the nasolacrimal duct. Behind this process a broad, thin plate, the **ethmoidal process**, ascends to join the uncinate process of the ethmoid; from its lower border a thin lamina, the **maxillary process**, curves downward and lateralward; it articulates with the maxilla and forms a part of the medial wall of the maxillary sinus. The **inferior border** is free, thick, and cellular in structure, more especially in the middle of the bone. Both **extremities** are more or less pointed, the posterior being the more tapering.

Ossification.—The inferior nasal concha is ossified from a single center, which appears about the fifth month of fetal life in the lateral wall of the cartilaginous nasal capsule.

Articulations.—The inferior nasal concha articulates with *four* bones: the ethmoid, maxilla, lacrimal, and palatine.

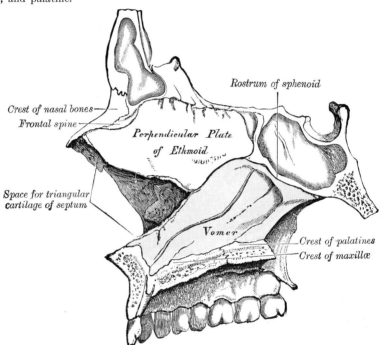

Fig. 187.—Median wall of left nasal cavity showing vomer *in situ*.

The Vomer.

The **vomer** is situated in the median plane, but its anterior portion is frequently bent to one or other side. It is thin, somewhat quadrilateral in shape, and forms the hinder and lower part of the nasal septum (Fig. 187); it has two surfaces and four borders. The **surfaces** (Fig. 188) are marked by small furrows for blood-vessels, and on each is the **nasopalatine groove**, which runs obliquely downward and forward, and lodges the nasopalatine nerve and vessels. The **superior border**, the thickest, presents a deep furrow, bounded on either side by a horizontal projecting ala of bone; the furrow receives the rostrum of the sphenoid, while the margins of the alæ articulate with the vaginal processes of the medial pterygoid plates of the sphenoid behind, and with the sphenoidal processes of the palatine bones in front. The **inferior border** articulates with the crest formed by the maxillæ and palatine bones. The **anterior border** is the longest and slopes downward and forward. Its upper half is fused with the perpendicular plate of the ethmoid; its lower half is grooved for the inferior margin of the septal cartilage of the nose. The **posterior border** is free, concave, and separates the choanæ. It is thick and bifid above, thin below.

Ossification.—At an early period the septum of the nose consists of a plate of cartilage, the *ethmovomerine cartilage.* The postero-superior part of this cartilage is ossified to form the perpendicular plate of the ethmoid; its antero-inferior portion persists as the septal cartilage, while the vomer is ossified in the membrane covering its postero-inferior part. Two ossific centers, one on either side of the middle line, appear about the eighth week of fetal life in this part of the membrane, and hence the vomer consists primarily of two lamellæ. About the third month

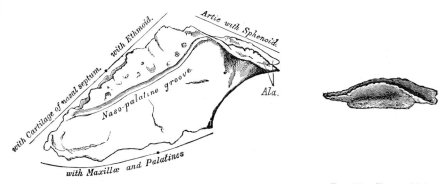

FIG. 188.—The vomer.   FIG 189.—Vomer of infant.

these unite below, and thus a deep groove is formed in which the cartilage is lodged. As growth proceeds, the union of the lamellæ extends upward and forward, and at the same time the intervening plate of cartilage undergoes absorption. By the age of puberty the lamellæ are almost completely united to form a median plate, but evidence of the bilaminar origin of the bone is seen in the everted alæ of its upper border and the groove on its anterior margin.

Articulations.—The vomer articulates with *six* bones: two of the cranium, the sphenoid and ethmoid; and four of the face, the two maxillæ and the two palatine bones; it also articulates with the septal cartilage of the nose.

THE EXTREMITIES.

The bones by which the upper and lower limbs are attached to the trunk constitute respectively the shoulder and pelvic girdles. The **shoulder girdle or girdle of the superior extremity** is formed by the scapulæ and clavicles, and is imperfect in front and behind. In front, however, it is completed by the upper end of the sternum, with which the medial ends of the clavicles articulate. Behind, it is widely imperfect, the scapulæ being connected to the trunk by muscles only. The **pelvic girdle or girdle of the inferior extremity** is formed by the hip bones, which articulate with each other in front, at the symphysis pubis. It is imperfect behind, but the gap is filled in by the upper part of the sacrum. The pelvic girdle, with the sacrum, is a complete ring, massive and comparatively rigid, in marked contrast to the lightness and mobility of the shoulder girdle.

THE BONES OF THE UPPER EXTREMITY (OSSA EXTREMITATIS SUPERIORIS).

The Clavicle (Clavicula; Collar Bone).

The **clavicle** (Figs. 190, 191) forms the anterior portion of the shoulder girdle. It is a long bone, curved somewhat like the italic letter f, and placed nearly horizontally at the upper and anterior part of the thorax, immediately above the first rib. It articulates medially with the manubrium sterni, and laterally with the acromion of the scapula.[1] It presents a double curvature, the convexity being directed forward at the sternal end, and the concavity at the scapular end. Its lateral third is flattened from above downward, while its medial two-thirds is of a rounded or prismatic form.

The **upper surface** of the **lateral** third is flat, rough, and marked by impressions for the attachments of the Deltoideus in front, and the Trapezius behind; between these impressions a small portion of the bone is subcutaneous. The **under surface** is flat. At its posterior border, near the point where the prismatic joins with the flattened portion, is a rough eminence, the **coracoid tuberosity** (*conoid tubercle*); this, in the natural position of the bone, surmounts the coracoid process of the

Sternal extremity   *Acromial extremity*

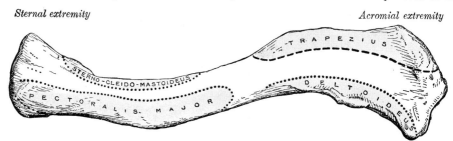

Fig. 190.—Left clavicle. Superior surface.

scapula, and gives attachment to the conoid ligament. From this tuberosity an oblique ridge, the **oblique** or **trapezoid ridge,** runs forward and lateralward, and afford attachment to the trapezoid ligament. The **anterior border** of the lateral third is concave, thin, and rough, and gives attachment to the Deltoideus. The **posterior border** is convex, rough, thicker than the anterior, and gives attachment to the Trapezius.

The medial two-thirds constitute the prismatic portion and is curved so as to be convex in front, concave behind. The **anterior border** is continuous with the anterior margin of the flat portion. Its lateral part is smooth, and corresponds to the interval between the attachments of the Pectoralis major and Deltoideus;

Articular capsule   *Articular capsule*

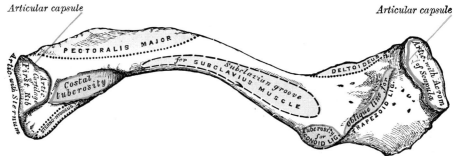

Fig. 191.—Left clavicle. Inferior surface.

its medial part forms the lower boundary of an elliptical surface for the attachment of the clavicular portion of the Pectoralis major, and approaches the posterior border of the bone. The **superior border** is continuous with the posterior margin of the flat portion, and separates the anterior from the posterior surface. Smooth and rounded laterally, it becomes rough toward the medial third for the attachment of the Sternocleidomastoideus, and ends at the upper angle of the sternal extremity. The **posterior** or **subclavian border** separates the posterior from the inferior surface, and extends from the coracoid tuberosity to the costal tuberosity;

---

[1] The clavicle acts especially as a fulcrum to enable the muscles to give lateral motion to the arm. It is accordingly absent in those animals whose fore-limbs are used only for progression, but is present for the most part in animals whose anterior extremities are clawed and used for prehension, though in some of them—as, for instance, in a large number of the carnivora—it is merely a rudimentary bone suspended among the muscles, and not articulating with either the scapula or sternum.

it forms the posterior boundary of the groove for the Subclavius, and gives attachment to a layer of cervical fascia which envelops the Omohyoideus. The **anterior surface** is included between the superior and anterior borders. Its lateral part looks upward, and is continuous with the superior surface of the flattened portion; it is smooth, convex, and nearly subcutaneous, being covered only by the Platysma. Medially it is divided by a narrow subcutaneous area into two parts: a lower, elliptical in form, and directed forward, for the attachment of the Pectoralis major; and an upper for the attachment of the Sternocleidmastoideus. The **posterior or cervical surface** is smooth, and looks backward toward the root of the neck. It is limited, above, by the superior border; below, by the subclavian border; medially, by the margin of the sternal extremity; and laterally, by the coracoid tuberosity. It is concave medio-laterally, and is in relation, by its lower part, with the transverse scapular vessels. This surface, at the junction of the curves of the bone, is also in relation with the brachial plexus of nerves and the subclavian vessels. It gives attachment, near the sternal extremity, to part of the Sternohyoideus; and presents, near the middle, an oblique foramen directed lateralward, which transmits the chief nutrient artery of the bone. Sometimes there are two foramina on the posterior surface, or one on the posterior and another on the inferior surface. The **inferior or subclavian surface** is bounded, in front, by the anterior border; behind, by the subclavian border. It is narrowed medially, but gradually increases in width laterally, and is continuous with the under surface of the flat portion. On its medial part is a broad rough surface, the **costal tuberosity** (*rhomboid impression*), rather more than 2 cm. in length, for the attachment of the costoclavicular ligament. The rest of this surface is occupied by a groove, which gives attachment to the Subclavius; the coracoclavicular fascia, which splits to enclose the muscle, is attached to the margins of the groove. Not infrequently this groove is subdivided longitudinally by a line which gives attachment to the intermuscular septum of the Subclavius.

The Sternal Extremity (*extremitas sternalis; internal extremity*).—The sternal extremity of the clavicle is triangular in form, directed medialward, and a little downward and forward; it presents an articular facet, concave from before backward, convex from above downward, which articulates with the manubrium sterni through the intervention of an articular disk. The lower part of the facet is continued on to the inferior surface of the bone as a small semi-oval area for articulation with the cartilage of the first rib. The circumference of the articular surface is rough, for the attachment of numerous ligaments; the upper angle gives attachment to the articular disk.

The Acromial Extremity (*extremitas acromialis; outer extremity*).—The acromial extremity presents a small, flattened, oval surface directed obliquely downward, for articulation with the acromion of the scapula. The circumference of the articular facet is rough, especially above, for the attachment of the acromio-clavicular ligaments.

In the female, the clavicle is generally shorter, thinner, less curved, and smoother than in the male. In those persons who perform considerable manual labor it becomes thicker and more curved, and its ridges for muscular attachment are prominently marked.

Structure.—The clavicle consists of cancellous tissue, enveloped by a compact layer, which is much thicker in the intermediate part than at the extremities of the bone.

Ossification.—The clavicle begins to ossify before any other bone in the body; it is ossified from *three* centers—viz., two primary centers, a medial and a lateral, for the body, which appear during the fifth or sixth week of fetal life; and a secondary center for the sternal end, which appears about the eighteenth or twentieth year, and unites with the rest of the bone about the twenty-fifth year.

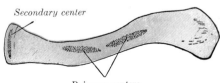

Secondary center

Primary centers

Fig. 192.—Diagram showing the three centers of ossification of the clavicle.

The Scapula (Shoulder Blade).

The **scapula** forms the posterior part of the shoulder girdle. It is a flat, triangular bone, with two surfaces, three borders, and three angles.

Surfaces.—The **costal** or **ventral surface** (Fig. 193) presents a broad concavity, the **subscapular fossa**. The medial two-thirds of the fossa are marked by several

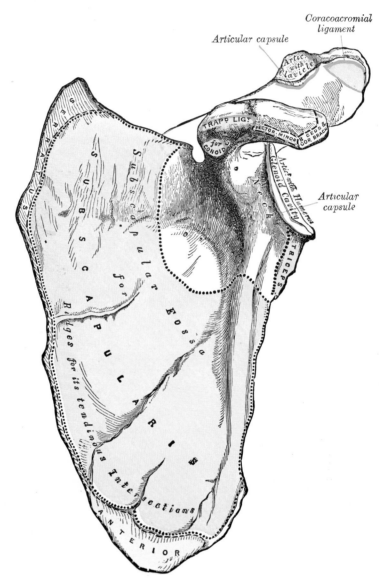

Fig. 193.—Left scapula. Costal surface.

oblique ridges, which run lateralward and upward. The ridges give attachment to the tendinous insertions, and the surfaces between them to the fleshy fibers, of the Subscapularis. The lateral third of the fossa is smooth and covered by the fibers of this muscle. The fossa is separated from the vertebral border by smooth triangular areas at the medial and inferior angles, and in the interval between these by a narrow ridge which is often deficient. These triangular areas and the intervening ridge afford attachment to the Serratus anterior. At the upper part of the fossa is a transverse depression, where the bone appears to be bent on itself along a line at right angles to and passing through the center of the glenoid cavity, forming a considerable angle, called the **subscapular angle**; this gives greater strength to the body of the bone by its arched form, while the summit of the arch serves to support the spine and acromion.

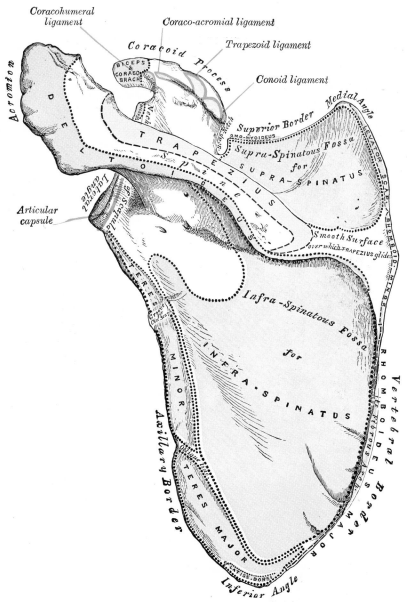

FIG. 194.—Left scapula. Dorsal surface.

The **dorsal surface** (Fig. 194) is arched from above downward, and is subdivided into two unequal parts by the spine; the portion above the spine is called the **supraspinatous fossa,** and that below it the **infraspinatous fossa.**

The **supraspinatous fossa,** the smaller of the two, is concave, smooth, and broader at its vertebral than at its humeral end; its medial two-thirds give origin to the Supraspinatus.

The **infraspinatous fossa** is much larger than the preceding; toward its vertebral margin a shallow concavity is seen at its upper part; its center presents a prominent convexity, while near the axillary border is a deep groove which runs from the upper toward the lower part. The medial two-thirds of the fossa give origin to the Infraspinatus; the lateral third is covered by this muscle.

The dorsal surface is marked near the axillary border by an elevated ridge, which runs from the lower part of the glenoid cavity, downward and backward to the vertebral border, about 2.5 cm. above the inferior angle. The ridge serves for the attachment of a fibrous septum, which separates the Infraspinatus from the Teres major and Teres minor. The surface between the ridge and the axillary border is narrow in the upper two-thirds of its extent, and is crossed near its center by a groove for the passage of the scapular circumflex vessels; it affords attachment to the Teres minor. Its lower third presents a broader, somewhat triangular surface, which gives origin to the Teres major, and over which the Latissimus dorsi glides; frequently the latter muscle takes origin by a few fibers from this part. The broad and narrow portions above alluded to are separated by an oblique line, which runs from the axillary border, downward and backward, to meet the elevated ridge: to it is attached a fibrous septum which separates the Teres muscles from each other.

The Spine (*spina scapulæ*).—The spine is a prominent plate of bone, which crosses obliquely the medial four-fifths of the dorsal surface of the scapula at its upper part, and separates the supra- from the infraspinatous fossa. It begins at the vertebral border by a smooth, triangular area over which the tendon of insertion of the lower part of the Trapezius glides, and, gradually becoming more elevated, ends in the acromion, which overhangs the shoulder-joint. The spine is triangular, and flattened from above downward, its apex being directed toward the vertebral border. It presents two surfaces and three borders. Its **superior surface** is concave; it assists in forming the supraspinatous fossa, and gives origin to part of the Supraspinatus. Its **inferior surface** forms part of the infraspinatous fossa, gives origin to a portion of the Infraspinatus, and presents near its center the orifice of a nutrient canal. Of the three borders, the **anterior** is attached to the dorsal surface of the bone; the **posterior, or crest of the spine, is** broad, and presents two lips and an intervening rough interval. The Trapezius is attached to the superior lip, and a rough tubercle is generally seen on that portion of the spine which receives the tendon of insertion of the lower part of this muscle. The Deltoideus is attached to the whole length of the inferior lip. The interval between the lips is subcutaneous and partly covered by the tendinous fibers of these muscles. The **lateral border, or base,** the shortest of the three, is slightly concave; its edge, thick and round, is continuous above with the under surface of the acromion, below with the neck of the scapula. It forms the medial boundary of the **great scapular notch,** which serves to connect the supra- and infraspinatous fossæ.

The Acromion.—The acromion forms the summit of the shoulder, and is a large, somewhat triangular or oblong process, flattened from behind forward, projecting at first lateralward, and then curving forward and upward, so as to overhang the glenoid cavity. Its **superior surface,** directed upward, backward, and lateralward, is convex, rough, and gives attachment to some fibers of the Deltoideus, and in the rest of its extent is subcutaneous. Its **inferior surface** is smooth and concave. Its **lateral border** is thick and irregular, and presents three or four tubercles for the tendinous origins of the Deltoideus. Its **medial border,** shorter than the lateral, is concave, gives attachment to a portion of the Trapezius, and presents about its center a small, oval surface for articulation with the acromial end of the clavicle.

Its **apex,** which corresponds to the point of meeting of these two borders in front, is thin, and has attached to it the coracoacromial ligament.

Borders.—Of the *three* borders of the scapula, the **superior** is the shortest and thinnest; it is concave, and extends from the medial angle to the base of the coracoid process. At its lateral part is a deep, semicircular notch, the **scapular notch,** formed partly by the base of the coracoid process. This notch is converted into a foramen by the superior transverse ligament, and serves for the passage of the suprascapular nerve; sometimes the ligament is ossified. The adjacent part of the superior border affords attachment to the Omohyoideus. The **axillary border** is the thickest of the three. It begins above at the lower margin of the glenoid cavity, and inclines obliquely downward and backward to the inferior angle. Immediately below the glenoid cavity is a rough impression, the **infraglenoid tuberosity,** about 2.5 cm. in length, which gives origin to the long head of the Triceps brachii; in front of this is a longitudinal groove, which extends as far as the lower third of this border, and affords origin to part of the Subscapularis. The inferior third is thin and sharp, and serves for the attachment of a few fibers of the Teres major behind, and of the Subscapularis in front. The **vertebral border**

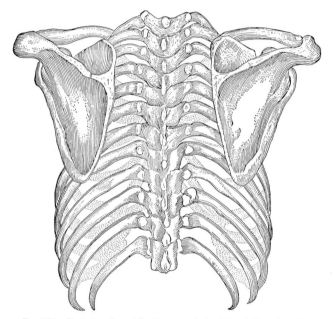

Fig. 195.—Posterior view of the thorax and shoulder girdle. (Morris.)

is the longest of the three, and extends from the medial to the inferior angle. It is arched, intermediate in thickness between the superior and the axillary borders, and the portion of it above the spine forms an obtuse angle with the part below. This border presents an anterior and a posterior lip, and an intermediate narrow area. The anterior lip affords attachment to the Serratus anterior; the posterior lip, to the Supraspinatus above the spine, the Infraspinatus below; the area between the two lips, to the Levator scapulæ above the triangular surface at the commencement of the spine, to the Rhomboideus minor on the edge of that surface, and to the Rhomboideus major below it; this last is attached by means of a fibrous arch, connected above to the lower part of the triangular surface at the base of the spine, and below to the lower part of the border.

Angles.—Of the *three* angles, the **medial,** formed by the junction of the superior and vertebral borders, is thin, smooth, rounded, inclined somewhat lateralward, and gives attachment to a few fibers of the Levator scapulæ. The **inferior angle,** thick and rough, is formed by the union of the vertebral and axillary borders; its dorsal surface affords attachment to the Teres major and frequently to a few fibers of the Latissimus dorsi. The **lateral angle** is the thickest part of the bone, and is sometimes called the head of the scapula. On it is a shallow pyriform, articular surface, the **glenoid cavity**, which is directed lateralward and forward and articulates with the head of the humerus; it is broader below than above and its vertical diameter is the longest. The surface is covered with cartilage in the fresh state; and its margins, slightly raised, give attachment to a fibrocartilaginous structure, the **glenoidallabrum**, which deepens the cavity. At its apex is a slight elevation, the **supraglenoid tuberosity**, to which the long head of the Biceps brachii is attached. The **neck** of the scapula is the slightly constricted portion which surrounds the head; it is more distinct below and behind than above and in front.

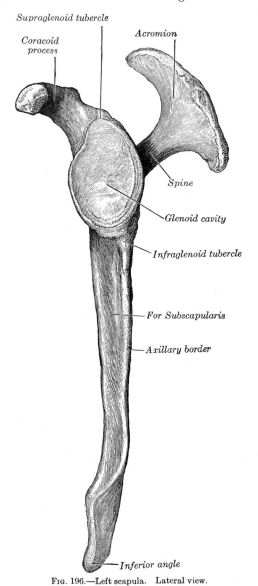

Supraglenoid tubercle

Coracoid process

Acromion

Spine

Glenoid cavity

Infraglenoid tubercle

For Subscapularis

Axillary border

Inferior angle

FIG. 196.—Left scapula. Lateral view.

The Coracoid Process (*processus coracoideus*). — The coracoid process is a thick curved process attached by a broad base to the upper part of the neck of the scapula; it runs at first upward and medialward; then, becoming smaller, it changes its direction, and projects forward and lateralward. The ascending portion, flattened from before backward, presents in front a smooth concave surface, across which the Subscapularis passes. The horizontal portion is flattened from above downward; its upper surface is convex and irregular, and gives attachment to the Pectoralis minor; its under surface is smooth; its medial and lateral borders are rough; the former gives attachment to the Pectoralis minor and the latter to the coracoacromial ligament; the apex is embraced by the conjoined tendon of origin of the Coracobrachialis and short head of the Biceps brachii and gives attachment to the coraco-clavicular fascia. On the medial part of the root of the coracoid process is a rough impression for the attachment of the conoid ligament; and running from it obliquely forward and lateralward, on to the upper surface of the horizontal portion, is an elevated ridge for the attachment of the trapezoid ligament.

Structure.—The head, processes, and the thickened parts of the bone, contain cancellous tissue; the rest consists of a thin layer of compact tissue. The central part of the supraspinatous fossa and the upper part of the infraspinatous fossa, but especially the former, are usually so thin as to be semitransparent; occasionally the bone is found wanting in this situation, and the adjacent muscles are separated only by fibrous tissue.

Ossification (Fig. 197).—The scapula is ossified from *seven* or more centers: one for the body, two for the coracoid process, two for the acromion, one for the vertebral border, and one for the inferior angle.

Ossification of the body begins about the second month of fetal life, by the formation of an irregular quadrilateral plate of bone, immediately behind the glenoid cavity. This plate extends so as to form the chief part of the bone, the spine growing up from its dorsal surface about the third month. At birth, a large part of the scapula is osseous, but the glenoid cavity, the coracoid process, the acromion, the vertebral border, and the inferior angle are cartilaginous. From the fifteenth to the eighteenth month after birth, ossification takes place in the middle of the coracoid process, which as a rule becomes joined with the rest of the bone about the fifteenth year. Between the fourteenth and twentieth years, ossification of the remaining parts takes place in quick succession, and usually in the following order; first, in the root of the coracoid process, in the form of a broad scale; secondly, near the base of the acromion; thirdly, in the inferior angle and contiguous part of the vertebral border; fourthly, near the extremity of the acromion; fifthly, in the vertebral border. The base of the acromion is formed by an extension from the spine; the two separate nuclei of the acromion unite, and then join with the extension from the spine. The upper third of the glenoid cavity is ossified from a separate center (subcoracoid), which makes its appearance between the tenth and eleventh years and joins between the sixteenth and the eighteenth. Further, an epiphyseal plate appears for the lower part of the glenoid cavity, while the tip of the coracoid process frequently presents

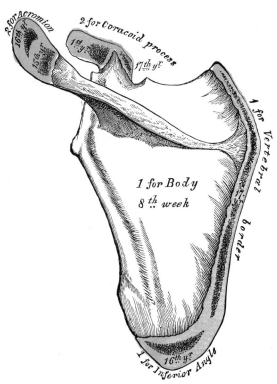

FIG. 197.—Plan of ossification of the scapula. From seven centers.

a separate nucleus. These various epiphyses are joined to the bone by the twenty-fifth year. Failure of bony union between the acromion and spine sometimes occurs, the junction being effected by fibrous tissue, or by an imperfect articulation; in some cases of supposed fracture of the acromion with ligamentous union, it is probable that the detached segment was never united to the rest of the bone.

The Humerus (Arm Bone).

The **humerus** (Figs. 200, 201) is the longest and largest bone of the upper extremity; it is divisible into a **body** and **two extremities.**

Upper Extremity.—The upper extremity consists of a large rounded *head* joined to the body by a constricted portion called the **neck,** and two eminences, the **greater** and **lesser tubercles.**

The Head (*caput humeri*).—The head (Fig. 198), nearly hemispherical in form, is directed upward, medialward, and a little backward, and articulates with the glenoid cavity of the scapula. The circumference of its articular surface is slightly constricted and is termed the **anatomical neck,** in contradistinction to a constriction below the tubercles called the **surgical neck** which is frequently the seat of fracture. Fracture of the anatomical neck rarely occurs.

The **Anatomical Neck** (*collum anatomicum*) is obliquely directed, forming an obtuse angle with the body. It is best marked in the lower half of its circumference; in the upper half it is represented by a narrow groove separating the head from the tubercles. It affords attachment to the articular capsule of the shoulder-joint, and is perforated by numerous vascular foramina.

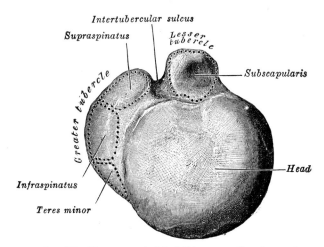

FIG. 198.—The upper end of the left humerus. Superior aspect.

The **Greater Tubercle** (*tuberculum majus; greater tuberosity*).—The greater tubercle is situated lateral to the head and lesser tubercle. Its upper surface is rounded and marked by three flat impressions: the highest of these gives insertion to the Supraspinatus; the middle to the Infraspinatus; the lowest one, and the body of the bone for about 2.5 cm. below it, to the Teres minor. The lateral surface of the greater tubercle is convex, rough, and continuous with the lateral surface of the body.

The **Lesser Tubercle** (*tuberculum minus; lesser tuberosity*).—The lesser tubercle, although smaller, is more prominent than the greater: it is situated in front, and is directed medialward and forward. Above and in front it presents an impression for the insertion of the tendon of the Subscapularis.

The tubercles are separated from each other by a deep groove, the **intertubercular groove** (*bicipital groove*), which lodges the long tendon of the Biceps brachii and transmits a branch of the anterior humeral circumflex artery to the shoulder-joint. It runs obliquely downward, and ends near the junction of the upper with the middle third of the bone. In the fresh state its upper part is covered with a thin layer of cartilage, lined by a prolongation of the synovial membrane of the shoulder-joint; its lower portion gives insertion to the tendon of the Latissimus dorsi. It is deep and narrow above, and becomes shallow and a little broader as it descends. Its lips are called, respectively, the **crests of the greater and lesser tubercles** (*bicipital ridges*), and form the upper parts of the anterior and medial borders of the body of the bone.

The **Body or Shaft** (*corpus humeri*).—The body is almost cylindrical in the upper half in its extent, prismatic and flattened below, and has three borders and three surfaces.

Borders.—The **anterior border** runs from the front of the greater tubercle above to the coronoid fossa below, separating the antero-medial from the antero-lateral surface. Its upper part is a prominent ridge, the crest of the greater tubercle; it serves for the insertion of the tendon of the Pectoralis major. About its center it forms the anterior boundary of the deltoid tuberosity; below, it is smooth and rounded, affording attachment to the Brachialis.

The **lateral border** runs from the back part of the greater tubercle to the lateral epicondyle, and separates the antero-lateral from the posterior surface. Its upper half is rounded and indistinctly marked, serving for the attachment of the lower part of the insertion of the Teres minor, and below this giving origin to the lateral head of the Triceps brachii; its center is traversed by a broad but shallow oblique depression, the **radial sulcus** (*musculospiral groove*). Its lower part forms a prominent, rough margin, a little curved from behind forward, the **lateral supra-condylar ridge,** which presents an anterior lip for the origin of the Brachioradialis above, and Extensor carpi radialis longus below, a posterior lip for the Triceps brachii, and an intermediate ridge for the attachment of the lateral intermuscular septum.

The **medial border** extends from the lesser tubercle to the medial epicondyle. Its upper third consists of a prominent ridge, the **crest of the lesser tubercle,** which gives insertion to the tendon of the Teres major. About its center is a slight impression for the insertion of the Coracobrachialis, and just below this is the entrance of the nutrient canal, directed downward; sometimes there is a second nutrient canal at the commencement of the radial sulcus. The inferior third of this border is raised into a slight ridge, the **medial supracondylar ridge,** which becomes very prominent below; it presents an anterior lip for the origin of the Brachialis, a pos_ terior lip for the medial head of the Triceps brachii, and an intermediate ridge for the attachment of the medial intermuscular septum.

Surfaces.—The **antero-lateral surface** is directed lateralward above, where it is smooth, rounded, and covered by the Deltoideus; forward and lateralward below, where it is slightly concave from above downward, and gives origin to part of the Brachialis. About the middle of this surface is a rough, triangular elevation, the **deltoid tuberosity** for the insertion of the Deltoideus; below this is the **radial sulcus,** directed obliquely from behind, forward, and downward, and transmitting the radial nerve and profunda artery.

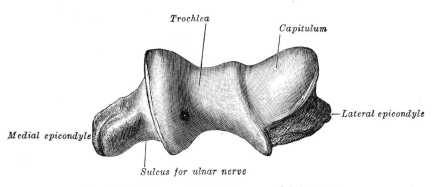

Fig. 199.—The lower end of the left humerus.   Inferior aspect.

The **antero-medial surface,** less extensive than the antero-lateral, is directed medialward above, forward and medialward below; its upper part is narrow, and forms the floor of the intertubercular groove which gives insertion to the tendon of the Latissimus dorsi; its middle part is slightly rough for the attachment of some of the fibers of the tendon of insertion of the Coracobrachialis; its lower part is smooth, concave from above downward, and gives origin to the Brachialis.

The **posterior surface** appears somewhat twisted, so that its upper part is

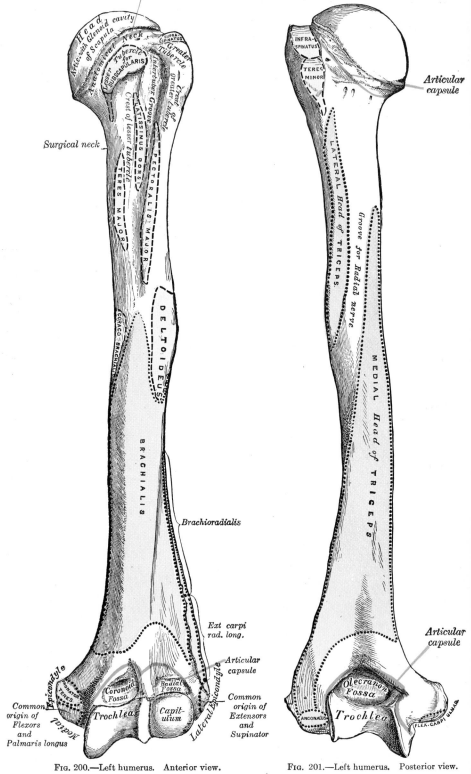

FIG. 200.—Left humerus. Anterior view.   FIG. 201.—Left humerus. Posterior view.

directed a little medialward, its lower part backward and a little lateralward. Nearly the whole of this surface is covered by the lateral and medial heads of the Triceps brachii, the former arising above, the latter below the radial sulcus.

The Lower Extremity.—The lower extremity is flattened from before backward, and curved slightly forward; it ends below in a broad, articular surface, which is divided into two parts by a slight ridge. Projecting on either side are the lateral and medial epicondyles. The **articular surface** extends a little lower than the epicondyles, and is curved slightly forward; its medial extremity occupies a lower level than the lateral. The lateral portion of this surface consists of a smooth, rounded eminence, named the **capitulum of the humerus**; it articulates with the cup-shaped depression on the head of the radius, and is limited to the front and lower part of the bone. On the medial side of this eminence is a shallow groove, in which is received the medial margin of the head of the radius. Above the front part of the capitulum is a slight depression, the **radial fossa**, which receives the anterior border of the head of the radius, when the forearm is flexed. The medial portion

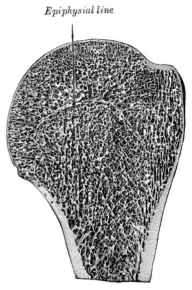

Epiphysial line

Fig. 202.—Longitudinal section of head of left humerus.

of the articular surface is named the **trochlea**, and presents a deep depression between two well-marked borders; it is convex from before backward, concave from side to side, and occupies the anterior, lower, and posterior parts of the extremity. The lateral border separates it from the groove which articulates with the margin of the head of the radius. The medial border is thicker, of greater length, and consequently more prominent, than the lateral. The grooved portion of the articular surface fits accurately within the semilunar notch of the ulna; it is broader and deeper on the posterior than on the anterior aspect of the bone, and is inclined obliquely downward and forward toward the medial side. Above the front part of the trochlea is a small depression, the **coronoid fossa**, which receives the coronoid process of the ulna during flexion of the forearm. Above the back part of the trochlea is a deep triangular depression, the **olecranon fossa**, in which the summit of the olecranon is received in extension of the forearm. These fossæ are separated from one another by a thin, transparent lamina of bone, which is sometimes perforated by a **supratrochlear foramen**; they are lined in the fresh state by the synovial membrane of the elbow-joint, and their margins afford attachment to the anterior and posterior ligaments of this articulation. The **lateral epicondyle** is a small, tuberculated eminence, curved a little forward, and giving attachment to the radial collateral ligament of the elbow-joint, and to a tendon common to the origin of the Supinator and some of the Extensor muscles. The **medial epicondyle**, larger and more prominent than the lateral, is directed a little backward; it gives attachment to the ulnar collateral ligament of the elbow-joint, to the Pronator teres, and to a common tendon of origin of most of the Flexor muscles of the forearm; the ulnar nerve runs in a groove on the back of this epicondyle. The epicondyles are continuous above with the supracondylar ridges.

Structure.—The extremities consist of cancellous tissue, covered with a thin, compact layer (Fig. 202); the body is composed of a cylinder of compact tissue, thicker at the center than toward the extremities, and contains a large medullary canal which extends along its whole length.

Ossification (Figs. 203, 204).—The humerus is ossified from *eight* centers, one for each of the following parts: the body, the head, the greater tubercle, the lesser tubercle, the capitulum, the trochlea, and one for each epicondyle. The center for the body appears near the middle of the bone in the eighth week of fetal life, and soon extends toward the extremities. At birth the humerus is ossified in nearly its whole length, only the extremities remaining cartilaginous. During the first year, sometimes before birth, ossification commences in the head of the bone, and during the third year the center for the greater tubercle, and during the fifth that for the lesser tubercle, make their appearance. By the sixth year the centers for the head and tubercles have joined, so as to form a single large epiphysis, which fuses with the body about the twentieth year. The conical shape of the proximal end of the diaphysis, where the epiphyseal cap fits over it as shown by the epiphyseal line in Figure 202, is an adult condition. In the fetus and newborn, the end of the diaphysis is flat; the conical shape is established during the first year and gradually reaches the height of the adult by the twelfth year. The lower end of the humerus is ossified as follows. At the end of the second year ossification begins in the capitulum, and extends medialward, to form the chief part of the articular end of the bone; the center for the medial part of the trochlea appears about the age of twelve. Ossification begins in the medial epicondyle about the fifth year, and in the lateral about the thirteenth or fourteenth year. About the sixteenth or seventeenth year, the lateral epicondyle and both portions of the articulating surface, having already joined, unite with the body, and at the eighteenth year the medial epicondyle becomes joined to it.

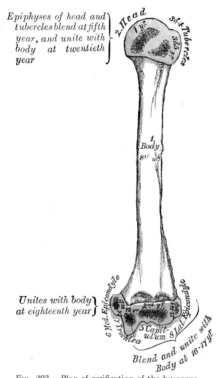

Epiphyses of head and tubercles blend at fifth year, and unite with body at twentieth year

Unites with body at eighteenth year

FIG. 203.—Plan of ossification of the humerus.

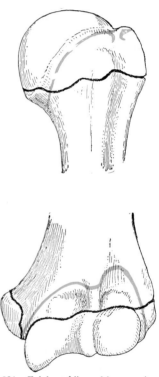

FIG. 204.—Epiphyseal lines of humerus in a young adult. Anterior aspect. The lines of attachment of the articular capsules are in blue.

Torsion of the Humerus is the term used to refer to the twisting of the bone about its longitudinal axis, that is, the change in the relation of the transverse, articular axes of the two ends of the bone to each other. This is entirely distinct and independent of the rotation of the whole limb referred to in the section on Embryology. The angle formed by the axes of the two ends of the bone is called the torsion angle. According to Evans and Krahl (1945), the angle measures 74° in the adult bone, the distal end having been twisted medially in relation to the proximal end. Two factors have been identified; a primary torsion which is hereditary and evolutionary, and a secondary which is ontogenetic. The primary torsion is found in all tetrapods, and in the evolutionary scale of mammals, the angle increases from 27° to 74°. The secondary torsion takes place at the proximal epiphyseal junction before the age of twenty, while cartilage is still present, and apparently is due to muscular pull since the lateral rotators are attached proximal and the medial rotators distal to the junction. There is no torsion in the diaphysis; the apparent twisting of this part of the bone is due to the surface markings associated with the spiral course of the radial nerve.

Variations.—A small, hook-shaped process of bone, the *supracondylar process*, varying from 2 to 20 mm. in length, is not infrequently found projecting from the antero-medial surface of the body of the humerus 5 cm. above the medial epicondyle. It is curved downward and forward, and its pointed end is connected to the medial border, just above the medial epicondyle, by a fibrous band, which gives origin to a portion of the Pronator teres; through the arch completed by this fibrous band the median nerve and brachial artery pass, when these structures deviate from their usual course. Sometimes the nerve alone is transmitted through it, or the nerve may be accompanied by the ulnar artery, in cases of high division of the brachial. A well-marked groove is usually found behind the process, in which the nerve and artery are lodged. This arch is the homologue of the *supracondyloid foramen* found in many animals, and probably serves in them to protect the nerve and artery from compression during the contraction of the muscles in this region.

The Ulna (Elbow Bone).

The **ulna** (Figs. 206, 207) is a long bone, prismatic in form, placed at the medial side of the forearm, parallel with the radius. It is divisible into a **body** and **two extremities.** Its upper extremity, of great thickness and strength, forms a large part of the elbow-joint; the bone diminishes in size from above downward, its lower extremity being very small, and excluded from the wrist-joint by the interposition of an articular disk.

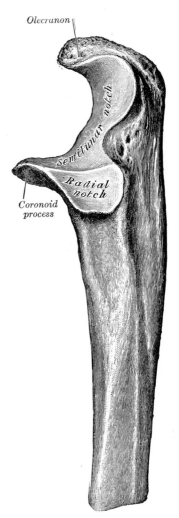

FIG. 205.—Upper extremity of left ulna. Lateral aspect.

The Upper Extremity (*proximal extremity*) (Fig. 205).—The upper extremity presents two curved processes, the **olecranon** and the **coronoid process;** and two concave, articular cavities, the **semilunar** and **radial notches.**

The Olecranon (*olecranon process*).—The olecranon is a large, thick, curved eminence, situated at the upper and back part of the ulna. It is bent forward at the summit so as to present a prominent lip which is received into the olecranon fossa of the humerus in extension of the forearm. Its **base** is contracted where it joins the body and the narrowest part of the upper end of the ulna. Its **posterior surface**, directed backward, is triangular, smooth, subcutaneous, and covered by a bursa. Its **superior surface** is of quadrilateral form, marked behind by a rough impression for the insertion of the Triceps brachii; and in front, near the margin, by a slight transverse groove for the attachment of part of the posterior ligament of the elbow-joint. Its **anterior surface** is smooth, concave, and forms the upper part of the semilunar notch. Its **borders** present continuations of the groove on the margin of the superior surface; they serve for the attachment of ligaments, viz., the back part of the ulnar collateral ligament medially, and the posterior ligament laterally. From the medial border a part of the Flexor carpi ulnaris arises; while to the lateral border the Anconæus is attached.

The Coronoid Process (*processus coronoideus*).—The coronoid process is a triangular eminence projecting forward from the upper and front part of the ulna. Its **base** is continuous with the body of the bone, and of considerable strength. Its **apex** is pointed, slightly curved upward, and in flexion of the

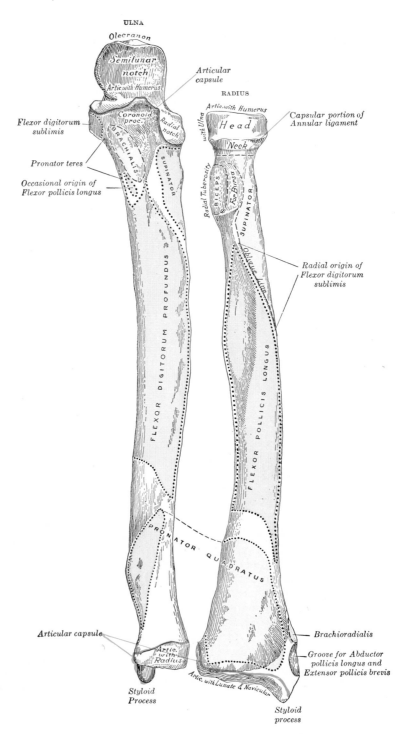

ULNA

Olecranon

Semilunar notch

Artic. with Humerus

Articular capsule

RADIUS

Artic. with Humerus

Head

Capsular portion of Annular ligament

Flexor digitorum sublimis

Coronoid proc.

Radial notch

with Ulna

Neck

BRACHIALIS

Radial Tuberosity

BICEPS

For. Bursa

Pronator teres

SUPINATOR

Occasional origin of Flexor pollicis longus

SUPINATOR

Oblique Line

Radial origin of Flexor digitorum sublimis

FLEXOR DIGITORUM PROFUNDUS

FLEXOR POLLICIS LONGUS

PRONATOR QUADRATUS

Articular capsule

Artic. with Radius

Brachioradialis

Groove for Abductor pollicis longus and Extensor pollicis brevis

Artic. with Lunate & Navicular

Styloid Process

Styloid process

FIG. 206.—The bones of the left forearm. Anterior aspect.

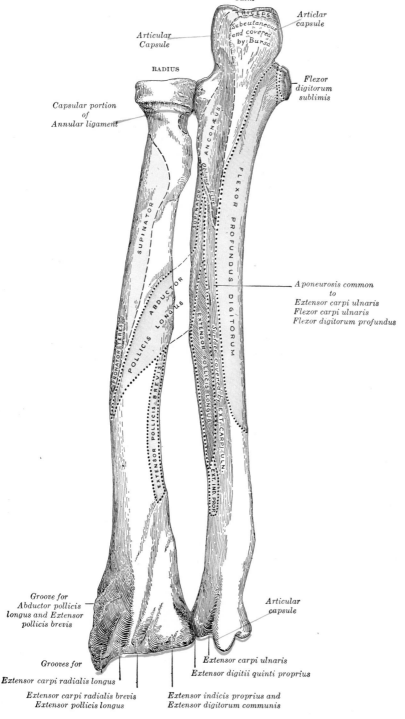

FIG 207.—The bones of the left forearm. Posterior aspect.

forearm is received into the coronoid fossa of the humerus. Its **upper surface** is smooth, concave, and forms the lower part of the semilunar notch. Its **antero-inferior surface** is concave, and marked by a rough impression for the insertion of the Brachialis. At the junction of this surface with the front of the body is a rough eminence, the **tuberosity of the ulna,** which gives insertion to a part of the Brachialis; to the lateral border of this tuberosity the oblique cord is attached. Its **lateral surface** presents a narrow, oblong, articular depression, the **radial notch.** Its **medial surface,** by its prominent, free margin, serves for the attachment of part of the ulnar collateral ligament. At the front part of this surface is a small rounded eminence for the origin of one head of the Flexor digitorum sublimis; behind the eminence is a depression for part of the origin of the Flexor digitorum profundus; descending from the eminence is a ridge which gives origin to one head of the Pronator teres. Frequently, the Flexor pollicis longus arises from the lower part of the coronoid process by a rounded bundle of muscular fibers.

The Semilunar Notch (*incisura semilunaris; greater sigmoid cavity*).—The semilunar notch is a large depression, formed by the olecranon and the coronoid process, and serving for articulation with the trochlea of the humerus. About the middle of either side of this notch is an indentation, which contracts it somewhat, and indicates the junction of the olecranon and the coronoid process. The notch is concave from above downward, and divided into a medial and a lateral portion by a smooth ridge running from the summit of the olecranon to the tip of the coronoid process. The medial portion is the larger, and is slightly concave transversely; the lateral is convex above, slightly concave below.

The Radial Notch (*incisura radialis; lesser sigmoid cavity*).—The radial notch is a narrow, oblong, articular depression on the lateral side of the coronoid process it receives the circumferential articular surface of the head of the radius. It is concave from before backward, and its prominent extremities serve for the attachment of the annular ligament.

The Body or Shaft (*corpus ulnæ*).—The body at its upper part is prismatic in form, and curved so as to be convex behind and lateralward; its central part is straight; its lower part is rounded, smooth, and bent a little lateralward. It tapers gradually from above downward, and has three borders and three surfaces.

Borders.—The **volar border** (*margo volaris; anterior border*) begins above at the prominent medial angle of the coronoid process, and ends below in front of the styloid process. Its upper part, well-defined, and its middle portion, smooth and rounded, give origin to the Flexor digitorum profundus; its lower fourth, called the **pronator ridge,** serves for the origin of the Pronator quadratus. This border separates the volar from the medial surface.

The **dorsal border** (*margo dorsalis; posterior border*) begins above at the apex of the triangular subcutaneous surface at the back part of the olecranon, and ends below at the back of the styloid process; it is well-marked in the upper three fourths, and gives attachment to an aponeurosis which affords a common origin to the Flexor carpi ulnaris, the Extensor carpi ulnaris, and the Flexor digitorum profundus; its lower fourth is smooth and rounded. This border separates the medial from the dorsal surface.

The **interosseous crest** (*crista interossea; external or interosseous border*) begins above by the union of two lines, which converge from the extremities of the radial notch and enclose between them a triangular space for the origin of part of the Supinator; it ends below at the head of the ulna. Its upper part is sharp, its lower fourth smooth and rounded. This crest gives attachment to the interosseous membrane, and separates the volar from the dorsal surface.

Surfaces.—The **volar surface** (*facies volaris; anterior surface*), much broader above than below, is concave in its upper three-fourths, and gives origin to the Flexor digitorum profundus; its lower fourth, also concave, is covered by the Pronator quadratus. The lower fourth is separated from the remaining portion by a ridge, directed obliquely downward and medialward, which marks the extent of origin of the Pronator quadratus. At the junction of the upper with the middle third of the bone is the nutrient canal, directed obliquely upward.

The **dorsal surface** (*facies dorsalis; posterior surface*) directed backward and lateralward, is broad and concave above; convex and somewhat narrower in the middle; narrow, smooth, and rounded below. On its upper part is an oblique ridge, which runs from the dorsal end of the radial notch, downward to the dorsal

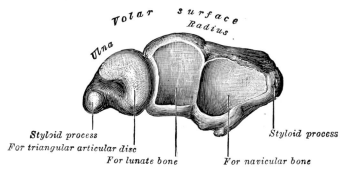

Fig. 208.—The lower ends of the left radius and ulna. Inferior aspect.

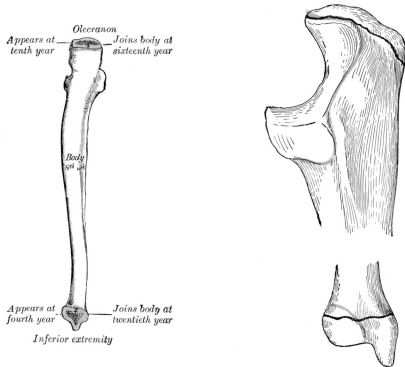

Fig. 209.—Plan of ossification of the ulna. From three centers.

Fig. 210.—Epiphyseal lines of ulna in a young adult. Lateral aspect. The lines of attachment of the articular capsules are in blue.

border; the triangular surface above this ridge receives the insertion of the Anconæus, while the upper part of the ridge affords attachment to the Supinator. Below this the surface is subdivided by a longitudinal ridge, sometimes called the **perpendicular line,** into two parts: the medial part is smooth, and covered by the Extensor carpi ulnaris; the lateral portion, wider and rougher, gives origin from above downward to the Supinator, the Abductor pollicis longus, the Extensor pollicis longus, and the Extensor indicis proprius.

The **medial surface** (*facies medialis; internal surface*) is broad and concave above, narrow and convex below. Its upper three-fourths give origin to the Flexor digitorum profundus; its lower fourth is subcutaneous.

The Lower Extremity (*distal extremity*).—The lower extremity of the ulna is small, and presents two eminences; the lateral and larger is a rounded, articular eminence, termed the head of the ulna; the medial, narrower and more projecting, is a non-articular eminence, the styloid process. The **head** presents an articular surface, part of which, of an oval or semilunar form, is directed downward, and articulates with the upper surface of the triangular articular disk which separates it from the wrist-joint; the remaining portion, directed lateralward, is narrow, convex, and received into the ulnar notch of the radius. The **styloid process** projects from the medial and back part of the bone; it descends a little lower than the head, and its rounded end affords attachment to the ulnar collateral ligament of the wrist-joint. The head is separated from the styloid process by a depression for the attachment of the apex of the triangular articular disk, and behind, by a shallow groove for the tendon of the Extensor carpi ulnaris.

Structure.—The long, narrow medullary cavity is enclosed in a strong wall of compact tissue which is thickest along the interosseous border and dorsal surface. At the extremities the compact layer thins. The compact layer is continued onto the back of the olecranon as a plate of close spongy bone with lamellae parallel. From the inner surface of this plate and the compact layer below it trabeculae arch forward toward the olecranon and coronoid and cross other trabeculae, passing backward over the medullary cavity from the upper part of the shaft below the coronoid. Below the coronoid process there is a small area of compact bone from which trabeculae curve upward to end obliquely to the surface of the semilunar notch which is coated with a thin layer of compact bone. The trabeculae at the lower end have a more longitudinal direction.

Ossification (Figs. 209, 210).—The ulna is ossified from *three* centers: one each for the body, the inferior extremity, and the top of the olecranon. Ossification begins near the middle of the body, about the eighth week of fetal life, and soon extends through the greater part of the bone. At birth the ends are cartilaginous. About the fourth year, a center appears in the middle of the head, and soon extends into the styloid process. About the tenth year, a center appears in the olecranon near its extremity, the chief part of this process being formed by an upward extension of the body. The upper epiphysis joins the body about the sixteenth, the lower about the twentieth year.

Articulations.—The ulna articulates with the humerus and radius.

The Radius.

The **radius** (Figs. 206, 207) is situated on the lateral side of the ulna, which exceeds it in length and size. Its upper end is small, and forms only a small part of the elbow-joint; but its lower end is large, and forms the chief part of the wrist-joint. It is a long bone, prismatic in form and slightly curved longitudinally. It has a body and two extremities.

The Upper Extremity (*proximal extremity*).—The upper extremity presents a head, neck, and tuberosity. The **head** is of a cylindrical form, and on its upper surface is a shallow cup or fovea for articulation with the capitulum of the humerus. The circumference of the head is smooth; it is broad medially where it articulates with the radial notch of the ulna, narrow in the rest of its extent, which is embraced by the annular ligament. The head is supported on a round, smooth, and constricted portion called the **neck**, on the back of which is a slight ridge for the insertion of part of the Supinator. Beneath the neck, on the medial side, is an eminence, the **radial tuberosity**; its surface is divided into a posterior, rough portion, for the insertion of the tendon of the Biceps brachii, and an anterior, smooth portion, on which a bursa is interposed between the tendon and the bone.

The Body or Shaft (*corpus radii*).—The body is prismoid in form, narrower above than below, and slightly curved, so as to be convex lateralward. It presents three borders and three surfaces.

Borders.—The **volar border** (*margo volaris; anterior border*) extends from the lower part of the tuberosity above to the anterior part of the base of the styloid process below, and separates the volar from the lateral surface. Its upper third is prominent, and from its oblique direction has received the name of the **oblique line of the radius**; it gives origin to the Flexor digitorum sublimis and Flexor pollicis longus; the surface above the line gives insertion to part of the Supinator. The middle third of the volar border is indistinct and rounded. The lower fourth is prominent, and gives insertion to the Pronator quadratus, and attachment to the dorsal carpal ligament; it ends in a small tubercle, into which the tendon of the Brachioradialis is inserted.

The **dorsal border** (*margo dorsalis; posterior border*) begins above at the back of the neck, and ends below at the posterior part of the base of the styloid process; it separates the posterior from the lateral surface. It is indistinct above and below, but well-marked in the middle third of the bone.

The **interosseous crest** (*crista interossea; internal or interosseous border*) begins above, at the back part of the tuberosity, and its upper part is rounded and indistinct; it becomes sharp and prominent as it descends, and at its lower part divides into two ridges which are continued to the anterior and posterior margins of the ulnar notch. To the posterior of the two ridges the lower part of the interosseous membrane is attached, while the triangular surface between the ridges gives insertion to part of the Pronator quadratus. This crest separates the volar from the dorsal surface, and gives attachment to the interosseous membrane.

Surface.—The **volar surface** (*facies volaris; anterior surface*) is concave in its upper three-fourths, and gives origin to the Flexor pollicis longus; it is broad and flat in its lower fourth, and affords insertion to the Pronator quadratus. A prominent ridge limits the insertion of the Pronator quadratus below, and between this and the inferior border is a triangular rough surface for the attachment of the volar radiocarpal ligament. At the junction of the upper and middle thirds of the volar surface is the nutrient foramen, which is directed obliquely upward.

The **dorsal surface** (*facies dorsalis; posterior surface*) is convex, and smooth in the upper third of its extent, and covered by the Supinator. Its middle third is broad, slightly concave, and gives origin to the Abductor pollicis longus above, and the Extensor pollicis brevis below. Its lower third is broad, convex, and covered by the tendons of the muscles which subsequently run in the grooves on the lower end of the bone.

The **lateral surface** (*facies lateralis; external surface*) is convex throughout its entire extent. Its upper third gives insertion to the Supinator. About its center is a rough ridge, for the insertion of the Pronator teres. Its lower part is narrow, and covered by the tendons of the Abductor pollicis longus and Extensor pollicis brevis.

The Lower Extremity.—The lower extremity is large, of quadrilateral form, and provided with two articular surfaces—one below, for the carpus, and another at the medial side, for the ulna The carpal articular surface is triangular, concave, smooth, and divided by a slight antero-posterior ridge into two parts. Of these, the lateral, triangular, articulates with the navicular bone; the medial, quadrilateral, with the lunate bone. The articular surface for the ulna is called the **ulnar notch** (*sigmoid cavity*) **of the radius**; it is narrow, concave, smooth, and articulates with the head of the ulna. These two articular surfaces are separated by a prominent ridge, to which the base of the triangular articular disk is attached; this disk separates the wrist-joint from the distal radioulnar articulation. This end of the bone has three non-articular surfaces—volar, dorsal, and lateral. The **volar surface**, rough and irregular, affords attachment to the volar radiocarpal ligament. The **dorsal surface** is convex, affords attachment to the dorsal radiocarpal ligament, and is marked by three grooves. Enumerated from the lateral side, the first groove is broad, but shallow, and subdivided into two by a slight ridge; the lateral of these two transmits the tendon of the Extensor carpi radialis longus, the medial the tendon of the Extensor carpi radialis brevis. The second is deep but narrow, and bounded laterally by a sharply defined ridge; it is directed obliquely from above downward and lateralward, and transmits the tendon of the Extensor pollicis longus. The third is broad, for the passage of the tendons of the Extensor indicis proprius and Extensor digitorum communis. The **lateral surface** is prolonged obliquely downward into a strong, conical projection, the **styloid process**, which gives attachment by its base to the tendon of the Brachioradialis, and by its apex to the radial collateral ligament of the wrist-joint. The lateral surface of this process is marked by a flat groove, for the tendons of the Abductor pollicis longus and Extensor pollicis brevis.

Structure.—The long narrow medullary cavity is enclosed in a strong wall of compact tissue which is thickest along the interosseous border and thinnest at the extremities except over the cup-shaped articular surface (fovea) of the head where it is thickened. The trabeculæ of the spongy tissue are somewhat arched at the upper end and pass upward from the compact layer of the shaft to the fovea capituli; they are crossed by others parallel to the surface of the fovea. The arrangement at the lower end is somewhat similar.

Ossification (Figs. 211, 212).—The radius is ossified from *three* centers: one for the body, and one for either extremity. That for the body makes its appearance near the center of the bone, during the eighth week of fetal life. About the end of the second year, ossification commences in the lower end; and at the fifth year, in the upper end. The upper epiphysis fuses with the body at the age of seventeen or eighteen years, the lower about the age of twenty. An additional center sometimes found in the radial tuberosity, appears about the fourteenth or fifteenth year.

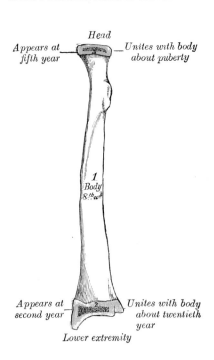

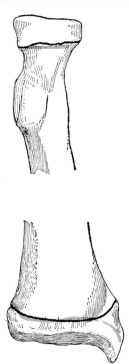

Fig. 211.—Plan of ossification of the radius. From three centers.

Fig. 212.—Epiphyseal lines of radius in a young adult. Anterior aspect. The line of attachment of the articular capsule of the wrist-joint is in blue.

THE HAND.

The skeleton of the hand (Figs. 213, 214) is subdivided into three segments: the **carpus** or **wrist bones**; the **metacarpus** or **bones of the palm**; and the **phalanges** or **bones of the digits**.

The Carpus (Ossa Carpi).

The **carpal bones**, eight in number, are arranged in two rows. Those of the proximal row, from the radial to the ulnar side, are named the **navicular, lunate, triangular**, and **pisiform**; those of the distal row, in the same order, are named the **greater multangular, lesser multangular, capitate**, and **hamate**.

Common Characteristics of the Carpal Bones.—Each bone (excepting the pisiform) presents six surfaces. Of these the *volar* or *anterior* and the *dorsal* or *posterior surfaces* are rough, for ligamentous attachment; the dorsal surfaces being the broader, except in the navicular and lunate. The *superior* or *proximal*, and *inferior* or *distal surfaces* are articular, the superior generally convex, the inferior concave; the *medial* and *lateral surfaces* are also articular where they are in contact with contiguous bones, otherwise they are rough and tuberculated. The structure in all is similar, viz., cancellous tissue enclosed in a layer of compact bone.

Bones of the Proximal Row (*upper row*).—**The Navicular Bone** (*os naviculare manus; scaphoid bone*) (Fig. 215).—The navicular bone is the largest bone of the proximal row, and has received its name from its fancied resemblance to a boat. It is situated at the radial side of the carpus, its long axis being from above downward, lateralward, and forward. The **superior surface** is convex, smooth, of triangular shape, and articulates with the lower end of the radius. The **inferior surface**, directed downward, lateralward, and backward, is also smooth, convex, and triangular, and is divided by a slight ridge into two parts, the lateral articulating with the greater multangular, the medial with the lesser multangular. On the **dorsal surface** is a narrow, rough groove, which runs the entire length of the bone, and serves for the attachment of ligaments. The **volar surface** is concave above, and elevated at its lower and lateral part into a rounded projection, the **tubercle**, which is directed forward and gives attachment to the transverse carpal ligament and sometimes origin to a few fibers of the Abductor pollicis brevis. The **lateral surface** is rough and narrow, and gives attachment to the radial collateral ligament of the wrist. The **medial surface** presents two articular facets; of these, the superior or smaller is flattened, of semilunar form, and articulates with the lunate bone; the inferior or larger is concave, forming with the lunate a concavity for the head of the capitate bone.

Articulations.—The navicular articulates with *five* bones: the radius proximally, greater and lesser multangulars distally, and capitate and lunate medially.

The Lunate Bone (*os lunatum; semilunar bone*) (Fig. 216).—The lunate bone may be distinguished by its deep concavity and crescentic outline. It is situated in the center of the proximal row of the carpus, between the navicular and triangular. The **superior surface**, convex and smooth, articulates with the radius. The **inferior surface** is deeply concave, and of greater extent from before backward than transversely: it articulates with the head of the capitate, and, by a long, narrow facet (separated by a ridge from the general surface), with the hamate. The **dorsal** and **volar surfaces** are rough, for the attachment of ligaments, the latter being the broader. The **lateral surface** presents a narrow, flattened, semilunar facet for articulation with the navicular. The **medial surface** is marked by a smooth, quadrilateral facet, for articulation with the triangular.

Articulations.—The lunate articulates with *five* bones: the radius proximally, capitate and hamate distally, navicular laterally, and triangular medially.

The Triangular Bone (*os triquetrum; cuneiform bone*) (Fig. 217).—The triangular bone may be distinguished by its pyramidal shape, and by an oval isolated facet for articulation with the pisiform bone. It is situated at the upper and ulnar side of the carpus. The **superior surface** presents a medial, rough, non-articular portion, and a lateral convex articular portion which articulates with the triangular articular disk of the wrist. The **inferior surface**, directed lateralward, is concave, sinuously curved, and smooth for articulation with the hamate. The **dorsal surface** is rough for the attachment of ligaments. The **volar surface** presents, on its medial part, an oval facet, for articulation with the pisiform; its lateral part is rough for ligamentous attachment. The **lateral surface**, the base of the pyramid, is marked by a flat, quadrilateral facet, for articulation with the lunate. The **medial surface,**

the summit of the pyramid, is pointed and roughened, for the attachment of the ulnar collateral ligament of the wrist.

Articulations.—The triangular articulates with *three* bones: the lunate laterally, the pisiform in front, the hamate distally; and with the triangular articular disk which separates it from the lower end of the ulna.

The Pisiform Bone (*os pisiforme*) (Fig. 218).—The pisiform bone may be known by its small size, and by its presenting a single articular facet. It is situated on a

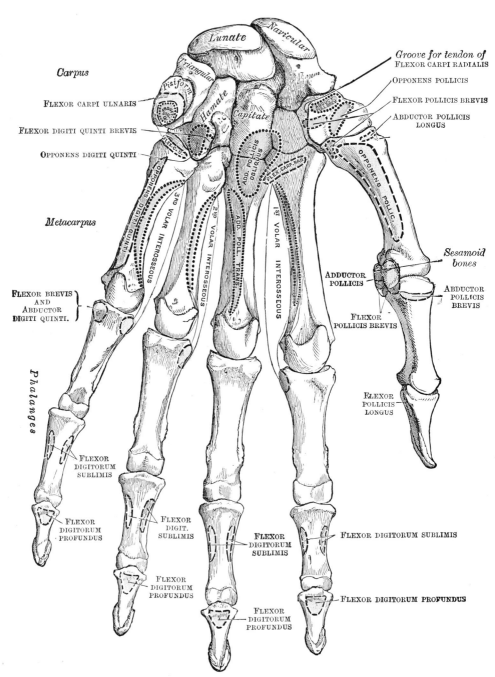

FIG. 213.—Bones of the left hand. Volar surface.

plane anterior to the other carpal bones and is spheroidal in form. Its **dorsal surface** presents a smooth, oval facet, for articulation with the triangular: this facet approaches the superior, but not the inferior border of the bone. The **volar surface** is rounded and rough, and gives attachment to the transverse carpal ligament, and to the Flexor carpi ulnaris and Abductor digiti quinti. The **lateral** and **medial surfaces** are also rough, the former being concave, the latter usually convex.

Articulation.—The pisiform articulates with *one* bone, the triangular.

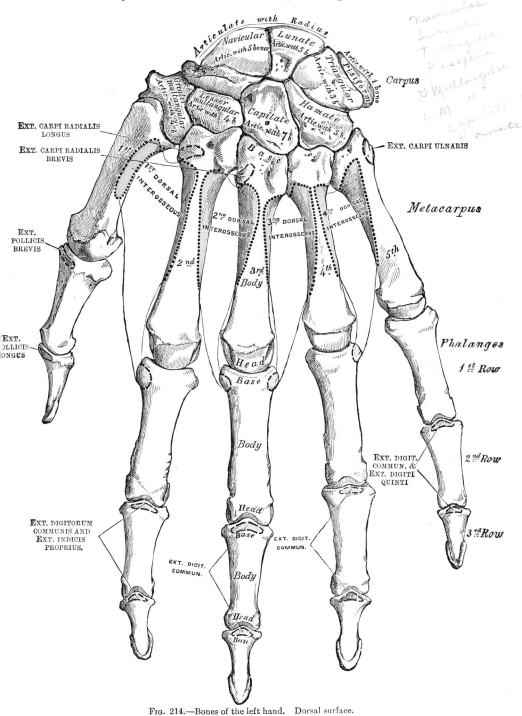

Fig. 214.—Bones of the left hand. Dorsal surface.

Bones of the Distal Row (*lower row*).—**The Greater Multangular Bone** (*os multangulum majus; trapezium*) (Fig. 219).—The greater multangular bone may be distinguished by a deep groove on its volar surface. It is situated at the radial side of the carpus, between the navicular and the first metacarpal bone. The

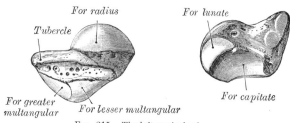

FIG. 215.—The left navicular bone.

superior surface is directed upward and medialward; medially it is smooth, and articulates with the navicular; laterally it is rough and continuous with the lateral surface. The **inferior surface** is oval, concave from side to side, convex from before

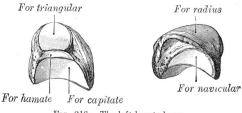

FIG. 216.—The left lunate bone.

backward, so as to form a saddle-shaped surface for articulation with the base of the first metacarpal bone. The **dorsal surface** is rough. The **volar surface** is narrow and rough. At its upper part is a deep groove, running from above obliquely

FIG. 217.—The left triangular bone.   FIG. 218.—The left pisiform bone.

downward and medialward, it transmits the tendon of the Flexor carpi radialis, and is bounded laterally by an oblique ridge. This surface gives origin to the Opponens pollicis and to the Abductor and Flexor pollicis brevis; it also affords

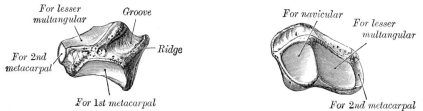

FIG. 219.—The left greater multangular bone.

attachment to the transverse carpal ligament. The **lateral surface** is broad and rough, for the attachment of ligaments. The **medial surface** presents two facets; the upper, large and concave, articulates with the lesser multangular; the lower, small and oval, with the base of the second metacarpal.

Articulations.—The greater multangular articulates with *four* bones: the navicular proximally, the first metacarpal distally, and the lesser multangular and second metacarpal medially.

The Lesser Multangular Bone (*os multangulum minus; trapezoid bone*) (Fig. 220). —The lesser multangular is the smallest bone in the distal row. It may be known by its wedge-shaped form, the broad end of the wedge constituting the dorsal, the narrow end the volar surface; and by its having four articular facets touching each other, and separated by sharp edges. The **superior surface**, quadrilateral, smooth, and slightly concave, articulates with the navicular. The **inferior surface** articulates with the proximal end of the second metacarpal bone; it is convex from side to side, concave from before backward and subdivided by an elevated ridge into two unequal facets. The **dorsal** and **volar** surfaces are rough for the attachment of ligaments, the former being the larger of the two. The **lateral surface**, convex and smooth, articulates with the greater multangular. The **medial surface** is concave and smooth in front, for articulation with the capitate; rough behind, for the attachment of an interosseous ligament.

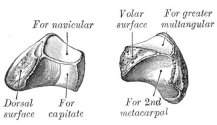

Fig. 220.—The left lesser multangular bone.

Articulations.—The lesser multangular articulates with *four* bones: the navicular proximally, second metacarpal distally, greater multangular laterally, and capitate medially.

The Capitate Bone (*os capitatum; os magnum*) (Fig. 221).—The capitate bone is the largest of the carpal bones, and occupies the center of the wrist. It presents, above, a rounded portion or head, which is received into the concavity formed by

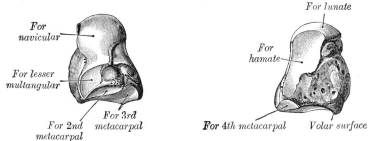

Fig. 221.—The left capitate bone.

the navicular and lunate; a constricted portion or neck; and below this, the body. The **superior surface** is round, smooth, and articulates with the lunate. The **inferior surface** is divided by two ridges into three facets, for articulation with the second,

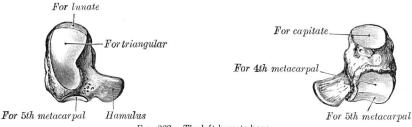

Fig. 222.—The left hamate bone.

third, and fourth metacarpal bones, that for the third being the largest. The **dorsal surface** is broad and rough. The **volar surface** is narrow, rounded, and rough, for the attachment of ligaments and a part of the Adductor pollicis obliquus.

The **lateral surface** articulates with the lesser multangular by a small facet at its anterior inferior angle, behind which is a rough depression for the attachment of an interosseous ligament. Above this is a deep, rough groove, forming part of the neck, and serving for the attachment of ligaments; it is bounded superiorly by a smooth, convex surface, for articulation with the navicular. The **medial surface** articulates with the hamate by a smooth, concave, oblong facet, which occupies its posterior and superior parts; it is rough in front, for the attachment of an interosseous ligament.

Articulations.—The capitate articulates with *seven* bones: the navicular and lunate proximally, the second, third, and fourth metacarpals distally, the lesser multangular on the radial side, and the hamate on the ulnar side.

The **Hamate Bone** (*os hamatum; unciform bone*) (Fig. 222).—The hamate bone may be readily distinguished by its wedge-shaped form, and the hook-like process which projects from its volar surface. It is situated at the medial and lower angle of the carpus, with its base downward, resting on the fourth and fifth metacarpal bones, and its apex directed upward and lateralward. The **superior surface**, the apex of the wedge, is narrow, convex, smooth, and articulates with the lunate. The **inferior surface** articulates with the fourth and fifth metacarpal bones, by concave facets which are separated by a ridge. The **dorsal surface** is triangular and rough for ligamentous attachment. The **volar surface** presents, at its lower and ulnar side, a curved, hook-like process, the **hamulus**, directed forward and lateralward. This process gives attachment, by its apex, to the transverse carpal ligament and the Flexor carpi ulnaris; by its medial surface to the Flexor brevis and Opponens digiti quinti; its lateral side is grooved for the passage of the Flexor tendons into the palm of the hand. It is one of the four eminences on the front of the carpus to which the transverse carpal ligament of the wrist is attached; the others being the pisiform medially, the oblique ridge of the greater multangular and the tubercle of the navicular laterally. The **medial surface** articulates with the triangular bone by an oblong facet, cut obliquely from above, downward and medialward. The *lateral surface* articulates with the capitate by its upper and posterior part, the remaining portion being rough, for the attachment of ligaments.

Articulations.—The hamate articulates with *five* bones: the lunate proximally, the fourth and fifth metacarpals distally, the triangular medially, the capitate laterally.

The Metacarpus (Fig. 213, 214).

The **metacarpus** consists of five cylindrical bones which are numbered from the lateral side (*ossa metacarpalia I–V*); each consists of a body and two extremities.

Common Characteristics of the Metacarpal Bones.—The Body (*corpus; shaft*).— The body is prismoid in form, and curved, so as to be convex in the longitudinal direction behind, concave in front. It presents three surfaces: medial, lateral, and dorsal. The **medial and lateral surfaces** are concave, for the attachment of the Interossei, and separated from one another by a prominent anterior ridge. The **dorsal surface** presents in its distal two-thirds a smooth, triangular, flattened area which is covered in the fresh state, by the tendons of the Extensor muscles. This surface is bounded by two lines, which commence in small tubercles situated on either side of the digital extremity, and, passing upward, converge and meet some distance above the center of the bone and form a ridge which runs along the rest of the dorsal surface to the carpal extremity. This ridge separates two sloping surfaces for the attachment of the Interossei dorsales. To the tubercles on the digital extremities are attached the collateral ligaments of the metacarpophalangeal joints.

The **Base** or **Carpal Extremity** (*basis*) is of a cuboidal form, and broader behind than in front: it articulates with the carpus, and with the adjoining metacarpal bones; its **dorsal** and **volar surfaces** are rough, for the attachment of ligaments.

The **Head** or **Digital Extremity** (*capitulum*) presents an oblong surface markedly convex from before backward, less so transversely, and flattened from side to side; it articulates with the proximal phalanx. It is broader, and extends farther upward, on the volar than on the dorsal aspect, and is longer in the antero-posterior than in the transverse diameter. On either side of the head is a tubercle for the attachment of the collateral ligament of the metacarpophalangeal joint. The **dorsal surface**, broad and flat, supports the Extensor tendons; the **volar surface** is grooved in the middle line for the passage of the Flexor tendons, and marked on either side by an articular eminence continuous with the terminal articular surface.

Characteristics of the Individual Metacarpal Bones.—The **First Metacarpal Bone** (*os metacarpale I; metacarpal bone of the thumb*) (Fig. 223) is shorter and

stouter than the others, diverges to a greater degree from the carpus, and its volar surface is directed toward the palm. The **body** is flattened and broad on its dorsal surface, and does not present the ridge which is found on the other metacarpal bones; its volar surface is concave from above downward. On its radial border is inserted the Opponens pollicis; its ulnar border gives origin to the lateral head of the first Interosseus dorsalis. The **base** presents a concavo-convex surface, for articulation with the greater multangular; it has no facets on its sides, but on its radial side is a tubercle for the insertion of the Abductor pollicis longus. The **head** is less convex than those of the other metacarpal bones, and is broader from side to side than from before backward. On its volar surface are two articular eminences, of which the lateral is the larger, for the two sesamoid bones in the tendons of the Flexor pollicis brevis.

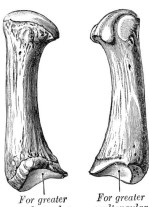

For greater multangular   *For greater multangular*

Fig. 223.—The first metacarpal. (Left.)

The Second Metacarpal Bone (*os metacarpale II; metacarpal bone of the index finger*) (Fig. 224) is the longest, and its base the largest, of the four remaining bones. Its **base** is prolonged upward and medialward, forming a prominent ridge. It presents four articular facets: three on the upper surface and one on the ulnar side. Of the facets on the upper surface the intermediate is the largest and is concave from side to side, convex from before backward for articulation with the lesser multangular; the lateral is small, flat and oval for articulation with the greater multangular; the medial, on the summit of the ridge, is long and narrow for articulation with the capitate. The facet on the ulnar side articulates with the third metacarpal. The Extensor carpi radialis longus is inserted on the dorsal surface and the Flexor carpi radialis on the volar surface of the base.

The Third Metacarpal Bone (*os metacarpale III; metacarpal bone of the middle finger*) (Fig. 225) is a little smaller than the second. The dorsal aspect of its **base** presents on its radial side a pyramidal eminence, the **styloid process**, which extends upward behind the capitate; immediately distal to this is a rough surface for the attachment of the Extensor carpi radialis brevis. The carpal articular facet is concave behind, flat in front, and articulates with the capitate. On the radial side is a smooth, concave facet for articulation with the second metacarpal, and on the ulnar side two small oval facets for the fourth metacarpal.

The Fourth Metacarpal Bone (*os metacarpale IV; metacarpal bone of the ring finger*) (Fig. 226) is shorter and smaller than the third. The **base** is small and quadrilateral; its superior surface presents two facets, a large one medially for articulation with the hamate, and a small one laterally for the capitate. On the radial side are two oval facets, for articulation with the third metacarpal; and on the ulnar side a single concave facet, for the fifth metacarpal.

The Fifth Metacarpal Bone (*os metacarpale V; metacarpal bone of the little finger*) (Fig. 227) presents on its **base** one facet on its superior surface, which is concavo-convex and articulates with the hamate, and one on its radial side, which articulates with the fourth metacarpal. On its ulnar side is a prominent tubercle for the inser-

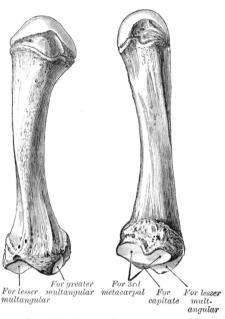

For lesser multangular   For greater multangular   For 3rd metacarpal   For capitate   For lesser multangular

Fig. 224.—The second metacarpal. (Left.)

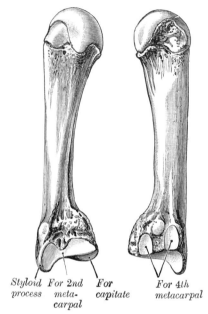

Styloid process   For 2nd metacarpal   For capitate   For 4th metacarpal

Fig. 225.—The third metacarpal. (Left.)

tion of the tendon of the Extensor carpi ulnaris. The dorsal surface of the body is divided by an oblique ridge, which extends from near the ulnar side of the base to the radial side of the head. The lateral part of this surface serves for the attach-

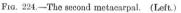

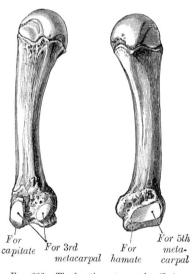

For capitate   For 3rd metacarpal   For hamate   For 5th metacarpal

Fig. 226.—The fourth metacarpal. (Left.)

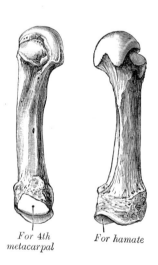

For 4th metacarpal   For hamate

Fig. 227.—The fifth metacarpal. (Left.)

ment of the fourth Interosseus dorsalis; the medial part is smooth, triangular, and covered by the Extensor tendons of the little finger.

Articulations.—Besides their phalangeal articulations, the metacarpal bones articulate as follows: the first with the greater multangular; the second with the greater multangular, lesser multangular, capitate and third metacarpal; the third with the capitate and second and fourth metacarpals; the fourth with the capitate, hamate, and third and fifth metacarpals; and the fifth with the hamate and fourth metacarpal.

The Phalanges of the Hand (Phalanges Digitorum Manus) (Fig. 213).

The **phalanges** are fourteen in number, three for each finger, and two for the thumb. Each consists of a body and two extremities. The **body** tapers from above downward, is convex posteriorly, concave in front from above downward, flat from side to side; its sides are marked by rough ridges which give attachment to the fibrous sheaths of the Flexor tendons. The **proximal extremities** of the bones of the first row present oval, concave articular surfaces, broader from side to side than from before backward. The **proximal extremity** of each of the bones of the second and third rows presents a double concavity separated by a median ridge. The **distal extremities** are smaller than the proximal, and each ends in two condyles separated by a shallow groove; the articular surface extends farther on the volar than on the dorsal surface, a condition best marked in the bones of the first row.

The **ungual phalanges** are convex on their dorsal and flat on their volar surfaces; they are recognized by their small size, and by a roughened, elevated surface of a horseshoe form on the volar surface of the distal extremity of each which serves to support the sensitive pulp of the finger.

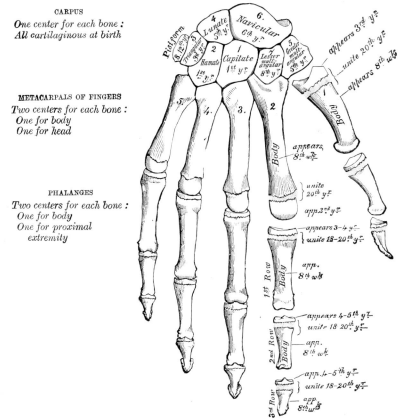

Fig. 228.—Plan of ossification of the hand.

Articulations.—In the four fingers the phalanges of the first row articulate with those of the second row and with the metacarpals; the phalanges of the second row with those of the first and third rows, and the ungual phalanges with those of the second row. In the thumb, which has only two phalanges, the first phalanx articulates by its proximal extremity with the metacarpal bone and by its distal with the ungual phalanx.

Ossification of the Bones of the Hand.—The **carpal bones** are each ossified from a single center, and ossification proceeds in the following order (Fig. 228): in the capitate and hamate, during the first year, the former preceding the latter; in the triangular, during the third year; in the lunate and greater multangular, during the fifth year, the former preceding the latter; in the navicular, during the sixth year; in the lesser multangular, during the eighth year; and in the pisiform, about the twelfth year. Ossification is usually bilaterally symmetrical (Pryor).

Occasionally an additional bone, the *os centrale*, is found on the back of the carpus, lying between the navicular, lesser multangular, and capitate. During the second month of fetal life it is represented by a small cartilaginous nodule, which usually fuses with the cartilaginous navicular. Sometimes the styloid process of the third metacarpal is detached and forms an additional ossicle.

The **metacarpal bones** are each ossified from *two* centers: one for the body and one for the distal extremity of each of the second, third, fourth, and fifth bones; one for the body and one for the base of the first metacarpal bone. The first metacarpal bone is therefore ossified in the same manner as the phalanges, and this has led some anatomists to regard the thumb as being made up of three phalanges, and not of a metacarpal bone and two phalanges. Ossification commences in the middle of the body about the eighth or ninth week of fetal life, the centers for the second and third metacarpals being the first, and that for the first metacarpal, the last, to appear; about the third year the distal extremities of the metacarpals of the fingers, and the base of the metacarpal of the thumb, begin to ossify; they unite with the bodies about the twentieth year.

The **phalanges** are each ossified from *two* centers: one for the body, and one for the proximal extremity. Ossification begins in the body, about the eighth week of fetal life. Ossification of the proximal extremity commences in the bones of the first row between the third and fourth years, and a year later in those of the second and third rows. The two centers become united in each row between the eighteenth and twentieth years.

In the ungual phalanges the centers for the bodies appear at the distal extremities of the phalanges, instead of at the middle of the bodies, as in the other phalanges. Moreover, of all the bones of the hand, the ungual phalanges are the first to ossify.

THE BONES OF THE LOWER EXTREMITY (OSSA EXTREMITATIS INFERIORIS).

The Hip Bone (Os Coxæ; Innominate Bone) (Fig. 229, 230).

The **hip bone** is a large, flattened, irregularly shaped bone, constricted in the center and expanded above and below. It meets its fellow on the opposite side in the middle line in front, and together they form the sides and anterior wall of the pelvic cavity. It consists of three parts, the **ilium, ischium,** and **pubis,** which are distinct from each other in the young subject, but are fused in the adult; the union of the three parts takes place in and around a large cup-shaped articular cavity, the **acetabulum,** which is situated near the middle of the outer surface of the bone. The **ilium,** so-called because it supports the flank, is the superior broad and expanded portion which extends upward from the acetabulum. The **ischium** is the lowest and strongest portion of the bone; it proceeds downward from the acetabulum, expands into a large tuberosity, and then, curving forward, forms, with the pubis, a large aperture, the **obturator foramen.** The **pubis** extends medialward and downward from the acetabulum and articulates in the middle line with the bone of the opposite side: it forms the front of the pelvis and supports the external organs of generation.

The Ilium (*os ilii*).—The ilium is divisible into two parts, the **body** and the **ala;** the separation is indicated on the internal surface by a curved line, the **arcuate line,** and on the external surface by the margin of the acetabulum.

The Body (*corpus oss. ilii*).—The body enters into the formation of the acetabulum, of which it forms rather less than two-fifths. Its **external surface** is partly articular, partly non-articular; the articular segment forms part of the lunate surface of the acetabulum, the non-articular portion contributes to the acetabular fossa. The **internal surface** of the body is part of the wall of the lesser pelvis and gives origin to some fibers of the Obturator internus. Below, it is continuous with the pelvic surfaces of the ischium and pubis, only a faint line indicating the place of union.

The Ala (*ala oss. ilii*).—The ala is the large expanded portion which bounds the greater pelvis laterally. It presents for examination two surfaces—an external and an internal—a crest, and two borders—an anterior and a posterior. The **external surface** (Fig. 229), known as the **dorsum ilii**, is directed backward and lateralward behind, and downward and lateralward in front. It is smooth, convex in front, deeply concave behind; bounded above by the crest, below by the upper border of the acetabulum, in front and behind by the anterior and posterior borders. This surface is crossed in an arched direction by three lines—the posterior, anterior, and inferior gluteal lines. The **posterior gluteal line** (*superior curved line*), the shortest of the three, begins at the crest, about 5 cm. in front of its posterior extremity; it is at first distinctly marked, but as it passes downward to the upper part of the greater sciatic notch, where it ends, it becomes less distinct, and is often altogether lost. Behind this line is a narrow semilunar surface, the upper part of which is rough and gives origin to a portion of the Glutæus maximus; the lower part is smooth and has no muscular fibers attached to it. The **anterior gluteal line** (*middle curved line*), the longest of the three, begins at the crest, about 4 cm. behind its anterior extremity, and, taking a curved direction downward and backward, ends at the upper part of the greater sciatic notch. The space between the anterior and posterior gluteal lines and the crest is concave, and gives origin to the Glutæus medius. Near the middle of this line a nutrient foramen is often seen. The **inferior gluteal line** (*inferior curved line*), the least distinct of the three, begins in front at the notch on the anterior border, and, curving backward and downward, ends near the middle of the greater sciatic notch. The surface of bone included between the anterior and inferior gluteal lines is concave from above downward, convex from before backward, and gives origin to the Glutæus minimus. Between the inferior gluteal line and the upper part of the acetabulum is a rough, shallow groove, from which the reflected tendon of the Rectus femoris arises.

The **internal surface** (Fig. 230) of the ala is bounded above by the crest, below, by the arcuate line; in front and behind, by the anterior and posterior borders. It presents a large, smooth, concave surface, called the **iliac fossa**, which gives origin to the Iliacus and is perforated at its inner part by a nutrient canal; and below this a smooth, rounded border, the **arcuate line** (**iliopectineal line**, Fig. 384), which runs downward, forward, and medialward. Behind the iliac fossa is a rough surface, divided into two portions, an anterior and a posterior. The **articular surface** (*auricular surface*), so called from its resemblance in shape to the ear, is coated with cartilage in the fresh state, and articulates with a similar surface on the side of the sacrum. The posterior portion, known as the **iliac tuberosity**, is elevated and rough, for the attachment of the posterior sacroiliac ligaments and for the origins of the Sacrospinalis and Multifidus. Below and in front of the auricular surface is the **preauricular sulcus,** more commonly present and better marked in the female than in the male; to it is attached the pelvic portion of the anterior sacroiliac ligament.

The **crest** of the ilium is convex in its general outline but is sinuously curved, being concave inward in front, concave outward behind. It is thinner at the center than at the extremities, and ends in the **anterior** and **posterior superior iliac spines.** The surface of the crest is broad, and divided into external and internal lips, and an intermediate line. About 5 cm. behind the anterior superior iliac spine there is a prominent tubercle on the outer lip. To the external lip are attached the Tensor fasciæ latæ, Obliquus externus abdominis, and Latissimus dorsi, and along its whole length the fascia lata; to the intermediate line the Obliquus internus abdominis; to the internal lip, the fascia iliaca, the Transversus abdominis, Quadratus lumborum, Sacrospinalis, and Iliacus.

The **anterior border** of the ala is concave. It presents two projections, separated by a notch. Of these, the uppermost, situated at the junction of the crest and anterior border, is called the **anterior superior iliac spine;** its outer border gives attachment to the fascia lata, and the Tensor fasciæ latæ, its inner border, to the Iliacus; while its extremity affords attachment to the inguinal ligament and gives origin to the Sartorius. Beneath this eminence is a notch from which the Sartorius takes origin and across which the lateral femoral cutaneous nerve passes. Below

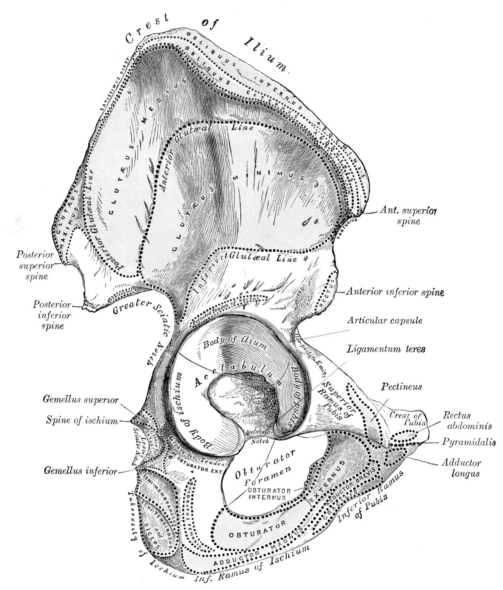

Fig. 229.—Right hip bone. External surface.

the notch is the **anterior inferior iliac spine,** which ends in the upper lip of the acetabulum; it gives attachment to the straight tendon of the Rectus femoris and to the iliofemoral ligament of the hip-joint. Medial to the anterior inferior spine is a broad, shallow groove, over which the Iliacus and Psoas major pass. This groove is bounded medially by an eminence, the **iliopectineal eminence,** which marks the point of union of the ilium and pubis.

The **posterior border** of the ala, shorter than the anterior, also presents two projections separated by a notch, the **posterior superior iliac spine** and the **posterior inferior iliac spine.** The former serves for the attachment of the oblique portion of the posterior sacroiliac ligaments and the Multifidus; the latter corresponds with the posterior extremity of the auricular surface. Below the posterior inferior spine is a deep notch, the **greater sciatic notch.**

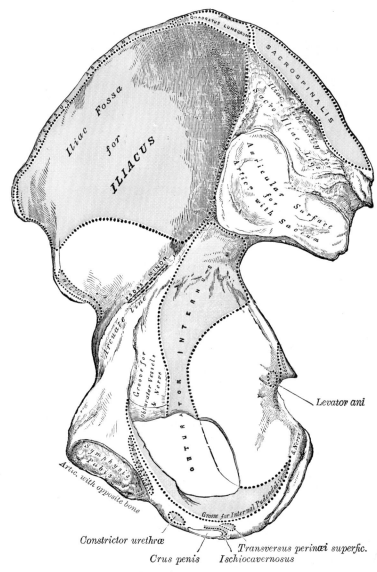

Fig. 230.—Right hip bone. Internal surface.

The Ischium (*os ischii*).—The ischium forms the lower and back part of the hip bone. It is divisible into three portions—a **body** and **two rami.**

The Body (*corpus oss. ischii*).—The body enters into and constitutes a little more than two-fifths of the acetabulum. Its **external surface** forms part of the lunate surface of the acetabulum and a portion of the acetabular fossa. Its **internal surface** is part of the wall of the lesser pelvis; it gives origin to some fibers of the

14

Obturator internus. Its anterior border projects as the **posterior obturator tubercle;** from its posterior border there extends backward a thin and pointed triangular eminence, the **ischial spine,** more or less elongated in different subjects. The external surface of the spine gives attachment to the Gemellus superior, its internal surface to the Coccygeus, Levator ani, and the pelvic fascia; while to the pointed extremity the sacrospinous ligament is attached. Above the spine is a large notch, the **greater sciatic notch,** converted into a foramen by the sacrospinous ligament; it transmits the Piriformis, the superior and inferior gluteal vessels and nerves, the sciatic and posterior femoral cutaneous nerves, the internal pudendal vessels, and nerve, and the nerves to the Obturator internus and Quadratus femoris. Of these, the superior gluteal vessels and nerve pass out above the Piriformis, the other structures below it. Below the spine is a smaller notch, the **lesser sciatic notch;** it is smooth, coated in the recent state with cartilage, the surface of which presents two or three ridges corresponding to the subdivisions of the tendon of the Obturator internus, which winds over it. It is converted into a foramen by the sacrotuberous and sacrospinous ligaments, and transmits the tendon of the Obturator internus, the nerve which supplies that muscle, and the internal pudendal vessels and nerve.

The Superior Ramus (*ramus superior oss. ischii; descending ramus*).—The superior ramus projects downward and backward from the body and presents for examination three surfaces: external, internal, and posterior. The **external surface** is quadrilateral in shape. It is bounded *above* by a groove which lodges the tendon of the Obturator externus; *below*, it is continuous with the inferior ramus; in *front* it is limited by the posterior margin of the obturator foramen; *behind*, a prominent margin separates it from the posterior surface. In front of this margin the surface gives origin to the Quadratus femoris, and anterior to this to some of the fibers of origin of the Obturator externus; the lower part of the surface gives origin to part of the Adductor magnus. The **internal surface** forms part of the bony wall of the lesser pelvis. In *front* it is limited by the posterior margin of the obturator foramen. *Below*, it is bounded by a sharp ridge which gives attachment to a falciform prolongation of the sacrotuberous ligament, and, more anteriorly, gives origin to the Transversus perinæi and Ischiocavernosus. *Posteriorly* the ramus forms a large swelling, the **tuberosity of the ischium,** which is divided into two portions: a lower, rough, somewhat triangular part, and an upper, smooth, quadrilateral portion. The lower portion is subdivided by a prominent longitudinal ridge, passing from base to apex, into two parts; the outer gives attachment to the Adductor magnus, the inner to the sacrotuberous ligament. The upper portion is subdivided into two areas by an oblique ridge, which runs downward and outward; from the upper and outer area the Semimembranosus arises; from the lower and inner, the long head of the Biceps femoris and the Semitendinosus.

The Inferior Ramus (*ramus inferior oss. ischii; ascending ramus*).—The inferior ramus is the thin, flattened part of the ischium, which ascends from the superior ramus, and joins the inferior ramus of the pubis—the junction being indicated in the adult by a raised line. The **outer surface** is uneven for the origin of the Obturator externus and some of the fibers of the Adductor magnus; its **inner surface** forms part of the anterior wall of the pelvis. Its **medial border** is thick, rough, slightly everted, forms part of the outlet of the pelvis, and presents two ridges and an intervening space. The ridges are continuous with similar ones on the inferior ramus of the pubis: to the outer is attached the deep layer of the superficial perineal fascia (*fascia of Colles*), and to the inner the inferior fascia of the urogenital diaphragm. If these two ridges be traced downward, they will be found to join with each other just behind the point of origin of the Transversus perinæi; here the two layers of fascia are inseparable behind the posterior border of the muscle. To the intervening space, just in front of the point of junction of the ridges, the

Transversus perinæi is attached, and in front of this a portion of the crus penis vel clitoridis and the Ischiocavernosus. Its **lateral border** is thin and sharp, and forms part of the medial margin of the obturator foramen.

The Pubis (*os pubis*).—The pubis, the anterior part of the hip bone, is divisible into a **body**, a **superior** and an **inferior ramus**.

The Body (*corpus oss. pubis*).—The body forms one-fifth of the acetabulum, contributing by its **external surface** both to the lunate surface and the acetabular fossa. Its **internal surface** enters into the formation of the wall of the lesser pelvis and gives origin to a portion of the Obturator internus.

The Superior Ramus (*ramus superior oss. pubis; ascending ramus*).—The superior ramus extends from the body to the median plane where it articulates with its fellow of the opposite side. It is conveniently described in two portions, viz., a medial flattened part and a narrow lateral prismoid portion.

The **Medial Portion** of the superior ramus, formerly described as the body of the pubis, is somewhat quadrilateral in shape, and presents for examination two surfaces and three borders. The **external surface** is rough, directed downward and outward, and serves for the origin of various muscles. The Adductor longus arises from the upper and medial angle, immediately below the crest; lower down, the Obturator externus, the Adductor brevis, and the upper part of the Gracilis take origin. The **internal surface**, convex from above downward, concave from side to side, is smooth, and forms part of the anterior wall of the pelvis. It gives origin to the Levator ani and Obturator internus, and attachment to the puboprostatic ligaments and to a few muscular fibers prolonged from the bladder. The **upper border** presents a prominent tubercle, the **pubic tubercle** (*pubic spine*), which projects forward; the inferior crus of the **subcutaneous inguinal ring** (*external abdominal ring*), and the **inguinal ligament** (*Poupart's ligament*) are attached to it. Passing upward and lateralward from the pubic tubercle is a well-defined ridge, forming a part of the **pecten pubis** which marks the brim of the lesser pelvis: to it are attached a portion of the **inguinal falx** (*conjoined tendon of Obliquus internus and Transversus*), the **lacunar ligament** (*Gimbernat's ligament*), and the **reflected inguinal ligament** (*triangular fascia*). Medial to the pubic tubercle is the **crest**, which extends from this process to the medial end of the bone. It affords attachment to the inguinal falx, and to the Rectus abdominis and Pyramidalis. The point of junction of the crest with the medial border of the bone is called the **angle**; to it, as well as to the symphysis, the superior crus of the subcutaneous inguinal ring is attached. The **medial border** is articular; it is oval, and is marked by eight or nine transverse ridges, or a series of nipple-like processes arranged in rows, separated by grooves; they serve for the attachment of a thin layer of cartilage, which intervenes between it and the interpubic fibrocartilaginous lamina. The **lateral border** presents a sharp margin, the **obturator crest**, which forms part of the circumference of the obturator foramen and affords attachment to the obturator membrane.

The **Lateral Portion** of the superior ramus has three surfaces: superior, inferior, and posterior. The **superior surface** presents the **iliopectineal line**, a continuation of the pecten pubis, already mentioned as commencing at the pubic tubercle. In front of this line, the surface of bone is triangular in form, wider laterally than medially, and is covered by the Pectineus. The surface is bounded, laterally, by a rough eminence, the **iliopectineal eminence**, which serves to indicate the point of junction of the ilium and pubis, and below by a prominent ridge which extends from the acetabular notch to the pubic tubercle. The **inferior surface** forms the upper boundary of the obturator foramen, and presents, laterally, a broad and deep, oblique groove, for the passage of the obturator vessels and nerve; and medially, a sharp margin, the **obturator crest**, forming part of the circumference of the obturator foramen, and giving attachment to the obturator membrane. The

posterior surface constitutes part of the anterior boundary of the lesser pelvis. It is smooth, convex from above downward, and affords origin to some fibers of the Obturator internus.

The Inferior Ramus (*ramus inferior oss. pubis; descending ramus*).—The inferior ramus is thin and flattened. It passes lateralward and downward from the medial end of the superior ramus; it becomes narrower as it descends and joins with the inferior ramus of the ischium below the obturator foramen. Its **external surface** is rough, for the origin of muscles—the Gracilis along its medial border, a portion of the Obturator externus where it enters into the formation of the obturator foramen, and between these two, the Adductores brevis and magnus, the former being the more medial. The **internal surface** is smooth, and gives origin to the Obturator internus, and, close to the medial margin, to the Constrictor urethræ. The **medial border** is thick, rough, and everted, especially in females. It presents two ridges, separated by an intervening space. The ridges extend downward, and are continuous with similar ridges on the inferior ramus of the ischium; to the external is attached the fascia of Colles, and to the internal the inferior fascia of the urogenital diaphragm. The **lateral border** is thin and sharp, forms part of the circumference of the obturator foramen, and gives attachment to the obturator membrane.

The Acetabulum (*cotyloid cavity*).—The acetabulum is a deep, cup-shaped, hemispherical depression, directed downward, lateralward, and forward. It is formed medially by the pubis, above by the ilium, laterally and below by the ischium; a little less than two-fifths is contributed by the ilium, a little more than two-fifths by the ischium, and the remaining fifth by the pubis. It is bounded by a prominent uneven rim, which is thick and strong above, and serves for the attachment of the **glenoidal labrum** (*cotyloid ligament*), which contracts its orifice, and deepens the surface for articulation. It presents below a deep notch, the **acetabular notch**, which is continuous with a circular non-articular depression, the **acetabular fossa**, at the bottom of the cavity: this depression is perforated by numerous apertures, and lodges a mass of fat. The notch is converted into a foramen by the transverse ligament; through the foramen nutrient vessels and nerves enter the joint; the margins of the notch serve for the attachment of the ligamentum teres. The rest of the acetabulum is formed by a curved articular surface, the **lunate surface**, for articulation with the head of the femur.

The Obturator Foramen (*foramen obturatum; thyroid foramen*).—The obturator foramen is a large aperture, situated between the ischium and pubis. In the male it is large and of an oval form, its longest diameter slanting obliquely from before backward; in the female it is smaller, and more triangular. It is bounded by a thin, uneven margin, to which a strong membrane is attached, and presents, superiorly, a deep groove, the **obturator groove**, which runs from the pelvis obliquely medialward and downward. This groove is converted into a canal by a ligamentous band, a specialized part of the obturator membrane, attached to two tubercles: one, the **posterior obturator tubercle**, on the medial border of the ischium, just in front of the acetabular notch; the other, the **anterior obturator tubercle**, on the obturator crest of the superior ramus of the pubis. Through the canal the obturator vessels and nerve pass out of the pelvis.

Structure.—The thicker parts of the bone consist of cancellous tissue, enclosed between two layers of compact tissue; the thinner parts, as at the bottom of the acetabulum and center of the iliac fossa, are usually semitransparent, and composed entirely of compact tissue.

Ossification (Fig. 231).—The hip bone is ossified from *eight* centers: *three* primary—one each for the ilium, ischium, and pubis; and *five* secondary—one each for the crest of the ilium, the anterior inferior spine (said to occur more frequently in the male than in the female), the tuberosity of the ischium, the pubic symphysis (more frequent in the female than in the male), and one or more for the Y-shaped piece at the bottom of the acetabulum. The centers appear in the following order: in the lower part of the ilium, immediately above the greater sciatic notch, about the eighth or ninth week of fetal life; in the superior ramus of the ischium, about the third month; in the superior ramus of the pubis, between the fourth and fifth months. At birth, the three primary centers are quite separate, the crest, the bottom of the acetabulum, the ischial tuberosity and the inferior rami of the ischium and pubis being still cartilaginous. By the seventh or eighth year, the inferior rami of the pubis and ischium are almost completely united by bone. About the thirteenth or fourteenth year, the three primary centers have extended their growth into the bottom of the acetabulum, and are there separated from each other by a Y-shaped portion of cartilage, which now presents traces of ossification, often by two or more centers. One of these, the *os acetabuli*, appears about the age of twelve, between the ilium and pubis, and fuses with them about the age of eighteen; it forms the pubic part of the acetabulum. The ilium and ischium then become joined, and lastly the pubis and ischium, through the intervention of this Y-shaped portion. At about the age of puberty, ossification takes place in each of the remaining portions, and they join with the rest of the bone between the twentieth and twenty-fifth years. Separate centers are frequently found for the pubic tubercle and the ischial spine, and for the crest and angle of the pubis.

Articulations.—The hip bone articulates with its fellow of the opposite side, and with the sacrum and femur.

By eight centers { *Three primary (Ilium, Ischium, and Pubis)*
 Five secondary

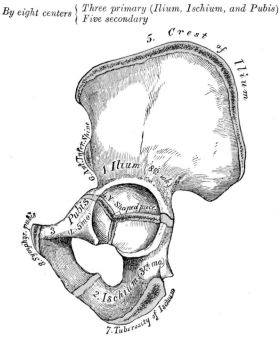

Fig. 231.—Plan of ossification of the hip bone. The three primary centers unite through a Y-shaped piece about puberty. Epiphyses appear about puberty, and unite about twenty-fifth year.

The Pelvis.

The **pelvis,** so called from its resemblance to a basin, is a bony ring, interposed between the movable vertebræ of the vertebral column which it supports, and the lower limbs upon which it rests; it is stronger and more massively constructed than the wall of the cranial or thoracic cavities, and is composed of four bones: the two **hip bones** laterally and in front and the **sacrum** and **coccyx** behind.

The pelvis is divided by an oblique plane passing through the prominence of the sacrum, the arcuate and pectineal lines, and the upper margin of the symphysis pubis, into the greater and the lesser pelvis. The circumference of this plane is termed the **linea terminalis** or **pelvic brim.**

The Greater or False Pelvis (*pelvis major*).—The greater pelvis is the expanded portion of the cavity situated above and in front of the pelvic brim. It is bounded on either side by the ilium; in *front* it is incomplete, presenting a wide interval between the anterior borders of the ilia, which is filled up in the fresh state by the parietes of the abdomen; behind is a deep notch on either side between the ilium and the base of the sacrum. It supports the intestines, and transmits part of their weight to the anterior wall of the abdomen.

The Lesser or True Pelvis (*pelvis minor*).—The lesser pelvis is that part of the pelvic cavity which is situated below and behind the pelvic brim. Its bony walls are more complete than those of the greater pelvis. For convenience of description, it is divided into an **inlet** bounded by the superior circumference, and **outlet** bounded by the inferior circumference, and a **cavity**.

The Superior Circumference.—The superior circumference forms the brim of the pelvis, the included space being called the **superior aperture** or **inlet** (*apertura pelvis* [*minoris*] *superior*) (Fig. 232). It is formed laterally by the pectineal and arcuate lines, in front by the crests of the pubes, and behind by the anterior margin of the base of the sacrum and sacrovertebral angle. The superior aperture is somewhat heart-shaped, obtusely pointed in front, diverging on either side, and encroached upon behind by the projection forward of the promontory of the sacrum. It has three principal diameters: antero-posterior, transverse, and oblique. The **antero-posterior** or **conjugate diameter** extends from the sacrovertebral angle to the sym-

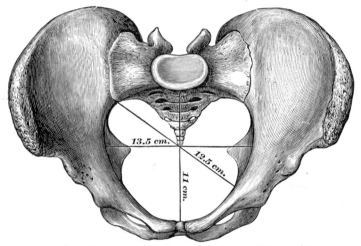

FIG. 232.—Diameters of superior aperture of lesser pelvis (female).

physis pubis; its average measurement is about 11 cm. in the female. The **transverse diameter** extends across the greatest width of the superior aperture, from the middle of the brim on one side to the same point on the opposite; its average measurement is about 13.5 cm. in the female. The **oblique diameter** extends from the iliopectineal eminence of one side to the sacroiliac articulation of the opposite side; its average measurement is about 12.5 cm. in the female.

The **cavity** of the lesser pelvis is bounded in front and below by the pubic symphysis and the superior rami of the pubes; above and behind, by the pelvic surfaces of the sacrum and coccyx, which, curving forward above and below, contract the superior and inferior apertures of the cavity; laterally, by a broad, smooth, quadrangular area of bone, corresponding to the inner surfaces of the body and superior ramus of the ischium and that part of the ilium which is below the arcuate line. From this description it will be seen that the cavity of the lesser pelvis is a short, curved canal, considerably deeper on its posterior than on its anterior wall. It contains, in the fresh subject, the pelvic colon, rectum, bladder, and some of the organs of generation. The rectum is placed at the back of the pelvis, in the curve of the sacrum and coccyx; the bladder is in front, behind the pubic symphysis. In the female the uterus and vagina occupy the interval between these viscera.

The Lower Circumference.—The lower circumference of the pelvis is very irregular; the space enclosed by it is named the **inferior aperture** or **outlet** (*apertura pelvis* [*minoris*] *inferior*) (Fig. 233), and is bounded behind by the point of the coccyx, and laterally by the ischial tuberosities. These eminences are separated by three notches: one in front, the **pubic arch**, formed by the convergence of the inferior rami of the ischium and pubis on either side. The other notches, one on either side, are formed by the sacrum and coccyx behind, the ischium in front, and

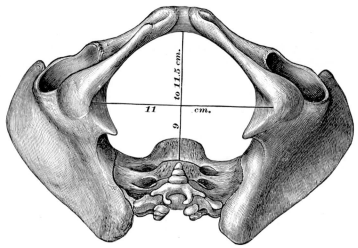

FIG. 233.—Diameters of inferior aperture of lesser pelvis (female).

the ilium above; they are called the **sciatic notches**; in the natural state they are converted into foramina by the sacrotuberous and sacrospinous ligaments. When the ligaments are *in situ*, the inferior aperture of the pelvis is lozenge-shaped, bounded, in front, by the pubic arcuate ligament and the inferior rami of the pubes and ischia; laterally, by the ischial tuberosities; and behind, by the sacrotuberous ligaments and the tip of the coccyx.

The diameters of the outlet of the pelvis are two, antero-posterior and transverse. The **antero-posterior diameter** extends from the tip of the coccyx to the lower part of the pubic symphysis; its measurement is from 9 to 11.5 cm. in the female. It varies with the length of the coccyx, and is capable of increase or diminution, on account of the mobility of that bone. The **transverse diameter**, measured between the posterior parts of the ischial tuberosities, is about 11 cm. in the female.

Axes (Fig. 234).—A line at right angles to the plane of the superior aperture at its center would, if prolonged, pass through the umbilicus above and the middle of the coccyx below; the axis of the superior aperture is therefore directed downward and backward. The axis of the inferior aperture, produced upward, would touch the base of the sacrum, and is also directed

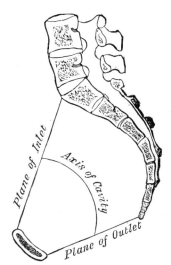

FIG. 234.—Median sagittal section of pelvis.

downward, and slightly backward. The axis of the cavity—*i. e.*, an axis at right angles to a series of planes between those of the superior and inferior apertures

—is curved like the cavity itself: this curve corresponds to the concavity of the sacrum and coccyx, the extremities being indicated by the central points of the superior and inferior apertures. A knowledge of the direction of these axes serves to explain the course of the fetus in its passage through the pelvis during parturition.

Position of the Pelvis (Fig. 234).—In the erect posture, the pelvis is placed obliquely with regard to the trunk: the plane of the superior aperture forms an angle of from 50° to 60°, and that of the inferior aperture one of about 15° with the horizontal plane. The pelvic surface of the symphysis pubis looks upward and backward, the concavity of the sacrum and coccyx downward and forward. The position of the pelvis in the erect posture may be indicated by holding it so that the anterior superior iliac spines and the front of the top of the symphysis pubis are in the same vertical plane.

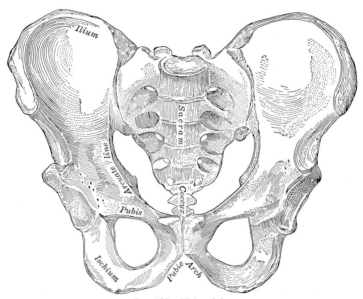

Fig. 235.—Male pelvis.

Differences between the Male and Female Pelves.—The *female* pelvis (Fig. 236) is distinguished from that of the *male* (Fig. 235) by its bones being more delicate and its depth less. The whole pelvis is less massive, and its muscular impressions are slightly marked. The ilia are less sloped, and the anterior iliac spines more widely separated; hence the greater lateral prominence of the hips. The preauricular sulcus is more commonly present and better marked. The superior aperture of the lesser pelvis is larger in the female than in the male; it is more nearly circular, and its obliquity is greater. The cavity is shallower and wider; the sacrum is shorter, wider, and its upper part is less curved; the obturator foramina are triangular in shape and smaller in size than in the male. The inferior aperture is larger and the coccyx more movable. The sciatic notches are wider and shallower, and the spines of the ischia project less inward. The acetabula are smaller and look more distinctly forward. The ischial tuberosities and the acetabula are wider apart, and the former are more everted. The pubic symphysis is less deep, and the pubic arch is wider and more rounded than in the male, where it is an angle rather than an arch.

The size of the pelvis varies not only in the two sexes, but also in different members of the same sex, and does not appear to be influenced in any way by the height of the individual. Women of short stature, as a rule, have broad pelves. Occasionally the pelvis is equally contracted in all its dimensions, so much so that all its diameters measure 12.5 mm. less than the average, and this even in well-formed women of average height. The principal divergences, however, are found at the superior aperture, and affect the relation of the antero-posterior to the transverse diameter. Thus the superior aperture may be elliptical either in a transverse or an antero-posterior direction, the transverse diameter in the former, and the antero-posterior in the latter, greatly exceeding the other diameters; in other instances it is almost circular.

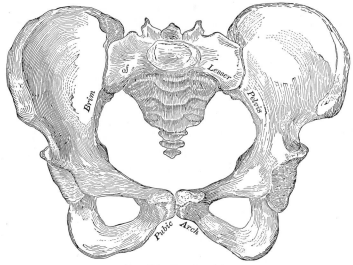

FIG. 236.—Female pelvis.

In the fetus, and for several years after birth, the pelvis is smaller in proportion than in the adult, and the projection of the sacrovertebral angle less marked. The characteristic differences between the male and female pelvis are distinctly indicated as early as the fourth month of fetal life.

The Femur (Thigh Bone).

The **femur** (Figs. 238, 239), the longest and strongest bone in the skeleton, is almost perfectly cylindrical in the greater part of its extent. In the erect posture it is not vertical, being separated above from its fellow by a considerable interval, which corresponds to the breadth of the pelvis, but inclining gradually downward and medialward, so as to approach its fellow toward its lower part, for the purpose of bringing the knee-joint near the line of gravity of the body. The degree of this inclination varies in different persons, and is greater in the female than in the male, on account of the greater breadth of the pelvis. The femur, like other long bones, is divisible into a **body** and **two extremities.**

The Upper Extremity (*proximal extremity,* Fig. 237).—The upper extremity presents for examination a **head,** a **neck,** a **greater** and a **lesser trochanter.**

The Head (*caput femoris*).—The head which is globular and forms rather more than a hemisphere, is directed upward, medialward, and a little forward, the greater part of its convexity being above and in front. Its surface is smooth, coated with cartilage in the fresh state, except over an ovoid depression, the **fovea capitis femoris,** which is situated a little below and behind the center of the head, and gives attachment to the ligamentum teres.

The Neck (*collum femoris*).—The neck is a flattened pyramidal process of bone, connecting the head with the body, and forming with the latter a wide angle opening medialward. The angle is widest in infancy, and becomes lessened during growth, so that at puberty it forms a gentle curve from the axis of the body of the bone. In the adult, the neck forms an angle of about 125° with the body, but this varies in inverse proportion to the development of the pelvis and the stature. In the female, in consequence of the increased width of the pelvis, the neck of the femur forms more nearly a right angle with the body than it does in the male. The angle decreases during the period of growth, but after full growth has been attained it does not usually undergo any change, even in old age; it varies considerably in different persons of the same age. It is smaller in short than in long bones, and when the pelvis is wide. In addition to projecting upward and medialward from the body of the femur, the neck also projects somewhat forward; the amount of this forward projection is extremely variable, but on an average is from 12° to 14°.

The neck is flattened from before backward, contracted in the middle, and broader laterally than medially. The vertical diameter of the lateral half is increased by the obliquity of the lower edge, which slopes downward to join the body at the level of the lesser trochanter, so that it measures one-third more than the antero-posterior diameter. The medial half is smaller and of a more circular shape. The **anterior surface** of the neck is perforated by numerous vascular foramina. Along the upper part of the line of junction of the anterior surface with the head is a shallow groove, best marked in elderly subjects; this groove lodges the orbicular fibers of the capsule of the hip-joint. The **posterior surface** is smooth, and is broader and more concave than the anterior: the posterior part of the capsule of the hip-joint is attached to it about 1 cm. above the intertrochanteric crest. The **superior border** is short and thick, and ends laterally at the greater trochanter; its surface is perforated by large foramina. The **inferior border**, long and narrow, curves a little backward, to end at the lesser trochanter.

The Trochanters.—The trochanters are prominent processes which afford leverage to the muscles that rotate the thigh on its axis. They are two in number, the greater and the lesser.

The **Greater Trochanter** (*trochanter major; great trochanter*) is a large, irregular, quadrilateral eminence, situated at the junction of the neck with the upper part of the body. It is directed a little lateralward and backward, and, in the adult, is about 1 cm. lower than the head. It has two surfaces and four borders. The **lateral surface**, quadrilateral in form, is broad, rough, convex, and marked by a diagonal impression, which extends from the postero-superior to the antero-inferior angle, and serves for the insertion of the tendon of the Glutæus medius. Above the impression is a triangular surface, sometimes rough for part of the tendon of the same muscle, sometimes smooth for the interposition of a bursa between the tendon and the bone. Below and behind the diagonal impression is a smooth, triangular surface, over which the tendon of the Glutæus maximus plays, a bursa being interposed. The **medial surface**, of much less extent than the lateral, presents at its base a deep depression, the **trochanteric fossa** (*digital fossa*), for the insertion of the tendon of the Obturator externus, and above and in front of this an impression for the insertion of the Obturator internus and Gemelli. The **superior border** is free; it is thick and irregular, and marked near the center by an impression for the insertion of the Piriformis. The **inferior border** corresponds to the line of junction of the base of the trochanter with the lateral surface of the body; it is marked by a rough, prominent, slightly curved ridge, which gives origin to the upper part of the Vastus lateralis. The **anterior border** is prominent and somewhat irregular; it affords insertion at its lateral part to the Glutæus minimus. The **posterior border** is very prominent and appears as a free, rounded edge, which bounds the back part of the trochanteric fossa.

The **Lesser Trochanter** (*trochanter minor; small trochanter*) is a conical eminence, which varies in size in different subjects; it projects from the lower and back part of the base of the neck. From its apex three well-marked borders extend; two of these are above—a **medial** continuous with the lower border of the neck, a **lateral** with the intertrochanteric crest; the **inferior border** is continuous with the middle division of the linea aspera. The **summit** of the trochanter is rough, and gives insertion to the tendon of the Psoas major.

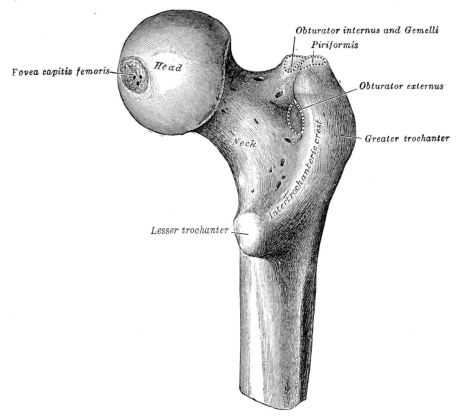

Fig. 237.—Upper extremity of right femur viewed from behind and above.

A prominence, of variable size, occurs at the junction of the upper part of the neck with the greater trochanter, and is called the **tubercle of the femur**; it is the point of meeting of five muscles: the Glutæus minimus laterally, the Vastus lateralis below, and the tendon of the Obturator internus and two Gemelli above. Running obliquely downward and medialward from the tubercle is the **intertrochanteric line** (*spiral line of the femur*); it winds around the medial side of the body of the bone, below the lesser trochanter, and ends about 5 cm. below this eminence in the linea aspera. Its upper half is rough, and affords attachment to the iliofemoral ligament of the hip-joint; its lower half is less prominent, and gives origin to the upper part of the Vastus medialis. Running obliquely downward and medialward from the summit of the greater trochanter on the posterior surface of the neck is a prominent ridge, the **intertrochanteric crest**. Its upper half forms the posterior border of the greater trochanter, and its lower half runs downward and medialward to the lesser trochanter. A slight ridge is sometimes seen com-

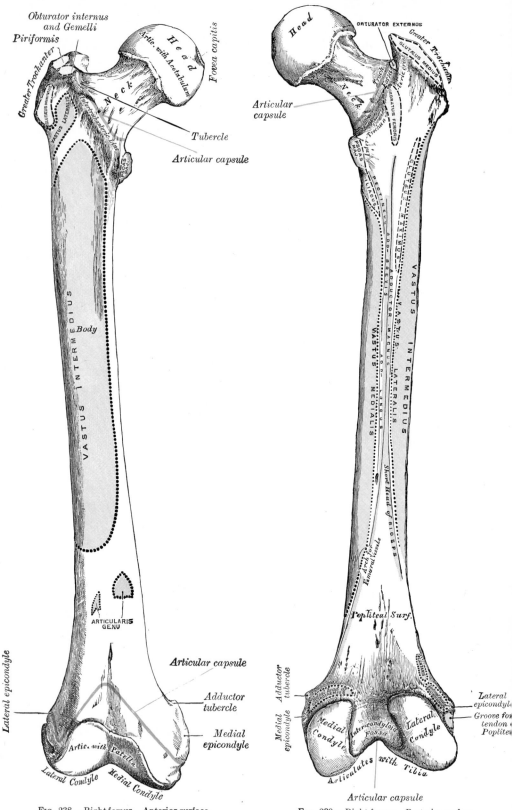

Obturator internus
and Gemelli

Piriformis

Greater Trochanter

Head

Artic. with Acetabulum

Fovea capitis

Neck

GLUTÆUS MINIMUS

VASTUS LATERALIS

Intertrochanteric line

Tubercle

Articular capsule

V A S T U S   I N T E R M E D I U S

Body

Lateral epicondyle

ARTICULARIS
GENU

Articular capsule

Adductor
tubercle

Medial
epicondyle

Artic. with Patella

Lateral Condyle

Medial Condyle

FIG. 238.—Right femur. Anterior surface.

(220)

Head

OBTURATOR EXTERNUS

Greater Trochanter

GLUTÆUS MEDIUS

Articular
capsule

Neck

QUADRATUS FEMORIS

Trochanteric crest

PSOAS
MAJOR

ILIACUS

PECTINEUS

ADDUCTOR BREVIS

ADDUCTOR MAGNUS

GLUTÆUS MAXIMUS

V A S T U S   L A T E R A L I S

VASTUS
MEDIALIS

ADD. LONGUS

Short Head of BICEPS

V A S T U S   I N T E R M E D I U S

Arteria and
Femoral vessels

Popliteal Surf.

Medial
epicondyle

Adductor
tubercle

Medial
Condyle

Intercondyloid
Fossa

Lateral
Condyle

Lateral
epicondyle

Groove for
tendon
Poplite

Articulates with Tibia

Articular capsule

FIG. 239.—Right femur. Posterior surface.

mencing about the middle of the intertrochanteric crest, and reaching vertically downward for about 5 cm. along the back part of the body: it is called the **linea quadrata,** and gives attachment to the Quadratus femoris and a few fibers of the Adductor magnus. Generally there is merely a slight thickening about the middle of the intertrochanteric crest, marking the attachment of the upper part of the Quadratus femoris.

The Body or Shaft (*corpus femoris*).—The body, almost cylindrical in form, is a little broader above than in the center, broadest and somewhat flattened from before backward below. It is slightly arched, so as to be convex in front, and concave behind, where it is strengthened by a prominent longitudinal ridge, the **linea aspera.** It presents for examination three borders, separating three surfaces. Of the borders, one, the linea aspera, is posterior, one is medial, and the other, lateral.

The **linea aspera** (Fig. 239) is a prominent longitudinal ridge or crest, on the middle third of the bone, presenting a medial and a lateral lip, and a narrow rough, intermediate line. Above, the linea aspera is prolonged by three ridges. The lateral ridge is very rough, and runs almost vertically upward to the base of the greater trochanter. It is termed the **gluteal tuberosity,** and gives attachment to part of the Glutæus maximus: its upper part is often elongated into a roughened crest, on which a more or less well-marked, rounded tubercle, the **third trochanter,** is occasionally developed. The intermediate ridge or **pectineal line** is continued to the base of the lesser trochanter and gives attachment to the Pectineus; the medial ridge is lost in the intertrochanteric line; between these two a portion of the Iliacus is inserted. Below, the linea aspera is prolonged into two ridges, enclosing between them a triangular area, the **popliteal surface,** upon which the popliteal artery rests. Of these two ridges, the lateral is the more prominent, and descends to the summit of the lateral condyle. The medial is less marked, especially at its upper part, where it is crossed by the femoral artery. It ends below at the summit of the medial condyle, in a small tubercle, the **adductor tubercle,** which affords insertion to the tendon of the Adductor magnus.

From the **medial lip** of the linea aspera and its prolongations above and below, the Vastus medialis arises; and from the **lateral lip** and its upward prolongation, the Vastus lateralis takes origin. The Adductor magnus is inserted into the linea aspera, and to its lateral prolongation above, and its medial prolongation below. Between the Vastus lateralis and the Adductor magnus two muscles are attached —viz., the Glutæus maximus inserted above, and the short head of the Biceps femoris arising below. Betweeen the Adductor magnus and the Vastus medialis four muscles are inserted: the Iliacus and Pectineus above; the Adductor brevis and Adductor longus below. The linea aspera is perforated a little below its center by the nutrient canal, which is directed obliquely upward.

The other two *borders* of the femur are only slightly marked: the **lateral border** extends from the antero-inferior angle of the greater trochanter to the anterior extremity of the lateral condyle; the **medial border** from the intertrochanteric line, at a point opposite the lesser trochanter, to the anterior extremity of the medial condyle.

The **anterior surface** includes that portion of the shaft which is situated between the lateral and medial borders. It is smooth, convex, broader above and below than in the center. From the upper three-fourths of this surface the Vastus intermedius arises; the lower fourth is separated from the muscle by the intervention of the synovial membrane of the knee-joint and a bursa; from the upper part of it the Articularis genu takes origin. The **lateral surface** includes the portion between the lateral border and the linea aspera; it is continuous above with the corresponding surface of the greater trochanter, below with that of the lateral condyle: from its upper three-fourths the Vastus intermedius takes origin. The **medial surface** includes the portion between the medial border and the linea aspera; it is continuous above with the lower border of the neck, below with the medial side of the medial condyle: it is covered by the Vastus medialis.

The Lower Extremity (*distal extremity*), (Fig. 240).—The lower extremity, larger than the upper, is somewhat cuboid in form, but its transverse diameter is greater than its antero-posterior; it consists of two oblong eminences known as the **condyles.** In front, the condyles are but slightly prominent, and are separated from one another by a smooth shallow articular depression called the **patellar surface**; behind, they project considerably, and the interval between them forms a deep notch, the **intercondyloid fossa.** The **lateral condyle** is the more prominent and is the broader both in its antero-posterior and transverse diameters, the **medial condyle** is the longer and, when the femur is held with its body perpendicular, projects to a lower level. When, however, the femur is in its natural oblique position the lower surfaces of the two condyles lie practically in the same horizontal plane. The condyles are not quite parallel with one another; the long axis of the lateral is almost directly antero-posterior, but that of the medial runs backward and medialward. Their opposed surfaces are small, rough, and concave, and form the walls of the intercondyloid fossa. This fossa is limited above by a ridge, the **intercondyloid**

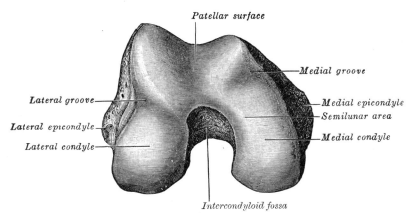

Fig. 240.—Lower extremity of right femur viewed from below.

line, and below by the central part of the posterior margin of the patellar surface. The posterior cruciate ligament of the knee-joint is attached to the lower and front part of the medial wall of the fossa and the anterior cruciate ligament to an impression on the upper and back part of its lateral wall. Each condyle is surmounted by an elevation, the epicondyle. The **medial epicondyle** is a large convex eminence to which the tibial collateral ligament of the knee-joint is attached. At its upper part is the adductor tubercle, already referred to, and behind it is a rough impression which gives origin to the medial head of the Gastrocnemius. The **lateral epicondyle**, smaller and less prominent than the medial, gives attachment to the fibular collateral ligament of the knee-joint. Directly below it is a small depression from which a smooth well-marked groove curves obliquely upward and backward to the posterior extremity of the condyle. This groove is separated from the articular surface of the condyle by a prominent lip across which a second, shallower groove runs vertically downward from the depression. In the fresh state these grooves are covered with cartilage. The Popliteus arises from the depression; its tendon lies in the oblique groove when the knee is flexed and in the vertical groove when the knee is extended. Above and behind the lateral epicondyle is an area for the origin of the lateral head of the Gastrocnemius, above and to the medial side of which the Plantaris arises.

The **articular surface** of the lower end of the femur occupies the anterior, inferior, and posterior surfaces of the condyles. Its front part is named the **patellar surface** and articulates with the patella; it presents a median groove which extends downward to the intercondyloid fossa and two convexities, the lateral of which is broader, more prominent, and extends farther upward than the medial. The lower and posterior parts of the articular surface constitute the **tibial surfaces** for articulation with the corresponding condyles of the tibia and menisci. These surfaces are separated from one another by the intercondyloid fossa and from the patellar surface by faint grooves which extend obliquely across the condyles. The lateral groove is the better marked; it runs lateralward and forward from the front part of the intercondyloid fossa, and expands to form a triangular depression. When the knee-joint is fully extended, the triangular depression rests upon the anterior portion of the lateral meniscus, and the medial part of the groove comes into contact with the medial margin of the lateral articular surface of the tibia in front of the lateral tubercle of the tibial intercondyloid eminence. The medial groove is less distinct than the lateral. It does not reach as far as the intercondyloid fossa and therefore exists only on the medial part of the condyle; it receives the anterior edge of the medial meniscus when the knee-joint is extended. Where the groove ceases laterally the patellar surface is seen to be continued backward as a semilunar area close to the anterior part of the intercondyloid fossa; this semilunar area articulates with the medial vertical facet of the patella in forced flexion of the knee-joint. The tibial surfaces of the condyles are convex from side to side and from before backward. Each presents a double curve, its posterior segment being an arc of a circle, its anterior, part of a cycloid.[1]

The Architecture of the Femur.—Koch[2] by mathematical analysis has "shown that in every part of the femur there is a remarkable adaptation of the inner structure of the bone to the mechanical requirements due to the load on the femur-head. The various parts of the femur taken together form a single mechanical structure wonderfully well-adapted for the efficient, economical transmission of the loads from the acetabulum to the tibia; a structure in which every element contributes its modicum of strength in the manner required by theoretical mechanics for maximum efficiency." "The internal structure is everywhere so formed as to provide in an efficient manner for all the internal stresses which occur due to the load on the femur-head. Throughout the femur, with the load on the femur-head, the bony material is arranged in the paths of the maximum internal stresses, which are thereby resisted with the greatest efficiency, and hence with maximum economy of material." "The conclusion is inevitable that the inner structure and outer form of the femur are governed by the conditions of maximum stress to which the bone is subjected normally by the preponderant load on the femur-head; that is, by the body weight transmitted to the femur-head through the acetabulum." "The femur obeys the mechanical laws that govern other elastic bodies under stress; the relation between the computed internal stresses due to the load on the femur-head, and the internal structure of the different portions of the femur is in very close agreement with the theoretical relations that should exist between stress and structure for maximum economy and efficiency; and, therefore, it is believed that the following laws of bone structure have been demonstrated for the femur:

"1. The inner structure and external form of human bone are closely adapted to the mechanical conditions existing at every point in the bone.

"2. The inner architecture of normal bone is determined by definite and exact requirements of mathematical and mechanical laws to produce a maximum of strength with a minimum of material."

The Inner Architecture of the Upper Femur.—"The spongy bone of the upper femur (to the lower limit of the lesser trochanter) is composed of two distinct systems of trabeculæ arranged in curved paths: one, which has its origin in the medial (inner) side of the shaft and curving upward in a fan-like radiation to the opposite side of the bone; the other, having origin in the lateral (outer) portion of the shaft and arching upward and medially to end in the upper surface of the greater trochanter, neck and head. These two systems intersect each other at right angles.

---

[1] A *cycloid* is a curve traced by a point in the circumference of a wheel when the wheel is rolled along in a straight line.

[2] The Laws of Bone Architecture. Am. Jour. of Anat., **21**, 1917. The following paragraphs are taken almost verbatim from Koch's article in which we have the first correct mathematical analysis of the femur in support of the theory of the functional form of bone proposed by Wolff and also by Roux.

"*A. Medial (Compressive) System of Trabeculæ.*—As the compact bone of the medial (inner) part of the shaft nears the head of the femur it gradually becomes thinner and finally reaches the articular surface of the head as a very thin layer. From a point at about the lower level of the lesser trochanter, $2\frac{1}{2}$ to 3 inches from the lower limit of the articular surface of the head, the trabeculæ branch off from the shaft in smooth curves, spreading radially to cross to the opposite side in two well-defined groups: a lower, or secondary group, and an upper, or principal group.

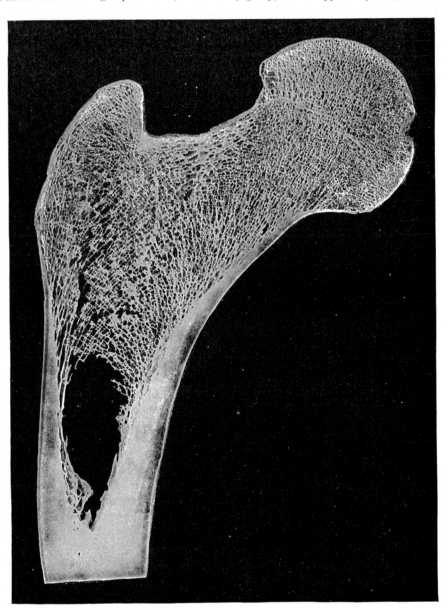

FIG. 241.—Frontal longitudinal midsection of upper femur.

"*a. The Secondary Compressive Group.*—This group of trabeculæ leaves the inner border of the shaft beginning at about the level of the lesser trochanter, and for a distance of almost 2 inches along the curving shaft, with which the separate trabeculæ make an angle of about 45 degrees. They curve outwardly and upwardly to cross in radiating smooth curves to the opposite side. The lower filaments end in the region of the greater trochanter: the adjacent filaments above these pursue a more nearly vertical course and end in the upper portion of the neck of the femur. The trabeculæ of this group are thin and with wide spaces between them. As they traverse the space between the medial and lateral surfaces of the bone they cross at right angles the system of curved trabeculæ which arise from the lateral (outer) portion of the shaft. (Figs. 241 and 242.)

"*b. The Principal Compressive Group.*—This group of trabeculæ (Figs. 244 and 246) springs from the medial portion of the shaft just above the group above-described, and spreads upward and in slightly radial smooth curved lines to reach the upper portion of the articular surface of the head of the femur. These trabeculæ are placed very closely together and are the thickest ones seen in the upper femur. They are a prolongation of the shaft from which they spring in straight lines which gradually curve to meet at right-angles the articular surface. There is no change as they cross the epiphyseal line. They also intersect at right-angles the system of lines which rise from the lateral side of the femur.

"This system of principal and secondary compressive trabeculæ corresponds in position and in curvature with the lines of maximum compressive stress, which were traced out in the mathematical analysis of this portion of the femur. (Figs. 242 and 244.)

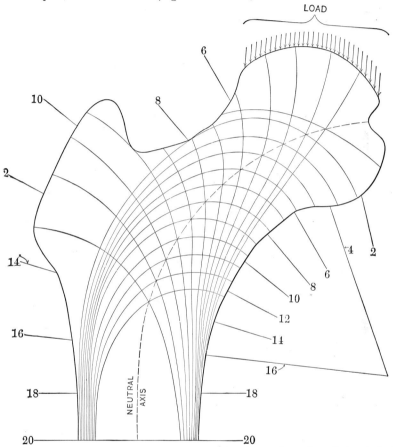

Fig. 242.—Diagram of the lines of stress in the upper femur, based upon the mathematical analysis of the right femur. These result from the combination of the different kinds of stresses at each point in the femur. (After Koch.)

"*B. Lateral (Tensile) System of Trabeculæ.*—As the compact bone of the outer portion of the shaft approaches the greater trochanter it gradually decreases in thickness. Beginning at a point about 1 inch below the level of the lower border of the greater trochanter, numerous thin trabeculæ are given off from the outer portion of the shaft. These trabeculæ lie in three distinct groups.

"*c. The Greater Trochanter Group.*—These trabeculæ rise from the outer part of the shaft just below the greater trochanter and rise in thin, curving lines to cross the region of the greater trochanter and end in its upper surface. Some of these filaments are poorly defined. This group intersects the trabeculæ of group (*a*) which rise from the opposite side. The trabeculæ of this group evidently carry small stresses, as is shown by their slenderness.

"*d. The Principal Tensile Group.*—This group springs from the outer part of the shaft immediately below group *c*, and curves convexly upward and inward in nearly parallel lines across the neck of the femur and ends in the inferior portion of the head. These trabeculæ are somewhat thinner and more widely spaced than those of the principal compressive group (*b*). All the trabeculæ of this group cross those of groups (*a*) and (*b*) at right angles. This group is the most important of the lateral system (tensile) and, as will be shown later, the greatest tensile stresses of the upper femur are carried by the trabeculæ of this group.

15

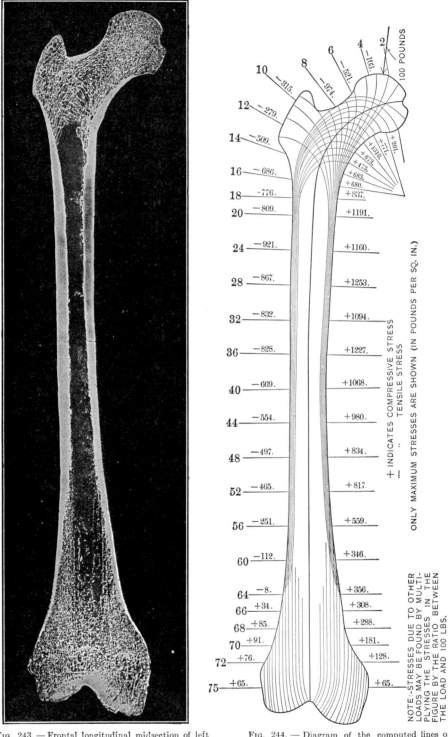

FIG. 243. — Frontal longitudinal midsection of left femur. Taken from the same subject as the one that was analyzed and shown in Figs. 244 and 245. ⅜ of natural size. (After Koch.)

FIG. 244. — Diagram of the computed lines of maximum stress in the normal femur. The section numbers 2, 4, 6, 8, etc., show the positions of the transverse sections analyzed. The amounts of the maximum tensile and compressive stress at the various sections are given for a load of 100 pounds on the femur-head. For the standing position ("at attention") these stresses are multiplied by 0.6, for walking by 1.6 and for running by 3.2. (After Koch.)

"*e. The Secondary Tensile Group.*—This group consists of the trabeculæ which spring from the outer side of the shaft and lie below those of the preceding group. They curve upward and medially across the axis of the femur and end more or less irregularly after crossing the midline, but a number of these filaments end in the medial portion of the shaft and neck. They cross at right angles the trabeculæ of group (*a*).

"In general, the trabeculæ of the tensile system are lighter in structure than those of the compressive system in corresponding positions. The significance of the difference in thickness of these two systems is that the thickness of the trabeculæ varies with the intensity of the stresses at any given point. Comparison of Fig. 241 with Fig. 242 will show that the trabeculæ of the compressive system carry heavier stresses than those of the tensile system in corresponding positions. For example, the maximum tensile stress at section 8 (Fig. 245) in the outermost fiber is 771 pounds per square inch, and at the corresponding point on the compressive side the compressive stress is 954 pounds per square inch. Similar comparisons may be made at other points, which confirm the conclusion that the thickness and closeness of spacing of the trabeculæ varies in proportion to the intensity of the stresses carried by them.

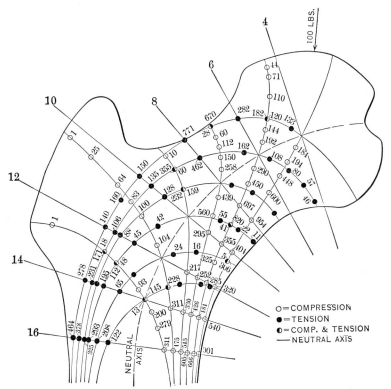

Fɪɢ. 245.—Intensity of the maximum tensile and compressive stresses in the upper femur. Computed for the load of 100 pounds on the right femur. Corresponds to the upper part of Fig. 244. (After Koch.)

"It will be seen that the trabeculæ lie exactly in the paths of the maximum tensile and compressive stresses (compare Figs. 241, 242 and 245), and hence these trabeculæ carry these stresses in the most economical manner. This is in accordance with the well-recognized principle of mechanics that the most direct manner of transmitting stress is in the direction in which the stress acts.

"Fig. 243 shows a longitudinal frontal section through the left femur, which is the mate of the right femur on which the mathematical analysis was made. In this midsection the system of tensile trabeculæ, which rises from the lateral (outer) part of the shaft and crosses over the central area to end in the medial portion of the shaft, neck and head, is clearly shown. This figure also shows the compressive system of trabeculæ which rises on the medial portion of the shaft and crosses the central area to end in the head, neck and greater trochanter. By comparing the position of these two systems of trabeculæ shown in Fig. 243 with the lines of maximum and minimum stresses shown in Figs. 242 and 244 it is seen that the tensile system of trabeculæ corresponds exactly with the position of the lines of maximum and minimum tensile stresses which were determined by mathematical analysis. In a similar manner, the compressive system of trabeculæ in Fig. 243 corresponds exactly with the lines of maximum and minimum compressive stresses computed by mathematical analysis.

"The amount of vertical shear varies almost uniformly from a maximum of 90 pounds (90 per cent. of the load on the femur-head) midway between sections 4 and 6, to a minimum of —5.7 pounds at section 18" (Fig. 245). There is a gradual diminution of the spongy bone from section 6 to section 18 parallel with the diminished intensities of the vertical shear.

1. The trabeculæ of the upper femur, as shown in frontal sections, are arranged in two general systems, compressive and tensile, which correspond in position with the lines of maximum and minimum stresses in the femur determined by the mathematical analysis of the femur as a mechancal structure.

2. The thickness and spacing of the trabeculæ vary with the intensity of the maximum stresses at various points in the upper femur, being thickest and most closely spaced in the regions where the greatest stresses occur.

3. The amount of bony material in the spongy bone of the upper femur varies in proportion to the intensity of the shearing force at the various sections.

4. The arrangement of the trabeculæ in the positions of maximum stresses is such that the greatest strength is secured with a minimum of material.

Significance of the Inner Architecture of the Shaft.—1. Economy for resisting shear. The shearing stresses are at a minimum in the shaft. "It is clear that a minimum amount of material will be required to resist the shearing stresses." As horizontal and vertical shearing stresses are most efficiently resisted by material placed near the neutral plane, in this region a minimum amount of material will be needed near the neutral axis. In the shaft there is very little if any material in the central space, practically the only material near the neutral plane being in the compact bone, but lying at a distance from the neutral axis. This conforms to the requirement of mechanics for economy, as a minimum of material is provided for resisting shearing stresses where these stresses are a minimum.

2. Economy for resisting bending moment. "The bending moment increases from a minimum at section 4 to a maximum between sections 16 and 18, then gradually decreases almost uniformly to 0 near section 75." "To resist bending moment stresses most effectively the material should be as far from the neutral axis as possible." It is evident that the hollow shaft of the femur is an efficient structure for resisting bending moment stresses, all of the material in the shaft being relatively at a considerable distance from the neutral axis. It is evident that the hollow shaft provides efficiently for resisting bending moment not only due to the load on the femur-head, but from any other loads tending to produce bending in other planes.

3. Economy for resisting axial stress.

The inner architecture of the shaft is adapted to resist in the most efficient manner the combined action of the minimal shearing forces and the axial and maximum bending stresses.

The structure of the shaft is such as to secure great strength with a relatively small amount of material.

The Distal Portion of the Femur.—In frontal section (Fig. 243) in the distal 6 inches of the femur "there are to be seen two main systems of trabeculæ, a longitudinal and a transverse system. The trabeculæ of the former rise from the inner wall of the shaft and continue in perfectly straight lines parallel to the axis of the shaft and proceed to the epiphyseal line, whence they continue in more or less curved lines to meet the articular surface of the knee-joint at right angles at every point. Near the center there are a few thin, delicate, longitudinal trabeculæ which spring from the longitudinal trabeculæ just described, to which they are joined by fine transverse filaments that lie in planes parallel to the sagittal plane.

"The trabeculæ of the transverse system are somewhat lighter in structure than those of the longitudinal system, and consist of numerous trabeculæ at right angles to the latter.

"As the distal end of the femur is approached the shaft gradually becomes thinner until the articular surface is reached, where there remains only a thin shell of compact bone. With the gradual thinning of the compact bone of the shaft, there is a simultaneous increase in the amount of the spongy bone, and a gradual flaring of the femur which gives this portion of the bone a gradually increasing gross area of cross-section.

"There is a marked thickening of the shell of bone in the region of the intercondyloid fossa where the anterior and posterior crucial ligaments are attached. This thickened area is about 0.4 inch in diameter and consists of compact bone from which a number of thick trabeculæ pass at right angles to the main longitudinal system. The inner structure of the bone is here evidently adapted to the efficient distribution of the stresses arising from this ligamentary attachment.

"Near the distal end of the femur the longitudinal trabeculæ gradually assume curved paths and end perpendicularly to the articular surface at every point. Such a structure is in accordance with the principles of mechanics, as stresses can be communicated through a frictionless joint only in a direction perpendicular to the joint surface at every point.

"With practically no increase in the amount of bony material used there is a greatly increased stability produced by the expansion of the lower femur from a hollow shaft of compact bone to a structure of much larger cross-section almost entirely composed of spongy bone.

"*Significance of the Inner Architecture of the Distal Part of the Femur.*—The function of the lower end of the femur is to transmit through a hinged joint the loads carried by the femur. For stability the width of the bearing on which the hinge action occurs should be relatively large. For economy of material the expansion of the end bearing should be as lightly constructed as is consistent with proper strength. In accordance with the principles of mechanics. . . . . ., the most efficient manner in which stresses are transmitted is by the arrangement of the resisting material in lines parallel to the direction in which the stresses occur and in the paths taken by the stresses. Theoretically the most efficient manner to attain these objects would be to prolong the innermost filaments of the bone as straight lines parallel to the longitudinal axis of the bone, and gradually to flare the outer shell of compact bone outward, and continuing to give off filaments of bone parallel to the longitudinal axis as the distal end of the femur is approached. These filaments should be well-braced transversely and each should carry its proportionate part of the total load, parallel to the longitudinal axis, transmitting it eventually to the articular surface, and in a direction perpendicular to that surface."

Referring to Fig. 243, it is seen that the large expansion of the bone is produced by the gradual transition of the hollow shaft of compact bone to cancellated bone, resulting in the production of a much larger volume. The trabeculæ are given off from the shaft in lines parallel to the longitudinal axis, and are braced transversely

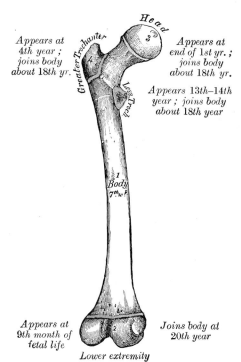

Appears at 4th year; joins body about 18th yr.

Appears at end of 1st yr.; joins body about 18th yr.

Appears 13th–14th year; joins body about 18th year

Appears at 9th month of fetal life

Joins body at 20th year

Lower extremity

FIG. 246.—Plan of ossification of the femur. From five centers.

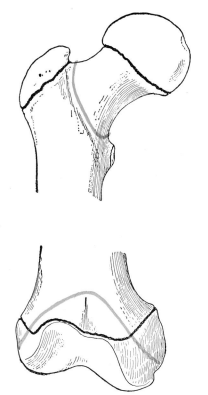

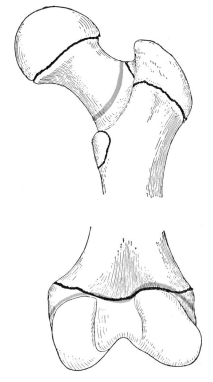

FIG. 247.—Epiphyseal lines of femur in a young adult. Anterior aspect. The lines of attachment of the articular capsules are in blue.

FIG. 248.—Epiphyseal lines of femur in a young adult. Posterior aspect. The lines of attachment of the articular capsules are in blue.

by two series of trabeculæ at right angles to each other, in the same manner as required theoretically for economy.

Although the action of the muscles exerts an appreciable effect on the stresses in the femur, it is relatively small and very complex to analyze and has not been considered in the above analysis.

Ossification (Figs. 246, 247, 248).—The femur is ossified from *five* centers: one for the body, one for the head, one for each trochanter, and one for the lower extremity. Of all the long bones, except the clavicle, it is the first to show traces of ossification; this commences in the middle of the body, at about the seventh week of fetal life, and rapidly extends upward and downward. The centers in the epiphyses appear in the following order: in the lower end of the bone, at the ninth month of fetal life (from this center the condyles and epicondyles are formed); in the head, at the end of the first year after birth; in the greater trochanter, during the fourth year; and in the lesser trochanter, between the thirteenth and fourteenth years. The order in which the epiphyses are joined to the body is the reverse of that of their appearance; they are not united until after puberty, the lesser trochanter being first joined, then the greater, then the head, and, lastly, the inferior extremity, which is not united until the twentieth year.

The Patella (Knee Cap).

The **patella** (Figs. 249, 250) is a flat, triangular bone, situated on the front of the knee-joint. It is usually regarded as a sesamoid bone, developed in the tendon of the Quadriceps femoris, and resembles these bones (1) in being developed in a tendon; (2) in its center of ossification presenting a knotty or tuberculated outline; (3) in being composed mainly of dense cancellous tissue. It serves to protect the front of the joint, and increases the leverage of the Quadriceps femoris by making it act at a greater angle. It has an anterior and a posterior surface three borders, and an apex.

Fig. 249.—Right patella. Anterior surface.

Fig. 250.—Right patella, Posterior surface.

Surfaces.—The **anterior surface** is convex, perforated by small apertures for the passage of nutrient vessels, and marked by numerous rough, longitudinal striæ. This surface is covered, in the recent state, by an expansion from the tendon of the Quadriceps femoris, which is continuous below with the superficial fibers of the ligamentum patellæ. It is separated from the integument by a bursa. The **posterior surface** presents above a smooth, oval, articular area, divided into two facets by a vertical ridge; the ridge corresponds to the groove on the patellar surface of the femur, and the facets to the medial and lateral parts of the same surface; the lateral facet is the broader and deeper. Below the articular surface is a rough, convex, non-articular area, the lower half of which gives attachment to the ligamentum patellæ; the upper half is separated from the head of the tibia by adipose tissue.

Borders.—The **base or superior border** is thick, and sloped from behind, downward, and forward: it gives attachment to that portion of the Quadriceps femoris which is derived from the Rectus femoris and Vastus intermedius. The **medial** and **lateral borders** are thinner and converge below: they give attachment to those portions of the Quadriceps femoris which are derived from the Vasti lateralis and medialis.

Apex.—The apex is pointed, and gives attachment to the ligamentum patellæ.

Structure.—The patella consists of a nearly uniform dense cancellous tissue, covered by a thin compact lamina. The cancelli immediately beneath the anterior surface are arranged parallel with it. In the rest of the bone they radiate from the articular surface toward the other parts of the bone.

Ossification.—The patella is ossified from a single center, which usually makes its appearance in the second or third year, but may be delayed until the sixth year. More rarely, the bone is developed by two centers, placed side by side. Ossification is completed about the age of puberty.

Articulation.—The patella articulates with the femur.

The Tibia (Shin Bone).

The **tibia** (Figs. 253, 254) is situated at the medial side of the leg, and, excepting the femur, is the longest bone of the skeleton. It is prismoid in form, expanded above, where it enters into the knee-joint, contracted in the lower third, and again enlarged but to a lesser extent below. In the male, its direction is vertical, and parallel with the bone of the opposite side; but in the female it has a slightly oblique direction downward and lateralward, to compensate for the greater obliquity of the femur. It has a **body** and **two extremities.**

The Upper Extremity (*proximal extremity*.)—The upper extremity is large, and expanded into two eminences, the **medial** and **lateral condyles.** The **superior articular surface** presents two smooth articular facets (Fig. 251). The medial facet, oval in shape, is slightly concave from side to side, and from before backward. The lateral,

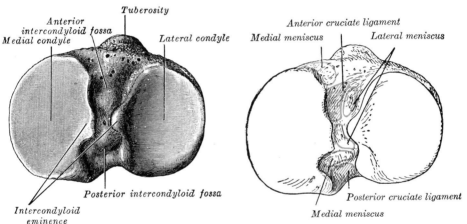

FIG. 251.—Upper surface of right tibia.

FIG. 252.—An outline of Fig. 251 showing the attachment of the menisci and cruciata ligaments.

nearly circular, is concave from side to side, but slightly convex from before backward, especially at its posterior part, where it is prolonged on to the posterior surface for a short distance. The central portions of these facets articulate with the condyles of the femur, while their peripheral portions support the menisci of the knee-joint, which here intervene between the two bones. Between the articular facets, but nearer the posterior than the anterior aspect of the bone, is the **intercondyloid eminence** (*spine of tibia*), surmounted on either side by a prominent tubercle, on to the sides of which the articular facets are prolonged; in front of and behind the intercondyloid eminence are rough depressions for the attachment of the anterior and posterior cruciate ligaments and the menisci. The **anterior surfaces** of the condyles are continuous with one another, forming a large somewhat flattened area; this area is triangular, broad above, and perforated by large vascular foramina; narrow below where it ends in a large oblong elevation, the **tuberosity of the tibia,** which gives attachment to the ligamentum patellæ; a bursa intervenes between the deep surface of the ligament and the part of the bone immediately above the tuberosity. *Posteriorly,* the condyles are separated from each other by a shallow depression, the **posterior intercondyloid fossa,** which gives attachment to part of the posterior cruciate ligament of the knee-joint. The **medial condyle** presents posteriorly a deep transverse groove, for the insertion of the tendon of

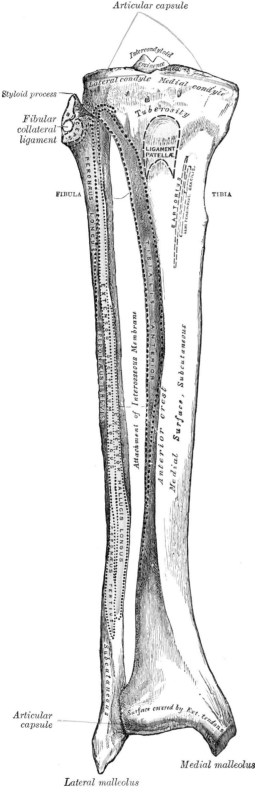

Articular capsule

Intercondyloid Eminence

Lateral condyle   Medial condyle

Styloid process

Fibular collateral ligament

Tuberosity

LIGAMENT PATELLÆ

FIBULA   TIBIA

SARTORIUS
SEMITENDINOSUS. GRACILIS.

Attachment of Interosseous Membrane

Anterior crest

Medial Surface, Subcutaneous

Subcutaneous

Articular capsule

Surface covered by Ext. tendons

Medial malleolus

Lateral malleolus

FIG. 253.—Bones of the right leg. Anterior surface.

the Semimembranosus. Its *medial surface* is convex, rough, and prominent; it gives attachment to the tibial collateral ligament. The **lateral condyle** presents posteriorly a flat articular facet, nearly circular in form, directed downward, backward, and lateralward, for articulation with the head of the fibula. Its *lateral surface* is convex, rough, and prominent in front: on it is an eminence, situated on a level with the upper border of the tuberosity and at the junction of its anterior and lateral surfaces, for the attachment of the iliotibial band. Just below this a part of the Extensor digitorum longus takes origin and a slip from the tendon of the Biceps femoris is inserted.

The Body or Shaft (*corpus tibiæ*). —The body has three borders and three surfaces.

Borders.—The **anterior crest** or **border**, the most prominent of the three, commences above at the tuberosity, and ends below at the anterior margin of the medial malleolus. It is sinuous and prominent in the upper two-thirds of its extent, but smooth and rounded below; it gives attachment to the deep fascia of the leg.

The **medial border** is smooth and rounded above and below, but more prominent in the center; it begins at the back part of the medial condyle, and ends at the posterior border of the medial malleolus; its upper part gives attachment to the tibial collateral ligament of the knee-joint to the extent of about 5 cm., and insertion to some fibers of the Popliteus; from its middle third some fibers of the Soleus and Flexor digitorum longus take origin.

The **interosseous crest** or **lateral border** is thin and prominent, especially its central part, and gives attachment to the interosseous membrane; it commences above in front of the fibular articular facet, and bifurcates below, to form the boundaries of a triangular rough surface, for the attachment of the interosseous ligament connecting the tibia and fibula.

Surfaces.—The **medial surface** is smooth, convex, and broader above than below; its upper third, directed forward and medialward, is covered by the aponeurosis derived from the tendon of the Sartorius, and by the tendons of the Gracilis and Semitendinosus, all of which are inserted nearly as far forward as the anterior crest; in the rest of its extent it is subcutaneous.

The **lateral surface** is narrower than the medial; its upper two-thirds present a shallow groove for the origin of the Tibialis anterior; its lower third is smooth, convex, curves gradually forward to the anterior aspect of the bone, and is covered by the tendons of the Tibialis anterior, Extensor hallucis longus, and Extensor digitorum longus, arranged in this order from the medial side.

The **posterior surface** (Fig. 254) presents, at its upper part, a prominent ridge, the **popliteal line,** which extends obliquely downward from the back part of the articular facet for the fibula to the medial border, at the junction of its upper and middle thirds; it marks the lower limit of the insertion of the Popliteus, serves for the attachment of the fascia covering this muscle, and gives origin to part of the Soleus, Flexor digitorum longus, and Tibialis posterior. The triangular area, above this line, gives insertion to the Popliteus. The middle third of the posterior surface is divided by a vertical ridge into two parts; the ridge begins at the popliteal line and is well-marked above, but indistinct below; the medial and broader portion gives origin to the Flexor digitorum longus, the lateral and narrower to part of the Tibialis posterior. The

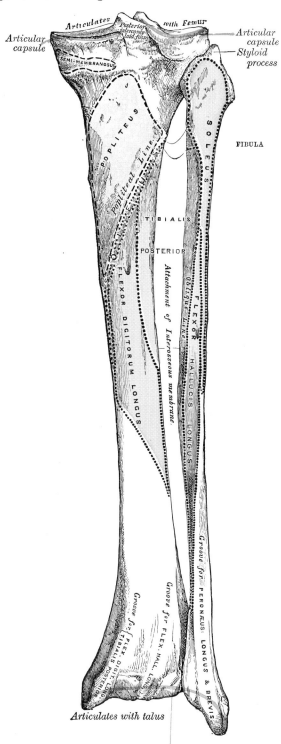

Fig. 254.—Bones of the right leg. Posterior surface.

remaining part of the posterior surface is smooth and covered by the Tibialis posterior, Flexor digitorum longus, and Flexor hallucis longus. Immediately below the popliteal line is the **nutrient foramen**, which is large and directed obliquely downward.

The Lower Extremity (*distal extremity*).—The lower extremity, much smaller than the upper, presents five surfaces; it is prolonged downward on its medial side as a strong process, the **medial malleolus.**

Surfaces.—The **inferior articular surface** is quadrilateral, and smooth for articulation with the talus. It is concave from before backward, broader in front than behind, and traversed from before backward by a slight elevation, separating two depressions. It is continuous with that on the medial malleolus.

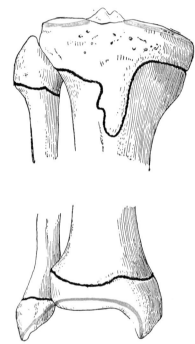
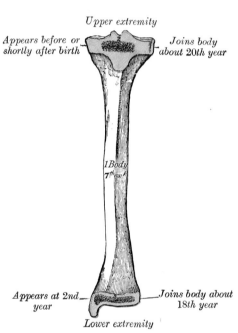
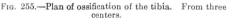

FIG. 255.—Plan of ossification of the tibia. From three centers.

FIG. 256.—Epiphysial lines of tibia and fibula in a young adult. Anterior aspect.

The **anterior surface** of the lower extremity is smooth and rounded above, and covered by the tendons of the Extensor muscles; its lower margin presents a rough transverse depression for the attachment of the articular capsule of the ankle-joint.

The **posterior surface** is traversed by a shallow groove directed obliquely downward and medialward, continuous with a similar groove on the posterior surface of the talus and serving for the passage of the tendon of the Flexor hallucis longus.

The **lateral surface** presents a triangular rough depression for the attachment of the inferior interosseous ligament connecting it with the fibula; the lower part of this depression is smooth, covered with cartilage in the fresh state, and articulates with the fibula. The surface is bounded by two prominent borders, continuous above with the interosseous crest; they afford attachment to the anterior and posterior ligaments of the lateral malleolus.

The **medial surface** is prolonged downward to form a strong pyramidal process, flattened from without inward—the **medial malleolus.** The *medial surface* of this process is convex and subcutaneous; its *lateral* or *articular surface* is smooth and slightly concave, and articulates with the talus; its *anterior border* is rough, for the attachment of the anterior fibers of the deltoid ligament of the ankle-joint;

its *posterior border* presents a broad groove, the **malleolar sulcus**, directed obliquely downward and medialward, and occasionally double; this sulcus lodges the tendons of the Tibialis posterior and Flexor digitorum longus. The *summit* of the medial malleolus is marked by a rough depression behind, for the attachment of the deltoid ligament.

Structure.—The structure of the tibia is like that of the other long bones. The compact wall of the body is thickest at the junction of the middle and lower thirds of the bone.

Ossification.—The tibia is ossified from *three* centers (Figs. 255, 256): one for the body and one for either extremity. Ossification begins in the center of the body, about the seventh week of fetal life, and gradually extends toward the extremities. The center for the upper epiphysis appears before or shortly after birth; it is flattened in form, and has a thin tongue-shaped process in front, which forms the tuberosity (Fig. 255); that for the lower epiphysis appears in the second year. The lower epiphysis joins the body at about the eighteenth, and the upper one joins about the twentieth year. Two additional centers occasionally exist, one for the tongue-shaped process of the upper epiphysis, which forms the tuberosity, and one for the medial malleolus.

The Fibula (Calf Bone).

The **fibula** (Figs. 253, 254) is placed on the lateral side of the tibia, with which it is connected above and below. It is the smaller of the two bones, and, in proportion to its length, the most slender of all the long bones. Its upper extremity is small, placed toward the back of the head of the tibia, below the level of the knee-joint, and excluded from the formation of this joint. Its lower extremity inclines a little forward, so as to be on a plane anterior to that of the upper end; it projects below the tibia, and forms the lateral part of the ankle-joint. The bone has a **body** and **two extremities**.

The Upper Extremity or Head (*capitulum fibulæ; proximal extremity*).—The upper extremity is of an irregular quadrate form, presenting above a flattened articular surface, directed upward, forward, and medialward, for articulation with a corresponding surface on the lateral condyle of the tibia. On the lateral side is a thick and rough prominence continued behind into a pointed eminence, the **apex** (*styloid process*), which projects upward from the posterior part of the head. The prominence, at its upper and lateral part, gives attachment to the tendon of the Biceps femoris and to the fibular collateral ligament of the knee-joint, the ligament dividing the tendon into two parts. The remaining part of the circumference of the head is rough, for the attachment of muscles and ligaments. It presents in front a tubercle for the origin of the upper and anterior fibers of the Peronæus longus, and a surface for the attachment of the anterior ligament of the head; and behind, another tubercle, for the attachment of the posterior ligament of the head and the origin of the upper fibers of the Soleus.

The Body or Shaft (*corpus fibulæ*).—The body presents four borders—the antero-lateral, the antero-medial, the postero-lateral, and the postero-medial; and four surfaces—anterior, posterior, medial, and lateral.

Borders.—The **antero-lateral border** begins above in front of the head, runs vertically downward to a little below the middle of the bone, and then curving somewhat lateralward, bifurcates so as to embrace a triangular subcutaneous surface immediately above the lateral malleolus. This border gives attachment to an intermuscular septum, which separates the Extensor muscles on the anterior surface of the leg from the Peronæi longus and brevis on the lateral surface.

The **antero-medial border**, or **interosseous crest**, is situated close to the medial side of the preceding, and runs nearly parallel with it in the upper third of its extent, but diverges from it in the lower two-thirds. It begins above just beneath the head of the bone (sometimes it is quite indistinct for about 2.5 cm. below the head), and ends at the apex of a rough triangular surface immediately above the articular facet of the lateral malleolus. It serves for the attachment of the interosseous membrane, which separates the Extensor muscles in front from the Flexor muscles behind.

The **postero-lateral border** is prominent; it begins above at the apex, and ends below in the posterior border of the lateral malleolus. It is directed lateralward above, backward in the middle of its course, backward, and a little medialward below, and gives attachment to an aponeurosis which separates the Peronæi on the lateral surface from the Flexor muscles on the posterior surface.

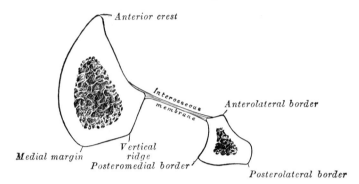

Fig. 257.—A transverse section through the right tibia and fibula, showing the attachment of the crural interosseous membrane.

The **postero-medial border**, sometimes called the **oblique line**, begins above at the medial side of the head, and ends by becoming continuous with the interosseous crest at the lower fourth of the bone. It is well-marked and prominent at the upper and middle parts of the bone. It gives attachment to an aponeurosis which seprates the Tibialis posterior from the Soleus and Flexor hallucis longus.

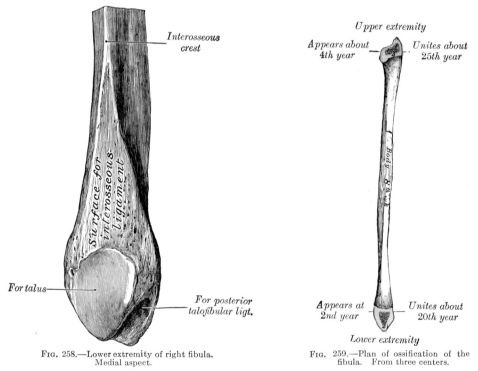

Fig. 258.—Lower extremity of right fibula. Medial aspect.

Fig. 259.—Plan of ossification of the fibula. From three centers.

Surfaces.—The **anterior surface** is the interval between the antero-lateral and antero-medial borders. It is extremely narrow and flat in the upper third of its extent; broader and grooved longitudinally in its lower third; it serves for the origin of three muscles: the Extensor digitorum longus, Extensor hallucis longus, and Peronæus tertius.

The **posterior surface** is the space included between the postero-lateral and the postero-medial borders; it is continuous below with the triangular area above the articular surface of the lateral malleolus; it is directed backward above, backward and medialward at its middle, directly medialward below. Its upper third is rough, for the origin of the Soleus; its lower part presents a triangular surface, connected to the tibia by a strong interosseous ligament; the intervening part of the surface is covered by the fibers of origin of the Flexor hallucis longus. Near the middle of this surface is the nutrient foramen, which is directed downward.

The **medial surface** is the interval included between the antero-medial and the postero-medial borders. It is grooved for the origin of the Tibialis posterior.

The **lateral surface** is the space between the antero-lateral and postero-lateral borders. It is broad, and often deeply grooved; it is directed lateralward in the upper two-thirds of its course, backward in the lower third, where it is continuous with the posterior border of the lateral malleolus. This surface gives origin to the Peronæi longus and brevis.

The Lower Extremity or Lateral Malleolus (*malleolus lateralis; distal extremity; external malleolus*).—The lower extremity is of a pyramidal form, and somewhat flattened from side to side; it descends to a lower level than the medial malleolus. The **lateral surface** is convex, subcutaneous, and continuous with the triangular, subcutaneous surface on the lateral side of the body. The **medial surface** (Fig. 258) presents in front a smooth triangular surface, convex from above downward, which articulates with a corresponding surface on the lateral side of the talus. Behind and beneath the articular surface is a rough depression, which gives attachment to the posterior talofibular ligament. The **anterior border** is thick and rough, and marked below by a depression for the attachment of the anterior talofibular ligament. The **posterior border** is broad and presents the shallow **malleolar sulcus,** for the passage of the tendons of the Peronæi longus and brevis. The **summit** is rounded, and give attachment to the calcaneofibular ligament.

Ossification.—The fibula is ossified from *three* centers (Fig. 259): one for the body, and one for either end. Ossification begins in the body about the eighth week of fetal life, and extends toward the extremities. At birth the ends are cartilaginous. Ossification commences in the lower end in the second year, and in the upper about the fourth year. The lower epiphysis, the first to ossify, unites with the body about the twentieth year; the upper epiphysis joins about the twenty-fifth year.

THE FOOT.

The skeleton of the foot (Figs. 260 and 261) consists of three parts: the **tarsus, metatarsus,** and **phalanges.**

The Tarsus (Ossa Tarsi).

The **tarsal bones** are seven in number, viz., the **calcaneus, talus, cuboid, navicular,** and the **first, second,** and **third cuneiforms.**

The Calcaneus (*os calcis*) (Figs. 262 to 265).—The calcaneus is the largest of the tarsal bones. It is situated at the lower and back part of the foot, serving to transmit the weight of the body to the ground, and forming a strong lever for the muscles of the calf. It is irregularly cuboidal in form, having its long axis directed forward and lateralward; it presents for examination six surfaces.

Surfaces.—The **superior surface** extends behind on to that part of the bone which projects backward to form the heel. This varies in length in different individuals, is convex from side to side, concave from before backward, and supports a mass of fat placed in front of the tendo calcaneus. In front of this area is a large usually somewhat oval-shaped facet, the **posterior articular surface,** which looks upward and forward; it is convex from behind forward, and articulates with the posterior

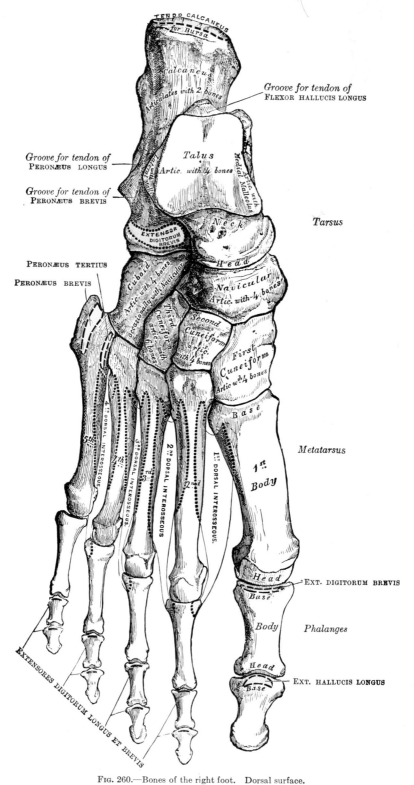

FIG. 260.—Bones of the right foot. Dorsal surface.

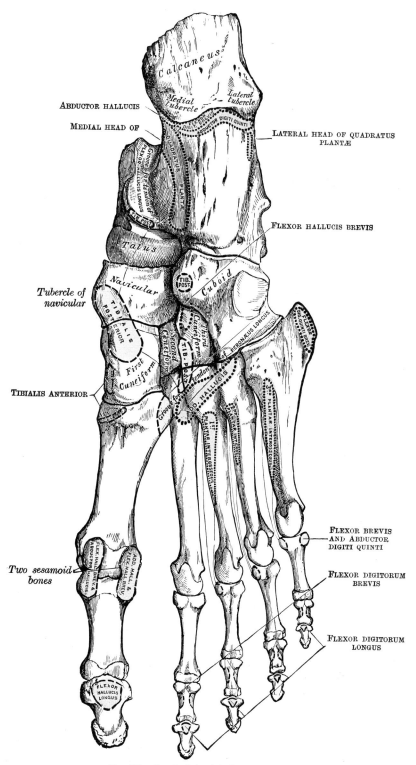

Fɪɢ 261.—Bones of the right foot.   Plantar surface.

calcaneal facet on the under surface of the talus. It is bounded anteriorly by a deep depression which is continued backward and medialward in the form of a groove, the **calcaneal sulcus.** In the articulated foot this sulcus lies below a similar one on the under surface of the talus, and the two form a canal (**sinus tarsi**) for the lodgement of the interosseous talocalcaneal ligament. In front and to the medial side of this groove is an elongated facet, concave from behind forward, and with its long axis directed forward and lateralward. This facet is frequently divided into two by a notch: of the two, the posterior, and larger is termed the **middle articular surface;** it is supported on a projecting process of bone, the **sustentaculum tali,** and articulates with the middle calcaneal facet on the under surface of the talus; the **anterior articular surface** is placed on the anterior part of the body, and articulates with the anterior calcaneal facet on the talus. The upper surface, anterior and lateral to the facets, is rough for the attachment of ligaments and for the origin of the Extensor digitorum brevis.

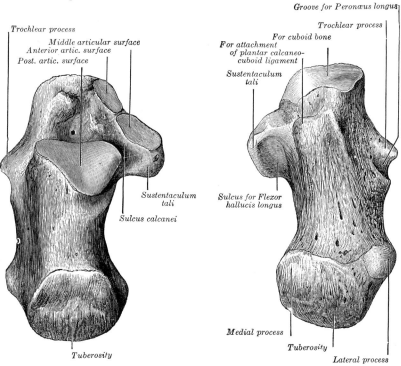

FIG. 262.—Left calcaneus, superior surface.   FIG. 263.—Left calcaneus, inferior surface.

The **inferior** or **plantar surface** is uneven, wider behind than in front, and convex from side to side; it is bounded posteriorly by a transverse elevation, the **calcaneal tuberosity,** which is depressed in the middle and prolonged at either end into a process; the **lateral process,** small, prominent, and rounded, gives origin to part of the Abductor digiti quinti; the **medial process,** broader and larger, gives attachment, by its prominent medial margin, to the Abductor hallucis, and in front to the Flexor digitorum brevis and the plantar aponeurosis; the depression between the processes gives origin to the Abductor digiti quinti. The rough surface in front of the processes gives attachment to the long plantar ligament, and to the lateral head of the Quadratus plantæ; while to a prominent tubercle nearer the anterior part of this surface, as well as to a transverse groove in front of the tubercle, is attached the plantar calcaneocuboid ligament.

The **lateral surface** is broad behind and narrow in front, flat and almost subcutaneous; near its center is a tubercle, for the attachment of the calcaneofibular ligament. At its upper and anterior part, this surface gives attachment to the lateral talocalcaneal ligament; and in front of the tubercle it presents a narrow surface marked by two oblique grooves. The grooves are separated by an elevated ridge, or tubercle, the **trochlear process** (*peroneal tubercle*), which varies much in size in different bones. The **superior groove** transmits the tendon of the Peronæus brevis; the **inferior groove**, that of the Peronæus longus.

The **medial surface** is deeply concave; it is directed obliquely downward and forward, and serves for the transmission of the plantar vessels and nerves into the sole of the foot; it affords origin to part of the Quadratus plantæ. At its upper

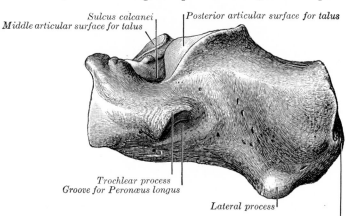

FIG. 264.—Left calcaneus, lateral surface.

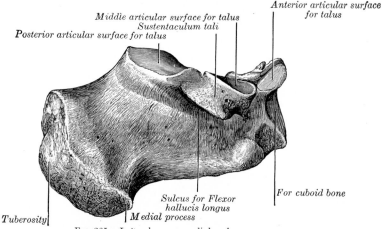

FIG. 265.—Left calcaneus, medial surface.

and forepart is a horizontal eminence, the **sustentaculum tali,** which gives attachment to a slip of the tendon of the Tibialis posterior. This eminence is concave above, and articulates with the middle calcaneal articular surface of the talus; below, it is grooved for the tendon of the Flexor hallucis longus; its anterior margin gives attachment to the plantar calcaneonavicular ligament, and its medial, to a part of the deltoid ligament of the ankle-joint.

The **anterior** or **cuboid articular surface** is of a somewhat triangular form. It is concave from above downward and lateralward, and convex in a direction at right angles to this. Its medial border gives attachment to the plantar calcaneonavicular ligament.

The **posterior surface** is prominent, convex, wider below than above, and divisible into three areas. The lowest of these is rough, and covered by the fatty and fibrous tissue of the heel; the middle, also rough, gives insertion to the tendo calcaneus and Plantaris; while the highest is smooth, and is covered by a bursa which intervenes between it and the tendo calcaneus.

Articulations.—The calcaneus articulates with two bones: the talus and cuboid.

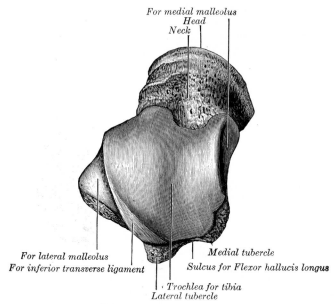

For medial malleolus
Head
Neck

For lateral malleolus
For inferior transverse ligament

Medial tubercle
Sulcus for Flexor hallucis longus

· Trochlea for tibia
Lateral tubercle

FIG. 266.—Left talus, from above.

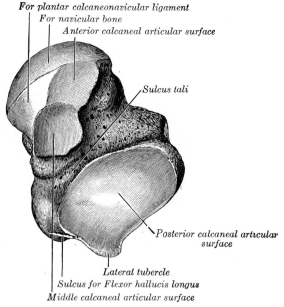

For plantar calcaneonavicular ligament
For navicular bone
Anterior calcaneal articular surface

Sulcus tali

Posterior calcaneal articular surface

Lateral tubercle
Sulcus for Flexor hallucis longus
Middle calcaneal articular surface

FIG. 267.—Left talus, from below.

The Talus (*astragalus; ankle bone*) (Figs. 266 to 269).—The talus is the second largest of the tarsal bones. It occupies the middle and upper part of the tarsus, supporting the tibia above, resting upon the calcaneus below, articulating on either side with the malleoli, and in front with the navicular. It consists of a **body**, a **neck**, and a **head**.

The **Body** (*corpus tali*).—The **superior surface** of the body presents, behind, a smooth trochlear surface, the **trochlea**, for articulation with the tibia. The trochlea is broader in front than behind, convex from before backward, slightly concave from side to side: in front it is continuous with the upper surface of the neck of the bone.

The **inferior surface** presents two articular areas, the posterior and middle calcaneal surfaces, separated from one another by a deep groove, the **sulcus tali**. The groove runs obliquely forward and lateralward, becoming gradually broader and deeper in front: in the articulated foot it lies above a similar groove upon the upper surface of the calcaneus, and forms, with it, a canal (**sinus tarsi**) filled up in the fresh state by the interosseous talocalcaneal ligament. The **posterior calcaneal articular surface** is large and of an oval or oblong form. It articulates

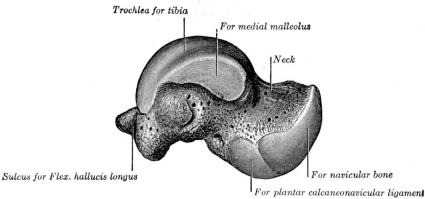

FIG. 268.—Left talus, medial surface.

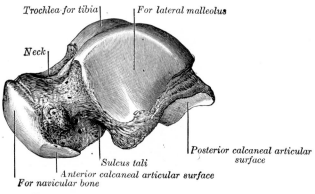

FIG. 269.—Left talus, lateral surface.

with the corresponding facet on the upper surface of the calcaneus, and is deeply concave in the direction of its long axis which runs forward and lateralward at an angle of about 45° with the median plane of the body. The **middle calcaneal articular surface** is small, oval in form and slightly convex; it articulates with the upper surface of the sustentaculum tali of the calcaneus.

The **medial surface** presents at its upper part a pear-shaped articular facet for the medial malleolus, continuous above with the trochlea; below the articular surface is a rough depression for the attachment of the deep portion of the deltoid ligament of the ankle-joint.

The **lateral surface** carries a large triangular facet, concave from above downward, for articulation with the lateral malleolus; its anterior half is continuous above with the trochlea; and in front of it is a rough depression for the attachment of the anterior talofibular ligament. Between the posterior half of the lateral border of the trochlea and the posterior part of the base of the fibular articular surface is a triangular facet which comes into contact with the transverse inferior tibiofibular ligament during flexion of the ankle-joint; below the base of this facet is a groove which affords attachment to the posterior talofibular ligament.

The **posterior surface** is narrow, and traversed by a groove running obliquely downward and medialward, and transmitting the tendon of the Flexor hallucis longus. Lateral to the groove is a prominent tubercle, the **posterior process,** to which the posterior talofibular ligament is attached; this process is sometimes separated from the rest of the talus, and is then known as the **os trigonum.** Medial to the groove is a second smaller tubercle.

The Neck (*collum tali*).—The neck is directed forward and medialward, and comprises the constricted portion of the bone between the body and the oval head. Its **upper** and **medial surfaces** are rough, for the attachment of ligaments; its **lateral surface** is concave and is continuous below with the deep groove for the interosseous talocalcaneal ligament.

The Head (*caput tali*).—The head looks forward and medialward; its **anterior articular** or **navicular surface** is large, oval, and convex. Its **inferior surface** has two facets, which are best seen in the fresh condition. The medial, situated in front of the middle calcaneal facet, is convex, triangular, or semi-oval in shape, and rests on the plantar calcaneonavicular ligament; the lateral, named the **anterior calcaneal articular surface,** is somewhat flattened, and articulates with the facet on the upper surface of the anterior part of the calcaneus.

Articulations.—The talus articulates with *four* bones: tibia, fibula, calcaneus, and navicular.

The Cuboid Bone (*os cuboideum*) (Figs. 270, 271).—The cuboid bone is placed on the lateral side of the foot, in front of the calcaneus, and behind the fourth and fifth metatarsal bones. It is of a pyramidal shape, its base being directed medialward.

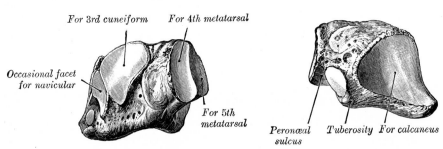

FIG. 270.—The left cuboid. Antero-medial view.　　　FIG. 271.—The left cuboid. Postero-lateral view.

Surfaces.—The **dorsal surface,** directed upward and lateralward, is rough, for the attachment of ligaments. The **plantar surface** presents in front a deep groove, the **peroneal sulcus,** which runs obliquely forward and medialward; it lodges the tendon of the Peronæus longus, and is bounded behind by a prominent ridge, to which the long plantar ligament is attached. The ridge ends laterally in an eminence, the **tuberosity,** the surface of which presents an oval facet; on this facet glides the sesamoid bone or cartilage frequently found in the tendon of the Peronæus longus. The surface of bone behind the groove is rough, for the attachment of the plantar calcaneocuboid ligament, a few fibers of the Flexor hallucis brevis, and a fasciculus from the tendon of the Tibialis posterior. The **lateral surface** presents a deep notch formed by the commencement of the peroneal sulcus. The posterior surface is smooth, triangular, and concavo-convex, for articulation with the anterior surface of the calcaneus; its infero-medial angle projects backward as a process which underlies and supports the anterior end of the calcaneus. The anterior surface, of smaller size, but also irregularly triangular, is divided by a vertical ridge into two facets: the medial, quadrilateral in form, articulates with the fourth metatarsal; the lateral, larger and more triangular, articulates with the fifth. The medial surface is broad, irregularly quadrilateral, and presents at its middle and upper part a smooth oval facet, for articulation with the third cuneiform; and behind this (occasionally) a smaller facet, for articulation with the navicular; it is rough in the rest of its extent, for the attachment of strong interosseous ligaments.

Articulations.—The cuboid articulates with *four* bones: the calcaneus, third cuneiform, and fourth and fifth metatarsals; occasionally with a fifth, the navicular.

The Navicular Bone (*os naviculare pedis; scaphoid bone*) (Figs. 272, 273).—The navicular bone is situated at the medial side of the tarsus, between the talus behind and the cuneiform bones in front.

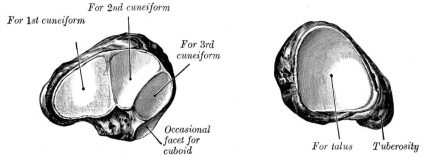

For 2nd cuneiform

For 1st cuneiform

For 3rd cuneiform

Occasional facet for cuboid

For talus   *Tuberosity*

Fig. 272.—The left navicular. Antero-lateral view.   Fig. 273.—The left navicular. Postero-medial view.

Surfaces.—The anterior surface is convex from side to side, and subdivided by two ridges into three facets, for articulation with the three cuneiform bones. The posterior surface is oval, concave, broader laterally than medially, and articulates with the rounded head of the talus. The dorsal surface is convex from side to side, and rough for the attachment of ligaments. The plantar surface is irregular, and also rough for the attachment of ligaments. The medial surface presents a rounded tuberosity, the lower part of which gives attachment to part of the tendon of the Tibialis posterior. The lateral surface is rough and irregular for the attachment of ligaments, and occasionally presents a small facet for articulation with the cuboid bone.

Articulations.—Then avicular articulates with *four* bones: the talus and the three cuneiforms; occasionally with a fifth, the cuboid.

The First Cuneiform Bone (*os cuneiforme primum; internal cuneiform*) (Figs. 274, 275).—The first cuneiform bone is the largest

For 1st metatarsal

For tendon of Tibialis anterior

Fig. 274.—The left first cuneiform. Antero-medial view.

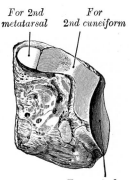

For 2nd metatarsal   *For 2nd cuneiform*

For navicular

Fig. 275.—The left first cuneiform. Postero-lateral view.

of the three cuneiforms. It is situated at the medial side of the foot, between the navicular behind and the base of the first metatarsal in front.

Surfaces.—The **medial surface** is subcutaneous, broad, and quadrilateral; at its anterior plantar angle is a smooth oval impression, into which part of the tendon of the Tibialis anterior is inserted; in the rest of its extent it is rough for the attachment of ligaments. The **lateral surface** is concave, presenting, along its superior and posterior borders a narrow L-shaped surface, the vertical limb and posterior part of the horizontal limb of which articulate with the second cuneiform, while the anterior part of the horizontal limb articulates with the second metatarsal bone: the rest of this surface is rough for the attachment of ligaments and part of the tendon of the Peronæus longus. The **anterior surface**, kidney-shaped and much larger than the posterior, articulates with the first metatarsal bone. The **posterior surface** is triangular, concave, and articulates with the most medial and largest of the three facets on the anterior surface of the navicular. The **plantar surface** is rough, and forms the base of the wedge; at its back part is a tuberosity for the insertion of part of the tendon of the Tibialis posterior. It also gives insertion in front to part of the tendon of the Tibialis anterior. The **dorsal surface** is the narrow end of the wedge, and is directed upward and lateralward; it is rough for the attachment of ligaments.

Articulations.—The first cuneiform articulates with *four* bones: the navicular, second cuneiform, and first and second metatarsals.

The Second Cuneiform Bone (*os cuneiforme secundum; middle cuneiform*) (Figs. 276, 277).—The second cuneiform bone, the smallest of the three, is of very regular wedge-like form, the thin end being directed downward. It is situated between the other two cuneiforms, and articulates with the navicular behind, and the second metatarsal in front.

Surfaces.—The **anterior surface**, triangular in form, and narrower than the posterior, articulates with the base of the second metatarsal bone. The **posterior surface**, also triangular, articulates with the intermediate facet on the anterior surface of the navicular. The **medial surface** carries an L-shaped articular facet, running along the superior and posterior borders, for articulation with the first cuneiform, and is rough in the rest of its extent for the attachment of ligaments. The **lateral surface** presents posteriorly a smooth facet for articulation with the third cuneiform bone. The **dorsal surface** forms the base of the wedge; it is quadrilateral and rough for the attachment of ligaments. The **plantar surface**, sharp and tuberculated, is also rough for the attachment of ligaments, and for the insertion of a slip from the tendon of the Tibialis posterior.

For 1st cuneiform

For navicular

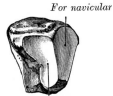

For 2nd metatarsal

For 3rd cuneiform

Fig. 276.—The left second cuneiform. Antero-medial view.

Fig. 277.—The left second cuneiform. Postero-lateral view.

Articulations.—The second cuneiform articulates with *four* bones: the navicular, first and third cuneiforms, and second metatarsal.

The Third Cuneiform Bone (*os cuneiforme tertium; external cuneiform*) (Figs. 279, 280).—The third cuneiform bone, intermediate in size between the two preceding, is wedge-shaped, the base being uppermost. It occupies the center of the front row of the tarsal bones, between the second cuneiform medially, the cuboid laterally, the navicular behind, and the third metatarsal in front.

Surfaces.—The **anterior surface**, triangular in form, articulates with the third metatarsal bone. The **posterior surface** articulates with the lateral facet on the anterior surface of the navicular, and is rough below for the attachment of ligamentous fibers. The **medial surface** presents an anterior and a posterior articular facet, separated by a rough depression: the anterior, sometimes divided, articulates with the lateral side of the base of the second metatarsal bone; the posterior skirts the posterior border, and articulates with the second cuneiform; the rough depression gives attachment to an interosseous ligament. The **lateral surface** also presents two articular facets, separated by a rough non-articular area; the anterior facet, situated at the superior angle of the bone, is small and semi-oval in shape, and articulates with the medial side of the base of the fourth metatarsal bone; the posterior and larger one is triangular or oval, and articulates with the cuboid; the rough, non-articular area serves for the attachment of an interosseous ligament. The three facets for articulation with the three metatarsal bones are continuous with one another; those for articulation with the second cuneiform and navicular are also continuous, but that for articulation with the cuboid is usually separate. The **dorsal surface** is of an oblong form, its postero-lateral angle being prolonged backward. The **plantar surface** is a rounded margin, and serves for the attachment of part of the tendon of the Tibialis posterior, part of the Flexor hallucis brevis, and ligaments.

Articulations.—The third cuneiform articulates with *six* bones: the navicular, second cuneiform, cuboid, and second, third, and fourth metatarsals.

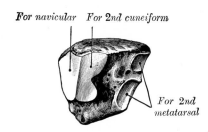

For navicular *For 2nd cuneiform*

For 2nd metatarsal

For 4th metatarsal *For cuboid*

For 3rd metatarsal

FIG. 278.—The left third cuneiform. Postero-medial view.

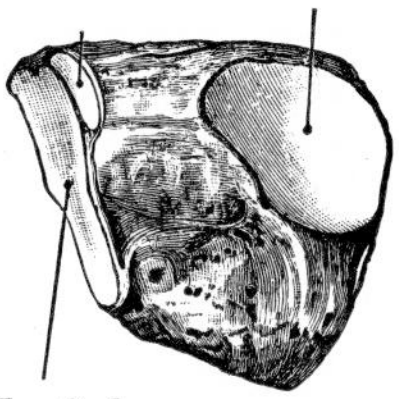

FIG. 279.—The third left cuneiform. Antero-lateral view.

The Metatarsus (Fig. 260, 261).

The **metatarsus** consists of five bones which are numbered from the medial side (*ossa metatarsalia* I.–V.); each presents for examination a **body** and **two extremities.**

Common Characteristics of the Metatarsal Bones.—The body is prismoid in form, tapers gradually from the tarsal to the phalangeal extremity, and is curved longitudinally, so as to be concave below, slightly convex above. The **base or posterior extremity** is wedge-shaped, articulating proximally with the tarsal bones, and by its sides with the contiguous metatarsal bones: its dorsal and plantar surfaces are rough for the attachment of ligaments. The **head or anterior extremity** presents a convex articular surface, oblong from above downward, and extending farther backward below than above. Its sides are flattened, and on each is a depression, surmounted by a tubercle, for ligamentous attachment. Its plantar surface is grooved antero-posteriorly for the passage of the Flexor tendons, and marked on either side by an articular eminence continuous with the terminal articular surface.

Characteristics of the Individual Metatarsal Bones. — The First Metatarsal Bone (*os metatarsale I; metatarsal bone of the great toe*) (Fig. 280).—The first metatarsal bone is remarkable for its great thickness, and is the shortest of the metatarsal bones. The **body** is strong, and of well-marked prismoid form. The **base** presents, as a rule, no articular facets on its sides, but occasionally on the lateral side there is an oval facet, by which it articulates with the second metatarsal. Its proximal articular surface is of large size and kidney-shaped; its circumference is grooved, for the tarsometatarsal ligaments, and medially gives insertion to part of the tendon of the Tibialis anterior; its plantar angle presents a rough oval prominence for the insertion of the tendon of the Peronæus longus. The **head** is large; on its plantar surface are two grooved facets, on which glide sesamoid bones; the facets are separated by a smooth elevation.

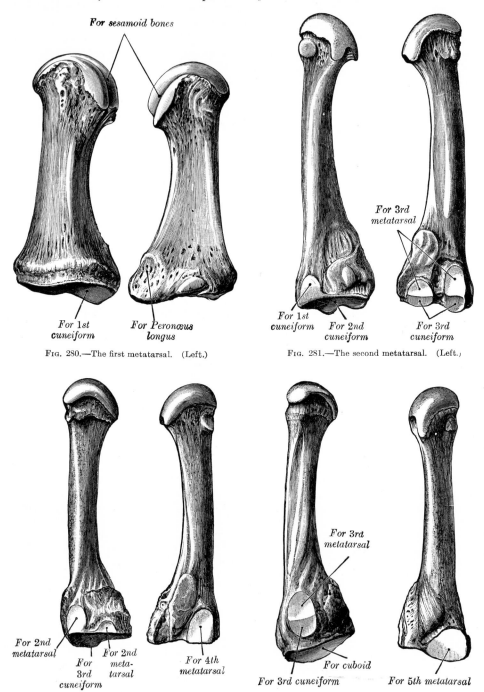

For sesamoid bones

For 1st cuneiform   *For Peronæus longus*

Fig. 280.—The first metatarsal. (Left.)

For 3rd metatarsal

For 1st cuneiform   *For 2nd cuneiform*   *For 3rd cuneiform*

Fig. 281.—The second metatarsal. (Left.)

For 2nd metatarsal   *For 3rd cuneiform*   *For 2nd metatarsal*   *For 4th metatarsal*

Fig. 282.—The third metatarsal. (Left.)

For 3rd metatarsal

For 3rd cuneiform   *For cuboid*   *For 5th metatarsal*

Fig. 283.—The fourth metatarsal. (Left.)

The Second Metatarsal Bone (*os metatarsale II*) (Fig. 281).—The second metatarsal bone is the longest of the metatarsal bones, being prolonged backward into the recess formed by the three cuneiform bones. Its **base** is broad above, narrow and rough below. It presents four articular surfaces: one behind, of a triangular form, for articulation with the second cuneiform; one at the upper part of its medial surface, for articulation with the first cuneiform; and two on its lateral surface, an upper and lower, separated by a rough non-articular interval. Each of these lateral articular surfaces is divided into two by a vertical ridge; the two anterior facets articulate with the third metatarsal; the two posterior (sometimes continuous) with the third cuneiform. A fifth facet is occasionally present for articulation with the first metatarsal; it is oval in shape, and is situated on the medial side of the body near the base.

The Third Metatarsal Bone (*os metatarsale III*) (Fig. 282).—The third metatarsal bone articulates proximally, by means of a triangular smooth surface, with the third cuneiform; medially, by two facets, with the second metatarsal; and laterally, by a single facet, with the fourth metatarsal. This last facet is situated at the dorsal angle of the base.

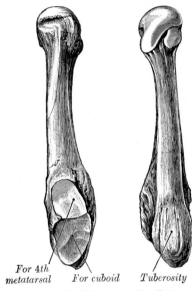

For 4th
metatarsal   For cuboid   Tuberosity

Fig. 284.—The fifth metatarsal. (Left.)

The Fourth Metatarsal Bone (*os metatarsale IV*) (Fig. 283).—The fourth metatarsal bone is smaller in size than the preceding; its **base** presents an oblique quadrilateral surface for articulation with the cuboid; a smooth facet on the medial side, divided by a ridge into an anterior portion for articulation with the third metatarsal, and a posterior portion for articulation with the third cuneiform; on the lateral side a single facet, for articulation with the fifth metatarsal.

The Fifth Metatarsal Bone (*os metatarsale V*) (Fig. 284).—The fifth metatarsal bone is recognized by a rough eminence, the **tuberosity,** on the lateral side of its base. The **base** articulates behind, by a triangular surface cut obliquely in a transverse direction, with the cuboid; and medially, with the fourth metatarsal. On the medial part of its dorsal surface is inserted the tendon of the Peronæus tertius and on the dorsal surface of the tuberosity that of the Peronæus brevis. A strong band of the plantar aponeurosis connects the projecting part of the tuberosity with the lateral process of the tuberosity of the calcaneus. The plantar surface of the base is grooved for the tendon of the Abductor digiti quinti, and gives origin to the Flexor digiti quinti brevis.

Articulations.—The base of each metatarsal bone articulates with one or more of the tarsal bones, and the head with one of the first row of phalanges. The first metatarsal articulates with the first cuneiform, the second with all three cuneiforms, the third with the third cuneiform, the fourth with the third cuneiform and the cuboid, and the fifth with the cuboid.

The Phalanges of the Foot (Phalanges Digitorum Pedis) (Fig. 260).

The **phalanges** of the foot correspond, in number and general arrangement, with those of the hand; there are two in the great toe, and three in each of the other toes. They differ from them, however, in their size, the bodies being much reduced in length, and, especially in the first row, laterally compressed.

First Row.—The **body** of each is compressed from side to side, convex above, concave below. The **base** is concave; and the **head** presents a trochlear surface for articulation with the second phalanx.

Second Row.—The phalanges of the second row are remarkably small and short, but rather broader than those of the first row.

The **ungual phalanges,** in form, resemble those of the fingers; but they are smaller and are flattened from above downward; each presents a broad base for articulation with the corresponding bone of the second row, and an expanded distal extremity for the support of the nail and end of the toe.

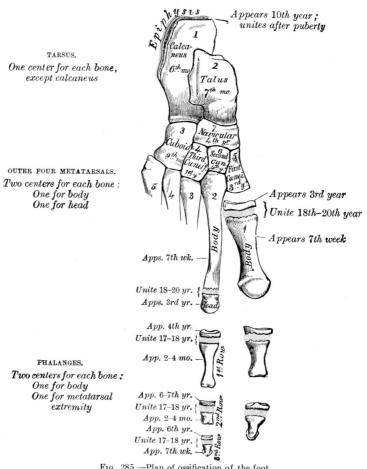

FIG. 285.—Plan of ossification of the foot.

Articulations.—In the second, third, fourth, and fifth toes the phalanges of the first row articulate behind with the metatarsal bones, and in front with the second phalanges, which in their turn articulate with the first and third: the ungual phalanges articulate with the second.

Ossification of the Bones of the Foot (Fig. 285).—The **tarsal bones** are each ossified from a *single* center, excepting the calcaneus, which has an epiphysis for its posterior extremity. The centers make their appearance in the following order: calcaneus at the sixth month of fetal life:

talus, about the seventh month; cuboid, at the ninth month; third cuneiform, during the first year; first cuneiform, in the third year; second cuneiform and navicular, in the fourth year. The epiphysis for the posterior extremity of the calcaneus appears at the tenth year, and unites with the rest of the bone soon after puberty. The posterior process of the talus is sometimes ossified from a separate center, and may remain distinct from the main mass of the bone, when it is named the *os trigonum*.

The **metatarsal bones** are each ossified from *two* centers: one for the body, and one for the head, of the second, third, fourth, and fifth metatarsals; one for the body, and one for the base, of the first metatarsal. Ossification commences in the center of the body about the ninth week, and extends toward either extremity. The center for the base of the first metatarsal appears about the third year; the centers for the heads of the other bones between the fifth and eighth years; they join the bodies between the eighteenth and twentieth years.

The **phalanges** are each ossified from *two* centers: one for the body, and one for the base. The center for the body appears about the tenth week, that for the base between the fourth and tenth years; it joins the body about the eighteenth year.

Comparison of the Bones of the Hand and Foot.

The hand and foot are constructed on somewhat similar principles, each consisting of a proximal part, the carpus or the tarsus, a middle portion, the metacarpus, or the metatarsus, and a terminal portion, the phalanges. The proximal part consists of a series of more or less cubical bones which allow a slight amount of gliding on one another and are chiefly concerned in distributing forces transmitted to or from the bones of the arm or leg. The middle part is made up of slightly movable long bones which assist the carpus or tarsus in distributing forces and also give greater breadth for the reception of such forces. The separation of the individual bones from one another allows of the attachments of the Interossei and protects the dorsi-palmar and dorsi-plantar vascular anastomoses. The terminal portion is the most movable, and its separate elements enjoy a varied range of movements, the chief of which are flexion and extension.

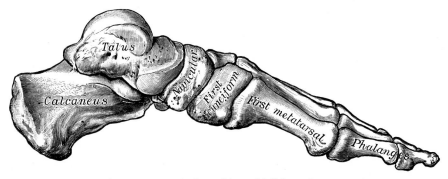

Fig. 286.—Skeleton of foot. Medial aspect.

The function of the hand and foot are, however, very different, and the general similarity between them is greatly modified to meet these requirements. Thus the foot forms a firm basis of support for the body in the erect posture, and is therefore more solidly built up and its component parts are less movable on each other than those of the hand. In the case of the phalanges the difference is readily noticeable; those of the foot are smaller and their movements are more limited than those of the hand. Very much more marked is the difference between the metacarpal bone of the thumb and the metatarsal bone of the great toe. The metacarpal bone of the thumb is constructed to permit of great mobility, is directed at an acute angle from that of the index finger, and is capable of a considerable range of movements at its articulation with the carpus. The metatarsal bone of the great toe assists in supporting the weight of the body, is constructed with great solidity, lies parallel with the other metatarsals, and has a very limited degree of mobility. The carpus is small in proportion to the rest of the hand, is placed in line with the forearm, and forms a transverse arch, the concavity of which constitutes a bed for the Flexor tendons and the palmar vessels and nerves. The tarsus forms a considerable part of the foot, and is placed at right angles to the leg, a position which is almost peculiar to man, and has relation to his erect posture. In order to allow of their supporting the weight of the body with the least expenditure of material the tarsus and a part of the metatarsus are constructed in a series of arches (Figs. 286, 287), the disposition of which will be considered after the articulations of the foot have been described.

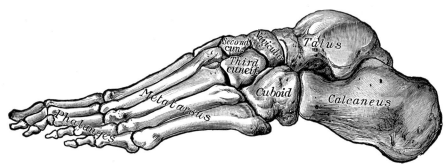

FIG. 287.—Skeleton of foot.   Lateral aspect.

The Sesamoid Bones (Ossa Sesamoidea).

Sesamoid bones are small more or less rounded masses embedded in certain tendons and usually related to joint surfaces. Their functions probably are to modify pressure, to diminish friction, and occasionally to alter the direction of a muscle pull. That they are not developed to meet certain physical requirements in the adult is evidenced by the fact that they are present as cartilaginous nodules in the fetus, and in greater numbers than in the adult. They must be regarded, according to Thilenius, as integral parts of the skeleton phylogenetically inherited. Physical necessities probably come into play in selecting and in regulating the degree of development of the original cartilaginous nodules. Nevertheless, irregular nodules of bone may appear as the result of intermittent pressure in certain regions, e. g., the "rider's bone," which is occasionally developed in the Adductor muscles of the thigh.

Sesamoid bones are invested by the fibrous tissue of the tendons, except on the surfaces in contact with the parts over which they glide, where they present smooth articular facets.

In the upper extremity the sesamoid bones of the joints are found only on the palmar surface of the hand. Two, of which the medial is the the larger, are constant at the metacarpophalangeal joint of the thumb; one is frequently present in the corresponding joint of the little finger, and one (or two) in the same joint of the index finger. Sesamoid bones are also found occasionally at the metacarpophalangeal joints of the middle and ring fingers, at the interphalangeal joint of the thumb and at the distal interphalangeal joint of the index finger.

In the lower extremity the largest sesamoid bone of the joints is the patella, developed in the tendon of the Quadriceps femoris. On the plantar aspect of the foot, two, of which the medial is the larger, are always present at the metatarsophalangeal joint of the great toe; one sometimes at the metatarsophalangeal joints of the second and fifth toes, one occasionally at the corresponding joint of the third and fourth toes, and one at the interphalangeal joint of the great toe.

Sesamoid bones apart from joints are seldom found in the tendons of the upper limb; one is sometimes seen in the tendon of the Biceps brachii opposite the radial tuberosity. They are, however, present in several of the tendons of the lower limb, viz., one in the tendon of the Peronæus longus, where it glides on the cuboid; one, appearing late in life, in the tendon of the Tibialis anterior, opposite the smooth facet of the first cuneiform bone; one in the tendon of the Tibialis posterior, opposite the medial side of the head of the talus; one in the lateral head of the Gastrocnemius, behind the lateral condyle of the femur; and one in the tendon of the Psoas major, where it glides over the pubis. Sesamoid bones are found occasionally in the tendon of the Glutæus maximus, as it passes over the greater trochanter, and in the tendons which wind around the medial and lateral malleoli.

BIBLIOGRAPHY

Embryology, Ossification and Growth

On the growth pattern of the human head from the third month to the eighth year of life. Brodie, A. G.: 1941. Am. J. Anat., Vol. 68, pp. 209–262.

Growth of the human tibia. Francis, C. C.: 1939. Am. J. Phys. Anthrop., Vol. 25, pp. 323–331.

Fetal age assessment by centers of ossification. Hill, A. H.: 1939. Am. J. Phys. Anthrop., Vol. 24, pp. 251–272.

Morphogenesis of the architecture of hip and thigh. Howell, A. B.: 1938. J. Morph., Vol. 62, pp. 177–218.

Observations on the bones of the skull in white and negro fetuses and infants. Limson, M.: 1932. Carnegie Cont. to Emb., Vol. 23, pp. 205–222.

A method for assessing the development of the hand skeleton. Michelson, N.: 1946. Am. J. Phys. Anthrop., Vol. 4, pp. 235–242.

A Study of the Development and Structure of the Vertebrate Skeleton. Murray, P. D. F.: 1936. Cambridge Univ. Press, London, x + 203 pp.

The developmental anatomy of the human osseous skeleton during the embryonic, fetal and circumnatal periods. Noback, C. R.: 1944. Anat. Rec., Vol. 88, pp. 91–125; Vol. 87, pp. 29–51.

Normal variations in the ossification of bones. Pryor, J. W.: 1939. J. Heredity, Vol. 30, pp. 249–255.

The origin of the vertebral column in the deer-mouse, Peromyscus maniculatus rufinus. Sensenig, E. C.: 1943. Anat. Rec., Vol. 86, pp. 123–141.

Atlas of Skeletal Maturation. Todd, T. W.: 1937. Mosby, St. Louis, 203 pp.

The sequence of epiphysial union in the opossum. Washburn, S. L.: 1946. Anat. Rec., Vol. 95, pp. 353–363.

Histology and Bone Formation

Perichondrial ossification and the fate of the perichondrium with special reference to that of the otic capsule. Bast, T. H.: 1944. Anat. Rec., Vol. 90, pp. 139–148.

Microscopic observations on new formation of cartilage and bone in the living mammal. Clark, E. R., and E. L.: 1942. Am. J. Anat., Vol. 70, pp. 167–200.

Length of lacunæ and number of canaliculi in bones of several mammals. Gray, D. J.: 1941. Anat. Rec., Vol. 81, pp. 163–169.

The composition of bone and the function of the bone cell. Huggins, C.: 1937. Physiol. Rev., Vol. 17, pp. 119–143.

Organizers and the growth of bone. Lacroix, P.: 1947. J. Bone and Joint Surg., Vol. 29, pp. 292–296.

Calcification and ossification. Calcification in normal growing bone. McLean, F. C., and W. Bloom: 1940. Anat. Rec., Vol. 78, pp. 333–359.

Observations on the pathology of rickets with particular reference to the changes at the cartilage-shaft junctions of the growing bones. Park, E. A.: 1939. Harvey Lectures, Vol. 34, pp. 157–213.

Osteology and Physical Anthropology

Skeletal change in ancient Greece. Angel, J. L.: 1946. Am. J. Phys. Anthrop., Vol. 4, pp. 69–97.

Determination of the condylo-diaphysial angle of the humerus. Bodel, J. K., Jr.: 1939. Am. J. Phys. Anthrop., Vol. 25, pp. 333–339.

The cranio-facial union in man. Cobb, W. M.: 1940. Am. J. Phys. Anthrop., Vol. 26, pp. 87–111.

Torsion of the lower extremity. Elftman, H.: 1945. Am. J. Phys. Anthrop., Vol. 3, pp. 255–265.

The torsion of the humerus: A phylogenetic survey from fish to man. Evans, F. G., and V. E. Krahl: 1945. Am. J. Anat., Vol. 76, pp. 303–337.

The tibial tuberosity and the insertion of the ligamentum patellæ. Hughes, E. S. R., and S. Sunderland: 1946. Anat. Rec., Vol. 96, pp. 439–444.

A Bibliography of Human Morphology, 1914–1939. Krogman, W.: 1941. Univ. Chicago Press, Chicago, xxxi + 385 pp.

The effects of partial starvation on somatotype: An analysis of material from the Minnesota starvation experiment. Lasker, G. W.: 1947. Am. J. Phys. Anthrop., Vol. 5, pp. 323–341.

The significance of the premaxillary diastema in Pithecanthropus robustus. (Skull IV.) Montagu, M. F. A.: 1946. Am. J. Phys. Anthrop., Vol. 4, pp. 193–198.

The comparative morphology of the vertebrate spinal column. Its form as related to function. Rockwell, H., F. G. Evans, and H. C. Pheasant: 1938. J. Morph., Vol. 63, pp. 87–117.

Popliteal facet in men who habitually squat. Shah, M. A.: 1945. Nature, Vol. 156, pp. 237–238.

The posture of the great ape hand in locomotion, and its phylogenetic implications. Straus, W. L., Jr.: 1940. Am. J. Phys. Anthrop., Vol. 27, pp. 199–207.

Variations and Anomalies

Variations in human scapulæ. Gray, D. J.: 1942. Am. J. Phys. Anthrop., Vol. 29, pp. 57–72.

Length of first, twelfth, and accessory ribs in American whites and negroes; their relationship to certain vertebral variations. Lanier, R. R., Jr.: 1944. Am. J. Phys. Anthrop., Vol. 2, pp. 137–146.

The os epipyramis or epitriquetrum. Saunders, R. L.: 1942. Anat. Rec., Vol. 84, pp. 17–22.

Variations of the female sacrum. Trotter, M., and G. S. Letterman: 1944. Surg., Gyn. and Obs., Vol. 78, pp. 419–424.

Experimental

Studies on bone mechanics in vitro. II. The role of tension and pressure in chondrogenesis. Glücksmann, A.: 1939. Anat. Rec., Vol. 73, pp. 39–55.

Skeletal variations resulting from the interaction of gene determined growth forces. Sawin, P. B.: 1946. Anat. Rec., Vol. 96, pp. 183–200.

The effect of facial paralysis on the growth of the skull of rat and rabbit. Washburn, S. L.: 1946. Anat. Rec., Vol. 94, pp. 163–168.

JOINTS AND LIGAMENTS.

THE bones of the skeleton are joined to one another at different parts of their surfaces, and such connections are termed **Joints** or **Articulations.** Where the joints are *immovable*, as in the articulations between practically all the bones of the skull, the adjacent margins of the bones are almost in contact, being separated merely by a thin layer of fibrous membrane, named the **sutural ligament.** In certain regions at the base of the skull this fibrous membrane is replaced by a layer of cartilage. Where *slight movement* combined with great strength is required, the osseous surfaces are united by tough and elastic **fibrocartilages,** as in the joints between the vertebral bodies, and in the interpubic articulation. In the *freely movable* joints the surfaces are completely separated; the bones forming the articulation are expanded for greater convenience of mutual connection, covered by **cartilage** and enveloped by **capsules** of fibrous tissue. The cells lining the interior of the fibrous capsule form an imperfect membrane—the **synovial membrane**—which secretes a lubricating fluid. The joints are strengthened by strong fibrous bands called **ligaments,** which extend between the bones forming the joint.

DEVELOPMENT OF THE JOINTS.

The mesoderm from which the different parts of the skeleton are formed shows at first no differentiation into masses corresponding with the individual bones. Thus continuous cores of mesoderm form the axes of the limb-buds and a continuous column of mesoderm the future vertebral column. The first indications of the bones and joints are circumscribed condensations of the mesoderm; these condensed parts become chondrified and finally ossified to form the bones of the skeleton. The intervening non-condensed portions consist at first of undifferentiated mesoderm, which may develop in one of three directions. It may be converted into fibrous tissue as in the case of the skull bones, a synarthrodial joint being the result, or it may become partly cartilaginous, in which case an amphiarthrodial joint is formed. Again, it may become looser in texture and a cavity ultimately appear in its midst; the cells lining the sides of this cavity form a synovial membrane and thus a diarthrodial joint is developed.

The tissue surrounding the original mesodermal core forms fibrous sheaths for the developing bones, *i. e.*, periosteum and perichondrium, which are continued between the ends of the bones over the synovial membrane as the capsules of the joints. These capsules are not of uniform thickness, so that in them may be recognized especially strengthened bands which are described as ligaments. This, however, is not the only method of formation of ligaments. In some cases by modification of, or derivations from, the tendons surrounding the joint, additional ligamentous bands are provided to further strengthen the articulations.

In several of the movable joints the mesoderm which originally existed between the ends of the bones does not become completely absorbed—a portion of it persists and forms an articular disk. These disks may be intimately associated in their development with the muscles surrounding the joint, *e. g.*, the menisci of the knee-joint, or with cartilaginous elements, representatives of skeletal structures, which are vestigial in human anatomy, *e. g.*, the articular disk of the sterno-clavicular joint.

(255)

HISTOLOGY

Bone.—Bone constitutes the fundamental element of all the joints. In the long bones, the extremities are the parts which form the articulations; they are generally somewhat enlarged; and consist of spongy cancellous tissue with a thin coating of compact substance. In the flat bones, the articulations usually take place at the edges; and in the short bones at various parts of their surfaces. The layer of compact bone which forms the joint surface, and to which the articular cartilage is attached, is called the **articular lamella.** It differs from ordinary bone tissue in that it contains no Haversian canals, and its lacunæ are larger and have no canaliculi. The vessels of the cancellous tissue, as they approach the articular lamella, turn back in loops, and do not perforate it; this layer is consequently denser and firmer than ordinary bone, and is evidently designed to form an unyielding support for the articular cartilage.

Cartilage.—Cartilage is a non-vascular structure which is found in various parts of the body—in adult life chiefly in the joints, in the parietes of the thorax, and in various tubes, such as the trachea and bronchi, nose, and ears, which require to be kept permanently open. In the fetus, at an early period, the greater part of the skeleton is cartilaginous; as this cartilage is afterward replaced by bone, it is called **temporary,** in contradistinction to that which remains unossified during the whole of life, and is called **permanent.**

Cartilage is divided, according to its minute structure, into **hyaline cartilage, white fibrocartilage,** and **yellow** or **elastic fibrocartilage.**

Hyaline Cartilage.—Hyaline cartilage consists of a gristly mass of a firm consistence, but of considerable elasticity and pearly bluish color. Except where it coats the articular ends of bones, it is covered externally by a fibrous membrane, the **perichondrium,** from the vessels of which it imbibes its nutritive fluids, being itself destitute of bloodvessels. It contains no nerves. Its intimate structure is very simple. If a thin slice be examined under the microscope, it will be found to consist of cells of a rounded or bluntly angular form, lying in groups of two or more in a granular or almost homogeneous matrix (Fig. 288). The cells, when arranged in groups of two or more, have generally straight outlines where they are in contact with each other, and in the rest of their circumference are rounded. They consist of clear translucent protoplasm in which fine interlacing filaments and minute granules are sometimes present; imbedded in this are one or two round nuclei, having the usual intranuclear network. The cells are contained in cavities in the matrix, called **cartilage lacunæ;** around these the matrix is arranged in concentric lines, as if it had been formed in successive portions around the cartilage cells. This constitutes the so-called **capsule of the space.** Each lacuna is generally occupied by a single cell, but during the division of the cells it may contain two, four, or eight cells.

The matrix is transparent and apparently without structure, or else presents a dimly granular appearance, like ground glass. Some observers have shown that the matrix of hyaline cartilage, and especially of the articular variety, after prolonged maceration, can be broken up into fine fibrils.

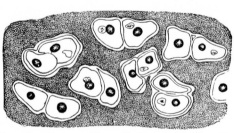

Fig. 288.—Human cartilage cells from the cricoid cartilage × 350.

These fibrils are probably of the same nature, chemically, as the white fibers of connective tissue. It is believed by some histologists that the matrix is permeated by a number of fine channels, which connect the lacunæ with each other, and that these canals communicate with the lymphatics of the perichondrium, and thus the structure is permeated by a current of nutrient fluid.

Articular cartilage, costal cartilage, and **temporary cartilage** are all of the hyaline variety. They present differences in the size, shape, and arrangement of their cells.

In **Articular Cartilage** (Fig. 289), which shows no tendency to ossification, the matrix is finely granular; the cells and nuclei are small, and are disposed parallel to the surface in the superficial part, while nearer to the bone they are arranged in vertical rows. Articular cartilages have a tendency to split in a vertical direction; in disease this tendency becomes very manifest. The free surface of articular cartilage, where it is exposed to friction, is not covered by perichondrium, although a layer of connective tissue continuous with that of the synovial membrane can be traced in the adult over a small part of its circumference, and here the cartilage cells are more or less branched and pass insensibly into the branched connective tissue corpuscles of the synovial membrane. Articular cartilage forms a thin incrustation upon the joint surfaces of the bones, and its elasticity enables it to break the force of concussions, while its smoothness affords ease and freedom of movement. It varies in thickness according to the shape of the articular surface

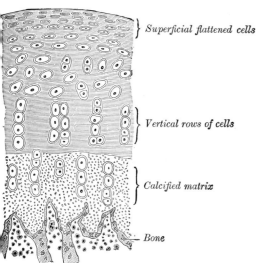

Superficial flattened cells

Vertical rows of cells

Calcified matrix

Bone

FIG. 289.—Vertical section of articular cartilage.

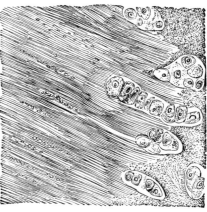

FIG. 290.—Costal cartilage from a man, aged seventy-six years, showing the development of fibrous structure in the matrix. In several portions of the specimen two or three generations of cells are seen enclosed in a parent cell wall. Highly magnified.

on which it lies; where this is convex the cartilage is thickest at the center, the reverse being the case on concave articular surfaces. It appears to derive its nutriment partly from the vessels of the neighboring synovial membrane and partly from those of the bone upon which it is implanted. Toynbee has shown that the minute vessels of the cancellous tissue as they approach the articular lamella dilate and form arches, and then return into the substance of the bone.

In **Costal Cartilage** the cells and nuclei are large, and the matrix has a tendency to fibrous striation, especially in old age (Fig. 290). In the thickest parts of the costal cartilages a few large vascular channels may be detected. This appears, at first sight, to be an exception to the statement that cartilage is a non-vascular tissue, but is not so really, for the vessels give no branches to the cartilage substance itself, and the channels may rather be looked upon as involutions of the perichondrium. The xiphoid process and the cartilages of the nose, larynx, and trachea (except the epiglottis and corniculate cartilages of the larynx, which are composed of elastic fibrocartilage) resemble the costal cartilages in microscopic characteristics. The arytenoid cartilage of the larynx shows a transition from hyaline cartilage at its base to elastic cartilage at the apex.

17

The hyaline cartilages, especially in adult and advanced life, are prone to calcify—that is to say, to have their matrix permeated by calcium salts without any appearance of true bone. The process of calcification, occurs frequently, in such cartilages as those of the trachea and in the costal cartilages, where it may be succeeded by conversion into true bone.

White Fibrocartilage.—White fibrocartilage consists of a mixture of white fibrous tissue and cartilaginous tissue in various proportions; to the former of these constituents it owes its flexibility and toughness, and to the latter its elasticity. When examined under the microscope it is found to be made up of fibrous connective tissue arranged in bundles, with cartilage cells between the bundles; the cells to a certain extent resemble tendon cells, but may be distinguished from them by being surrounded by a concentrically striated area of cartilage matrix and by being less flattened (Fig. 291). The white fibrocartilages admit of arrangement into four groups—**interarticular, connecting, circumferential,** and **stratiform.**

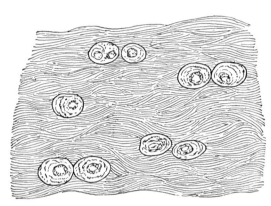

FIG. 291.—White fibrocartilage from an intervertebral fibrocartilage.

1. The **Interarticular Fibrocartilages** (*menisci*) are flattened fibrocartilaginous plates, of a round, oval, triangular, or sickle-like form, interposed between the articular cartilages of certain joints. They are free on both surfaces, usually thinner toward the center than at the circumference, and held in position by the attachment of their margins and extremities to the surrounding ligaments. The synovial surfaces of the joints are prolonged over them. They are found in the temporomandibular, sternoclavicular, acrominoclavicular, wrist, and knee joints—*i. e.*, in those joints which are most exposed to violent concussion and subject to frequent movement. Their uses are to obliterate the intervals between opposed surfaces in their various motions; to increase the depths of the articular surfaces and give ease to the gliding movements; to moderate the effects of great pressure and deaden the intensity of the shocks to which the parts may be subjected. It should be pointed out that these interarticular fibrocartilages serve an important purpose in increasing the varieties of movement in a joint. Thus in the knee joint there are two kinds of motion, viz., angular movement and rotation, although it is a hinge joint, in which, as a rule, only one variety of motion is permitted; the former movement takes place between the condyles of the femur and the interarticular cartilages, the latter between the cartilages and the head of the tibia.

2. The **Connecting Fibrocartilages** are interposed between the bony surfaces of those joints which admit of only slight mobility, as between the bodies of the vertebræ. They form disks which are closely adherent to the opposed surfaces. Each disk is composed of concentric rings of fibrous tissue, with cartilaginous laminæ interposed, the former tissue predominating toward the circumference, the latter toward the center.

3. The **Circumferential Fibrocartilages** consist of rims of fibrocartilage, which surround the margins of some of the articular cavities, *e. g.*, the glenoidal labrum of the hip, and of the shoulder; they serve to deepen the articular cavities and to protect their edges.

4. The **Stratiform Fibrocartilages** are those which form a thin coating to osseous grooves through which the tendons of certain muscles glide. Small masses of fibro-cartilage are also developed in the tendons of some muscles, where they glide over bones, as in the tendons of the Peronæus longus and Tibialis posterior.

The distinguishing feature of cartilage chemically is that it yields on boiling a substance called **chondrin**, very similar to gelatin, but differing from it in several of its reactions. It is now believed that chondrin is not a simple body, but a mixture of gelatin with mucinoid substances, chief among which, perhaps, is a compound termed **chondro-mucoid**.

Ligaments.—Ligaments are composed mainly of bundles of **collagenous fibers** placed parallel with, or closely interlaced with one another, and present a white, shining, silvery appearance. They are pliant and flexible, so as to allow perfect freedom of movement, but strong, tough, and inextensible, so as not to yield readily to applied force. Some ligaments consist entirely of **yellow elastic tissue**, as the ligamenta flava which connect together the laminæ of adjacent vertebræ, and the ligamentum nuchæ in the lower animals. In these cases the elasticity of the ligament is intended to act as a substitute for muscular power.

The Articular Capsules.—The articular capsules form complete envelopes for the freely movable joints. Each capsule consists of two strata—an **external** (*stratum fibrosum*) composed of white fibrous tissue, and an **internal** (*stratum synoviale*) which is a specialized layer, and is usually described separately as the synovial membrane.

The **fibrous capsule** is attached to the whole circumference of the articular end of each bone entering into the joint, and thus entirely surrounds the articulation.

The **synovial membrane** covers the inner surface of the fibrous capsule, forming a closed sac called the **synovial cavity**. It is composed of loose connective tissue, cellular in some places, fibrous in others, and it has a free surface which elaborates a thick, viscous, glairy fluid, similar to the white of an egg and termed, therefore, **synovia** or **synovial fluid**. The synovial membrane covers tendons which pass through the joint, such as the tendon of the Popliteus in the knee, and the long head of the Biceps in the shoulder. The membrane is not closely applied to the inner surface of the fibrous capsule, but is thrown into folds, fringes, or projections which are composed of connective tissue, fat, and blood vessels. These folds commonly surround the margin of the articular cartilage, filling in clefts and crevices, and in some joints, such as the knee, forming large pads of fat. The synovial cavity of a normal joint contains only enough synovial fluid to moisten and lubricate the synovial surfaces, but in an injured or inflamed joint, the fluid may accumulate in painful amounts. Part of the lining of the synovial cavity is provided by the surface of the articular cartilage which is moistened by the synovia but is not covered by the synovial membrane.

Similar to the synovial cavities of true joints are the synovial tendon sheaths and synovial bursæ which have an inner lining equivalent to the synovial membrane of a joint and are lubricated by a fluid very similar to synovial fluid.

The **Synovial Tendon Sheaths** (*vaginæ mucosæ*) facilitate the gliding of tendons which pass through fibrous and bony tunnels such as those under the transverse carpal ligament of the wrist. These sheaths are closed sacs, one layer of the synovial membrane lining the tunnel, the other reflected over the surface of the tendon.

Synovial Bursæ (*bursæ mucosæ*) are clefts in the connective tissue between muscles, tendons, ligaments, and bones. They are made into closed sacs by a synovial lining, similar to that of a true joint, which may in some cases be continuous through and opening in the wall with the lining of a joint cavity. They facilitate the gliding of muscles or tendons over bony or ligamentous prominences, and are named according to their location, subcutaneous, submuscular, and subtendinous.

CLASSIFICATION OF JOINTS.

The articulations are divided into three classes: **synarthroses** or immovable, **amphiarthroses** or slightly movable, and **diarthroses** or freely movable, joints.

Synarthroses (*immovable articulations*).—Synarthroses include all those articulations in which the surfaces of the bones are in almost direct contact, fastened together by intervening connective tissue or hyaline cartilage, and in which there is no appreciable motion, as in the joints between the bones of the skull, excepting those of the mandible. There are four varieties of synarthrosis: **sutura, schindylesis, gomphosis**, and **synchondrosis**.

Sutura.—Sutura is that form of articulation where the contiguous margins of the bones are united by a thin layer of fibrous tissue; it is met with only in the skull (Fig. 292). When the margins of the bones are connected by a series of processes, and indentations interlocked together, the articulation is termed a **true suture** (*sutura vera*); and of this there are three varieties: sutura dentata, serrata, and limbosa. The margins of the bones are not in direct contact, being separated by a thin layer of fibrous tissue, continuous externally with the pericranium, internally with the dura mater. The **sutura dentata** is so called from the tooth-like form of the projecting processes, as in the suture between the parietal bones. In the

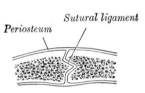

Periosteum   *Sutural ligament*

Fig. 292.—Section across the sagittal suture.

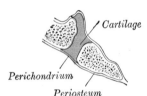

Cartilage

Perichondrium

Periosteum

Fig. 293.—Section through occipitosphenoid synchondrosis of an infant.

sutura serrata the edges of the bones are serrated like the teeth of a fine saw, as between the two portions of the frontal bone. In the **sutura limbosa**, there is besides the interlocking, a certain degree of bevelling of the articular surfaces, so that the bones overlap one another, as in the suture between the parietal and frontal bones. When the articulation is formed by roughened surfaces placed in apposition with one another, it is termed a **false suture** (*sutura notha*), of which there are two kinds: the **sutura squamosa**, formed by the overlapping of contiguous bones by broad bevelled margins, as in the squamosal suture between the temporal and parietal, and the **sutura harmonia**, where there is simple apposition of contiguous rough surfaces, as in the articulation between the maxillæ, or between the horizontal parts of the palatine bones.

Schindylesis.—Schindylesis is that form of articulation in which a thin plate of bone is received into a cleft or fissure formed by the separation of two laminæ in another bone, as in the articulation of the rostrum of the sphenoid and perpendicular plate of the ethmoid with the vomer, or in the reception of the latter in the fissure between the maxillæ and between the palatine bones.

Gomphosis.—Gomphosis is articulation by the insertion of a conical process into a socket; this is not illustrated by any articulation between bones, properly so called, but is seen in the articulations of the roots of the teeth with the alveoli of the mandible and maxillæ.

Synchondrosis.—Where the connecting medium is cartilage the joint is termed a synchondrosis (Fig. 293). This is a temporary form of joint, for the cartilage is converted into bone before adult life. Such joints are found between the epiphyses and bodies of long bones, between the occipital and the sphenoid at, and for some years after, birth, and between the petrous portion of the temporal and the jugular process of the occipital.

Amphiarthroses (*slightly movable articulations*).—In these articulations the contiguous bony surfaces are either connected by broad flattened disks of fibrocartilage, of a more or less complex structure, as in the articulations between the bodies of the vertebræ; or are united by an interosseous ligament, as in the inferior tibiofibular articulation. The first form is termed a **symphysis** (Fig. 294), the second a **syndesmosis**.

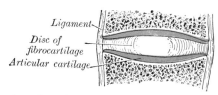

Ligament

Disc of fibrocartilage

Articular cartilage

FIG. 294.—Diagrammatic section of a symphysis.

Diarthroses (*freely movable articulations*).—This class includes the greater number of the joints in the body. In a diarthrodial joint the contiguous bony surfaces are covered with articular cartilage, and connected by ligaments lined by synovial membrane (Fig. 295). The joint may be divided, completely or incompletely, by an **articular disk** or **meniscus**, the periphery of which is continuous with the fibrous capsule while its free surfaces are covered by synovial membrane (Fig. 296).

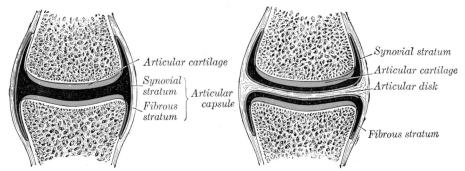

Articular cartilage

Synovial stratum *Articular capsule*

Fibrous stratum

FIG. 295.—Diagrammatic section of a diarthrodial joint.

Synovial stratum

Articular cartilage

Articular disk

Fibrous stratum

FIG. 296.—Diagrammatic section of a diarthrodial joint, with an articular disk.

The varieties of joints in this class have been determined by the kind of motion permitted in each. There are two varieties in which the movement is uniaxial, that is to say, all movements take place around one axis. In one form, the **ginglymus**, this axis is, practically speaking, transverse; in the other, the **trochoid** or **pivot-joint**, it is longitudinal. There are two varieties where the movement is biaxial, or around two horizontal axes at right angles to each other, or at any intervening axis between the two. These are the **condyloid** and the **saddle-joint**. There is one form where the movement is polyaxial, the **enarthrosis** or **ball-and-socket joint;** and finally there are the **arthrodia** or **gliding joints**.

Ginglymus or Hinge-joint.—In this form the articular surfaces are moulded to each other in such a manner as to permit motion only in one plane, forward and backward, the extent of motion at the same time being considerable. The direction which the distal bone takes in this motion is seldom in the same plane as that of the axis of the proximal bone; there is usually a certain amount of deviation from the straight line during flexion. The articular surfaces are connected together by strong collateral ligaments, which form their chief bond of union. The best examples of ginglymus are the interphalangeal joints and the joint between the humerus and ulna; the knee- and ankle-joints are less typical, as they allow a slight degree of rotation or of side-to-side movement in certain positions of the limb.

Trochoid or Pivot-joint (*articulatio trochoidea; rotary joint*).—Where the movement is limited to rotation, the joint is formed by a pivot-like process turning within a ring, or a ring on a pivot, the ring being formed partly of bone, partly of ligament. In the proximal radioulnar articulation, the ring is formed by the radial notch of the ulna and the annular ligament; here, the head of the radius rotates within the ring. In the articulation of the odontoid process of the axis with the atlas the ring is formed in front by the anterior arch, and behind by the transverse ligament of the atlas; here, the ring rotates around the odontoid process.

Condyloid Articulation (*articulatio ellipsoidea*).—In this form of joint, an ovoid articular surface, or condyle, is received into an elliptical cavity in such a manner as to permit of flexion, extension, adduction, abduction, and circumduction, but no axial rotation. The wrist-joint is an example of this form of articulation.

Saddle Joint (*articulatio sellaris*).—In this variety the opposing surfaces are reciprocally concavo-convex. The movements are the same as in the preceding form; that is to say, flexion, extension, adduction, abduction, and circumduction are allowed; but no axial rotation. The best example of this form is the carpo-metacarpal joint of the thumb.

Enarthrosis (*ball-and-socket joints*).—Enarthrosis is a joint in which the distal bone is capable of motion around an indefinite number of axes, which have one common center. It is formed by the reception of a globular head into a cup-like cavity, hence the name "ball-and-socket." Examples of this form of articulation are found in the hip and shoulder.

Arthrodia (*gliding joints*) is a joint which admits of only gliding movement; it is formed by the apposition of plane surfaces, or one slightly concave, the other slightly convex, the amount of motion between them being limited by the ligaments or osseous processes surrounding the articulation. It is the form present in the joints between the articular processes of the vertebræ, the carpal joints, except that of the capitate with the navicular and lunate, and the tarsal joints with the exception of that between the talus and the navicular.

THE KINDS OF MOVEMENT ADMITTED IN JOINTS.

The movements admissible in joints may be divided into four kinds: **gliding** and **angular movements, circumduction,** and **rotation.** These movements are often, however, more or less combined in the various joints, so as to produce an infinite variety, and it is seldom that only one kind of motion is found in any particular joint.

Gliding Movement.—Gliding movement is the simplest kind of motion that can take place in a joint, one surface gliding or moving over another without any angular or rotatory movement. It is common to all movable joints; but in some, as in most of the articulations of the carpus and tarsus, it is the only motion permitted. This movement is not confined to plane surfaces, but may exist between any two contiguous surfaces, of whatever form.

Angular movements increase or decrease the angle between two adjoining bones. Flexion and extension, abduction and adduction are the common examples.

Flexion occurs when the angle between adjoining bones is decreased as when the forearm, hand or fingers are moved forward and upward, the thigh forward and upward, the lower leg backward and upward and the foot upward. In the erect posture the foot is normally in flexion. Further flexion is often designated as dorsi-flexion. When the hand is overextended or bent backward the term dorsi-flexion also applies.

Extension occurs when the angle between adjoining bones is increased, as when an arm or a leg is straightened. Extension of the foot is often designated as plantar-flexion.

Abduction occurs when an arm or a leg is moved away from the mid-sagittal plane, or when the fingers and toes are moved away from the median longitudinal axis of the hand or foot.

Adduction occurs when an arm or a leg is moved toward or beyond the mid-sagittal plane or when the fingers or toes are moved toward the median longitudinal axis of the hand or foot.

Circumduction.—Circumduction is that form of motion which takes place between the head of a bone and its articular cavity, when the bone is made to circumscribe a conical space; the base of the cone is described by the distal end of the bone, the apex is in the articular cavity; this kind of motion is best seen in the shoulder- and hip-joints.

Rotation.—Rotation is a form of movement in which a bone moves around a central axis without undergoing any displacement from this axis; the axis of rotation may lie in a separate bone, as in the case of the pivot formed by the odontoid process of the axis vertebræ around which the atlas turns; or a bone may rotate around its own longitudinal axis, as in the rotation of the humerus at the shoulder-joint; or the axis of rotation may not be quite parallel to the long axis of the bone, as in the movement of the radius on the ulna during pronation and supination of the hand, where it is represented by a line connecting the center of the head of the radius above with the center of the head of the ulna below.

In **supination** the radius and ulna are parallel, and palm faces forward or upward.

In **pronation** the radius is rotated diagonally across the ulna and the palm faces backward or downward.

Ligamentous Action of Muscles.—The movements of the different joints of a limb are combined by means of the long muscles passing over more than one joint. These, when relaxed and stretched to their greatest extent, act as elastic ligaments in restraining certain movements of one joint, except when combined with corresponding movements of the other—the latter movements being usually in the opposite direction. Thus the shortness of the hamstring muscles prevents complete flexion of the hip, unless the knee-joint is also flexed so as to bring their attachments nearer together. The uses of this arrangement are threefold: (1) It coördinates the kinds of movements which are the most habitual and necessary, and enables them to be performed with the least expenditure of power. (2) It enables the short muscles which pass over only one joint to act upon more than one. (3) It provides the joints with ligaments which, while they are of very great power in resisting movements to an extent incompatible with the mechanism of the joint, at the same time spontaneously yield when necessary.

ARTICULATIONS OF THE TRUNK.

These may be divided into the following groups, viz.:

I. Of the Vertebral Column.
II. Of the Atlas with the Axis.
III. Of the Vertebral Column with the Cranium.
IV. Of the Mandible.
V. Of the Ribs with the Vertebræ.
VI. Of the Cartilages of the Ribs with the Sternum, and with Each Other.
VII. Of the Sternum.
VIII. Of the Vertebral Column with the Pelvis.
IX. Of the Pelvis.

I. Articulations of the Vertebral Column.

The articulations of the vertebral column consist of (1) a series of amphiarthrodial joints between the vertebral bodies, and (2) a series of diathrodial joints between the vertebral arches.

1. **Articulations of Vertebral Bodies** (*intercentral ligaments*).—The articulations between the bodies of the vertebræ are amphiarthrodial joints, and the individual vertebræ move only slightly on each other. When, however, this slight degree

of movement between the pairs of bones takes place in all the joints of the vertebral column, the total range of movement is very considerable. The ligaments of these articulations are the following:

The Anterior Longitudinal. The Posterior Longitudinal.
The Intervertebral Fibrocartilages.

The Anterior Longitudinal Ligament (*ligamentum longitudinale anterius; anterior common ligament*) (Figs. 297, 308).—The anterior longitudinal ligament is a broad and strong band of fibers, which extends along the anterior surfaces of the bodies of the vertebræ, from the axis to the sacrum. It is broader below than above, thicker in the thoracic than in the cervical and lumbar regions, and somewhat thicker opposite the bodies of the vertebræ than opposite the intervertebral fibro-cartilages. It is attached, above, to the body of the axis, where it is continuous with the anterior atlantoaxial ligament, and extends down as far as the upper

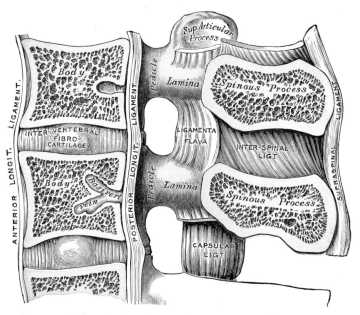

Fig. 297.—Median sagittal section of two lumbar vertebræ and their ligaments.

part of the front of the sacrum. It consists of dense longitudinal fibers, which are intimately adherent to the intervertebral fibrocartilages and the prominent margins of the vertebræ, but not to the middle parts of the bodies. In the latter situation the ligament is thick and serves to fill up the concavities on the anterior surfaces, and to make the front of the vertebral column more even. It is composed of several layers of fibers, which vary in length, but are closely interlaced with each other. The most superficial fibers are the longest and extend between four or five vertebræ. A second, subjacent set extends between two or three vertebræ; while a third set, the shortest and deepest, reaches from one vertebra to the next. At the sides of the bodies the ligament consists of a few short fibers which pass from one vertebra to the next, separated from the concavities of the vertebral bodies by oval apertures for the passage of vessels.

The Posterior Longitudinal Ligament (*ligamentum longitudinale posterius; posterior common ligament*) (Figs. 297, 298).—The posterior longitudinal ligament is situated within the vertebral canal, and extends along the posterior surfaces of the bodies of the vertebræ, from the body of the axis, where it is continuous with the membrana tectoria, to the sacrum. It is broader above than below, and thicker in the thoracic than in the cervical and lumbar regions. In the situation of the intervertebral fibrocartilages and contiguous margins of the vertebræ, where the ligament is more intimately adherent, it is broad, and in the thoracic and lumbar regions presents a series of dentations with intervening concave margins; but it is narrow and thick over the centers of the bodies, from which it is separated by the basivertebral veins. This ligament is composed of smooth, shining, longitudinal fibers, denser and more compact than those of the anterior ligament, and consists of superficial layers occupying the interval between three or four vertebræ, and deeper layers which extend between adjacent vertebræ.

The Intervertebral Fibrocartilages (*fibrocartilagines intervertebrales; intervertebral disks*) (Figs. 297, 309).—The intervertebral fibrocartilages are interposed between the adjacent surfaces of the bodies of the vertebræ, from the axis to the sacrum, and form the chief bonds of connection between the vertebræ. They vary in shape, size, and thickness, in different parts of the vertebral column. In *shape* and *size* they correspond with the surfaces of the bodies between which they are placed, except in the cervical region, where they are slightly smaller from side to side than the corresponding bodies. In *thickness* they vary not only in the different regions of the column, but in different parts of the same fibrocartilage; they are thicker

in front than behind in the cervical and lumbar regions, and thus contribute to the anterior convexities of these parts of the column; while they are of nearly uniform thickness in the thoracic region, the anterior concavity of this part of the column being most entirely owing to the shape of the vertebral bodies. The intervertebral fibrocartilages constitute about one-fourth of the length of the vertebral column, exclusive of the first two vertebræ; but this amount is not equally distributed between the various bones, the cervical and lumbar portions having, in proportion to their length, a much greater amount than the thoracic region, with the result that these parts possess greater pliancy and freedom of movement. The intervertebral fibrocartilages are adherent, by their surfaces, to thin layers of hyaline cartilage which cover the upper and under surfaces of the bodies of the vertebræ; in

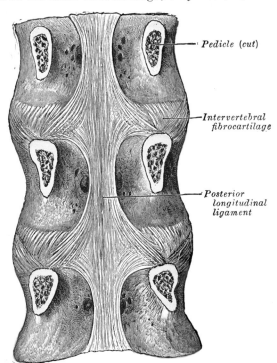

FIG. 298.—Posterior longitudinal ligament of the vertebræ in the lumbar region.

the lower cervical vertebræ, however, small joints lined by synovial membrane are occasionally present between the upper surfaces of the bodies and the margins of the fibrocartilages on either side. By their circumferences the intervertebral fibrocartilages are closely connected in front to the anterior, and behind to the posterior, longitudinal ligaments. In the thoracic region they are joined laterally, by means of the interarticular ligaments, to the heads of those ribs which articulate with two vertebræ.

Structure of the Intervertebral Fibrocartilages.—Each is composed, at its circumference, of laminæ of fibrous tissue and fibrocartilage, forming the *annulus fibrosus;* and, at its center, of a soft, pulpy, highly elastic substance, of a yellowish color, which projects considerably above the surrounding level when the disk is divided horizontally. This pulpy substance (*nucleus pulposus*), especially well-developed in the lumbar region, is the remains of the notochord. The laminæ are arranged concentrically; the outermost consist of ordinary fibrous tissue, the others of white fibrocartilage. The laminæ are not quite vertical in their direction, those near the circumference being curved outward and closely approximated; while those nearest the center curve in the opposite direction, and are somewhat more widely separated. The fibers of which each lamina is composed are directed, for the most part, obliquely from above downward, the fibers of adjacent laminæ passing in opposite directions and varying in every layer; so that the fibers of one layer are directed across those of another, like the limbs of the letter X. This laminar arrangement belongs to about the outer half of each fibrocartilage. The pulpy substance presents no such arrangement, and consists of a fine fibrous matrix, containing angular cells united to form a reticular structure.

The intervertebral fibrocartilages are important shock absorbers. Under pressure the highly elastic nucleus pulposus becomes flatter and broader and pushes the more resistant fibrous laminæ outward in all directions.

2. Articulations of Vertebral Arches.—The joints between the articular processes of the vertebræ belong to the arthrodial variety and are enveloped by capsules lined by synovial membranes; while the laminæ, spinous and transverse processes are connected by the following ligaments: (Fig. 303).

The Ligamenta Flava.
The Supraspinal.
The Ligamentum Nuchæ.
The Interspinal.
The Intertransverse.

The Articular Capsules (*capsulæ articulares; capsular ligaments*) (Fig. 297).—The articular capsules are thin and loose, and are attached to the margins of the articular processes of adjacent vertebræ. They are longer and looser in the cervical than in the thoracic and lumbar regions (Fig. 303).

The Ligamenta Flava (*ligmenta subflava*) (Fig. 299).—The ligamenta flava connect the laminæ of adjacent vertebræ, from the axis to the first segment of the sacrum. They are best seen from the interior of the vertebral canal; when looked at from the outer surface they appear short,

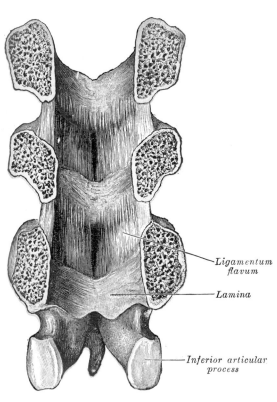

Ligamentum flavum

Lamina

Inferior articular process

Fig. 299.—The ligamenta flava of the lumbar region. Anterior aspect.

being overlapped by the laminæ. Each ligament consists of two lateral portions which commence one on either side of the roots of the articular processes, and extend backward to the point where the laminæ meet to form the spinous process; the posterior margins of the two portions are in contact and to a certain extent united, slight intervals being left for the passage of small vessels. Each consists of yellow elastic tissue, the fibers of which, almost perpendicular in direction, are attached to the anterior surface of the lamina above, some distance from its inferior margin, and to the posterior surface and upper margin of the lamina below. In the cervical region the ligaments are thin, but broad and long; they are thicker in the thoracic region and thickest in the lumbar region. Their marked elasticity serves to preserve the upright posture, and to assist the vertebral column in resuming it after flexion.

The Supraspinal Ligament (*ligamentum supraspinale; supraspinous ligament*) (Fig. 297).—The supraspinal ligament is a strong fibrous cord, which connects together the apices of the spinous processes from the seventh cervical vertebra to the sacrum; at the points of attachment to the tips of the spinous processes fibro-cartilage is developed in the ligament. It is thicker and broader in the lumbar than in the thoracic region, and intimately blended, in both situations, with the neighboring fascia. The most superficial fibers of this ligament extend over three or four vertebræ; those more deeply seated pass between two or three vertebræ; while the deepest connect the spinous processes of neighboring vertebræ. Between the spinous processes it is continuous with the interspinal ligaments. It is continued upward to the external occipital protuberance and median nuchal line, as the ligamentum nuchæ.

The Ligamentum Nuchæ.—The ligamentum nuchæ is a fibrous membrane, which, in the neck, represents the supraspinal ligaments of the lower vertebræ. It extends from the external occipital protuberance and median nuchal line to the spinous process of the seventh cervical vertebra. From its anterior border a fibrous lamina is given off, which is attached to the posterior tubercle of the atlas, and to the spinous processes of the cervical vertebræ, and forms a septum between the muscles on either side of the neck. In man it is merely the rudiment of an important elastic ligament, which, in some of the lower animals, serves to sustain the weight of the head.

The Interspinal Ligaments (*ligamenta interspinalia; interspinous ligaments*) (Fig. 297).—The interspinal ligaments thin and membranous, connect adjoining spinous processes and extend from the root to the apex of each process. They meet the ligamenta flava in front and the supraspinal ligament behind. They are narrow and elongated in the thoracic region; broader, thicker, and quadrilateral in form in the lumbar region; and only slightly developed in the neck.

The Intertransverse Ligaments (*ligamenta intertransversaria*).—The intertransverse ligaments are interposed between the transverse processes. In the cervical region they consist of a few irregular, scattered fibers; in the thoracic region they are rounded cords intimately connected with the deep muscles of the back; in the lumbar region they are thin and membranous.

Movements.—The movements permitted in the vertebral column are: *flexion, extension, lateral flexion, circumduction,* and *rotation.*

In **flexion,** or movement forward, the anterior longitudinal ligment is relaxed, and the intervertebral fibrocartilages are compressed in front; while the posterior longitudinal ligament, the ligamenta flava, and the inter- and supraspinal ligaments are stretched, as well as the posterior fibers of the intervertebral fibrocartilages. The interspaces between the laminæ are widened, and the inferior articular processes glide upward, upon the superior articular processes of the subjacent vertebræ. Tension of the extensor muscles of the back is the most important factor in limiting the movement. Flexion is the most extensive of all the movements of the vertebral column, and is freest in the cervical region.

In **extension,** or movement backward, an exactly opposite disposition of the parts takes place. This movement is limited by the anterior longitudinal ligament, and by the approximation of the spinous processes. It is freest in the cervical and lumbar regions.

In **lateral flexion,** the sides of the intervertebral fibrocartilages are compressed, the extent of motion being limited by the resistance offered by the surrounding ligaments. This movement may take place in any part of the column, but is freest in the cervical and lumbar regions.

Circumduction is very limited, and is merely a succession of the preceding movements.

Rotation is produced by the twisting of the intervertebral fibrocartilages; this, although only slight between any two vertebræ, allows of a considerable extent of movement when it takes place in the whole length of the column, the front of the upper part of the column being turned to one or other side. This movement occurs to a slight extent in the cervical region, is freer in the upper part of the thoracic region, and absent in the lumbar region.

The extent and variety of the movements are influenced by the shape and direction of the articular surfaces. In the *cervical* region the upward inclination of the superior articular surfaces allows of free flexion and extension. Extension can be carried farther than flexion; at the upper end of the region it is checked by the locking of the posterior edges of the superior atlantal facets in the condyloid fossæ of the occipital bone; at the lower end it is limited by a mechanism whereby the inferior articular processes of the seventh cervical vertebra slip into grooves behind and below the superior articular processes of the first thoracic. Flexion is arrested just beyond the point where the cervical convexity is straightened; the movement is checked by the apposition of the projecting lower lips of the bodies of the vertebræ with the shelving surfaces on the bodies of the subjacent vertebræ. Lateral flexion and rotation are free in the cervical region; they are, however, always combined. The upward and medial inclinations of the superior articular surfaces impart a rotatory movement during lateral flexion, while pure rotation is prevented by the slight medial slope of these surfaces.

In the **thoracic region,** notably in its upper part, all the movements are limited in order to reduce interference with respiration to a minimum. The almost complete absence of an upward inclination of the superior articular surfaces prohibits any marked flexion, while extension is checked by the contact of the inferior articular margins with the laminæ, and the contact of the spinous processes with one another. The mechanism between the seventh cervical and the first thoracic vertebræ, which limits extension of the cervical region, will also serve to limit flexion of the thoracic region when the neck is extended. Rotation is free in the thoracic region: the superior articular processes are segments of a cylinder whose axis is in the mid-ventral line of the vertebral bodies. The direction of the articular facets would allow of free lateral flexion, but this movement is considerably limited in the upper part of the region by the resistance of the ribs and sternum.

In the **lumbar region** extension is free and wider in range than flexion. The inferior articular facets are not in close apposition with the superior facets of the subjacent vertebræ, and on this account a considerable amount of lateral flexion is permitted. For the same reason a slight amount of rotation can be carried out, but this is so soon checked by the interlocking of the articular surfaces that it is negligible.

The *principal muscles* which produce *flexion* are the Sternocleidomastoideus, Longus capitis, and Longus colli; the Scaleni; the abdominal muscles and the Psoas major. *Extension* is produced by the intrinsic muscles of the back, assisted in the neck by the Splenius, Semispinales dorsi and cervicis, and the Multifidus. *Lateral* motion is produced by the intrinsic muscles of the back by the Splenius, the Scaleni, the Quadratus lumborum, and the Psoas major, the muscles of one side only acting; and *rotation* by the action of the following muscles of one side only, viz., the Sternocleidomastoideus, the Longus capitis, the Scaleni, the Multifidus, the Semispinalis capitis, and the abdominal muscles.

II. Articulation of the Atlas with the Epistropheus or Axis (Articulatio Atlantoepistrophica).

The articulation of the atlas with the axis comprises three joints. There is a pivot articulation, **median atlanto-axial joint,** between the odontoid process of the axis and the ring formed by the anterior arch and the transverse ligament of the atlas (see Fig. 302); here there are two synovial cavities: one between the posterior surface of the anterior arch of the atlas and the front of the odontoid process; the other between the anterior surface of the ligament and the back of the process. Between the articular processes of the two bones there is on either side an arthrodial or gliding joint, **lateral atlanto-axial joint.** The ligaments are:

Two Articular Capsules.	The Posterior Atlantoaxial.
The Anterior Atlantoaxial.	The Transverse.

The Articular Capsules (*capsulæ articulares; capsular ligaments*).—The articular capsules are thin and loose, and connect the margins of the lateral masses of the atlas with those of the posterior articular surfaces of the axis. Each is strengthened at its posterior and medial part by an **accessory ligament,** which is attached below to the body of the axis near the base of the odontoid process, and above to the lateral mass of the atlas near the transverse ligament.

The Anterior Atlantoaxial Ligament (Fig. 300).—This ligament is a strong membrane, fixed, *above*, to the lower border of the anterior arch of the atlas; *below*

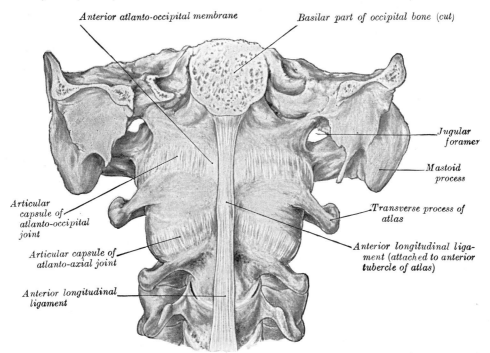

Anterior atlanto-occipital membrane

Basilar part of occipital bone (cut)

Jugular foramen

Mastoid process

Articular capsule of atlanto-occipital joint

Transverse process of atlas

Articular capsule of atlanto-axial joint

Anterior longitudinal ligament (attached to anterior tubercle of atlas)

Anterior longitudinal ligament

Fig. 300.—The atlantoöccipital and atlantoaxial joints. Anterior aspect. On each side a small, occasional, synovial joint is shown between the lateral part of the upper surface of the body of the third cervical vertebra and the bevelled, inferior surface of the body of the axis. The joint cavities have been opened.

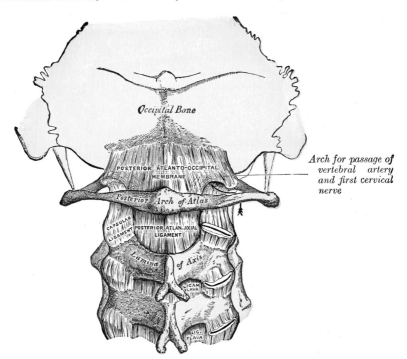

Occipital Bone

POSTERIOR ATLANTO-OCCIPITAL MEMBRANE

Arch for passage of vertebral artery and first cervical nerve

Posterior Arch of Atlas

CAPSULAR LIGAMENT

POSTERIOR ATLAN. AXIAL LIGAMENT

Lamina of Axis

LIGAM. FLAVA

LIG. FLAVA

Fig. 301.—Posterior atlantoöccipital membrane and atlantoaxial ligament.

to the front of the body of the axis. It is strengthened in the middle line by a rounded cord, which connects the tubercle on the anterior arch of the atlas to the body of the axis, and is a continuation upward of the anterior longitudinal ligament. The ligament is in relation, in front, with the Longi capitis.

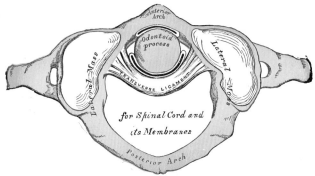

Fɪɢ. 302.—Articulation between odontoid process and atlas.

The Posterior Atlantoaxial Ligament (Fig. 304).—This ligament is a broad, thin membrane attached, *above*, to the lower border of the posterior arch of the atlas; *below*, to the upper edges of the laminæ of the axis. It supplies the place of the ligamenta flava, and is in relation, *behind*, with the Obliqui capitis inferiores.

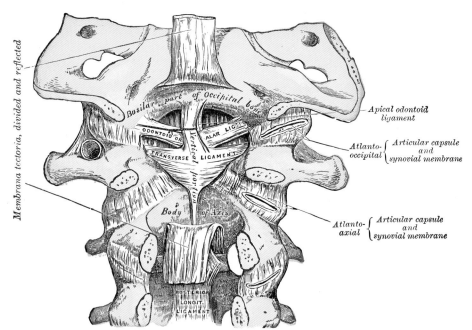

Fɪɢ. 303.—Membrana tectoria, transverse, and alar ligaments.

The Transverse Ligament of the Atlas (*ligamentum transversum atlantis*) (Figs. 302, 303, 304).—The transverse ligament of the atlas is a thick, strong band, which arches across the ring of the atlas, and retains the odontoid process in contact with the anterior arch. It is concave in front, convex behind, broader and thicker in the middle than at the ends, and firmly attached on either side to a small tubercle on the medial surface of the lateral mass of the atlas. As it crosses the odontoid process, a small fasciculus (*crus superius*) is prolonged upward, and another (*crus inferius*) downward, from the superficial or posterior fibers of the ligament. The former is attached to the basilar part of the occipital bone, in close relation with the membrana tectoria; the latter is fixed to the posterior surface of the body of the axis; hence, the whole ligament is named the **cruciate ligament of the atlas.** The transverse ligament divides the ring of the atlas into two unequal parts:

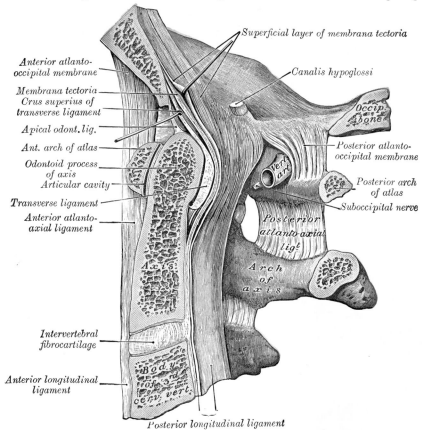

FIG. 304.—Median sagitta lsection through the occipital bone and first three cervical vertebræ. (Spalteholz.)

of these, the posterior and larger serves for the transmission of the medulla spinalis and its membranes and the accessory nerves; the anterior and smaller contains the odontoid process. The neck of the odontoid process is constricted where it is embraced posteriorly by the transverse ligament, so that this ligament suffices to retain the odontoid process in position after all the other ligaments have been divided.

Synovial Membranes.—There is a synovial membrane for each joint; the joint cavity between the odontoid process and the transverse ligament is often continuous with those of the atlanto-occipital articulations.

Movements.—The opposed articular surfaces of the atlas and axis are not reciprocally curved; both surfaces are convex in their long axes. When, therefore, the upper facet glides forward on the lower it also descends; the fibers of the articular capsule are relaxed in a vertical direction, and will then permit of movement in an antero-posterior direction. By this means a shorter capsule suffices and the strength of the joint is materially increased.

This joint allows the rotation of the atlas (and, with it, the skull) upon the axis, the extent of rotation being limited by the alar ligaments.

The principal muscles by which these movements are produced are the Sternocleidomastoideus and Semispinalis capitis of one side, acting with the Longus capitis, Splenius, Longissimus capitis, Rectus capitis posterior major, and Obliqui capitis superior and inferior of the other side.

III. Articulations of the Vertebral Column with the Cranium.

Articulation of the Atlas with the Occipital Bone (*articulatio atlantoöccipitalis*).—The atlanto-occipital joint of each side lies between the superior articular facet of the lateral mass of the atlas and the condyle of the occipital bone; it is condyloid in type. The articular surfaces are reciprocally curved. The ligaments connecting the bones are:

Two Articular Capsules.	The Posterior Atlantoöccipital
The Anterior Atlantoöccipital	membrane.
membrane.	Two Lateral Atlantoöccipital.

The Articular Capsules (*capsulæ articulares; capsular ligaments*).—The articular capsules surround the condyles of the occipital bone, and connect them with the articular processes of the atlas: they are thin and loose (Fig. 303).

The Anterior Atlantoöccipital Membrane (*membrana atlantoöccipitalis anterior; anterior atlantoöccipital ligament*) (Fig. 300).—The anterior atlantoöccipital membrane is broad and composed of densely woven fibers, which pass between the anterior margin of the foramen magnum above, and the upper border of the anterior arch of the atlas below; laterally, it is continuous with the articular capsules; in front, it is strengthened in the middle line by a strong, rounded cord, which connects the basilar part of the occipital bone to the tubercle on the anterior arch of the atlas. This membrane is in relation in *front* with the Recti capitis anteriores, *behind* with the alar ligaments.

The Posterior Atlantoöccipital Membrane (*membrana atlantoöccipitalis posterior; posterior atlantoöccipital ligament*) (Fig. 301).—The posterior atlantoöccipital membrane, broad but thin, is connected above, to the posterior margin of the foramen magnum; below, to the upper border of the posterior arch of the atlas. On either side this membrane is defective below, over the groove for the vertebral artery, and forms with this groove an opening for the entrance of the artery and the exit of the suboccipital nerve. The free border of the membrane, arching over the artery and nerve, is sometimes ossified. The membrane is in relation, *behind*, with the Recti capitis posteriores minores and Obliqui capitis superiores; in *front*, with the dura mater of the vertebral canal, to which it is intimately adherent.

The Lateral Ligaments.—The lateral ligaments are thickened portions of the articular capsules reinforced by bundles of fibrous tissue, and are directed obliquely upward and medialward; they are attached above to the jugular processes of the occipital bone, and below to the bases of the transverse processes of the atlas.

Synovial Membranes.—There are two synovial membranes: one lining each of the articular capsules. The joints frequently communicate with that between the posterior surface of the odontoid process and the transverse ligament of the atlas.

Movements.—The movements permitted in this joint are (*a*) flexion and extension, which give rise to the ordinary forward and backward nodding of the head, and (*b*) slight lateral motion to one or other side. *Flexion* is produced mainly by the action of the Longi capitis and Recti capitis anteriores; *extension* by the Recti capitis posteriores major and minor, the Obliquus superior, the Semispinalis capitis, Splenius capitis, Sternocleidomastoideus, and upper fibers of the Trapezius. The Recti laterales are concerned in the *lateral movement*, assisted by the Trapezius, Splenius capitis, Semispinalis capitis, and the Sternocleidomastoideus of the same side, all acting together.

Ligaments Connecting the Axis with the Occipital Bone.—

The Membrana Tectoria.	Two Alar.	The Apical Odontoid.

The Membrana Tectoria (*occipitoaxial ligament*) (Figs. 303, 304).—The membrana tectoria is situated within the vertebral canal. It is a broad, strong band which covers the odontoid process and its ligaments, and appears to be a prolongation upward of the posterior longitudinal ligament of the vertebral column. It is fixed, below, to the posterior surface of the body of the axis, and, expanding as it ascends, is attached to the basilar groove of the occipital bone, in front of the foramen magnum, where it blends with the cranial dura mater. Its anterior surface is in relation with the transverse ligament of the atlas, and its posterior surface with the dura mater.

The Alar Ligaments (*ligamenta alaria; odontoid ligaments*) (Fig. 303).—The alar ligaments are strong, rounded cords, which arise one on either side of the upper part of the odontoid process, and, passing obliquely upward and lateralward, are inserted into the rough depressions on the medial sides of the condyles of the occipital bone. In the triangular interval between these ligaments is another fibrous cord, the **apical odontoid ligament** (Fig. 304), which extends from the tip of the odontoid process to the anterior margin of the foramen magnum, being intimately blended with the deep portion of the anterior atlantoöccipital membrane and superior crus of the transverse ligament of the atlas. It is regarded as a rudimentary intervertebral fibrocartilage, and in it traces of the notochord may persist. The alar ligaments limit rotation of the cranium and therefore receive the name of **check ligaments.**

In addition to the ligaments which unite the atlas and axis to the skull, the ligamentum nuchæ (page 267) must be regarded as one of the ligaments connecting the vertebral column with the cranium.

IV. Articulation of the Mandible (Articulatio Mandibularis; Temporo-mandibular Articulation).

This is a ginglymo-arthrodial joint; the parts entering into its formation on either side are: the anterior part of the mandibular fossa of the temporal bone and the articular tubercle above; and the condyle of the mandible below. The ligaments of the joint are the following:

The Articular Capsule.	The Sphenomandibular.
The Temporomandibular.	The Articular Disk.
	The Stylomandibular.

The Articular Capsule (*capsula articularis; capsular ligament*).—The articular capsule is a thin, loose envelope, attached above to the circumference of the mandibular fossa and the articular tubercle immediately in front; below, to the neck of the condyle of the mandible.

The Temporomandibular Ligament (*ligamentum temporomandibulare; external lateral ligament*) (Fig. 305).—The temporomandibular ligament consists of two short, narrow fasciculi, one in front of the other, attached, above, to the lateral surface of the zygomatic arch and to the tubercle on its lower border; below, to the lateral surface and posterior border of the neck of the mandible. It is broader above than below, and its fibers are directed obliquely downward and backward. It is covered by the parotid gland, and by the integument.

The Sphenomandibular Ligament (*ligamentum sphenomandibulare; internal lateral ligament*) (Fig. 306).—The sphenomandibular ligament is a flat, thin band which is attached above to the spina angularis of the sphenoid bone, and, becoming broader as it descends, is fixed to the lingula of the mandibular foramen. Its lateral surface is in relation, above, with the Pterygoideus externus; lower down, it is separated from the neck of the condyle by the internal maxillary vessels; still lower, the interior alveolar vessels and nerve and a lobule of the parotid gland lie between it and the ramus of the mandible. Its medial surface is in relation with the Pterygoideus internus.

The Articular Disk (*discus articularis; interarticular fibrocartilage; articular meniscus*) (Fig. 307).—The articular disk is a thin, oval plate, placed between the

18

condyle of the mandible and the mandibular fossa. Its upper surface is concavo-convex from before backward, to accommodate itself to the form of the mandibular fossa and the articular tubercle. Its under surface, in contact with the condyle, is concave. Its circumference is connected to the articular capsule; and in

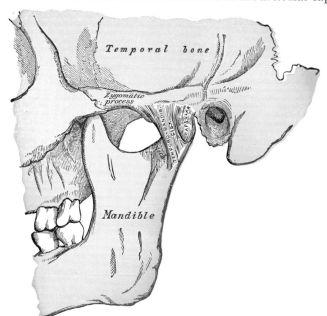

Fig. 305.—Articulation of the mandible. Lateral aspect.

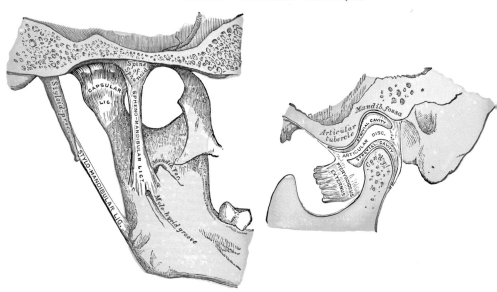

Fig. 306.—Articulation of the mandible. Medial aspect.

Fig. 307.—Sagittal section of the articulation of the mandible.

front to the tendon of the Pterygoideus externus. It is thicker at its periphery, especially behind, than at its center. The fibers of which it is composed have a concentric arrangement, more apparent at the circumference than at the center. It divides the joint into two cavities, each of which is furnished with a synovial membrane.

The Synovial Membranes.—The synovial membranes, two in number, are placed one above, and the other below, the articular disk. The upper one, the larger and looser of the two, is continued from the margin of the cartilage covering the mandibular fossa and articular tubercle on to the upper surface of the disk. The lower one passes from the under surface of the disk to the neck of the condyle, being prolonged a little farther downward behind than in front. The articular disk is sometimes perforated in its center, and the two cavities then communicate with each other.

The Stylomandibular Ligament (*ligamentum stylomandibulare*); *stylomaxillary ligament* (Fig. 306).—The stylomandibular ligament is a specialized band of the cervical fascia, which extends from near the apex of the styloid process of the temporal bone to the angle and posterior border of the ramus of the mandible, between the Masseter and Pterygoideus internus. This ligament separates the parotid from the submaxillary gland, and from its deep surface some fibers of the Styloglossus take origin. Although classed among the ligaments of the temporomandibular joint, it can only be considered as accessory to it.

The **nerves** of the temporomandibular joint are derived from the auriculotemporal and masseteric branches of the mandibular nerve, the **arteries** from the superficial temporal branch of the external carotid.

Movements.—The movements in this articulation are the opening and closing of the jaws, protrusion of the mandible, and lateral displacement of the mandible. It must be born in mind that there are two parts to this articulation—one between the condyle and the articular disk, and the other between the disk and the mandibular fossa. When the jaws are opened and closed, motion takes place in both parts; the disk glides on the articular tubercle, and the condyle moves on the disk like a hinge, causing the mandible to rotate about a center of suspension near the angle of the mandible. This somewhat moveable center is provided by the attachment of the sphenomandibular ligament to the lingula, and the sling formed by the Masseter and the Pterygoideus internus. When the jaws are opened, the angle of the mandible remains more or less fixed in position; the condyle glides forward as the short arm of a lever, and the chin, as the long arm of the lever, describes a wide arc. The motion between the condyle and the articular disk is largely one of accommodation to the change in position. When the jaws are closed, some of the force is applied to the condyle as a fulcrum, especially in biting with the incisors, but in chewing with the molars, the pressure comes more directly between the teeth, the condyle acting as a guide more than as a fulcrum. In protruding the mandible, both disks glide forward in the mandibular fossa, the usual rotation of opening the jaws being prevented by the synergetic action of the closing muscles. In lateral displacement of the mandible, one disk glides forward while the other remains in place. In grinding or chewing movements; there is first a lateral displacement of the mandible by a forward movement of one condyle, and then the mandible is brought back into place by the action of the closing muscles and the meshing of the teeth. The condyles may be displaced alternately, or the same one may be displaced repeatedly as in chewing with the teeth of one side.

The jaws are opened, that is, the mandible is depressed, by the Pterygoideus externus, assisted by the Digastricus, Mylohyoideus, and Geniohyoideus. The jaws are closed, that is, the mandible elevated, by the Masseter, Pterygoideus internus, and Temporalis. It is protruded by the simultaneous action of the Pterygoidei externi of both sides and the synergetic action of the closing muscles. It is drawn backward by the posterior fibers of the Temporalis, and displaced laterally by the action of the Pterygoideus externus of one side.

V. Costovertebral Articulations (Articulationes Costovertebrales).

The articulations of the ribs with the vertebral column may be divided into two sets, one connecting the heads of the ribs with the bodies of the vertebræ, another uniting the necks and tubercles of the ribs with the transverse processes.

1. **Articulations of the Heads of the Ribs** (*articulationes capitulorum; costocentral articulations*) (Fig. 308).—These constitute a series of gliding or arthrodial joints, and are formed by the articulation of the heads of the typical ribs with the facets on the contiguous margins of the bodies of the thoracic vertebræ and with the intervertebral fibrocartilages between them; the first, tenth, eleventh, and twelfth ribs each articulate with a single vertebra. The ligaments of the joints are:

The Articular Capsule.   The Radiate.   The Interarticular.

The Articular Capsule (*capsula articularis; capsular ligament*).—The articular capsule surrounds the joint, being composed of short, strong fibers, connecting the head of the rib with the circumference of the articular cavity formed by the intervertebral fibrocartilage and the adjacent vertebræ. It is most distinct at the upper and lower parts of the articulation; some of its upper fibers pass through the intervertebral foramen to the back of the intervertebral fibrocartilage, while its posterior fibers are continuous with the ligament of the neck of the rib.

The Radiate Ligament (*ligamentum capituli costæ radiatum; anterior costovertebral or stellate ligament*).—The radiate ligament connects the anterior part of the head of each rib with the side of the bodies of two vertebræ, and the intervertebral fibrocartilage between them. It consists of three flat fasciculi, which are attached to the anterior part of the head of the rib, just beyond the articular sur-

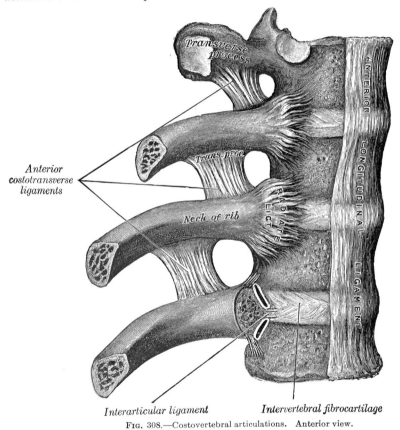

Anterior costotransverse ligaments

Interarticular ligament   Intervertebral fibrocartilage

Fig. 308.—Costovertebral articulations. Anterior view.

face. The superior fasciculus ascends and is connected with the body of the vertebra above; the inferior one descends to the body of the vertebra below; the middle one, the smallest and least distinct, is horizontal and is attached to the intervertebral fibrocartilage. The radiate ligament is in relation, in *front*, with the thoracic ganglia of the sympathetic trunk, the pleura, and, on the right side, with the azygos vein; *behind*, with the interarticular ligament and synovial membranes.

In the case of the first rib, this ligament is not divided into three fasciculi, but its fibers are attached to the body of the last cervical vertebra, as well as to that of the first thoracic. In the articulations of the heads of the tenth, eleventh, and twelfth ribs, each of which articulates with a single vertebra, the triradiate arrangement does not exist; but the fibers of the ligament in each case are connected to the vertebra above, as well as to that with which the rib articulates.

The Interarticular Ligament (*ligamentum capituli costæ interarticulare*).—The interarticular ligament is situated in the interior of the joint. It consists of a short band of fibers, flattened from above downward, attached by one extremity to the crest separating the two articular facets on the head of the rib, and by the other to the intervertebral fibrocartilage; it divides the joint into two cavities. Each cavity has a synovial membrane. In the joints of the first, tenth, eleventh, and twelfth ribs, the interarticular ligament does not exist; consequently, there is but one cavity and one synovial membrane in each of these articulations.

2. **Costotransverse Articulations** (*articulationes costotransversariæ*) (Fig. 309).—The articular portion of the tubercle of the rib forms with the articular surface on the adjacent transverse process an arthrodial joint.

In the eleventh and twelfth ribs this articulation is wanting.

The ligaments of the joint are:

The Articular Capsule.   The Posterior Costotransverse.
The Anterior Costotransverse.   The Ligament of the Neck of the Rib.
            The Ligament of the Tubercle of the Rib.

The Articular Capsule (*capsula articularis; capsular ligament*).—The articular capsule is a thin membrane attached to the circumferences of the articular surfaces, and lined by a synovial membrane.

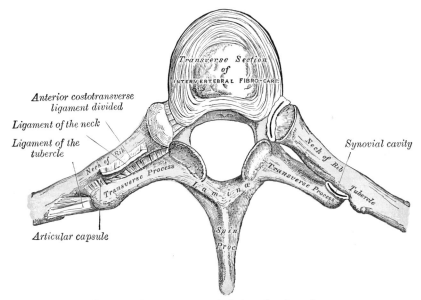

Fɪɢ. 309.—Costotransverse articulation. Seen from above.

The Anterior Costotransverse Ligament (*ligamentum costotransversarium anterius; anterior superior ligament*).—The anterior costotransverse ligament is attached below to the sharp crest on the upper border of the neck of the rib, and passes obliquely upward and lateralward to the lower border of the transverse process immediately above. It is in relation, in front, with the intercostal vessels and nerves; its medial border is thickened and free, and bounds an aperture which transmits the posterior branches of the intercostal vessels and nerves; its lateral border is continuous with a thin aponeurosis, which covers the Intercostalis externus.

The first rib has no anterior costotransverse ligament. A band of fibers, the **lumbocostal ligament,** in series with the anterior costotransverse ligaments, connects the neck of the twelfth rib to the base of the transverse process of the first lumbar vertebra; it is merely a thickened portion of the lumbocostal aponeurosis or anterior layer of the lumbodorsal fascia.

The Posterior Costotransverse Ligament (*ligamentum costotransversarium posterius*). —The posterior costotransverse ligament is a feeble band which is attached below to the neck of the rib and passes upward and medialward to the base of the transverse process and lateral border of the inferior articular process of the vertebra above.

The Ligament of the Neck of the Rib (*ligamentum colli costæ; middle costotransverse or interosseous ligament*).—The ligament of the neck of the rib consists of short but strong fibers, connecting the rough surface on the back of the neck of the rib with the anterior surface of the adjacent transverse process. A rudimentary ligament may be present in the case of the eleventh and twelfth ribs.

The Ligament of the Tubercle of the Rib (*ligamentum tuberculi costæ; posterior costotransverse ligament*).—The ligament of the tubercle of the rib is a short but thick and strong fasciculus, which passes obliquely from the apex of the transverse process to the rough non-articular portion of the tubercle of the rib. The ligaments attached to the upper ribs ascend from the transverse processes; they are shorter and more oblique than those attached to the inferior ribs, which descend slightly.

Movements.—The heads of the ribs are so closely connected to the bodies of the vertebræ by the radiate and interarticular ligaments that only slight gliding movements of the articular surfaces on one another can take place. Similarly, the strong ligaments binding the necks and tubercles of the ribs to the transverse processes limit the movements of the costotransverse joints to slight gliding, the nature of which is determined by the shape and direction of the articular surfaces. In the upper six ribs the articular surfaces on the tubercles are oval in shape and convex from above downward; they fit into corresponding concavities on the *anterior surfaces* of the transverse process, so that upward and downward movements of the tubercles are associated with rotation of the rib neck on its long axis. In the seventh, eighth, ninth, and tenth ribs the articular surfaces on the tubercles are flat, and are directed obliquely downward, medialward, and backward. The surfaces with which they articulate are placed on the *upper margins* of the transverse processes; when, therefore, the tubercles are drawn up they are at the same time carried backward and medialward. The two joints, costocentral and costotransverse, move simultaneously and in the same directions, the total effect being that the neck of the rib moves as if on a single joint, of which the costocentral and costotransverse articulations form the ends. In the upper six ribs the neck of the rib moves but slightly upward and downward; its chief movement is one of rotation around its own long axis, rotation backward being associated with depression, rotation forward with elevation. In the seventh, eighth, ninth, and tenth ribs the neck of the rib moves upward, backward, and medialward, or downward, forward, and lateralward; very slight rotation accompanies these movements.

VI.   Sternocostal Articulations (Articulationes Sternocostales; Costosternal Articulations) (Fig. 310).

The articulations of the cartilages of the true ribs with the sternum are arthrodial joints, with the exception of the first, in which the cartilage is directly united with the sternum, and which is, therefore, a synarthrodial articulation. The ligaments connecting them are:

The Articular Capsules.	The Intra-articular Sternocostal.
The Radiate Sternocostal.	The Costoxiphoid.

The Articular Capsules (*capsulæ articulares; capsular ligaments*).—The articular capsules surround the joints between the cartilages of the true ribs and the sternum. They are very thin, intimately blended with the radiate sternocostal ligaments, and strengthened at the upper and lower parts of the articulations by a few fibers, which connect the cartilages to the side of the sternum.

The Radiate Sternocostal Ligaments (*ligamenta sternocostalia radiata; chondrosternal or sternocostal ligaments*).—These ligaments consist of broad and thin membranous bands that radiate from the front and back of the sternal ends of the cartilages of the true ribs to the anterior and posterior surfaces of the sternum. They are composed of fasciculi which pass in different directions. The **superior fasciculi** ascend obliquely, the **inferior fasciculi** descend obliquely, and the **middle fasciculi** run horizontally. The superficial fibers are the longest; they intermingle with the fibers of the ligaments above and below them, with those of the opposite

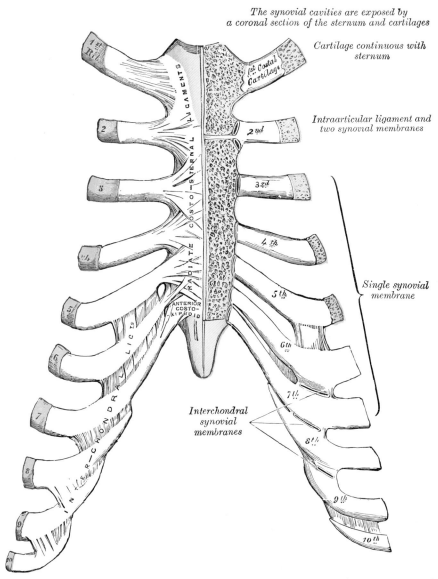

Fig. 310.—Sternocostal and interchondral articulations. Anterior view.

side, and in front with the tendinous fibers of origin of the Pectoralis major, forming a thick fibrous membrane (**membrana sterni**) which envelopes the sternum. This is more distinct at the lower than at the upper part of the bone.

The Intra-articular Sternocostal Ligament (*ligamentum sternocostale interarticulare; interarticular chondrosternal ligament*).—This ligament is found constantly only between the second costal cartilages and the sternum. The cartilage of the *second* *rib* is connected with the sternum by means of an intra-articular ligament, attached by one end to the cartilage of the rib, and by the other to the fibrocartilage which unites the manubrium and body of the sternum. This articulation is provided with two synovial membranes. Occasionally the cartilage of the *third rib* is connected with the first and second pieces of the body of the sternum by an interarticular ligament. Still more rarely, similar ligaments are found in the other four joints of the series. In the lower two the ligament sometimes completely obliterates the cavity, so as to convert the articulation into an amphiarthrosis.

The Costoxiphoid Ligaments (*ligamenta costoxiphoidea; chondroxiphoid ligaments*). —These ligaments connect the anterior and posterior surfaces of the seventh costal cartilage, and sometimes those of the sixth, to the front and back of the xiphoid process. They vary in length and breadth in different subjects; those on the back of the joint are less distinct than those in front.

Synovial Membranes.—There is no synovial membrane between the first costal cartilage and the sternum, as this cartilage is directly continuous with the manubrium. There are two in the articulation of the second costal cartilage and generally one in each of the other joints; but those of the sixth and seventh sternocostal joints are sometimes absent; where an intra-articular ligament is present, there are two synovial cavities. After middle life the articular surfaces lose their polish, become roughened, and the synovial membranes apparently disappear. In old age, the cartilages of most of the ribs become continuous with the sternum, and the joint cavities are consequently obliterated.

Movements.—Slight gliding movements are permitted in the sternocostal articulations.

Interchondral Articulations (*articulationes interchondrales; articulations of the cartilages of the ribs with each other*) (Fig. 310).—The contiguous borders of the sixth, seventh, and eighth, and sometimes those of the ninth and tenth, costal cartilages articulate with each other by small, smooth, oblong facets. Each articulation is enclosed in a thin **articular capsule,** lined by **synovial membrane** and strengthened laterally and medially by ligamentous fibers (**interchondral ligaments**) which pass from one cartilage to the other. Sometimes the fifth costal cartilages, more rarely the ninth and tenth, articulate by their lower borders with the adjoining cartilages by small oval facets; more frequently the connection is by a few ligamentous fibers.

Costochondral Articulations.—The lateral end of each costal cartilage is received into a depression in the sternal end of the rib, and the two are held together by the periosteum.

VII.　Articulations of the Sternum.

The **manubriosternal articulation.**—The manubrium is united to the body of the sternum by fibrocartilage. It occasionally ossifies in advanced life. About one-third of the fibrocartilages develop a synovial cavity. The two bones are also connected by fibrous tissue.

The **xiphisternal articulation** between the xiphoid process and the body of the sternum is cartilaginous. It is usually ossified by the fifteenth year.

Mechanism of the Thorax.—Each rib possesses its own range and variety of movements, but the movements of all are combined in the respiratory excursions of the thorax. Each rib may be regarded as a lever the fulcrum of which is situated immediately outside the costotransverse articulation, so that when the body of the rib is elevated the neck is depressed and *vice versa*; from the disproportion in length of the arms of the lever a slight movement at the vertebral end of the rib is greatly magnified at the anterior extremity.

The anterior ends of the ribs lie on a lower plane than the posterior; when therefore the body of the rib is elevated the anterior extremity is thrust also forward. Again, the middle of the body of the rib lies in a plane below that passing through the two extremities, so that when the body is elevated relatively to its ends it is at the same time carried outward from the median plane of the thorax. Further, each rib forms the segment of a curve which is greater than that of the rib immediately above, and therefore the elevation of a rib increases the transverse diameter of the thorax in the plane to which it is raised. The modifications of the rib movements at their vertebral ends have already been described (page 278). Further modifications result from the attachments of their anterior extremities, and it is convenient therefore to consider separately the movements of the ribs of the three groups—vertebrosternal, vertebrochondral, and vertebral.

Vertebrosternal Ribs (Figs. 311, 312).—The first rib differs from the others of this group in that its attachment to the sternum is a rigid one; this is counterbalanced to some extent by the fact that its head possesses no interarticular ligament, and is therefore more movable. The first pair of ribs with the manubrium sterni move as a single piece, the anterior portion being elevated by rotatory movements at the vertebral extremities. In normal quiet respiration the movement of this arc is practically *nil;* when it does occur the anterior part is raised and carried forward, increasing the antero-posterior and transverse diameters of this region of the chest. The movement of the second rib is also slight in normal respiration, as its anterior extremity is fixed to the manubrium, and prevented therefore from moving upward. The sternocostal articulation, however, allows the middle of the body of the rib to be drawn up, and

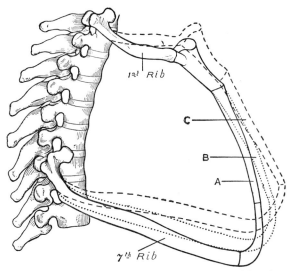

FIG. 311.—Lateral view of first and seventh ribs in position, showing the movements of the sternum and ribs in *A,* ordinary expiration; *B,* quiet inspiration; *C,* deep inspiration.

in this way the transverse thoracic diameter is increased. Elevation of the third, fourth, fifth, and sixth ribs raises and thrusts forward their anterior extremities, the greater part of the movement being effected by the rotation of the rib neck backward. The thrust of the anterior extremities carries forward and upward the body of the sternum, which moves on the joint

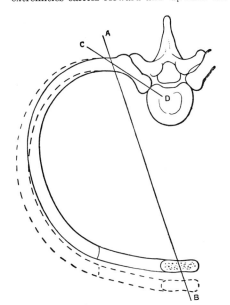
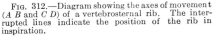

FIG. 312.—Diagram showing the axes of movement (*A B* and *C D*) of a vertebrosternal rib. The interrupted lines indicate the position of the rib in inspiration.

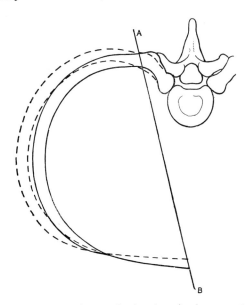

FIG. 313.—Diagram showing the axis of movement (*A B*) of a vertebrochondral rib. The interrupted lines indicate the position of the rib in inspiration.

between it and the manubrium, and thus the antero-posterior thoracic diameter is increased. This movement is, however, soon arrested, and the elevating force is then expended in raising the middle part of the body of the rib and everting its lower border; at the same time the costochondral angle is opened out. By these latter movements a considerable increase in the transverse diameter of the thorax is effected.

Vertebrochondral Ribs (Fig. 313).—The seventh rib is included with this group, as it conforms more closely to their type. While the movements of these ribs assist in enlarging the thorax for respiratory purposes, they are also concerned in increasing the upper abdominal space for viscera displaced by the action of the diaphragm. The costal cartilages articulate with one another, so that each pushes up that above it, the final thrust being directed to pushing forward and upward the lower end of the body of the sternum. The amount of elevation of the anterior extremities is limited on account of the very slight rotation of the rib neck. Elevation of the shaft is accompanied by an outward and backward movement; the outward movement everts the anterior end of the rib and opens up the subcostal angle, while the backward movement pulls back the anterior extremity and counteracts the forward thrust due to its elevation; this latter is most noticeable in the lower ribs, which are the shortest. The total result is a considerable increase in the transverse and a diminution in the median antero-posterior diameter of the upper part of the abdomen; at the same time, however, the lateral antero-posterior diameters of the abdomen are increased.

Vertebral Ribs.—Since these ribs have free anterior extremities and only costocentral articulations with no interarticular ligaments, they are capable of slight movements in all directions When the other ribs are elevated these are depressed and fixed to form points of action for the diaphragm.

VIII. Articulation of the Vertebral Column with the Pelvis.

The ligaments connecting the fifth lumbar vertebra with the sacrum are similar to those which join the movable segments of the vertebral column with each other —viz.: 1. The continuation downward of the anterior and posterior longitudinal ligaments. 2. The intervertebral fibrocartilage, connecting the body of the fifth lumbar to that of the first sacral vertebra and forming an amphiarthrodial joint. 3. Ligamenta flava, uniting the laminæ of the fifth lumbar vertebra with those of the first sacral. 4. Capsules connecting the articular processes and forming a double arthrodia. 5. Inter- and supraspinal ligaments.

On either side an additional ligament, the **iliolumbar,** connects the pelvis with the vertebral column.

The Iliolumbar Ligament (*ligamentum iliolumbale*) (Fig. 314).—The iliolumbar ligament is attached above to the lower and front part of the transverse process of the fifth lumbar vertebra. It radiates as it passes lateralward and is attached by two main bands to the pelvis. The lower bands run to the base of the sacrum, blending with the anterior sacroiliac ligament; the upper is attached to the crest of the ilium immediately in front of the sacroiliac articulation, and is continuous above with the lumbodorsal fascia. In *front*, it is in relation with the Psoas major; *behind*, with the muscles occupying the vertebral groove; *above*, with the Quadratus lumborum.

IX. Articulations of the Pelvis.

The ligaments connecting the bones of the pelvis with each other may be divided into four groups: 1. Those connecting the sacrum and ilium. 2. Those passing between the sacrum and ischium. 3. Those uniting the sacrum and coccyx. 4. Those between the two pubic bones.

1. **Sacroiliac Articulation** (*articulatio sacroiliaca*).—The sacroiliac articulation is an amphiarthrodial joint, formed between the auricular surfaces of the sacrum and the ilium. The articular surface of each bone is covered with a thin plate of cartilage, thicker on the sacrum than on the ilium. These cartilaginous plates are in close contact with each other, and to a certain extent are united together by irregular patches of softer fibrocartilage, and at their upper and posterior part by fine interosseous fibers. In a considerable part of their extent, especially in advanced life, they are separated by a space containing a synovia-like fluid, and

hence the joint presents the characteristics of a diarthrosis. The ligaments of the joint are:

The Anterior Sacroiliac. The Posterior Sacroiliac.
The Interosseous.

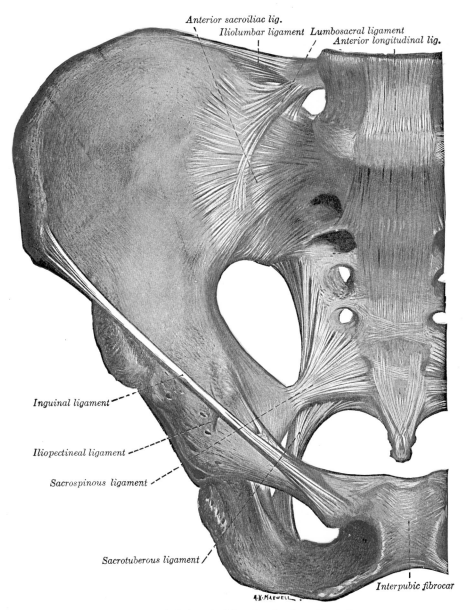

Fig. 314.—Articulations of pelvis. Anterior view. (Quain.)

The Anterior Sacroiliac Ligament (*ligamentum sacroiliacum anterius*) (Fig. 314).—
The anterior sacroiliac ligament consists of numerous thin bands, which connect
the anterior surface of the lateral part of the sacrum to the margin of the auricular
surface of the ilium and to the preauricular sulcus.

The Posterior Sacroiliac Ligament (*ligamentum sacroiliacum posterius*) (Fig. 315).
—The posterior sacroiliac ligament is situated in a deep depression between the
sacrum and ilium behind; it is strong and forms the chief bond of union between
the bones. It consists of numerous fasciculi, which pass between the bones in

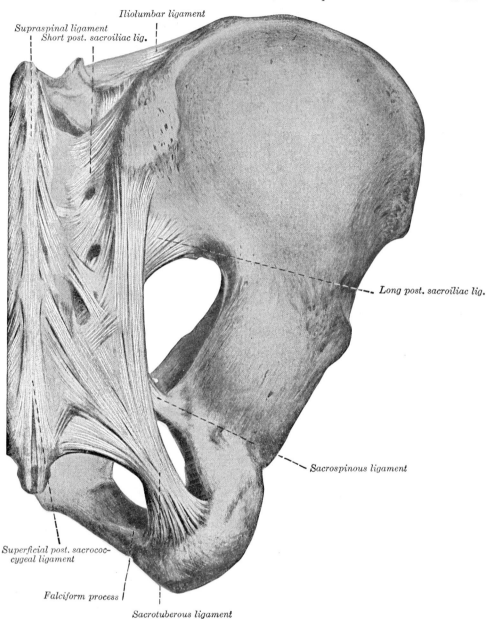

Iliolumbar ligament

Supraspinal ligament
Short post. sacroiliac lig.

Long post. sacroiliac lig.

Sacrospinous ligament

Superficial post. sacrococ-
cygeal ligament

Falciform process

Sacrotuberous ligament

FIG. 315.—Articulations of pelvis. Posterior view. (Quain.)

various directions. The upper part (**short posterior sacroiliac ligament**) is nearly
horizontal in direction, and passes from the first and second transverse tubercles
on the back of the sacrum to the tuberosity of the ilium. The lower part (**long
posterior sacroiliac ligament**) is oblique in direction; it is attached by one extremity

to the third transverse tubercle of the back of the sacrum, and by the other to the posterior superior spine of the ilium, where it merges with the upper part of the sacrotuberous ligament.

The Interosseous Sacroiliac Ligament (*ligamentum sacroiliacum interosseum*).— This ligament lies deep to the posterior ligament, and consists of a series of short, strong fibers connecting the tuberosities of the sacrum and ilium.

2. Ligaments Connecting the Sacrum and Ischium (Fig. 315).

The Sacrotuberous.   The Sacrospinous.

The Sacrotuberous Ligament (*ligamentum sacrotuberosum; great or posterior sacrosciatic ligament*).—The sacrotuberous ligament is situated at the lower and back part of the pelvis. It is flat, and triangular in form; narrower in the middle than at the ends; attached by its broad base to the posterior inferior spine of the ilium, to the fourth and fifth transverse tubercles of the sacrum, and to the lower part of the lateral margin of that bone and the coccyx. Passing obliquely downward, forward, and lateralward, it becomes narrow and thick, but at its insertion into the inner margin of the tuberosity of the ischium, it increases in breadth, and is prolonged forward along the inner margin of the ramus, as the **falciform process**, the free concave edge of which gives attachment to the obturator fascia; one of its surfaces is turned toward the perineum, the other toward the Obturator internus. The lower border of the ligament is directly continuous with the tendon of origin of the long head of the Biceps femoris, and by many is believed to be the proximal end of this tendon, cut off by the projection of the tuberosity of the ischium.

Relations.—The *posterior surface* of this ligament gives origin, by its whole extent, to the Glutæus maximus. Its *anterior surface* is in part united to the sacrospinous ligament. Its *upper border* forms, above, the posterior boundary of the greater sciatic foramen, and, below, the posterior boundary of the lesser sciatic foramen. Its *lower border* forms part of the boundary of the perineum. It is pierced by the coccygeal nerve and the coccygeal branch of the inferior gluteal artery.

The Sacrospinous Ligament (*ligamentum sacrospinosum; small or anterior sacrosciatic ligament*).—The sacrospinous ligament is thin, and triangular in form; it is attached by its apex to the spine of the ischium, and medially, by its broad base, to the lateral margins of the sacrum and coccyx, in front of the sacrotuberous ligament with which its fibers are intermingled.

Relations.—It is in relation, *anteriorly*, with the Coccygeus muscle, to which it is closely connected; *posteriorly*, it is covered by the sacrotuberous ligament, and crossed by the internal pudendal vessels and nerve. Its *upper border* forms the lower boundary of the greater sciatic foramen; its *lower border*, part of the margin of the lesser sciatic foramen.

These two ligaments convert the sciatic notches into foramina. The **greater sciatic foramen** is bounded, in *front* and *above*, by the posterior border of the hip bone; *behind*, by the sacrotuberous ligament; and *below*, by the sacrospinous ligament. It is partially filled up, in the recent state, by the Piriformis which leaves the pelvis through it. Above this muscle, the superior gluteal vessels and nerve emerge from the pelvis; and below it, the inferior gluteal vessels and nerve, the internal pudendal vessels and nerve, the sciatic and posterior femoral cutaneous nerves, and the nerves to the Obturator internus and Quadratus femoris make their exit from the pelvis. The **lesser sciatic foramen** is bounded, in *front*, by the tuberosity of the ischium; *above*, by the spine of the ischium and sacrospinous ligament; *behind*, by the sacrotuberous ligament. It transmits the tendon of the Obturator internus, its nerve, and the internal pudendal vessels and nerve.

3. **Sacrococcygeal Symphysis** (*symphysis sacrococcygea; articulation of the sacrum and coccyx*).—This articulation is an amphiarthrodial joint, formed between the oval surface at the apex of the sacrum, and the base of the coccyx. It is homol-

ogous with the joints between the bodies of the vertebræ. and is connected by similar ligaments. They are:

The Anterior Sacrococcygeal.	The Lateral Sacrococcygeal.
The Posterior Sacrococcygeal.	The Interposed Fibrocartilage.

The Interarticular.

The Anterior Sacrococcygeal Ligament (*ligamentum sacrococcygeum anterius*).—This consists of a few irregular fibers, which descend from the anterior surface of the sacrum to the front of the coccyx, blending with the periosteum.

The Posterior Sacrococcygeal Ligament (*ligamentum sacrococcygeum posterius*).—This is a flat band, which arises from the margin of the lower orifice of the sacral canal, and descends to be inserted into the posterior surface of the coccyx. This ligament completes the lower and back part of the sacral canal, and is divisible into a short deep portion and a longer superficial part. It is in relation, behind, with the Glutæus maximus.

The Lateral Sacrococcygeal Ligament (*ligamentum sacrococcygeum laterale; intertransverse ligament*).—The lateral sacrococcygeal ligament exists on either side and connects the transverse process of the coccyx to the lower lateral angle of the sacrum; it completes the foramen for the fifth sacral nerve.

A disk of **fibrocartilage** is interposed between the contiguous surfaces of the sacrum and coccyx; it differs from those between the bodies of the vertebræ in that it is thinner, and its central part is firmer in texture. It is somewhat thicker in front and behind than at the sides. Occasionally the coccyx is freely movable on the sacrum, most notably during pregnancy; in such cases a synovial membrane is present.

The **Interarticular Ligaments** are thin bands, which unite the cornua of the two bones.

The different segments of the coccyx are connected together by the extension downward of the anterior and posterior sacrococcygeal ligaments, thin annular disks of fibrocartilage being interposed between the segments. In the adult male, all the pieces become ossified together at a comparatively early period; but in the female, this does not commonly occur until a later period of life. At more advanced age the joint between the sacrum and coccyx is obliterated.

Movements.—The movements which take place between the sacrum and coccyx, and between the different pieces of the latter bone, are forward and backward; they are very limited. Their extent increases during pregnancy.

4. **The Pubic Symphysis** (*symphysis ossium pubis; articulation of the pubic bones*) (Fig. 316).—The articulation between the pubic bones is an amphiarthrodial joint, formed between the two oval articular surfaces of the bones. The ligaments of this articulation are:

The Superior Pubic.	The Arcuate Pubic.

The Interpubic Fibrocartilaginous Lamina.

The Superior Pubic Ligament (*ligamentum pubicum superius*).—The superior pubic ligament connects together the two pubic bones superiorly, extending laterally as far as the pubic tubercles.

The Arcuate Pubic Ligament (*ligamentum arcuatum pubis; inferior pubic or subpubic ligament*.—The arcuate pubic ligament is a thick, triangular arch of ligamentous fibers, connecting together the two pubic bones below, and forming the upper boundary of the pubic arch. *Above*, it is blended with the interpubic fibrocartilaginous lamina; *laterally*, it is attached to the inferior rami of the pubic bones; *below*, it is free and is separated from the fascia of the urogenital diaphragm by an opening through which the deep dorsal vein of the penis passes into the pelvis.

The Interpubic Fibrocartilaginous Lamina (*lamina fibrocartilaginea interpubica; interpubic disk*).—The interpubic fibrocartilaginous lamina connects the opposed surfaces of the pubic bones. Each of these surfaces is covered by a thin layer of hyaline cartilage firmly joined to the bone by a series of nipple-like processes which accurately fit into corresponding depressions on the osseous surfaces. These opposed cartilaginous surfaces are connected together by an intermediate lamina of fibrocartilage which varies in thickness in different subjects. It often contains a cavity in its interior, probably formed by the softening and absorption of the fibrocartilage, since it rarely appears before the tenth year of life and is not lined by synovial membrane (Fig. 316). In front the lamina is strengthened by decussating fibers which pass obliquely from one bone to the other and interlace with fibers of the aponeuroses of the Oblique externi and the medial tendons of origin of the Recti abdominis.

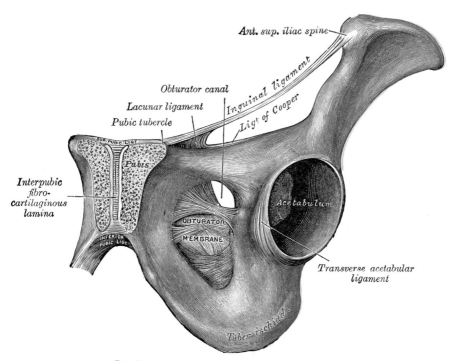

Fig. 316.—Symphysis pubis exposed by a coronal section.

Mechanism of the Pelvis.—The pelvic girdle supports and protects the contained viscera and affords surfaces for the attachments of the trunk and lower limb muscles. Its most important mechanical function, however, is to transmit the weight of the trunk and upper limbs to the lower extremities.

It may be divided into two arches by a vertical plane passing through the acetabular cavities; the posterior of these arches is the one chiefly concerned in the function of transmitting the weight. Its essential parts are the upper three sacral vertebræ and two strong pillars of bone running from the sacroiliac articulations to the acetabular cavities. For the reception and diffusion of the weight each acetabular cavity is strengthened by two additional bars running toward the pubis and ischium. In order to lessen concussion in rapid changes of distribution of the weight, joints (sacroiliac articulations) are interposed between the sacrum and the iliac bones; an accessory joint (pubic symphysis) exists in the middle of the anterior arch. The sacrum forms the summit of the posterior arch; the weight transmitted falls on it at the lumbosacral articulation and, theoretically, has a component in each of two directions. One component of the force is expended in driving the sacrum downward and backward between the iliac bones, while the other thrusts the upper end of the sacrum downward and forward toward the pelvic cavity.

The movements of the sacrum are regulated by its form. Viewed as a whole, it presents the shape of a wedge with its base upward and forward. The first component of the force is therefore acting against the resistance of the wedge, and its tendency to separate the iliac bones is resisted by the sacroiliac and iliolumbar ligaments and by the ligaments of the pubic symphysis.

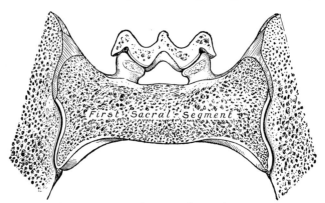

Fig. 317.—Corona section of anterior sacral segment.

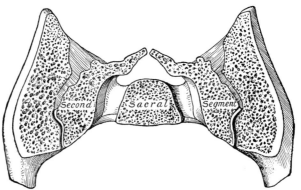

Fig. 318.—Corona section of middle sacral segment.

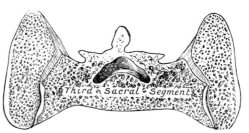

Fig. 319.—Coronal section of posterior sacral segment.

If a series of coronal sections of the sacroiliac joints be made, it will be found possible to divide the articular portion of the sacrum into three segments: anterior, middle, and posterior. In the **anterior segment** (Fig. 317), which involves the first sacral vertebra, the articular surfaces show slight sinuosities and are almost parallel to one another; the distance between their dorsal margins is, however, slightly greater than that between their ventral margins. This segment therefore presents a slight wedge shape with the truncated apex downward. The **middle segment** (Fig. 318) is a narrow band across the centers of the articulations. Its dorsal width is distinctly greater than its ventral, so that the segment is more definitely wedge-shaped, the truncated apex being again directed downward. Each articular surface presents in the center a marked concavity from above downward and into this a corresponding convexity of the iliac articular surface fits, forming an interlocking mechanism. In the **posterior segment** (Fig. 319) the ventral width is greater than the dorsal, so that the wedge form is the reverse of those of the other segments—*i. e.*, the truncated apex is directed upward. The articular surfaces are only slightly concave.

Dislocation downward and forward of the sacrum by the second component of the force applied to it is prevented therefore by the middle segment, which interposes the resistance of its wedge shape and that of the interlocking mechanism on its surfaces; a rotatory movement, however, is produced by which the anterior segment is tilted downward and the posterior upward; the axis of this rotation passes through the dorsal part of the middle segment. The movement of the anterior segment is slightly limited by its wedge form, but chiefly by the posterior and interosseous sacroiliac ligaments; that of the posterior segment is checked to a slight extent by its wedge form, but the chief limiting factors are the sacrotuberous and sacrospinous ligaments. In all these movements the effect of the sacroiliac and iliolumbar ligaments and the ligaments of the symphysis pubis in resisting the separation of the iliac bones must be recognized.

During pregnancy the pelvic joints and ligaments are relaxed, and capable therefore of more extensive movements. When the fetus is being expelled the force is applied to the front of the sacrum. Upward dislocation is again prevented by the interlocking mechanism of the middle segment. As the fetal head passes the anterior segment the latter is carried upward, enlarging the antero-posterior diameter of the pelvic inlet; when the head reaches the posterior segment this also is pressed upward against the resistance of its wedge, the movement only being possible by the laxity of the joints and the stretching of the sacrotuberous and sacrospinous ligaments.

ARTICULATIONS OF THE UPPER EXTREMITY.

The articulations of the Upper Extremity may be arranged as follows:

I. Sternoclavicular.	VI. Wrist.
II. Acromioclavicular.	VII. Intercarpal.
III. Shoulder.	VIII. Carpometacarpal.
IV. Elbow.	IX. Intermetacarpal.
V. Radioulnar.	X. Metacarpophalangeal.

XI. Articulations of the Digits.

I. Sternoclavicular Articulation (Articulatio Sternoclavicularis) (Fig. 322).

The sternoclavicular articulation is a double arthrodial joint. The parts entering into its formation are the sternal end of the clavicle, the upper and lateral part of the manubrium sterni, and the cartilage of the first rib. The articular surface of the clavicle is much larger than that of the sternum, and is invested with a layer of fibrocartilage, which is thicker than that on the latter bone. The ligaments of this joint are:

The Articular Capsule.	The Interclavicular.
The Anterior Sternoclavicular.	The Costoclavicular.
The Posterior Sternoclavicular.	The Articular Disk.

The Articular Capsule (*capsula articularis; capsular ligament*).—The articular capsule surrounds the articulation and varies in thickness and strength. In front and behind it is of considerable thickness, and forms the anterior and posterior sternoclavicular ligaments; but above, and especially below, it is thin and partakes more of the character of areolar than of true fibrous tissue.

The Anterior Sternoclavicular Ligament (*ligamentum sternoclaviculare anterior*).— The anterior sternoclavicular ligament is a broad band of fibers, covering the anterior surface of the articulation; it is attached *above* to the upper and front part of the sternal end of the clavicle, and, passing obliquely downward and medialward, is attached below to the front of the upper part of the manubrium sterni. This ligament is covered by the sternal portion of the Sternocleidomastoideus and the integument; *behind*, it is in relation with the capsule, the articular disk, and the two synovial membranes.

The Posterior Sternoclavicular Ligament (*ligamentum sternoclaviculare posterius*).— The posterior sternoclavicular ligament is a similar band of fibers, covering the posterior surface of the articulation; it is attached above to the upper and back

19

part of the sternal end of the clavicle, and, passing obliquely downward and medialward, is fixed below to the back of the upper part of the manubrium sterni. It is in relation, in *front*, with the articular disk and synovial membranes; *behind*, with the Sternohyoideus and Sternothyreoideus.

The Interclavicular Ligament (*ligamentum interclaviculare*).—This ligament is a flattened band, which varies considerably in form and size in different individuals, it passes in a curved direction from the upper part of the sternal end of one clavicle to that of the other, and is also attached to the upper margin of the sternum. It is in relation, in *front*, with the integument and Sternocleidomastoidei; *behind*, with the Sternothyreoidei.

The Costoclavicular Ligament (*ligamentum costoclaviculare; rhomboid ligament*).— This ligament is short, flat, strong, and rhomboid in form. Attached below to the upper and medial part of the cartilage of the first rib, it ascends obliquely backward and lateralward, and is fixed above to the costal tuberosity on the under surface of the clavicle. It is in relation, in *front*, with the tendon of origin of the Subclavius; *behind*, with the subclavian vein.

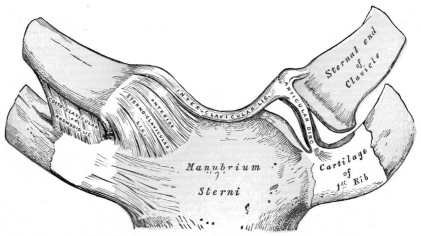

FIG. 320.—Sternoclavicular articulation. Anterior view.

The Articular Disk (*discus articularis*).—The articular disk is flat and nearly circular, interposed between the articulating surfaces of the sternum and clavicle. It is attached, *above*, to the upper and posterior border of the articular surface of the clavicle; *below*, to the cartilage of the first rib, near its junction with the sternum; and by its circumference to the interclavicular and anterior and posterior sternoclavicular ligaments. It is thicker at the circumference, especially its upper and back part, than at its center. It divides the joint into two cavities, each of which is furnished with a synovial membrane.

Synovial Membranes.—Of the two synovial membranes found in this articulation, the lateral is reflected from the sternal end of the clavicle, over the adjacent surface of the articular disk, and around the margin of the facet on the cartilage of the first rib; the medial is attached to the margin of the articular surface of the sternum and clothes the adjacent surface of the articular disk; the latter is the larger of the two.

Movements.—This articulation admits of a limited amount of motion in nearly every direction—upward, downward, backward, forward, as well as circumduction. When these movements take place in the joint, the clavicle in its motion carries the scapula with it, this bone gliding on the outer surface of the chest. This joint therefore forms the center from which all movements of the supporting arch of the shoulder originate, and is the only point of articulation of the shoulder girdle with the trunk. The movements attendant on elevation and depression of the shoulder take place between the clavicle and the articular disk, the bone rotating upon the ligament on an axis drawn from before backward through its own articular facet; when the shoulder is moved forward and backward, the clavicle, with the articular disk rolls to and fro on the articular surface of the sternum, revolving, with a sliding movement, around an axis drawn nearly vertically through the sternum; in the circumduction of the shoulder, which is compounded of these two movements, the clavicle revolves upon the articular disk and the latter, with the clavicle, roll supon the sternum. Elevation of the shoulder is limited principally by the costoclavicular ligament; depression, by the interclavicular ligament and articular disk. The muscles which *raise* the shoulder are the upper fibers of the Trapezius, the Levator scapulæ, and the clavicular head of the Sternocleidomastoideus, assisted to a certain extent by the Rhomboidei, which pull the vertebral border of the scapula backward and upward and so raise the shoulder. The *depression* of the shoulder is principally effected by gravity assisted by the Subclavius, Pectoralis minor and lower fibers of the Trapezius. The shoulder is drawn *backward* by the Rhomboidei and the middle and lower fibers of the Trapezius, and *forward* by the Serratus anterior and Pectoralis minor.

II. Acromioclavicular Articulation (Articulatio Acromioclavicularis; Scapuloclavicular Articulation) (Fig. 321).

The acromioclavicular articulation is an arthrodial joint between the acromial end of the clavicle and the medial margin of the acromion of the scapula. Its ligaments are:

The Articular Capsule.	The Articular Disk.
The Superior Acromioclavicular.	The Coracoclavicular {Trapezoid and Conoid.
The Inferior Acromioclavicular.	

The Articular Capsule (*capsula articularis; capsular ligament*).—The articular capsule completely surrounds the articular margins, and is strengthened above and below by the superior and inferior acromioclavicular ligaments.

The Superior Acromioclavicular Ligament (*ligamentum acromioclaviculare*).—This ligament is a quadrilateral band, covering the superior part of the articulation, and extending between the upper part of the acromial end of the clavicle and the adjoining part of the upper surface of the acromion. It is composed of parallel fibers, which interlace with the aponeuroses of the Trapezius and Deltoideus; *below*, it is in contact with the articular disk when this is present.

The Inferior Acromioclavicular Ligament.—This ligament is somewhat thinner than the preceding; it covers the under part of the articulation, and is attached to the adjoining surfaces of the two bones. It is in relation, *above*, in rare cases with the articular disk; *below*, with the tendon of the Supraspinatus.

The Articular Disk (*discus articularis*).—The articular disk is frequently absent in this articulation. When present, it generally only partially separates the articular surfaces, and occupies the upper part of the articulation. More rarely, it completely divides the joint into two cavities.

The Synovial Membrane.—There is usually only one synovial membrane in this articulation, but when a complete articular disk is present, there are two.

The Coracoclavicular Ligament (*ligamentum coracoclaviculare*) (Fig. 321).—This ligament serves to connect the clavicle with the coracoid process of the scapula. It does not properly belong to this articulation, but is usually described with it, since it forms a most efficient means of retaining the clavicle in contact with the acromion. It consists of two fasciculi, called the **trapezoid** and **conoid ligaments.**

The Trapezoid Ligament (*ligamentum trapezoideum*), the anterior and lateral fasciculus, is broad, thin, and quadrilateral: it is placed obliquely between the coracoid process and the clavicle. It is attached, *below*, to the upper surface of the coracoid process; *above*, to the oblique ridge on the under surface of the clavicle. Its anterior border is free; its posterior border is joined with the conoid ligament, the two forming, by their junction, an angle projecting backward.

The Conoid Ligament (*ligamentum conoideum*), the posterior and medial fasciculus, is a dense band of fibers, conical in form, with its base directed upward. It is attached by its apex to a rough impression at the base of the coracoid process, medial to the trapezoid ligament; above, by its expanded base, to the coracoid tuberosity on the under surface of the clavicle, and to a line proceeding medial-ward from it for 1.25 cm. These ligaments are in relation, in *front*, with the Subclavius and Deltoideus; *behind*, with the Trapezius.

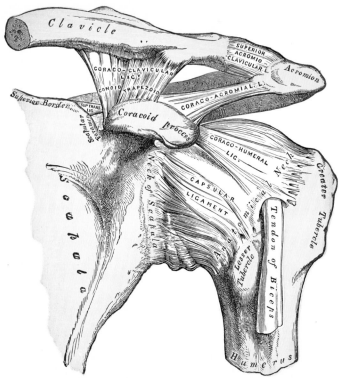

Fig. 321.—The left shoulder and acromioclavicular joints, and the proper ligaments of the scapula.

Movements.—The movements of this articulation are of two kinds: (1) a gliding motion of the articular end of the clavicle on the acromion; (2) rotation of the scapula forward and backward upon the clavicle. The extent of this rotation is limited by the two portions of the coracoclavicular ligament, the trapezoid limiting rotation forward, and the conoid backward.

The acromioclavicular joint has important functions in the movements of the upper extremity. It has been well pointed out by Humphry, that if there had been no joint between the clavicle and scapula, the circular movement of the scapula on the ribs (as in throwing the shoulders backward or forward) would have been attended with a greater alteration in the direction of the shoulder than is consistent with the free use of the arm in such positions, and it would have been impossible to give a blow straight forward with the full force of the arm; that is to say, with the combined force of the scapula, arm, and forearm. "This joint," as he happily says, "is so adjusted as to enable either bone to turn in a hinge-like manner upon a vertical axis drawn through the other, and it permits the surfaces of the scapula, like the baskets in a roundabout swing, to look the same way in every position, or nearly so." Again, when the whole arch formed by the clavicle and scapula rises and falls (in elevation or depression of the shoulder), the joint between these Two bones enables the scapula still to maintain its lower part in contact with the ribs.

THE LIGAMENTS OF THE SCAPULA (Fig. 321).

Coracoacromial, Superior and Inferior Transverse.

The Coracoacromial Ligament (*ligamentum coracoacromiale*).—This ligament is a strong triangular band, extending between the coracoid process and the acromion.

It is attached, by its apex, to the summit of the acromion just in front of the articular surface for the clavicle; and by its broad base to the whole length of the lateral border of the coracoid process. This ligament, together with the coracoid process and the acromion, forms a vault for the protection of the head of the humerus. It is in relation, *above*, with the clavicle and under surface of the Deltoideus; *below*, with the tendon of the Supraspinatus, a bursa being interposed. Its lateral border is continuous with a dense lamina that passes beneath the Deltoideus upon the tendons of the Supraspinatus and Infraspinatus. The ligament is sometimes described as consisting of two marginal bands and a thinner intervening portion, the two bands being attached respectively to the apex and the base of the coracoid process, and joining together at the acromion. When the Pectoralis minor is inserted, as occasionally is the case, into the capsule of the shoulder-joint instead of into the coracoid process, it passes between these two bands, and the intervening portion of the ligament is then deficient.

The Superior Transverse Ligament (*ligamentum transversum scapulæ superius; transverse* or *suprascapular ligament*).—This ligament converts the scapular notch into a foramen. It is a thin and flat fasciculus, narrower at the middle than at the extremities, attached by one end to the base of the coracoid process, and by the other to the medial end of the scapular notch. The suprascapular nerve runs through the foramen; the transverse scapular vessels cross over the ligament. The ligament is sometimes ossified.

The Inferior Transverse Ligament (*ligamentum transversum scapulæ interius; spinoglenoid ligament*).—This ligament is a weak membranous band, situated behind the neck of the scapula and stretching from the lateral border of the spine to the margin of the glenoid cavity. It forms an arch under which the transverse scapular vessels and suprascapular nerve enter the infraspinatous fossa.

III. Humeral Articulation or Shoulder-joint (Articulatio Humeri) (Fig. 321).

The shoulder-joint is an enarthrodial or ball-and-socket joint. The bones entering into its formation are the hemispherical head of the humerus and the shallow glenoid cavity of the scapula, an arrangement which permits of very considerable movement, while the joint itself is protected against displacement by the tendons which surround it. The ligaments do not maintain the joint surfaces in apposition, because when they alone remain the humerus can be separated to a considerable extent from the glenoid cavity; their use, therefore, is to limit the amount of movement. The joint is protected above by an arch, formed by the coracoid process, the acromion, and the coracoacromial ligament. The articular cartilage on the head of the humerus is thicker at the center than at the circumference, the reverse being the case with the articular cartilage of the glenoid cavity. The ligaments of the shoulder are:

The Articular Capsule.	The Glenohumeral.
The Coracohumeral.	The Transverse Humeral.
	The Glenoidal Labrum.

The Articular Capsule (*capsula articularis; capsular ligament*) (Fig. 323).—The articular capsule completely encircles the joint, being attached, above, to the circumference of the glenoid cavity beyond the glenoidal labrum; below, to the anatomical neck of the humerus, approaching nearer to the articular cartilage above than in the rest of its extent. It is thicker above and below than elsewhere, and is so remarkably loose and lax, that it has no action in keeping the bones in contact, but allows them to be separated from each other more than 2.5 cm., an evident provision for that extreme freedom of movement which is peculiar to this articulation. It is strengthened, *above*, by the Supraspinatus; *below*, by the long head of the Triceps brachii; *behind,* by the tendons of the Infraspinatus and Teres minor; and in *front,* by the tendon of the Subscapularis. There are usually three openings in the capsule. One anteriorly, below the coracoid process, establishes a communication between the joint and a bursa beneath the tendon of the Sub-

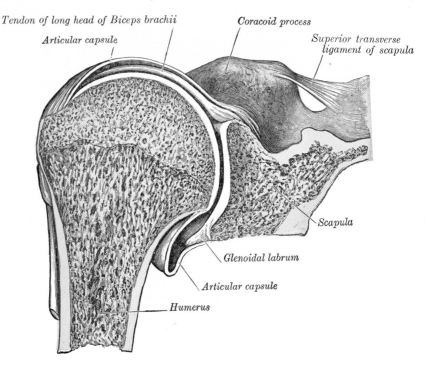

Tendon of long head of Biceps brachii   *Coracoid process*

Articular capsule   *Superior transverse ligament of scapula*

Scapula

Glenoidal labrum

Articular capsule

Humerus

Fig. 322.—A section through the shoulder-joint.

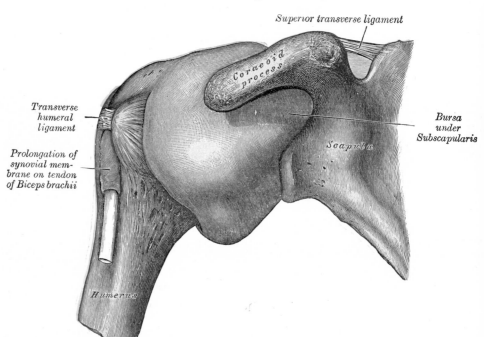

Superior transverse ligament

Coracoid process

Transverse humeral ligament

Bursa under Subscapularis

Scapula

Prolongation of synovial membrane on tendon of Biceps brachii

Humerus

Fig. 323 —Capsule of shoulder-joint (distended). Anterior aspect.

scapularis. The second, which is not constant, is at the posterior part, where an opening sometimes exists between the joint and a bursal sac under the tendon of the Infraspinatus. The third is between the tubercles of the humerus, for the passage of the long tendon of the Biceps brachii.

The Coracohumeral Ligament (*ligamentum coracohumerale*).—This ligament is a broad band which strengthens the upper part of the capsule. It arises from the lateral border of the coracoid process, and passes obliquely downward and lateralward to the front of the greater tubercle of the humerus, blending with the tendon of the Supraspinatus. This ligament is intimately united to the capsule by its hinder and lower border; but its anterior and upper border presents a free edge, which overlaps the capsule.

Glenohumeral Ligaments.—In addition to the coracohumeral ligament, three supplemental bands, which are named the **glenohumeral ligaments**, strengthen the capsule. These may be best seen by opening the capsule at the back of the joint and removing the head of the humerus. One on the medial side of the joint passes from the medial edge of the glenoid cavity to the lower part of the lesser tubercle of the humerus. A second at the lower part of the joint extends from the under edge of the glenoid cavity to the under part of the anatomical neck of the humerus. A third at the upper part of the joint is fixed above to the apex of the glenoid cavity close to the root of the coracoid process, and passing downward along the medial edge of the tendon of the Biceps brachii, is attached below to a small depression above the lesser tubercle of the humerus. In addition to these, the capsule is strengthened in front by two bands derived from the tendons of the Pectoralis major and Teres major respectively.

The Transverse Humeral Ligament (Fig. 323) is a broad band passing from the lesser to the greater tubercle of the humerus, and always limited to that portion of the bone which lies above the epiiphyseal line. It converts the intertubercula groove into a canal, and is the homologue of the strong process of bone which connects the summits of the two tubercles in the musk ox.

The Glenoidal Labrum (*labrium glenoidale; glenoid ligament*) is a fibrocartilaginous rim attached around the margin of the glenoid cavity. It is triangular on section, the base being fixed to the circumference of the cavity, while the free edge is thin and sharp. It is continuous above with the tendon of the long head of the Biceps brachii, which gives off two fasciculi to blend with the fibrous tissue of the labrum. It deepens the articular cavity, and protects the edges of the bone (Fig. 324).

Synovial Membrane.—The synovial membrane is reflected from the margin of the glenoid cavity over the labrum; it is then reflected over the inner surface of the capsule, and covers the lower part and sides of the anatomical neck of the humerus as far as the articular cartilage on the head of the bone. The tendon of the long head of the Biceps brachii passes through the capsule and is enclosed in a tubular sheath of synovial membrane, which is reflected upon it from the summit of the glenoid cavity and is continued around the tendon into the intertubercular groove as far as the surgical neck of the humerus (Fig. 323). The tendon thus traverses the articulation, but it is not contained within the synovial cavity (Fig. 322).

Bursæ.—The bursæ in the neighborhood of the shoulder-joint are the following: (1) A constant bursa is situated between the tendon of the Subscapularis muscle and the capsule; it communicates with the synovial cavity through an opening in the front of the capsule; (2) a bursa which occasionally communicates with the joint is sometimes found between the tendon of the Infraspinatus and the capsule; (3) a large bursa exists between the under surface of the Deltoideus and the capsule, but does not communicate with the joint; this bursa is prolonged under the acromion and coraco-acromial ligament, and intervenes between these structures and the capsule; (4) a large bursa is situated on the summit of the acromion; (5) a bursa is frequently found between the coracoid process and the capsule; (6) a bursa exists beneath the Coracobrachialis; (7) one lies between the Teres major and the long head of the Triceps brachii; (8) one is placed in front of, and another behind, the tendon of the Latissimus dorsi.

The **muscles** in relation with the joint are, *above*, the Supraspinatus; *below*, the long head of the Triceps brachii; in *front*, the Subscapularis; *behind*, the Infraspinatus and Teres minor; *within*, the tendon of the long head of the Biceps brachii. The Deltoideus covers the articulation in front, behind, and laterally.

The **arteries** supplying the joint are articular branches of the anterior and posterior humeral circumflex, and transverse scapular.

The **nerves** are derived from the axillary and suprascapular.

Movements.—The shoulder-joint is capable of every variety of movement, flexion, extension, abduction, adduction, circumduction, and rotation. The humerus is *flexed* (drawn forward) by the Pectoralis major, anterior fibers of the Deltoideus, Coracobrachialis, and when the forearm is flexed, by the Biceps brachii; *extended* (drawn backward) by the Latissimus dorsi, Teres major, posterior fibers of the Deltoideus, and, when the forearm is extended, by the Triceps brachii; it is *abducted* by the Deltoideus and Supraspinatus; it is *adducted* by the Subscapularis, Pectoralis major, Latissimus dorsi, and Teres major, and by the weight of the limb; it is *rotated outward* by the Infraspinatus and Teres minor; and it is *rotated inward* by the Subscapularis, Latissimus dorsi, Teres major, Pectoralis major, and the anterior fibers of the Deltoideus.

The most striking peculiarities in this joint are: (1) The large size of the head of the humerus in comparison with the depth of the glenoid cavity, even when this latter is supplemented by the glenoidal labrum. (2) The looseness of the capsule of the joint. (3) The intimate connection of the capsule with the muscles attached to the head of the humerus. (4) The peculiar relation of the tendon of the long head of the Biceps brachii to the joint.

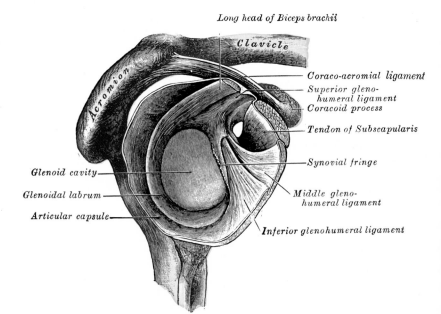

FIG. 324.—Interior of shoulder-joint. Lateral aspect.

It is in consequence of the relative sizes of the two articular surfaces, and the looseness of the articular capsule, that the joint enjoys such free movement in all directions. The arm can be carried considerably farther by the movements of the scapula, involving, of course, motion at the acromio- and sternoclavicular joints. These joints are therefore to be regarded as accessory structures to the shoulder-joint (see pages 290 and 292). The extent of the scapular movements is very considerable, especially in extreme elevation of the arm, a movement best accomplished when the arm is thrown somewhat forward and outward, because the margin of the head of the humerus is by no means a true circle; its greatest diameter is from the intertubercular groove, downward, medialward, and backward, and the greatest elevation of the arm can be obtained by rolling its articular surface in the direction of this measurement. The great width of the central portion of the humeral head also allows of very free horizontal movement when the arm is raised to a right angle, in which movement the arch formed by the acromion, the coracoid process and the coracoacromial ligament, constitutes a sort of supplemental articular cavity for the head of the bone.

The looseness of the capsule is so great that the humeral head will fall away from the scapula about 2.5 cm. when the muscles are dissected from around the joint. The articular surfaces of the two bones are held in contact, not so much by the capsule as by the surrounding muscles, an arrangement which allows very easy movement in the joint, especially when the muscles are not under tension. In all ordinary positions of the joint, the capsule is not put on the stretch, but extreme movements are checked by the tension of appropriate portions of the capsule, as well as by other ligaments and certain muscles.

The scapula is capable of being moved upward and downward, forward and backward, or, by a combination of these movements, circumducted on the wall of the chest. The muscles which *raise* the scapula are the upper fibers of the Trapezius, the Levator scapulæ, and the Rhomboidei; those which *depress* it are the lower fibers of the Trapezius, the Pectoralis minor, and, through the clavicle, the Subclavius. The scapula is drawn *backward* by the Rhomboidei and the middle and lower fibers of the Trapezius, and *forward* by the Serratus anterior and Pectoralis minor, assisted, when the arm is fixed, by the Pectoralis major. The mobility of the scapula is very considerable, and greatly assists the movements of the arm at the shoulder-joint. This mobility is of special importance in ankylosis of the shoulder-joint, the movements of this bone compensating to a very great extent for the immobility of the joint.

Raising of the arm above the head, either by carrying it forward in flexion or to the side in abduction, is brought about by the combined activity of the shoulder joint and rotation of the scapula on the chest wall. Although it has been customary to separate the movement into two parts, one, raising the arm to the horizontal, the other, from horizontal to overhead, such a distinction is artificial. During practically all of both parts of the movement, the ratio of motion in the two articulations is that of two parts glenohumeral to one part scapulothoracic. If motion in the glenohumeral articulation is destroyed by ankylosis, therefore, only one-third of the whole movement of 60° of motion will be retained in the compensatory motion of the scapulo-thoracic articulation.

The intimate union of the tendons of the Supraspinatus, Infraspinatus, Teres minor and Subscapularis with the capsule, converts these muscles into elastic and spontaneously acting ligaments of the joint.

The peculiar relations of the tendon of the long head of the Biceps brachii to the shoulder-joint appear to subserve various purposes. In the first place, by its connection with both the shoulder and elbow the muscle harmonizes the action of the two joints, and acts as an elastic ligament in all positions, in the manner previously discussed (see page 263). It strengthens the upper part of the articular cavity, and prevents the head of the humerus from being pressed up against the acromion, when the Deltoideus contracts; it thus fixes the head of the humerus as the center of motion in the glenoid cavity. By its passage along the intertubercular groove it assists in steadying the head of the humerus in the various movements of the arm. When the arm is raised from the side it assists the Supraspinatus and Infraspinatus in rotating the head of the humerus in the glenoid cavity. It also holds the head of the bone firmly in contact with the glenoid cavity, and prevents its slipping over its lower edge, or being displaced by the action of the Latissimus dorsi and Pectoralis major, as in climbing and many other movements.

IV. Elbow-joint (Articulatio Cubiti) (Figs. 325, 326, 327).

The elbow-joint is a ginglymus or hinge-joint. The trochlea of the humerus is received into the semilunar notch of the ulna, and the capitulum of the humerus articulates with the fovea on the head of the radius. The articular surfaces are connected together by a **capsule**, which is thickened medially and laterally into the **ulnar collateral** and the **radial collateral** ligaments.

The Articular Capsule (Fig. 325).—The anterior part is a broad and thin fibrous layer covering the anterior surface of the joint. It is attached to the *front* of the medial epicondyle and to the front of the humerus immediately above the coronoid and radial fossæ; *below,* to the anterior surface of the coronoid process of the ulna and to the annular ligament (page 301), being continuous on either side with the collateral ligaments. Its superficial fibers pass obliquely from the medial epicondyle of the humerus to the annular ligament. The middle fibers, vertical in direction, pass from the upper part of the coronoid depression and become partly blended with the preceding, but are inserted mainly into the anterior surface of the coronoid process. The deep or transverse set intersects these at right angles. It is in relation, in *front,* with the Brachialis, except at its most lateral part.

The posterior part (Fig. 326), is thin and membranous, and consists of transverse and oblique fibers. *Above,* it is attached to the humerus immediately behind the capitulum and close to the medial margin of the trochlea, to the margins of the olecranon fossa, and to the back of the lateral epicondyle some little distance from the trochlea. *Below,* it is fixed to the upper and lateral margins of the olecranon, to the posterior part of the annular ligament, and to the ulna behind the radial notch. The transverse fibers form a strong band which bridges across the olecranon fossa; under

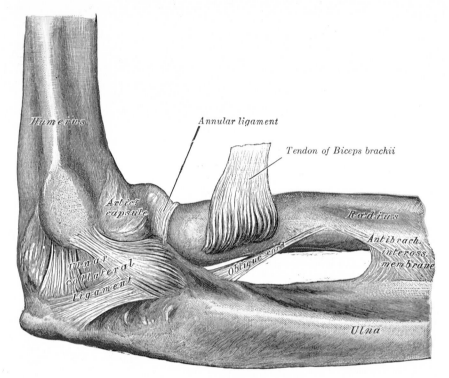

FIG. 325.—The left elbow-joint. Medial aspect.

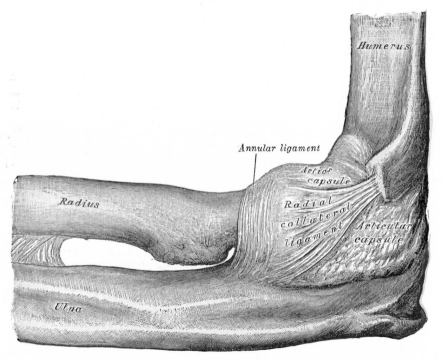

FIG. 326.—The left elbow-joint. Lateral aspect.

cover of this band a pouch of synovial membrane and a pad of fat project into the upper part of the fossa when the joint is extended. In the fat are a few scattered fibrous bundles, which pass from the deep surface of the transverse band to the upper part of the fossa. It is in relation, *behind,* with the tendon of the Triceps brachii and the Anconæus.

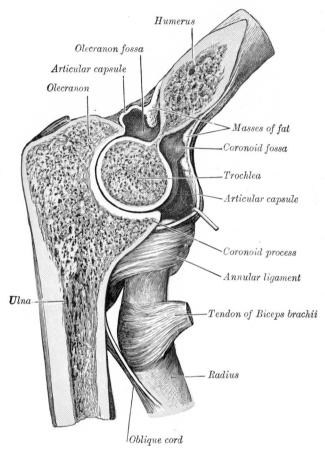

Humerus

Olecranon fossa

Articular capsule

Olecranon

Masses of fat

Coronoid fossa

Trochlea

Articular capsule

Coronoid process

Annular ligament

Ulna

Tendon of Biceps brachii

Radius

Oblique cord

Fɪɢ. 327.—Sagittal section through the left elbow-joint.

The Ulnar Collateral Ligament (*ligamentum collaterale ulnare; internal lateral ligament*) (Fig. 325).—This ligament is a thick triangular band consisting of two portions, an anterior and posterior united by a thinner intermediate portion. The **anterior portion,** directed obliquely forward, is attached, *above,* by its apex, to the front part of the medial epicondyle of the humerus; and, *below,* by its broad base to the medial margin of the coronoid process. The **posterior portion,** also of triangular form, is attached, *above,* by its apex, to the lower and back part of the medial epicondyle; *below,* to the medial margin of the olecranon. Between these two bands a few intermediate fibers descend from the medial epicondyle to blend with a *transverse band* which bridges across the notch between the olecranon and the coronoid process. This ligament is in relation with the Triceps brachii and Flexor carpi ulnaris and the ulnar nerve, and gives origin to part of the Flexor digitorum sublimis.

The Radial Collateral Ligament (*ligamentum collaterale radiale; external lateral ligament*) (Fig. 326).—This ligament is a short and narrow fibrous band, less distinct than the ulnar collateral, attached, *above,* to a depression below the lateral epicondyle of the humerus; *below,* to the annular ligament, some of its most posterior fibers passing over that ligament, to be inserted into the lateral margin of the ulna. It is intimately blended with the tendon of origin of the Supinator.

Synovial Membrane (Figs. 328, 329).—The synovial membrane is very extensive. It extends from the margin of the articular surface of the humerus, and lines the coronoid, radial and olecranon fossæ on that bone; it is reflected over the deep surface of the capsule and forms a pouch between the radial notch, the deep surface of the annular ligament, and the circumference of the head of the radius. Projecting between the radius and ulna into the cavity is a crescentic fold of synovial membrane, suggesting the division of the joint into two; one the humeroradial, the other the humeroulnar.

Between the capsule and the synovial membrane are three masses of fat: the largest, over the olecranon fossa, is pressed into the fossa by the Triceps brachii during the flexion; the second, over the coronoid fossa, and the third, over the radial fossa, are pressed by the Brachialis into their respective fossæ during extension.

The **muscles** in relation with the joint are, in *front,* the Brachialis; *behind,* the Triceps brachii and Anconæus; *laterally,* the Supinator, and the common tendon of origin of the Extensor muscles; *medially,* the common tendon of origin of the Flexor muscles, and the Flexor carpi ulnaris.

The **arteries** supplying the joint are derived from the anastomosis between the profunda and the superior and inferior ulnar collateral branches of the brachial, with the anterior, posterior, and interosseous recurrent branches of the ulnar, and the recurrent branch of the radial. These vessels form a complete anastomotic network around the joint.

The **nerves** of the joint are a twig from the ulnar, as it passes between the medial condyle and the olecranon; a filament from the musculocutaneous, and two from the median.

Movements.—The elbow-joint comprises three different portions—viz., the joint between the ulna and humerus, that between the head of the radius and the humerus, and the proximal radioulnar articulation, described below. All these articular surfaces are enveloped by a common synovial membrane, and the movements of the whole joint should be studied together. The combination of the movements of flexion and extension of the forearm with those of pronation and supination of the hand, which is ensured by the two being performed at the same joint, is essential to the accuracy of the various minute movements of the hand.

The portion of the joint between the ulna and humerus is a simple hinge-joint, and allows of movements of flexion and extension only. Owing to the obliquity of the trochlea of the humerus, this movement does not take place in the antero-posterior plane of the body of the humerus. When the forearm is extended and supinated, the axes of the arm and forearm are not in the same line; the arm forms an obtuse angle with the forearm, the hand and forearm being directed lateralward. During flexion, however, the forearm and the hand tend to approach the middle line of the body, and thus enable the hand to be easily carried to the face. The accurate adaptation of the trochlea of the humerus, with its prominences and depressions, to the semilunar notch of the ulna, prevents any lateral movement. *Flexion* is produced by the action of the Biceps brachii and Brachialis, assisted by the Brachioradialis and the muscles arising from the medial condyle of the humerus; *extension,* by the Triceps brachii and Anconæus, assisted by the Extensors of the wrist, the Extensor digitorum communis, and the Extensor digiti quinti proprius.

The joint between the head of the radius and the capitulum of the humerus is an arthrodial joint. The bony surfaces would of themselves constitute an enarthrosis and allow of movement in all directions, were it not for the annular ligament, by which the head of the radius is bound to the radial notch of the ulna, and which prevents any separation of the two bones laterally. It is to the same ligament that the head of the radius owes its security from dislocation, which would otherwise tend to occur, from the shallowness of the cup-like surface on the head of the radius. In fact, but for this ligament, the tendon of the Biceps brachii would be liable to pull the head of the radius out of the joint. The head of the radius is not in complete contact with the capitulum of the humerus in all positions of the joint. The capitulum occupies only the anterior and inferior surfaces of the lower end of the humerus, so that in complete extension a part of the radial head can be plainly felt projecting at the back of the articulation. In full flexion the movement of the radial head is hampered by the compression of the surrounding soft parts, so that the freest rotatory movement of the radius on the humerus (pronation and supination) takes place in semiflexion, in which position the two articular surfaces are in most intimate contact. Flexion and extension of the elbow-joint are limited by the tension of the structures on the front and back of the joint; the limitation of flexion is also aided by the soft structures of the arm and forearm coming into contact.

In any position of flexion or extension, the radius, carrying the hand with it, can be rotated in the proximal radioulnar joint. The hand is directly articulated to the lower surface of the radius only, and the ulnar notch on the lower end of the radius travels around the lower end of the ulna. The latter bone is excluded from the wrist-joint by the articular disk. Thus, rotation of the head of the radius around an axis passing through the center of the radial head of the humerus imparts circular movement to the hand through a very considerable arc.

V. Radioulnar Articulations (Articulatio Radioulnaris).

The articulation of the radius with the ulna is effected by ligaments which connect together the extremities as well as the bodies of these bones. The ligaments may, consequently, be subdivided into three sets: 1, those of the proximal radioulnar articulation; 2, the middle radioulnar ligaments; 3, those of the distal radioulnar articulation.

Proximal Radioulnar Articulation (*articulatio radioulnaris proximalis; superior radioulnar joint*).—This articulation is a trochoid or pivot-joint between the circumference of the head of the radius and the ring formed by the radial notch of the ulna and the *annular ligament.*

The Annular Ligament (*ligamentum annulare radii; orbicular ligament*) (Fig. 330). —This ligament is a strong band of fibers, which encircles the head of the radius, and retains it in contact with the radial notch of the ulna. It forms about four-fifths of the osseo-fibrous ring, and is attached to the anterior and posterior margins of the radial notch; a few of its lower fibers are continued around below the cavity and form at this level a complete fibrous ring. Its upper border blends with the anterior and posterior ligaments of the elbow, while from its lower border a thin loose membrane passes to be attached to the neck of the radius; a thickened band which extends from the inferior border of the annular ligament below the radial notch to the neck of the radius is known as the **quadrate ligament**. The superficial surface of the annular ligament is strengthened by the radial collateral ligament of the elbow, and affords origin to part of the Supinator. Its deep surface is smooth, and lined by synovial membrane, which is continuous with that of the elbow-joint.

Movements.—The movements allowed in this articulation are limited to rotatory movements of the head of the radius within the ring formed by the annular ligament and the radial notch of the ulna; rotation forward being called *pronation;* rotation backward, *supination.* Supination is performed by the Biceps brachii and Supinator, assisted to a slight extent by the Extensor muscles of the thumb. Pronation is performed by the Pronator teres and Pronator quadratus.

Middle Radioulnar Union.—The shafts of the radius and ulna are connected by the Oblique Cord and the Interosseous Membrane.

The Oblique Cord (*chorda obliqua; oblique ligament*) (Fig. 325).—The oblique cord is a small, flattened band, extending downward and lateralward, from the lateral side of the tubercle of the ulna at the base of the coronoid process to the radius a little below the radial tuberosity. Its fibers run in the opposite direction to those of the interosseous membrane. It is sometimes wanting.

The Interosseous Membrane (*membrana interossea antebrachii*).—The interosseous membrane is a broad and thin plane of fibrous tissue descending obliquely downward and medialward, from the interosseous crest of the radius to that of the ulna; the lower part of the membrane is attached to the posterior of the two lines into which the interosseous crest of the radius divides. It is deficient above, commencing about 2.5 cm. beneath the tuberosity of the radius; is broader in the middle than at either end; and presents an oval aperture a little above its lower margin for the passage of the volar interosseous vessels to the back of the forearm. This membrane serves to connect the bones, and to increase the extent of surface for the attachment of the deep muscles. Between its upper border and the oblique cord is a gap, through which the dorsal interosseous vessels pass. Two or three fibrous bands are occasionally found on the dorsal surface of this membrane; they descend obliquely from the ulna toward the radius, and have consequently a direction contrary to that of the other fibers. The membrane is in relation, in *front*, by its upper three-fourths, with the Flexor pollicis longus on the radial side, and with the Flexor digitorum profundus on the ulnar, lying in the interval between which are the volar interosseous vessels and nerve; by its lower fourth with the Pronator quadratus; *behind*, with the Supinator, Abductor pollicis longus, Extensor pollicis

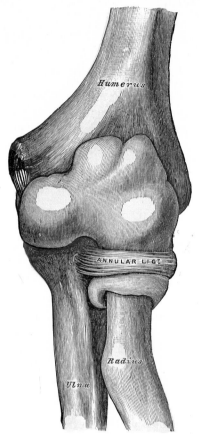

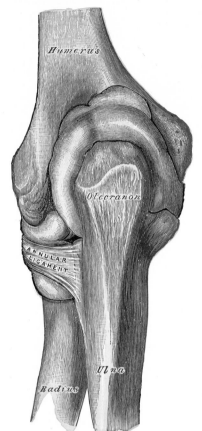

FIG. 328.—Capsule of elbow-joint (distended). Anterior aspect.

FIG. 329.—Capsule of elbow-joint (distended). Posterior aspect.

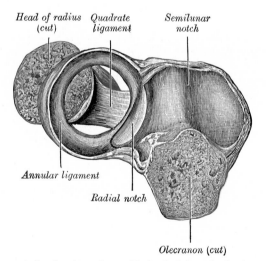

FIG. 330.—Annular ligament of radius, from above. The head of the radius has been sawn off and the bone dislodged from the ligament.

brevis, Extensor pollicis longus, Extensor indicis proprius; and, near the wrist, with the volar interosseous artery and dorsal interosseous nerve.

Distal Radioulnar Articulation (*articulatio radioulnaris distalis; inferior radio-ulnar joint*).—This is a pivot-joint formed between the head of the ulna and the ulnar notch on the lower end of the radius. The articular surfaces are connected together by the following ligaments:

The Volar Radioulnar.   The Dorsal Radioulnar.
The Articular Disk.

The Volar Radioulnar Ligament (*anterior radioulnar ligament*) (Fig. 331).—This ligament is a narrow band of fibers extending from the anterior margin of the ulnar notch of the radius to the front of the head of the ulna.

The Dorsal Radioulnar Ligament (*posterior radioulnar ligament*) (Fig. 332).—This ligament extends between corresponding surfaces on the dorsal aspect of the articulation.

The Articular Disk (*discus articularis; triangular fibrocartilage*) (Fig. 333).—The articular disk is triangular in shape, and is placed transversely beneath the head of the ulna, binding the lower ends of the ulna and radius firmly together. Its periphery is thicker than its center, which is occasionally perforated. It is attached by its apex to a depression between the styloid process and the head of the ulna; and by its base, which is thin, to the prominent edge of the radius, which separates the ulnar notch from the carpal articular surface. Its margins are united to the ligaments of the wrist-joint. Its **upper surface**, smooth and concave, articulates with the head of the ulna, forming an arthrodial joint; its **under surface**, also concave and smooth, forms part of the wrist-joint and articulates with the triangular bone and medial part of the lunate. Both surfaces are clothed by synovial membrane; the upper, by that of the distal radioulnar articulation, the under, by that of the wrist.

Synovial Membrane (Fig. 333).—The synovial membrane of this articulation is extremely loose, and extends upward as a recess (*recessus sacciformis*) between the radius and the ulna.

Movements.—The movements in the distal radioulnar articulation consist of rotation of the lower end of the radius around an axis which passes through the center of the head of the ulna. When the radius rotates forward, *pronation* of the forearm and hand is the result; and when backward *supination*. It will thus be seen that in pronation and supination the radius describes the segment of a cone, the axis of which extends from the center of the head of the radius to the middle of the head of the ulna. In this movement the head of the ulna is not stationary, but describes a curve in a direction opposite to that taken by the head of the radius. This, however, is not to be regarded as a rotation of the ulna—the curve which the head of this bone describes is due to a combined antero-posterior and rotatory movement, the former taking place almost entirely at the elbow-joint, the latter at the shoulder-joint.

VI. Radiocarpal Articulation or Wrist-joint (Articulatio Radiocarpea)
(Figs. 331, 332).

The wrist-joint is a condyloid articulation. The parts forming it are the distal end of the radius and under surface of the articular disk above; and the navicular, lunate, and triangular bones below. The articular surface of the radius and the under surface of the articular disk form together a transversely elliptical concave surface. The superior articular surfaces of the navicular, lunate, and triangular form a smooth convex surface, the **condyle**, which is received into the concavity. The joint is surrounded by a capsule and strengthened by the following ligaments:

The Volar Radiocarpal.   The Ulnar Collateral.
The Dorsal Radiocarpal.   The Radial Collateral.

The Volar Radiocarpal Ligament (*ligamentum radiocarpeum volare; anterior ligament*) (Fig. 331).—This ligament is a broad membranous band, attached above to the anterior margin of the lower end of the radius, to its styloid process, and to the front of the lower end of the ulna; its fibers pass downward and medialward to be inserted into the volar surfaces of the navicular, lunate, and triangular bones, some being continued to the capitate. In addition to this broad membrane, there is a rounded fasciculus, superficial to the rest, which reaches from the base of the styloid process of the ulna to the lunate and triangular bones. The ligament is perforated by apertures for the passage of vessels, and is in relation,

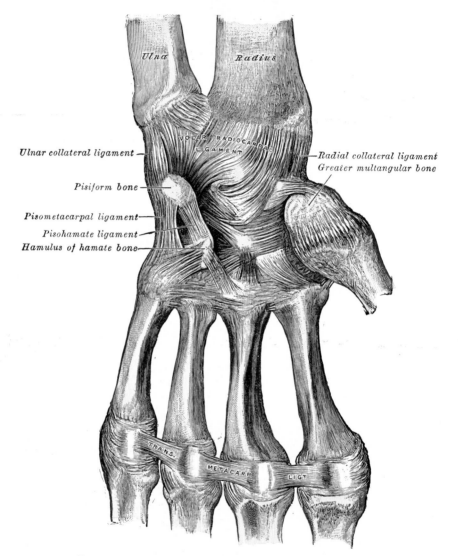

FIG. 331.—The ligaments of the left wrist and metacarpus. Volar aspect.

in *front*, with the tendons of the Flexor digitorum profundus and Flexor pollicis longus; *behind*, it is closely adherent to the anterior border of the articular disk of the distal radioulnar articulation.

The Dorsal Radiocarpal Ligament (*ligamentum radiocarpeum dorsale; posterior ligament*) (Fig. 332).—The dorsal radiocarpal ligament less thick and strong than the volar, is attached, *above*, to the posterior border of the lower end of the radius; its fibers are directed obliquely downward and medialward, and are fixed, *below*, to the dorsal surfaces of the navicular, lunate, and triangular, being continuous with those of the dorsal intercarpal ligaments. It is in relation, *behind*, with the Extensor tendons of the fingers; in *front*, it is blended with the articular disk.

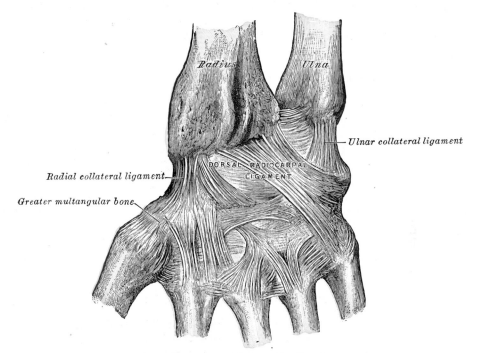

FIG. 332.—The ligaments of the left wrist. Dorsal aspect.

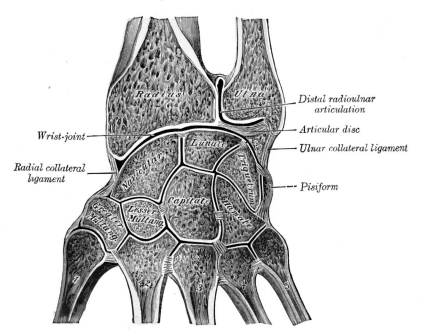

FIG. 333.—Vertical section through the articulations at the wrist, showing the synovial cavities.

The Ulnar Collateral Ligament (*ligamentum collaterale carpi ulnare; internal lateral ligament*) (Fig. 331).—The ulnar collateral ligament is a rounded cord,

20

attached above to the end of the styloid process of the ulna, and dividing below into two fasciculi, one of which is attached to the medial side of the triangular bone, the other to the pisiform and transverse carpal ligament.

The Radial Collateral Ligament (*ligamentum collaterale carpi radiale; external lateral ligament*) (Fig. 332).—The radial collateral ligament extends from the tip of the styloid process of the radius to the radial side of the navicular, some of its fibers being prolonged to the greater multangular bone and the transverse carpal ligament. It is in relation with the radial artery, which separates the ligament from the tendons of the Abductor pollicis longus and Extensor pollicis brevis.

Synovial Membrane (Fig. 333).—The synovial membrane lines the deep surfaces of the ligaments above described, extending from the margin of the lower end of the radius and articular disk above to the margins of the articular surfaces of the carpal bones below. It is loose and lax, and presents numerous folds, especially behind.

The wrist-joint is covered in front by the Flexor, and behind by the Extensor tendons.

The **arteries** supplying the joint are the volar and dorsal carpal branches of the radial and ulnar, the volar and dorsal metacarpals, and some ascending branches from the deep volar arch.

The **nerves** are derived from the ulnar and dorsal interosseous.

Movements.—The movements permitted in this joint are flexion, extension, abduction, adduction, and circumduction. They will be studied with those of the carpus, with which they are combined.

VII. Intercarpal Articulations (Articulationes Intercarpeæ; Articulations of the Carpus).

These articulations may be subdivided into three sets:

1. The Articulations of the Proximal Row of Carpal Bones.
2. The Articulations of the Distal Row of Carpal Bones.
3. The Articulations of the Two Rows with each Other.

Articulations of the Proximal Row of Carpal Bones.—These are arthrodial joints. The navicular, lunate, and triangular are connected by dorsal, volar, and interosseous ligaments.

The Dorsal Ligaments (*ligamenta intercarpea dorsalia*).—The dorsal ligaments, two in number, are placed transversely behind the bones of the first row; they connect the navicular and lunate, and the lunate and triangular.

The Volar ligaments (*ligamenta intercarpea volaria; palmar ligaments*).—The volar ligaments, also two, connect the navicular and lunate, and the lunate and triangular; they are less strong than the dorsal, and placed very deeply behind the Flexor tendons and the volar radiocarpal ligament.

The Interosseous Ligaments (*ligamenta intercarpea interossea*) (Fig. 333).—The interosseous ligaments are two narrow bundles, one connecting the lunate with the navicular, the other joining it to the triangular. They are on a level with the superior surfaces of these bones, and their upper surfaces are smooth, and form part of the convex articular surface of the wrist-joint.

The ligaments connecting the pisiform bone are the articular capsule and the two volar ligaments.

The **articular capsule** is a thin membrane which connects the pisiform to the triangular; it is lined by synovial membrane.

The two **volar ligaments** are strong fibrous bands; one, the **pisohamate ligament**, connects the pisiform to the hamate, the other, the **pisometacarpal ligament**, joins the pisiform to the base of the fifth metacarpal bone (Fig. 331). These ligaments are, in reality, prolongations of the tendon of the Flexor carpi ulnaris.

Articulations of the Distal Row of Carpal Bones.—These also are arthrodial joints; the bones are connected by dorsal, volar, and interosseous ligaments.

The Dorsal Ligaments (*ligamenta intercarpea dorsalia*).—The dorsal ligaments, three in number, extend transversely from one bone to another on the dorsal surface, connecting the greater with the lesser multangular, the lesser multangular with the capitate, and the capitate with the hamate.

The Volar Ligaments (*ligamenta intercarpea volaria; palmar ligaments*).—The volar ligaments, also three, have a similar arrangement on the volar surface.

The Interosseous Ligaments (*ligamenta intercarpea interossea*).—The three interosseous ligaments are much thicker than those of the first row; one is placed between the capitate and the hamate, a second between the capitate and the lesser multangular, and a third between the greater and lesser multangulars. The first is much the strongest, and the third is sometimes wanting.

Articulations of the Two Rows of Carpal Bones with Each Other.—The joint between the navicular, lunate, and triangular on the one hand, and the second row of carpal bones on the other, is named the **midcarpal joint**, and is made up of three distinct portions: in the center the head of the capitate and the superior surface of the hamate articulate with the deep cup-shaped cavity formed by the navicular and lunate, and constitute a sort of ball-and-socket joint. On the radial side the greater and lesser multangulars articulate with the navicular, and on the ulnar side the hamate articulates with the triangular, forming gliding joints.

The ligaments are: volar, dorsal, ulnar and radial collateral.

The Volar Ligaments (*ligamenta intercarpea volaria; anterior or palmar ligaments*). —The volar ligaments consist of short fibers, which pass, for the most part, from the volar surfaces of the bones of the first row to the front of the capitate.

The Dorsal Ligaments (*ligamenta intercarpea dorsalia; posterior ligaments*).— The dorsal ligaments consist of short, irregular bundles passing between the dorsal surfaces of the bones of the first and second rows.

The Collateral Ligaments (*lateral ligaments*).—The collateral ligaments are very short; one is placed on the radial, the other on the ulnar side of the carpus; the former, the stronger and more distinct, connects the navicular and greater multangular, the latter the triangular and hamate; they are continuous with the collateral ligaments of the wrist-joint. In addition to these ligaments, a slender interosseous band sometimes connects the capitate and the navicular.

Synovial Membrane.—The synovial membrane of the carpus is very extensive (Fig. 333), and bounds a synovial cavity of very irregular shape. The upper portion of the cavity intervenes between the under surfaces of the navicular, lunate, and triangular bones and the upper surfaces of the bones of the second row. It sends two prolongations upward—between the navicular and lunate, and the lunate and triangular—and three prolongations downward between the four bones of the second row. The prolongation between the greater and lesser multangulars, or that between the lesser multangular and capitate, is, owing to the absence of the interosseous ligament, often continuous with the cavity of the carpometacarpal joints, sometimes of the second, third, fourth, and fifth metacarpal bones, sometimes of the second and third only. In the latter condition the joint between the hamate and the fourth and fifth metacarpal bones has a separate synovial membrane. The synovial cavities of these joints are prolonged for a short distance between the bases of the metacarpal bones. There is a separate synovial membrane between the pisiform and triangular.

Movements.—The articulation of the hand and wrist considered as a whole involves four articular surfaces: (*a*) the inferior surfaces of the radius and articular disk; (*b*) the superior surfaces of the navicular, lunate, and triangular, the pisiform having no essential part in the movement of the hand; (*c*) the S-shaped surface formed by the inferior surfaces of the navicular, lunate, and triangular; (*d*) the reciprocal surface formed by the upper surfaces of the bones of the second row. These four surfaces form two joints: (1) a proximal, the wrist-joint proper; and (2) a distal, the mid-carpal joint.

1. The wrist-joint proper is a true condyloid articulation, and therefore all movements but rotation are permitted. Flexion and extension are the most free, and of these a greater amount of extension than of flexion is permitted, since the articulating surfaces extend farther on the dorsal than on the volar surfaces of the carpal bones. In this movement the carpal bones rotate on a transverse axis drawn between the tips of the styloid processes of the radius and ulna. A certain amount of adduction (or ulnar flexion) and abduction (or radial flexion) is also permitted. The

former is considerably greater in extent than the latter on account of the shortness of the styloid process of the ulna, abduction being soon limited by the contact of the styloid process of the radius with the greater multangular. In this movement the carpus revolves upon an antero-posterior axis drawn through the center of the wrist. Finally, circumduction is permitted by the combined and consecutive movements of adduction, extension, abduction, and flexion. No rotation is possible, but the effect of rotation is obtained by the pronation and supination of the radius on the ulna. The movement of *flexion* is performed by the Flexor carpi radialis, the Flexor carpi ulnaris, and the Palmaris longus; *extension* by the Extensores carpi radiales longus and brevis and the Extensor carpi ulnaris; *adduction* (ulnar flexion) by the Flexor carpi ulnaris and the Extensor carpi ulnaris; and *abduction* (radial flexion) by the Abductor pollicis longus, the Extensors of the thumb, and the Extensores carpi radiales longus and brevis and the Flexor carpi radialis. When the fingers are extended, flexion of the wrist is performed by the Flexores carpi radialis and ulnaris and extension is aided by the Extensor digitorum communis. When the fingers are flexed, flexion of the wrist is aided by the Flexores digitorum sublimis and profundus, and extension is performed by the Extensores carpi radiales and ulnaris.

2. The chief movements permitted in the mid-carpal joint are flexion and extension and a slight amount of rotation. In flexion and extension, which are the movements most freely enjoyed, the greater and lesser multangulars on the radial side and the hamate on the ulnar side glide forward and backward on the navicular and triangular respectively, while the head of the capitate and the superior surface of the hamate rotate in the cup-shaped cavity of the navicular and lunate. Flexion at this joint is freer than extension. A very trifling amount of rotation is also permitted, the head of the capitate rotating around a vertical axis drawn through its own center, while at the same time a slight gliding movement takes place in the lateral and medial portions of the joint.

VIII. Carpometacarpal Articulations (Articulationes Carpometacarpeæ).

Carpometacarpal Articulation of the Thumb (*articulatio carpometacarpea pollicis*). —This is a joint of reciprocal reception between the first metacarpal and the greater multangular; it enjoys great freedom of movement on account of the configuration of its articular surfaces, which are saddle-shaped. The joint is surrounded by a capsule, which is thick but loose, and passes from the circumference of the base of the metacarpal bone to the rough edge bounding the articular surface of the greater multangular; it is thickest laterally and dorsally, and is lined by synovial membrane.

Movements.—In this articulation the movements permitted are flexion and extension in the plane of the palm of the hand, abduction and adduction in a plane at right angles to the palm, circumduction, and opposition. It is by the movement of opposition that the tip of the thumb is brought into contact with the volar surfaces of the slightly flexed fingers. This movement is effected through the medium of a small sloping facet on the anterior lip of the saddle-shaped articular surface of the greater multangular. The Flexor muscles pull the corresponding part of the articular surface of the metacarpal bone on to this facet, and the movement of opposition is then carried out by the Adductors.

Flexion of this joint is produced by the Flexores pollicis longus and brevis, assisted by the Opponens pollicis and the Adductor pollicis. Extension is effected mainly by the Abductor pollicis longus, assisted by the Extensores pollicis longus and brevis. Adduction is carried out by the Adductor; abduction mainly by the Abductores pollicis longus and brevis, assisted by the Extensors.

Articulations of the Other Four Metacarpal Bones with the Carpus (*articulationes carpometacarpeæ*).—The joints between the carpus and the second, third, fourth, and fifth metacarpal bones are arthrodial. The bones are united by dorsal, volar, and interosseous ligaments.

The Dorsal Ligaments (*ligamenta carpometacarpea dorsalia*).—The dorsal ligaments, the strongest and most distinct, connect the carpal and metacarpal bones on their dorsal surfaces. The second metacarpal bone receives two fasciculi, one from the greater, the other from the lesser multangular; the third metacarpal receives two, one each from the lesser multangular and capitate; the fourth two, one each from the capitate and hamate; the fifth receives a single fasciculus from the hamate, and this is continuous with a similar ligament on the volar surface, forming an incomplete capsule.

The Volar Ligaments (*ligamenta carpometacarpea volaria; palmar ligaments*).— The volar ligaments have a somewhat similar arrangement, with the exception of those of the third metacarpal, which are three in number: a lateral one from the greater multangular, situated superficial to the sheath of the tendon of the Flexor carpi radialis; an intermediate one from the capitate; and a medial one from the hamate.

The Interosseous Ligaments.—The interosseous ligaments consist of short, thick fibers, and are limited to one part of the carpometacarpal articulation; they connect the contiguous inferior angles of the capitate and hamate with the adjacent surfaces of the third and fourth metacarpal bones.

Synovial Membrane.—The synovial membrane is a continuation of that of the intercarpal joints. Occasionally, the joint between the hamate and the fourth and fifth metacarpal bones has a separate synovial membrane.

The synovial membranes of the wrist and carpus (Fig. 333) are thus seen to be five in number. The *first* passes from the lower end of the ulnar to the ulnar notch of the radius, and lines the upper surface of the articular disk. The *second* passes from the articular disk and the lower end of the radius above, to the bones of the first row below. The *third*, the most extensive, passes between the contiguous margins of the two rows of carpal bones, and sometimes, in the event of one of the interosseous ligaments being absent, between the bones of the second row to the carpal extremities of the second, third, fourth, and fifth metacarpal bones. The *fourth* extends from the margin of the greater multangular to the metacarpal bone of the thumb. The *fifth* runs between the adjacent margins of the triangular and pisiform bones. Occasionally the fourth and fifth carpometacarpal joints have a separate synovial membrane.

Movements.—The movements permitted in the carpometacarpal articulations of the fingers are limited to slight gliding of the articular surfaces upon each other, the extent of which varies in the different joints. The metacarpal bone of the little finger is most movable, then that of the ring finger; the metacarpal bones of the index and middle fingers are almost immovable.

IX. Intermetacarpal Articulations (**Articulationes Intermetacarpeæ; Articulations of the Metacarpal Bones with Each Other**).

The bases of the second, third, fourth and fifth metacarpal bones articulate with one another by small surfaces covered with cartilage, and are connected together by dorsal, volar, and interosseous ligaments.

The **dorsal** (*ligamenta basium oss. metacarp. dorsalia*) and **volar ligaments** (*ligamenta basium oss. metacarp. volaria; palmar ligaments*) pass transversely from one bone to another on the dorsal and volar surfaces. The **interosseous ligaments** (*ligamenta basium oss. metacarp. interossea*) connect their contiguous surfaces, just distal to their collateral articular facets.

The **synovial membrane** for these joints is continuous with that of the carpometacarpal articulations.

The Transverse Metacarpal Ligament (*ligamentum capitulorum [oss. metacarpalium] transversum*) (Fig. 334).—This ligament is a narrow fibrous band, which runs across the volar surfaces of the heads of the second, third, fourth and fifth metacarpal bones, connecting them together. It is blended with the volar (glenoid) ligaments of the metacarpophalangeal articulations. Its volar surface is concave where the Flexor tendons pass over it; behind it the tendons of the Interossei pass to their insertions.

X. Metacarpophalangeal Articulations (**Articulationes Metacarpophalangeæ; Metacarpophalangeal Joints**) (Figs. 334, 335).

These articulations are of the condyloid kind, formed by the reception of the rounded heads of the metacarpal bones into shallow cavities on the proximal ends of the first phalanges, with the exception of that of the thumb, which presents more of the characters of a ginglymoid joint. Each joint has a volar and two collateral ligaments.

The Volar Ligaments (*glenoid ligaments of Cruveilhier; palmar or vaginal ligaments*). —The volar ligaments are thick, dense, fibrocartilaginous structures, placed upon the volar surfaces of the joints in the intervals between the collateral ligaments, to which they are connected; they are loosely united to the metacarpal bones, but are very firmly attached to the bases of the first phalanges. Their volar surfaces are intimately blended with the transverse metacarpal ligament, and present grooves for the passage of the Flexor tendons, the sheaths surrounding which are connected to the sides of the grooves. Their deep surfaces form parts of the articular facets for the heads of the metacarpal bones, and are lined by synovial membranes.

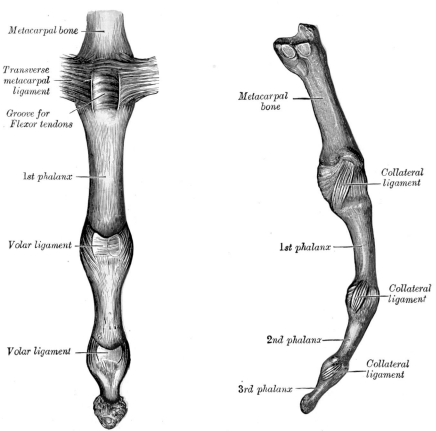

FIG. 334.—Metacarpophalangeal articulation and articulations of digit. Volar aspect.

FIG. 335.—Metacarpophalangeal articulation and articulations of digit. Ulnar aspect.

The Collateral Ligaments (*ligamenta collateralia; lateral ligaments*).—The collateral ligaments are strong, rounded cords, placed on the sides of the joints; each is attached by one extremity to the posterior tubercle and adjacent depression on the side of the head of the metacarpal bone, and by the other to the contiguous extremity of the phalanx.

The dorsal surfaces of these joints are covered by the expansions of the Extensor tendons, together with some loose areolar tissue which connects the deep surfaces of the tendons to the bones.

Movements.—The movements which occur in these joints are flexion, extension, adduction, abduction, and circumduction; the movements of abduction and adduction are very limited, and cannot be performed when the fingers are flexed.

XI. Articulations of the Digits (Articulationes Digitorum Manus; Interphalangeal Joints) (Figs. 334, 335).

The interphalangeal articulations are hinge-joints; each has a volar and two collateral ligaments. The arrangement of these ligaments is similar to those in the metacarpophalangeal articulations. The Extensor tendons supply the place of posterior ligaments.

Movements.—The only movements permitted in the interphalangeal joints are flexion and extension; these movements are more extensive between the first and second phalanges than between the second and third. The amount of flexion is very considerable, but extension is limited by the volar and collateral ligaments.

Muscles Acting on the Joints of the Digits.—Flexion of the metacarpophalangeal joints of the fingers is effected by the Flexores digitorum sublimis and profundus, Lumbricales, and Interossei, assisted in the case of the little finger by the Flexor digiti quinti brevis. Extension is produced by the Extensor digitorum communis, Extensor indicis proprius, and Extensor digiti quinti proprius.

Flexion of the interphalangeal joints of the fingers is accomplished by the Flexor digitorum profundus acting on the proximal and distal joints and by the Flexor digitorum sublimis acting on the proximal joints. Extension is effected mainly by the Lumbricales and Interossei, the long Extensors having little or no action upon these joints.

Flexion of the metacarpophalangeal joint of the thumb is effected by the Flexores pollicis longus and brevis; extension by the Extensores pollicis longus and brevis. Flexion of the interphalangeal joint is accomplished by the Flexor pollicis longus, and extension by the Extensor pollicis longus.

ARTICULATIONS OF THE LOWER EXTREMITY.

The articulations of the Lower Extremity comprise the following:

I. Hip.
II. Knee.
III. Tibiofibular.
IV. Ankle.
V. Intertarsal.
VI. Tarsometatarsal.
VII. Intermetatarsal.
VIII. Metatarsophalangeal.
IX. Articulations of the Digits.

I. Coxal Articulation or Hip-joint (Articulatio Coxæ).

This articulation is an enarthrodial or ball-and-socket joint, formed by the reception of the head of the femur into the cup-shaped cavity of the acetabulum. The articular cartilage on the head of the femur, thicker at the center than at the circumference, covers the entire surface with the exception of the fovea capitis femoris, to which the ligamentum teres is attached; that on the acetabulum forms an incomplete marginal ring, the lunate surface. Within the lunate surface there is a circular depression devoid of cartilage, occupied in the fresh state by a mass of fat, covered by synovial membrane. The ligaments of the joint are:

The Articular Capsule.
The Iliofemoral.
The Ischiocapsular.
The Pubocapsular.
The Ligamentum Teres Femoris.
The Glenoidal Labrum.
The Transverse Acetabular

The Articular Capsule (*capsula articularis; capsular ligament*) (Figs. 336, 337).—The articular capsule is strong and dense. *Above*, it is attached to the margin of the acetabulum 5 to 6 mm. beyond the glenoidal labrum behind; but in *front*, it is attached to the outer margin of the labrum, and, opposite to the notch where the margin of the cavity is deficient, it is connected to the transverse ligament, and by a few fibers to the edge of the obturator foramen. It surrounds the neck of the femur, and is attached, in *front*, to the intertrochanteric line; *above*, to the base of the neck; *behind,* to the neck, about 1.25 cm. above the intertrochanteric crest; *below,* to the lower part of the neck, close to the lesser trochanter. From its femoral attachment some of the fibers are reflected upward along the neck as longitudinal bands, termed **retinacula.** The capsule is much thicker at the upper and forepart of the joint, where the greatest amount of resistance is required; behind and below, it is thin and loose. It consists of two sets of fibers, circular and longitudinal. The circular fibers, **zona orbicularis,** are most abundant at the lower and back part of the capsule (Fig. 339), and form a sling or collar around the neck of the femur. Anteriorly they blend with the deep surface of the iliofemoral ligament, and gain an attachment to the anterior inferior iliac spine. The longitudinal fibers are greatest in amount at the upper and front part of the capsule, where they are reinforced by distinct bands, or accessory ligaments, of which the

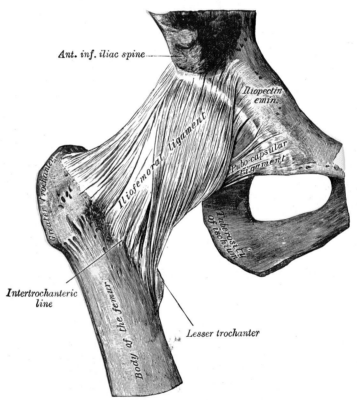

Fig. 336.—Right hip-joint from the front. (Spalteholz.)

most important is the **iliofemoral ligament.** The other accessory bands are known as the **pubocapsular** and the **ischiocapsular ligaments.** The external surface of the capsule is rough, covered by numerous muscles, and separated in front from the Psoas major and Iliacus by a bursa, which not infrequently communicates by a circular aperture with the cavity of the joint.

The Iliofemoral Ligament (*ligamentum iliofemorale; Y-ligament; ligament of Bigelow*) (Fig. 336).—The iliofemoral ligament is a band of great strength which lies in front of the joint; it is intimately connected with the capsule, and serves to strengthen it in this situation. It is attached, *above,* to the lower part of the anterior inferior iliac spine; *below,* it divides into two bands, one of which passes downward and is fixed to the lower part of the intertrochanteric line; the other is directed downward and lateralward and is attached to the upper part of the same line. Between the two bands is a thinner part of the capsule. In some cases there is no division, and the ligament spreads out into a flat triangular band which is attached to the whole length of the intertrochanteric line. This ligament is frequently called the Y-shaped ligament of Bigelow; and its upper band is sometimes named the **iliotrochanteric ligament.**

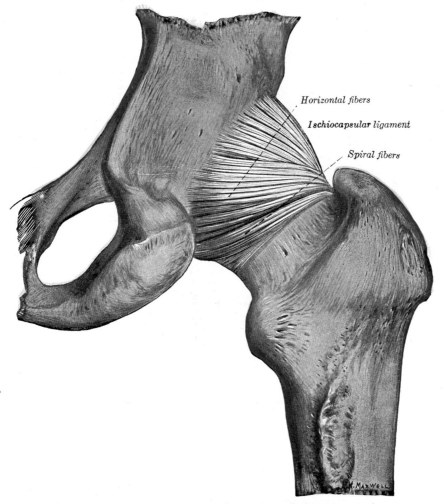

Horizontal fibers

Ischiocapsular ligament

Spiral fibers

Fig. 337.—The hip-joint from behind. (Quain.)

The **Pubocapsular Ligament** (*ligamentum pubocapsulare; pubofemoral ligament*).— This ligament is attached, *above*, to the obturator crest and the superior ramus of the pubis; *below*, it blends with the capsule and with the deep surface of the vertical band of the iliofemoral ligament.

The **Ischiocapsular Ligament** (*ligamentum ischiocapsulare; ischiocapsular band; ligament of Bertin*).—The ischiocapsular ligament consists of a triangular band of strong fibers, which spring from the ischium below and behind the acetabulum, and blend with the circular fibers of the capsule (Fig. 337).

The **Ligamentum Teres Femoris** (Fig. 338).—The ligamentum teres femoris is a triangular, somewhat flattened band implanted by its apex into the antero-superior part of the fovea capitis femoris; its base is attached by two bands, one into either side of the acetabular notch, and between these bony attachments it blends with the transverse ligament. It is ensheathed by the synovial membrane, and varies greatly in strength in different subjects; occasionally only the synovial fold exists, and in rare cases even this is absent. The ligament is made tense when the thigh is semiflexed and the limb then adducted or rotated outward; it is, on the other hand, relaxed when the limb is abducted. It has, however, but little influence as a ligament.

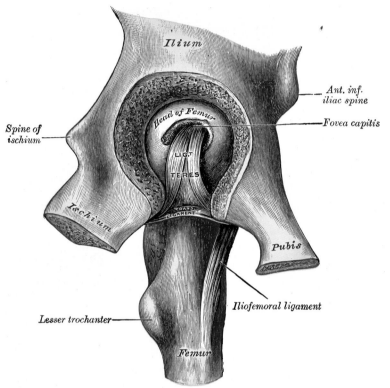

Fig. 338.—Left hip-joint, opened by removing the floor of the acetabulum from within the pelvis.

The Glenoidal Labrum (*labrum glenoidale; cotyloid ligament*).—The glenoidal labrum is a fibrocartilaginous rim attached to the margin of the acetabulum, the cavity of which it deepens; at the same time it protects the edge of the bone, and fills up the inequalities of its surface. It bridges over the notch as the **transverse ligament**, and thus forms a complete circle, which closely surrounds the head of the femur and assists in holding it in its place. It is triangular on section, its base being attached to the margin of the acetabulum, while its opposite edge is free and sharp. Its two surfaces are invested by synovial membrane, the external one being in contact with the capsule, the internal one being inclined inward so as to narrow the acetabulum, and embrace the cartilaginous surface of the head of the femur. It is much thicker above and behind than below and in front, and consists of compact fibers.

The Transverse Acetabular Ligament (*ligamentum transversum acetabuli; transverse ligament*).—This ligament is in reality a portion of the glenoidal labrum, though differing from it in having no cartilage cells among its fibers. It consists of strong, flattened fibers, which cross the acetabular notch, and convert it into a foramen through which the nutrient vessels enter the joint.

Synovial Membrane (Fig. 340).—The synovial membrane is very extensive. Commencing at the margin of the cartilaginous surface of the head of the femur, it covers the portion of the

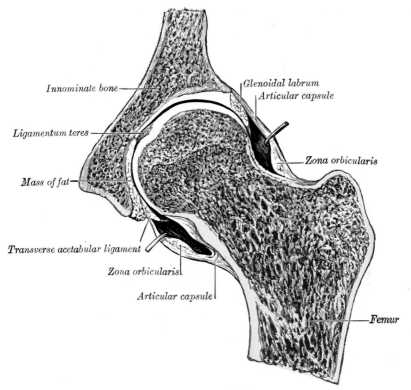

Innominate bone

Ligamentum teres

Mass of fat

Transverse acetabular ligament

Zona orbicularis

Articular capsule

Glenoidal labrum

Articular capsule

Zona orbicularis

Femur

FIG. 339.—A section through the hip-joint.

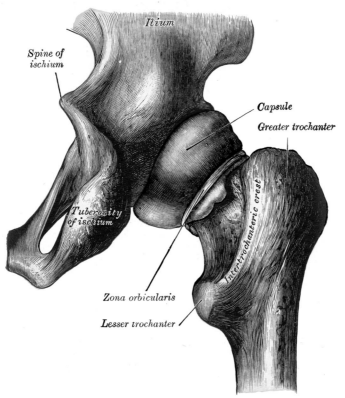

Ilium

Spine of ischium

Tuberosity of ischium

Zona orbicularis

Lesser trochanter

Capsule

Greater trochanter

Intertrochanteric crest

FIG. 340.—Capsule of hip-joint (distended). Posterior aspect.

neck which is contained within the joint; from the neck it is reflected on the internal surface of the capsule, covers both surfaces of the glenoidal labrum and the mass of fat contained in the depression at the bottom of the acetabulum, and ensheathes the ligamentum teres as far as the head of the femur. The joint cavity sometimes communicates through a hole in the capsule between the vertical band of the iliofemoral ligament and the pubocapsular ligament with a bursa situated on the deep surfaces of the Psoas major and Iliacus.

The **muscles** in relation with the joint are, in *front*, the Psoas major and Iliacus, separated from the capsule by a bursa; *above*, the reflected head of the Rectus femoris and Glutæus minimus, the latter being closely adherent to the capsule; *medially*, the Obturator externus and Pectineus; *behind*, the Piriformis, Gemellus superior, Obturator internus, Gemellus inferior, Obturator externus, and Quadratus femoris (Fig. 341).

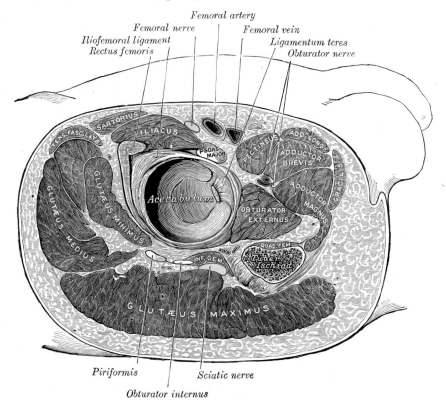

FIG. 341.—Structures surrounding right hip-joint.

The **arteries** supplying the joint are derived from the obturator, medial femoral circumflex, and superior and inferior gluteals.

The **nerves** are articular branches from the sacral plexus, sciatic, obturator, accessory obturator, and a filament from the branch of the femoral supplying the Rectus femoris.

Movements.—The movements of the hip are very extensive, and consist of flexion, extension, adduction, abduction, circumduction, and rotation.

The length of the neck of the femur and its inclinations to the body of the bone have the effect of converting the angular movements of flexion, extension, adduction, and abduction partially into rotatory movements in the joint. Thus when the thigh is flexed or extended, the head of the femur, on account of the *medial* inclination of the neck, rotates within the acetabulum with only a slight amount of gliding to and fro. The *forward* slope of the neck similarly affects the movements of adduction and abduction. Conversely rotation of the thigh which is permitted by the *upward* inclination of the neck, is not a simple rotation of the head of the femur in the acetabulum, but is accompanied by a certain amount of gliding.

The hip-joint presents a very striking contrast to the shoulder-joint in the much more complete mechanical arrangements for its security and for the limitation of its movements. In the shoulder, as has been seen, the head of the humerus is not adapted at all in size to the glenoid cavity, and is hardly restrained in any of its ordinary movements by the capsule. In the hip-joint, on the contrary, the head of the femur is closely fitted to the acetabulum for an area extending over nearly half a sphere, and at the margin of the bony cup it is still more closely embraced by the glenoidal labrum, so that the head of the femur is held in its place by that ligament even when the fibers of the capsule have been quite divided. The iliofemoral ligament is the strongest of all the ligaments in the body, and is put on the stretch by any attempt to extend the femur beyond a straight line with the trunk. That is to say, this ligament is the chief agent in maintaining the erect position without muscular fatigue; for a vertical line passing through the center of gravity of the trunk falls behind the centers of rotation in the hip-joints, and therefore the pelvis tends to fall backward, but is prevented by the tension of the iliofemoral ligaments. The security of the joint may be provided for also by the two bones being directly united through the ligamentum teres; but it is doubtful whether this ligament has much influence upon the mechanism of the joint. When the knee is flexed, flexion of the hip-joint is arrested by the soft parts of the thigh and abdomen being brought into contact, and when the knee is extended, by the action of the hamstring muscles; extension is checked by the tension of the iliofemoral ligament; adduction by the thighs coming into contact; adduction with flexion by the lateral band of the iliofemoral ligament and the lateral part of the capsule; abduction by the medial band of the iliofemoral ligament and the pubocapsular ligament; rotation outward by the lateral band of the iliofemoral ligament; and rotation inward by the ischiocapsular ligament and the hinder part of the capsule. The muscles which *flex* the femur on the pelvis are the Psoas major, Iliacus, Tensor fasciæ latæ Rectus femoris, Sartorius, Pectineus, Adductores longus and brevis, and the anterior fibers of the Glutæi medius and minimus. *Extension* is mainly performed by the Glutæus maximus, assisted by the hamstring muscles and the ischial head of the Adductor magnus. The thigh is *adducted* by the Adductores magnus, longus, and brevis, the Pectineus, and the Gracilis, and *abducted* by the Glutæi medius and minimus. The muscles which *rotate* the thigh *inward* are the Glutæus minimus and the anterior fibers of the Glutæus medius, the Tensor fasciæ latæ the Adductores longus, brevis, and magnus, the Pectineus, and the Iliacus and Psoas major; while those which rotate it *outward* are the posterior fibers of the Glutæus medius, the Piriformis, Obturatores externus and internus, Gemelli superior and inferior, Quadratus femoris, Glutæus maximus, and the Sartorius.

II. The Knee-joint (Articulatio Genu).

The knee-joint was formerly described as a ginglymus or hinge-joint, but is really of a much more complicated character. It must be regarded as consisting of three articulations in one: two condyloid joints, one between each condyle of the femur and the corresponding meniscus and condyle of the tibia; and a third between the patella and the femur, partly arthrodial, but not completely so, since the articular surfaces are not mutually adapted to each other, so that the movement is not a simple gliding one. This view of the construction of the knee-joint receives confirmation from the study of the articulation in some of the lower mammals, where, corresponding to these three subdivisions, three synovial cavities are sometimes found, either entirely distinct or only connected together by small communications. This view is further rendered probable by the existence in the middle of the joint of the two cruciate ligaments, which must be regarded as the collateral ligaments of the medial and lateral joints. The existence of the patellar fold of synovial membrane would further indicate a tendency to separation of the synovial cavity into two minor sacs, one corresponding to the lateral and the other to the medial joint.

The bones are connected together by the following ligaments:

The Articular Capsule.	The Anterior Cruciate.
The Ligamentum Patellæ.	The Posterior Cruciate.
The Oblique Popliteal.	The Medial and Lateral Menisci.
The Arcuate Popliteal.	The Transverse.
The Tibial Collateral.	The Coronary.
The Fibular Collateral.	

The Articular Capsule (*capsula articularis; capsular ligament*) (Fig. 342).—The articular capsule consists of a thin, but strong, fibrous membrane which is strengthened in almost its entire extent by bands inseparably connected with it. Above and in front, beneath the tendon of the Quadriceps femoris, it is represented only by the synovial membrane. Its chief strengthening bands are derived from the fascia lata and from the tendons surrounding the joint. In front, expansions from the Vasti and from the fascia lata and its iliotibial band fill in the intervals between the anterior and collateral ligaments, constituting the **medial** and **lateral patellar retinacula.** Behind the capsule consists of vertical fibers which arise from the condyles and from the sides of the intercondyloid fossa of the femur;

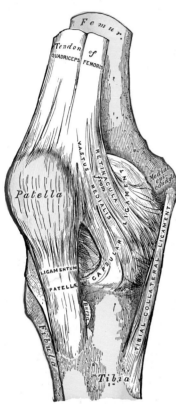

FIG. 342.—Right knee-joint. Anterior view.

the posterior part of the capsule is therefore situated on the sides of and in front of the cruciate ligaments, which are thus excluded from the joint cavity. Behind the cruciate ligaments is the oblique popliteal ligament which is augmented by fibers derived from the tendon of the Semimembranosus. Laterally, a prolongation from the iliotibial band fills in the interval between the oblique popliteal and the fibular collateral ligaments, and partly covers the latter. Medially, expansions from the Sartorius and Semimembranosus pass upward to the tibial collateral ligament and strengthen the capsule.

The Ligamentum Patellæ (*anterior ligament*) (Fig. 342).—The ligamentum patellæ is the central portion of the common tendon of the Quadriceps femoris, which is continued from the patella to the tuberosity of the tibia. It is a strong, flat, ligamentous band, about 8 cm. in length, attached, *above*, to the apex and adjoining margins of the patella and the rough depression on its posterior surface; *below*, to the tuberosity of the tibia; its superficial fibers are continuous over the front of the patella with those of the tendon of the Quadriceps femoris. The medial and lateral portions of the tendon of the Quadriceps pass down on either side of the patella, to be inserted into the upper extremity of the tibia on either side of the tuberosity; these portions merge into the capsule, as stated above, forming the medial and lateral patellar retinacula. The posterior surface of the ligamentum patellæ is separated from the synovial membrane of the joint by a large infrapatellar pad of fat, and from the tibia by a bursa.

The Oblique Popliteal Ligament (*ligamentum popliteum obliquum; posterior ligament*) (Fig. 343).—This ligament is a broad, flat, fibrous band, formed of fasciculi separated from one another by apertures for the passage of vessels and nerves. It is attached above to the upper margin of the intercondyloid fossa and posterior surface of the femur close to the articular margins of the condyles, and below to the posterior margin of the head of the tibia. Superficial to the main part of the ligament is a strong fasciculus, derived from the tendon of the Semimembranosus and passing from the back part of the medial condyle of the tibia obliquely upward and lateralward to the back part of the lateral condyle of the femur. The oblique popliteal ligament forms part of the floor of the popliteal fossa, and the popliteal artery rests upon it.

The Arcuate Popliteal Ligament (Fig. 343).—This ligament arches downward from the lateral condyle of the femur to the posterior surface of the capsular ligament. It is connected to the styloid process of the head of the fibula by two converging bands.

The Tibial Collateral Ligament (*ligamentum collaterale tibiale; internal lateral ligament*) (Fig. 342).—The tibial collateral is a broad, flat, membranous band, situated nearer to the back than to the front of the joint. It is attached, *above*, to the medial condyle of the femur immediately below the adductor tubercle; *below*, to the medial condyle and medial surface of the body of the tibia. The fibers of the posterior part of the ligament are short and incline backward as they descend; they are inserted into the tibia above the groove for the Semimembranosus. The anterior part of the ligament is a flattened band, about 10 cm. long, which inclines forward as it descends. It is inserted into the medial surface of the body of the tibia about 2.5 cm. below the level of the condyle. It is crossed, at its lower part, by the tendons of the Sartorius, Gracilis, and Semitendinosus, a bursa being interposed. Its deep surface covers the inferior medial genicular vessels and nerve and the anterior portion of the tendon of the Semimembranosus, with which it is connected by a few fibers; it is intimately adherent to the medial meniscus.

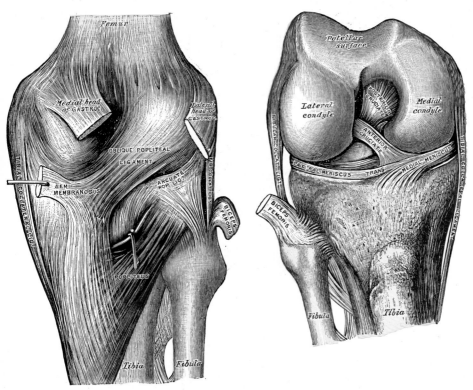

FIG. 343.—The right knee-joint.
Posterior aspect.

FIG. 344.—The right knee-joint. Dissected
from the front.

The Fibular Collateral Ligament (*ligamentum collaterale fibulare; external lateral or long external lateral ligament*) (Fig. 345).—The fibular collateral is a strong, rounded, fibrous cord, attached, *above*, to the back part of the lateral condyle of the femur, immediately above the groove for the tendon of the Popliteus; *below*, to the lateral side of the head of the fibula, in front of the styloid process. The greater part of its lateral surface is covered by the tendon of the Biceps femoris; the tendon, however, divides at its insertion into two parts, which are separated by the ligament. Deep to the ligament are the tendon of the Popliteus, and the inferior lateral genicular vessels and nerve. The ligament has no attachment to the lateral meniscus.

An inconstant bundle of fibers, the **short fibular collateral ligament,** is placed behind and parallel with the preceding, attached, *above,* to the lower and back part of the lateral condyle of the femur; *below,* to the summit of the styloid process of the fibula. Passing deep to it are the tendon of the Popliteus, and the inferior lateral genicular vessels and nerve.

The Cruciate Ligaments (*ligamenta cruciata genu; crucial ligaments*).—The cruciate ligaments are of considerable strength, situated in the middle of the joint, nearer to its posterior than to its anterior surface. They are called *cruciate* because they cross each other somewhat like the lines of the letter X; and have received the names **anterior** and **posterior,** from the position of their attachments to the tibia.

The Anterior Cruciate Ligament (*ligamentum cruciatum anterius; external crucial ligament*) (Fig. 344) is attached to the depression in front of the intercondyloid eminence of the tibia, being blended with the anterior extremity of the lateral meniscus; it passes upward, backward, and lateralward, and is fixed into the medial and back part of the lateral condyle of the femur. (See Fig. 254, page 233.)

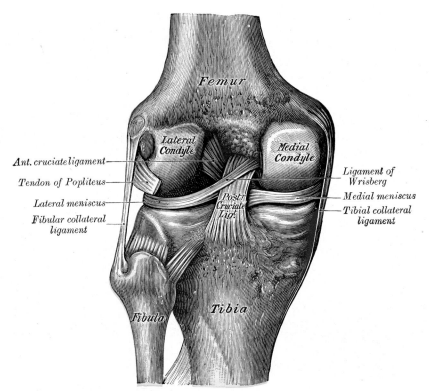

FIG. 345.—Left knee-joint from behind, showing interior ligaments.

The Posterior Cruciate Ligament (*ligamentum cruciatum posterius; internal crucial ligament*) (Fig. 345) is stronger, but shorter and less oblique in its direction, than the anterior. It is attached to the posterior intercondyloid fossa of the tibia, and to the posterior extremity of the lateral meniscus; and passes upward, forward, and medialward, to be fixed into the lateral and front part of the medial condyle of the femur. (See Fig. 254, page 233.)

The Menisci (*semilunar fibrocartilages*) (Fig. 346).—The menisci are two crescentic lamellæ, which serve to deepen the surfaces of the head of the tibia for articulation with the condyles of the femur. The peripheral border of each meniscus is thick, convex, and attached to the inside of the capsule of the joint; the opposite border is thin, concave, and free. The upper surfaces of the menisci are concave, and in contact with the condyles of the femur; their lower surfaces are flat, and rest upon the head of the tibia; both surfaces are smooth, and invested by synovial membrane. Each meniscus covers approximately the peripheral two-thirds of the corresponding articular surface of the tibia.

The **medial meniscus** (*meniscus medialis; internal semilunar fibrocartilage*) is nearly semicircular in form, a little elongated from before backward, and broader behind than in front; its anterior end, thin and pointed, is attached to the anterior intercondyloid fossa of the tibia, in front of the anterior cruciate ligament; its posterior end is fixed to the posterior intercondyloid fossa of the tibia, between the attachments of the lateral meniscus and the posterior cruciate ligament.

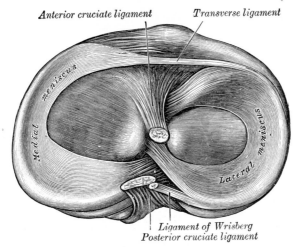

Anterior cruciate ligament   *Transverse ligament*

Ligament of Wrisberg
Posterior cruciate ligament

Fig. 346.—Head of right tibia seen from above, showing menisci and attachments of ligaments.

The **lateral meniscus** (*meniscus lateralis; external semilunar fibrocartilage*) is nearly circular and covers a larger portion of the articular surface than the medial one. It is grooved laterally for the tendon of the Popliteus, which separates it from the fibular collateral ligament. Its anterior end is attached in front of the intercondyloid eminence of the tibia, lateral to, and behind, the anterior cruciate ligament, with which it blends; the posterior end is attached behind the intercondyloid eminence of the tibia and in front of the posterior end of the medial meniscus. The anterior attachment of the lateral meniscus is twisted on itself so that its free margin looks backward and upward, its anterior end resting on a sloping shelf of bone on the front of the lateral process of the intercondyloid eminence. Close to its posterior attachment it sends off a strong fasciculus, the **ligament of Wrisberg** (Figs. 345, 346), which passes upward and medialward, to be inserted into the medial condyle of the femur, immediately behind the attachment of the posterior cruciate ligament. Occasionally a small fasciculus passes forward to be inserted into the lateral part of the anterior cruciate ligament. The lateral meniscus gives off from its anterior convex margin a fasciculus which forms the transverse ligament.

The **Transverse Ligament** (*ligamentum transversum genu*).—The transverse ligament connects the anterior convex margin of the lateral meniscus to the anterior end of the medial meniscus; its thickness varies considerably in different subjects, and it is sometimes absent.

The **coronary ligaments** are merely portions of the capsule, which connect the periphery of each meniscus with the margin of the head of the tibia.

21

Synovial Membrane.—The synovial membrane of the knee-joint is the largest and most extensive in the body. Commencing at the upper border of the patella, it forms a large cul-de-sac
beneath the Quadriceps femoris (Figs. 347, 348) on the lower part of the front of the femur,
and frequently communicates with a bursa interposed between the tendon and the front of the
femur. The pouch of synovial membrane between the Quadriceps and front of the femur is
supported, during the movements of the knee, by a small muscle, the Articularis genu, which
is inserted into it. On either side of the patella, the synovial membrane extends beneath the
aponeuroses of the Vasti, and more especially beneath that of the Vastus medialis. Below the
patella it is separated from the ligamentum patellæ by a considerable quantity of fat, known as

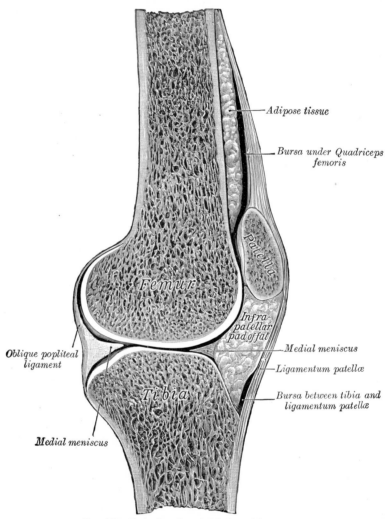

Adipose tissue

*Bursa under Quadriceps
femoris*

Patella

Femur

*Infra-
patellar
pad of fat*

Medial meniscus

Ligamentum patellæ

*Bursa between tibia and
ligamentum patellæ*

*Oblique popliteal
ligament*

Tibia

Medial meniscus

Fɪɢ. 347.—Sagittal section of right knee-joint.

the **infrapatellar pad.** From the medial and lateral borders of the articular surface of the patella,
reduplications of the synovial membrane project into the interior of the joint. These form two
fringe-like folds termed the **alar folds;** below, these folds converge and are continued as a single
band, the **patellar fold** (*ligamentum mucosum*), to the front of the intercondyloid fossa of the femur.
On either side of the joint, the synovial membrane passes downward from the femur, lining the
capsule to its point of attachment to the menisci; it may then be traced over the upper surfaces
of these to their free borders, and thence along their under surfaces to the tibia (Figs. 348, 349).
At the back part of the lateral meniscus it forms a cul-de-sac between the groove on its surface
and the tendon of the Popliteus; it is reflected across the front of the cruciate ligaments, which
are therefore situated outside the synovial cavity.

Bursæ.—The bursæ near the knee-joint are the following: In front there are *four* bursæ: a large one is interposed between the patella and the skin, a small one between the upper part of the tibia and the ligamentum patellæ, a third between the lower part of the tuberosity of the tibia and the skin, and a fourth between the anterior surface of the lower part of the femur and the deep surface of the Quadriceps femoris, usually communicating with the knee-joint. Laterally there are four bursæ: (1) one (which sometimes communicates with the joint) between the lateral head of the Gastrocnemius and the capsule; (2) one between the fibular collateral ligament and the tendon of the Biceps; (3) one between the fibular collateral ligament and the tendon of the Popliteus (this is sometimes only an expansion from the next bursa); (4) one between the tendon of the Popliteus and the lateral condyle of the femur, usually an extension from the synovial membrane of the joint. Medially, there are five bursæ: (1) one between the medial head of the Gastrocnemius and the capsule; this sends a prolongation between the tendon of the

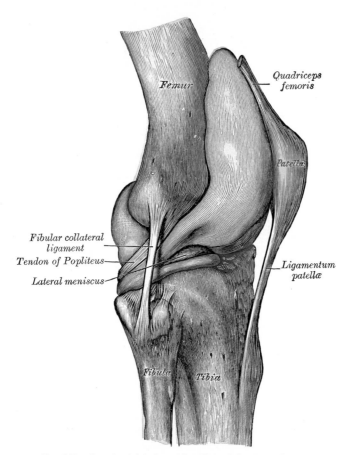

FIG. 348.—Capsule of right knee-joint (distended). Lateral aspect.

medial head of the Gastrocnemius and the tendon of the Semimembranosus and often communicates with the joint; (2) one superficial to the tibial collateral ligament, between it and the tendons of the Sartorius, Gracilis, and Semitendinosus; (3) one deep to the tibial collateral ligament, between it and the tendon of the Semimembranosus (this is sometimes only an expansion from the next bursa); (4) one between the tendon of the Semimembranosus and the head of the tibia; (5) occasionally there is a bursa between the tendons of the Semimembranosus and Semitendinosus.

Structures Around the Joint.—In front, and at the sides, is the Quadriceps femoris; laterally the tendons of the Biceps femoris and Popliteus and the common peroneal nerve; medially, the Sartorius, Gracilis, Semitendinosus, and Semimembranosus; behind, the popliteal vessels and the tibial nerve, Popliteus, Plantaris, and medial and lateral heads of the Gastrocnemius some lymph glands, and fat.

The **arteries** supplying the joint are the highest genicular (anastomotica magna), a branch of the femoral, the genicular branches of the popliteal, the recurrent branches of the anterior tibial, and the descending branch from the lateral femoral circumflex of the profunda femoris.

The **nerves** are derived from the obturator, femoral, tibial, and common peroneal.

Movements.—The movements which take place at the knee-joint are flexion and extension, and, in certain positions of the joint, internal and external rotation. The movements of flexion and extension at this joint differ from those in a typical hinge-joint, such as the elbow, in that (*a*) the axis around which motion takes place is not a fixed one, but shifts forward during extension and backward during flexion; (*b*) the commencement of flexion and the end of extension are accompanied by rotatory movements associated with the fixation of the limb in a position of great stability. The movement from full flexion to full extension may therefore be described in three phases:

1. In the fully flexed condition the posterior parts of the femoral condyles rest on the corresponding portions of the meniscotibial surfaces, and in this position a slight amount of simple rolling movement is allowed.

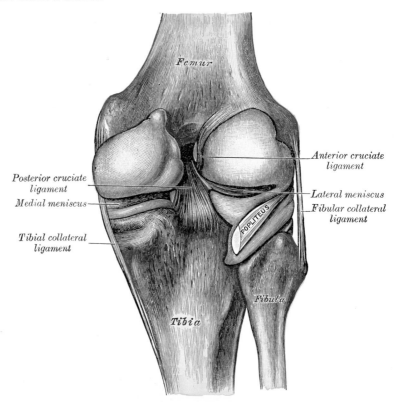

Fig. 349.—Capsule of right knee-joint (distended). Posterior aspect.

2. During the passage of the limb from the flexed to the extended position a gliding movement is superposed on the rolling, so that the axis, which at the commencement is represented by a line through the inner and outer condyles of the femur, gradually shifts forward. In this part of the movement, the posterior two-thirds of the tibial articular surfaces of the two femoral condyles are involved, and as these have similar curvatures and are parallel to one another, they move forward equally.

3. The lateral condyle of the femur is brought almost to rest by the tightening of the anterior cruciate ligament; it moves, however, slightly forward and medialward, pushing before it the anterior part of the lateral meniscus. The tibial surface on the medial condyle is prolonged farther forward than that on the lateral, and this prolongation is directed lateralward. When, therefore, the movement forward of the condyles is checked by the anterior cruciate ligament, continued muscular action causes the medial condyle, dragging with it the meniscus, to travel backward and medialward, thus producing an internal rotation of the thigh on the leg. When the position of full extension is reached the lateral part of the groove on the lateral condyle is pressed against the anterior part of the corresponding meniscus, while the medial part of the

groove rests on the articular margin in front of the lateral process of the tibial intercondyloid eminence. Into the groove on the medial condyle is fitted the anterior part of the medial meniscus, while the anterior cruciate ligament and the articular margin in front of the medial process of the tibial intercondyloid eminence are received into the forepart of the intercondyloid fossa of the femur. This third phase by which all these parts are brought into accurate apposition is known as the "screwing home," or locking movement of the joint.

The complete movement of flexion is the converse of that described above, and is therefore preceded by an external rotation of the femur which unlocks the extended joint.

The axes around which the movements of flexion and extension take place are not precisely at right angles to either bone; in flexion, the femur and tibia are in the same plane, but in extension the one bone forms an angle, opening lateralward with the other.

In addition to the rotatory movements associated with the completion of extension and the initiation of flexion, rotation inward or outward can be effected when the joint is partially flexed; these movements take place mainly between the tibia and the menisci, and are freest when the leg is bent at right angles with the thigh.

Movements of Patella.—The articular surface of the patella is indistinctly divided into seven facets—upper, middle, and lower horizontal pairs, and a medial perpendicular facet (Fig. 350).

When the knee is forcibly flexed, the medial perpendicular facet is in contact with the semilunar surface on the lateral part of the medial condyle; this semilunar surface is a prolongation backward of the medial part of the patellar surface. As the leg is carried from the flexed to the extended position, first the highest pair, then the middle pair, and lastly the lowest pair of horizontal facets is successively brought into contact with the patellar surface of the femur. In the extended position, when the Quadriceps femoris is relaxed, the patella lies loosely on the front of the lower end of the femur.

FIG. 350.—Posterior surface of the right patella, showing diagrammatically the areas of contact with the femur in different positions of the knee.

During flexion, the ligamentum patellæ is put upon the stretch, and in extreme flexion the posterior cruciate ligament, the oblique popliteal, and collateral ligaments, and, to a slight extent, the anterior cruciate ligament, are relaxed. Flexion is checked during life by the contact of the leg with the thigh. When the knee-joint is fully extended the oblique popliteal and collateral ligaments, the anterior cruciate ligament, and the posterior cruciate ligament, are rendered tense; in the act of extending the knee, the ligamentum patellæ is tightened by the Quadriceps femoris, but in full extension with the heel supported it is relaxed. Rotation inward is checked by the anterior cruciate ligament; rotation outward tends to uncross and relax the cruciate ligaments, but is checked by the tibial collateral ligament. The main function of the cruciate ligament is to act as a direct bond between the tibia and femur and to prevent the former bone from being carried too far backward or forward. They also assist the collateral ligaments in resisting any bending of the joint to either side. The menisci are intended, as it seems, to adapt the surfaces of the tibia to the shape of the femoral condyles to a certain extent, so as to fill up the intervals which would otherwise be left in the varying positions of the joint, and to obviate the jars which would be so frequently transmitted up the limb in jumping or by falls on the feet; also to permit of the two varieties of motion, flexion and extension, and rotation, as explained above. The patella is a great defence to the front of the knee-joint, and distributes upon a large and tolerably even surface, during kneeling, the pressure which would otherwise fall upon the prominent ridges of the condyles; it also affords leverage to the Quadriceps femoris.

When standing erect in the attitude of "attention," the weight of the body falls in front of a line carried across the centers of the knee-joints, and therefore tends to produce overextension of the articulations; this, however, is prevented by the tension of the anterior cruciate, oblique popliteal, and collateral ligaments.

Extension of the leg on the thigh is performed by the Quadriceps femoris; *flexion* by the Biceps femoris, Semitendinosus, and Semimembranosus, assisted by the Gracilis, Sartorius, Gastrocnemius, Popliteus, and Plantaris. *Rotation outward* is effected by the Biceps femoris, and *rotation inward* by the Popliteus, Semitendinosus, and, to a slight extent, the Semimembranosus, the Sartorius, and the Gracilis. The Popliteus comes into action especially at the commencement of the movement of flexion of the knee; by its contraction the leg is rotated inward, or, if the tibia be fixed, the thigh is rotated outward, and the knee-joint is unlocked.

III. Articulations between the Tibia and Fibula.

The tibia and fibula are connected by: (1) the Tibiofibular articulation; (2) the interosseous membrane; (3) the Tibiofibular syndesmosis.

Tibiofibular Articulation (*articulatio tibiofibularis; superior tibiofibular articulation*).—This articulation is an arthrodial joint between the lateral condyle of the tibia and the head of the fibula. The contiguous surfaces of the bones present flat, oval facets covered with cartilage and connected together by an articular capsule and by anterior and posterior ligaments.

The Articular Capsule (*capsula articularis; capsular ligament*).—The articular capsule surrounds the articulation, being attached around the margins of the articular facets on the tibia and fibula; it is much thicker in front than behind.

The Anterior Ligament (*anterior superior ligament*).—The anterior ligament of the head of the fibula (Fig. 344) consists of two or three broad and flat bands, which pass obliquely upward from the front of the head of the fibula to the front of the lateral condyle of the tibia.

The Posterior Ligament (*posterior superior ligament*).—The posterior ligament of the head of the fibula (Fig. 345) is a single thick and broad band, which passes obliquely upward from the back of the head of the fibula to the back of the lateral condyle of the tibia. It is covered by the tendon of the Popliteus.

Synovial Membrane.—A synovial membrane lines the capsule; it is continuous with that of the knee-joint in occasional cases when the two joints communicate.

Interosseous Membrane (*membrana interossea cruris; middle tibiofibular ligament*).—An interosseous membrane extends between the interosseous crests of the tibia and fibula, and separates the muscles on the front from those on the back of the leg. It consists of a thin, aponeurotic lamina composed of oblique fibers, which for the most part run downward and lateralward; some few fibers, however, pass in the opposite direction. It is broader above than below. Its upper margin does not quite reach the tibiofibular joint, but presents a free concave border, above which is a large, oval aperture for the passage of the anterior tibial vessels to the front of the leg. In its lower part is an opening for the passage of the anterior peroneal vessels. It is continuous below with the interosseous ligament of the tibiofibular syndesmosis, and presents numerous perforations for the passage of small vessels. It is in relation, in *front*, with the Tibialis anterior, Extensor digitorum longus, Extensor hallucis longus, Peronæus tertius, and the anterior tibial vessels and deep peroneal nerve; *behind*, with the Tibialis posterior and Flexor hallucis longus.

Tibiofibular Syndesmosis (*syndesmosis tibiofibularis; inferior tibiofibular articulation*).—This syndesmosis is formed by the rough, convex surface of the medial side of the lower end of the fibula, and a rough concave surface on the lateral side of the tibia. Below, to the extent of about 4 mm. these surfaces are smooth, and covered with cartilage, which is continuous with that of the ankle-joint. The ligaments are: anterior, posterior, inferior transverse, and interosseous.

The Anterior Ligament (*ligamentum malleoli lateralis anterius; anterior inferior tibiofibular ligament*).—The anterior ligament (Fig. 352) is a flat, triangular band of fibers, broader below than above, which extends obliquely downward and lateralward between the adjacent margins of the tibia and fibula, on the front aspect of the syndesmosis. It is in relation, in *front*, with the Peronæus tertius, the aponeurosis of the leg, and the integument; *behind*, with the interosseous ligament; and lies in contact with the cartilage covering the talus.

The Posterior Ligament (*ligamentum malleoli lateralis posterius; posterior inferior tibiofibular ligament*).—The posterior ligament (Fig. 352), smaller than the preceding, is disposed in a similar manner on the posterior surface of the syndesmosis.

The Inferior Transverse Ligament.—The inferior transverse ligament lies in front of the posterior ligament, and is a strong, thick band, of yellowish fibers which passes transversely across the back of the joint, from the lateral malleolus to the posterior border of the articular surface of the tibia, almost as far as its malleolar process. This ligament projects below the margin of the bones, and forms part of the articulating surface for the talus.

The Interosseous Ligament.—The interosseous ligament consists of numerous short, strong, fibrous bands, which pass between the contiguous rough surfaces of the tibia and fibula, and constitute the chief bond of union between the bones. It is continuous, above, with the interosseous membrane (Fig. 354).

Synovial Membrane.—The synovial membrane associated with the small arthrodial part of this joint is continuous with that of the ankle-joint.

IV. Talocrural Articulation or Ankle-joint (Articulatio Talocruralis; Tibiotarsal Articulation).

The ankle-joint is a ginglymus, or hinge-joint. The structures entering into its formation are the lower end of the tibia and its malleolus, the malleolus of the

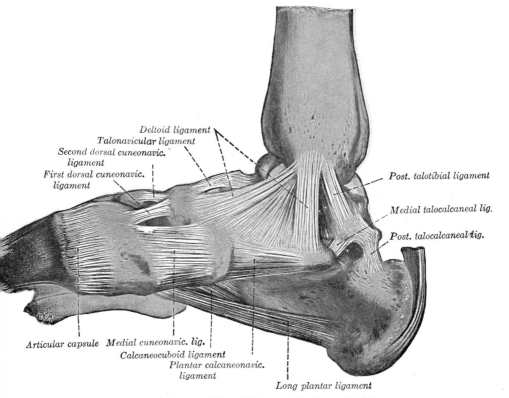

Fig. 351.—Ligaments of the medial aspect of the foot. (Quain.)

fibula, and the inferior transverse ligament, which together form a mortise for the reception of the upper convex surface of the talus and its medial and lateral facets. The bones are connected by the following ligaments:

The Articular Capsule.	The Anterior Talofibular.
The Deltoid.	The Posterior Talofibular.
	The Calcaneofibular.

The Articular Capsule (*capsula articularis; capsular ligament*).—The articular capsule surrounds the joints, and is attached, *above*, to the borders of the articular surfaces of the tibia and malleoli; and *below*, to the talus around its upper articular surface. The anterior part of the capsule (*anterior ligament*) is a broad, thin, membranous layer, attached, *above*, to the anterior margin of the lower end of the tibia; *below*, to the talus, in front of its superior articular surface. It is in relation, in *front*, with the Extensor tendons of the toes, the tendons of the Tibialis anterior and Peronæus tertius, and the anterior tibial vessels and deep peroneal nerve. The posterior part of the capsule (*posterior ligament*) is very thin, and consists principally of transverse fibers. It is attached, *above*, to the margin of the articular surface of the tibia, blending with the transverse ligament; *below*, to the talus behind its superior articular facet. Laterally, it is somewhat thickened, and is attached to the hollow on the medial surface of the lateral malleolus.

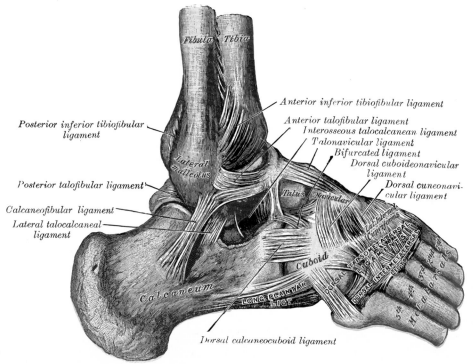

FIG. 352.—The ligaments of the right ankle and tarsus. Lateral aspect.

The Deltoid Ligament (*ligamentum deltoideum; internal lateral ligament*) (Fig. 351).—The deltoid ligament is a strong, flat, triangular band, attached, *above*, to the apex and anterior and posterior borders of the medial malleolus. It consists of two sets of fibers, superficial and deep. Of the superficial fibers the most anterior (*tibionavicular*) pass forward to be inserted into the tuberosity of the navicular bone, and immediately behind this they blend with the medial margin of the plantar calcaneonavicular ligament; the middle (*calcaneotibial*) descend almost perpendicularly to be inserted into the whole length of the sustentaculum tali of the calcaneus; the posterior fibers (*posterior talotibial*) pass backward and lateralward to be attached to the inner side of the talus, and to the prominent tubercle on its posterior surface, medial to the groove for the tendon of the Flexor hallucis longus. The deep fibers (*anterior talotibial*) are attached, *above*, to the tip of the medial malleolus, and, *below*, to the medial surface of the talus. The deltoid ligament is covered by the tendons of the Tibialis posterior and Flexor digitorum longus.

The anterior and posterior talofibular and the calcaneofibular ligaments were formerly described as the three fasciculi of the *external lateral ligament* of the ankle-joint.

The Anterior Talofibular Ligament (*ligamentum talofibulare anterius*) (Fig. 352). —The anterior talofibular ligament, the shortest of the three, passes from the anterior margin of the fibular malleolus, forward and medially, to the talus, in front of its lateral articular facet.

The Posterior Talofibular Ligament (*ligamentum talofibulare posterius*) (Fig. 352). —The posterior talofibular ligament, the strongest and most deeply seated, runs almost horizontally from the depression at the medial and back part of the fibular malleolus to a prominent tubercle on the posterior surface of the talus immediately lateral to the groove for the tendon of the Flexor hallucis longus.

The Calcaneofibular Ligament (*ligamentum calcaneofibulare*) (Fig. 352).—The calcaneofibular ligament, the longest of the three, is a narrow, rounded cord, running from the apex of the fibular malleolus downward and slightly backward to a tubercle on the lateral surface of the calcaneus. It is covered by the tendons of the Peronæi longus and brevis.

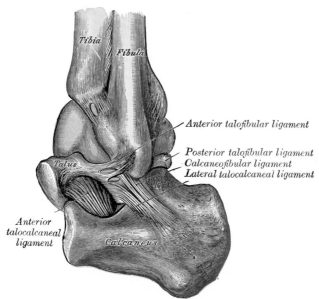

Fig. 353.—Capsule of left talocrural articulation (distended).   Lateral aspect.

Synovial Membrane (Fig. 353).—The synovial membrane invests the deep surfaces of the ligaments, and sends a small process upward between the lower ends of the tibia and fibula.

Relations.—The tendons, vessels, and nerves in connection with the joint are, in *front*, from the medial side, the Tibialis anterior, Extensor hallucis longus, anterior tibial vessels, deep peroneal nerve, Extensor digitorum longus, and Peronæus tertius; *behind*, from the medial side, the Tibialis posterior, Flexor digitorum longus, posterior tibial vessels, tibial nerve, Flexor hallucis longus; and, in the groove behind the fibular malleolus, the tendons of the Peronæi longus and brevis.

The **arteries** supplying the joint are derived from the malleolar branches of the anterior tibial and the peroneal.

The **nerves** are derived from the deep peroneal and tibial.

Movements.—When the body is in the erect position, the foot is at right angles to the leg. The movements of the joint are those of dorsiflexion and plantar flexion; dorsiflexion consists in the approximation of the dorsum of the foot to the front of the leg, while in plantar flexion the heel is drawn up and the toes pointed downward. The range of movement varies in different individuals from about 50° to 90°. The transverse axis about which movement takes place is slightly oblique. The malleoli tightly embrace the talus in all positions of the joint, so that any slight degree of side-to-side movement which may exist is simply due to stretching of the ligaments of the talofibular syndesmosis, and slight bending of the body of the fibula. The superior articular surface of the talus is broader in front than behind. In dorsiflexion, therefore, greater space is required between the two malleoli. This is obtained by a slight outward rotatory movement of the lower end of the fibula and a stretching of the ligaments of the syndesmosis; this lateral movement is facilitated by a slight gliding at the tibiofibular articulation, and possibly also by the bending of the body of the fibula. Of the ligaments, the deltoid is of very great power—so much so, that it usually resists a force which fractures the process of bone to which it is attached. Its middle portion, together with the calcaneofibular ligament, binds the bones of the leg firmly to the foot, and resists displacement in every direction. Its anterior and posterior fibers limit plantar flexion and dorsal flexion of the foot and the anterior fibers also limit abduction. The posterior talofibular ligament assists the calcaneofibular in resisting the displacement of the foot backward, and deepens the cavity for the reception of the talus. The anterior talofibular is a security against the displacement of the foot forward, and limits plantar flexion of the joint.

The movements of inversion and eversion of the foot, together with the minute changes in form by which it is applied to the ground or takes hold of an object in climbing, etc., are mainly effected in the tarsal joints; the joint which enjoys the greatest amount of motion being that between the talus and calcaneus behind and the navicular and cuboid in front. This is often called the **transverse tarsal joint,** and it can, with the subordinate joints of the tarsus, replace the ankle-joint in a great measure when the latter has become ankylosed.

Plantar flexion of the foot upon the tibia and fibula is produced by the Gastrocnemius, Soleus, Plantaris, Tibialis posterior, Poronæi longus and brevis, Flexor digitorum longus, and Flexor hallucis longus; *dorsiflexion,* by the Tibialis anterior, Peronæus tertius, Extensor digitorum longus, and Extensor hallucis longus.

V. Intertarsal Articulations (Articulationes Intertarseæ; Articulations of the Tarsus).

Talocalcaneal Articulation (*articulatio talocalcanea; articulation of the calcaneus and astragalus; calcaneo-astragaloid articulation*).—The articulations between the calcaneus and talus are two in number—anterior and posterior. Of these, the anterior forms part of the talocalcaneonavicular joint, and will be described with that articulation. The posterior or talocalcaneal articulation is formed between the posterior calcaneal facet on the inferior surface of the talus, and the posterior facet on the superior surface of the calcaneus. It is an arthrodial joint, and the two bones are connected by an articular capsule and by anterior, posterior, lateral, medial, and interosseous talocalcaneal ligaments.

The Articular Capsule (*capsula articularis*).—The articular capsule envelops the joint, and consists for the most part of short fibers, which are split up into distinct slips; between these there is only a weak fibrous investment.

The Anterior Talocalcaneal Ligament (*ligamentum talocalcaneum anterius; anterior calcaneo-astragaloid ligament*) (Figs. 353, 356).—The anterior talocalcaneal ligament extends from the front and lateral surface of the neck of the talus to the superior surface of the calcaneus. It forms the posterior boundary of the talocalcaneonavicular joint, and is sometimes described as the **anterior interosseous ligament.**

The Posterior Talocalcaneal Ligament (*ligamentum talocalcaneum posterius; posterior calcaneo-astragaloid ligament*) (Fig. 351).—The posterior talocalcaneal ligament connects the lateral tubercle of the talus with the upper and medial part of the calcaneus; it is a short band, and its fibers radiate from their narrow attachment to the talus.

The Lateral Talocalcaneal Ligament (*ligamentum talocalcaneum laterale; external calcaneo-astragaloid ligament*) (Figs. 353, 356).—The lateral talocalcaneal ligament is a short, strong fasciculus, passing from the lateral surface of the talus, immediately beneath its fibular facet to the lateral surface of the calcaneus. It is placed in front of, but on a deeper plane than, the calcaneofibular ligament, with the fibers of which it is parallel.

The Medial Talocalcaneal Ligament (*ligamentum talocalcaneum mediale; internal calcaneo-astragaloid ligament*).—The medial talocalcaneal ligament connects the medial tubercle of the back of the talus with the back of the sustentaculum tali. Its fibers blend with those of the plantar calcaneonavicular ligament (Fig. 351).

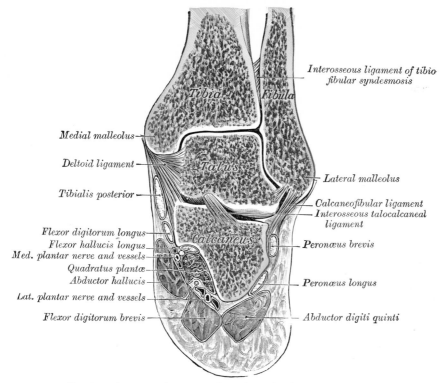

FIG. 354.—Corona section through right talocrural and talocalcaneal joints.

The Interosseous Talocalcaneal Ligament (*ligamentum talocalcaneum interosseum*) (Figs. 354, 356).—The interosseous talocalcaneal ligament forms the chief bond of union between the bones. It is, in fact, a portion of the united capsules of the talocalcaneonavicular and the talocalcaneal joints, and consists of two partially united layers of fibers, one belonging to the former and the other to the latter joint. It is attached, *above*, to the groove between the articular facets of the under surface of the talus; *below*, to a corresponding depression on the upper surface of the calcaneus. It is very thick and strong, being at least 2.5 cm. in breadth from side to side, and serves to bind the calcaneus and talus firmly together.

Synovial Membrane (Fig. 357).—The synovial membrane lines the capsule of the joint, and is distinct from the other synovial membranes of the tarsus.

Movements.—The movements permitted between the talus and calcaneus are limited to gliding of the one bone on the other backward and forward and from side to side.

Talocalcaneonavicular Articulation (*articulatio talocalcaneonavicularis*).—This articulation is an arthrodial joint: the rounded head of the talus being received into the concavity formed by the posterior surface of the navicular, the anterior articular surface of the calcaneus, and the upper surface of the plantar calcaneonavicular ligament. There are two ligaments in this joint: the articular capsule and the dorsal talonavicular.

The **Articular Capsule** (*capsula articularis*).—The articular capsule is imperfectly developed except posteriorly, where it is considerably thickened and forms, with a part of the capsule of the talocalcaneal joint, the strong interosseous ligament which fills in the canal formed by the opposing grooves on the calcaneus and talus, as above mentioned.

The **Dorsal Talonavicular Ligament** (*ligamentum talonaviculare dorsale; superior astragalonavicular ligament*) (Fig. 351).—This ligament is a broad, thin band, which connects the neck of the talus to the dorsal surface of the navicular bone; it is covered by the Extensor tendons. The plantar calcaneonavicular supplies the place of a plantar ligament for this joint.

Synovial Membrane.—The synovial membrane lines all parts of the capsule of the joint.

Movements.—This articulation permits of a considerable range of gliding movements, and some rotation; its feeble construction allows occasionally of dislocation of the other bones of the tarsus from the talus.

Calcaneocuboid Articulation (*articulatio calcaneocuboidea; articulation of the calcaneus with the cuboid*).—The ligaments connecting the calcaneus with the cuboid are five in number, viz., the articular capsule, the dorsal calcaneocuboid, part of the bifurcated, the long plantar, and the plantar calcaneocuboid.

The **Articular Capsule** (*capsula articularis*).—The articular capsule is an imperfectly developed investment, containing certain strengthened bands, which form the other ligaments of the joint.

The **Dorsal Calcaneocuboid Ligament** (*ligamentum calcaneocuboideum dorsale; superior calcaneocuboid ligament*) (Fig. 352).—The dorsal calcaneocuboid ligament is a thin but broad fasciculus, which passes between the contiguous surfaces of the calcaneus and cuboid, on the dorsal surface of the joint.

The **Bifurcated Ligament** (*ligamentum bifurcatum; internal calcaneocuboid; interosseous ligament*) (Fig. 352, 356).—The bifurcated ligament is a strong band, attached behind to the deep hollow on the upper surface of the calcaneus and dividing in front in a Y-shaped manner into a calcaneocuboid and a calcaneonavicular part. The **calcaneocuboid part** is fixed to the medial side of the cuboid and forms one of the principal bonds between the first and second rows of the tarsal bones. The **calcaneonavicular part** is attached to the lateral side of the navicular.

The **Long Plantar Ligament** (*ligamentum plantare longum; long calcaneocuboid ligament; superficial long plantar ligament*) (Fig. 355).—The long plantar ligament is the longest of all the ligaments of the tarsus: it is attached *behind* to the plantar surface of the calcaneus in front of the tuberosity, and in *front* to the tuberosity on the plantar surface of the cuboid bone, the more superficial fibers being continued forward to the bases of the third, fourth and fifth, and occasionally also the second metatarsal bones. This ligament converts the groove on the plantar surface of the cuboid into a canal for the tendon of the Peronæus longus.

The **Plantar Calcaneocuboid Ligament** (*ligamentum calcaneocuboideum plantare; short calcaneocuboid ligament; short plantar ligament*) (Fig. 355).—The plantar calcaneocuboid ligament lies nearer to the bones than the preceding, from which it is separated by a little areolar tissue. It is a short but wide band of great strength, and extends from the tubercle and the depression in front of it, on the forepart of the plantar surface of the calcaneus, to the plantar surface of the cuboid behind the peroneal groove.

Synovial Membrane.—The synovial membrane lines the inner surface of the capsule and is distinct from that of the other tarsal articulations (Fig. 357).

Movements.—The movements permitted between the calcaneus and cuboid are limited to slight gliding movements of the bones upon each other.

The *transverse tarsal joint* is formed by the articulation of the calcaneus with the cuboid, and the articulation of the talus with the navicular. The movement which takes place in this joint is more extensive than that in the other tarsal joints, and consists of a sort of rotation by means of which the foot may be slightly flexed or extended, the sole being at the same time carried medially (inverted) or laterally (everted).

The Ligaments Connecting the Calcaneus and Navicular.—Though the calcaneus and navicular do not directly articulate, they are connected by two ligaments: the calcaneonavicular part of the bifurcated, and the plantar calcaneonavicular.

The **calcaneonavicular part of the bifurcated ligament** is described on page 332.

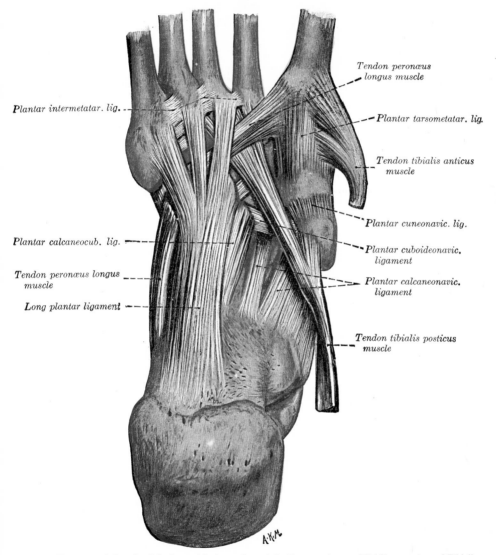

Plantar intermetatar. lig.

Plantar calcaneocub. lig.

Tendon peronæus longus muscle

Long plantar ligament

Tendon peronæus longus muscle

Plantar tarsometatar. lig.

Tendon tibialis anticus muscle

Plantar cuneonavic. lig.

Plantar cuboideonavic. ligament

Plantar calcaneonavic. ligament

Tendon tibialis posticus muscle

Fig. 355.—Ligaments of the sole of the foot, with the tendons of the Peronæus longus, Tibialis posterior and Tibialis anterior muscles. (Quain.)

The **Plantar Calcaneonavicular Ligament** (*ligamentum calcaneonaviculare plantare; inferior or internal calcaneonavicular ligament; calcaneonavicular ligament*) (Figs. 351, 355).—The plantar calcaneonavicular ligament is a broad and thick band of fibers, which connects the anterior margin of the sustentaculum tali of the calcaneus to the plantar surface of the navicular. This ligament not only serves to connect the calcaneus and navicular, but supports the head of the talus, forming part of the articular cavity in which it is received. The **dorsal surface** of the ligament presents a fibrocartilaginous facet, lined by the synovial membrane, and upon this a portion of the head of the talus rests. Its **plantar surface** is supported by the tendon of the Tibialis posterior; its **medial border** is blended with the forepart of the deltoid ligament of the ankle-joint.

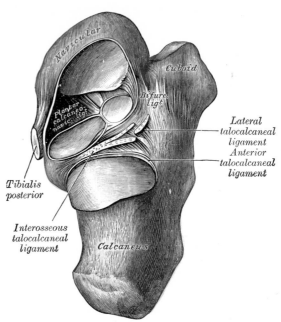

Fig. 356.—Talocalcaneal and talocalcaneonavicular articulations exposed from above by removing the talus.

The plantar calcaneonavicular ligament, by supporting the head of the talus, is principally concerned in maintaining the arch of the foot. When it yields, the head of the talus is pressed downward, medialward, and forward by the weight of the body, and the foot becomes flattened, expanded, and turned lateralward, and exhibits the condition known as *flat-foot*. This ligament contains a considerable amount of elastic fibers, so as to give elasticity to the arch and spring to the foot; hence it is sometimes called the "spring" ligament. It is supported, on its plantar surface, by the tendon of the Tibialis posterior, which spreads out at its insertion into a number of fasciculi, to be attached to most of the tarsal and metatarsal bones. This helps to prevent undue stretching of the ligament.

Cuneonavicular Articulation (*articulatio cuneonavicularis; articulation of the navicular with the cuneiform bones*).—The navicular is connected to the three cuneiform bones by dorsal and plantar ligaments.

The Dorsal Ligaments (*ligamenta navicularicuneiformia dorsalia*).—The dorsal ligaments are three small bundles, one attached to each of the cuneiform bones. The bundle connecting the navicular with the first cuneiform is continuous around the medial side of the articulation with the plantar ligament which unites these two bones (Figs. 351, 352).

The Plantar Ligaments (*ligamenta navicularicuneiformia plantaria*).—The plantar ligaments have a similar arrangement to the dorsal, and are strengthened by slips from the tendon of the Tibialis posterior (Fig. 355).

Synovial Membrane.—The synovial membrane of these joints is part of the great tarsal synovial membrane (Fig. 357).

Movements.—Mere gliding movements are permitted between the navicular and cuneiform bones.

Cuboideonavicular Articulation.—The navicular bone is connected with the cuboid by dorsal, plantar, and interosseous ligaments.

The Dorsal Ligament (*ligamentum cuboideonaviculare dorsale*).—The dorsal ligament extends obliquely forward and lateralward from the navicular to the cuboid bone (Fig. 355).

The Plantar Ligament (*ligamentum cuboideonaviculare plantare*).—The plantar ligament passes nearly transversely between these two bones (Fig. 355).

The Interosseous Ligament.—The interosseous ligament consists of strong transverse fibers, and connects the rough non-articular portions of the adjacent surfaces of the two bones Fig. 357).

Synovial Membrane.—The synovial membrane of this joint is part of the great tarsal synovial membrane (Fig. 357).

Movements.—The movements permitted between the navicular and cuboid bones are limited to a slight gliding upon each other.

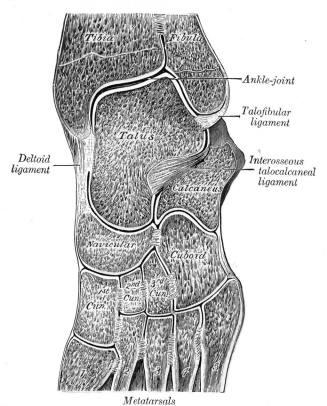

Fig. 357.—Oblique section of left intertarsal and tarsometatarsal articulations, showing the synovial cavities.

Intercuneiform and Cuneocuboid Articulations.—The three cuneiform bones and the cuboid are connected together by dorsal, plantar, and interosseous ligaments.

The Dorsal Ligaments (*ligamenta intercuneiformia dorsalia*).—The dorsal ligaments consist of three transverse bands: one connects the first with the second cuneiform, another the second with the third cuneiform, and another the third cuneiform with the cuboid.

The Plantar Ligaments (*ligamenta intercuneiformia plantaria*).—The plantar ligaments have a similar arrangement to the dorsal, and are strengthened by slips from the tendon of the Tibialis posterior.

The Interosseous Ligaments (*ligamenta intercuneiformia interossea*).—The interosseous ligaments consist of strong transverse fibers which pass between the rough non-articular portions of the adjacent surfaces of the bones (Fig. 357).

Synovial Membrane.—The synovial membrane of these joints is part of the great tarsal synovial membrane (Fig. 357).

Movements.—The movements permitted between these bones are limited to a slight gliding upon each other.

VI. Tarsometatarsal Articulations (Articulationes Tarsometatarseæ).

These are arthrodial joints. The bones entering into their formation are the first, second, and third cuneiforms, and the cuboid, which articulate with the bases of the metatarsal bones. The first metatarsal bone articulates with the first cuneiform; the second is deeply wedged in between the first and third cuneiforms articulating by its base with the second cuneiform; the third articulates with the third cuneiform; the fourth, with the cuboid and third cuneiform; and the fifth, with the cuboid. The bones are connected by dorsal, plantar, and interosseous ligaments.

The **Dorsal Ligaments** (*ligamenta tarsometatarsea dorsalia*).—The dorsal ligaments are strong, flat bands. The first metatarsal is joined to the first cuneiform by a broad, thin band; the second has three, one from each cuneiform bone; the third has one from the third cuneiform; the fourth has one from the third cuneiform and one from the cuboid; and the fifth, one from the cuboid (Figs. 351, 352).

The **Plantar Ligaments** (*ligamenta tarsometatarsea plantaria*).—The plantar ligaments consist of longitudinal and oblique bands, disposed with less regularity than the dorsal ligaments. Those for the first and second metatarsals are the strongest; the second and third metatarsals are joined by oblique bands to the first cuneiform; the fourth and fifth metatarsals are connected by a few fibers to the cuboid (Fig. 355).

The **Interosseous Ligaments** (*ligamenta cuneometatarsea interossea*).—The interosseous ligaments are two or three in number. The first is the strongest, and passes from the lateral surface of the first cuneiform to the adjacent angle of the second metatarsal. The second or middle which is the smallest and is less constant than the others, passes from the third cuneiform to the lateral aspect of the second metatarsal. The third connects the lateral angle of the third cuneiform with the adjacent side of the base of the third metatarsal.

Synovial Membrane (Fig. 357).—The synovial membrane between the first cuneiform and the first metatarsal forms a distinct sac. The synovial membrane between the second and third cuneiforms behind, and the second and third metatarsal bones in front, is part of the great tarsal synovial membrane. Two prolongations are sent forward from it, one between the adjacent sides of the second and third, and another between those of the third and fourth metatarsal bones. The synovial membrane between the cuboid and the fourth and fifth metatarsal bones forms a distinct sac. From it a prolongation is sent forward between the fourth and fifth metatarsal bones.

Movements.—The movements permitted between the tarsal and metatarsal bones are limited to slight gliding of the bones upon each other.

Nerve Supply.—The intertarsal and tarsometatarsal joints are supplied by the deep peroneal nerve.

VII. Intermetatarsal Articulations (Articulationes Intermetatarseæ).

The bases of the four lateral metatarsals are are connected by the dorsal, plantar, and interosseous ligaments.

The first metatarsal is connected with the second by interosseous fibers only; the fibers are weak and may be largely replaced by a bursa between indistinct facets on the two bones.

The **Dorsal Ligaments** (*ligamenta basium* [*oss. metatars.*] *dorsalia*) pass transversely between the dorsal surfaces of the bases of the adjacent metatarsal bones.

The **Plantar Ligaments** (*ligamenta basium* [*oss. metatars*] *plantaria*).—The plantar ligaments have a similar arrangement to the dorsal.

The Interosseous Ligaments (*ligamenta basium* [*oss. metatars.*] *interossea*).—The interosseous ligaments consist of strong transverse fibers which connect the rough non-articular portions of the adjacent surfaces.

Synovial Membranes (Fig. 357).—The synovial membranes between the second and third, and the third and fourth metatarsal bones are part of the great tarsal synovial membrane; that between the fourth and fifth is a prolongation of the synovial membrane of the cuboideometatarsal joint.

Movements.—The movement permitted between the tarsal ends of the metatarsal bones is limited to a slight gliding of the articular surfaces upon one another.

The heads of all the metatarsal bones are connected together by the transverse metatarsal ligament.

The Transverse Metatarsal Ligament.—The transverse metatarsal ligament is a narrow band which runs across and connects together the heads of all the metatarsal bones; it is blended anteriorly with the plantar (glenoid) ligaments of the metatarsophalangeal articulations. Its plantar surface is concave where the Flexor tendons run below it; above it the tendons of the Interossei pass to their insertions. It differs from the transverse metacarpal ligament in that it connects the metatarsal to the others.

The Synovial Membranes in the Tarsal and Tarsometatarsal Joints (Fig. 357).—The synovial membranes found in the articulations of the tarsus and metatarsus are six in number: one for the talocalcaneal articulation; a second for the talocalcaneonavicular articulation; a third for the calcaneocuboid articulation; and a fourth for the cuneonavicular, intercuneiform, and cuneocuboid articulations, the articulations of the second and third cuneiforms with the bases of the second and third metatarsal bones, and the adjacent surfaces of the bases of the second, third, and fourth metatarsal bones; a fifth for the first cuneiform with the metatarsal bone of the great toe; and a sixth for the articulation of the cuboid with the fourth and fifth metatarsal bones. A small synovial cavity is sometimes found between the contiguous surfaces of the navicular and cuboid bones.

VIII. Metatarsophalangeal Articulations (Articulationes Metatarsophalangeæ).

The metatarsophalangeal articulations are of the condyloid kind, formed by the reception of the rounded heads of the metatarsal bones in shallow cavities on the ends of the first phalanges.

The ligaments are the plantar and two collateral.

The Plantar Ligaments (*ligamenta accessoria plantaria; glenoid ligaments of Cruveilhier*).—The plantar ligaments are thick, dense, fibrous structures. They are placed on the plantar surfaces of the joints in the intervals between the collateral ligaments, to which they are connected; they are loosely united to the metatarsal bones, but very firmly to the bases of the first phalanges. Their plantar surfaces are intimately blended with the transverse metatarsal ligament, and grooved for the passage of the Flexor tendons, the sheaths surrounding which are connected to the sides of the grooves. Their deep surfaces form part of the articular facets for the heads of the metatarsal bones, and are lined by synovial membrane.

The Collateral Ligaments (*ligamenta collateralia; lateral ligaments*).—The collateral ligaments are strong, rounded cords, placed one on either side of each joint, and attached, by one end, to the posterior tubercle on the side of the head of the metatarsal bone, and, by the other, to the contiguous extremity of the phalanx.

The place of **dorsal ligaments** is supplied by the Extensor tendons on the dorsal surfaces of the joints.

Movements.—The movements permitted in the metatarsophalangeal articulations are flexion extension, abduction, and adduction.

IX. Articulations of the Digits (Articulationes Digitorum Pedis; Articulations of the Phalanges).

The interphalangeal articulations are ginglymoid joints, and each has a plantar and two collateral ligaments.

The arrangement of these ligaments is similar to that in the metatarsophalangeal articulations: the Extensor tendons supply the places of dorsal ligaments.

Movements.—The only movements permitted in the joints of the digits are flexion and extension; these movements are more extensive between the first and second phalanges than between the second and third. The amount of flexion is very considerable, but extension is limited by the plantar and collateral ligaments.

Arches of the Foot.

The **longitudinal arch** is formed by the seven tarsal and the five metatarsal bones (Figs. 286, 287) and the ligaments which bind them together. The multiplicity of parts gives resiliency. The arch rests posteriorly on the calcaneal tuberosity and anteriorly on the heads of the five metatarsals. In the standing position, 25 per cent of the body weight is distributed to each calcaneum and 25 per cent to the heads of the five metatarsals of each foot, in proportion of about 1 part for metatarsal I to 2.5 parts for metatarsals II to V. The greater part of the tension stress on the longitudinal arch is borne by the plantar ligaments (Fig. 355). Only about 15 to 20 per cent of the stress is borne by the tibialis posterior and the peroneal muscles. When the body is raised on the ball of one foot, the stress on the arch is increased four times.

In addition to the longitudinal arch the foot presents a series of **transverse arches**. At the posterior part of the metatarsus and the anterior part of the tarsus the arches are complete, but in the middle of the tarsus they present more the characters of half-domes the concavities of which are directed downward and medialward, so that when the medial borders of the feet are placed in apposition a complete tarsal dome is formed. The transverse arches are strengthened by the interosseous, plantar, and dorsal ligaments, by the short muscles of the first and fifth toes (especially the transverse head of the Adductor hallucis), and by the Peronæus longus, whose tendon stretches across between the piers of the arches.

BIBLIOGRAPHY

Histology, Physiology and General

The physiology of articular structures. Bauer, W., M. W. Ropes, and H. Waine: 1940. Physiol. Rev., Vol. 20, pp. 272–312.

The cytology of normal human synovial fluid. Coggeshall, H. C., C. F. Warren, and W. Bauer: 1940. Anat. Rec., Vol. 77, pp. 129–144.

Influence of the nervous system on bone and joints. Corbin, K. B., and J. C. Hinsey: 1939. Anat. Rec., Vol. 75, pp. 307–317.

The synovial membrane of joints and bursæ. Key, J. A.: 1932. Special Cytology, E. V. Cowdry, 2nd Ed., Hoeber, New York, Vol. 2, pp. 1055–1085.

The origin and nature of normal synovial fluid. Ropes, M. W., G. A. Bennett, and W. Bauer: 1939. J. Clin. Invest., Vol. 18, pp. 351–372.

A note on the fibrillar structure of hyaline cartilage. Ruth, E. B.: 1946. Anat. Rec., Vol. 96, pp. 93–99.

Temporo-mandibular Joint

Movements of the jaw and how they are effected. Lord, F. P.: 1937. Internat. J. Orthodontia, Vol. 23, pp. 557–571.

Applied Anatomy of the Head and Neck. Shapiro, H. H.: 1947. Lippincott, Phila., 2nd ed., xiv + 303 pp.

The temporomandibular joint and the auditory function. Shapiro, H. H., and R. C. Truex: 1943. J. Am. Dental Assn., Vol. 30, pp. 1147–1168.

The "mandibular sling." Stein, M. R.: 1939. Dental Survey, Vol. 15, pp. 883–887.

Joints of Axial Skeleton

The intervertebral disc: its microscopic anatomy and pathology. Coventry, M. B., R. K. Ghormley, and J. W. Kernohan: 1945. J. Bone and Joint Surg., Vol. 27, pp. 105–112, 233–247, and 460–474.

The human sternochondral joints. Gray, D. J., and E. D. Gardner: 1943. Anat. Rec., Vol. 87, 235–253.

The anatomy and development of the sacro-iliac joint in man. Schunke, G. B.: 1938. Anat. Rec., Vol. 72, pp. 313–331.

Accessory sacro-iliac articulations in the higher primates and their significance. Stewart, T. D.: 1938. Am. J. Phys. Anthrop., Vol. 24, pp. 43–59.

Low-back pain. The anatomical structure of the lumbar region, including variations. Willis, T. A.: 1937. J. Bone and Joint Surg., Vol. 19, pp. 745–748.

Shoulder Joint

Rupture of the supraspinatus tendon. Codman, E. A.: 1937. J. Bone and Joint Surg., Vol. 19, pp. 643–652.

Observations on the function of the shoulder joint. Inman, V. T., J. B. Saunders, and L. C. Abbott: 1944. J. Bone and Joint Surg., Vol. 26, pp. 1–30.

The shoulder joint. Observations on the anatomy and physiology. Jones, L.: 1942. Surg., Gyn. and Obs., Vol. 75, pp. 433–444.

The coraco-humeral ligament of the human shoulder. Kaplan, E. B.: 1943. Bull. Hosp. Joint Dis., Vol. 4, pp. 62–65.

The movements of the shoulder-joint, with special reference to rupture of the supraspinatus tendon. Martin, C. P.: 1940. Am. J. Anat., Vol. 66, pp. 213–234.

Lesions of the musculotendinous cuff of the shoulder. I. The exposure and treatment of tears with retraction. McLaughlin, H. L.: 1944. J. Bone and Joint Surg., Vol. 26, pp. 31–51.

A comparative study of the clavicular ligaments of the rat, rabbit, cat, and dog. Sandstrom, C. J., and A. Saltzman: 1944. Anat. Rec., Vol. 89, pp. 23–32.

Elbow, Wrist and Hand

The carrying angle of the human arm as a secondary sex character. Atkinson, W. B., and H. Elftman: 1945. Anat. Rec., Vol. 91, pp. 49–52.

A comparison of the action of extension of the knee and elbow joints in man. Haxton, H. A.: 1945. Anat. Rec., Vol. 93, pp. 279–286.

A note on the piso-triquetral joint. Kropp, B. N.: 1945. Anat. Rec., Vol. 92, pp. 91–92.

Hip Joint

The position of the external hip joint in the above-the-knee prosthesis with pelvic suspension. Buchanan, A. R., and B. E. Robinson: 1946. J. Bone and Joint Surg., Vol. 28, pp. 71–80.

Hip motions. Ghormley, J. W.: 1944. Am. J. Surg., Vol. 66, pp. 24–30.

Embryology of human hip joint. Strayer, L. M., Jr.: 1943. Yale J. Biol. and Med., Vol. 16, pp. 13–26.

Knee Joint

Injuries to the ligaments of the knee joint. Abbott, L. C., J. B. Saunders, F. C. Bost, and C. E. Anderson: 1944. J. Bone and Joint Surg., Vol. 26, pp. 503–521.

Surgical approaches to the knee joint. Abbott, L. C., and W. F. Carpenter: 1945. J. Bone and Joint Surg., Vol. 27, pp. 277–310.

The mechanics of the ligaments and menisci of the knee joint. Brantigan, O. C., and A. F. Voshell: 1941. J. Bone and Joint Surg., Vol. 23, pp. 44–66.

The tibial collateral ligament: its function, its bursæ, and its relation to the medial meniscus. Brantigan, O. C., and A. F. Voshell: 1943. J. Bone and Joint Surg., Vol. 25, pp. 121–131.

Ligaments of the knee joint: relationship of ligament of Humphry to ligament of Wrisberg. Brantigan, O. C., and A. F. Voshell: 1946. J. Bone and Joint Surg., Vol. 28, pp. 66–67.

On the menisci of the knee joint in American whites and negroes. Charles, C. M.: 1935. Anat. Rec., Vol. 63, pp. 355–364.

The distribution and termination of nerves in the knee joint of the cat. Gardner, E.: 1944. J. Comp. Neur., Vol. 80, pp. 11–32.

The tetrapod knee joint. Haines, R. W.: 1942. J. Anat., Vol. 76, pp. 270–301.

The roentgen anatomy of the knee joint: an experimental analysis. Lachmann, E.: 1937. Radiology, Vol. 29, pp. 455–471.

Absorption of trypan blue from the human knee joint. Saunders, R. L., and E. G. Young: 1947. J. Bone and Joint Surg., Vol. 29, pp. 301–304.

Ankle Joint and Foot

The human foot. An experimental study of its mechanics and the role of its muscles and liagments in the support of the arch. Jones, R. L.: 1941. Am. J. Anat., Vol. 68, pp. 1–39.

Distribution of compression forces in the joints of the human foot. Manter, J. T.: 1946. Anat. Rec., Vol. 96, pp. 313–321.

The Human Foot: Its Evolution, Physiology and Functional Disorders. Morton, D. J.: 1935. Columbia Univ. Press, New York, xiii + 244 pp.

Bursæ

Trabeculæ traversing human bursæ. Schneider, C. L.: 1943. Anat. Rec., Vol. 87, pp. 151–163.

The prenatal incidence, structure and development of some human synovial bursæ. Black, B. M.: 1934. Anat. Rec., Vol. 60, pp. 333–355.

MUSCLES AND FASCIÆ.

THE muscles are the organs of voluntary motion, and by their contraction, move the various parts of the body. The energy of their contraction is made mechanically effective by means of the tendons, aponeuroses, and fasciæ which secure the ends of the muscles and control the direction of their pull. They form the dark, reddish masses that are popularly known as flesh, and account for approximately 40 per cent of the body weight. They vary greatly in size. The Gastrocnemius forms the bulk of the calf of the leg; the Sartorius is nearly 2 feet in length, and the Stapedius, a tiny muscle of the middle ear, weighs 0.1 gm. and is 2 to 3 mm. in length. In addition to these muscles, which are properly called **voluntary, skeletal,** or **striated muscles,** there are other muscular tissues which are not under voluntary control, such as the cardiac muscle of the heart and the smooth muscle of the intestines. They are described in chapters dealing with the viscera.

DEVELOPMENT OF THE MUSCLES.

Both the cross-striated and smooth muscles, with the exception of a few that are of ectodermal origin, arise from the mesoderm. The intrinsic muscles of the trunk are derived from the myotomes while the muscles of the head and limbs differentiate directly from the mesoderm.

The Myotomic Muscles.—The intrinsic muscles of the trunk which are derived directly from the myotomes are conveniently treated in two groups, the deep muscles of the back and the thoraco-abdominal muscles.

The deep muscles of the back extend from the sacral to the occipital region and vary much in length and size. They act chiefly on the vertebral column. The shorter muscles, such as the Interspinales, Intertransversarii, the deeper layers of the Multifidus, the Rotatores, Levatores costarum, Obliquus capitis inferior, Obliquus capitis superior and Rectus capitis posterior minor which extend between adjoining vertebræ, retain the primitive segmentation of the myotomes. Other muscles, such as the Splenius capitis, Splenius cervicis, Sacrospinalis, Semispinalis, Multifidus, Iliocostalis, Longissimus, Spinales, Semispinales, and Rectus capitis posterior major, which extend over several vertebræ, are formed by the fusion of successive myotomes and the splitting into longitudinal columns.

The fascia lumbo-dorsalis develops between the true myotomic muscles and the more superficial ones which migrate over the back such as the Trapezius, Rhomboideus, and Latissimus.

The anterior vertebral muscles, the Longus colli, Longus capitis, Rectus capitis anterior and Rectus capitis lateralis are derived from the ventral part of the cervical myotomes as are probably also the Scaleni.

The thoraco-abdominal muscles arise through the ventral extension of the thoracic myotomes into the body wall. This process takes place coincidently with the ventral extension of the ribs. In the thoracic region the primitive myotomic segments still persist as the intercostal muscles, but over the abdomen these ventral myotomic processes fuse into a sheet which splits in various ways to form the Rectus, the Obliquus externus and internus, and the Transversalis. Such muscles as the Pectoralis major and minor and the Serratus anterior do not belong to the above group.

(341)

The Ventrolateral Muscles of the Neck.—The intrinsic muscles of the tongue, the Infrahyoid muscles and the diaphragm are derived from a more or less continuous premuscle mass which extends on each side from the tongue into the lateral region of the upper half of the neck and into it early extend the hypoglossal and branches of the upper cervical nerves. The two halves which form the Infrahyoid muscles and the diaphragm are at first widely separated from each other by the heart. As the latter descends into the thorax the diaphragmatic portion of each lateral mass is carried with its nerve down into the thorax and the laterally placed Infrahyoid muscles move toward the midventral line of the neck.

Muscles of the Shoulder Girdle and Arm.—The Trapezius and Sternocleidomastoideus arise from a common premuscle mass in the occipital region just caudal to the last branchial arch; as the mass increases in size it spreads downward to the shoulder girdle to which it later becomes attached. It also spreads backward and downward to the spinous processes, gaining attachment at a still later period.

The Levator scapulæ, Serratus anterior and the Rhomboids arise from premuscle tissue in the lower cervical region and undergo extensive migration.

The Latissimus dorsi and Teres major are associated in their origin from the premuscle sheath of the arm as are also the two Pectoral muscles when the arm bud lies in the lower cervical region.

The intrinsic muscles of the arm develop *in situ* from the mesoderm of the arm bud and probably do not receive cells or buds from the myotomes. The nerves enter the arm bud when it still lies in the cervical region and as the arm shifts caudally over the thorax the lower cervical nerves which unite to form the brachial plexus, acquire a caudal direction.

The Muscles of the Leg.—The muscles of the leg like those of the arm develop *in situ* from the mesoderm of the leg bud, the myotomes apparently taking no part in their formation.

The Muscles of the Head.—The muscles of the orbit arise from the mesoderm over the dorsal and caudal sides of the optic stalk.

The muscles of mastication arise from the mesoderm of the mandibular arch. The mandibular division of the trigeminal nerve enters this premuscle mass before it splits into the Temporal, Masseter and Pterygoideus.

The facial muscles (muscles of expression) arise from the mesoderm of the hyoid arch. The facial nerve enters this mass before it begins to split, and as the muscle mass spreads out over the face and head and neck it splits more or less incompletely into the various muscles.

The early differentiation of the muscular system apparently goes on independently of the nervous system and only later does it appear that muscles are dependent on the functional stimuli of the nerves for their continued existence and growth. Although the nervous system does not influence muscle differentiation, the nerves, owing to their early attachments to the muscle rudiments, are in a general way indicators of the position of origin of many of the muscles and likewise in many instances the nerves indicate the paths along which the developing muscles have migrated during development. The muscle of the diaphragm, for example, has its origin in the region of the fourth and fifth cervical segments. The phrenic nerve enters the muscle mass while the latter is in this region and is drawn out as the diaphragm migrates through the thorax. The Trapezius and Sternocleidomastoideus arise in the lateral occipital region as a common muscle mass, into which at a very early period the nervus accessorius extends and as the muscle mass migrates and extends caudally the nerve is carried with it. The Pectoralis major and minor arise in the cervical region, receive their nerves while in this position and as the muscle mass migrates and extends caudally over the thorax the nerves are carried along. The Latissimus dorsi and Serratus anterior are excellent examples of migrating muscles whose nerve supply indicates their origin in the cervical region. The Rectus abdominis and the other abdominal muscles migrate or shift from a lateral to a ventrolateral or abdominal position, carrying with them the nerves.

The facial nerve, which early enters the common facial muscle mass of the second branchial or hyoid arch, is dragged about with the muscle as it spreads over the head and face and neck, and as the muscle splits into the various muscles of expression, the nerve is correspondingly split. The mandibular division of the trigeminal nerve enters at an early time the muscle mass in the mandibular arch and as this mass splits and migrates apart to form the muscles of mastication the nerve splits into its various branches.

The nerve supply then serves as a key to the common origin of certain groups of muscles. The muscles supplied by the oculomotor nerve arise from a single mass in the eye region; the lingual muscles arise from a common mass supplied by the hypoglossal nerve.

STRUCTURE OF MUSCLE.

The **skeletal** or **voluntary** muscles are called **striated muscles** because they consist of long threadlike fibers which, under the microscope, are seen to be crossed by regularly placed, parallel, transverse bands or cross-striations. The smallest independent units of the tissue are the muscle fibers. They are just within the limit of visibility with the naked eye, measuring from 0.01 to 0.1 mm. in diameter, and from 1 mm. to 12 cm. in length. They are cylindrical unless crowded against each

Fig. 358.—Transverse section of human striped muscle fibers. × 255.

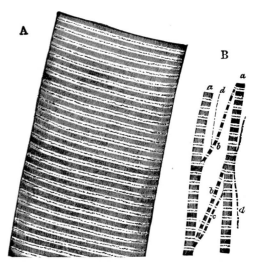

Fig. 359.—*A*. Portion of a medium-sized human muscular fiber. Magnified nearly 800 diameters. *B*. Separated bundles of fibrils, equally magnified. *a, a*, Larger, *b, b*, smaller collections. *c.* Still smaller. *d, d.* The smallest which could be detached.

other, and have either blunt or tapering ends. They do not divide or anastomose, but may occasionally be split for a short distance near their terminations. The maximum length of fiber, except in very long muscles, is approximately 10 cm., and if the muscular fasciculi are of this length or shorter, the majority of fibers extend from one tendon to the other. If the fasciculi are longer, however, the fibers have one termination at a tendon and the other within the muscle, or in the case of a very long muscle like the Sartorius, both terminations may be within the muscle.

Each **muscle fiber** is a multinucleated cell. It has an outer membrane called the **sarcolemma** within which lie the nuclei and the contractile, cross-striated substance. The **nuclei** are flat oval discs, and usually are closely applied to the inner surface of the sarcolemma in adult human fibers. They are irregularly placed throughout the length of the fiber, and vary in number according to the size of the fiber, several hundred occurring in a larger one. About each nucleus there is a small amount of **cytoplasm** which may contain mitochondria and a Golgi body.

The **cross-striated substance** is composed of a cytoplasmic matrix, the **sarcoplasm**, within which the long filamentous **myofibrillæ** are embedded and more or less evenly distributed across the fiber. The fibrillæ impart to the fiber a fine longitudinal marking or striation which is less regular and distinct than the cross-striation. They are usually 0.002 mm. or less in diameter in human muscle. The cross-striated appearance is due to the fact that the myofibrillæ are made up of alternating birefringent and monorefringent segments which are evenly spaced at intervals of approximately 0.003 mm., unless the fiber is distorted by contraction. During contraction the cross stripes become narrower or crowded together, and when the fiber is stretched they become wider or farther apart. The cross-striations have been given various names and designations, and have been used, along with other lines, bands, discs, and membranes, as the basis for many diverse theories of muscular contraction.

The sarcoplasm contains numerous granular bodies called *sarcosomes*, as well as tiny *droplets of fat*, scattered among the myofibrillæ. The fat droplets may be abundant in well nourished individuals. Glycogen may appear to be concentrated in the sarcosomes in fixed and stained material, but in the living fiber it is diffusely distributed. The relative amount of sarcoplasm and myofibrillæ varies in individual fibers. Those with a greater concentration of fibrillæ are pale in appearance in the fresh condition; those with more sarcoplasm are darker. These **light and dark fibers** are intermingled in most human muscles, and are not as sharply demarcated as in animals or birds with light and dark flesh.

Most muscles are connected with bones, cartilages, or ligaments, and usually through the intervention of tendons or aponeuroses. The latter may be long, or the muscle may seem to connect directly with the bone or cartilage. Muscles may also attach to the skin (facial muscles), a mucous membrane (tongue), a fibrous plate (ocular muscles), or form circular bands (sphincter muscles).

The **attachment of the ends of the muscle fibers** is the same in principle whether the fasciculi end in a tendon or are connected directly with bones or cartilage. Each muscle fiber has a distinct termination which is rounded, conical, or truncated, and is covered by sarcolemma. The reticular fibrillæ of the endomysium become thickened and are closely adherent to the end of the fiber as they pass over it, and they continue on beyond it into the tendon, where they become the actual substance of the tendon. In muscles which appear to attach directly to bones, cartilages, or other structures, the reticular endomysium becomes continuous with the periosteum, or other fibrous layer in the same manner as with a tendon. When the muscle fibers terminate within instead of at the end of a fasciculus, as in long muscles, the ends may be either blunt or long and tapering, and they are secured in place by the merging of their terminal reticular endomysium with the endomysium of neighboring fibers.

The muscle, considered as a contractile organ, has a parenchyma composed of muscle fibers, and an intrinsic **connective tissue stroma**. Each fiber is surrounded by a very delicate, close-meshed network of reticular connective tissue fibrillæ. This net, together with a few collagenous and elastic fibers which bind contiguous muscle fibers together, is known as the **endomysium**. Groups of a dozen or more fibers are brought together into bundles or **fasciculi** and enclosed by a thin lamella of collagenous and elastic fibers known as the perimysium. The **perimysium** also includes all the connective tissue which binds the fasciculi into larger groups and forms fibrous septa throughout the muscle. The concentration of connective tissue which envelopes the entire muscle is known as the **epimysium**. It should not be confused with the definitive fascial membranes which are described below. It may be well developed, or quite delicate, as it is where the muscle glides freely under a strong fascial sheet, or it may lose its identity and become fused with a fascial membrane if the latter is used by the muscle fibers for their attachment.

The **arrangement of the fasciculi**, and the manner in which they approach the tendons has many variations. In some muscles, the fasciculi are parallel with the longitudinal axis and terminate at either end in flat tendons. In others, the fasciculi converge, like the plumes of a feather, to one side of a tendon which runs the entire length of a muscle, forming a **pennifrom** muscle like the Semimembranosus. If they converge to both sides of a tendon, as in the Rectus femoris, they are called **bipenniform**, or if they converge to several tendons, as in the Deltoideus, they are called **multipenniform**. The fasciculi may converge from a broad surface to a narrow tendinous point, as in the Temporalis, and be called **radiated**.

This arrangement of fasciculi is correlated with the power of the muscles. Those with comparatively few fasciculi, extending the length of the muscle, have a greater range of motion but not as much power. Penniform muscles, with a large number of fasciculi distributed along their tendons, have greater power but smaller range of motion.

The names of the muscles have been derived from: (*a*) their situation, as the Brachialis, Pectoralis, Supraspinatus; (*b*) their direction, as the Rectus, Obliquus, and Transversus abdominis; (*c*) their action, as Flexors, Extensors; (*d*) their shape, as the Deltoideus, Trapezius, Rhomboideus; (*e*) the number of divisions, as the Biceps, Triceps, Quadriceps; (*f*) their points of attachment, as the Sternocleidomastoideus, Omohyoideus.

The attachments of the two ends of a muscle are called the **origin** and the **insertion**. The origin is the more fixed and proximal end, the insertion the more movable and distal end. For example, the Pectoralis major arises or has its origin from the ribs and clavicle, and its insertion is into the humerus. If the individual were climbing a tree, however, the origin and insertion might seem to be reversed, and the hand be more fixed and the body more movable. The designations of the origins and insertions in the following descriptions are more or less arbitrary, therefore, and a matter of convention among anatomists. The section on bones should be consulted for graphic illustration of these attachments; the origins are shown in red, the insertions in blue.

Vessels and Nerves of Striated Muscle.—The **capillaries** of **striped muscle** are very abundant, and form a sort of rectangular network, the branches of which run longitudinally in the endomysium between the muscular fibers, and are joined at short intervals by transverse anastomosing branches.. The larger vascular channels, arteries and veins are found only in the perimysium, between the muscular fasciculi. **Nerves** are profusely distributed to striped muscle. For mode of termination see section on Neurology. The existence of **lymphatic vessels** in striped muscle has not been ascertained, though they have been found in tendons and in the sheaths of the muscles.

CONNECTIVE TISSUES.

The connective tissues include the connecting and supporting tissues in all parts of the body except the central nervous system. Every organ has its capsule or stroma of connective tissue, and the entire body is supported by the skeleton. The muscles are particularly closely associated with the connective tissues because the latter make it possible for the muscles to perform their functions. Thus, the bones are the rigid levers, they are made movable by the joints, and the force of muscular contraction is transmitted to them by the tendons. The connective tissues are composed largely of intercellular material. They are classified according to the character of this intercellular matrix, and their particular mechanical properties are based upon it.

Bone (described as a tissue on page 68) has a tough fibrous matrix which has been made rigid by the deposit of mineral salts. It can withstand the stress of either compression or tension to a remarkable degree.

Cartilage (described on page 256) has a firm, more or less solid, but elastic matrix which may or may not have fibers imbedded in it. It withstands compression especially well and tension to a considerable extent.

Fibrous connective tissue has many varieties which involve the relative concentrations of the different kinds of fibers and the fluid ground substance. They are: (1) dense fibrous, (a) organized or (b) unorganized; (2) loose fibrous, (a) fibroelastic, (b) fibroareolar, (c) adipose, and (d) reticular.

Dense fibrous connective tissue occurs either organized into specific organs such as the tendons, aponeuroses, and ligaments, or formed into unorganized bands and membranes of a less specific nature. The *organized fibrous connective tissues* consist of compact parallel bundles of collagenous fibers. They are pliable and inelastic, and are able to withstand great tensional but comparatively small compressional stress. An exception to the inelasticity is found in the large ligamentum nuchæ of some lower animals and the corresponding human ligamenta flava which are composed almost entirely of elastic fibers. In the *unorganized dense fibrous connective tissue* the collagenous bundles are interwoven rather than arranged into parallel bundles. Examples are the periosteum of bones, the corium of the skin, the dura mater, and many of the fascial membranes. This type of fibrous connective tissue is very strong in resisting tensional stress, and it withstands stresses in many directions instead of in one particular direction as in the case of a tendon.

Loose fibrous connective tissue is the most pervasive of all tissues, with the exception of the blood. It has a strong binding power but is very pliable and somewhat stretchable since it contains elastic fibers as well as collagenous bundles, and even the latter are loosely interwoven and easily displaced. Between the fibers there are comparatively wide interstices or *areolæ* which are filled with ground substance or tissue fluid. When this tissue is comparatively strong and closely woven, as in the capsules of organs, it is called *fibro-elastic tissue*. When it is loosely woven and weak, as in the fascial clefts, it is called *fibro-areolar* or *areolar tissue*.

The most delicate connective tissue, that which surrounds individual cells, muscle fibers, or the acini of glands, is composed of very fine fibrils woven into a network, and is called **reticular tissue**. It merges into the fibro-elastic connective tissue of the capsule and stroma of the organs, wherever the smallest units of the organ are grouped into lobules, fasciculi, etc.

The specific cells of fibrous connective tissue, commonly called fibroblasts, usually are quite widely separated and distributed, but in certain parts of the body, and especially in well nourished individuals, the cells are clumped together and each contains a large vesicle of fat. Where these fat cells occur in considerable concentration, the tissue is called **adipose tissue**. Adipose tissue is commonly found as a packing or padding tissue; it fills pockets, rounds out contours, and forms soft cushions.

TENDONS AND APONEUROSES.

Tendons are white, glistening, fibrous cords, varying in length and thickness, sometimes round, sometimes flattened, of great tensile strength, flexible, and practically inelastic. They consist of white fibrous or collagenous bundles which are firmly united together and whose fibrils have a parallel course. Except where they are attached, the tendons have a sheath of delicate fibro-elastic connective tissue, and the larger ones have a stroma of thin internal septa as well. They are very sparingly supplied with bloodvessels, the smaller tendons presenting no trace of them in their interior. They are supplied with sensory nerves whose fibers have specialized terminations called the organs of Golgi and which mediate a special stereognostic sensibility.

Aponeuroses are fibrous membranes, of a pearly white color, iridescent, and glistening, which represent very much flattened tendons. They consist of closely packed, parallel, collagenous bundles, and by this characteristic may be differentiated from the fibrous membranes of fascia which have their collagenous bundles more irregularly interwoven. They are only sparingly supplied with bloodvessels.

The aponeuroses and tendons are, indeed, parts of the muscles, and are utilized by the muscles to exert the force of contraction. They are in the direct line of muscular pull, and in this regard they differ from the fascial membranes which enclose or guide the muscles and tendons. It is customary to regard the ultimate attachment, that is, the origin and insertion of the muscle, as the terminal attachment of the tendon or aponeurosis to the bone, rather than the termination of the fasciculi of contractile fibers at the tendon.

FASCIÆ.

The dissectable, fibrous connective tissues of the body, other than the specifically organized structures, tendons, aponeuroses, and ligaments, are called fasciæ. This same term is used also in a more restricted sense to indicate local connective tissue membranes which enclose a part of the body, or invest muscles or other structures. Although the term will be used most commonly with its restricted meaning of fibrous membranes, it is essential that the concept be borne in mind that the latter are part of the general connective tissues. This allows one to regard all the fascial structures as a part of a functional as well as morphological system in which the connective tissue varies in thickness, in density, in accumulation of fat, and in relative amounts of collagenous fibers, elastic fibers, and tissue fluid according to local requirements.

The entire fascial system is made up of three subdivisions: the **superficial fascia,** the **deep fascia,** and the **subserous fascia.** The deep fascia is the principal somatic fascia which invests and penetrates between the structures which form the body wall and appendages. It is the most extensive of the three and calls for the major part of our attention. The superficial fascia is the subcutaneous layer which intervenes between the deep fascia and the skin. The subserous fascia lies within the body cavities; it forms the fibrous layer of the serous membranes (pleura, pericardium, and peritoneum), covers and supports the viscera, and attaches the parietal layer of the serous membranes to the deep fascia of the internal surface of the body wall.

The **Superficial Fascia** (*tela subcutanea*) is continuous over the entire body between the skin and the deep fascial investment of the specialized structures of the body, such as muscles. It is composed of two layers. The outer one, often called the *panniculus adiposus*, normally contains an accumulation of fat. The latter may be several centimeters thick, or it may, in emaciated individuals, be almost entirely lacking. The inner layer is a thin membrane which ordinarily has no fat and has a generous amount of elastic tissue. The two layers are quite adherent in most regions but they can be separated by careful dissection, particularly in the lower anterior abdominal wall. Between the two layers lie the superficial arteries, veins, nerves, and lymphatics, the mammary glands, most of the facial muscles, the platysma, and one or two other muscles.

The superficial fascia in many parts of the body glides freely over the deep fascia, producing the characteristic movability of the skin in an area like the back of the hand. In these areas, the two fasciæ can be dissected apart easily by a probing finger or blunt instrument. They are separated, in other words, by a fascial cleft. At certain other points on the body surface, especially over bony prominences, the two fasciæ are closely adherent. They retain their individuality even here, however, and do not become continuous with each other.

The **deep fascia** is represented characteristically by the gray felt-like membranes immediately covering the muscles. It comprises a rather intricate series of sheets and bands which hold the muscles and other structures in their proper relative positions, separating them from each other for independent function as well as joining them together into an integrated whole. The intrinsic connective tissue of the capsules or stroma of these structures is not included in this fascia. In the case of a muscle, the epimysium may be fused with the overlying fascia and lose its identity, as in the Triceps, or it may be separated from the fascia by a cleft and retain its individuality, as in the Biceps.

The membranes of the deep fascia are organized into a continuous or never ending system. The periosteum of the bones (and perichondrium of cartilage), and the ligaments may assist in establishing this continuity. The membranes split, on occasion, in order to surround (invest) muscles or other structures and unite again into single sheets. These phenomena of splitting and fusing are important because it is by their means that any sheet of fascia can be traced to any other sheet and can be shown to make eventual attachment to the skeleton.

The deep fascia, although a continuous system, may be subdivided for the purpose of description into three parts. First, the **outer investing layer** (*Deep Subcutaneous System of Gallaudet*) is an extensive sheet which covers the trunk, neck, limbs, and part of the head, and lies just under the subcutaneous superficial fascia. Second, in the trunk there is another extensive sheet, the **internal investing layer** (*Deep Subserous System of Gallaudet*), which covers the internal surface of the body wall, that is, it lines the thoracic and abdominal cavities and, in turn, is covered internally by the Subserous Fascia (see below). The third portion comprises the manifold **intermediate membranes** which are derived from the two investing layers by splitting and attachment, and which lie between the muscles and other structures throughout the body.

The mechanical function of fascia is particularly well developed in the deep fascia and is responsible for its many local variations and specializations. A membrane may be thickened, either for strength or padding; it may be fused with another membrane or split into several sheets; it may be separated from another membrane by a plane of cleavage; or it may combine with other membranes to form compartments for groups of muscles. These specializations will be described in greater detail.

The thickening of a membrane for greater strength, especially if it receives the direct pull of a muscle, is by the addition of parallel bundles of collagenous fibers which impart to it the white, glistening appearance of an aponeurosis. A membrane of this type may lie between the origins of two muscles whose fibers pull in approximately the same direction, as, for example, the forearm muscles originating on the epicondyles of the humerus, in which case it is called an intermuscular septum. Such a strengthened membrane may cover a muscle and be used by it for a surface of attachment as in the case of the outer investing layer of the forearm. An extreme instance is that of the fascia lata of the thigh, whose iliotibial band is in fact the principal tendon of insertion for the Gluteus maximus and the Tensor fasciæ latæ muscles. This aponeurotic function of fascia has led to some confusion. Certain fibrous membranes retain the name fascia when they are actually aponeuroses and, conversely, some authors, particularly the French, are inclined to call even the unspecialized membranes aponeuroses.

A band of fascia may act as a ligament. This is the case with the greatly strengthened portion of the clavipectoral fascia, the costocoracoid membrane, which, by its attachment to the coracoid process and ribs, serves as a ligament for the articulations of the clavicle. Another important specialization is shown by the annular ligaments and retinacula at the wrist and ankle which provide tunnels for the long tendons of the hand and foot.

Lamination of a fascial membrane is found where there is a thickening without a corresponding increase in strength. The membrane splits into two leaves which are separated by a pad of connective tissue containing fat and an occasional blood-vessel or lymph node. An example of this is the lamination of the outer cervical fascia above the sternum which is ambiguously called the suprasternal (Burns') space.

A **fascial compartment** is a portion of the body which is walled off by fascial membranes. Characteristically, it contains a muscle or a group of muscles but in some instances other structures are included. A typical example is offered by the flexor and extensor compartments of the arm, where the substance of the arm, enclosed by brachial fascia, is divided into the two compartments by the medial and lateral intermuscular septa. In many descriptions of fascia, such compartments are ambiguously called spaces or potential spaces. For example, the mediastinum is frequently called a "space" containing the heart, great vessels, esophagus, etc., whereas in reality it is a compartment enclosed by mediastinal fascia. Any "potential space" must be sought in the area of cleavage which separates the parietal pericardium from the sternum except at the pericardiosternal ligaments. Another confusing use of the word space was mentioned in the preceding paragraph, that is, to refer to a lamination and thickening of a fascial membrane.

The **fascial cleft** is an important specialization which is greatly in need of emphasis. It is a place of cleavage which separates two contiguous fascial surfaces. It may be described also as a stratum rich in fluid but poor in traversing fibers which allows two fascial surfaces to move more or less freely over each other and makes them easy to separate in dissection. The degree of separation may vary from an almost complete detachment to a comparatively strong adhesion, depending on the need for motion between the parts. The cleft between the superficial fascia and the deep fascia has already been mentioned. The cleft between a muscle and an overlying, restraining fascial membrane, like the Biceps and brachial fascia, is actually between the epimysium of the muscle and the true fascial sheet. The cleft between two adjacent muscles is likely to be between the simple epimysium of each muscle, but the latter may, in some instances, be thickened into a true fascial sheet.

A **bursa** represents the final step in the development of an efficient device for freedom of motion between contiguous connective tissue surfaces. It is a relatively small, circumscribed area in which all traversing fibers have been lost. The result is a pocket of complete separation, the lining of which provides two opposed, lubricated surfaces similar to the synovial membranes of a joint. Characteristically, a bursa is found where a tendon glides directly over the periosteum of a bone. The **synovial tendon sheaths** of the hand and foot are specialized bursæ.

Just as there are adaptations for separation of membranes, there are adaptations for attachment. Fascial membranes may fuse with each other, as in the case of the outer investing and middle cervical fasciæ near the hyoid bone. They may attach to bones, as the clavipectoral fasciæ to the clavicle. The attachment in some instances is very secure, in others it is separable by dissection. The relation between two contiguous fascial membranes, therefore, may vary from the complete separation at a bursa, or the functional separation of a fascial cleft, through progressive degrees of adhesion and attachment up to complete fusion.

The names of particular parts of the fascia are derived most commonly and most appropriately from the regions of the body which they occupy or the structures which they cover. For example, the brachial fascia encloses the arm and the deltoid fascia covers the Deltoideus muscle. Some fasciæ have descriptive names, such as the fascia lata from its broad extent on the thigh or the fascia cribrosa from its many holes. A few are named from their attachments, for example, the fascia clavipectoralis or coracoclavicularis.

Eponyms which are taken from the names of persons who first described or emphasized particular portions or concepts of fascia are used very commonly by authors of clinical treatises. In most instances such nomenclature is of doubtful value anatomically, but is worthy of preservation because it emphasizes the importance of a certain fascia in operative procedures or in pathological processes such as the spread of infection. The identification of any specific fascial membrane is intrinsically difficult because the fascia has the same histological structure as the ligament, aponeurosis, and periosteum to which it may be attached, and the continuity of the whole system makes the setting of exact boundaries and limitations a matter of arbitrary definition.

The **Subserous** or **Visceral Fascia** (*tela subserosa*; *superficial subserous fascia of Gallaudet*) lies between the internal investing layer of deep fascia and the serous membranes lining the body cavities, in much the same way as the subcutaneous superficial fascia lies between the skin and the deep fascia. It is very thin in some areas, as between the pleura and the chest wall. It is thick in other areas and, except in emaciated individuals, forms a pad of adipose tissue like that surrounding the kidney. It is not separable into outer and inner layers, as is the superficial fascia, but it may be irregularly laminated in the adipose accumulations, especially in well nourished individuals. As a general rule, only the fascia of the parietal serous membrane is given in a description, but it should be remembered that this parietal layer is continuous with the visceral layer carried over to the organs at the reflections of the serous membranes and at the mesenteries.

A cleft of variable prominence separates the subserous fascia from the deep fascia as it does in the case of the subcutaneous and deep fasciæ. It allows a considerable amount of sliding motion between the two fasciæ and makes it possible to dissect them apart. Where both fasciæ are thin and delicate, it is difficult to identify and separate them.

Complications and problems of identification and naming of fasciæ arise in the regions where internal structures penetrate the wall of the body cavity. For example, the rectum penetrates the pelvic diaphragm, the spermatic cord penetrates the abdominal wall through the inguinal canal, and the trachea and esophagus leave the thoracic cavity to enter the neck, and, in so doing, they introduce transitions between the subserous, deep, and superficial fasciæ.

Careful study of the fascia has been made, for the most part, in restricted areas instead of throughout the body as a complete system. Interest has stemmed from its obvious importance in surgery and pathology. It is logical, however, to weave the fascia into a functional system. Its function is predominantly mechanical in the normal body, except for the activity of the various types of cells which are visitors within its meshes and which are beyond the scope of this discussion. The understanding and learning of the fasciæ are much easier on the basis of this mechanical function than on the basis of surgical and pathological importance, and the latter becomes easily comprehensible only with the knowledge of function as a background. One very important mechanical function must not be overlooked even if it is seldom mentioned, namely, that of supporting and carrying the bloodvessels, nerves and lymphatics.

Although much advantage might be gained by presenting the fasciæ in a separate chapter, it has been decided to retain the usual method of describing them with the muscles. Should the reader desire a systematic treatment of the fasciæ, he may obtain it by leafing through the pages of the chapter on muscles, reading only the sections on fascia. A study of the muscles or other structures in a particular region is recommended as a preliminary to the reading of the description of the fascia.

MUSCLE ACTION.

When a muscle contracts, it acts upon movable parts to bring about certain movements. These actions of the muscle should be studied from three points of view: (*a*) *individual action*, (*b*) *group actions*, and (*c*) *action correlated with the nerve supply*. The individual action is closely associated with the anatomy of a muscle because mechanically, the action is the direct result of the attachment of its two ends. It is not necessarily true, however, that the action in the living body is the same as that deduced from observing its attachments, nor even from pulling on it in a dead subject, because incidental actions may not be utilized or may even be suppressed in the living body. A knowledge of individual action is of practical value to a surgeon in the diagnosis and treatment of displacements due to fractures. Group actions are related to the functions as well as the anatomy of the muscles. It is seldom possible for a person to make a single muscle contract at will. In other words, the movements, not the muscles, are represented in the central nervous system. A muscle may be associated with one group for one action and a different group for another, possibly even antagonistic action. A correlation of the knowledge of the action with the nerve supply is of practical value in the diagnosis of lesions of the peripheral and central nervous system, and in the treatment of such lesions. Frequently there is a correspondence between groups of muscles arranged according to nerve supply and those arranged according to common actions.

Practically every muscle acting upon a joint is matched by another muscle which has an opposite action. Each muscle of such a pair is the **antagonist** of the other, for example, the Biceps brachii, a flexor, and the Triceps, an extensor, are antagonists at the elbow. The performance of most movements requires the combined action of a number of muscles; those which act directly to bring about the desired movement are called the **prime movers**; those which act to hold the part of the body in an appropriate position are called **fixation muscles**. It happens frequently that the prime movers have actions other than the one desired, in which case the antagonists of the undesired action come into play; these are the **synergists**. For example, in closing the fist, the prime movers are the Flexores digitorum sublimis and profundus, the Flexor pollicis longus, and the small muscles of the thumb; the fixation muscles are the Triceps, Biceps, Brachialis, and the muscles about the shoulder which hold the arm in position; the synergetic muscles are the Extensores carpi radialis and ulnaris, which prevent flexion of the wrist. In some instances, when an act is performed with extreme force, muscles which are not required for a moderate performance come to the assistance of the prime movers, and these are known as *emergency muscles*. For example, the flexors of the fingers may flex the wrist in emergency. A further point which must be borne in mind is that the force of gravity may be the prime mover, in which case, the antagonists of the muscles which might be expected to be the prime movers are the muscles which act, and they do so to retard and control the movement caused by gravity.

Individual muscles cannot always be treated as single mechanical units, with regard to their actions. Different parts of the same muscle may have different and even antagonistic actions; for example, the anterior part of the Deltoideus flexes, but the posterior portion extends the arm. Two adjacent muscles like the Infraspinatus and the Teres minor, on the other hand, may have the same action.

No study of muscles is complete without observations of the muscles in their normal positions in the living body. It is recommended that students find an opportunity to make this study. The surface markings associated with the muscles are illustrated in the last chapter of the book.

THE MUSCLES AND FASCIÆ OF THE HEAD.

The muscles of the head may be arranged in groups, of which the following two will be described in this chapter:

I. The Facial Muscles.　　　　　　II. The Muscles of Mastication.

In addition to these two groups, other muscles occupying positions in the head are described in other, more appropriate parts of the book: (1) The Ocular Muscles; (2) The Muscles of the Auditory Ossicles; (3) The Muscles of the Tongue; and (4) The Muscles of the Pharynx.

I. THE FACIAL MUSCLES.

The **facial muscles** (*muscles of expression*) are cutaneous muscles, lying within the layers of the superficial fascia. In general, they arise, either from fascia or from the bones of the face, and insert into the skin. The individual muscles seldom remain separate and distinct throughout their length because of a tendency to merge with their neighbors at their terminations or attachments. They may be grouped into: (1) the muscles of the scalp; (2) the extrinsic muscles of the ear; (3) the muscles of the eyelid; (4) the muscles of the nose; (5) the muscles of the mouth. An additional muscle, the Platysma, really belongs to the facial group but will be described with the muscles of the neck.

1. The Muscles and Fasciæ of the Scalp.

Epicranius.　　　　　　Occipitalis.　　　　　　Frontalis.

The **superficial fascia** (*tela subcutanea*) of the head invests the facial muscles and carries the superficial bloodvessels and nerves. It varies considerably in thickness and texture in different areas but everywhere has an abundant blood and nerve supply. Above the superior nuchal and temporal lines, and anterior to the Masseter muscle there is no deep fascia underlying it other than the periosteum of the bones. Under the scalp, the superficial fascia is very thick and tough, and over the cranial vault, the muscular stratum is represented by the broad epicranial aponeurosis or galea aponeurotica. A fascial cleft, such as that commonly found under the superficial fascia in the rest of the body, is very prominent in this region and separates the galea from the pericranium or cranial periosteum. It accounts for the movability of the scalp and makes possible the sudden accumulation of large amounts of blood in the hematomas following blows upon the head. Over the forehead, the superficial layers of the fascia are much thinner than in the scalp and the skin is closely attached to the underlying Frontalis. Over the eyelids, it is devoid of fat and is composed of a loose areolar tissue which is easily distended and infiltrated with tissue fluid in edema, or blood in ecchymosis or hemorrhage. On the cheeks and lips, it contains a considerable amount of fat and is tougher and more fibrous, especially in men. The superficial fascia is reduced over the cartilages of the nose and external ear, the skin being closely bound to the underlying perichondrium. The superficial fascia of the face is directly continuous over the mandible with that of the neck, and that of the scalp merges posteriorly with the similar fibrous layer of the back of the neck.

The skin of the scalp is thicker than in any other part of the body. The hair follicles are closely set together, have numerous sebaceous glands, and extend deeply into the superficial fascia. The subcutaneous fat is broken up into granular lobules, and is mattressed into a firm layer by the many fibrous bands which secure the skin to the deeper layers of the superficial fascia.

The **Epicranius** (*Occipitofrontalis*) (Fig. 360) is a broad muscular and tendinous layer which covers the top of the skull, from the occipital bone to the eyebrow. It consists of two thin, broad, muscular bellies, the Occipitalis and the Frontalis, connected by an extensive intermediate aponeurosis, the galea aponeurotica.

The **Occipitalis**, quadrilateral in form, *arises* by short tendinous fibers from the lateral two-thirds of the superior nuchal line of the occipital bone, and from the mastoid part of the temporal. The muscular fasciculi ascend in a parallel course toward the vertex and *end* in the galea aponeurotica. Between the two Occipitales there is a considerable, though variable, interval which is occupied by a prolongation of the galea.

The **Frontalis**, also quadrilateral in form, is broader than the Occipitalis and its fasciculi are longer, finer and paler in color. It has no bony attachments. Its medial fibers are continuous with those of the Procerus; its intermediate fibers blend with the Corrugator and Orbicularis oculi; and its lateral fibers are blended with the latter muscle also, over the zygomatic process of the frontal bone. From these attachments the fibers are directed upward, and join the galea aponeurotica below the coronal suture. The medial margins of the Frontales are joined together for some distance above the root of the nose.

The **galea aponeurotica** (*epicranial aponeurosis*) covers the upper part of the cranium between the Frontales and Occipitales. In addition to its attachment to these muscle bellies, it is attached behind, in the interval between the two Occipitales, to the external occipital protuberance and the highest nuchal line of the occipital bone. In front, it forms a short, narrow prolongation between the two Frontales. On either side, it gives origin to the Auriculares anterior and superior; at this point it loses its aponeurotic character, and is continuous over the temporal fascia with a layer of laminated areolar tissue. It is closely connected to the integument by the firm, dense, adipose layer of superficial fascia and is separated from the pericranium by the fascial cleft which allows the aponeurosis, carrying with it the integument, to move through a considerable distance.

Action.—The Frontalis raises the eyebrow and the skin over the root of the nose and, at the same time, draws the scalp forward, throwing the skin of the forehead into transverse wrinkles. The Occipitalis draws the scalp backward. In the ordinary action of the muscles, the scalp is fixed by the Occipitales and the eyebrows elevated by the Frontales, giving the face an expression of surprise; if the action is exaggerated, the eyebrows are raised still farther and the forehead wrinkled as in an expression of fright or horror.

Nerves.—The Frontalis is supplied by the temporal branches, and the Occipitalis by the posterior auricular branch of the facial nerve.

Variations.—Both Frontalis and Occipitalis may vary considerably in size and in extent; either may be absent; the muscles of the two sides may fuse in the middle line; the Frontales may interdigitate across the line; the Occipitalis may fuse with the Auricularis posterior.

A thin muscular slip, the **Transversus nuchæ** or **Occipitalis minor**, is present in 25 per cent of the cases; it arises from the external occipital protuberance or from the superior nuchal line, either superficial or deep to the Trapezius; it is frequently inserted with the Auricularis posterior, but may join the posterior edge of the Sternocleidomastoideus.

2. The Extrinsic Muscles of the Ear.

The **Auricularis anterior** (*Attrahens aurem*) (Fig. 360), the smallest of the three extrinsic muscles of the ear, is thin, fan-shaped, and its fasciculi are pale, delicate, and indistinct. It *arises* from the anterior portion of the galea aponeurotica or its fascial prolongation into the anterior temporal area, and its fibers converge to be *inserted* into a projection on the front of the helix.

23

The **Auricularis superior** (*Attolens aurem*) (Fig. 360), the largest of the three, is thin and fan-shaped. Its fibers *arise* from the galea aponeurotica, and converge to be *inserted* by a thin flattened tendon into the upper part of the cranial surface of the auricula.

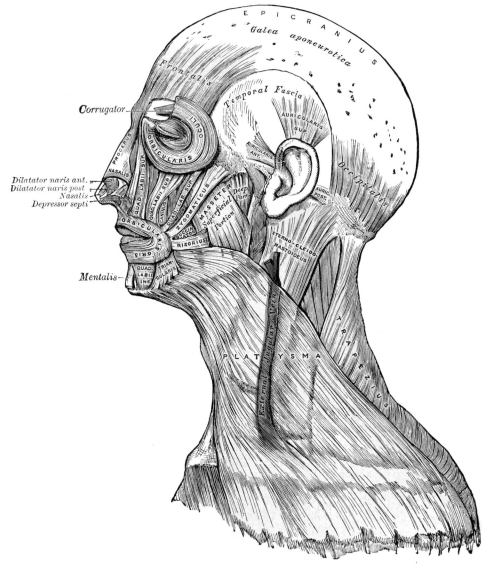

Fig. 360.—Muscles of the head, face, and neck.

The **Auricularis posterior** (*Retrahens aurem*) (Fig. 360) consists of two or three fleshy fasciculi which *arise* from the mastoid portion of the temporal bone by short aponeurotic fibers. They are *inserted* into the lower part of the cranial surface of the concha.

Actions.—The Auricularis anterior draws the auricula forward and upward, the Auricularis superior draws it upward, and the posterior draws it backward. In man these muscles seem to act more in conjunction with the Frontalis and Occipitalls to move the scalp than to move the auricula, but in some individuals they can be used to execute voluntary movements of the auricula.

Nerves.—The Auriculares anterior and superior are supplied by the temporal branches, the Auricularis posterior by the posterior auricular branch of the facial nerve.

Variations.—The auricular muscles vary greatly in thickness and extent or rarely may be absent. An *Auriculo-frontalis* or *Temporalis superficialis* may occupy the interval between the Frontalis and the Auricularis anterior or superior.

3. The Muscles of the Eyelids.

Levator palpebræ superioris.   Orbicularis oculi.   Corrugator.

The Levator palpebræ superioris is described with the Anatomy of the Eye.

The **Orbicularis oculi** (*Orbicularis palpebrarum*) (Fig. 361) *arises* from the nasal part of the frontal bone, from the frontal process of the maxilla in front of the lacrimal groove, and from the anterior surface and borders of a short fibrous band

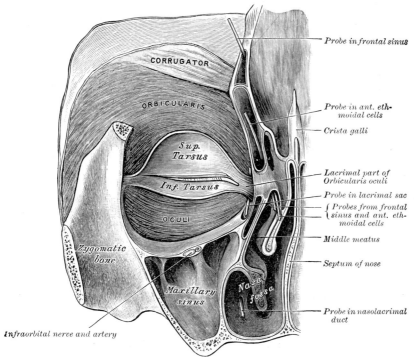

Fig. 361.—Left orbicularis oculi, seen from behind.

the **medial palpebral ligament.** From this origin, the fibers are directed lateral-ward, forming a broad and thin layer, which occupies the eyelids or palpebræ, surrounds the circumference of the orbit, and spreads over the temple, and down-ward on the cheek. The **palpebral portion** of the muscle is thin and pale; it *arises* from the bifurcation of the medial palpebral ligament, forms a series of concentric curves, and is *inserted* into the lateral palpebral raphé. The **orbital portion** is thicker and of a reddish color; its fibers form a complete ellipse without interruption at the lateral palpebral commissure; the upper fibers of this portion blend with the Frontalis and Corrugator. The **lacrimal part** (*Tensor tarsi*) is a small, thin muscle, about 6 mm. in breadth and 12 mm. in length, situated behind the medial palpebral ligament and lacrimal sac (Fig. 361). It *arises* from the posterior crest and adjacent part of the orbital surface of the lacrimal bone, and passing behind the lacrimal sac, divides into two slips, upper and lower, which are *inserted* into the superior and inferior tarsi medial to the puncta lacrimalia; occasionally it is very indistinct.

The **medial palpebral ligament** (*tendo oculi*), about 4 mm. in length and 2 mm. in breadth, is attached to the frontal process of the maxilla in front of the lacrimal groove. Crossing the lacrimal sac, it divides into two parts, upper and lower, each attached to the medial end of the corresponding tarsus. As the ligament crosses the lacrimal sac, a strong aponeurotic lamina is given off from its posterior surface; this expands over the sac, and is attached to the posterior lacrimal crest.

The **lateral palpebral raphé** is a much weaker structure than the medial palpebral ligament. It is attached to the margin of the frontosphenoidal process of the zygomatic bone, and passes medialward to the lateral commissure of the eyelids, where it divides into two slips, which are attached to the margins of the respective tarsi.

The **Corrugator** (*Corrugator supercilii*) is a small, narrow, pyramidal muscle, placed at the medial end of the eyebrow, beneath the Frontalis and Orbicularis oculi. It *arises* from the medial end of the superciliary arch; and its fibers pass upward and lateralward, between the palpebral and orbital portions of the Orbicularis oculi, and are *inserted* into the deep surface of the skin, above the middle of the orbital arch.

Actions.—The Orbicularis oculi is the sphincter muscle of the eyelids. The palpebral portion closes the lids gently, as in blinking or in sleep; the orbital portion is used as well in stronger closing, like winking with one eye. When the entire muscle is brought into action, the skin of the forehead, temple, and cheek is drawn toward the medial angle of the orbit, and the eyelids are firmly closed, as in photophobia. The skin thus drawn upon is thrown into folds, especially radiating from the lateral angle of the eyelids; these folds become permanent in old age, and form the so-called "crows' feet." The Levator palpebræ superioris is the direct antagonist of this muscle; it raises the upper eyelid and exposes the front of the bulb of the eye. Each time the eyelids are closed through the action of the Orbicularis, the medial palpebral ligament is tightened, the wall of the lacrimal sac is thus drawn lateralward and forward, so that a vacuum is made in it, and the tears are sucked along the lacrimal canals into it. The lacrimal part of the Orbicularis oculi draws the eyelids and the ends of the lacrimal canals medialward and compresses them against the surface of the globe of the eye, thus placing them in the most favorable situation for receiving the tears; it also compresses the lacrimal sac. The Corrugator draws the eyebrow downward and medialward, producing the vertical wrinkles of the forehead. It is the "frowning" muscle, and may be regarded as the principal muscle in the expression of suffering.

Nerves.—Nerves from the temporal and zygomatic branches of the facial nerve.

Variations.—The Orbicularis varies in extent and may be fused with neighboring muscles.

4. The Muscles of the Nose (Fig. 360).

Procerus.	Depressor septi.
Nasalis.	Dilatator naris posterior.

Dilatator naris anterior.

The **Procerus** (*Pyramidalis nasi*) is a small pyramidal slip *arising* by tendinous fibers from the fascia covering the lower part of the nasal bone and upper part of the lateral nasal cartilage; it is *inserted* into the skin over the lower part of the forehead between the two eyebrows, its fibers decussating with those of the Frontalis.

The **Nasalis** (*Compressor naris*) consists of two parts, transverse and alar. The **transverse part** *arises* from the maxilla, above and lateral to the incisive fossa; its fibers proceed upward and medialward, expanding into a thin aponeurosis which is continuous on the bridge of the nose with that of the muscle of the opposite side, and with the aponeurosis of the Procerus. The **alar part** is attached by one end to the greater alar cartilage, and by the other to the integument at the point of the nose.

The **Depressor septi** (*Depressor alæ nasi*) *arises* from the incisive fossa of the maxilla; its fibers ascend to be *inserted* into the septum and back part of the ala of the nose. It lies between the mucous membrane and muscular structure of the lip.

The **Dilatator naris posterior** is placed partly beneath the Quadratus labii superioris. It *arises* from the margin of the nasal notch of the maxilla, and from the lesser alar cartilages, and is *inserted* into the skin near the margin of the nostril.

The **Dilatator naris anterior** is a delicate fasciculus, passing from the greater alar cartilage to the integument near the margin of the nostril; it is situated in front of the preceding.

Actions.—The Procerus draws down the medial angle of the eyebrows and produces transverse wrinkles over the bridge of the nose. The two Dilatatores enlarge the aperture of the nares. Their action in ordinary breathing is to resist the tendency of the nostrils to close from atmospheric pressure, but in difficult breathing, as well as in some emotions, such as anger, they contract strongly. The Depressor septi is a direct antagonist of the other muscles of the nose, drawing the ala of the nose downward, and thereby constricting the aperture of the nares. The Nasalis depresses the cartilaginous part of the nose and draws the ala toward the septum.

Nerves.—Nerves from the buccal branches of the facial nerve.

Variations.—These muscles vary in size and strength or may be absent.

5. The Muscles of the Mouth (Fig. 360).

Quadratus labii superioris.   Quadratus labii inferioris.
Caninus.   Triangularis.
Zygomaticus.   Mentalis.
Risorius.   Orbicularis oris.
Buccinator.

The **Quadratus labii superioris** is a broad sheet, the origin of which extends from the side of the nose to the zygomatic bone. Its medial fibers form the **angular head**, which *arises* by a pointed extremity from the upper part of the frontal process of the maxilla and passing obliquely downward and lateralward divides into two slips. One of these is *inserted* into the greater alar cartilage and skin of the nose; the other is prolonged into the lateral part of the upper lip, blending with the infraorbital head and with the Orbicularis oris. The intermediate portion or **infraorbital head** *arises* from the lower margin of the orbit immediately above the infraorbital foramen, some of its fibers being attached to the maxilla, others to the zygomatic bone. Its fibers converge, to be *inserted* into the muscular substance of the upper lip between the angular head and the Caninus. The lateral fibers, forming the **zygomatic head**, *arise* from the malar surface of the zygomatic bone immediately behind the zygomaticomaxillary suture and pass downward and medialward to the upper lip.

The **Caninus** (*Levator anguli oris*) *arises* from the canine fossa, immediately below the infraorbital foramen; its fibers are *inserted* into the angle of the mouth, intermingling with those of the Zygomaticus, Triangularis, and Orbicularis oris.

The **Zygomaticus** (*Zygomaticus major*) *arises* from the zygomatic bone, in front of the zygomaticotemporal suture, and descending obliquely with a medial inclination, is *inserted* into the angle of the mouth, where it blends with the fibers of the Caninus, Orbicularis oris, and Triangularis.

Actions.—The Quadratus labii superioris is the proper elevator of the upper lip, carrying it at the same time a little forward. Its angular head acts as a dilator of the naris; the infraorbital and zygomatic heads assist in forming the nasolabial furrow, which passes from the side of the nose to the upper lip and gives to the face an expression of sadness. When the whole muscle is in action it gives to the countenance an expression of contempt and disdain. The Quadratus labii superioris raises the angle of the mouth and assists the Caninus in producing the nasolabial furrow. The Zygomaticus draws the angle of the mouth backward and upward, as in laughing.

Nerves.—Nerves from the buccal branches of the facial nerve.

Variations.—These muscles, especially the zygomatic head of the Quadratus superior, vary in extent and the degree of fusion with each other or with neighboring muscles.

The **Risorius** *arises* in the fascia over the Masseter and, passing horizontally forward, superficial to the Platysma, is *inserted* into the skin at the angle of the mouth (Fig. 360.)

The **Quadratus labii inferioris** (*Depressor labii inferioris; Quadratus menti*) is a small quadrilateral muscle. It *arises* from the oblique line of the mandible, between the symphysis and the mental foramen, and passes upward and medial-ward, to be *inserted* into the integument of the lower lip, its fibers blending with the Orbicularis oris, and with those of its fellow of the opposite side. At its origin it is continuous with the fibers of the Platysma. Much yellow fat is intermingled with the fibers of this muscle.

The **Triangularis** (*Depressor anguli oris*) *arises* from the oblique line of the mandible, whence its fibers converge, to be *inserted*, by a narrow fasciculus, into the angle of the mouth. At its origin it is continuous with the Platysma, and at its insertion with the Orbicularis oris and Risorius; some of its fibers are directly continuous with those of the Caninus.

The **Mentalis** (*Levator menti*) is a small conical fasciculus, situated at the side of the frenulum of the lower lip. It *arises* from the incisive fossa of the mandible, and descends to be *inserted* into the integument of the chin.

Actions.—The Risorius retracts the angle of the mouth. The Quadratus labii inferioris draws the lower lip directly downward and a little lateralward, as in the expression of irony. The Tri-angularis depresses the angle of the mouth, being the antagonist of the Caninus and Zygomaticus; acting with the Caninus, it draws the angle of the mouth medialward. The Mentalis raises and protrudes the lower lip, and at the same time wrinkles the skin of the chin, expressing doubt or disdain. The Platysma acts with this group, retracting and depressing the angle of the mouth.

Nerves.—Nerves from the mandibular and buccal branches of the facial nerve.

Variations.—The Risorius varies greatly; it may be absent, doubled, greatly enlarged, or blended with the Platysma. The Quadratus labii inferioris is continuous with the Platysma to a greater or lesser extent. The Mentalis varies in size and connection with the Platysma. The Triangularis may be in two or three separate parts; its anterior fibers may cross under the chin to join the Transversus menti.

The **Transversus menti**, found in more than half the bodies, is a small muscle which crosses the midline just under the chin. It is frequently continuous with the Triangularis.

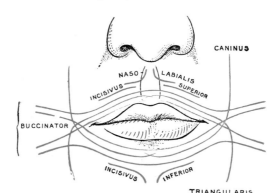

Fig. 362.—Scheme showing arrangement of fibers of Orbicularis oris.

The **Orbicularis oris** (Fig. 362) is not a simple sphincter muscle like the Orbic-ularis oculi; it consists of numerous strata of muscular fibers surrounding the orifice of the mouth but having different direction. It consists partly of fibers derived from the other facial muscles which are inserted into the lips, and partly of fibers proper to the lips. Of the former, a considerable number are derived from the Buccinator and form the deeper stratum of the Orbicularis. Some of the Buccinator fibers—namely, those near the middle of the muscle—decussate at the angle of the mouth, those arising from the maxilla passing to the lower lip, and those from the mandible to the upper lip. The uppermost and lowermost fibers of the Buccinator pass across the lips from side to side without decussation. Superficial to this stratum is a second, formed on either side by the Caninus and

Triangularis, which cross each other at the angle of the mouth; those from the Caninus passing to the lower lip, and those from the Triangularis to the upper lip, along which they run, to be inserted into the skin near the median line. In addition to these there are fibers from the Quadratus labii superioris, the Zygomaticus, and the Quadratus labii inferioris; these intermingle with the transverse fibers

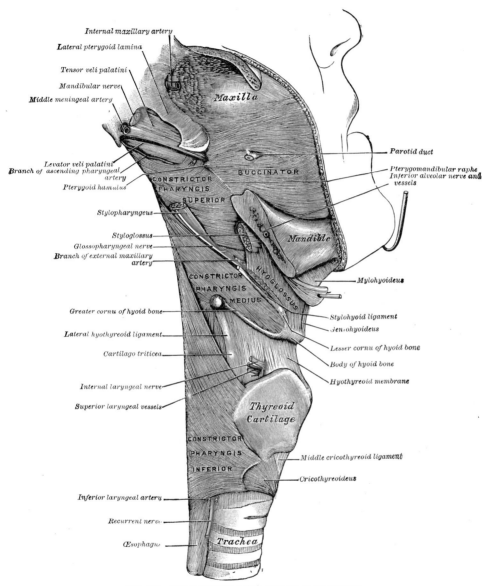

FIG. 363.—The Buccinator and the muscles of the pharynx.

above described, and have principally an oblique direction. The proper fibers of the lips are oblique, and pass from the under surface of the skin to the mucous membrane, through the thickness of the lip. Finally there are fibers by which the muscle is connected with the maxillæ and the septum of the nose above and with the mandible below. In the upper lip these consist of two bands, lateral and medial, on either side of the middle line; the **lateral band** (*m. incisivus labii superioris*) *arises* from the alveolar border of the maxilla, opposite the lateral incisor tooth, and arching lateralward is continuous with the other muscles at the angle of the mouth; the **medial band** (*m. nasolabialis*) connects the upper lip to the back of the septum of the nose. The interval between the two medial bands corresponds with the depression, called the **philtrum**, seen on the lip beneath the septum of the nose. The additional fibers for the lower lip constitute a slip (*m. incisivus labii inferioris*) on either side of the middle line; this arises from the mandible, lateral to the Mentalis, and intermingles with the other muscles at the angle of the mouth.

Actions.—The Orbicularis oris in its ordinary action effects the direct closure of the lips; by its deep fibers, assisted by the oblique ones, it closely applies the lips to the alveolar arch. The superficial part, consisting principally of the decussating fibers, brings the lips together and also protrudes them forward.

Nerves.—The buccal branches of the facial nerve.

The **Buccinator** (Fig. 363) is the principal muscle of the cheek and forms the lateral wall of the oral cavity. It lies deeper than the other facial muscles, is quadrilateral in form, and occupies the interval between the maxilla and mandible, lateral to the teeth. It *arises* from the outer surfaces of the alveolar processes of the maxilla above and mandible below, alongside of the three molar teeth, and in between, from the pterygomandibular raphé, a tendinous inscription giving origin to both the Buccinator and the Constrictor pharyngis superior. The fibers of the upper and lower portions follow a slightly converging course forward, and *insert* by blending with the deeper stratum of muscle fibers in the corresponding lips. The fibers of the central portion converge toward the angle of the mouth and decussate, those from above becoming continuous with the Orbicularis oris of the lower lip, those from below with that of the upper lip. The superficial surface of the Buccinator is covered by the buccopharyngeal fascia and the buccal fat pad; the deep surface is in relation with the buccal glands and mucous membrane of the mouth. It is pierced by the duct of the parotid gland opposite the upper second molar tooth.

Action.—The Buccinator compresses the cheek and is, therefore, an important accessory muscle of mastication, holding the food under the immediate pressure of the teeth. When the cheeks have been distended with air, the Buccinators compress it and tend to force it out between the lips as in blowing a trumpet (Latin buccinator, a trumpet player).

Nerve.—The motor fibers to the Buccinator come from the facial nerve through its buccal branches. The buccinator nerve (from the trigeminal) is sensory only, in this area.

The **Pterygomandibular Raphé** (*pterygomandibular ligament*) (Fig. 363) is a tendinous inscription between the Buccinator and the Constrictor pharyngis superior which gives origin to the middle portion of both muscles. Except for this tendinous interruption, the Constrictor, Buccinator and Orbicularis oris would form a continuous sphincter-like band of muscle. The raphé is held in place by its attachment superiorly to the pterygoid hamulus and inferiorly to the posterior end of the mylohyoid line of the mandible. Its relations are the same as those of the two muscles, its medial surface being covered by the mucous membrane of the mouth and its lateral surface being separated from the ramus of the mandible by a quantity of adipose tissue, the buccal fat pad.

Buccal Fat Pad (*corpus adiposum buccæ, suctorial pad*), a circumscribed or encapsulated mass of fat, lies superficial to the Buccinator at the anterior border of the Masseter. A well defined fascial cleft separates it from the superficial fascia and facial muscles. From this main mass of adipose tissue, narrow prolongations extend deeply between the Masseter and the Temporalis and upward under the deep temporal fascia. Some of the tissue continues still more deeply into the infratemporal fossa, separating the Pterygoideus externus and Temporalis from the maxilla, and filling in between the various structures and the bony fossæ. The mass superficial to the Buccinator is particularly prominent in infants, and is called the suctorial pad because it is supposed to assist in the act of sucking.

II. THE MUSCLES OF MASTICATION.

Temporalis.   Pterygoideus internus.
  Masseter.   Pterygoideus externus.

The **Temporal Fascia** (*fascia temporalis*) (Fig. 366) is a strong, fibrous sheet, aponeurotic in appearance, which covers the Temporalis and is used by it for the attachment of its fibers. It is the most cranial extension of the deep fascia; above it, the deep fascia is represented only by the pericranium. It is covered by the superficial fascia which includes the Galea aponeurotica and Auricularis superior above, the Orbicularis oculi anteriorly, and just in front of the ear it is crossed by the superficial temporal vessels and auriculotemporal nerve. Its uppermost portion is a thin, single sheet, attached to the entire extent of the superior temporal line. Its lower portion, near the attachment to the zygomatic arch, is thickened and laminated. The inner leaf ends by attaching to the medial border of the arch; the outer leaf, after attaching to the lateral border, continues downward below the arch as the masseteric fascia. Between the leaves is a small quantity of fat, the orbital branch of the superficial temporal artery, and a filament from the zygomatic branch of the maxillary nerve.

The **Parotideomasseteric Fascia** (*fascia parotideomasseterica*) (Fig. 366) covers the lateral surface of the Masseter and splits to enclose the parotid gland. It is attached to the zygomatic arch above, is continuous with the suprahyoid portion of the cervical fascia below, and with the cervical fascia over the Sternocleidomastoideus posteriorly. The sheet which covers the superficial surface of the gland is fused with dense and tough superficial fascia, is intimately mingled with its capsule, and sends numerous irregular septa into its substance so that this gland cannot be shelled out, as can the submaxillary gland. The layer on the deep surface of the gland follows this surface behind the ramus of the mandible and there fuses with the fascia of the posterior belly of the Digastricus into a strong band, the stylomandibular ligament. The fascia covering the Masseter, the **masseteric fascia,** terminates anteriorly by encircling the ramus of the mandible and becoming continuous with the fascia of the Pterygoideus internus deep to the bone. The masseteric fascia is attached to the border of the mandible inferiorly and posteriorly, completing a compartment which encloses the muscle except at its upper, deep portion where there is a communication with the tissue spaces about the insertion of the Temporalis.

The **pterygoid fascia** invests the Pterygoideus internus and externus muscles. It is continuous below, at the angle of the mandible, with the masseteric and investing cervical fascias where the latter are attached to the bone. In this region also, it is continuous with the thickened band known as the stylomandibular ligament. It extends upward and forward along the deep surface of the Pterygoideus internus to be attached with the origin of the muscle to the pterygoid process of the sphenoid bone. This sheet of fascia is attached to the mandible at both the borders of the inferior half of the muscle, but as the muscle angles away from the mandible toward its origin, the fascia wraps around the muscle forming a sheet on its superficial surface. This superficial sheet, continuing upward, splits to invest the Pterygoideus externus and is attached to the skull with the origin of this muscle. The fascia between the two Pterygoidei is attached to the skull along a line extending from the lateral pterygoid plate to the spina angularis of the sphenoid bone. The part attached to the spina angularis is thickened into a strong band which is attached below to the lingula of the mandible, forming the sphenomandibular ligament (page 273). Another band, the **pterygospinous ligament,** extends from the spine, between the two Pterygoidei, to the posterior margin of the lateral pterygoid plate. Occasionally this band is ossified, creating, between its upper border and the skull, a **pterygospinous foramen** which transmits the branches of the mandibular division of the trigeminal nerve to the muscles of mastication. Between the sphenomandibular ligament and the neck of the mandible, there is an interval which affords a passage for the internal maxillary vessels into the infratemporal fossa. The fascia on the surface of the Pterygoideus externus is in relation with the pterygoid plexus of veins. Deep to the pterygoid and deep temporal fasciæ the layer of soft adipose tissue which is an extension of the buccal fat pad separates these fasciæ from the buccopharyngeal fascia and neighboring structures.

The masticator compartment contains the four muscles of mastication and the ramus and posterior part of the body of the mandible. It is enclosed superficially by the masseteric and temporal fasciæ and deeply by the pterygoid and deep temporal fasciæ.

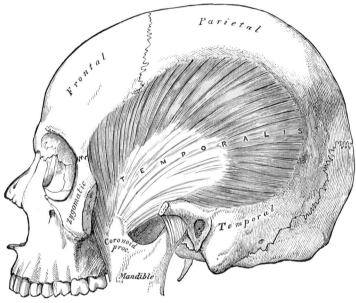

Fig. 364.—The Temporalis; the zygomatic arch and Masseter have been removed.

The **Temporalis** (*Temporal muscle*) (Fig. 364) is a broad, radiating muscle, situated at the side of the head. It *arises* from the whole of the temporal fossa and from the deep surface of the temporal fascia. Its fibers converge as they descend, and end in a tendon, which passes deep to the zygomatic arch and is *inserted* into the medial surface, apex, and anterior border of the coronoid process, and the anterior border of the ramus of the mandible nearly as far forward as the last molar tooth.

Action.—Closes the jaws. The posterior portion retracts the mandible.

Nerves.—Anterior and posterior deep temporal nerves from the mandibular division of the trigeminal nerve.

The **Masseter** (Fig. 360) is a thick, somewhat quadrilateral muscle, consisting of two portions, superficial and deep. The *superficial portion*, the larger, *arises* by a thick, tendinous aponeurosis from the zygomatic process of the maxilla, and from the anterior two-thirds of the lower border of the zygomatic arch: its fibers pass downward and backward, to be *inserted* into the angle and lower half of the lateral surface of the ramus of the mandible. The *deep portion* is much smaller, and more muscular in texture; it *arises* from the posterior third of the lower border and from the whole of the medial surface of the zygomatic arch; its fibers pass downward and forward, to be *inserted* into the upper half of the ramus and the lateral surface of the coronoid process of the mandible. The deep portion of the muscle is partly concealed, in front, by the superficial portion; behind, it is covered by the parotid gland. The fibers of the two portions are continuous at their insertion.

Action.—Closes the jaws.
Nerve.—The masseteric nerve from the mandibular division of the trigeminal nerve.

The **Pterygoideus internus** (*Internal pterygoid muscles* (Fig. 365) is a thick, quadrilateral muscle occupying a position on the inside of the ramus of the mandible similar to that of the Masseter on the outside. It *arises* from the medial surface of the lateral pterygoid plate and the grooved surface of the pyramidal process of the palatine bone; it has a second slip of origin from the lateral surfaces of the pyramidal process of the palatine and tuberosity of the maxilla. The second slip lies superficial to the Pterygoideus externus while the main mass of the muscle lies deep. Its fibers pass downward, lateralward, and backward, and are *inserted*, by a strong tendinous lamina, into the lower and back part of the medial surface of the ramus and angle of the mandible, as high as the mandibular foramen. The upper portion of the muscle is separated from the mandible by the sphenomandibular ligament, the internal maxillary vessels, the inferior alveolar vessels and nerve, and the lingual nerve. The medial surface of the muscle is closely related to the Tensor veli palatini above and to the Constrictor pharyngis superior lower down.

Action.—Closes the jaws.
Nerve.—The internal pterygoid nerve from the mandibular division of the trigeminal nerve.

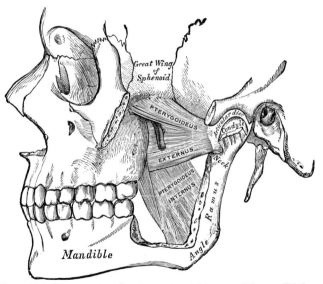

Fig. 365.—The Pterygoidei; the zygomatic arch and a portion of the ramus of the mandible have been removed.

The **Mandibular Sling.**—The Masseter and the Pterygoideus internus are so placed that they suspend the angle of the mandible in a sling. They form a functional articulation between the mandible and the maxilla, with the temporomandibular joint acting as a guide, in a fashion similar to the articulation between the scapula and the thorax, with the clavicle as a guide. When the mouth is opened and closed, the mandible moves about a center of rotation established by the attachment of the sling and the sphenomandibular ligament.

The **Pterygoideus externus** (*External pterygoid muscle*) (Fig. 365) is a short, thick muscle, somewhat conical in form, which extends almost horizontally between the infratemporal fossa and the condyle of the mandible. It *arises* by two heads; an **upper** from the lower part of the lateral surface of the great wing of the sphenoid and from the infratemporal crest; a **lower** from the lateral surface of the lateral pterygoid plate. Its fibers pass horizontally backward and lateralward, to be *inserted* into a depression in front of the neck of the condyle of the mandible, and into the front margin of the articular disk of the temporomandibular articulation.

Action.—Opens the jaws; protrudes the mandible; moves mandible from side to side.

Nerve.—The external pterygoid nerve from the mandibular division of the trigeminal nerve.

Group Actions.—The Temporalis, Masseter and Pterygoideus internus close the jaws. Biting with the incisor teeth is performed by the Masseter and Pterygoideus internus primarily, to some extent by the anterior portion of the Temporalis. Biting or chewing with the molars calls all three into maximal action. Opening of the jaws is performed primarily by the Pterygoideus externus pulling forward on the condyle and rotating the mandible about the center of rotation near the angle (see page 275). It is assisted, at the beginning of the action, by the Mylohyoideus, Digastricus, and Geniohyoideus. When the mouth is opened against great resistance, in addition to the above, the infrahyoid muscles act to fix the hyoid, and other suprahyoid muscles probably come into action. The Platysma is practically without action unless the corners of the mouth are widely drawn back. The Pterygoideus externus protrudes the jaw when accompanied by appropriate synergetic action of the closing muscles. The Pterygoideus internus assists in this action only as a synergist, along with the other closing muscles, when they prevent the rotation which opens the jaws widely. If the Pterygoideus externus of one side acts, the corresponding side of the mandible is drawn forward while the opposite condyle remains comparatively fixed, and side-to-side movements, such as those occurring in the triturition of food, take place. The mandible is retracted by the posterior fibers of the Temporalis.

THE FASCIÆ AND MUSCLES OF THE ANTERO–LATERAL REGION OF THE NECK.

The antero-lateral muscles of the neck may be arranged into the following groups:

I. Superficial Cervical.

II. Lateral Cervical.

III. Suprahyoid.

IV. Infrahyoid.

V. Anterior Vertebral.

VI. Lateral Vertebral.

I. THE SUPERFICIAL CERVICAL MUSCLE.

Platysma.

The **Superficial Fascia** (*tela subcutanea*) in the anterior and lateral regions of the neck is thinner and less dense than the facial portion with which it is continuous over the border of the mandible and the parotid gland. It has imbedded in its deeper layers the fibers of the Platysma muscle, and it is separated from the deep fascia by a distinct fascial cleft which facilitates the action of the muscle and increases the movability of the skin in this region. It is continuous over the clavicle with the superficial fascia of the pectoral and deltoid regions. Posteriorly, it is continuous with the superficial fascia of the back of the neck which is thick, tough, fibrous, and adherent to the deep fascia.

The **Platysma** (Fig. 360) is a broad sheet *arising* from the fascia covering the upper parts of the Pectoralis major and Deltoideus; its fibers cross the clavicle, and proceed obliquely upward and medialward along the side of the neck. The anterior fibers interlace, below and behind the symphysis menti, with the fibers of the muscle of the opposite side; the posterior fibers cross the mandible, some being inserted into the bone below the oblique line, others into the skin and subcutaneous tissue of the lower part of the face, many of these fibers blending with the muscles about the angle and lower part of the mouth. Sometimes fibers can be traced to the Zygomaticus, or to the margin of the Orbicularis oculi. Beneath the Platysma, the external jugular vein descends from the angle of the mandible to the clavicle.

Action.—Draws the outer part of the lower lip downward and backward, widening the aperture at the corners of the mouth as in an expression of horror, and assists in opening the jaws when the mouth is opened as above. When all its fibers act maximally, it pulls the skin up from the clavicular region, increasing the diameter of the neck and relieving the pressure of a tight collar.

Nerve.—The cervical branch of the facial nerve.

Variations.—The platysma may be composed of delicate, pale, scattered fasciculi, or may form a broad layer of robust, dark fasciculi; it may be deficient or reach well below the clavicle; it may extend into the face for a very short distance or may continue as high as the zygoma or the ear. Decussation of fasciculi in the middle line anteriorly is common. The muscle may be absent.

The **Occipitalis minor** may extend, as a more or less independent band, from the fascia over the Trapezius to the fascia over the insertion of the Sternocleidomastoideus.

CERVICAL FASCIÆ

The **Fascia Colli** (*deep cervical fascia*) (Fig. 366) forms important transitions and connections, as might be expected, because the neck itself is a connecting structure, joining the head with the thorax and making many contributions to the upper limb. Its components are complex and form various compartments and fascial clefts which are of major surgical interest because of these associations.

Cervical Triangles.—Two triangular areas are formed in the neck by the oblique course of the Sternocleidomastoideus muscle. The **Anterior Triangle** is bounded by the middle line anteriorly, the Sternocleidomastoideus laterally, and the body of the mandible superiorly. The **Posterior Triangle** is bounded by the clavicle below, and by the adjacent borders of the Sternocleidomastoideus and Trapezius above.

The Fascia Colli may be divided, first, according to area, into suprahyoid and infrahyoid portions. Both of these, in turn, may be subdivided into smaller portions for the purpose of description. The suprahyoid subdivisions are: (1) the investing fascia, and (2) the deeper portion which is associated with the mandible and the floor of the mouth. The infrahyoid may be subdivided into: (1) the investing fascia; (2) the prevertebral fascia; (3) the middle cervical fascia; (4) the visceral fascia, and (5) the carotid sheath.

Fascia of the Suprahyoid Region.—Since the suprahyoid region is as much a part of the head as of the neck, it will be necessary to include descriptions of certain head fasciæ for the sake of clarity and continuity. It is convenient and logical, moreover, to look upon the fascia of the head as the cranial portion of the cervical fascia, and trace them both to the same superior termination and attachment.

The **investing fascia of the suprahyoid region** (Fig. 368) extends upward from its attachment to the hyoid bone and is attached to the whole length of the inferior border of the mandible. It covers the anterior belly of the Digastricus, is adherent to its sheath, and is continuous across the middle line. More laterally, it splits to enclose the submaxillary gland in a sheath which is separated from the intrinsic capsule of the gland by a fascial cleft. The sheet on the deep surface of the gland lies over the Stylohyoideus and the intermediate tendon of the Digastricus, and, by a fusion with their fascial covering, forms a band which is carried up to the styloid process, prolonging the lower boundary of the suprahyoid compartment posteriorly from the hyoid bone. The sheets of the superficial and deep surfaces of the submaxillary gland come together for a short distance near the angle of the mandible and separate again to ensheath the parotid gland. The external layer of the parotid portion extends upward over the angle of the mandible as the parotideo-masseteric fascia and attaches to the zygomatic arch. It is closely adherent to the capsule of the gland which cannot, therefore, be shelled out readily, as is the case

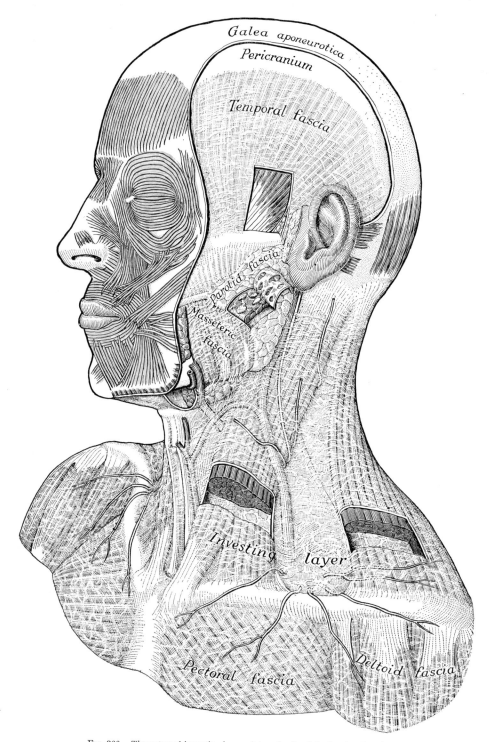

FIG. 366.—The external investing layer of deep fascia of the head and neck.

with the submaxillary gland. The fascia at the posterior border of the parotid gland is very tough where the superficial layer joins the deeper layer. It splits again to enclose the Sternocleidomastoideus, is attached to the mastoid process of the temporal bone, and is then continuous with the fascia of the back of the neck.

The deeper layers of fascia in the anterior portion of the suprahyoid region form individual sheaths for the muscles and are attached to the hyoid bone, below, and to the mandible, the styloid process, or the tongue, above. More laterally, the portion of the investing layer between the submaxillary and parotid glands, extends deeply to fuse with the fascia of the posterior belly of the Digastricus. The result is a strong band which continues upward between the deep surface of the parotid and the posterior belly of the Digastricus; it is attached, above, to the styloid process and below, to the angle of the mandible, and is known as the stylomandibular ligament.

The suprahyoid compartment is closed by the attachment of the investing fascia to the border of the mandible above and to the hyoid bone below. It is continuous across the middle line anteriorly and reaches up to the floor of the mouth in the region of the sublingual gland and tongue. The fascial clefts between structures in this compartment are continuous posteriorly into the fascial cleft which lies superficial to the buccopharyngeal fascia (the lateral pharyngeal cleft) and into the region of the deep extensions of the buccal fat pad. The fascial clefts in the floor of the mouth and about the sublingual gland communicate with the cleft surrounding the submaxillary gland by extending around the posterior border of the Mylohyoideus.

The **fascia of the infrahyoid region** includes most of what is commonly called the deep cervical fascia (fascia colli).

The **investing layer of cervical fascia** (Fig. 366) in the infrahyoid region is not sharply marked off from the investing fascia of adjacent regions with which it is continuous, and the fascia of one side is continuous across the middle line with the fascia of the other side. It splits into two sheets to invest the two prominent superficial muscles, the Sternocleidomastoideus and the Trapezius, but it covers the anterior and posterior triangles as a single sheet except just above the sternum. It is continuous, superiorly, with the fascia of the suprahyoid region, and inferiorly, with the pectoral and deltoid fasciæ. It has bony attachments superiorly, inferiorly, and posteriorly. The anterior portion of its superior attachment is to the hyoid bone; the lateral and posterior portion is to the mandible, mastoid process, and superior nuchal line through its continuity with the suprahyoid and posterior cervical fasciæ. Through its continuity with the posterior cervical fascia also, it is attached posteriorly to the spinous process of the seventh cervical vertebra and the ligamentum nuchæ. The inferior attachment is to the acromion, the clavicle, and the manubrium sterni. Extending upward from the manubrial attachment between the sternal origins of the Sternocleidomastoidei for 3 or 4 cm., there is a thickening due to lamination. The outer lamina is attached to the anterior border of the manubrium, the inner lamina to the posterior border and the interclavicular ligament. The shallow interval between the two laminæ, mostly filled with fat, is called the **suprasternal space** (*Space of Burns*) (Fig. 368.) It contains the lower portions of the anterior jugular veins and their transverse connecting branch (arcus venosus), the sternal heads of the Sternocleidomastoidei, and sometimes a lymph node. The anterior jugulars, in order to reach the external jugulars, traverse extensions of the laminated interval which are prolonged laterally behind the heads of the Sternocleidomastoidei (*cul de sac of Gruber*) (Fig. 368). The external and anterior jugular veins, through most of their course in the neck, appear to lie between the superficial and deep fasciæ but actually are imbedded in the superficial surface of the investing sheet.

The **prevertebral fascia** (Figs. 367, 372) is the anterior portion of a larger complex, the vertebral fascia, which encloses the vertebral column and its muscles. The cervical portion of the prevertebral fascia is part of a larger sheet which goes by that name and which lies on the anterior surface of the vertebral column from the skull to the coccyx. In the neck, it extends laterally across the anterior surface of the Longus colli and capitis, and the Rectus capitis anterior and lateralis muscles, and is then secured to the tips of the transverse processes. From this attachment,

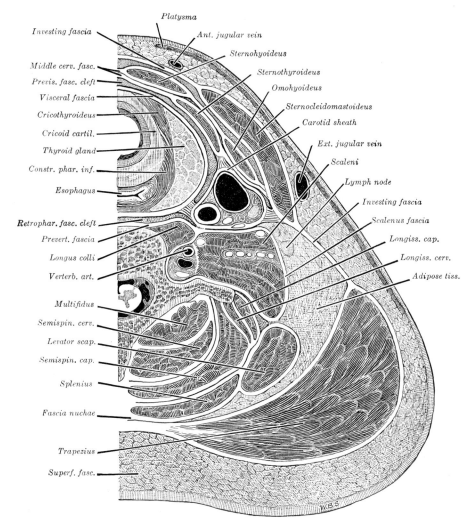

Fig. 367.—Section of the neck at about the level of the sixth cervical vertebra. Showing the arrangement of the fascia colli.

it is continuous laterally with the fascia which covers the Levator scapulæ and Splenius, and completes the enclosure of the vertebral compartment posteriorly by attaching to the spinous processes of the vertebræ. Below, it extends over the superficial surface of the Scalenus anterior, medius, and posterior muscles to become continuous with the fascia of the thoracic wall. The fascia on the deep surface of the scalenus group of muscles forms part of a conical, fibrous dome, called **Sibson's fascia**, which arches over the cupula of the lung. It varies considerably in its thickness and composition; it is reinforced frequently by fibrous bands, and, in some cases, by muscle fibers, the latter being called the **Scalenus minimus**. It is attached to the transverse process of the seventh cervical vertebra and to the medial border of the first rib, and merges with the carotid sheath where the latter is pierced by the subclavian artery. Below the first rib it becomes continuous with the endothoracic fascia. As the spinal nerves emerge from between the Scalenus medius and anterior muscles, on their way to the brachial plexus, they are covered by a prolongation from the scalenus portion of the prevertebral fascia. This prolongation encloses the nerves and the subclavian artery and vein and extends under the clavicle into the axilla as the axillary sheath.

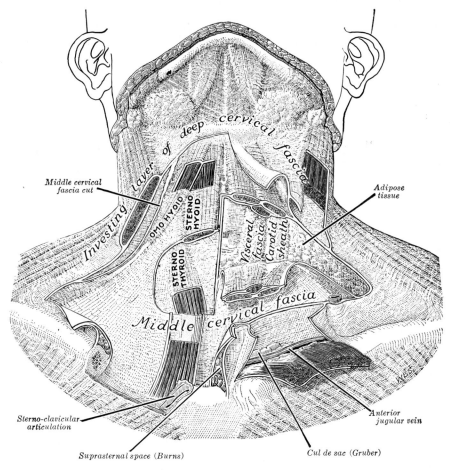

FIG. 368.—The middle cervical fascia.

The prevertebral fascia is separated from the visceral fascia by the **retropharyngeal fascial cleft** (*retropharyngeal space*). In the lateral region, the prevertebral fascia is adherent to the investing fascia of the neck under the Sternocleidomastoideus and superiorly in the Posterior Triangle. In the lower part of the Posterior Triangle a considerable pad of adipose tissue occupies the interval between the prevertebral and investing sheets and surrounds the axillary sheath as it passes under the clavicle.

The **middle cervical fascia** (Fig. 368) invests the two layers of infrahyoid muscles and has, therefore, a superficial, a deep, and a middle sheet. Above, all three sheets are attached to the hyoid bone and the outer sheet is also fused with the external

24

investing fascia for a short distance below the bone. At the lateral border of the Omohyoideus, the superficial and deep sheets come together and are fused to the deep surface of the investing membrane of the neck. No independent representation of this fascia, therefore, is found in the posterior triangle above the Omohyoideus. Below, all three layers are attached to the posterior surface of the sternum along with the muscles they invest. In the supraclavicular region, the fascia is securely fastened to the clavicle and is looped over the inferior belly of the Omohyoideus like a sleeve with the medial part thickened into a pulley for the intermediate tendon. Under cover of the Sternocleidomastoideus, the lateral border of the fascia is attached to the carotid sheath. A fascial cleft separates the deep surface of the fascia from the underlying visceral fascia, especially inferior to the thyroid cartilage.

The **cervical visceral fascia** (Fig. 367) is a roughly tubular prolongation of the visceral fascia of the mediastinum. It forms a compartment enclosing the esophagus and trachea as they enter the neck from the thorax, and farther superiorly, the pharynx, larynx, and thyroid gland. It extends superiorly into the head and is attached to the base of the skull at the pharyngeal tubercle, with the Constrictor pharyngis superior and the pharyngeal aponeurosis, and to the pterygoid hamulus and the mandible with the pterygomandibular raphé. The portion covering the Constrictor superior continues anteriorly over the Buccinator and is called the buccopharyngeal fascia. That covering the Constrictor medius is continuous anteriorly with the fascia over the Hyoglossus and Genioglossus, and with them, is attached to the hyoid bone.

A **perivisceral fascial cleft** (Fig. 367) almost completely surrounds the visceral fascia and separates it from the middle cervical fascia antero-laterally, from the carotid sheath laterally, and from the prevertebral fascia posteriorly, leaving the enclosed esophagus and pharynx relatively free for the movement of swallowing. Postero-laterally, however, the visceral fascia has a narrow attachment along its whole length to the tips of the transverse processes, at which point, it is fused also with the carotid sheath and prevertebral fascia. This attachment subdivides the entire perivisceral fascial cleft into anterior and posterior portions. The anterior portion, sometimes named the **previsceral cleft,** is in relation to that part of the visceral fascia frequently called the **pretracheal fascia,** that is, the part covering the trachea, larynx, and thyroid gland. The posterior portion of the cleft, between the pharynx and the prevertebral fascia, is called the retropharyngeal cleft (see above) and is of surgical importance because of its continuation downward behind the esophagus into the thorax.

The **carotid sheath** (Fig. 367) forms a tubular investment for the carotid artery, internal jugular vein and vagus nerve. It is attached medially to the visceral fascia by means of a sheet, the **alar fascia,** which is fused with the latter along the posterior middle line of the pharynx from the skull to the level of the seventh cervical vertebra. The sheath is attached posteriorly to the prevertebral fascia along the line of the tips of the transverse processes. Laterally, it is fused with the investing fascia on the deep surface of the Sternocleidomastoideus, and anteriorly, it is fused with the middle cervical fascia along the lateral border of the Sterno-thyroideus. In the upper part of the neck the sheath is fused with the fascia of the Stylohyoideus and posterior belly of the Digastricus as it passes deep to them and finally is fastened to the skull with its enclosed structures. In the root of the neck the sheath is adherent to the sternum and first rib, fuses with the scalenus fascia, and finally becomes continuous with the fibrous pericardium. The cervical sympathetic trunk is imbedded in the fascia of the posterior wall of the sheath and is not actually within the sheath.

II. THE LATERAL CERVICAL MUSCLES.

Trapezius and Sternocleidomastoideus.

The Trapezius is described on page 423.

The **Sternocleidomastoideus** (*Sternomastoid muscle*) (Fig. 369) passes obliquely across the side of the neck. It is thick and narrow at its central part, but broader and thinner at either end. It *arises* from the sternum and clavicle by two heads. The **medial or sternal head** is a rounded fasciculus, tendinous in front, fleshy behind, which *arises* from the upper part of the anterior surface of the manubrium sterni, and is directed upward, lateralward, and backward. The **lateral or clavicular head** composed of fleshy and aponeurotic fibers, *arises* from the superior border and anterior surface of the medial third of the clavicle; it is directed almost vertically upward. The two heads are separated from one another at their origins by a triangular interval, but gradually blend, below the middle of the neck, into a thick, rounded muscle which is *inserted*, by a strong tendon, into the lateral surface of the mastoid process, from its apex to its superior border, and by a thin aponeurosis into the lateral half of the superior nuchal line of the occipital bone.

Action.—The muscle of one side bends the cervical vertebral column laterally, drawing the head toward the shoulder of the same side, and at the same time rotates it, pointing the chin upward, and to the opposite side. Both muscles acting together flex the vertebral column, bringing the head forward and at the same time elevating the chin.

Nerves.—The spinal part of the accessory nerve and branches from the anterior rami of the second and third cervical nerves.

Variations.—The Sternocleidomastoideus varies much in the extent of its origin from the clavicle: in some cases the clavicular head may be as narrow as the sternal; in others it may be as much as 7.5 cm. in breadth. When the clavicular origin is broad, it is occasionally subdivided into several slips, separated by narrow intervals. More rarely, the adjoining margins of the Sternocleidomastoideus and Trapezius have been found in contact. The *Supraclavicularis muscle* arises from the manubrium behind the Sternocleidomastoideus and passes behind the Sternocleidomastoideus to the upper surface of the clavicle.

III. THE SUPRAHYOID MUSCLES (Figs. 369, 370).

Digastricus.   Mylohyoideus.
Stylohyoideus.   Geniohyoideus.

The **Digastricus** (*Digastric muscle*) consists of two fleshy bellies united by an intermediate rounded tendon. It lies below the body of the mandible, and extends, in a curved form, from the mastoid process to the symphysis menti. The **posterior belly**, longer than the anterior, *arises* from the mastoid notch of the temporal bone and passes downward and forward. The **anterior belly** *arises* from a depression on the inner side of the lower border of the mandible, close to the symphysis, and passes downward and backward. The two bellies end in an intermediate tendon which perforates the Stylohyoideus muscle, and is held in connection with the side of the body and the greater cornu of the hyoid bone by a fibrous loop, which is sometimes lined by a mucous sheath. A broad aponeurotic layer is given off from the tendon of the Digastricus on either side, to be attached to the body and greater cornu of the hyoid bone; this is termed the **suprahyoid aponeurosis**.

Action.—Raises the hyoid bone; assists in opening the jaws. The anterior belly draws the hyoid forward, the posterior backward.

Nerve.—Anterior belly by the mylohyoid nerve from the inferior alveolar branch of the mandibular division of the trigeminal; posterior belly by a branch of the facial nerve.

Variations are numerous. The posterior belly may arise partly or entirely from the styloid process. or be connected by a slip to the middle or inferior constrictor; the anterior belly may be double or extra slips from this belly may pass to the jaw or Mylohyoideus or decussate with a similar slip on opposite side; anterior belly may be absent and posterior belly inserted into the middle of the jaw or hyoid bone. The tendon may pass in front, more rarely behind the Stylohyoideus. The *Mentohyoideus muscle* passes from the body of hyoid bone to chin.

The Digastricus divides the anterior triangle of the neck into three smaller triangles (1) the **submaxillary triangle,** bounded above by the lower border of the body of the mandible, and a line drawn from its angle to the Sternocleidomastoideus, below by the posterior belly of the Digastricus and the Stylohyoideus, in front by the anterior belly of the Digastricus; (2) the **carotid triangle,** bounded above by the posterior belly of the Digastricus and Stylohyoideus, behind by the Sternocleidomastoideus, below by the Omohyoideus; (3) the **suprahyoid** or **submental triangle,** bounded laterally by the anterior belly of the Digastricus, medially by the middle line of the neck from the hyoid bone to the symphysis menti, and inferiorly by the body of the hyoid bone.

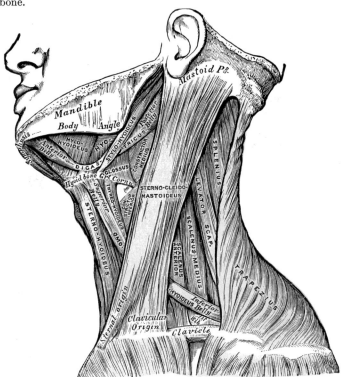

Fig. 369.—Muscles of the neck. Lateral view.

The **Stylohyoideus** (*Stylohyoid muscle*) is a slender muscle, lying in front of, and above, the posterior belly of the Digastricus. It *arises* from the back and lateral surface of the styloid process, near the base; and, passing downward and forward, is *inserted* into the body of the hyoid bone, at its junction with the greater cornu, and just above the Omohyoideus. It is perforated, near its insertion, by the tendon of the Digastricus.

Action.—Draws the hyoid bone upward and backward.

Nerve.—A branch of the facial nerve.

Variations.—It may be absent or doubled, lie beneath the carotid artery, or be inserted into the Omohyoideus, Thyreohyoideus, or Mylohyoideus.

The **Stylohyoid Ligament** (*ligamentum stylohyoideum*).—In connection with the Stylohyoideus muscle a ligamentous band, the **stylohyoid ligament,** may be described. It is a fibrous cord, which is attached to the tip of the styloid process of the temporal and the lesser cornu of the hyoid bone. It frequently contains a little cartilage in its center, is often partially ossified, and in many animals forms a distinct bone, the **epihyal.**

The **Mylohyoideus** (*Mylohyoid muscle*), flat and triangular, is situated immediately above the anterior belly of the Digastricus, and forms, with its fellow of the opposite side, a muscular floor for the cavity of the mouth. It *arises* from the whole length of the mylohyoid line of the mandible, extending from the symphysis in front to the last molar tooth behind. The posterior fibers pass medialward and slightly downward, to be *inserted* into the body of the hyoid bone. The middle and anterior fibers are *inserted* into a median fibrous raphé extending from the symphysis menti to the hyoid bone, where they join at an angle with the fibers of the opposite muscle. This median raphé is sometimes wanting; the fibers of the two muscles are then continuous.

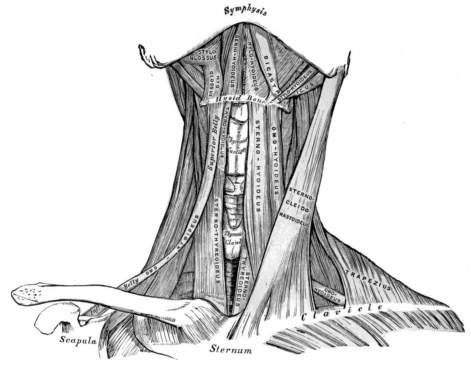

Fig. 370.—Muscles of the neck. Anterior view.

Action.—Raises the hyoid bone and tongue.

Nerve.—The mylohyoid nerve from the inferior alveolar branch of the mandibular division of the trigeminal nerve.

Variations.—It may be united to or replaced by the anterior belly of the Digastricus; accessory slips to other hyoid muscles are frequent.

The **Geniohyoideus** (*Geniohyoid muscle*) is a narrow muscle, situated above the medial border of the Mylohyoideus. It *arises* from the inferior mental spine on the back of the symphysis menti, and runs backward and slightly downward, to be *inserted* into the anterior surface of the body of the hyoid bone; it lies in contact with its fellow of the opposite side.

Action.—Draws the hyoid bone and tongue forward.

Nerve.—A branch of the hypoglossal nerve containing fibers communicated to it by the first cervical nerve.

Variations.—It may be blended with the one on opposite side or double; slips to greater cornu of hyoid bone and Genioglossus occur.

Group Actions.—These muscles perform two very important actions. During deglutition, they raise the hyoid bone, and with it the base of the tongue; when the hyoid bone is fixed by its depressors and those of the larynx, they depress the mandible. During the first act of deglutition, when the mass of food is being driven from the mouth into the pharynx, the hyoid bone and with it the tongue, is carried upward and forward by the anterior bellies of the Digastrici, the Mylohyoidei, and Geniohyoidei. In the second act, when the mass is passing through the pharynx, the direct elevation of the hyoid bone takes place by the combined action of all the muscles; and after the food has passed, the hyoid bone is carried upward and backward by the posterior bellies of the Digastrici and the Stylohyoidei, which assist in preventing the return of the food into the mouth.

IV. THE INFRAHYOID MUSCLES (Figs. 369, 370).

Sternohyoideus.   Thyreohyoideus.
Sternothyreoideus.   Omohyoideus.

The **Sternohyoideus** (*Sternohyoid muscle*) is a thin, narrow muscle, which *arises* from the posterior surface of the medial end of the clavicle, the posterior sterno-clavicular ligament, and the upper and posterior part of the manubrium sterni. Passing upward and medialward, it is *inserted*, by short, tendinous fibers, into the lower border of the body of the hyoid bone. Below, this muscle is separated from its fellow by a considerable interval; but the two muscles come into contact with one another in the middle of their course, and from this upward, lie side by side. It sometimes presents, immediately above its origin, a transverse tendinous inscription.

> **Action.**—Draws the hyoid bone downward.
> **Nerve.**—Branch of the ansa hypoglossi containing fibers from the first three cervical nerves.
> **Variations.**—Doubling; accessory slips (Cleidohyoideus); absence.

The **Sternothyreoideus** (*Sternothyroid muscle*) is shorter and wider than the preceding muscle, beneath which it is situated. It *arises* from the posterior surface of the manubrium sterni, below the origin of the Sternohyoideus, and from the edge of the cartilage of the first rib, and sometimes that of the second rib, it is *inserted* into the oblique line on the lamina of the thyroid cartilage. This muscle is in close contact with its fellow at the lower part of the neck, but diverges somewhat as it ascends; it is occasionally traversed by a transverse or oblique tendinous inscription.

> **Action.**—Draws the thyroid cartilage downward.
> **Nerve.**—Branch of the ansa hypoglossi containing fibers from the first three cervical nerves.
> **Variations.**—Doubling; absence; accessory slips to Thyreohyoideus, Inferior constrictor, or carotid sheath.

The **Thyreohyoideus** (*Thyrohyoid muscle*) is a small, quadrilateral muscle appearing like an upward continuation of the Sternothyreoideus. It *arises* from the oblique line on the lamina of the thyroid cartilage, and is *inserted* into the lower border of the greater cornu of the hyoid bone.

> **Action.**—Draws the hyoid bone downward, or if the latter is fixed, draws the thyroid cartilage upward.
> **Nerve.**—Fibers from the first and second cervical nerves by way of a communication to the hypoglossal nerve and through its descendens hypoglossi branch.

The **Omohyoideus** (*Omohyoid muscle*) consists of two fleshy bellies united by a central tendon. It *arises* from the upper border of the scapula, and occasionally from the superior transverse ligament which crosses the scapular notch, its extent of attachment to the scapula varying from a few millimetres to 2.5 cm. From this origin, the inferior belly forms a flat, narrow fasciculus, which inclines forward and slightly upward across the lower part of the neck, being bound down to the clavicle by a fibrous expansion; it then passes behind the Sternocleidomastoideus, becomes tendinous and changes its direction, forming an obtuse angle. It ends in the superior belly, which passes almost vertically upward, close to the lateral border of the Sternohyoideus, to be inserted into the lower border of the body of the hyoid bone, lateral to the insertion of the Sternohyoideus. The central tendon of this muscle varies much in length and form, and is held in position by a process of the deep cervical fascia, which sheaths it, and is prolonged down to be attached to the clavicle and first rib; it is by this means that the angular form of the muscle is maintained.

Action.—Draws the hyoid bone downward.
Nerves.—Branches of the ansa hypoglossi containing fibers from the first three cervical nerves.
Variations.—Doubling; absence; origin from clavicle; absence or doubling of either belly.

The inferior belly of the Omohyoideus divides the posterior triangle of the neck into an upper or **occipital triangle** and a lower or **subclavian triangle**, while its superior belly divides the anterior triangle into an upper or **carotid triangle** and a lower or **muscular triangle.**
Group Actions.—These muscles depress the larynx and hyoid, after they have been drawn up with the pharynx in the act of deglutition. The Omohyoidei not only depress the hyoid bone, but carry it backward and to one or the other side. They are concerned especially in prolonged inspiratory efforts; for by rendering the lower part of the cervical fascia tense they lessen the inward suction of the soft parts, which would otherwise compress the great vessels and the apices of the lungs.

V. THE ANTERIOR VERTEBRAL MUSCLES (Fig. 371).

Longus colli.   Rectus capitis anterior.
Longus capitis.   Rectus capitis lateralis.

The **Longus colli** is situated on the anterior surface of the vertebral column, between the atlas and the third thoracic vertebra. It is broad in the middle, narrow and pointed at either end, and consists of three portions, a superior oblique, an inferior oblique, and a vertical. The **superior oblique portion** *arises* from the anterior tubercles of the transverse processes of the third, fourth, and fifth cervical vertebræ; and, ascending obliquely with a medial inclination, is *inserted* by a narrow tendon into the tubercle on the anterior arch of the atlas. The **inferior oblique portion**, the smallest part of the muscle, *arises* from the front of the bodies of the first two or three thoracic vertebræ; and, ascending obliquely in a lateral direction, is *inserted* into the anterior tubercles of the transverse processes of the fifth and sixth cervical vertebræ. The **vertical portion** *arises*, below, from the front of the bodies of the upper three thoracic and lower three cervical vertebræ, and is *inserted* into the front of the bodies of the second, third, and fourth cervical vertebræ.

Action.—Flexes the neck and slightly rotates the cervical portion of the vertebral column.
Nerve.—Branches from the second to the seventh cervical nerves.

The **Longus capitis** (*Rectus capitis anticus major*), broad and thick above, narrow below, *arises* by four tendinous slips, from the anterior tubercles of the transverse processes of the third, fourth, fifth, and sixth cervical vertebræ, and ascends, converging toward its fellow of the opposite side, to be *inserted* into the inferior surface of the basilar part of the occipital bone.

Action.—Flexes the head.
Nerve.—Branches from the first, second, and third cervical nerves.

The **Rectus capitis anterior** (*Rectus capitis anticus minor*) is a short, flat muscle, situated immediately behind the upper part of the Longus capitis. It *arises* from the anterior surface of the lateral mass of the atlas, and from the root of its transverse process, and passing obliquely upward and medialward, is *inserted* into the inferior surface of the basilar part of the occipital bone immediately in front of the foramen magnum.

Action.—Flexes the head.
Nerve.—Branches of the loop between the first and second cervical nerves.

The **Rectus capitis lateralis,** a short, flat muscle, *arises* from the upper surface of the transverse process of the atlas, and is *inserted* into the under surface of the jugular process of the occipital bone.

Action.—Bends the head laterally.

Nerve.—Branches of the loop between the first and second cervical nerves.

Group Actions.—The Longus capitis and Rectus anterior are the direct antagonists of the muscles at the back of the neck, serving to restore the head to its natural position after it has been drawn backward. These muscles also flex the head, and from their obliquity, rotate it, so as to turn the face to one or the other side. The Rectus lateralis, acting on one side, bends the head laterally.

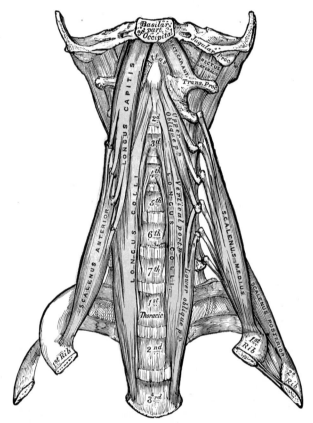

Fig. 371.—The anterior vertebral muscles.

VI. THE LATERAL VERTEBRAL MUSCLES (Fig. 371).

Scalenus anterior.　　　　　　　　　　　　　Scalenus medius.

Scalenus posterior.

The **Scalenus anterior** (*Scalenus anticus*) lies deeply at the side of the neck, behind the Sternocleidomastoideus. It *arises* from the anterior tubercles of the transverse processes of the third, fourth, fifth, and sixth cervical vertebræ, and descending, almost vertically, is *inserted* by a narrow, flat tendon into the scalene tubercle on the inner border of the first rib, and into the ridge on the upper surface of the rib in front of the subclavian groove.

The **Scalenus medius,** the largest and longest of the three Scaleni, *arises* from the posterior tubercles of the transverse processes of the lower six cervical vertebræ, and descending along the side of the vertebral column, is *inserted* by a broad attachment into the upper surface of the first rib, between the tubercle and the subclavian groove.

Action.—Raise the first rib; bend and slightly rotate the neck.
Nerves.—Branches of the lower cervical nerves.

The **Scalenus posterior** (*Scalenus posticus*), the smallest and most deeply seated of the three Scaleni, *arises*, by two or three separate tendons, from the posterior tubercles of the transverse processes of the lower two or three cervical vertebræ, and is *inserted* by a thin tendon into the outer surface of the second rib, behind the attachment of the Serratus anterior. It is occasionally blended with the Scalenus medius.

Action.—Raises the second rib; bends and slightly rotates the neck.
Nerve.—Branches of anterior rami of last three cervical nerves.
Group Actions.—When the Scaleni act from above, they elevate the first and second ribs, and are, therefore, inspiratory muscles. Acting from below, they bend the vertebral column to one or other side; if the muscles of both sides act, the vertebral column is slightly flexed.
Variations.—The Scaleni muscles vary considerably in their attachments and in the arrangement of their fibers. A slip from the Scalenus anticus may pass behind the subclavian artery. The Scalenus posticus may be absent or extend to the third rib. The *Scalenus pleuralis muscle* extends from the transverse process of the seventh cervical vertebra to the fascia supporting the dome of the pleura and inner border of first rib.

THE FASCIÆ AND MUSCLES OF THE TRUNK.

The muscles of the trunk may be arranged in six groups:

I. Deep Muscles of the Back. IV. Muscles of the Abdomen.
II. Suboccipital Muscles. V. Muscles of the Pelvis.
III. Muscles of the Thorax. VI. Muscles of the Perineum.

I. THE DEEP MUSCLES OF THE BACK (Fig. 373).

The deep or intrinsic muscles of the back consist of a complex, serially arranged group of muscles, extending from the pelvis to the skull, which may be looked upon as a single muscle functionally, the extensor of the vertebral column. Two subgroups may be identified: (*A*) A superficial stratum with fasciculi mainly crossing laterally as they ascend may be called the transverso-costal group:

Splenius capitis. Splenius cervicis
Sacrospinalis (Iliocostalis, Longissimus, Spinalis)

(*B*) The deeper stratum has fasciculi coursing mainly upward and medially, and may be called the transverso-spinal group:

Semispinalis. Rotatores. Interspinales.
Multifidus. Intertransversarii.

The **Nuchal Fascia** (*fascia nuchæ*) (Fig. 367) is the cervical portion of the more extensive vertebral fascia and is continuous below with the lumbodorsal fascia. It covers the Splenius capitis and cervicis, and near the skull, the upper portion of the Semispinalis capitis. With these muscles, it is attached to the skull just below the superior nuchal line, the ligamentum nuchæ, and the spinous processes of the seventh cervical and upper six thoracic vertebræ. In the upper part of the neck it is more or less adherent to the fascia of the under surface of the Trapezius. Lower, a distinct fascial cleft separates it from the fascia of the Serratus posterior superior and Rhomboidei.

The deeper muscles of the neck are enclosed by fascial septa which form compartments for each muscle. A fascial cleft separates the Splenius from the Semispinalis capitis. A considerable layer of adipose tissue and a fascial cleft intervene between the latter and the Semispinalis cervicis. In this adipose layer are found the deep cervical bloodvessels. The fascia covering the Semispinalis cervicis continues upward from the atlas to form the thick adherent covering of the suboccipital muscles. The fasciæ of the several muscles which attach to the transverse processes of the cervical vertebræ are either fused or continuous, the scalenus fascia becoming continuous with the splenius and serratus posterior superior fascia under cover of the Levator scapulæ.

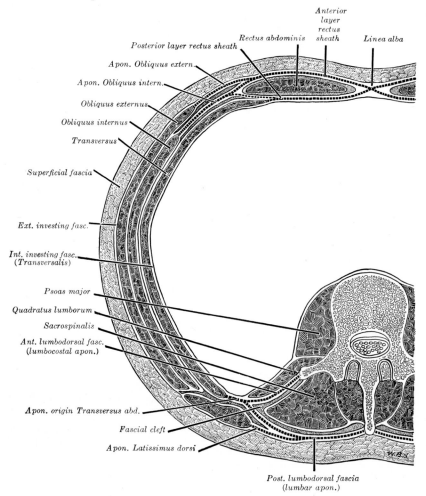

FIG. 372.—Fasciæ and aponeuroses of abdominal wall in cross-section through third lumbar vertebra. Semidiagrammatic.

Lumbodorsal Fascia (*fascia lumbodorsalis*) (Figs. 372, 381, 391).—The name lumbodorsal fascia is given to a rather varied fascial complex. It is, in general terms, the subdivision of the vertebral fascia which forms the sheath of the Sacrospinalis muscle. It should be looked upon primarily as an intermediate stratum, derived from the fascia of the trunk deep to the large limb muscles. It becomes part of the investing fascia of the body, however, in the lower half of the trunk, because in that region the aponeurosis of the Latissimus dorsi is incorporated in it.

Above, it is continuous with the fascia nuchæ. Medially, it is attached to the spines of the vertebræ, the supraspinal ligaments, and the medial crest of the sacrum; below, to the iliac crests and lateral crests of the sacrum. Laterally, in the thorax, it is attached to the angles of the ribs and intercostal fascia, and in the lumbar region, it is continuous with the aponeurosis of origin of the Transversus abdominis muscle. In the upper part of the thorax, where it is covered by the Rhomboidei, it is thin, gray, and transparent. It retains this consistency also under the fleshy fibers of the upper part of the Latissimus dorsi. More caudally, it is a thick, white, glistening sheet which serves as the origin of the Latissimus and is called the lumbar aponeurosis. Caudal to the twelfth rib, since it can no longer attach to the ribs, the line of attachment along the lateral border of the Sacrospinalis, becomes a line of fusion between the fascia covering the dorsal surface of this muscle (**the posterior layer of the lumbodorsal fascia**) and the fascia on the deep surface of the muscle (**the anterior layer of the lumbodorsal fascia**). From this fusion, the fascia extends laterally as a single sheet, the aponeurosis of origin of the Transversus abdominis muscle. This portion of the fascia may be described in another way. The aponeurosis of origin of the Transversus abdominis, in seeking to attach to the vertebræ, meets interference at the lateral border of the Sacrospinalis and splits, therefore, to enclose the latter in a superficial and deep sheet. The superficial sheet, the **lumbar aponeurosis** or lumbodorsal fascia (posterior layer), extends over the dorsal surface of the Sacrospinalis and attaches to the spines. The deep sheet, the **lumbocostal aponeurosis** (anterior layer of the lumbodorsal fascia), extends over the deep surface of the Sacrospinalis and attaches to the transverse processes. The lumbocostal aponeurosis is a strong sheet reaching from the lower border of the twelfth rib to the crest of the ilium. Its fiber bundles radiate out from attachments to the tips of the transverse processes of the lumbar vertebræ. It lies deep to the Sacrospinalis, and superficial to the Quadratus lumborum and Psoas major muscles. The upper portion, attached to the twelfth rib and the transverse process of the first lumbar vertebra, is more specifically named the **lumbocostal ligament**.

A. Transverso-costal Muscles.

The **Splenius capitis** (Fig. 391) *arises* from the lower half of the ligamentum nuchæ, from the spinous process of the seventh cervical vertebra, and from the spinous processes of the upper three or four thoracic vertebræ. The fibers of the muscle are directed upward and lateralward and are *inserted* into the rough surface on the occipital bone just below the lateral third of the superior nuchal line, and, under cover of the Sternocleidomastoideus, into the mastoid process of the temporal bone.

The **Splenius cervicis** (*Splenius colli*) (Fig. 391) *arises* by a narrow tendinous band from the spinous processes of the third to the sixth thoracic vertebræ; it is *inserted*, by tendinous fasciculi, into the posterior tubercles of the transverse processes of the upper two or three cervical vertebræ.

Action.—Draw the head and neck backward and laterally, and rotate them, turning the face toward the same side. Both sides acting together extend the head and neck.

Nerves.—Lateral branches of the posterior rami of the middle and lower cervical nerves.

Variations.—The origin is frequently moved up or down one or two vertebræ. Accessory slips are occasionally found.

The **Sacrospinalis** (*Erector spinæ*) (Fig. 373), and its prolongations in the thoracic and cervical regions, lie in the groove on the side of the vertebral column. They are covered in the lumbar and thoracic regions by the lumbodorsal fascia, and in the cervical region by the nuchal fascia. This large muscular and tendinous mass varies in size and structure at different parts of the vertebral column. In

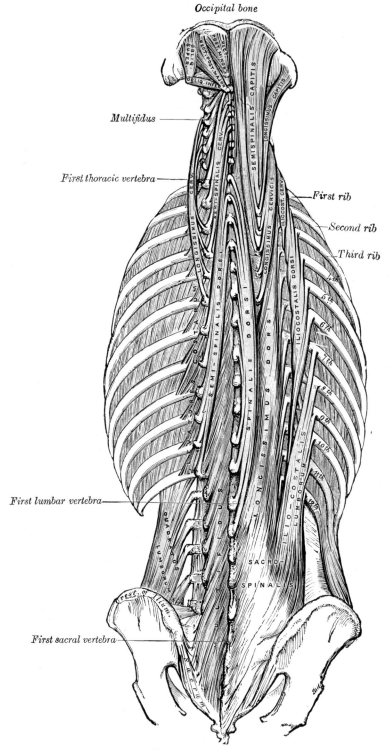

FIG. 373.—Deep muscles of the back.

the sacral region it is narrow and pointed, and at its origin chiefly tendinous in structure. In the lumbar region it is larger, and forms a thick fleshy mass which, in its upward course, is subdivided into three columns; these gradually diminish in size as they ascend to be inserted into the vertebræ and ribs.

The Sacrospinalis *arises* from the anterior surface of a broad and thick tendon, which is attached to the middle crest of the sacrum, to the spinous processes of the lumbar and the eleventh and twelfth thoracic vertebræ, and the supraspinal ligament, to the back part of the inner lip of the iliac crests and to the lateral crests of the sacrum, where it blends with the sacrotuberous and posterior sacro-iliac ligaments. Some of its fibers are continuous with the fibers of origin of the Glutæus maximus. The muscular fibers form a large fleshy mass which splits, in the upper lumbar region into three columns, viz., a lateral, the **Iliocostalis**, an intermediate, the **Longissimus**, and a medial, the **Spinalis**. Each of these consists from below upward, of three parts, as follows:

Lateral Column.	*Intermediate Column.*	*Medial Column.*
Iliocostalis.	Longissimus.	Spinalis.
I. lumborum.	L. dorsi.	S. dorsi.
I. dorsi.	L. cervicis.	S. cervicis.
I. cervicis.	L. capitis.	S. capitis.

The **Iliocostalis lumborum** (*Iliocostalis muscle; Sacrolumbalis muscle*) is *inserted*, by six or seven flattened tendons, into the inferior borders of the angles of the lower six or seven ribs.

The **Iliocostalis dorsi** (*Musculus accessorius*) *arises* by flattened tendons from the upper borders of the angles of the lower six ribs medial to the tendons of insertion of the Iliocostalis lumborum; these become muscular, and are *inserted* into the upper borders of the angles of the upper six ribs and into the back of the transverse process of the seventh cervical vertebra.

The **Iliocostalis cervicis** (*Cervicalis ascendens*) *arises* from the angles of the third, fourth, fifth, and sixth ribs, and is *inserted* into the posterior tubercles of the transverse processes of the fourth, fifth, and sixth cervical vertebræ.

Action.—Extend the vertebral column and bend it to one side; lumborum and dorsi draw the ribs downward.

Nerve.—Branches of the posterior rami of the spinal nerves.

The **Longissimus dorsi** is the intermediate and largest of the continuations of the Sacrospinalis. In the lumbar region, where it is as yet blended with the Iliocostalis lumborum and Spinalis, some of its fibers are attached to the whole length of the posterior surfaces of the transverse processes and the accessory processes of the lumbar vertebræ, and to the anterior layer of the lumbodorsal fascia (lumbocostal aponeurosis). In the thoracic region it is *inserted*, by rounded tendons, into the tips of the transverse processes of all the thoracic vertebræ, and by fleshy processes into the lower nine or ten ribs between their tubercles and angles.

The **Longissimus cervicis** (*Transversalis cervicis*), situated medial to the Longissimus dorsi, *arises* by long thin tendons from the summits of the transverse processes of the upper four or five thoracic vertebræ, and is *inserted* by similar tendons into the posterior tubercles of the transverse processes of the cervical vertebræ from the second to the sixth inclusive.

Action.—Extend the vertebral column and bend it to one side; draw the ribs downward.

Nerve.—Branches of the posterior rami of the spinal nerves.

The **Longissimus capitis** (*Trachelomastoid muscle*) lies medial to the Longissimus cervicis, between it and the Semispinalis capitis. It *arises* by tendons from the transverse processes of the upper four or five thoracic vertebræ along with the cervicis, and the articular processes of the lower three or four cervical vertebræ, and is *inserted* into the posterior margin of the mastoid process, beneath the Splenius capitis and Sternocleidomastoideus. In the upper part of the neck, where the capitis and cervicis diverge toward their insertions, the Longissimus mass is crossed by the Splenius cervicis. The latter's insertion separates that of the L. capitis from that of the L. cervicis, and where it crosses them, their muscular fasciculi are replaced by a tendinous inscription.

Action.—Extends the head; the muscle of one side acting alone bends the head to the same side and rotates the face toward that side.
Nerve.—Branches of the posterior rami of the middle and lower cervical nerves.

The **Spinalis dorsi**, the medial continuation of the Sacrospinalis, is scarcely separable as a distinct muscle. It is situated at the medial side of the Longissimus dorsi, and is intimately blended with it; it *arises* by three or four tendons from the spinous processes of the first two lumbar and the last two thoracic vertebræ: these, uniting, form a small muscle which is *inserted* by separate tendons into the spinous processes of the upper thoracic vertebræ, the number varying from four to eight. It is intimately united with the Semispinalis dorsi, situated beneath it.

The **Spinalis cervicis** (*Spinalis colli*) is an inconstant muscle, which *arises* from the lower part of the ligamentum nuchæ, the spinous process of the seventh cervical, and sometimes from the spinous processes of the first and second thoracic vertebræ, and is *inserted* into the spinous process of the axis, and occasionally into the spinous processes of the two vertebræ below it.

The **Spinalis capitis** (*Biventer cervicis*) is usually inseparably connected with the Semispinalis capitis (see below).

Action.—Extend the vertebral column.
Nerve.—Branches of the posterior rami of the spinal nerves.

B. Transverso-spinal Muscles.

The **Semispinalis dorsi** consists of thin, narrow, fleshy fasciculi, interposed between tendons of considerable length. It *arises* by a series of small tendons from the transverse processes of the sixth to the tenth thoracic vertebræ, and is *inserted*, by tendons, into the spinous processes of the upper four thoracic and lower two cervical vertebræ.

The **Semispinalis cervicis** (*Semispinalis colli*), thicker than the preceding, *arises* by a series of tendinous and fleshy fibers from the transverse processes of the upper five or six thoracic vertebræ, and is inserted into the cervical spinous processes, from the axis to the fifth inclusive. The fasciculus connected with the axis is the largest, and is chiefly muscular in structure.

Action.—Extend the vertebral column and rotate it toward the opposite side.
Nerve.—Branches of the posterior rami of the spinal nerves.

The **Semispinalis capitis** (*Complexus*) is situated at the upper and back part of the neck, beneath the Splenius, and medial to the Longissimus cervicis and capitis. It *arises* by a series of tendons from the tips of the transverse processes of the upper six or seven thoracic and the seventh cervical vertebræ, and from the articular processes of the three cervical above this. The tendons, uniting, form a broad muscle, which passes upward, and is *inserted* between the superior and inferior nuchal lines of the occipital bone. The medial part, usually more or less distinct from the remainder of the muscle, is frequently termed the **Spinalis capitis**; it is also named the **Biventer cervicis** since it is traversed by an imperfect tendinous inscription.

Action.—Extends the head and rotates it toward the opposite side.
Nerve.—Branches of the posterior rami of the cervical nerves.

The **Multifidus** (*Multifidus spinæ*) consists of a number of fleshy and tendinous fasciculi, which fill up the groove on either side of the spinous processes of the vertebræ, from the sacrum to the axis. In the sacral region, these fasciculi *arise* from the back of the sacrum, as low as the fourth sacral foramen, from the aponeurosis of origin of the Sacrospinalis, from the medial surface of the posterior superior iliac spine, and from the posterior sacroiliac ligaments; in the lumbar region, from all the mamillary processes; in the thoracic region, from all the transverse processes; and in the cervical region, from the articular processes of the lower four vertebræ. Each fasciculus ascends obliquely, crossing over from two to four vertebræ in its course toward the middle line, and is inserted into the spinous process of one of the vertebræ, from the last lumbar to the axis. The fasciculi vary in length and depth of position; the longest and most superficial pass from one vertebra to the fifth above; those somewhat deeper are shorter and cross three vertebræ; the deepest and shortest cross two. The Rotatores longi (see below) are sometimes included in the Multifidus.

Action.—Extends the vertebral column and rotates it toward the opposite side.
Nerve.—Branches of the posterior rami of the spinal nerves.

The **Rotatores** (*Rotatores spinæ*) are a series of small muscles which form the deepest layer in the groove between the spinous and transverse processes. They lie beneath the Multifidus and cannot be distinguished readily from its deepest fibers. They are found along the entire length of the vertebral column from the sacrum to the axis. They arise from the transverse process of one vertebra and insert at the base of the spinous process of the vertebra above. The **Rotatores longi** cross one vertebra in their oblique course. The **Rotatores breves** insert in the next succeeding vertebra and run in an almost horizontal direction.

Action.—Extend the vertebral column and rotate it toward the opposite side.
Nerve.—Branches of the posterior rami of the spinal nerves.

The **Interspinales** are short muscular fasciculi, placed in pairs between the spinous processes of the contiguous vertebræ, one on either side of the interspinal ligament. In the *cervical region* they are most distinct, and consist of six pairs, the first being situated between the axis and third vertebra, and the last between the seventh cervical and the first thoracic. They are small narrow bundles, attached, above and below, to the apices of the spinous processes. In the *thoracic region*, they are found between the first and second vertebræ, and sometimes between the second and third, and between the eleventh and twelfth. In the *lumbar region* there are four pairs in the intervals between the five lumbar vertebræ. There is also occasionally one between the last thoracic and first lumbar, and one between the fifth lumbar and the sacrum.

Action.—Extend the vertebral column.
Nerves.—Branches of the posterior rami of the spinal nerves.

The **Extensor coccygis** is a slender muscular fasciculus, which is not always present; it extends over the lower part of the posterior surface of the sacrum and coccyx. It *arises* by tendinous fibers from the last segment of the sacrum, or first piece of the coccyx, and passes downward to be *inserted* into the lower part of the coccyx. It is a rudiment of the Extensor muscle of the caudal vertebræ of the lower animals.

The **Intertransversarii** (*Intertransversales*) are small muscles placed between the transverse processes of the vertebræ. In the *cervical region* they are best developed, consisting of rounded muscular and tendinous fasciculi, and are placed in pairs, passing between the anterior and the posterior tubercles respectively of the transverse processes of two contiguous vertebræ, and separated from one another by an anterior primary division of the cervical nerve, which lies in the groove between them. The muscles connecting the anterior tubercles are termed the **Intertransversarii anteriores**; those between the posterior tubercles, the **Inter-transversarii posteriores**.   There are seven pairs of these muscles, the first pair being between the atlas and axis, and the last pair between the seventh cervical and first thoracic vertebræ.   In the *thoracic region* they are present between the transverse processes of the lower three thoracic vertebræ, and between the transverse processes of the last thoracic and the first lumbar.   In the *lumbar region* they are arranged in pairs, on either side of the vertebral column, one set occupying the entire interspace between the transverse processes of the lumbar vertebræ, the **Intertransversarii laterales**; the other set, **Intertransversarii mediales**, passing from the accessory process of one vertebra to the mammillary of the vertebra below.

Action.—Bend the vertebral column laterally.

Nerve.—The anteriores, posteriores, and laterales by branches of the anterior rami of the spinal nerves; the mediales by branches of the posterior rami.

II.   THE SUBOCCIPITAL MUSCLES (Figs. 373, 374).

Rectus capitis posterior major.	Obliquus capitis inferior.
Rectus capitis posterior minor.	Obliquus capitis superior.

The **Rectus capitis posterior major** (*Rectus capitis posticus major*) *arises* by a pointed tendon from the spinous process of the axis, and, becoming broader as it ascends, is *inserted* into the lateral part of the inferior nuchal line of the occipital bone and the surface of the bone immediately below the line.   As the muscles of the two sides pass upward and lateralward, they leave between them a triangular space, in which the Recti capitis posteriores minores are seen.

Action.—Extends the head and rotates it to the same side.

Nerve.—A branch of the posterior ramus of the suboccipital nerve.

The **Rectus capitis posterior minor** (*Rectus capitis posticus minor*) *arises* by a narrow pointed tendon from the tubercle on the posterior arch of the atlas, and, widening as it ascends, is *inserted* into the medial part of the inferior nuchal line of the occipital bone and the surface between it and the foramen magnum.

Action.—Extends the head.

Nerve.—A branch of the posterior ramus of the suboccipital nerve.

The **Obliquus capitis inferior** (*Obliquus inferior*), the larger of the two Oblique muscles, *arises* from the apex of the spinous process of the axis, and passes lateral-ward and slightly upward, to be *inserted* into the lower and back part of the transverse process of the atlas.

Action.—Rotates the atlas, turning the face toward the same side.

Nerve.—A branch of the posterior ramus of the suboccipital nerve.

The **Obliquus capitis superior** (*Obliquus superior*), narrow below, wide and expanded above, *arises* by tendinous fibers from the upper surface of the transverse process of the atlas, joining with the insertion of the preceding.   It passes upward and medialward, and is *inserted* into the occipital bone, between the superior and inferior nuchal lines, lateral to the Semispinalis capitis.

Action.—Extends the head and bends it laterally.

Nerve.—A branch of the posterior ramus of the suboccipital nerve.

The Suboccipital Triangle.—Between the Obliqui and the Rectus capitis posterior major is **the suboccipital triangle.**   It is bounded, *above* and *medially*, by the Rectus capitis posterior major; *above* and *laterally*, by the Obliquus capitis superior; *below* and *laterally*, by the Obliquus capitis inferior.   It is covered by a layer of dense fibro-fatty tissue, situated beneath the Semispinalis capitis.   The floor is formed by the posterior occipito-atlantal membrane, and the posterior arch of the atlas.   In the deep groove on the upper surface of the posterior arch of the atlas are the vertebral artery and the first cervical or suboccipital nerve.   (Fig. 374.)

Group Actions.—The Sacrospinalis and its upward continuations and the Spinales maintain the vertebral column in the erect posture; they also serve to bend the trunk backward when it is required to counterbalance the influence of any weight at the front of the body—as, for instance, when a heavy weight is suspended from the neck, or when there is any great abdominal distension, as in pregnancy or dropsy; the peculiar gait under such circumstances depends upon the vertebral column being drawn backward, by the counterbalancing action of the Sacrospinales. The muscles which form the continuation of the Sacrospinales on to the head and neck steady those parts and fix them in the upright position. If the Iliocostalis lumborum and Longissimus dorsi of one side act, they serve to draw down the chest and vertebral column to the correspond-

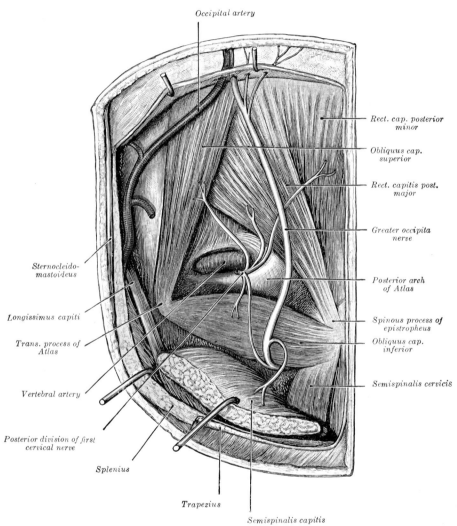

Fig. 374.—The left suboccipital triangle and muscles.

ing side. The Iliocostales cervicis, taking their fixed points from the cervical vertebræ, elevate those ribs to which they are attached; taking their fixed points from the ribs, both muscles help to extend the neck; while one muscle bends the neck to its own side. The Multifidus acts successively upon the different parts of the column; thus, the sacrum furnishes a fixed point from which the fasciculi of this muscle act upon the lumbar region; which in turn becomes the fixed point for the fasciculi moving the thoracic region, and so on throughout the entire length of the column. The Multifidus also serves to rotate the column, so that the front of the trunk is turned to the side opposite to that from which the muscle acts, this muscle being assisted in its action by the Obliquus externus abdominis.

25

III. THE MUSCLES OF THE THORAX.

Intercostales externi.

Intercostales interni.

Subcostales.

Transversus thoracis.

Levatores costarum.

Serratus posterior superior.

Serratus posterior inferior.

Diaphragm.

Fascia.—The superficial fascia (tela subcutanea) and the outer layers of deep fascia of the thorax are described with the pectoral region (page 426) and back (page 422). The thoracic cage proper, composed of ribs and intercostal muscles, is covered inside and outside by thin membranes of deep fascia. The outer membrane is the external intercostal fascia, the inner one is the endothoracic fascia.

The **External Intercostal Fascia** covers the external surface of the Intercostales externi, the anterior intercostal membranes and the intervening surfaces of the ribs, costal cartilages and sternum. Above, it is continuous with the scalenus fascia; below, with the fascia between the external and internal oblique muscles of the abdomen. Posteriorly, it splits at the border of the Sacrospinalis into an outer membrane, the lumbodorsal fascia, and an inner membrane which continues on the surface of the Intercostales externi and Levatores costarum and forms an intermuscular septum between these muscles and the Sacrospinalis.

Between the Intercostales externi and interni is a thin layer of fascia to which both muscles are adherent.

The **Endothoracic Fascia** (*fascia endothoracica*) is the internal investing fascia, that is, the deep fascia which lines the inside of the thoracic cavity. It covers the internal surface of the Intercostales interni and intervening ribs, the Subcostales, Transversus thoracis, and Diaphragm, and posteriorly, it includes the thoracic portion of the prevertebral fascia which covers the bodies of the vertebræ and intervertebral discs. It is continuous, above, with the cervical prevertebral fascia, with the scalenus fascia (Sibson's) along the inner border of the first rib, and, behind the sternum, with the middle cervical fascia. It covers the entire thoracic surface of the diaphragm and is continuous with the internal investing fascia of the abdominal cavity (transversalis fascia, endoabdominal fascia) behind the diaphragm at the lumbocostal arches and through the aortic hiatus.

The **Subserous Fascia** (*visceral fascia*) (page 350) intervenes between the endothoracic fascia and the pleura, and provides the connective tissue investment for the mediastinal structures. It is more fully described with the lungs.

The **Intercostales** (*Intercostal muscles*) (Fig. 379) are two thin planes of muscular and tendinous fibers occupying each of the intercostal spaces. They are named **external** and **internal** from their surface relations—the external being superficial to the internal.

The **Intercostales externi** (*External intercostals*) are *eleven* in number on either side. They extend from the tubercles of the ribs behind, to the cartilages of the ribs in front, where they end in thin membranes, the **anterior intercostal membranes**, which are continued forward to the sternum. Each *arises* from the lower border of a rib, and is *inserted* into the upper border of the rib below. In the two lower spaces they extend to the ends of the cartilages, and in the upper two or three spaces they do not quite reach the ends of the ribs. They are thicker than the Intercostales interni, and their fibers are directed obliquely downward and lateralward on the back of the thorax, and downward, forward, and medialward on the front.

Action.—Draw adjacent ribs together. With the first rib fixed by the Scaleni, they lift the ribs, increasing the volume of the thoracic cavity.

Nerves.—Intercostal nerves.

Variations.—Continuation with the Obliquus externus or Serratus anterior: A *Supracostalis muscle,* from the anterior end of the first rib down to the second, third or fourth ribs occasionally occurs.

The **Intercostales interni** (*Internal intercostals*) are also *eleven* in number on either side. They commence anteriorly at the sternum, in the interspaces between the cartilages of the true ribs, and at the anterior extremities of the cartilages of the false ribs, and extend backward as far as the angles of the ribs, whence they are continued to the vertebral column by thin aponeuroses, the **posterior intercostal membranes**. Each *arises* from the ridge on the inner surface of a rib, as well as from the corresponding costal cartilage, and is *inserted* into the upper border of the rib below. Their fibers are also directed obliquely, but pass in a direction opposite to those of the Intercostales externi.

The **Subcostales** (*Intracostales*) consist of muscular and aponeurotic fasciculi, which are usually well-developed only in the lower part of the thorax; each *arises* from the inner surface of one rib near its angle, and is *inserted* into the inner surface of the second or third rib below. Their fibers run in the same direction as those of the Intercostales interni.

Action.—Draw adjacent ribs together. With the last rib fixed by the Quadratus lumborum, they lower the ribs, decreasing the volume of the thoracic cavity.
Nerves.—Intercostal nerves.

The **Transversus thoracis** (*Triangularis sterni*) is a thin plane of muscular and tendinous fibers, situated upon the inner surface of the front wall of the chest (Fig. 375). It *arises* on either side from the lower third of the posterior surface of the body of the sternum, from the posterior surface of the xiphoid process, and from the sternal ends of the costal cartilages of the lower three or four true ribs. Its fibers diverge upward and lateralward, to be *inserted* by slips into the lower borders and inner surfaces of the costal cartilages of the second, third, fourth, fifth, and sixth ribs. The lowest fibers of this muscle are horizontal in their direction, and are continuous with those of the Transversus abdominis; the intermediate fibers are oblique, while the highest are almost vertical. This muscle varies in its attachments, not only in different subjects, but on opposite sides of the same subject.

Action.—Draws the anterior portion of the ribs downward, decreasing the thoracic cavity.
Nerve. — Branches of the intercostal nerves.

The **Levatores costarum** (Fig. 373), *twelve* in number on either side, are small tendinous and fleshy bundles, which *arise* from the ends of the transverse processes of the seventh cervical and upper eleven thoracic vertebræ; they pass obliquely downward and lateralward, like the fibers of the Intercostales externi, and each is *inserted* into the outer surface of the rib immediately below the vertebra from which it takes origin, between the tubercle and the angle (**Levatores costarum breves**). Each of the four lower muscles divides into two fasciculi, one of which is inserted as above described; the other passes down to the second rib below its origin (**Levatores costarum longi**).

Action.—Raise the ribs, increasing the thoracic cavity; extend the vertebral column, bend it laterally and rotate it slightly toward the opposite side.
Nerves.—Branches of the intercostal nerves.

The **Serratus posterior superior** (*Serratus posticus superior*) is a thin, quadrilateral muscle, situated at the upper and back part of the thorax. It *arises* by a thin and broad aponeurosis from the lower part of the ligamentum nuchae, from the spinous processes of the seventh cervical and upper two or three thoracic vertebræ and from the supraspinal ligament. Inclining downward and lateralward it becomes muscular, and is *inserted*, by four fleshy digitations, into the upper borders of the second, third, fourth, and fifth ribs, a little beyond their angles.

Action.—Raises the ribs to which it is attached, increasing the thoracic cavity.
Nerve.—Branches of the rami anteriores of the upper four thoracic nerves.
Variations.—Increase or decrease in size and number of slips or entire absence.

The **Serratus posterior inferior** (*Serratus posticus inferior*) (Fig. 391) is situated at the junction of the thoracic and lumbar regions: it is of an irregularly quadrilateral form, broader than the preceding, and separated from it by a wide interval. It *arises* by a thin aponeurosis from the spinous processes of the lower two thoracic and upper two or three lumbar vertebræ, and from the supraspinal ligament. Passing obliquely upward and lateralward, it becomes fleshy, and divides into four

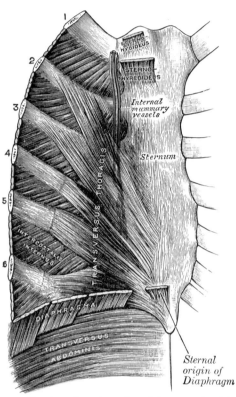

Fig. 375.—Posterior surface of sternum and costal cartilages, showing Transversus thoracis.

flat digitations, which are *inserted* into the inferior borders of the lower four ribs, a little beyond their angles. The thin aponeurosis of origin is intimately blended with the lumbodorsal fascia, and aponeurosis of the Latissimus dorsi.

Action.—Draws the ribs to which it is attached outward and downward, counteracting the inward pull of the Diaphragm.

Nerve.—Branches of the anterior rami of the ninth to twelfth thoracic nerves.

Variations.—Increase or decrease in size and number of slips or entire absence.

The **Diaphragm** (Fig. 376) is a dome-shaped musculofibrous septum which separates the thoracic from the abdominal cavity, its convex upper surface forming the floor of the former, and its concave under surface the roof of the latter. Its peripheral part consists of muscular fibers which take origin from the circumference of the thoracic outlet and converge to be *inserted* into a central tendon.

The muscular fibers may be grouped according to their origins into three parts—sternal, costal, and lumbar. The **sternal part** *arises* by two fleshy slips from the back of the xiphoid process; the **costal part** from the inner surfaces of the cartilages and adjacent portions of the lower six ribs on either side, interdigitating with the Transversus abdominis; and the **lumbar part** from aponeurotic arches, named the lumbocostal arches, and from the lumbar vertebræ by two pillars or **crura**. There are two lumbocostal arches, a medial and a lateral, on either side.

The **Medial Lumbocostal Arch** (*arcus lumbocostalis medialis* [*Halleri*]; *internal arcuate ligament*) is a tendinous arch in the fascia covering the upper part of the Psoas major; medially, it is continuous with the lateral tendinous margin of the corresponding crus, and is attached to the side of the body of the first or second lumbar vertebra; laterally, it is fixed to the front of the transverse process of the first and, sometimes also, to that of the second lumbar vertebra.

The **Lateral Lumbocostal Arch** (*arcus lumbocostalis lateralis* [*Halleri*]; *external arcuate ligament*) arches across the upper part of the Quadratus lumborum, and is attached, medially, to the front of the transverse process of the first lumbar vertebra, and, laterally, to the tip and lower margin of the twelfth rib.

The Crura.—At their origins the crura are tendinous in structure, and blend with the anterior longitudinal ligament of the vertebral column. The **right crus,**

larger and longer than the left, *arises* from the anterior surfaces of the bodies and intervertebral fibrocartilages of the upper three lumbar vertebræ, while the **left crus** *arises* from the corresponding parts of the upper two only. The medial tendinous margins of the crura pass forward and medialward, and meet in the middle line to form an arch across the front of the aorta; this arch is often poorly defined.

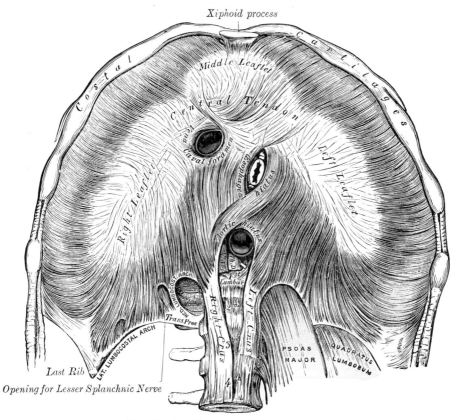

Fig. 376.—The diaphragm. Under surface.

From this series of origins the fibers of the diaphragm converge to be inserted into the central tendon. The fibers arising from the xiphoid process are very short, and occasionally aponeurotic; those from the medial and lateral lumbocostal arches, and more especially those from the ribs and their cartilages, are longer, and describe marked curves as they ascend and converge to their insertion. The fibers of the crura diverge as they ascend, the most lateral being directed upward and lateralward to the central tendon. The medial fibers of the right crus ascend on the left side of the esophageal hiatus, and occasionally a fasciculus of the left crus crosses the aorta and runs obliquely through the fibers of the right crus toward the vena caval foramen.

The Central Tendon.—The central tendon of the diaphragm is a thin but strong aponeurosis situated near the center of the vault formed by the muscle, but somewhat closer to the front than to the back of the thorax, so that the posterior muscular fibers are the longer. It is situated immediately below the pericardium, with which it is partially blended. It is shaped somewhat like a trefoil leaf, consisting of three divisions or leaflets separated from one another by slight indentations.

The right leaflet is the largest, the middle, directed toward the xiphoid process, the next in size, and the left the smallest. In structure the tendon is composed of several planes of fibers, which intersect one another at various angles and unite into straight or curved bundles—an arrangement which gives it additional strength.

Openings in the Diaphragm.—The diaphragm is pierced by a series of apertures to permit of the passage of structures between the thorax and abdomen. Three large openings—the **aortic**, the **esophageal**, and the **vena caval**—and a series of smaller ones are described.

The **aortic hiatus** is the lowest and most posterior of the large apertures; it lies at the level of the twelfth thoracic vertebra. Strictly speaking, it is not an aperture in the diaphragm but an osseoaponeurotic opening between it and the vertebral column, and therefore behind the diaphragm; occasionally some tendinous fibers prolonged across the bodies of the vertebræ from the medial parts of the lower ends of the crura pass behind the aorta, and thus convert the hiatus into a fibrous ring. The hiatus is situated slightly to the left of the middle line, and is bounded in front by the crura, and behind by the body of the first lumbar vertebra. Through it pass the aorta, the azygos vein, and the thoracic duct; occasionally the azygos vein is transmitted through the right crus.

The **esophageal hiatus** is situated in the muscular part of the diaphragm at the level of the tenth thoracic vertebra, and is elliptical in shape. It is placed above, in front, and a little to the left of the aortic hiatus, and transmits the esophagus, the vagus nerves, and some small esophageal bloodvessels.

The **vena caval foramen** is the highest of the three, and is situated about the level of the fibrocartilage between the eighth and ninth thoracic vertebræ. It is quadrilateral in form, and is placed at the junction of the right and middle leaflets of the central tendon, so that its margins are tendinous. It transmits the inferior vena cava, the wall of which is adherent to the margins of the opening, and some branches of the right phrenic nerve.

Of the **lesser apertures,** two in the right crus transmit the greater and lesser right splanchnic nerves; three in the left crus give passage to the greater and lesser left splanchnic nerves and the hemiazygos vein. The gangliated trunks of the sympathetic usually enter the abdominal cavity behind the diaphragm, under the medial lumbocostal arches.

On either side two small intervals exist at which the muscular fibers of the diaphragm are deficient and are replaced by areolar tissue. One between the sternal and costal parts transmits the superior epigastric branch of the internal mammary artery and some lymphatics from the abdominal wall and convex surface of the liver. The other, between the fibers springing from the medial and lateral lumbocostal arches, is less constant; when this interval exists, the upper and back part of the kidney is separated from the pleura by areolar tissue only.

Action.—Draws the central tendon downward. This action has two effects: (*a*) it tends to increase the volume and decrease the pressure within the thoracic cavity, and (*b*) it tends to decrease the volume and increase the pressure within the abdominal cavity. During inspiration, the lowering of the diaphragm decreases the pressure within the thorax, and air is forced into the lungs through the open larynx and trachea by the pressure of the atmosphere. At the same time, the descending diaphragm presses against the abdominal viscera, forcing them downward against the passive resistance of the abdominal and pelvic muscles, and causing the anterior abdominal wall to protrude slightly. The pressure within the abdominal cavity is greatly increased when the abdominal muscles and the diaphragm contract actively at the same time, and this increase in pressure tends to make the abdominal viscera discharge their contents as in micturition, defecation, emesis, and parturition. The portion of the diaphragm about the esophageal hiatus is supposed to have a sphincteric action on the esophagus.

Nerve.—The phrenic nerve from the cervical plexus, containing mainly fibers from the fourth, but also some from the third and fifth cervical nerves.

Variations.—The sternal portion of the muscle is sometimes wanting and more rarely defects occur in the lateral part of the central tendon or adjoining muscle fibers.

The **Movements of Respiration** are inspiration, caused by an increase in the thoracic cavity, and expiration, caused by a decrease in the cavity. The increase in the volume of the cavity is the result of muscular action and is brought about in two ways: (*a*) by the descent of the diaphragm from contraction of its muscle, and (*b*) by the expansion of the thoracic wall through the action of certain muscles on the ribs, sternum, and vertebral column. The decrease in volume with expiration may be passive, due to the elastic recoil of the thoracic wall and the tissues of the lungs and bronchi. The decrease may also be the result of muscular action, in which case, (*a*) the abdominal muscles force the diaphragm upward by increasing the abdominal pressure, and (*b*) the thoracic wall is contracted by the action of certain muscles on the ribs and vertebral column.

Quiet Inspiration.—The diaphragm contracts, increasing the vertical diameter of the thoracic cavity. The first and second ribs remain fixed by the inertia and resistance of the cervical structures, and the remaining ribs, except the last two, are brought upward toward them by the contraction of the Intercostales externi. The upward motion of the ribs, due to their position and to the obliquity of their axis of rotation, enlarges the antero-posterior and transverse diameters of the thorax according to the movements described on page 280.

Traditionally, there are two types of quiet inspiration, diaphragmatic and costal, but under normal conditions there is a mixture of both types, although one or the other may show decided predominance in individual cases. Diaphragmatic breathing is also called abdominal because the visible result of contraction of the diaphragm is protrusion of the abdominal wall. To contrast with this, costal breathing is also called thoracic breathing. Costal breathing predominates in recumbency and it is said to be more frequent in women, while diaphragmatic is more frequent in men.

Quiet Expiration.—The normal resting position of the thorax is that found at the end of a quiet expiration. This position is restored without muscular effort after a quiet inspiration by the recoil of the structures which were displaced by the inspiratory act. The displacement of the anterior abdominal wall is overcome by the tonus of the abdominal muscles. The ribs are restored from their displacement by the elasticity of the ligaments and cartilages which hold them in place. The extensive network of elastic fibers which permeates the pulmonary tissue retracts the lungs wherever possible, and the bronchial tree, which has been elongated by the descent of the diaphragm, helps to draw the latter back up by its elastic recoil.

Deep Inspiration.—All the actions of quiet inspiration are increased in extent. In addition, the first two ribs are raised by the Scaleni and the Sternocleidomastoideus, and the remaining ribs are raised more forcibly by the additional action of the Levatores costarum and the Serratus posterior superior. The ribs are raised still farther by a straightening of the vertebral column through contraction of the Sacrospinalis. After the abdominal viscera have been forced downward by the diaphragm to a considerable extent, the abdominal muscles offer increased resistance, and the viscera may then act as a point of fixation for the diaphragm so that its further contraction raises the ribs.

Forced Inspiration.—In patients with great air hunger, all the muscles of the body seem to combine and coördinate to assist in breathing. The Levator scapulæ, the Trapezius, and the Rhomboidei elevate and fix the scapula which is then used as an origin by the Pectoralis minor to draw the ribs upward. If the patient further fixes the shoulder girdle by grasping the back of a chair or end of the bed, the Pectoralis major and the Serratus anterior will also raise the ribs.

Forced Expiration.—In forced expiration, muscles are called into play. The last two ribs are pulled downward and fixed by the Quadratus lumborum, and the other ribs are drawn downward toward them by the Intercostales interni and the Serrati posteriores inferiores. The muscles of the abdominal wall, by pressing on the abdominal viscera, force the diaphragm upward, and the same muscles, by flexing the vertebral column, assist in lowering the ribs.

Position of the Diaphragm.—The height of the diaphragm is constantly varying during respiration; it also varies with the degree of distension of the stomach and intestines and with the size of the liver. After a forced expiration the right cupola is on a level in front with the fourth costal cartilage, at the side with the fifth, sixth, and seventh ribs, and behind with the eighth rib; the left cupola is a little lower than the right. The absolute range of movement between deep inspiration and deep expiration averages in the male and female 30 mm. on the right side and 28 mm. on the left; in quiet respiration the average movement is 12.5 mm. on the right side and 12 mm. on the left.

Radiography shows that the height of the diaphragm in the thorax varies considerably with the position of the body. It stands highest when the body is horizontal and the patient on his back, and in this position it performs the largest respiratory excursions with normal breathing. When the body is erect the dome of the diaphragm falls, and its respiratory movements become smaller. The dome falls still lower when the sitting posture is assumed, and in this position its respiratory excursions are smallest. These facts may, perhaps, explain why it is that patients suffering from severe dyspnœa are most comfortable and least short of breath when they sit up. When the body is horizontal and the patient on his side, the two halves of the diaphragm do not behave alike. The uppermost half sinks to a level lower even than when the patient sits, and moves little with respiration; the lower half rises higher in the thorax than it does when the patient is supine, and its respiratory excursions are much increased. In unilateral disease of the pleura or lungs analogous interference with the position or movement of the diaphragm can generally be observed radiographically.

It appears that the position of the diaphragm in the thorax depends upon three main factors, viz.: (1) the elastic retraction of the lung tissue, tending to pull it upward; (2) the pressure exerted on its under surface by the viscera; this naturally tends to be a negative pressure, or downward suction, when the patient sits or stands, and positive, or an upward pressure, when he reclines; (3) the intra-abdominal tension due to the abdominal muscles. These are in a state of contraction in the standing position and not in the sitting; hence the diaphragm, when the patient stands, is pushed up higher than when he sits.

The following figures represent the average changes which occur during deepest possible respiration. The manubrium sterni moves 30 mm. in an upward and 14 mm. in a forward direction; the width of the subcostal angle, at a level of 30 mm. below the articulation between the body of the sternum and the xiphoid process, is increased by 26 mm.; the umbilicus is retracted and drawn upward for a distance of 13 mm.

IV. THE FASCIÆ AND MUSCLES OF THE ABDOMEN.

The muscles of the abdomen may be divided into two groups: (1) the **antero-lateral muscles**; (2) the **posterior muscles**.

1. The Antero-lateral Muscles of the Abdomen.

Obliquus externus abdominis.	Transversus abdominis.
Obliquus internus abdominis.	Rectus abdominis.
Pyramidalis.	

The **Superficial Fascia** (*tela subcutanea*) (Fig. 378) of the anterior abdominal wall is soft and movable, and likely to contain fat. It is continuous, above, with the superficial fascia of the thorax; below, with that of the thigh and external genitalia; and laterally, it gradually becomes tougher and more resistant as it changes into the fascia of the back. In the lower portion, below the umbilicus, its superficial and deep layers are unusually distinct and can be separated easily by dissection. This unaccustomed divisibility and certain other peculiar features have been emphasized by giving the two layers in this region special names, Camper's fascia and Scarpa's fascia.

The **superficial layer of the superficial fascia** (*Camper's Fascia*) is a genuine panniculus adiposus. It may be several centimeters thick in obese individuals, in which case it is likely to be irregularly divisible into laminæ. It is continuous over the inguinal ligament with the similar and corresponding layer of the thigh. In the male, as it continues down on the penis and scrotum, it loses its fat and, fusing with the deep layer, assists in the formation of the special fascia of these organs called the dartos. In the female, it retains some of the adipose tissue as it is continued into the labia majora. In both sexes, it is prolonged backward in the groove between the external genitalia and the thigh and is there continuous with the superficial layer of the superficial fascia of the perineum and medial surface of the thigh.

The **deep layer of the superficial fascia** (*Scarpa's Fascia*) is a membranous sheet which usually contains no adipose tissue. It is composed, in considerable part, of yellow elastic fibers, and probably corresponds to the tunica abdominalis, an elastic layer which contributes to the support of the viscera and inguinal mammæ in some lower mammals. It forms a continuous sheet across the middle line, and is attached to the linea alba as it passes across it. Above and laterally, it loses its identity as a special layer in the superficial fascia of the upper abdomen and back. Below, it passes over the inguinal ligament and is securely attached either to the ligament itself or to the fascia lata just beyond it. Inferior to the ligament, the corresponding layer is called the fascia cribrosa as it covers and fills in the fossa ovalis (saphenous opening). At the medial end of the inguinal ligament, it passes over the external inguinal ring without being attached and continues into the penis and scrotum. It continues along the groove between the scrotum (labium majus) and thigh into the perineum where it is called the fascia of Colles. As the superficial fascia comes to lie under the skin of the scrotum and penis, its two layers are fused into a single tunic called the dartos. Here the superficial layer loses its fat and acquires a layer of scattered smooth muscle cells which attach to the skin and throw it into folds or rugæ. In the middle line, over the symphysis pubis, it is thickened by the addition of numerous, closely set, strong bands which extend down to the dorsum and sides of the penis forming the **ligamentum fundiforme penis.**

The fascial cleft which separates Scarpa's from the deep fascia over the lower portion of the aponeurosis of the Obliquus externus is quite definite and of considerable clinical interest because of its continuity with a similar cleft in the perineum. It is limited upward, toward the umbilicus, by an adhesion of Scarpa's fascia to the deep fascia, and laterally, by the former's closer attachment over the muscular portion of the external oblique. It is limited, downward and laterally, by a firm attachment either to the inguinal ligament or to the fascia lata just below it. Over the medial portion of the inguinal ligament and the external inguinal ring, however, the two fasciæ are not attached, so that the cleft follows along the narrow groove between the scrotum (labium) and thigh, with the cleft between Colles' fascia and the external perineal fascia. From this groove, it is continuous medially with the cleft under the very movable dartos of the scrotum and penis, but it is abruptly limited laterally by an attachment to the deep fascia over the pubic ramus where the adductor muscles of the medial side of the thigh originate. In obese individuals there may be accumulations of adipose tissue between the cleft and the deep surface of Scarpa's fascia. The superficial inferior epigastric and circumflex iliac blood-vessels lie between Camper's and Scarpa's fasciæ but are attached to the superficial surface of Scarpa's layer.

Deep Fascia (*Fascia innominata; Gallaudet's fascia*).—The **outer investing layer** of deep fascia is easily identified in the lateral portion of the anterior abdominal wall where it covers the fleshy fibers of the Obliquus externus abdominis. It is continuous with the fascia of the Latissimus dorsi and Pectoralis major. More medially, over the aponeurosis of the Obliquus externus, it is so firmly adherent that it may escape recognition. Its presence is easily demonstrated in dissection, however, by scraping it back until the glistening fibers of the aponeurosis beneath are revealed. Above, it covers the upper end of the rectus sheath and is continuous with the pectoral fascia. Below, it is firmly attached to the inguinal ligament and joins the deep fascia emerging from under that ligament to become the fascia lata of the thigh. It covers the external inguinal ring as a distinct and separate layer, and there, reinforced by the fascia of the inner surface of the aponeurosis, gives rise to a tubular prolongation, the external spermatic (intercrural) fascia, which is the coat of the spermatic cord and testis just deep to the dartos. Near the middle line, it is attached to the pubic bone and is then continuous with deep fascia investing the penis. Over the lower end of the linea alba it is thickened into a strong, fibrous triangle, the **suspensory ligament of the penis,** which attaches the dorsum of the penis to the symphysis and arcuate pubic ligament. At the medial end of the inguinal ligament and lowest medial portion of the aponeurosis of the external oblique, it is attached to the pubic ramus and arcuate pubic ligament and is then continuous posteriorly, over the Ischiocavernosus muscle, with the external perineal fascia. Laterally in this region, beyond its attachment to the ramus, it is continuous with the fascia covering the adductor muscles of the medial side of the thigh.

The **Obliquus externus abdominis** (*External or descending oblique muscle*) (Fig. 377), situated on the lateral and anterior parts of the abdomen, is the largest and the most superficial of the three flat muscles in this region. It is broad, thin, and irregularly quadrilateral, its muscular portion occupying the side, its aponeurosis the anterior wall of the abdomen. It *arises*, by eight fleshy digitations, from the external surfaces and inferior borders of the lower eight ribs; these digitations are arranged in an oblique line which runs downward and backward, the upper ones being attached close to the cartilages of the corresponding ribs, the lowest to the apex of the cartilage of the last rib, the intermediate ones to the ribs at

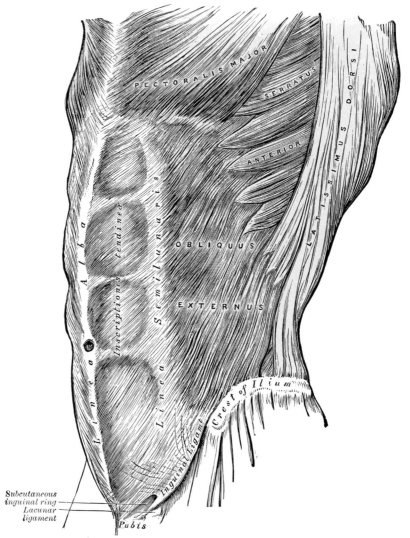

Fig. 377.—The Obliquus externus abdominis.

some distance from their cartilages. The five superior serrations increase in size from above downward, and are received between corresponding processes of the Serratus anterior; the three lower ones diminish in size from above downward and receive between them corresponding processes from the Latissimus dorsi. The muscular fasciculi from the last two ribs pass nearly vertically downward and are *inserted* into the anterior half of the outer lip of the iliac crest; the rest of the fasciculi, directed downward and forward, terminate in the broad abdominal aponeurosis by means of which most of the muscle reaches its final *insertion*, the linea alba.

Action.—Compresses the abdominal contents, assisting in micturition, defecation, emesis, parturition, and forced expiration. Both sides acting together flex the vertebral column, drawing the pubis toward the xiphoid process. One side alone bends the vertebral column laterally and rotates it, bringing the shoulder of the same side forward.

Nerve.—Branches of the eighth to twelfth intercostal, and the iliohypogastric and ilioinguinal nerves.

The **aponeurosis of the Obliquus externus abdominis** (Figs. 377, 378) is a strong membrane whose tendinous bundles continue, for the most part, in the direction of the muscular fasciculi, downward and medialward. It covers the entire front of the abdomen, lying superficial to the Rectus abdominis and helping to form its sheath. The fibers of the two sides interlace in the middle line to form the linea alba, the real insertion of the muscle, which extends from the xiphoid process to the symphysis pubis. The uppermost part of the aponeurosis serves as the origin for the lower fibers of the Pectoralis major. The lowermost portion ends in a very strong, thickened, free border which gives up its function as the tendon for the muscle and becomes, instead, a ligament attached to the anterior superior spine of the ilium at one end and to the pubic tubercle at the other. This is the **inguinal ligament.** Near its medial end, the free border is curled under like a sling to support the spermatic cord. Its attachment to the pubic bone is fanned out along the pectineal line beyond the pubic tubercle, leaving a crescentic free border which is called the **lacunar ligament.** Some of these fibers, after curling under and attaching to the bone, double back upward behind the main aponeurosis in a triangular sheet called the **reflected inguinal ligament.** The tendinous bundles of the aponeurosis just above the inguinal ligament separate from each other near the pubis to leave a narrow triangular opening which is called the **subcutaneous inguinal ring,** and which gives passage to the spermatic cord (round ligament in the female). Lateral to this opening, the aponeurosis contains, in addition to the bundles running in the usual direction, some scattered, transverse, reinforcing bundles which sweep medialward and upward in curved lines from the inguinal ligament. These are called **intercrural fibers.** In the above description, the aponeurosis has been treated as if it belonged solely to the Obliquus externus. This is advantageous for the presentation of the subcutaneous inguinal ring and associated structures, but it gives an incomplete picture because the aponeurosis serves also as the insertion of the Obliquus internus and Transversus, and it forms the sheath of the Rectus abdominis.

The **Inguinal Ligament** (*ligamentum inguinale; Poupart's ligament*) (Figs. 314, 378).—The inguinal ligament is the thickened lower border of the aponeurosis of the Obliquus externus. It extends from the anterior superior iliac spine to the pubic tubercle in a curved line with its convexity downward. It is attached securely to the fascia lata by means of its own fascia, the fascia innominata, and its lateral third is attached also to the fused transversalis and iliac fasciæ, as the latter emerge from under the ligament on the surface of the Iliacus muscle. Medial to its attachment to the iliac fascia, it arches over the femoral vessels as they enter the thigh. In the formation of the inguinal ligament, the aponeurosis folds or curves inward from the surface, especially toward the medial attachment, and forms a narrow sling for the support of the spermatic cord. The attachment of the incurved portion doubles back like the letter U, following along the pectineal line of the superior ramus of the pubis as a strong band called Cooper's ligament and leaving a crescentic free border with the concavity facing laterally. This crescentic fold is called the lacunar ligament.

The **Lacunar Ligament** (*ligamentum lacunare* [*Gimbernati*]; *Gimbernat's ligament*)

(Fig. 316).—The lacunar ligament is the medial end of the inguinal ligament which is rolled under the spermatic cord and is attached along the pectineal line just lateral to the pubic tubercle. When it is viewed through the subcutaneous inguinal ring, after the spermatic cord has been removed, it appears to be a triangular fibrous membrane, about 1.25 cm. long, with a crescentic base, concave laterally, and with an apex medially at the pubic tubercle. It lies almost horizontally, in the erect posture, with the spermatic cord resting on its superior surface. Against its concave lateral border lies the medial wall of the femoral canal.

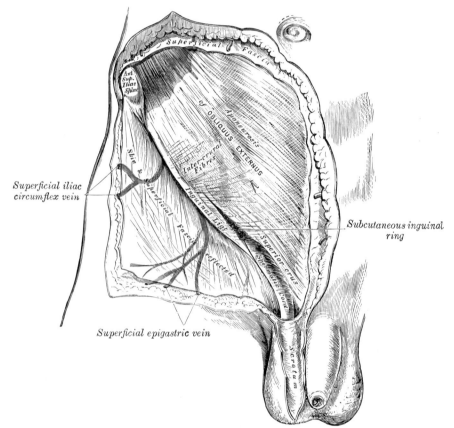

FIG. 378.—The subcutaneous inguinal ring.

The **Reflected Inguinal Ligament** (*ligamentum inguinale reflexum [Collesi]*; *triangular fascia*) (Fig. 380).—The reflected inguinal ligament is a triangular, tendinous sheet 2 or 3 cm. wide extending from the medial part of the inguinal ring to the linea alba. The fibers are attached to the pectineal line along with the lacunar ligament, or they may seem to be a continuation of that ligament; they course upward and medially, behind or deep to the main aponeurosis of the external oblique, and interlace with the fibers of the latter in the linea alba. The ligament may be independent, but more often it is fused either with the aponeurosis of the external oblique or with the falx inguinalis which lies deep to it. Frequently it seems to be entirely lacking.

The **Subcutaneous Inguinal Ring** (*annulus inguinalis subcutaneous; superficial or external inguinal ring; external abdominal ring*) (Fig. 378).—The subcutaneous inguinal ring is the opening in the aponeurosis of the Obliquus externus abdominis just above and lateral to the pubis, through which the spermatic cord (round ligament of the uterus) passes. It is a narrow triangle, pointing upward and laterally in the direction of the fibers of the aponeurosis. Its base is at the crest of the pubis; the sides are the margins of the opening in the aponeurosis and are called the crura of the ring. The **inferior** (lateral) **crus** (*external pillar*) is the stronger and is formed by the portion of the inguinal ligament which is attached to the pubic tubercle; it is curved and turned under into a narrow sling upon which the spermatic cord rests. The **superior** (medial) **crus** (*internal pillar*), thin and flat, is merely the part of the aponeurosis next to the opening and is not marked off except as it is attached to the front of the symphysis pubis. The triangular opening in the aponeurosis is converted by fascia into an oval ring, 2.5 cm. long and 1.25 cm. wide. The fascia of the superficial surface of the aponeurosis, called the fascia innominata by Gallaudet, fuses with the fascia of the deep surface and fills in the angular, lateral por-

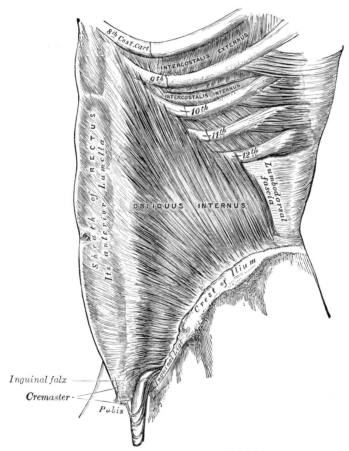

Fig. 379.—The Obliquus internus abdominis.

tion of the opening. A tubular prolongation of this fascia is continued down into the scrotum, enclosing the spermatic cord and testis in a sheath called the external spermatic fascia (intercrural or intercolumnar fascia). This intercrural fascia, so named because it occupies the space between the crura of the ring, is not to be confused with the intercrural fibers which are a part of the aponeurosis itself and reinforce the latter above the ring. The subcutaneous inguinal ring gives passage to the ilioinguinal nerve as well as to the spermatic cord or round ligament; it is larger in men than in women because of the greater size of the spermatic cord.

The Pectineal Ligament (*Cooper's Ligament*) (Fig. 316) is a narrow band of strong aponeurotic fibers which continues laterally from the lacunar ligament along the pectineal line of the pubis. It is firmly attached to the bone along this line and its medial end is continuous with the lacunar ligament. It diminishes in size gradually toward its lateral extremity at the iliopectineal eminence. It is aponeurotic rather than fascial in origin, and to it are attached parts of the iliopectineal, pectineal, and transversalis fasciæ. It forms the posterior or deep boundary of the lacuna vasorum through which the femoral vessels pass under the inguinal ligament.

The **Obliquus internus abdominis** (*Internal or ascending oblique muscle*) (Fig. 379), situated in the lateral and anterior part of the abdominal wall, is of an irregularly quadrilateral form, and is smaller and thinner than the Obliquus externus under which it lies. It *arises* by fleshy fibers from the lateral half of the inguinal ligament and the nearby iliac fascia from the anterior two-thirds of the middle lip of the iliac crest, and from the lower portion of the lumbar aponeurosis (posterior layer of the lumbodorsal fascia) near the crest. The posterior fasciculi pass almost vertically upward to be *inserted* into the inferior borders of the cartilages of the lower three or four ribs by fleshy digitations which appear to be continuations of the internal intercostal muscles. The remainder of the fasciculi which arise from the iliac crest diverge as they spread over the side of the abdomen and terminate in the region of the linea semilunaris, in an aponeurosis which fuses with the aponeuroses of the externus and the transversus at a variable distance from the middle line. By means of the aponeurosis the muscle makes its final *insertion* into the linea alba. The fibers of the aponeurosis assist in the formation of the rectus sheath, some passing anterior and some posterior to the latter muscle. The fasciculi arising from the inguinal ligament are less compact and paler than the rest, and descending, form an arch over the spermatic cord (round ligament). They terminate in a tendinous sheet, which they share with the Transversus, and which is not fused with the aponeurosis of the externus but is independently inserted into the pubis and medial part of the pectineal line behind the lacunar ligament, forming what is known as the *falx inguinalis*.

Action.—Compresses the abdominal contents, assisting in micturition, defecation, emesis, parturition, and forced expiration. Both sides acting together flex the vertebral column, drawing the costal cartilages downward toward the pubis. One side acting alone bends the vertebral column laterally and rotates it, bringing the shoulder of the opposite side forward.

Nerves.—Branches of the eighth to twelfth intercostal, and the iliohypogastric and ilioinguinal nerves.

Variations.—Occasionally, tendinous inscriptions occur from the tips of the tenth or eleventh cartilages or even from the ninth; an additional slip to the ninth cartilage is sometimes found; separation between iliac and inguinal parts may occur.

The **Cremaster** (Fig. 380) is a thin muscular layer whose fasciculi are separate and spread out over the spermatic cord in a series of loops. It *arises* from the middle of the inguinal ligament as a continuation of the Obliquus internus, and is *inserted* by a small pointed tendon into the tubercle and crest of the pubis and into the front of the sheath of the Rectus abdominis. The fasciculi form a compact layer as they lie within the inguinal canal, but after they pass out of the subcutaneous inguinal ring they form a series of loops, the longest of which extend down as far as the testis and are attached to the tunica vaginalis. The interval between the loops is occupied by fascia which is a fused continuation of the fasciæ of the deep and superficial surfaces of the Obliquus internus and which may be called the cremasteric fascia. The muscular loops and the fascia together make up a single layer which forms the middle tunic of the spermatic cord.

Action.—Draws the testis up toward the subcutaneous inguinal ring.

Nerve.—The external spermatic branch of the genitofemoral nerve.

The **Transversus abdominis** (*Transversalis muscle*) (Fig. 381), so called from the direction of its fibers, is the internal of the flat muscles of the abdomen, being placed immediately beneath the Obliquus internus. It *arises* by fleshy fibers from the lateral third of the inguinal ligament, from the anterior three-fourths of the inner lip of the iliac crest, from the lumbodorsal fascia, and from the inner surface of the cartilages of the lower six ribs. The origin from the ribs is by means of digitations which are separated from similar digitations of the Diaphragm (Fig. 375) by a narrow fibrous raphé; viewed from the interior of the abdomen, the two muscles appear to be components of a single stratum of muscle. The fasciculi of the Transversus, except the lowermost, pass horizontally forward, and terminate in an aponeurosis which fuses with the aponeurosis of the Obliquus internus, and joins the aponeurosis of the opposite side to form the *insertion* of the muscle into the linea alba. The aponeurosis assists in the formation of the sheath of the Rectus as follows: the upper portion passes entirely behind the Rectus; a portion extending for a variable distance below the umbilicus splits and interdigitates with the aponeurosis of the Obliquus internus contributing to both the anterior and posterior layers of the sheath; and the lowest part, below the linea semicircularis, a curved fibrous border approximately half way between the umbilicus and the pubis, passes entirely in front of the Rectus. The fasciculi of the lowest portion of the muscle pass downward as well as forward, *terminating* in the falx inguinalis along with the lowest fasciculi of the Obliquus internus. The muscle ends inferiorly in a free border which forms an arch extending from the lateral part of the inguinal ligament to the pubis, a short distance above the abdominal inguinal ring and spermatic cord.

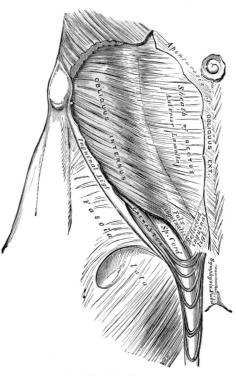

Fig. 380.—The Cremaster.

Action.—Constricts the abdomen, compressing the contents and assisting in micturition, defecation, emesis, parturition, and forced expiration.

Nerve.—Branches of the seventh to twelfth intercostal, and the iliohypogastric and ilioinguinal nerves.

Variations.—It may be more or less fused with the Obliquus internus or absent. The spermatic cord may pierce its lower border. Slender muscle slips from the iliopectineal line to transversalis fascia, the aponeurosis of the Transversus abdominis, or the outer end of the linea semicircularis and other slender slips are occasionally found.

The **Inguinal Falx** (*falx inguinalis aponeurotica; conjoined tendon of Internal oblique and Transversalis muscles*) (Figs. 380, 382, 383) is the lower terminal portion of the common aponeurosis of the Obliquus internus and Transversus abdominis muscles. It is inserted into the crest of the pubis and pectineal line immediately behind the subcutaneous inguinal ring, giving strength to a potentially weak point in the anterior abdominal wall. There is a wide variation in its width, strength, composition, and degree of union with neighboring aponeurotic and fascial structures. It may be narrow with a high arch, scarcely reaching the lateral part of the external inguinal ring, or it may be a broad, strong band, arching close to the inguinal ligament, and greatly reinforcing the abdominal wall in the region of the ring. In many cases it could be called the conjoined muscle instead of the conjoined tendon because the muscular fasciculi continue almost to the pubis. Not infrequently it is intimately fused with the reflected inguinal ligament which lies between it and the aponeurosis of the Obliquus externus. It may be reinforced on its deep surface by fusion with Henle's ligament.

The **Rectus abdominis** (Fig. 381) is a long flat muscle, which extends along the whole length of the front of the abdomen, and is separated from its fellow of the opposite side by the linea alba. It is much broader, but thinner, above than below, and *arises* by two tendons; the lateral or larger is attached to the crest of the pubis, the medial interlaces with its fellow of the opposite side, and is connected with the ligaments covering the front of the symphysis pubis. The muscle is *inserted* by three portions of unequal size into the cartilages of the fifth, sixth, and seventh ribs. The upper portion, attached principally to the cartilage of the fifth rib, usually has some fibers of insertion into the anterior extremity of the rib itself. Some fibers are occasionally connected with the costoxiphoid ligaments, and the side of the xiphoid process.

The Rectus is crossed by fibrous bands, three in number, which are named the **tendinous inscriptions;** one is usually situated opposite the umbilicus, one at the extremity of the xiphoid process, and the third about midway between the xiphoid process and the umbilicus. These inscriptions pass transversely or obliquely across the muscle in a zigzag course; they rarely extend completely through its substance and may pass only halfway across it; they are intimately adherent in front to the sheath of the muscle. Sometimes one or two additional inscriptions, generally incomplete, are present below the umbilicus.

Action.—Flexes the vertebral column, particularly the lumbar portion, drawing the sternum toward the pubis; tenses the anterior abdominal wall, and assists in compressing the abdominal contents.

Nerves.—Branches of the seventh to twelfth intercostal nerves; the seventh supplies the portion above the first tendinous inscription, the eighth the portion between the first and second inscriptions, and the ninth the portion between the lower two inscriptions.

Variations.—The Rectus may insert as high as the fourth or third rib or may fail to reach the fifth. Fibers may spring from the lower part of the linea alba. Both the aponeurotic composition and the position of the linea semicircularis vary considerably.

The **sheath of the Rectus abdominis** (*vagina m. recti abdominis*) (Fig. 379, 381).— The Rectus abdominis is enclosed in a sheath which holds it in position but does not restrict its motion during contraction because it is separated from the muscle by a fascial cleft. The sheath is formed by the aponeuroses of the Obliquus externus, Obliquus internus, and Transversus which preserve their identity in some regions, but fuse or interlace in others. At the lateral border of the Rectus, they form two membranes, the anterior and posterior lamellæ of the sheath. The aponeurosis of the externus keeps its position anterior to the Rectus throughout its entire length, but fuses with that of the internus at a variable distance from the middle line. The line of fusion is close to the linea alba at the pubis and below the umbilicus, and gradually angles outward and upward, but remains medial to the lateral border of the Rectus. Thus a surgical incision over the Rectus, below the umbilicus, will go through the aponeuroses of the externus and internus as separate layers before it reaches the Rectus muscle itself. The aponeurosis of the internus, above the umbilicus, splits into two lamellæ, one of which passes anterior to the Rectus and fuses with the externus as just described; the other passes posterior to the Rectus and fuses with the aponeurosis of the Transversus to form the posterior lamella of the sheath. Above the costal margin, to which the internus is attached, the costal cartilages and xiphoid process of the sternum take the place of the aponeurotic sheath, posteriorly. The posterior lamella of the internus aponeurosis is attached to the cartilages; the anterior lamella ends abruptly in a fibrous band similar to the linea semicircularis, the Rectus above this point being covered only by the externus aponeurosis. The aponeurosis of the Transversus, above the umbilicus, passes entirely posterior to the Rectus and fuses with the internus as just described. Below the umbilicus, the behavior of the aponeuroses is more complicated and more variable. At an inconstant distance above the pubis, usually about half way, the

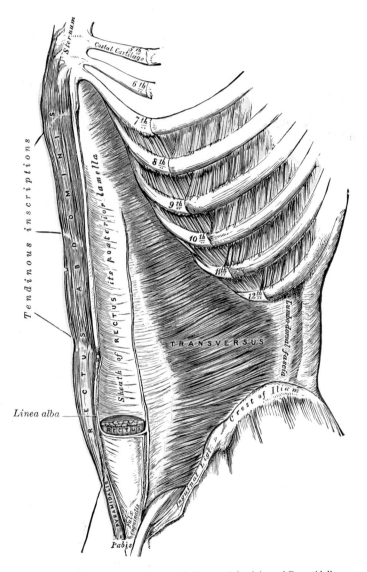

Fig. 381.—The Transversus abdominis, Rectus abdominis, and Pyramidalis.

contribution of the aponeuroses to the posterior lamella of the sheath ceases abruptly in a curved line, the **semicircular line of Douglas.** Below this line all the aponeurotic fibers of all three muscles pass anterior to the Rectus. Between the umbilicus and the semicircular line, the aponeuroses of the internus and Transversus fuse and interdigitate, and tendinous bundles from both may pass either anterior or posterior to the Rectus. Usually a short distance above the linea semicircularis, the internus terminates its contribution to the posterior lamella and the Transversus only

26

remains; hence, in the majority of instances, the linea is formed by the fibers of the Transversus alone. Below the linea, the sheath is formed by a portion of the endoabdominal or transversalis fascia. This portion of the sheath is occasionally reinforced by scattered tendinous bundles from the Transversus and by thickened laminæ of the subserous fascia. The sheath contains, besides the Rectus muscle, the Pyramidalis muscle, the superior and inferior epigastric arteries and veins, and branches of the intercostal nerves.

The **Pyramidalis** (Fig. 381) is a small triangular muscle, placed at the lower part of the abdomen, in front of the Rectus, and contained in the sheath of that muscle. It *arises* by tendinous fibers from the front of the pubis and the anterior pubic ligament; the fleshy portion of the muscle passes upward, diminishing in size as it ascends, and ends by a pointed extremity which is *inserted* into the linea alba, midway between the umbilicus and pubis.

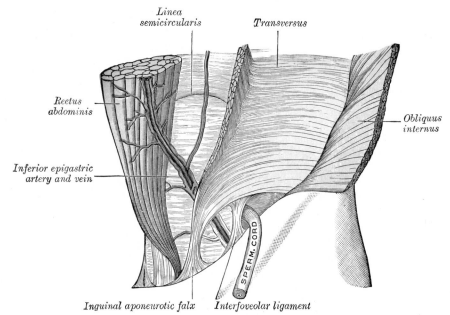

Fig. 382.—The interfoveolar ligament, seen from in front. (Modified from Braune.)

Action.—Tenses the linea alba.

Nerve.—Branch of the twelfth thoracic nerve.

Variations.—The Pyramidalis is wanting in 10 per cent, the lower end of the Rectus then becomes proportionately large. It may vary from 1.5 to 12 cm. in length, averaging 6.8 cm.; it is occasionally double on one or both sides, and the two sides may be unequal.

The **Linea alba** (Fig. 377) is the name given to the portion of the anterior abdominal aponeurosis or Rectus sheath in the middle line. It represents the insertion of the Obliquus externus and internus and the Transversus by the fusion of their aponeuroses with those of the opposite side; the fibers interlace and the three aponeuroses are fused into a single tendinous band which extends from the xiphoid process to the symphysis pubis. It is broader above, where the Recti are separated from each other by a considerable interval; a surgical incision above the umbilicus in the middle line will go through the linea as a single aponeurotic layer. It is narrower below, where the Recti are more closely placed; a surgical incision in the middle line below the umbilicus seldom follows the linea and will, in consequence, go through the anterior and posterior lamellæ of the Rectus sheath as individual layers. The lower end of the linea alba has a double attachment; the superficial one passes in front of the medial heads of the Recti to the symphysis pubis; the deeper one spreads out into a triangular sheet behind the Recti, attaches to the posterior lip of the crest of the pubis, and is named the **adminiculum lineæ albæ.** The umbilicus, which is an aperture for the passage of the umbilical vessels in the fetus, is closed in the adult and has the form of a hard fibrous ring or plate of scar tissue within the linea alba.

The **Linea Semicircularis** (*semicircular line or fold of Douglas*) (Fig. 382) is a curved tendinous band, with convexity upward, in the posterior lamella of the Rectus sheath below the umbilicus. It marks the lower limit of the aponeurotic portion of the posterior lamella, the latter being composed of transversalis fascia below the line. Its origin from the lateral border of the sheath may be from 4 to 13 cm., average 8 cm., from the pubis; its arched course may be horizontal or upward, but is most frequently downward; its insertion is into the linea alba, or occasionally as far down as the pubic crest. The tendinous bundles of the linea semicircularis are usually derived from the aponeurosis of the Transversus abdominis, but may be from the Obliquus internus, or from an interlacing of fibers from both the Transversus and the internus. A secondary linea may be found above the primary one, especially in those instances which have the primary linea formed by the Transversus, in which case the secondary is formed by the Obliquus internus.

The **Linea Semilunaris** (Fig. 377) is a slightly curved line on the anterior abdominal wall running approximately parallel with the median line, and lying about half way between the latter and the side of the body. It marks the lateral border of the Rectus abdominis, and can be seen as a shallow groove in the living subject, when that muscle is tensed. The abdominal wall is thin, particularly along the lower part of this line, where it is composed only of the aponeuroses of the Obliqui and Transversus, and their fasciæ. At its upper end, it is thicker where the muscular fasciculi of the Transversus extend under the Rectus for a variable distance.

Group Actions.—If pelvis and thorax are fixed, the abdominal muscles compress the abdominal viscera by constricting the cavity of the abdomen, in which action they are materially assisted by the descent of the diaphragm. By these means assistance is given in expelling the feces from the rectum, the urine from the bladder, the fetus from the uterus, and the contents of the stomach in vomiting.

If the pelvis and vertebral column be fixed, these muscles compress the lower part of the thorax, materially assisting expiration. If the pelvis alone be fixed, the thorax is bent directly forward, when the muscles of both sides act; when the muscles of only one side contract, the trunk is bent toward that side and rotated toward the opposite side.

If the thorax be fixed, the muscles, acting together, draw the pelvis upward, as in climbing; or, acting singly, they draw the pelvis upward, and bend the vertebral column to one side or the other. The Recti, acting from below, depress the thorax, and consequently flex the vertebral column; when acting from above, they flex the pelvis upon the vertebral column.

The **Transversalis Fascia** (*endoabdominal fascia*).—The **internal investing layer** of deep fascia which lines the entire wall of the abdomen is now generally called the Transversalis Fascia. It may even include the pelvic portion of this internal layer. Formerly, the name was applied only to the deep fascia covering the internal surface of the Transversus (Transversalis) abdominis muscle, but, because this muscle occupies a large proportion of the surface of the abdominal cavity, the name has gradually become adopted for the entire internal sheet. Various subdivisions of it are still referred to by their more specific designations; for example, the names iliac, psoas, or obturator fascia are used for the portions covering these muscles. This internal fascia is of great surgical interest and is extremely complex; in different areas it covers muscles, aponeuroses, bones, and ligaments; it may be very thin and adherent in one place or thickened and independent in another; it gives rise to specialized structures, such as tubular investments, and from it are derived certain components of important extra-abdominal fasciæ. It is a gray, felt-like membrane, sometimes transparent, sometimes thickened into strong bands, but seldom aponeurotic in appearance, and, except in obese individuals, contains no fat. Between this membrane and the peritoneum there is a layer of subserous fascia which may contain fat.

The definitive part of the transversalis fascia, that covering the internal surface of the muscular portion of the Transversus muscle, is readily identified by dissection. Over the aponeurosis of this muscle, however, it is thin and so closely adherent that only with difficulty can it be dissected free. Upward from the muscular portion of the Transversus, the fascia continues onto the diaphragm and covers its entire abdominal surface. It is thin and adherent over the muscular portion as well as over the central tendon. Ventrally, the fascia over the Transversus aponeurosis of one side is continuous across the middle line with that of the other side. Dorsally, as it leaves the muscular fasciculi of the Transversus, it continues for a short distance over the aponeurosis of origin of this muscle and then covers the Quadratus lumborum and Psoas muscles. From the Psoas it covers the crura of the diaphragm, the bodies and discs of the lumbar vertebræ, and is then continuous with the fascia of the Psoas of the other side. As the dorsal origin of the diaphragm crosses the Quadratus and Psoas, the fascia is thickened into the strong, fibrous lumbocostal arches. Downward from the muscular portion of the Transversus and the Quadratus lumborum, the fascia is attached to the bone along the crest of the ilium and continues into the greater pelvis on the surface of the Iliacus muscle. It is continuous, from the Iliacus and Psoas muscles, with the pelvic fascia which is described in the section dealing with the muscles of that region. The fascia on the internal surface of the anterior wall below the umbilicus requires an especially detailed description.

In a medial direction from the muscular fasciculi of the Transversus, the transversalis fascia below the umbilicus continues on the aponeurosis toward the middle line. The portion below the linea semicircularis, however, splits at the lateral border of the Rectus into two sheets; the thin anterior sheet continues on the aponeurosis and passes with it anterior to the Rectus; a thick posterior sheet forms the posterior lamina of the Rectus sheath and represents the internal investing or endoabdominal fascia in this area. Lateral to the lower part of the Rectus, the transversalis fascia continues downward on the Transversus aponeurosis to its lower limit, covering there the falx inguinalis, and passing over the free border of the Transversus aponeurosis as it forms an arch extending from the crest of the pubic bone to the lateral part of the inguinal ligament. The fascial membranes on both the deep and superficial surfaces of the Transversus fuse into a single sheet at this free border, providing a reinforced transversalis to bridge the interval between the arch and the inguinal ligament.

At a point just above the middle of the inguinal ligament, a tubular prolongation of this reinforced fascia is carried outward on the ductus deferens and internal spermatic vessels as they leave the abdominal cavity. This tubular investment is the inner coat of the spermatic cord and testis and is known as the internal spermatic or infundibuliform fascia. The ductus and vessels leave the abdominal cavity at a point which is called the abdominal or internal inguinal ring and they follow an oblique course through the abdominal wall in a tunnel called the inguinal canal. The lateral part of this canal, that is, before it has begun to penetrate the internal oblique muscle, has transversalis fascia for its posterior wall. The fascia is loosely attached to the inguinal ligament and has two thickenings near the ring, one extending upward is called the interfoveolar ligament, one extending downward is called the deep crural arch.

The **Interfoveolar Ligament** (*Hesselbach's ligament*) (Fig. 382) forms a crescentic medial boundary for the internal inguinal ring. It may be poorly defined or it may be a strong band whose fibers fan out medially as it follows the upward course of the deep inferior epigastric artery. It forms a slight ridge, not always visible but usually palpable from the interior of the abdominal cavity, which extends upward from the middle of the inguinal ligament, dividing the shallow fossa above the ligament into two parts, a **medial** and a **lateral inguinal fovea**. The internal inguinal ring, through which the ductus deferens leaves the abdominal cavity, is in the lateral fovea and it is here that the sac of an indirect inguinal hernia penetrates the abdominal wall. In the medial fovea, a triangular area is marked out by the inguinal ligament, the lateral boundary of the Rectus abdominis, and the inferior deep epigastric artery. This is *Hesselbach's triangle* and is the site of a direct inguinal hernia.

The **Deep Crural Arch** (*iliopubic tract*) is the downward extension of the transversalis fascia from the region of the internal inguinal ring. It arches across the external iliac vessels as they pass under the inguinal ligament and marks the transition from transversalis fascia to femoral sheath. Laterally, it is attached to the iliac fascia where the latter gives origin to the lower fibers of the Transversus muscle. Medially, it follows the downward curve of the lacunar ligament. It may be a strong band or it may be poorly defined and appear to be merely the proximal part of the femoral sheath.

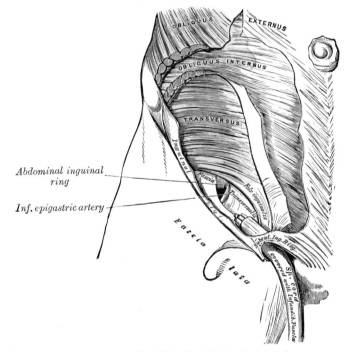

Abdominal inguinal ring

Inf. epigastric artery

Fig. 383.—The abdominal inguinal ring.

The **Abdominal Inguinal Ring** (*annulus inguinalis abdominis; internal or deep inguinal ring*) (Figs. 383, 539) is the name given to the interruption in the transversalis fascia where the spermatic cord (round ligament in the female) penetrates the anterior abdominal wall, carrying with it a sleeve-like investment of the transversalis fascia called the internal spermatic fascia. It is situated midway between the anterior superior iliac spine and the symphysis pubis, and about 1.25 cm. above the inguinal ligament (Fig. 383). It is of an oval form, the long axis of the oval being vertical. It varies in size, fitting rather closely about the penetrating structures unless it has been distended by the sac of an indirect inguinal hernia. It is bounded, above, by the arched lower margin of the Transversus abdominis;

medially, by the interfoveolar ligament accompanying the inferior deep epigastric vessels, and below, by the iliopubic tract.

The **Inguinal Canal** (*canalis inguinalis; spermatic canal*) is the tunnel in the lower anterior abdominal wall through which the spermatic cord (round ligament in the female) passes. Its internal (lateral) end is at the abdominal inguinal ring; its external (medial) end is at the subcutaneous inguinal ring. It is about 4 cm. long and takes an oblique course parallel with and a little above the inguinal ligament. It is bounded superficially by the skin, superficial fascia, aponeurosis of the Obliquus externus, and, in its lateral third, by the Obliquus internus; deeply, from medial to lateral ends, by the reflected inguinal ligament, the inguinal falx, the transversalis fascia, subserous fascia and peritoneum; proximally, by the arched fibers of the Obliquus internus and Transversus; distally, by the inguinal ligament, and at its medial end, the lacunar ligament. Through it pass the spermatic cord (round ligament), the ilioinguinal nerve, the internal spermatic vessels, and the Cremaster muscle.

Subserous Fascia (*subperitoneal fascia, superficial subserous fascia* [*Gallaudet*], *extraperitoneal connective tissue*).—Intervening between the internal investing layer of deep fascia of the abdominal wall and the peritoneum is the fibro-elastic connective tissue which supports the peritoneum. This subserous fascia resembles the subcutaneous superficial fascia in that it supports a free surface epithelial layer, it commonly contains adipose tissue in varying thicknesses, and it is frequently separated from the deep fascia by a fascial cleft. Not only does it have a parietal portion supporting the peritoneum of the abdominal wall, but it has a visceral portion which continues out over the viscera at the peritoneal reflections, and which accompanies the bloodvessels into the mesenteries. The subserous fascia has localized thickenings and accumulations of fat which are associated with the particular requirements of the different regions; these are described in the chapters dealing with the viscera.

The subserous fascia in the pelvis is uninterruptedly continuous with that of the abdomen. It is described in the chapter dealing with the pelvic viscera.

2. The Posterior Muscles of the Abdomen.

Psoas major.	Iliacus.
Psoas minor.	Quadratus lumborum.

The Psoas major, the Psoas minor, and the Iliacus, with the fasciæ covering them, will be described with the muscles of the lower extremity.

Fascia Covering the Quadratus Lumborum.—The transversalis (internal investing, endoabdominal) fascia covers the lateral portion of the Quadratus lumborum on its ventral surface. Since the medial portion of the muscle is overlapped by the Psoas, the fascia continues medially between the muscles and is attached to the bases of the transverse processes of the lumbar vertebræ. Its superior portion is thickened into a strong band, called the lateral lumbocostal arch (see Diaphragm), which is attached to the transverse process of the first lumbar vertebra, and the apex and lower border of the last rib. Inferiorly, the fascia is attached to the crest of the ilium, and is then continuous with the iliac fascia. At the lateral border of the muscle, the fascia fuses with the combined fascia and aponeurosis of origin of the Transversus. The latter, extending medially from this point of fusion, covers the dorsal surface of the Quadratus. The more medial portion of this aponeurotic sheet lies between the Quadratus and the Sacrospinalis and is named the lumbar aponeurosis (anterior layer of the lumbodorsal fascia).

The **Quadratus lumborum** (Fig. 373, page 380) is irregularly quadrilateral in shape, and broader below than above. It *arises* by aponeurotic fibers from the iliolumbar ligament and the adjacent portion of the iliac crest for about 5 cm., and is *inserted* into the lower border of the last rib for about half its length, and by four small tendons into the apices of the transverse processes of the upper four lumbar vertebræ. Occasionally a second portion of this muscle is found in front of the preceding. It *arises* from the upper borders of the transverse processes of the lower three or four lumbar vertebræ, and is *inserted* into the lower margin of the last rib. In front of the Quadratus lumborum are the colon, the kidney, the Psoas major and minor, and the diaphragm; between the fascia and the muscle are the twelfth thoracic, ilioinguinal, and iliohypogastric nerves.

Action.—Draws the last rib toward the pelvis and flexes the lumbar vertebral column laterally toward the side of the muscle acting. Fixes the last two ribs in forced expiration.

Nerves.—Branches of the twelfth thoracic and first lumbar nerves.

Variations.—The number of attachments to the vertebræ and the extent of its attachment to the last rib vary.

V. THE MUSCLES AND FASCIÆ OF THE PELVIS.

Levator ani.	Obturator internus.
Coccygeus.	Piriformis.

The muscles within the pelvis may be divided into two groups: (1) the true pelvic muscles, the Levator ani and Coccygeus; (2) the muscles of the lower limb which originate within the pelvis and thus form part of the pelvic wall, the Obturator internus and the Piriformis. The muscles of the second group will be described later with the muscles of the lower limb, but their fasciæ will be considered here because they form an important part of the pelvic fascia.

The **Pelvic Diaphragm** (*diaphragma pelvis*) is composed of the Levator ani and Coccygeus muscles together with the fasciæ covering their internal and external surfaces. It stretches across the pelvic cavity like a hammock. It is the most inferior portion of the body wall, closing the abdominopelvic cavity, restraining the abdominal contents, and giving support to the pelvic viscera. It is pierced by the anal canal, the urethra, and the vagina, and is reinforced in the perineum by the special muscles and fasciæ associated with these structures. The pelvic diaphragm and the structures of the perineum are intimately associated both structurally and functionally and an accurate knowledge of one cannot be obtained without study of the other.

The **Levator ani** (Fig. 384) is a broad, thin muscle forming the hammock-like floor of the pelvis. Although the muscles of the two sides are separated from each other anteriorly, and are inserted into a raphé posteriorly, they function as a single sheet across the middle line forming the principal part of the pelvic diaphragm. It *arises*, anteriorly, from the inner surface of the superior ramus of the pubis lateral to the symphysis; posteriorly, from the inner surface of the spine of the ischium; and between these two points, from the *arcus tendineus musculi levatoris ani*. The latter is a thickened band of the obturator fascia attached posteriorly to the spine of the ischium and anteriorly to the pubic bone at the anterior margin of the obturator membrane. The fasciculi pass posteriorly and medially in the floor of the pelvis and are *inserted* into the side of the last two segments of the coccyx, the anococcygeal raphé, the Sphincter ani externus, and the central tendinous point of the perineum. The *anococcygeal raphé* is the narrow fibrous band extending from the coccyx to the posterior margin of the anus where the muscles of the two sides join each other in the middle line.

The Levator ani generally shows a separation into two parts, more distinct in lower mammals than in man, the Pubococcygeus and the Iliococcygeus.

The **Pubococcygeus** arises from the dorsal surface of the pubis along an oblique line extending from the lower part of the symphysis to the obturator canal. The muscular fasciculi pass posteriorly, more or less parallel with the middle line, and terminate by joining the fibers from the other side. The lateral margin of the muscle may be separated from the Iliococcygeus by a narrow interval or it may be overlapped by the latter muscle. The medial margin is separated from the muscle of the other side by an interval known as the genital hiatus which allows the passage of the urethra, vagina, and rectum. The most anterior fasciculi, which are also the most medial, pass in close relation to the prostate and insert into the

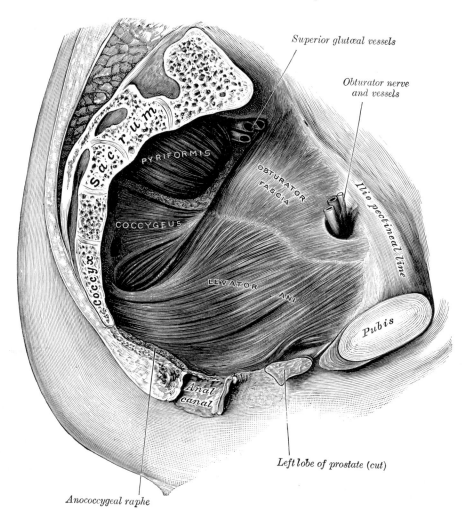

Fig. 384.—Left Levator ani from within.

central tendinous point just in front of the anus. This portion has been called the *Levator prostatæ*. In the female, this anterior portion has a similar relationship to the vagina. The majority of the fasciculi pass horizontally backward beside the anal canal, the superficial ones joining the anococcygeal raphé, the deeper ones joining the muscle of the other side to form a loop or sling about the rectum. This portion is called the *Puborectalis muscle*.

The **Iliococcygeus** arises from the arcus tendineus m. levatoris ani and the spine of the ischium, and inserts into the last two segments of the coccyx and the anococcygeal raphé. Its fasciculi pass medially as well as downward and backward which helps to distinguish them from the fasciculi of the Pubococcygeus.

Action.—Supports and slightly raises the pelvic floor, resisting increased intra-abdominal pressure, as during forced expiration. The Pubococcygeus draws the anus toward the pubis and constricts it.

Nerve.—Branches of the pudendal plexus, containing fibers from the fourth, sometimes also the third or fifth sacral nerves.

Variations.—The degree of distinctness of the Pubococcygeus and Iliococcygeus varies; the latter may be replaced by fibrous tissue.

The **Coccygeus** (Fig. 384) is situated behind the preceding. It is a triangular plane of muscular and tendinous fibers, *arising* by its apex from the spine of the ischium and sacrospinous ligament, and *inserted* by its base into the margin of the coccyx and into the side of the lowest piece of the sacrum. It assists the Levator ani and Piriformis in closing in the back part of the outlet of the pelvis.

Action.—Draws the coccyx forward, supporting the pelvic floor against intra-abdominal pressure.

Nerve.—Branches of the pudendal plexus, containing fibers from the fourth and fifth sacral nerves.

Variations.—The iliosacralis is an occasional band of muscle, ventral to the Coccygeus, attached to the iliopectineal line and the lateral border of the sacrum.

The **Sacrococcygeus anterior** is a muscular or tendinous slip from the lower sacral vertebræ to the coccyx, representing the vestige of the Depressor caudæ of lower mammals.

The **Sacrococcygeus posterior** is a slip from the dorsal aspect of the sacrum to the coccyx.

Pelvic Fascia (*fascia pelvis*).—The **internal investing fascia of the pelvis** covers the Levator ani and Coccygeus and the intrapelvic portions of the Obturator internus and Piriformis muscles. It belongs to the same category of fascia as the endo-abdominal or transversalis and is directly continuous with the latter over the brim of the lesser pelvis where it is attached to or fused with the periosteum of the symphysis and superior ramus of the pubis, the ilium along the arcuate or ilio-pectineal line, and the promontory of the sacrum. From these attachments, it sweeps downward and across the middle line, attaching to the anococcygeal raphé posteriorly and blending with the fasciæ of the anal canal and urogenital structures anteriorly. Although it is a continuous sheet, for convenience in description it is divided into (1) piriformis fascia, (2) obturator fascia and (3) supra-anal fascia.

The **fascia of the Piriformis** is very thin and is attached to the front of the sacrum and the sides of the greater sciatic foramen; it is prolonged outward through the greater sciatic foramen, joins the fascia of the external surface of the muscle at its lower border, and, becoming extrapelvic, forms part of the deep gluteal fascia. At its sacral attachment around the margins of the anterior sacral foramina it comes into intimate association with and ensheathes the nerves emerging from these foramina. Hence the sacral nerves are frequently described as lying behind the fascia. The internal iliac vessels and their branches, on the other hand, lie in the subperitoneal tissue in front of the fascia, and the branches to the gluteal region emerge in special sheaths of this tissue, above and below the Piriformis muscle.

Obturator Fascia (*fascia obturatoria*) (Fig. 385).—The fascia covering the Obturator internus muscle is partly intrapelvic and partly extrapelvic. This condition can best be understood if the intrapelvic portion is pictured as having incorporated in it the aponeurosis of origin of the Levator ani. It is as if the Levator had at one time been attached to the pelvic brim above the Obturator (a condition found in lower primates) but had slipped downward for a variable distance, usually about half the length of the muscle. At this point, the origin of the Levator is visible as a thickened band called the **arcus tendineus musculi levatoris ani**. Posteriorly, the arcus always ends by attaching to the spine of the ischium; anteriorly, it varies, but usually attaches to the anterior margin of the obturator membrane or the pubic bone medial to it. Since the Levator closes the aperture of the pelvis, the arcus marks the boundary between the intra- and extrapelvic portions of the obturator fascia. The intrapelvic portion usually is not aponeurotic in appearance and may be quite thin except at the arcus tendineus. Anteriorly, the obturator fascia is attached to the upper border of the obturator membrane or the pubic bone just in front of the obturator canal. It forms a tubular investment for the obturator nerve and vessels as they leave the pelvis through the obturator canal. Above, its attachment to the bone gradually angles upward from the obturator membrane until it reaches the iliopectineal line near the sacroiliac articulation. Posteriorly, it is attached to the margin of the greater sciatic notch down to the spine of the ischium. At the arcus tindineus of the Levator ani, the obturator fascia splits into three sheets; the outer one continues as the extrapelvic obturator fascia, the other two cover the external and internal surfaces of the pelvic diaphragm. The extrapelvic portion of the obturator fascia follows the muscle downward into the ischiorectal fossa and will be described with the perineum.

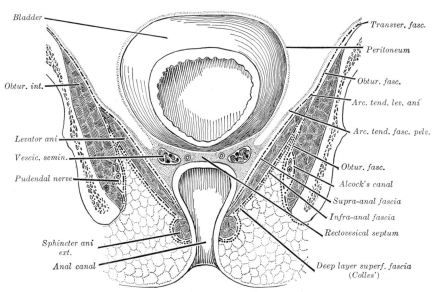

Fig. 385.—Fasciæ of pelvis and anal region of perineum. Diagram of coronal section.

The **Supra-anal Fascia** (*fascia diaphragmatis pelvis superior*) (Fig. 385) covers the internal surface of the Levator ani and Coccygeus muscles. Anteriorly, above the Pubococcygeus part of the Levator, it is attached to the pubic bone. Laterally, above the Iliococcygeus, it is continuous with the intrapelvic obturator fascia at the arcus tendineus of the Levator ani. Posteriorly, it covers the Coccygeus and becomes continuous with the fascia of the Piriformis. Behind the rectum, the fascia of the two sides is continuous across the middle line over the anococcygeal raphé. In front of the rectum, in the genital hiatus where the medial borders of the Pubococcygei of the two sides do not meet, the supra-anal fascia joins the infra-anal fascia to assist in the formation of the deep layer of the urogenital diaphragm. (See perineum).

Subserous Fascia (*tela subserosa*) (Fig. 386).—The subserous fascia of the pelvis not only covers the parietal wall and the viscera, but also acts as a padding tissue for the viscera in the lower part of the pelvis. It forms important ligaments, folds, and bands which are described in the chapter dealing with the pelvic viscera.

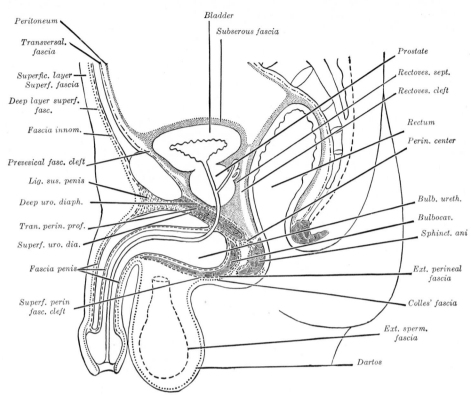

Fig. 386.—Fasciæ of pelvis and perineum in median sagittal section. Diagram.

VI. THE FASCIÆ AND MUSCLES OF THE PERINEUM.

The perineum corresponds to the outlet of the pelvis. Its deep boundaries are—in *front,* the pubic arch and the arcuate ligament of the pubis; *behind,* the tip of the coccyx; and on either side the inferior rami of the pubis and ischium, and the sacrotuberous ligament. The space is somewhat lozenge-shaped and is limited on the surface of the body by the scrotum in front, by the buttocks behind, and laterally by the medial side of the thigh. A line drawn transversely across in front of the ischial tuberosities divides the space into two portions. The posterior contains the termination of the anal canal and is known as the **anal region;** the anterior, which contains the external urogenital organs, is termed the **urogenital region.**

The **Superficial Fascia** (*tela subcutanea, fascia superficialis perinei*).—The superficial fascia of the perineum is divisible into two layers, superficial and deep, which are similar to and continuous with the corresponding layers of the anterior abdominal wall. The deep layer is called the fascia of Colles instead of Scarpa. The superficial layer, corresponding to Camper's fascia, usually is not specifically named, although it has been called Cruveilhier's fascia.

The **superficial layer of superficial fascia** in the anterior part of the perineum, that is, over the urogenital region, contains a considerable amount of adipose tissue and is likely to be irregularly laminated. Anteriorly, in the groove between the scrotum and the thigh, it is directly continuous with the corresponding layer (Camper's fascia) on the anterior abdominal wall. More medially, it is combined with the deep layer into the dartos tunic of the scrotum in the male, while in the female, it forms the greater part of the labium majus. Laterally, it is continuous with the superficial layer of the thigh. Posteriorly, it becomes the superficial layer of the anal region.

The superficial layer in the anal region is greatly thickened into a mass of fat which occupies the ischiorectal fossa. It is continuous posteriorly with the superficial fascia of the gluteal region and posterior thigh. Over the ischial tuberosities, the fibrous tissue is increased in amount, forming a tough pad.

Ischiorectal Fossa (*fossa ischiorectalis*) (Fig. 387).—The fossa is somewhat prismatic, in the shape of a wedge, with its base at the perineum and its apex deep in the pelvis where the Levator ani and Obturator internus come together. It is bounded medially, by the infra-anal fascia covering the Levator ani and Sphincter ani externus; laterally, by the obturator fascia over the extrapelvic portion of the Obturator internus, and by the tuberosity of the ischium; anteriorly, by the posterior borders of the Transversus perinæi superficialis and profundus; posteriorly, by the fascia over the Glutæus maximus and the sacrotuberous ligament. The superficial boundary is the skin, and the fossa is occupied by a mass of adipose tissue belonging to the superficial layer of the superficial fascia. The superficial and deep layers of the superficial fascia are not separable in the fossa and both are securely attached to the deep fascia covering the entire surface of the fossa. The posterior portion of the Transversus perinæi profundus is separated from the Levator ani for a short distance, so that the ischiorectal mass of fat has an *anterior process* which projects under the posterior border of the Transversus muscles. The adipose tissue is traversed by fibrous bands and incomplete septa. It is crossed transversely by the inferior hemorrhoidal vessels and nerves; at the back part are the perineal and perforating cutaneous branches of the pudendal plexus; while from the forepart, the posterior scrotal (or labial) vessels and nerves emerge. The internal pudendal vessels and pudendal nerve lie deep to the obturator fascia on the lateral wall of the fossa in a special reduplication of the fascia known as Alcock's canal.

Deep Layer of Superficial Fascia of Perineum (*Colles' fascia*) (Figs. 386, 387, 388).— The deep layer of superficial fascia in the urogenital region of the perineum is a distinctive structure. It is a strong membrane but does not have the white glistening appearance of an aponeurosis. It has a slightly yellow color due to its content of elastic fibers and is smooth in texture, its fibrous nature not being detectable with the naked eye. This characteristic texture is of assistance frequently in differentiating it from the deep fascia in the region. Anteriorly, it is directly continuous with the deep layer of superficial abdominal fascia (Scarpa's fascia) in the groove between the scrotum (labium) and thigh. More medially, it joins the superficial layer in the formation of the **dartos tunic** of the scrotum. In the middle line, it is attached to the superficial fascia along the raphé and continues anteriorly into the **septum of the scrotum**. Laterally, it is firmly adherent to the medial surface of the thigh along the ischiopubic ramus at the origin of the adductor muscles. In the anterior part of this area, it is continuous with the fascia cribrosa which covers the fossa ovalis (saphenous opening). Posteriorly, it dips inward toward the ischiorectal fossa around the posterior border of the Transversus perinæi superficialis and becomes firmly attached to the deep fascia along the posterior border of the Transversus perinæi profundus. It is attached also, with all the other layers, to the central tendinous point of the perineum. There is a distinct fascial cleft between it (Colles' fascia) and the external perineal fascia (deep fascia) (Figs. 386, 388) over the Bulbocavernosus, Ischiocavernosus, and Transversus perinæi superficialis muscles. This **superficial perineal cleft** is continuous with the cleft under Scarpa's fascia on the anterior abdominal wall but is closed off laterally and posteriorly by the attachments described above.

In the anal region, the deep layer of the superficial fascia is adherent both to the superficial layer and to the deep fascia. From its attachment to the posterior border of the Transversus perinæi profundus mentioned above, it continues deeply into the ischiorectal fossa in close apposition to the infra-anal fascia on the Levator ani muscle. At the origin of this muscle, it folds back sharply over the extrapelvic portion of the obturator fascia. Posteriorly, it leaves the ischiorectal fossa along the border of the gluteal region and posterior thigh.

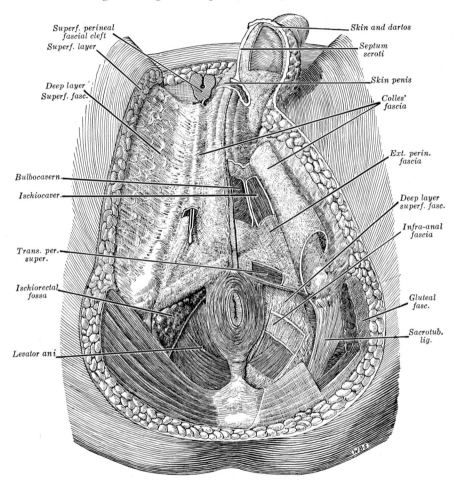

Fig. 387.—Fasciæ of perineum. Dissection of superficial layers.

Deep Fascia.—The deep fascia of the perineum consists of the obturator fascia, the infra-anal fascia, and the fasciæ over two groups of small muscles which are associated with the urogenital organs and occupy a position superficial to the pelvic diaphragm in the urogenital region of the perineum. The phenomena of splitting, fusion, and cleavage are prominent features of the fascia in this region. The clinical interest and importance of these fasciæ have made them the subject of numerous treatises in which the various parts are segregated and given special names. In the following description these parts will be considered individually but an attempt will be made to correlate the diverse terminology into a consistent description. A certain amount of repetition will be unavoidable.

Obturator Fascia (*fascia obturatoria*) (Fig. 386).—The fascia covering the extra-pelvic portion of the Obturator internus forms the lateral wall of the ischiorectal fossa, and is, therefore, a portion of the external investing layer of deep fascia of the body. Above, it meets the infra-anal fascia at a sharp angle in the deepest part of the fossa. Its inferior portion, extending from the lesser sciatic foramen to the ischial tuberosity, is thickened and splits to enclose the pudendal nerve and internal pudendal vessels in a fibrous tunnel called **Alcock's canal.** Anteriorly, it is attached to the ischiopubic ramus, and the fibrous sheath of Alcock's canal merges with the external perineal fascia and the superficial fascia of the urogenital diaphragm where branches of the nerve and vessels enter the superficial and deep perineal compartments described below.

The **Infra-anal Fascia** (*fascia diaphragmatis pelvis inferior*) (Fig. 386).—The infra-anal fascia is the deep fascia of the superficial (inferior, external) surface of the Levator ani and Coccygeus muscles. It is adherent to the muscle throughout. Above, the portion on the Iliococcygeus is continuous with the extra-pelvic obturator fascia at the arcus tendineus of the Levator ani; the portion over the Pubococcygeus is attached to the ischiopubic ramus and the pubic bone at the origin of the muscle. Between the medial borders of the two Pubococcygei, it joins the supra-anal fascia to form a thick sheet in the genital hiatus. Behind the rectum, it is continuous from side to side over the anococcygeal raphé where it is firmly attached. More posteriorly and laterally, it bridges the slight interval between the Levator ani and Coccygeus, and then binds the latter muscle to the lower edge of the sacrospinous ligament. From this ligament, it passes outward from the ischiorectal fossa along the overhanging lower border of the Glutæus maximus where it becomes continuous with the gluteal fascia. In the region of the anus, it invests the Sphincter ani externus and just anterior to the anus, it is firmly attached to the other perineal layers at the central tendinous point.

If the infra-anal fascia is traced forward from the ischiorectal fossa, it will be seen to split into three sheets at a transverse line connecting the anterior extremities of the ischial tuberosities. The deepest of the three continues on the surface of the Levator ani, and, lying between this muscle and the Transversus perinæi profundus, it is called the deep layer of the urogenital diaphragm. This is the sheet which joins the supra-anal fascia in the genital hiatus to form the thick membrane which binds the two medial borders of the Pubococcygei together. The middle sheet covers the superficial surface of the Transversus profundus and is called the superficial layer of the urogenital diaphragm. The most superficial of the three sheets curves outward around the posterior border of the Transversus perinæi superficialis and is the external perineal fascia.

The **Urogenital Diaphragm** (*diaphragma urogenitale*).—The Transversus perinæi profundus muscle is covered internally and externally by fascial membranes which are called respectively the deep and superficial layers of the urogenital diaphragm. The muscle and the two fasciæ taken together constitute the urogenital diaphragm. According to this, it is synonymous with the deep perineal compartment (pouch, interspace) and its contents, which will be described below. The urogenital diaphragm, as it has just been defined, is assisted in its rôle of a supporting structure by the portion of the Levator ani over which it lies and by the superficial perineal muscles and their fasciæ.

The **Genital Hiatus** is the interval in the middle line between the medial borders of the two Pubococcygeus portions of the Levator ani muscle. It is through this hiatus that the urethra passes in both sexes and the vagina in the female. It is filled in by fibrous tissue derived from the fascia of the Levator ani (the supra-anal and infra-anal fasciæ) and the deep layer of the urogenital diaphragm.

The **Deep** (*superior; internal*) **Layer of the Urogenital Diaphragm** (*fascia diaphragmatis urogenitalis superior*) is a flat triangular membrane stretching across the interval between the ischiopubic rami. It lies between the Transversus perinæi profundus and the Pubococcygeus portions of the Levator ani and represents, therefore, the fused fascial membranes of both these muscles. It represents also, in the genital hiatus between the medial borders of the two Pubococcygei, a fusion with still a third membrane, the supra-anal fascia. It is securely attached to the symphysis pubis anteriorly and joins the other perineal layers in the central tendinous point posteriorly. Laterally, it is attached to the medial borders of the ischiopubic rami along with the superficial layer of the diaphragm and there it is continuous with the obturator fascia. The middle portion, which occupies the genital hiatus, is thickened to fill in the gap between the two Pubococcygei and bind their medial borders together. It is pierced by the urethra and the vagina and blends with their walls as they pass through. The prostate gland rests on its pelvic surface and the connective tissue of the inferior portion of the gland's capsule blends with it intimately. The attachment of the fascia to the pubic bone and the blending with the prostatic capsule make the anterior part of the fascia a true **ligament of the prostate**. The tissue attachments may form three strands, a **middle puboprostatic**

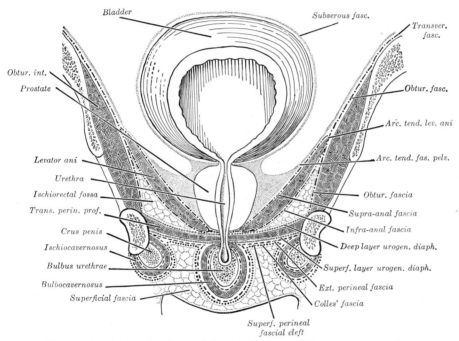

Fig. 388.—Fasciæ of pelvis and urogenital region of perineum. Diagram of coronal section.

ligament to the symphysis and two **lateral puboprostatic ligaments** to the pubic bone at the points where the anterior ends of the arcus tendinei of the Levatores ani are attached. At the posterior border of the deep Transversus, it is fused with the superficial layer of the urogenital diaphragm, closing the deep perineal compartment.

The **Superficial** (*inferior, external*) **Layer of the Urogenital Diaphragm** (*fascia diaphragmatis urogenitalis inferior*) (Figs. 386, 388) is a flat triangular membrane which, like the preceding, bridges the angular interval between the ischiopubic rami. It is attached laterally to the medial borders of the rami from the arcuate pubic ligament to the ischial tuberosities. Along these same borders, the deep layer of the diaphragm is attached more deeply and the crura of the penis more superficially. The middle portion of the fascia is pierced by the urethra and vagina and blends with their walls. It is perforated also by the arteries to the bulb, the ducts of the bulbourethral glands, the deep arteries of the penis, and the dorsal arteries and nerves of the penis. The part posterior to the urethra blends with the fascia of the bulb and, because of its attachment to the rami laterally, is sometimes called the **ligament of the bulb.** At these lateral attachments, the fascia blends with that of the crura also. The part anterior to the urethra arches across the subpubic angle and is sometimes called the **ligmæntum transversum pelvis.** The latter is separated from the symphysis and arcuate pubic ligament by an opening for the passage of the dorsal vein of the penis. At the posterior border of the deep Transversus muscle, the superficial and deep layers of the diaphragm fuse into a single layer and blend with the infra-anal fascia of the ischiorectal fossa.

The **External Perineal Fascia** (*inferior perineal fascia of Gallaudet*) (Figs. 387, 388) is the external investing fascia, that is, the most superficial layer of the deep fascia in the urogenital region of the perineum. It covers approximately the same triangular area as the preceding but it is not flat because it must accommodate itself to the contours of the superficial perineal muscles. It is attached laterally to the ischiopubic ramus at the outer border of the Ischiocavernosus. From this attachment it passes anteriorly along the groove between the scrotum and thigh, there becoming continuous with the external oblique fascia (fascia innominata) of the anterior abdominal wall and, more laterally, with the fascia lata of the medial surface of the thigh. It invests the Ischiocavernosus and Bulbocavernosus muscles and, in the interval between them, dips down to the level of the superficial layer of the urogenital diaphragm for a short distance and is there adherent to it. It follows the muscles just mentioned forward to the root of the penis and, at their insertion, it joins the fascia of the crura and bulb to become the **deep fascia of the penis** (*Buck's fascia*). Posteriorly, the fascia invests the Transversus perinæi superficialis. It passes deeply around the posterior border of this muscle into the ischiorectal fossa until it meets the deep Transversus where the two Transversi are in contact with each other. Here it fuses with the fascia of the urogenital diaphragm, and with it blends into the single layer of infra-anal fascia in the ischiorectal fossa. The fusion of this fascia with the fascia of the urogenital diaphragm posteriorly, its attachment to the ischiopubic rami laterally, and its fusion with the fascia of the penis anteriorly make it the superficial layer of a closed compartment, the superficial perineal compartment (pouch, interspace). The deep layer of the compartment is the superficial layer of the urogenital diaphragm. The fascial cleft which is superficial to the external perineal fascia, that is, which lies between it and Colles' fascia, should not be included in the compartment.

The **Perineal Center** is often called the **central tendinous point** (Fig. 386) in the male and often simply the perineum in the female. It is the mass of tissue in the middle line between the anus and the bulb in the male and between the anus and vagina in the female. It is approximately 2 cm. in width and depth in the male and about twice this dimension in the female. It is composed predominantly of fibrous tissue since it represents the fusion of the following: Infra-anal fascia (deep layer of the urogenital diaphragm), superficial layer of the urogenital diaphragm, external perineal fascia, and Colles' fascia. It contains a few muscular fibers also, principally from the Pubococcygeus and Sphincter ani externus, and it has attached to it besides these two muscles, the Transversus perinæi profundus and superficialis, and the Bulbocavernosus. It is directly continuous anteriorly with the fibrous tissue which fills in the genital hiatus between the two Pubococcygei. It is continuous deeply into the pelvis with the rectoprostatic and rectovesical septum in the male and the rectovaginal septum in the female. It is the time honored route of approach to the bladder and prostate from the perineum and it is the site of the perineal tears which are frequently a result of child bearing.

The **Triangular Ligament** is a name frequently given to the urogenital diaphragm, that is, the Transversus perinæi profundus and its superficial and deep fascial membranes. The name is less commonly used for the superficial fascia of the uro-genital diaphragm alone, without the muscle or the other fascia.

The **Deep Perineal Compartment** (*deep perineal pouch; deep perineal interspace*) is formed by the deep and superficial layers of the urogenital diaphragm. The compartment and its contents, therefore, form the urogenital diaphragm. The compartment is principally occupied by the Transversus perinæi profundus but contains also: the Sphincter urethræ membranaceæ and the membranous portion of the urethra; the bulbourethral glands (vestibular glands in the female) and their ducts; the internal pudendal vessels; the deep dorsal vein of the penis, and the dorsal nerve of the penis. The internal pudendal artery enters the compartment posteriorly and its branches to the bulb, to the urethra, the deep and the dorsal arteries of the penis, pierce the superficial fascia of the urogenital diaphragm to reach their destination.

The **Superficial Perineal Compartment** (*pouch*; *interspace*) is bounded by the superficial layer of the urogenital diaphragm and the external perineal fascia. It contains the Bulbocavernosus, Ischiocavernosus, and Transversus perinæi super-ficialis muscles, and is traversed by the perineal vessels and nerve. The usual description of this compartment, in which Colles' fascia forms the superficial boundary, is erroneous. The superficial boundary is a layer of deep fascia, the external investing perineal fascia (inferior perineal fascia, Gallaudet). There is a distinct **superficial perineal fascial cleft** between the latter and Colles' fascia (Figs. 386, 388).

Clinical Considerations.—The fascial cleft between the external perineal fascia and Colles' fascia has long been included erroneously in the superficial perineal pouch. When extravasated urine or hemorrhage finds its way into the tissue under Colles' fascia, it is not in the pouch but in the fascial cleft superficial to it. If it were in the pouch, it would infiltrate the superficial muscles and be restricted in its spread to the area covered by these muscles. Clinical experience has shown that it actually does spread along the groove between the scrotum and thigh to the anterior abdominal wall in the fascial cleft under Scarpa's fascia and into the scrotum and penis in the fascial cleft under the dartos. The spread is restricted posteriorly by the termination of the fascial cleft where Colles' fascia is attached to the infra-anal fascia at the posterior border of the Transversus perinæi profundus muscle, and laterally where it is attached to the fascia lata.

The muscles of the perineum may be divided into two groups:

    1. Those of the urogenital region: A, In the male; B, In the female.
    2. Those of the anal region.

1. A. The Muscles of the Urogenital Region in the Male (Fig. 389).

Superficial Group:
Transversus perinæi superficialis.
Bulbocavernosus.
Ischiocavernosus.

Deep Group:
Transversus perinæi profundus.
Sphincter urethræ membranaceæ.

The **Transversus perinæi superficialis** (*Transversus perinæi; Superficial transverse perineal muscle*) is a narrow muscular slip, which passes more or less transversely across the perineal space in front of the anus. It *arises* by tendinous fibers from the inner and forepart of the tuberosity of the ischium, and, running medialward, is inserted into the central tendinous point of the perineum, joining in this situa-tion with the muscle of the opposite side, with the Sphincter ani externus behind, and with the Bulbocavernosus in front. In some cases, the fibers of the deeper layer of the Sphincter ani externus decussate in front of the anus and are continued into this muscle. Occasionally it gives off fibers, which join with the Bulbocavernosus of the same side.

Actions.—The simultaneous contraction of the two muscles serves to fix the central tendinous point of the perineum.

Variations are numerous. It may be absent or double, or insert into Bulbocavernosus or External sphincter.

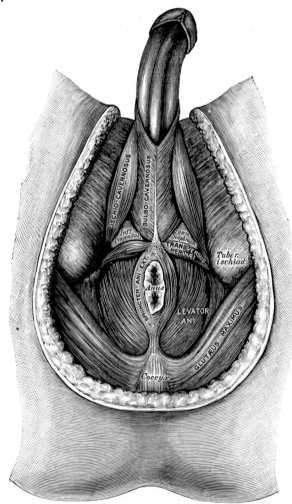

Fig. 389.—Muscles of male perineum.

The **Bulbocavernosus** (*Ejaculator urinæ; Accelerator urinæ*) is placed in the middle line of the perineum, in front of the anus. It consists of two symmetrical parts, united along the median line by a tendinous raphé. It *arises* from the central tendinous point of the perineum and from the median raphé in front. Its fibers diverge like the barbs of a feather; the most posterior form a thin layer, which is lost on the superficial fascia of the urogenital diaphragm; the middle fibers encircle the bulk and adjacent parts of the corpus cavernosum urethræ, and join with the fibers of the opposite side, on the upper part of the corpus cavernosum urethræ, in a strong aponeurosis; the anterior fibers spread out over the side of the corpus cavernosum penis to be inserted partly into that body, anterior to the Ischiocavernosus, occasionally extending to the pubis, and partly ending in a tendinous expansion which covers the dorsal vessels of the penis. The latter fibers are best seen by dividing the muscle longitudinally, and reflecting it from the surface of the corpus cavernosum urethræ.

Actions.—This muscle serves to empty the canal of the urethra, after the bladder has expelled its contents; during the greater part of the act of micturition its fibers are relaxed, and it only comes into action at the end of the process. The middle fibers are supposed by Krause to assist in the erection of the corpus cavernosum urethræ, by compressing the erectile tissue of the bulb. The anterior fibers, according to Tyrrel, also contribute to the erection of the penis by compressing the deep dorsal vein of the penis as they are inserted into, and continuous with, the fascia of the penis.

The **Ischiocavernosus** (*Erector penis*) covers the crus penis. It is an elongated muscle, broader in the middle than at either end, and situated on the lateral boundary of the perineum. It *arises* by tendinous and fleshy fibers from the inner surface of the tuberosity of the ischium, behind the crus penis; and from the rami of the pubis and ischium on either side of the crus. From these points, fleshy fibers proceed, and end in an aponeurosis which is *inserted* into the sides and under surface of the crus penis.

Action.—The Ischiocavernosus compresses the crus penis, and retards the return of the blood through the veins, and thus serves to maintain the organ erect.

The **Transversus perinæi profundus** *arises* from the inferior rami of the ischium and runs to the median line, where it interlaces in a tendinous raphé with its fellow of the opposite side. It lies in the same plane as the Sphincter urethræ membranaceæ; formerly the two muscles were described together as the **Constrictor urethræ.**

The **Sphincter urethræ membranaceæ** surrounds the whole length of the membranous portion of the urethra, and is enclosed in the fasciæ of the urogenital diaphragm. Its *external* fibers *arise* from the junction of the inferior rami of the pubis and ischium to the extent of 1.25 to 2 cm., and from the neighboring fasciæ. They arch across the front of the urethra and bulbourethral glands, pass around the urethra, and behind it unite with the muscle of the opposite side, by means of a tendinous raphé. Its *innermost* fibers form a continuous circular investment for the membranous urethra.

Actions.—The muscles of both sides act together as a sphincter, compressing the membranous portion of the urethra. During the transmission of fluids they, like the Bulbocavernosus, are relaxed, and only come into action at the end of the process to eject the last drops of the fluid.

Nerve Supply.—The perineal branch of the pudendal nerve supplies this group of muscles.

1. B. The Muscles of the Urogenital Region in the Female (Fig. 390).

Transversus perinæi superficialis.	Ischiocavernosus.
Bulbocavernosus.	Transversus perinæi profundus.
Sphincter urethræ membranaceæ.	

The **Transversus perinæi superficialis** (*Transversus perinæi; Superficial transverse perineal muscle*) in the female is a narrow muscular slip, which *arises* by a small tendon from the inner and forepart of the tuberosity of the ischium, and is inserted into the central tendinous point of the perineum, joining in this situation with the muscle of the opposite side, the Sphincter ani externus behind, and the Bulbocavernosus in front.

Action.—The simultaneous contraction of the two muscles serves to fix the central tendinous point of the perineum.

The **Bulbocavernosus** (*Sphincter vaginæ*) surrounds the orifice of the vagina. It covers the lateral parts of the vestibular bulbs, and is attached posteriorly to the central tendinous point of the perineum, where it blends with the Sphincter ani externus. Its fibers pass forward on either side of the vagina to be inserted into the corpora cavernosa clitoridis, a fasciculus crossing over the body of the organ so as to compress the deep dorsal vein.

Actions.—The Bulbocavernosus diminishes the orifice of the vagina. The anterior fibers contribute to the erection of the clitoris, as they are inserted into and are continuous with the fascia of the clitoris, compressing the deep dorsal vein during the contraction of the muscle.

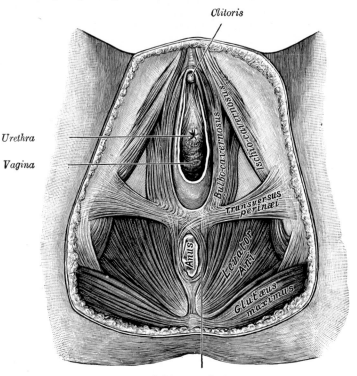

Fig. 390.—Muscles of the female perineum.   (Modified from a drawing by Peter Thompson.)

The **Ischiocavernosus** (*Erector clitoridis*) is smaller than the corresponding muscle in the male. It covers the unattached surface of the crus clitoridis. It is an elongated muscle, broader at the middle than at either end, and situated on the side of the lateral boundary of the perineum. It *arises* by tendinous and fleshy fibers from the inner surface of the tuberosity of the ischium, behind the crus clitoridis; from the surface of the crus; and from the adjacent portion of the ramus of the ischium. From these points fleshy fibers succeed, and end in an aponeurosis, which is inserted into the sides and under surface of the crus clitoridis.

Actions.—The Ischiocavernosus compresses the crus clitoridis and retards the return of blood through the veins, and thus serves to maintain the organ erect.

The **fascia of the urogenital diaphragm** in the female is not so strong as in the male. It is attached to the pubic arch, its apex being connected with the arcuate pubic ligament. It is divided in the middle line by the aperture of the vagina, with the external coat of which it becomes blended, and in front of this is perforated by the urethra. Its posterior border is continuous, as in the male, with the deep layer of the superficial fascia around the Transversus perinæi superficialis.

Like the corresponding fascia in the male, it consists of two layers, between which are to be found the following structures: the deep dorsal vein of the clitoris, a portion of the urethra and the Constrictor urethra muscle, the larger vestibular glands and their ducts; the internal pudendal vessels and the dorsal nerves of the clitoris; the arteries and nerves of the bulbi vestibuli, and a plexus of veins.

The **Transversus perinæi profundus** *arises* from the inferior rami of the ischium and runs across to the side of the vagina. The Sphincter urethræ membranaceæ (*Constrictor urethræ*), like the corresponding muscle on the male, consists of external and internal fibers. The *external* fibers arise on either side from the margin of the inferior ramus of the pubis. They are directed across the pubic arch in front of the urethra, and pass around it to blend with the muscular fibers of the opposite side, between the urethra and vagina. The *innermost* fibers encircle the lower end of the urethra.

Nerve Supply.—The muscles of this group are supplied by the perineal branch of the pudendal.

2. The Muscles of the Anal Region.

Corrugator cutis ani.   Sphincter ani externus.   Sphincter ani internus.

The Corrugator Cutis Ani.—Around the anus is a thin stratum of involuntary muscular fiber, which radiates from the orifice. *Medially* the fibers fade off into the submucous tissue, while *laterally* they blend with the true skin. By its contraction it raises the skin into ridges around the margin of the anus.

The **Sphincter ani externus** (*External sphincter ani*) (Fig 390) is a flat plane of muscular fibers, elliptical in shape and intimately adherent to the integument surrounding the margin of the anus. It measures about 8 to 10 cm. in length, from its anterior to its posterior extremity, and is about 2.5 cm. broad opposite the anus. It consists of two strata, superficial and deep. The *superficial*, constituting the main portion of the muscle, arises from a narrow tendinous band, the **anococcygeal raphé**, which stretches from the tip of the coccyx to the posterior margin of the anus; it forms two flattened planes of muscular tissue, which encircle the anus and meet in front to be inserted into the central tendinous point of the perineum, joining with the Transversus perinæi superficialis, the Levator ani, and the Bulbocavernosus. The *deeper portion* forms a complete sphincter to the anal canal. Its fibers surround the canal, closely applied to the Sphincter ani internus, and in front blend with the other muscles at the central point of the perineum. In a considerable proportion of cases the fibers decussate in front of the anus, and are continuous with the Transversi perinæi superficiales. Posteriorly, they are not attached to the coccyx, but are continuous with those of the opposite side behind the anal canal. The upper edge of the muscle is ill-defined, since fibers are given off from it to join the Levator ani.

Actions.—The action of this muscle is peculiar. (1) It is, like other muscles, always in a state of tonic contraction, and having no antagonistic muscle it keeps the anal canal and orifice closed. (2) It can be put into a condition of greater contraction under the influence of the will, so as more firmly to occlude the anal aperture, in expiratory efforts unconnected with defecation. (3) Taking its fixed point at the coccyx, it helps to fix the central point of the perineum, so that the Bulbocavernosus may act from this fixed point.

Nerve Supply.—A branch from the fourth sacral and twigs from the inferior hemorrhoidal branch of the pudendal supply the muscle.

The **Sphincter ani internus** (*Internal sphincter ani*) is a muscular ring which surrounds about 2.5 cm. of the anal canal; its inferior border is in contact with, but quite separate from, the Sphincter ani externus. It is about 5 mm. thick, and is formed by an aggregation of the involuntary circular fibers of the intestine. Its lower border is about 6 mm. from the orifice of the anus.

Actions.—Its action is entirely involuntary. It helps the Sphincter ani externus to occlude the anal aperture and aids in the expulsion of the feces.

THE MUSCLES AND FASCIÆ OF THE UPPER EXTREMITY.

The muscles of the upper extremity are divisible into groups, corresponding with the different regions of the limb.

 I. Muscles Connecting the Upper Extremity to the Vertebral Column.
 II. Muscles Connecting the Upper Extremity to the Anterior and Lateral Thoracic Walls.
 III. Muscles of the Shoulder.
 IV. Muscles of the Arm.
 V. Muscles of the Forearm.
 VI. Muscles of the Hand.

I. THE MUSCLES CONNECTING THE UPPER EXTREMITY TO THE VERTEBRAL COLUMN.

Trapezius.   Rhomboideus major.
Latissimus dorsi.   Rhomboideus minor.
                    Levator scapulæ.

The **Superficial Fascia** (*tela subcutanea*) of the back is a thick fibrous and fatty layer which extends from the scalp to the gluteal region as a comparatively uniform sheet. At the sides of the neck and trunk, it gradually changes into the thinner or softer fascia of the ventral regions. The dermal fibrous layer is thick, and is bound down to the deeper layers by numerous heavy bands and septa which divide the fat into small granular lobules, and mattress the entire layer into a tough, resilient pad. The fascial cleft, usually present between the superficial and deep fascia, is lacking in the dorsal area, making the superficial fascia firmer and less movable than in the ventral area.

Deep Fascia.—The **investing layer of deep fascia** is attached in the middle line to the ligamentum nuchæ, the supraspinal ligament, and to the spinous processes of all vertebræ caudal to the sixth cervical. It splits to enclose the Trapezius and the fleshy portion of the Latissimus dorsi, but in the neck, it covers the posterior triangle as a single layer, and there becomes continuous with the anterior cervical fascia. It is attached, over the shoulder, to the acromion and spine of the scapula, and is then continuous with the deltoid fascia. Laterally from the Latissimus, it is continuous with the axillary fascia and the fascia covering the Obliquus abdominis externus. Over the fleshy portions of the Trapezius and Latissimus, it is gray and felt-like, but strong and adherent both to the superficial fascia and to the muscles. In the triangular area between the Trapezius, Deltoideus, and Latissimus it is white and glistening, forming the aponeurosis of the Infraspinatus. In the lumbar region it is greatly strengthened by having incorporated in it the aponeurosis of origin of the Latissimus dorsi. This portion is called the lumbar aponeurosis or the posterior layer of the lumbodorsal fascia (page 378).

The fascia of the deep surface of the Trapezius is thickened by an accumulation of adipose tissue similar to that under the Pectoralis major. It contains the branches of the superficial cervical and transverse cervical arteries, and the accessory nerve. It is separated from the underlying structures by a distinct fascial cleft. The fascia of the deep surface of the fleshy portion of the Latissimus is similar to that of the Trapezius, but over the aponeurosis it loses its identity as a separate layer, and is fused with the lumbodorsal fascia.

The Rhomboidei and the Levator scapulæ are enclosed in their own proper fascial sheaths which are attached to the vertebræ and to the vertebral border of the scapula. The fascia of the superficial surface, after attaching to the border of the scapula, continues laterally as the supra and infraspinatus fasciæ. That of the deep surface continues laterally on the deep surface of the Serratus anterior. A distinct fascial cleft separates both superficial and deep surfaces of the Rhomboidei from contiguous structures. The fascia of the Levator is more adherent to surrounding structures and is continuous with the scalenus fascia in the posterior triangle of the neck. In the interval between the superior and the inferior Serrati posteriores, it is possible to dissect out a thin membrane which lies in the same plane as these muscles, but distinct from the fascia of the underlying Sacrospinalis and the overlying Latissimus and Rhomboidei. This may represent the vestige of a continuous Serratus muscle like that found in some lower animals.

The **Trapezius** (Fig. 391) is a flat, triangular muscle, covering the upper and back part of the neck and shoulders. It *arises* from the external occipital protuberance and the medial third of the superior nuchal line of the occipital bone, from the ligamentum nuchæ, the spinous process of the seventh cervical, and the spinous processes of all the thoracic vertebræ, and from the corresponding portion of the supraspinal ligament. From this origin, the superior fibers proceed downward and lateralward, the inferior upward and lateralward, and the middle horizontally; the superior fibers are *inserted* into the posterior border of the lateral third of the clavicle; the middle fibers into the medial margin of the acromion, and into the superior lip of the posterior border of the spine of the scapula; the inferior fibers converge near the scapula, and end in an aponeurosis, which glides over the smooth triangular surface on the medial end of the spine, to be inserted into a tubercle at the apex of this smooth triangular surface. At its occipital origin, the Trapezius is connected to the bone by a thin fibrous lamina, firmly adherent to the skin. At the middle it is connected to the spinous processes by a broad semi-elliptical aponeurosis, which reaches from the sixth cervical to the third thoracic vertebra, and forms, with that of the opposite muscle, a tendinous ellipse. The rest of the muscle arises by numerous short tendinous fibers. The two Trapezius muscles together resemble a trapezium, or diamond-shaped quadrangle: two angles corresponding to the shoulders; a third to the occipital protuberance; and the fourth to the spinous process of the twelfth thoracic vertebra.

Action.—All parts, acting together, rotate the scapula, raising the point of the shoulder in full abduction and flexion of the arm. They also adduct the scapula, that is, draw it medially toward the vertebral column. The upper part acting alone, draws the scapula upward, bracing the shoulder. The lower part acting alone, draws the scapula downward. The upper part of one side draws the head toward the same side, and turns the face to the opposite side; both sides together draw the head directly backward.

Nerve.—The spinal accessory (spinal part of eleventh cranial) nerve and branches from the anterior rami of the third and fourth cervical nerves.

Variations.—The attachments to the thoracic vertebræ are often reduced, the lower ones being absent. The occipital attachment may be small or wanting. The clavicular attachment may be reduced, but is more often increased, and may cover the posterior triangle. The cervical and thoracic portions may be separate. The muscles of the two sides are seldom symmetrical, and complete absence has been described. Aberrant bundles are not uncommon.

The **Latissimus dorsi** (Fig. 391) is a large triangular muscle which covers the lumbar and lower half of the posterior thoracic region. Its *origin* is principally in a broad aponeurosis, the lumbar aponeurosis (posterior layer of the lumbodorsal fascia, see page 378), by means of which it is attached to the spinous processes of the lower six thoracic, the lumbar, and the sacral vertebræ, to the supraspinal ligament, and to the posterior part of the crest of the ilium. It also *arises* by muscular fasciculi from the external lip of the crest of the ilium lateral to the margin of the Sacrospinalis, and from the lower three or four ribs by fleshy digitations which are interposed between similar processes of the Obliquus externus abdominis (Fig. 377). From this extensive origin, the fasciculi converge toward the shoulder; those of the upper part are almost horizontal, and, as they pass over the inferior angle of the scapula, are joined by additional fasciculi arising from this bone. The muscle curves around the lower border of the Teres major, and is twisted upon itself, so that the superior fibers become at first posterior and then inferior, and the vertical fibers at first anterior and then superior. It ends in a quadrilateral tendon, about 7 cm. long, which passes in front of the tendon of the Teres major, and is *inserted* into the bottom of the intertubercular groove of the humerus; its insertion extends higher on the humerus than that of the tendon of the Pectoralis major. The lower border of its tendon is united with that of the Teres major, the surfaces of the two being separated near their insertions by a bursa; another bursa is sometimes interposed between the muscle and the inferior angle of the scapula. The tendon of the muscle gives off an expansion to the deep fascia of the arm.

Action.—Extends, adducts, and rotates the arm medially; draws the shoulder downward and backward.

Nerve.—The thoracodorsal (long subscapular) nerve from the brachial plexus, containing fibers from the sixth, seventh and eighth cervical nerves.

Variations.—The number of thoracic vertebræ to which it is attached varies from four to seven or eight; the number of costal attachments varies; muscle fibers may or may not reach the crest of the ilium.

A muscular slip, the **axillary arch,** varying from 7 to 10 cm. in length, and from 5 to 15 mm. in breadth, occasionally springs from the upper edge of the Latissimus dorsi about the middle of the posterior fold of the axilla, and crosses the axilla in front of the axillary vessels and nerves, to join the under surface of the tendon of the Pectoralis major, the Coracobrachialis, or the fascia over the Biceps brachii. This axillary arch crosses the axillary artery, just above the spot usually selected for the application of a ligature, and may mislead the surgeon during the operation. It is present in about 7 per cent. of subjects and may be easily recognized by the transverse direction of its fibers.

A fibrous slip usually passes from the lower border of the tendon of the Latissimus dorsi, near its insertion, to the long head of the Triceps brachii. This is occasionally muscular, and is the representative of the *Dorsoepitrochlearis brachii* of apes.

The **lumbar triangle of Petit** is a small triangular interval which separates the lateral margin of the lower portion of the Latissimus dorsi from the Obliquus externus abdominis just above the ilium. The base of the triangle is the iliac crest, and its floor is the Obliquus internus abdominis.

The **triangle of auscultation** is a triangle associated with the upper portion of the Latissimus. It is bounded above by the Trapezius, below by the Latissimus dorsi, and laterally by the vertebral border of the scapula. The floor is partly formed by the Rhomboideus major. If the scapula is drawn forward by folding the arms across the chest, and the trunk bent forward, parts of the sixth and seventh ribs and their interspace become subcutaneous and accessible for auscultation.

The **Rhomboideus major** (Fig. 391) *arises* by tendinous fibers from the spinous processes of the second, third, fourth, and fifth thoracic vertebræ and the supraspinal ligament, and is *inserted* into a narrow tendinous arch, attached above to the lower part of the triangular surface at the root of the spine of the scapula; below to the inferior angle, the arch being connected to the vertebral border by a thin membrane. When the arch extends, as it occasionally does, only a short distance, the muscular fibers are inserted directly into the scapula.

The **Rhomboideus minor** (Fig. 391) arises from the lower part of the ligamentum nuchæ and from the spinous processes of the seventh cervical and first thoracic vertebræ. It is *inserted* into the base of the triangular smooth surface at the root of the spine of the scapula, and is usually separated from the Rhomboideus major by a slight interval, but the adjacent margins of the two muscles are occasionally united.

Action.—Adduct the scapula, that is, draw it medially toward the vertebral column, at the same time supporting it and drawing it slightly upward. The lower part of the major rotates the scapula to depress the lateral angle, assisting in adduction of the arm.

Nerve.—The dorsal scapular nerve from the brachial plexus, containing fibers from the fifth cervical nerve.

Variations.—The vertebral and scapular attachments of the two muscles vary in extent. A small slip from the scapula to the occipital bone close to the minor occasionally occurs, the *Rhomboideus occipitalis muscle.*

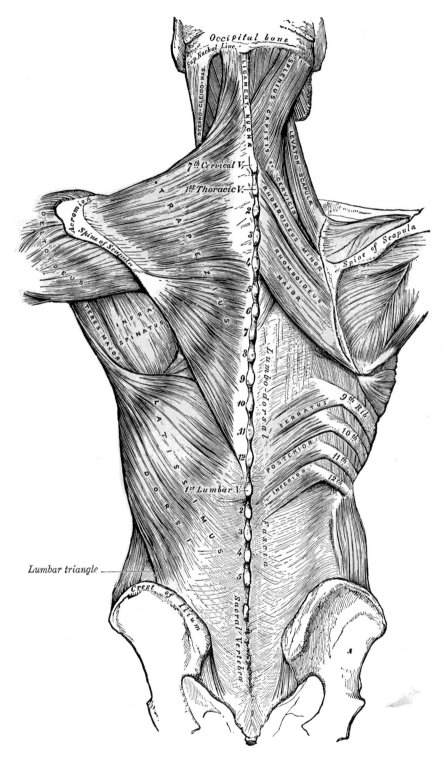

FIG. 391.—Muscles connecting the upper extremity to the vertebral column.

The **Levator scapulæ** (*Levator anguli scapulæ*) (Fig. 391) is situated at the back and side of the neck. It *arises* by tendinous slips from the transverse processes of the atlas and axis and from the posterior tubercles of the transverse processes of the third and fourth cervical vertebræ. It is *inserted* into the vertebral border of the scapula, between the medial angle and the triangular smooth surface at the root of the spine.

Action.—Raises the scapula, tending to draw it medialward and rotate it to lower the lateral angle. With the scapula fixed, it bends the neck laterally and rotates it slightly toward the same side.

Nerves.—Branches of the third and fourth cervical nerves from the cervical plexus, and frequently the lower portion by a branch of the dorsal scapular nerve containing fibers from the fifth cervical nerve.

Variations.—The number of vertebral attachments varies; a slip may extend to the occipital or mastoid, to the Trapezius, Scalene or Serratus anterior, or to the first or second rib. The muscle may be subdivided into several distinct parts from origin to insertion. *Levator claviculæ* from the transverse processes of one or two upper cervical vertebræ to the outer end of the clavicle corresponds to a muscle of lower animals. More or less union with the Serratus anterior.

II. THE MUSCLES CONNECTING THE UPPER EXTREMITY TO THE ANTERIOR AND LATERAL THORACIC WALLS.

Pectoralis major.   Subclavius.
Pectoralis minor.   Serratus anterior.

The **superficial fascia** (*tela subcutanea*) of the pectoral region is continuous with that of the neck and upper limb above, the abdomen below, and the axilla laterally. The fasciculi of the Platysma muscle extend down from the neck for a variable distance between its superficial and deep layers. In the female, the adipose tissue is increased and molded into a rounded mass which gives the bulk and form to the mamma. The parenchyma of the mammary gland is imbedded in this fat. The connective tissue stroma, distributed between the lobes of the gland, is thickened into fibrous bands, called **ligamenta suspensoria** or **Cooper's ligaments,** which secure the skin to the deep layer of the superficial fascia. A fascial cleft separates the superficial fascia from the deep fascia. Through these fascial structures, a carcinoma may make its presence known either by pulling on Cooper's ligaments and dimpling the skin like an orange peel, or by interfering with the normal movability of the gland through adhesions between the superficial and deep fasciæ.

Pectoral Fascia (*fascia pectoralis*) (Fig. 392).—The pectoral fascia is a membranous sheet of deep fascia which consists of the external investing fascia over the Pectoralis major, and a deeper layer enclosing its under surface. It is more or less adherent throughout and attached, with the origin of the muscle, to the clavicle and sternum, and with the insertion, to the humerus. The external layer is continuous medially, across the middle line, with the pectoral fascia of the other side; superiorly and laterally, with the brachial fascia which covers the Coracobrachialis and Biceps; and inferiorly, with the axillary, thoracic, and abdominal investing fasciæ. At the lower sternocostal and abdominal origins of the muscle, it is aponeurotic and is blended with the sheath of the Rectus abdominis. The deeper layer, covering the deep surface of the muscle and adherent to it, is thickened by a considerable pad of fat in which the thoracoacromial bloodvessels and anterior thoracic nerves are imbedded. A definite fascial cleft separates this layer from the underlying clavipectoral fascia. The external and the deeper layers come together at both borders of the muscle, forming a closed compartment. At the superior border, the fascia separates again to enclose the Deltoideus; at the inferior border, however, a single sheet is formed which becomes immediately the axillary fascia.

The **Clavipectoral Fascia** (*fascia coracoclavicularis*) (Fig. 392) is an intermediate stratum of deep fascia which lies between the Pectoralis major and the thoracic wall. It invests the Pectoralis minor and Subclavius, and extends from the clavicle to the axillary fascia. Its attachment to the clavicle is by means of two membranes which lie superficial and deep to the Subclavius, and which are separated from each other by the insertion of the muscle. The two sheets form a compartment for the muscle by fusing, at its inferior border, into a single sheet which stretches across the interval between the Subclavius and the Pectoralis minor. The portion superficial to the Subclavius is greatly strengthened by the addition of fibrous bundles which continue laterally beyond the muscle, and attach to the coracoid process, forming the **costocoracoid ligament.** This strong band, attached to the coracoid process, the clavicle, and the first rib, serves as an important ligament for the clavicular articulations. From its attachment to the coracoid process, the fascia passes downward as a thin sheet, investing the Pectoralis minor on both its sur-

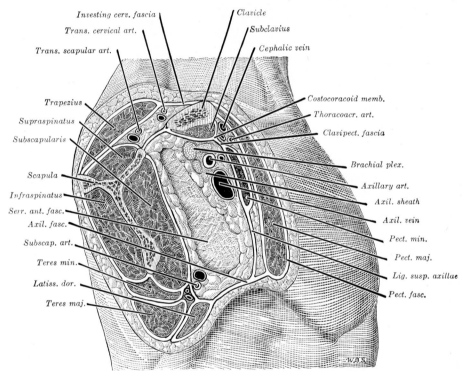

Fig. 392.—Fasciæ of axillary and pectoral regions in sagittal section.

faces, and attaching to the ribs with the origin of the latter muscle. Between the ribs it is continuous with the external intercostal fascia. At the superior border of the Pectoralis minor, the two layers investing the muscle fuse into the single sheet which bridges the triangular interval between the Pectoralis minor and Subclavius. This single sheet is thin, below the ligament, and has one or more holes or defects through which pass the thoracoacromial artery and vein, the cephalic vein, and the lateral anterior thoracic nerve. The portion of the fascia between the upper border of the Pectoralis minor and the clavicle, including the costocoracoid ligament, has been named the **fascia coracoclavicularis.** At the inferior or lateral border of the Pectoralis minor, the two layers combine again into a single sheet which passes into the axilla, and fuses with the deep surface of the axillary fascia a short distance from the lateral border of the Pectoralis major. The axillary sheath, enclosing the axillary vessels and nerves of the brachial plexus, passes under the lateral portion of the clavipectoral fascia, but is partially separated from it by some of the adipose tissue of the deep axillary fossa.

Axillary Fascia (*fascia axillaris*) (Fig. 392).—The portion of the investing fascia which crosses the interval between the lateral borders of the Pectoralis major and Latissimus dorsi dips inward to form the hollow of the armpit. It is adherent to the superficial fascia, and there are openings through which the adipose tissue of the latter is continuous with that in the deeper axillary fossa. It is continuous with the pectoral, latissimus, serratus, and brachial fasciæ. Fused with its deep surface,

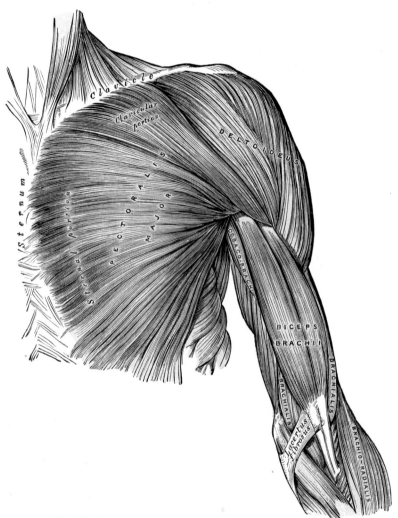

Fig. 393.—Superficial muscles of the chest and front of the arm.

in the hollow of the armpit, is the termination of the clavipectoral fascia which has continued laterally from the Pectoralis minor. The latter fascia has been named the **suspensory ligament of the axilla** because it is believed that the hollow, seen when the arm is abducted, is produced mainly by the traction of this fascia on the axillary floor.

The **axilla** (Fig. 394, "Axillary Space"), in anatomical usage comprises more than the externally visible armpit. It includes the fossa between the medial side of the arm and the lateral surface of the chest wall, inside or deep to the axillary investing layer described above. It is commonly called a space, but should be recognised as a pyramidal compartment filled with adipose tissue, vessels, nerves, and lymph nodes. The walls of the fossa are formed by the fascial coverings of the following muscles: anteriorly, the Pectoralis major and minor; posteriorly, the Latissimus dorsi, Teres major, and Subscapularis; medially, the Serratus anterior; laterally, the Coracobrachialis and Biceps. At the apex of the fossa, between the first rib, clavicle, and base of the coracoid process, the adipose padding tissue is continuous with the mass of similar tissue in the posterior triangle of the

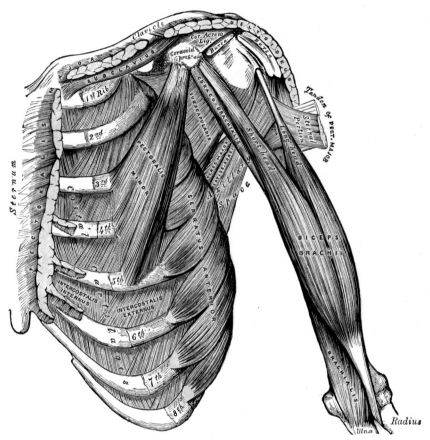

Fig. 394.—Deep muscles of the chest and front of the arm, with the boundaries of the axilla.

neck. At the apex also, the fascia of the first two ribs and first intercostal space is continuous with the scalenus fascia. In this region, the latter fascia gives a tubular investment, called the **axillary sheath,** to the large vessels and nerves of the arm. The sheath is partially adherent to the clavipectoral fascia on the deep surface of the Subclavius and Pectoralis minor as it passes under them, and then, after traversing the lateral wall of the axilla along the Coracobrachialis, it becomes fused with the anterior surface of the medial intermuscular septum of the arm.

The **Pectoralis major** (Fig. 393) is a thick, fan-shaped muscle, situated at the upper and forepart of the chest. It *arises* from the anterior surface of the sternal half of the clavicle; from half the breadth of the anterior surface of the sternum, as low down as the attachment of the cartilage of the sixth or seventh rib; from the cartilages of all the true ribs, with the exception, frequently, of the first or seventh, or both, and from the aponeurosis of the Obliquus externus abdominis. From this extensive origin the fibers converge toward their insertion; those arising from the clavicle pass obliquely downward and lateralward, and are usually separated from the rest by a slight interval; those from the lower part of the sternum, and the cartilages of the lower true ribs, run upward and lateralward; while the middle fibers pass horizontally. They all end in a flat tendon, about 5 cm. broad, which is *inserted* into the crest of the greater tubercle of the humerus. This tendon consists of two laminæ, placed one in front of the other, and usually blended together below. The anterior lamina, the thicker, receives the clavicular and the uppermost sternal fibers; they are inserted in the same order as that in which they arise: that is to say, the most lateral of the clavicular fibers are inserted at the upper part of the anterior lamina; the uppermost sternal fibers pass down to the lower part of the lamina which extends as low as the tendon of the Deltoideus and joins with it. The posterior lamina of the tendon receives the attachment of the greater part of the sternal portion and the deep fibers, *i. e.*, those from the costal cartilages. These deep fibers, and particularly those from the lower costal cartilages, ascend the higher, turning backward successively behind the superficial and upper ones, so that the tendon appears to be twisted. The posterior lamina reaches higher on the humerus than the anterior one, and from it an expansion is given off which covers the intertubercular groove and blends with the capsule of the shoulder-joint. From the deepest fibers of this lamina at its insertion an expansion is given off which lines the intertubercular groove, while from the lower border of the tendon a third expansion passes downward to the fascia of the arm.

Action.—Flexes, adducts, and rotates the arm medially. The clavicular portion draws the arm or the shoulder, if the arm is at the side, upward, forward, and medialward; the sternocostal portion draws the arm or shoulder forward, medialward, and downward.

Nerves.—Medial and lateral anterior thoracic nerves from the brachial plexus, containing fibers from the fifth, sixth, seventh, eighth cervical, and first thoracic nerves.

Variations.—The more frequent variations are greater or less extent of attachment to the ribs and sternum, varying size of the abdominal part or its absence, greater or less extent of separation of sternocostal and clavicular parts, fusion of clavicular part with deltoid, decussation in front of the sternum. Deficiency or absence of the sternocostal part is not uncommon. Absence of the clavicular part is less frequent. Rarely the whole muscle is wanting.

Costocoracoideus is a muscular band occasionally found arising from the ribs or aponeurosis of the External oblique between the Pectoralis major and Latissimus dorsi and inserted into the coracoid process.

Chondro-epitrochlearis is a muscular slip occasionally found arising from the costal cartilages or from the aponeurosis of the External oblique below the Pectoralis major or from the Pectoralis major itself. The insertion is variable on the inner side of the arm to fascia, intermuscular septum or internal condyle.

Sternalis, in front of the sternal end of the Pectoralis major parallel to the margin of the sternum. It is supplied by the anterior thoracic nerves and is probably a misplaced part of the pectoralis.

The **Pectoralis minor** (Fig. 394) is a thin, triangular muscle, situated at the upper part of the thorax, beneath the Pectoralis major. It *arises* from the upper margins and outer surfaces of the third, fourth, and fifth ribs, near their cartilages, and from the aponeuroses covering the Intercostales; the fibers pass upward and lateralward and converge to form a flat tendon, which is inserted into the medial border and upper surface of the coracoid process of the scapula.

Action.—Draws the scapula forward and downward, and rotates it to lower the lateral angle, as in adduction of the arm. Raises the third, fourth, and fifth ribs in forced inspiration, the scapula being fixed by the Levator scapulæ.

Nerve.—The medial anterior thoracic nerve from the brachial plexus, containing fibers from the eighth cervical and first thoracic nerves.

Variations.—Origin from second, third and fourth or fifth ribs. The tendon of insertion may extend over the coracoid process to the greater tubercle. May be split into several parts. Absence rare.

Pectoralis minimus, first rib-cartilage to coracoid process. Rare.

The **Subclavius** (Fig. 394) is a small cylindrical muscle, placed between the clavicle and the first rib. It *arises* by a short, thick tendon from the first rib and its cartilage at their junction, in front of the costoclavicular ligament; the fleshy fibers proceed obliquely upward and lateralward, to be *inserted* into the groove on the under surface of the clavicle between the costoclavicular and conoid ligaments.

Actions.—Draws the shoulder forward and downward.

Nerve.—A special nerve from the lateral trunk of the brachial plexus containing fibers from the fifth and sixth cervical nerves.

Variations.—Insertion into coracoid process instead of clavicle or into both clavicle and coracoid process. *Sternoscapular* fasciculus to the upper border of scapula. *Sternoclavicularis* from manubrium to clavicle between Pectoralis major and coracoclavicular fascia.

The **Serratus anterior** (*Serratus magnus*) (Fig. 394) is a thin muscular sheet, situated between the ribs and the scapula at the upper and lateral part of the chest. It *arises* by fleshy digitations from the outer surfaces and superior borders of the upper eight or nine ribs, and from the aponeuroses covering the intervening Intercostales. Each digitation (except the first) arises from the corresponding rib; the first springs from the first and second ribs; and from the fascia covering the first intercostal space. From this extensive attachment the fibers pass backward, closely applied to the chest-wall, and reach the vertebral border of the scapula, and are inserted into its ventral surface in the following manner. The first digitation is *inserted* into a triangular area on the ventral surface of the medial angle. The next two digitations spread out to form a thin, triangular sheet, the base of which is directed backward and is inserted into nearly the whole length of the ventral surface of the vertebral border. The lower five or six digitations converge to form a fan-shaped mass, the apex of which is inserted, by muscular and tendinous fibers, into a triangular impression on the ventral surface of the inferior angle. The lower four slips interdigitate at their origins with the upper five slips of the Obliquus externus abdominis.

Action.—Rotates the scapula, raising the point of the shoulder as in full flexion and abduction of the arm. Draws the scapula forward as in the act of pushing. The upper digitation may draw the scapula downward and forward; the lower digitations draw the scapula downward.

Nerve.—The long thoracic nerve from the brachial plexus, containing fibers from the fifth, sixth, and seventh cervical nerves.

Variations.—Attachment to tenth rib. Absence of attachments to first rib, to one or more of the lower ribs. Division into three parts; absence or defect of middle part. Union with Levator scapulæ, External intercostals or External oblique.

III. THE MUSCLES AND FASCIÆ OF THE SHOULDER.

Deltoideus.   Infraspinatus.
Subscapularis.   Teres minor.
Supraspinatus.   Teres major.

Deltoid Fascia.—The deltoid portion of the investing fascia covers the Deltoideus. Above, it is attached to the clavicle, acromion, and spine of the scapula. Below, it is continuous with the brachial fascia. In front, it bridges the narrow triangular interval between the adjacent borders of the Deltoideus and the Pectoralis major. In this interval, called Mohrenheim's triangle, the fascia is thick but is pierced by the cephalic vein and deltoid branch of the thoracoacromial artery. The deltoid fascia is stronger posteriorly, and continues into the Infraspinatus fascia. Along both borders of the Deltoideus, the investing layer joins the fascia of the deep surface to form a closed compartment. Both layers are adherent to the muscle. The deep layer may contain adipose tissue, and is separated by a distinct fascial cleft from the underlying humerus, subdeltoid bursa, shoulder joint, and associated tendons and ligaments.

The **Deltoideus** (*Deltoid muscle*) (Fig. 393) is a large, thick, triangular muscle, which covers the shoulder-joint in front, behind, and laterally. It *arises* from the anterior border and upper surface of the lateral third of the clavicle; from the lateral margin and upper surface of the acromion, and from the lower lip of the posterior border of the spine of the scapula, as far back as the triangular surface at its medial end. From this extensive origin the fibers converge toward their insertion, the middle passing vertically, the anterior obliquely backward and lateralward, the posterior obliquely forward and lateralward; they unite in a thick tendon, which is *inserted* into the deltoid prominence on the middle of the lateral side of the body of the humerus. At its insertion the muscle gives off an expansion to the deep fascia of the arm. This muscle is remarkably coarse in texture, and the arrangement of its fibers is somewhat peculiar; the central portion of the muscle—that is to say, the part arising from the acromion—consists of oblique fibers; these arise in a bipenniform manner from the sides of the tendinous intersections, generally four in number, which are attached above to the acromion and pass downward parallel to one another in the substance of the muscle. The oblique fibers thus formed are inserted into similar tendinous intersections, generally three in number, which pass upward from the insertion of the muscle and alternate with the descending septa. The portions of the muscle arising from the clavicle and spine of the scapula are not arranged in this manner, but are inserted into the margins of the inferior tendon.

Action.—As a whole abducts the arm. The clavicular and adjacent part of the acromial portions flex the arm; the spinous and adjacent part of the acromial portions extend the arm. The most ventral portion rotates the arm medially, the most dorsal portion laterally.

Nerve.—The axillary nerve from the brachial plexus, containing fibers from the fifth and sixth cervical nerves.

Variations.—Large variations uncommon. More or less splitting common. Continuation into the Trapezius; fusion with the Pectoralis major; additional slips from the vertebral border of the scapula, infraspinous fascia and axillary border of scapula not uncommon. Insertion varies in extent or rarely is prolonged to origin of Brachioradialis.

Subscapular Fascia (*fascia subscapularis*).—The subscapular fascia is a thin membrane attached to the entire circumference of the subscapular fossa, and affording attachment by its deep surface to some of the fibers of the Subscapularis.

The **Subscapularis** (Fig. 394) is a large triangular muscle which fills the subscapular fossa, and *arises* from its medial two-thirds and from the lower two-thirds of the groove on the axillary border of the bone. Some fibers *arise* from tendinous laminæ which intersect the muscle and are attached to ridges on the bone; others from an aponeurosis, which separates the muscle from the Teres major and the long head of the Triceps brachii. The fibers pass lateralward, and, gradually converging, end in a tendon which is *inserted* into the lesser tubercle of the humerus and the front of the capsule of the shoulder-joint. The tendon of the muscle is separated from the neck of the scapula by a large bursa, which communicates with the cavity of the shoulder-joint through an aperture in the capsule.

Action.—Rotates the arm medially. It assists in both flexion and extension, and abduction and adduction, depending on the position of the arm. Draws the humerus toward the glenoid fossa strengthening the shoulder joint.

Nerves.—The upper and lower subscapular nerves from the brachial plexus, containing fibers from the fifth and sixth cervical nerves.

Supraspinatous Fascia (*fascia supraspinata*).—The supraspinatous fascia completes the osseofibrous case in which the Supraspinatus muscle is contained; it affords attachment, by its deep surface, to some of the fibers of the muscle. It is thick medially, but thinner laterally under the coracoacromial ligament.

The **Supraspinatus** (Fig. 395) occupies the whole of the supraspinatous fossa, *arising* from its medial two-thirds, and from the strong supraspinatous fascia. The muscular fibers converge to a tendon, which crosses the upper part of the shoulder-joint, and is *inserted* into the highest of the three impressions on the greater tubercle of the humerus; the tendon is intimately adherent to the tendon of the Infraspinatus and to the capsule of the shoulder-joint.

Action.—Abducts the arm. Draws the humerus toward the glenoid fossa, strengthening the shoulder joint. It is a weak lateral rotator and flexor.

Nerve.—Branches of the suprascapular nerve from the brachial plexus, containing fibers from the fifth cervical nerve.

Infraspinatous Fascia (*fascia infraspinata*).—The infraspinatous fascia is a dense fibrous membrane, covering the Infraspinatous muscle and fixed to the circumference of the infraspinatous fossa; it affords attachment, by its deep surface, to some fibers of that muscle. It is intimately attached to the deltoid fascia along the overlapping border of the Deltoideus.

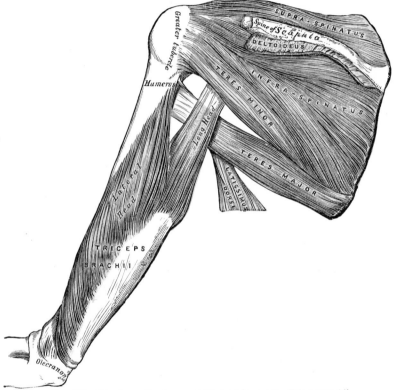

Fig. 395.—Muscles on the dorsum of the scapula, and the Triceps brachii.

The **Infraspinatus** (Fig. 395) is a thick triangular muscle, which occupies the chief part of the infraspinatous fossa; it *arises* by fleshy fibers from its medial two-thirds, and by tendinous fibers from the ridges on its surface; it also arises from the infraspinatous fascia which covers it, and separates it from the Teres major and minor. The fibers converge to a tendon, which glides over the lateral border of the spine of the scapula, and, passing across the posterior part of the capsule of the shoulder-joint, is *inserted* into the middle impression on the greater tubercle of the humerus, where it is fused with its neighbors. The tendon of this muscle is sometimes separated from the capsule of the shoulder-joint by a bursa, which may communicate with the joint cavity.

28

Action.—Rotates the arm laterally. The upper part abducts, the lower part adducts. Draws the humerus toward the glenoid fossa, strengthening the shoulder joint.

Nerve.—The suprascapular nerve from the brachial plexus, containing fibers from the fifth and sixth cervical nerves.

The **Teres minor** (Fig. 395) is a narrow, elongated muscle, which *arises* from the dorsal surface of the axillary border of the scapula for the upper two-thirds of its extent, and from two aponeurotic laminæ, one of which separates it from the Infraspinatus, the other from the Teres major. Its fibers run obliquely upward and lateralward; the upper ones end in a tendon which is *inserted* into the lowest of the three impressions on the greater tubercle of the humerus; the lowest fibers are *inserted* directly into the humerus immediately below this impression. The tendon of this muscle passes across, and is united with, the posterior part of the capsule of the shoulder-joint.

Action.—Rotates the arm laterally and weakly adducts it. Draws the humerus toward the glenoid fossa, strengthening the shoulder joint.

Nerve.—A branch of the axillary nerve, containing fibers from the fifth cervical.

Variations.—It is sometimes inseparable from the Infraspinatus.

The **Teres major** (Fig. 395) is a thick but somewhat flattened muscle, which *arises* from the oval area on the dorsal surface of the inferior angle of the scapula, and from the fibrous septa interposed between the muscle and the Teres minor and Infraspinatus; the fibers are directed upward and lateralward, and end in a flat tendon, about 5 cm. long, which is *inserted* into the crest of the lesser tubercle of the humerus. The tendon, at its insertion, lies behind that of the Latissimus dorsi, from which it is separated by a bursa, the two tendons being, however, united along their lower borders for a short distance.

Action.—Adducts, extends, and rotates the arm medially.

Nerve.—A branch of the lower subscapular nerve from the brachial plexus, containing fibers from the fifth and sixth cervical nerves.

Group Action of Muscles About the Shoulder.—Flexion of the arm is brought about by the anterior part of the Deltoideus, Coracobrachialis, and short head of the Biceps, acting on the shoulder joint and by the Trapezius and Serratus anterior rotating the scapula on the chest wall to raise the point of the shoulder. The clavicular part of the Pectoralis major also acts until the arm is raised above the shoulder. Extension of the arm is brought about by the Latissimus dorsi, acting on both the shoulder joint and the scapula, and it is strongly assisted by the lower part of the Pectoralis major except in hyperextension. The Teres major, posterior Deltoideus, and long head of the Triceps act on the shoulder joint, and the scapula is rotated downward by the Pectoralis minor, and drawn backward by the Rhomboidei and Trapezius. The arm is abducted by the Deltoideus and Supraspinatus, acting on the shoulder joint and by the Trapezius and Serratus anterior rotating the scapula to raise the shoulder. The arm is adducted by the Pectoralis major and Latissimus dorsi, by the Coracobrachialis and Teres major acting on the shoulder joint, by the Pectoralis minor rotating the scapula downward, and by the lower portion of the Trapezius drawing the scapula downward. Medial rotation is brought about primarily by the Subscapularis and Teres major when it is performed as a voluntary act, but the Pectoralis major and Latissimus dorsi have strong medial rotating power incidental to their contraction. Lateral rotation is brought about by the Infraspinatus and Teres minor. Independent movements of the scapula are elevation by the Levator scapulæ and upper part of the Trapezius; depression by the Pectoralis minor, lower Trapezius and lower Serratus anterior; drawing it forward (abduction of scapula) by the Serratus anterior, as in pushing; drawing it backward (adduction of scapula) by the Rhomboidei and Trapezius.

IV. THE MUSCLES AND FASCIÆ OF THE ARM.

Coracobrachialis.   Brachialis.
Biceps brachii.   Triceps brachii.

Brachial Fascia (*fascia brachii; deep fascia of the arm*) (Fig. 396).—The portion of the investing fascia which covers the arm is a strong membrane but is not, for the most part, distinctly aponeurotic. It is continuous above with the deltoid, pectoral, and axillary fasciæ; it is attached below to the epicondyles of the humerus and the olecranon, and is then continuous with the antebrachial fascia. Beginning at the attachment to the epicondyles and prolonged upward into the arm are two intermuscular septa, medial and lateral, which divide the arm into flexor and extensor compartments. The **lateral intermuscular septum** (*septum intermusculare [humeri] laterale*) is attached along the lateral supracondylar ridge and is fused with the under surface of the investing brachial fascia. Its lower extremity is the lateral epicondyle, its upper, the insertion of the Deltoideus where it continues into the deltoid fascia. Its dorsal surface is used by the Triceps for the origin of some of its fibers; the ventral surface by the Brachialis, Brachioradialis, and Extensor carpi radialis longus. Its lower portion is pierced by the radial nerve and the radial collateral branch of the profunda artery. The **medial intermuscular septum** (*septum intermusculare [humeri] mediale*) is attached to the medial supracondylar ridge and extends from the medial epicondyle, below, to the Teres major and Latissimus dorsi insertions, above. Some of the fibers of the Triceps originate on its dorsal surface and some of the Brachialis on its ventral surface. It is pierced, near the epicondyle, by the ulnar nerve and superior ulnar collateral artery. The medial septum appears very much thicker than the lateral because the axillary sheath, containing the main vessels and nerves of the arm, blends with its ventral surface, and the nerves and vessels continue this close association down to the elbow. The two intermuscular septa and the investing fascia of the posterior aspect of the arm form the posterior or extensor compartment which contains the Triceps, radial nerve, and profunda artery. The anterior or flexor compartment contains the Biceps, Brachialis, part of the Coracobrachialis, the brachial vessels, and the median and ulnar nerves. The relationship of the investing fascia to the muscles is different on the dorsal and ventral aspects of the arm. That over the Triceps is adherent to the muscle and is used in part for its origin. That over the Biceps is separated from the muscle by a distinct fascial cleft which is continued around the deep surface of the muscle, also separating it from the Brachialis. The ventral investing fascia, medially, just below the middle of the arm, is pierced by the basilic vein.

The **Coracobrachialis** (Fig. 394), the smallest of the three muscles in this region, is situated at the upper and medial part of the arm. It *arises* from the apex of the coracoid process, in common with the short head of the Biceps brachii, and from the intermuscular septum between the two muscles; it is *inserted* by means of a flat tendon into an impression at the middle of the medial surface and border of the body of the humerus between the origins of the Triceps brachii and Brachialis. It is perforated by the musculocutaneous nerve.

Action.—Flexes and adducts the arm.

Nerve.—A branch of the musculocutaneous nerve, containing fibers from the sixth and seventh cervical nerves.

Variations.—A bony head may reach the medial epicondyle; a short head more rarely found may insert into the lesser tubercle.

The **Biceps brachii** (*Biceps; Biceps flexor cubiti*) (Fig. 394) is a long fusiform muscle, placed on the front of the arm, and *arising* by two heads, from which circumstance it has received its name. The **short head** *arises* by a thick flattened tendon from the apex of the coracoid process, in common with the Coracobrachialis. The **long head** *arises* from the supraglenoid tuberosity at the upper margin of the glenoid cavity, and is continuous with the glenoidal labrum. This tendon, enclosed in a special sheath of the synovial membrane of the shoulder-joint, arches over the head of the humerus; it emerges from the capsule through an opening close to the humeral attachment of the ligament, and descends in the intertubercular groove; it is retained in the groove by the transverse humeral ligament and by a fibrous prolongation from the tendon of the Pectoralis major. Each tendon is succeeded by an elongated muscular belly, and the two bellies, although closely applied to each other, can readily be separated until within about 7.5 cm. of the elbow-joint. Here they end in a flattened tendon, which is inserted into the rough posterior portion of the tuberosity of the radius, a bursa being interposed between the tendon and the front part of the tuberosity. As the tendon of the muscle approaches the radius it is twisted upon itself, so that its anterior surface becomes lateral and is applied to the tuberosity of the radius at its insertion. Opposite the bend of the elbow the tendon gives off, from its medial side, a broad aponeurosis, the **lacertus fibrosus** (*bicipital fascia*) which passes obliquely downward and medialward across the brachial artery, and is continuous with the deep fascia covering the origins of the Flexor muscles of the forearm (Fig. 393).

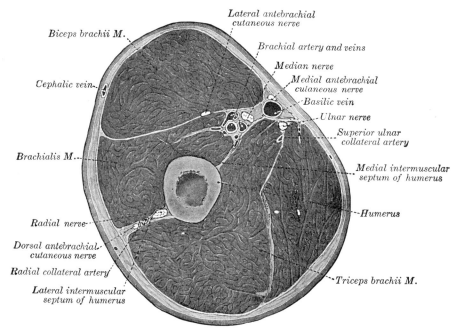

Fig. 396.—Cross-section through the middle of upper arm. (Eycleshymer and Schoemaker.)

Action.—Flexes the arm, flexes the forearm, and supinates the hand. The long head draws the humerus toward the glenoid fossa, strengthening the shoulder joint.

Nerves.—Branches of the musculocutaneous nerve, containing fibers from the fifth and sixth cervical nerves.

Variations.—A third head (10 per cent.) to the Biceps brachii is occasionally found, arising at the upper and medial part of the Brachialis, with the fibers of which it is continuous, and inserted into the lacertus fibrosus and medial side of the tendon of the muscle. In most cases this additional slip lies behind the brachial artery in its course down the arm. In some instances the third head consists of two slips, which pass down, one in front of and the other behind the artery, concealing the vessel in the lower half of the arm. More rarely a fourth head occurs arising from the outer side of the humerus, from the intertubercular groove, or from the greater tubercle. Other heads are occasionally found. Slips sometimes pass from the inner border of the muscle over the brachial artery to the medial intermuscular septum, or the medial epicondyle; more rarely to the Pronator teres or Brachialis. The long head may be absent or arise from the intertubercular groove.

The **Brachialis** (*Brachialis anticus*) (Fig. 394) covers the front of the elbow-joint and the lower half of the humerus. It *arises* from the lower half of the front of the humerus, commencing above at the insertion of the Deltoideus, which it embraces by two angular processes. Its origin extends below to within 2.5 cm. of the margin of the articular surface. It also arises from the intermuscular septa, but more extensively from the medial than the lateral; it is separated from the lateral below by the Brachioradialis and Extensor carpi radialis longus. Its fibers converge to a thick tendon, which is *inserted* into the tuberosity of the ulna and the rough depression on the anterior surface of the coronoid process.

Action.—Flexes the forearm.

Nerve.—A branch of the musculocutaneous nerve, containing fibers from the fifth and sixth cervical nerves; usually an additional small branch of the radial and occasionally of the median nerve.

Variations.—Occasionally doubled; additional slips to the Supinator, Pronator teres, Biceps, lacertus fibrosus, or radius are more rarely found.

The **Triceps brachii** (*Triceps; Triceps extensor cubiti*) (Fig. 395) is situated on the back of the arm, extending the entire length of the dorsal surface of the humerus. It is of large size, and arises by three heads (long, lateral, and medial), hence its name.

The **long head** *arises* by a flattened tendon from the infraglenoid tuberosity of the scapula, being blended at its upper part with the capsule of the shoulder-joint; the muscular fibers pass downward between the two other heads of the muscle, and join with them in the tendon of insertion.

The **lateral head** *arises* from the posterior surface of the body of the humerus, between the insertion of the Teres minor and the upper part of the groove for the radial nerve, and from the lateral border of the humerus and the lateral intermuscular septum; the fibers from this origin converge toward the tendon of insertion.

The **medial head**, which really should be called the **deep head**, *arises* from the posterior surface of the body of the humerus, below the groove for the radial nerve; it is narrow and pointed above, and extends from the insertion of the Teres major to within 2.5 cm. of the trochlea: it also arises from the medial border of the humerus and from the back of the whole length of the medial intermuscular septum. Some of the fibers are directed downward to the olecranon, while other converge to the tendon of insertion.

The **tendon of the Triceps brachii** begins about the middle of the muscle: it consists of two aponeurotic laminæ, one of which is subcutaneous and covers the back of the lower half of the muscle; the other is more deeply seated in the substance of the muscle. After receiving the attachment of the muscular fibers, the two lamellæ join together above the elbow, and are inserted, for the most part, into the posterior portion of the upper surface of the olecranon; a band of fibers is, however, continued downward, on the lateral side, over the Anconæus, to blend with the deep fascia of the forearm.

The long head of the Triceps brachii descends between the Teres minor and Teres major, dividing the triangular space between these two muscles and the humerus into two smaller spaces, one triangular, the other quadrangular (Fig. 395). The triangular space contains the scapular circumflex vessels; it is bounded by the Teres minor above, the Teres major below, and the scapular head of the Triceps laterally. The quadrangular space transmits the posterior humeral circumflex vessels and the axillary nerve; it is bounded by the Teres minor and capsule of the shoulder-joint above, the Teres major below, the long head of the Triceps brachii medially, and the humerus laterally.

Action.—Extends the forearm. The long head extends and adducts the arm.

Nerves.—Branches of the radial nerve, containing fibers from the seventh and eighth cervical nerves.

Variations.—A fourth head from the inner part of the humerus; a slip between Triceps and Latissimus dorsi corresponding to the *Dorso-epitrochlearis.*

The **Subanconæus** is the name given to a few fibers which spring from the deep surface of the lower part of the Triceps brachii, and are inserted into the posterior ligament and synovial membrane of the elbow-joint.

Group Actions.—Flexion at the elbow is brought about by the Brachialis, a pure flexor, by the Biceps which also has strong Supinating action, and by the Brachioradialis, also a pure flexor. In spite of its old name, Supinator longus, the Brachioradialis does not assist in voluntary supination or pronation; it may have incidental action in restoring the forearm to the middle position from the extreme of either one. The Pronator teres contracts, but its action may be synergetic to counteract the supination of the Biceps. Other forearm muscles may be used in very strong flexion or in cases of paralysis, provided the proper position of pronation or supination is first obtained. Extension of the elbow is performed by the Triceps and Anconæus.

V. THE MUSCLES AND FASCIÆ OF THE FOREARM.

Antebrachial Fascia (*fascia antebrachii; deep fascia of the forearm*) (Fig. 400).— The portion of the investing fascia which covers the upper forearm is a strong aponeurotic sheet, closely adherent to the underlying muscles. Above, it is continuous with the brachial fascia and is attached to the epicondyles of the humerus and the olecranon. Below, it is attached to the distal portions of the radius and ulna and is continued into the fascia of the hand. It is attached to the dorsal border of the ulna through most of its length, closing off the flexor and extensor compartments of the forearm. In the proximal two-thirds of the forearm, the underlying muscles utilize the deep surface of the investing fascia for attachment of their fibers, and the area for attachment is increased further by the strong intermuscular septa which extend deeply toward the bones, between the adjacent muscles. The volar fascia is visibly thickened by collagenous bundles, derived from the tendon of the biceps, which fan out medially into a distinct aponeurosis called the **lacertus fibrosus**. The dorsal portion is thickened, even more than the volar, by bundles from the Triceps tendon. Near the distal ends of the radius and ulna, the fascia is abruptly thickened by the addition of prominent, annular, collagenous bundles which form the volar and dorsal carpal ligaments. In the distal third of the forearm, the muscles and tendons are separated from the overlying fascia and from each other by fascial clefts. The antebrachial fascia is pierced in several places by vessels and nerves, the largest aperture being for the branch of the median cubital vein which communicates with the deep veins in the antecubital fossa. The radius, ulna, and interossous membrane form a septum dividing the forearm into dorsal or extensor and volar or flexor compartments.

In the **dorsal compartment**, a fascial cleft separates the superficial from the deep muscles, especially near the wrist, but it is closed medially and laterally, not communicating with other clefts. In the **volar compartment**, the fascial cleft is more extensive and may communicate with the fascial clefts of the palm. It is especially evident between the surface of the Pronator quadratus and the overlying muscles and tendons, and is here called the **anterior interosseous cleft**. It continues proximally between the Flexores profundus and sublimis and may follow along the ulnar vessels and nerve to the antecubital fossa. At the wrist it is in contact with the proximal end of the flexor tendon sheaths (radial and ulnar bursæ) and may continue distally under these sheaths into the middle palmar cleft.

The antebrachial or forearm muscles may be divided into a **volar** and a **dorsal group**.

1. The Volar Antebrachial Muscles.

These muscles are divided for convenience of description into two groups, superficial and deep.

The Superficial Group (Fig. 397).

Pronator teres.	Palmaris longus.
Flexor carpi radialis.	Flexor carpi ulnaris.
Flexor digitorum sublimis.	

The muscles of this group take origin from the medial epicondyle of the humerus by a common tendon; they receive additional fibers from the deep fascia of the forearm near the elbow, and from the septa which pass from this fascia between the individual muscles.

The **Pronator teres** has two heads of origin—humeral and ulnar. The **humeral head,** the larger and more superficial, *arises* immediately above the medial epicondyle, and from the tendon common to the origin of the other muscles; also from the intermuscular septum between it and the Flexor carpi radialis and from the antebrachial fascia. The **ulnar head** is a thin fasciculus, which *arises* from the medial side of the coronoid process of the ulna, and joins the preceding at an acute angle. The median nerve enters the forearm between the two heads of the muscle, and is separated from the ulnar artery by the ulnar head. The muscle passes obliquely across the forearm, and ends in a flat tendon, which is inserted into a rough impression at the middle of the lateral surface of the body of the radius. The lateral border of the muscle forms the medial boundary of a triangular hollow situated in front of the elbow-joint and containing the brachial artery, median nerve, and tendon of the Biceps brachii.

Action.—Pronates the hand.

Nerve.—A branch of the median nerve, containing fibers from the sixth and seventh cervical nerves.

Variations.—Absence of ulnar head; additional slips from the medial intermuscular septum, from the Biceps and from the Brachialis anterior occasionally occur.

The **Flexor carpi radialis** lies on the medial side of the preceding muscle. It *arises* from the medial epicondyle by the common tendon; from the fascia of the forearm; and from the intermuscular septa between it and the Pronator teres laterally, the Palmaris longus medially, and the Flexor digitorum sublimis beneath. Slender and aponeurotic in structure at its commencement, it increases in size, and ends in a tendon which forms rather more than the lower half of its length. This tendon passes through a canal in the lateral part of the transverse carpal ligament and runs through a groove on the greater multangular bone; the groove is converted into a canal by fibrous tissue, and lined by a synovial sheath. The tendon is inserted into the base of the second metacarpal bone, and sends a slip to the base of the third metacarpal bone. The radial artery, in the lower part of the forearm, lies between the tendon of this muscle and the Brachioradialis.

Action.—Flexes the hand and helps to abduct it.

Nerve.—A branch of the median nerve, containing fibers from the sixth and seventh cervical nerves.

Variations.—Slips from the tendon of the Biceps, the lacertus fibrosus, the coronoid, and the radius have been found. Its insertion often varies and may be mostly into the annular ligament, the trapezium, or the fourth metacarpal as well as the second or third. The muscle may be absent.

The **Palmaris longus** is a slender, fusiform muscle, lying on the medial side of the preceding. It *arises* from the medial epicondyle of the humerus by the common tendon, from the intermuscular septa between it and the adjacent muscles, and from the antebrachial fascia. It ends in a slender, flattened tendon, which passes over the upper part of the transverse carpal ligament, and is *inserted* into the central part of the transverse carpal ligament and into the palmar aponeurosis, frequently sending a tendinous slip to the short muscles of the thumb.

Action.—Flexes the hand.

Nerve.—A branch of the median nerve, containing fibers from the sixth and seventh cervical nerves.

Variations.—One of the most variable muscles in the body. This muscle is often absent about (10 per cent.), and is subject to many variations; it may be tendinous above and muscular below; or it may be muscular in the center with a tendon above and below; or it may present two muscular bundles with a central tendon; or finally it may consist solely of a tendinous band. The muscle may be double. Slips of origin from the coronoid process or from the radius have been seen.

Partial or complete insertion into the fascia of the forearm, into the tendon of the Flexor carpi ulnaris and pisiform bone, into the navicular, and into the muscles of the little finger have been observed.

The **Flexor carpi ulnaris** lies along the ulnar side of the forearm. It *arises* by two heads, humeral and ulnar, connected by a tendinous arch, beneath which the ulnar nerve and posterior ulnar recurrent artery pass.

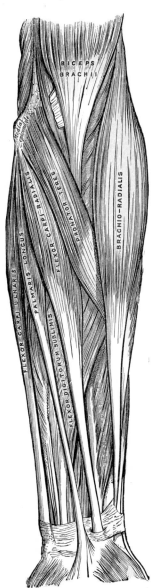

The **humeral head** *arises* from the medial epicondyle of the humerus by the common tendon; the **ulnar head** *arises* from the medial margin of the olecranon and from the upper two-thirds of the dorsal border of the ulna by an aponeurosis, common to it and the Extensor carpi ulnaris and Flexor digitorum profundus; and from the intermuscular septum between it and the Flexor digitorum sublimis. The fibers end in a tendon, which occupies the anterior part of the lower half of the muscle and is *inserted* into the pisiform bone, and is prolonged from this to the hamate and fifth metacarpal bones by the pisohamate and pisometacarpal ligaments; it is also attached by a few fibers to the transverse carpal ligament. The ulnar vessels and nerve lie on the lateral side of the tendon of this muscle, in the lower two-thirds of the forearm.

Action.—Flexes and adducts the hand.

Nerve.—A branch of the ulnar nerve, containing fibers from the eighth cervical and first thoracic nerves.

Variations.—Slips of origin from the coronoid. The *Epitrochleo-anconæus*, a small muscle often present runs from the back of the inner condyle to the olecranon, over the ulnar nerve.

The **Flexor digitorum sublimis** is placed beneath the previous muscle; it is the largest of the muscles of the superficial group, and arises by three heads —humeral, ulnar, and radial. The **humeral head** *arises* from the medial epicondyle of the humerus by the common tendon, from the ulnar collateral ligament of the elbow-joint, and from the intermuscular septa between it and the preceding muscles. The **ulnar head** *arises* from the medial side of the coronoid process, above the ulnar origin of the Pronator teres (see Fig. 206, page 190). The **radial head** *arises* from the oblique line of the radius, extending from the radial tuberosity to the insertion of the Pronator teres. The muscle speedily separates into two planes of muscular fibers, superficial and deep: the superficial plane divides into two parts which end in tendons for the middle and ring fingers; the deep plane gives off a muscular slip to join the portion of the superficial plane which is associated with the tendon of the ring finger, and then divides into two parts, which end in tendons for the index and little fingers. As the four tendons thus formed pass beneath the transverse carpal ligament into the palm of the hand, they are arranged in pairs, the superficial pair going to the middle and ring fingers, the deep pair to the index and little fingers. The tendons diverge from one another in the palm and form dorsal relations to the superficial volar arch and digital branches of the median and ulnar nerves. Opposite the bases of the first phalanges each

FIG. 397.—Front of the left forearm. Superficial muscles.

tendon divides into two slips to allow of the passage of the corresponding tendon of the Flexor digitorum profundus; the two slips then reunite and form a grooved channel for the reception of the accompanying tendon of the Flexor digitorum profundus. Finally the tendon divides and is inserted into the sides of the second phalanx about its middle.

Action.—Flexes the second phalanx of each finger; by continued action, flexes the first phalanx and hand.

Nerves.—Branches of the median nerve, containing fibers from the seventh and eighth cervical and first thoracic nerves.

Variations.—Absence of radial head, of little finger portion; accessory slips from ulnar tuberosity to the index and middle finger portions; from the inner head to the Flexor profundus; from the ulnar or annular ligament to the little finger.

The Deep Group (Fig. 398).

Flexor digitorum profundus.
Flexor pollicis longus.
Pronator quadratus.

The **Flexor digitorum profundus** is situated on the ulnar side of the forearm, immediately beneath the superficial Flexors. It *arises* from the upper three-fourths of the volar and medial surfaces of the body of the ulna, embracing the insertion of the Brachialis above, and extending below to within a short distance of the Pronator quadratus. It also arises from a depression on the medial side of the coronoid process; by an aponeurosis from the upper three-fourths of the dorsal border of the ulna, in common with the Flexor and Extensor carpi ulnaris; and from the ulnar half of the interosseous membrane. The muscle ends in four tendons which run under the transverse carpal ligament dorsal to the tendons of the Flexor digitorum sublimis. Opposite the first phalanges the tendons pass through the openings in the tendons of the Flexor digitorum sublimis, and are finally *inserted* into the bases of the last phalanges. The portion of the muscle for the index finger is usually distinct throughout, but the

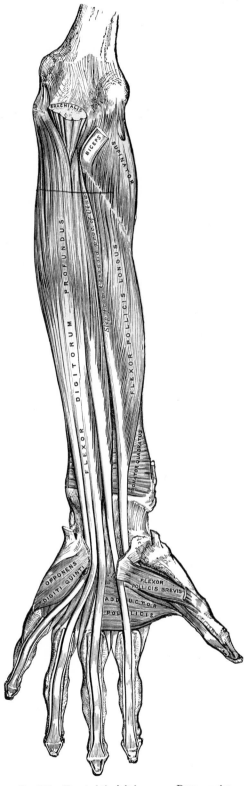

Fig. 398.—Front of the left forearm. Deep muscles.

tendons for the middle, ring, and little fingers are connected together by areolar tissue and tendinous slips, as far as the palm of the hand.

Distal to the metacarpophalangeal joints, the tendons of the Flexores digitorum sublimis and profoundus lie in strong ligamentous tunnels, the digital **fibrous tendon sheaths** (page 454 and Fig. 410). Each tunnel is lined by the **synovial tendon sheath,** a lubricated layer which is reflected on the contained tendons. Within each digital sheath, the tendons of the sublimis and profoundus are connected to each other and to the phalanges by tendinous bands called **vincula tendinum** (Fig. 399). There are two types of vincula: (*a*) the **vincula brevia,** which are two in number in each finger, are fan-shaped expansions near the termination of the tendons, one con-

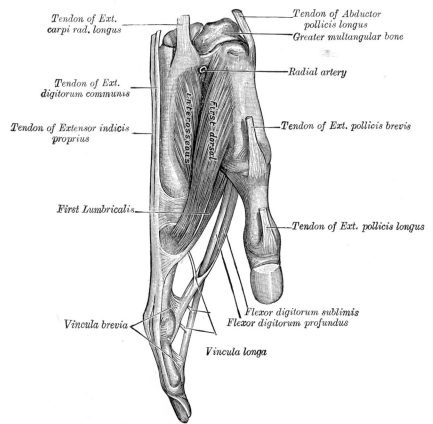

Fig. 399.—Tendons of forefinger and vincula tendinum.

necting the sublimis tendon to the front of the proximal interphalangeal joint and the head of the first phalanx, and the other connecting the profundus tendon to the front of the second interphalangeal joint and the head of the second phalanx; (*b*) the **vincula longa** are slender, independent bands which are found in two positions: one pair of them in each finger connects the under surface of the profundus tendon to the subjacent sublimis tendon after the former has passed through the split in the latter; another pair, or a single band, connects the sublimis tendon to the proximal end of the first phalanx.

Action.—Flexes the terminal phalanx of each finger; by continued action flexes the other phalanges and to some extent the hand.

Nerves.—A branch of the volar interosseous nerve from the median and a branch of the ulnar, containing fibers from the eighth cervical and first thoracic nerves.

Variations.—The index finger portion may arise partly from the upper part of the radius. Slips from the inner head of the Flexor sublimis, medial epicondyle, or the coronoid are found. Connection with the Flexor pollicis longus.

Four small muscles, the Lumbricales, are connected with the tendons of the Flexor profundus in the palm. They will be described with the muscles of the hand (page 462).

The **Flexor pollicis longus** is situated on the radial side of the forearm, lying in the same plane as the preceding. It *arises* from the grooved volar surface of the body of the radius, extending from immediately below the tuberosity and oblique line to within a short distance of the Pronator quadratus. It *arises* also from the adjacent part of the interosseous membrane, and generally by a fleshy

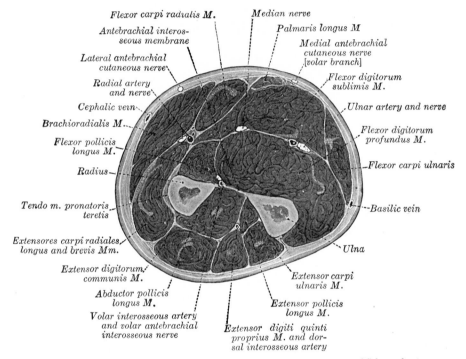

Flexor carpi radialis M.
Antebrachial interosseous membrane
Lateral antebrachial cutaneous nerve
Radial artery and nerve
Cephalic vein
Brachioradialis M.
Flexor pollicis longus M.
Radius
Tendo m. pronatoris teretis
Extensores carpi radiales, longus and brevis Mm.
Extensor digitorum communis M.
Abductor pollicis longus M.
Volar interosseous artery and volar antebrachial interosseous nerve

Median nerve
Palmaris longus M
Medial antebrachial cutaneous nerve [volar branch]
Flexor digitorum sublimis M.
Ulnar artery and nerve
Flexor digitorum profundus M.
Flexor carpi ulnaris
Basilic vein
Ulna
Extensor carpi ulnaris M.
Extensor pollicis longus M.
Extensor digiti quinti proprius M. and dorsal interosseous artery

Fɪɢ. 400.—Cross-section through the middle of the forearm. (Eycleshymer and Schoemaker.)

slip from the medial border of the coronoid process, or from the medial epicondyle of the humerus. The fibers end in a flattened tendon, which passes beneath the transverse carpal ligament, is then lodged between the lateral head of the Flexor pollicis brevis and the oblique part of the Adductor pollicis, and, entering an osseoaponeurotic canal similar to those for the Flexor tendons of the fingers, is *inserted* into the base of the distal phalanx of the thumb. The volar interosseous nerve and vessels pass downward on the front of the interosseous membrane between the Flexor pollicis longus and Flexor digitorum profundus.

Action.—Flexes the second phalanx of the thumb; by continued action, flexes the first phalanx, and flexes and adducts the metacarpal.

Nerve.—A branch of the volar interosseous nerve from the median, containing fibers from the eighth cervical and first thoracic nerves.

Variations.—Slips may connect with Flexor sublimis, or Profundus, or Pronator teres. An additional tendon to the index finger is sometimes found.

The **Pronator quadratus** is a small, flat, quadrilateral muscle, extending across the front of the lower parts of the radius and ulna. It *arises* from the pronator ridge on the lower part of the volar surface of the body of the ulna; from the medial part of the volar surface of the lower fourth of the ulna; and from a strong aponeurosis which covers the medial third of the muscle. The fibers pass lateralward and slightly downward, to be inserted into the lower fourth of the lateral border and the volar surface of the body of the radius. The deeper fibers of the muscle are inserted into the triangular area above the ulnar notch of the radius—an attachment comparable with the origin of the Supinator from the triangular area below the radial notch of the ulna.

Action.—Pronates the hand.

Nerve.—A branch of the volar interosseous nerve from the median, containing fibers from the eighth cervical and first thoracic nerves.

Variations.—Rarely absent; split into two or three layers; increased attachment upward or downward.

2. The Dorsal Antebrachial Muscles.

These muscles are divided for convenience of description into two groups, superficial and deep.

The Superficial Group (Fig. 401).

Brachioradialis.	Extensor digitorum communis.
Extensor carpi radialis longus.	Extensor digiti quinti proprius.
Extensor carpi radialis brevis.	Extensor carpi ulnaris.

Anconæus.

The **Brachioradialis** (*Supinator longus*) is the most superficial muscle on the radial side of the forearm. It *arises* from the upper two-thirds of the lateral supracondylar ridge of the humerus, and from the lateral intermuscular septum, being limited above by the groove for the radial nerve. Interposed between it and the Brachialis are the radial nerve and the anastomosis between the radial collateral branch of the profunda artery and the radial recurrent. The fibers end above the middle of the forearm in a flat tendon, which is *inserted* into the lateral side of the base of the styloid process of the radius. The tendon is crossed near its insertion by the tendons of the Abductor pollicis longus and Extensor pollicis brevis; on its ulnar side is the radial artery.

Action.—Flexes the forearm.

Nerve.—A branch of the radial nerve, containing fibers from the fifth and sixth cervical nerves.

Variations.—Fusion with the Brachialis; tendon of insertion may be divided into two or three slips; insertion partial or complete into the middle of the radius, fasciculi to the tendon of the Biceps, the tuberosity or oblique line of the radius; slips to the Extensor carpi radialis longus or Abductor pollicis longus; absence; rarely doubled.

The **Extensor carpi radialis longus** (*Extensor carpi radialis longior*) is placed partly beneath the Brachioradialis. It *arises* from the lower third of the lateral supracondylar ridge of the humerus, from the lateral intermuscular septum, and by a few fibers from the common tendon of origin of the Extensor muscles of the forearm. The fibers end at the upper third of the forearm in a flat tendon, which runs along the lateral border of the radius, beneath the Abductor pollicis longus and Extensor pollicis brevis; it then passes beneath the dorsal carpal ligament, where it lies in a groove on the back of the radius common to it and the Extensor carpi radialis brevis, immediately behind the styloid process. It is *inserted* into the dorsal surface of the base of the second metacarpal bone, on its radial side (Fig. 399).

Action.—Extends and abducts the hand.

Nerve.—A branch of the radial nerve, containing fibers from the sixth and seventh cervical nerves.

The **Extensor carpi radialis brevis** (*Extensor carpi radialis brevior*) is shorter and thicker than the preceding muscle, beneath which it is placed. It *arises* from the lateral epicondyle of the humerus, by a tendon common to it and the three following muscles; from the radial collateral ligament of the elbow-joint; from a strong aponeurosis which covers its surface; and from the intermuscular septa between it and the adjacent muscles. The fibers end about the middle of the forearm in a flat tendon, which is closely connected with that of the preceding muscle, and accompanies it to the wrist; it passes beneath the Abductor pollicis longus and Extensor pollicis brevis, then beneath the dorsal carpal ligament, and is *inserted* into the dorsal surface of the base of the third metacarpal bone on its radial side. Under the dorsal carpal ligament the tendon lies on the back of the radius in a shallow groove, to the ulnar side of that which lodges the tendon of the Extensor carpi radialis longus, and separated from it by a faint ridge.

The tendons of the two preceding muscles pass through the same compartment of the dorsal carpal ligament in a single synovial sheath.

Action.—Extends and may abduct the hand.

Nerve.—A branch of the radial nerve, containing fibers from the sixth and seventh cervical nerves.

Variations.—Either muscle may split into two or three tendons of insertion to the second and third or even the fourth metacarpal. The two muscles may unite into a single belly with two tendons. Cross slips between the two muscles may occur. The *Extensor carpi radialis intermedius* rarely arises as a distinct muscle from the humerus, but is not uncommon as an accessory slip from one or both muscles to the second or third or both metacarpals. The *Extensor carpi radialis accessorius* is occasionally found arising from the humerus with or below the Extensor carpi radialis longus and inserted into the first metacarpal, the Abductor pollicis brevis, the First dorsal interosseus, or elsewhere.

The **Extensor digitorum communis** *arises* from the lateral epicondyle of the humerus, by the common tendon; from the intermuscular septa between it and the adjacent muscles, and from the antebrachial fascia. It divides below into four tendons, which pass, together with that of the Extensor indicis proprius, through a separate compartment of the dorsal carpal ligament, within a synovial sheath. The tendons then diverge on the back of the hand, and are *inserted* into the second and third phalanges of the fingers in the following manner. Opposite the metacarpophalangeal articulation each tendon is bound by fasciculi to the collateral ligaments and serves as the dorsal ligament of this joint; after having crossed the joint, it spreads out into a broad aponeurosis, which covers the dorsal surface of the first phalanx and is reinforced, in this situation, by the tendons of the Interossei and Lumbricales. Opposite the first interphalangeal joint this aponeurosis divides into three slips; an intermediate and two collateral: the former is inserted into the base of the second phalanx; and the two collateral, which are continued onward along the sides of the second phalanx, unite by their contiguous margins, and are *inserted* into the dorsal surface of the last phalanx. As the tendons cross the interphalangeal joints, they furnish them with dorsal ligaments. The tendon to the index finger is accompanied by the Extensor indicis proprius, which lies on its ulnar side. On the back of the hand, the tendons to the middle, ring, and little fingers are connected by obliquely placed bands. Occasionally the first tendon is connected to the second by a thin transverse band.

Action.—Extends the phalanges, and by continued action, extends the wrist.

Nerve.—A branch of the deep radial nerve, containing fibers from the sixth, seventh, and eighth cervical nerves.

Variations.—An increase or decrease in the number of tendons is common; an additional slip to the thumb is sometimes present.

The **Extensor digiti quinti proprius** (*Extensor minimi digiti*) is a slender muscle placed on the medial side of the Extensor digitorum communis, with which it is

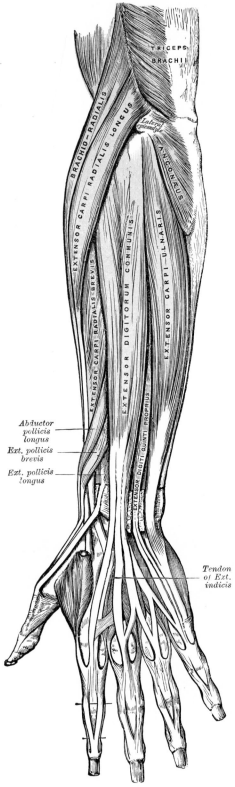

Abductor
pollicis
longus

Ext. pollicis
brevis

Ext. pollicis
longus

Tendon
of Ext.
indicis

Fig. 401.—Posterior surface of the forearm.
Superficial muscles.

generally connected. It *arises* from the common Extensor tendon by a thin tendinous slip, from the intermuscular septa between it and the adjacent muscles. Its tendon runs through a compartment of the dorsal carpal ligament behind the distal radio-ulnar joint, then divides into two as it crosses the hand, and finally joins the expansion of the Extensor digitorum communis tendon on the dorsum of the first phalanx of the little finger.

Action.—Extends the little finger.

Nerve.—A branch of the deep radial nerve, containing fibers from the sixth, seventh, and eighth cervical nerves.

Variations.—An additional fibrous slip from the lateral epicondyle; the tendon of insertion may not divide or may send a slip to the ring finger. Absence of muscle rare; fusion of the belly with the Extensor digitorum communis not uncommon.

The **Extensor carpi ulnaris** lies on the ulnar side of the forearm. It *arises* from the lateral epicondyle of the humerus, by the common tendon; by an aponeurosis from the dorsal border of the ulna in common with the Flexor carpi ulnaris and the Flexor digitorum profundus; and from the deep fascia of the forearm. It ends in a tendon, which runs in a groove between the head and the styloid process of the ulna, passing through a separate compartment of the dorsal carpal ligament, and is *inserted* into the prominent tubercle on the ulnar side of the base of the fifth metacarpal bone.

Action.—Extends and adducts the hand.

Nerve.—A branch of the deep radial nerve, containing fibers from the sixth, seventh, and eighth cervical nerves.

Variations.—Doubling; reduction to tendinous band; insertion partially into fourth metacarpal. In many cases (52 per cent.) a slip is continued from the insertion of the tendon anteriorly over the Opponens digiti quinti, to the fascia covering that muscle, the metacarpal bone, the capsule of the metacarpophalangeal articulation, or the first phalanx of the little finger. This slip may be replaced by a muscular fasciculus arising from or near the pisiform.

The **Anconæus** is a small triangular muscle which is placed on the back of the elbow-joint, and appears to be a continuation of the Triceps brachii. It *arises* by a separate tendon from the back part of the lateral epicondyle of the humerus; its fibers diverge and are *inserted* into the side of the olecranon, and upper fourth of the dorsal surface of the body of the ulna.

Action.—Extends the forearm.
Nerve.—A branch of radial nerve, containing fibers from the seventh and eighth cervical nerves.

The Deep Group (Fig. 402).

Supinator.
Abductor pollicis longus.
Extensor pollicis brevis.
Extensor pollicis longus.
Extensor indicis proprius.

The **Supinator** (*Supinator brevis*) (Fig. 403) is a broad muscle, curved around the upper third of the radius. It consists of two planes of fibers, between which the deep branch of the radial nerve lies. The two planes *arise* in common—the superficial one by tendinous and the deeper by muscular

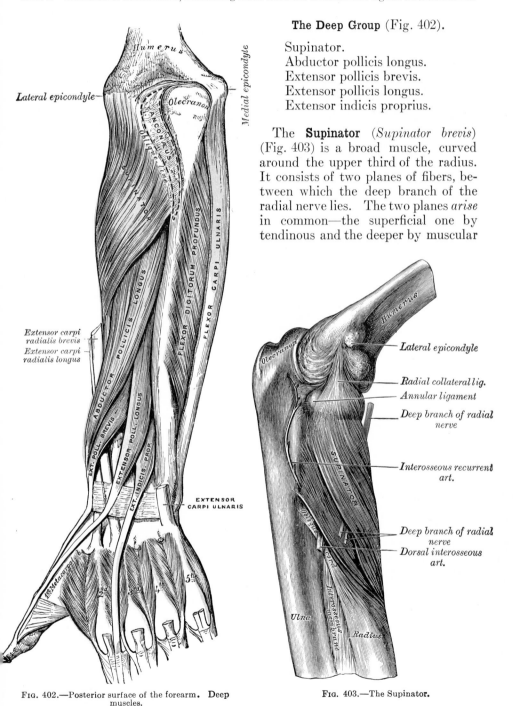

Fɪɢ. 402.—Posterior surface of the forearm. **Deep muscles.**

Fɪɢ. 403.—The Supinator.

fibers—from the lateral epicondyle of the humerus; from the radial collateral ligament of the elbow-joint, and the annular ligament; from the ridge on the ulna,
which runs obliquely downward from the dorsal end of the radial notch; from the
triangular depression below the notch; and from a tendinous expansion which
covers the surface of the muscle. The superficial fibers surround the upper part
of the radius, and are inserted into the lateral edge of the radial tuberosity and
the oblique line of the radius, as low down as the insertion of the Pronator teres.
The upper fibers of the deeper plane form a sling-like fasciculus, which encircles
the neck of the radius above the tuberosity and is attached to the back part of
its medial surface; the greater part of this portion of the muscle is inserted into
the dorsal and lateral surfaces of the body of the radius, midway between the
oblique line and the head of the bone.

Action.—Supinates the hand.
Nerve.—A branch of the deep radial nerve, containing fibers from the sixth cervical nerve.

The **Abductor pollicis longus** (*Extensor ossis metacarpi pollicis*) lies immediately
below the Supinator and is sometimes united with it. It *arises* from the lateral
part of the dorsal surface of the body of the ulna below the insertion of the Anconæus, from the interosseous membrane, and from the middle third of the dorsal
surface of the body of the radius. Passing obliquely downward and lateralward,
it ends in a tendon, which runs through a groove on the lateral side of the lower
end of the radius, accompanied by the tendon of the Extensor pollicis brevis, and
is *inserted* into the radial side of the base of the first metacarpal bone (Fig. 399).
It occasionally gives off two slips near its insertion: one to the greater multangular
bone and the other to blend with the origin of the Abductor pollicis brevis.

Action.—Abducts the thumb and, by continued action, the wrist.
Nerve.—A branch of the deep radial nerve, containing fibers from the sixth and seventh cervical
nerves.
Variations.—More or less doubling of muscle and tendon with insertion of the extra tendon
into the first metacarpal, the greater multangular, or into the Abductor pollicis brevis or Opponens
pollicis.

The **Extensor pollicis brevis** (*Extensor primi internodii pollicis*) lies on the
medial side of, and is closely connected with, the Abductor pollicis longus. It *arises*
from the dorsal surface of the body of the radius below that muscle, and from the
interosseous membrane. Its direction is similar to that of the Abductor pollicis
longus, its tendon passing through the same groove on the lateral side of the lower
end of the radius, to be *inserted* into the base of the first phalanx of the thumb
(Fig. 399).

Action.—Extends the first phalanx of the thumb and, by continued action, abducts the hand
Nerve.—A branch of the deep radial nerve, containing fibers from the sixth and seventh cervical·
nerves.
Variations.—Absence; fusion of tendon with that of the Extensor pollicis longus.

The **Extensor pollicis longus** (*Extensor secundi internodii pollicis*) is much larger
than the preceding muscle, the origin of which it partly covers. It *arises* from
the lateral part of the middle third of the dorsal surface of the body of the ulna
below the origin of the Abductor pollicis longus, and from the interosseous membrane. It ends in a tendon, which passes through a separate compartment in the
dorsal carpal ligament, lying in a narrow, oblique groove on the back of the lower
end of the radius. It then crosses obliquely the tendons of the Extensores carpi
radiales longus and brevis, and is separated from the Extensor brevis pollicis by a
triangular interval (the anatomical snuff-box), in which the radial artery is found;
and is finally *inserted* into the base of the last phalanx of the thumb. The radial
artery is crossed by the tendons of the Abductor pollicis longus and of the Extensores
pollicis longus and brevis.

Action.—Extends the second phalanx of the thumb and, by continued action, abducts the hand.

Nerve.—A branch of the deep radial nerve, containing fibers from the sixth, seventh, and eighth cervical nerves.

The **Extensor indicis proprius** (*Extensor indicis*) is a narrow, elongated muscle, placed medial to, and parallel with, the preceding. It *arises*, from the dorsal surface of the body of the ulna below the origin of the Extensor pollicis longus, and from the interosseous membrane. Its tendon passes under the dorsal carpal ligament in the same compartment as that which transmits the tendons of the Extensor digitorum communis, and opposite the head of the second metacarpal bone, joins the ulnar side of the tendon of the Extensor digitorum communis which belongs to the index finger.

Action.—Extends and to some extent adducts the index finger.

Nerve.—A branch of the deep radial nerve, containing fibers from the sixth, seventh, and eighth cervical nerves.

Variations.—Doubling; the ulnar part may pass beneath the dorsal carpal ligament with the Extensor digitorum communis; a slip from the tendon may pass to the index finger.

Group Actions.—Flexion at the wrist is brought about by the Flexor carpi ulnaris, Flexor carpi radialis, and Palmaris longus. The Flexores digitorum sublimis and profundus are not used in voluntary flexion at the wrist unless they are prevented from flexing the fingers. The extensors of the wrist are the Extensores carpi radialis longus and brevis, and the Extensor carpi ulnaris. The Extensor digitorum communis may act if the fingers are prevented from extending. Abduction (radial flexion) at the wrist is performed by the Flexor carpi radialis, Extensores carpi radialis longus and brevis, and Abductor pollicis longus. Adduction (ulnar flexion) at the wrist is performed by the Flexor carpi ulnaris and Extensor carpi ulnaris. Pronation of the hand is brought about by the Pronator teres and Pronator quadratus. Supination is performed by the Biceps and the Supinator. Group actions of muscles inserting on the digits are presented after the description of the muscles of the hand.

VI. THE MUSCLES AND FASCIÆ OF THE HAND.

The muscles of the hand are subdivided into three groups: (1) those of the thumb, which occupy the radial side and produce the **thenar eminence**; (2) those of the little finger, which occupy the ulnar side and give rise to the **hypothenar eminence**; (3) those in the middle of the palm and between the metacarpal bones.

Superficial Fascia (*tela subcutanea*).—The superficial fascia of the volar surface of the forearm changes its character abruptly at the distal crease of the wrist from a delicate movable tissue into the tough cushion which covers the palm and palmar surface of the digits. The latter contains a considerable amount of fat, but cannot be separated readily into superficial and deep layers. The adipose tissue is permeated by strong fibrous bands and septa which break it up into small granular lobules and bind it securely to the deep fascia. The dermis is very compact, and not only protects the underlying structures, but also offers resistance to the progress of infectious processes seeking to point toward the surface; at the same time, the vertical direction of the fibrous bands tends to guide the spread of the infection into deeper layers. The superficial fascia is adherent to the deep fascia over the entire palm, but the union is especially strong at the skin creases of the wrist, the major creases of the palm, and the creases of the digits. At the medial and lateral borders of the hand and digits, the fascia changes its character rather abruptly as it becomes continuous with the corresponding layer of the dorsum.

The superficial fascia of the dorsum of the hand and digits is delicate and movable, like that of the forearm with which it is continuous. Its two layers can be identified; the superficial one is thin but may contain a small amount of fat; the deep one is a definite fibrous sheet and supports the superficial veins and cutaneous nerves. It is separated from the deep fascia by a distinct fascial cleft, the dorsal subcutaneous cleft (described below), which imparts the characteristic movability to the skin of the back of the hand.

29

Deep Fascia of the Wrist.—The antebrachial fascia at the wrist is thickened into an annular band or cuff which holds the tendons of the forearm muscles close against the wrist. For convenience in description, it is divided into two parts, the volar carpal ligament and the dorsal carpal ligament. An additional band, the transverse carpal ligament, is distal to the volar carpal ligament and lies at a slightly deeper

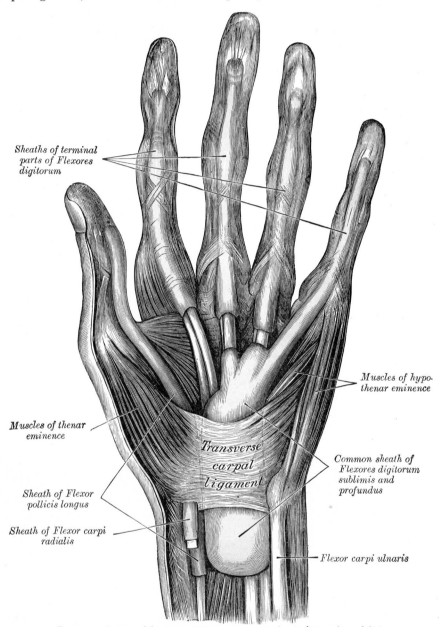

Sheaths of terminal parts of Flexores digitorum

Muscles of hypo-thenar eminence

Muscles of thenar eminence

Transverse carpal ligament

Common sheath of Flexores digitorum sublimis and profundus

Sheath of Flexor pollicis longus

Sheath of Flexor carpi radialis

Flexor carpi ulnaris

Fig. 404.—The synovial sheaths of the tendons on the front of the wrist and digits.

level. It is not strictly a fascial derivative, coming rather from the tendons and ligaments of the carpus, but it will be described here because of its close association with the fascia.

The **Volar Carpal Ligament** (*ligamentum carpi volare*) (Fig. 410), not to be confused with the transverse carpal ligament described below, is the distal portion of the investing antebrachial fascia which is abruptly thickened at the wrist by the addition of strong transverse collagenous bundles. It is attached medially and laterally to the styloid processes of the ulna and radius and under it lie the tendons of the flexor muscles. Its distal border is difficult to determine because it merges

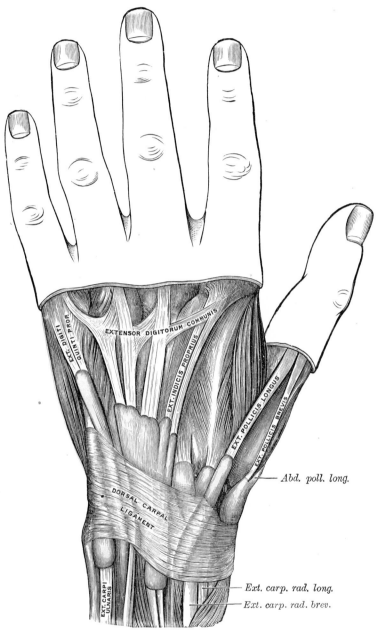

Fig. 405.—The synovial sheaths of the tendons on the back of the wrist.

with the transverse carpal ligament, except where the ulnar artery emerges from under the volar carpal to lie superficial to the transverse carpal ligament.

The relations of the flexor tendons to each other and to the nerves and blood-vessels in the wrist are of great surgical interest because they are frequently severed in industrial injuries and must be sutured back into place. These relations are quite constant unless actual muscular variations or anomalies occur, and are shown in Figure 406.

Transverse Carpal Ligament (*ligamentum carpi transversum; anterior annular ligament*) (Figs. 404, 410).—The transverse carpal ligament is a thick fibrous band which arches over the deep groove on the volar surface of the carpal bones, forming a tunnel through which the long flexor tendons and the median nerve pass. It is attached, medially, to the pisiform and the hamulus of the hamate, and laterally, to the tuberosity of the navicular, and the medial part of the volar surface and ridge of the greater multangular. Its proximal border is partly merged with the distal border of the volar carpal ligament, but the latter belongs to a definitely different and more superficial stratum, and is separated from it by the ulnar artery and nerve. It is attached to the palmar aponeurosis, which lies superficial to it, and contributes oblique crossed fibers to the deep surface of the aponeurosis. It is attached to the greater multangular in two parts, one on either side of the groove in which the tendon of the Flexor carpi radialis lies. The Flexor carpi ulnaris, at its insertion, contributes tendinous fibers to the ligament and the short muscles of the thumb and little finger arise from it to a large extent.

The **Synovial Sheaths of the Flexor Tendons at the Wrist** (Fig. 404).—As the tendons pass under the transverse carpal ligament, they are enclosed in two specialized synovial sacs; the larger one, for all the tendons of the Flexores digitorum sublimis and profundus, is called the **ulnar bursa**; the smaller one, for the Flexor pollicis longus, is called the **radial bursa**. They extend proximally into the forearm for about 2.5 cm. beyond the transverse carpal ligament. The radial bursa extends distally to the terminal phalanx of the thumb where the Flexor pollicis longus inserts. The ulnar bursa continues distally beyond the middle of the palm as the digital sheath for the little finger, but it is greatly reduced in diameter at the middle of the metacarpal bones by the formation of terminal diverticula about the tendons of the second, third, and fourth digits. The tendons to the second, third, and fourth digits, therefore, are without synovial sheaths for a short distance in the middle of the palm, but they have independent digital sheaths beginning proximally over the heads of their metacarpal bones and continuing distally to the terminal phalanges, where the profundus inserts.

Dorsal Carpal Ligament (*ligamentum carpi dorsale; posterior annular ligament*) (Figs. 402, 405).—The dorsal carpal ligament, under which the extensor tendons lie, is the distal portion of the investing antebrachial fascia which is thickened abruptly by the addition of transverse collagenous bundles. The latter take a somewhat oblique course, extending distalward as they cross from the radial to the ulnar side. The ligament is attached, medially, to the styloid process of the ulna, and to the triangular and pisiform bones, and laterally, to the lateral margin of the radius. Between these medial and lateral borders, it is attached to the ridges on the dorsal surface of the radius.

The **Synovial Sheaths of the Extensor Tendons at the Wrist** (Fig. 405).—Between the dorsal carpal ligament and the carpal bones, six tunnels are formed for the passage of tendons, each tunnel having a separate synovial sheath. One is found in each of the following positions (Fig. 406): (1) on the lateral side of the styloid process of the radius, for the tendons of the Abductor pollicis longus and Extensor pollicis brevis; (2) dorsal to the styloid process, for the tendons of the Extensores carpi radialis longus and brevis; (3) about the middle of the dorsal surface of the radius, for the tendon of the Extensor pollicis longus; (4) more medially, for the tendons of the Extensor digitorum communis and Extensor indicis proprius; (5) opposite the interval between the radius and ulna, for the Extensor digiti quinti proprius; (6) between the head and styloid process of the ulna, for the tendon of the Extensor carpi ulnaris. The sheaths lining these tunnels all begin proximal to the dorsal carpal ligament; those for the tendons of the Abductor pollicis longus, Extensor pollicis brevis, Extensores carpi radialis, and Extensor carpi ulnaris stop immediately proximal to the bases of the metacarpal bones, while the sheaths for the Extensor digitorum communis, Extensor indicis proprius, and Extensor digiti quinti proprius are prolonged to the junction of the proximal and intermediate thirds of the metacarpus.

Deep Fascia of the Palm.—The investing layer of deep fascia in the palm is continuous with the antebrachial fascia which is represented, in the wrist, by the volar carpal ligament. It is continuous also with the fascia of the dorsum at the borders of the hand, attaching to the fifth metacarpal bone medially, and the first and second metacarpal bones laterally, as it passes over them. The thenar fascia, over the muscular eminence at the radial side of the hand, and the hypothenar fascia, over the eminence of the ulnar side, are similar in texture to the antebrachial fascia, but that in the central part of the palm is greatly strengthened into what is called the palmar aponeurosis.

Palmar Aponeurosis (Fig. 407).—The Palmar aponeurosis is made up of two components: (*a*) a thick superficial stratum of longitudinal bundles which are the direct continuation of the tendon of the Palmaris longus, and (*b*) a thinner deep stratum of transverse fibers which is continuous with the volar carpal ligament. The two strata are intimately fused and partly interwoven. The deeper portion is securely attached to the transverse carpal ligament and the latter may contribute obliquely running fibers to the aponeurosis. The longitudinal bundles of the superficial stratum form a uniform layer in the proximal part of the palm, but distally, they fan out and are segregated into divergent bands which extend toward the bases of the digits, covering the long flexor tendons. The four bands to the fingers are heavier and more constant than the one to the thumb. Each of these bands has a double termination, the superficial part attaching to the skin, and the deeper part ending in the flexor tendon sheath. The most superficial fibers attach to the skin at the distal crease of the palm; other superficial fibers terminate at the crease at the base of the digit. The deeper portion of each band contributes to the fibrous tendon sheath in two ways: some of the fibers continue distally into the digit, assisting in the formation of the digital sheath; the greater number of fibers, however, form two arching ligamentous bands, on each side of the tendon, which penetrate deeply toward the metacarpal bone. They attach to the bone and send fibers to the transverse metacarpal ligament, thus completing the formation of the tunnel which lies on the head of the metacarpal bone. In the central part of the palm, as the longitudinal bands diverge and separate from each other, the intervals between them are occupied by transverse fibers which represent the distal thickening of the deeper stratum of the aponeurosis. These transverse fibers, making up what is called the **superficial transverse metacarpal ligament,** extend as far distally as the heads of the metacarpal bones, but from here to the webs between the digits, the intervals are not covered by aponeurosis. In this distal, uncovered portion, therefore, the digital vessels and nerves, and the tendons of the Lumbricales are more readily accessible to the surgeon. The intervals are closed distally by other transverse fibers which occupy and support the webs between the digits and which are variously named the **fasciculi transversi,** the **superficial transverse ligament of the fingers,** the **interdigital ligament,** and the **ligamentum natatorium.** They attach to the digital sheaths at the bases of the first phalanges and merge into the fibrous septa of the sides of the fingers known as the **cutaneous ligaments of the phalanges.** The digital vessels and nerves enter the digits deep to the fasciculi transversi and lie against the cutaneous ligaments of the phalanges in their course toward the ends of the fingers. As mentioned above, the band of longitudinal fibers from the palmar aponeurosis which extends toward the thumb is not as robust as the other four. Some of its fibers attach to the longitudinal crease of the palm, many of them fuse with the fascia of the thenar eminence, and a comparatively small number assist in the formation of the sheath for the Flexor pollicis longus tendon. When the Palmaris longus is absent, a condition which occurs in 13 per cent of the hands, the attachment of the palmar aponeurosis to the transverse carpal ligament is strengthened to compensate for the loss of continuity with the Palmaris tendon. The Palmaris brevis is a small but constant muscle which lies superficial to the hypothenar fascia; it has its origin at the ulnar border of the palmar aponeurosis and inserts into the skin of the ulnar border of the palm. The palmar aponeurosis is fused, at its radial border, with the fascial membrane of the thenar eminence, and from this line of union, a membrane is continued deeply into the palm and is attached to the first metacarpal bone, forming the **thenar septum**. Similarly, the aponeurosis is fused with the hypothenar fascia, and from this union a septum is continued deeply to the fifth metacarpal, forming the **hypothenar septum**. These two septa divide the palm into three compartments: a thenar, a hypothenar, and a central compartment (see below).

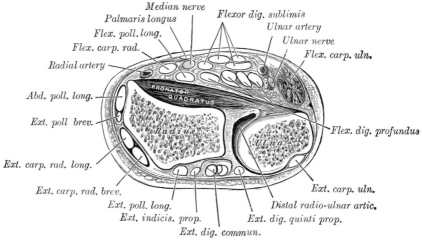

Fig. 406.—Transverse section across distal ends of radius and ulna.

Digital Tendon Sheaths.—The tendons of the Flexores digitorum sublimis and profundus are held in position along the digits by strong fibrous tunnels (Fig. 410). The tunnels or canals are formed by the volar surfaces of the phalanges and by strong collagenous bands which arch over the tendons and are attached to the margins of the phalanges on either side. Opposite the middle of the proximal and second phalanges, the bands (*digital vaginal ligaments*) are very strong and their fibers are transverse. Opposite the joints they are much thinner, and consist of annular and cruciate ligamentous fibers. At their proximal ends, the digital sheaths merge with the deeper parts of the palmar aponeurosis. Within each of the five fibrous digital sheaths, there is a synovial tendon sheath; that for the thumb is continuous with the radial bursa; that for the little finger with the ulnar bursa; those for the other three fingers are closed proximally at the metacarpophalangeal joints (Fig. 404).

Deep Fascia of the Dorsum of the Hand.—The investing layer of deep fascia of the dorsum of the hand is directly continuous with the antebrachial fascia which is thickened at the wrist by the addition of annular collagenous bundles into the dorsal carpal ligament. It is continuous, at the medial side of the hand, with the hypothenar fascia, after being attached to the dorsum of the fifth metacarpal bone. At the lateral border of the hand, it is continuous with the fascia over the first Interosseus dorsalis, after being attached to the dorsum of the second metacarpal bone and with the thenar fascia, after being attached to the first metacarpal bone. The investing fascia forms the superficial boundary of a flat compartment which contains the tendons of the extensors of the digits.

The fascia of the dorsum of the thumb corresponds to that of the hand proper whose investing and subaponeurotic fasciæ fuse into a single layer at its lateral border. This single layer, after being attached to the dorsum of the second metacarpal bone, continues laterally over the first Interosseus dorsalis, in the web between the thumb and the index finger, and is attached to the ulnar border of the first metacarpal bone. It separates again into two layers which form a compartment for the extensor tendons of the thumb, and then, reunited into a single sheet, attaches to the radial border of the first metacarpal, where it becomes continuous with the thenar fascia.

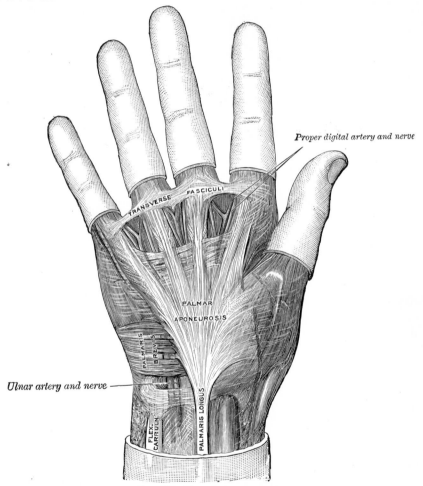

Fig. 407.—The palmar aponeurosis.

Fascial Compartments of the Hand.—The **thenar compartment** (not to be confused with the thenar fascial cleft or space) occupies the thenar eminence of the palm and contains the short muscles of the thumb with the exception of the Adductores. The boundary is formed by the investing layer of deep fascia and its inward continuation, the thenar septum, which lies between the Adductores and the Flexor brevis. The compartment is closed by the attachment of this fascia proximally, to the carpal bones and transverse carpal ligament; distally, to the first phalanx at the insertion of the enclosed muscles; dorsally, along the subcutaneous border of the first metacarpal bone, and ventrally, by the attachment of the thenar septum along the Adductores. In addition to the Abductor brevis, the Flexor brevis and the Opponens, the compartment contains the first metacarpal bone, the superficial volar branch of the radial artery, and a portion of the tendon of the Flexor pollicis longus enclosed in the radial bursa. Within the compartment, the muscles are enclosed in their individual fascial sheaths, and for the most part, are separated from each other by fascial clefts, but these clefts do not communicate with each other nor with the major fascial clefts of the palm.

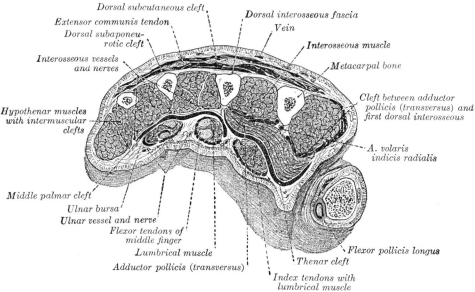

Fig. 408.—Transverse section across the wrist and digits. (Kanavel).

The **hypothenar compartment** occupies the hypothenar eminence and contains the short muscles of the little finger. It is enclosed by the hypothenar investing fascia and the hypothenar septum which lies between the Flexor digiti quinti brevis and the third Interosseus volaris. The fascia forms a closed compartment by attaching along the fifth metacarpal bone on both the dorsal and volar aspects of the muscles which it surrounds. Within the compartment, the individual muscles are enclosed in fascial sheaths of their own and are separated from each other by fascial clefts, but these clefts do not communicate with each other nor with the major fascial cleft of the palm.

The **central compartment** is bounded, medially and laterally, by the thenar and hypothenar fascial septa; superficially, by the palmar aponeurosis; and deeply, by a fascial membrane which covers the deep surface of the long flexor tendon mass. It contains the Flexores digitorum sublimis and profundus tendons, the Lumbricales, the superficial volar arch, the palmar branch of the medial nerve, and the superficial branch of the ulnar nerve. The compartment is narrow proximally, but widens distally as the tendons diverge toward their fingers. It is closed proximally, as far as fascial attachments are concerned, but the tendon sheaths within it extend back into the forearm, and its tissues merge distally with those of the webs and digits.

The **Interosseus-adductor Compartment.**—The compartments of the palm are separated from the dorsal portion of the hand by a septum which is made up principally of the Interossei and the Adductores pollicis, and which may be called accordingly, the interosseus-adductor compartment. It is enclosed by two fascial membranes which are continuous with each other around its medial and lateral borders. The membrane on the dorsal surface, called the **dorsal interosseous fascia**, covers and is adherent to the dorsal surfaces of the second to fifth metacarpal bones and the intervening dorsal Interossei. The palmar surface is covered by the **volar interosseous fascia** in the ulnar half, and by the fascia of the Adductores in the radial half. The compartment is closed by the attachment of these membranes at the origins of the muscles, proximally, and at their insertions, distally. It contains the second, third, fourth, and fifth metacarpal bones, all the Interossei, the Adductores transversus and obliquus, the deep volar arch, and the deep branch of the ulnar nerve. The Adductores and the Interossei have been placed in the same rather than in separate compartments because the entire muscle mass lies deep to the palmar compartments (Fig. 408) and is separated from it by the major fascial cleft of the palm. A fascial cleft may separate the two Adductores from each other and from the first dorsal Interosseus, and these clefts may communicate with the thenar cleft or with the tissue spaces of the web between the thumb and index finger.

The **dorsal tendon compartment** is enclosed, superficially, by the investing fascia, and deeply, by a membrane of fascia covering the deep surface of the extensor tendon mass called the **dorsal subaponeurotic fascia**. The compartment is closed at the sides of the hand by the fusion of the two membranes into a single sheet where both are attached to the dorsum of the second and fifth metacarpal bones. It is closed distally by the fusion of the two layers at the webs between the fingers and their attachment to the joint capsules and tendinous expansions of the digits. It is closed proximally by the fusion with the tendon sheaths which pass under the dorsal carpal ligament. The compartment is separated from the superficial fascia by the subcutaneous fascial cleft, and from the dorsal interosseus fascia by the subaponeurotic fascial cleft.

Fascial Clefts (*fascial spaces*) **of the Palm** (Fig. 408).—The term fascial cleft is preferable to fascial space because the latter quite frequently leads to ambiguity and the former agrees with the description in other parts of this book (see pages 347-351). Fascial clefts are planes of cleavage between fascial membranes and should not be confused with fascial compartments which are enclosures formed by fascial membranes and contain muscles, bones, or other structures. Fascial clefts may occur inside of compartments or may lie between compartments.

The major fascial cleft of the palm lies between the fascia covering the deep surface of the long flexor tendon mass and the fascia covering the Adductores and the Interossei of the medial portion of the hand; that is, it lies between the central palmar compartment and the interosseus adductor compartment. Delicate membranous septa of variable number and extent attach to the metacarpal bones distally, and extend toward the wrist, producing more or less complete subdivisions of the cleft. The septum which is attached to the middle metacarpal bone is more constant and better developed than the rest and is commonly described as subdividing the cleft into two parts, the middle palmar cleft and the thenar cleft (Kanavel, 1942).

The **middle palmar cleft** (*middle palmar space*) is triangular in shape and separates the deep surface of the long flexor tendons from the Interossei in the central part of the palm. It lies between the volar interosseous fascia and the fascia covering the deep surface of the long flexor tendon compartment. The cleft may be closed at the wrist by adhesion between the fascial membranes at the transverse carpal ligament, or it may be continued proximally, deep to the ulnar bursa, and communicate with the anterior interosseous cleft of the forearm. It is closed, medially, by the attachment of the hypothenar septum to the fifth metacarpal bone, and laterally, from the thenar cleft by a transparent fibrous membrane which is attached along the middle metacarpal bone. This membrane, instead of attaching to the flexor tendon mass directly over the middle metacarpal, takes an oblique course toward the region of the second metacarpal, causing the middle palmar cleft to extend into the radial portion of the palm so that it overlaps the thenar cleft to some extent. The membrane between the middle palmar and the thenar cleft may be incomplete proximally, allowing the two clefts to communicate with each other. Closely associated with the middle palmar cleft, acting as diverticula, are the clefts surrounding the third, fourth, and fifth Lumbricales, called the **lumbrical canals.**

The **thenar cleft** (*thenar space*) (Fig. 408) overlies the volar surface of the Adductores pollicis. It is bounded, medially, by the membrane which is attached to the middle metacarpal bone and which separates it from the middle palmar cleft; laterally, by the thenar septum and the first metacarpal bone; proximally, by the transverse carpal ligament, and distally, by the extent of the Adductor transversus. The thenar cleft is commonly continuous with the cleft between the two Adductores and between the latter and the first dorsal Interosseus. It may communicate with the middle palmar cleft, proximally, and it usually has a diverticulum extending along the first Lumbricalis, the lumbrical canal.

The **lumbrical canals** are the tubular fascial clefts which separate the Lumbricales from the denser connective tissue which surrounds them. These clefts are closely associated with, or act as diverticula for, the major fascial clefts of the palm in the following way: the cleft of the first lumbrical with the thenar cleft, that of the second, third, and fourth with the middle palmar cleft.

Smaller independent fascial clefts are found between the individual muscles of the thenar and hypothenar groups. A cleft of variable extent may be found superficial to the palmar aponeurosis, lying between it and the superficial fascia in the center of the palm.

The **dorsal subcutaneous cleft** (*dorsal subcutaneous fascial space*) (Fig. 408) separates the superficial fascia from the deep fascia. It extends distally out into the fingers and proximally into the forearm. It is closed at the borders of the hand by the attachment of the superficial fascia to the deep fascia of the palm, and it has no communication with the dorsal subaponeurotic cleft.

The **dorsal subaponeurotic fascial cleft** (*dorsal subaponeurotic fascial space*) (Fig. 408) separates the dorsal subaponeurotic fascia from the dorsal interosseus fascia. It is closed at the sides of the hand by the fusion of the two membranes near their attachment to the second and the fifth metacarpal bones. It is closed distally by the fusion of the two layers and their union with the joint capsules and extensor expansions of the digits. Proximally, it is obliterated by the attachment of the tendon sheaths to the bones and ligaments of the wrist. This cleft does not communicate with the dorsal subcutaneous cleft, nor with the palmar clefts, and it does not pass from the hand into the forearm.

Variations.—The flexor tendons to the index finger and the first Lumbricalis may be enclosed in a separate compartment. In this case, there are two membranes attached to the middle metacarpal bone. One has the usual position, extending obliquely toward the radial side of the hand and overlying the thenar cleft; the other extends directly toward the deep surface of the flexor tendon mass and attaches along the flexors to the middle finger. The index compartment is bounded by these two membranes and the palmar aponeurosis. The portion of the middle palmar cleft which usually lies superficial to the thenar cleft is within the index compartment, and the lumbrical canal for this finger leads into this cleft rather than the thenar cleft.

Surgical Considerations.—An understanding of the relationship of the fascial clefts to each other and to the tendon sheaths may best be reached by a brief review of the probable spread of an infective process, independent of the participation of the bloodvessels or lymphatics.

A subcutaneous abscess on the dorsum of the hand or in the webs could be expected to point at the surface locally because of the softness of the tissues; in the palm, it might reach the surface or spread to the webs, but would not be likely to penetrate the palmar aponeurosis. An abscess of the index finger, after penetrating to the deeper tissues might progress proximally until it arrived in the lumbrical canal, and through this path, reach the thenar cleft. From the other three fingers, it might reach the middle palmar cleft by a similar path. It might progress from either of these deep palmar clefts to the other, or, if the swelling and edema would permit, it might reach the cleft of the forearm. An infection involving a digital flexor tendon sheath, if it occurred in the little finger or the thumb, would quickly follow the sheath into the ulnar or radial bursæ, and after a period of time, the latter could rupture into the volar fascial cleft of the forearm. If the infection were in the index finger, the tendon sheath might be expected to rupture into the thenar cleft; if in the middle or fourth finger, it would rupture into the middle palmar cleft. An infection of the dorsal subcutaneous cleft could be expected to reach the surface locally. An infection in the dorsal subaponeurotic cleft would be expected to spread throughout the entire cleft, and then eventually rupture into the webs or at the sides of the hand.

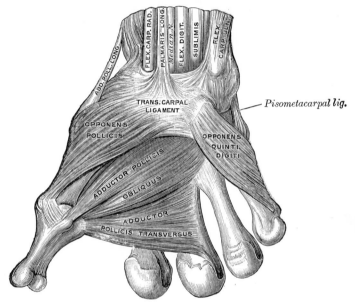

FIG. 409.—The muscles of the thumb.

1. The Thenar Muscles (Figs. 409, 410).

Abductor pollicis brevis.
Opponens pollicis.
Flexor pollicis brevis.
Adductor pollicis (obliquus).
Adductor pollicis (transversus).

The **Abductor pollicis brevis** (*Abductor pollicis*) is a thin, flat muscle, placed most superficially in the thenar region. It *arises* from the transverse carpal ligament, the tuberosity of the navicular, and the ridge of the greater multangular, frequently by two distinct slips. Running lateralward and distalward, it is *inserted* by a thin, flat tendon into the radial side of the base of the first phalanx of the thumb and the capsule of the metacarpophalangeal articulation.

Action.—Abducts the thumb, that is, draws it away in a plane at right angles to that of the palm of the hand.

Nerve.—A branch of the median nerve, containing fibers from the sixth and seventh cervical nerves.

The **Opponens pollicis** is a small, triangular muscle, placed beneath the preceding. It *arises* from the ridge on the greater multangular and from the transverse carpal ligament, passes distalward and lateralward, and is *inserted* into the whole length of the metacarpal bone of the thumb on its radial side.

Action.—Abducts, flexes, and rotates the metacarpal of the thumb, bringing the thumb out in front of the palm to face the fingers.

Nerve.—A branch of the median nerve, containing fibers from the sixth and seventh cervical nerves.

The **Flexor pollicis brevis** consists of two portions, lateral and medial. The **lateral** and more **superficial portion** *arises* from the lower border of the transverse carpal ligament and the lower part of the ridge on the greater multangular bone; it passes along the radial side of the tendon of the Flexor pollicis longus, and,

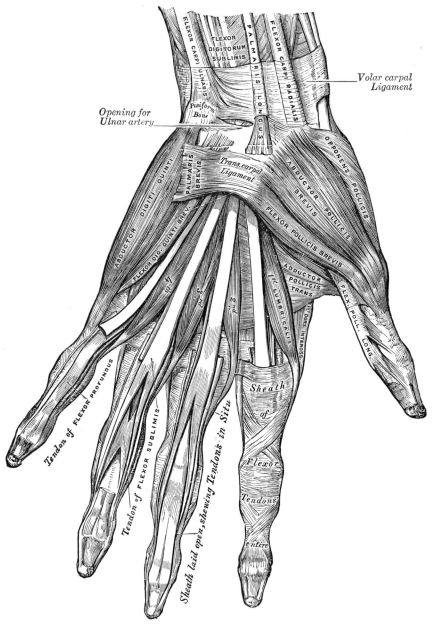

Fig. 410.—The muscles of the left hand. Palmar surface.

becoming tendinous, is *inserted* into the radial side of the base of the first phalanx of the thumb; in its tendon of insertion there is a sesamoid bone. The **medial** and **deeper portion** of the muscle is very small, and *arises* from the ulnar side of the first metacarpal bone between the Adductor pollicis (obliquus) and the lateral head of the first Interosseous dorsalis, and is *inserted* into the ulnar side of the base of the first phalanx with the Adductor pollicis (obliquus). The medial part of the Flexor brevis pollicis is sometimes described as the **first Interosseous volaris.**

Action.—Flexes and adducts the thumb.
Nerve.—A branch of the median nerve, containing fibers from the sixth and seventh cervical nerves.

The **Adductor pollicis (obliquus)** (*Adductor obliquus pollicis*) *arises* by several slips from the capitate bone, the bases of the second and third metacarpals, the intercarpal ligaments, and the sheath of the tendon of the Flexor carpi radialis. From this origin the greater number of fibers pass obliquely distalward and converge to a tendon, which, uniting with the tendons of the medial portion of the Flexor pollicis brevis and the transverse part of the Adductor, is *inserted* into the ulnar side of the base of the first phalanx of the thumb, a sesamoid bone being present in the tendon. A considerable fasciculus, however, passes more obliquely beneath the tendon of the Flexor pollicis longus to join the lateral portion of the Flexor brevis and the Abductor pollicis brevis.

The **Adductor pollicis (transversus)** (*Adductor transversus pollicis*) (Fig. 409) is the most deeply seated of this group of muscles. It is of a triangular form arising by a broad base from the distal two-thirds of the volar surface of the third metacarpal bone; the fibers converge, to be *inserted* with the medial part of the Flexor pollicis brevis and the Adductor pollicis (obliquus) into the ulnar side of the base of the first phalanx of the thumb.

Action.—Adducts, that is, brings the thumb toward the palm.
Nerve.—A branch of the deep palmar branch of the ulnar, containing fibers from the eighth cervical and first thoracic nerves.
Variations.—The Abductor pollicis brevis is often divided into an outer and an inner part; accessory slips from the tendon of the Abductor pollicis longus or Palmaris longus, more rarely from the Extensor carpi radialis longus, from the styloid process or Opponens pollicis or from the skin over the thenar eminence. The deep head of the Flexor pollicis brevis may be absent or enlarged. The two adductors vary in their relative extent and in the closeness of their connection. The Adductor obliquus may receive a slip from the transverse metacarpal ligament.

2. The Hypothenar Muscles (Figs. 409, 410).

Palmaris brevis.
Abductor digiti quinti.

Flexor digiti quinti brevis.
Opponens digiti quinti.

The **Palmaris brevis** is a thin, quadrilateral muscle, placed beneath the integument of the ulnar side of the hand. It *arises* by tendinous fasciculi from the transverse carpal ligament and palmar aponeurosis; the fleshy fibers are *inserted* into the skin on the ulnar border of the palm of the hand.

Action.—Draws the skin at the ulnar side of the palm toward the middle of the palm, increasing the height of the hypothenar eminence, as in clenching the fist. Holds the hypothenar subcutaneous pad in place, as in catching a ball.
Nerve.—A branch of the ulnar nerve, containing fibers from the eighth cervical nerve.

The **Abductor digiti quinti** (*Abductor minimi digiti*) is situated on the ulnar border of the palm of the hand. It *arises* from the pisiform bone and from the tendon of the Flexor carpi ulnaris, and ends in a flat tendon, which divides into two slips; one is *inserted* into the ulnar side of the base of the first phalanx of the little finger; the other into the ulnar border of the aponeurosis of the Extensor digiti quinti proprius.

Action.—Abducts the little finger and flexes its proximal phalanx.
Nerve.—A branch of the ulnar nerve, containing fibers from the eighth cervical and first thoracic nerves.

The **Flexor digiti quinti brevis** (*Flexor brevis minimi digiti*) lies on the same plane as the preceding muscle, on its radial side. It *arises* from the convex surface of the hamulus of the hamate bone, and the volar surface of the transverse carpal ligament, and is *inserted* into the ulnar side of the base of the first phalanx of the little finger. It is separated from the Abductor, at its origin, by the deep branches of the ulnar artery and nerve. This muscle is sometimes wanting; the Abductor is then, usually, of large size.

Action.—Flexes the little finger.

Nerve.—A branch of the ulnar nerve, containing fibers from the eighth cervical and first thoracic nerves.

The **Opponens digiti quinti** (*Opponens minimi digiti*) (Fig. 409) is of a triangular form, and placed immediately beneath the preceding muscles. It *arises* from the convexity of the hamulus of the hamate bone, and contiguous portion of the transverse carpal ligament; it is inserted into the whole length of the metacarpal bone of the little finger, along its ulnar margin.

Action.—Abducts, flexes, and rotates the fifth metacarpal in bringing the little finger out to face the thumb.

Nerve.—A branch of the ulnar nerve, containing fibers from the eighth cervical and first thoracic nerves.

Variations.—The Palmaris brevis varies greatly in size. The Abductor digiti quinti may be divided into two or three slips or united with the Flexor digiti quinti brevis. Accessory head from the tendon of the Flexor carpi ulnaris, the transverse carpal ligament, the fascia of the forearm or the tendon of the Palmaris longus. A portion of the muscle may insert into the metacarpal, or separate slips the *Pisimetacarpus*, *Pisiuncinatus* or the *Pisiannularis* muscle may exist.

3. The Intermediate Muscles.

Lumbricales.   Interossei.

The **Lumbricales** (Fig. 410) are four small fleshy fasciculi, associated with the tendons of the Flexor digitorum profundus. The first and second *arise* from the radial sides and volar surfaces of the tendons of the index and middle fingers respectively; the third, from the contiguous sides of the tendons of the middle and ring fingers; and the fourth, from the contiguous sides of the tendons of the ring and little fingers. Each passes to the radial side of the corresponding finger, and opposite the metacarpophalangeal articulation is *inserted* into the tendinous expansion of the Extensor digitorum communis covering the dorsal aspect of the finger.

Action.—Flex the metacarpophalangeal joints and extend the two distal phalanges.

Nerves.—The first and second Lumbricales by branches of the third and fourth digital branches of the median nerve, containing fibers from the sixth and seventh cervical nerves. The third and fourth by branches of the deep palmar branch of the ulnar, containing fibers from the eighth cervical nerve. The third Lumbrical may receive twigs from both nerves or all its fibers from the median nerve.

Variations.—The Lumbricales vary in number from two to five or six and there is considerable variation in insertions.

The **Interossei** (Figs. 411, 412) are so named from occupying the intervals between the metacarpal bones, and are divided into two sets, a dorsal and a volar.

The **Interossei dorsales** (*Dorsal interossei*) are *four* in number, and occupy the intervals between the metacarpal bones. They are bipenniform muscles, each *arising* by two heads from the adjacent sides of the metacarpal bones, but more extensively from the metacarpal bone of the finger into which the muscle is inserted. They are inserted into the bases of the first phalanges and into the aponeuroses of the tendons of the Extensor digitorum communis. Between the double origin of each of these muscles is a narrow triangular interval; through the first of these the radial artery passes; through each of the other three a perforating branch from the deep volar arch is transmitted.

The **first** or **Abductor indicis** is larger than the others. It is flat, triangular in form, and *arises* by two heads, separated by a fibrous arch for the passage of the radial artery from the dorsum to the palm of the hand. The lateral head *arises* from the proximal half of the ulnar border of the first metacarpal bone; the medial head, from almost the entire length of the radial border of the second metacarpal bone; the tendon is inserted into the radial side of the index finger. The **second** and **third** are inserted into the middle finger, the former into its radial, the latter into its ulnar side. The **fourth** is inserted into the ulnar side of the ring finger.

Action.—Abduct the fingers from an imaginary line drawn through the axis of the middle finger; flex the metacarpophalangeal joint and extend the two distal phalanges.

Nerves.—Branches from the deep palmar branch of the ulnar, containing fibers from the eighth cervical and first thoracic nerves.

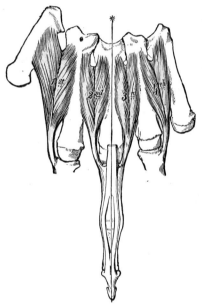
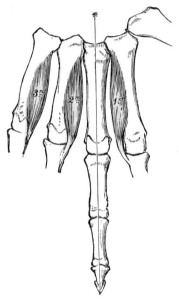

Fig. 411.—The Interossei dorsales of left hand.   Fig. 412.—The Interossei volares of left hand.

The **Interossei volares** (*Palmar interossei*), three in number, are smaller than the Interossei dorsales, and placed upon the volar surfaces of the metacarpal bones, rather than between them. Each *arises* from the entire length of the metacarpal bone of one finger, and is *inserted* into the side of the base of the first phalanx and aponeurotic expansion of the Extensor communis tendon to the same finger.

The **first** *arises* from the ulnar side of the second metacarpal bone, and is *inserted* into the same side of the first phalanx of the index finger. The **second** *arises* from the radial side of the fourth metacarpal bone, and is *inserted* into the same side of the ring finger. The **third** *arises* from the radial side of the fifth metacarpal bone, and is *inserted* into the same side of the little finger. From this account it may be seen that each finger is provided with two Interossei, with the exception of the little finger, in which the Abductor takes the place of one of the pair.

As already mentioned (p. 461), the medial head of the Flexor pollicis brevis is sometimes described as the **Interosseus volaris primus**.

Action.—Adduct the fingers toward an imaginary line through the axis of the middle finger; flex the metacarpophalangeal joint and extend the two distal phalanges.

Nerves.—Branches from the deep palmar branch of the ulnar, containing fibers from the eighth cervical and first thoracic nerves.

Group Actions.—Flexion of the fingers in grasping an object is performed by the Flexores digitorum sublimis and profundus. The wrist extensors contract synergetically to prevent flexion of the wrist. The characteristic action of the profundus, to flex the terminal phalanx, can be carried out independently as a freak by some individuals. The action of both muscles on the two terminal phalanges can be performed independently of the proximal phalanx by calling into play the synergetic action of the Extensor digitorum communis on the proximal phalanx. Flexion of the proximal phalanx at the same time as extension of the two distal joints is performed by the Interossei dorsales and volares, and the Lumbricales.

Extension of the proximal phalanges is performed by the Extensor digitorum communis, Extensor indicis proprius, and Extensor digiti quinti proprius. The wrist flexors contract synergetically to prevent extension at the wrist. The long extensors have a weak action on the two terminal joints, and must be assisted in this action by the Lumbricales and the Interossei.

Abduction of the fingers is performed by the Interossei dorsales and the Abductor digiti quinti, considering the axis of the middle finger as the center of the hand. Full abduction can be carried out only if the fingers are extended, because of restrictions in the joints. Adduction of the fingers is performed by the Interossei volares, and can be performed with the fingers either flexed or extended.

The thumb is so placed that its plane of flexion and extension is at right angles to that of the fingers. Flexion and extension of the thumb, therefore, are in the same plane as abduction and adduction of the fingers; abduction and adduction of the thumb are in the same plane as flexion and extension of the fingers. Flexion of the distal phalanx is performed by the Flexor pollicis longus; of the proximal phalanx alone by the Flexor pollicis brevis. Extension of the distal phalanx is performed by the Extensor pollicis longus, the proximal phalanx by the Extensor pollicis brevis. Abduction of the thumb is by the Abductores pollicis longus and brevis; adduction by the Adductor pollicis. It is seldom that extension or abduction are performed independently of each other, most normal activity being a mixture of the two movements. When the thumb is used in grasping, first, as a preliminary, it is abducted by the Abductores, and rotated by the Opponens so that its palmar surface faces the palm of the hand, and then finally, the actual grasping is performed largely by the Flexor pollicis longus.

THE MUSCLES AND FASCIÆ OF THE LOWER EXTREMITY.

The muscles of the lower extremity are subdivided into groups corresponding with the different regions of the limb.

I. Muscles of the Iliac Region.　　　III. Muscles of the Leg.
II. Muscles of the Thigh.　　　　　IV. Muscles of the Foot.

THE MUSCLES AND FASCIÆ OF THE ILIAC REGION (Fig. 413).

Psoas major.　　　　　　Psoas minor.　　　　　Iliacus.

The fascia covering the intra-abdominal surface of the Iliacus and Psoas is part of the endo-abdominal or internal investing layer of deep fascia, but, as it follows these muscles under the inguinal ligament out into the thigh, it becomes continuous with the fascia lata which is a portion of the external investing fascia. In this way, it forms an important direct continuity between the internal and the external investing layers of deep fascia. The endo-abdominal portion of this fascia is covered internally by subserous fascia.

Iliac Fascia (*fascia iliaca*).—The endo-abdominal portion of the iliac fascia is attached at its cephalic limit to the entire length of the inner lip of the crest of the ilium, along with the muscle. Above that, it is continuous with the definitive transversalis fascia except near the vertebral column where it is continuous with the quadratus lumborum fascia. It is continuous medially, with the psoas fascia, and, after attaching to the arcuate line of the ilium, it is continued down into the lesser pelvis as the obturator internus fascia. At the inguinal ligament, it meets and fuses with the transversalis fascia of the lateral portion of the anterior abdominal wall to form a single sheet which follows the surface of the Iliacus under the ligament out into the thigh. It is securely attached to the ligament, as it passes under it, and at this point the origins of the Obliquus internus and Transversus abdominis are attached to the iliac fascia as well as to the inguinal ligament. In the thigh, it becomes continuous with the part of the fascia lata over the Sartorius, laterally, and with the iliopectineal fascia, medially.

Psoas Fascia.—The cephalic extremity of the psoas fascia is intimately blended with the medial lumbocostal arch of the Diaphragm, which stretches from the bodies to the transverse processes of the first or second lumbar vertebræ. It is attached, medially, by a series of arched processes to the intervertebral fibrocartilages and prominent margins of the vertebræ, and to the upper part of the sacrum. The intervals left between these arched processes and the constricted bodies of the vertebræ transmit the lumbar arteries and veins, and the filaments of the sympathetic trunk. It is continuous laterally with the quadratus lumborum and iliac fasciæ. At the inguinal ligament and in the thigh, the psoas and iliac fasciæ combine to make up part of a complex called the iliopectineal fascia.

Iliopectinal Fascia (*fascia iliopectinea*).—The iliopectineal fascia is made up of three interconnected portions: (*a*) the fascia covering the femoral portions of the Iliacus and Psoas; (*b*) the fascia over the proximal portion of the Pectineus, and (*c*) a thickened band which dips down between the Psoas and the femoral vessels as they pass under the inguinal ligament. The fascia as a whole is continuous, under the inguinal ligament, with the endo-abdominal iliac, psoas, and transversalis fasciæ. Parts (*a*) and (*b*) together form a sheet which is the floor of the femoral (Scarpa's) triangle. At the junction of the iliopsoas and pectineal portions of this fascia, there is a firm attachment to the iliopectineal eminence of the ilium and to the pubocapsular ligament of the hip joint. From the attachment to the iliopectineal eminence, the fascia passes outward as a thickened band (*c*, above) between the Psoas and the femoral vessels toward the inguinal ligament to which it becomes attached (Fig. 314). This band divides the interval beneath the inguinal ligament, that is, between the ligament and the pelvic bone, into two parts known as the lacuna musculorum and the lacuna vasorum. The **lacuna musculorum** contains the Iliacus and Psoas, and the femoral nerve. The **lacuna vasorum** contains the femoral artery and vein, and the femoral canal (page 630).

30

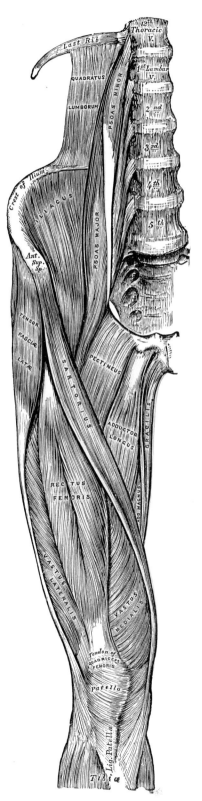

Fig. 413 —Muscles of the iliac and anterior femoral regions.

The **Iliopsoas** is frequently regarded as a single muscle but it is here divided into its two parts, the Psoas major and the Iliacus, for convenience of description.

The **Psoas major** (*Psoas magnus*) (Fig. 413) is a long fusiform muscle placed on the side of the lumbar region of the vertebral column and brim of the lesser pelvis. It *arises* (1) from the anterior surfaces of the bases and lower borders of the transverse processes of all the lumbar vertebræ; (2) from the sides of the bodies and the corresponding intervertebral fibrocartilages of the last thoracic and all the lumbar vertebræ by five slips, each of which is attached to the adjacent upper and lower margins of two vertebræ, and to the intervertebral fibrocartilage; (3) from a series of tendinous arches which extend across the constricted parts of the bodies of the lumbar vertebræ between the previous slips; the lumbar arteries and veins, and filaments from the sympathetic trunk pass beneath these tendinous arches. The muscle proceeds downward across the brim of the lesser pelvis, and diminishing gradually in size, passes beneath the inguinal ligament and in front of the capsule of the hip-joint and ends in a tendon which also receives nearly the whole of the fibers of the Iliacus and is *inserted* into the lesser trochanter of the femur. A large bursa which may communicate with the cavity of the hip-joint, separates the tendon from the pubis and the capsule of the joint.

Action.—Flexes the thigh and rotates it medially; flexes the lumbar vertebral column and bends it laterally.

Nerves.—Branches of the lumbar plexus, containing fibers from the second and third lumbar nerves.

The **Psoas minor** (*Psoas parvus*) is a long slender muscle, placed in front of the Psoas major. It *arises* from the sides of the bodies of the twelfth thoracic and first lumbar vertebræ and from the fibrocartilage between them. It ends in a long flat tendon which is *inserted* into the pectineal line and iliopectineal eminence, and, by its lateral border, into the iliac fascia. This muscle is often absent.

Action.—Flexes the pelvis and lumbar vertebral column.

Nerve.—A branch of the first lumbar nerve.

The **Iliacus** is a flat, triangular muscle, which fills the iliac fossa. It *arises* from the upper two-thirds of this fossa, and from the inner lip of the iliac crest; behind, from the anterior sacroiliac and the iliolumbar ligaments, and base of the sacrum; in front, it reaches as far as the anterior superior and anterior inferior iliac spines, and the notch between them. The fibers converge to be inserted into the lateral side of the tendon of the Psoas major, some of them being prolonged on to the body of the femur for about 2.5 cm. below and in front of the lesser trochanter.

Action.—Flexes the thigh and rotates it medially.

Nerves.—Branches of the femoral nerve, containing fibers from the second and third lumbar nerves.

Variations.—The *Iliacus minor* or *Iliocapsularis*, a small detached part of the Iliacus is frequently present. It arises from the anterior inferior spine of the ilium and is inserted into the lower part of the intertrochanteric line of the femur or into the iliofemoral ligament.

II. THE MUSCLES AND FASCIÆ OF THE THIGH.

Superficial Fascia (*tela subcutanea*).—The superficial fascia forms a prominent layer over the entire thigh. It usually contains a considerable amount of fat, but it varies in thickness in different regions. It is continuous with the superficial fascia of the abdomen, the leg, and, over the gluteal region, with the back. It may be separated into a superficial fatty layer and a deep membranous layer between which are found the superficial vessels and nerves, the superficial inguinal lymph nodes, and the great saphenous vein. In well-nourished individuals, the adipose tissue of the superficial layer is usually divided into two or three subsidiary layers by fibrous membranes which are associated with the emergence of the superficial nerves. The deep or fibrous layer is adherent to the fascia lata a little below the inguinal ligament and along the upper medial portion of the thigh. It is attached to the margin of the fossa ovalis (saphenous opening), and fills the opening itself with an irregular layer of spongy tissue, called the **fascia cribrosa** (Fig. 572) because it is pierced by numerous openings for the passage of the saphenous vein and other blood and lymphatic vessels.

A large subcutaneous bursa is found in the superficial fascia over the patella.

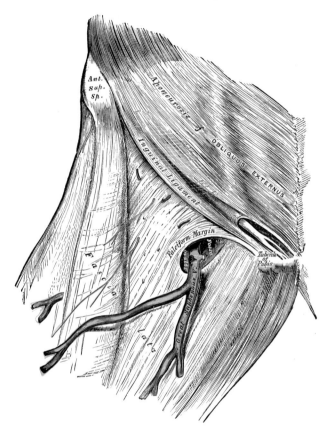

Fig. 414.—The fossa ovalis.

Fascia Lata (Fig. 414).—The external investing fascia of the thigh is named fascia lata from its broad extent. Its thick, lateral portion is commonly taken to be typical of its texture, but it is thin in some areas where it has not been reinforced by fibrous contributions from the tendons. Proximally, it is continuous with the external abdominal and lumbodorsal fasciæ after being attached to the pelvic bone and inguinal ligament; distally it is continuous with the fascia of the leg. The *medial portion* lies over the Adductor group of muscles and is thin, grey, and not aponeurotic. It is attached to the ischial tuberosity and ischiopubic ramus, and beyond this is continuous with the external perineal fascia. At the knee it is thick and aponeurotic, having been strengthened by fibers from the tendon of the Sartorius. The *anterior portion* is attached to the pubic tubercle, inguinal ligament, and anterior superior iliac spine. Just distal to the lateral half of the inguinal ligament, it is a single sheet formed by the fusion of three abdominal fasciæ. Of these, the most superficial is the external fascia over the aponeurosis of the Obliquus externus (fascia innominata) which passes superficial to the inguinal ligament; the middle one is the transversalis fascia of the anterior abdominal wall which passes under the inguinal ligament; the internal one also passes under the inguinal ligament and is the continuation of the iliac fascia. Distal to the medial half of the inguinal ligament, the middle and internal layers just mentioned fail to join the fascia lata at the ligament and continue into the thigh as the anterior and posterior portions of the femoral sheath. The fascia lata in this medial region over the femoral vessels is thickened and laminated and has an opening through it, called the fossa ovalis (see below), for the passage of the great saphenous vein. The outer lamina is attached to the pubic tubercle along with the inguinal ligament; it has a free falciform margin which crosses the proximal end of the great saphenous vein and spirals outward, downward, and behind the vein to join the deep lamina medial to the vein. The two laminæ are separated by a pad of adipose tissue. The anterior portion of the fascia lata is thicker than the medial, but is truly aponeurotic only near the knee where it is reinforced by fibers from the tendons of the Vasti. It is separated from the underlying Sartorius and Quadriceps by a fascial space, except near the knee. The *lateral portion* is a thick strong aponeurosis, containing the tendinous fibers of insertion of the Glutæus maximus and the Tensor fasciæ latæ. It is attached proximally to the crest of the ilium and the back of the sacrum. Between the iliac crest and the superior border of the Glutæus maximus, it is thickened by vertical tendinous bundles and is known as the **gluteal aponeurosis** (Fig. 417) which is used by the Glutæus medius for part of its origin. At the border of the maximus it splits to enclose the muscle; the external layer of this **gluteal fascia** is thin, is closely bound to the superficial fascia and the muscle, and sends septa down between large bundles of the muscle. In the region over the great trochanter, the muscular fasciculi end in a broad tendon which is imbedded in the fascia lata and is called the **iliotibial band** (*tractus iliotibialis*). Below the anterior part of the iliac crest, the fascia splits to enclose the Tensor fasciæ latæ which is inserted into the iliotibial band below the maximus. The iliotibial band is separated from the underlying Vastus lateralis by a distinct fascial cleft. It is inserted into the tibia and is blended with fibrous expansions from the Vastus lateralis and Biceps femoris. The *posterior portion* of the fascia lata is formed proximally by the union of the two layers of fascia enclosing the Glutæus maximus at its inferior border. It covers the hamstring muscles and the popliteal fossa.

Two strong intermuscular septa (Fig. 415) connect the deep surface of the fascia lata with the linea aspera of the femur. The **lateral intermuscular septum** is the stronger; it separates the Vastus lateralis from the Biceps femoris and is used by both muscles for the attachment of their fibers. It extends from the insertion of the Glutæus maximus to the lateral condyle. The **medial intermuscular septum** lies between the Vastus medialis and the Adductores and Pectineus. Its outer portion near the fascia lata, splits to enclose the Sartorius and contributes to the formation of the adductor canal (Hunter's canal) about the femoral vessels.

The **Fossa Ovalis** (*saphenous opening*) (Fig. 414) is an oval aperture in the fascia lata in the proximal part of the thigh, a little below the medial end of the inguinal ligament. The great saphenous vein passes through it just before it joins the femoral vein. The fascia lata in this part of the thigh is thickened by lamination into two leaves separated by fat. The superficial leaf is attached to the inguinal ligament and pubic tubercle. It ends abruptly in a free border, the **falciform margin of the fossa**, which forms a spiral of one turn beginning at the pubic tubercle, coursing at first in a lateral direction superficial to the vein, then down along the vein and back medially under the vein. Medial to the vein the superficial leaf merges with the deep leaf. The proximal and lateral part of the falciform margin is called the **superior cornu**, the medial and distal part the **inferior cornu**. The deep leaf is formed by the pectineal, iliopectineal, and iliac fasciæ. The fossa ovalis is filled in and covered over by a thickened pad derived from the deep layer of superficial fascia, called the fascia cribrosa.

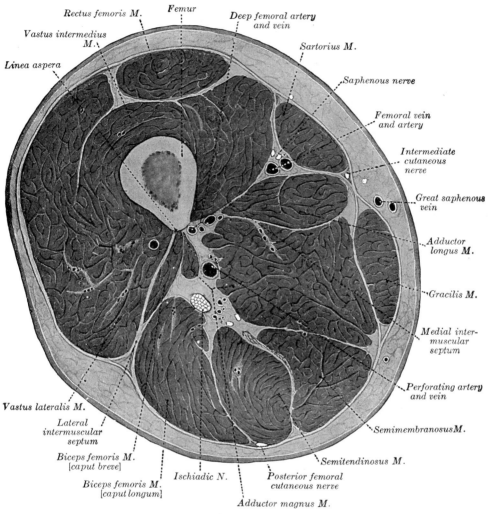

Fig. 415.—Cross-section through the middle of the thigh. (Eycleshymer and Schoemaker).

1. The Anterior Femoral Muscles (Fig. 413).

Sartorius.

Quadriceps femoris.
{ Rectus femoris.
Vastus lateralis.
Vastus medialis.
Vastus intermedius.

Articularis genu.

The **Sartorius,** the longest muscle in the body, is narrow and ribbon-like; it *arises* by tendinous fibers from the anterior superior iliac spine and the upper half of the notch below it. It passes obliquely across the upper and anterior part of the thigh, from the lateral to the medial side of the limb, then descends vertically, as far as the medial side of the knee, passing behind the medial condyle of the femur. It ends in a tendon which curves obliquely forward and expands into a broad aponeurosis, which is *inserted*, in front of the Gracilis and Semitendinosus, into the upper part of the medial surface of the body of the tibia, nearly as far forward as the anterior crest. The upper part of the aponeurosis is curved backward over the upper edge of the tendon of the Gracilis so as to be inserted behind it. An offset, from its upper margin, blends with the capsule of the knee-joint, and another from its lower border, with the fascia on the medial side of the leg.

Action.—Flexes the thigh and rotates it laterally. Flexes the leg and, after it is flexed, rotates it slightly medially.

Nerves.—Branches, usually two in number, from the femoral nerve containing fibers from the second and third lumbar nerves. The first branch is distributed to the proximal portion of the muscle and arises in common with the intermediate anterior cutaneous nerve; the second branch is distributed to the distal portion.

Variations.—Slips of origin from the outer end of the inguinal ligament, the notch of the ilium the ilio-pectineal line or the pubis occur. The muscle may be split into two parts, and one part may be inserted into the fascia lata, the femur, the ligament of the patella or the tendon of the Semitendinosus. The tendon of insertion may end in the fascia lata, the capsule of the knee-joint, or the fascia of the leg. The muscle may be absent.

The **Quadriceps femoris** (*Quadriceps extensor*) includes the four remaining muscles on the front of the thigh. It is the great extensor muscle of the leg, forming a large fleshy mass which covers the front and sides of the femur. It is subdivided into separate portions, which have received distinctive names. One occupying the middle of the thigh, and connected above with the ilium, is called from its straight course the **Rectus femoris.** The other three lie in immediate connection with the body of the femur, which they cover from the trochanters to the condyles. The portion on the lateral side of the femur is termed the **Vastus lateralis**; that covering the medial side, the **Vastus medialis**; and that in front, the **Vastus intermedius.**

The **Rectus femoris** is situated in the middle of the front of the thigh; it is fusiform in shape, and its superficial fibers are arranged in a bipenniform manner, the deep fibers running straight down to the deep aponeurosis. It *arises* by two tendons: one, the anterior or straight, from the anterior inferior iliac spine; the other, the posterior or reflected, from a groove above the brim of the acetabulum. The two unite at an acute angle, and spread into an aponeurosis which is prolonged downward on the anterior surface of the muscle, and from this the muscular fibers arise. The muscle ends in a broad and thick aponeurosis which occupies the lower two-thirds of its posterior surface, and, gradually becoming narrowed into a flattened tendon, is *inserted* into the base of the patella.

The **Vastus lateralis** (*Vastus externus*) is the largest part of the Quadriceps femoris. It *arises* by a broad aponeurosis, which is attached to the upper part of the intertrochanteric line, to the anterior and inferior borders of the greater trochanter, to the lateral lip of the gluteal tuberosity, and to the upper half of the lateral lip of the linea aspera; this aponeurosis covers the upper three-fourths of the muscle, and from its deep surface many fibers take origin. A few additional fibers arise from the tendon of the Glutæus maximus, and from the lateral intermuscular septum between the Vastus lateralis and short head of the Biceps femoris. The fibers form a large fleshy mass, which is attached to a strong aponeurosis, placed on the deep surface of the lower part of the muscle; this aponeurosis becomes contracted and thickened into a flat tendon inserted into the lateral border of the patella, blending with the Quadriceps femoris tendon, and giving an expansion to the capsule of the knee-joint.

The Vastus medialis and Vastus intermedius appear to be inseparably united, but when the Rectus femoris has been reflected a narrow interval will be observed extending upward from the medial border of the patella between the two muscles, and the separation may be continued as far as the lower part of the intertrochanteric line, where, however, the two muscles are frequently continuous.

The **Vastus medialis** (*Vastus internus*) *arises* from the lower half of the inter-trochanteric line, the medial lip of the linea aspera, the upper part of the medial supracondylar line, the tendons of the Adductor longus and the Adductor magnus and the medial intermuscular septum. Its fibers are directed downward and forward, and are chiefly attached to an aponeurosis which lies on the deep surface of the muscle and is *inserted* into the medial border of the patella and the Quadriceps femoris tendon, an expansion being sent to the capsule of the knee-joint.

The **Vastus intermedius** (*Crureus*) *arises* from the front and lateral surfaces of the body of the femur in its upper two-thirds and from the lower part of the lateral intermuscular septum. Its fibers end in a superficial aponeurosis, which forms the deep part of the Quadriceps femoris tendon.

The **tendons** of the different portions of the Quadriceps unite at the lower part of the thigh, so as to form a single strong tendon, which is inserted into the ba:e of the patella, some few fibers passing over it to blend with the ligmentatum patellæ. More properly, the patella may be regarded as a sesamoid bone, developed in the tendon of the Quadriceps; and the ligamentum patellæ, which is continued from the apex of the patella to the tuberosity of the tibia, as the proper tendon of insertion of the muscle, the medial and lateral patellar retinacula (see p. 318) being expansions from its borders. A bursa, which usually communicates with the cavity of the knee-joint, is situated between the femur and the portion of the Quadriceps tendon above the patella; another is interposed between the tendon and the upper part of the front of the tibia; and a third, the **prepatellar bursa,** is placed over the patella itself.

Action.—The entire Quadriceps extends the leg. The Rectus femoris also flexes the thigh.

Nerves.—Branches of the femoral nerve containing fibers from the second, third, and fourth lumbar nerves.

The **Articularis genu** (*Subcrureus*) is a small muscle, usually distinct from the Vastus intermedius, but occasionally blended with it; it *arises* from the anterior surface of the lower part of the body of the femur, and is inserted into the upper part of the synovial membrane of the knee-joint. It sometimes consists of several separate muscular bundles.

Action.—Draws the articular capsule upward.

Nerve.—A branch of the nerve to the Vastus intermedius.

2. The Medial Femoral Muscles.

Gracilis. Adductor longus. Adductor magnus.
Pectineus. Adductor brevis.

The **Gracilis** (Fig. 413) is the most superficial muscle on the medial side of the thigh. It is thin and flattened, broad above, narrow and tapering below. It *arises* by a thin aponeurosis from the anterior margins of the lower half of the symphysis pubis and the upper half of the pubic arch. The fibers run vertically downward, and end in a rounded tendon, which passes behind the medial condyle of the femur, curves around the medial condyle of the tibia, where it becomes flattened, and is *inserted* into the upper part of the medial surface of the body of the tibia, below the condyle. A few of the fibers of the lower part of the tendon are prolonged into the deep fascia of the leg. At its insertion the tendon is situated immediately above that of the Semitendinosus, and its upper edge is overlapped by the tendon of the Sartorius, with which it is in part blended. It is separated from the tibial collateral ligament of the knee-joint, by a bursa common to it and the tendon of the Semitendinosus.

Action.—Adducts the thigh. Flexes the leg, and after it is flexed, assists in its medial rotation.

Nerve.—A branch of the anterior division of the obturator nerve containing fibers from the third and fourth lumbar nerves.

The **Pectineus** (Fig. 413) is a flat, quadrangular muscle, situated at the anterior part of the upper and medial aspect of the thigh. It *arises* from the pectineal line, and to a slight extent from the surface of bone in front of it, between the iliopectineal eminence and tubercle of the pubis, and from the fascia covering the anterior surface of the muscle; the fibers pass downward, backward, and lateralward, to be inserted into a rough line leading from the lesser trochanter to the linea aspera.

Action.—Flexes and adducts the thigh, and rotates it medially.

Nerve.—Usually a branch of the femoral nerve containing fibers from the second, third, and fourth lumbar nerves. When an accessory obturator is present, one of its branches is distributed to the Pectineus. It may receive a branch from the obturator nerve.

Variations.—The Pectineus may consist of two incompletely separated strata; the lateral or dorsal stratum is supplied by a branch of the femoral nerve or the accessory obturator if present; the medial or ventral stratum, when present, is supplied by the obturator nerve. The muscle may be attached to or inserted into the capsule of the hip joint.

The **Adductor longus** (Fig. 416), the most superficial of the three Adductores, is a triangular muscle, lying in the same plane as the Pectineus. It *arises* by a flat, narrow tendon, from the front of the pubis, at the angle of junction of the crest with the symphysis; and soon expands into a broad fleshy belly. This passes downward, backward, and lateralward, and is *inserted*, by an aponeurosis, into the linea aspera, between the Vastus medialis and the Adductor magnus, with both of which it is usually blended.

Action.—Adducts, flexes, and tends to rotate the thigh medially.

Nerve.—A branch of the anterior division of the obturator nerve containing fibers from the third and fourth lumbar nerves.

Variations.—The Adductor longus may be double, may extend to the knee, or be more or less united with the Pectineus.

The **Adductor brevis** (Fig. 416) is situated immediately behind the two preceding muscles. It is somewhat triangular in form, and *arises* by a narrow origin from the outer surface of the inferior ramus of the pubis, between the Gracilis and Obturator externus. Its fibers, passing backward, lateralward, and downward, are *inserted*, by an aponeurosis, into the line leading from the lesser trochanter to the linea aspera and into the upper part of the linea aspera, immediately behind the Pectineus and upper part of the Adductor longus.

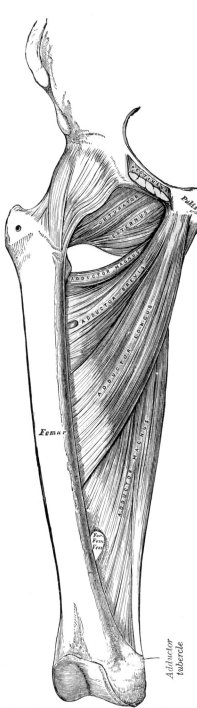

Fig. 416.—Deep muscles of the medial femoral region.

Action.—Adducts, flexes, and tends to rotate the thigh medially.

Nerve.—A branch of the obturator nerve, usually from its anterior division, containing fibers from the third and fourth lumbar nerves.

Variations.—The Adductor brevis may be divided into two or three parts, or it may be united with the Adductor magnus.

The **Adductor magnus** (Fig. 416) is a large triangular muscle, situated on the medial side of the thigh. It *arises* from a small part of the inferior ramus of the pubis, from the inferior ramus of the ischium, and from the outer margin of the inferior part of the tuberosity of the ischium. Those fibers which arise from the ramus of the pubis are short, horizontal in direction, and are inserted into the rough line leading from the greater trochanter to the linea aspera, medial to the Glutæus maximus; those from the ramus of the ischium are directed downward and lateralward with different degrees of obliquity, to be *inserted*, by means of a broad aponeurosis, into the linea aspera and the upper part of its medial prolongation below. The medial portion of the muscle, composed principally of the fibers arising from the tuberosity of the ischium, forms a thick fleshy mass consisting of coarse bundles which descend almost vertically, and end about the lower third of the thigh in a rounded tendon which is inserted into the adductor tubercle on the medial condyle of the femur, and is connected by a fibrous expansion to the line leading upward from the tubercle to the linea aspera. At the *insertion* of the muscle, there is a series of osseoaponeurotic openings, formed by tendinous arches attached to the bone. The upper four openings are small, and give passage to the perforating branches of the profunda femoris artery. The lowest is of large size, and transmits the femoral vessels to the popliteal fossa.

Action.—The entire muscle adducts the thigh powerfully. The upper portion rotates the thigh medially and flexes it; the lower portion extends it powerfully and rotates it laterally.

Nerves.—Branches of the posterior division of the obturator nerve containing fibers from the third and fourth lumbar nerves, and in addition a branch from the sciatic nerve.

Variations.—The Adductor magnus is composed of three superimposed portions, the superior is frequently distinct but the middle and inferior are usually fused. The ischiocondylar or inferior portion is derived from the flexor or hamstring muscles of lower forms and is the portion supplied by the sciatic nerve. The magnus may be fused with the Quadratus femoris, or with either the Adductor longus or brevis.

The **Adductor minimus** is the name given to the superior portion of the Adductor magnus when it forms a distinct muscle.

3. The Muscles of the Gluteal Region (Figs. 417, 418).

Glutæus maximus.
Glutæus medius.
Glutæus minimus.
Tensor fasciæ latæ.
Piriformis.

Obturator internus.
Gemellus superior.
Gemellus inferior.
Quadratus femoris.
Obturator externus.

The **Glutæus maximus**, the most superficial muscle in the gluteal region, is a broad and thick fleshy mass of a quadrilateral shape, and forms the prominence of the nates. Its large size is one of the most characteristic features of the muscular system in man, connected as it is with the power he has of maintaining the trunk in the erect posture. The muscle is remarkably coarse in structure, being made up of fasciculi lying parallel with one another and collected together into large bundles separated by fibrous septa. It *arises* from the posterior gluteal line of the ilium, and the rough portion of bone including the crest, immediately above and behind it; from the posterior surface of the lower part of the sacrum and the side of the coccyx; from the aponeurosis of the Sacrospinalis, the sacrotuberous ligament, and the fascia (gluteal aponeurosis) covering the Glutæus medius.

The fibers are directed obliquely downward and lateralward; those forming the upper and larger portion of the muscle, together with the superficial fibers of the lower portion, end in a thick tendinous lamina, which passes across the greater trochanter, and is *inserted* into the iliotibial band of the fascia lata; the deeper fibers of the lower portion of the muscle are inserted into the gluteal tuberosity between the Vastus lateralis and Adductor magnus.

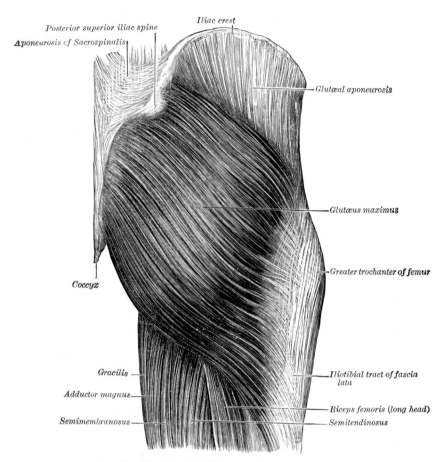

FIG. 417.—The right Glutæus maximus muscle.

Action.—Extends and laterally rotates the thigh. Through the iliotibial band, it braces the knee when the latter is fully extended.

Nerve.—The inferior gluteal nerve, containing fibers from the fifth lumbar and first and second sacral nerves.

Bursæ.—Three **bursæ** are usually found in relation with the deep surface of this muscle. One of these, of large size, and generally multilocular, separates it from the greater trochanter; a second, often wanting, is situated on the tuberosity of the ischium; a third is found between the tendon of the muscle and that of the Vastus lateralis.

The **Glutæus medius** is a broad, thick, radiating muscle, situated on the outer surface of the pelvis. Its posterior third is covered by the Glutæus maximus, its anterior two-thirds by the gluteal aponeurosis, which separates it from the superficial fascia and integument. It *arises* from the outer surface of the ilium between the iliac crest and posterior gluteal line above, and the anterior gluteal line below; it also *arises* from the gluteal aponeurosis covering its outer surface. The fibers converge to a strong flattened tendon, which is *inserted* into the oblique ridge which runs downward and forward on the lateral surface of the greater trochanter. A bursa separates the tendon of the muscle from the surface of the trochanter over which it glides.

Action.—Abducts the thigh and rotates it medially. The anterior portion flexes and rotates medially; the posterior portion extends and rotates laterally.

Nerve.—Branches of the superior gluteal nerve, containing fibers from the fourth and fifth lumbar and first sacral nerves.

Variations.—The posterior border may be more or less closely united to the Piriformis, or some of the fibers end on its tendon.

The **Glutæus minimus** (Fig. 418) the smallest of the three Glutæi, is placed immediately beneath the preceding. It is fan-shaped, *arising* from the outer surface of the ilium, between the anterior and inferior gluteal lines, and behind, from the margin of the greater sciatic notch. The fibers converge to the deep surface of a radiated aponeurosis, and this ends in a tendon which is inserted into an impression on the anterior border of the greater trochanter, and gives an expansion to the capsule of the hip-joint. A bursa is interposed between the tendon and the greater trochanter. Between the Glutæus medius and Glutæus minimus are the deep branches of the superior gluteal vessels and the superior gluteal nerve. The deep surface of the Glutæus minimus is in relation with the reflected tendon of the Rectus femoris and the capsule of the hip-joint.

Action.—Rotates the thigh medially, abducts it, and to some extent, flexes it.

Nerve.—Branch of the superior gluteal nerve, containing fibers from the fourth and fifth lumbar and first sacral nerves.

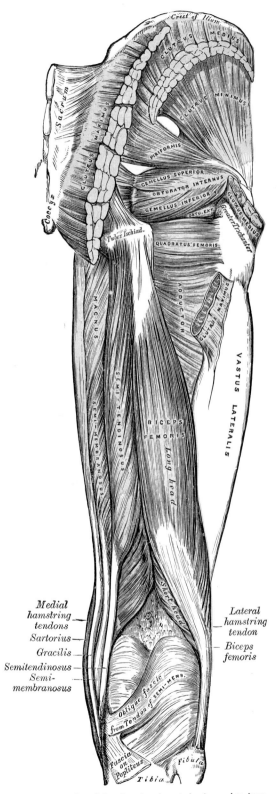

Fig. 418.—Muscles of the gluteal and posterior femoral regions.

Variations.—The muscle may be divided into an anterior and a posterior part, or it may send slips to the Piriformis, the Gemellus superior or the outer part of the origin of the Vastus lateralis.

The **Tensor fasciæ latæ** (*Tensor fasciæ femoris*) (Fig. 413) *arises* from the anterior part of the outer lip of the iliac crest; from the outer surface of the anterior superior iliac spine, and part of the outer border of the notch below it, between the Glutæus medius and Sartorius; and from the deep surface of the fascia lata. It is *inserted* between the two layers of the iliotibial band of the fascia lata about the junction of the middle and upper thirds of the thigh.

Action.—Flexes the thigh and, to some extent, rotates it medially.

Nerve.—A branch of the superior gluteal nerve to the Glutæus minimus, containing fibers from the fourth and fifth lumbar and first sacral nerves.

The **Piriformis** is a flat muscle, pyramidal in shape, lying almost parallel with the posterior margin of the Glutæus medius. It is situated partly within the pelvis against its posterior wall, and partly at the back of the hip-joint. It *arises* from the front of the sacrum by three fleshy digitations, attached to the portions of bone between the first, second, third, and fourth anterior sacral foramina, and to the grooves leading from the foramina: a few fibers also arise from the margin of the greater sciatic foramen, and from the anterior surface of the sacrotuberous ligament. The muscle passes out of the pelvis through the greater sciatic foramen, the upper part of which it fills, and is *inserted* by a rounded tendon into the upper border of the greater trochanter behind, but often partly blended with, the common tendon of the Obturator internus and Gemelli (Fig. 418.)

Action.—Rotates the thigh laterally, abducts and, to some extent, extends it.

Nerve.—One or two branches from the second sacral or the first and second sacral nerves.

Variations.—It is frequently pierced by the common peroneal nerve and thus divided more or less into two parts. It may be united with the Glutæus medius, or send fibers to the Glutæus minimus or receive fibers from the Gemellus superior. It may have only one or two sacral attachments or be inserted into the capsule of the hip-joint. It may be absent.

Obturator Membrane (Fig. 316, page 287).—The obturator membrane is a thin fibrous sheet, which almost completely closes the obturator foramen. Its fibers are arranged in interlacing bundles mainly transverse in direction; the uppermost bundle is attached to the obturator tubercles and completes the obturator canal for the passage of the obturator vessels and nerve. The membrane is attached to the sharp margin of the obturator foramen except at its lower lateral angle, where it is fixed to the pelvic surface of the inferior ramus of the ischium, *i. e.*, within the margin. The two obturator muscles arise partly from the opposite surfaces of this membrane.

The **Obturator internus** is situated partly within the lesser pelvis, and partly at the back of the hip-joint. It *arises* from the inner surface of the antero-lateral wall of the pelvis, where it surrounds the greater part of the obturator foramen, being attached to the inferior rami of the pubis and ischium, and at the side to the inner surface of the hip bone below and behind the pelvic brim, reaching from the upper part of the greater sciatic foramen above and behind to the obturator foramen below and in front. It also arises from the pelvic surface of the obturator membrane except in the posterior part, from the tendinous arch which completes the canal for the passage of the obturator vessels and nerve, and to a slight extent from the obturator fascia, which covers the muscle. The fibers converge rapidly toward the lesser sciatic foramen, and end in four or five tendinous bands, which are found on the deep surface of the muscle; these bands are reflected at a right angle over the grooved surface of the ischium between its spine and tuberosity. This bony surface is covered by smooth cartilage, which is separated from the tendon by a bursa, and presents one or more ridges corresponding with the furrows between the tendinous bands. These bands leave the pelvis through the lesser sciatic foramen and unite into a single flattened tendon, which passes horizontally across the capsule of the hip-joint, and, after receiving the attachments of the Gemelli, is *inserted* into the forepart of the medial surface of the greater trochanter above the trochanteric fossa. A bursa, narrow and elongated in form, is usually found between the tendon and the capsule of the hip-joint; it occasionally communicates with the bursa between the tendon and the ischium.

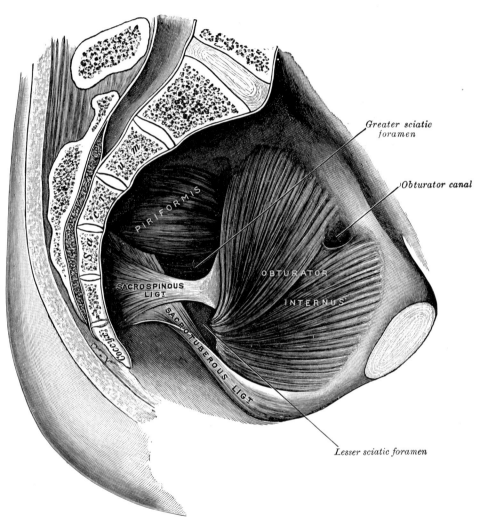

Fig. 419.—The left Obturator internus. Pelvic aspect.

Action.—Rotates the thigh laterally; extends and abducts when the thigh is flexed.
Nerves.—A special nerve from the sacral plexus, containing fibers from the lumbosacral trunk (fifth lumbar) and first and second sacral nerves.

The **Gemelli** are two small muscular fasciculi, accessories to the tendon of the Obturator internus which is received into a groove between them (Fig. 418).

The **Gemellus superior,** the smaller of the two, *arises* from the outer surface of the spine of the ischium, blends with the upper part of the tendon of the Obturator internus, and is *inserted* with it into the medial surface of the greater trochanter.

The **Gemellus inferior** *arises* from the upper part of the tuberosity of the ischium, immediately below the groove for the Obturator internus tendon. It blends with the lower part of the tendon of the Obturator internus, and is *inserted* with it into the medial surface of the greater trochanter.

Action.—Rotate the thigh laterally.

Nerves.—A branch of the nerve to the Obturator internus supplies the superior; a branch of the nerve to the Quadratus femoris supplies the inferior.

Variations.—The Gemelli vary in size; the superior is smaller and is more frequently absent. The inferior is more frequently bound intimately to the Obturator internus. The superior may be fused with the Piriformis or Glutæus minimus, the inferior with the Quadratus femoris.

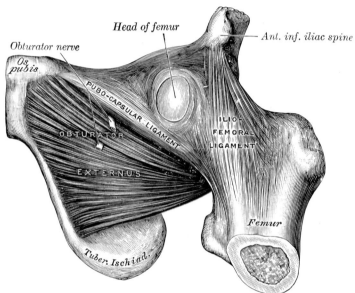

Fig. 420.—The Obturator externus.

The **Quadratus femoris** (Fig. 418) is a flat, quadrilateral muscle; between the Gemellus inferior and the upper margin of the Adductor magnus; it is separated from the latter by the terminal branches of the medial femoral circumflex vessels. It *arises* from the upper part of the external border of the tuberosity of the ischium, and is *inserted* into the upper part of the linea quadrata—that is, the line which extends vertically downward from the intertrochanteric crest. A bursa is often found between the front of this muscle and the lesser trochaner.

Action.—Rotates the thigh laterally.

Nerve.—A special branch from the sacral plexus, containing fibers from the lumbosacral trunk (fourth and fifth lumbar) and first sacral nerves.

Variations.—Absence of the Quadratus femoris has been reported in 1 or 2 per cent, but this may be apparent only, because it is fused either with the Gemellus inferior or the Adductor magnus. It may be double at its insertion, the posterior part having the usual attachment to the femur, the anterior part attaching to the intertrochanteric crest.

The **Obturator externus** (Fig. 420) is a flat, triangular muscle, which covers the outer surface of the anterior wall of the pelvis. It *arises* from the margin of bone immediately around the medial side of the obturator foramen, viz., from the rami of the pubis, and the inferior ramus of the ischium; it also arises from the medial two-thirds of the outer surface of the obturator membrane, and from the tendinous arch which completes the canal for the passage of the obturator vessels and nerves. The fibers springing from the pubic arch extend on to the inner surface of the bone, where they obtain a narrow origin between the margin of the foramen and the attachment of the obturator membrane. The fibers converge and pass backward, lateralward, and upward, and end in a tendon which runs across the back of the neck of the femur and lower part of the capsule of the hip-joint and is *inserted* into the trochanteric fossa of the femur. The obturator vessels lie between the muscle and the obturator membrane; the anterior branch of the obturator nerve reaches the thigh by passing in front of the muscle, and the posterior branch by piercing it.

Action.—Rotates the thigh laterally.

Nerve.—A branch of the obturator nerve, containing fibers from the third and fourth lumbar nerves.

Group Action of Muscles About the Hip Joint.—Extension of the thigh is performed by the Glutæus maximus and Adductor magnus, the former is most powerful in a position of lateral rotation, the latter in medial rotation. The Glutæus medius acts synergetically to neutralize the adduction of the magnus and the lateral rotation of the maximus. The hamstring muscles extend the thigh, but are used for this action only if it accompanies flexion of the leg.

Flexion of the thigh is performed by the Iliopsoas, Tensor fasciæ latæ, Pectineus, and Sartorius. The action is initiated by the Tensor, Pectineus, and Sartorius; stronger and final action is by the Iliopsoas; the Adductor longus assists. Positions of medial or lateral rotation have only slight effect. The Rectus femoris flexes, but only if the muscle is acting as an extensor at the knee.

Abduction of the thigh is performed by the Glutæus medius and minimus, the latter especially in a position of medial rotation. Adduction is performed by the Adductores magnus, longus, brevis, and the Gracilis.

Lateral rotation of the thigh is performed by the Obturator externus and internus, Gemelli Piriformis, and Quadratus femoris. Other muscles, such as the Glutæus maximus, have incidental power for lateral rotation but are not used for pure rotatory action. Medial rotation is performed by the Glutæus minimus and anterior Glutæus medius. The Tensor fasciæ latæ, the Adductores and Iliopsoas have incidental power for this action.

4. The Posterior Femoral Muscles (Hamstring Muscles) (Fig. 418).

The **Biceps femoris** (*Biceps*) is situated on the posterior and lateral aspect of the thigh. It has two heads of origin; one, the **long head**, *arises* from the lower and inner impression on the back part of the tuberosity of the ischium, by a tendon common to it and the Semitendinosus, and from the lower part of the sacrotuberous ligament; the other, the **short head**, *arises* from the lateral lip of the linea aspera, between the Adductor magnus and Vastus lateralis, extending up almost as high as the insertion of the Glutæus maximus; from the lateral prolongation of the linea aspera to within 5 cm. of the lateral condyle; and from the lateral intermuscular septum. The fibers of the long head form a fusiform belly, which passes obliquely downward and lateralward across the sciatic nerve to end in an aponeurosis which covers the posterior surface of the muscle, and receives the fibers of the short head; this aponeurosis becomes gradually contracted into a tendon, which is *inserted* into the lateral side of the head of the fibula, and by a small slip into the lateral condyle of the tibia. At its insertion the tendon divides into two portions, which embrace the fibular collateral ligament of the knee-joint. From the posterior border of the tendon a thin expansion is given off to the fascia of the leg. The tendon of insertion of this muscle forms the lateral hamstring; the common peroneal nerve descends along its medial border.

Action.—Flexes the leg, and after it is flexed, rotates it laterally. The long head extends the thigh and tends to rotate it laterally.

Nerves.—The long head is supplied by branches, usually two, from the tibial portion of the sciatic nerve, containing fibers from the first three sacral nerves. The nerve to the short head comes from the peroneal portion and contains fibers from the fifth lumbar and first two sacral nerves.

Variations.—The short head may be absent; additional heads may arise from the ischial tuberosity, the linea aspera, the medial supracondylar ridge of the femur or from various other parts. A slip may pass to the Gastrocnemius.

The **Semitendinosus**, remarkable for the great length of its tendon of insertion, is situated at the posterior and medial aspect of the thigh. It *arises* from the lower and medial impression on the tuberosity of the ischium, by a tendon common to it and the long head of the Biceps femoris; it also arises from an aponeurosis which connects the adjacent surfaces of the two muscles to the extent of about 7.5 cm. from their origin. The muscle is fusiform and ends a little below the middle of the thigh in a long round tendon which lies along the medial side of the popliteal fossa; it then curves around the medial condyle of the tibia and passes over the tibial collateral ligament of the knee-joint, from which it is separated by a bursa and is *inserted* into the upper part of the medial surface of the body of the tibia, nearly as far forward as its anterior crest. At its insertion it gives off from its lower border a prolongation to the deep fascia of the leg and lies behind the tendon of the Sartorius, and below that of the Gracilis, to which it is united. A tendinous intersection is usually observed about the middle of the muscle.

> **Action.**—Flexes the leg, and, after it is flexed, rotates it medially; extends the thigh.
>
> **Nerves.**—Usually two branches of the tibial portion of the sciatic, containing fibers from the fifth lumbar and first two sacral nerves.

The **Semimembranosus,** so called from its membranous tendon of origin, is situated at the back and medial side of the thigh. It *arises* by a thick tendon from the upper and outer impression on the tuberosity of the ischium, above and lateral to the Biceps femoris and Semitendinosus. The tendon of origin expands into an aponeurosis, which covers the upper part of the anterior surface of the muscle; from this aponeurosis muscular fibers arise, and converge to another aponeurosis which covers the lower part of the posterior surface of the muscle and contracts into the tendon of insertion. It is *inserted* mainly into the horizontal groove on the posterior medial aspect of the medial condyle of the tibia. The tendon of insertion gives off certain fibrous expansions: one, of considerable size, passes upward and lateralward to be *inserted* into the back part of the lateral condyle of the femur, forming part of the oblique popliteal ligament of the knee-joint; a second is continued downward to the fascia which covers the Popliteus muscle; while a few fibers join the tibial collateral ligament of the joint and the fascia of the leg. The muscle overlaps the upper part of the popliteal vessels.

> **Action.**—Flexes the leg, and, after it is flexed, tends to rotate it medially. Extends the thigh.
>
> **Nerve.**—Several branches from the tibial portion of the sciatic nerve, containing fibers from the fifth lumbar and first two sacral nerves.
>
> **Variations.**—It may be reduced or absent, or double, arising mainly from the sacrotuberous ligament and giving a slip to the femur or Adductor magnus.

The tendons of insertion of the two preceding muscles form the medial hamstrings.

> **Group Actions at the Knee.**—Extension of the leg is performed by the Quadriceps femoris; *i. e.*, the Rectus femoris, Vastus lateralis, Vastus medialis, and Vastus intermedius. Flexion is performed by the hamstring muscles; *i. e.*, the Biceps femoris, Semitendinosus, and Semimembranosus, and by the Popliteus. The Sartorius and Gracilis act in full flexion and against resistance. The Gastrocnemius has flexing action but is used more as a protective agent to prevent hyperextension. Lateral rotation of the flexed knee is performed by the Biceps femoris; medial rotation by the Popliteus and, to a lesser extent, by the medial hamstrings.

III. THE MUSCLES AND FASCIÆ OF THE LEG.

The muscles of the leg may be divided into three groups: anterior, posterior, and lateral.

1. The Anterior Crural Muscles (Fig. 421).

Deep Fascia (*fascia cruris*).—The deep fascia of the leg forms a complete investment to the muscles, and is fused with the periosteum over the subcutaneous surfaces of the bones. It is continuous *above* with the fascia lata, and is attached around the knee to the patella, the ligamentum patellæ, the tuberosity and condyles of the tibia, and the head of the fibula. *Behind,* it forms the popliteal fascia, covering in the popliteal fossa; here it is strengthened by transverse fibers, and perforated by the small saphenous vein. It receives an expansion from the tendon of the Biceps femoris laterally, and from the tendons of the Sartorius, Gracilis, Semitendinosus, and Semimembranosus medially; in *front,* it blends with the periosteum covering the subcutaneous surface of the tibia, and with that covering the head and malleolus of the fibula; below, it is continuous with the transverse crural and laciniate ligaments. It is thick and dense in the upper and anterior part of the leg, and gives attachment, by its deep surface, to the Tibialis anterior and Extensor digitorum longus; but thinner behind, where it covers the Gastrocnemius and Soleus. It gives off from its deep surface, on the lateral side of the leg, two strong intermuscular septa, the **anterior** and **posterior peroneal septa,** which enclose the Peronæi longus and brevis, and separate them from the muscles of the anterior and posterior crural regions, and several more slender processes which enclose the individual muscles in each region. A broad transverse intermuscular septum, called the **deep transverse fascia of the leg,** intervenes between the superficial and deep posterior crural muscles.

The **Tibialis anterior** (*Tibialis anticus*) is situated on the lateral side of the tibia; it is thick and fleshy above, tendinous below. It *arises* from the lateral condyle and upper half or two-thirds of the lateral surface of the body of the tibia; from the adjoining part of the interosseous membrane; from the deep surface of the fascia; and from the intermuscular septum between it and the Extensor digitorum longus. The fibers run vertically downward, and end in a tendon, which is apparent on the anterior surface of the muscle at the lower third of the leg. After passing through the most medial compartments of the transverse and cruciate crural ligaments, it is *inserted* into the medial and under surface of the first cuneiform bone, and the base of the first metatarsal bone. This muscle overlaps the anterior tibial vessels and deep peroneal nerve in the upper part of the leg.

Action.—Dorsally flexes and supinates (adducts and inverts) the foot.

Nerve.—Branch of the deep peroneal nerve, containing fibers from the fourth and fifth lumbar and first sacral nerves.

Variations.—A deep portion of the muscle is rarely inserted into the talus, or a tendinous slip may pass to the head of the first metatarsal bone or the base of the first phalanx of the great toe. The *Tibiofascialis anterior,* a small muscle from the lower part of the tibia to the transverse or cruciate crural ligaments or deep fascia.

The **Extensor hallucis longus** (*Extensor proprius hallucis*) is a thin muscle, situated between the Tibialis anterior and the Extensor digitorum longus. It *arises* from the anterior surface of the fibula for about the middle two-fourths of its extent, medial to the origin of the Extensor digitorum longus; it also *arises* from the interosseous membrane to a similar extent. The anterior tibial vessels and deep peroneal nerve lie between it and the Tibialis anterior. The fibers pass downward, and end in a tendon, which occupies the anterior border of the muscle, passes through a distinct compartment in the cruciate crural ligament, crosses from the lateral to the medial side of the anterior tibial vessels near the bend of the ankle, and is *inserted* into the base of the distal phalanx of the great toe. Opposite the metatarso-phalangeal articulation, the tendon gives off a thin prolongation on either side, to cover the surface of the joint. An expansion from the medial side of the tendon is usually inserted into the base of the proximal phalanx.

Action.—Extends proximal phalanx of great toe. Dorsally flexes and supinates the foot.

Nerve.—Branch of the deep peroneal nerve, containing fibers from the fourth and fifth lumbar and first sacral nerves.

Variations.—Occasionally united at its origin with the Extensor digitorum longus. *Extensor ossis metatarsi hallucis,* a small muscle, sometimes found as a slip from the Extensor hallucis longus, or from the Tibialis anterior, or from the Extensor digitorum longus, or as a distinct muscle; it traverses the same compartment of the transverse ligament with the Extensor hallucis longus.

31

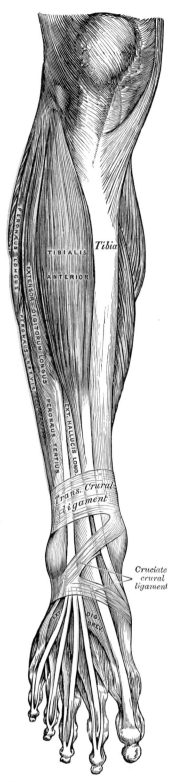

FIG. 421.—Muscles of the front of the leg.

The **Extensor digitorum longus** is a penniform muscle, situated at the lateral part of the front of the leg. It *arises* from the lateral condyle of the tibia; from the upper three-fourths of the anterior surface of the body of the fibula; from the upper part of the interosseous membrane; from the deep surface of the fascia; and from the intermuscular septa between it and the Tibialis anterior on the medial, and the Peronæi on the lateral side. Between it and the Tibialis anterior are the upper portions of the anterior tibial vessels and deep peroneal nerve. The tendon passes under the transverse and cruciate crural ligaments in company with the Peronæus tertius, and divides into four slips, which run forward on the dorsum of the foot, and are *inserted* into the second and third phalanges of the four lesser toes. The tendons to the second, third, and fourth toes are each joined, opposite the metatarso-phalangeal articulation, on the lateral side by a tendon of the Extensor digitorum brevis. The tendons are inserted in the following manner: each receives a fibrous expansion from the Interossei and Lumbricalis, and then spreads out into a broad aponeurosis, which covers the dorsal surface of the first phalanx: this aponeurosis, at the articulation of the first with the second phalanx, divides into three slips—an intermediate, which is inserted into the base of the second phalanx; and two collateral slips, which, after uniting on the dorsal surface of the second phalanx, are continued onward, to be inserted into the base of the third phalanx.

Action.—Extends the proximal phalanges of the four small toes. Dorsally flexes and pronates the foot.

Nerve.—Branches of the deep peroneal nerve, containing fibers from the fourth and fifth lumbar and first sacral nerves.

Variations.—This muscle varies considerably in the modes of origin and the arrangement of its various tendons. The tendons to the second and fifth toes may be found doubled, or extra slips are given off from one or more tendons to their corresponding metatarsal bones, or to the short extensor, or to one of the interosseous muscles. A slip to the great toe from the innermost tendon has been found.

The **Peronæus tertius** is a part of the Extensor digitorum longus, and might be described as its fifth tendon. The fibers belonging to this tendon *arise* from the lower third or more of the anterior surface of the fibula; from the lower part of the interosseous membrane; and from an intermuscular septum between it and the Peronæus brevis. The tendon, after passing under the transverse and cruciate crural ligaments in the same canal as the Extensor digitorum longus, is *inserted* into the dorsal surface of the base of the metatarsal bone of the little toe.

Action.—Dorsally flexes and pronates the foot.
Nerve.—Branch of the deep peroneal nerve, containing fibers from the fourth and fifth lumbar and first sacral nerves.

2. The Posterior Crural Muscles.

The muscles of the back of the leg are subdivided into two groups—superficial and deep. Those of the superficial group constitute a powerful muscular mass, forming the calf of the leg. Their large size is one of the most characteristic features of the muscular apparatus in man, and bears a direct relation to his erect posture and his mode of locomotion.

The Superficial Group (Fig. 422).

Gastrocnemius. Soleus. Plantaris.

The **Gastrocnemius** is the most superficial muscle, and forms the greater part of the calf. It *arises* by two heads, which are connected to the condyles of the femur by strong, flat tendons. The **medial** and **larger head** takes its origin from a depression at the upper and back part of the medial condyle and from the adjacent part of the femur. The **lateral head** *arises* from an impression on the side of the lateral condyle and from the posterior surface of the femur immediately above the lateral part of the condyle. Both heads, also, *arise* from the subjacent part of the capsule of the knee. Each tendon spreads out into an aponeurosis, which covers the posterior surface of that portion of the muscle to which it belongs. From the anterior surfaces of these tendinous expansions, muscular fibers are given off; those of the medial head being thicker and extending lower than those of the lateral. The fibers unite at an angle in the middle line of the muscle in a tendinous raphé, which expands into a broad aponeurosis on the anterior surface of the muscle, and into this the remaining fibers are inserted. The aponeurosis, gradually contracting, unites with the tendon of the Soleus, and forms with it the tendo calcaneus.

Action.—Plantar flexes the foot (points the toe); flexes the leg; tends to supinate the foot.
Nerves.—Branches of the tibial nerve, containing fibers from the first and second sacral nerves.
Variations.—Absence of the outer head or of the entire muscle. Extra slips from the popliteal surface of the femur.

The **Soleus** is a broad flat muscle situated immediately in front of the Gastrocnemius. It *arises* by tendinous fibers from the back of the head of the fibula, and from the upper third of the posterior surface of the body of the bone; from the popliteal line, and the middle third of the medial border of the tibia; some fibers also arise from a tendinous arch placed between the tibial and fibular origins of the muscle, in front of which the popliteal vessels and tibial nerve run. The fibers end in an aponeurosis which covers the posterior surface of the muscle, and, gradually becoming thicker and narrower, joins with the tendon of the Gastrocnemius, and forms with it the tendo calcaneus.

Action.—Plantar flexes the foot.
Nerve.—Branch of the tibialis, containing fibers from the first and second sacral nerves.
Variations.—Accessory head to its lower and inner part usually ending in the tendocalcaneus, or the calcaneus, or the laciniate ligament.

The Gastrocnemius and Soleus together form a muscular mass which is occasionally described as the **Triceps suræ**: its tendon of insertion is the tendo calcaneus.

Tendo Calcaneus (*tendo Achillis*).—The tendo calcaneus, the common tendon of the Gastrocnemius and Soleus, is the thickest and strongest in the body. It is about

15 cm. long, and begins near the middle of the leg, but receives fleshy fibers on its anterior surface, almost to its lower end. Gradually becoming contracted below, it is inserted into the middle part of the posterior surface of the calcaneus, a bursa being interposed between the tendon and the upper part of this surface. The tendon spreads out somewhat at its lower end, so that its narrowest part is about 4 cm. above its insertion. It is covered by the fascia and the integument, and is separated from the deep muscles and vessels by a considerable interval filled up with areolar and adipose tissue. Along its lateral side, but superficial to it, is the small saphenous vein.

The **Plantaris** is placed between the Gastrocnemius and Soleus. It *arises* from the lower part of the lateral prolongation of the linea aspera, and from the oblique popliteal ligament of the knee-joint. It forms a small fusiform belly, from 7 to 10 cm. long, ending in a long slender tendon which crosses obliquely between the two muscles of the calf, and runs along the medial border of the tendo calcaneus, to be *inserted* with it into the posterior part of the calcaneus. This muscle is sometimes double, and at other times wanting. Occasionally, its tendon is lost in the laciniate ligament, or in the fascia of the leg.

Action.—Plantar flexes the foot; flexes the leg.

Nerve.—Branch of the tibial nerve, containing fibers from the fourth and fifth lumbar and first sacral nerves.

The Deep Group (Fig. 423).

Popliteus.   Flexor digitorum longus.
Flexor hallucis longus.   Tibialis posterior.

Deep Transverse Fascia.—The deep transverse fascia of the leg is a transversely placed, intermuscular septum, between the superficial and deep muscles of the back of the leg. At the sides it is connected to the margins of the tibia and fibula. *Above*, where it covers the Popliteus, it is thick and dense, and receives an expansion from the tendon of the Semimembranosus; it is thinner in the middle of the leg; but *below*, where it covers the tendons passing behind the malleoli, it is thickened and continuous with the laciniate ligament.

The **Popliteus** is a thin, flat, triangular muscle, which forms the lower part of the floor of the popliteal fossa. It *arises* by a strong tendon about 2.5 cm. long, from a depression at the anterior part of the groove on the lateral condyle of the femur, and to a small extent from the oblique popliteal ligament of the knee-joint; and is *inserted* into the medial two-thirds of the triangular surface above the popliteal line on the posterior surface of the body of the tibia, and into the tendinous expansion covering the surface of the muscle.

Action.—Flexes the leg and rotates it medially.

Nerve.—Branch of the tibial nerve, containing fibers from the fourth and fifth lumbar and first sacral nerves.

Variations.—Additional head from the sesamoid bone in the outer head of the Gastrocnemius. *Popliteus minor*, rare, origin from femur on the inner side of the Plantaris, insertion into the posterior ligament of the knee-joint. *Peroneotibialis*, 14 per cent., origin inner side of the head of the fibula, insertion into the upper end of the oblique line of the tibia, it lies beneath the Popliteus.

The **Flexor hallucis longus** is situated on the fibular side of the leg. It *arises* from the inferior two-thirds of the posterior surface of the body of the fibula, with the exception of 2.5 cm. at its lowest part; from the lower part of the interosseous membrane; from an intermuscular septum between it and the Peronæi, laterally, and from the fascia covering the Tibialis posterior, medially. The fibers pass obliquely downward and backward, and end in a tendon which occupies nearly the whole length of the posterior surface of the muscle. This tendon lies in a groove which crosses the posterior surface of the lower end of the tibia, the posterior surface of the talus, and the under surface of the sustentaculum tali of the calcaneus; in the sole of the foot it runs forward between the two heads of the Flexor hallucis brevis, and is *inserted* into the base of the last phalanx of the great toe.

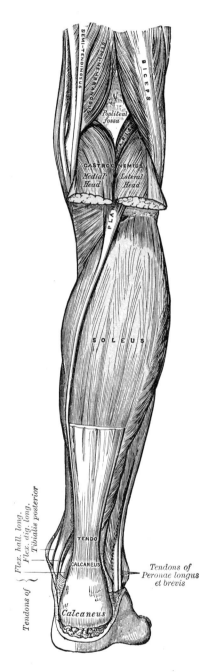

FIG. 422.—Muscles of the back of the leg. Superficial layer.

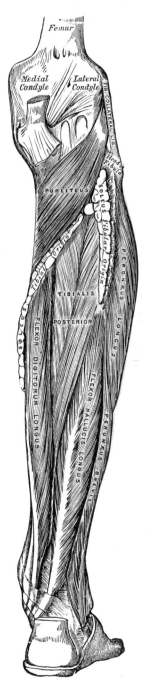

FIG. 423.—Muscles of the back of the leg. Deep layer.

The grooves on the talus and calcaneus, which contain the tendon of the muscle, are converted by tendinous fibers into distinct canals, lined by a synovial sheath.

As the tendon passes forward in the sole of the foot, it is situated above, and crosses from the lateral to the medial side of the tendon of the Flexor digitorum longus, to which it is connected by a fibrous slip.

Action.—Flexes second phalanx of great toe. Plantar flexes and supinates the foot.

Nerve.—Branch of the tibial nerve, containing fibers from the fifth lumbar and first and second sacral nerves.

Variations.—Usually a slip runs to the Flexor digitorum and frequently an additional slip runs from the Flexor digitorum to the Flexor hallucis. *Peroneocalcaneus internus*, rare, origin below or outside the Flexor hallucis from the back of the fibula, passes over the sustentaculum tali with the Flexor hallucis and is inserted into the calcaneum.

The **Flexor digitorum longus** is situated on the tibial side of the leg. At its origin it is thin and pointed, but it gradually increases in size as it descends. It *arises* from the posterior surface of the body of the tibia, from immediately below the popliteal line to within 7 or 8 cm. of its lower extremity, medial to the tibial origin of the Tibialis posterior; it also *arises* from the fascia covering the Tibialis posterior. The fibers end in a tendon, which runs nearly the whole length of the posterior surface of the muscle. This tendon passes behind the medial malleolus, in a groove, common to it and the Tibialis posterior, but separated from the latter by a fibrous septum, each tendon being contained in a special compartment lined by a separate synovial sheath. It passes obliquely forward and lateralward, superficial to the deltoid ligament of the ankle-joint, into the sole of the foot (Fig. 428), where it crosses below the tendon of the Flexor hallucis longus, and receives from it a strong tendinous slip. It then expands and is joined by the Quadratus plantæ, and finally divides into four tendons, which are *inserted* into the bases of the last phalanges of the second, third, fourth, and fifth toes, each tendon passing through an opening in the corresponding tendon of the Flexor digitorum brevis opposite the base of the first phalanx.

Action.—Flexes the terminal phalanges of the four small toes. Plantar flexes and supinates the foot.

Nerve.—Branch of the tibial nerve, containing fibers from the fifth lumbar and first sacral, nerves.

Variations.—*Flexor accessorius longus digitorum*, not infrequent, origin from fibula, or tibia, or the deep fascia and ending in a tendon which, after passing beneath the laciniate ligament joins the tendon of the long flexor or the Quadratus plantæ.

The **Tibialis posterior** (*Tibialis posticus*) lies between the two preceding muscles, and is the most deeply seated of the muscles on the back of the leg. It begins above by two pointed processes, separated by an angular interval through which the anterior tibial vessels pass forward to the front of the leg. It *arises* from the whole of the posterior surface of the interosseous membrane, excepting its lowest part; from the lateral portion of the posterior surface of the body of the tibia, between the commencement of the popliteal line above and the junction of the middle and lower thirds of the body below; and from the upper two-thirds of the medial surface of the fibula; some fibers also arise from the deep transverse fascia, and from the intermuscular septa separating it from the adjacent muscles. In the lower fourth of the leg its tendon passes in front of that of the Flexor digitorum longus and lies with it in a groove behind the medial malleolus, but enclosed in a separate sheath; it next passes under the laciniate and over the deltoid ligament into the foot, and then beneath the plantar calcaneonavicular ligament. The tendon contains a sesamoid fibrocartilage, as it runs under the plantar calcaneonavicular ligament. It is *inserted* into the tuberosity of the navicular bone, and gives off fibrous expansions, one of which passes backward to the sustentaculum tali of the calcaneus, others forward and lateralward to the three cuneiforms, the cuboid, and the bases of the second, third, and fourth metatarsal bones.

Action.—Supinates (adducts and inverts), and plantar flexes the foot.

Nerve.—Branch of the tibial nerve, containing fibers from the fifth lumbar and first sacral nerves.

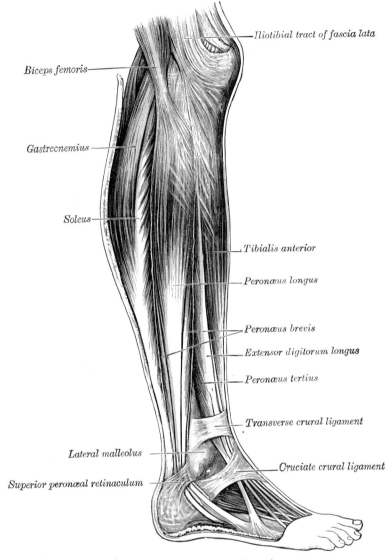

Iliotibial tract of fascia lata

Biceps femoris

Gastrecnemius

Soleus

Tibialis anterior

Peronæus longus

Peronæus brevis

Extensor digitorum longus

Peronæus tertius

Transverse crural ligament

Lateral malleolus

Cruciate crural ligament

Superior peronæal retinaculum

Fig. 424.—The right lateral crural muscles.

3. The Lateral Crural Muscles (Fig. 424).

Peronæus longus   Peronæus brevis.

The **Peronæus longus** is situated at the upper part of the lateral side of the leg, and is the more superficial of the two muscles. It *arises* from the head and upper two-thirds of the lateral surface of the body of the fibula, from the deep surface of the fascia, and from the intermuscular septa between it and the muscles on the front and back of the leg; occasionally also by a few fibers from the lateral condyle of the tibia. Between its attachments to the head and to the body of the fibula there is a gap through which the common peroneal nerve passes to the front of the leg. It ends in a long tendon, which runs behind the lateral malleolus, in a groove common to it and the tendon of the Peronæus brevis, behind which it lies; the groove is converted into a canal by the superior peroneal retinaculum, and the tendons in it are contained in a common synovial sheath. The tendon then extends obliquely forward across the lateral side of the calcaneus, below the trochlear process, and the tendon of the Peronæus brevis, and under cover of the inferior peroneal retinaculum. It crosses the lateral side of the cuboid, and then runs on the under surface of that bone in a groove which is converted into a canal by the long plantar ligament; the tendon then crosses the sole of the foot obliquely, and is inserted into the lateral side of the base of the first metatarsal bone and the lateral side of the first cuneiform. Occasionally it sends a slip to the base of the second metatarsal bone. The tendon changes its direction at two points: first, behind the lateral malleolus; secondly, on the cuboid bone; in both of these situations the tendon is thickened, and, in the latter, a sesamoid fibrocartilage (sometimes a bone), is usually developed in its substance.

Action.—Pronates (abducts and everts) and plantar flexes the foot.

Nerve.—Branch of the superficial peroneal nerve, containing fibers from the fourth and fifth lumbar and first sacral nerves.

The **Peronæus brevis** lies under cover of the Peronæus longus, and is a shorter and smaller muscle. It *arises* from the lower two-thirds of the lateral surface of the body of the fibula; medial to the Peronæus longus; and from the intermuscular septa separating it from the adjacent muscles on the front and back of the leg. The fibers pass vertically downward, and end in a tendon which runs behind the lateral malleolus along with but in front of that of the preceding muscle, the two tendons being enclosed in the same compartment, and lubricated by a common synovial sheath. It then runs forward on the lateral side of the calcaneus, above the trochlear process and the tendon of the Peronæus longus, and is *inserted* into the tuberosity at the base of the fifth metatarsal bone, on its lateral side.

On the lateral surface of the calcaneus the tendons of the Peronæi longus and brevis occupy separate osseoaponeurotic canals formed by the calcaneus and the peroneal retinacula; each tendon is enveloped by a forward prolongation of the common synovial sheath.

Action.—Pronates (everts and abducts) and plantar flexes the foot.

Nerve.—Branch of the superficial peroneal nerve, containing fibers from the fourth and fifth lumbar and first sacral nerves.

Variations.—Fusion of the two peronæi is rare. A slip from the Peronæus longus to the base of the third, fourth or fifth metatarsal bone, or to the Adductor hallucis is occasionally seen.

Peronæus accessorius, origin from the fibula between the longus and brevis, joins the tendon of the longus in the sole of the foot.

Peronæus quinti digiti, rare, origin lower fourth of the fibula under the brevis, insertion into the Extensor aponeurosis of the little toe. More common as a slip of the tendon of the Peronæus brevis.

Peronæus quartus, 13 per cent. (Gruber), origin back of fibula between the brevis and the Flexor hallucis, insertion into the peroneal spine of the calcaneum, (*peroneocalcaneus externum*), or less frequently into the tuberosity of the cuboid (*peroneocuboideus*).

Group Actions at the Ankle.—Plantar flexion of the foot is brought about by the Gastrocnemius and Soleus, the Plantaris, the Peronæi longus and brevis, and the Tibialis posterior. The Peronæi and Tibialis posterior act alone if there is no resistance to be overcome. The Flexores digitorum and hallucis come into action to meet great resistance. The Gastrocnemius supinating and the Peronæi pronating are synergetic.

Dorsal flexion of the foot is performed by the Tibialis anterior, Extensores digitorum and hallucis longi, and Peronæus tertius. The Peronæus brevis acts synergetically along with the Extensor digitorum and Peronæus tertius to neutralize the inversion of the Tibialis anterior and Extensor hallucis.

Supination of the Foot (combined adduction and inversion).—The Tibiales anterior and posterior are the principal supinators. The posterior adducts more powerfully, the anterior inverts more powerfully. The Gastrocnemius tends to supinate and acts synergetically against the dorsal flexion of the Tibialis anterior.

Pronation of the foot (combined abduction and eversion) is performed by the Peronæi. The Peronæus brevis abducts more strongly and acts slightly before the longus; the longus everts more strongly. The Peronæus tertius acts when it is present. The Extensor digitorum longus acts as an emergency muscle.

THE FASCIA AROUND THE ANKLE.

Fibrous bands, or thickened portions of the fascia, bind down the tendons in front of and behind the ankle in their passage to the foot. They comprise three ligaments, viz., the **transverse crural**, the **cruciate crural** and the **laciniate**; and the **superior and inferior peroneal retinacula**.

Transverse Crural Ligament (*ligamentum transversum cruris; upper part of anterior annular ligament*) (Fig. 425).—The transverse crural ligament binds down the tendons of Extensor digitorum longus, Extensor hallucis longus, Peronæus tertius, and Tibialis anterior as they descend on the front of the tibia and fibula; under it are found also the anterior tibial vessels and deep peroneal nerve. It is attached laterally to the lower end of the fibula, and medially to the tibia; above it is continuous with the fascia of the leg.

Cruciate Crural Ligament (*ligamentum cruciatum cruris; lower part of anterior annular ligament*) (Figs. 425, 426).—The cruciate crural ligament is a Y-shaped band placed in front of the ankle-joint, the stem of the Y being attached laterally to the upper surface of the calcaneus, in front of the depression for the interosseous talocalcanean ligament; it is directed medialward as a double layer, one lamina passing in front of, and the other behind, the tendons of the Peronæus tertius and Extensor digitorum longus. At the medial border of the latter tendon these two layers join together, forming a compartment in which the tendons are enclosed. From the medial extremity of this sheath the two limbs of the Y diverge: one is directed upward and medialward, to be attached to the tibial malleolus, passing over the Extensor hallucis longus and the vessels and nerves, but enclosing the Tibialis anterior by a splitting of its fibers. The other limb extends downward and medialward, to be attached to the border of the plantar aponeurosis, and passes over the tendons of the Extensor hallucis longus and Tibialis anterior and also the vessels and nerves.

Laciniate Ligament (*ligamentum laciniatum; internal annular ligament*).—The laciniate ligament is a strong fibrous band, extending from the tibial malleolus above to the margin of the calcaneus below, converting a series of bony grooves in this situation into canals for the passage of the tendons of the Flexor muscles and the posterior tibial vessels and tibial nerve into the sole of the foot. It is continuous by its upper border with the deep fascia of the leg, and by its lower border with the plantar aponeurosis and the fibers of origin of the Abductor hallucis muscle. Enumerated from the medial side, the four canals which it forms transmit the tendon of the Tibialis posterior; the tendon of the Flexor digitorum longus; the posterior tibial vessels and tibial nerve, which run through a broad space beneath the ligament; and lastly, in a canal formed partly by the talus, the tendon of the Flexor hallucis longus (Fig. 426, not labelled).

Peroneal Retinacula.—The peroneal retinacula are fibrous bands which bind down the tendons of the Peronæi longus and brevis as they run across the lateral side of the ankle. The fibers of the **superior retinaculum** (*external annular ligament*) are attached *above* to the lateral malleolus and *below* to the lateral surface of the calcaneus. The fibers of the **inferior retinaculum** are continuous in *front* with those of the cruciate crural ligament; *behind* they are attached to the lateral surface of the calcaneus; some of the fibers are fixed to the peroneal trochlea, forming a septum between the tendons of the Peronæi longus and brevis.

The Synovial Sheaths of the Tendons Around the Ankle.—All the tendons crossing the ankle-joint are enclosed for part of their length in synovial sheaths which have an almost uniform length of about 8 cm. each. On the *front* of the ankle (Fig. 425) the sheath for the Tibialis anterior extends from the upper margin of the transverse crural ligament to the interval between the diverging limbs of the cruciate

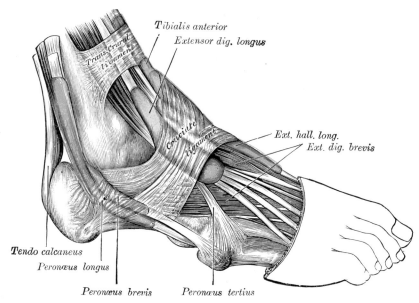

FIG. 425.—The synovial sheaths of the tendons around the ankle. Lateral aspect.

ligament; those for the Extensor digitorum longus and Extensor hallucis longus reach upward to just above the level of the tips of the malleoli, the former being the higher. The sheath of the Extensor hallucis longus is prolonged on to the base

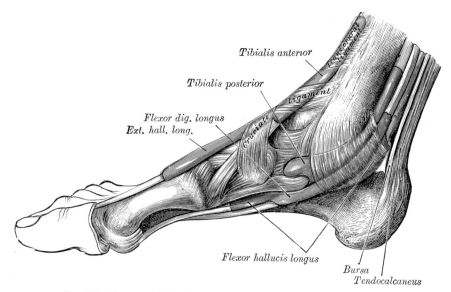

FIG. 426.—The synovial sheaths of the tendons around the ankle. Medial aspect.

of the first metatarsal bone, while that of the Extensor digitorum longus reaches only to the level of the base of the fifth metatarsal. On the *medial side* of the ankle (Fig. 426) the sheath for the Tibialis posterior extends highest up—to about

4 cm. above the tip of the malleolus—while below it stops just short of the tuberosity of the navicular. The sheath for Flexor hallucis longus reaches up to the level of the tip of the malleolus, while that for the Flexor digitorum longus is slightly higher; the former is continued to the base of the first metatarsal, but the latter stops opposite the first cuneiform bone.

On the *lateral side* of the ankle (Fig. 425) a sheath which is single for the greater part of its extent encloses the Peronæi longus and brevis. It extends upward for about 4 cm. above the tip of the malleolus and downward and forward for about the same distance.

IV. THE MUSCLES AND FASCIÆ OF THE FOOT.

1. The Dorsal Muscle of the Foot.

The **fascia** on the dorsum of the foot is a thin membranous layer, continuous above with the transverse and cruciate crural ligaments; on either side it blends with the plantar aponeurosis; anteriorly it forms a sheath for the tendons on the dorsum of the foot.

The **Extensor digitorum brevis** (Fig. 425) is a broad, thin muscle, which *arises* from the forepart of the upper and lateral surfaces of the calcaneus, in front of the groove for the Peronæus brevis; from the lateral talocalcanean ligament; and from the common limb of the cruciate crural ligament. It passes obliquely across the dorsum of the foot, and ends in four tendons. The most medial, which is the largest, is *inserted* into the dorsal surface of the base of the first phalanx of the great toe, crossing the dorsalis pedis artery; it is frequently described as a separate muscle—the **Extensor hallucis brevis.** The other three are *inserted* into the lateral sides of the tendons of the Extensor digitorum longus of the second, third, and fourth toes.

Action.—Extends the proximal phalanges of the great and the adjacent three small toes.

Nerve.—Branch of the deep peroneal nerve, containing fibers from fifth lumbar and first sacral nerves.

Variations.—Accessory slips of origin from the talus and navicular, or from the external cuneiform and third metatarsal bones to the second slip of the muscle, and one from the cuboid to the third slip have been observed. The tendons vary in number and position; they may be reduced to two, or one of them may be doubled, or an additional slip may pass to the little toe. A supernumerary slip ending on one of the metatarsophalangeal articulations, or joining a dorsal interosseous muscle is not uncommon. Deep slips between this muscle and the Dorsal interossei occur.

2. The Plantar Muscles of the Foot.

Plantar Aponeurosis (*aponeurosis plantaris; plantar fascia*).—The plantar aponeurosis is of great strength, and consists of pearly white glistening fibers, disposed, for the most part, longitudinally: it is divided into central, lateral, and medial portions.

The **central portion**, the thickest, is narrow behind and *attached* to the medial process of the tuberosity of the calcaneus, posterior to the origin of the Flexor digitorum brevis; and becoming broader and thinner in front, divides near the heads of the metatarsal bones into five processes, one for each of the toes. Each of these processes divides opposite the metatarsophalangeal articulation into two strata, superficial and deep. The superficial stratum is *inserted* into the skin of the transverse sulcus which separates the toes from the sole. The deeper stratum divides into two slips which embrace the side of the Flexor tendons of the toes, and blend with the sheaths of the tendons, and with the transverse metatarsal ligament, thus forming a series of arches through which the tendons of the short and long Flexors pass to the toes. The intervals left between the five processes allow the digital vessels and nerves and the tendons of the Lumbricales to become superficial.   At the point of division of the aponeurosis, numerous transverse fasciculi are superadded; these serve to increase the strength of the aponeurosis at this part by binding the processes together, and connecting them with the integument.   The central portion of the plantar aponeurosis is continuous with the lateral and medial portions and sends upward into the foot, at the lines of junction, two strong vertical intermuscular septa, broader in front than behind, which separate the intermediate from the lateral and medial plantar groups of muscles; from these again are derived thinner transverse septa which separate the various layers of muscles in this region.   The upper surface of this aponeurosis gives origin behind to the Flexor digitorum brevis.

The lateral and medial portions of the plantar aponeurosis are thinner than the central piece, and cover the sides of the sole of the foot.

The **lateral portion** covers the under surface of the Abductor digiti quinti; it is thin in front and thick behind, where it forms a strong band between the lateral process of the tuberosity of the calcaneus and the base of the fifth metatarsal bone; it is continuous medially with the central portion of the plantar aponeurosis, and laterally with the dorsal fascia.

The **medial portion** is thin, and covers the under surface of the Abductor hallucis; it is *attached* behind to the laciniate ligament, and is continuous around the side of the foot with the dorsal fascia, and laterally with the central portion of the plantar aponeurosis.

The muscles in the plantar region of the foot may be divided into three groups, in a similar manner to those in the hand.   Those of the medial plantar region are connected with the great toe, and corrrespond with those of the thumb; those of the lateral plantar region are connected with the little toe, and correspond with those of the little finger; and those of the intermediate plantar region are connected with the tendons intervening between the two former groups.   But in order to facilitate the description of these muscles, it is more convenient to divide them into four layers, in the order in which they are successively exposed.

The First Layer (Fig. 427).

Abductor hallucis.   Flexor digitorum brevis.
                        Abductor digiti quinti.

The **Abductor hallucis** lies along the medial border of the foot and covers the origins of the plantar vessels and nerves.   It *arises* from the medial process of the tuberosity of the calcaneus, from the laciniate ligament, from the plantar aponeurosis, and from the intermuscular septum between it and the Flexor digitorum brevis.   The fibers end in a tendon, which is *inserted*, together with the medial tendon of the Flexor hallucis brevis, into the tibial side of the base of the first phalanx of the great toe.

Action.—Abducts the great toe.
Nerve.—Branch of the medial plantar nerve, containing fibers from the fourth and fifth lumbar nerves.

The **Flexor digitorum brevis** lies in the middle of the sole of the foot, immediately above the central part of the plantar aponeurosis, with which it is firmly united.   Its deep surface is separated from the lateral plantar vessels and nerves by a thin layer of fascia.   It *arises* by a narrow tendon, from the medial process of the tuberosity of the calcaneus, from the central part of the plantar aponeurosis, and from the intermuscular septa between it and the adjacent muscles.   It passes forward, and divides into four tendons, one for each of the four lesser toes.   Opposite the bases of the first phalanges, each tendon divides into two slips, to allow of the passage of the corresponding tendon of the Flexor digitorum longus; the two portions of the tendon then unite and form a grooved channel for the reception of the accompanying long Flexor tendon. Finally, it divides a second time, and is *inserted* into the sides of the second phalanx about its middle. The mode of division of the tendons of the Flexor digitorum brevis, and of their insertion into the phalanges, is analogous to that of the tendons of the Flexor digitorum sublimis in the hand.

Action.—Flexes the second phalanges of the four small toes.

Nerve.—Branch of the medial plantar nerve, containing fibers from the fourth and fifth lumbar nerves.

Variations.—Slip to the little toe frequently wanting, 23 per cent; or it may be replaced by a small fusiform muscle arising from the long flexor tendon or from the Quadratus plantæ.

Fibrous Sheaths of the Flexor Tendons.—The terminal portions of the tendons of the long and short Flexor muscles are contained in osseoaponeurotic canals similar in their arrangement to those in the fingers. These canals are formed above by the phalanges and below by fibrous bands, which arch across the tendons, and are attached on either side to the margins of the phalanges. Opposite the bodies of the proximal and second phalanges the fibrous bands are strong, and the fibers are transverse; but opposite the joints they are much thinner, and the fibers are directed obliquely. Each canal contains a synovial sheath, which is reflected on the contained tendons.

The **Abductor digiti quinti** (*Abductor minimi digiti*) lies along the lateral border of the foot, and is in relation by its medial margin with the lateral plantar vessels and nerves. It *arises*, by a broad origin, from the lateral process of the tuberosity of the calcaneus, from the under surface of the calcaneus between the two processes of the tuberosity, from the forepart of the medial process, from the plantar aponeurosis, and from the intermuscular septum between it and the Flexor digitorum brevis. Its tendon, after gliding over a smooth facet on the under surface of the base of the fifth metatarsal bone, is *inserted*, with the Flexor digiti quinti brevis, into the fibular side of the base of the first phalanx of the fifth toe.

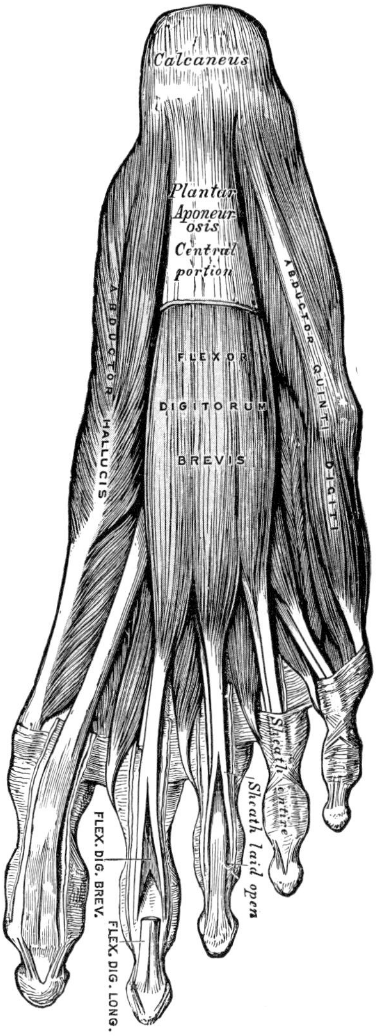

Action.—Abducts the small toe.

Nerve.—Branch of the lateral plantar nerve, containing fibers from the first and second sacral nerves.

Variations.—Slips of origin from the tuberosity at the base of the fifth metatarsal. *Abductor ossis metatarsi quinti*, origin external tubercle of the calcaneus, insertion into tuberosity of the fifth metatarsal bone in common with or beneath the outer margin of the plantar fascia.

Fig. 427.—Muscles of the sole of the foot. First layer.

The Second Layer (Fig. 428).

Quadratus plantæ.   Lumbricales.

The **Quadratus plantæ** (*Flexor accessorius*) is separated from the muscles of the first layer by the lateral plantar vessels and nerve. It *arises* by two heads, which are separated from each other by the long plantar ligament: the **medial or larger head** is muscular, and is attached to the medial concave surface of the calcaneus, below the groove which lodges the tendon of the Flexor hallucis longus; the **lateral head,** flat and tendinous, *arises* from the lateral border of the inferior surface of the calcaneus, in front of the lateral process of its tuberosity, and from the long plantar ligament. The two portions join at an acute angle, and end in a flattened band which is *inserted* into the lateral margin and upper and under surfaces of the tendon of the Flexor digitorum longus, forming a kind of groove, in which the tendon is lodged. It usually sends slips to those tendons of the Flexor digitorum longus which pass to the second, third, and fourth toes.

Action.—Flexes the terminal phalanges of the four small toes.

Nerve.—Branch of the lateral plantar nerve, containing fibers from the first and second sacral nerves.

Variations.—Lateral head often wanting; entire muscle absent. Variation in the number of digital tendons to which fibers can be traced. Most frequent offsets are sent to the second, third and fourth toes; in many cases to the fifth as well; occasionally to two toes only.

The **Lumbricales** are four small muscles, accessory to the tendons of the Flexor digitorum longus and numbered from the medial side of the foot; they *arise* from these tendons, as far back as their angles of division, each springing from two tendons, except the first. The muscles end in tendons, which pass forward on the medial sides of the four lesser toes, and are *inserted* into the expansions of the tendons of the Extensor digitorum longus on the dorsal surfaces of the first phalanges.

Action.—Flex the proximal phalanges and extend the two distal phalanges of the four small toes.

Nerves.—The first Lumbricalis by a branch of the medial plantar nerve, containing fibers from the fourth and fifth lumbar nerves; the other three Lumbricales by branches of the lateral plantar nerve containing fibers from the first and second sacral nerves.

Variations.—Absence of one or more; doubling of the third or fourth. Insertion partly or wholly into the first phalanges.

The Third Layer (Fig. 429).

Flexor hallucis brevis.   Adductor hallucis.

Flexor digiti quinti brevis.

The **Flexor hallucis brevis** *arises,* by a pointed tendinous process, from the medial part of the under surface of the cuboid bone, from the contiguous portion of the third cuneiform, and from the prolongation of the tendon of the Tibialis posterior which is attached to that bone. It divides in front into two portions, which are inserted into the medial and lateral sides of the base of the first phalanx of the great toe, a sesamoid bone being present in each tendon at its insertion. The **medial portion** is blended with the Abductor hallucis previous to its insertion; the **lateral portion** with the Adductor hallucis; the tendon of the Flexor hallucis longus lies in a groove between them; the lateral portion is sometimes described as the **first Interosseous plantaris.**

Action.—Flexes the proximal phalanx of the great toe.

Nerve.—Branch of the medial plantar nerve, containing fibers from the fourth and fifth lumbar and first sacral nerves.

Variations.—Origin subject to considerable variation; it often receives fibers from the calcaneus or long plantar ligament. Attachment to the cuboid sometimes wanting. Slip to first phalanx of the second toe.

The **Adductor hallucis** (*Adductor obliquus hallucis*) *arises* by two heads—oblique and transverse. The **oblique head** is a large, thick, fleshy mass, crossing the foot obliquely and occupying the hollow space under the first, second, third, and fourth metatarsal bones. It *arises* from the bases of the second, third, and fourth metatarsal bones, and from the sheath of the tendon of the Peronæus longus, and is *inserted*, together with the lateral portion of the Flexor hallucis brevis, into the lateral side of the base of the first phalanx of the great toe. The **transverse head**

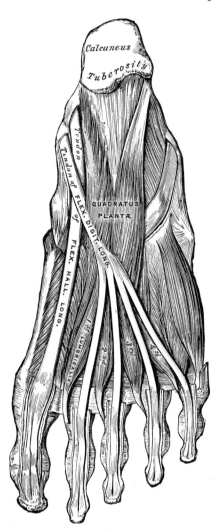

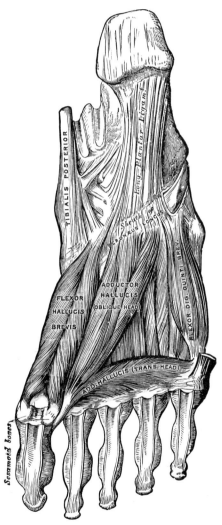

FIG. 428.—Muscles of the sole of the foot.
Second layer.

FIG. 429.—Muscles of the sole of the foot.
Third layer.

(*Transversus pedis*) is a narrow, flat fasciculus which *arises* from the plantar metatarsophalangeal ligaments of the third, fourth, and fifth toes (sometimes only from the third and fourth), and from the transverse ligament of the metatarsus. It is *inserted* into the lateral side of the base of the first phalanx of the great toe, its fibers blending with the tendon of insertion of the oblique head.

Action.—Adducts the great toe.

Nerve.—Branch of the lateral plantar nerve, containing fibers from the first and second sacral nerves.

Variations.—Slips to the base of the first phalanx of the second toe. *Opponens hallucis*, occasional slips from the adductor to the metatarsal bone of the great toe.

The Abductor, Flexor brevis, and Adductor of the great toe, like the similar muscles of the thumb, give off, at their insertions, fibrous expansions to blend with the tendons of the Extensor hallucis longus.

The **Flexor digiti quinti brevis** (*Flexor brevis minimi digiti*) lies under the metatarsal bone of the little toe, and resembles one of the Interossei. It *arises* from the base of the fifth metatarsal bone, and from the sheath of the Peronæus longus; its tendon is *inserted* into the lateral side of the base of the first phalanx of the fifth toe. Occasionally a few of the deeper fibers are inserted into the lateral part of the distal half of the fifth metatarsal bone; these are described by some as a distinct muscle, the **Opponens digiti quinti.**

Action.—Flexes the proximal phalanx of the small toe.

Nerve.—Branch of the lateral plantar nerve, containing fibers from the first and second sacral nerves.

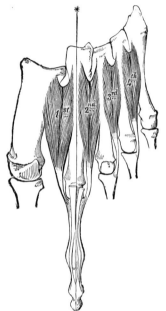

FIG. 430.—The Interossei dorsales. Left foot.

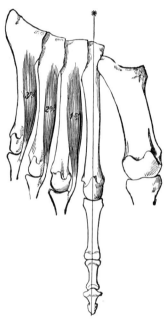

FIG. 431.—The Interossei plantares. Left foot.

The Fourth Layer.

Interossei.

The **Interossei** in the foot are similar to those in the hand, with this exception, that they are grouped around the middle line of the *second* digit, instead of that of the *third*. They are seven in number, and consist of two groups, dorsal and plantar.

The **Interossei dorsales** (*Dorsal interossei*) (Fig. 431), *four* in number, are situated between the metatarsal bones. They are bipenniform muscles, each *arising* by two heads from the adjacent sides of the metatarsal bones between which it is placed; their tendons are *inserted* into the bases of the first phalanges, and into the aponeurosis of the tendons of the Extensor digitorum longus. In the angular interval left between the heads of each of the three lateral muscles, one of the perforating arteries passes to the dorsum of the foot; through the space between the heads of the first muscle the deep plantar branch of the dorsalis pedis artery enters the sole of the foot. The first is *inserted* into the medial side of the second toe; the other three are *inserted* into the lateral sides of the second, third, and fourth toes.

Action.—Abduct the toes from the longitudinal axis of the second toe. Flex the proximal and extend the distal phalanges.

Nerves.—Branches of the lateral plantar nerve, containing fibers from the first and second sacral nerves.

The **Interossei plantares** (*Plantar interossei*) (Fig. 431), *three* in number, lie beneath rather than between the metatarsal bones, and each is connected with but one metatarsal bone. They *arise* from the bases and medial sides of the bodies of the third, fourth, and fifth metatarsal bones, and are *inserted* into the medial sides of the bases of the first phalanges of the same toes, and into the aponeuroses of the tendons of the Extensor digitorum longus.

Action.—Adduct the toes toward the axis of the second toe. Flex the proximal and extend the distal phalanges.

Nerve.—Branches of the lateral plantar nerve, containing fibers from the first and second sacral nerves.

Group Actions of Foot Muscles.—Flexion of the distal phalanges of the four small toes is performed by the Flexor digitorum longus and the Quadratus plantæ. The latter is really a part of the long flexor correcting the direction of its pull. Flexion of the second phalanges is by the Flexor digitorum brevis. Flexion of the proximal phalanges is by the Interossei and Lumbricales, with added strength given to the small toe by its Flexor brevis and Abductor. Flexion of the second phalanx of the great toe is performed by the Flexor hallucis longus; of the proximal phalanx by the Flexor hallucis brevis, Abductor hallucis, and Adductor hallucis.

Extension of the distal phalanges of all toes is performed by the Interossei, Lumbricales, Abductor digiti quinti, and Abductor hallucis. Extension of all toes is performed by the Extensor digitorum longus, Extensor hallucis longus, and Extensor digitorum brevis.

Abduction and adduction of the toes is toward the longitudinal axis of the second digit, rather than the third as in the hand. The abductors are the Interossei dorsales, Abductor hallucis, and Abductor digiti quinti. The adductors are the Interossei plantares and Adductor hallucis.

BIBLIOGRAPHY.

MUSCLES

HISTOLOGY OF MUSCLE

A cytological study of fatigued muscle. ADELHELM, E.: 1938. Anat. Rec., Vol. 70, pp. 473–481.
Wave mechanics in striated muscle. XIX. Experimental variation in number and pattern of living muscle striæ produced by heat. CAREY, E. J., W. ZEIT, and L. MASSOPUST: 1942. Am. J. Anat., Vol. 70, pp. 119–133.
The attachment of skeletal muscle fibers. Goss, C. M.: 1944. Am. J. Anat., Vol. 74, pp. 259–289.
The structural changes in striped muscle during contraction. JORDON, H. E.: 1933. Physiol. Rev., Vol. 13, pp. 301–324.
The development of the muscle-tendon attachment in the rat. LONG, M. E.: 1947. Am. J. Anat., Vol. 81, pp. 159–197.
Vitamin E and muscle pigment in the rat. MASON, K. E., and A. F. EMMEL: 1945. Anat. Rec., Vol. 92, pp. 33–59.
Studies of living muscles. SPEIDEL, C. C.: 1938. Am. J. Anat., Vol. 62, pp. 179–235.

MYOLOGY

Variations in the origin of the m. trapezius. BEATON, L. E., and B. J. ANSON: 1942. Anat. Rec., Vol. 83, pp. 41–46.
The comparative anatomy of the dorsal interosseous muscles. CAMPBELL, B.: 1939. Anat. Rec., Vol. 73, pp. 115–125.
The extensor indicis proprius muscle. CAULDWELL, E. W., B. J. ANSON, and R. R. WRIGHT: 1943. Quart. Bull., Northwestern U. Med. School, Vol. 17, pp. 267–279.
The plantaris muscle. DASELER, E. H., and B. J. ANSON: 1943. J. Bone and Joint Surg., Vol. 25, pp. 822–827.
The accessory tendon of the flexor pollicis longus muscle. DYKES, J., and B. J. ANSON: 1944. Anat. Rec., Vol. 90, pp. 83–87.
Some anomalous hamstring muscles. GRAY, D. J.: 1945. Anat. Rec., Vol. 91, pp. 33–38.

32

Phylogeny of the distal musculature of the pectoral appendage. HOWELL, A. B.: 1936. J. Morph., Vol. 60, pp. 287–315.

Variations of the interosseous muscles of the human foot. MANTER, J. T.: 1945. Anat. Rec., Vol. 93, pp. 117–124.

Anthropological significance of the musculus pyramidalis and its variability in man. MONTAGU, M. F. ASHLEY: 1939. Am. J. Phys. Anthrop., Vol. 25, pp. 435–490.

The palmaris longus muscle and tendon. A study of 1600 extremities. REIMANN, A. F., E. H. DASELER, B. J. ANSON, and L. E. BEATON: 1944. Anat. Rec., Vol. 89, pp. 495–505.

The m. pectoralis minor in American whites and American negroes. SEIB, G. A.: 1938. Am. J. Phys. Anthrop., Vol. 23, pp. 389–419.

The homologies of the forearm flexors: Urodeles, lizards, mammals. STRAUS, W. L., JR.: 1942. Am. J. Anat., Vol. 70, pp. 281–316.

Absence of superior gemellus muscle in American whites and negroes. TERRY, R. J.: 1942. Am. J. Phys. Anthrop., Vol. 29, pp. 47–56.

INNERVATION OF MUSCLES

Demonstration of the nerve to the levator glandulæ thyreoideæ muscle. KEYES, E. L.: 1940. Anat. Rec., Vol. 77, pp. 293–295.

The innervation of the flexor digitorum profundus and lumbrical muscles. SUNDERLAND, S.: 1945. Anat. Rec., Vol. 93, pp. 317–321.

The innervation of the first dorsal interosseous muscle of the hand. SUNDERLAND, S.: 1946. Anat. Rec., Vol. 95, pp. 7–10.

Loss of nerve endings in degenerated skeletal muscles of young vitamin E deficient rats. TELFORD, I. R.: 1941. Anat. Rec., Vol. 81, pp. 171–181.

ABDOMINAL WALL, INGUINAL REGION, AND PELVIS

The anatomy of the region of inguinal hernia. ANSON, B. J., E. H. MORGAN, and C. B. McVAY: 1942. Quart. Bull., Northwestern U. Med. School, Vol. 16, pp. 128–141.

Studies on the inguinal region. I. The conjoined aponeurosis versus the conjoined tendon. CHANDLER, S. B., and M. SCHADEWALD: 1944. Anat. Rec., Vol. 89, pp. 339–343.

Constitution of the sheath of the rectus abdominis muscle. CHOUKE, K. S.: 1935. Anat. Rec., Vol. 61, pp. 341–349.

A working model to demonstrate the anatomical relationships of inguinal herniæ. COLE, A. E.: 1941. Anat. Rec., Vol. 79, pp. 53–56.

The evolution of the pelvic floor of primates. ELFTMAN, H. O.: 1932. Am. J. Anat., Vol. 51, pp. 307–346.

The pelvic diaphragm in the female. Its form, function and a method of repair for laceration. HILL, H., and D. T. VAN DEL: 1932. Surg. Gyn. and Obs., Vol. 54, pp. 108–116.

Anatomy of the inguinal region. HOWELL, A. B.: 1939. Surgery, Vol. 6, pp. 653–662.

Composition of the rectus sheath. McVAY, C. B., and B. J. ANSON: 1940. Anat. Rec., Vol. 77, pp. 213–225.

The inguinal canal of primates. MILLER, R. A.: 1947. Am. J. Anat., Vol. 80, pp. 117–142.

Anatomy of the attachments of the diaphragm: Their relation to the problems of the surgery of diaphragmatic hernia. RIVES, J. D., and D. D. BAKER: 1942. Ann. Surg., Vol. 115, pp. 745–755.

MUSCLE ACTIONS

Experimental studies on the movements of the mammalian tongue. II. The protrusion mechanism of the tongue (dog). BENNETT, G. A., and R. C. HUTCHINSON: 1946. Anat. Rec., Vol. 94, pp. 57–83.

The actions of the extensor digitorum communis, interosseous and lumbrical muscles. SUNDERLAND, S.: 1945. Am. J. Anat., Vol. 77, pp. 189–217.

EXPERIMENTAL

Studies on transplanted embryonic limbs of the chick. I. The development of muscle in nerveless and in innervated grafts. EASTLICK, H. L.: 1943. J. Exp. Zool., Vol. 93, pp. 27–49.

Form and behavior of adult mammalian skeletal muscle *in vitro*. POGOGEFF, I. A., and M. R. MURRAY: 1946. Anat. Rec., Vol. 95, pp. 321–335.

The functional results of muscle transposition in the hind limb of the rat. SPERRY, R. W.: 1940. J. Comp. Neur., Vol. 73, pp. 379–404.

A comparison of growth, differentiation, activity and action currents of heart and skeletal muscle in tissue culture. SZEPSENWOL, J.: 1946. Anat. Rec., Vol. 95, pp. 125–146.

Tendon Sheaths and Tendons

The tensile strength of human tendons. CRONKITE, A. E.: 1936. Anat. Rec., Vol. 64, pp. 173–186.

A study of the tendon sheaths of the foot and their relation to infection. GRODINSKY, M.: 1930. Surg., Gyn. and Obst., Vol. 51, pp. 460–468.

Infections of the Hand. KANAVEL, A. B.: 1939. Lea & Febiger, Phila., 7th Ed., 503 pp.

Surgical anatomy of the flexor tendons of the wrist. KAPLAN, E. B.: 1945. J. Bone and Joint Surg., Vol. 27, pp. 368–372.

FASCIÆ

General and Comprehensive

A Description of the Planes of Fascia of the Human Body. GALLAUDET, B. B.: 1931. Columbia U. Press, New York, v + 75 pp.

Fasciæ of the Human Body and Their Relation to the Organs They Envelop. SINGER, E.: 1935. William Wood, Baltimore, ix + 105 pp.

Connective Tissues

Some observations on the pre-adipose cells. CHANG, CH.: 1940. Anat. Rec., Vol. 77, pp. 397–406.

Microscopic studies of the new formation of fat in living adult rabbits. CLARK, E. R., and E. L.: 1940. Am. J. Anat., Vol. 67, pp. 255–285.

Structural changes associated with advancing age in the thyroid gland of the female rat with particular reference to alterations in the connective tissue. LANSING, W., and J. M. WOLFE: 1944. Anat. Rec., Vol. 88, pp. 311–325.

Electron microscope investigations of the structure of collagen. SCHMITT, F. O., C. E. HALL, and M. A. JAKUS: 1942. J. Cell and Comp. Physiol., Vol. 20, pp. 11–33.

Studies on the development of connective tissue in transparent chambers in the rabbit's ear. STEARNS, M. L.: 1940. Am. J. Anat., Vol. 66, pp. 133–176.

Adipose tissue, a neglected subject. WELLS, H. G.: 1940. J. Amer. Med. Assn., Vol. 114, pp. 2177–2183 and 2284–2289.

Head, Neck and Thorax

The relation of the spread of infection to fascial planes in the neck and thorax. COLLER, F. A., and L. YGLESIAS: 1937. Surgery, Vol. 1, pp. 323–337.

The fasciæ and fascial spaces of the head, neck and adjacent regions. GRODINSKY, M., and E. A. HOLYOKE: 1938. Am. J. Anat., Vol. 63, pp. 367–408.

Description of a fascia situated between the serratus anterior muscle and the thorax. LEE, F. C.: 1941. Anat. Rec., Vol. 81, pp. 35–41.

Note on a fascia underneath the pectoralis major muscle. LEE, F. C.: 1944. Anat. Rec., Vol. 90, pp. 45–49.

Hand

The midpalmar compartment, associated spaces and limiting layers. ANSON, B. J., and F. L. ASHLEY: 1940. Anat. Rec., Vol. 78, pp. 389–407.

Clinical and anatomical investigations of deep fascial space infections of the hand. FLYNN, J. E.: 1942. Am. J. Surg., Vol. 55, pp. 467–475.

The cutaneous ligaments of the digits. GRAYSON, J.: 1941. J. Anat., Vol. 75, pp. 164–165.

The fasciæ and fascial spaces of the palm. GRODINSKY, M., and E. A. HOLYOKE: 1941. Anat. Rec., Vol. 79, pp. 435–451.

The Principles of Anatomy as Seen in the Hand. JONES, F. W.: 1942. Baillière, Tindall & Cox, London, 2nd Ed., x + 418 pp.

Infections of the Hand. KANAVEL, A. B.: 1939. Lea & Febiger, Phila., 7th Ed., 503 pp.

The palmar fascia in connection with Dupuytren's contracture. KAPLAN, E. B.: 1938. Surgery, Vol. 4, pp. 415–422.

Lower Extremity

The fossa ovalis, and related blood vessels. ANSON, B. J., and C. B. McVAY: 1938. Anat. Rec., Vol. 72, pp. 399–404.

A study of the fascial spaces of the foot and their bearing on infections. GRODINSKY, M.: 1929. Surg., Gyn. and Obs., Vol. 49, pp. 737–751.

Abdomen

The cone of renal fascia in the adult white male. CONGDON, E. D., and J. N. EDSON: 1941. Anat. Rec., Vol. 80, pp. 289–313.

Fasciæ of fusion and elements of fused enteric mesenteries in the human adult. CONGDON, E. D., R. BLUMBERG, and W. HENRY: 1942. Am. J. Anat., Vol. 70, pp. 251–279.

Gross structure of the subcutaneous layer of the anterior and lateral trunk in the male. CONGDON, E. D., J. N. EDSON, and S. YANITELLI: 1946. Am. J. Anat., Vol. 79, pp. 399–429.

The urachus, its anatomy and associated fasciæ. HAMMOND, G. L. YGLESIAS, and J. E. DAVIS 1941. Anat. Rec., Vol. 80, pp. 271–287.

A note on the renal fascia. MARTIN, C. P.: 1942. J. Anat., Vol. 77, pp. 101–103.

The third inguinal ring. MCGREGOR, A. L.: 1929. Surg., Gyn. and Obs., Vol. 49, pp. 273–307

The renal fascia and its relation to the transversalis fascia. TOBIN, C. E.: 1944. Anat. Rec. Vol. 89, pp. 295–311.

Continuity of the fasciæ lining the abdomen, pelvis, and spermatic cord. TOBIN, C. E., J. A BENJAMIN, and J. C. WELLS: 1946. Surg., Gyn. and Obs., Vol. 83, pp. 575–596.

Importance and distribution of the transversalis fascia from the viewpoint of the surgeon. ZIEMAN S. A.: 1942. Arch. Surg., Vol. 45, pp. 926–934.

PELVIS AND PERINEUM

The pelvic outlet—its practical application. DAVIES, J. W.: 1934. Surg., Gyn. and Obs., Vol. 58 pp. 70–78.

An histological study of the perivaginal fascia in a nullipara. GOFF, B. H.: 1931. Surg., Gyn and Obs., Vol. 52, pp. 32–42.

Aponeurotic and fascial continuities in the abdomen, pelvis and thigh. MCVAY, C. B., and B. J ANSON: 1940. Anat. Rec., Vol. 76, pp. 213–231.

The ischial callosities of primates. MILLER, R. A.: 1945. Am. J. Anat., Vol. 76, pp. 67–91.

The fascia surrounding the vagina, its origin and arrangement. SEARS, N. P.: 1933. Am. J Obs. and Gyn., Vol. 25, pp. 484–492.

Anatomical study and clinical consideration of the fasciæ limiting urinary extravasation from the penile urethra. TOBIN, C. E., and J. A. BENJAMIN: 1944. Surg., Gyn. and Obs., Vol. 79, pp. 195–204.

Anatomical and surgical restudy of Denonvilliers' fascia. TOBIN, C. E., and J. A. BENJAMIN 1945. Surg., Gyn. and Obs., Vol. 80, pp. 373–388.

Value of Buck's and Colles' fasciæ. WESSON, M. B.: 1945. J. Urol., Vol. 53, pp. 365–372

THE BLOOD VASCULAR SYSTEM.

THE heart is the central organ of the blood vascular system, and is a muscular pump; by its contraction the blood is pumped to all parts of the body through series of tubes, termed **arteries**. The arteries undergo enormous ramification in their course throughout the body, and end in minute vessels, called **arterioles**, which in turn open into a close-meshed network of microscopic vessels, termed **capillaries**. After the blood has passed through the capillaries it is collected into a series of venules which unite to form **veins**, by which it is returned to the heart.

The human heart is divided by septa into right and left halves, and each half further divided into two cavities, an upper termed the **atrium** and a lower the **ventricle**. The heart therefore consists of four chambers, two, the right atrium and right ventricle, forming the right half, and two, the left atrium and left ventricle the left half. Venous blood, with waste products of metabolism and CO_2 from the tissues is carried from all parts of the body by the veins to the right atrium. From there it passes into the right ventricle and is pumped by the heart through the pulmonary artery into the lungs. As the blood passes through the pulmonary capillaries CO_2 is given off into the air spaces and O_2 taken up. The oxygenated blood is returned to the left atrium by the pulmonary veins, passes into the left ventricle and is pumped through the aorta and distributed by numerous arterial branches and capillaries to all the tissues of the body. The arterial blood in the tissue capillaries gives up O_2 and takes up CO_2, and as venous blood is carried by the veins back to the heart. This passage of the blood through the heart and bloodvessels is termed the **circulation of the blood.**

The course of the blood from the left ventricle through the body to the right side of the heart constitutes the greater or **systemic circulation**, while its passage from the right ventricle through the lungs to the left side of the heart is termed the lesser or **pulmonary circulation.**

It is necessary, however, to state that the blood which circulates through the spleen, pancreas, stomach, small intestine, and the greater part of the large intestine is not returned directly from these organs to the heart, but is conveyed by the **portal vein** to the liver. In the liver this vein divides, like an artery, and ultimately ends in capillary-like vessels (*sinusoids*), from which the rootlets of a series of veins, called the **hepatic veins**, arise; these carry the blood into the inferior vena cava, whence it is conveyed to the right atrium. From this it will be seen that the blood contained in the portal vein passes through two sets of capillaries: (1) the capillaries in the spleen, pancreas, stomach, etc., and (2) the sinusoids in the liver. The blood in the portal vein carries certain of the products of digestion: the carbohydrates, which are mostly taken up by the liver cells and stored as glycogen, and the protein products which remain in solution and are carried into the general circulation to the various tissues and organs of the body.

Speaking generally, the arteries may be said to contain pure (oxygenated) and the veins impure blood (blood containing less oxygen). This is true of the systemic, but not of the pulmonary vessels, since it has been seen that the impure blood is conveyed from the heart to the lungs by the pulmonary arteries, and the pure blood returned from the lungs to the heart by the pulmonary veins. Arteries, therefore, must be defined as vessels which convey blood *from* the heart, and veins as vessels which return blood *to* the heart.

(501)

DEVELOPMENT OF THE VASCULAR SYSTEM.

Bloodvessels first make their appearance in several scattered *vascular are* which are developed simultaneously between the entoderm and the mesoderm the yolk-sac, later the same process occurs in the body of the embryo. Here a ne type of cell, the **angioblast** or **vasoformative cell**, is usually described as differentiati from the mesoderm. It may be that the angioblasts are derived directly fro the primitive streak and are as independent a race of cells as the mesoblas These cells as they divide form small, dense masses which soon join with simil masses to form **plexuses**. Within these solid plexuses and also within the isolat masses of angioblasts plasma collects and the lumen develops. The flattened ce at the periphery form the endothelium. The nucleated red blood corpuscles devel from small masses of the original angioblast left attached to the inner wall of t lumen. Such a mass is known as a blood island and hemoglobin gradually accum lates within it. Later the cells on the surface round up, giving the mass a mulberr like appearance. Then the red blood cells break loose and are carried away in t plasma. Such free blood cells continue to divide. Blood islands have been seen the area vasculosa, in the omphalomesenteric vein and arteries, and in the dors aorta. All the vessels of the body are derived from capillary plexuses and ul mately the extension of such plexuses is confined to sprouts from ones already la down.

Eternod describes the circulation in an embryo which he estimated to be abo thirteen days old (Fig. 433). The rudiment of the heart is situated immediate below the fore-gut and consists of a short stem. It gives off two vessels, the prim tive aortæ, which run backward, one on either side of the notochord, and then pa into the body-stalk along which they are carried to the chorion. From the chorion villi the blood is returned by a pair of umbilical veins which unite in the body-sta to form a single vessel and subsequently encircle the mouth of the yolk-sac a open into the heart. At the junction of the yolk-sac and body-stalk each ve is joined by a branch from the vascular plexus of the yolk-sac.

By the forward growth and flexure of the head the pericardial area and t anterior portions of the primitive aortæ are folded backward on the ventral aspe of the fore-gut, and the original relation of the somatopleure and splanchnopleu layers of the pericardial area is reversed. Each primitive aorta now consists of ventral and a dorsal part connected anteriorly by an arch; these three parts a named respectively the anterior ventral aorta, the dorsal aorta, and the first aort arch. The vitelline veins which enter the embryo through the anterior wall of t umbilical orifice are now continuous with the posterior ends of the anterior ventr aorta. With the formation of the tail-fold the posterior parts of the primitive aort are carried forward in a ventral direction to form the posterior ventral aortæ an primary caudal arches. In the pericardial region the two primitive aortæ gro together, and fuse to form a single tubular heart, the posterior end of which receiv the two vitelline veins, while from its anterior end the two anterior ventral aort emerge. The first cephalic arches pass through the mandibular arches, and behir them five additional pairs subsequently develop, so that altogether six pairs aortic arches are formed; the fifth arches are very transitory vessels connecting th ventral aortæ with the dorsal ends of the sixth arches. By the rhythmical contra tion of the tubular heart the blood is forced through the aortæ and bloodvessels the vascular area, from which it is returned to the heart by the vitelline vein This constitutes the **vitelline circulation,** and by means of it nutriment is absorbe from the yolk (vitellus.)

The vitelline veins at first open separately into the posterior end of the tubula heart, but after a time their terminal portions fuse to form a single vessel. The vitelline veins ultimately drain the blood from the digestive tube, and are modified to form the portal vein. This modification is caused by the growth of the liver,

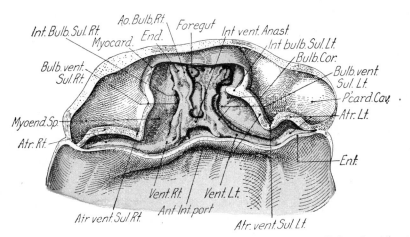

Fig. 432.—Heart from human embryo 1.8 mm. long. Pericardial and myocardial walls have been dissected off. *Ant. Int. port.*, anterior intestinal portal. *Ao. bulb*, aortic bulb. *Atr.*, atrium. *Atr. vent. sul.*, atrio-ventricular sulcus, *Bulb. cor.*, bulbus cordis. *Bulb vent. sul.*, bulbo-ventricular sulcus. *End.*, endocardium. *Ent*, entoderm. *Int. vent. anast.*, interventricular anastomosis. *Int. bulb. sul.*, interbulbar sulcus. *Myocard.*, myocardium. *Myoend. sp.*, myo-endocardial space. *Pcard. cav.*, pericardial cavity. *Vent.*, ventricle. (Davis.)

which interrupts their direct continuity with the heart; and the blood returned by them circulates through the liver before reaching the heart.

With the atrophy of the yolk-sac the vitelline circulation diminishes and ultimately ceases, while an increasing amount of blood is carried through the umbilical arteries to the villi of the chorion. Subsequently, as the non-placental chorionic villi atrophy, their vessels disappear; and then the umbilical arteries convey the whole of their contents to the placenta, whence it is returned to the heart by the umbilical veins. In this manner the placental circulation is established, and by means of it nutritive materials are absorbed from, and waste products given up to the maternal blood.

The umbilical veins, like the vitelline, undergo interruption in the developing

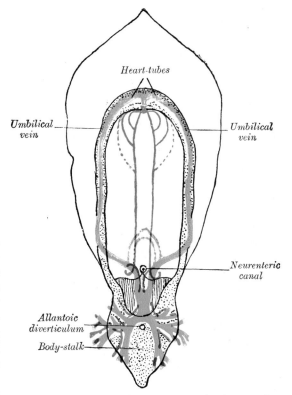

Fig. 433.—Diagram of the vascular channels in a human embryo of the second week. (After Eternod.) The red lines are the dorsal aortæ continued into the umbilical arteries. The red dotted lines are the ventral aortæ, and the blue dotted lines the vitelline veins.

liver, and the blood returned by them passes through this organ before reaching the heart. Ultimately the right umbilical vein shrivels up and disappears.

During the occurrence of these changes great alterations take place in the primitive heart and bloodvessels.

The Development of the Heart.—Both the myocardium and the endocardium are derived from bilateral but incompletely separated primordia which unite at an early stage to form the primitive tubular heart (Fig. 432). The bulbar ends of

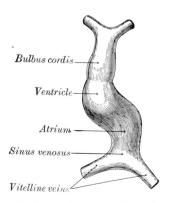

Bulbus cordis

Ventricle

Atrium

Sinus venosus

Vitelline veins

Fig. 434.—Diagram to illustrate the simple tubular condition of the heart. (Drawn from Ecker-Ziegler model.)

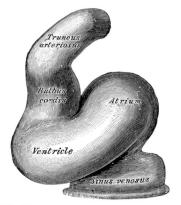

Truncus arteriosus

Bulbus cordis

Atrium

Ventricle

Sinus venosus

Fig. 435.—Heart of human embryo of about fourteen days. (From model by His.)

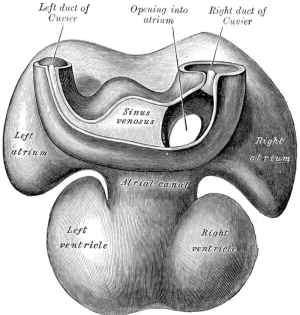

Left duct of Cuvier

Opening into atrium

Right duct of Cuvier

Sinus venosus

Left atrium

Right atrium

Atrial canal

Left ventricle

Right ventricle

Fig. 436.—Dorsal surface of heart of human embryo of thirty-five days. (From model by His.)

the primordia are continuous with the primitive aortæ and the atrial ends with the vitello-umbilical trunks. The simple tubular heart becomes elongated and bent on itself so as to form an S-shaped loop, the anterior part bending to the right and the posterior part to the left. The intermediate portion arches transversely from left to right, and then turns sharply forward into the anterior part of the loop. Slight constrictions make their appearance in the tube and divide it from behind forward into five parts, viz.: (1) the **sinus venosus**; (2) the **primitive atrium**; (3)

the **primitive ventricle**; (4) the **bulbus cordis,** and (5) the **truncus arteriosus** (Figs. 434, 435). The constriction between the atrium and ventricle constitutes the **atrial canal,** and indicates the site of the future atrio-ventricular valves.

The **sinus venosus** is at first situated in the septum transversum (a layer of mesoderm in which the liver and the central tendon of the diaphragm are developed) behind the primitive atrium, and is formed by the union of the vitelline veins. The veins or ducts of Cuvier from the body of the embryo and the umbilical veins from the placenta subsequently open into it (Fig. 435). The sinus is at first placed transversely, and opens by a median aperture into the primitive atrium. Soon, however, it assumes an oblique position, and becomes crescentic in form; its right half or horn increases more rapidly than the left, and the opening into the atrium now communicates with the right portion of the atrial cavity. The right horn and transverse portion of the sinus ultimately become incorporated with and

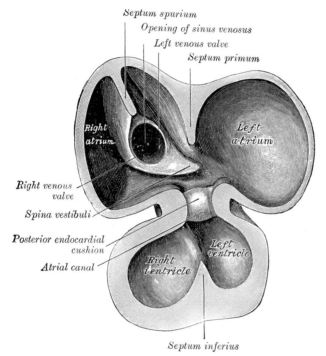

FIG. 437.—Interior of dorsal half of heart from a human embryo of about thirty days. (From model by His.)

form a part of the adult right atrium, the line of union between it and the auricula being indicated in the interior of the atrium by a vertical crest, the **crista terminalis of His.** The left horn, which ultimately receives only the left duct of Cuvier, persists as the coronary sinus (Fig. 436). The vitelline and umbilical veins are soon replaced by a single vessel, the **inferior vena cava,** and the three veins (inferior vena cava and right and left Cuvierian ducts) open into the dorsal aspect of the atrium by a common slit-like aperture (Fig. 437). The upper part of this aperture represents the opening of the permanent superior vena cava, the lower that of the inferior vena cava, and the intermediate part the orifice of the coronary sinus. The slit-like aperture lies obliquely, and is guarded by two valves, the **right** and **left venous valves;** above the opening these unite with each other and are continuous with a fold named the **septum spurium;** below the opening they fuse to form a triangular thickening—the **spina vestibuli.** The right venous valve is retained; a small septum, the **sinus septum,** grows from the posterior wall of the sinus venosus to fuse with the valve and divide it into two parts—an upper, the valve of the inferior vena cava, and a lower, the valve of the coronary sinus (Fig. 439). The extreme upper portion of the right venous valve, together with the septum spurium, form the crista terminalis already mentioned. The upper and middle thirds of the left venous valve disappear; the lower third is continued into the spina vestibuli, and later fuses with the septum secundum of the atria and takes part in the formation of the limbus fossæ ovalis.

The atrial canal is at first a short straight tube connecting the atrial with the ventricular portion of the heart, but its growth is relatively slow, and it becomes overlapped by the atria and ventricles so that its position on the surface of the heart is indicated only by an annular constriction (Fig. 438). Its lumen is reduced to a transverse slit, and two thickenings appear, one on its dorsal and another on its ventral wall. These thickenings, or **endocardial cushions** (Fig. 437) as they are termed, project into the canal, and, meeting in the middle line, unite to form the **septum intermedium** which divides the canal into two channels, the future right and left atrioventricular orifices.

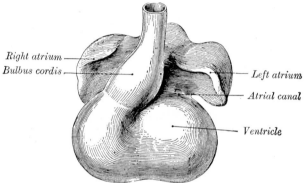

Right atrium —
Bulbus cordis —
— Left atrium
— Atrial canal
— Ventricle

FIG. 438.—Heart showing expansion of the atria. (Drawn from Ecker-Ziegler model.)

The **primitive atrium** grows rapidly and partially encircles the bulbus cordis; the groove against which the bulbus cordis lies is the first indication of a division into right and left atria. The cavity of the primitive atrium becomes subdivided into right and left chambers by a septum, the **septum primum** (Fig. 437), which grows downward into the cavity. For a time the atria communicate with each other by an opening, the **ostium primum of Born,** below the free margin of the septum. This opening is closed by the union of the septum primum with the septum intermedium, and the communication between the atria is reëstablished through an opening which is developed in the upper part of the septum primum; this opening is known as the **foramen ovale** (*ostium secundum of Born*) and persists until birth. A second septum, the **septum secundum** (Fig. 439), semilunar in shape, grows downward from the upper wall of the atrium immediately to the right of the primary septum and foramen ovale. Shortly after birth it fuses with the primary septum, and by this means the foramen ovale is closed, but sometimes the fusion is incomplete and the upper part of the foramen remains patent. The limbus fossæ ovalis denotes the free margin of the septum secundum. Issuing from each lung is a pair of pulmonary veins; each pair unites to form a single vessel, and these in turn join in a common trunk which opens into the left atrium. Subsequently the common trunk and the two vessels forming it expand and form the vestibule or greater part of the atrium, the expansion reaching as far as the openings of the four vessels, so that in the adult all four veins open separately into the left atrium.

The **primitive ventricle** becomes divided by a septum, the **septum inferius** or **ventricular septum** (Figs. 437, 438), which grows upward from the lower part of the ventricle, its position being indicated on the surface of the heart by a furrow. Its dorsal part increases more rapidly than its ventral portion, and fuses with the dorsal part of the septum intermedium. For a time an interventricular foramen exists above its ventral portion (Fig. 439), but this foramen is ultimately closed by the fusion of the aortic septum with the ventricular septum.

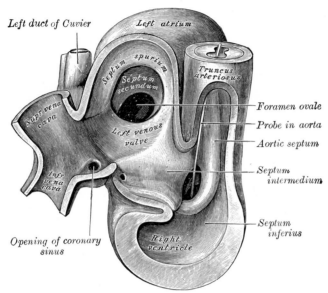

Fig. 439.—Interior of heart of human embryo of about thirty-five days.

When the heart assumes its S-shaped form, the **bulbus cordis** lies ventral to, and in front of, the primitive ventricle. The adjacent walls of the bulbus cordis and ventricle approximate, fuse, and finally disappear, and the bulbus cordis now

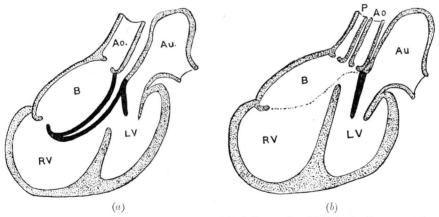

(a)   (b)

Fig. 440.—Diagrams to illustrate the transformation of the bulbus cordis. (Keith.) *Ao.* Truncus arteriosus.
Au. Atrium. *B.* Bulbus cordis. *RV.* Right ventricle. *LV.* Left ventricle. *P.* Pulmonary artery.

communicates freely with the right ventricle, while the junction of the bulbus with the truncus arteriosus is brought directly ventral to and applied to the atrial canal. By the upgrowth of the ventricular septum, the bulbus cordis is, in great measure, separated from the left ventricle, but remains an integral part of the right ventricle, of which it forms the infundibulum (Fig. 440).

The **truncus arteriosus** and **bulbus cordis** are divided by the **aortic septum** (Fig. 441). This makes its appearance in three portions. (1) Two distal ridge-like thickenings project into the lumen of the tube; these increase in size, and ultimately meet and fuse to form a septum, which takes a spiral course toward the proximal end of the truncus arteriosus. It divides the distal part of the truncus into two vessels, the aorta and pulmonary artery, which lie side by side above, but near the heart the pulmonary artery is in front of the aorta. (2) Four endocardial cushions appear in the proximal part of the truncus arteriosus in the region of the

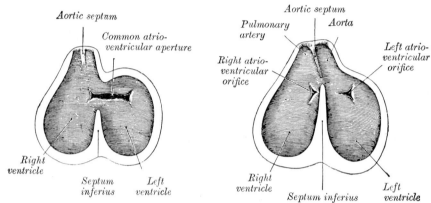

Fig. 441.—Diagrams to show the development of the septum of the aortic bulb and of the ventricles. (Born.)

future semilunar valves; the manner in which these are related to the aortic septum is described below. (3) Two endocardial thickenings—anterior and posterior—develop in the bulbus cordis and unite to form a short septum; this joins above with the aortic septum and below with the ventricular septum. The septum grows down into the ventricle as an oblique partition, which ultimately blends with the ventricular septum in such a way as to bring the bulbus cordis into communication with the pulmonary artery, and, through the latter, with the sixth pair of aortic arches; while the left ventricle is brought into continuity with the aorta, which communicates with the remaining aortic arches.

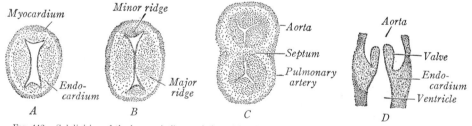

Fig. 442.—Subdivision of the human bulbus and the origin of the semilunar valves. *A–C*, Transverse sections, at five to seven weeks (× 27). *D*, Longitudinal section, at seven weeks (× 45). (Arey's Developmental Anatomy, courtesy of W. B. Saunders Co.)

The Valves of the Heart.—The atrioventricular valves are developed in relation to the atrial canal. By the upward expansion of the bases of the ventricles the canal becomes invaginated into the ventricular cavities. The invaginated margin forms the rudiments of the lateral cusps of the atrioventricular valves; the mesial or septal cusps of the valves are developed as downward prolongations of the septum intermedium. The aortic and pulmonary semilunar valves are formed from four endocardial thickenings—an anterior, a posterior, and two lateral—which appear at the proximal end of the truncus arteriosus. As the aortic septum grows downward it divides each of the lateral thickenings into two, thus giving rise to six thickenings—the rudiments of the semilunar valves—three at the aortic and three at the pulmonary orifice (Fig. 442).

Further Development of the Arteries.—Recent observations show that practically none of the main vessels of the adult arises as such in the embryo. In the site of each vessel a capillary network forms, and, by the enlargement of definite paths in this, the larger arteries and veins are developed. The branches of the main arteries are not always simple modifications of the vessels of the capillary network, but may arise as new outgrowths from the enlarged stem.

It has been seen (page 502) that each primitive aorta consists of a ventral and a dorsal part which are continuous through the first aortic arch. The dorsal aortæ at first run backward separately on either side of the notochord, but about the fourth week the caudal portions fuse to form a single trunk, the descending aorta. The first aortic arches run through the mandibular arches, and behind them four additional pairs are developed within the visceral arches; so that, in all, five pairs

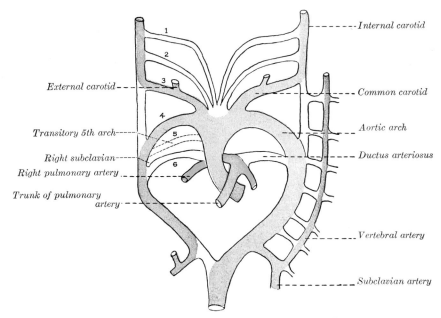

FIG. 443.—Scheme of the aortic arches and their destination. (Modified from Kollmann.)

of aortic arches are formed (Fig. 443). The existence of the aortic arches is the result of the interposition of the pharynx, with its pouches, in the path of the blood stream from the heart to the dorsal aortæ. Since the arterial end of the heart at first lies below the cranial end of the pharynx and later shifts backward relative to it, the aortic arches develop in regular order from before backward. As the more caudal ones are completed, the first and then the second undergo involution. The first arch is strongly developed and the only one present in the 3-mm. embryo shown in Figs. 444 and 445. By the time the embryo is 4-mm. in length the first arch has about disappeared, the second arch has formed, reached its greatest extent and then diminished in size, and the third arch is well developed (Figs. 446 and 447). The fourth arch may be complete and the dorsal and ventral sprouts for the pulmonary arch may be present. In a 5-mm. embryo the third and fourth arches are in a condition of maximum development and the dorsal and ventral sprouts of the pulmonary arches have nearly met (Figs. 448 and 449). The pulmonary arches are usually complete in the 6-mm. embryo. The right one soon begins to regress and disappears by the time the embryo is 12 to 13 mm. in length. The third aortic arches also disappear at about the same time (Figs. 450, 451 and 452). There is some evidence for the occasional occurrence of an additional aortic arch between

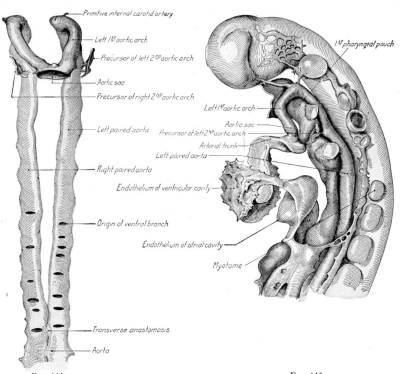

FIGS. 444 and 445.—Ventral and lateral views of the cranial portion of the arterial system of a 3 mm. human embryo. The first aortic arch is at its maximum development and the dorsal and ventral outgrowths, which are to aid in the formation of the second arch are just appearing. (Congdon).

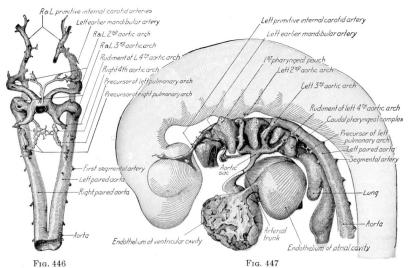

FIGS. 446 and 447.—Ventral and lateral views of an embryo 4 mm. in length, in which the first arch has gone, the second is much reduced, and the third well developed. Dorsal and ventral outgrowths for the fourth and probably the pulmonary arch (fifth) are present. (Congdon).

the fourth arch and the pulmonary arch. In such cases it would be the fifth and the pulmonary the sixth (Fig. 443).

The Ventral Aorta consists of a single short **arterial trunk** which connects the heart with the aortic sac and from the latter arise the aortic arches. According to Congdon there are no paired ventral aortæ in man. From the arterial trunk and sac there are formed the innominate artery, a short portion of the aortic arch and a portion of the pulmonary artery.

The Aortic Arches.—The first and second arches disappear early, but the dorsal end of the second gives origin to the stapedial artery, a vessel which atrophies in man but persists in some mammals. It passes through the ring of the stapes and divides into supraorbital, infraorbital, and mandibular branches which follow the

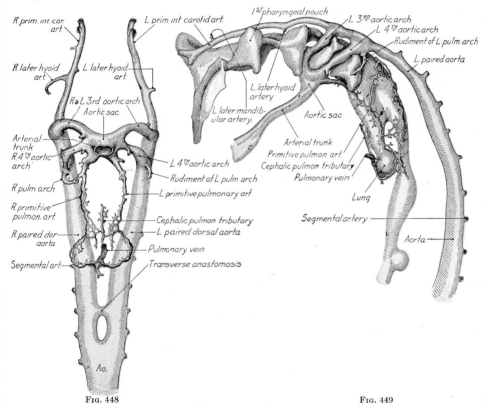

FIG. 448

FIG. 449

FIGS. 448 and 449.—Ventral and lateral views of a 5 mm. embryo. The third and fourth arches are in a condition of maximum development, the dorsal and ventral sprouts for the pulmonary arches have nearly met. The primitive pulmonary arches are already of considerable length. (Congdon.)

three divisions of the trigeminal nerve. The infraorbital and mandibular arise from a common stem, the terminal part of which anastomoses with the external carotid. On the obliteration of the stapedial artery this anastomosis enlarges and forms the internal maxillary artery, and the branches of the stapedial artery are now branches of this vessel. The common stem of the infraorbital and mandibular branches passes between the two roots of the auriculotemporal nerve and becomes the middle meningeal artery; the original supraorbital branch of the stapedial is represented by the orbital twigs of the middle meningeal. The third aortic arch constitutes the common carotid and the commencement of the internal carotid artery, and is therefore named the **carotid arch**. From it arises the external carotid according to Congdon. The fourth right arch forms the right subclavian as far as the origin of its internal mammary branch; while the fourth left arch constitutes the arch of the aorta between the origin of the left carotid artery and the termination of the ductus arteriosus. The fifth right arch disappears; the fifth left arch gives off the pulmonary arteries and forms the ductus arteriosus; this duct remains pervious during the whole of fetal life, but is obliterated a few days after birth. His showed that in the early embryo the right and left arches each gives a branch to the lungs, but that later both pulmonary arteries take origin from the left arch.

The Dorsal Aortæ.—In front of the third aortic arches the dorsal aortæ persist and form the continuations of the internal carotid arteries; these arteries pass to the brain and each divides into an anterior and a posterior branch, the former giving off the ophthalmic and the anterior and middle cerebral arteries, while the latter turns back and joins the cerebral part of the vertebral artery. Behind the third arch the right dorsal aorta disappears as far as the point where the two dorsal aortæ fuse to form the descending aorta. The part of the left dorsal aorta between the third and fourth arches disappears, while the remainder persists to form the descending part of the arch of the aorta. A constriction, the **aortic isthmus**, is sometimes seen in the aorta between the origin of the left subclavian and the attachment of the ductus arteriosus.

Sometimes the right subclavian artery arises from the aortic arch distal to the origin of the left subclavian and passes upward and to the right behind the trachea and esophagus. This condition may be explained by the persistence of the right dorsal aorta and the obliteration of the fourth right arch.

The heart originally lies on the ventral aspect of the pharynx, immediately behind the stomodeum. With the elongation of the neck and the development of the lungs it recedes within the thorax, and, as a consequence, the ventral aorta is drawn out and the original position of the fourth and fifth arches is greatly modified. Thus, on the right side the fourth recedes to the root of the neck, while on the left side it is withdrawn within the thorax. The recurrent nerves originally pass to the larynx under the fifth pair of arches, and are therefore pulled backward with the descent of these structures, so that in the adult the left nerve hooks around the ligamentum arteriosum; owing to the disappearance of the fifth right arch the right nerve hooks around that immediately above it, *i. e.*, the commencement of the subclavian artery. Segmental arteries arise from the primitive dorsal aortæ and course between successive segments. The seventh segmental artery is of special interest, since it forms the lower end of the vertebral artery and, when the forelimb bud appears, sends a branch to it (the subclavian artery). From the seventh segmental arteries the entire left subclavian and the greater part of the right subclavian are formed. The second pair of segmental arteries accompany the hypoglossal nerves to the brain and are named the hypoglossal arteries. Each sends forward a branch which forms the cerebral part of the vertebral artery and anastomoses with the posterior branch of the internal carotid. The two vertebrals unite on the ventral surface of the hind-brain to form the basilar artery. Later the hypoglossal artery atrophies and the vertebral is connected with the first segmental artery. The cervical part of the vertebral is developed from a longitudinal anastomosis between the first seven segmental arteries, so that the seventh of these ultimately becomes the source of the artery. As a result of the growth of the upper limb the subclavian artery increases greatly in size and the vertebral then appears to spring from it.

Recent observations show that several segmental arteries contribute branches to the upper limb-bud and form in it a free capillary anastomosis. Of these branches, only one, viz., that derived from the seventh segmental artery, persists to form the subclavian artery. The subclavian artery is prolonged into the limb under the names of the axillary and brachial arteries, and these together constitute the arterial stem for the upper arm, the direct continuation of this stem in the forearm is the volar interosseous artery. A branch which accompanies the median nerve soon increases in size and forms the main vessel (median artery) of the forearm,

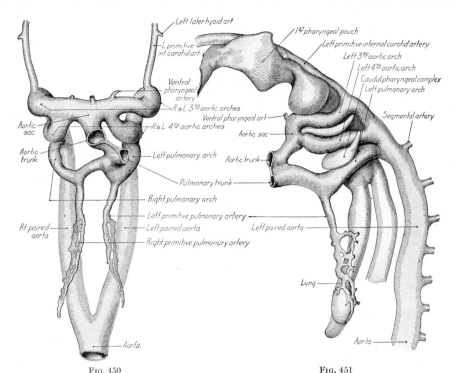

FIG. 450   FIG. 451

FIGS. 450 and 451.—Ventral and lateral views of an 11-mm. embryo. The pulmonary arches are complete and the right is already regressing. The third arch is bent cranially at its dorsal end. (Congdon.)

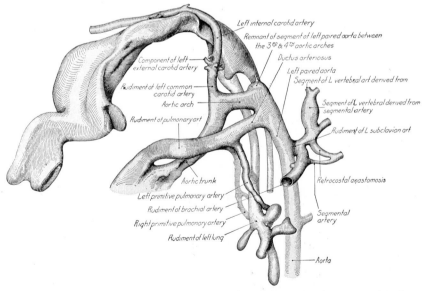

FIG. 452.—Lateral view of a 14 mm. embryo. The last indications of the aortic arch system are just disappearing (Congdon.)

33

while the volar interosseous diminishes. Later the radial and ulnar arteries are developed as branches of the brachial part of the stem and coincidently with their enlargement the median artery recedes; occasionally it persists as a vessel of some considerable size and then accompanies the median nerve into the palm of the hand.

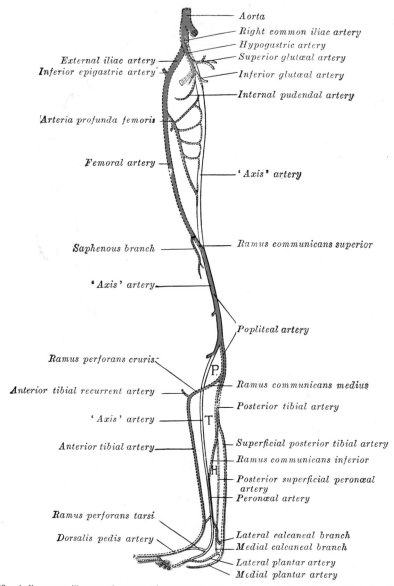

Fig. 453.—A diagram to illustrate the general development of the arteries of the lower limb. The letter *P* indicates the position of the Popliteus: *T*, that of the Tibialis posterior; *H*, that of the Flexor hallucis longus. (H. D. Senior.)

According to Senior (Fig. 453) the primary arterial trunk or "axis" artery of the embryonic lower limb arises from the dorsal root of the umbilical artery, and courses along the dorsal surface of the thigh, knee and leg. The femoral artery springs from the external iliac and forms a new channel along the ventral side of the thigh to its communication with the axis artery above the knee. As this channel increases in size that part of the axis artery proximal to the communication disappears, except its upper end which persists as the inferior gluteal artery. Two other segments of the axial artery persist; one forms the proximal part of the popliteal artery, and the other forms a part of the peroneal artery.

Further Development of the Veins.—The formation of the great veins of the embryo may be best considered by dividing them into two groups, **visceral** and **parietal**.

The Visceral Veins.—The visceral veins are the two **vitelline** or **omphalomesenteric veins** bringing the blood from the yolk-sac, and the two **umbilical veins** returning the blood from the placenta; these four veins open close together into the sinus venosus.

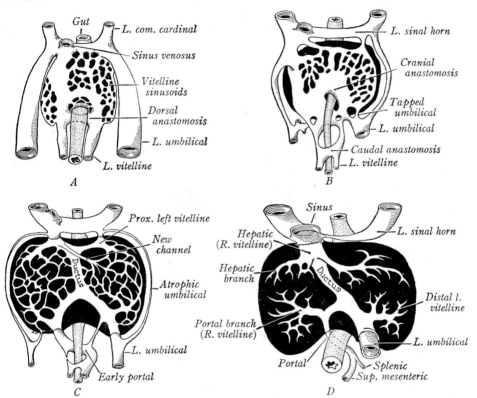

Fig. 454.—Transformation of the human, vitelline and umbilical veins in the region of the liver, seen in ventral view (adapted). *A*, At 4.5 mm.; *B*, at 5 mm.; *C*, at 6 mm.; *D*, at 9 mm. (Arey's Developmental Anatomy, courtesy of W. B. Saunders Co.)

The **Vitelline Veins** run upward at first in front, and subsequently on either side of the intestinal canal. They unite on the ventral aspect of the canal, and beyond this are connected to one another by two anastomotic branches, one on the dorsal, and the other on the ventral aspect of the duodenal portion of the intestine, which is thus encircled by two venous rings (Fig. 454); into the middle or dorsal anastomosis the superior mesenteric vein opens. The portions of the veins above the upper ring become interrupted by the developing liver and broken up by it into a plexus of small capillary-like vessels termed **sinusoids** (Minot). The branches conveying the blood to this plexus are named the **venæ advehentes,** and become the branches of the portal vein; while the vessels draining the plexus into the sinus venosus are termed the **venæ revehentes,** and form the future hepatic veins (Figs. 454, 455). Ultimately the left vena revehens no longer communicates directly with the sinus venosus, but opens into the right vena revehens. The persistent part of the upper venous ring, above the opening of the superior mesenteric vein, forms the trunk of the portal vein.

The two **Umbilical Veins** fuse early to form a single trunk in the body-stalk, but remain separate within the embryo and pass forward to the sinus venosus in the side walls of the body. Like the vitelline veins, their direct connection with the sinus venosus becomes interrupted by the developing liver, and thus at this stage all the blood from the yolk-sac and placenta passes through the substance of the liver before it reaches the heart. The right umbilical and right vitelline veins shrivel and disappear; the left umbilical, on the other hand, becomes enlarged and opens into the upper venous ring of the vitelline veins. With the atrophy of the yolk-sac the left vitelline vein also undergoes atrophy and disappears. Finally a direct branch is established between this ring and the right hepatic vein; this branch is named the **ductus venosus**, and, enlarging rapidly,

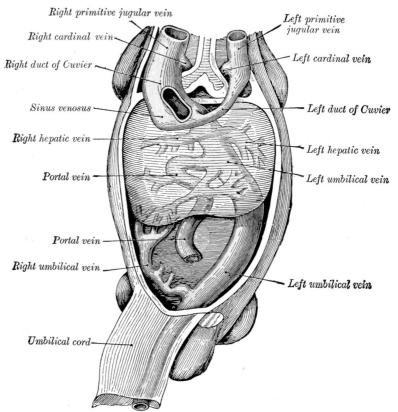

FIG. 455.—Human embryo with heart and anterior body-wall removed to show the sinus venosus and its tributaries
(After His.)

it forms a wide channel through which most of the blood, returned from the placenta, is carried direct to the heart without passing through the liver. A small proportion of the blood from the placenta is, however, conveyed from the left umbilical vein to the liver through the left vena advehens. The left umbilical vein and the ductus venosus undergo atrophy and obliteration after birth, and form respectively the ligamentum teres and ligamentum venosum of the liver.

The Parietal Veins.—The first indication of a parietal system consists in the appearance of two short transverse veins, the **ducts of Cuvier**, which open, one on either side, into the sinus venosus. Each of these ducts receives an ascending and descending vein. The ascending veins return the blood from the parietes of the trunk and from the Wolffian bodies, and are called **cardinal veins** or postcardinal veins. The descending veins return the blood from the head, and are called **primitive jugular veins** or precardial veins (Fig. 456). The blood from the lower limbs is collected by the right and left iliac and hypogastric veins, which, in the earlier stages of development, open into the corresponding right and left cardinal veins; later, a transverse branch (the left common iliac vein) is dev:loped between the lower parts of the two cardinal veins (Fig. 458), and through this the blood is carried into the right cardinal vein. The portion of the left cardinal vein below the left renal vein atrophies and disappears up to the point of entrance of the left spermatic vein; the portion above the left renal vein persists as the hemiazygos and accessory hemiazygos veins and the lower portion of the highest left intercostal vein. The right cardinal vein which now receives the blood from both lower extremities, forms a large venous trunk along the posterior abdominal wall; up to the level of the renal veins it forms the lower part of the inferior vena cava. Above the level of the renal veins the right cardinal vein persists as the azygos vein and receives the right intercostal veins, while the hemiazygos veins are brought into communication with it by the development of transverse branches in front of the vertebral column (Figs. 458, 459).

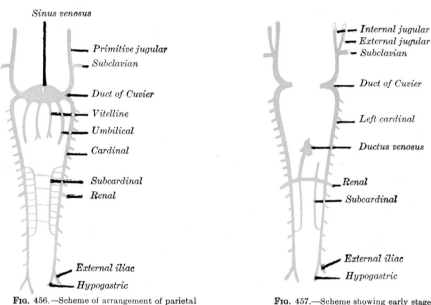

FIG. 456.—Scheme of arrangement of parietal veins.

FIG. 457.—Scheme showing early stages of development of the inferior vena cava.

Inferior Vena Cava.—The development of the inferior vena cava is associated with the formation of two veins, the **subcardinal veins** (Figs. 456, 457). These lie parallel to, and on the ventral aspect of, the cardinal veins, and originate as longitudinal anastomosing channels which link up the tributaries from the mesentery to the cardinal veins; they communicate with the cardinal veins above and below, and also by a series of transverse branches. The two subcardinals are for a time connected with each other in front of the aorta by cross branches, but these disappear and are replaced by a single transverse channel at the level where the renal veins join the cardinals, and at the same level a cross communication is established on either side between the cardinal and subcardinal (Fig. 457). The portion of the right subcardinal behind this cross communication disappears, while that in front, *i. e.*, the prerenal part, forms a connection with the ductus venosus at the point of opening of the hepatic veins, and, rapidly enlarging, receives the blood by cross-communications from the postrenal part of the right supracardinal, a vein which develops later, dorsal to the cardinal. In this manner a single trunk, the **inferior vena cava** (Fig. 459), is formed, and consists of the proximal part of the ductus venosus, the prerenal part of the right subcardinal vein, the postrenal part of the right supracardinal vein, and the cross branch which joins these two veins. The left subcardinal disappears, except the part immediately in front of

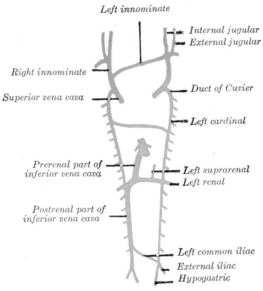

Left innominate

Internal jugular
External jugular
Right innominate
Duct of Cuvier
Superior vena cava
Left cardinal
Prerenal part of inferior vena cava
Left suprarenal
Left renal
Postrenal part of inferior vena cava
Left common iliac
External iliac
Hypogastric

Fɪɢ. 458.—Diagram showing development of main cross branches between jugulars and between cardinals.

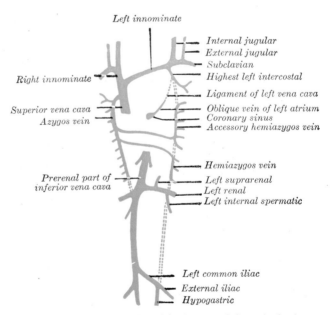

Left innominate

Internal jugular
External jugular
Subclavian
Right innominate
Highest left intercostal
Ligament of left vena cava
Superior vena cava
Oblique vein of left atrium
Azygos vein
Coronary sinus
Accessory hemiazygos vein
Hemiazygos vein
Prerenal part of inferior vena cava
Left suprarenal
Left renal
Left internal spermatic
Left common iliac
External iliac
Hypogastric

Fɪɢ. 459.—Diagram showing completion of development of the parietal veins.

the renal vein, which is retained as the left suprarenal vein. The spermatic (or ovarian) vein opens into the postrenal part of the corresponding cardinal vein. This portion of the right cardinal, as already explained, forms the lower part of the inferior vena cava, so that the right spermatic opens directly into that vessel. The postrenal segment of the left cardinal disappears, with the exception of the portion between the spermatic and renal vein, which is retained as the terminal part of the left spermatic vein.

In consequence of the atrophy of the Wolffian bodies the cardinal veins diminish in size; the primitive jugular veins, on the other hand, become enlarged, owing to the rapid development of the head and brain. They are further augmented by receiving the veins (*subclavian*) from the upper extremities, and so come to form the chief veins of the Cuvierian ducts; these ducts gradually assume an almost vertical position in consequence of the descent of the heart into the thorax. The right and left Cuvierian ducts are originally of the same diameter, and are frequently termed the **right** and **left superior venæ cavæ.** By the development of a transverse branch, the **left innominate vein** between the two primitive jugular veins, the blood is carried across from the left to the right primitive jugular (Figs. 458, 459). The portion of the right primitive jugular vein between the left innominate and the azygos vein forms the upper part of the superior vena cava of the adult; the lower part of this vessel, *i. e.*, below the entrance of the azygos vein, is formed by the right Cuvierian duct. Below the origin of the transverse branch, the left primitive jugular vein and left Cuvierian duct atrophy, the former constituting the upper part of the highest left intercostal vein, while the latter is represented by the ligament of the left vena cava, **vestigial fold of Marshall,** and the oblique vein of the left atrium, **oblique vein of Marshall** (Fig. 459). Both right and left superior venæ cavæ are present in some animals, and are occasionally found in the adult human being. The oblique vein of the left atrium passes downward across the back of the left atrium to open into the coronary sinus, which, as already indicated, represents the persistent left horn of the sinus venosus.

Venous Sinuses of the Dura Mater.—The primary arrangement for drainage of the capillaries of the head (Figs. 460, 467) consists of a primary head vein which starts in the region of the midbrain and runs caudalward along the side of the brain tube to terminate at the duct of Cuvier. The primary head vein drains three plexuses of capillaries: the anterior dural plexus, the middle dural plexus and the posterior dural plexus. The growth of the cartilaginous capsule of the ear and the growth and alteration in form of the brain bring about changes in this primary arrangement (Figs. 462–467). Owing to the growth of the otic capsule and middle ear the course of the primary head vein becomes unfavorable and a segment of it becomes obliterated. To make the necessary adjustment an anastomosis is established above the otic capsule (Fig. 462) and the middle plexus drains into the posterior plexus. Then the anterior plexus fuses with the middle plexus (Fig. 463) and drains through it and the newly established channel, dorsal to the otic capsule. All that remains of the primary head vein is the cardinal portion or internal jugular and the part in the region of the trigeminal nerve which may be called the cavernous sinus. Into it drain the orbital veins. The drainage from the cavernous sinus is now upward through the original trunk of the middle plexus, which is now the superior petrosal sinus, into the newly established dorsal channel. This dorsal channel is the transverse sinus (Figs. 464–467). The inferior petrosal sinus appears later (Fig. 465). From the anterior plexus a sagittal plexus extends forward from which develops the superior sagittal sinus (Figs. 463–467). The straight sinus is formed in the ventral part of the sagittal plexus. As the hemispheres extend backward these sinuses elongate by incorporating the more caudal loops of the plexus. The anterior part of the sinus is completed first.

The external jugular vein at first drains the region behind the ear (posterior auricular) and enters the primitive jugular as a lateral tributary. A group of veins from the face and lingual region converge to form a common vein, the linguo-facial, which also terminates in the primitive jugular. Later, cross communications develop between the external jugular and the linguo-facial, with the result that the posterior group of facial veins is transferred to the external jugular.

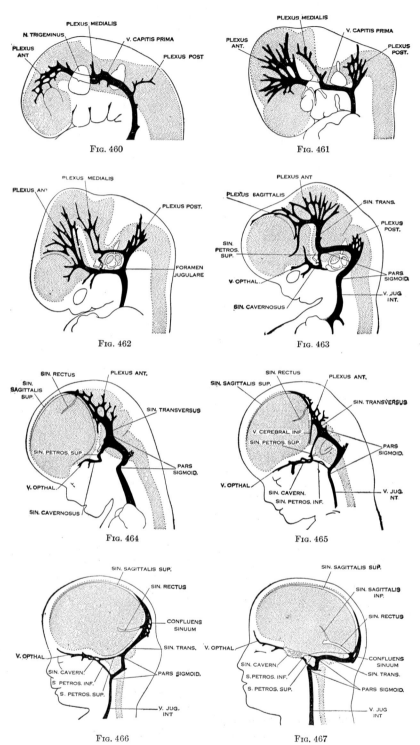

Figs. 460 to 467.—Profile drawings of the dural veins showing principal stages in their development in human embryos from 4 mm. to birth. It is of particular interest to notice their adaptation to the growth and changes in the form of the central nervous system. Fig. 460, 4 mm.; Fig. 461, 14 mm.; Fig. 462, 18 mm.; Fig. 463, 21 mm.; Fig. 464, 35 mm.; Fig. 465, 50 mm. crown-rump length; Fig. 466, 80 mm crown-rump length; Fig. 467, adult. (After Streeter.)

Structure of Arteries (Fig. 468).—The arteries are composed of three coats: an internal or endothelial coat (*tunica intima*); a middle or muscular coat (*tunica media*); and an external or connective-tissue coat (*tunica adventitia*).

The **inner coat** (*tunica intima*) can be separated from the middle by a little maceration, or it may be stripped off in small pieces; but, on account of its friability, it cannot be separated as a complete membrane. It is a fine, transparent, colorless structure which is highly elastic, and, after death, is commonly corrugated into longitudinal wrinkles. The inner coat consists of: (1) A layer of pavement endothelium, the cells of which are polygonal, oval, or fusiform, and have very distinct round or oval nuclei. This endothelium is brought into view most distinctly by staining with nitrate of silver. (2) A subendothelial layer, consisting of delicate connective tissue with branched cells lying in the interspaces of the tissue; in arteries of less than 2 mm. in diameter the subendothelial layer consists of a single stratum of stellate cells, and the connective tissue is largely developed only in vessels of a considerable size. (3) An elastic or fenestrated layer, which consists of a membrane containing a network of elastic fibers, having principally a longitudinal direction, and in which, under the microscope, small elongated apertures or perforations may be seen, giving it a fenestrated appearance. This membrane or internal elastic layer forms the chief thickness of the inner coat, and can be separated into several layers, some of which present the appearance of a net-work of longitudinal elastic fibers, and others a more membranous character, marked by pale lines having a longitudinal direction. In minute arteries the fenestrated membrane is a very thin layer; but in the larger arteries, and especially in the aorta, it has a very considerable thickness.

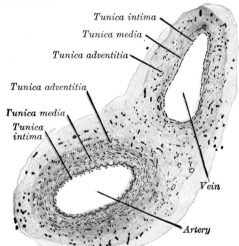

Fig. 468.—A transverse section through an artery and a vein of a child aged thirteen months. Stained with hematoxylin and eosin. × 20.

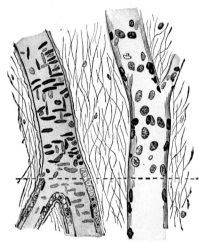

Fig. 469.—Small artery and vein, pia mater of sheep. × 250. Surface view above the interrupted line; longitudinal section below. Artery in red; vein in blue.

The **middle coat** (*tunica media*) is distinguished from the inner by its color and by the transverse arrangement of its fibers. In the smaller arteries it consists principally of plain muscle fibers in fine bundles, arranged in lamellæ and disposed circularly around the vessel. These lamellæ vary in number according to the size of the vessel; the smallest arteries having only a single layer (Fig. 469), and those slightly larger three or four layers. It is to this coat that the thickness of the wall of the artery is mainly due (Fig. 468). In the larger arteries, as the iliac, femoral, and carotid, elastic fibers unite to form lamellæ which alternate with the layers of muscular fibers; these lamellæ are united to one another by elastic fibers which pass between the muscular bundles, and are connected with the fenestrated membrane of the inner coat (Fig. 470). In the largest arteries, as the aorta and innominate, the amount of elastic tissue is very considerable; in these vessels a few bundles of white connective tissue also have been found in the middle coat. The muscle fiber cells are about 50μ in length and contain well-marked, rod-shaped nuclei, which are often slightly curved.

The **external coat** (*tunica adventitia*) consists mainly of fine and closely felted bundles of white connective tissue, but also contains elastic fibers in all but the smallest arteries. The elastic tissue is much more abundant next the tunica media, and it is sometimes described as forming here, between the adventitia and media, a special layer, the **tunica elastica externa.** This layer is most marked in arteries of medium size. In the largest vessels the external coat is relatively thin; but in small arteries it is of greater proportionate thickness. In the smaller arteries it consists of a single layer of white connective tissue and elastic fibers; while in the smallest arteries, just above capillaries, the elastic fibers are wanting, and the connective tissue of which the coat is composed becomes more nearly homogeneous the nearer it approaches the capillaries, and is gradually reduced to a thin membranous envelope, which finally disappears.

Some arteries have extremely thin walls in proportion to their size; this is especially the case in those situated in the cavity of the cranium and vertebral canal, the difference depending on the thinness of the external and middle coats.

The arteries, in their distribution throughout the body, are included in thin fibro-areolar investments, which form their **sheaths.** The vessel is loosely connected with its sheath by delicate areolar tissue; and the sheath usually encloses the accompanying veins, and sometimes a nerve. Some arteries, as those in the cranium, are not included in sheaths.

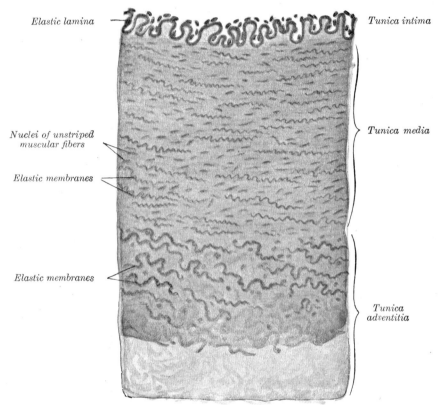

Fig. 470.—A transverse section through the wall of a femoral artery of a dog.   × 250.

All the larger arteries, like the other organs of the body, are supplied with bloodvessels. These nutrient vessels, called the **vasa vasorum,** *arise* from a branch of the artery, or from a neighboring vessel, at some considerable distance from the point at which they are distributed; they ramify in the loose areolar tissue connecting the artery with its sheath, and are distributed to the external coat, but do not, in man, penetrate the other coats; in some of the larger mammals a few vessels have been traced into the middle coat. Minute veins return the blood from these vessels; they empty themselves into the vein or veins accompanying the artery. Lymphatic vessels are also present in the outer coat.

Arteries are also supplied with nerves, which are derived from the sympathetic, but may pass through the cerebrospinal nerves. They form intricate plexuses upon the surfaces of the larger trunks, and run along the smaller arteries as single filaments, or bundles of filaments which twist around the vessel and unite with each other in a plexiform manner. The branches derived from these plexuses penetrate the external coat and are distributed principally to the muscular tissue of the middle coat, and thus regulate, by causing the contraction and relaxation of this tissue the amount of blood sent to any part.

The Capillaries.—The smaller arterial branches (excepting those of the cavernous structure of the sexual organs, of the splenic pulp, and of the placenta) terminate in networks of vessels which pervade nearly every tissue of the body. These vessels, from their minute size, are termed capillaries. They are interposed between the smallest branches of the arteries and the commencing veins, constituting a network, the branches of which maintain the same diameter throughout; the meshes of the network are more uniform in shape and size than those formed by the anastomoses of the small arteries and veins.

The *diameters* of the capillaries vary in the different tissues of the body, the usual size being about 8μ. The smallest are those of the brain and the mucous membrane of the intestines; and the largest those of the skin and the marrow of bone, where they are stated to be as large as 20μ in diameter. The *form* of the capillary net varies in the different tissues, the meshes being generally rounded or elongated.

The *rounded form of mesh* is most common, and prevails where there is a dense network, as in the lungs, in most glands and mucous membranes, and in the cutis; the meshes are not of an absolutely circular outline, but more or less angular, sometimes nearly quadrangular, or polygonal, or more often irregular.

Elongated meshes are observed in the muscles and nerves, the meshes resembling parallelograms in form, the long axis of the mesh running parallel with the long axis of the nerve or muscle. Sometimes the capillaries have a *looped arrangement;* a single vessel projecting from the common network and returning after forming one or more loops, as in the papillæ of the tongue and skin.

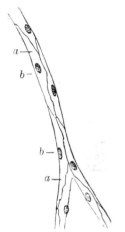

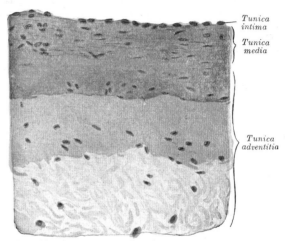

Tunica
intima

Tunica
media

Tunica
adventitia

FIG. 471.—Capillaries from the mesentery of a guinea-pig, after treatment with solution of nitrate of silver. *a.* Cells. *b.* Their nuclei.

FIG. 472.—A transverse section through the wall of a femoral vein of a dog. $\times$ 250. The elastic tissue is not differentiated in this preparation.

The number of the capillaries and the size of the meshes determine the degree of vascularity of a part. The closest network and the smallest interspaces are found in the lungs and in the choroid coat of the eye. In these situations the interspaces are smaller than the capillary vessels themselves. In the intertubular plexus of the kidney, in the conjunctiva, and in the cutis, the interspaces are from three to four times as large as the capillaries which form them; and in the brain from eight to ten times as large as the capillaries in the long diameters of the meshes, and from four to six times as large in their transverse diameters. In the adventitia of arteries the width of the meshes is ten times that of the capillary vessels. As a general rule, the more active the function of the organ, the closer is its capillary net and the larger its supply of blood; the meshes of the network are very narrow in all growing parts, in the glands, and in the mucous membranes, wider in bones and ligaments which are comparatively inactive; bloodvessels are nearly absent in tendons, in which very little organic change occurs after their formation. In the liver the capillaries take a more or less radial course toward the intralobular vein, and their walls may be incomplete, so that the blood comes into direct contact with the liver cells. These vessels in the liver are not true capillaries but "sinusoids;" they are developed by the growth of columns of liver cells into the blood spaces of the embryonic organ, have an irregular lumen and have very little, if any, connective tissue covering.

Structure.—The wall of a capillary consists of a fine transparent endothelial layer, composed of cells joined edge to edge by an interstitial cement substance, and continuous with the endothelial cells which line the arteries and veins. When stained with nitrate of silver the edges which bound the endothelial cells are brought into view (Fig. 471). These cells are of large size and of an irregular polygonal or lanceolate shape, each containing an oval nucleus which may be displayed by carmine or hematoxylin. Between their edges, at various points of their meeting, roundish dark spots are sometimes seen, which have been described as stomata, though they are closed by intercellular substance. They have been believed to be the situations through which the colorless corpuscles of the blood, when migrating from the bloodvessels, emerge; but this view is not universally accepted.

In many situations a delicate sheath or envelope of branched nucleated connective tissue cells is found around the simple capillary tube, particularly in the larger ones; and in other places, especially in the glands, the capillaries are invested with retiform connective tissue. In certain organs where true connective tissue is absent and the blood capillaries come into direct contact with actively secreting epithelium, the endothelial cells themselves are able (according to Corner) to lay down the supporting framework of the gland in the form of reticular fibers.

Structure of Veins.—The veins, like the arteries, are composed of three coats: internal, middle, and external; and these coats are, with the necessary modifications, analogous to the coats of the arteries; the internal being the endothelial, the middle the muscular, and the external the connective tissue or areolar (Fig. 472). The main difference between the veins and the arteries is in the comparative weakness of the middle coat in the former.

In the smallest veins the three coats are hardly to be distinguished (Fig. 469). The endothelium is supported on a membrane separable into two layers, the outer of which is the thicker, and consists of a delicate, nucleated membrane (*adventitia*), while the inner is composed of a network of longitudinal elastic fibers (*media*). In the veins next above these in size (0.4 mm. in diameter), according to Kölliker, a connective tissue layer containing numerous muscle fibers circularly disposed can be traced, forming the middle coat, while the elastic and connective tissue elements of the outer coat become more distinctly perceptible. In the middle-sized veins the typical structure of these vessels becomes clear. The endothelium is of the same character as in the arteries, but its cells are more oval and less fusiform. It is supported by a connective tissue layer, consisting of a delicate network of branched cells, and external to this is a layer of elastic fibers disposed in the form of a network in place of the definite fenestrated membrane seen in the arteries. This constitutes the **internal coat.** The **middle coat** is composed of a thick layer of connective tissue with elastic fibers, intermixed, in some veins, with a transverse layer of muscular tissue. The white fibrous element is in considerable excess, and the elastic fibers are in much smaller proportion in the veins than in the arteries. The **outer coat** consists, as in the arteries, of areolar tissue, with longitudinal elastic fibers. In the largest veins the outer coat is from two to five times thicker than the middle coat, and contains a large number of longitudinal muscular fibers. These are most distinct in the inferior vena cava, especially at the termination of this vein in the heart, in the trunks of the hepatic veins, in all the large trunks of the portal vein, and in the external iliac, renal, and azygos veins. In the renal and portal veins they extend through the whole thickness of the outer coat, but in the other veins mentioned a layer of connective and elastic tissue is found external to the muscular fibers. All the large veins which open into the heart are covered for a short distance with a layer of striped muscular tissue continued on to them from the heart. Muscular tissue is wanting: (1) in the veins of the maternal part of the placenta; (2) in the venous sinuses of the dura mater and the veins of the pia mater of the brain and medulla spinalis; (3) in the veins of the retina; (4) in the veins of the cancellous tissue of bones; (5) in the venous spaces of the corpora cavernosa. The veins of the above-mentioned parts consist of an internal endothelial lining supported on one or more layers of areolar tissue.

Most veins are provided with valves which serve to prevent the reflux of the blood. Each valve is formed by a reduplication of the inner coat, strengthened by connective tissue and elastic fibers, and is covered on both surfaces with endothelium, the arrangement of which differs on the two surfaces. On the surface of the valve next the wall of the vein the cells are arranged transversely; while on the other surface, over which the current of blood flows, the cells are arranged longitudinally in the direction of the current. Most commonly two such valves are found placed opposite one another, more especially in the smaller veins or in the larger trunks at the point where they are joined by smaller branches; occasionally there are three and sometimes only one. The valves are semilunar. They are attached by their convex edges to the wall of the vein; the concave margins are free, directed in the course of the venous current, and lie in close apposition with the wall of the vein as long as the current of blood takes its natural course; if, however, any regurgitation takes place, the valves become distended, their opposed edges are brought into contact, and the current is interrupted. The wall of the vein on the cardiac side of the point of attachment of each valve is expanded into a pouch or sinus, which gives to the vessel, when injected or distended with blood, a knotted appearance. The valves are very numerous in the veins of the extremities, especially of the lower extremities, these vessels having to conduct the blood against the force of gravity. They are absent in the very small veins, *i. e.*, those less than 2 mm. in diameter, also in the venæ cavæ, hepatic, renal, uterine, and ovarian veins. A few valves are found in each spermatic vein, and one also at its point of junction with the renal vein or inferior vena cava respectively. The cerebral and spinal veins, the veins of the cancellated tissue of bone, the pulmonary veins, and the umbilical vein and its branches, are also destitute of valves. A few valves are occasionally found in the azygos and intercostal veins. Rudimentary valves are found in the tributaries of the portal venous system.

The veins, like the arteries, are supplied with nutrient vessels, **vasa vasorum.** Nerves also are distributed to them in the same manner as to the arteries, but in much less abundance.

THE BLOOD.

The blood is an opaque, rather viscid fluid, of a bright red or scarlet color when it flows from the arteries, of a dark red or purple color when it flows from the veins. It is salty to the taste, and has a peculiar faint odor and an alkaline reaction. Its specific gravity is about 1.06, and its temperature is generally about 37° C., though varying slightly in different parts of the body.

General Composition of the Blood.—Blood consists of a faintly yellow fluid, the **plasma** or **liquor sanguinis**, in which are suspended numerous minute particles, the **blood corpuscles**, the majority of which are colored and give to the blood its red tint. If a drop of blood be placed in a thin layer on a glass slide and examined under the microscope, a number of these corpuscles will be seen floating in the plasma.

The **Blood Corpuscles** are of three kinds: (1) **colored corpuscles** or **erythrocytes;** (2) **colorless corpuscles** or **leucocytes;** (3) **blood platelets.**

1. **Colored or red corpuscles** (*erythrocytes*), when examined under the microscope, are seen to be circular disks, biconcave in profile. The disk has no nucleus, but, in consequence of its biconcave shape, presents, according to the alterations of focus under an ordinary high power, a central part, sometimes bright, sometimes dark, which has the appearance of a nucleus (Fig. 473, *a*). It is to the aggregation of the red corpuscles that the blood owes its red hue, although when examined by transmitted light their color appears to be only a faint reddish-yellow. The corpuscles vary slightly in size even in the same drop of blood, but the average diameter is about 7.5μ,[1] and the

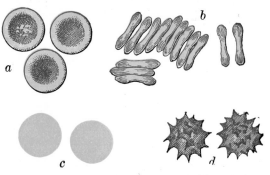

Fig. 473.—Human red blood corpuscles. Highly magnified. *a.* Seen from the surface. *b.* Seen in profile and forming rouleaux. *c.* Rendered spherical by water. *d.* Rendered crenate by salt solution.

thickness about 2μ. Besides these there are found in normal blood smaller (extreme 6 μ) and larger (extreme 9 μ) erythrocytes the distribution curve of which follows the law of chance. This curve is "regular" in healthy individuals but shifts in disease, *i. e.,* more small cells (microcytes) of still small diameters (4 to 6 μ) may appear, *e. g.,* in "secondary" anemia after hemorrhage or in hemolytic jaundice, or more large cells (macrocytes) of still larger diameter (9 to 12 μ), *e. g.,* in pernicious anemia, may be present. The number of red corpuscles in the blood is enormous; between 4,000,000 and 5,000,000 are contained in a cubic millimeter. Power states that the red corpuscles of an adult would present an aggregate surface of about 3000 square yards.

If the web of a living frog's foot be spread out and examined under the microscope the blood is seen to flow in a continuous stream through the vessels, and the corpuscles show no tendency to adhere to each other or to the wall of the vessel. Doubtless the same is the case in the human body; but when human blood is drawn and examined on a slide without reagents the corpuscles tend to collect into heaps like rouleaux of coins (Fig. 473, *b*). It has been suggested that this phenomenon may be explained by alteration in surface tension. During life the red corpuscles may be seen to change their shape under pressure so as to adapt themselves, to some extent, to the size of the vessel. They are, however, highly elastic, and speedily recover their shape when the pressure is removed. They are readily influenced by

[1] A micromillimeter (μ) is 1/1000 of a millimeter or 1/25000 of an inch.

the medium in which they are placed. In hypotonic solutions they swell up, become spherical (Fig. 473, *c*), and the hemoglobin is dissolved out (hemolysis) so that the envelope can barely be distinguished as a faint circular outline (ghosts of red blood corpuscles). In hypertonic solutions the red blood corpuscles assume a stellate or crenated appearance; this process is reversible. An isotonic salt solution merely separates the blood corpuscles mechanically, without changing their shape. Two views are held with regard to the structure of the erythrocytes. The older view, that of Rollett, supposes that the corpuscle consists of a sponge work or stroma permeated by a solution of hemoglobin. Schäfer, on the other hand, believes that the hemoglobin solution is contained within an envelope or membrane, and the facts stated above with regard to the osmotic behavior of the erythrocyte support this belief. The envelope consists mainly of lecithin, cholesterin, and nucleoprotein.

The **white corpuscles or leucocytes** are of various sizes, the majority are larger than the red corpuscles, and measure about 10 μ in diameter. On the average from 7000 to 12,000 leucocytes are found in each cubic millimetre of blood.

These small amœboid cells are differentiated from each other chiefly by their nuclei, by the occurrence or non-occurrence of granules in their protoplasm, and by the staining reactions of these granules when present (Fig. 474). (1) The most numerous (60 per cent.) and important of the white blood corpuscles are irregular in shape, and are characterized by nuclei which often consist of two or more connected parts. They are therefore called polymorphonuclear leucocytes. Their protoplasm contains a number of very fine granules which may be stained by a variety of dyes, but their characteristic reaction is with the neutral dye when stained with mixtures such as eosin-methylene blue (neutrophil granules). Because of these two characteristics this type of leucocyte is usually referred to as the **polymorphonuclear neutrophil leucocyte.** (2) A second variety comprises from 1 to 4 per cent. of the leucocytes; they are larger than the previous kind, and are made up of coarsely granular protoplasm, the granules being highly refractile and grouped around nuclei of a simpler configuration than that of the neutrophil leucocytes, *i. e.*, they are bilobed or (in a very small percentage) trilobed nuclei or they may be simply horseshoe-shaped (Fig. 474*a*). The granules stain deeply with eosin and the cells are therefore termed **eosinophils.** (3) The third variety is called the **mast cell.** There are two types which have nothing in common except an identical basophil metachromatic staining reaction of their granules. The one type occurs in the connective tissue (histogenous mast cell), the other occurs in the blood and is called mast leucocyte or **basophil.** These basophils constitute about .45 per cent. of the white corpuscles in human blood, *i. e.*, there are approximately 35 of them found in 1 cubic millimeter of blood. Their nuclei are polymorphous although the segmentation is less pronounced than in the other types of granular leucocytes.

The non-granular leucocytes which account for the remaining one-third of white blood cells are divided into two groups, the lymphocytes (20 to 25 per cent.) and the monocytes (3.5 per cent.). They occur not only in the blood but also in the lymphatic and connective tissue. The **lymphocytes** are the smallest of the white blood cells. They average 6 to 8 μ in diameter. The more or less spherical, heavily staining nucleus fills the cell almost entirely so that the cytoplasm appears only as a thin border around the nucleus. The cytoplasm as a rule is pale blue in the usual blood stains. The **monocytes,** measuring up to 10 to 11 μ in diameter, may have segmented or rounded nuclei of varying shapes. They have usually a larger amount of cytoplasm than the large lymphocytes from which they are sometimes difficult to differentiate. Monocytes are highly phagocytic. Many lodge in the liver sinusoids and in the spleen where they ingest and digest erythrocytes and cellular debris and enlarge into **macrophages.** Many monocytes also migrate out of the capillaries into the tissues. Here they act as the great scavengers of the body and enlarge into macrophages as they ingest and digest escaped erythrocytes and debris. Some authors believe that monocytes become transformed into fibroblasts in inflammatory areas and in wound healing.

The **blood platelets** are discoid or irregularly shaped, colorless, refractile bodies, much smaller than the red corpuscles. They are cellular particles derived from the megacaryocytes of the bone marrow. Their movement is passive, but they have a great adhesive power and stickiness which is of importance for their function, which is to hasten the coagulation of the blood. Their number, according to different authors using different methods of counting, is 180,000 to 800,000 per cubic millimeter of blood.

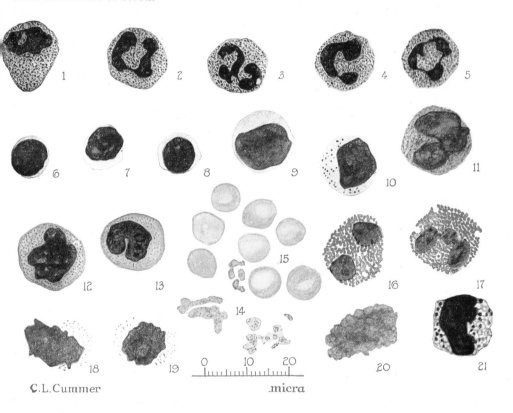

C.L.Cummer   .micra

Fig. 474.—Types of cells found in normal blood. Colored by Wright's stain. All cells drawn with the same magnification and outlined with the camera lucida for the purpose of comparing sizes. × 1150. Nos. 1 to 5, inclusive, neutrophiles; 6, 7, 8, lymphocytes; 9 to 13, monocytes; 14, platelets; 15, a group of red blood cells; 16, 17, eosinophiles; 18, 19, 20, "basket cells," degenerated leucocytes; 21, basophilic leucocyte. (Cummer's Laboratory Methods.)

THE THORACIC CAVITY.

The heart and lungs are situated in the thorax, the walls of which afford them protection. The heart lies between the two lungs, and is enclosed within a fibrous bag, the **pericardium**, while each lung is invested by a serous membrane the **pleura**. The skeleton of the thorax, and the shape and boundaries of the cavity, have already been described (page 95).

The Cavity of the Thorax.—The capacity of the cavity of the thorax does not correspond to its apparent size externally, because (1) the space enclosed by the lower ribs is occupied by some of the abdominal viscera; and (2) the cavity extends above the anterior parts of the first ribs into the neck. The size of the thoracic cavity varies constantly during life with the movements of the ribs and diaphragm, and with the degree of distention of the abdominal viscera. From the collapsed state of the lungs as seen when the thorax is opened in the dead body, it would appear as if the viscera only partly filled the cavity, but during life there is no vacant space, that which is seen after death being filled by the expanded lungs.

The Upper Opening of the Thorax.—The structures which pass through the upper opening of the thorax are, from before backward, in or near the middle line, the Sternohyoideus and Sternothyreoideus muscles, the remains of the thymus, the inferior thyroid veins, the trachea, esophagus, thoracic duct, and the Longus colli muscles; at the sides, the innominate artery, the left common carotid, left subclavian and internal mammary arteries and the costocervical trunks, the innominate veins, the vagus, cardiac, phrenic, and sympathetic nerves, the greater parts of the anterior divisions of the first thoracic nerves, and the recurrent nerve of the left side. The apex of each lung, covered by the pleura, also projects through this aperture, a little above the level of the sternal end of the first rib.

The Lower Opening of the Thorax.—The lower opening of the thorax is wider transversely than from before backward. It slopes obliquely downward and backward, so that the thoracic cavity is much deeper behind than in front. The diaphragm (see page 402) closes the opening and forms the floor of the thorax. The floor is flatter at the center than at the sides, and higher on the right side than on the left; in the dead body the right side reaches the level of the upper border of the fifth costal cartilage, while the left extends only to the corresponding part of the sixth costal cartilage. From the highest point on each side the floor slopes suddenly downward to the costal and vertebral attachments of the diaphragm; this slope is more marked behind than in front, so that only a narrow space is left between the diaphragm and the posterior wall of the thorax.

THE PERICARDIUM.

The **pericardium** (Fig. 475) is a fibro-serous sac, in which the heart and the roots of the great vessels are contained. It is placed behind the sternum and the cartilages of the third, fourth, fifth, sixth, and seventh ribs of the left side, in the mediastinum.

In **front**, it is separated from the anterior wall of the thorax, in the greater part of its extent, by the lungs and pleuræ; but a small area, somewhat variable in size, and usually corresponding with the left half of the lower portion of the body of the sternum and the medial ends of the cartilages of the fourth and fifth ribs of the left side, comes into direct relationship with the chest wall. The lower extremity of the thymus, in the child, is in contact with the front of the upper part of the pericardium. **Behind** it are the bronchi, the esophagus, the descending thoracic aorta, and the posterior part of the mediastinal surface of each lung. **Laterally,** it is covered by the pleuræ, and is in relation with the mediastinal surfaces of the lungs; the phrenic nerve, with its accompanying vessels, descends between the pericardium and pleura on either side. The inner surface of the pericardium is in contact with the heart and roots of the great vessels.

Structure of the Pericardium.—It consists of an inner serous layer and an outer fibrous layer. The inner **serous layer** is a delicate membrane composed of a single layer of flattened mesothelial cells resting on loose connective tissue which connects it with the fibrous layer.

The serous layer is continuous with the **epicardium** at the junction of the pericardium and the great vessels of the heart. The epicardium covers the heart and great vessels. The enclosed sac, the **pericardial cavity**, is merely a potential space. Under normal conditions the serous layer of the pericardium is everywhere in contact with the serous layer of the epicardium, the contact surfaces being moistened by a slight amount of serous fluid.

The portion of the epicardium which covers the vessels is arranged in the form of two tubes. The aorta and pulmonary artery are enclosed in one tube, the **arterial mesocardium.** The superior and inferior venæ cavæ and the four pulmonary veins are enclosed in a second tube, the **venous mesocardium,** the attachment of which to the parietal layer presents the shape of an inverted U. The *cul-de-sac* enclosed between the limbs of the U lies behind the left atrium and is known as the **oblique sinus,** while the passage between the venous and arterial mesocardia—*i. e.*, between the aorta and pulmonary artery in front and the atria behind—is termed the **transverse sinus.**

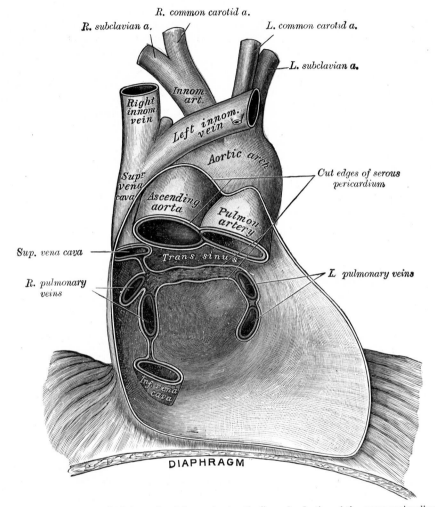

Fig. 475.—Posterior wall of the pericardial sac, showing the lines of reflection of the serous pericardium on the great vessels.

The **fibrous layer** forms a flask-shaped bag, the neck of which is closed by its fusion with the external coats of the great vessels, while its base is attached to the central tendon and the muscular fibers of the left side of the diaphragm. In some of the lower mammals the base is either completely separated from the diaphragm or joined to it by some loose areolar tissue; in man much of its diaphragmatic attachment consists of loose fibrous tissue which can be readily broken down, but over a small area the central tendon of the diaphragm and the pericardium are completely fused. Above, the fibrous layer not only blends with the external coats of the great vessels, but is continuous with the pretracheal layer of the deep cervical fascia. By means of these upper and lower connections it is securely anchored within the thoracic cavity. It is also attached to the posterior surface of the sternum by the **superior** and **inferior sternopericardiac ligaments;** the upper passing to the manubrium, and the lower to the xiphoid process.

34

The vessels receiving fibrous prolongations from this membrane are: the aorta, the superior vena cava, the right and left pulmonary arteries, and the four pulmonary veins. The inferior vena cava enters the pericardium through the central tendon of the diaphragm, and receives no covering from the fibrous layer.

The Ligament of the Left Vena Cava.—Between the left pulmonary artery and subjacent pulmonary vein is a triangular fold of the serous pericardium; it is known as the **ligament of the left vena cava** (*vestigial fold of Marshall*). It is formed by the duplicature of the serous layer over the remnant of the lower part of the left superior vena cava (*duct of Cuvier*), which becomes obliterated during fetal life, and remains as a fibrous band stretching from the highest left intercostal vein to the left atrium, where it is continuous with a small vein, **the vein of the left atrium** (*oblique vein of Marshall*), which opens into the coronary sinus.

The **arteries** of the pericardium are branches of the internal mammary and its musculophrenic branch, and from the descending thoracic aorta.

The **nerves** of the pericardium are branches of the vagus and phrenic nerves, and the sympathetic trunks.

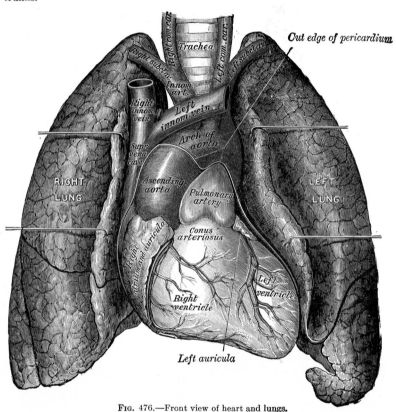

Fig. 476.—Front view of heart and lungs.

THE HEART (COR).

The **heart** is a hollow muscular organ of a somewhat conical form; it lies between the lungs in the middle mediastinum and is enclosed in the pericardium (Fig. 476). It is placed obliquely in the chest behind the body of the sternum and adjoining parts of the rib cartilages, and projects farther into the left than into the right half of the thoracic cavity, so that about one-third of it is situated on the right and two-thirds on the left of the median plane.

Size.—The heart, in the adult, measures about 12 cm. in length, 8 to 9 cm. in breadth at the broadest part, and 6 cm. in thickness. Its weight, in the male, varies from 280 to 340 grams; in the female, from 230 to 280 grams. The heart continues to increase in weight and size up to an advanced period of life; this increase is more marked in men than in women.

Component Parts.—As has already been stated (page 501), the heart is subdivided by septa into right and left halves, and a constriction subdivides each half of the organ into two cavities, the upper cavity being called the **atrium**, the lower the **ventricle**. The heart therefore consists of four chambers, viz., right and left atria, and right and left ventricles.

The division of the heart into four cavities is indicated on its surface by grooves. The atria are separated from the ventricles by the **coronary sulcus** (*auriculo-ventricular groove*); this contains the trunks of the nutrient vessels of the heart, and is deficient in front, where it is crossed by the root of the pulmonary artery.

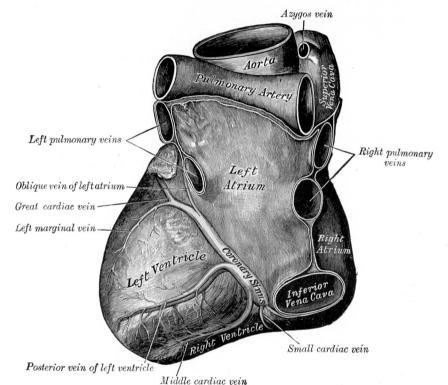

FIG. 477.—Base and diaphragmatic surface of heart.

The **interatrial groove**, separating the two atria, is scarcely marked on the posterior surface, while anteriorly it is hidden by the pulmonary artery and aorta. The ventricles are separated by two grooves, one of which, the **anterior longitudinal sulcus**, is situated on the sternocostal surface of the heart, close to its left margin, the other **posterior longitudinal sulcus**, on the diaphragmatic surface near the right margin; these grooves extend from the base of the ventricular portion to a notch, the **incisura apicis cordis**, on the acute margin of the heart just to the right of the apex.

The **base** (*basis cordis*) (Fig. 477), directed upward, backward, and to the right, is separated from the fifth, sixth, seventh, and eighth thoracic vertebræ by the esophagus, aorta, and thoracic duct. It is formed mainly by the left atrium, and, to a small extent, by the back part of the right atrium. Somewhat quadrilateral in form, it is in relation above with the bifurcation of the pulmonary artery, and is bounded below by the posterior part of the coronary sulcus, containing the coronary sinus. On the right it is limited by the sulcus terminalis of the right atrium, and on the left by the ligament of the left vena cava and the oblique vein of the left atrium. The four pulmonary veins, two on either side, open into the left atrium, while the superior vena cava opens into the upper, and the inferior vena cava into the lower, part of the right atrium.

The Apex (*apex cordis*).—The apex is directed downward, forward, and to the left, and is overlapped by the left lung and pleura: it lies behind the fifth left intercostal space, 8 to 9 cm. from the mid-sternal line, or about 4 cm. below and 2 mm. to the medial side of the left mammary papilla.

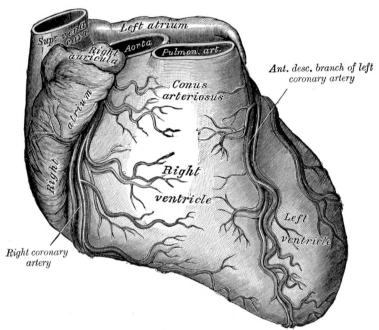

FIG. 478.—Sternocostal surface of heart.

The **sternocostal surface** (Fig. 478) is directed forward, upward, and to the left. Its lower part is convex, formed chiefly by the right ventricle, and traversed near its left margin by the anterior longitudinal sulcus. Its upper part is separated from the lower by the coronary sulcus, and is formed by the atria; it presents a deep concavity (Fig. 480), occupied by the ascending aorta and the pulmonary artery.

The **diaphragmatic surface** (Fig. 477), directed downward and slightly backward, is formed by the ventricles, and rests upon the central tendon and a small part of the left muscular portion of the diaphragm. It is separated from the base by the posterior part of the coronary sulcus, and is traversed obliquely by the posterior longitudinal sulcus.

The **right margin** of the heart is long, and is formed by the right atrium above and the right ventricle below. The atrial portion is rounded and almost vertical; it is situated behind the third, fourth, and fifth right costal cartilages about 1.25 cm. from the margin of the sternum. The ventricular portion, thin and sharp, is named the **acute margin**; it is nearly horizontal, and extends from the sternal end of the sixth right costal cartilage to the apex of the heart.

The **left** or **obtuse margin** is shorter, full, and rounded: it is formed mainly by the left ventricle, but to a slight extent, above, by the left atrium. It extends from a point in the second left intercostal space, about 2.5 cm. from the sternal margin, obliquely downward, with a convexity to the left, to the apex of the heart.

Right Atrium (*atrium dextrum; right auricle*).—The right atrium is larger than the left, but its walls are somewhat thinner, measuring about 2 mm.; its cavity is capable of containing about 57 c.c. It consists of two parts: a principal cavity, or **sinus venarum**, situated posteriorly, and an anterior, smaller portion, the **auricula.**

Sinus Venarum (*sinus venosus*).—The sinus venarum is the large quadrangular cavity placed between the two venæ cavæ. Its walls, which are extremely thin, are connected below with the right ventricle, and medially with the left atrium, but are free in the rest of their extent.

Auricula (*auricula dextra; right auricular appendix*).—The auricula is a small conical muscular pouch, the margins of which present a dentated edge. It projects from the upper and front part of the sinus forward and toward the left side, overlapping the root of the aorta.

The separation of the auricula from the sinus venarum is indicated externally by a groove, the **terminal sulcus,** which extends from the front of the superior vena cava to the front of the inferior vena cava, and represents the line of union of the sinus venosus of the embryo with the primitive atrium. On the inner wall of the atrium the separation is marked by a vertical, smooth, muscular ridge, the **terminal crest.** Behind the crest the internal surface of the atrium is smooth, while in front of it the muscular fibers of the wall are raised into parallel ridges resembling the teeth of a comb, and hence named the **musculi pectinati.**

Its interior (Fig. 479) presents the following parts for examination:

Openings
{
Superior vena cava.
Inferior vena cava.
Coronary sinus.
Foramina venarum minimarum.
Atrioventricular.
}

Valves
{
Valve of the inferior vena cava.
Valve of the coronary sinus.
}

Fossa ovalis.
Limbus fossæ ovalis.
Intervenous tubercle.
Musculi pectinati.
Crista terminalis.

The **superior vena cava** returns the blood from the upper half of the body, and opens into the upper and back part of the atrium, the direction of its orifice being downward and forward. Its opening has no valve.

The **inferior vena cava,** larger than the superior, returns the blood from the lower half of the body, and opens into the lowest part of the atrium, near the atrial septum, its orifice being directed upward and backward, and guarded by a rudimentary valve, the **valve of the inferior vena cava** (*Eustachian valve*). The blood entering the atrium through the superior vena cava is directed downward and forward, *i. e.,* toward the atrioventricular orifice, while that entering through the inferior vena cava is directed upward and backward, toward the atrial septum. This is the normal direction of the two currents in fetal life.

The **coronary sinus** opens into the atrium, between the orifice of the inferior vena cava and the atrioventricular opening. It returns blood from the substance of the heart and is protected by a semicircular valve, the **valve of the coronary sinus** (*valve of Thebesius*).

The **foramina venarum minimarum** (*foramina Thebesii*) are the orifices of minute veins (*venæ cordis minimæ*), which return blood directly from the muscular substance of the heart.

The **atrioventricular opening** (*tricuspid orifice*) is the large oval aperture of communication between the atrium and the ventricle; it will be described with the right ventricle.

The **valve of the inferior vena cava** (*valvula venæ cavæ inferioris* [*Eustachii*]; *Eustachian valve*) is situated in front of the orifice of the inferior vena cava. It is semilunar in form, its convex margin being attached to the anterior margin of the orifice; its concave margin, which is free, ends in two cornua, of which the left is continuous with the anterior edge of the limbus fossæ ovalis while the right is lost on the wall of the atrium. The valve is formed by a duplicature of the lining membrane of the atrium, containing a few muscular fibers. *In the fetus* this valve is of large size, and serves to direct the blood from the inferior vena cava, through the foramen ovale, into the left atrium. *In the adult* it occasionally persists, and may assist in preventing the reflux of blood into the inferior vena cava; more commonly it is small, and may present a cribriform or filamentous appearance; sometimes it is altogether wanting.

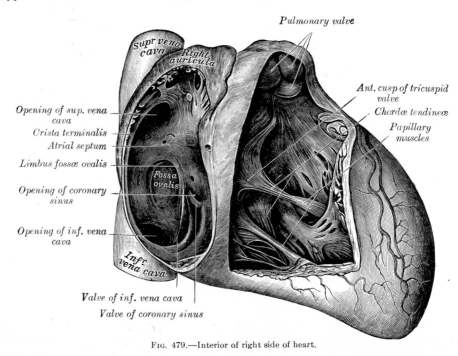

Pulmonary valve

Supr vena cava *Right auricula*

Opening of sup. vena cava
Crista terminalis
Atrial septum
Limbus fossæ ovalis
Fossa ovalis
Opening of coronary sinus
Opening of inf. vena cava
Infr vena cava

Ant. cusp of tricuspid valve
Chordæ tendineæ
Papillary muscles

Valve of inf. vena cava
Valve of coronary sinus

Fig. 479.—Interior of right side of heart.

The **valve of the coronary sinus** (*valvula sinus coronarii* [*Thebesii*]; *Thebesian valve*) is a semicircular fold of the lining membrane of the atrium, at the orifice of the coronary sinus. It prevents the regurgitation of blood into the sinus during the contraction of the atrium. This valve may be double or it may be cribriform.

The **fossa ovalis** is an oval depression on the septal wall of the atrium, and corresponds to the situation of the foramen ovale in the fetus. It is situated at the lower part of the septum, above and to the left of the orifice of the inferior vena cava.

The **limbus fossæ ovalis** (*annulus ovalis*) is the prominent oval margin of the fossa ovalis. It is most distinct above and at the sides of the fossa; below, it is deficient. A small slit-like valvular opening is occasionally found, at the upper margin of the fossa, leading upward beneath the limbus, into the left atrium; it is the remains of the fetal aperture between the two atria.

The **intervenous tubercle** (*tuberculum intervenosum; tubercle of Lower*) is a small projection on the posterior wall of the atrium, above the fossa ovalis. It is distinct in the hearts of quadrupeds, but in man is scarcely visible. It was supposed by

Lower to direct the blood from the superior vena cava toward the atrioventricular opening.

Right Ventricle (*ventriculus dexter*).—The right ventricle is triangular in form, and extends from the right atrium to near the apex of the heart. Its antero-superior surface is rounded and convex, and forms the larger part of the sterno-costal surface of the heart. Its under surface is flattened, rests upon the diaphragm, and forms a small part of the diaphragmatic surface of the heart. Its posterior wall is formed by the ventricular septum, which bulges into the right ventricle, so that a transverse section of the cavity presents a semilunar outline. Its upper and left angle forms a conical pouch, the **conus arteriosus**, from which the pulmonary artery arises. A tendinous band, which may be named the **tendon of the conus arteriosus**, extends upward from the right atrioventricular fibrous ring and connects the posterior surface of the conus arteriosus to the aorta. The wall of the right ventricle is thinner than that of the left, the proportion between them being as 1 to 3; it is thickest at the base, and gradually becomes thinner toward the apex. The cavity equals in size that of the left ventricle, and is capable of containing about 85 c.c.

Its interior (Fig. 479) presents the following parts for examination:

Openings {Right atrioventricular. {Pulmonary artery. Valves {Tricuspid. {Pulmonary.
Trabeculæ carneæ. Chordæ tendineæ.

The **right atrioventricular orifice** is the large oval aperture of communication between the right atrium and ventricle. Situated at the base of the ventricle, it measures about 4 cm. in diameter and is surrounded by a fibrous ring, covered by the lining membrane of the heart; it is considerably larger than the corresponding aperture on the left side, being sufficient to admit the ends of four fingers It is guarded by the tricuspid valve.

The **opening of the pulmonary artery** is circular in form, and situated at the summit of the conus arteriosus, close to the ventricular septum. It is placed above and to the left of the atrioventricular opening, and is guarded by the pulmonary semilunar valves.

The **tricuspid valve** (*valvula tricuspidalis*) (Figs. 479, 481) consists of three somewhat triangular cusps or segments. The largest cusp is interposed between the atrioventricular orifice and the conus arteriosus and is termed the **anterior or infundibular cusp**. A second, the **posterior or marginal cusp**, is in relation to the right margin of the ventricle, and a third, the **medial or septal cusp**, to the ventricular septum. They are formed by duplicatures of the lining membrane of the heart, strengthened by intervening layers of fibrous tissue: their central parts are thick and strong, their marginal portions thin and translucent, and in the angles between the latter small intermediate segments are sometimes seen. Their bases are attached to a fibrous ring surrounding the atrioventricular orifice and are also joined to each other so as to form a continuous annular membrane, while their apices project into the ventricular cavity. Their atrial surfaces, directed toward the blood current from the atrium, are smooth; their ventricular surfaces, directed toward the wall of the ventricle, are rough and irregular, and, together with the apices and margins of the cusps, give attachment to a number of delicate tendinous cords, the **chordæ tendineæ**.

The **trabeculæ carneæ** (*columnæ carneæ*) are rounded or irregular muscular columns which project from the whole of the inner surface of the ventricle, with the exception of the conus arteriosus. They are of three kinds: some are attached along their entire length on one side and merely form prominent ridges, others are fixed at their extremities but free in the middle, while a third set (*musculi* *papillares*) are continuous by their bases with the wall of the ventricle, while their apices give origin to the chordæ tendineæ which pass to be attached to the segments of the tricuspid valve. There are two papillary muscles, anterior and posterior: of these, the anterior is the larger, and its chordæ tendineæ are connected with the anterior and posterior cusps of the valve: the posterior papillary muscle sometimes consists of two or three parts; its chordæ tendineæ are connected with the posterior and medial cusps. In addition to these, some chordæ tendineæ spring directly from the ventricular septum, or from small papillary eminences on it, and pass to the anterior and medial cusps. A muscular band, well-marked in sheep and some other animals, frequently extends from the base of the anterior papillary muscle to the ventricular septum. From its attachments it may assist in preventing overdistension of the ventricle, and so has been named the **moderator band.**

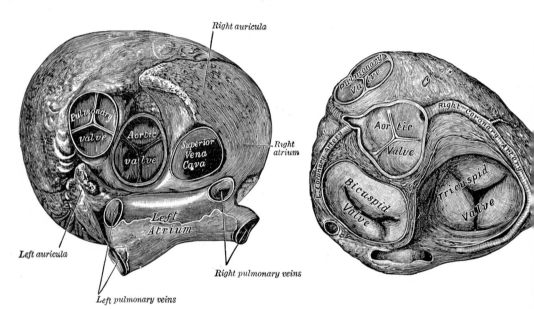

FIG. 480.—The heart. Superior aspect.

FIG. 481.—Base of ventricles exposed by removal of the atria.

The **pulmonary semilunar valves** (Fig. 480) are three in number, two in front and one behind, formed by duplicatures of the lining membrane, strengthened by fibrous tissue. They are attached, by their convex margins, to the wall of the artery, at its junction with the ventricle, their free borders being directed upward into the lumen of the vessel. The free and attached margins of each are strengthened by tendinous fibers, and the former presents, at its middle, a thickened nodule (*corpus Arantii*). From this nodule tendinous fibers radiate through the segment to its attached margin, but are absent from two narrow crescentic portions, the **lunulæ,** placed one on either side of the nodule immediately adjoining the free margin. Between the semilunar valves and the wall of the pulmonary artery are three **pouches or sinuses** (*sinuses of Valsalva*).

Left Atrium (*atrium sinistum; left auricle*).—The left atrium is rather smaller than the right, but its walls are thicker, measuring about 3 mm.; it consists, like the right, of two parts, a **principal cavity** and an **auricula.**

The **principal cavity** is cuboidal in form, and concealed, in front, by the pulmonary artery and aorta; in front and to the right it is separated from the right atrium by the atrial septum; opening into it on either side are the two pulmonary veins.

Auricula (*auricula sinistra; left auricular appendix*).—The auricula is somewhat constricted at its junction with the principal cavity; it is longer, narrower, and more curved than that of the right side, and its margins are more deeply indented. It is directed forward and toward the right and overlaps the root of the pulmonary artery.

The interior of the left atrium (Fig. 482) presents the following parts for examination:

> Openings of the four pulmonary veins.
> Left atrioventricular opening.
> Musculi pectinati.

The **pulmonary veins**, four in number, open into the upper part of the posterior surface of the left atrium—two on either side of its middle line: they are not provided with valves. The two left veins frequently end by a common opening.

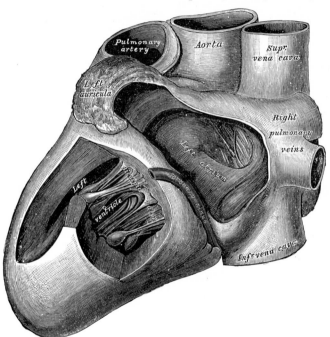

Fig. 482.—Interior of left side of heart.

The **left atrioventricular opening** is the aperture between the left atrium and ventricle, and is rather smaller than the corresponding opening on the right side.

The **musculi pectinati**, fewer and smaller than in the right auricula, are confined to the inner surface of the auricula.

On the atrial septum may be seen a lunated impression, bounded below by a crescentic ridge, the concavity of which is turned upward. The depression is just above the fossa ovalis of the right atrium.

Left Ventricle (*ventriculus sinister*).—The left ventricle is longer and more conical in shape than the right, and on transverse section its concavity presents an oval or nearly circular outline. It forms a small part of the sternocostal surface and a considerable part of the diaphragmatic surface of the heart; it also forms the apex of the heart. Its walls are about three times as thick as those of the right ventricle.

Its interior (Fig. 482) presents the following parts for examination:

Openings { Left atrioventricular. / Aortic. } Valves { Bicuspid or Mitral. / Aortic. }
Trabeculæ carneæ. Chordæ tendineæ.

The **left atrioventricular opening** (*mitral orifice*) is placed below and to the left of the aortic orifice. It is a little smaller than the corresponding aperture of the opposite side, admitting only two fingers. It is surrounded by a dense fibrous ring, covered by the lining membrane of the heart, and is guarded by the bicuspid or mitral valve.

The **aortic opening** is a circular aperture, in front and to the right of the atrioventricular, from which it is separated by the anterior cusp of the bicuspid valve. Its orifice is guarded by the **aortic semilunar valves.** The portion of the ventricle immediately below the aortic orifice is termed the **aortic vestibule,** and possesses fibrous instead of muscular walls.

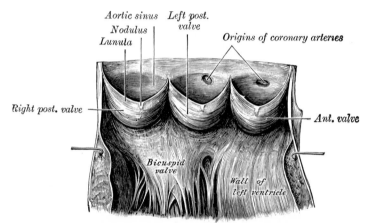

FIG. 483.—Aorta laid open to show the semilunar valves.

The **bicuspid** or **mitral valve** (*valvula bicuspidalis* [*mitralis*]) (Figs. 480, 481, is attached to the circumference of the left atrioventricular orifice in the same way that the tricuspid valve is on the opposite side. It consists of two triangular cusps, formed by duplicatures of the lining membrane, strengthened by fibrous tissue, and containing a few muscular fibers. The cusps are of unequal size, and are larger, thicker, and stronger than those of the tricuspid valve. The larger cusp is placed in front and to the right between the atrioventricular and aortic orifices, and is known as the **anterior** or **aortic cusp**; the smaller or **posterior cusp** is placed behind and to the left of the opening. Two smaller cusps are usually found at the angles of junction of the larger. The cusps of the bicuspid valve are furnished with chordæ tendineæ, which are attached in a manner similar to those on the right side; they are, however, thicker, stronger, and less numerous.

The **aortic semilunar valves** (Figs. 480, 483) are three in number, and surround the orifice of the aorta; two are posterior (right and left) and one anterior. They are similar in structure, and in their mode of attachment, to the pulmonary semilunar valves, but are larger, thicker, and stronger; the lunulæ are more distinct, and the noduli or corpora Arantii thicker and more prominent. Opposite the valves the aorta presents slight dilatations, the **aortic sinuses** (*sinuses of Valsalva*), which are larger than those at the origin of the pulmonary artery.

The **trabeculæ carneæ** are of three kinds, like those upon the right side, but they are more numerous, and present a dense interlacement, especially at the apex, and upon the posterior wall of the ventricle. The **musculi papillares** are two in number, one being connected to the anterior, the other to the posterior wall; they are of large size, and end in rounded extremities from which the chordæ tendineæ arise. The chordæ tendineæ from each papillary muscle are connected to both cusps of the bicuspid valve.

Ventricular Septum (*septum ventriculorum; interventricular septum*) (Fig. 484).— The ventricular septum is directed obliquely backward and to the right, and is curved with the convexity toward the right ventricle: its margins correspond with the anterior and posterior longitudinal sulci. The greater portion of it is thick and muscular and constitutes the **muscular ventricular septum,** but its upper and posterior part, which separates the aortic vestibule from the lower part of the right atrium and upper part of the right ventricle, is thin and fibrous, and is termed the **membranous ventricular septum.** An abnormal communication may exist between the ventricles at this part owing to defective development of the membranous septum.

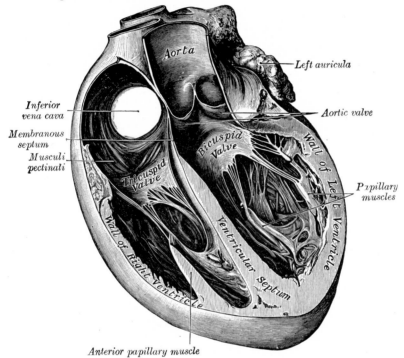

Fig. 484.—Section of the heart showing the ventricular septum.

The Heart-wall.—The heart-wall is covered by a serous layer of flat mesothelial cells, the **epicardium,** and lined by the **endocardium.** Between these two membranes is the muscular wall or **myocardium.**

The **endocardium** is a thin, smooth membrane which lines and gives the glistening appearance to the inner surface of the heart; it assists in forming the valves by its reduplications, and is continuous with the lining membrane of the large bloodvessels. It consists of connective tissue and elastic fibers, and is attached to the muscular structure by loose elastic tissue which contains bloodvessels and nerves; its free surface is covered by endothelial cells.

The **fibrous rings** surround the atrioventricular and arterial orifices, and are stronger upon the left than on the right side of the heart. The atrioventricular rings serve for the attachment of the muscular fibers of the atria and ventricles, and for the attachment of the bicuspid and tricuspid valves. The left atrioventricular ring is closely connected, by its right margin, with the aortic arterial ring; between these and the right atrioventricular ring is a triangular mass of fibrous tissue, the **trigonum fibrosum,** which represents the basal thickening of the membranous ventricular septum. Lastly, there is the tendon of the conus arteriosus extending from the trigonum fibrosum and right atrioventricular fibrous ring to the posterior side of the conus. It is intimately blended with the right anterior aspect of the aortic fibrous ring.

The **muscular structure of the heart** consists of bands of fibers, which present an exceedingly intricate interlacement. They comprise (*a*) the fibers of the atria, (*b*) the fibers of the ventricles, and (*c*) the atrioventricular bundle of His.

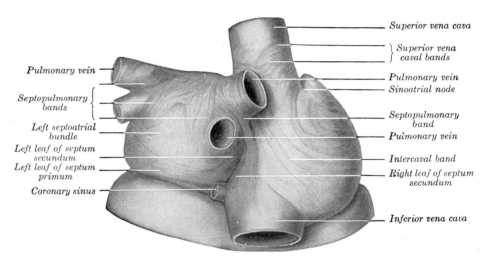

FIG. 485.—External bundles on the posterior surface of the atria. (Papez.)

The principal **muscle bundles of the atria** radiate from one central area which surrounds the orifice of the superior vena cava and is for the most part buried in the anterior part of the atrial septum; in front and to the right of the orifice of the vena cava it comes to the external surface. The portion that appears in the groove

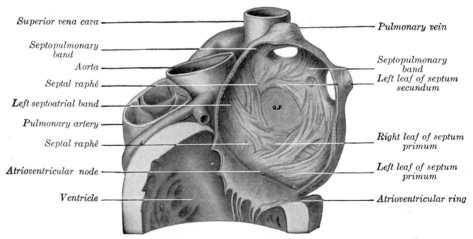

FIG. 486.—Muscle bands that radiate from the septal raphé in the left surface of the atrial septum. (Papez.)

between the vena cava and the right atrium has been designated the **sinoatrial node**; it is the seat of impulse formation for the atria in the normally beating heart. The portion that is buried in the atrial septum has been named the **septal raphé** by Papez. It provides an apparent mechanical support for many of the larger muscle bundles of both atria. The fibers of the sinoatrial node resemble those of the atrioventricular node. With the exception of the interatrial bundle, which connects the anterior surfaces of the two atria, the various muscle bundles are confined to their respective atria. These bundles radiate from either side of the septal raphé, which lies in front of the oval fossa, into the walls of the atria, the sinous venosus and the superior vena cava. According to Papez there are about fifteen muscle bundles which make up the walls of the two atria. They merge into one another more or less.

The **muscle bundles of the ventricles** probably all arise from the tendinous structures at the base, converge in spiral courses toward the apex for varying distances and then turn spirally upward to be inserted on the opposite side of these same tendinous structures. The superficial fibers pass to the vortex at the apex of the left ventricle before they turn upward while the deep ones turn upward at varying distances without reaching the apex.

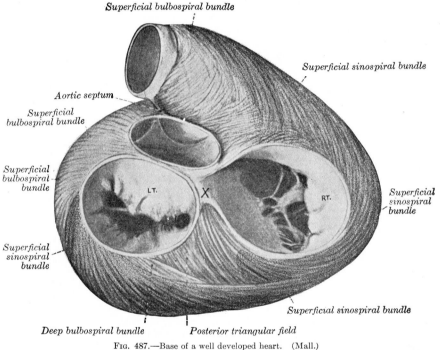

Fig. 487.—Base of a well developed heart. (Mall.)

The **superficial bulbospiral bundle** arises from the conus, left side of the aortic septum, aortic ring and left atrioventricular ring, passes apicalward and somewhat toward the right to the posterior horn of the vortex of the left ventricle. At their origin the fibers form a broad thin sheet that becomes thick and narrow at the apex where the bundle twists on itself and continues upward in a spiral manner on the inner surface of the left ventricle, spreading out into a thin sheet that is inserted on the opposite side of the tendinous structures from which it arose. These fibers make nearly a double circle around the heart somewhat like a figure 8 that is open at the top. As the fibers pass toward the apex they lie superficial to the deep bulbospiral bundle and as they pass upward from the apex they partly blend and partly pass on the inner side of it in directions nearly at right angles to their superficial fibers.

The **superficial sinospiral bundle** arises as a thin layer from the posterior sides of the left and right atrioventricular rings and from the right side of the latter. The fibers pass more horizontally around the heart to the apex than do those of the bulbospiral bundle. They pass completely around the right ventricle across the posterior and anterior longitudinal sulci gradually converging as they approach the apex and enter the anterior horn of the left vortex as a narrow thick band that twists upon itself to encircle the apex as it passes upward into the papillary muscles and inner wall of the left ventricle to become attached to the fibrous rings either by the chordæ tendineæ and the valve leaves or directly by the fibers themselves. These fibers likewise course around the heart somewhat in the form of a figure 8 that is open at the top and small at the bottom.

As the bundle enters the vortex it is joined by fibers from the longitudinal bundle of the right ventricle and fibers of the interventricular bundle from the papillæ of the right ventricle. Many of these pass into the papillæ of the left ventricle.

Many fibers from both the bulbospiral and sinospiral muscle bundles enter the interventricular septum as they pass into the anterior longitudinal sulcus. Consequently if the superficial fibers are cut across toward the right side of the posterior longitudinal sulcus the two ventricles can be pulled apart more readily than by a cut along the anterior sulcus. By turning back the superficial fibers the deep bulbospiral bundle is exposed.

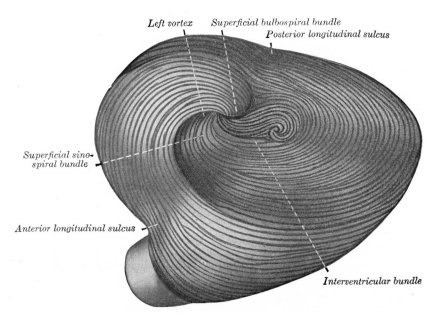

FIG. 488.—Apex of heart to show the two vortices. (Mall.)

The **deep bulbospiral bundle** arises immediately beneath the superficial bundle from the left side of the left ostia. The fibers pass downward to the right and enter the septum through the posterior longitudinal sulcus. They then encircle the left ventricle without reaching the apex after turning upon themselves on the apical side of the ring and blend with the fibers of the superficial bundle as they pass spirally upward to be inserted on the opposite sides of the fibrous rings of the left side. These fibers likewise seem to form an open figure 8 with both loops of about the same size.

The **deep sinospiral bundle** is more especially concerned with the right ventricle although its fibers communicate freely with the papillary muscles of both ventricles. Its fibers arise from the posterior part of the left ostium and pass diagonally into the deeper layer of the wall of the right ventricle where they turn upward to the conus and membranous septum. Some of them probably pass through the right vortex.

The **interventricular bundles** are represented in part by the longitudinal bundle of the right ventricle which passes through the septum and must be cut in order to unroll the heart, and by the interpapillary bands.

The **circular bands of the conus** are relatively simple and extend from one side of the tendon of the conus around the root of the pulmonary artery and the conus to the opposite side of the tendon.

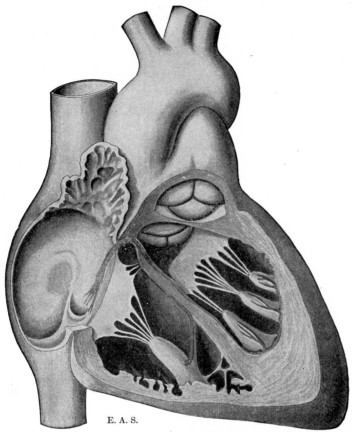

E. A. S.

Fig. 489.—Schematic representation of the atrioventricular bundle of His. The bundle, represented in red, originates near the orifice of the coronary sinus, undergoes slight enlargement to form a node, passes forward to the ventricular septum, and divides into two limbs. The ultimate distribution cannot be completely shown in this diagram.

The general arrangement of the fibers is such that the heart is twisted during systole, as one wrings out a wet rag, obliterating the ventricular cavities and forcing the blood out.

The **sinoatrial node** located at the junction of the superior vena cava and right atrium consists of modified muscle fibers. From it fibers extend to the vena cava and over the atrial wall. Contraction impulses probably start in this node, spread over the atrium and are then transmitted by the atrioventricular bundle to the ventricles. It is sometimes called the "pacemaker" of the heart.

The **atrioventricular bundle of His** (Fig. 489), is the only direct muscular connection known to exist between the atria and the ventricles. Its cells differ from ordinary cardiac muscle cells in being more spindle-shaped. They are also more loosely arranged and have a richer vascular supply than the rest of the heart muscle. It arises in connection with a small collection of spindle-shaped cells, the atrioventricular node. The **atrioventricular node** lies near the orifice of the coronary sinus in the annular and septal fibers of the right atrium; from it the atrioventricular bundle passes forward in the lower part of the membranous septum, and divides into right and left fasciculi. These run down in the right and left ventricles, one on either side of the ventricular septum, covered by endocardium. In the lower parts of the ventricles they break up into numerous strands which end in the papillary muscles and in the ventricular muscle generally. The bundle and its divisions are enveloped in a sheath of connective tissue; by injecting this sheath with India ink the ramifications of the bundle can be demonstrated. The greater portion of the atrioventricular bundle consists of narrow, somewhat fusiform fibers, but its terminal strands are composed of Purkinje fibers.

A. Morison has shown that in the sheep and pig the atrioventricular bundle "is a great avenue for the transmission of nerves from the auricular to the ventricular heart; large and numerous nerve trunks entering the bundle and coursing with it." From these, branches pass off and form plexuses around groups of Purkinje fibers, and from these plexuses fine fibrils go to innervate individual cells.

Clinical and experimental evidence go to prove that this bundle conveys the impulse to systolic contraction from the atrial septum to the ventricles.

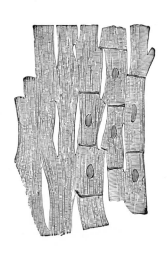

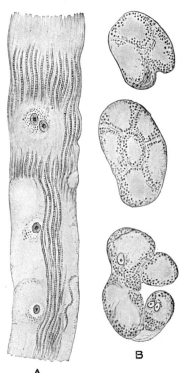

A

B

Fig. 490.—Anastomosing muscular fibers of the heart seen in a longitudinal section. On the right the limits of the separate cells with their nuclei are exhibited somewhat diagrammatically.

Fig 491.—Purkinje's fibers from the sheep's heart. *A*. In longitudinal section. *B*. In transverse section.

Cardiac Muscular Tissue.—The fibers of the heart differ very remarkably from those of other striped muscles. They are smaller by one-third, and their transverse striæ are by no means so well-marked. The fibers are made up of distinct quadrangular cells, joined end to end (Fig. 490). Each cell contains a clear oval nucleus, situated near its center. The extremities of the cells have a tendency to branch or divide, the subdivisions uniting with offsets from other cells, and thus producing an anastomosis of the fibers. The connective tissue between the bundles of fibers is much less than in ordinary striped muscle, and no sarcolemma has been proved to exist.

Purkinje Fibers (Fig. 491).—Between the endocardium and the ordinary cardiac muscle are found, imbedded in a small amount of connective tissue, peculiar fibers known as Purkinje fibers. They are found in certain mammals and in birds, and can be best seen in the sheep's heart, where they form a considerable portion of the moderator band and also appear as gelatinous-looking strands on the inner walls of the atria and ventricles. They also occur in the human heart associated with the terminal distributions of the bundle of His. The fibers are very much larger in size than the cardiac cells and differ from them in several ways. In longitudinal section they are quadrilateral in shape, being about twice as long as they are broad. The central portion of each fiber contains one or more nuclei and is made up of granular protoplasm, with no indication of striations, while the peripheral portion is clear and has distinct transverse striations. The fibers are intimately connected with each other, possess no definite sarcolemma, and do not branch.

Vessels and Nerves.—The **arteries** supplying the heart are the right and left coronary from the aorta; the **veins** end in the right atrium.

The **lymphatics** end in the thoracic and right lymphatic ducts.

The **nerves** are derived from the cardiac plexus, which is formed partly from the vagi, and partly from the sympathetic trunks. They are freely distributed both on the surface and in the substance of the heart, the separate nerve filaments being furnished with small ganglia.

The Cardiac Cycle and the Actions of the Valves.—By the contractions of the heart the blood is pumped through the arteries to all parts of the body. These contractions occur regularly and at the rate of about seventy per minute. Each wave of contraction or *period of activity* is followed by a *period of rest*, the two periods constituting what is known as a **cardiac cycle**.

Each cardiac cycle consists of three phases, which succeed each other as follows: (1) a short simultaneous contraction of both atria, termed the **atrial systole**, followed, after a slight pause, by (2) a simultaneous, but more prolonged, contraction of both ventricles, named the **ventricular systole**, and (3) a **period of rest**, during which the whole heart is relaxed. The atrial contraction commences around the venous openings, and sweeping over the atria forces their contents through the atrioventricular openings into the ventricles, regurgitation into the veins being prevented by the contraction of their muscular coats. When the ventricles contract, the tricuspid and bicuspid valves are closed, and prevent the passage of the blood back into the atria; the musculi papillares at the same time are shortened, and, pulling on the chordæ tendineæ, prevent the inversion of the valves into the atria. As soon as the pressure in the ventricles exceeds that in the pulmonary artery and aorta, the valves guarding the orifices of these vessels are opened and the blood is driven from the right ventricle into the pulmonary artery and from the left into the aorta. The moment the systole of the ventricle ceases, the pressure of the blood in the pulmonary artery and aorta closes the pulmonary and aortic semilunar valves to prevent regurgitation of blood into the ventricles, the valves remaining shut until reopened by the next ventricular systole. During the period of rest the tension of the tricuspid and bicuspid valves is relaxed, and blood is flowing from the veins into the atria, being aspirated by negative intrathoracic pressure, and slightly also from the atria into the ventricles. The average duration of a cardiac cycle is about $\frac{8}{10}$ of a second, made up as follows:

Atrial systole, $\frac{1}{10}$. Atrial diastole, $\frac{7}{10}$.

Ventricular systole, $\frac{3}{10}$. Ventricular diastole, $\frac{5}{10}$.

Total systole, $\frac{4}{10}$. Complete diastole, $\frac{4}{10}$.

The rhythmical action of the heart is *muscular* in origin—that is to say, the heart muscle itself possesses the inherent property of contraction apart from any nervous stimulation. The more embryonic the muscle the better is it able to initiate and propagate the contraction wave; this explains why the normal systole of the heart starts at the entrance of the veins, for there the muscle is most embryonic in its histological appearance. At the atrioventricular junction there is a slight pause

35

in the wave of muscular contraction. To obviate this so far as possible a peculiar band of marked embryonic type passes across the junction and so carries on the contraction wave to the ventricles. This band, composed of special fibers, is the atrioventricular bundle of His (p. 543). The nerves, although not concerned in originating the contractions of the heart muscle, play an important rôle in regulating their force and frequency in order to subserve the physiological needs of the organism.

PECULIARITIES IN THE VASCULAR SYSTEM OF THE FETUS.

The chief peculiarities of the fetal heart are the direct communication between the atria through the foramen ovale, and the large size of the valve of the inferior vena cava. Among other peculiarities the following may be noted. (1) In early fetal life the heart lies immediately below the mandibular arch and is relatively large in size. As development proceeds it is gradually drawn within the thorax, but at first it lies in the middle line; toward the end of pregnancy it gradually becomes oblique in direction. (2) For a time the atrial portion exceeds the ventricular in size, and the walls of the ventricles are of equal thickness: toward the end of fetal life the ventricular portion becomes the larger and the wall of the left ventricle exceeds that of the right in thickness. (3) Its size is large as compared with that of the rest of the body, the proportion at the second month being 1 to 50, and at birth, 1 to 120, while in the adult the average is about 1 to 160.

The **foramen ovale**, situated at the lower part of the atrial septum, forms a free communication between the atria until the end of fetal life. A septum (*septum secundum*) grows down from the upper wall of the atrium to the right of the primary septum in which the foramen ovale is situated; shortly after birth it fuses with the primary septum and the foramen ovale is obliterated.

The **valve of the inferior vena cava** serves to direct the blood from that vessel through the foramen ovale into the left atrium.

The peculiarities in the arterial system of the fetus are the communication between the pulmonary artery and the aorta by means of the ductus arteriosus, and the continuation of the hypogastric arteries as the umbilical arteries to the placenta.

The **ductus arteriosus** is a short tube, about 1.25 cm. in length at birth, and 4.4 mm. in diameter. In the early condition it forms the continuation of the pulmonary artery, and opens into the aorta, just beyond the origin of the left subclavian artery; and so conducts the greater amount of the blood from the right ventricle into the aorta. When the branches of the pulmonary artery have become larger relatively to the ductus arteriosus, the latter is chiefly connected to the left pulmonary artery.

The **hypogastric arteries** run along the sides of the bladder and thence upward on the back of the anterior abdominal wall to the umbilicus; here they pass out of the abdomen and are continued as the **umbilical arteries** in the umbilical cord to the placenta. They convey the fetal blood to the placenta.

The peculiarities in the venous system of the fetus are the communications established between the placenta and the liver and portal vein, through the umbilical vein; and between the umbilical vein and the inferior vena cava through the ductus venosus.

Fetal Circulation (Fig. 492).—The fetal blood is returned from the placenta to the fetus by the umbilical vein. This vein enters the abdomen at the umbilicus, and passes upward along the free margin of the falciform ligament of the liver to the under surface of that organ, where it gives off two or three branches, one of large size to the left lobe, and others to the lobus quadratus and lobus caudatus.

At the **porta hepatis** (*transverse fissure of the liver*) it divides into two branches: of these, the larger is joined by the portal vein, and enters the right lobe; the smaller is continued upward, under the name of the **ductus venosus,** and joins

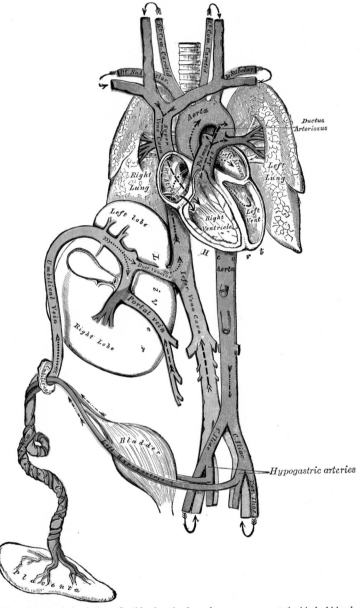

Fig. 492.—Plan of the fetal circulation. In this plan the figured arrows represent the kind of blood, as well as the direction which it takes in the vessels. Thus—arterial blood is figured >-------->; venous blood, > – – – >; mixed (arterial and venous) blood, >– –-- –>.

the inferior vena cava. The blood, therefore, which traverses the umbilical vein, passes to the inferior vena cava in three different ways. A considerable quantity circulates through the liver with the portal venous blood, before entering the inferior vena cava by the hepatic veins; some enters the liver directly, and is carried to the inferior vena cava by the hepatic veins; the remainder passes directly into the inferior vena cava through the ductus venosus.

In the inferior vena cava, the blood carried by the ductus venosus and hepatic veins becomes mixed with that returning from the lower extremities and abdominal wall. It enters the right atrium, and, guided by the valve of the inferior vena cava, passes through the foramen ovale into the left atrium, where it mixes with a small quantity of blood returned from the lungs by the pulmonary veins. From the left atrium it passes into the left ventricle; and from the left ventricle into the aorta, by means of which it is distributed almost entirely to the head and upper extremities, a small quantity being probably carried into the descending aorta. From the head and upper extremities the blood is returned by the superior vena cava to the right atrium, where it mixes with a small portion of the blood from the inferior vena cava. From the right atrium it descends into the right ventricle, and thence passes into the pulmonary artery. The lungs of the fetus being inactive, only a small quantity of the blood of the pulmonary artery is distributed to them by the right and left pulmonary arteries, and returned by the pulmonary veins to the left atrium: the greater part passes through the ductus arteriosus into the aorta, where it mixes with a small quantity of the blood transmitted by the left ventricle into the aorta. Through this vessel it descends, and is in part distributed to the lower extremities and the viscera of the abdomen and pelvis, but the greater amount is conveyed by the umbilical arteries to the placenta.

From the preceding account of the circulation of the blood in the fetus the following facts will be evident: (1) The placenta serves the purposes of nutrition and excretion, receiving the impure blood from the fetus, and returning it purified and charged with additional nutritive material. (2) Nearly all the blood of the umbilical vein traverses the liver before entering the inferior vena cava; hence the large size of the liver, especially at an early period of fetal life. (3) The right atrium is the point of meeting of a double current, the blood in the inferior vena cava being guided by the valve of this vessel into the left atrium, while that in the superior vena cava descends into the right ventricle. At an early period of fetal life it is highly probable that the two streams are quite distinct; for the inferior vena cava opens almost directly into the left atrium, and the valve of the inferior vena cava would exclude the current from the right ventricle. At a later period, as the separation between the two atria becomes more distinct, it seems probable that some mixture of the two streams must take place. (4) The pure blood carried from the placenta to the fetus by the umbilical vein, mixed with the blood from the portal vein and inferior vena cava, passes almost directly to the arch of the aorta, and is distributed by the branches of that vessel to the head and upper extremities. (5) The blood contained in the descending aorta, chiefly derived from that which has already circulated through the head and limbs, together with a small quantity from the left ventricle, is distributed to the abdomen and lower extremities.

Changes in the Vascular System at Birth.—At birth, when respiration is established, an increased amount of blood from the pulmonary artery passes through the lungs, and the placental circulation is cut off. The foramen ovale gradually decreases in size during the first month, but a small opening usually persists until the last third of the first year and often later; the valvular fold above mentioned adheres to the margin of the foramen for the greater part of its circumference, but a slit-like opening is left between the two atria above, and this sometimes persists.

The **ductus arteriosus** begins to contract immediately after respiration is established, and its lumen slowly becomes obliterated; it ultimately degenerates into an impervious cord, the **ligamentum arteriosum**, which connects the left pulmonary artery to the arch of the aorta. (Fig. 495.)

Of the **hypogastric arteries**, the parts extending from the sides of the bladder to the umbilicus become obliterated between the second and fifth days after birth, and project as fibrous cords, the **lateral umbilical ligaments**, toward the abdominal cavity, carrying on them folds of peritoneum. (Fig. 530.)

The **umbilical vein** and **ductus venosus** are obliterated between the first and fifth days after birth; the former becomes the ligamentum teres, the latter the ligamentum venosum, of the liver. The hepatic half of the ductus venosus may remain open, receive tributaries from the liver and thus function as a hepatic vein in the adult. (Fig. 1072.)

BIBLIOGRAPHY.

BLOOD

An experimental analysis of hematopoiesis in the rat yolk sac. BLOCK, M.: 1946. Anat. Rec., Vol. 96, pp. 289-311.
Locomotion of blood cells in tissue cultures. DE BRUYN, P. P. H.: 1944. Anat. Rec., Vol. 89, pp. 43-63.
Extramedullary blood production. JORDAN, H. E.: 1942. Physiol. Rev., Vol. 22, pp. 375-384.
An experimental study of the cytology of human peripheral blood neutrophiles and lymphocytes. RICHTER, K. M.: 1942. J. Morph., Vol. 71, pp. 53-75.

CAPILLARIES

The permeability of the arterioles, capillaries and venules of the living rabbit to the vital dye T-1824. ABELL, R. G.: 1940. Anat. Rec., Vol. 78, pp. 215-231.
Topography and function of the mesenteric capillary circulation. CHAMBERS, R., and B. W. ZWEIFACH: 1944. Am. J. Anat., Vol. 75, pp. 173-205.
Caliber changes in minute blood-vessels observed in the living mammal. CLARK, E. R., and E. L. 1943. Am. J. Anat., Vol. 73, pp. 215-250.
Capillary pressure and capillary permeability. LANDIS, E. M.: 1934. Physiol. Rev., Vol. 14, pp. 404-481.
The structural basis of permeability and other functions of blood capillaries. ZWEIFACH, B. W.: 1940. Cold Spring Harbor Symp., Vol. 8, pp. 216-223.

HEART

Prediction of heart weight in man. GRAY, H., and E. MAHAN: 1943. Am. J. Phys. Anthrop., Vol. 1, pp. 271-287.
The incidence and size of the moderator band in man and in mammals. TRUEX, R. C., and L. J. WARSHAW: 1942. Anat. Rec., Vol. 82, pp. 361-372.

HISTOLOGY

A determination of the diameters of ventricular myocardial fibers in man and other mammals. ASHLEY, L. M.: 1945. Am. J. Anat., Vol. 77, pp. 325-363.
Further observations on the differentiation of cardiac muscle in tissue cultures. Goss, C. M.: 1933. Arch. exper. Zellfors., Vol. 14, pp. 175-201.
Effect of trypan blue upon cardiac explants in tissue culture. HETHERINGTON, D. C.: 1944. Proc. Soc. Exp. Biol. and Med., Vol. 57, pp. 194-196.
On the muscular architecture of the vertebrate ventricle. SHANER, R. F.: 1924. J. Anat., Vol. 58, pp. 59-70.
Histology of the moderator band in man and other mammals with special reference to the conduction system. TRUEX, R. C., and W. M. COPENHAVER: 1947. Am. J. Anat., Vol. 80, pp. 173-201.

EMBRYOLOGY

Studies of the fœtal circulation and of certain changes that take place after birth. BARCLAY, A. E., J. BARCROFT, D. H. BARRON, K. J. FRANKLIN, and M. M. L. PRICHARD: 1941. Am. J. Anat., Vol. 69, pp. 383-406.
The development of the heart in the rat. BURLINGAME, P. L., and J. A. LONG: 1939. Univ. Cal. Publ. Zool., Vol. 43, pp. 249-320.
Initiation of beat and intrinsic contraction rates in the different parts of the Amblystoma heart. COPENHAVER, W. M.: 1939. J. Exp. Zool., Vol. 80, pp. 193-224.
Development of the human heart from its first appearance to the stage found in embryos of 20 paired somites. DAVIS, C. L.: 1927. Carnegie Cont. to Emb., Vol. 19, pp. 245-284.
The first contractions of the heart in rat embryos. Goss, C. M.: 1938. Anat. Rec., Vol. 70, pp. 505-524.

A note on the closure of the foramen ovale and the postnatal changes of the ventricles in the human heart. KEEN, J. A.: 1942. J. Anat., Vol. 77, pp. 104–109.

The partitioning of the truncus and conus and the formation of the membranous portion of the interventricular septum in the human heart. KRAMER, T. C.: 1942. Am. J. Anat., Vol. 71, pp. 343–370.

A theory of transposition of the arterial trunks based on the phylogenetic and ontogenetic development of the heart. LEV, M., and O. SAPHIR: 1945. Arch. Path., Vol. 39, pp. 172–183.

The closure of the foramen ovale. PATTEN, B. M.: 1931. Am. J. Anat., Vol. 48, pp. 19-44.

The initiation of contraction in the embryonic chick heart. PATTEN, B. M., and KRAMER, T. C.: 1933. Am. J. Anat., Vol. 53, pp. 349–375.

EXPERIMENTAL EMBRYOLOGY

Self-differentiation and induction in the heart of Amblystoma. BACON, R. L.: 1945. J. Exp. Zool., Vol. 98, pp. 87–125.

The intrinsic pulsation rates of fragments of the embryonic chick heart. BARRY, A.: 1942. J. Exp. Zool., Vol. 91, pp. 119-130.

Heteroplastic transplantation of the sinus venosus between two species of Amblystoma. COPENHAVER, W. M.: 1945. J. Exp. Zool., Vol. 100, pp. 203-216.

Physiological contraction of double hearts in rabbit embryos. DWINNELL, L. A.: 1939. Proc. Soc. Exp. Biol. and Med., Vol. 42, pp. 264–267.

A study of double hearts produced experimentally in embryos of Amblystoma punctatum. FALES, D. E.: 1946. J. Exp. Zool., Vol. 101, pp. 281–298.

The physiology of the embryonic mammalian heart before circulation. Goss, C. M.: 1942. Am. J. Physiol., Vol. 137, pp. 146–152.

Transplantation of sino-atrium to conus in the embryonic heart *in vitro*. PAFF, G. H.: 1936. Am. J. Physiol., Vol. 117, pp. 313–317.

Micromoving pictures and electrocardiographic records of age changes in embryonic heart action. PATTEN, B. M.: 1944. West. J. Surg., Vol. 52, pp. 325-329.

ANOMALIES AND VARIATIONS

A multiple anomaly of the human heart and pulmonary veins. ATKINSON, W. J., JR., J. L. DEAN, E. H. KENNERDELL, and C. J. LAMBERTSEN: 1940. Anat. Rec., Vol. 78, pp. 383–388.

Apical pericardial adhesion resembling the reptilian gubernaculum cordis. COBB, W. M.: 1944. Anat. Rec., Vol. 89, pp. 87-91.

Developmental defects at the foramen ovale. PATTEN, B. M.: 1938. Am. J. Path., Vol. 14, pp. 135–162.

Congenital anomalies of the heart. POYNTER, C. W. M.: 1919. Nebraska Univ. Studies, Vol. 19, pp. 1–102.

A five-chambered human heart. SINCLAIR, J. G.: 1944. Anat. Rec., Vol. 90, pp. 41–43.

Congenital pericardial defects. SUNDERLAND, S., and R. J. WRIGHT–SMITH: 1944. Brit. Heart J., Vol. 6, pp. 167–175.

INNERVATION

The role of the nerves in the action of acetylcholine on the embryonic heart. ARMSTRONG, P. B.: 1935. J. Physiol., Vol. 84, pp. 20-32.

Studies on the innervation of the heart. NONIDEZ, J. F.: 1939. Am. J. Anat., Vol. 65, pp. 361–413.

Structure and innervation of conductive system of heart of dog and rhesus monkey. NONIDEZ, J. F.: 1943. Am. Heart J., Vol. 26, pp. 577-597.

BLOOD SUPPLY

Arteriæ coronariæ (cordis) in the higher primates. CHASE, R. E., and C. F. DE GARIS: 1939. Am. J. Phys. Anthrop., Vol. 24, pp. 427-448.

The arterial blood vascular distribution to the left and right ventricles of the human heart. GROSS, L., and M. A. KUGEL: 1933. Am. Heart J., Vol. 9, pp. 165–177.

The nature of the vascular communications between the coronary arteries and the chambers of the heart. WEARN, J. T., S. R. METTIER, T. G. KLUMPP, and L. J. ZSCHIESCHE: 1933. Am. Heart J., Vol. 9, pp. 143–164.

SURGERY OF HEART AND GREAT VESSELS

The surgical treatment of congenital pulmonic stenosis. BLALOCK, A.: 1946. Ann. Surg., Vol. 124, pp. 879-887.

A symposium on cardiac surgery; basic considerations. Cox, P. L.: 1947. McGill M. J., Vol. 16, pp. 11–22.

Heart catheterization in the investigation of congenital heart disease. JOHNSON, A. L., D. G. WOLLIN, and J. B. ROSS: 1947. Canada Med. Assn. J., Vol. 56, pp. 249–255.

THE ARTERIES.

THE distribution of the systemic arteries is like a highly ramified tree, the common trunk of which, formed by the aorta, commences at the left ventricle, while the smallest ramifications extend to the peripheral parts of the body and the contained organs. Arteries are found in all parts of the body, except in the hairs, nails, epidermis, cartilages, and cornea; the larger trunks usually occupy the most protected situations, running, in the limbs, along the flexor surface, where they are less exposed to injury.

There is considerable variation in the mode of division of the arteries: occasionally a short trunk subdivides into several branches at the same point, as may be observed in the celiac artery and the thyrocervical trunk: the vessel may give off several branches in succession, and still continue as the main trunk, as is seen in the arteries of the limbs; or the division may be dichotomous, as, for instance, when the aorta divides into the two common iliacs.

A branch of an artery is smaller than the trunk from which it arises; but if an artery divides into two branches, the combined sectional area of the two vessels is, in nearly every instance, somewhat greater than that of the trunk; and the combined sectional area of all the arterial branches greatly exceeds that of the aorta; so that the arteries collectively may be regarded as a cone, the apex of which corresponds to the aorta, and the base to the capillary system.

The arteries, in their distribution, communicate with one another, forming what are called **anastomoses**, and these communications are very free between the large as well as between the smaller branches. The anastomosis between trunks of equal size is found where great activity of the circulation is requisite, as in the brain; here the two vertebral arteries unite to form the basilar, and the two anterior cerebral arteries are connected by a short communicating trunk; it is also found in the abdomen, where the intestinal arteries have very ample anastomoses between their larger branches. In the limbs the anastomoses are most numerous and of largest size around the joints, the branches of an artery above uniting with branches from the vessels below. These anastomoses are of considerable interest to the surgeon, as it is by their enlargement that a **collateral circulation** is established after the application of a ligature to an artery. The smaller branches of arteries anastomose more frequently than the larger; and between the smallest twigs these anastomoses become so numerous as to constitute a close network that pervades nearly every tissue of the body. Of particular interest are anastomoses between arteries and veins which permit the shunting of the blood from an artery to a vein without its passing through the capillaries. The arteriovenous anastomoses in such organs as the kidney or the salivary glands appear to be of significance for the special functions of these organs. In the tips of the fingers where arteriovenous anastomoses occur also frequently, they may play a rôle in thermoregulation. The morphological and physiological aspects of arteriovenous anastomoses are manifold and are as yet not fully understood.

Throughout the body generally the larger arterial branches pursue a fairly straight course, but in certain situations they are tortuous. Thus the external maxillary artery in its course over the face, and the arteries of the lips, are extremely tortuous, accommodating themselves to the movements of the parts. The uterine arteries are also tortuous, accommodating themselves to the increase of size which the uterus undergoes during pregnancy.

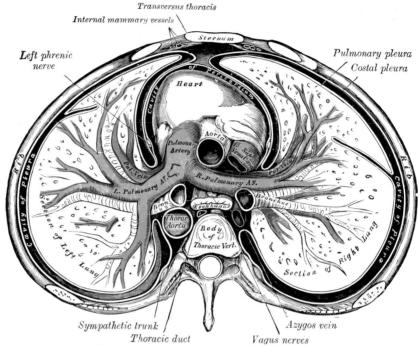

FIG. 493.—Transverse section of thorax, showing relations of pulmonary artery.

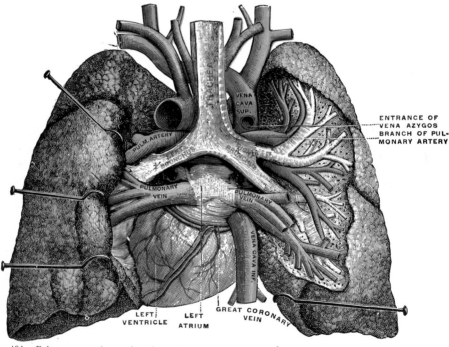

FIG. 494.—Pulmonary vessels, seen in a dorsal view of the heart and lungs. The lungs have been pulled away from the median line, and a part of the right lung has been cut away to display the air-ducts and bloodvessels

The Pulmonary Artery (**A. Pulmonalis**) (Figs. 493, 494).

The **pulmonary artery** conveys the venous blood from the right ventricle of the heart to the lungs. It is a short, wide vessel, about 5 cm. in length and 3 cm. in diameter, *arising* from the conus arteriosus of the right ventricle. It extends obliquely upward and backward, passing at first in front and then to the left of the ascending aorta, as far as the under surface of the aortic arch, where it divides, about the level of the fibrocartilage between the fifth and sixth thoracic vertebræ, into right and left branches of nearly equal size.

Relations.—This entire vessel is contained within the pericardium. It is enclosed with the ascending aorta in a single tube of the visceral layer of the serous pericardium, which is continued upward upon them from the base of the heart. The fibrous layer of the pericardium is gradually lost upon the external coats of the two branches of the artery. In *front*, the pulmonary artery is separated from the anterior end of the second left intercostal space by the pleura and left lung, in addition to the pericardium; at first it is anterior to the ascending aorta, and higher up lies in front of the left atrium on a plane posterior to the ascending aorta. On *either side* of its origin is the auricula of the corresponding atrium and a coronary artery, the left coronary artery passing, in the first part of its course, behind the vessel. The superficial part of the cardiac plexus lies above its bifurcation, between it and the arch of the aorta.

The **right branch of the pulmonary artery** (*ramus dexter a. pulmonalis*), longer and larger than the left, runs horizontally to the right, behind the ascending aorta and superior vena cava and in front of the right bronchus, to the root of the right lung, where it divides into two branches. The lower and larger of these goes to the middle and lower lobes; the upper and smaller is distributed to the upper lobe.

The **left branch of the pulmonary artery** (*ramus sinister a. pulmonalis*), shorter and somewhat smaller than the right, passes horizontally in front of the descending aorta and left bronchus to the root of the left lung, where it divides into two branches, one for each lobe of the lung.

Above, it is connected to the concavity of the aortic arch by the **ligamentum arteriosum**, on the left of which is the left recurrent nerve, and on the right the superficial part of the cardiac plexus. *Below*, it is joined to the upper left pulmonary vein by the ligament of the left vena cava.

The terminal branches of the pulmonary arteries will be described with the lungs.

THE AORTA.

The **aorta** is the main trunk of a series of vessels which convey the oxygenated blood to the tissues of the body for their nutrition. It commences at the upper part of the left ventricle, where it is about 3 cm. in diameter, and after ascending for a short distance, arches backward and to the left side, over the root of the left lung; it then descends within the thorax on the left side of the vertebral column, passes into the abdominal cavity through the aortic hiatus in the diaphragm, and ends, considerably diminished in size (about 1.75 cm. in diameter), opposite the lower border of the fourth lumbar vertebra, by dividing into the right and left common iliac arteries. Hence it is described in several portions, viz., the **ascending aorta**, the **arch of the aorta**, and the **descending aorta**, which last is again divided into the **thoracic** and **abdominal aortæ**.

THE ASCENDING AORTA (AORTA ASCENDENS) (Fig. 495).

The **ascending aorta** is about 5 cm. in length. It commences at the upper part of the base of the left ventricle, on a level with the lower border of the third costal cartilage behind the left half of the sternum; it curves obliquely upward, anteriorly, and to the right, in the direction of the heart's axis, as high as the upper border of the second right costal cartilage, and lying about 6 cm. behind the posterior surface of the sternum. At its origin, opposite the segments of the aortic valve, are three small dilatations called the **aortic sinuses**. At the union of the ascending aorta with the aortic arch the caliber of the vessel is increased by a bulging of its right wall, and on transverse section presents a somewhat oval figure. The ascending aorta is contained within the pericardium, and is enclosed in a tube of the serous pericardium, common to it and the pulmonary artery.

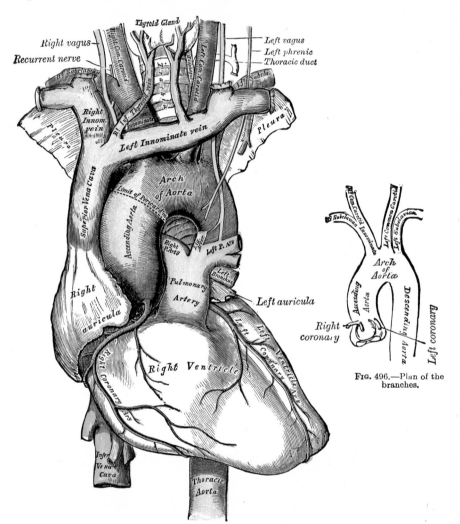

FIG. 496.—Plan of the branches.

FIG. 495.—The arch of the aorta, and its branches.

Relations.—The ascending aorta is covered at its commencement by the trunk of the pulmonary artery and the right auricula, and, higher up, is separated from the sternum by the pericardium, the right pleura, the anterior margin of the right lung, some loose areolar tissue, and the remains of the thymus; *posteriorly*, it rests upon the left atrium and right pulmonary artery. On the *right side*, it is in relation with the superior vena cava and right atrium, the former lying partly behind it; on the *left side*, with the pulmonary artery.

Branches.—The **Right Coronary Artery** (*a. coronaria* [*cordis*] *dextra*) *arises* from the anterior aortic sinus. It passes at first between the conus arteriosus and the right auricula and then runs in the right portion of the coronary sulcus, coursing at first from the left to right and then on the diaphragmatic surface of the heart from right to left as far as the posterior longitudinal sulcus, down which it is continued to the apex of the heart as the **posterior descending branch.** A large **marginal branch** follows the acute margin of the heart and supplies branches to both surfaces of the right ventricle. It also gives twigs to the right atrium and to the part of the left ventricle which adjoins the posterior longitudinal sulcus. It is poorly developed in 11 per cent. of cases.

The **Left Coronary Artery** (*a. coronaria* [*cordis*] *sinistra*), larger than the right, arises from the left posterior aortic sinus and divides into an anterior descending and a circumflex branch. The **anterior descending branch** passes at first behind the pulmonary artery and then comes forward between that vessel and the left auricula to reach the anterior longitudinal sulcus, along which it descends to the incisura apicis cordis; it gives branches to both ventricles. The **circumflex branch** follows the left part of the coronary sulcus, running first to the left and then to the right, reaching nearly as far as the posterior longitudinal sulcus; it gives branches to the left atrium and ventricle. There is a free anastomosis between the minute branches of the two coronary arteries in the substance of the heart.

Variations.—These vessels occasionally arise by a common trunk, or their number may be increased to three, the additional branch being of small size. More rarely, there are two additional branches.

THE ARCH OF THE AORTA (ARCUS AORTÆ; TRANSVERSE AORTA) (Fig. 495).

The **arch of the aorta** begins at the level of the upper border of the second sterno-costal articulation of the right side, and runs at first upward, backward, and to the left in front of the trachea; it is then directed backward on the left side of the trachea and finally passes downward on the left side of the body of the fourth thoracic vertebra, at the lower border of which it becomes continuous with the descending aorta. It thus forms two curvatures: one with its convexity upward, the other with its convexity forward and to the left. Its upper border is usually about 2.5 cm. below the superior border of the manubrium sterni.

Relations.—The arch of the aorta is covered *anteriorly* by the pleuræ and anterior margins of the lungs, and by the remains of the thymus. As the vessel runs backward its *left* side is in contact with the left lung and pleura. Passing downward on the left side of this part of the arch are four nerves; in order from before backward these are, the left phrenic, the lower of the superior cardiac branches of the left vagus, the superior cardiac branch of the left sympathetic, and the trunk of the left vagus. As the last nerve crosses the arch it gives off its recurrent branch, which hooks around below the vessel and then passes upward on its right side. The highest left intercostal vein runs obliquely upward and forward on the left side of the arch, between the phrenic and vagus nerves. On the *right* are the deep part of the cardiac plexus, the left recurrent nerve, the esophagus, and the thoracic duct; the trachea lies behind and to the right of the vessel. *Above* are the innominate, left common carotid, and left subclavian arteries, which arise from the convexity of the arch and are crossed close to their origins by the left innominate vein. *Below* are the bifurcation of the pulmonary artery, the left bronchus, the ligamentum arteriosum, the superficial part of the cardiac plexus, and the left recurrent nerve. As already stated, the ligamentum arteriosum connects the commencement of the left pulmonary artery to the aortic arch.

Between the origin of the left subclavian artery and the attachment of the ductus arteriosus the lumen of the fetal aorta is considerably narrowed, forming what is termed the **aortic isthmus,** while immediately beyond the ductus arteriosus the vessel presents a fusiform dilation which His has named the **aortic spindle**—the point of junction of the two parts being marked in the concavity of the arch by an indentation or angle. These conditions persist, to some extent, in the adult, where His found that the average diameter of the spindle exceeded that of the isthmus by 3 mm.

Variations.—The height to which the aorta rises in the thorax is usually about 2.5 cm. below the upper border of the sternum; but it may ascend nearly to the top of the bone. Occasionally it is found 4 cm., more rarely from 5 to 8 cm. below this point. Sometimes the aorta arches over the root of the right lung (right aortic arch) instead of over that of the left, and passes down on the right side of the vertebral column, a condition which is found in birds. In such cases all the thoracic and abdominal viscera are transposed. Less frequently the aorta, after arching over the root of the right lung, is directed to its usual position on the left side of the vertebral column; this peculiarity is not accompanied by transposition of the viscera. The aorta occasionally divides, as in some quadrupeds, into an ascending and a descending trunk, the former of which is directed vertically upward, and subdivides into three branches, to supply the head and upper extremities. Sometimes the aorta subdivides near its origin into two branches, which soon reunite. In one of these cases the esophagus and trachea were found to pass through the interval between the two branches; this is the normal condition of the vessel in the reptilia.

Branches (Figs. 495, 496).—The branches given off from the arch of the aorta are three in number: the **innominate**, the **left common carotid**, and the **left subclavian**, in 83 to 94 per cent. of cadavers, according to various reports.

Variations.—The branches, instead of arising from the highest part of the arch, may spring from the commencement of the arch or upper part of the ascending aorta; or the distance between them at their origins may be increased or diminished, the most frequent change in this respect being the approximation of the left carotid toward the innominate artery.

The *number* of the primary branches may be reduced to one, or more commonly two; the left carotid arising from the innominate artery; or (more rarely) the carotid and subclavian arteries of the left side arising from a left innominate artery. But the number may be increased to four, from the right carotid and subclavian arteries arising directly from the aorta, the innominate being absent. In most of these latter cases the right subclavian has been found to arise from the left end of the arch; in other cases it is the second or third branch given off, instead of the first. Another common form in which there are four primary branches is that in which the left vertebral artery arises from the arch of the aorta between the left carotid and subclavian arteries. Lastly, the number of trunks from the arch may be increased to five or six; in these instances, the external and internal carotids arise separately from the arch, the common carotid being absent on one or both sides. In some few cases six branches have been found, and this condition is associated with the origin of both vertebral arteries from the arch.

When the aorta arches over to the right side, the three branches have a reverse arrangement; the innominate artery is a left one, and the right carotid and subclavian arise separately. In other cases, where the aorta takes its usual course, the two carotids may be joined in a common trunk, and the subclavians arise separately from the arch, the right subclavian generally arising from the left end.

In some instances other arteries spring from the arch of the aorta. Of these the most common are the bronchial, one or both, and the thyreoidea ima; but the internal mammary and the inferior thyroid have been seen to arise from this vessel.

The Innominate Artery (A. Anonyma; Brachiocephalic Artery) (Fig. 495).

The **innominate artery** is the largest branch of the arch of the aorta, and is from 4 to 5 cm. in length. It *arises*, on a level with the upper border of the second right costal cartilage, from the commencement of the arch of the aorta, on a plane anterior to the origin of the left carotid; it ascends obliquely upward, backward, and to the right to the level of the upper border of the right sternoclavicular articulation, where it divides into the right common carotid and right subclavian arteries.

Relations.—*Anteriorly*, it is separated from the manubrium sterni by the Sternohyoideus and Sternothyreoideus, the remains of the thymus, the left innominate and right inferior thyroid veins which cross its root, and sometimes the superior cardiac branches of the right vagus. *Posterior* to it is the trachea, which it crosses obliquely. On the *right side* are the right innominate vein, the superior vena cava, the right phrenic nerve, and the pleura; and on the *left side*, the remains of the thymus, the origin of the left common carotid artery, the inferior thyroid veins, and the trachea.

Branches.—The innominate artery usually gives off no branches; but occasionally a small branch, the **thyreoidea ima**, arises from it. Sometimes it gives off a **thymic or bronchial branch**.

The **thyreoidea ima** (*a. thyreoidea ima*) ascends in front of the trachea to the lower part of the thyroid gland, which it supplies. It varies greatly in size, and appears to compensate for deficiency or absence of one of the other thyroid vessels. It occasionally arises from the aorta, the right common carotid, the subclavian or the internal mammary.

Variations.—The innominate artery sometimes divides above the level of the sternoclavicular joint; less frequently below it. It may be absent, the right subclavian and the right common carotid then arising directly from the aorta. When the aortic arch is on the right side, the innominate is directed to the left side of the neck.

THE ARTERIES OF THE HEAD AND NECK.

The principal arteries of supply to the head and neck are the two **common carotids**; each divides into two branches, viz., (1) the **external carotid**, supplying the exterior of the head, the face, and the greater part of the neck; (2) the **internal carotid**, supplying to a great extent the parts within the cranial and orbital cavities.

THE COMMON CAROTID ARTERY (A. CAROTIS COMMUNIS).

The **common carotid arteries** differ in length and in their mode of origin. The *right* begins at the bifurcation of the innominate artery behind the sternoclavicular joint and is confined to the neck. The *left* springs from the highest part of the arch of the aorta to the left of, and on a plane posterior to the innominate artery, and therefore consists of a thoracic and a cervical portion.

The **thoracic portion of the left common carotid artery** ascends from the arch of the aorta through the superior mediastinum to the level of the left sternoclavicular joint, where it is continuous with the cervical portion.

Relations.—*In front*, it is separated from the manubrium sterni by the Sternohyoideus and Sternothyreoideus, the anterior portions of the left pleura and lung, the left innominate vein, and the remains of the thymus; *behind*, it lies on the trachea, esophagus, left recurrent nerve, and thoracic duct. To its *right side* below is the innominate artery, and above, the trachea, the inferior thyroid veins, and the remains of the thymus; to its *left side* are the left vagus and phrenic nerves, left pleura, and lung. The left subclavian artery is posterior and slightly lateral to it.

The **cervical portions** of the common carotids resemble each other so closely that one description will apply to both (Fig. 497). Each vessel passes obliquely upward, from behind the sternoclavicular articulation, to the level of the upper border of the thyroid cartilage, where it divides into the external and internal carotid arteries.

At the lower part of the neck the two common carotid arteries are separated by a very narrow interval which contains the trachea; but at the upper part, the thyroid gland, the larynx and pharynx project forward between the two vessels. The common carotid artery is contained in a sheath, which is derived from the deep cervical fascia and encloses also the internal jugular vein and vagus nerve, the vein lying lateral to the artery, and the nerve between the artery and vein, on a plane posterior to both. On opening the sheath, each of these three structures is seen to have a separate fibrous investment.

Relations.—At the lower part of the neck, the common carotid artery is very deep, being *covered by* the integument, superficial fascia, Platysma, and deep cervical fascia, the Sternocleidomastoideus, Sternohyoideus, Sternothyreoideus, and Omohyoideus; in the upper part of its course it is more superficial, being covered merely by the integument, the superficial fascia, Platysma, deep cervical fascia, and medial margin of the Sternocleidomastoideus. When the latter muscle is drawn backward, the artery is seen to be contained in a triangular space, the **carotid triangle**, bounded behind by the Sternocleidomastoideus, above by the Stylohyoideus and posterior belly of the Digastricus, and below by the superior belly of the Omohyoideus. This part of the artery is crossed obliquely, from its medial to its lateral side, by the sternocleidomastoid branch of the superior thyroid artery; it is also crossed by the superior and middle thyroid veins which end in the internal jugular; in front of its sheath is the descending branch of the hypoglossal nerve, this filament being joined by one or two branches from the cervical nerves, which cross the vessel obliquely. Sometimes the descending branch of the hypoglossal nerve is contained within the sheath. The superior thyroid vein crosses the artery near its termination, and the middle thyroid vein a little below the level of the cricoid cartilage; the anterior jugular vein crosses the artery just above the clavicle, but is separated from it by the

Sternohyoideus and Sternothyreoideus. *Behind*, the artery is separated from the transverse processes of the cervical vertebræ by the Longus colli and Longus capitis, the sympathetic trunk being interposed between it and the muscles. The inferior thyroid artery crosses behind the lower part of the vessel. *Medially*, it is in relation with the esophagus, trachea, and thyroid gland (which overlaps it), the inferior thyroid artery and recurrent nerve being interposed; higher up, with the larynx and pharynx. *Lateral* to the artery are the internal jugular vein and vagus nerve.

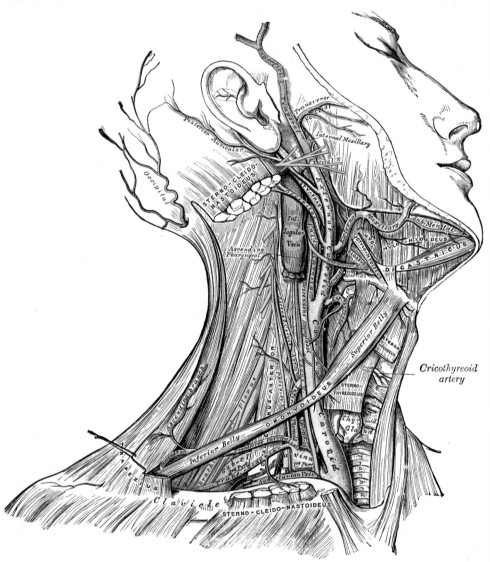

Cricothyreoid artery

Fig. 497.—Superficial dissection of the right side of the neck, showing the carotid and subclavian arteries.

At the lower part of the neck, the right recurrent nerve crosses obliquely behind the artery; the right internal jugular vein diverges from the artery, but the left approaches and often overlaps the lower part of the artery.

Behind the angle of bifurcation of the common carotid artery is a reddish-brown oval body, known as the **glomus caroticum** (*carotid body*). It is a small neuro-vascular structure, oval or wedge-shaped, containing some large chromaffin cells.

Variations.—The *right common carotid* may arise above the level of the upper border of the sternoclavicular articulation; this variation occurs in about 12 per cent. of cases. In other cases the artery may arise as a separate branch from the arch of the aorta, or in conjunction with the left carotid. The *left common carotid* varies in its origin more than the right. In the majority of abnormal cases it arises with the innominate artery; if that artery is absent, the two carotids may arise by a single trunk. In the majority of abnormal cases the point of division occurs higher than usual, the artery dividing opposite or even above the hyoid bone; more rarely, it occurs below, opposite the middle of the larynx, or the lower border of the cricoid cartilage. Very rarely, the common carotid ascends in the neck without any subdivision, either the external or the internal carotid being wanting; and in a few cases the common carotid has been found to be absent, the external and internal carotids arising directly from the arch of the aorta.

The common carotid usually gives off no branch previous to its bifurcation, but it occasionally gives origin to the superior thyroid or its laryngeal branch, the ascending pharyngeal, the inferior thyroid, or, more rarely, the vertebral artery.

Collateral Circulation.—After ligature of the common carotid, the collateral circulation can be perfectly established, by the free communication which exists between the carotid arteries of opposite sides, both without and within the cranium, and by enlargement of the branches of the subclavian artery on the side corresponding to that on which the vessel has been tied. The chief communications outside the skull take place between the superior and inferior thyroid arteries, and the profunda cervicis and ramus descendens of the occipital; the vertebral supplies blood to the branches of the internal carotid within the cranium.

The External Carotid Artery (**A. Carotis Externa**) (Fig. 497).

The **external carotid artery** begins opposite the upper border of the thyroid cartilage, and curving slightly passes upward and forward, and then inclines backward to the space behind the neck of the mandible, where it divides into the superficial temporal and internal maxillary arteries. It rapidly diminishes in size in its course up the neck, owing to the number and large size of the branches given off from it. In the child, it is somewhat smaller than the internal carotid; but in the adult, the two vessels are of nearly equal size. At its origin, this artery is more superficial, and placed nearer the mid-line than the internal carotid, and is contained within the carotid triangle.

Relations.—The external carotid artery is *covered by* the skin, superficial fascia, Platysma, deep fascia, and anterior margin of the Sternocleidomastoideus; it is crossed by the hypoglossal nerve, by the lingual, ranine, common facial, and superior thyroid veins; and by the Digastricus and Stylohyoideus; higher up it passes deeply into the substance of the parotid gland, where it lies deep to the facial nerve and the junction of the temporal and internal maxillary veins. *Medial* to it are the hyoid bone, the wall of the pharynx, the superior laryngeal nerve, and a portion of the parotid gland. *Lateral* to it, in the lower part of its course, is the internal carotid artery. *Posterior* to it, near its origin, is the superior laryngeal nerve; and higher up, it is separated from the internal carotid by the Styloglossus and Stylopharyngeus, the glossopharyngeal nerve, the pharyngeal branch of the vagus, and part of the parotid gland.

Branches.—The branches of the external carotid artery may be divided into four sets.

Anterior.	*Posterior.*	*Ascending.*	*Terminal.*
Superior Thyroid.	Occipital.	Ascending	Superficial Temporal.
Lingual.	Posterior Auricular.	Pharyngeal.	Internal Maxillary.
External Maxillary.			

1. The **superior thyroid artery** (*a. thyreoidea superior*) (Fig. 497) *arises* from the external carotid artery just below the level of the greater cornu of the hyoid bone and ends in the thyroid gland. In 16 per cent. of cases, the superior thyroid arises from the common carotid.

Relations.—From its origin under the anterior border of the Sternocleidomastoideus it runs upward and forward for a short distance in the carotid triangle, where it is covered by the skin, Platysma, and fascia; it then arches downward beneath the Omohyoideus, Sternohyoideus, and Sternothyreoideus. To its medial side are the Constrictor pharyngis inferior and the external branch of the superior laryngeal nerve.

Branches.—It distributes twigs to the adjacent muscles, and usually two main branches to the thyroid gland; one, the larger, supplies principally the anterior surface; on the isthmus of the gland it anastomoses with the corresponding artery of the opposite side; a second branch descends on the posterior surface of the gland and anastomoses with the inferior thyroid artery.

Besides the arteries distributed to the muscles and to the thyroid gland, the branches of the superior thyroid are:

Hyoid.   Superior Laryngeal.
Sternocleidomastoid.   Cricothyroid.

The **Hyoid Branch** (*ramus hyoideus; infrahyoid branch*) is small and runs along the lower border of the hyoid bone beneath the Thyreohyoideus and anastomoses with the vessel of the opposite side.

The **Sternocleidomastoid Branch** (*ramus sternocleidomastoideus; sternomastoid branch*) runs downward and lateralward across the sheath of the common carotid artery, and supplies the Sternocleidomastoideus and neighboring muscles and integument; it frequently *arises* as a separate branch from the external carotid.

The **Superior Laryngeal Artery** (*a. laryngea superior*), larger than either of the preceding, accompanies the internal laryngeal branch of the superior laryngeal nerve, beneath the Thyreohyoideus; it pierces the hyothyroid membrane, and supplies the muscles, mucous membrane, and glands of the larynx, anastomosing with the branch from the opposite side. It sometimes (13 per cent.) arises separately from the external carotid.

The **Cricothyroid Branch** (*ramus cricothyreoideus*) is small and runs transversely across the cricothyroid membrane, communicating with the artery of the opposite side.

2. The **lingual artery** (*a. lingualis*) (Fig. 502) *arises* from the external carotid opposite the tip of the greater cornu of the hyoid bone, and between the superior thyroid and external maxillary arteries; it first runs obliquely upward and medialward above the greater cornu of the hyoid bone, then curves downward and forward, forming a loop which is crossed by the hypoglossal nerve, and passing beneath the Digastricus and Stylohyoideus it runs horizontally forward, beneath the Hyoglossus, and finally, ascending almost perpendicularly to the tongue, turns forward on its lower surface as far as the tip, under the name of the **profunda linguæ**.

Relations.—Its first, or oblique, portion is superficial, and is contained within the carotid triangle; it rests upon the Constrictor pharyngis medius, and is covered by the Platysma and the fascia of the neck. Its second, or curved, portion also lies upon the Constrictor pharyngis medius, being covered at first by the tendon of the Digastricus and by the Stylohyoideus, and afterward by the Hyoglossus. Its third, or horizontal, portion lies between the Hyoglossus and Genioglossus. The fourth, or terminal part, under the name of the **profunda linguæ** (*ranine artery*) runs along the under surface of the tongue to its tip; here it is superficial, being covered only by the mucous membrane; above it is the Longitudinalis inferior, and on the medial side the Genioglossus. The hypoglossal nerve crosses the first part of the lingual artery, but is separated from the second part by the Hyoglossus.

Branches.—The branches of the lingual artery are:

Hyoid.   Sublingual.
Dorsales linguæ.   Profunda linguæ.

The **Hyoid Branch** (*ramus hyoideus; suprahyoid branch*) runs along the upper border of the hyoid bone, supplying the muscles attached to it and anastomosing with its fellow of the opposite side.

The **Dorsal Lingual Arteries** (*a. dorsales linguæ; rami dorsales linguæ*) consist usually of two or three small branches which *arise* beneath the Hyoglossus; they ascend to the back part of the dorsum of the tongue, and supply the mucous membrane in this situation, the glossopalatine arch, the tonsil, soft palate, and epiglottis; anastomosing with the vessels of the opposite side.

The **Sublingual Artery** (*a. sublingualis*) *arises* at the anterior margin of the Hyoglossus, and runs forward between the Genioglossus and Mylohyoideus to the sublingual gland. It supplies the gland and gives branches to the Mylohyoideus and neighboring muscles, and to the mucous membrane of the mouth and gums. One branch runs behind the alveolar process of the mandible in the substance of the gum to anastomose with a similar artery from the other side; another pierces the Mylohyoideus and anastomoses with the submental branch of the external maxillary artery.

The **Deep Lingual Artery** (*a. profunda linguæ; ranine artery*) is the terminal portion of the lingual artery; it pursues a tortuous course, running along the under surface of the tongue, below the Longitudinalis inferior, and above the mucous membrane; it lies on the lateral side of the Genioglossus, accompanied by the lingual nerve. It anastomoses with the artery of the opposite side at the tip of the tongue.

3. The **external maxillary artery** (*a. maxillaris externa; facial artery*) (Fig. 498), *arises* in the carotid triangle a little above the lingual artery and, sheltered by the ramus of the mandible, passes obliquely up beneath the Digastricus and Stylohyoideus, over which it arches to enter a groove on the posterior surface of the submaxillary gland. It then curves upward over the body of the mandible at the antero-inferior angle of the Masseter; passes forward and upward across the cheek to the angle of the mouth, then ascends along the side of the nose, and ends at the medial commissure of the eye, under the name of the **angular artery**. This vessel, both in the neck and on the face, is remarkably tortuous: in the neck, to accommodate itself to the movements of the pharynx in deglutition; and in the face, to the movements of the mandible, lips, and cheeks.

Relations.—*In the neck*, its origin is superficial, being covered by the integument, Platysma, and fascia; it then passes beneath the Digastricus and Stylohyoideus muscles and part of the submaxillary gland, and frequently beneath the hypoglossal nerve. It lies upon the Constrictores pharyngis medius and superior, the latter of which separates it, at the summit of its arch, from the lower and back part of the tonsil. *On the face*, where it passes over the body of the mandible, it is comparatively superficial, lying immediately beneath the Platysma. In its course over the face, it is covered by the integument, the fat of the cheek, and, near the angle of the mouth, by the Platysma, Risorius, and Zygomaticus. It rests on the Buccinator and Caninus, and passes either over or under the infraorbital head of the Quadratus labii superioris. The anterior facial vein lies lateral to the artery, and takes a more direct course across the face, where it is separated from the artery by a considerable interval. In the neck it lies superficial to the artery. The branches of the facial nerve cross the artery from behind forward.

Branches.—The branches of the artery may be divided into two sets: those given off in the neck (*cervical*), and those on the face (*facial*).

Cervical Branches.	*Facial Branches.*
Ascending Palatine.	Inferior Labial.
Tonsillar.	Superior Labial.
Glandular.	Lateral Nasal.
Submental.	Angular.
Muscular.	Muscular.

The **Ascending Palatine Artery** (*a. palatina ascendens*) (Fig. 502) *arises* close to the origin of the external maxillary artery and passes up between the Styloglossus

36

and Stylopharyngeus to the side of the pharynx, along which it is continued between the Constrictor pharyngis superior and the Pterygoideus internus to near the base of the skull. It divides near the Levator veli palatini into two branches: one follows the course of this muscle, and, winding over the upper border of the Constrictor pharyngis superior, supplies the soft palate and the palatine glands, anastomosing with its fellow of the opposite side and with the descending palatine branch of the internal maxillary artery; the other pierces the Constrictor pharyngis superior and supplies the palatine tonsil and auditory tube, anastomosing with the tonsillar and ascending pharyngeal arteries.

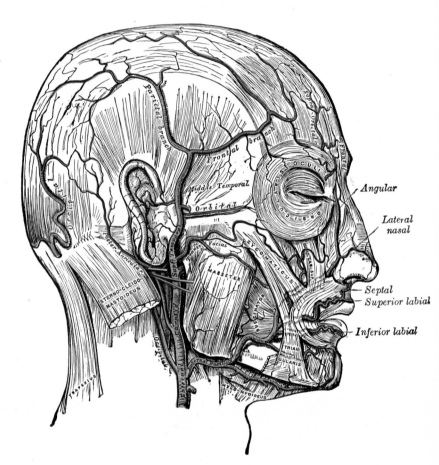

FIG. 498.—The arteries of the face and scalp.[1]

The **Tonsillar Branch** (*ramus tonsillaris*) (Fig. 502) ascends between the Pterygoideus internus and Styloglossus, and then along the side of the pharynx, perforating the Constrictor pharyngis superior, to ramify in the substance of the palatine tonsil and root of the tongue.

The **Glandular Branches** (*rami glandulares; submaxillary branches*) consist of three or four large vessels, which supply the submaxillary gland, some being prolonged to the neighboring muscles, lymph glands, and integument.

---

[1] The muscular tissue of the lips must be supposed to have been cut away, in order to show the course of the labial arteries.

The **Submental Artery** (*a. submentalis*) the largest of the cervical branches, is given off from the facial artery just as that vessel quits the submaxillary gland: it runs forward upon the Mylohyoideus, just below the body of the mandible, and beneath the Digastricus. It supplies the surrounding muscles, and anastomoses with the sublingual artery and with the mylohyoid branch of the inferior alveolar; at the symphysis menti it turns upward over the border of the mandible and divides into a superficial and a deep branch. The superficial branch passes between the integument and Quadratus labii inferioris, and anastomoses with the inferior labial artery; the deep branch runs between the muscle and the bone, supplies the lip, and anastomoses with the inferior labial and mental arteries.

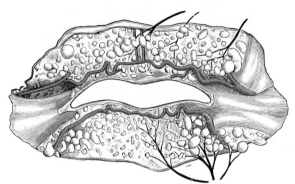

FIG. 499.—The labial arteries, the glands of the lips, and the nerves of the right side seen from the posterior surface after removal of the mucous membrane. (Poirier and Charpy.)

The **Inferior Labial Artery** (*a. labialis inferior*) *arises* near the angle of the mouth; it passes upward and forward beneath the Triangularis and, penetrating the Orbicularis oris, runs a tortuous course along the edge of the lower lip between this muscle and the mucous membrane. It supplies the labial glands, the mucous membrane, and the muscles of the lower lip; and anastomoses with the artery of the opposite side, and with the mental branch of the inferior alveolar artery.

The **Superior Labial Artery** (*a. labialis superior*), larger and more tortuous than the inferior, follows a similar course along the edge of the upper lip, lying between the mucous membrane and the Orbicularis oris, anastomosing with the artery of the opposite side. It supplies the upper lip, and gives off two or three vessels which ascend to the nose; a **septal branch** ramifies on the nasal septum as far as the point of the nose, and an **alar branch** supplies the ala of the nose.

The **Lateral Nasal** branch is derived from the external maxillary as that vessel ascends along the side of the nose. It supplies the ala and dorsum of the nose, anastomosing with its fellow, with the septal and alar branches, with the dorsal nasal branch of the ophthalmic, and with the infraorbital branch of the internal maxillary.

The **Angular Artery** (*a. angularis*) is the terminal part of the external maxillary; it ascends to the medial angle of the orbit, imbedded in the fibers of the angular head of the Quadratus labii superioris, and accompanied by the angular vein. On the cheek it distributes branches which anastomose with the infraorbital; after supplying the lacrimal sac and Orbicularis oculi, it ends by anastomosing with the dorsal nasal branch of the ophthalmic artery.

The **Muscular Branches** in the neck are distributed to the Pterygoideus internus and Stylohyoideus, and on the face to the Masseter and Buccinator. The anastomoses of the external maxillary artery are very numerous, not only with the vessel of the opposite side, but, *in the neck*, with the sublingual branch of the lingual, with the ascending pharyngeal, and by its ascending palatine and tonsillar branches with the palatine branch of the internal maxillary; *on the face*, with the mental branch of the inferior alveolar as it emerges from the mental foramen, with the transverse facial branch of the superficial temporal, with the infraorbital branch of the internal maxillary, and with the dorsal nasal branch of the ophthalmic.

The external maxillary artery not infrequently arises in common with the lingual. It varies in size and in the extent to which it supplies the face; it occasionally ends as the submental, and not infrequently extends only as high as the angle of the mouth or nose. The deficiency is then compensated for by enlargement of one of the neighboring arteries.

4. The **occipital artery** (*a. occipitalis*) (Fig. 498) *arises* from the posterior part of the external carotid, opposite the external maxillary, near the lower margin of the posterior belly of the Digastricus, and ends in the posterior part of the scalp.

Course and Relations.—At its origin, it is covered by the posterior belly of the Digastricus and the Stylohyoideus, and the hypoglossal nerve winds around it from behind forward; higher up, it crosses the internal carotid artery, the internal jugular vein, and the vagus and accessory nerves. It next ascends to the interval between the transverse process of the atlas and the mastoid process of the temporal bone, and passes horizontally backward, grooving the surface of the latter bone, being covered by the Sternocleidomastoideus, Splenius capitis, Longissimus capitis, and Digastricus, and resting upon the Rectus capitis lateralis, the Obliquus superior, and Semispinalis capitis. It then changes its course and runs vertically upward, pierces the fascia connecting the cranial attachment of the Trapezius with the Sternocleidomastoideus, and ascends in a tortuous course in the superficial fascia of the scalp, where it divides into numerous branches, which reach as high as the vertex of the skull and anastomose with the posterior auricular and superficial temporal arteries. Its terminal portion is accompanied by the greater occipital nerve.

Branches.—The branches of the occipital artery are:

Muscular.	Sternocleidomastoid.	Auricular.
Meningeal.	Descending.	

The **Muscular Branches** (*rami musculares*) supply the Digastricus, Stylohyoideus, Splenius, and Longissimus capitis.

The **Sternocleidomastoid Artery** (*a. sternocleidomastoidea; sternomastoid artery*) generally *arises* from the occipital close to its commencement, but sometimes springs directly from the external carotid. It passes downward and backward over the hypoglossal nerve, and enters the substance of the muscle, in company with the accessory nerve.

The **Auricular Branch** (*ramus auricularis*) supplies the back of the concha and frequently gives off a branch, which enters the skull through the mastoid foramen and supplies the dura mater, the diploë, and the mastoid cells; this latter branch sometimes arises from the occipital artery, and is then known as the **mastoid branch.**

The **Meningeal Branch** (*ramus meningeus; dural branch*) ascends with the internal jugular vein, and enters the skull through the jugular foramen and condyloid canal, to supply the dura mater in the posterior fossa.

The **Descending Branch** (*ramus descendens; arteria princeps cervicis*) (Fig. 502), the largest branch of the occipital, descends on the back of the neck, and divides into a superficial and deep portion. The superficial portion runs beneath the Splenius, giving off branches which pierce that muscle to supply the Trapezius and anastomose with the ascending branch of the transverse cervical: the deep portion runs down between the Semispinales capitis and cervicis, and anastomoses with the vertebral and with the a. profunda cervicalis, a branch of the costocervical trunk. The anastomosis between these vessels assists in establishing the collateral circulation after ligature of the common carotid or subclavian artery.

The terminal branches of the occipital artery are distributed to the back of the head: they are very tortuous, and lie between the integument and Occipitalis, anastomosing with the artery of the opposite side and with the posterior auricular and temporal arteries, and supplying the Occipitalis, the integument, and pericranium.   One of the terminal branches may give off a meningeal twig which passes through the parietal foramen.

5. The **posterior auricular artery** (*a. auricularis posterior*) (Fig. 498) is small and *arises* from the external carotid, above the Digastricus and Stylohyoideus, opposite the apex of the styloid process.   It ascends, under cover of the parotid gland, on the styloid process of the temporal bone, to the groove between the cartilage of the ear and the mastoid process, immediately above which it divides into its auricular and occipital branches.

Branches.—Besides several small branches to the Digastricus, Stylohyoideus, and Sternocleidomastoideus, and to the parotid gland, this vessel gives off three branches:

Stylomastoid.   Auricular.   Occipital.

The **Stylomastoid Artery** (*a. stylomastoidea*) enters the stylomastoid foramen and supplies the tympanic cavity, the tympanic antrum and mastoid cells, and the semicircular canals.   In the young subject a branch from this vessel forms, with the anterior tympanic artery from the internal maxillary, a vascular circle, which surrounds the tympanic membrane, and from which delicate vessels ramify on that membrane.   It anastomoses with the superficial petrosal branch of the middle meningeal artery by a twig which enters the hiatus canalis facialis.

The **Auricular Branch** (*ramus auricularis*) ascends behind the ear, beneath the Auricularis posterior, and is distributed to the back of the auricula, upon which it ramifies minutely, some branches curving around the margin of the cartilage, others perforating it, to supply the anterior surface.   It anastomoses with the parietal and anterior auricular branches of the superficial temporal.

The **Occipital Branch** (*ramus occipitalis*) passes backward, over the Sternocleido- mastoideus, to the scalp above and behind the ear.   It supplies the Occipitalis and the scalp in this situation and anastomoses with the occipital artery.

6. The **ascending pharyngeal artery** (*a. pharyngea ascendens*) (Fig. 502), the smallest branch of the external carotid, is a long, slender vessel, deeply seated in the neck, beneath the other branches of the external carotid and under the Stylo- pharyngeus.   It *arises* from the back part of the external carotid, near the com- mencement of that vessel, and ascends vertically between the internal carotid and the side of the pharynx, anterior to the Longus capitis, to the under surface of the base of the skull.   In 14 per cent. of cases it arises from the occipital artery.

Branches.—Its branches are:

Pharyngeal.   Prevertebral.
Palatine.   Inferior Tympanic.
                  Posterior Meningeal.

The **Pharyngeal Branches** (*rami pharyngei*) are three or four in number.   Two of these descend to supply the Constrictores pharyngis medius and inferior and the Stylopharyngeus, ramifying in their substance and in the mucous membrane lining them.

The **Palatine Branch** varies in size, and may take the place of the ascending palatine branch of the external maxillary artery, when that vessel is small.   It passes inward upon the Constrictor pharyngis superior, sends ramifications to the soft palate and tonsil, and supplies a branch to the auditory tube.

The **Prevertebral Branches** are numerous small vessels, which supply the Longi capitis and colli, the sympathetic trunk, the hypoglossal and vagus nerves, and the lymph glands; they anastomose with the ascending cervical artery.

The **Inferior Tympanic Artery** (*a. tympanica inferior*) is a small branch which passes through a minute foramen in the petrous portion of the temporal bone, in company with the tympanic branch of the glossopharyngeal nerve, to supply the medial wall of the tympanic cavity and anastomose with the other tympanic arteries.

The **Meningeal Branches** are several small vessels, which supply the dura mater. One, the **posterior meningeal**, enters the cranium through the jugular foramen; a second passes through the foramen lacerum; and occasionally a third through the canal for the hypoglossal nerve.

7. The **superficial temporal artery** (*a. temporalis superficialis*) (Fig. 498), the smaller of the two terminal branches of the external carotid, appears, from its direction, to be the continuation of that vessel. It begins in the substance of the parotid gland, behind the neck of the mandible, and crosses over the posterior root of the zygomatic process of the temporal bone; about 5 cm. above this process it divides into two branches, a frontal and a parietal.

Relations.—As it crosses the zygomatic process, it is covered by the Auricularis anterior muscle, and by a dense fascia; it is crossed by the temporal and zygomatic branches of the facial nerve and one or two veins, and is accompanied by the auriculotemporal nerve, which lies immediately behind it. Just above the zygomatic process and in front of the auricle, the superficial temporal artery is quite superficial, being covered only by skin and fascia, and can easily be felt pulsating. This artery is often used for determining the pulse, particularly by anesthetists.

Branches.—Besides some twigs to the parotid gland, to the temporomandibular joint, and to the Masseter muscle, its branches are:

Transverse Facial.	Anterior Auricular.
Middle Temporal.	Frontal.
Parietal.	

The **Transverse Facial Artery** (*a. transversa faciei*) is given off from the superficial temporal before that vessel quits the parotid gland; running forward through the substance of the gland, it passes transversely across the side of the face, between the parotid duct and the lower border of the zygomatic arch, and divides into numerous branches, which supply the parotid gland and duct, the Masseter, and the integument, and anastomose with the external maxillary, masseteric, buccinator, and infraorbital arteries. This vessel rests on the Masseter, and is accompanied by one or two branches of the facial nerve.

The **Middle Temporal Artery** (*a. temporalis media*) *arises* immediately above the zygomatic arch, and, perforating the temporal fascia, gives branches to the Temporalis, anastomosing with the deep temporal branches of the internal maxillary. It occasionally gives off a **zygomaticoörbital branch**, which runs along the upper border of the zygomatic arch, between the two layers of the temporal fascia, to the lateral angle of the orbit. This branch, which may arise directly from the superficial temporal artery, supplies the Orbicularis oculi, and anastomoses with the lacrimal and palpebral branches of the ophthalmic artery.

The **Anterior Auricular Branches** (*rami auriculares anteriores*) are distributed to the anterior portion of the auricula, the lobule, and part of the external meatus, anastomosing with the posterior auricular.

The **Frontal Branch** (*ramus frontalis; anterior temporal*) runs tortuously upward and forward to the forehead, supplying the muscles, integument, and pericranium in this region, and anastomosing with the supraorbital and frontal arteries.

The **Parietal Branch** (*ramus parietalis; posterior temporal*) larger than the frontal, curves upward and backward on the side of the head, lying superficial to the temporal fascia, and anastomosing with its fellow of the opposite side, and with the posterior auricular and occipital arteries.

8. The **internal maxillary artery** (*a. maxillaris interna*) (Fig. 500), the larger of the two terminal branches of the external carotid, *arises* behind the neck of the mandible, and is at first imbedded in the substance of the parotid gland; it passes

forward between the ramus of the mandible and the sphenomandibular ligament, and then runs, either superficial or deep to the Pterygoideus externus, to the pterygopalatine fossa. It supplies the deep structures of the face, and may be divided into **mandibular, pterygoid,** and **pterygopalatine portions.**

The **first** or **mandibular portion** passes horizontally forward, between the ramus of the mandible and the sphenomandibular ligament, where it lies parallel to and a little below the auriculotemporal nerve; it crosses the inferior alveolar nerve, and runs along the lower border of the Pterygoideus externus.

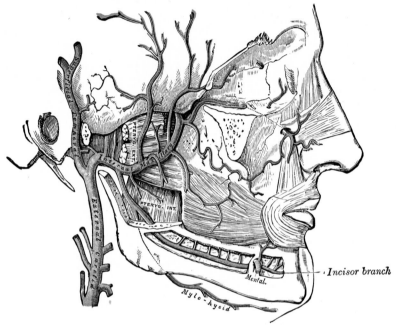

Fig. 500.—Plan of branches of internal maxillary artery.

The **second** or **pterygoid portion** runs obliquely forward and upward under cover of the ramus of the mandible and insertion of the Temporalis, on the superficial (very frequently on the deep) surface of the Pterygoideus externus; it then passes between the two heads of origin of this muscle and enters the fossa.

The **third** or **pterygopalatine portion** lies in the pterygopalatine fossa lateral to the sphenopalatine ganglion.

The branches of this vessel may be divided into three groups (Fig. 501), corresponding to its three divisions.

Branches of the First or Mandibular Portions.—

Anterior Tympanic.	Middle Meningeal.
Deep Auricular.	Accessory Meningeal.
Inferior Alveolar.	

The **Anterior Tympanic Artery** (*a. tympanica anterior; tympanic artery*) passes upward behind the temporomandibular articulation, enters the tympanic cavity through the petrotympanic fissure, and ramifies upon the tympanic membrane, forming a vascular circle around the membrane with the stylomastoid branch of the posterior auricular, and anastomosing with the artery of the pterygoid canal and with the caroticotympanic branch from the internal carotid.

The **Deep Auricular Artery** (*a. auricularis profunda*) often *arises* in common with the preceding. It ascends in the substance of the parotid gland, behind the temporomandibular articulation, pierces the cartilaginous or bony wall of the external acoustic meatus, and supplies its cuticular lining and the outer surface of the tympanic membrane. It gives a branch to the temporomandibular joint.

The **Middle Meningeal Artery** (*a. meningea media; medidural artery*) is the largest of the arteries which supply the dura mater. It ascends between the spheno-mandibular ligament and the Pterygoideus externus, and between the two roots of the auriculotemporal nerve to the foramen spinosum of the sphenoid bone, through which it enters the cranium; it then runs forward in a groove on the great wing of the sphenoid bone, and divides into two branches, anterior and posterior. The **anterior branch**, the larger, crosses the great wing of the sphenoid, reaches the

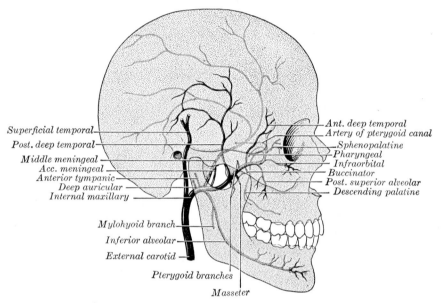

Superficial temporal —
Post. deep temporal —
Middle meningeal —
Acc. meningeal —
Anterior tympanic —
Deep auricular —
Internal maxillary —

Ant. deep temporal
Artery of pterygoid canal
Sphenopalatine
Pharyngeal
Infraorbital
Buccinator
Post. superior alveolar
Descending palatine

Mylohyoid branch —
Inferior alveolar —
External carotid —

Pterygoid branches

Masseter

Fig. 501.—Plan of branches of internal maxillary artery.

groove, or canal, in the sphenoidal angle of the parietal bone, and then divides into branches which spread out between the dura mater and internal surface of the cranium, some passing upward as far as the vertex, and others backward to the occipital region. The **posterior branch** curves backward on the squama of the temporal bone, and, reaching the parietal some distance in front of its mastoid angle, divides into branches which supply the posterior part of the dura mater and cranium. The branches of the middle meningeal artery are distributed partly to the dura mater, but chiefly to the bones; they anastomose with the arteries of the opposite side, and with the anterior and posterior meningeal.

The middle meningeal, on entering the cranium, gives off the following branches: (1) Numerous small vessels supply the semilunar ganglion and the dura mater nearby. (2) A **superficial petrosal** branch enters the hiatus of the facial canal, supplies the facial nerve, and anastomoses with the stylomastoid branch of the posterior auricular artery. (3) A **superior tympanic artery** runs in the canal for the Tensor tympani, and supplies this muscle and the lining membrane of the canal. (4) **Orbital branches** pass through the superior orbital fissure or through separate canals in the great wing of the sphenoid, to anastomose with the lacrimal or other branches of the ophthalmic artery. (5) **Temporal branches** pass through foramina in the great wing of the sphenoid, and anastomose in the temporal fossa with the deep temporal arteries.

The **Accessory Meningeal Branch** (*ramus meningeus accessorius; small meningeal or parvidural branch*) is sometimes derived from the preceding. It enters the skull through the foramen ovale, and supplies the semilunar ganglion and dura mater.

The **Inferior Alveolar Artery** (*a. alveolaris inferior; inferior dental artery*) descends with the inferior alveolar nerve to the mandibular foramen on the medial surface of the ramus of the mandible. It runs along the mandibular canal in the substance of the bone, accompanied by the nerve, and opposite the first premolar tooth divides into two branches, incisor and mental. The **incisor branch** is continued forward beneath the incisor teeth as far as the mid-line, where it anastomoses with the artery of the opposite side; the **mental branch** emerges with the nerve from the mental foramen, supplies the chin, and anastomoses with the submental and inferior labial arteries. Near its origin the inferior alveolar artery gives off a **lingual branch** which descends with the lingual nerve and supplies the mucous membrane of the mouth. As the inferior alveolar artery enters the foramen, it gives off a **mylohyoid branch** which runs in the mylohyoid groove, and ramifies on the under surface of the Mylohyoideus. The inferior alveolar artery and its incisor branch, during their course through the substance of the bone, give off a few twigs which are lost in the cancellous tissue, and a series of branches which correspond in number to the roots of the teeth: these enter the minute apertures at the extremities of the roots, and supply the pulp of the teeth.

Branches of the Second or Pterygoid Portion.—

Deep Temporal.	Masseteric.
Pterygoid.	Buccinator.

The **Deep Temporal Branches**, two in number, **anterior** and **posterior**, ascend between the Temporalis and the pericranium; they supply the muscle, and anastomose with the middle temporal artery; the anterior communicates with the lacrimal artery by means of small branches which perforate the zygomatic bone and great wing of the sphenoid.

The **Pterygoid Branches** (*rami pterygoidei*), irregular in number and origin, supply the Pterygoidei.

The **Masseteric Artery** (*a. masseterica*) is small and passes lateralward through the mandibular notch to the deep surface of the Masseter. It supplies the muscle, and anastomoses with the masseteric branches of the external maxillary and with the transverse facial artery.

The **Buccinator Artery** (*a. buccinatoria; buccal artery*) is small and runs obliquely forward, between the Pterygoideus internus and the insertion of the Temporalis, to the outer surface of the Buccinator, to which it is distributed, anastomosing with branches of the external maxillary and with the infraorbital.

Branches of the Third or Pterygopalatine Portion.—

Posterior Superior Alveolar.	Artery of the Pterygoid Canal.
Infraorbital.	Pharyngeal.
Descending Palatine.	Sphenopalatine.

The **Posterior Superior Alveolar Artery** (*a. alveolaris superior posterior; alveolar or posterior dental artery*) is given off from the internal maxillary, frequently in conjunction with the infraorbital, just as the trunk of the vessel is passing into the pterygopalatine fossa. Descending upon the tuberosity of the maxilla, it divides into numerous branches, some of which enter the alveolar canals, to supply the molar and premolar teeth and the lining of the maxillary sinus, while others continue forward on the alveolar process to supply the gums.

The **Infraorbital Artery** (*a. infraorbitalis*) appears, from its direction, to be the continuation of the trunk of the internal maxillary, but often *arises* in conjunction with the posterior superior alveolar. It runs along the infraorbital groove and canal with the infraorbital nerve, and emerges on the face through the infraorbital foramen, beneath the infraorbital head of the Quadratus labii superioris. While in the canal, it gives off (*a*) **orbital branches** which assist in supplying the Rectus inferior and Obliquus inferior and the lacrimal sac, and (*b*) **anterior superior alveolar branches** which descend through the anterior alveolar canals to supply the upper incisor and canine teeth and the mucous membrane of the maxillary sinus. On the face, some branches pass upward to the medial angle of the orbit and the lacrimal sac, anastomosing with the angular branch of the external maxillary artery; others run toward the nose, anastomosing with the dorsal nasal branch of the ophthalmic; and others descend between the Quadratus labii superioris and the Caninus, and anastomose with the external maxillary, transverse facial, and buccinator arteries. The four remaining branches *arise* from that portion of the internal maxillary which is contained in the pterygopalatine fossa.

The **Descending Palatine Artery** (*a. palatina descendens*) descends through the pterygopalatine canal with the anterior palatine branch of the sphenopalatine ganglion, and, emerging from the greater palatine foramen, runs forward in a groove on the medial side of the alveolar border of the hard palate to the incisive canal; the terminal branch of the artery passes upward through this canal to anastomose with the sphenopalatine artery. Branches are distributed to the gums, the palatine glands, and the mucous membrane of the roof of the mouth; while in the pterygo-palatine canal it gives off twigs which descend in the lesser palatine canals to supply the soft palate and palatine tonsil, anastomosing with the ascending palatine artery.

The **Artery of the Pterygoid Canal** (*a. canalis pterygoidei; Vidian artery*) passes backward along the pterygoid canal with the corresponding nerve. It is distributed to the upper part of the pharynx and to the auditory tube, sending into the tympanic cavity a small branch which anastomoses with the other tympanic arteries.

The **Pharyngeal Branch** is very small; it runs backward through the pharyngeal canal with the pharyngeal nerve, and is distributed to the upper part of the pharynx and to the auditory tube.

The **Sphenopalatine Artery** (*a. sphenopalatina; nasopalatine artery*) passes through the sphenopalatine foramen into the cavity of the nose, at the back part of the superior meatus. Here it gives off its **posterior lateral nasal branches** which spread forward over the conchæ and meatuses, anastomose with the ethmoidal arteries and the nasal branches of the descending palatine, and assist in supplying the frontal, maxillary, ethmoidal, and sphenoidal sinuses. Crossing the under surface of the sphenoid, the sphenopalatine artery ends on the nasal septum as the **posterior septal branches**; these anastomose with the ethmoidal arteries and the septal branch of the superior labial; one branch descends in a groove on the vomer to the incisive canal and anastomoses with the descending palatine artery.

The Internal Carotid Artery (A. Carotis Interna) (Fig. 502).

The **internal carotid artery** supplies the anterior part of the brain, the eye and its appendages, and sends branches to the forehead and nose. Its size, in the adult, is equal to that of the external carotid, though, in the child, it is larger than that vessel. It is remarkable for the number of curvatures that it presents in different parts of its course. It occasionally has one or two flexures near the base of the skull, while in its passage through the carotid canal and along the side of the body of the sphenoid bone it describes a double curvature and resembles the italic letter *S*.

The Carotid Sinus.—The carotid sinus, a slight dilatation of the terminal portion of the common carotid artery and of the internal carotid artery at its origin from the common carotid, or a dilatation 1 cm. in length of the internal carotid only, is an important organ for the regulation of systemic blood-pressure. Special nervous end-organs in its modified wall respond to increase and to decrease in blood-pressure and through a reflex arc, probably via the carotid branch of the glossopharyngeal nerve, convey stimuli to the medulla which result in increasing or decreasing the rate of the heart beat.

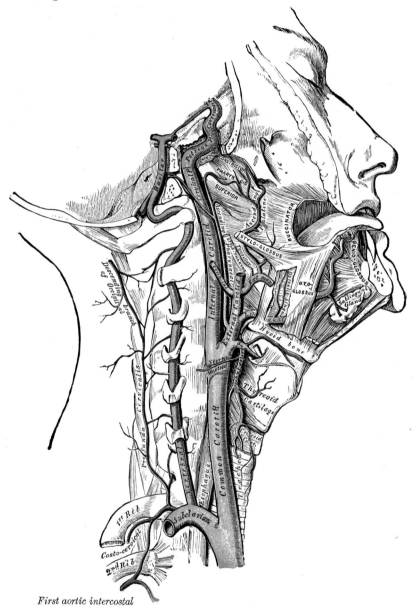

Fig. 502.—The internal carotid and vertebral arteries. Right side.

Course and Relations.—In considering the course and relations of this vessel it may be divided into four portions: **cervical, petrous, cavernous,** and **cerebral.**

Cervical Portion.—This portion of the internal carotid begins at the bifurcation of the common carotid, opposite the upper border of the thyroid cartilage, and runs perpendicularly upward, in front of the transverse processes of the upper three cervical vertebræ, to the carotid canal in the petrous portion of the temporal bone. It is comparatively superficial at its commencement, where it is contained in the carotid triangle, and lies behind and lateral to the external carotid, overlapped by the Sternocleidomastoideus, and covered by the deep fascia, Platysma, and integument: it then passes beneath the parotid gland, being crossed by the hypoglossal nerve, the

Digastricus and Stylohyoideus, and the occipital and posterior auricular arteries. Higher up, it is separated from the external carotid by the Styloglossus and Stylopharyngeus, the tip of the styloid process and the stylohyoid ligament, the glossopharyngeal nerve and the pharyngeal branch of the vagus. It is in relation, *behind*, with the Longus capitis, the superior cervical ganglion of the sympathetic trunk, and the superior laryngeal nerve; *laterally*, with the internal jugular vein and vagus nerve, the nerve lying on a plane posterior to the artery; *medially*, with the pharynx, superior laryngeal nerve, and ascending pharyngeal artery. At the base of the skull the glossopharyngeal, vagus, accessory, and hypoglossal nerves lie between the artery and the internal jugular vein.

Petrous Portion.—When the internal carotid artery enters the canal in the petrous portion of the temporal bone, it first ascends a short distance, then curves forward and medialward, and again ascends as it leaves the canal to enter the cavity of the skull between the lingula and petrosal process of the sphenoid. The artery lies at first in front of the cochlea and tympanic cavity; from the latter cavity it is separated by a thin, bony lamella, which is cribriform in the young subject, and often partly absorbed in old age. Farther forward it is separated from the semilunar ganglion by a thin plate of bone, which forms the floor of the fossa for the ganglion and the roof of the horizontal portion of the canal. Frequently this bony plate is more or less deficient, and then the ganglion is separated from the artery by fibrous membrane. The artery is separated from the bony wall of the carotid canal by a prolongation of dura mater, and is surrounded by a number of small veins and by filaments of the carotid plexus, derived from the ascending branch of the superior cervical ganglion of the sympathetic trunk.

Cavernous Portion.—In this part of its course, the artery is situated between the layers of the dura mater forming the cavernous sinus, but covered by the lining membrane of the sinus. It at first ascends toward the posterior clinoid process, then passes forward by the side of the body of the sphenoid bone, and again curves upward on the medial side of the anterior clinoid process, and perforates the dura mater forming the roof of the sinus. This portion of the artery is surrounded by filaments of the sympathetic nerve, and on its lateral side is the abducent nerve.

Cerebral Portion.—Having perforated the dura mater on the medial side of the anterior clinoid process, the internal carotid passes between the optic and oculomotor nerves to the anterior perforated substance at the medial extremity of the lateral cerebral fissure, where it gives off its terminal or cerebral branches.

Variations.—The length of the internal carotid varies according to the length of the neck, and also according to the point of bifurcation of the common carotid. It arises sometimes from the arch of the aorta. The course of the artery, instead of being straight, may be very tortuous. A few instances are recorded in which this vessel was altogether absent; in one of these the common carotid passed up the neck, and gave off the usual branches of the external carotid; the cranial portion of the internal carotid was replaced by two branches of the internal maxillary, which entered the skull through the foramen rotundum and foramen ovale, and joined to form a single vessel.

Branches.—The cervical portion of the internal carotid gives off no branches. Those from the other portions are:

From the Petrous Portion	{ Caroticotympanic. { Artery of the Pterygoid Canal.
From the Cavernous Portion	{ Cavernous. { Hypophyseal. { Semilunar. { Anterior Meningeal. { Ophthalmic.
From the Cerebral Portion	{ Anterior Cerebral. { Middle Cerebral. { Posterior Communicating. { Choroidal.

1. The **caroticotympanic branch** (*ramus caroticotympanicus; tympanic branch*) is small; it enters the tympanic cavity through a minute foramen in the carotid canal, and anostomoses with the anterior tympanic branch of the internal maxillary, and with the stylomastoid artery.

2. The **artery of the pterygoid canal** (*a. canalis pterygoidei* [*Vidii*]; *Vidian artery*) is a small, inconstant branch which passes into the pterygoid canal and anastomoses with a branch of the internal maxillary artery.

3. The **cavernous branches** are numerous small vessels which supply the hypophysis, the semilunar ganglion, and the walls of the cavernous and inferior petrosal sinuses. Some of them anastomose with branches of the middle meningeal.

4. The **hypophyseal branches** are one or two minute vessels supplying the hypophysis.

5. The **semilunar branches** are small vessels to the semilunar ganglion.

6. The **anterior meningeal branch** (*a. meningea anterior*) is a small branch which passes over the small wing of the sphenoid to supply the dura mater of the anterior cranial fossa; it anastomoses with the meningeal branch from the posterior ethmoidal artery.

7. The **ophthalmic artery** (*a. ophthalmica*) (Fig. 503) *arises* from the internal carotid, just as that vessel is emerging from the cavernous sinus, on the medial side of the anterior clinoid process, and enters the orbital cavity through the optic foramen, below and lateral to the optic nerve. It then passes over the nerve to reach the medial wall of the orbit, and thence horizontally forward, beneath the lower border of the Obliquus superior, and divides into two terminal branches, the **frontal** and **dorsal nasal**. As the artery crosses, the optic nerve is accompanied by the nasociliary nerve, and is separated from the frontal nerve by the Rectus superior and Levator palpebræ superioris. The artery runs below, rather than above, the optic nerve in 15 per cent. of cases.

Branches.—The branches of the ophthalmic artery may be divided into an **orbital group**, distributed to the orbit and surrounding parts; and an **ocular group**, to the muscles and bulb of the eye.

Orbital Group.	*Ocular Group.*
Lacrimal.	Central Artery of the Retina.
Supraorbital.	Short Posterior Ciliary.
Posterior Ethmoidal.	Long Posterior Ciliary.
Anterior Ethmoidal.	Anterior Ciliary.
Medial Palpebral.	Muscular.
Frontal.	
Dorsal Nasal.	

The **Lacrimal Artery** (*a. lacrimalis*) *arises* close to the optic foramen, not infrequently before it enters the orbit, and is one of the largest branches derived from the ophthalmic. It accompanies the lacrimal nerve along the upper border of the Rectus lateralis, and supplies the lacrimal gland. Its terminal branches, escaping from the gland, are distributed to the eyelids and conjunctiva: of those supplying the eyelids, two are of considerable size and are named the **lateral palpebral arteries**; they run medialward in the upper and lower lids respectively and anastomose with the medial palpebral arteries, forming an arterial circle in this situation. The lacrimal artery gives off one or two **zygomatic branches**, one of which passes through the zygomatico-temporal foramen, to reach the temporal fossa, and anastomoses with the deep temporal arteries; another appears on the cheek through the zygomatico-facial foramen, and anastomoses with the transverse facial. A **recurrent branch** passes backward through the lateral part of the superior orbital fissure to the dura mater, and anastomoses with a branch of the middle meningeal artery. The lacrimal artery is sometimes derived from one of the anterior branches of the middle meningeal artery.

The **Supraorbital Artery** (*a. supraorbitalis*) springs from the ophthalmic as that vessel is crossing over the optic nerve. It passes upward on the medial borders of the Rectus superior and Levator palpebræ, and meeting the supraorbital nerve, accompanies it between the periosteum and Levator palpebræ to the supraorbital foramen; passing through this it divides into a superficial and a deep branch, which supply the integument, the muscles, and the pericranium of the forehead, anastomosing with the frontal, the frontal branch of the superficial temporal, and the artery of the opposite side. This artery in the orbit supplies the Rectus superior and the Levator palpebræ, and sends a branch across the pulley of the Obliquus superior, to supply the parts at the medial palpebral commissure. At the supra-orbital foramen it frequently transmits a branch to the diploë.

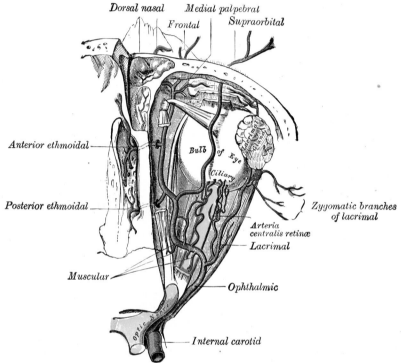

FIG. 503.—The ophthalmic artery and its branches.

The **Ethmoidal Arteries** are two in number: **posterior** and **anterior**. The **posterior ethmoidal artery**, the smaller, passes through the posterior ethmoidal canal, supplies the posterior ethmoidal cells, and, entering the cranium, gives off a meningeal branch to the dura mater, and nasal branches which descend into the nasal cavity through apertures in the cribriform plate, anastomosing with branches of the sphenopalatine. The **anterior ethmoidal artery** accompanies the nasociliary nerve through the anterior ethmoidal canal, supplies the anterior and middle ethmoidal cells and frontal sinus, and, entering the cranium, gives off a meningeal branch to the dura mater, and nasal branches; these latter descend into the nasal cavity through the slit by the side of the crista galli, and, running along the groove on the inner surface of the nasal bone, supply branches to the lateral wall and septum of the nose, and a terminal branch which appears on the dorsum of the nose between the nasal bone and the lateral cartilage.

The **Medial Palpebral Arteries** (*aa. palpebrales mediales; internal palpebral arteries*), two in number, **superior** and **inferior**, *arise* from the ophthalmic, opposite the pulley of the Obliquus superior; they leave the orbit to encircle the eyelids near their free margins, forming a superior and an inferior arch, between the

Orbicularis oculi and the tarsi. The **superior palpebral** anastomoses, at the lateral angle of the orbit, with the zygomaticoörbital branch of the temporal artery and with the upper of the two lateral palpebral branches from the lacrimal artery; the **inferior palpebral** anastomoses, at the lateral angle of the orbit, with the lower of the two lateral palpebral branches from the lacrimal and with the transverse facial artery, and, at the medial part of the lid, with a branch from the angular artery. From this last anastomosis a branch passes to the nasolacrimal duct, ramifying in its mucous membrane, as far as the inferior meatus of the nasal cavity.

The **Frontal Artery** (*a. frontalis*), one of the terminal branches of the ophthalmic, leaves the orbit at its medial angle with the supratrochlear nerve, and, ascending on the forehead, supplies the integument, muscles, and pericranium, anastomosing with the supraorbital artery, and with the artery of the opposite side.

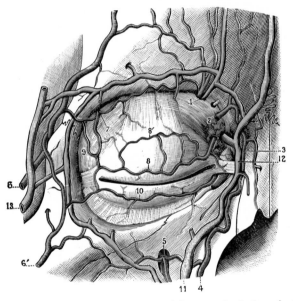

Fig. 504.—Bloodvessels of the eyelids, front view. 1, supraorbital artery and vein; 2, nasal artery; 3, angular artery, the terminal branch of 4, the facial artery; 5, infraorbital artery; 6, anterior branch of the superficial temporal artery; 6', malar branch of the transverse artery of the face; 7, lacrimal artery; 8, superior palpebral artery with 8', its external arch; 9, anastomoses of the superior palpebral with the superficial temporal and lacrimal; 10, inferior palpebral artery; 11, facial vein; 12, angular vein; 13, branch of the superficial temporal vein. (Testut.)

The **Dorsal Nasal Artery** (*a. dorsalis nasi; nasal artery*), the other terminal branch of the ophthalmic, emerges from the orbit above the medial palpebral ligament, and, after giving a twig to the upper part of the lacrimal sac, divides into two branches, one of which crosses the root of the nose, and anastomoses with the angular artery, the other runs along the dorsum of the nose, supplies its outer surface; and anastomoses with the artery of the opposite side, and with the lateral nasal branch of the external maxillary.

The **Central Artery of the Retina** (*a. centralis retinæ*) is the first and one of the smallest branches of the ophthalmic artery. It runs for a short distance within the dural sheath of the optic nerve, but about 1.25 cm. behind the eyeball it pierces the nerve obliquely, and runs forward in the center of its substance to the retina. Its mode of distribution will be described with the anatomy of the eye. It may be a branch of the lacrimal artery (Fig. 503). There is an arteria cilio-retinalis in 13 per cent. of cases (Adachi).

The **Ciliary Arteries** (*aa. ciliares*) are divisible into three groups, the long and short, the posterior, and the anterior. The **short posterior ciliary arteries,** from six to twelve in number, arise from the ophthalmic, or its branches; they pass forward around the optic nerve to the posterior part of the eyeball, pierce the sclera around the entrance of the nerve, and supply the choroid and ciliary processes. The **long posterior ciliary arteries,** two in number, pierce the posterior part of the sclera at some little distance from the optic nerve, and run forward, along either side of the eyeball, between the sclera and choroid, to the ciliary muscle, where they divide into two branches; these form an arterial circle, the **circulus arteriosus major,** around the circumference of the iris, from which numerous converging branches run, in the substance of the iris, to its pupillary margin, where they form a second arterial circle, the **circulus arteriosus minor.** The **anterior ciliary arteries** are derived from the muscular branches; they run to the front of the eyeball in company with the tendons of the Recti, form a vascular zone beneath the conjunctiva, and then pierce the sclera a short distance from the cornea and end in the circulus arteriosus major.

The **Muscular Branches,** (*rami musculares*), two in number, **superior and inferior,** frequently spring from a common trunk. The **superior,** often wanting, supplies the Levator palpebræ superioris, Rectus superior, and Obliquus superior. The **inferior,** more commonly present, passes forward between the optic nerve and Rectus inferior, and is distributed to the Recti lateralis, medialis, and inferior, and the Obliquus inferior. This vessel gives off most of the anterior ciliary arteries. Additional muscular branches are given off from the lacrimal and supraorbital arteries, or from the trunk of the ophthalmic.

8. The **anterior cerebral artery** (*a. cerebri anterior*) (Figs. 505, 506, 507) *arises* from the internal carotid, at the medial extremity of the lateral cerebral fissure. It passes forward and medialward across the anterior perforated substance, above the optic nerve, to the commencement of the longitudinal fissure. Here it comes into close relationship with the opposite artery, to which it is connected by a short trunk, the **anterior communicating artery.** From this point the two vessels run side by side in the longitudinal fissure, curve around the genu of the corpus callosum, and, turning backward, continue along the upper surface of the corpus callosum to its posterior part, where they end by anastomosing with the posterior cerebral arteries.

Branches.—In its first part the anterior cerebral artery gives off twigs which pierce the anterior perforated substance and the lamina terminalis, and supply the rostrum of the corpus callosum and the septum pellucidum. A larger branch, phylogenetically one of the oldest of the cerebral arteries, takes a recurrent course laterally over the anterior perforated substance (recurrent branch of the anterior cerebral artery, Shellshear; medial striate artery, Abbie). This medial striate artery supplies the lower anterior portion of the basal nuclei, *i. e.,* the lower part of the head of the caudate nucleus, the lower part of the frontal pole of the putamen, the frontal pole of the globus pallidus, and the anterior limb of the internal capsule up to the dorsal limit of the globus pallidus. The inferior or orbital branches of the anterior cerebral artery are distributed to the orbital surface of the frontal lobe, where they supply the olfactory lobe, gyrus rectus, and internal orbital gyrus. The anterior or prefrontal branches supply a part of the superior frontal gyrus, and send twigs over the edge of the hemisphere to the superior and middle frontal gyri and upper part of the anterior central gyrus. The **middle branches** supply the corpus callosum, the cingulate gyrus, the medial surface of the superior frontal gyrus, and the upper part of the anterior central gyrus. The **posterior branches** supply the precuneus and adjacent lateral surface of the hemisphere.

The **Anterior Communicating Artery** (*a. communicans anterior*) connects the two anterior cerebral arteries across the commencement of the longitudinal fissure. Sometimes this vessel is wanting, the two arteries joining to form a single trunk, which afterward divides; or it may be wholly, or partially, divided into two. Its length averages about 4 mm., but varies greatly. It gives off some antero-medial branches.

9. The **middle cerebral artery** (*a. cerebri media*) (Figs. 505, 506), the largest branch of the internal carotid, runs at first lateralward in the lateral cerebral or Sylvian fissure and then backward and upward on the surface of the insula, where it divides into a number of branches which are distributed to the lateral surface of the cerebral hemisphere.

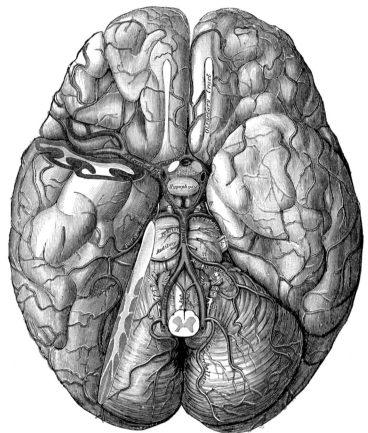

Fig. 505.—The arteries of the base of the brain. The temporal pole of the cerebrum and a portion of the cerebellar hemisphere have been removed on the right side.

Branches.—At its commencement the middle cerebral artery gives off the lateral striate arteries which supply the basal nuclei, *i. e.*, the whole of the putamen except the lower anterior pole, the upper part of the head and the whole of the body of the caudate nucleus, the lateral part of the globus pallidus, and the capsula interna above the level of the globus pallidus. It is not possible to distinguish among the branches of the lateral striate arteries any individual artery such as the "lenticulo-striate" artery of Duret or the "artery of cerebral hemorrhage" of Charcot. The thalamus is nowhere supplied by branches of the middle cerebral artery. Branches supplying cortical areas may be designated as follows: An inferior lateral frontal branch supplies the inferior frontal gyrus (Broca's convolution) and the lateral part of the orbital surface of the frontal lobe. An ascending frontal branch supplies the anterior central gyrus. An ascending parietal branch is distributed to the posterior central gyrus and the lower part of the superior parietal lobule.

37

A parietotemporal branch supplies the supramarginal and angular gyri, and the posterior parts of the superior and middle temporal gyri. Temporal branches, two or three in number, are distributed to the lateral surface of the temporal lobe.

10. The **posterior communicating artery** (*a. communicans posterior*) (Fig. 505) runs backward from the internal carotid, and anastomoses with the posterior cerebral, a branch of the basilar. It varies in size, being sometimes small, and

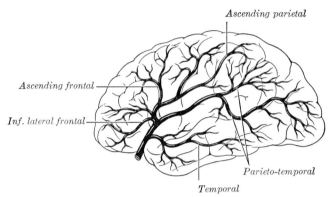

Ascending parietal

Ascending frontal

Inf. lateral frontal

Parieto-temporal

Temporal

FIG. 506.—Branches of the middle cerebral artery to the lateral surface of the cerebral hemisphere. (Modified after Foix.)

occasionally so large that the posterior cerebral may be considered as arising from the internal carotid rather than from the basilar. It is frequently larger on one side than on the other. Branches of the posterior communicating artery enter the base of the brain between the infundibulum and the optic tract, and supply the genu and about the anterior one-third of the posterior limb of the internal capsule. There are also branches to the anterior one-third of the thalamus (exclusive of the anterior nucleus) and to the walls of the third ventricle.

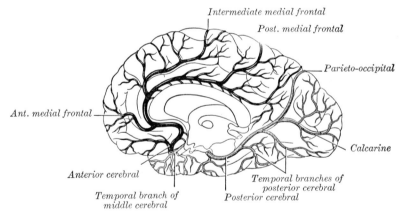

Intermediate medial frontal

Post. medial frontal

Parieto-occipital

Ant. medial frontal

Calcarine

Anterior cerebral

Temporal branches of posterior cerebral

Temporal branch of middle cerebral

Posterior cerebral

FIG. 507.—Medial surface of cerebral hemisphere, showing areas supplied by cerebral arteries.

11. The **anterior choroidal artery** (*a. chorioidea; choroid artery*) is, next to the middle cerebral artery, the most important source of supply to the internal capsule. The artery arises from the internal carotid near the origin of the posterior communicating artery, and takes its course along the optic tract, and around the cerebral peduncle as far as the lateral geniculate body, where its main branches turn to enter the choroid plexus of the inferior horn of the lateral ventricle. In its

course it gives branches to the optic tract, the cerebral peduncle, and the base of the brain. These branches terminate in the lateral geniculate body, the tail of the caudate nucleus, and the posterior two-thirds of the posterior limb of the internal capsule as far as the dorsal limit of the globus pallidus. The infralenticular and retrolenticular portions of the internal capsule are also vascularized by branches of the anterior choroidal artery.

THE ARTERIES OF THE BRAIN.

Since the mode of distribution of the vessels of the brain has an important bearing upon a considerable number of the pathological lesions which may occur in this part of the nervous system, it is im-portant to consider a little more in detail the manner in which the vessels are distributed.

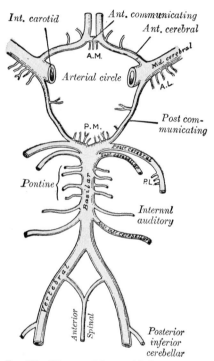

The cerebral arteries are derived from the internal carotid and vertebral, which at the base of the brain form a remarkable anasto-mosis known as the **arterial circle of Willis**. It is formed in front by the anterior cere-bral arteries, branches of the internal carotid, which are connected together by the anterior communicating; behind by the two posterior cerebral arteries, branches of the basilar, which are connected on either side with the internal carotid by the posterior commu-nicating (Figs. 505, 508). The parts of the brain included within this arterial circle are the lamina terminalis, the optic chiasma, the infundibulum, the tuber cinereum, the corpora mammillaria, and the posterior perforated substance.

The three trunks which together supply each cerebral hemisphere arise from the arterial circle of Willis. From its anterior part proceed the two anterior cerebrals, from its antero-lateral parts the middle cerebrals, and from its posterior part the posterior cerebrals. Each of these principal arteries gives origin to the numerous vessels which supply the brain substance. They

FIG. 508.—Diagram of the arterial circulation at the base of the brain. *A.L.* Antero-lateral. *A.M.* Antero-medial. *P.L.* Postero-lateral. *P.M.* Postero-medial ganglionic branches.

contribute to a continuous complex network of capillaries, which is of different density in various parts of the central nervous system, probably in conjunction with the varying requirements of the different structures. Thus the gray matter of the brain has a much denser capillary bed than the white matter. The arteries on the surface of the brain anastomose freely, but within the central nervous system arterial anastomoses are rare. There is no evidence for the existence of arterio-venous anastomoses either in the pia or within the central nervous system. While true anatomical end-arteries exist in certain mammals, in man end- or terminal arteries do not exist in a strict anatomical sense, *i. e.*, there are no arteries which have no connections with neighboring vessels. However, the lack of sufficiently large and numerous anastomoses, and the high vulnerability of the nervous tissue in case of lack of oxygen, when an artery is occluded, greatly reduces the chances that an effi-cient collateral circulation might take care of the needs of the ischemic area. This ischemic area corresponds in its extent to the area of supply of the occluded vessel.

The arteries of the brain may, therefore, be considered as functional end- or terminal arteries, though anatomically they are not strictly what Cohnheim designated as terminal arteries.

THE ARTERIES OF THE UPPER EXTREMITY

The artery which supplies the upper extremity continues as a single trunk from its commencement down to the elbow; but different portions of it have received different names, according to the regions through which they pass. That part of the vessel which extends from its origin to the outer border of the first rib is termed the **subclavian;** beyond this point to the lower border of the axilla it is named the **axillary;** and from the lower margin of the axillary space to the bend of the elbow it is termed **brachial;** here the trunk ends by dividing into two branches the **radial** and **ulnar.**

THE SUBCLAVIAN ARTERY (A. SUBCLAVIA) (Fig. 509).

On the right side the **subclavian artery** *arises* from the innominate artery behind the right sternoclavicular articulation; on the left side it springs from the arch of the aorta. The two vessels, therefore, in the first part of their course, differ in length, direction, and relation with neighboring structures.

In order to facilitate the description, each subclavian artery is divided into three parts. The first portion extends from the origin of the vessel to the medial border of the Scalenus anterior; the second lies behind this muscle; and the third extends from the lateral margin of the muscle to the outer border of the first rib, where it becomes the axillary artery. The first portions of the two vessels require separate descriptions; the second and third parts of the two arteries are practically alike.

First Part of the Right Subclavian Artery (Figs. 495, 509).—The first part of the right subclavian artery *arises* from the innominate artery, behind the upper part of the right sternoclavicular articulation, and passes upward and lateralward to the medial margin of the Scalenus anterior. It ascends a little above the clavicle, the extent to which it does so varying in different cases.

Relations.—It is covered, *in front,* by the integument, superficial fascia, Platysma, deep fascia, the clavicular origin of the Sternocleidomastoideus, the Sternohyoideus, and Sternothyreoideus, and another layer of the deep fascia. It is crossed by the internal jugular and vertebral veins, by the vagus nerve and the cardiac branches of the vagus and sympathetic, and by the subclavian loop of the sympathetic trunk which forms a ring around the vessel. The anterior jugular vein is directed lateralward in front of the artery, but is separated from it by the Sternohyoideus and Sternothyreoideus. *Below and behind* the artery is the pleura, which separates it from the apex of the lung; *behind* is the sympathetic trunk, the Longus colli and the first thoracic vertebra. The right recurrent nerve winds around the lower and back part of the vessel.

First Part of the Left Subclavian Artery (Fig. 495).—The first part of the left subclavian artery *arises* from the arch of the aorta, behind the left common carotid and at the level of the fourth thoracic vertebra; it ascends in the superior mediastinal cavity to the root of the neck and then arches lateralward to the medial border of the Scalenus anterior.

Relations.—It is in relation, *in front,* with the vagus, cardiac, and phrenic nerves, which lie parallel with it, the left common carotid artery, left internal jugular and vertebral veins, and the commencement of the left innominate vein, and is covered by the Sternothyreoideus, Sternohyoideus, and Sternocleidomastoideus; *behind,* it is in relation with the esophagus, thoracic duct, left recurrent nerve, inferior cervical ganglion of the sympathetic trunk, and Longus colli; higher up, however, the esophagus and thoracic duct lie to its right side; the latter ultimately arching over the vessel to join the angle of union between the subclavian and internal jugular veins. *Medial* to it are the esophagus, trachea, thoracic duct, and left recurrent nerve; *lateral* to it, the left pleura and lung.

Second and Third Parts of the Subclavian Artery (Fig. 509).—The second **portion** of the subclavian artery lies behind the Scalenus anterior; it is very short, and forms the highest part of the arch described by the vessel.

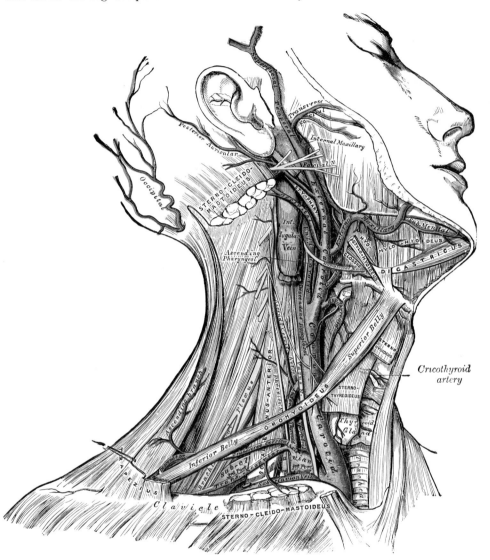

Cricothyroid artery

FIG. 509.—Superficial dissection of the right side of the neck, showing the carotid and subclavian arteries.

Relations.—It is covered *in front,* by the skin, superficial fascia, Platysma, deep cervical fascia, Sternocleidomastoideus, and Scalenus anterior. On the right side of the neck the phrenic nerve is separated from the second part of the artery by the Scalenus anterior, while on the left side it crosses the first part of the artery close to the medial edge of the muscle. *Behind* the vessel are the pleura and the Scalenus medius; *above,* the brachial plexus of nerves; *below,* the pleura. The subclavian vein lies below and in front of the artery, separated from it by the Scalenus anterior.

The **third portion** of the subclavian artery runs downward and lateralward from the lateral margin of the Scalenus anterior to the outer border of the first rib, where it becomes the axillary artery. This is the most superficial portion of the vessel, and is contained in the subclavian triangle.

Relations.—It is covered, *in front*, by the skin, the superficial fascia, the Platysma, the supraclavicular nerves, and the deep cervical fascia. The external jugular vein crosses its medial part and receives the transverse scapular, transverse cervical, and anterior jugular veins, which frequently form a plexus in front of the artery. Behind the veins, the nerve to the Subclavius descends in front of the artery. The terminal part of the artery lies behind the clavicle and the Subclavius and is crossed by the transverse scapular vessels. The subclavian vein is in front of and at a slightly lower level than the artery. *Behind*, it lies on the lowest trunk of the brachial plexus, which intervenes between it and the Scalenus medius. *Above* and to its *lateral* side are the upper trunks of the brachial plexus and the Omohyoideus. *Below*, it rests on the upper surface of the first rib.

Variations.—The subclavian arteries vary in their origin, their course, and the height to which they rise in the neck.

The origin of the right subclavian from the innominate takes place, in some cases, above the sternoclavicular articulation, and occasionally, but less frequently, below that joint. The artery may arise as a separate trunk from the arch of the aorta, and in such cases it may be either the first, second, third, or even the last branch derived from that vessel; in the majority, however, it is the first or last, rarely the second or third. When it is the first branch, it occupies the ordinary position of the innominate artery; when the second or third, it gains its usual position by passing behind the right carotid; and when the last branch, it arises from the left extremity of the arch, and passes obliquely toward the right side, usually behind the trachea, esophagus, and right carotid, sometimes between the esophagus and trachea, to the upper border of the first rib, whence it follows its ordinary course. In very rare instances, this vessel arises from the thoracic aorta, as low down as the fourth thoracic vertebra. Occasionally, it perforates the Scalenus anterior; more rarely it passes in front of that muscle. Sometimes the subclavian vein passes with the artery behind the Scalenus anterior. The artery may ascend as high as 4 cm. above the clavicle, or any intermediate point between this and the upper border of the bone, the right subclavian usually ascending higher than the left.

The left subclavian is occasionally joined at its origin with the left carotid.

The left subclavian artery is more deeply placed than the right in the first part of its course, and, as a rule, does not reach quite as high a level in the neck. The posterior border of the Sternocleidomastoideus corresponds pretty closely to the lateral border of the Scalenus anterior, so that the third portion of the artery, the part most accessible for operation, lies immediately lateral to the posterior border of the Sternocleidomastoideus.

Collateral Circulation.—After ligature of the third part of the subclavian artery, the collateral circulation is established mainly by anastomoses between the transverse scapular, the descending ramus of the transverse cervical artery, and the subscapular artery, also by an anastomosis between branches of the internal mammary and lateral thoracic and subscapular arteries.

Branches.—The branches of the subclavian artery are:

Vertebral.   Internal mammary.
Thyrocervical.   Costocervical.
                    Transverse cervical.

The first four branches generally arise from the first portion on the left side, but the costocervical trunk springs more frequently from the second portion on the right side. On both sides the first three branches arise close together at the medial border of the Scalenus anterior, leaving, in the majority of cases, a free interval of from 1.25 to 2.5 cm. between the commencement of the artery and the origin of the nearest branch. The transverse cervical is much less constant than the other branches, and when present is the only branch of the third portion of the artery.

1. The **vertebral artery** (*a. vertebralis*) (Fig. 502), is the first branch of the subclavian, and *arises* from the upper and back part of the first portion of the vessel. It is surrounded by a plexus of nerve fibers derived from the inferior cervical ganglion of the sympathetic trunk, and ascends through the foramina in the transverse processes of the upper six cervical vertebræ; it then winds behind the superior articular process of the atlas and, entering the skull through the foramen magnum, unites, at the lower border of the pons, with the vessel of the opposite side to form the basilar artery.

Relations.—The vertebral artery may be divided into four parts: The **first part** runs upward and backward between the Longus colli and the Scalenus anterior. In front of it are the internal jugular and vertebral veins, and it is crossed by the inferior thyroid artery; the left vertebral is crossed by the thoracic duct also. Behind it are the transverse process of the seventh cervical vertebra, the sympathetic trunk and its inferior cervical ganglion. The **second part** runs upward through the foramina in the transverse processes of the upper six cervical vertebræ, and is surrounded by branches from the inferior cervical sympathetic ganglion and by a plexus of veins which unite to form the vertebral vein at the lower part of the neck. It is situated in front of the trunks of the cervical nerves, and pursues an almost vertical course as far as the transverse process of the axis, above which it runs upward and lateralward to the foramen in the transverse process of the atlas. The **third part** issues from the latter foramen on the medial side of the Rectus capitis lateralis, and curves backward behind the superior articular process of the atlas, the anterior ramus of the first cervical nerve being on its medial side; it then lies in the groove on the upper surface of the posterior arch of the atlas, and enters the vertebral canal by passing beneath the posterior atlantoöccipital membrane. This part of the artery is covered by the Semispinalis capitis and is contained in the **suboccipital triangle**—a triangular space bounded by the Rectus capitis posterior major, the Obliquus superior, and the Obliquus inferior. The first cervical or suboccipital nerve lies between the artery and the posterior arch of the atlas. The **fourth part** pierces the dura mater and inclines medialward to the front of the medulla oblongata; it is placed between the hypoglossal nerve and the anterior root of the first cervical nerve and beneath the first digitation of the ligamentum denticulatum. At the lower border of the pons it unites with the vessel of the opposite side to form the basilar artery.

Branches.—The branches of the vertebral artery may be divided into two sets: those given off in the neck, and those within the cranium.

Cervical Branches.	*Cranial Branches*
Spinal.	Meningeal.
Muscular.	Posterior Spinal.
	Anterior Spinal.
	Posterior Inferior Cerebellar.
	Medullary.

Spinal Branches (*rami spinales*) enter the vertebral canal through the intervertebral foramina, and each divides into two branches. Of these, one passes along the roots of the nerves to supply the medulla spinalis and its membranes, anastomosing with the other arteries of the medulla spinalis; the other divides into an ascending and a descending branch, which unite with similar branches from the arteries above and below, so that two lateral anastomotic chains are formed on the posterior surfaces of the bodies of the vertebræ, near the attachment of the pedicles. From these anastomotic chains branches are supplied to the periosteum and the bodies of the vertebræ, and others form communications with similar branches from the opposite side; from these communications small twigs arise which join similar branches above and below, to form a central anastomotic chain on the posterior surface of the bodies of the vertebræ.

Muscular Branches are given off to the deep muscles of the neck, where the vertebral artery curves around the articular process of the atlas. They anastomose with the occipital, and with the ascending and deep cervical arteries.

The **Meningeal Branch** (*ramus meningeus; posterior meningeal branch*) springs from the vertebral at the level of the foramen magnum, ramifies between the bone and dura mater in the cerebellar fossa, and supplies the falx cerebelli. It is frequently represented by one or two small branches.

The **Posterior Spinal Artery** (*a. spinalis posterior; dorsal spinal artery*) *arises* from the vertebral, at the side of the medulla oblongata; passing backward, it descends on this structure, lying in front of the posterior roots of the spinal nerves, and is reinforced by a succession of small branches, which enter the vertebral canal through the intervertebral foramina; by means of these it is continued to the lower part of the medulla spinalis, and to the cauda equina. Branches from the posterior spinal arteries form a free anastomosis around the posterior roots of the spinal nerves, and communicate, by means of very tortuous transverse branches, with the vessels of the opposite side. Close to its origin each gives off an ascending branch, which ends at the side of the fourth ventricle.

The **Anterior Spinal Artery** (*a. spinalis anterior; ventral spinal artery*) is a small branch, which *arises* near the termination of the vertebral, and, descending in front of the medulla oblongata, unites with its fellow of the opposite side at the level of the foramen magnum. One of these vessels is usually larger than the other, but occasionally they are about equal in size. The single trunk, thus formed, descends on the front of the medulla spinalis, and is reinforced by a succession of small branches which enter the vertebral canal through the intervertebral foramina; these branches are derived from the vertebral and the ascending cervical of the inferior thyroid in the neck; from the intercostals in the thorax; and from the lumbar, iliolumbar, and lateral sacral arteries in the abdomen and pelvis. They unite, by means of ascending and descending branches, to form a single anterior median artery, which extends as far as the lower part of the medulla spinalis, and is continued as a slender twig on the filum terminale. This vessel is placed in the pia mater along the anterior median fissure; it supplies that membrane, and the substance of the medulla spinalis, and sends off branches at its lower part to be distributed to the cauda equina.

The **Posterior Inferior Cerebellar Artery** (*a. cerebelli inferior posterior*) (Fig. 505), the largest branch of the vertebral, winds backward around the upper part of the medulla oblongata, passing between the origins of the vagus and accessory nerves, over the inferior peduncle to the under surface of the cerebellum, where it divides into two branches. The **medial branch** is continued backward to the notch between the two hemispheres of the cerebellum; while the **lateral** supplies the under surface of the cerebellum, as far as its lateral border, where it anastomoses with the anterior inferior cerebellar and the superior cerebellar branches of the basilar artery. Branches from this artery supply the choroid plexus of the fourth ventricle.

The **Medullary Arteries** (*bulbar arteries*) are several minute vessels which spring from the vertebral and its branches and are distributed to the medulla oblongata.

The **Basilar Artery** (*a. basilaris*) (Fig. 505), so named from its position at the base of the skull, is a single trunk formed by the junction of the two vertebral arteries: it extends from the lower to the upper border of the pons, lying in its median groove, under cover of the arachnoid. It ends by dividing into the two posterior cerebral arteries.

Its **branches**, on either side, are the following:

Pontine.	Anterior Inferior Cerebellar.
Internal Auditory.	Superior Cerebellar.
	Posterior Cerebral.

The **pontine branches** (*rami ad pontem; transverse branches*) are a number of small vessels which come off at right angles from either side of the basilar artery and supply the pons and adjacent parts of the brain.

The **internal auditory artery** (*a. auditiva interna; auditory artery*), a long slender branch, *arises* from near the middle of the artery; it accompanies the acoustic nerve through the internal acoustic meatus, and is distributed to the internal ear. It often (60 per cent., Stopford) arises from the anterior inferior cerebellar artery.

The **anterior inferior cerebellar artery** (*a. cerebelli inferior anterior*) passes backward to be distributed to the anterior part of the under surface of the cerebellum, anastomosing with the posterior inferior cerebellar branch of the vertebral.

The **superior cerebellar artery** (*a. cerebelli superior*) *arises* near the termination of the basilar. It passes lateralward, immediately below the oculomotor nerve, which separates it from the posterior cerebral artery, winds around the cerebral eduncle, close to the trochlear nerve, and, arriving at the upper surface of the erebellum, divides into branches which ramify in the pia mater and anastomose ʋith those of the inferior cerebellar arteries. Several branches go to the pineal ody, the anterior medullary velum, and the tela chorioidea of the third ventricle.

The **posterior cerebral artery** (*a. cerebri posterior*) (Figs. 505, 507, 510) is larger ʰan the preceding, from which it is separated near its origin by the oculomotor erve. Passing lateralward, parallel to the superior cerebellar artery, and receiving ʰe posterior communicating from the internal carotid, it winds around the cerebral eduncle, and reaches the tentorial surface of the occipital lobe of the cerebrum, ʰere it breaks up into branches for the supply of the temporal and occipital lobes. t may be a branch of the internal carotid, in as many as 7 per cent. of cases.

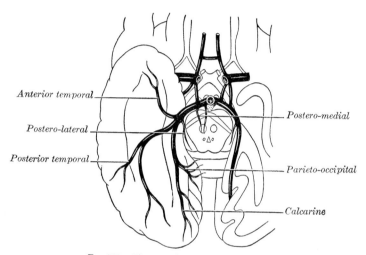

Anterior temporal

Postero-lateral

Posterior temporal

Postero-medial

Parieto-occipital

Calcarine

FIG. 510.—The posterior cerebral artery. (After Foix.)

The **branches** of the posterior cerebral artery are as follows:

Posterior-medial Central.	Anterior Temporal.
Posterior Choroidal.	Posterior Temporal.
Postero-lateral Central.	Calcarine.
Parietoöccipital.	

The **postero-medial branches** (Fig. 510) are a group of small arteries which arise ᵗ the commencement of the posterior cerebral artery. These, with similar branches om the posterior communicating, pierce the posterior perforated substance, and ᵃpply the medial surfaces of the thalami and the walls of the third ventricle. The ᵖsterior choroidal branches run forward beneath the splenium of the corpus cal-ᵒsum, and supply the tela chorioidea of the third ventricle and the choroid plexus. ʰe **postero-lateral branches** are small arteries which arise from the posterior cerebral ᵗery after it has turned around the cerebral peduncle; they supply the posterior ᵒrtion of the thalamus. The **anterior temporal branches** are distributed to the ᵘncus and the anterior part of the fusiform gyrus; the **posterior temporal**, to the ᵘsiform and the inferior temporal gyri; the **calcarine**, to the cuneus and gyrus ᵑgualis and the back part of the convex surface of the occipital lobe; and the ᵃrietoöccipital, to the cuneus and the precuneus.

2. The **thryocervical trunk** (*truncus thyreocervicalis; thyroid axis*) (Fig. 509) is ᵇort and thick; it *arises* from the front of the first portion of the subclavian artery, ᵒse to the medial border of the Scalenus anterior, and divides almost immediately ᵗo three branches, the **inferior thyroid, transverse scapular,** and **superficial cervical.**

The **Inferior Thyroid Artery** (*a. thyreoidea inferior*) passes upward, in front of th
vertebral artery and Longus colli; then turns medialward behind the carotid sheat
and its contents, and also behind the sympathetic trunk, the middle cervica
ganglion resting upon the vessel. Reaching the lower border of the thyroid glan
it divides into two branches, which supply the postero-inferior parts of the glanc
and anastomose with the superior thyroid, and with the corresponding artery c
the opposite side. The recurrent nerve passes upward generally behind, but occa
sionally in front, of the artery.

The **branches** of the inferior thyroid are:

Inferior Laryngeal..	Esophageal.
Tracheal.	Ascending Cervical.

Muscular.

The **inferior laryngeal artery** (*a. laryngea inferior*) ascends upon the trachea t
the back part of the larynx under cover of the Constrictor pharyngis inferior, i
company with the recurrent nerve, and supplies the muscles and mucous mem
brane of this part, anastomosing with the branch from the opposite side, and wit
the superior laryngeal branch of the superior thyroid artery.

The **tracheal branches** (*rami tracheales*) are distributed upon the trachea, an
anastomose below with the bronchial arteries.

The **esophageal branches** (*rami œsophagei*) supply the esophagus, and anasto
mose with the esophageal branches of the aorta.

The **ascending cervical artery** (*a. cervicalis ascendens*) is a small branch whic
arises from the inferior thyroid as that vessel passes behind the carotid sheath
it runs up on the anterior tubercles of the transverse processes of the cervic
vertebræ in the interval between the Scalenus anterior and Longus capitis. T
the muscles of the neck it gives twigs which anastomose with branches of th
vertebral, sending one or two spinal branches into the vertebral canal throug
the intervertebral foramina to be distributed to the medulla spinalis and its men
branes, and to the bodies of the vertebræ, in the same manner as the spinal branch
from the vertebral. It anastomoses with the ascending pharyngeal and occipit
arteries.

The **muscular branches** supply the depressors of the hyoid bone, and the Longu
colli, Scalenus anterior, and Constrictor pharyngis inferior.

The **Transverse Scapular Artery** (*a. transversa scapulæ; suprascapular artery*) pass
at first downward and lateralward across the Scalenus anterior and phren
nerve, being covered by the Sternocleidomastoideus; it then crosses the subclavia
artery and the brachial plexus, and runs behind and parallel with the clavicle ar
Subclavius, and beneath the inferior belly of the Omohyoideus, to the superi
border of the scapula; it passes over the superior transverse ligament of the scapu
which separates it from the suprascapular nerve, and enters the supraspinous fos
(Fig. 511). In this situation it lies close to the bone, and ramifies between it ar
the Supraspinatus, to which it supplies branches. It then descends behind the ne
of the scapula, through the great scapular notch and under cover of the inferi
transverse ligament, to reach the infraspinous fossa, where it anastomoses with th
scapular circumflex and the descending branch of the transverse cervical. Besid
distributing branches to the Sternocleidomastoideus, Subclavius, and neighbori
muscles, it gives off a **suprasternal branch**, which crosses over the sternal end of t
clavicle to the skin of the upper part of the chest; and an **acromial branch**, whi
pierces the Trapezius and supplies the skin over the acromion, anastomosing wi
the thoracoacromial artery. As the artery passes over the superior transver
ligament of the scapula, it sends a branch into the subscapular fossa, where
ramifies beneath the Subscapularis, and anastomoses with the subscapular arte

and with the descending branch of the transverse cervical. It also sends articular branches to the acromioclavicular and shoulder-joints, and a nutrient artery to the clavicle.

The **Superficial Cervical Artery** (*a. cervicalis superficialis*) passes laterally across the Scalenus anterior and phrenic nerve above the transverse scapular artery and, diverging from the latter, it follows a slightly upward course to reach the anterior margin of the Trapezius, where it divides into an ascending and a descending branch. Medially, it lies deep to the Sternocleidomastoideus; laterally, it is covered only by deep cervical fascia and the Platysma, except where it is crossed by the inferior belly of the Omohyoideus, lying between the latter and the divisions of the brachial plexus. The ascending branch follows the anterior margin of the Trapezius, distributing branches to it and to the neighboring muscles and lymph nodes, and anastomosing with the superficial branch of the descending ramus of the occipital artery. The descending branch also lies against the deep surface of the Trapezius, supplying it with branches and accompanying the accessory nerve.

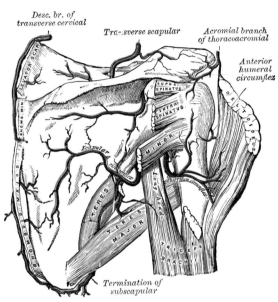

FIG. 511.—The scapular and circumflex arteries.

The superficial cervical and the transverse cervical arteries are combined into a common trunk in approximately half the cases, in which condition the common trunk arises from the thyrocervical trunk and follows the course of the superficial cervical to the margin of the Trapezius, as illustrated in Fig. 509.

3. The **internal mammary artery** (*a. mammaria interna*) (Fig. 512) *arises* from the under surface of the first portion of the subclavian, opposite the thryocervical trunk. It descends behind the cartilages of the upper six ribs at a distance of about 1.25 cm. from the margin of the sternum, and at the level of the sixth intercostal space divides into the **musculophrenic** and **superior epigastric arteries.**

Relations.—It is directed at first downward, forward, and medialward behind the sternal end of the clavicle, the subclavian and internal jugular veins, and the first costal cartilage, and passes forward close to the lateral side of the innominate vein. As it enters the thorax the phrenic nerve crosses from its lateral to its medial side. Below the first costal cartilage it descends almost vertically to its point of bifurcation. It is covered in front by the cartilages of the upper six ribs and the intervening Intercostales interni and anterior intercostal membranes, and is crossed by the terminal portions of the upper six intercostal nerves. It rests on the pleura, as far as the third costal cartilage; below this level, upon the Transversus thoracis. It is accompanied by a pair of veins; these unite above to form a single vessel, which runs medial to the artery and ends in the corresponding innominate vein.

Branches.—The branches of the internal mammary are:

Pericardiacophrenic.	Intercostal.
Anterior Mediastinal.	Perforating.
Pericardial.	Musculophrenic.
Sternal.	Superior Epigastric.

The **Pericardiacophrenic Artery** (*a. pericardiacophrenica*; *a. comes nervi phrenici*) is a long slender branch, which accompanies the phrenic nerve, between the pleura and pericardium, to the diaphragm, to which it is distributed; it anastomoses with the musculophrenic and inferior phrenic arteries.

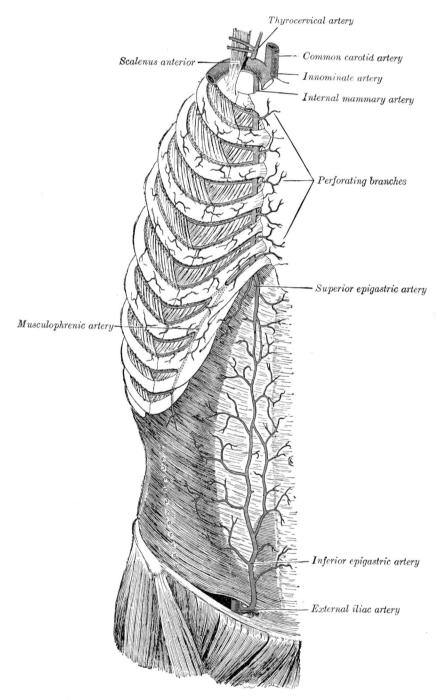

Thyrocervical artery

Scalenus anterior

Common carotid artery

Innominate artery

Internal mammary artery

Perforating branches

Superior epigastric artery

Musculophrenic artery

Inferior epigastric artery

External iliac artery

Fig. 512.—The internal mammary artery and its branches. The intercostal branches lie at first between the pleura and the internal intercostal muscles, then between the internal and external intercostal muscles. (The figure does not indicate these relationships.)

The **Anterior Mediastinal Arteries** (*aa. mediastinales anteriores; mediastinal arteries*) are small vessels, distributed to the areolar tissue and lymph glands in the anterior mediastinal cavity, and to the remains of the thymus.

The **Pericardial Branches** supply the upper part of the anterior surface of the pericardium; the lower part receives branches from the musculophrenic artery.

The **Sternal Branches** (*rami sternales*) are distributed to the Transversus thoracis, and to the posterior surface of the sternum.

The anterior mediastinal, pericardial, and sternal branches, together with some twigs from the pericardiacophrenic, anastomose with branches from the intercostal and bronchial arteries, and form a **subpleural mediastinal plexus**.

The **Intercostal Branches** (*rami intercostales; anterior intercostal arteries*) supply the upper five or six intercostal spaces. Two in number in each space, these small vessels pass lateralward, one lying near the lower margin of the rib above, and the other near the upper margin of the rib below, and anastomose with the intercostal arteries from the aorta. They are at first situated between the pleura and the Intercostales interni, and then between the Intercostales interni and externi. They supply the Intercostales and, by branches which perforate the Intercostales externi, the Pectorales and the mamma.

The **Perforating Branches** (*rami perforantes*) pierce the chest wall in the first five or six intercostal spaces. They pass forward through the internal intercostal muscles and the Pectoralis major, and curving lateralward, supply the Pectoralis major and the integument. Those which correspond to the second, third, and fourth spaces give branches to the mamma in the female, and during lactation are of large size.

The **Musculophrenic Artery** (*a. musculophrenica*) is directed obliquely downward and lateralward, behind the cartilages of the false ribs; it perforates the diaphragm at the eighth or ninth costal cartilage, and ends, considerably reduced in size, opposite the last intercostal space. It gives off intercostal branches to the seventh, eighth, and ninth intercostal spaces; these diminish in size as the spaces decrease in length, and are distributed in a manner precisely similar to the intercostals from the internal mammary. The musculophrenic also gives branches to the lower part of the pericardium, and others which run backward to the diaphragm, and downward to the abdominal muscles.

The **Superior Epigastric Artery** (*a. epigastrica superior*) continues in the original direction of the internal mammary; it descends through the interval between the costal and sternal attachments of the diaphragm, and enters the sheath of the Rectus abdominis, at first lying behind the muscle, and then perforating and supplying it, and anastomosing with the inferior epigastric artery from the external iliac. Branches perforate the anterior wall of the sheath of the Rectus, and supply the other muscles of the abdomen and the integument, and a small branch passes in front of the xiphoid process and anastomoses with the artery of the opposite side. It also gives some twigs to the diaphragm, while from the artery of the right side small branches extend into the falciform ligament of the liver and anastomose with the hepatic artery.

4. The **costocervical trunk** (*truncus costocervicalis; superior intercostal artery*), absent in 10 per cent. of cadavers (Fig. 502), *arises* from the upper and back part of the subclavian artery, behind the Scalenus anterior on the right side, and medial to that muscle on the left side. Passing backward, it gives off the **profunda cervicalis**, and, continuing as the **highest intercostal artery**, descends behind the pleura in front of the necks of the first and second ribs, and anastomoses with the first aortic intercostal. As it crosses the neck of the first rib it lies medial to the anterior division of the first thoracic nerve, and lateral to the first thoracic ganglion of the sympathetic trunk.

In the first intercostal space, it gives off a branch which is distributed in a manner similar to the distribution of the aortic intercostals. The branch for the second intercostal space usually joins with one from the highest aortic intercostal artery. This branch is not constant, but is more commonly found on the right side; when absent, its place is supplied by an intercostal branch from the aorta. Each intercostal gives off a posterior branch which goes to the posterior vertebral muscles, and sends a small spinal branch through the corresponding intervertebral foramen to the medulla spinalis and its membranes.

The **Profunda Cervicalis** (*a. cervicalis profunda; deep cervical branch*) *arises*, in most cases, from the costocervical trunk, and is analogous to the posterior branch of an aortic intercostal artery: occasionally it is a separate branch from the subclavian artery. Passing backward, above the eighth cervical nerve and between the transverse process of the seventh cervical vertebra and the neck of the first rib, it runs up the back of the neck, between the Semispinales capitis and colli, as high as the axis vertebra, supplying these and adjacent muscles, and anastomosing with the deep division of the descending branch of the occipital, and with branches of the vertebral. It gives off a spinal twig which enters the canal through the intervertebral foramen between the seventh cervical and first thoracic vertebræ.

5. The **Transverse Cervical Artery** (*a. transversa colli; transversalis colli artery*) arises with about equal frequency (1) as an independent branch from the third portion of the subclavian or (2) combined into a common trunk with the superficial cervical. From its independent origin, between the lateral border of the Scalenus anterior and the brachial plexus, the artery passes upward for a short distance, then loops around the plexus, frequently passing between the anterior and posterior divisions of the upper trunk, and courses downward toward the scapula. At the Levator scapulæ it divides into an ascending and a descending branch. The **ascending branch** (*ramus ascendens*) supplies the Levator scapulæ and neighboring deep cervical muscles. The **descending branch** (*posterior scapular artery; ramus descendens*) (Fig. 511) usually double, passes beneath the Levator scapulæ to the medial angle of the scapula, and then descends anterior to the Rhomboidei along the vertebral border of that bone as far as the inferior angle. The medial division is accompanied by the dorsal scapular nerve. The lateral division lies on the costal surface of the Serratus anterior muscle and is usually larger than the medial division. The descending branch of the transverse cervical supplies the Rhomboidei, Latissimus dorsi and Trapezius, and anastomoses with the transverse scapular and subscapular arteries and with the posterior branches of some of the intercostal arteries.

The common trunk, when present, arises from the thyrocervical, is called the transverse cervical (Fig. 509), follows the course described for the superficial cervical, and, at the border of the Trapezius, divides into an ascending branch whose distribution corresponds to the superficial cervical, and a descending branch whose distribution corresponds to the transverse cervical artery.

THE AXILLA.

The axilla is a pyramidal space, situated between the upper lateral part of the chest and the medial side of the arm (see p. 428).

Boundaries.—The *apex*, which is directed upward toward the root of the neck, corresponds to the interval between the outer border of the first rib, the superior border of the scapula, and the posterior surface of the clavicle, and through it the axillary vessels and nerves pass. The *base*, directed downward, is broad at the chest but narrow and pointed at the arm; it is formed by the integument and a thick layer of fascia, the **axillary fascia**, extending between the lower border of the Pectoralis major in front, and the lower border of the Latissimus dorsi behind. The *anterior wall* is formed by the Pectorales major and minor, the former covering the whole of this wall, the latter only its central part. The space between the upper border of the Pectoralis minor and the clavicle is occupied by the coracoclavicular fascia. The *posterior wall*, which extends somewhat lower than the anterior, is formed by the Subscapularis above, the Teres major and Latissimus dorsi below. On the *medial side* are the first four ribs with their corresponding Intercostales, and part of the Serratus anterior. On the *lateral side*, where the anterior and posterior walls converge, the space is narrow, and bounded by the humerus, the Coracobrachialis, and the Biceps brachii.

Contents.—It contains the axillary vessels, and the brachial plexus of nerves, with their branches, some branches of the intercostal nerves, and a large number of lymph glands, together with a quantity of fat and loose areolar tissue. The axillary artery and vein, with the brachial plexus of nerves, extend obliquely along the lateral boundary of the axilla, from its apex to its base, and are placed much nearer to the anterior than to the posterior wall, the vein lying to the thoracic side of the artery and partially concealing it. At the forepart of the axilla, in contact with the Pectorales, are the thoracic branches of the axillary artery, and along the lower margin of the Pectoralis minor the lateral thoracic artery extends to the side of the chest. At the back, in contact with the lower margin of the Subscapularis, are the subscapular vessels and nerves; winding around the lateral border of this muscle are the scapular circumflex vessels; and, close to the neck of the humerus, the posterior humeral circumflex vessels and the axillary nerve curve backward to the shoulder. Along the medial or thoracic side no vessel of any importance exists, the upper part of the space being crossed merely by a few small branches from the highest thoracic artery. There are some important nerves, however, in this situation, viz., the long thoracic nerve, descending on the surface of the Serratus anterior, to which it is distributed; and the intercostobrachial nerve, perforating the upper and anterior part of this wall, and passing across the axilla to the medial side of the arm.

The position and arrangement of the lymph nodes are described in the section on Lymphatics.

The Axillary Artery (A. Axillaris) (Fig. 513).

The **axillary artery**, the continuation of the subclavian, commences at the outer border of the first rib, and ends at the lower border of the tendon of the Teres major, where it takes the name of brachial. Its direction varies with the position of the limb; thus the vessel is nearly straight when the arm is directed at right angles with the trunk, concave upward when the arm is elevated above this, and convex upward and lateralward when the arm lies by the side. At its origin the artery is very deeply situated, but near its termination is superficial, being covered only by the skin and fascia. To facilitate the description of the vessel it is divided into three portions; the first part lies above, the second behind, and the third below the Pectoralis minor. Its branches are subject to great variation.

Relations.—The **first portion** of the axillary artery is covered *anteriorly* by the clavicular portion of the Pectoralis major and the coracoclavicular fascia, and is crossed by the lateral anterior thoracic nerve, and the thoracoacromial and cephalic veins; *posterior* to it are the first intercostal space, the corresponding Intercostalis externus, the first and second digitations of the Serratus anterior, and the long thoracic and medial anterior thoracic nerves, and the medial cord of the brachial plexus; on its *lateral side* is the brachial plexus, from which it is separated by a little areolar tissue; on its *medial*, or thoracic side, is the axillary vein which overlaps the artery. It is enclosed, together with the axillary vein and the brachial plexus, in a fibrous sheath —the **axillary sheath**—continuous above with the deep cervical fascia.

The **second portion** of the axillary artery is covered, *anteriorly*, by the Pectorales major and minor; posterior to it are the posterior cord of the brachial plexus, and some areolar tissue which intervenes between it and the Subscapularis; on the *medial side* is the axillary vein, separated from the artery by the medial cord of the brachial plexus and the medial anterior thoracic nerve; on the *lateral side* is the lateral cord of the brachial plexus. The brachial plexus thus surrounds the artery on three sides, and separates it from direct contact with the vein and adjacent muscles

The **third portion** of the axillary artery extends from the lower border of the Pectoralis minor to the lower border of the tendon of the Teres major. *In front*, it is covered by the lower part of the Pectoralis major above, but only by the integument and fascia below; *behind*, it is in relation with the lower part of the Subscapularis, and the tendons of the Latissimus dorsi and Teres major; on its *lateral side* is the Coracobrachialis, and on its *medial* or thoracic side, the axillary vein. The nerves of the brachial plexus bear the following relations to this part of the artery on the *lateral side* are the lateral head and the trunk of the median, and the musculocutaneous for a short distance; on the *medial side* the ulnar (between the vein and artery) and medial brachial cutaneous (to the medial side of the vein); *in front* are the medial head of the median and the medial antebrachial cutaneous, and *behind*, the radial and axillary, the latter only as far as the lower border of the Subscapularis.

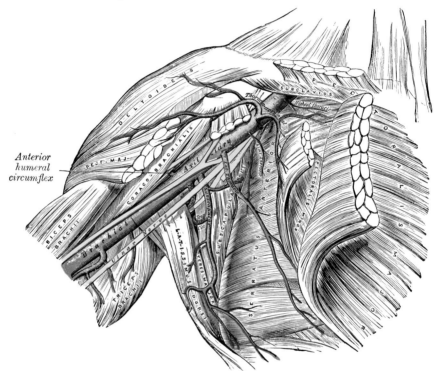

Anterior
humeral
circumflex

FIG. 513.—The axillary artery and its branches.

Collateral Circulation after Ligature of the Axillary Artery.—If the artery be tied above the origin of the thoracoacromial, the collateral circulation will be carried on by the same branches as after the ligature of the third part of the subclavian; if at a lower point, between the thoracoacromial and the subscapular, the latter vessel, by its free anastomosis with the transverse scapular and transverse cervical branches of the subclavian, will become the chief agent in carrying on the circulation; the lateral thoracic, if it be below the ligature, will materially contribute by its anastomoses with the intercostal and internal mammary arteries. If the point included in the ligature is below the origin of the subscapular artery, it will probably also be below the origins of the two humeral circumflex arteries. The chief agents in restoring the circulation will then be the subscapular and the two humeral circumflex arteries anastomosing with the a. profunda brachii.

Branches.—The branches of the axillary are:

From first part, Highest Thoracic.   *From second part* { Thoracoacromial.
                                                                  { Lateral Thoracic.

                  { Subscapular.
From third part { Posterior Humeral Circumflex.
                  { Anterior Humeral Circumflex.

1. The **highest thoracic artery** (*a. thoracalis suprema; superior thoracic artery*) is a small vessel, which may *arise* from the thoracoacromial or may be absent.

Running forward and medialward along the upper border of the Pectoralis minor, it passes between it and the Pectoralis major to the side of the chest. It supplies branches to these muscles, and to the parietes of the thorax, and anastomoses with the internal mammary and intercostal arteries.

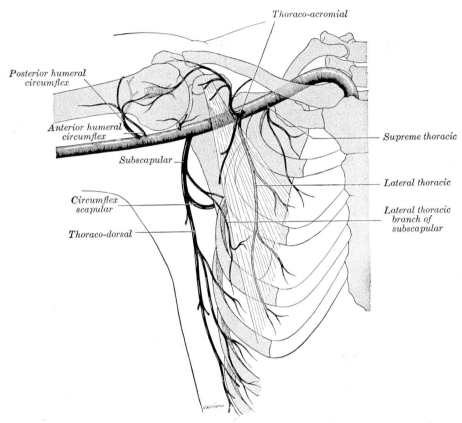

Fig. 514.—The axillary artery. A type found in approximately 33 per cent. of cases, according to DeGaris and Swartley.

2. The **thoracoacromial artery** (*a. thoracoacromialis; acromiothoracic artery; thoracic axis*) is a short trunk, which *arises* from the forepart of the axillary artery, its origin being generally overlapped by the upper edge of the Pectoralis minor Projecting forward to the upper border of this muscle, it pierces the coracoclavicular fascia and divides into four branches—pectoral, acromial, clavicular, and deltoid. The **pectoral branch** descends between the two Pectorales, and is distributed to them and to the mamma, anastomosing with the intercostal branches of the internal mammary and with the lateral thoracic. The **acromial branch** runs lateralward over the coracoid process and under the Deltoideus, to which it gives branches; it then pierces that muscle and ends on the acromion in an arterial network formed by branches from the transverse scapular, thoracoacromial, and posterior humeral circumflex arteries. The **clavicular branch** runs upward and medialward to the sternoclavicular joint, supplying this articulation, and the Subclavius. The **deltoid** (*humeral*) **branch**, often arising with the acromial, crosses over the Pectoralis minor and passes in the same groove as the cephalic vein, between the Pectoralis major and Deltoideus, and gives branches to both muscles.

3. The **lateral thoracic artery** (*a. thoracalis lateralis; long thoracic artery; external mammary artery*) follows the lower border of the Pectoralis minor to the side of the chest, supplying the Serratus anterior and the Pectoralis, and sending branches

38

across the axilla to the axillary glands and Subscapularis; it anastomoses with the internal mammary, subscapular, and intercostal arteries, and with the pectoral branch of the thoracoacromial. In the female it supplies an **external mammary branch** which turns around the free edge of the Pectoralis major and supplies the mamma. The lateral thoracic artery is often (60 per cent.) a branch either of the thoracoacromial artery or of the subscapular artery. It comes directly from the axillary only in about 30 per cent. of cases.

4. The **subscapular artery** (*a. subscapularis*) the largest branch of the axillary artery, *arises* at the lower border of the Subscapularis, gives off, 4 cm. from its origin, the **scapular circumflex artery**, and continues as the **thoraco-dorsal artery** (Fig. 514) to the inferior angle of the scapula. It anastomoses with the lateral thoracic, the intercostals, and the descending branch of the transverse cervical and ends in the neighboring muscles.

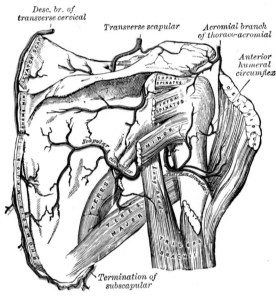

FIG. 515.—The scapular and circumflex arteries.

The **Scapular Circumflex Artery** (*a. circumflexa scapulæ; dorsalis scapulæ artery*) is generally larger than the continuation of the subscapular. It curves around the axillary border of the scapula, traversing the space between the Subscapularis above, the Teres major below, and the long head of the Triceps laterally (Fig. 515); it enters the infraspinous fossa under cover of the Teres minor, and anastomoses with the transverse scapular artery and the descending branch of the transverse cervical. In its course it gives off two branches: one (*infrascapular*) enters the subscapular fossa beneath the Subscapularis, which it supplies, anastomosing with the transverse scapular artery and the descending branch of the transverse cervical; the other is continued along the axillary border of the scapula, between the Teres major and minor, and at the dorsal surface of the inferior angle anastomoses with the descending branch of the transverse cervical. In addition to these, small branches are distributed to the back part of the Deltoideus and the long head of the Triceps brachii, anastomosing with an ascending branch of the a. profunda brachii.

5. The **posterior humeral circumflex artery** (*a. circumflexa humeri posterior; posterior circumflex artery*) (Fig. 515) *arises* from the axillary artery at the lower border of the Subscapularis, and runs backward with the axillary nerve through the quadrangular space bounded by the Subscapularis and Teres minor above, the Teres major below, the long head of the Triceps brachii medially, and the surgical neck of the humerus laterally. It winds around the neck of the humerus and is distributed to the Deltoideus and shoulder-joint, anastomosing with the anterior humeral circumflex and profunda brachii.

6. The **anterior humeral circumflex artery** (*a. circumflexa humeri anterior; anterior circumflex artery*) (Fig. 515), considerably smaller than the posterior, *arises* nearly opposite it, from the lateral side of the axillary artery. It runs horizontally, beneath the Coracobrachialis and short head of the Biceps brachii, in front of the neck of the humerus. On reaching the intertubercular sulcus, it gives off a branch which

ascends in the sulcus to supply the head of the humerus and the shoulder-joint. The trunk of the vessel is then continued onward beneath the long head of the Biceps brachii and the Deltoideus, and anastomoses with the posterior humeral circumflex artery. The anterior humeral circumflex artery often arises in common with the posterior humeral circumflex, or may be represented by three or four very small branches.

The Brachial Artery (A. Brachialis) (Fig. 516).

The **brachial artery** commences at the lower margin of the tendon of the Teres major, and, passing down the arm, ends about 1 cm. below the bend of the elbow, where it divides into the **radial and ulnar arteries.** At first the brachial artery lies medial to the humerus; but as it runs down the arm it gradually gets in front of the bone, and at the bend of the elbow it lies midway between its two epicondyles.

Relations.—The artery is superficial throughout its entire extent, being covered, *in front*, by the integument and the superficial and deep fasciæ; the lacertus fibrosus (*bicipital fascia*) lies in front of it opposite the elbow and separates it from the vena mediana cubiti; the median nerve crosses from its lateral to its medial side opposite the insertion of the Coracobrachialis. *Behind*, it is separated from the long head of the Triceps brachii by the radial nerve and a. profunda brachii. It then lies upon the medial head of the Triceps brachii, next upon the insertion of the Coracobrachialis, and lastly on the Brachialis. *Laterally*, it is in relation above with the median nerve and the Coracobrachialis, below with the Biceps brachii, the two muscles overlapping the artery to a considerable extent. *Medially*, its upper half is in relation with the medial antebrachial cutaneous and ulnar nerves, its lower half with the median nerve. The basilic vein lies on its medial side, but is separated from it in the lower part of the arm by the deep fascia. The artery is accompanied by two venæ comitantes, which lie in close contact with it, and are connected together at intervals by short transverse branches.

The **Antecubital Fossa.**—At the bend of the elbow the brachial artery sinks deeply into a triangular interval, the **antecubital fossa.** The base of the triangle is directed

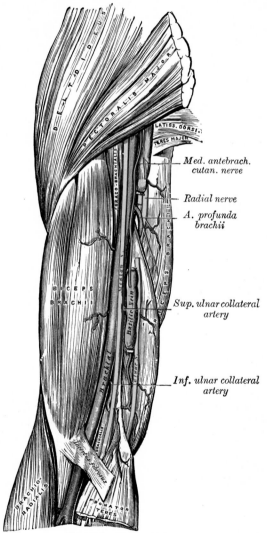

*Med. antebrach.
cutan. nerve*

Radial nerve

*A. profunda
brachii*

*Sup. ulnar collateral
artery*

*Inf. ulnar collateral
artery*

FIG. 516.—The brachial artery.

upward, and is represented by a line connecting the two epicondyles of the humerus; the sides are formed by the medial edge of the Brachioradialis and the lateral margin of the Pronator teres; the floor is formed by the Brachialis and Supinator. This space contains the brachial artery, with its accompanying veins; the radial and ulnar arteries; the median nerve; and the tendon of the Biceps brachii. The brachial artery occupies the middle of the space, and divides opposite the neck of the radius into the radial and ulnar arteries; it is covered, *in front*, by the integument, the superficial fascia, and the vena mediana cubiti, the last being separated from the artery by the lacertus fibrosus. *Behind* it is

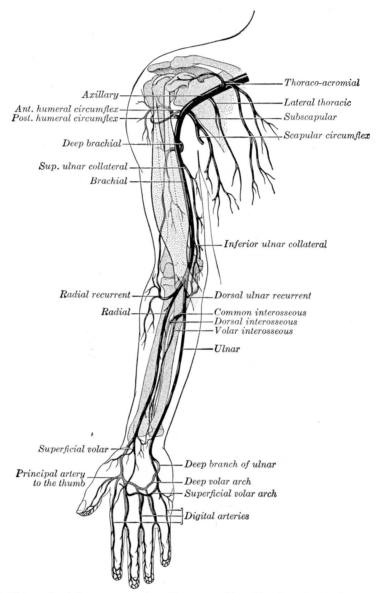

FIG. 517.—The arteries of the upper extremity. The pattern of branching shown in this diagram is probably the most frequent type.

the Brachialis which separates it from the elbow-joint. The median nerve lies close to the medial side of the artery, above, but is separated from it below by the ulnar head of the Pronator teres. The tendon of the Biceps brachii lies to the lateral side of the artery.

The radial nerve lies normally just outside the fossa between the Supinator and the Brachioradialis, but may be exposed through the fossa by drawing the Brachioradialis laterally.

Variations of the Brachial Artery.—The brachial artery, accompanied by the median nerve may leave the medial border of the Biceps brachii, and descend toward the medial epicondyle of the humerus; in such cases it usually passes behind the *supracondylar process* of the humerus, from which a fibrous arch is thrown over the artery; it then runs beneath or through the substance of the Pronator teres, to the bend of the elbow. This variation bears considerable analogy with the normal condition of the artery in some of the carnivora; it has been referred to in the description of the humerus (p. 189).

A frequent variation is the superficial brachial artery, which may continue into the forearm to form a superficial antebrachial artery. The superficial brachial may rejoin the brachial distally. Frequently the brachial artery divides at a higher level than usual, and the vessels concerned in this high division are three, viz., radial, ulnar, and interosseous. Most frequently the radial is given off high up, the other limb of the bifurcation consisting of the ulnar and interosseous; in some instances the ulnar arises above the ordinary level, and the radial and interosseous form the other limb of the division; occasionally the interosseous arises high up.

Sometimes, long slender vessels, *vasa aberrantia*, connect the brachial or the axillary artery with one of the arteries of the forearm, or branches from them. These vessels usually join the radial.

Collateral Circulation.—After the application of a ligature to the brachial artery in the upper third of the arm, the circulation is carried on by branches from the humeral circumflex and subscapular arteries anastomosing with ascending branches from the profunda brachii. If the artery be tied *below* the origin of the profunda brachii and superior ulnar collateral, the circulation is maintained by the branches of these two arteries anastomosing with the inferior ulnar collateral, the radial and ulnar recurrents, and the dorsal interosseous.

Branches.—The branches of the brachial artery are:

Profunda Brachii.   Superior Ulnar Collateral.
Nutrient.   Inferior Ulnar Collateral.
                            Muscular.

1. The **arteria profunda brachii** (*superior profunda artery*), the largest branch, *arises* from the medial and back part of the brachial, just below the lower border of the Teres major. It passes deeply into the arm between the long and lateral heads of the Triceps brachii and then accompanies the radial nerve in the spiral groove between the lateral and medial heads of the Triceps, on the posterior aspect of the humerus, and terminates by dividing into the radial collateral and the middle collateral branches. It gives muscular branches to the Deltoideus and to the other muscles between which it lies. An occasional **nutrient artery** enters the humerus posterior to the deltoid tuberosity. The **ascending branch** runs proximally between the long and lateral heads of the Triceps to anastomose with the posterior humeral circumflex artery. The **radial collateral branch**, frequently described as the terminal portion of the profunda, continues with the radial nerve into the forearm. It lies deep to the lateral head of the Triceps until it reaches the lateral supracondylar ridge where it pierces the lateral intermuscular septum, descends between the Brachioradialis and the Brachialis to the volar aspect of the lateral epicondyle, and ends by anastomosing with the radial recurrent artery. Just before it pierces the intermuscular septum, it gives off a branch which descends to the posterior aspect of the lateral epicondyle and there joins the anastomosis about the olecranon. The **middle collateral** branch enters the substance of the long and medial heads of the Triceps and descends along the posterior aspect of the humerus to the elbow where it anastomoses with the interosseous recurrent and joins the anastomosis about the olecranon.

2. The **nutrient artery** (*a. nutricia humeri*) of the body of the humerus arises about the middle of the arm and enters the nutrient canal near the insertion of the Coracobrachialis.

3. The **superior ulnar collateral artery** (*a. collateralis ulnaris superior; inferior profunda artery*), of small size, *arises* from the brachial a little below the middle of the arm; it frequently springs from the upper part of the a. profunda brachii. It pierces the medial intermuscular septum, and descends on the surface of the medial head of the Triceps brachii to the space between the medial epicondyle and

olecranon, accompanied by the ulnar nerve, and ends under the Flexor carpi ulnaris by anastomosing with the posterior ulnar recurrent, and inferior ulnar collateral. It sometimes sends a branch in front of the medial epicondyle, to anastomose with the anterior ulnar recurrent.

4. The **inferior ulnar collateral artery** (*a. collateralis ulnaris inferior; anastomotica magna artery*) *arises* about 5 cm. above the elbow. It passes medialward upon the Brachialis, and piercing the medial intermuscular septum, winds around the back of the humerus between the Triceps brachii and the bone, forming, by its junction with the profunda brachii, an arch above the olecranon fossa. As the vessel lies on the Brachialis, it gives off branches which ascend to join the superior ulnar collateral: others descend in front of the medial epicondyle, to anastomose with the anterior ulnar recurrent. Behind the medial epicondyle a branch anastomoses with the superior ulnar collateral and posterior ulnar recurrent arteries.

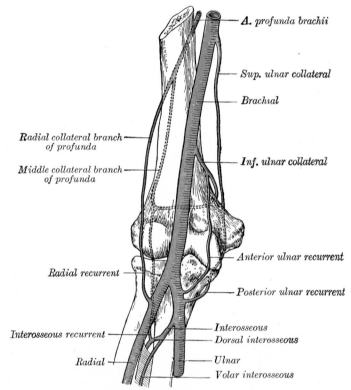

A. profunda brachii

Sup. ulnar collateral

Brachial

Radial collateral branch of profunda

Middle collateral branch of profunda

Inf. ulnar collateral

Anterior ulnar recurrent

Radial recurrent

Posterior ulnar recurrent

Interosseous recurrent

Interosseous
Dorsal interosseous

Radial

Ulnar
Volar interosseous

Fig. 518.—Diagram of the anastomosis around the elbow-joint.

5. The **muscular branches** (*rami musculares*), three or four in number, are distributed to the Coracobrachialis, Biceps brachii, and Brachialis.

The Anastomosis Around the Elbow-joint (Fig. 518).—The vessels engaged in this anastomosis may be conveniently divided into those *in front* of and those *behind* the medial and lateral epicondyles of the humerus. The branches anastomosing *in front* of the medial epicondyle are: the anterior branch of the inferior ulnar collateral, the anterior ulnar recurrent, and the anterior branch of the superior ulnar collateral. Those *behind* the medial epicondyle are: the inferior ulnar collateral, the posterior ulnar recurrent, and the posterior branch of the superior ulnar collateral. The branches anastomosing *in front* of the lateral epicondyle are: the radial recurrent and the radial collateral branch of the profunda brachii. Those *behind* the lateral epicondyle (perhaps better described as situated between the lateral epicondyle and the olecranon) are: the inferior ulnar collateral, the interosseous recurrent, and the middle collateral branch of the profunda brachii. There is also an arch of anastomosis above the olecranon, formed by the interosseous recurrent joining with the inferior ulnar collateral and posterior ulnar recurrent (Fig. 521).

The Radial Artery (A. Radialis)
(Fig. 519).

The **radial artery** appears, from its direction, to be a continuation of the brachial, but it is smaller in caliber than the ulnar. It commences at the bifurcation of the brachial, just below the bend of the elbow, and passes along the radial side of the forearm to the wrist. It then winds backward, around the lateral side of the carpus, beneath the tendons of the Abductor pollicis longus and Extensores pollicis longus and brevis to the upper end of the space between the metacarpal bones of the thumb and index finger. Finally it passes forward between the two heads of the first Interosseous dorsalis, into the palm of the hand, where it crosses the metacarpal bones and at the ulnar side of the hand unites with the deep volar branch of the ulnar artery to form the deep volar arch.

Relations.—(*a*) *In the forearm* the artery extends from the neck of the radius to the forepart of the styloid process, being placed to the medial side of the body of the bone above, and in front of it below. Its upper part is overlapped by the fleshy belly of the Brachioradialis; the rest of the artery is superficial, being covered by the integument and the superficial and deep fasciæ. In its course downward, it lies upon the tendon of the Biceps brachii, the Supinator, the Pronator teres, the radial origin of the Flexor digitorum sublimis, the Flexor pollicis longus, the Pronator quadratus, and the lower end of the radius. In the upper third of its course it lies between the

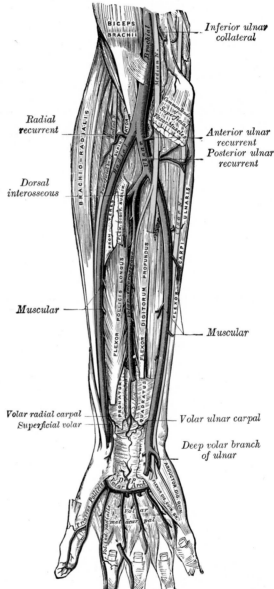

Fig. 519.—Ulnar and radial arteries. Deep view.

Brachioradialis and the Pronator teres; in the lower two-thirds, between the tendons of the Brachioradialis and Flexor carpi radialis. The superficial branch of the radial nerve is close to the lateral side of the artery in the middle third of its course; and some filaments of the lateral antebrachial cutaneous nerve run along the lower part of the artery as it winds around the wrist. The vessel is accompanied by a pair of venæ comitantes throughout its whole course.

(*b*) *At the wrist* the artery reaches the back of the carpus by passing between the radial collateral ligament of the wrist and the tendons of the Abductor pollicis longus and Extensor pollicis brevis. It then descends on the navicular and greater multangular bones, and before disappearing between the heads of the first Interosseus dorsalis is crossed by the tendon of the Extensor pollicis longus. In the interval between the two Extensores pollicis it is crossed by the digital rami of the superficial branch of the radial nerve which go to the thumb and index finger.

(c) *In the hand*, it passes from the upper end of the first interosseous space, between the heads of the first Interosseus dorsalis, transversely across the palm between the Adductor pollicis obliquus and Adductor pollicis transversus, but sometimes piercing the latter muscle, to the base of the metacarpal bone of the little finger, where it anastomoses with the deep volar branch from the ulnar artery, completing the **deep volar arch** (Fig. 519).

Variations.—The origin of the radial artery is, in nearly one case in eight, higher than usual. In the forearm it deviates less frequently from its normal position than the ulnar. It has been found lying on the deep fascia instead of beneath it. It has also been observed on the surface of the Brachioradialis, instead of under its medial border; and in turning around the wrist, it has been seen lying on, instead of beneath, the Extensor tendons of the thumb. A large *median* artery may replace the radial in the formation of the volar arches.

Branches.—The branches of the radial artery may be divided into three groups, corresponding with the three regions in which the vessel is situated.

In the Forearm.	*At the Wrist.*	*In the Hand.*
Radial Recurrent.	Dorsal Carpal.	Princeps Pollicis.
Muscular.	First Dorsal Metacarpal.	Volaris Indicis Radialis.
Volar Carpal.		Volar Metacarpal.
Superficial Volar.		Perforating.
		Recurrent.

The **radial recurrent artery** (*a. recurrens radialis*) *arises* immediately below the elbow. It ascends between the branches of the radial nerve, lying on the Supinator and then between the Brachioradialis and Brachialis, supplying these muscles and the elbow-joint, and anastomosing with the radial collateral branch of the profunda brachii.

The **muscular branches** (*rami musculares*) are distributed to the muscles on the radial side of the forearm.

The **volar carpal branch** (*ramus carpeus volaris; anterior radial carpal artery*) is a small vessel which *arises* near the lower border of the Pronator quadratus, and, running across the front of the carpus, anastomoses with the volar carpal branch of the ulnar artery. This anastomosis is joined by a branch from the volar interosseous above, and by recurrent branches from the deep volar arch below, thus forming a **volar carpal net-work** which supplies the articulations of the wrist.

The **superficial volar branch** (*ramus volaris superficialis; superficialis volæ artery*) *arises* from the radial artery, where this vessel is about to wind around the lateral side of the wrist. Running forward, it passes through, occasionally over, the muscles of the ball of the thumb, which it supplies, and sometimes anastomoses with the terminal portion of the ulnar artery, completing the **superficial volar arch.** This vessel varies considerably in size: usually it is very small, and ends in the muscles of the thumb; sometimes it is as large as the continuation of the radial.

The **dorsal carpal branch** (*ramus carpeus dorsalis; posterior radial carpal artery*) is a small vessel which *arises* beneath the Extensor tendons of the thumb; crossing the carpus transversely toward the medial border of the hand, it anastomoses with the dorsal carpal branch of the ulnar and with the volar and dorsal interosseous arteries to form a **dorsal carpal network.** From this network are given off three slender **dorsal metacarpal arteries,** which run downward on the second, third, and fourth Interossei dorsales and bifurcate into the dorsal digital branches for the supply of the adjacent sides of the middle, ring, and little fingers respectively, communicating with the proper volar digital branches of the superficial volar arch. Near their origins they anastomose with the deep volar arch by the **superior perforating arteries,** and near their points of bifurcation with the common volar digital vessels of the superficial volar arch by the **inferior perforating arteries.**

The **first dorsal metacarpal** *arises* just before the radial artery passes between the two heads of the first Interosseous dorsalis and divides almost immediately into two branches which supply the adjacent sides of the thumb and index finger; the radial side of the thumb receives a branch directly from the radial artery.

The **arteria princeps pollicis** *arises* from the radial just as it turns medialward to the deep part of the hand; it descends between the first Interosseous dorsalis and Adductor pollicis obliquus, along the ulnar side of the metacarpal bone of the thumb to the base of the first phalanx, where it lies beneath the tendon of the Flexor pollicis longus and divides into two branches. These make their appearance between the medial and lateral insertions of the Adductor pollicis obliquus, and run along the sides of the thumb, forming on the volar surface of the last phalanx an arch, from which branches are distributed to the integument and subcutaneous tissue of the thumb.

The **arteria volaris indicis radialis** (*radialis indicis artery*) *arises* close to the preceding, descends between the first Interosseus dorsalis and Adductor pollicis transversus, and runs along the radial side of the index finger to its extremity, where it anastomoses with the proper digital artery, supplying the ulnar side of the finger. At the lower border of the Adductor pollicis transversus this vessel anastomoses with the princeps pollicis, and gives a communicating branch to the superficial volar arch. The a. princeps pollicis and a. volaris indicis radialis may spring from a common trunk termed the **first volar metacarpal artery.**

The **deep volar arch** (*arcus volaris profundus; deep palmar arch*) (Fig. 519) is formed by the anastomosis of the terminal part of the radial artery with the deep volar branch of the ulnar. It lies upon the carpal extremities of the metacarpal bones and on the Interossei, being covered by the Adductor pollicis obliquus, the Flexor tendons of the fingers, and the Lumbricales. The deep volar arch lies deep to the ulnar nerve in 63 per cent. of cases; superficial, that is to say volar to the ulnar nerve, in 34 per cent. of cases. It is occasionally (2.5 per cent.) double and encircles the ulnar nerve.

The **volar metacarpal arteries** (*aa. metacarpeæ volares; palmar interosseous arteries*), three or four in number, arise from the convexity of the deep volar arch; they run distally upon the Interossei, and anastomose at the clefts of the fingers with the common digital branches of the superficial volar arch.

The **perforating branches** (*rami perforantes*), three in number, pass backward from the deep volar arch, through the second, third, and fourth interosseous spaces and between the heads of the corresponding Interossei dorsales, to anastomose with the dorsal metacarpal arteries.

The **recurrent branches** *arise* from the concavity of the deep volar arch. They ascend in front of the wrist, supply the intercarpal articulations, and end in the volar carpal network.

The Ulnar Artery (A. Ulnaris) (Fig. 519).

The **ulnar artery**, the larger of the two terminal branches of the brachial, begins a little below the bend of the elbow, and, passing obliquely downward, reaches the ulnar side of the forearm at a point about midway between the elbow and the wrist. It then runs along the ulnar border to the wrist, crosses the transverse carpal ligament on the radial side of the pisiform bone, and immediately beyond this bone divides into two branches, which enter into the formation of the superficial and deep volar arches.

Relations.—(*a*) *In the forearm.*—In its *upper half*, it is deeply seated, being covered by the Pronator teres, Flexor carpi radialis, Palmaris longus, and Flexor digitorum sublimis; it lies upon the Brachialis and Flexor digitorum profundus. The median nerve is in relation with the medial side of the artery for about 2.5 cm. and then crosses the vessel, being separated from it by the ulnar head of the Pronator teres. In the *lower half* of the forearm it lies upon the Flexor digitorum profundus, being covered by the integument and the superficial and deep fasciæ, and placed between the Flexor carpi ulnaris and Flexor digitorum sublimis. It is accompanied by two venæ comitantes, and is overlapped in its middle third by the Flexor carpi ulnaris; the ulnar nerve lies on the medial side of the lower two-thirds of the artery, and the palmar cutaneous branch of the nerve descends on the lower part of the vessel to the palm of the hand.

(b) *At the wrist* (Fig. 519) the ulnar artery is covered by the integument and the volar carpal ligament, and lies upon the transverse carpal ligament. On its medial side is the pisiform bone, and, somewhat behind the artery, the ulnar nerve.

Variations.—The ulnar artery varies in its origin in the proportion of about one in thirteen cases; it may arise about 5 to 7 cm. below the elbow, but frequently higher. Variations in the position of this vessel are more common than in the radial. When its origin is normal, the course of the vessel is rarely changed. When it arises high up, it is almost invariably superficial to the Flexor muscles in the forearm, lying commonly beneath the fascia, more rarely between the fascia and integument. In a few cases, its position was subcutaneous in the upper part of the forearm, and subaponeurotic in the lower part.

Branches.—The branches of the ulnar artery may be arranged in the following groups:

In the Forearm { Anterior Recurrent.
Posterior Recurrent.
Common Interosseous.
Muscular.

At the Wrist { Volar Carpal.
Dorsal Carpal.

In the Hand { Deep Volar.
Superficial Volar Arch.

The **anterior ulnar recurrent artery** (*a. recurrens ulnaris anterior*) *arises* immediately below the elbow-joint, runs upward between the Brachialis and Pronator teres, supplies twigs to those muscles, and, in front of the medial epicondyle, anastomoses with the superior and inferior ulnar collateral arteries.

The **posterior ulnar recurrent artery** (*a. recurrens ulnaris posterior*) is much larger, and *arises* somewhat lower than the preceding. It passes backward and medialward on the Flexor digitorum profundus, behind the Flexor digitorum sublimis, and ascends behind the medial epicondyle of the humerus. Between this process and the olecranon, it lies beneath the Flexor carpi ulnaris, and ascending between the

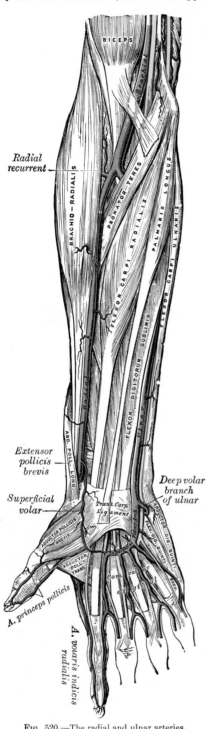

Fig. 520.—The radial and ulnar arteries.

heads of that muscle, in relation with the ulnar nerve, it supplies the neighboring muscles and the elbow-joint, and anastomoses with the superior and inferior ulnar collateral and the interosseous recurrent arteries (Fig. 521).

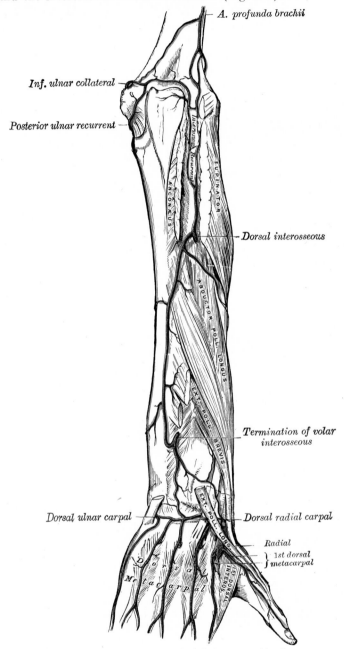

FIG. 521.—Arteries of the back of the forearm and hand.

The **common interosseous artery** (*a. interossea communis*) (Fig. 519), about 1 cm. in length, *arises* immediately below the tuberosity of the radius, and, passing backward to the upper border of the interosseous membrane, divides into two branches, the **volar** and **dorsal interosseous** arteries.

The **Volar Interosseous Artery** (*a. interossea volaris; anterior interosseous artery*) (Fig. 519), passes down the forearm on the volar surface of the interosseous membrane. It is accompanied by the volar interosseous branch of the median nerve, and overlapped by the contiguous margins of the Flexor digitorum profundus and Flexor pollicis longus, giving off **muscular branches**, and the **nutrient arteries** of the radius and ulna. At the upper border of the Pronator quadratus it pierces the interosseous membrane and reaches the back of the forearm, where it anastomoses with the dorsal interosseous artery (Fig. 521). It then descends, in company with the terminal portion of the dorsal interosseous nerve, to the back of the wrist to join the dorsal carpal net-work. The volar interosseous artery gives off a slender branch, the **arteria mediana**, which accompanies the median nerve, and gives offsets to its substance; this artery is sometimes much enlarged, and runs with the nerve into the palm of the hand. Before it pierces the interosseous membrane the volar interosseous sends a branch downward behind the Pronator quadratus to join the volar carpal network.

The **Dorsal Interosseous Artery** (*a. interossea dorsalis; posterior interosseous artery*) (Fig. 521) passes backward either over or between the oblique cord and the upper border of the interosseous membrane. It appears between the contiguous borders of the Supinator and the Abductor pollicis longus, and runs down the back of the forearm between the superficial and deep layers of muscles, to both of which it distributes branches. Upon the Abductor pollicis longus and the Extensor pollicis brevis, it is accompanied by the dorsal interosseous nerve. At the lower part of the forearm it anastomoses with the termination of the volar interosseous artery, and with the dorsal carpal network. It gives off, near its origin, the **interosseous recurrent artery,** which ascends to the interval between the lateral epicondyle and olecranon, on or through the fibers of the Supinator, but beneath the Anconæus, and anastomoses with the middle collateral branch of the profunda brachii, the posterior ulnar recurrent and the inferior ulnar collateral.

The **muscular branches** (*rami musculares*) are distributed to the muscles along the ulnar side of the forearm.

The **volar carpal branch** (*ramus carpeus volares; anterior ulnar carpal artery*) is a small vessel which crosses the front of the carpus beneath the tendons of the Flexor digitorum profundus, and anastomoses with the corresponding branch of the radial artery.

The **dorsal carpal branch** (*ramus carpeus dorsalis; posterior ulnar carpal artery*) *arises* immediately above the pisiform bone, and winds backward beneath the tendon of the Flexor carpi ulnaris; it passes across the dorsal surface of the carpus beneath the Extensor tendons, to anastomose with a corresponding branch of the radial artery. Immediately after its origin, it gives off a small branch, which runs along the ulnar side of the fifth metacarpal bone, and supplies the ulnar side of the dorsal surface of the little finger.

The **deep volar branch** (*ramus volaris profundus; profunda branch*) (Fig. 520) passes between the Abductor digiti quinti and Flexor digiti quinti brevis and through the origin of the Opponens digiti quinti; it anastomoses with the radial artery, and completes the deep volar arch.

The **superficial volar arch** (*arcus volaris superficialis; superficial palmar arch*) (Fig. 520) is formed by the ulnar artery, and is usually completed by a branch from the a. volaris indicis radialis, but sometimes by the superficial volar, the median, or by a branch from the a. princeps pollicis of the radial artery. The arch curves across the palm, its convexity downward.

Relations.—The superficial volar arch is covered by the skin, the Palmaris brevis, and the palmar aponeurosis. It lies upon the transverse carpal ligament, the Flexor digiti quinti brevis and Opponens digiti quinti, the tendons of the Flexor digitorum sublimis, the Lumbricales, and the divisions of the median and ulnar nerves.

Three **Common Volar Digital Arteries** (*aa. digitales volares communes; palmar digital arteries*) (Fig. 520) *arise* from the convexity of the arch and proceed downward on the second, third, and fourth Lumbricales. Each receives the corresponding volar metacarpal artery and then divides into a pair of **proper volar digital arteries** (*aa. digitales volares propriœ; collateral digital arteries*) which run along the contiguous sides of the index, middle, ring, and little fingers, behind the corresponding digital nerves; they anastomose freely in the subcutaneous tissue of the finger tips and by smaller branches near the interphalangeal joints. Each gives off a couple of dorsal branches which anastomose with the dorsal digital arteries, and supply the soft parts on the back of the second and third phalanges, including the matrix of the finger-nail. The proper volar digital artery for medial side of the little finger springs from the ulnar artery under cover of the Palmaris brevis.

THE ARTERIES OF THE TRUNK.

THE DESCENDING AORTA.

The **descending aorta** is divided into two portions, the **thoracic** and **abdominal,** in correspondence with the two great cavities of the trunk in which it is situated

The Thoracic Aorta (Aorta Thoracalis) (Fig. 522).

The **thoracic aorta** is contained in the posterior mediastinal cavity. It begins at the lower border of the fourth thoracic vertebra where it is continuous with the aortic arch, and ends in front of the lower border of the twelfth at the aortic hiatus in the diaphragm. At its commencement, it is situated on the left of the vertebral column; it approaches the median line as it descends; and, at its termination, lies directly in front of the column. The vessel describes a curve which is concave forward, and as the branches given off from it are small, its diminution in size is inconsiderable.

Relations.—It is in relation, *anteriorly*, from above downward, with the root of the left lung, the pericardium, the esophagus, and the diaphragm; *posteriorly*, with the vertebral column and the hemiazygos veins; on the *right side*, with the azygos vein and thoracic duct; on the *left side*, with the left pleura and lung. The esophagus, with its accompanying plexus of nerves, lies on the right side of the aorta above; but at the lower part of the thorax it is placed in front of the aorta, and, close to the diaphragm, is situated on its left side.

Branches of the Thoracic Aorta.—

Visceral	Pericardial. Bronchial. Esophageal. Mediastinal.	*Parietal*	Intercostal. Subcostal. Superior Phrenic.

The **pericardial branches** (*rami pericardiaci*) consist of a few small vessels which are distributed to the posterior surface of the pericardium.

The **bronchial arteries** (*aa. bronchiales*) vary in number, size, and origin. There is as a rule only one **right bronchial artery**, which *arises* from the first aortic intercostal, or from the upper left bronchial artery. The **left bronchial arteries** are usually two in number, and *arise* from the thoracic aorta. The upper left bronchial arises opposite the fifth thoracic vertebra, the lower just below the level of the left bronchus. Each vessel runs on the back part of its bronchus, dividing and subdividing along the bronchial tubes, supplying them, the areolar tissue of the lungs, the bronchial lymph glands, and the esophagus.

The **esophageal arteries** (*aa. œsophageæ*) four or five in number, *arise* from the front of the aorta, and pass obliquely downward to the esophagus, forming a chain of anastomoses along that tube, anastomosing with the esophageal branches of the inferior thyroid arteries above, and with ascending branches from the left inferior phrenic and left gastric arteries below.

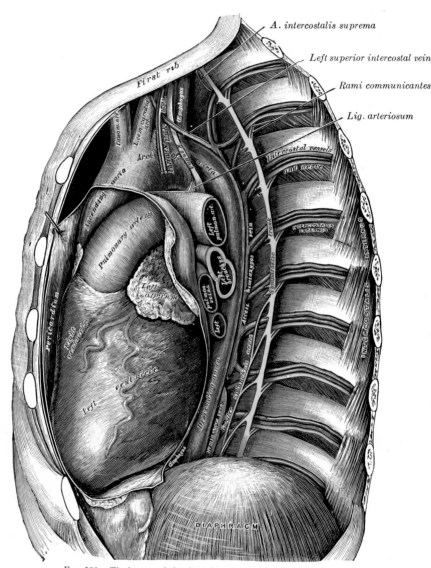

Fig. 522.—The heart and the thoracic aorta. Left lateral aspect.

The **mediastinal branches** (*rami mediastinales*) are numerous small vessels which supply the lymph glands and loose areolar tissue in the posterior mediastinum.

Intercostal Arteries (*aa. intercostales*).—There are usually nine pairs of aortic intercostal arteries. They *arise* from the back of the aorta, and are distributed to the lower nine intercostal spaces, the first two spaces being supplied by the highest intercostal artery, a branch of the costocervical trunk of the subclavian. The right aortic intercostals are longer than the left, on account of the position of the aorta on the left side of the vertebral column; they pass across the vertebræ behind the esophagus, thoracic duct, and vena azygos, and are covered by the right lung and pleura. The **left** aortic intercostals run backward on the sides of the vertebræ and are covered by the left lung and pleura; the upper two vessels are crossed by the highest left intercostal vein, the lower vessels by the hemiazygos veins. The further course of the intercostal arteries is practically the same on both sides. Opposite the heads of the ribs the sympathetic trunk passes downward in front of them, and the splanchnic nerves also descend in front by the lower arteries. Each artery then divides into an **anterior** and a **posterior ramus.**

The **Anterior Ramus** crosses the corresponding intercostal space obliquely toward the angle of the upper rib, and thence is continued forward in the costal groove. It is placed at first between the pleura and the posterior intercostal membrane, then it pierces this membrane, and lies between it and the Intercostalis externus as far as the angle of the rib; from this onward it runs between the Intercostalis externus and Intercostalis internus, and anastomoses in front with the intercostal branch of the internal mammary or the musculophrenic. Each artery is accompanied by a vein and a nerve, the former being above and the latter below the artery, except in the upper spaces, where the nerve is at first above the artery. The first aortic intercostal artery anastomoses with the intercostal branch of the costocervical trunk, and may form the chief supply of the second intercostal space. The lower two intercostal arteries are continued anteriorly from the intercostal spaces into the abdominal wall, and anastomose with the subcostal, superior epigastric, and lumbar arteries.

Branches.—The anterior rami give off the following branches:

Collateral Intercostal.	Lateral Cutaneous.
Muscular.	Mammary.

The **collateral intercostal branch** comes off from the intercostal artery near the angle of the rib, and descends to the upper border of the rib below, along which it courses to anastomose with the intercostal branch of the internal mammary.

Muscular branches are given to the Intercostales and Pectorales and to the Serratus anterior; they anastomose with the highest and lateral thoracic branches of the axillary artery.

The **lateral cutaneous branches** accompany the lateral cutaneous branches of the thoracic nerves.

Mammary branches are given off by the vessels in the third, fourth, and fifth spaces. They supply the mamma, and increase considerably in size during the period of lactation.

The **Posterior Ramus** runs backward through a space which is bounded above and below by the necks of the ribs, medially by the body of a vertebra, and laterally by an anterior costotransverse ligament. It gives off a **spinal branch** which enters the vertebral canal through the intervertebral foramen and is distributed to the medulla spinalis and its membranes and the vertebræ. It then courses over the transverse process with the posterior division of the thoracic nerve, supplies branches to the muscles of the back and cutaneous branches which accompany the corresponding cutaneous branches of the posterior division of the nerve.

The **subcostal arteries,** so named because they lie below the last ribs, constitute the lowest pair of branches derived from the thoracic aorta, and are in series with the intercostal arteries. Each passes along the lower border of the twelfth rib behind the kidney and in front of the Quadratus lumborum muscle, and is accompanied by the twelfth thoracic nerve. It then pierces the posterior aponeurosis of the Transversus abdominis, and, passing forward between this muscle and the

Obliquus internus, anastomoses with the superior epigastric, lower intercostal, and lumbar arteries. Each subcostal artery gives off a posterior branch which has a distribution similar to that of the posterior ramus of an intercostal artery.

The **superior phrenic branches** are small and *arise* from the lower part of the thoracic aorta; they are distributed to the posterior part of the upper surface of the diaphragm, and anastomose with the musculophrenic and pericardiacophrenic arteries.

A small **aberrant artery** is sometimes found *arising* from the right side of the thoracic aorta near the origin of the right bronchial. It passes upward and to the right behind the trachea and the esophagus, and may anastomose with the highest right intercostal artery. It represents the remains of the right dorsal aorta, and in a small proportion of cases is enlarged to form the first part of the right subclavian artery.

The Abdominal Aorta (Aorta Abdominalis) (Fig. 523).

The **abdominal aorta** begins at the aortic hiatus of the diaphragm, in front of the lower border of the body of the last thoracic vertebra, and, descending in front of the vertebral column, ends on the body of the fourth lumbar vertebra, commonly a little to the left of the mid-line, by dividing into the two common iliac arteries. It diminishes rapidly in size, in consequence of the many large branches which it gives off. As it lies upon the bodies of the vertebræ, the curve which it describes is convex forward, the summit of the convexity corresponding to the third lumbar vertebra.

Relations.—The abdominal aorta is covered, *anteriorly*, by the lesser omentum and stomach, behind which are the branches of the celiac artery and the celiac plexus; below these, by the lienal vein, the pancreas, the left renal vein, the inferior part of the duodenum, the mesentery, and aortic plexus. *Posteriorly*, it is separated from the lumbar vertebræ and intervertebral fibrocartilages by the anterior longitudinal ligament and left lumbar veins. On the *right side* it is in relation above with the azygos vein, cisterna chyli, thoracic duct, and the right crus of the diaphragm—the last separating it from the upper part of the inferior vena cava, and from the right celiac ganglion; the inferior vena cava is in contact with the aorta below. On the *left side* are the left crus of the diaphragm, the left celiac ganglion, the ascending part of the duodenum, and some coils of the small intestine.

Collateral Circulation.—The collateral circulation would be carried on by the anastomoses between the internal mammary and the inferior epigastric; by the free communication between the superior and inferior mesenterics, if the ligature were placed between these vessels; or by the anastomosis between the inferior mesenteric and the internal pudendal, when (as is more common) the point of ligature is below the origin of the inferior mesenteric; and possibly by the anastomoses of the lumbar arteries with the branches of the hypogastric.

Branches.—The branches of the abdominal aorta may be divided into three sets: visceral, parietal, and terminal.

Visceral Branches.	*Parietal Branches.*
Celiac.	Inferior Phrenics.
Superior Mesenteric.	Lumbars.
Inferior Mesenteric.	Middle Sacral.
Middle Suprarenals.	
Renals.	
Internal Spermatics.	*Terminal Branches.*
Ovarian (in the female).	Common Iliacs.

Of the visceral branches, the celiac artery and the superior and inferior mesenteric arteries are unpaired, while the suprarenals, renals, internal spermatics, and ovarian are paired. Of the parietal branches the inferior phrenics and lumbars are paired; the middle sacral is unpaired. The terminal branches are paired.

The **celiac artery** (*a. cœliaca; celiac axis*) (Figs. 524, 525) is a short thick trunk, about 1.25 cm. in length, which *arises* from the front of the aorta, just below the aortic hiatus of the diaphragm, and, passing nearly horizontally forward, divides into three large branches, the **left gastric**, the **hepatic**, and the **splenic**; it occasionally gives off one of the inferior phrenic arteries.

Relations.—The celiac artery is covered by the lesser omentum. On the *right side* it is in relation with the right celiac ganglion and the caudate process of the liver; on the *left side*, with the left celiac ganglion and the cardiac end of the stomach. *Below*, it is in relation to the upper border of the pancreas, and the lienal vein.

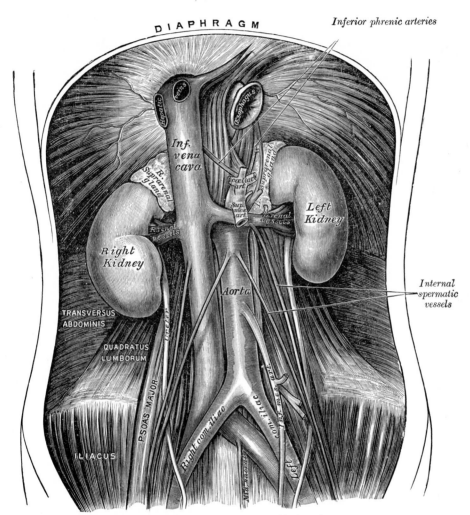

FIG. 523.—The abdominal aorta and its branches.

1. The **Left Gastric Artery** (*a. gastrica sinistra; gastric or coronary artery*), the smallest of the three branches of the celiac artery, passes upward and to the left, posterior to the omental bursa, to the cardiac orifice of the stomach. Here it distributes branches to the esophagus, which anastomose with the aortic esophageal arteries; others supply the cardiac part of the stomach, anastomosing with branches of the lienal artery. It then runs from left to right, along the lesser curvature of the stomach to the pylorus, between the layers of the lesser omentum; it gives branches to both surfaces of the stomach and anastomoses with the right gastric artery. The left gastric artery arises directly from the aorta in 7.5 per cent. of cases. In 17 per

cent. of cadavers (Adachi) the left gastric also gives off a left accessory hepatic artery.

2. The **Hepatic Artery** (*a. hepatica*) in the adult is intermediate in size between the left gastric and lienal; in the fetus, it is the largest of the three branches of the celiac artery. It is first directed forward and to the right, to the upper margin of the superior part of the duodenum, forming the lower boundary of the epiploic foramen (*foramen of Winslow*). It then crosses the portal vein anteriorly and ascends between the layers of the lesser omentum, and in front of the epiploic foramen, to the porta hepatis, where it divides into two branches, right and left, which supply the corresponding lobes of the liver, accompanying the ramifications of the portal vein and hepatic ducts. The hepatic artery, in its course along the right border of the lesser omentum, is in relation with the common bile-duct and portal vein, the duct lying to the right of the artery, and the vein behind. In 12 per cent. of cadavers there is an accessory right hepatic artery arising from the superior mesenteric artery.

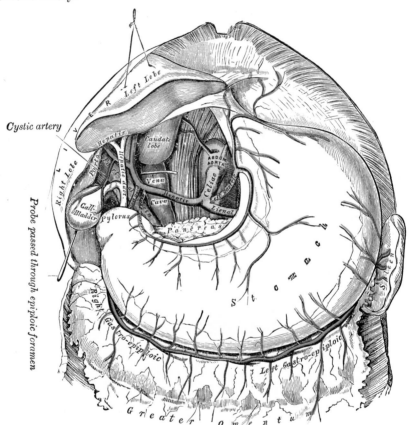

Fig. 524,—The celiac artery and its branches; the liver has been raised, and the lesser omentum and anterior layer of the greater omentum removed.

Its branches are:

> Right Gastric.
>
> Gastroduodenal { Right Gastroepiploic.
> { Superior Pancreaticoduodenal.
>
> Cystic.

The **right gastric artery** (*a. gastrica dextra; pyloric artery*) *arises* from the hepatic (or from the superior mesenteric in 12 per cent. of bodies) above the pylorus, descends to the pyloric end of the stomach, and passes from right to left along its lesser curvature, supplying it with branches, and anastomosing with the left gastric artery.

The **gastroduodenal artery** (*a. gastroduodenalis*) (Fig. 525) is a short but large branch, which descends, near the pylorus, between the superior part of the duodenum and the neck of the pancreas, and divides at the lower border of the duodenum into two branches, the **right gastroepiploic** and the **superior pancreaticoduodenal**. Before dividing it gives off two or three small branches to the pyloric end of the stomach and to the pancreas.

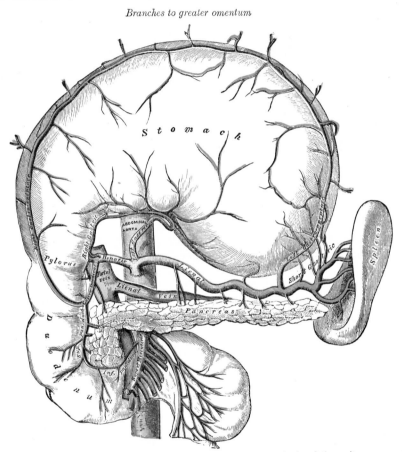

FIG. 525.—The celiac artery and its branches; the stomach has been raised and the peritoneum removed.

The **right gastroepiploic artery** (*a. gastroepiploica dextra*) runs from right to left along the greater curvature of the stomach, between the layers of the greater omentum, anastomosing with the left gastroepiploic branch of the lienal artery. Except at the pylorus, where it is in contact with the stomach, it lies about a finger's breadth from the greater curvature. This vessel gives off numerous branches, some of which ascend to supply both surfaces of the stomach, while others descend to supply the greater omentum and anastomose with branches of the middle colic.

The **superior pancreaticoduodenal artery** (*a. pancreaticoduodenalis superior*) descends between the contiguous margins of the duodenum and pancreas. It supplies both these organs, and anastomoses with the inferior pancreaticoduodenal branch of the superior mesenteric artery, and with the pancreatic branches of the lienal artery.

The **cystic artery** (*a. cystica*) (Fig. 524), usually a branch of the right hepatic, passes downward and forward along the neck of the gall-bladder, and divides into two branches, one of which ramifies on the free surface, the other on the attached surface of the gall-bladder.

3. The **Lienal** or **Splenic Artery** (*a. lienalis*), the largest branch of the celiac artery, is remarkable for the tortuosity of its course. It passes horizontally to the left side, behind the stomach and the omental bursa of the peritoneum, and along the upper border of the pancreas, accompanied by the lienal vein, which lies below it; it crosses in front of the upper part of the left kidney, and, on nearing the spleen, divides into branches, some of which enter the hilum of that organ between the two layers of the phrenicolienal ligament to be distributed to the tissues of the spleen; some are given to the pancreas, while others pass to the greater curvature of the stomach between the layers of the gastrolienal ligament. Its **branches** are:

Pancreatic.	Short Gastric.	Left Gastroepiploic.

The **pancreatic branches** (*rami pancreatici*) are numerous small vessels derived from the lienal as it runs behind the upper border of the pancreas, supplying its body and tail. One of these, larger than the rest, is sometimes given off near the tail of the pancreas; it runs from left to right near the posterior surface of the gland, following the course of the pancreatic duct, and is called the **arteria pancreatica magna.** These vessels anastomose with the pancreatic branches of the pancreatico-duodenal and superior mesenteric arteries.

The **short gastric arteries** (*aa. gastricæ breves; vasa brevia*) consist of from five to seven small branches, which *arise* from the end of the lienal artery, and from its terminal divisions. They pass from left to right, between the layers of the gastro-lienal ligament, and are distributed to the greater curvature of the stomach, anastomosing with branches of the left gastric and left gastroepiploic arteries.

The **left gastroepiploic artery** (*a. gastroepiploica sinistra*) the largest branch of the lienal, runs from left to right about a finger's breadth or more from the greater curvature of the stomach, between the layers of the greater omentum, and anastomoses with the right gastroepiploic. In its course it distributes several ascending branches to both surfaces of the stomach; others descend to supply the greater omentum and anastomose with branches of the middle colic.

The **superior mesenteric artery** (*a. mesenterica superior*) (Fig. 526) is a large vessel which supplies the whole length of the small intestine, except the superior part of the duodenum; it also supplies the cecum and the ascending part of the colon and about one-half of the transverse part of the colon. It arises from the front of the aorta, about 1.25 cm. below the celiac artery, at the level of the first lumbar vertebra, and is crossed at its origin by the lienal vein and the neck of the pancreas. It passes downward and forward, anterior to the processus uncinatus of the head of the pancreas and inferior part of the duodenum, and descends between the layers of the mesentery to the right iliac fossa, where, considerably diminished in size, it anastomoses with one of its own branches, viz., the ileocolic. In its course it crosses in front of the inferior vena cava, the right ureter and Psoas major, and forms an arch, the convexity of which is directed forward and downward to the left side, the concavity backward and upward to the right. It is accompanied by the superior mesenteric vein, which lies to its right side, and it is surrounded by the superior mesenteric plexus of nerves. Occasionally it arises from the aorta by a common trunk with the coeliac axis.

Branches.—Its branches are:

Inferior Pancreaticoduodenal.	Ileocolic.
Intestinal.	Right Colic.
Middle Colic.	

The **Inferior Pancreaticoduodenal Artery** (*a. pancreaticoduodenalis inferior*) is given off from the superior mesenteric or from its first intestinal branch, opposite the upper border of the inferior part of the duodenum. It courses to the right between the head of the pancreas and duodenum, and then ascends to anastomose with the superior pancreaticoduodenal artery. It distributes branches to the head of the pancreas and to the descending and inferior parts of the duodenum.

The **Intestinal Arteries** (*aa. intestinales; vasa intestini tenuis*) arise from the convex side of the superior mesenteric artery, are usually from twelve to fifteen in number, and are distributed to the jejunum and ileum. They run nearly parallel with

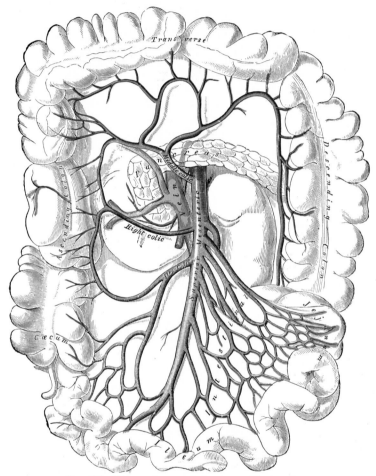

Fig. 526.—The superior mesenteric artery and its branches.

one another between the layers of the mesentery, each vessel dividing into two branches, which unite with adjacent branches, forming a series of arches, the convexities of which are directed toward the intestine (Fig. 527). From this first set of arches branches arise, which unite with similar branches from above and below, thus forming a second series of arches; from the lower branches of the artery, a third, a fourth, or even a fifth series of arches may be formed, diminishing in size the nearer they approach the intestine. In the short, upper part of the mesentery only one set of arches exists, but as the depth of the mesentery increases, second, third, fourth, or even fifth groups are developed. From the terminal arches numerous small straight vessels arise which encircle the intestine, upon

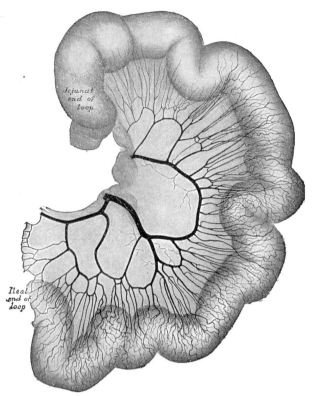

Fig. 527.—Loop of small intestine showing distribution of intestinal arteries. (From a preparation by Mr. Hamilton Drummond). The vessels were injected while the gut was *in situ;* the gut was then removed, and an *x*-ray photograph taken.

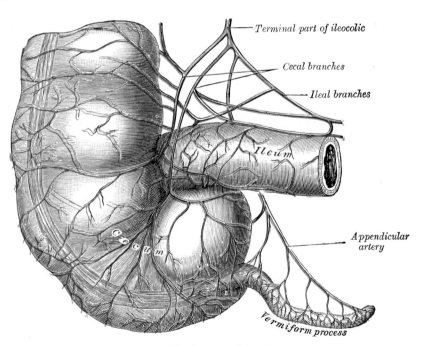

Fig. 528 —Arteries of cecum and vermiform process.

which they are distributed, ramifying between its coats. From the intestinal arteries small branches are given off to the lymph glands and other structures between the layers of the mesentery.

The **Ileocolic Artery** (*a. ileocolica*) is the lowest branch arising from the concavity of the superior mesenteric artery. It passes downward and to the right behind the peritoneum toward the right iliac fossa, where it divides into a superior and an inferior branch; the inferior anastomoses with the end of the superior mesenteric artery, the superior with the right colic artery.

The inferior branch of the ileocolic runs toward the upper border of the ileocolic junction and supplies the following branches (Fig. 528): (*a*) **colic**, which pass upward on the ascending colon; (*b*) **anterior** and **posterior cecal**, which are distributed to the front and back of the cecum; (*c*) an **appendicular artery**, which descends behind the termination of the ileum and enters the mesenteriole of the vermiform process; it runs near the free margin of this mesenteriole and ends in branches which supply the vermiform process; and (*d*) **ileal**, which run upward and to the left on the lower part of the ileum, and anastomose with the termination of the superior mesenteric.

The **Right Colic Artery** (*a. colica dextra*) *arises* from about the middle of the concavity of the superior mesenteric artery, or from a stem common to it and the ileocolic. It passes to the right behind the peritoneum, and in front of the right internal spermatic or ovarian vessels, the right ureter and the Psoas major, toward the middle of the ascending colon; sometimes the vessel lies at a higher level, and crosses the descending part of the duodenum and the lower end of the right kidney. At the colon it divides into a descending branch, which anastomoses with the ileocolic, and an ascending branch, which anastomoses with the middle colic. These branches form arches, from the convexity of which vessels are distributed to the ascending colon.

The **Middle Colic Artery** (*a. colica media*) *arises* from the superior mesenteric just below the pancreas and, passing downward and forward between the layers of the transverse mesocolon, divides into two branches, right and left; the former anastomoses with the right colic; the latter with the left colic, a branch of the inferior mesenteric. The arches thus formed are placed about two fingers' breadth from the transverse colon, to which they distribute branches.

The **inferior mesenteric artery** (*a. mesenterica inferior*) (Fig. 529) supplies the left half of the transverse part of the colon, the whole of the descending and iliac parts of the colon, the sigmoid colon, and the greater part of the rectum. It is smaller than the superior mesenteric, and *arises* from the aorta, about 3 or 4 cm. above its division into the common iliacs and close to the lower border of the inferior part of the duodenum, at the level of the middle of the third lumbar vertebra. It passes downward posterior to the peritoneum, lying at first anterior to and then on the left side of the aorta. It crosses the left common iliac artery and is continued into the lesser pelvis under the name of the **superior hemorrhoidal artery**, which descends between the two layers of the sigmoid mesocolon and ends on the upper part of the rectum.

Branches.—Its branches are:

Left Colic. Sigmoid. Superior Hemorrhoidal.

The **Left Colic Artery** (*a. colica sinistra*) runs to the left behind the peritoneum and in front of the Psoas major, and after a short, but variable, course divides into an ascending and a descending branch; the stem of the artery or its branches cross the left ureter and left internal spermatic vessels. The ascending branch crosses in front of the left kidney and ends, between the two layers of the transverse mesocolon, by anastomosing with the middle colic artery; the descending branch anastomoses with the highest sigmoid artery. From the arches formed by these anastomoses branches are distributed to the descending colon and the left part of the transverse colon.

The **Sigmoid Arteries** (*aa. sigmoideæ*) (Fig. 529), two or three in number, run obliquely downward and to the left behind the peritoneum and in front of the Psoas major, ureter, and internal spermatic vessels. Their branches supply the lower part of the descending colon, the iliac colon, and the sigmoid or pelvic colon; anastomosing above with the left colic, and below with the superior hemorrhoidal artery.

The **Superior Hemorrhoidal Artery** (*a. hæmorrhoidalis superior*) (Fig. 529), the continuation of the inferior mesenteric, descends into the pelvis between the layers

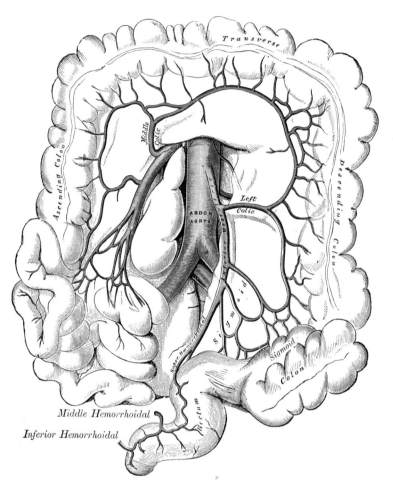

Fig. 529.—The inferior mesenteric artery and its branches.

of the mesentery of the sigmoid colon, crossing, in its course, the left common iliac vessels. It divides, opposite the third sacral vertebra, into two branches, which descend one on either side of the rectum, and about 10 or 12 cm. from the anus break up into several small branches. These pierce the muscular coat of the bowel and run downward, as straight vessels, placed at regular intervals from each other in the wall of the gut between its muscular and mucous coats, to the level of the Sphincter ani internus; here they form a series of loops around the lower end of the rectum, and communicate with the middle hemorrhoidal branches of the hypogastric, and with the inferior hemorrhoidal branches of the internal pudendal.

The **middle suprarenal arteries** (*aa. suprarenales mediæ; middle capsular arteries; suprarenal arteries*) are two small vessels which *arise*, one from either side of the aorta, opposite the superior mesenteric artery. They pass lateralward and slightly upward, over the crura of the diaphragm, to the suprarenal glands, where they anastomose with suprarenal branches of the inferior phrenic and renal arteries. In the fetus these arteries are of large size.

The **renal arteries** (*aa. renales*) (Fig. 523) are two large trunks, which *arise* from the side of the aorta, immediately below the superior mesenteric artery, at the level of the disk between the first and second lumbar vertebræ. Each is directed across the crus of the diaphragm, so as to form nearly a right angle with the aorta. The right is longer than the left, on account of the position of the aorta; it passes behind the inferior vena cava, the right renal vein, the head of the pancreas, and the descending part of the duodenum. The left is somewhat higher than the right; it lies behind the left renal vein, the body of the pancreas and the lienal vein, and is crossed by the inferior mesenteric vein. Before reaching the hilum of the kidney, each artery divides into four or five branches; the greater number of these lie between the renal vein and ureter, the vein being in front, the ureter behind, with one or more branches usually behind the ureter. Each vessel gives off some small **inferior suprarenal branches** to the suprarenal gland, the ureter, and the surrounding cellular tissue and muscles. One or two accessory renal arteries are frequently found (23 per cent.), more especially on the left side. They usually arise from the aorta, and may come off above or below the main artery, the former being the more common position. Instead of entering the kidney at the hilus, they usually pierce the upper or lower part of the gland.

The **internal spermatic arteries** (*aa. spermaticæ internæ; spermatic arteries*) (Fig. 523) are distributed to the testes. They are two slender vessels of considerable length, and *arise* from the front of the aorta a little below the renal arteries. Each passes obliquely downward and lateralward behind the peritoneum, resting on the Psoas major, the right spermatic lying in front of the inferior vena cava and behind the middle colic and ileocolic arteries and the terminal part of the ileum, the left behind the left colic and sigmoid arteries and the iliac colon. Each crosses obliquely over the ureter and the lower part of the external iliac artery to reach the abdominal inguinal ring, through which it passes, and accompanies the other constituents of the spermatic cord along the inguinal canal to the scrotum, where it becomes tortuous, and divides into several branches. Two or three of these accompany the ductus deferens, and supply the epididymis, anastomosing with the artery of the ductus deferens; others pierce the back part of the tunica albuginea, and supply the substance of the testis. The internal spermatic artery supplies one or two small branches to the ureter, and in the inguinal canal gives one or two twigs to the Cremaster.

The **ovarian arteries** (*aa. ovaricæ*) are the arteries in the female corresponding to the internal spermatic in the male. They supply the ovaries, are shorter than the internal spermatics, and do not pass out of the abdominal cavity. The origin and course of the first part of each artery are the same as those of the internal spermatic, but on arriving at the upper opening of the lesser pelvis the ovarian artery passes inward, between the two layers of the ovariopelvic ligament and of the broad ligament of the uterus, to be distributed to the ovary. Small branches are given to the ureter and the uterine tube, and one passes on to the side of the uterus, and unites with the uterine artery. Other offsets are continued on the round ligament of the uterus, through the inguinal canal, to the integument of the labium majus and groin.

At an early period of fetal life, when the testes or ovaries lie by the side of the vertebral column, below the kidneys, the internal spermatic or ovarian arteries are short; but with the descent of these organs into the scrotum or lesser pelvis, the arteries are gradually lengthened.

The **inferior phrenic arteries** (*aa. phrenicæ inferiores*) (Fig. 523) are two small vessels, which supply the diaphragm but present much variety in their origin. They may *arise* separately from the front of the aorta, immediately above the celiac artery, or from one of the renal arteries, or by a common trunk, which may spring either from the aorta or from the celiac artery. They diverge from one another across the crura of the diaphragm, and then run obliquely upward and lateralward upon its under surface. The left phrenic passes behind the esophagus, and runs forward on the left side of the esophageal hiatus. The right phrenic passes behind the inferior vena cava, and along the right side of the foramen which transmits that vein. Near the back part of the central tendon each vessel divides into a medial and a lateral branch. The **medial branch** curves forward, and anastomoses with its fellow of the opposite side, and with the musculophrenic and pericardiaco-phrenic arteries. The **lateral branch** passes toward the side of the thorax, and anastomoses with the lower intercostal arteries, and with the musculophrenic. The lateral branch of the right phrenic gives off a few vessels to the inferior vena cava; and the left one, some branches to the esophagus. Each vessel gives off **superior suprarenal branches** to the suprarenal gland of its own side. The spleen and the liver also receive a few twigs from the left and right vessels respectively.

The **lumbar arteries** (*aa. lumbales*) are in series with the intercostals. They are usually four in number on either side, and *arise* from the back of the aorta, opposite the bodies of the upper four lumbar vertebræ. A fifth pair, small in size, is occasionally present arising from the middle sacral artery. The lumbar arteries run lateralward and backward on the bodies of the lumbar vertebræ, behind the sympathetic trunk, to the intervals between the adjacent transverse processes, and are then continued into the abdominal wall. The arteries of the right side pass behind the inferior vena cava, and the upper two on each side run behind the corresponding crus of the diaphragm. The arteries of both sides pass beneath the tendinous arches which give origin to the Psoas major, and are then continued behind this muscle and the lumbar plexus. They now cross the Quadratus lumborum, the upper three arteries running behind, the last usually in front of the muscle. At the lateral border of the Quadratus lumborum they pierce the posterior aponeurosis of the Transversus abdominis and are carried forward between this muscle and the Obliquus internus. They anastomose with the lower intercostal, the subcostal, the iliolumbar, the deep iliac circumflex, and the inferior epigastric arteries.

Branches.—In the interval between the adjacent transverse processes each lumbar artery gives off a **posterior ramus** which is continued backward between the transverse processes and is distributed to the muscles and skin of the back; it furnishes a **spinal branch** which enters the vertebral canal and is distributed in a manner similar to the spinal branches of the posterior rami of the intercostal arteries (page 607). **Muscular branches** are supplied from each lumbar artery and from its posterior ramus to the neighboring muscles.

The **middle sacral artery** (*a. sacralis media*) (Fig. 523) is a small vessel, which *arises* from the back of the aorta, a little above its bifurcation. It descends in the mid-line in front of the fourth and fifth lumbar vertebræ, the sacrum and coccyx, and ends in the glomus coccygeum (*coccygeal gland*). From it, minute branches are said to pass to the posterior surface of the rectum. On the last lumbar vertebra it anastomoses with the lumbar branch of the iliolumbar artery; in front of the sacrum it anastomoses with the lateral sacral arteries, and sends offsets into the anterior sacral foramina. It is crossed by the left common iliac vein, and is accompanied by a pair of venæ comitantes; these unite to form a single vessel, which opens into the left common iliac vein.

THE COMMON ILIAC ARTERIES (AA. ILIACÆ COMMUNES) (Figs. 523, 530).

The abdominal aorta divides on the left side of the body of the fourth lumbar vertebra into the two **common iliac arteries**, each about 5 cm. in length. They diverge from the end of the aorta, pass downward and lateralward, and divide, opposite the intervertebral fibrocartilage between the last lumbar vertebra and the sacrum, into two branches, the **external iliac** and **hypogastric arteries**; the former supplies the lower extremity; the latter, the viscera and parietes of the pelvis.

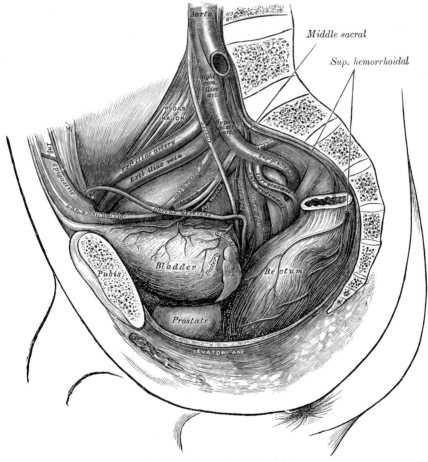

Fig. 530.—The arteries of the pelvis.

The **right common iliac artery** (Fig. 530) is usually somewhat longer than the left, and passes more obliquely across the body of the last lumbar vertebra. *In front* of it are the peritoneum, the small intestines, branches of the sympathetic nerves, and, at its point of division, the ureter. *Behind*, it is separated from the bodies of the fourth and fifth lumbar vertebræ, and the intervening fibrocartilage, by the terminations of the two common iliac veins and the commencement of the inferior vena cava. *Laterally*, it is in relation, above, with the inferior vena cava and the right common iliac vein; and, below, with the Psoas major. *Medial* to it, above, is the left common iliac vein.

The **left common iliac artery** is in relation, *in front*, with the peritoneum, the small intestines, branches of the sympathetic nerves, and the superior hemorrhoidal artery; and is crossed at its point of bifurcation by the ureter. It rests on the bodies of the fourth and fifth lumbar vertebræ, and the intervening fibrocartilage. The left common iliac vein lies partly *medial* to, and partly behind the artery; *laterally*, the artery is in relation with the Psoas major.

Branches.—The common iliac arteries give off small branches to the peritoneum, Psoas major, ureters, and the surrounding areolar tissue, and occasionally give origin to the iliolumbar, or accessory renal arteries.

Variations.—The *point of origin* varies according to the bifurcation of the aorta. In three-fourths of a large number of cases, the aorta bifurcated either upon the fourth lumbar vertebra, or upon the fibrocartilage between it and the fifth; the bifurcation being, in one case out of nine, below, and in one out of eleven, above this point. In about 80 per cent. of the cases the aorta bifurcated within 1.25 cm. above or below the level of the crest of the ilium; more frequently below than above.

The *point of division* varies greatly. In two-thirds of a large number of cases it was between the last lumbar vertebra and the upper border of the sacrum; being above that point in one case out of eight, and below it in one case out of six. The left common iliac artery divides lower down more frequently than the right.

The *relative lengths*, also, of the two common iliac arteries vary. The right common iliac was the longer in sixty-three cases; the left in fifty-two; while they were equal in fifty-three. The length of the arteries varied, in five-sevenths of the cases examined, from 3.5 to 7.5 cm.; in about half of the remaining cases the artery was longer, and in the other half, shorter; the minimum length being less than 1.25 cm., the maximum, 11 cm. In rare instances, the right common iliac has been found wanting, the external iliac and hypogastric arising directly from the aorta.

Collateral Circulation.—The principal agents in carrying on the collateral circulation after the application of a ligature to the common iliac are: the anastomoses of the hemorrhoidal branches of the hypogastric with the superior hemorrhoidal from the inferior mesenteric; of the uterine, ovarian, and vesical arteries of the opposite sides; of the lateral sacral with the middle sacral artery; of the inferior epigastric with the internal mammary, inferior intercostal, and lumbar arteries; of the deep iliac circumflex with the lumbar arteries; of the iliolumbar with the last lumbar artery; of the obturator artery, by means of its pubic branch, with the vessel of the opposite side and with the inferior epigastric.

The Hypogastric Artery (A. Hypogastrica; Internal Iliac Artery) (Figs. 530, 531).

The **hypogastric artery** supplies the walls and viscera of the pelvis, the buttock, the generative organs, and the medial side of the thigh. It is a short, thick vessel, smaller than the external iliac, and about 4 cm. in length. It *arises* at the bifurcation of the common iliac, opposite the lumbosacral articulation, and, passing downward to the upper margin of the greater sciatic foramen, divides into two large trunks, an **anterior** and a **posterior**.

Relations.—It is in relation *in front* with the ureter; *behind*, with the internal iliac vein, the lumbosacral trunk, and the Piriformis muscle; *laterally*, near its origin, with the external iliac vein, which lies between it and the Psoas major muscle; lower down, with the obturator nerve.

In the fetus, the hypogastric artery is twice as large as the external iliac, and is the direct continuation of the common iliac. It ascends along the side of the bladder, and runs upward on the back of the anterior wall of the abdomen to the umbilicus, converging toward its fellow of the opposite side. Having passed through the umbilical opening, the two arteries, now termed **umbilical,** enter the umbilical cord, where they are coiled around the umbilical vein, and ultimately ramify in the placenta.

At birth, when the placental circulation ceases, the pelvic portion only of the artery remains patent and constitutes the hypogastric and the first part of the superior vesical artery of the adult; the remainder of the vessel is converted into a solid fibrous cord, the **lateral umbilical ligament** (*obliterated hypogastric artery*) which extends from the pelvis to the umbilicus.

Variations.—The branches of the hypogastric artery are subject to great variation. Any two of the following branches, the superior gluteal, the inferior gluteal, or the internal pudendal, may have a common trunk. The iliolumbar occasionally arises from the common iliac. The obturator artery may arise either from the anterior trunk or posterior trunk of the hypogastric. The branches to be described fit the majority of cases, according to Poirier and Charpy.

Collateral Circulation.—The circulation after ligature of the hypogastric artery is carried on by the anastomoses of the uterine and ovarian arteries; of the vesical arteries of the two sides; of the hemorrhoidal branches of the hypogastric with those from the inferior mesenteric; of the obturator artery, by means of its pubic branch, with the vessel of the opposite side, and with the inferior epigastric and medial femoral circumflex; of the circumflex and perforating branches of the profunda femoris with the inferior gluteal; of the superior gluteal with the posterior branches of the lateral sacral arteries; of the iliolumbar with the last lumbar; of the lateral sacral with the middle sacral; and of the iliac circumflex with the iliolumbar and superior gluteal.

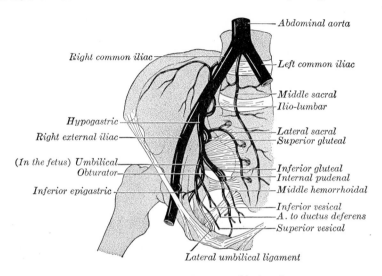

Fig. 531.—The hypogastric artery and its branches.

Branches.—The branches of the hypogastric artery are:

From the Anterior Trunk.	*From the Posterior Trunk.*
Superior Vesical.	Iliolumbar.
Middle Vesical.	Lateral Sacral.
Inferior Vesical.	Superior Gluteal.
Middle Hemorrhoidal.	
Obturator.	
Internal Pudendal.	
Inferior Gluteal.	
Uterine ⎫ *In the Female.*	
Vaginal ⎭	

The **superior vesical artery** (*a. vesicalis superior*) supplies numerous branches to the upper part of the bladder. From one of these a slender vessel, the **artery to the ductus deferens,** takes origin and accompanies the duct in its course to the testis, where it anastomoses with the internal spermatic artery. Other branches supply the ureter. The first part of the superior vesical artery represents the terminal section of the previous portion of the fetal hypogastric artery.

The **middle vesical artery** (*a. vesicalis medialis*), usually a branch of the superior, is distributed to the fundus of the bladder and the vesiculæ seminales.

The **inferior vesical artery** (*a. vesicalis inferior*) frequently *arises* in common with the middle hemorrhoidal, and is distributed to the fundus of the bladder, the prostate, and the vesiculæ seminales. The branches to the prostate communicate with the corresponding vessels of the opposite side.

The **middle hemorrhoidal artery** (*a. hæmorrhoidalis media*) usually *arises* with the preceding vessel. It is distributed to the rectum, anastomosing with the inferior vesical and with the superior and inferior hemorrhoidal arteries. It gives offsets to the vesiculæ seminales and prostate.

The **uterine artery** (*a. uterina*) (Fig. 532) springs from the anterior division of the hypogastric and runs medialward on the Levator ani and toward the cervix uteri; about 2 cm. from the cervix it crosses above and in front of the ureter, to which it supplies a small branch. Reaching the side of the uterus it ascends in a tortuous manner between the two layers of the broad ligament to the junction of the uterine tube and uterus. It then runs lateralward toward the hilus of the ovary, and ends by joining with the ovarian artery. It supplies branches to the cervix uteri and others which descend on the vagina; the latter anastomose with branches of the vaginal arteries and form with them two median longitudinal vessels—the **azygos arteries of the vagina**—one of which runs down in front of and the other behind the vagina. It supplies numerous branches to the body of the uterus, and from its terminal portion twigs are distributed to the uterine tube and the round ligament of the uterus.

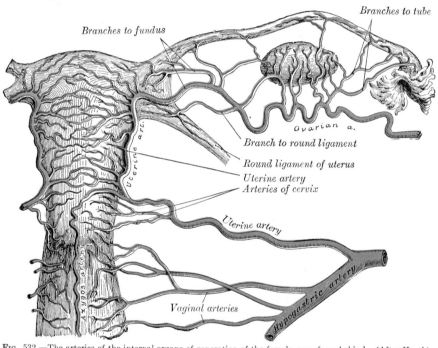

FIG. 532.—The arteries of the internal organs of generation of the female, seen from behind. (After Hyrtl.)

The **vaginal artery** (*a. vaginalis*) usually corresponds to the inferior vesical in the male; it descends upon the vagina, supplying its mucous membrane, and sends branches to the bulb of the vestibule, the fundus of the bladder, and the contiguous part of the rectum. It assists in forming the azygos arteries of the vagina, and is frequently represented by two or three branches.

The **obturator artery** (*a. obturatoria*) passes forward and downward on the lateral wall of the pelvis, to the upper part of the obturator foramen, and, escaping from the pelvic cavity through the obturator canal, it divides into an **anterior** and a **posterior branch.** In the pelvic cavity this vessel is in relation, laterally, with the obturator fascia; medially, with the ureter, ductus deferens, and peritoneum; while a little below it is the obturator nerve.

Branches.—*Inside the pelvis* the obturator artery gives off **iliac branches** to the iliac fossa, which supply the bone and the Iliacus, and anastomose with the ilio-lumbar artery; a **vesical branch,** which runs backward to supply the bladder; and a **pubic branch,** which is given off from the vessel just before it leaves the pelvic cavity. The pubic branch ascends upon the back of the pubis, communicating with the opposite corresponding vessel, and with the inferior epigastric artery.

Outside the pelvis, the obturator artery divides at the upper margin of the obturator foramen, into an anterior and a posterior branch which encircle the foramen under cover of the Obturator externus.

The **anterior branch** runs forward on the outer surface of the obturator membrane curving downward along the anterior margin of the foramen. It distributes branches to the Obturator externus, Pectineus, Adductores, and Gracilis, anastomosing with the posterior branch and with the medial femoral circumflex artery.

The **posterior branch** follows the posterior margin of the foramen and divides into two branches. One runs anteriorly on the inferior ramus of the ischium where it anastomoses with the anterior branch of the obturator. The other branch gives twigs to the muscles attached to the ischial tuberosity and anastomoses with the inferior gluteal. It also supplies an articular branch which enters the hip-joint through the acetabular notch, ramifies in the fat at the bottom of the acetabulum and sends a twig along the ligamentum teres to the head of the femur.

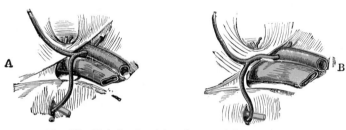

Fig. 533.—Variations in origin and course of obturator artery.

Variations.—The obturator artery sometimes arises from the main stem or from the posterior trunk of the hypogastric, or it may spring from the superior gluteal artery. It arises in common with the inferior gluteal in 24 per cent. of cases (Lipschütz). Various authors describe the obturator as arising in from 13 per cent. to 28 per cent. of cases from the inferior epigastric or even from the external iliac; in this case it descends almost vertically to the upper part of the obturator foramen. This origin represents the enlargement of the anastomosis that is normally present. The artery in this course usually lies in contact with the external iliac vein, and on the lateral side of the femoral ring (Fig. 533 A); in such cases it would not be endangered in the operation for strangulated femoral hernia. Occasionally, however, it curves along the free margin of the lacunar ligament (Fig. 533 B), and if in such circumstances a femoral hernia occurred, the vessel would almost completely encircle the neck of the hernial sac, and would be in great danger of being wounded if an operation were performed for strangulation.

The **internal pudendal artery** (*a. pudenda interna; internal pudic artery*) is the smaller of the two terminal branches of the anterior trunk of the hypogastric, and supplies the external organs of generation. Though the course of the artery is the same in the two sexes, the vessel is smaller in the female than in the male, and the distribution of its branches somewhat different. The description of its arrangement in the male will first be given, and subsequently the differences which it presents in the female will be mentioned.

The **internal pudendal artery in the male** passes downward and outward to the lower border of the greater sciatic foramen, and emerges from the pelvis between the Piriformis and Coccygeus; it then crosses the ischial spine, and enters the perineum through the lesser sciatic foramen. The artery now crosses the Obturator internus, along the lateral wall of the ischiorectal fossa, being situated about 4 cm.

above the lower margin of the ischial tuberosity. It gradually approaches the margin of the inferior ramus of the ischium and passes forward between the two layers of the fascia of the urogenital diaphragm; it then runs forward along the medial margin of the inferior ramus of the pubis, and about 1.25 cm. behind the pubic arcuate ligament it divides into the **dorsal and deep arteries of the penis,** but it may pierce the superficial fascia of the urogenital diaphragm before doing so.

Relations.—Within the pelvis, it lies in front of the Piriformis muscle, the sacral plexus of nerves, and the inferior gluteal artery. Crossing the ischial spine, it is covered by the Glutæus maximus and overlaps by the sacrotuberous ligament. Here the pudendal nerve lies to the medial side and the nerve to the Obturator internus to the lateral side. In the perineum it lies on the lateral wall of the ischiorectal fossa, in a canal (*Alcock's canal*) formed by the splitting of the obturator fascia. It is accompanied by a pair of venæ comitantes and the pudendal nerve.

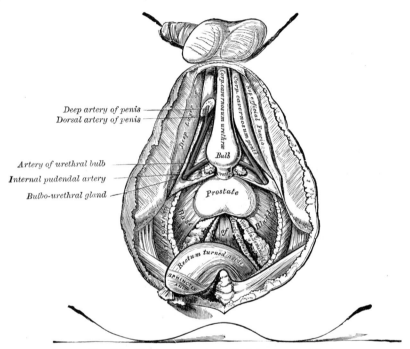

Fig. 534.—The deeper branches of the internal pudendal artery.

Variations.—The internal pudendal artery is sometimes smaller than usual, or fails to give off one or two of its usual branches; in such cases the deficiency is supplied by branches derived from an additional vessel, the **accessory pudendal,** which generally arises from the internal pudendal artery before its exit from the greater sciatic foramen. It passes forward along the lower part of the bladder and across the side of the prostate to the root of the penis, where it perforates the urogenital diaphragm, and gives off the branches usually derived from the internal pudendal artery. The deficiency most frequently met with is that in which the internal pudendal ends as the artery of the urethral bulb, the dorsal and deep arteries of the penis being derived from the accessory pudendal. The internal pudendal artery may also end as the perineal, the artery of the urethral bulb being derived, with the other two branches, from the accessory vessel. Occasionally the accessory pudendal artery is derived from one of the other branches of the hypogastric artery, most frequently the inferior vesical or the obturator.

Branches.—The branches of the internal pudendal artery (Figs. 534, 535) are:

Muscular.	Artery of the Urethral Bulb.
Inferior Hemorrhoidal.	Urethral.
Perineal.	Deep Artery of the Penis.

Dorsal Artery of the Penis.

The **Muscular Branches** consist of two sets: one given off in the pelvis; the other, as the vessel crosses the ischial spine. The former consists of several small offsets which supply the Levator ani, the Obturator internus, the Piriformis, and the Coccygeus. The branches given off outside the pelvis are distributed to the adjacent parts of the Glutæus maximus and external rotator muscles. They anastomose with branches of the inferior gluteal artery.

The **Inferior Hemorrhoidal Artery** (*a. hæmorrhoidalis inferior*) *arises* from the internal pudendal as it passes above the ischial tuberosity. Piercing the wall of Alcock's canal it divides into two or three branches which cross the ischiorectal fossa, and are distributed to the muscles and integument of the anal region, and send offshoots around the lower edge of the Glutæus maximus to the skin of the buttock. They anastomose with the corresponding vessels of the opposite side, with the superior and middle hemorrhoidal, and with the perineal artery.

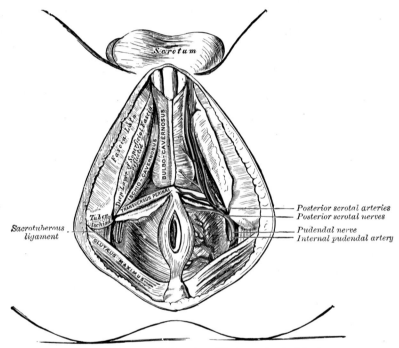

Fɪɢ. 535.—The superficial branches of the internal pudendal artery.

The **Perineal Artery** (*a. perinei; superficial perineal artery*) *arises* from the internal pudendal, in front of the preceding branches, and turns upward, crossing either over or under the Transverus perinæi superficialis, and runs forward, parallel to the pubic arch, in the interspace between the Bulbocavernosus and Ischiocavernosus, both of which it supplies, and finally divides into several **posterior scrotal branches** which are distributed to the skin and dartos tunic of the scrotum. As it crosses the Transversus perinæi superficialis it gives off the **transverse perineal artery** which runs transversely on the cutaneous surface of the muscle, and anastomoses with the corresponding vessel of the opposite side and with the perineal and inferior hemorrhoidal arteries. It supplies the Transversus perinæi superficialis and the structures between the anus and the urethral bulb.

The **Artery of the Urethral Bulb** (*a. bulbi urethræ*) is a short vessel of large caliber which *arises* from the internal pudendal between the two layers of fascia of the urogenital diaphragm; it passes medialward, pierces the inferior fascia of the urogenital diaphragm, and gives off branches which ramify in the bulb of the urethra and in

40

the posterior part of the corpus cavernosum urethræ. It gives off a small branch to the bulbo-urethral gland.

The **Urethral Artery** (*a. urethralis*) *arises* a short distance in front of the artery of the urethral bulb. It runs forward and medialward, pierces the inferior fascia of the urogenital diaphragm and enters the corpus cavernosum urethræ, in which it is continued forward to the glans penis.

The **Deep Artery of the Penis** (*a. profunda penis; artery to the corpus cavernosum*), one of the terminal branches of the internal pudendal, *arises* from that vessel while it is situated between the two fasciæ of the urogenital diaphragm; it pierces the superficial layer, and, entering the crus penis obliquely, runs forward in the center of the corpus cavernosum penis, to which its branches are distributed.

The **Dorsal Artery of the Penis** (*a. dorsalis penis*) ascends between the crus penis and the pubic symphysis, and, piercing the superficial fascia of the urogenital diaphragm, passes between the two layers of the suspensory ligament of the penis, and runs forward on the dorsum of the penis to the glans, where it divides into two branches, which supply the glans and prepuce. On the penis, it lies between the dorsal nerve and deep dorsal vein, the former being on its lateral side. It supplies the integument and fibrous sheath of the corpus cavernosum penis, sending branches through the sheath to anastomose with the preceding vessel.

The **internal pudendal artery in the female** is smaller than in the male. Its origin and course are similar, and there is considerable analogy in the distribution of its branches. The perineal artery supplies the labia pudendi; the artery of the bulb supplies the bulbus vestibuli and the erectile tissue of the vagina; the deep artery of the clitoris supplies the corpus cavernosum clitoridis; and the dorsal artery of the clitoris supplies the dorsum of that organ, and ends in the glans and prepuce of the clitoris.

The **inferior gluteal artery** (*a. glutæa inferior; sciatic artery*) (Fig. 536), the larger of the two terminal branches of the anterior trunk of the hypogastric, is distributed chiefly to the buttocks and back of the thigh. It passes posteriorly between the first and second sacral nerves, or between the second and third sacral nerves, and then descends between the piriformis and coccygeus muscles through the lower part of the sciatic foramen to the gluteal region. It then descends in the interval between the greater trochanter of the femur and tuberosity of the ischium, accompanied by the sciatic and posterior femoral cutaneous nerves and covered by the Glutæus maximus, is continued down the back of the thigh, supplying the skin, and anastomosing with branches of the perforating arteries.

Inside the pelvis it distributes branches to the Piriformis, Coccygeus, and Levator ani; some branches which supply the fat around the rectum, and occasionally take the place of the middle hemorrhoidal artery; and vesical branches to the fundus of the bladder, vesiculæ seminales, and prostate. *Outside the pelvis* it gives off the following branches:

Muscular.	Anastomotic.
Coccygeal.	Articular.
Comitans Nervi Ischiadici.	Cutaneous.

The **Muscular Branches** supply the Glutæus maximus, anastomosing with the superior gluteal artery in the substance of the muscle; the external rotators, anastomosing with the internal pudendal artery; and the muscles attached to the tuberosity of the ischium, anastomosing with the posterior branch of the obturator and the medial femoral circumflex arteries.

The **Coccygeal Branches** run medialward, pierce the sacrotuberous ligament, and supply the Glutæus maximus, the integument, and other structures on the back of the coccyx.

The **Arteria Comitans Nervi Ischiadici** is a long, slender vessel, which accompanies the sciatic nerve for a short distance; it then penetrates it, and runs in its substance to the lower part of the thigh.

The **Anastomotic** is directed downward across the external rotators, and assists in forming the so-called **crucial anastomosis** by joining with the first perforating and medial and lateral femoral circumflex arteries.

The **Articular Branch**, generally derived from the anastomotic, is distributed to the capsule of the hip-joint.

The **Cutaneous Branches** are distributed to the skin of the buttock and back of the thigh.

The **iliolumbar artery** (*a. iliolumbalis*), a branch of the posterior trunk of the hypogastric, turns upward behind the obturator nerve and the external iliac vessels, to the medial border of the Psoas major, behind which it divides into a lumbar and an iliac branch.

The **Lumbar Branch** (*ramus lumbalis*) supplies the Psoas major and Quadratus lumborum, anastomoses with the last lumbar artery, and sends a small **spinal branch** through the intervertebral foramen between the last lumbar vertebra and the sacrum, into the vertebral canal, to supply the cauda equina.

The **Iliac Branch** (*ramus iliacus*) descends to supply the Iliacus; some offsets, running between the muscle and the bone, anastomose with the iliac branches of the obturator; one of these enters an oblique canal to supply the bone, while others run along the crest of the ilium, distributing branches to the gluteal and abdominal muscles, and anastomosing in their course with the superior gluteal, iliac circumflex, and lateral femoral circumflex arteries.

The **lateral sacral arteries** (*aa. sacrales laterales*) (Fig. 530) *arise* from the posterior division of the hypogastric; there are usually two, a **superior** and an **inferior**.

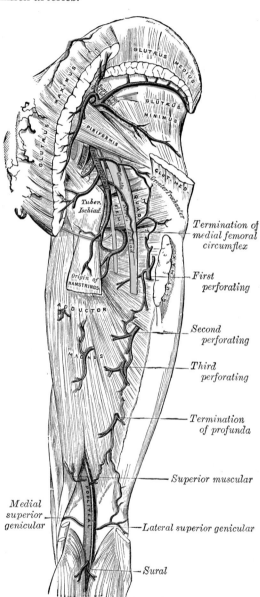

Fig. 536.—The arteries of the gluteal and posterior femoral regions.

The **superior**, of large size, passes medialward, and, after anastomosing with branches from the middle sacral, enters the first or second anterior sacral foramen, supplies branches to the contents of the sacral canal, and, escaping by the corresponding posterior sacral foramen, is distributed to the skin and muscles on the dorsum of the sacrum, anastomosing with the superior gluteal.

The **inferior** runs obliquely across the front of the Piriformis and the sacral nerves to the medial side of the anterior sacral foramina, descends on the front of the sacrum, and anastomoses over the coccyx with the middle sacral and opposite the lateral sacral artery. In its course it gives off branches, which enter the anterior sacral foramina; these, after supplying the contents of the sacral canal, emerge by the posterior sacral foramina, and are distributed to the muscles and skin on the dorsal surface of the sacrum, anastomosing with the gluteal arteries.

The **superior gluteal artery** (*a. glutæa superior; gluteal artery*) (Fig. 536) is the largest branch of the hypogastric, and appears to be the continuation of the posterior division of that vessel. It is a short artery which runs backward between the lumbosacral trunk and the first sacral nerve, and, passing out of the pelvis above the upper border of the Piriformis, immediately divides into a **superficial** and a **deep branch**. Within the pelvis it gives off a few branches to the Iliacus, Piriformis, and Obturator internus, and before quitting that cavity, a nutrient artery which enters the ilium.

The **superficial branch** enters the deep surface of the Glutæus maximus, and divides into numerous branches, some of which supply the muscle and anastomose with the inferior gluteal, while others perforate its tendinous origin, and supply the integument covering the posterior surface of the sacrum, anastomosing with the posterior branches of the lateral sacral arteries.

The **deep branch** lies under the Glutæus medius and almost immediately subdivides into two. Of these, the **superior division**, continuing the original course of the vessel, passes along the upper border of the Glutæus minimus to the anterior-superior spine of the ilium, anastomosing with the deep iliac circumflex artery and the ascending branch of the lateral femoral circumflex artery. The **inferior division** crosses the Glutæus minimus obliquely to the greater trochanter, distributing branches to the Glutæi and anastomoses with the lateral femoral circumflex artery. Some branches pierce the Glutæus minimus and supply the hip-joint.

The External Iliac Artery (A. Iliaca Externa) (Fig. 530).

The **external iliac artery** is larger than the hypogastric, and passes obliquely downward and lateralward along the medial border of the Psoas major, from the bifurcation of the common iliac to a point beneath the inguinal ligament, midway between the anterior superior spine of the ilium and the symphysis pubis, where it enters the thigh and becomes the femoral artery.

Relations.—*In front and medially*, the artery is in relation with the peritoneum, subperitoneal areolar tissue, the termination of the ileum and frequently the vermiform process on the right side, and, on the left, the sigmoid colon and a thin layer of fascia, derived from the iliac fascia, which surrounds the artery and vein. In the female it is crossed at its origin by the ovarian vessels, and occasionally by the ureter. The internal spermatic vessels lie for some distance upon it near its termination, and it is crossed in this situation by the external spermatic branch of the genitofemoral nerve and the deep iliac circumflex vein; the ductus deferens in the male, and the round ligament of the uterus in the female, curve down across its medial side. *Behind*, it is in relation with the medial border of the Psoas major, from which it is separated by the iliac fascia. At the upper part of its course, the external iliac vein lies partly behind it, but lower down lies entirely to its medial side. *Laterally*, it rests against the Psoas major, from which it is separated by the iliac fascia. Numerous lymphatic vessels and lymph glands lie on the front and on the medial side of the vessel.

Collateral Circulation.—The principal anastomoses in carrying on the collateral circulation, after the application of a ligature to the external iliac, are: the iliolumbar with the iliac circumflex; the superior gluteal with the lateral femoral circumflex; the obturator with the medial femoral circumflex; the inferior gluteal with the first perforating and circumflex branches of the profunda artery; and the internal pudendal with the external pudendal. When the obturator arises from the inferior epigastric, it is supplied with blood by branches, from either the hypogastric, the lateral sacral, or the internal pudendal. The inferior epigastric receives its supply from the internal mammary and lower intercostal arteries, and from the hypogastric by the anastomoses of its branches with the obturator.

Branches.—Besides several small branches to the Psoas major and the neighboring lymph glands, the external iliac gives off two branches of considerable size:

Inferior Epigastric.   Deep Iliac Circumflex.

The **inferior epigastric artery** (*a. epigastrica inferior; deep epigastric artery*) (Fig. 539) *arises* from the external iliac, immediately above the inguinal ligament. It curves forward in the subperitoneal tissue, and then ascends obliquely along the medial margin of the abdominal inguinal ring; continuing its course upward, it pierces the transversalis fascia, and, passing in front of the linea semicircularis, ascends between the Rectus abdominis and the posterior lamella of its sheath. It finally divides into numerous branches, which anastomose, above the umbilicus, with the superior epigastric branch of the internal mammary and with the lower intercostal arteries (Fig. 512). As the inferior epigastric artery passes obliquely upward from its origin it lies along the lower and medial margins of the abdominal inguinal ring, and behind the commencement of the spermatic cord. The ductus deferens, as it leaves the spermatic cord in the male, or the round ligament of the uterus in the female, winds around the lateral and posterior aspects of the artery.

Branches.—The branches of the vessel are: the **external spermatic artery** (*cremasteric artery*), which accompanies the spermatic cord, and supplies the Cremaster and other coverings of the cord, anastomosing with the internal spermatic artery (in the female it is very small and accompanies the round ligament); a **pubic branch** which runs along the inguinal ligament, and then descends along the medial margin of the femoral ring to the back of the pubis, and there anastomoses with the pubic branch of the obturator artery; **muscular branches**, some of which are distributed to the abdominal muscles and peritoneum, anastomosing with the iliac circumflex and lumbar arteries; branches which perforate the tendon of the Obliquus externus, and supply the integument, anastomosing with branches of the superficial epigastric.

Variations.—The origin of the inferior epigastric may take place from any part of the external iliac between the inguinal ligament and a point 6 cm. above it; or it may arise below this ligament, from the femoral. It frequently springs from the external iliac, by a common trunk with the obturator. Sometimes it arises from the obturator, the latter vessel being furnished by the hypogastric, or it may be formed of two branches, one derived from the external iliac, the other from the hypogastric.

The **deep iliac circumflex artery** (*a. circumflexa ilii profunda*) *arises* from the lateral aspect of the external iliac nearly opposite the inferior epigastric artery. It ascends obliquely lateralward behind the inguinal ligament, contained in a fibrous sheath formed by the junction of the transversalis fascia and iliac fascia, to the anterior superior iliac spine, where it anastomoses with the ascending branch of the lateral femoral circumflex artery. It then pierces the transversalis fascia and passes along the inner lip of the crest of the ilium to about its middle, where it perforates the Transversus, and runs backward between that muscle and the Obliquus internus, to anastomose with the iliolumbar and superior gluteal arteries. Opposite the anterior superior spine of the ilium it gives off a large branch, which ascends between the Obliquus internus and Transversus muscles, supplying them, and anastomosing with the lumbar and inferior epigastric arteries.

THE ARTERIES OF THE LOWER EXTREMITY.

The artery which supplies the greater part of the lower extremity is the direct continuation of the external iliac. It runs as a single trunk from the inguinal ligament to the lower border of the Popliteus, where it divides into two branches, the **anterior** and **posterior tibial.** The upper part of the main trunk is named the **femoral,** the lower part the **popliteal.**

THE FEMORAL ARTERY (A. FEMORALIS) (Figs. 541, 542).

The **femoral artery** begins immediately behind the inguinal ligament, midway between the anterior superior spine of the ilium and the symphysis pubis, and passes down the front and medial side of the thigh. It ends at the junction of the middle with the lower third of the thigh, where it passes through an opening in the Adductor magnus to become the popliteal artery. The vessel, at the upper part of the thigh, lies in front of the hip-joint; in the lower part of its course it lies to the medial side of the body of the femur, and between these two parts, where it crosses the angle between the head and body, the vessel is some distance from the bone. The first 4 cm. of the vessel is enclosed, together with the femoral vein,

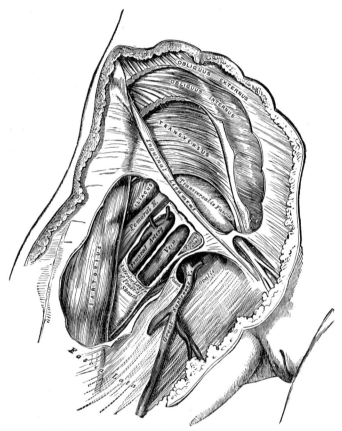

FIG. 537.—Femoral sheath laid open to show its three compartments.

in a fibrous sheath—the **femoral sheath.** In the upper third of the thigh the femoral artery is contained in the **femoral triangle** (*Scarpa's triangle*), and in the middle third of the thigh, in the **adductor canal** (*Hunter's canal*).

The **femoral sheath** (*crural sheath*) (Figs. 537, 538) is formed by a prolongation downward, behind the inguinal ligament, of the fasciæ which line the abdomen, the transversalis fascia being continued down in front of the femoral vessels and the iliac fascia behind them. The sheath assumes the form of a short funnel, the wide end of which is directed upward, while the lower, narrow end fuses with the fascial investment of the vessels, about 4 cm. below the inguinal ligament. It is strengthened in front by a band termed the **deep crural arch** (page 405). The lateral wall of the sheath is vertical and is perforated by the lumboinguinal nerve; the medial wall is directed obliquely downward and lateralward, and is pierced by the great saphenous vein and by some lymphatic vessels. The sheath is divided by two vertical partitions which stretch between its anterior and posterior walls. The lateral compartment contains the femoral artery, and the intermediate the femoral

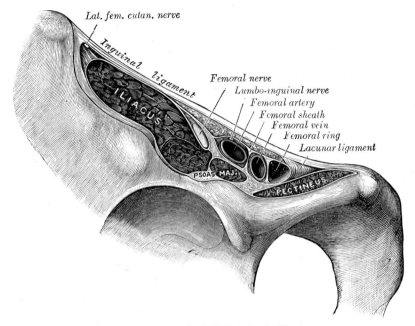

Fig. 538.—Structures passing behind the inguinal ligament.

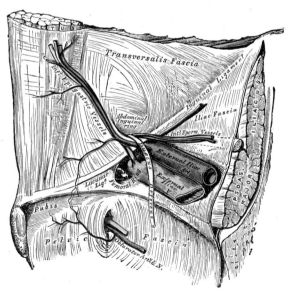

Fig. 539.—The relations of the femoral and abdominal inguinal rings, seen from within the abdomen. Right side.

vein, while the medial and smallest compartment is named the **femoral canal**, and contains some lymphatic vessels and a lymph gland imbedded in a small amount of areolar tissue. The femoral canal is conical and measures about 1.25 cm. in length. Its base, directed upward and named the **femoral ring**, is oval in form, its long diameter being directed transversely and measuring about 1.25 cm. The femoral ring (Figs. 538, 539) is bounded in *front* by the inguinal ligament, *behind* by the Pectineus covered by the pectineal fascia, *medially* by the crescentic base of the lacunar ligament, and *laterally* by the fibrous septum on the medial side of the

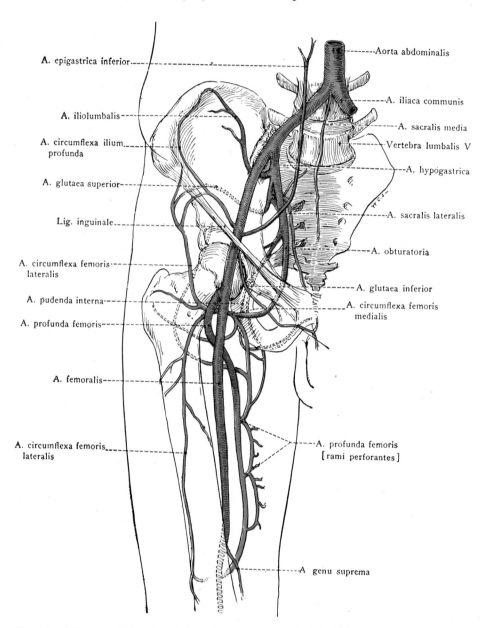

A. epigastrica inferior

Aorta abdominalis

A. iliolumbalis

A. iliaca communis

A. circumflexa ilium profunda

A. sacralis media

A. glutaea superior

Vertebra lumbalis V

Lig. inguinale

A. hypógastrica

A. circumflexa femoris lateralis

A. sacralis lateralis

A. pudenda interna

A. obturatoria

A. profunda femoris

A. glutaea inferior

A. femoralis

A. circumflexa femoris medialis

A. circumflexa femoris lateralis

A. profunda femoris [rami perforantes]

A genu suprema

Fig. 540.—Collateral circulation about the hip and the upper part of the right thigh. (Eycleshymer and Jones).

femoral vein. The spermatic cord in the male and the round ligament of the uterus in the female lie immediately above the anterior margin of the ring, while the inferior epigastric vessels are close to its upper and lateral angle. The femoral ring is closed by a somewhat condensed portion of the extraperitoneal fatty tissue, named the **septum femorale** (*crural septum*), the abdominal surface of which suports a small lymph gland and is covered by the parietal layer of the peritoneum. The septum femorale is pierced by numerous lymphatic vessels passing from the deep inguinal to the external iliac lymph nodes. The parietal peritoneum above t presents a slight depression named the **femoral fossa.**

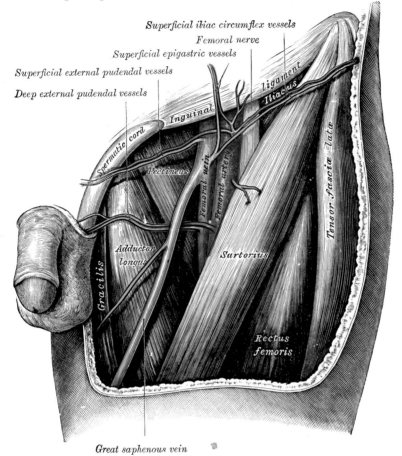

Fig. 541.—The left femoral triangle.

The **femoral triangle** (*trigonum femorale; Scarpa's triangle*) (Fig. 541) corresponds o the depression seen immediately below the fold of the groin. Its apex is directed downward, and the sides are formed laterally by the Sartorius, medially by the Adductor longus, and above by the inguinal ligament. The floor of the space is formed from its lateral to its medial side by the Iliacus, Psoas major, Pectineus, and in some cases a small part of the Adductor brevis; it is divided into two nearly equal parts by the femoral vessels, which extend from near the middle of its base to its apex: the artery giving off its superficial and profunda branches, the vein receiving the deep femoral and great saphenous tributaries. On the lateral side of the femoral artery is the femoral nerve with its branches. Besides the vessels and nerves, this space contains some fat and lymphatics.

The **adductor canal** (*canalis adductorius; Hunter's canal*) is an aponeurotic tunnel in the middle third of the thigh, extending from the apex of the femoral triangle to the opening in the Adductor magnus. It is bounded, in front and laterally, by the Vastus medialis; behind by the Adductores longus and magnus; and is covered by a strong aponeurosis which extends from the Vastus medialis, across the femoral vessels to the Adductores longus and magnus; lying on the aponeurosis is the Sartorius muscle. The canal contains the femoral artery and vein, the saphenous nerve, and the nerve to the Vastus medialis.

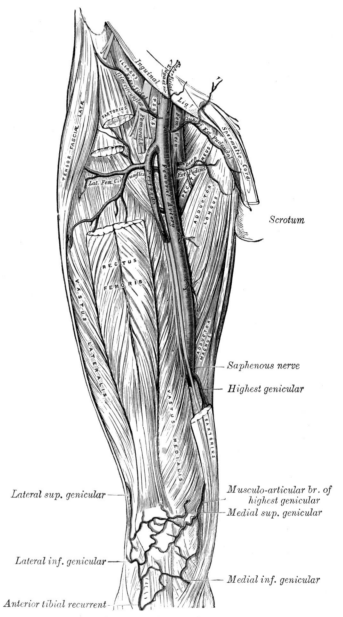

Fig. 542.—The femoral artery.

Relations of the Femoral Artery.—In the *femoral triangle* (Fig. 541) the artery is superficial, *In front* of it are the skin and superficial fascia, the superficial subinguinal lymph glands, the superficial iliac circumflex vein, the superficial layer of the fascia lata and the anterior part of the femoral sheath. The lumboinguinal nerve courses for a short distance within the lateral compartment of the femoral sheath, and lies at first in front and then lateral to the artery. Near the apex of the femoral triangle the medial branch of the anterior femoral cutaneous nerve crosses the artery from its lateral to its medial side.

Behind the artery are the posterior part of the femoral sheath, the pectineal fascia, the medial part of the tendon of the Psoas major, the Pectineus and the Adductor longus. The artery is separated from the capsule of the hip-joint by the tendon of the Psoas major, from the Pectineus by the femoral vein and profunda vessels, and from the Adductor longus by the femoral vein. The nerve to the Pectineus passes medialward behind the artery. On the *lateral* side of the artery, but separated from it by some fibers of the Psoas major, is the femoral nerve. The femoral vein is on the medial side of the upper part of the artery, but is behind the vessel in the lower part of the femoral triangle.

In the *adductor canal* (Fig. 542) the femoral artery is more deeply situated, being covered by the integument, the superficial and deep fasciæ, the Sartorius and the fibrous roof of the canal; the saphenous nerve crosses from its lateral to its medial side. Behind the artery are the Adductores longus and magnus; in front and lateral to it is the Vastus medialis. The femoral vein lies posterior to the upper part, and lateral to the lower part of the artery.

Variations.—Several cases are recorded in which the femoral artery divided into two trunks below the origin of the profunda, and became reunited near the opening in the Adductor magnus, so as to form a single popliteal artery. One occurred in a patient who was operated upon for popliteal aneurism. A few cases have been recorded in which the femoral artery was absent, its place being supplied by the inferior gluteal artery which accompanied the sciatic nerve to the popliteal fossa. The external iliac in these cases was small, and terminated in the profunda. The femoral vein is occasionally placed along the medial side of the artery throughout the entire extent of the femoral triangle; or it may be split so that a large vein is placed on either side of the artery for a greater or lesser distance.

Collateral Circulation.—After ligature of the femoral artery, the main channels for carrying on the circulation are the anastomoses between—(1) the superior and inferior gluteal branches of the hypogastric with the medial and lateral femoral circumflex and first perforating branches of the profunda femoris; (2) the obturator branch of the hypogastric with the medial femoral circumflex of the profunda; (3) the internal pudendal of the hypogastric with the superficial and deep external pudendal of the femoral; (4) the deep iliac circumflex of the external iliac with the lateral femoral circumflex of the profunda and the superficial iliac circumflex of the femoral, and (5) the inferior gluteal of the hypogastric with the perforating branches of the profunda.

Branches.—The branches of the femoral artery are:

Superficial Epigastric.   Deep External Pudendal.
Superficial Iliac Circumflex.   Muscular.
Superficial External Pudendal.   Profunda Femoris.
Highest Genicular.

The **superficial epigastric artery** (*a. epigastrica superficialis*) *arises* from the front of the femoral artery about 1 cm. below the inguinal ligament, and, passing through the femoral sheath and the fascia cribrosa, turns upward in front of the inguinal ligament, and ascends between the two layers of the superficial fascia of the abdominal wall nearly to the umbilicus. It distributes branches to the superficial subinguinal lymph glands, the superficial fascia, and the integument; it anastomoses with branches of the inferior epigastric, and with its fellow opposite.

The **superficial iliac circumflex artery** (*a. circumflexa ilii superficialis*), smallest of the cutaneous branches, *arises* close to the preceding, and, piercing the fascia lata, runs lateralward, parallel with the inguinal ligament, to the crest of the ilium; it divides into branches which supply the integument of the groin, and the superficial subinguinal lymph glands, anastomosing with the deep iliac circumflex, superior gluteal and lateral femoral circumflex arteries.

The **superficial external pudendal artery** (*a. pudenda externa superficialis; superficial external pudic artery*) *arises* from the medial side of the femoral artery, close to the preceding vessels, and, after piercing the femoral sheath and fascia cribrosa, courses medialward, across the spermatic cord (or round ligament in the female), to be distributed to the integument on the lower part of the abdomen, the penis and scrotum in the male, and the labium majus in the female, anastomosing with branches of the internal pudendal.

The **deep external pudendal artery** (*a. pudenda externa profunda; deep external pudic artery*), more deeply seated than the preceding, passes medialward across the Pectineus and the Adductor longus muscles; it is covered by the fascia lata, which it pierces at the medial side of the thigh, and is distributed, in the male, to the integument of the scrotum and perineum, in the female to the labium majus; its branches anastomose with the scrotal (or labial) branches of the perineal artery.

Muscular branches (*rami musculares*) are supplied by the femoral artery to the Sartorius, Vastus medialis, and Adductores.

The **profunda femoris artery** (*a. profunda femoris; deep femoral artery*) (Fig. 542) is a large vessel *arising* from the lateral and back part of the femoral artery, from 2 to 5 cm. below the inguinal ligament. At first it lies lateral to the femoral artery; it then runs behind it and the femoral vein to the medial side of the femur, and, passing downward behind the Adductor longus, ends at the lower third of the thigh in a small branch, which pierces the Adductor magnus, and is distributed on the back of the thigh to the hamstring muscles. The terminal part of the profunda is sometimes named the **fourth perforating artery**.

Relations.—*Behind it*, from above downward, are the Iliacus, Pectineus, Adductor brevis, and Adductor magnus. *In front* it is separated from the femoral artery by the femoral and profunda veins above and by the Adductor longus below. *Laterally*, the origin of the Vastus medialis intervenes between it and the femur.

Variations.—This vessel sometimes arises from the medial side, and, more rarely, from the back of the femoral artery; but a more important peculiarity, from a surgical point of view, is that relating to the height at which the vessel arises. In three-fourths of a large number of cases it arose from 2.25 to 5 cm. below the inguinal ligament; in a few cases the distance was less than 2.25 cm.; more rarely, opposite the ligament; and in one case above the inguinal ligament, from the external iliac. Occasionally the distance between the origin of the vessel and the inguinal ligament exceeds 5 cm.

Branches.—The profunda gives off the following branches: (Fig. 540)

Medial Femoral Circumflex.	Perforating.
Lateral Femoral Circumflex.	Muscular.

The **Medial Femoral Circumflex Artery** (*a. circumflexa femoris medialis; internal circumflex artery*) *arises* from the medial aspect of the profunda, and winds around the medial side of the femur, passing first between the Pectineus and Psoas major, and then between the Obturator externus and the Adductor brevis. At the upper border of the Adductor brevis it gives off two branches: one goes to the Adductores, the Gracilis, and Obturator externus, and anastomoses with the obturator artery; the other descends beneath the Adductor brevis, to supply it and the Adductor magnus; the continuation of the vessel passes backward and divides into superficial, deep, and acetabular branches. The **superficial branch** appears between the Quadratus femoris and upper border of the Adductor magnus, and anastomoses with the inferior gluteal, lateral femoral circumflex, and first perforating arteries (*crucial anastomosis*). The **deep branch** runs obliquely upward upon the tendon of the Obturator externus and in front of the Quadratus femoris toward the trochanteric fossa, where it anastomoses with twigs from the gluteal arteries. The **acetabular branch** *arises* opposite the acetabular notch and enters the hip-joint beneath the transverse ligament in company with an articular branch from the obturator artery; it supplies the fat in the bottom of the acetabulum, and continues along the round ligament to the head of the femur.

The **Lateral Femoral Circumflex Artery** (*a. circumflexa femoris lateralis; external circumflex artery*) *arises* from the lateral side of the profunda, passes horizontally between the divisions of the femoral nerve, and behind the Sartorius and Rectus femoris, and divides into ascending, transverse, and descending branches. The **ascending branch** passes upward, beneath the Tensor fasciæ latæ, to the lateral aspect of the hip, and anastomoses with the terminal branches of the superior gluteal and deep iliac circumflex arteries. The **descending branch** runs downward, behind the Rectus femoris, upon the Vastus lateralis, to which it gives offsets; one long branch descends in the muscle as far as the knee, and anastomoses with the superior lateral genicular branch of the popliteal artery. It is accompanied by the branch of the femoral nerve to the Vastus lateralis. The **transverse branch,** the smallest branch if present, but often absent, passes lateralward over the Vastus intermedius, pierces the Vastus lateralis, and winds around the femur, just below the greater trochanter, anastomosing on the back of the thigh with the medial femoral circumflex, inferior gluteal, and first perforating arteries.

The medial circumflex artery arises independently from the femoral in from 19 to 26.5 per cent. of cases, according to various authors. The lateral circumflex artery arises independently from the femoral as frequently as 18 per cent. of the time. The two circumflex arteries may arise by a common trunk from the profunda femoris.

The **Perforating Arteries** (Fig. 536), usually three in number, are so named because they perforate the tendon of the Adductor magnus to reach the back of the thigh. They pass backward close to the linea aspera of the femur under cover of small tendinous arches in the muscle. The first is given off above the Adductor brevis, the second in front of that muscle, and the third immediately below it.

The **first perforating artery** (*a. perforans prima*) passes backward between the Pectineus and Adductor brevis (sometimes perforating the latter); it pierces the Adductor magnus close to the linea aspera. It gives branches to the Adductores brevis and magnus, Biceps femoris, and Glutæus maximus, and anastomoses with the inferior gluteal, medial and lateral femoral circumflex and second perforating arteries. (Fig. 540)

The **second perforating artery** (*a. perforans secunda*), larger than the first, pierces the tendons of the Adductores brevis and magnus, and divides into ascending and descending branches, which supply the posterior femoral muscles, anastomosing with the first and third perforating. The second artery frequently *arises* in common with the first. The **nutrient artery** of the femur is usually given off from the second perforating artery; when two nutrient arteries exist, they usually spring from the first and third perforating vessels.

The **third perforating artery** (*a. perforans tertia*) is given off below the Adductor brevis; it pierces the Adductor magnus, and divides into branches which supply the posterior femoral muscles; anastomosing above with the higher perforating arteries, and below with the terminal branches of the profunda and the muscular branches of the popliteal. The nutrient artery of the femur may arise from this branch. The termination of the profunda artery, already described, is sometimes termed the **fourth perforating artery.**

Numerous **muscular branches** *arise* from the profunda; some of these end in the Adductores, others pierce the Adductor magnus, give branches to the hamstrings, and anastomose with the medial femoral circumflex artery and with the superior muscular branches of the popliteal.

The **highest genicular artery** (*a. genus suprema; anastomotica magna artery*) (Fig. 542) *arises* from the femoral just before it passes through the opening in the tendon of the Adductor magnus, and immediately divides into a saphenous and a musculo-articular branch. The **saphenous branch** pierces the aponeurotic covering of the adductor canal, and accompanies the saphenous nerve to the medial side of the knee. It passes between the Sartorius and Gracilis, and, piercing the fascia lata, is distributed to the integument of the upper and medial part of the leg, anastomosing with the medial inferior genicular artery. The **musculo-articular branch** descends in the substance of the Vastus medialis, and in front of the tendon of the Adductor magnus, to the medial side of the knee, where it anastomoses with the medial superior genicular artery and anterior recurrent tibial artery. A branch from this vessel crosses above the patellar surface of the femur, forming an anastomotic arch with the lateral superior genicular artery, and supplying branches to the knee-joint.

THE POPLITEAL FOSSA (Fig. 543).

Boundaries.—The popliteal fossa or space is a lozenge-shaped space, at the back of the knee-joint. Laterally it is bounded by the Biceps femoris above, and by the Plantaris and the lateral head of the Gastrocnemius below; medially it is limited by the Semitendinous and Semimembranosus above, and by the medial head of the Gastrocnemius below. The floor is formed by the popliteal surface of the femur, the oblique popliteal ligament of the knee-joint, the upper end of the tibia, and the fascia covering the Popliteus; the fossa is covered by the fascia lata.

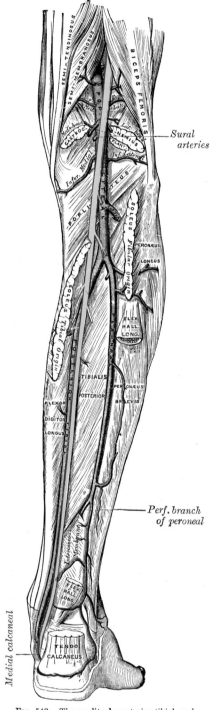

FIG. 543.—The popliteal, posterior tibial, and peroneal arteries.

Contents.—The popliteal fossa contains the popliteal vessels, the tibial and the common peroneal nerves, the termination of the small saphenous vein, the lower part of the posterior femoral cutaneous nerve, the articular branch from the obturator nerve, a few small lymph nodes, and a considerable amount of fat. The tibial nerve descends through the middle of the fossa, lying under the deep fascia and crossing the vessels posteriorly from the lateral to the medial side. The common peroneal nerve descends on the lateral side of the upper part of the fossa, close to the tendon of the Biceps femoris. On the floor of the fossa are the popliteal vessels, the vein being superficial to the artery and united to it by dense areolar tissue; the vein is a thick-walled vessel, at first lateral to the artery, and then crossing it posteriorly to gain its medial side below; sometimes it is double, the artery lying between the two veins, which are usually connected by short transverse branches. The articular branch from the obturator nerve descends upon the artery to the knee-joint. The popliteal lymph nodes, six or seven in number, are imbedded in the fat; one lies beneath the popliteal fascia near the termination of the external saphenous vein, another between the popliteal artery and the back of the knee-joint, while others are placed alongside the popliteal vessel. Arising from the artery, and passing off from it at right angles, are its genicular branches.

The Popliteal Artery (A. Poplitea) (Fig. 543).

The **popliteal artery** is the continuation of the femoral, and courses through the popliteal fossa. It extends from the opening in the Adductor magnus, at the junction of the middle and lower thirds of the thigh, downward and lateralward to the intercondyloid fossa of the femur, and then vertically downward to the lower border of the Popliteus, where it divides into anterior and posterior tibial arteries.

Relations.—In *front* of the artery from above downward are the popliteal surface of the femur (which is separated from the vessel by some fat), the back of the knee-joint, and the fascia covering the Popliteus. *Behind*, it is overlapped by the Semimembranosus above, and is covered by the Gastrocnemius and Plantaris below. In the middle part of its course the artery is separated from the integument and fasciæ by a quantity of fat, and is crossed from the lateral to the medial side by the tibial nerve and the popliteal vein, the vein being between the nerve and the artery and closely adherent to the latter. On its *lateral* side, above, are the Biceps femoris, the tibial nerve, the popliteal vein, and the lateral condyle of the femur; below, the Plantaris and the lateral head of the Gastrocnemius. On its *medial* side, above, are the Semimembranosus and the medial condyle of the femur; below, the tibial nerve, the popliteal vein, and the medial head of the Gastrocnemius. The relations of the popliteal lymph glands to the artery are described above.

Variations in Point of Division.—Occasionally the popliteal artery divides into its terminal branches opposite the knee-joint. The anterior tibial under these circumstances usually passes in front of the Popliteus.

Unusual Branches.—The artery sometimes divides into the anterior tibial and peroneal, the posterior tibial being wanting, or very small. Occasionally it divides into three branches, the anterior and posterior tibial, and peroneal.

Branches.—The branches of the popliteal artery are:

Muscular { Superior / Sural.

Cutaneous.

Medial Superior Genicular

Lateral Superior Genicular.

Middle Genicular.

Medial Inferior Genicular.

Lateral Inferior Genicular.

The two or three **superior muscular branches** *arise* from the upper part of the artery, and are distributed to the lower parts of the Adductor magnus and hamstring muscles, anastomosing with the endings of the profunda femoris.

The **sural arteries** (*aa. surales; inferior muscular arteries*) are two large branches, which are distributed to the Gastrocnemius, Soleus, and Plantaris. They *arise* from the popliteal artery opposite the knee-joint.

The **cutaneous branches** *arise* either from the popliteal artery or from some of its branches; they descend between the two heads of the Gastrocnemius, and, piercing the deep fascia, are distributed to the skin of the back of the leg. One branch usually accompanies the small saphenous vein.

The **superior genicular arteries** (*aa. genus superiores; superior articular arteries*) (Figs. 542, 543), two in number, *arise* one on either side of the popliteal, and wind around the femur immediately above its condyles to the front of the knee-joint. The **medial superior genicular** runs in front of the Semimembranosus and Semitendinosus, above the medial head of the Gastrocnemius, and passes beneath the tendon of the Adductor magnus. It divides into two branches, one of which supplies the Vastus medialis, anastomosing with the highest genicular and medial inferior genicular arteries; the other ramifies close to the surface of the femur, supplying it and the knee-joint, and anastomosing with the lateral superior genicular artery. The medial superior genicular artery is frequently of small size, a condition, which is associated with an increase in the size of the highest genicular. The **lateral superior genicular** passes above the lateral condyle of the femur, beneath the tendon of the Biceps femoris, and divides into a superficial and a deep branch; the superficial branch supplies the Vastus lateralis, and anastomoses with the descending branch of the lateral femoral circumflex and the lateral inferior genicular arteries; the deep branch supplies the lower part of the femur and knee-joint, and forms an anastomotic arch across the front of the bone with the highest genicular and the medial inferior genicular arteries.

The **middle genicular artery** (*a. genus media; azygos articular artery*) is a small branch, *arising* opposite the back of the knee-joint. It pierces the oblique popliteal ligament, and supplies the ligaments and synovial membrane in the interior of the articulation.

The **inferior genicular arteries** (*aa. genus inferiores; inferior articular arteries*) (Figs. 542, 543), two in number, *arise* from the popliteal beneath the Gastrocnemius. The **medial inferior genicular** first descends along the upper margin of the Popliteus, to which it gives branches; it then passes below the medial condyle of the tibia, beneath the tibial collateral ligament, at the anterior border of which it ascends to the front and medial side of the joint, to supply the upper end of the tibia and the articulation of the knee, anastomosing with the lateral inferior and medial superior genicular arteries. The **lateral inferior genicular** runs lateralward above the head of the fibula to the front of the knee-joint, passing beneath the lateral head of the Gastrocnemius, the fibular collateral ligament, and the tendon of the Biceps femoris. It ends by dividing into branches, which anastomose with the medial inferior and lateral superior genicular arteries, and with the anterior recurrent tibial artery.

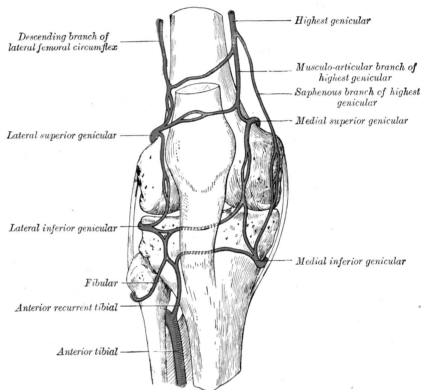

Descending branch of lateral femoral circumflex

Highest genicular

Musculo-articular branch of highest genicular

Saphenous branch of highest genicular

Medial superior genicular

Lateral superior genicular

Lateral inferior genicular

Medial inferior genicular

Fibular

Anterior recurrent tibial

Anterior tibial

Fig. 544.—Circumpatellar anastomosis.

The Anastomosis Around the Knee-joint (Fig. 544).—Around and above the patella, and on the contiguous ends of the femur and tibia, is an intricate net-work of vessels forming a superficial and a deep plexus. The **superficial plexus** is situated in the superficial fascia around the patella, and forms three well-defined arches: one, above the upper border of the patella, in the loose connective tissue over the Quadriceps femoris; the other two, below the level of the patella, are situated in the fat behind the ligamentum patellæ. The **deep plexus**, which forms a close net-work of vessels, lies on the lower end of the femur and upper end of the tibia around their articular surfaces, and sends numerous offsets into the interior of the joint. The arteries which form this plexus are the two medial and the two lateral genicular branches of the popliteal, the highest genicular, the descending branch of the lateral femoral circumflex, and the anterior recurrent tibial.

The Anterior Tibial Artery (A. Tibialis Anterior) (Fig. 545).

The **anterior tibial artery** commences at the bifurcation of the popliteal, at the lower border of the Popliteus, passes forward between the two heads of the Tibialis posterior, and through the aperture above the upper border of the interosseous membrane, to the deep part of the front of the leg: it here lies close to the medial side of the neck of the fibula. It then descends on the anterior surface of the interosseous membrane, gradually approaching the tibia; at the lower part of the leg it lies on this bone, and then on the front of the ankle-joint, where it is more superficial, and becomes the **dorsalis pedis.**

Relations.—In the upper two-thirds of its extent, the anterior tibial artery rests upon the interosseous membrane; in the lower third, upon the front of the tibia, and the anterior ligament of the ankle-joint. In the upper third of its course, it lies between the Tibialis anterior and Extensor digitorum longus; in the middle third between the Tibialis anterior and Extensor hallucis longus. At the ankle it is crossed from the lateral to the medial side by the tendon of the Extensor hallucis longus, lying between it and the first tendon of the Extensor digitorum longus. It is covered in the upper two-thirds by the muscles which lie on either side of it, and by the deep fascia; in the lower third, by the integument and fascia, and the transverse and cruciate crural ligaments.

The anterior tibial artery is accompanied by a pair of venæ comitantes which lie one on either side of the artery; the deep peroneal nerve, coursing around the lateral side of the neck of the fibula, comes into relation with the lateral side of the artery shortly after it has reached the front of the leg; about the middle of the leg the nerve is in front of the artery; at the lower part it is generally again on the lateral side.

Variations.—This vessel may be diminished in size, may be deficient to a greater or less extent or may be entirely wanting, its place being supplied by perforating branches from the posterior tibial, or by the perforating branch of the peroneal artery. The artery occasionally deviates toward the fibular side of the leg, regaining its usual position at the front of the ankle. In rare instances the vessel has been found to approach the surface in the middle of the leg, being covered merely by the integument and fascia below that point.

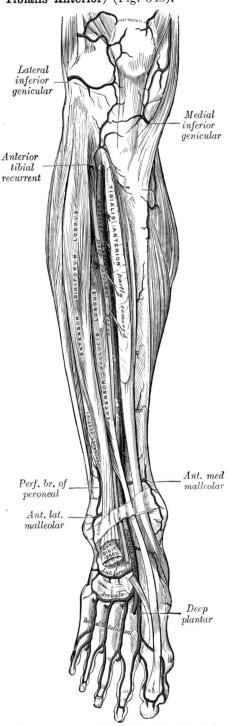

Fig. 545.—Anterior tibial and dorsalis pedis arteries.

Branches.—The branches of the anterior tibial artery are:

Posterior Tibial Recurrent.   Muscular.
Fibular.   Anterior Medial Malleolar.
Anterior Tibial Recurrent.   Anterior Lateral Malleolar.

The **posterior tibial recurrent artery** (*a. recurrens tibialis posterior*) an inconstant branch, is given off from the anterior tibial before that vessel passes through the interosseous space. It ascends in front of the Popliteus, which it supplies, and anastomoses with the inferior genicular branches of the popliteal artery, giving an offset to the tibiofibular joint.

The **fibular artery** is sometimes derived from the anterior tibial, sometimes from the posterior tibial. It passes lateralward, around the neck of the fibula, through the Soleus, which it supplies, and ends in the substance of the Peroneus longus.

The **anterior tibial recurrent artery** (*a. recurrens tibialis anterior*) *arises* from the anterior tibial, as soon as that vessel has passed through the interosseous space; it ascends in the Tibialis anterior, ramifies on the front and sides of the knee-joint, and assists in the formation of the patellar plexus by anastomosing with the genicular branches of the popliteal, and with the highest genicular artery.

The **muscular branches** (*rami musculares*) are numerous; they are distributed to the muscles which lie on either side of the vessel, some piercing the deep fascia to supply the integument, others passing through the interosseous membrane, and anastomosing with branches of the posterior tibial and peroneal arteries.

The **anterior medial malleolar artery** (*a. malleolaris anterior medialis; internal malleolar artery*) *arises* about 5 cm. above the ankle-joint, and passes behind the tendons of the Extensor hallucis longus and Tibialis anterior, to the medial side of the ankle, upon which it ramifies, anastomosing with branches of the posterior tibial and medial plantar arteries and with the medial calcaneal from the posterior tibial.

The **anterior lateral malleolar artery** (*a. malleolaris anterior lateralis; external malleolar artery*) passes beneath the tendons of the Extensor digitorum longus and Peronæus tertius and supplies the lateral side of the ankle, anastomosing with the perforating branch of the peroneal artery, and with ascending twigs from the lateral tarsal artery.

The arteries around the ankle-joint anastomose freely with one another and form net-works below the corresponding malleoli. The **medial malleolar net-work** is formed by the anterior medial malleolar branch of the anterior tibial, the medial tarsal branches of the dorsalis pedis, the posterior medial malleolar and medial calcaneal branches of the posterior tibial and branches from the medial plantar artery. The **lateral malleolar net-work** is formed by the anterior lateral malleolar branch of the anterior tibial, the lateral tarsal branch of the dorsalis pedis, the perforating and the lateral calcaneal branches of the peroneal, and twigs from the lateral plantar artery. The anterior medial and anterior lateral malleolar arteries often branch from the dorsalis pedis.

The Dorsalis Pedis Artery (**A. Dorsalis Pedis**) (Fig. 545).

The **arteria dorsalis pedis,** the continuation of the anterior tibial, passes forward from the ankle-joint along the tibial side of the dorsum of the foot to the proximal part of the first intermetatarsal space, where it divides into two branches, the **first dorsal metatarsal** and the **deep plantar.**

Relations.—This vessel, in its course forward, rests upon the front of the articular capsule of the ankle-joint, the talus, navicular, and second cuneiform bones, and the ligaments connecting them, being covered by the integument, fascia and cruciate ligament, and crossed near its termination by the first tendon of the Extensor digitorum brevis. On its *tibial side* is the tendon of the Extensor hallucis longus; on its *fibular side*, the first tendon of the Extensor digitorum longus, and the termination of the deep peroneal nerve. It is accompanied by two veins.

Variations.—The dorsal artery of the foot may be larger than usual, to compensate for a deficient plantar artery; or its terminal branches to the toes may be absent, the toes then being supplied by the medial plantar; or its place may be taken by a large perforating branch of the peroneal artery, in 3 per cent. of bodies. It frequently curves lateralward, lying lateral to the line between the middle of the ankle and the back part of the first interosseous space. In 12 per cent of bodies the dorsalis pedis is so small that it may be spoken of as absent.

Branches.—The branches of the arteria dorsalis pedis are:

Lateral Tarsal.	Arcuate.
Medial Tarsal.	First Dorsal Metatarsal.

Deep Plantar.

The **lateral tarsal artery** (*a. tarsea lateralis; tarsal artery*) *arises* from the dorsalis pedis, as that vessel crosses the navicular bone; it passes in an arched direction lateralward, lying upon the tarsal bones, and covered by the Extensor digitorum brevis; it supplies this muscle and the articulations of the tarsus, and anastomoses with branches of the arcuate, anterior lateral malleolar and lateral plantar arteries, and with the perforating branch of the peroneal artery.

The **medial tarsal arteries** (*aa. tarseæ mediales*) are two or three small branches which ramify on the medial border of the foot and join the medial malleolar network.

The **arcuate artery** (*a. arcuata; metatarsal artery*) *arises* a little anterior to the lateral tarsal artery; it passes lateralward, over the bases of the metatarsal bones, beneath the tendons of the Extensor digitorum brevis, its direction being influenced by its point of origin; and it anastomoses with the lateral tarsal and lateral plantar arteries. This vessel gives off the **second, third,** and **fourth dorsal metatarsal arteries,** which run forward upon the corresponding Interossei dorsales; in the clefts between the toes, each divides into two dorsal digital branches for the adjoining toes. At the proximal parts of the interosseous spaces these vessels receive the posterior perforating branches from the plantar arch, and at the distal parts of the spaces they are joined by the anterior perforating branches, from the plantar metatarsal arteries. The fourth dorsal metatarsal artery gives off a branch which supplies the lateral side of the fifth toe. The arcuate artery is a vessel of significant size in only 50 per cent. of bodies.

The **first dorsal metatarsal artery** (*a. dorsalis hallucis*) runs forward on the first Interosseous dorsalis, and at the cleft between the first and second toes divides into two branches, one of which passes beneath the tendon of the Extensor hallucis longus, and is distributed to the medial border of the great toe; the other bifurcates to supply the adjoining sides of the great and second toes.

The **deep plantar artery** (*ramus plantaris profundus; communicating artery*) descends into the sole of the foot, between the two heads of the first Interosseous dorsalis, and unites with the termination of the lateral plantar artery, to complete the plantar arch. It sends a branch along the medial side of the great toe, and continues forward along the first interosseous space as the **first plantar metatarsal artery,** which bifurcates for the supply of the adjacent sides of the first and second toes.

The Posterior Tibial Artery (**A. Tibialis Posterior**) (Fig. 543).

The **posterior tibial artery** begins at the lower border of the Popliteus, opposite the interval between the tibia and fibula; it extends obliquely downward, and, as it descends, it approaches the tibial side of the leg, lying behind the tibia, and in the lower part of its course is situated midway between the medial malleolus and the medial process of the calcaneal tuberosity. Here it divides beneath the origin of the Abductor hallucis into the **medial and lateral plantar arteries.**

Relations.—The posterior tibial artery lies successively upon the Tibialis posterior, the Flexor digitorum longus, the tibia, and the back of the ankle-joint. It is covered by the deep transverse fascia of the leg, which separates it above from the Gastrocnemius and Soleus; at its termination it is covered by the Abductor hallucis. In the lower third of the leg, where it is more superficial, it is covered only by the integument and fascia, and runs parallel with the medial border of the tendo calcaneus. It is accompanied by two veins, and by the tibial nerve, which lies at first to the medial side of the artery, but soon crosses it posteriorly, and is in the greater part of its course on its lateral side.

Behind the medial malleolus, the tendons, bloodvessels, and nerve are arranged, under cover of the laciniate ligament, in the following order from the medial to the lateral side: (1) the tendons of the Tibialis posterior and Flexor digitorum longus, lying in the same groove, behind the malleolus, the former being the more medial. Next is the posterior tibial artery, with a vein on either side of it; and lateral to the vessels is the tibial nerve; about 1.25 cm. nearer the heel is the tendon of the Flexor hallucis longus.

Variations in Size.—The posterior tibial is not infrequently smaller than usual, or absent, its place being supplied by a large peroneal artery, which either joins the small posterior tibial artery, or continues alone to the sole of the foot.

Branches.—The branches of the posterior tibial artery are:

Peroneal.	Posterior Medial Malleolar.
Nutrient.	Communicating.
Muscular.	Medial Calcaneal.

The **peroneal artery** (*a. peronœa*) is deeply seated on the back of the fibular side of the leg. It *arises* from the posterior tibial, about 2.5 cm. below the lower border of the Popliteus, passes obliquely toward the fibula, and then descends along the medial side of that bone, contained in a fibrous canal between the Tibialis posterior and the Flexor hallucis longus, or in the substance of the latter muscle. It then runs behind the tibiofibular syndesmosis and divides into lateral calcaneal branches which ramify on the lateral and posterior surfaces of the calcaneus.

It is covered, in the *upper* part of its course, by the Soleus and deep transverse fascia of the leg; *below,* by the Flexor hallucis longus.

Peculiarities in Origin.—The peroneal artery may arise 7 or 8 cm. below the Popliteus, or from the posterior tibial high up, or even from the popliteal.

Its size is more frequently increased than diminished; and then it either reinforces the posterior tibial by its junction with it, or altogether takes the place of the posterior tibial in the lower part of the leg and foot, the latter vessel only existing as a short muscular branch. In those rare cases where the peroneal artery is smaller than usual, a branch from the posterior tibial supplies its place; and a branch from the anterior tibial compensates for the diminished anterior peroneal artery. In one case the peroneal artery was entirely wanting.

Branches.—The branches of the peroneal are:

Muscular.	Perforating.
Nutrient (Tibial and Fibular).	Communicating.
Lateral Calcaneal.	

The **muscular branches** of the peroneal artery go to the Soleus, Tibialis posterior, Flexor hallucis longus, and Peronei.

The **nutrient artery** (*a. nutricia fibulæ*) is directed downward into the fibula.

The **perforating branch** (*ramus perforans; anterior peroneal artery*) pierces the interosseous membrane, about 5 cm. above the lateral malleolus, to reach the front of the leg, where it anastomoses with the anterior lateral malleolar; it then passes down in front of the tibiofibular syndesmosis, gives branches to the tarsus, and anastomoses with the lateral tarsal. The perforating branch is sometimes enlarged (3 per cent. of cases), and takes the place of the dorsalis pedis artery. In 50 per cent. of bodies, it anastomoses with a lateral branch of the anterior tibial, proximal to the anterior lateral malleolar.

The **communicating branch** (*ramus communicans*) is given off from the peroneal about 2.5 cm. from its lower end, and joins the communicating branch of the posterior tibial.

The **lateral calcaneal** (*ramus calcaneus lateralis; external calcaneal*) are the terminal branches of the peroneal artery; they pass to the lateral side of the heel, and communicate with the lateral malleolar and, on the back of the heel, with the medial calcaneal arteries.

The **nutrient artery** (*a. nutricia tibiæ*) of the tibia *arises* from the posterior tibial, near its origin, and after supplying a few muscular branches enters the nutrient canal of the bone, which it traverses obliquely from above downward. This is the largest nutrient artery of bone in the body.

The **muscular branches** of the posterior tibial are distributed to the Soleus and deep muscles along the back of the leg.

The **posterior medial malleolar artery** (*a. malleolaris posterior medialis; internal malleolar artery*) is a small branch which winds around the tibial malleolus and ends in the medial malleolar net-work.

The **communicating branch** (*ramus communicans*) runs transversely across the back of the tibia, about 5 cm. above its lower end, beneath the Flexor hallucis longus, and joins the communicating branch of the peroneal.

The **medial calcaneal** (*rami calcanei mediales; internal calcaneal*) are several large arteries which *arise* from the posterior tibial just before its division; they pierce the laciniate ligament and are distributed to the fat and integument behind the tendo calcaneus and about the heel, and to the muscles on the tibial side of the sole, anastomosing with the peroneal and medial malleolar and, on the back of the heel, with the lateral calcaneal arteries.

The **medial plantar artery** (*a. plantaris medialis; internal plantar artery*) (Figs. 546 and 547), much smaller than the lateral, passes forward along the medial side of the foot. It is at first situated above the Abductor hallucis, and then between it and the Flexor digitorum brevis, both of which it supplies. At the base of the first metatarsal bone, where it is much diminished in size, it passes along the medial border of the first toe, anastomosing with the first dorsal metatarsal artery. Small superficial digital branches accompany the digital branches of the medial plantar nerve and join the plantar metatarsal arteries of the first three spaces.

The **lateral plantar artery** (*a. plantaris lateralis; external plantar artery*), much larger than the medial, passes obliquely lateralward and forward to the base of the fifth metatarsal bone. It then turns medialward to the interval between the bases of the first and second metatarsal bones, where it unites with the deep plantar branch of the dorsalis pedis artery, thus completing the **plantar arch.** As this artery passes lateralward, it is first placed between the calcaneus and Abductor hallucis, and then between the Flexor digitorum brevis and Quadratus plantæ; as it runs forward to the base of the little toe it lies more superficially between the Flexor digitorum brevis and Abductor digiti quinti, covered by the plantar aponeurosis and integument. The remaining portion of the vessel is deeply situated; it extends from the base of the fifth metatarsal bone to the proximal part of the first interosseous space, and forms the plantar arch; it is convex forward, lies below the bases of the second, third, and fourth metatarsal bones and the corresponding Interossei, and upon the oblique part of the Adductor hallucis.

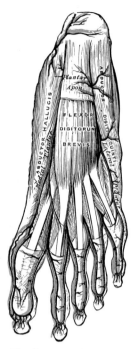

Fig. 546.—The plantar arteries.   Superficial view.

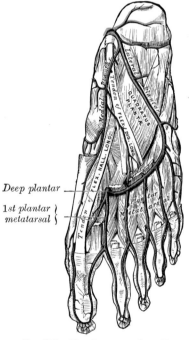

Deep plantar

1st plantar }
metatarsal }

Fig. 547.—The plantar arteries.   Deep view.

Branches.—The plantar arch, besides distributing numerous branches to the muscles, integument, and fasciæ in the sole, gives off the following branches:

Perforating.   Plantar Metatarsal.

The **Perforating Branches** (*rami perforantes*) are *three* in number; they ascend through the proximal parts of the second, third, and fourth interosseous spaces, between the heads of the Interossei dorsales, and anastomose with the dorsal metatarsal arteries.

The **Plantar Metatarsal Arteries** (*aa. metatarseœ plantares; digital branches*) are *four* in number, and run forward between the metatarsal bones and in contact with the Interossei. Each divides into a pair of plantar digital arteries which supply the adjacent sides of the toes. Near their points of division each sends upward an **anterior perforating branch** to join the corresponding dorsal metatarsal artery. The **first plantar metatarsal artery** (*arteria princeps hallucis*) springs from the junction between the lateral plantar and deep plantar arteries and sends a digital branch to the medial side of the first toe. The digital branch for the lateral side of the fifth toe arises from the lateral plantar artery near the base of the fifth metatarsal bone.

BIBLIOGRAPHY.

ARTERIES

Variations in origin and course of the hepatic artery and its branches. BROWNE, E. Z.: 1940. Surgery, Vol. 8, pp. 424–445.

Mammary arteries. CARR, B. W., W. E. BISHOP, and B. J. ANSON: 1942. Quart. Bull. Northwestern Univ. Med. School, Vol. 16, pp. 150–154.

The visceral branches of the abdominal aorta: Topographical relationships. CAULDWELL, E. W., and B. J. ANSON: 1943. Am. J. Anat., Vol. 73, pp. 27–57.

The aortic arch in primates. DE GARIS, C. F.: 1941. Am. J. Phys. Anthrop., Vol. 28, pp. 41–74.

The retroduodenal artery. EDWARDS, L. F.: 1941. Anat. Rec., Vol. 81, pp. 351–355.

The arterial network supplying the dorsum of the foot. HUBER, J. F.: 1941. Anat. Rec., Vol. 80, pp. 373–391.

The variational anatomy of the spleen and splenic artery. MICHELS, N. A.: 1942. Am. J. Anat., Vol. 70, pp. 21–72.

Observations upon the arrangement of the axillary artery and brachial plexus. MILLER, R. A.: 1939. Am. J. Anat., Vol. 64, pp. 143–163.

The inferior phrenic artery: Origin and suprarenal branches. PICK, J. W., and B. J. ANSON: 1940. Anat. Rec., Vol. 78, pp. 413–427.

The origin of the obturator artery. PICK, J. W., B. J. ANSON, and F. L. ASHLEY: 1942. Am. J. Anat., Vol. 70, pp. 317–343.

The origins of transverse cervical and of transverse scapular arteries in American whites and negroes. READ, W. T., and M. TROTTER: 1941. Am. J. Phys. Anthrop., Vol. 28, pp. 239–247.

Arteries and veins in the mammalian brain. SCHARRER, E.: 1940. Anat. Rec., Vol. 78, pp. 173–196.

A note on the formation of the plantar arterial arch of the human foot. VANN, H. M.: 1943. Anat. Rec., Vol. 85, pp. 269–275.

PULMONARY ARTERY AND DUCTUS ARTERIOSUS

Observations on the ductus arteriosus of the guinea pig in relation to its method of closure. KENNEDY, J. A., and S. L. CLARK: 1941. Anat. Rec., Vol. 79, pp. 349–371.

The ductus arteriosus in the human fetus and newborn infant. NOBACK, G. J., and I. REHMAN: 1941. Anat. Rec., Vol. 81, pp. 505–527.

Anomalies of the cardio-pulmonary circuit compensated without a ductus arteriosus. SINCLAIR, J. G., and N. D. SCHOFIELD: 1944. Anat. Rec., Vol. 90, pp. 209–215.

ANOMALIES AND VARIATIONS

Transposition of the aorta and the pulmonary artery. BREMER, J. L.: 1942. Arch. Path., Vol. 34, pp. 1016–1030.

A rare type of anomalous ophthalmic artery in a negro. HARVEY, J. C., and L. M. HOWARD: 1945. Anat. Rec., Vol. 92, pp. 87–90.

An anomalous middle meningeal artery. Low, F. N.: 1946. Anat. Rec., Vol. 95, pp. 347–351.

Variations in the origin of arteries derived from the aortic arch, in American whites and negroes. McDonald, J. J., and B. J. Anson: 1940. Am. J. Phys. Anthrop., Vol. 27, pp. 91–107.

Report of an unusual cœliacomesenteric trunk with unique distribution and anastomoses. Munger, R. S.: 1941. Anat. Rec., Vol. 80, pp. 55–59.

Arterial anomalies pertaining to the aortic arches and the branches arising from them. Poynter, C. W. M.: 1916. Nebraska Univ. Studies, Vol. 16, pp. 229–345.

Congenital anomalies of the arteries and veins of the human body with bibliography. Poynter, C. W. M.: 1923. Nebraska Univ. Studies, Vol. 22, pp. 1–106.

An interpretation of the recorded arterial anomalies of the human leg and foot. Senior, H. D.: 1919. J. Anat., Vol. 53, pp. 130–171.

COLLATERAL CIRCULATION

Collateral circulation following an obstruction of the abdominal aorta. Baylin, G. J.: 1939. Anat. Rec., Vol. 75, pp. 405–408.

COMPARATIVE ANATOMY AND PHYSICAL ANTHROPOLOGY

The hypogastric artery in American whites and negroes. Ashley, F. L., and B. J. Anson: 1941. Am. J. Phys. Anthrop., Vol. 28, pp. 381–395.

The coronary arteries in 266 hearts of rhesus monkey. Chase, R. E.: 1938. Am. J. Phys. Anthrop., Vol. 23, pp. 299–320.

Branches of the aortic arch in 153 rhesus monkeys. De Garis, C. F.: 1938. Anat. Rec., Vol. 70, pp. 251–262.

The origin of branches of the axillary artery in the Chinese. Ming-Tzu, P.: 1940. Am. J. Phys. Anthrop., Vol. 27, pp. 269–279.

The level of termination of the popliteal artery in the white and the negro. Trotter, M.: 1940. Am. J. Phys. Anthrop., Vol. 27, pp. 109–118.

HISTOLOGY

A study of the structure of the media of the distributing arteries by the method of microdissection. Strong, K. C.: 1938. Anat. Rec., Vol. 72, pp. 151–167.

EMBRYOLOGY

Transformation of the aortic arch system during the development of the human embryo. Congdon, E. D.: 1922. Carnegie Cont. Emb., Vol. 14, pp. 47–110.

The development of the cardiac-coronary circulatory system. Goldsmith, J. B., and H. W. Butler: 1937. Am. J. Anat., Vol. 60, pp. 185–201.

The development of the arteries of the human lower extremity. Senior, H. D.: 1919. Am. J. Anat., Vol. 25, pp. 55–95.

An interpretation of the recorded arterial anomalies of the human pelvis and thigh. Senior, H. D.: 1925. Am. J. Anat., Vol. 36, pp. 1–46.

ARTERIOVENOUS ANASTOMOSIS

Observations on living arteriovenous anastomoses as seen in transparent chambers introduced into the rabbit's ear. Clark, E. R., and E. L. 1934. Am. J. Anat., Vol. 54, pp. 229–286.

THE VEINS.

THE **Veins** convey the blood from the capillaries to the heart. They consist of two distinct sets of vessels, the **pulmonary** and **systemic**. The **Pulmonary Veins**, unlike other veins, contain arterial blood, which they return from the lungs to the left atrium of the heart. The **Systemic Veins** return the venous blood from the body generally to the right atrium of the heart.

The **Portal Vein**, an appendage to the systemic venous system, is confined to the abdominal cavity, and returns the venous blood from the spleen and the viscera of digestion to the liver. This vessel ramifies in the substance of the liver and there breaks up into a minute network of capillary-like vessels from which the blood is conveyed by the hepatic veins to the inferior vena cava.

The veins commence by minute plexuses which receive the blood from the capillaries. The branches arising from these plexuses unite together into trunks, and these, in their passage toward the heart, constantly increase in size as they receive tributaries, or join other veins. The veins are larger and altogether more numerous than the arteries; hence, the entire capacity of the venous system is much greater than that of the arterial; the capacity of the pulmonary veins, however, only slightly exceeds that of the pulmonary arteries. The veins are cylindrical like the arteries; their walls, however, are thin and they collapse when the vessels are empty, and the uniformity of their surfaces is interrupted at intervals by slight constrictions, which indicate the existence of valves in their interior. They communicate very freely with one another, especially in certain regions of the body; and these communications exist between the larger trunks as well as between the smaller branches. Thus, between the venous sinuses of the cranium, and between the veins of the neck, where obstruction would be attended with imminent danger to the cerebral venous system, large and frequent anastomoses are found. The same free communication exists between the veins throughout the whole extent of the vertebral canal, and between the veins composing the various venous plexuses in the abdomen and pelvis, e. g., the spermatic, uterine, vesical, and pudendal.

The systemic venous channels are subdivided into three sets, viz., **superficial** and **deep veins**, and **venous sinuses**.

The **Superficial Veins** (*cutaneous veins*) are found between the layers of the superficial fascia immediately beneath the skin; they return the blood from these structures, and communicate with the deep veins by perforating the deep fascia.

The **Deep Veins** accompany the arteries, and are usually enclosed in the same sheaths with those vessels. With the smaller arteries—as the radial, ulnar, brachial, tibial, peroneal—they exist generally in pairs, one lying on each side of the vessel, and are called **venæ comitantes**. The larger arteries—such as the axillary, sub-clavian, popliteal, and femoral—have usually only one accompanying vein. In certain organs of the body, however, the deep veins do not accompany the arteries; for instance, the veins in the skull and vertebral canal, the hepatic veins in the liver, and the larger veins returning blood from the bones.

Venous Sinuses, found only in the interior of the skull, consist of canals formed by separation of the two layers of the dura mater; their outer coat consists of fibrous tissue, their inner of an endothelial layer continuous with the lining of the veins.

THE PULMONARY VEINS (VENÆ PULMONALES).

The **pulmonary veins** return the arterialized blood from the lungs to the left atrium of the heart. They are four in number, two from each lung, and are destitute of valves. They commence in a capillary net-work upon the walls of the air sacs, where they are continuous with the capillary ramifications of the pulmonary artery, and, joining together, form one vessel for each lobule. These vessels uniting successively, form a single trunk for each lobe, three for the right, and two for the left lung. The vein from the middle lobe of the right lung generally unites with that from the upper lobe, so that ultimately two trunks from each lung are formed; they perforate the fibrous layer of the pericardium and open separately into the upper and back part of the left atrium. Occasionally the three veins on the right side remain separate. Not infrequently the two left pulmonary veins end by a common opening.

At the root of the lung, the superior pulmonary vein lies in front of and a little below the pulmonary artery; the inferior is situated at the lowest part of the hilum of the lung and on a plane posterior to the upper vein. Behind the pulmonary artery is the bronchus.

Within the pericardium, their anterior surfaces are invested by its serous layer.

The right pulmonary veins pass behind the right atrium and superior vena cava; the left in front of the descending thoracic aorta.

THE SYSTEMIC VEINS.

The **systemic veins** may be arranged into three groups: (1) The **veins of the heart.** (2) The veins of the **upper extremities, head, neck,** and **thorax,** which end in the superior vena cava. (3) The veins of the **lower extremities, abdomen,** and **pelvis,** which end in the inferior vena cava.

THE VEINS OF THE HEART (VV. Cordis) (Fig. 548).

Coronary Sinus (*sinus coronarius*).—Most of the veins of the heart open into the coronary sinus. This is a wide venous channel about 2.25 cm. in length situated in the posterior part of the coronary sulcus, and covered by muscular fibers from the left atrium. It ends in the right atrium between the opening of the inferior vena cava and the atrioventricular aperture, its orifice being guarded by an incompetent semilunar valve, the **valve of the coronary sinus** (*valve of Thebesius*).

Tributaries.—Its tributaries are the great, small, and middle cardiac veins, the posterior vein of the left ventricle, and the oblique vein of the left atrium, all of which, except the last, are provided with valves at their orifices.

1. The **Great Cardiac Vein** (*v. cordis magna; left coronary vein*) begins at the apex of the heart and ascends along the anterior longitudinal sulcus to the base of the ventricles. It then curves to the left in the coronary sulcus, and reaching the back of the heart, opens into the left extremity of the coronary sinus. It receives tributaries from the left atrium and from both ventricles: one, the **left marginal vein,** is of considerable size, and ascends along the left margin of the heart.

2. The **Small Cardiac Vein** (*v. cordis parva; right coronary vein*) runs in the coronary sulcus between the right atrium and ventricle, and opens into the right extremity of the coronary sinus. It receives blood from the back of the right atrium and ventricle; the **right marginal vein** ascends along the right margin of the heart and joins it in the coronary sulcus, or opens directly into the right atrium.

3. The **Middle Cardiac Vein** (*v. cordis media*) commences at the apex of the heart, ascends in the posterior longitudinal sulcus, and ends in the coronary sinus near its right extremity.

4. The **Posterior Vein of the Left Ventricle** (*v. posterior ventriculi sinistri*) runs on the diaphragmatic surface of the left ventricle to the coronary sinus, but may end in the great cardiac vein.

5. The **Oblique Vein of the Left Atrium** (*v. obliqua atrii sinistri* [*Marshalli*]; *oblique vein of Marshall*) is a small vessel which descends obliquely on the back of the left atrium and ends in the coronary sinus near its left extremity; it is continuous above with the **ligament of the left vena cava** (*lig. venæ cavæ sinistræ; vestigial fold of Marshall*), and the two structures form the remnant of the left Cuvierian duct.

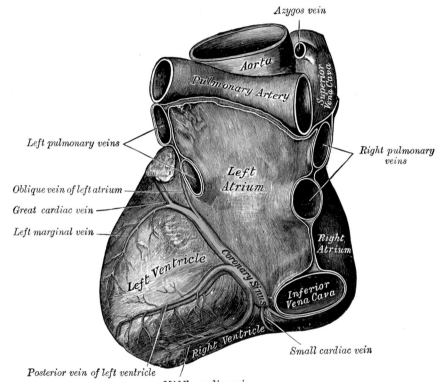

Fig. 548.—Base and diaphragmatic surface of heart.

The following cardiac veins do not end in the coronary sinus: (1) the **anterior cardiac veins**, comprising three or four small vessels which collect blood from the front of the right ventricle and open into the right atrium; the right marginal vein frequently opens into the right atrium, and is therefore sometimes regarded as belonging to this group; (2) the **smallest cardiac veins** (*veins of Thebesius*), consisting of a number of minute veins which arise in the muscular wall of the heart; the majority open into the atria, but a few end in the ventricles.

THE VEINS OF THE HEAD AND NECK.

The veins of the head and neck may be subdivided into three groups: (1) The **veins of the exterior of the head and face.** (2) The **veins of the neck.** (3) The **diploic veins, the veins of the brain,** and the **venous sinuses of the dura mater.**

The Veins of the Exterior of the Head and Face (Fig. 549).

The veins of the exterior of the head and face are:

Frontal.	Superficial Temporal
Supraorbital.	Internal Maxillary.
Angular.	Posterior Facial.
Anterior Facial.	Posterior Auricular.
Occipital.	

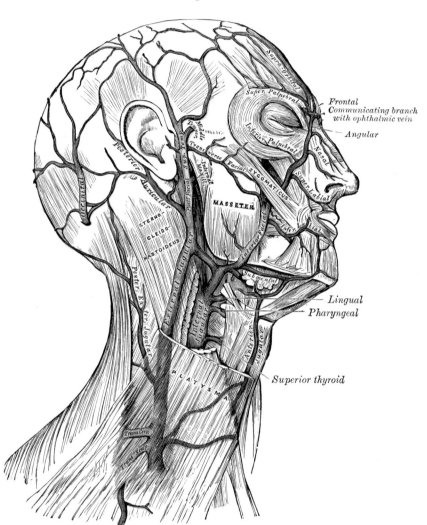

Fig. 549.—Veins of the head and neck.

The **frontal vein** (*v. frontalis*) *begins* on the forehead in a venous plexus which communicates with the frontal branches of the superficial temporal vein. The veins converge to form a single trunk, which runs downward near the middle line of the forehead parallel with the vein of the opposite side. The two veins are joined, at the root of the nose, by a transverse branch, called the **nasal arch**, which receives some small veins from the dorsum of the nose. At the root of the nose the veins diverge, and, each at the medial angle of the orbit, joins the **supraorbital vein,** to form the **angular vein**. Occasionally the frontal veins join to form a single trunk, which bifurcates at the root of the nose into the two angular veins.

The **supraorbital vein** (*v. supraorbitalis*) *begins* on the forehead where it communicates with the frontal branch of the superficial temporal vein. It runs downward superficial to the Frontalis muscle, and joins the frontal vein at the medial angle of the orbit to form the **angular vein**. Previous to its junction with the frontal vein, it sends through the supraorbital notch into the orbit a branch which communicates with the ophthalmic vein; as this vessel passes through the notch, it receives the frontal diploic vein through a foramen at the bottom of the notch.

The **angular vein** (*v. angularis*) *formed* by the junction of the frontal and supraorbital veins, runs obliquely downward, on the side of the root of the nose, to the level of the lower margin of the orbit, where it becomes the anterior facial vein. It receives the veins of the ala nasi, and communicates with the superior ophthalmic vein through the nasofrontal vein, thus establishing an important anastomosis between the anterior facial vein and the cavernous sinus.

The **anterior facial vein** (*v. facialis anterior; facial vein*) *commences* at the side of the root of the nose, and is a direct continuation of the angular vein. It lies behind the external maxillary (facial) artery and follows a less tortuous course. It runs obliquely downward and backward, beneath the Zygomaticus and zygomatic head of the Quadratus labii superioris, descends along the anterior border and then on the superficial surface of the Masseter, crosses over the body of the mandible, and passes obliquely backward, beneath the Platysma and cervical fascia, superficial to the submaxillary gland, the Digastricus and Stylohyoideus. It unites with the posterior facial vein to form the **common facial vein**, which crosses the external carotid artery and enters the internal jugular vein at a variable point below the hyoid bone. From near its termination a communicating branch often runs down the anterior border of the Sternocleidomastoideus to join the lower part of the anterior jugular vein. The facial vein has no valves, and its walls are not so flaccid as most superficial veins.

Tributaries.—The anterior facial vein receives a branch of considerable size, the **deep facial vein**, from the pterygoid venous plexus. It is also joined by the superior and inferior palpebral, the superior and inferior labial, the buccinator and the masseteric veins. Below the mandible it receives the submental, palatine, and submaxillary veins, and, generally, the vena comitans of the hypoglossal nerve.

The **superficial temporal vein** (*v. temporalis superficialis*) *begins* on the side and vertex of the skull in a plexus which communicates with the frontal and supraorbital veins, with the corresponding vein of the opposite side, and with the posterior auricular and occipital veins. From this net-work frontal and parietal branches arise, and unite above the zygomatic arch to form the trunk of the vein, which is joined in this situation by the **middle temporal vein**, from the substance of the Temporalis. It then crosses the posterior root of the zygomatic arch, enters the substance of the parotid gland, and unites with the internal maxillary vein to form the **posterior facial vein**.

Tributaries.—The superficial temporal vein receives in its course some parotid veins, articular veins from the temporomandibular joint, anterior auricular veins from the auricula, and the **transverse facial** from the side of the face. The middle temporal vein receives the **orbital vein**, which is formed by some lateral palpebral branches, and passes backward between the layers of the temporal fascia to join the superficial temporal vein.

The **pterygoid plexus** (*plexus pterygoideus*) (Fig. 562) is of considerable size, and is situated between the Temporalis and Pterygoideus externus, and partly between the two Pterygoidei. It receives tributaries corresponding with the branches of the internal maxillary artery. Thus it receives the sphenopalatine, the middle meningeal, the deep temporal, the pterygoid, masseteric, buccinator, alveolar, and some palatine veins, and a branch which communicates with the ophthalmic vein through the inferior orbital fissure. This plexus communicates freely with the anterior facial vein; it also communicates with the cavernous sinus, by branches through the foramen Vesalii, foramen ovale, and foramen lacerum.

The **internal maxillary vein** (*v. maxillaris interna*) is a short trunk which accompanies the first part of the internal maxillary artery. It is *formed* by a confluence of the veins of the pterygoid plexus, and passes backward between the spheno-mandibular ligament and the neck of the mandible, and unites with the temporal vein to form the posterior facial vein (Fig. 562, not labelled).

The **posterior facial vein** (*v. facialis posterior; temporomaxillary vein*), *formed* by the union of the superficial temporal and internal maxillary veins, descends in the substance of the parotid gland, superficial to the external carotid artery but beneath the facial nerve, between the ramus of the mandible and the Sternocleido-mastoideus muscle. It divides into two branches, an **anterior**, which passes forward and unites with the anterior facial vein to form the common facial vein and a **posterior**, which, joined by the posterior auricular vein, becomes the external jugular vein.

The **posterior auricular vein** (*v. auricularis posterior*) *begins* upon the side of the head, in a plexus which communicates with the tributaries of the occipital, and superficial temporal veins. It descends behind the auricula, and joins the posterior division of the posterior facial vein to form the external jugular. It receives the stylomastoid vein, and some tributaries from the cranial surface of the auricula.

The **occipital vein** (*v. occipitalis*) *begins* in a plexus at the back part of the vertex of the skull, From the plexus emerges a single vessel, which pierces the cranial attachment of the Trapezius and, dipping into the suboccipital triangle, joins the deep cervical and vertebral veins. Occasionally it follows the course of the occipital artery and ends in the internal jugular; in other instances, it joins the posterior auricular and through it opens into the external jugular. The parietal emissary vein connects it with the superior sagittal sinus; and as it passes across the mastoid portion of the temporal bone, it receives the mastoid emissary vein which connects it with the transverse sinus. The occipital diploic vein sometimes joins it.

The Veins of the Neck (Fig. 550).

The veins of the neck, which return the blood from the head and face, are:

External Jugular.	Anterior Jugular.
Posterior External Jugular.	Internal Jugular.

Vertebral.

The **external jugular vein** (*v. jugularis externa*) receives the greater part of the blood from the exterior of the cranium and the deep parts of the face, being formed by the junction of the posterior division of the posterior facial with the posterior auricular vein. It commences in the substance of the parotid gland, on a level with the angle of the mandible, and runs perpendicularly down the neck, in the direction of a line drawn from the angle of the mandible to the middle of the clavicle at the posterior border of the Sternocleidomastoideus. In its course it crosses the Sternocleidomastoideus obliquely, and in the subclavian triangle perforates the deep fascia, and ends in the subclavian vein, lateral to or in front of the Scalenus anterior. It is separated from the Sternocleidomastoideus by the investing layer of the deep cervical fascia, and is covered by the Platysma, the superficial fascia, and the integument; it crosses the cutaneous cervical nerve, and its upper half runs parallel with the great auricular nerve. The external jugular vein varies in size, bearing an inverse proportion to the other veins of the neck, it is occasionally double. It is provided with two pairs of valves, the lower pair being placed at its entrance into the subclavian vein, the upper in most cases about 4 cm. above the clavicle. The portion of vein between the two sets of valves is often dilated, and is termed the **sinus**. These valves do not prevent the regurgitation of the blood, or the passage of injection from below upward.

Tributaries.—This vein receives the occipital occasionally, the posterior external jugular, and, near its termination, the transverse cervical, transverse scapular, and anterior jugular veins; in the substance of the parotid, a large branch of communication from the internal jugular joins it.

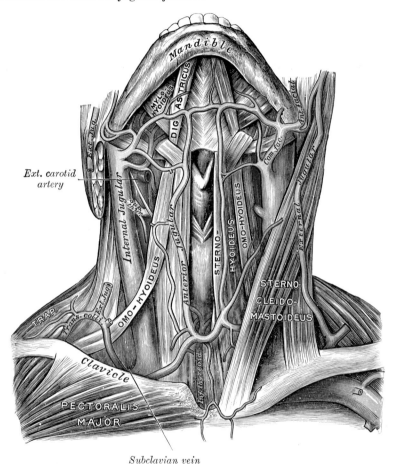

Fig. 550.—The veins of the neck, viewed from in front. (Spalteholz.)

The **posterior external jugular vein** (*v. jugularis posterior*) *begins* in the occipital region and returns the blood from the skin and superficial muscles in the upper and back part of the neck, lying between the Splenius and Trapezius. It runs down the back part of the neck, and opens into the external jugular vein just below the middle of its course.

The **anterior jugular vein** (*v. jugularis anterior*) *begins* near the hyoid bone by the confluence of several superficial veins from the submaxillary region. It descends between the median line and the anterior border of the Sternocleidomastoideus, and, at the lower part of the neck, passes beneath that muscle to open into the termination of the external jugular, or, in some instances, into the subclavian vein (Figs. 549, 550). It varies considerably in size, bearing usually an inverse proportion to the external jugular; most frequently there are two anterior jugulars, a right and left; but sometimes only one. Its tributaries are some laryngeal veins, and occasionally a small thyroid vein. Just above the sternum the two anterior jugular veins communicate by a transverse trunk, the **venous jugular arch**, which receives tributaries from the inferior thyroid veins; each also communicates with the internal jugular. There are no valves in this vein.

The **internal jugular vein** (*v. jugularis interna*) collects the blood from the brain, from the superficial parts of the face, and from the neck. It is directly continuous with the transverse sinus, and begins in the posterior compartment of the jugular foramen, at the base of the skull. At its origin it is somewhat dilated, and this dilatation is called the **superior bulb**. It runs down the side of the neck in a vertical direction, lying at first lateral to the internal carotid artery, and then lateral to the common carotid, and at the root of the neck unites with the subclavian vein to form the innominate vein; a little above its termination is a second dilatation, the **inferior bulb**. Above, it lies upon the Rectus capitis lateralis, behind the internal carotid artery and the nerves passing through the jugular foramen; lower down, the vein and artery lie upon the same plane, the glossopharyngeal and hypoglossal nerves passing forward between them; the vagus descends between and behind the vein and the artery in the same sheath, and the accessory runs obliquely backward, superficial or deep to the vein. At the root of the neck the right internal jugular vein is placed at a little distance from the common carotid artery, and

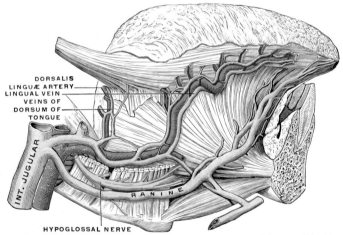

FIG. 551.—Veins of the tongue. The hypoglossal nerve has been displaced downward in this preparation. (Testut after Hirschfeld.)

crosses the first part of the subclavian artery, while the left internal jugular vein usually overlaps the common carotid artery. The left vein is generally smaller than the right, and each contains a pair of valves, which are placed about 2.5 cm. above the termination of the vessel.

Tributaries.—This vein receives in its course the inferior petrosal sinus, the common facial, lingual, pharyngeal, superior and middle thyroid veins, and sometimes the occipital. The thoracic duct on the left side and the right lymphatic duct on the right side open into the angle of union of the internal jugular and subclavian veins.

The **Inferior Petrosal Sinus** (*sinus petrosus inferior*) *leaves* the skull through the anterior part of the jugular foramen, and joins the superior bulb of the internal jugular vein.

The **Lingual Veins** (*vv. linguales*) *begin* on the dorsum, sides, and under surface of the tongue, and, passing backward along the course of the lingual artery, end in the internal jugular vein. The vena comitans of the hypoglossal nerve (**ranine** vein), a branch of considerable size, begins below the tip of the tongue, and may join the lingual; generally, however, it passes backward on the Hyoglossus, and joins the common facial.

The **Pharyngeal Veins** (*vv. pharyngeæ*) *begin* in the **pharyngeal plexus** on the outer surface of the pharynx, and, after receiving some posterior meningeal veins and the vein of the pterygoid canal, end in the internal jugular. They occasionally open into the facial, lingual, or superior thyroid vein.

The **Superior Thyroid Vein** (*v. thyreoidea superioris*) (Fig. 552) *begins* in the substance and on the surface of the thyroid gland, by tributaries corresponding with the branches of the superior thyroid artery, and ends in the upper part of the internal jugular vein. It receives the superior laryngeal and cricothyroid veins.

The **Middle Thyroid Vein** (Fig. 553) collects the blood from the lower part of the thyroid gland, and after being joined by some veins from the larynx and trachea, ends in the lower part of the internal jugular vein.

The **common facial** and **occipital veins** have been described.

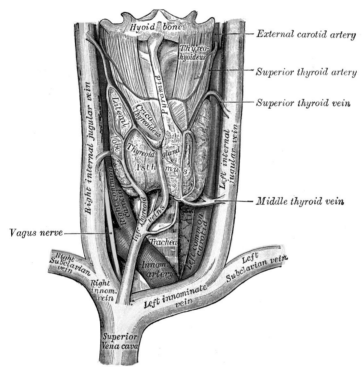

Fig. 552.—The veins of the thyroid gland.

The **vertebral vein** (*v. vertebralis*) is formed in the suboccipital triangle, from numerous small tributaries which spring from the internal vertebral venous plexuses and issue from the vertebral canal above the posterior arch of the atlas. They unite with small veins from the deep muscles at the upper part of the back of the neck, and form a vessel which enters the foramen in the transverse process of the atlas, and descends, forming a dense plexus around the vertebral artery, in the canal formed by the foramina transversaria of the cervical vertebræ. This plexus ends in a single trunk, which emerges from the foramen transversarium of the sixth cervical vertebra, and opens at the root of the neck into the back part of the innominate vein near its origin, its mouth being guarded by a pair of valves. On the right side, it crosses the first part of the subclavian artery.

42

Tributaries.—The vertebral vein communicates with the transverse sinus by a vein which passes through the condyloid canal, when that canal exists. It receives branches from the occipital vein and from the prevertebral muscles, from

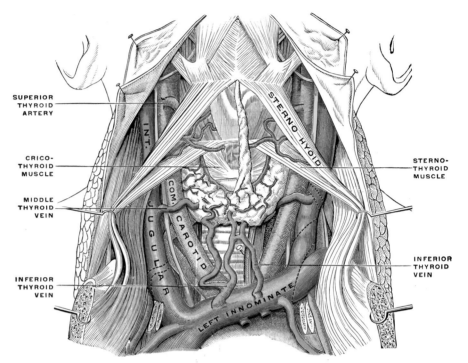

FIG. 553.—The middle and inferior thyroid veins. (Poirier and Charpy.)

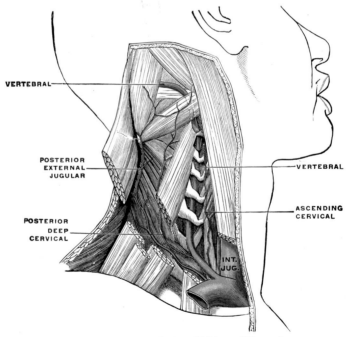

FIG. 554.—The vertebral vein. (Poirier and Charpy.)

the internal and external vertebral venous plexuses, from the anterior vertebral and the deep cervical veins; close to its termination it is sometimes joined by the first intercostal vein.

The **Anterior Vertebral Vein** *commences* in a plexus around the transverse processes of the upper cervical vertebræ, descends in company with the ascending cervical artery between the Scalenus anterior and Longus capitis muscles, and opens into the terminal part of the vertebral vein.

The **Deep Cervical Vein** (*v. cervicalis profunda; posterior vertebral or posterior deep cervical vein*) accompanies its artery between the Semispinales capitis and colli. It *begins* in the suboccipital region by communicating branches from the occipital vein and by small veins from the deep muscles at the back of the neck. It receives tributaries from the plexuses around the spinous processes of the cervical vertebræ, and terminates in the lower part of the vertebral vein.

The Diploic Veins (Venæ Diploicæ) (Fig. 555).

The **diploic veins** occupy channels in the diploë of the cranial bones. They are large and exhibit at irregular intervals pouch-like dilatations; their walls are thin, and formed of endothelium resting upon a layer of elastic tissue.

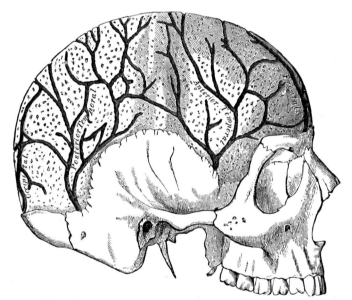

FIG. 555.—Veins of the diploë as displayed by the removal of the outer table of the skull.

So long as the cranial bones are separable from one another, these veins are confined to particular bones; but when the sutures are obliterated, they unite with each other, and increase in size. They communicate with the meningeal veins and the sinuses of the dura mater, and with the veins of the pericranium. They consist of (1) the **frontal**, which opens into the supraorbital vein and the superior sagittal sinus; (2) the **anterior temporal**, which, confined chiefly to the frontal bone, opens into the sphenoparietal sinus and into one of the deep temporal veins, through an aperture in the great wing of the sphenoid; (3) the **posterior temporal**, which is in the parietal bone, and ends in the transverse sinus, through an aperture at the mastoid angle of the parietal bone or through the mastoid foramen; and (4) the **occipital**, the largest of the four, which is confined to the occipital bone, and opens either externally into the occipital vein, or internally into the transverse sinus or into the confluence of the sinuses (*torcular Herophili*).

The Veins of the Brain.

The veins of the brain possess no valves, and their walls, owing to the absence of muscular tissue, are extremely thin. They pierce the arachnoid membrane and the inner or meningeal layer of the dura mater, and open into the cranial venous sinuses. They may be divided into two sets, **cerebral** and **cerebellar**.

The **cerebral veins** (*vv. cerebri*) are divisible into external and internal groups according as they drain the outer surfaces or the inner parts of the hemispheres.

The **external veins** are the superior, inferior, and middle cerebral.

The **Superior Cerebral Veins** (*vv. cerebri superiores*), eight to twelve in number, drain the superior, lateral, and medial surfaces of the hemispheres, most of them being lodged in the sulci between the gyri, while some run across the gyri. They open into the superior sagittal sinus; the anterior vein runs nearly at right angles to the sinus; the posterior and larger veins are directed obliquely forward and open into the sinus in a direction more or less opposed to the current of the blood contained within it.

The **Middle Cerebral Vein** (*v. cerebri media; superficial Sylvian vein*) *begins* on the lateral surface of the hemisphere, and, running along the lateral cerebral fissure, ends in the cavernous or the sphenoparietal sinus. It is connected (*a*) with the superior sagittal sinus by the **great anastomotic vein of Trolard**, which opens into one of the superior cerebral veins; (*b*) with the transverse sinus by the **posterior anastomotic vein of Labbé**, which courses over the temporal lobe.

The **Inferior Cerebral Veins** (*vv. cerebri inferiores*), of small size, drain the under surfaces of the hemispheres. Those on the orbital surface of the frontal lobe join the superior cerebral veins, and through these open into the superior sagittal sinus; those of the temporal lobe anastomose with the middle cerebral and basal veins, and join the cavernous, sphenoparietal, and superior petrosal sinuses.

The **basal vein** is formed at the anterior perforated substance by the union of (*a*) a small **anterior cerebral vein** which accompanies the anterior cerebral artery, (*b*) the **deep middle cerebral vein** (*deep Sylvian vein*), which receives tributaries from the insula and neighboring gyri, and runs in the lower part of the lateral cerebral fissure, and (*c*) the **inferior striate veins**, which leave the corpus striatum through the anterior perforated substance. The basal vein passes backward around the cerebral peduncle, and ends in the internal cerebral vein (*vein of Galen*); it receives tributaries from the interpeduncular fossa, the inferior horn of the lateral ventricle, the hippocampal gyrus, and the mid-brain.

The **Internal Cerebral Veins** (*vv. cerebri internæ; veins of Galen; deep cerebral veins*) drain the deep parts of the hemisphere and are two in number; each is formed near the interventricular foramen by the union of the **terminal** and **choroid veins**. They run backward parallel with one another, between the layers of the tela chorioidea of the third ventricle, and beneath the splenium of the corpus callosum, where they unite to form a short trunk, the **great cerebral vein**; just before their union each receives the corresponding basal vein.

The **terminal vein** (*v. terminalis; vena corporis striati*) *commences* in the groove between the corpus striatum and thalamus, receives numerous veins from both of these parts, and unites behind the crus fornicis with the choroid vein, to form one of the internal cerebral veins. The **choroid vein** runs along the whole length of the choroid plexus, and receives veins from the hippocampus, the fornix, and the corpus callosum.

The **Great Cerebral Vein** (*v. cerebri magna* [*Galeni*]; *great vein of Galen*) (Fig. 556), formed by the union of the two internal cerebral veins, is a short median trunk which curves backward and upward around the splenium of the corpus callosum and ends in the anterior extremity of the straight sinus. (Fig. 559)

The **cerebellar veins** are placed on the surface of the cerebellum, and are disposed in two sets, superior and inferior. The **superior cerebellar veins** (*vv. cerebelli superiores*) pass partly forward and medialward, across the superior vermis, to end in the straight sinus and the internal cerebral veins, partly lateralward to the transverse and superior petrosal sinuses. The **inferior cerebellar veins** (*vv. cerebelli inferiores*) of large size, end in the transverse, superior petrosal, and occipital sinuses.

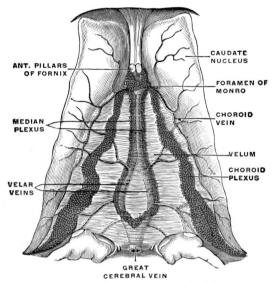

CAUDATE NUCLEUS

ANT. PILLARS OF FORNIX

FORAMEN OF MONRO

CHOROID VEIN

MEDIAN PLEXUS

VELUM

CHOROID PLEXUS

VELAR VEINS

GREAT CEREBRAL VEIN

Fig. 556.—Velum interpositum. (Poirier and Charpy.)

The Sinuses of the Dura Mater (Sinus Duræ Matris). Ophthalmic Veins and Emissary Veins.

The **sinuses of the dura mater** are venous channels which drain the blood from the brain; they are devoid of valves, and are situated between the two layers of the dura mater and lined by endothelium continuous with that which lines the veins. They may be divided into two groups: (1) a **postero-superior**, at the upper and back part of the skull, and (2) an **antero-inferior**, at the base of the skull.

The postero-superior group comprises the

Superior Sagittal.	Straight.
Inferior Sagittal.	Two Transverse.
Occipital.	

The **superior sagittal sinus** (*sinus sagittalis superior; superior longitudinal sinus*) (Figs. 557, 558) occupies the attached or convex margin of the falx cerebri. Commencing at the foramen cæcum, through which it receives a vein from the nasal cavity, it runs from before backward, grooving the inner surface of the frontal, the adjacent margins of the two parietals, and the superior division of the cruciate eminence of the occipital; near the internal occipital protuberance it deviates to one or other side (usually the right), and is continued as the corresponding transverse sinus. It is triangular in section, narrow in front, and gradually increases in size as it passes backward. Its inner surface presents the openings of the superior cerebral veins, which run, for the most part, obliquely forward, and open chiefly at the back part of the sinus, their orifices being concealed by fibrous folds; numerous fibrous bands (*chordæ Willisii*) extend transversely across the inferior angle of the sinus; and, lastly, small openings communicate with irregularly shaped venous spaces (*venous lacunæ*) in the dura mater near the sinus. There are usually three lacunæ on either side of the sinus: a small frontal, a large parietal, and an occipital, intermediate in size between the other two. Most of the cerebral veins from the outer surface of the hemisphere open into these lacunæ, and numerous **arachnoid granulations** (*Pacchionian bodies*) project into them from below. The superior sagittal sinus receives the superior cerebral veins, veins from the diploë and dura mater, and, near the posterior extremity of the sagittal suture, veins from the pericranium, which pass through the parietal foramina.

Numerous communications exist between this sinus and the veins of the nose, scalp, and diploë.

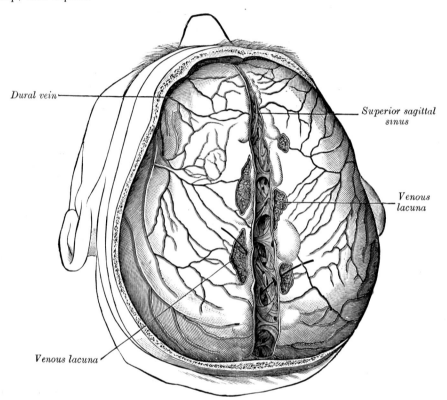

Fig. 557.—Superior sagittal sinus laid open after removal of the skull cap. The chordæ Willisii are clearly seen. The venous lacunæ are also well shown; from two of them probes are passed into the superior sagittal sinus. (Poirier and Charpy.)

The **inferior sagittal sinus** (*sinus sagittalis inferior; inferior longitudinal sinus*) (Fig. 558) is contained in the posterior half or two-thirds of the free margin of the falx cerebri. It is of a cylindrical form, increases in size as it passes backward, and ends in the straight sinus. It receives several veins from the falx cerebri, and occasionally a few from the medial surfaces of the hemispheres.

The **straight sinus** (*sinus rectus; tentorial sinus*) (Fig. 559) is situated at the line of junction of the falx cerebri with the tentorium cerebelli. It is triangular in section, increases in size as it proceeds backward, and runs downward and backward from the end of the inferior sagittal sinus to the transverse sinus of the opposite side to that into which the superior sagittal sinus is prolonged. Its terminal part communicates by a cross branch with the confluence of the sinuses. Besides the inferior sagittal sinus, it receives the great cerebral vein (*great vein of Galen*) and the superior cerebellar veins. A few transverse bands cross its interior.

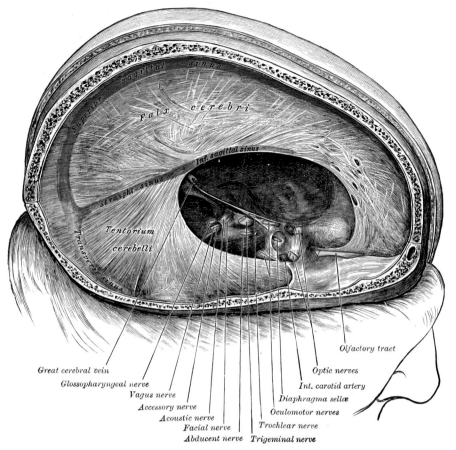

FIG. 558.—Dura matter and its processes exposed by removing part of the right half of the skull, and the brain.

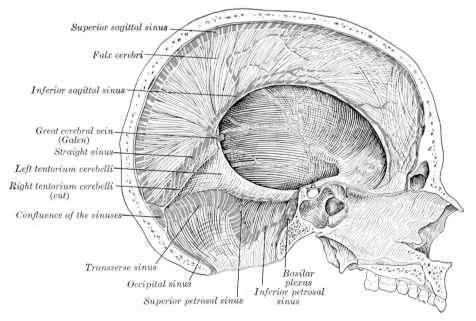

FIG. 559.—Sagittal section of the skull, showing the sinuses of the dura.

The **transverse sinuses** (*sinus transversus; lateral sinuses*) (Fig. 560) are of large size and begin at the internal occipital protuberance; one, generally the right, being the direct continuation of the superior sagittal sinus, the other of the straight sinus. Each transverse sinus passes lateralward and forward, describing a slight curve with its convexity upward, to the base of the petrous portion of the temporal bone, and lies, in this part of its course, in the attached margin of the tentorium cerebelli; it then leaves the tentorium and curves downward and medialward to reach the jugular foramen, where it ends in the internal jugular vein. In its course it rests upon the squama of the occipital, the mastoid angle

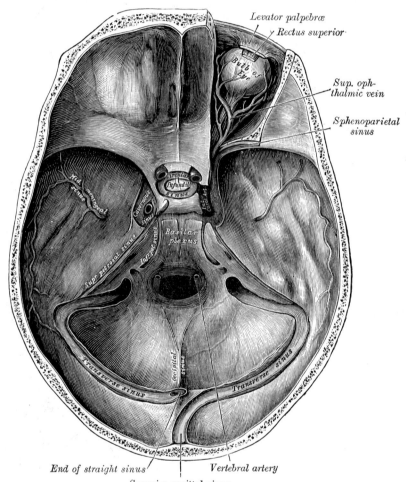

Fig. 560.—The sinuses at the base of the skull.

of the parietal, the mastoid part of the temporal, and, just before its termination, the jugular process of the occipital; the portion which occupies the groove on the mastoid part of the temporal is sometimes termed the **sigmoid sinus**. The transverse sinuses are frequently of unequal size, that formed by the superior sagittal sinus being the larger; they increase in size as they proceed from behind forward. On transverse section the horizontal portion exhibits a prismatic, the curved portion a semicylindrical form. They receive the blood from the superior petrosal sinuses at the base of the petrous portion of the temporal bone; they communicate with the veins of the pericranium by means of the mastoid and condyloid emissary veins; and they receive some of the inferior cerebral and inferior cerebellar veins, and some veins from the diploë. The **petrosquamous sinus**, when present, runs backward along the junction of the squama and petrous portion of the temporal, and opens into the transverse sinus.

The **occipital sinus** (*sinus occipitalis*) (Fig. 560) is the smallest of the cranial sinuses. It is situated in the attached margin of the falx cerebelli, and is generally single, but occasionally there are two. It commences around the margin of the foramen magnum by several small venous channels, one of which joins the terminal part of the transverse sinus; it communicates with the posterior internal vertebral venous plexuses and ends in the confluence of the sinuses.

The **Confluence of the Sinuses** (*confluens sinuum; torcular Herophili* (Fig. 559) is the dilated junction of three tributary sinuses, the superior sagittal, the straight, and the occipital with the two large transverse sinuses. The direction of currents within the confluence is such that the right transverse sinus usually receives the greater part of its blood from the superior sagittal sinus and the left from the straight sinus.

The anterior-inferior group of sinuses comprises the

Two Cavernous.	Two Superior Petrosal.
Two Intercavernous.	Two Inferior Petrosal.
	Basilar Plexus.	

The **cavernous sinuses** (*sinus cavernosus*) (Figs. 560, 561) are so named because they present a reticulated structure, due to their being traversed by numerous interlacing filaments. They are of irregular form, larger behind than in front, and are placed one on either side of the body of the sphenoid bone, extending from the superior orbital fissure to the apex of the petrous portion of the temporal bone. Each opens behind into the petrosal sinuses. On the medial wall of each sinus is the internal carotid artery, accompanied by filaments of the carotid plexus; near the artery is the abducent nerve; on the lateral wall are the oculomotor and trochlear nerves, and the ophthalmic and maxillary divisions of

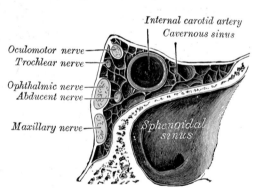

FIG. 561.—Oblique section through the cavernous sinus.

the trigeminal nerve (Fig. 561). These structures are separated from the blood flowing along the sinus by the lining membrane of the sinus. The cavernous sinus receives the superior ophthalmic vein through the superior orbital fissure, some of the cerebral veins, and also the small **sphenoparietal sinus**, which courses along the under surface of the small wing of the sphenoid. It communicates with the transverse sinus by means of the superior petrosal sinus; with the internal jugular vein through the inferior petrosal sinus and a plexus of veins on the internal carotid artery; with the pterygoid venous plexus through the foramen Vesalii, foramen ovale, and foramen lacerum, and with the angular vein through the ophthalmic vein. The two sinuses also communicate with each other by means of the anterior and posterior intercavernous sinuses.

The **ophthalmic veins** (Fig. 562), **superior** and **inferior**, are devoid of valves.

The **Superior Ophthalmic Vein** (*v. ophthalmica superior*) begins at the inner angle of the orbit in a vein named the **nasofrontal** which communicates anteriorly with the angular vein; it pursues the same course as the ophthalmic artery, and receives tributaries corresponding to the branches of that vessel. Forming a short single trunk, it passes between the two heads of the Rectus lateralis and through the medial part of the superior orbital fissure, and ends in the cavernous sinus.

The **Inferior Ophthalmic Vein** (*v. ophthalmica inferior*) begins in a venous net-work at the forepart of the floor and medial wall of the orbit; it receives some veins from the Rectus inferior, Obliquus inferior, lacrimal sac and eyelids, runs backward in the lower part of the orbit and divides into two branches. One of these passes through the inferior orbital fissure and joins the pterygoid venous plexus, while the other enters the cranium through the superior orbital fissure and ends in the cavernous sinus, either by a separate opening, or more frequently in common with the superior ophthalmic vein.

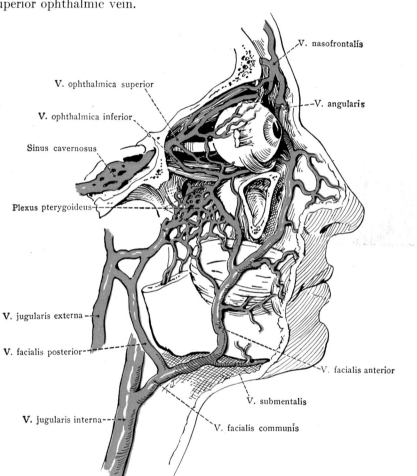

FIG. 562.—Principal veins of face and orbit. (Eycleshymer and Jones.)

The **intercavernous sinuses** (*sinus intercavernosi*) (Fig. 560) are two in number, an anterior and a posterior, and connect the two cavernous sinuses across the midline. The **anterior** passes in front of the hypophysis cerebri, the **posterior** behind it, and they form with the cavernous sinuses a venous circle (**circular sinus**) around the hypophysis. The anterior one is usually the larger of the two, and one or other is occasionally absent.

The **superior petrosal sinus** (*sinus petrosus superior*) (Fig. 560) small and narrow, connects the cavernous with the transverse sinus. It runs lateralward and backward, from the posterior end of the cavernous sinus, over the trigeminal nerve, and lies in the attached margin of the tentorium cerebelli and in the superior petrosal sulcus of the temporal bone; it joins the transverse sinus where the latter curves downward on the inner surface of the mastoid part of the temporal. It receives cerebellar and inferior cerebral veins, and veins from the tympanic cavity.

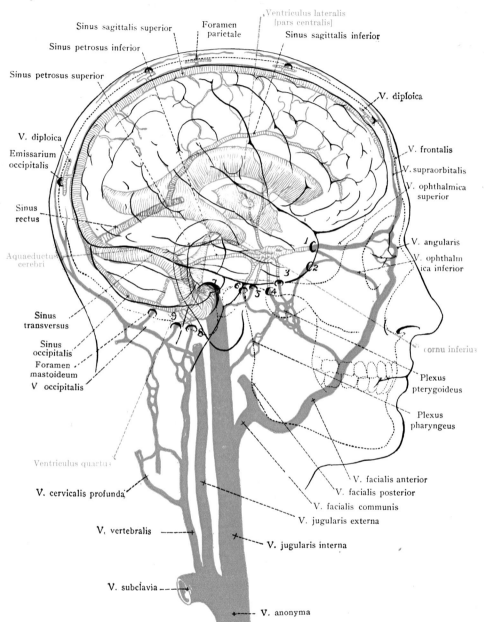

FIG. 563.—Venous drainage of the head and neck. The cerebral ventricles are projected in red The veins in their extra-cranial portions are shown in deep blue; the intra-cranial portions in light blue. The numbers indicate the foramina through which these veins enter the cranium. These are: *1.* Fissura orbitalis superior. *2.* Fissura orbitalis inferior. *3.* Foramen ovale. *4.* Foramen spinosum. *5.* Foramen lacerum. *6.* Canalis caroticus. *7.* Foramen jugulare. *8.* Canalis hypoglossi. *9.* Canalis condyloideus. The black inverted crescents indicate openings through which emissary veins pass. (Eycleshymer and Jones.)

The **inferior petrosal sinus** (*sinus petrosus inferior*) (Fig. 560) is situated in the inferior petrosal sulcus formed by the junction of the petrous part of the temporal with the basilar part of the occipital. It begins in the postero-inferior part of the cavernous sinus, and, passing through the anterior part of the jugular foramen, ends in the superior bulb of the internal jugular vein. The inferior petrosal sinus receives the internal auditory veins and also veins from the medulla oblongata, pons, and under surface of the cerebellum.

The exact relation of the parts to one another in the jugular foramen is as follows: the inferior petrosal sinus lies medially and anteriorly with the meningeal branch of the ascending pharyngeal artery, and is directed obliquely downward and backward; the transverse sinus is situated at the lateral and back part of the foramen with a meningeal branch of the occipital artery, and between the two sinuses are the glossopharyngeal, vagus, and accessory nerves. These three sets of structures are divided from each other by two processes of fibrous tissue. The junction of the inferior petrosal sinus with the internal jugular vein takes place on the lateral aspect of the nerves.

The **basilar plexus** (*plexus basilaris; transverse or basilar sinus*) (Fig. 560) consists of several interlacing venous channels between the layers of the dura mater over the basilar part of the occipital bone, and serves to connect the two inferior petrosal sinuses. It communicates with the anterior vertebral venous plexus.

Emissary Veins (*venæ emissariæ*). (Fig. 563)—The emissary veins pass through the cranial wall and establish communication between the sinuses inside the skull and the veins external to it. Some are always present, others only occasionally. The principal emissary veins are the following: (1) A mastoid emissary vein, usually present, runs through the mastoid foramen and unites the transverse sinus with the posterior auricular or with the occipital vein. (2) A parietal emissary vein passes through the parietal foramen and connects the superior sagittal sinus with the veins of the scalp. (3) A net-work of minute veins (*rete canalis hypoglossi*) traverses the hypoglossal canal and joins the transverse sinus with the vertebral vein and deep veins of the neck. (4) An inconstant condyloid emissary vein passes through the condyloid canal and connects the transverse sinus with the deep veins of the neck. (5) A net-work of veins (*rete foraminis ovalis*) unites the cavernous sinus with the pterygoid plexus through the foramen ovale. (6) Two or three small veins run through the foramen lacerum and connect the cavernous sinus with the pterygoid plexus. (7) The emissary vein of the foramen of Vesalius connects the same parts. (8) An internal carotid plexus of veins traverses the carotid canal and unites the cavernous sinus with the internal jugular vein. (9) A vein is transmitted through the foramen cæcum and connects the superior sagittal sinus with the veins of the nasal cavity.

THE VEINS OF THE UPPER EXTREMITY AND THORAX.

The veins of the upper extremity are divided into two sets, **superficial** and **deep**; the two sets anastomose frequently with each other. The superficial veins are placed immediately beneath the integument between the two layers of superficial fascia. The deep veins accompany the arteries, and constitute the venæ comitantes of those vessels. Both sets are provided with valves, which are more numerous in the deep than in the superficial veins.

The Superficial Veins of the Upper Extremity.

The **superficial veins** of the upper extremity are the **digital, metacarpal, cephalic, basilic, median.**

Digital Veins.—The **dorsal digital veins** pass along the sides of the fingers and are joined to one another by oblique communicating branches. Those from the adjacent sides of the fingers unite to form three **dorsal metacarpal veins** (Fig. 564), which end in a dorsal venous net-work on the back of the hand. The radial part of the net-work is joined by the dorsal digital vein from the radial side of the index finger and by the dorsal digital veins of the thumb, and is prolonged upward as the cephalic vein. The ulnar part of the net-work receives the dorsal digital vein of the ulnar side of the little finger and is continued upward as the basilic vein. A communicating branch frequently connects the dorsal venous network with the cephalic vein about the middle of the forearm.

The **volar digital veins** on each finger are connected to the dorsal digital veins by oblique **intercapitular veins**. They drain into a venous plexus which is situated over the thenar and hypothenar eminences and across the front of the wrist.

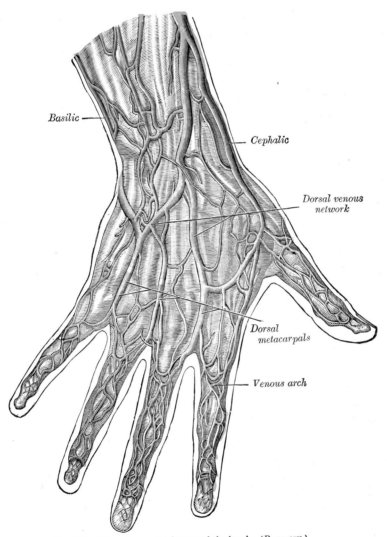

Fig. 564.—The veins on the dorsum of the hand. (Bourgery.)

The **cephalic vein** (Fig. 565) *begins* in the radial part of the dorsal venous net-work and winds upward around the radial border of the forearm, receiving tribu-taries from both surfaces. Below the front of the elbow it gives off the **vena mediana cubiti** (*median cubital vein*), which receives a communicating branch from the deep veins of the forearm and passes across to join the basilic vein. The cephalic vein then ascends in front of the elbow in the groove between the Brachioradialis and the Biceps brachii. It crosses superficial to the musculocutaneous nerve and ascends in the groove along the lateral border of the Biceps brachii. In the upper third of the arm it passes between the Pectoralis major and Deltoideus, where it is accompanied by the deltoid branch of the thoracoacromial artery. It pierces the clavipectoral fascia and, crossing the axillary artery, ends in the axillary vein just below the clavicle. Sometimes it communicates with the external jugular vein by a branch which ascends in front of the clavicle.

, The **accessory cephalic vein** (*v. cephalica accessoria*) *arises* either from a small tributary plexus on the back of the forearm or from the ulnar side of the dorsal venous net-work; it joins the cephalic below the elbow. In some cases the accessory cephalic springs from the cephalic above the wrist and joins it again higher up. A large oblique branch frequently connects the basilic and cephalic veins on the back of the forearm.

The **basilic vein** (*v. basilica*) (Fig. 565) *begins* in the ulnar part of the dorsal venous network. It runs up the posterior surface of the ulnar side of the forearm and inclines forward to the anterior surface below the elbow, where it is joined by the vena mediana cubiti. It ascends obliquely in the groove between the Biceps brachii and Pronator teres and crosses the brachial artery, from which it is separated by the lacertus fibrosus; filaments of the medial antebrachial cutaneous nerve pass both in front of and behind this portion of the vein. It then runs upward along the medial border of the Biceps brachii, perforates the deep fascia a little below the middle of the arm, and, ascending on the medial side of the brachial artery to the lower border of the Teres major joins the brachial to form the axillary vein.

The **median antebrachial vein** (*v. mediana antebrachii*) drains the venous plexus on the volar surface of the hand. It ascends on the ulnar side of the front of the forearm and ends in the basilic vein or in the vena mediana cubiti; in a small proportion of cases it divides into two branches, one of which joins the basilic, the other the cephalic, below the elbow.

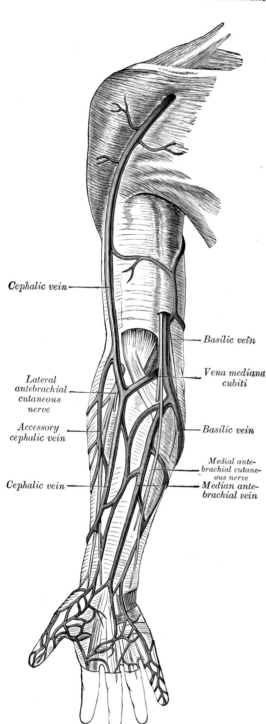

Cephalic vein

Lateral antebrachial cutaneous nerve

Accessory cephalic vein

Cephalic vein

Basilic vein

Vena mediana cubiti

Basilic vein

Medial antebrachial cutaneous nerve

Median antebrachial vein

Fig. 565.—The superficial veins of the upper extremity.

There is considerable variation in the superficial veins of the forearm. The basilic may be much larger than the cephalic and drain a correspondingly larger area, or the reverse may be true. The median antebrachial vein may be absent as a definite vessel. The median cubital vein may split into a distinct Y; one arm of the Y draining into the cephalic, the other into the basilic. In this case one branch is called the **median cephalic vein**, the other the **median basilic vein**.

The Deep Veins of the Upper Extremity.

The **deep veins** follow the course of the arteries, forming their venæ comitantes. They are generally arranged in pairs, and are situated one on either side of the corresponding artery, and connected at intervals by short transverse branches.

Deep Veins of the Hand.—Each of the superficial and deep volar arterial arches is accompanied by a pair of venæ comitantes which constitute the **superficial** and **deep volar venous arches,** and receive the veins corresponding to the branches of the arterial arches; thus the **common volar digital veins,** formed by the union of the **proper volar digital veins,** open into the superficial, and the **volar metacarpal veins** into the deep volar venous arches. The **dorsal metacarpal veins** receive perforating branches from the volar metacarpal veins and end in the radial veins and the superficial veins on the dorsum of the wrist.

The **deep veins of the forearm** are the venæ comitantes of the radial and ulnar arteries and constitute respectively the upward continuations of the deep and superficial volar venous arches; they unite in front of the elbow to form the brachial veins. The radial veins are smaller than the ulnar and receive the dorsal metacarpal veins. The ulnar veins receive tributaries from the deep volar venous arches and communicate with the super-

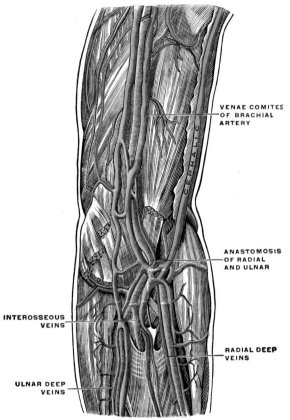

FIG. 566.—The deep veins of the upper extremity. (Bourgery.)

ficial veins at the wrist; near the elbow they receive the volar and dorsal interosseous veins and send a large communicating branch (profunda vein) to the vena mediana cubiti.

The **brachial veins** (*vv. brachiales*) are placed one on either side of the brachial artery, receiving tributaries corresponding with the branches given off from that vessel; near the lower margin of the Subscapularis, they join the axillary vein; the medial one frequently joins the basilic vein.

These deep veins have numerous anastomoses, not only with each other, but also with the superficial veins.

The **axillary vein** (*v. axillaris*) begins at the junction of the basilic and brachial veins near the lower border of the Teres major, and ends at the outer border of the first rib, by becoming the subclavian vein. In addition to the tributaries which correspond to the branches of the axillary artery, it receives the cephalic vein near its termination and may receive an additional deeper brachial comitans near its beginning. It lies on the medial side of the artery, which it partly overlaps; between the two vessels are the medial cord of the brachial plexus, the median, the ulnar, and the medial anterior thoracic nerves. It is provided with a pair of valves opposite the lower border of the Subscapularis; valves are also found at the ends of the cephalic and subscapular veins.

The **subclavian vein** (*v. subclavia*), the continuation of the axillary, extends from the outer border of the first rib to the sternal end of the clavicle, where it unites with the internal jugular to form the innominate vein. It is in relation, in

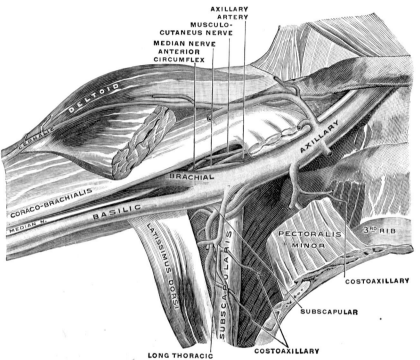

Fig. 567.—The veins of the right axilla, viewed from in front. (Spalteholz.)

front, with the clavicle and Subclavius; *behind* and *above*, with the subclavian artery, from which it is separated medially by the Scalenus anterior and the phrenic nerve. *Below*, it rests in a depression on the first rib and upon the pleura. It is usually provided with a pair of valves, which are situated about 2.5 cm. from its termination.

The subclavian vein occasionally rises in the neck to a level with the third part of the subclavian artery, and occasionally passes with this vessel behind the Scalenus anterior.

Tributaries.—This vein receives the external jugular vein, sometimes the anterior jugular vein, and occasionally a small branch, which ascends in front of the clavicle, from the cephalic. At its angle of junction with the internal jugular, the left subclavian vein receives the thoracic duct, and the right subclavian vein the right lymphatic duct.

The Veins of the Thorax (Fig. 568)

The **innominate veins** (*vv. anonymæ; brachiocephalic veins*) are two large trunks, one on either side of the root of the neck, and formed by the union of the internal jugular and subclavian veins of the corresponding side; they lack valves.

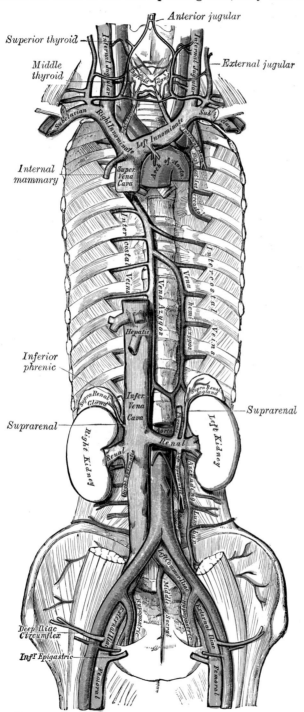

Fig. 568.—The venæ cavæ and azygos veins, with their tributaries.

The **Right Innominate Vein** (*v. anonyma dextra*) is a short vessel, about 2.5 cm. in length, which begins behind the sternal end of the clavicle, and, passing almost vertically downward, joins with the left innominate vein just below the cartilage of the first rib, close to the right border of the sternum, to form the superior vena cava. It lies in front and to the right of the innominate artery; on its right side are the phrenic nerve and the pleura, which are interposed between it and the apex of the lung. This vein, at its commencement, receives the right vertebral vein; and, lower down, the right internal mammary and right inferior thyroid veins, and sometimes the vein from the first intercostal space.

The **Left Innominate Vein** (*v. anonyma sinistra*), about 6 cm. in length, *begins* behind the sternal end of the clavicle and runs obliquely downward and to the right behind the upper half of the manubrium sterni to the sternal end of the first right costal cartilage, where it unites with the right innominate vein to form the **superior vena cava.** It is separated from the manubrium sterni by the Sterno-hyoideus and Sternothyreoideus, the thymus or its remains, and some loose areolar tissue. Behind it are the three large arteries, innominate, left common carotid, and left subclavian, arising from the aortic arch, together with the vagus and phrenic nerves. The left innominate vein may occupy a higher level, crossing the jugular notch and lying directly in front of the trachea.

Tributaries.—Its tributaries are the left vertebral, left internal mammary, left inferior thyroid, and the left highest intercostal veins, and occasionally some thymic and pericardiac veins.

Variations.—Sometimes the innominate veins open separately into the right atrium; in such cases the right vein takes the ordinary course of the superior vena cava; the left vein—*left superior vena cava*, as it is then termed—which may communicate by a small branch with the right one, passes in front of the root of the left lung, and, turning to the back of the heart, ends in the right atrium. This occasional condition in the adult is due to the persistence of the early fetal condition, and is the normal state of things in birds and some mammalia.

The **internal mammary veins** (*vv. mammariæ internæ*) are venæ comitantes to the lower half of the internal mammary artery, and receive tributaries corresponding to the branches of the artery. They then unite to form a single trunk, which runs up on the medial side of the artery and ends in the corresponding innominate vein. The **superior phrenic vein,** *i. e.,* the vein accompanying the pericardiacophrenic artery, usually opens into the internal mammary vein.

The **inferior thyroid veins** (*vv. thyreoideæ inferiores*) two, frequently three or four, in number, *arise* in the venous plexus on the thyroid gland, communicating with the middle and superior thyroid veins. They form a plexus in front of the trachea, behind the Sternothyreoidei. From this plexus, a left vein descends and joins the left innominate trunk, and a right vein passes obliquely downward and to the right across the innominate artery to open into the right innominate vein, just at its junction with the superior vena cava; sometimes the right and left veins open by a common trunk in the latter situation. These veins receive esophageal tracheal, and inferior laryngeal veins, and are provided with valves at their terminations in the innominate veins. (Fig. 533)

The **highest intercostal veins** (*v. intercostalis suprema; superior intercostal veins*) (right and left) drain the blood from the upper three or four intercostal spaces. The **right vein** (*v. intercostalis suprema dextra*) passes downward and opens into the vena azygos; the **left vein** (*v. intercostalis suprema sinistra*) runs across the arch of the aorta and the origins of the left subclavian and left common carotid arteries and opens into the left innominate vein. It usually receives the left bronchial vein, and sometimes the left superior phrenic vein, and communicates below with the accessory hemiazygos vein.

The **superior vena cava** (*v. cava superior*) drains the blood from the upper half of the body. It measures about 7 cm. in length, and is formed by the junction of the two innominate veins. It *begins* immediately below the cartilage of the right first rib close to the sternum, and, descending vertically behind the first and second intercostal spaces, ends in the upper part of the right atrium opposite the upper border of the third right costal cartilage: the lower half of the vessel is within the pericardium. It describes a slight curve, the convexity of which is to the right.

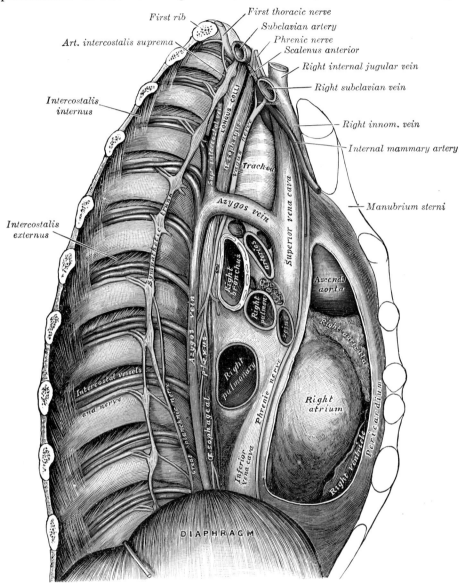

FIG. 569.—The mediastinum, from the right side.

Relations.—*In front* are the anterior margins of the right lung and pleura with the pericardium intervening below; these separate it from the first and second intercostal spaces and from the second and third right costal cartilages; *behind* it are the root of the right lung and the right vagus nerve. On its *right side* are the phrenic nerve and right pleura; on its *left side*, the commencement of the innominate artery and the ascending aorta, the latter overlapping it. Just before it pierces the pericardium, it receives the azygos vein and several small veins from the pericardium and other contents of the mediastinal cavity. The portion contained within the pericardium is covered, in front and laterally, by the serous layer of the membrane. The superior vena cava has no valves.

The **azygos vein** (*v. azygos; vena azygos major*) *begins* opposite the first or second lumbar vertebra, by a branch, the **ascending lumbar vein** (page 686); sometimes by a branch from the right renal vein, or from the inferior vena cava. It enters the thorax through the aortic hiatus in the diaphragm, and passes along the right side of the vertebral column to the fourth thoracic vertebra, where it arches forward over the root of the right lung, and ends in the superior vena cava, just before that vessel pierces the pericardium. In the aortic hiatus, it lies with the thoracic duct on the right side of the aorta; in the thorax it lies upon the intercostal arteries, on the right side of the aorta and thoracic duct, and is partly covered by pleura.

Tributaries.—It receives the right subcostal and intercostal veins, the upper three or four of these latter opening by a common stem, the highest superior intercostal vein. It receives the hemiazygos veins, several esophageal, mediastinal, and pericardial veins, and, near its termination, the right bronchial vein. A few imperfect valves are found in the azygos vein; but the valves of its tributaries are complete.

The intercostal veins on the left side, below the upper three intercostal spaces, usually form two trunks, named the **hemiazygos** and **accessory hemiazygos veins**.

The **Hemiazygos Vein** (*v. hemiazygos; vena azygos minor inferior*) *begins* in the left ascending lumbar or renal vein. It enters the thorax, through the left crus of the diaphragm, and, ascending on the left side of the vertebral column, as high as the ninth thoracic vertebra, passes across the column, behind the aorta, esophagus, and thoracic duct, to end in the azygos vein. It receives the lower four or five intercostal veins and the subcostal vein of the left side, and some esophageal and mediastinal veins.

The **Accessory Hemiazygos Vein** (*v. hemiazygos accessoria; vena azygos minor superior*) descends on the left side of the vertebral column, and varies inversely in size with the highest left intercostal vein. It receives veins from the three or four intercostal spaces between the highest left intercostal vein and highest tributary of the hemiazygos; the left bronchial vein sometimes opens into it. It either crosses the body of the eighth thoracic vertebra to join the azygos vein or ends in the hemiazygos. When this vein is small, or altogether wanting, the left highest intercostal vein may extend as low as the fifth or sixth intercostal space.

In obstruction of the inferior vena cava, the azygos and hemiazygos veins are the principal means by which the venous circulation is carried on, connecting as they do the superior and inferior venæ cavæ, and communicating with the common iliac veins by the ascending lumbar veins and with many of the tributaries of the inferior vena cava.

The **Bronchial Veins** (*vv. bronchiales*) return the blood from the larger bronchi, and from the structures at the roots of the lungs; that of the right side opens into the azygos vein, near its termination; that of the left side, into the highest left intercostal or the accessory hemiazygos vein. A considerable quantity of the blood which is carried to the lungs through the bronchial arteries is returned to the left side of the heart through the pulmonary veins.

The Veins of the Vertebral Column (Figs. 570, 571).

The veins which drain the blood from the vertebral column, the neighboring muscles, and the meninges of the medulla spinalis form intricate plexuses extending along the entire length of the column; these plexuses may be divided into two groups, external and internal, according to their positions inside or outside the vertebral canal. The plexuses of the two groups anastomose freely with each other and end in the intervertebral veins.

The **external vertebral venous plexuses** (*plexus venosi vertebrales externi; extraspinal veins*) best marked in the cervical region, consist of anterior and posterior plexuses which anastomose freely with each other. The **anterior external plexuses** lie in front of the bodies of the vertebræ, communicate with the basivertebral and intervertebral veins, and receive tributaries from the vertebral bodies. The **posterior external plexuses** are placed partly on the posterior surfaces of the vertebral arches and their processes, and partly between the deep dorsal muscles. They are best developed in the cervical region, and there anastomose with the vertebral, occipital, and deep cervical veins.

The **internal vertebral venous plexuses** (*plexus venosi vertebrales interni; intraspinal veins*) lie within the vertebral canal between the dura mater and the vertebræ, and receive tributaries from the bones and from the medulla spinalis. They form a closer net-work than the external plexuses, and, running mainly in a vertical direction, form four longitudinal veins, two in front and two behind; they therefore may be divided into anterior and posterior groups. The **anterior internal plexuses** consist of large veins which lie on the posterior surfaces of the vertebral bodies and intervertebral fibrocartilages on either side of the posterior longitudinal ligament; under cover of this ligament they are connected by transverse branches into which the basivertebral veins open. The **posterior internal plexuses** are placed, one on

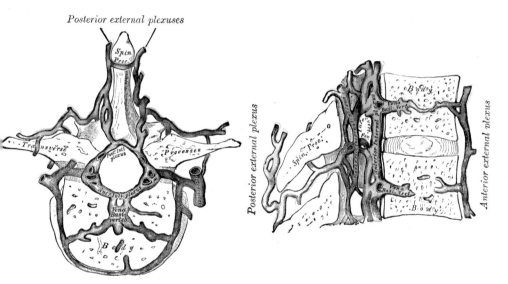

Fig. 570.—Transverse section of a thoracic vertebra, showing the vertebral venous plexuses.

Fig. 571.—Median sagittal section of two thoracic vertebræ, showing the vertebral venous plexuses.

either side of the middle line in front of the vertebral arches and ligamenta flava, and anastomose by veins passing through those ligaments with the posterior external plexuses. The anterior and posterior plexuses communicate freely with one another by a series of **venous rings** (*retia venosa vertebrarum*), one opposite each vertebra. Around the foramen magnum they form an intricate net-work which opens into the vertebral veins and is connected above with the occipital sinus, the basilar plexus, the condyloid emissary vein, and the rete canalis hypoglossi.

The **basivertebral veins** (*vv. basivertebrales*) emerge from the foramina on the posterior surfaces of the vertebral bodies. They are contained in large, tortuous channels in the substance of the bones, similar in every respect to those found in the diploë of the cranial bones. They communicate through small openings on the front and sides of the bodies of the vertebræ with the anterior external vertebral plexuses, and converge behind to the principal canal, which is sometimes double toward its posterior part, and open by valved orifices into the transverse branches which unite the anterior internal vertebral plexuses. They become greatly enlarged in advanced age.

The **intervertebral veins** (*vv. intervertebrales*) accompany the spinal nerves through the intervertebral foramina; they receive the veins from the medulla spinalis, drain the internal and external vertebral plexuses and end in the vertebral, intercostal, lumbar, and lateral sacral veins, their orifices being provided with valves.

The **veins of the medulla spinalis** (*vv. spinales; veins of the spinal cord*) are situated in the pia mater and form a minute, tortuous, venous plexus. They emerge chiefly from the median fissures of the medulla spinalis and are largest in the lumbar region. In this plexus there are (1) two median longitudinal veins, one in front of the anterior fissure, and the other behind the posterior sulcus of the cord, and (2) four lateral longitudinal veins which run behind the nerve roots. They end in the intervertebral veins. Near the base of the skull they unite, and form two or three small trunks, which communicate with the vertebral veins, and then end in the inferior cerebellar veins, or in the inferior petrosal sinuses.

According to Batson (1940) the veins of the vertebral column constitute a system paralleling the caval system. He reached this conclusion as a result of X-ray studies of human cadavers and living animals. A thin solution of radiopaque material which he injected into the dorsal vein of the penis in a cadaver found its way readily into the veins of the entire vertebral column, the skull, and the interior of the cranium. The material drained from the dorsal vein of the penis into the prostatic plexus and then followed communications with the veins of the sacrum, ilium, lumbar vertebræ, upper femur, and the venæ vasorum of the large femoral blood vessels, without traversing the main caval tributaries. Similarly, material injected into a small breast vein found its way into the veins of the clavicle, the intercostal veins, the head of the humerus, cervical vertebræ, and dural sinuses without following the caval paths. Thorium dioxide injected into the dorsal vein of the penis of an anæsthetized monkey drained into the caval system when the animal was undisturbed, but if its abdomen was put under pressure with a binder, simulating the increased intra-abdominal pressure of coughing or straining, the material drained into the veins of the vertebræ. Batson believes that the spread of metastases from tumors and abscesses, in many cases such as the metastases to the pelvic bones from the prostate, can be explained only through the channels of the vertebral venous system and its extensive communication with the caval system. When the pressure within the thorax and abdomen is increased by coughing or straining, the blood may flow along the vertebral system rather than the caval and it may even be forced into the vertebral veins from the viscera.

THE VEINS OF THE LOWER EXTREMITY, ABDOMEN, AND PELVIS.

The veins of the lower extremity are subdivided, like those of the upper, into two sets, **superficial** and **deep**; the superficial veins are placed beneath the integument between the two layers of superficial fascia; the deep veins accompany the arteries. Both sets of veins are provided with valves, which are more numerous in the deep than in the superficial set. Valves are also more numerous in the veins of the lower than in those of the upper limb.

The Superficial Veins of the Lower Extremity.

The **superficial veins** of the lower extremity are the **great** and **small saphenous veins** and their tributaries.

On the **dorsum of the foot** the **dorsal digital veins** receive, in the clefts between the toes, the **intercapitular veins** from the plantar cutaneous venous arch and join to form short **common digital veins** which unite across the distal ends of the metatarsal bones in a **dorsal venous arch**. Proximal to this arch is an irregular venous net-work which receives tributaries from the deep veins and is joined at the sides of the foot by a **medial** and a **lateral marginal vein**, formed mainly by the union of branches from the superficial parts of the sole of the foot.

On the **sole of the foot** the superficial veins form a **plantar cutaneous venous arch** which extends across the roots of the toes and opens at the sides of the foot into the medial and lateral marginal veins. Proximal to this arch is a **plantar cutaneous venous net-work** which is especially dense in the fat beneath the heel; this net-work communicates with the cutaneous venous arch and with the deep veins, but is chiefly drained into the medial and lateral marginal veins.

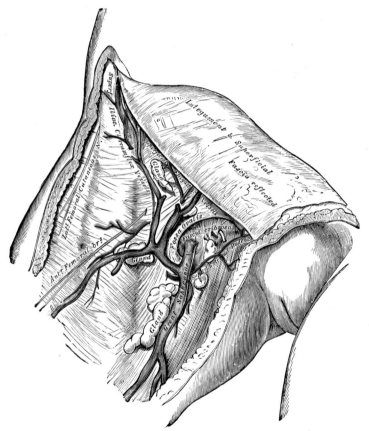

Fig. 572.—The great saphenous vein and its tributaries at the fossa ovalis.

The **great saphenous vein** (*v. saphena magna; internal or long saphenous vein*) (Fig. 573), the longest vein in the body, *begins* in the medial marginal vein of the dorsum of the foot and ends in the femoral vein about 3 cm. below the inguinal ligament. It ascends in front of the tibial malleolus and along the medial side of the leg in relation with the saphenous nerve. It runs upward behind the medial condyles of the tibia and femur and along the medial side of the thigh and, passing through the fossa ovalis, ends in the femoral vein.

Tributaries.—At the ankle it receives branches from the sole of the foot through the medial marginal vein; in the leg it anastomoses freely with the small saphenous vein, communicates with the anterior and posterior tibial veins and receives many cutaneous veins; in the thigh it communicates with the femoral vein and receives numerous tributaries; those from the medial and posterior parts of the thigh frequently unite to form a large **accessory saphenous vein** which joins the main vein at a variable level. Near the fossa ovalis (Fig. 572) it is joined by the super-

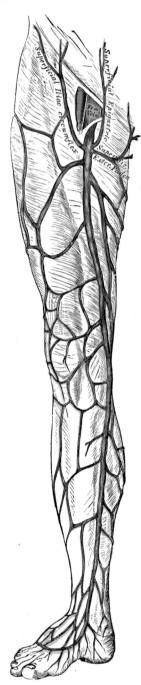

ficial epigastric, superficial iliac circumflex, and superficial external pudendal veins. A vein, named the **thoracoepigastric**, runs along the lateral aspect of the trunk between the superficial epigastric vein and the lateral thoracic vein and establishes an important communication between the femoral and axillary veins.

The valves in the great saphenous vein vary from ten to twenty in number; they are more numerous in the leg than in the thigh.

The **small saphenous vein** (*v. saphena parva; external or short saphenous vein*) (Fig. 574) *begins* behind the lateral malleolus as a continuation of

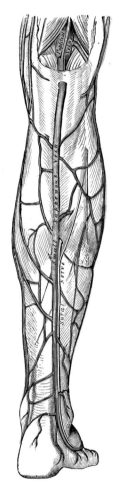

FIG. 574.—The small saphenous vein.

FIG. 573.—The great saphenous vein and its tributaries.

the lateral marginal vein; it first ascends along the lateral margin of the tendo calcanei, and then crosses it to reach the middle of the back of the leg. Running directly upward, it perforates the deep fascia in the lower part of the popliteal fossa, and ends in the popliteal vein, between the heads of the Gastrocnemius. It communicates with the deep veins on the dorsum of the foot, and receives numerous large tributaries from the back of the leg. Before it pierces the deep fascia, it gives off a branch which runs upward and forward to join the great saphenous vein. The small saphenous vein possesses from nine to twelve valves, one of which is always found near its termination in the popliteal vein. In the lower third of the leg the small saphenous vein is in close relation with the sural nerve, in the upper two-thirds with the medial sural cutaneous nerve.

The Deep Veins of the Lower Extremity.

The **deep veins** of the lower extremity accompany the arteries and their branches; they possess numerous valves.

The **plantar digital veins** (*vv. digitales plantares*) *arise* from plexuses on the plantar surfaces of the digits, and, after sending **intercapitular veins** to join the dorsal digital veins, unite to form four **metatarsal veins**; these run backward in the metatarsal spaces, communicate, by means of perforating veins, with the veins on the dorsum of the foot, and unite to form the **deep plantar venous arch** which lies alongside the plantar arterial arch. From the deep plantar venous arch the **medial** and **lateral plantar veins** run backward close to the corresponding arteries and, after communicating with the great and small saphenous veins, unite behind the medial malleolus to form the posterior tibial veins.

The **posterior tibial veins** (*vv. tibiales posteriores*) accompany the posterior tibial artery, and are joined by the **peroneal veins**.

The **anterior tibial veins** (*vv. tibiales anteriores*) are the upward continuation of the venæ comitantes of the dorsalis pedis artery. They leave the front of the leg by passing between the tibia and fibula, over the interosseous membrane, and unite with the posterior tibial, to form the **popliteal vein**.

The **Popliteal Vein** (*v. poplitea*) (Fig. 575) is formed by the junction of the anterior and posterior tibial veins at the lower border of the Popliteus; it ascends through the popliteal fossa to the aperture in the Adductor magnus, where it becomes the femoral vein. In the lower part of its course it is placed medial to the artery; between the heads of the Gastrocnemius it is superficial to that vessel; but above the knee-joint, it is close to its lateral side. It receives tributaries corresponding to the branches of the popliteal artery, and it also receives the small saphenous vein. The valves in the popliteal vein are usually four in number.

The **femoral vein** (*v. femoralis*) accompanies the femoral artery through the upper two-thirds of the thigh. In the lower part of its course it lies lateral to the artery; higher up, it is behind it; and at the inguinal ligament, it lies on its medial side, and on the same plane. It receives numerous muscular tributaries, and about 4 cm. below the inguinal ligament is joined by the v. profunda femoris; near its termination it is joined by the great saphenous vein. The valves in the femoral vein are three in number.

FIG. 575.—The popliteal vein.

The **Deep Femoral Vein** (*v. profunda femoris*) receives tributaries corresponding to the perforating branches of the profunda artery, and through these establishes communications with the popliteal vein below and the inferior gluteal vein above. It also receives the medial and lateral femoral circumflex veins.

The Veins of the Abdomen and Pelvis (Figs. 577).

The **external iliac vein** (*v. iliaca externa*), the upward continuation of the femoral vein, begins behind the inguinal ligament, and, passing upward along the brim of the lesser pelvis, ends opposite the sacroiliac articulation, by uniting with the hypogastric vein to form the common iliac vein. On the right side, it lies at first medial to the artery: but, as it passes upward, gradually inclines behind it. On the left side, it lies altogether on the medial side of the artery. It frequently contains one, sometimes two, valves.

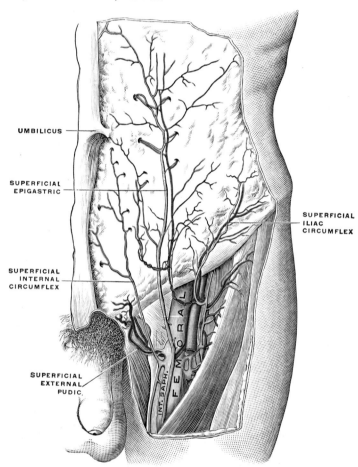

Fig. 576.—The femoral vein and its tributaries. (Poirier and Charpy.)

Tributaries.—The external iliac vein receives the inferior epigastric, deep iliac circumflex, and pubic veins.

The **Inferior Epigastric Vein** (*v. epigastrica inferior; deep epigastric vein*) is formed by the union of the venæ comitantes of the inferior epigastric artery, which communicate above with the superior epigastric vein; it joins the external iliac about 1.25 cm. above the inguinal ligament.

The **Deep Iliac Circumflex Vein** (*v. circumflexa ilii profunda*) is formed by the union of the venæ comitantes of the deep iliac circumflex artery, and joins the external iliac vein about 2 cm. above the inguinal ligament.

The **Pubic Vein** communicates with the obturator vein in the obturator foramen, and ascends on the back of the pubis to the external iliac vein.

The **hypogastric vein** (*v. hypogastrica; internal iliac vein*) *begins* near the upper part of the greater sciatic foramen, passes upward behind and slightly medial to the hypogastric artery and, at the brim of the pelvis, joins with the external iliac to form the common iliac vein.

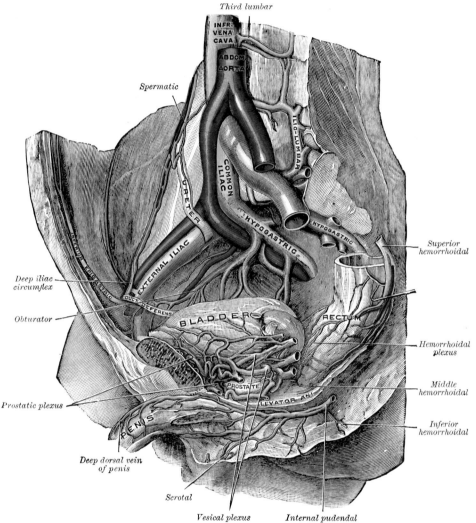

Fig. 577.—The veins of the right half of the male pelvis. (Spalteholz.)

Tributaries.—With the exception of the fetal umbilical vein which passes upward and backward from the umbilicus to the liver, and the iliolumbar vein which usually joins the common iliac vein, the tributaries of the hypogastric vein correspond with the branches of the hypogastric artery. It receives (*a*) the **gluteal, internal pudendal,** and **obturator veins,** which have their origins outside the pelvis; (*b*) the **lateral sacral veins,** which lie in front of the sacrum; and (*c*) the **middle hemorrhoidal, vesical, uterine,** and **vaginal veins,** which originate in venous plexuses connected with the pelvic viscera.

1. The **Superior Gluteal Veins** (*vv. glutaeæ superiores; gluteal veins*) are venæ comitantes of the superior gluteal artery; they receive tributaries from the buttock corresponding with the branches of the artery, and enter the pelvis through the greater sciatic foramen, above the Piriformis, and frequently unite before ending in the hypogastric vein.

2. The **Inferior Gluteal Veins** (*vv. glutaeœ inferiores; sciatic veins*), or venæ comitantes of the inferior gluteal artery, *begin* on the upper part of the back of the thigh, where they anastomose with the medial femoral circumflex and first perforating veins. They enter the pelvis through the lower part of the greater sciatic foramen and join to form a single stem which opens into the lower part of the hypogastric vein.

3. The **Internal Pudendal Veins** (*internal pudic veins*) are the venæ comitantes of the internal pudendal artery. They *begin* in the deep veins of the penis which issue from the corpus cavernosum penis, accompany the internal pudendal artery, and unite to form a single vessel, which ends in the hypogastric vein. They receive the veins from the urethral bulb, and the perineal and inferior hemorrhoidal veins. The deep dorsal vein of the penis communicates with the internal pudendal veins, but ends mainly in the pudendal plexus.

4. The **Obturator Vein** (*v. obturatoria*) *begins* in the upper portion of the adductor region of the thigh and enters the pelvis through the upper part of the obturator foramen. It runs backward and upward on the lateral wall of the pelvis below the obturator artery, and then passes between the ureter and the hypogastric artery, to end in the hypogastric vein.

5. The **Lateral Sacral Veins** (*vv. sacrales laterales*) accompany the lateral sacral arteries on the anterior surface of the sacrum and end in the hypogastric vein.

6. The **Middle Hemorrhoidal Vein** (*v. hœmorrhoidalis media*) takes origin in the hemorrhoidal plexus and receives tributaries from the bladder, prostate, and seminal vesicle; it runs lateralward on the pelvic surface of the Levator ani to end in the hypogastric vein.

The **hemorrhoidal plexus** (*plexus hœmorrhoidalis*) surrounds the rectum, and communicates in front with the vesical plexus in the male, and the uterovaginal plexus in the female. It consists of two parts, an **internal** in the submucosa, and an **external** outside of the muscular coat. The internal plexus presents a series of dilated pouches which are arranged in a circle around the tube, immediately above the anal orifice, and are connected by transverse branches.

The lower part of the external plexus is drained by the inferior hemorrhoidal veins into the internal pudendal vein; the middle part by the middle hemorrhoidal vein which joins the hypogastric vein; and the upper part by the superior hemorrhoidal vein which forms the commencement of the inferior mesenteric vein, a tributary of the portal vein. A free communication between the portal and systemic venous systems is established through the hemorrhoidal plexus.

The veins of the hemorrhoidal plexus are contained in very loose, connective tissue, so that they get less support from surrounding structures than most other veins, and are less capable of resisting increased blood-pressure.

The **pudendal plexus** (*plexus pudendalis; vesicoprostatic plexus*) lies behind the arcuate pubic ligament and the lower part of the symphysis pubis, and in front of the bladder and prostate. Its chief tributary is the deep dorsal vein of the penis, but it also receives branches from the front of the bladder and prostate. It communicates with the vesical plexus and with the internal pudendal vein and drains into the vesical and hypogastric veins. The **prostatic veins** form a well-marked **prostatic plexus** which lies partly in the fascial sheath of the prostate and partly between the sheath and the prostatic capsule. It communicates with the pudendal and vesical plexuses.

The **vesical plexus** (*plexus vesicalis*) envelops the lower part of the bladder and the base of the prostate and communicates with the pudendal and prostatic plexuses. It is drained, by means of several vesical veins, into the hypogastric veins.

The **Dorsal Veins of the Penis** (*vv. dorsales penis*) are two in number, a superficial and a deep. The **superficial vein** drains the prepuce and skin of the penis, and, running backward in the subcutaneous tissue, inclines to the right or left, and opens into the corresponding superficial external pudendal vein, a tributary of the great saphenous vein. The **deep vein** lies beneath the deep fascia of the penis; it receives the blood from the glans penis and corpora cavernosa penis and courses backward in the mid-line between the dorsal arteries; near the root of the penis it passes between the two parts of the suspensory ligament and then through an aperture between the arcuate pubic ligament and the transverse ligament of the pelvis, and divides into two branches, which enter the pudendal plexus. The deep vein also communicates below the symphysis pubis with the internal pudendal vein.

The **uterine plexuses** lie along the sides and superior angles of the uterus between the two layers of the broad ligament, and communicate with the ovarian and vaginal plexuses. They are drained by a pair of uterine veins on either side: these *arise* from the lower part of the plexuses, opposite the external orifice of the uterus, and open into the corresponding hypogastric vein.

The **vaginal plexuses** are placed at the sides of the vagina; they communicate with the uterine, vesical, and hemorrhoidal plexuses, and are drained by the vaginal veins, one on either side, into the hypogastric veins.

The **common iliac veins** (*vv. iliacæ communes*) are formed by the union of the external iliac and hypogastric veins, in front of the sacroiliac articulation; passing obliquely upward toward the right side, they end upon the fifth lumbar vertebra, by uniting with each other at an acute angle to form the inferior vena cava. The **right common iliac** is shorter than the left, nearly vertical in

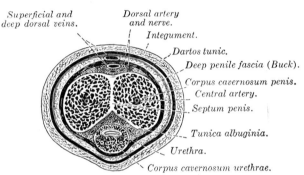

Superficial and deep dorsal veins.
Dorsal artery and nerve.
Integument.
Dartos tunic.
Deep penile fascia (Buck).
Corpus cavernosum penis.
Central artery.
Septum penis.
Tunica albuginia.
Urethra.
Corpus cavernosum urethrae.

FIG. 578.—The penis in transverse section showing the bloodvessels.

its direction, and ascends behind and then lateral to its corresponding artery. The **left common iliac,** longer than the right and more oblique in its course, is at first situated on the medial side of the corresponding artery, and then behind the right common iliac. Each common iliac receives the iliolumbar, and sometimes the lateral sacral veins. The left receives, in addition, the middle sacral vein. No valves are found in these veins.

The **Middle Sacral Veins** (*vv. sacrales mediales*) accompany the corresponding artery along the front of the sacrum, and join to form a single vein, which ends in the left common iliac vein; sometimes in the angle of junction of the two iliac veins.

Variations.—The left common iliac vein, instead of joining with the right in its usual position, occasionally ascends on the left side of the aorta as high as the kidney, where, after receiving the left renal vein, it crosses over the aorta, and then joins with the right vein to form the vena cava. In these cases, the two common iliacs are connected by a small communicating branch at the spot where they are usually united. This variation represents a persisting left lumbar supracardinal.

The **inferior vena cava** (*v. cava inferior*) (Fig. 568), returns to the heart the blood from the parts below the diaphragm. It is formed by the junction of the two common iliac veins, on the right side of the fifth lumbar vertebra. It ascends along the front of the vertebral column, on the right side of the aorta, and, having reached the liver, is continued in a groove on its posterior surface. It then perforates the diaphragm between the median and right portions of its central tendon; it subsequently inclines forward and medialward for about 2.5 cm., and, piercing the fibrous pericardium, passes behind the serous pericardium to open into the lower and back part of the right atrium. In front of its atrial orifice is a semilunar valve, termed the **valve of the inferior vena cava**: this is rudimentary in the adult, but is of large size and exercises an important function in the fetus (see page 546).

Relations.—The *abdominal portion* of the inferior vena cava is in relation *in front*, from below upward, with the right common iliac artery, the mesentery, the right internal spermatic artery, the inferior part of the duodenum, the pancreas, the common bile duct, the portal vein, and the posterior surface of the liver; the last partly overlaps and occasionally completely surrounds it; *behind*, with the vertebral column, the right Psoas major, the right crus of the diaphragm, the right inferior phrenic, suprarenal, renal and lumbar arteries, right sympathetic trunk and right celiac ganglion, and the medial part of the right suprarenal gland; on the *right side*, with the right kidney and ureter; on the *left side*, with the aorta, right crus of the diaphragm, and the caudate lobe of the liver.

The *thoracic portion* is only about 2.5 cm. in length, and is situated partly inside and partly outside the pericardial sac. The *extrapericardial part* is separated from the right pleura and lung by a fibrous band, named the **right phrenicopericardiac ligament.** This ligament, often feebly marked, is attached below to the margin of the vena-caval opening in the diaphragm, and above to the pericardium in front of and behind the root of the right lung. The *intrapericardiac part* is very short, and is covered antero-laterally by the serous layer of the pericardium.

Variations.—This vessel is sometimes placed on the left side of the aorta, as high as the left renal vein, and, after receiving this vein, crosses over to its usual position on the right side; or it may be placed altogether on the left side of the aorta, and in such a case the abdominal and thoracic viscera, together with the great vessels, are all transposed. Most of the variations are due to the persistence of the left lumbar supracardinal vein of the embryo. Occasionally the inferior vena cava joins the azygos vein, which is then of large size. In such cases, the superior vena cava receives all the blood from the body before transmitting it to the right atrium, except the blood from the hepatic veins, which passes directly into the right atrium.

Tributaries.—The inferior vena cava receives the following veins:

Lumbar.	Renal.	Inferior Phrenic.
Right Spermatic or Ovarian.	Suprarenal.	Hepatic.

The **Lumbar Veins** (*vv. lumbales*) *four* in number on each side, collect the blood by dorsal tributaries from the muscles and integument of the loins, and by abdominal tributaries from the walls of the abdomen, where they communicate with the epigastric veins. At the vertebral column, they receive veins from the vertebral plexuses, and then pass forward, around the sides of the bodies of the vertebræ, beneath the Psoas major, and end in the back part of the inferior cava. The left lumbar veins are longer than the right, and pass behind the aorta. The lumbar veins are connected together by a longitudinal vein which passes in front of the transverse processes of the lumbar vertebræ, and is called the **ascending lumbar;** it forms the most frequent origin of the corresponding azygos or hemiazygos vein, and serves to connect the common iliac, iliolumbar, and azygos or hemiazygos veins of its own side of the body.

The **Spermatic Veins** (*vv. spermaticæ*) (Fig. 580) emerge from the back of the testis, and receive tributaries from the epididymis; they unite and form a convoluted plexus, called the **pampiniform plexus,** which constitutes the greater mass of the spermatic cord; the vessels composing this plexus are very numerous, and ascend along the cord, in front of the ductus deferens. Below the subcutaneous inguinal ring they unite to form three or four veins, which pass along the inguinal canal, and, entering the abdomen through the abdominal inguinal ring, coalesce to form two veins, which ascend on the Psoas major, behind the peritoneum, lying one on either side of the internal spermatic artery. These unite to form a single vein, which opens on the right side into the inferior vena cava, at an acute angle; on the left side into the left renal vein, at a right angle. The spermatic veins are provided with valves.[1] The left spermatic vein passes behind the iliac colon, and is thus exposed to pressure from the contents of that part of the bowel.

---

[1] Rivington has pointed out that valves are usually found at the orifices of both the right and left spermatic veins. When no valves exist at the opening of the left spermatic vein into the left renal vein, valves are generally present in the left renal vein within 6 mm. from the orifice of the spermatic vein.—Journal of Anatomy and Physiol., vol. 7, 163.

The **Ovarian Veins** (*vv. ovaricæ*) correspond with the spermatic in the male; they form a plexus in the broad ligament near the ovary and uterine tube, and communicate with the uterine plexus. They end in the same way as the spermatic veins in the male. Valves are occasionally found in these veins. Like the uterine veins, they become much enlarged during pregnancy.

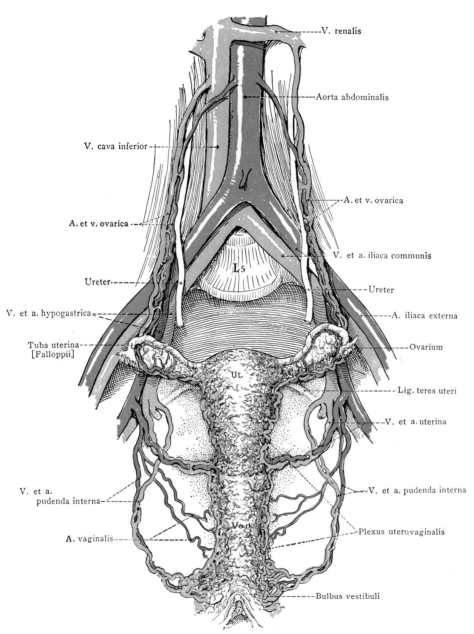

Fig. 579.—The blood vessels of the female pelvis, showing chief source of blood supply of the uterus and vagina. (Eycleshymer and Jones.)

The **Renal Veins** (*vv. renales*) are of large size, and placed in front of the renal arteries. The left is longer than the right, and passes in front of the aorta, just below the origin of the superior mesenteric artery. It receives the left spermatic and left inferior phrenic veins, and, generally, the left suprarenal vein. It opens into the inferior vena cava at a slightly higher level than the right.

The **Suprarenal Veins** (*vv. suprarenales*) are two in number: the right ends in the inferior vena cava; the left, in the left renal or left inferior phrenic vein.

The **Inferior Phrenic Veins** (*vv. phrenicæ inferiores*) follow the course of the inferior phrenic arteries; the right ends in the inferior vena cava; the left is often represented by two branches, one of which ends in the left renal or suprarenal vein, while the other passes in front of the esophageal hiatus in the diaphragm and opens into the inferior vena cava.

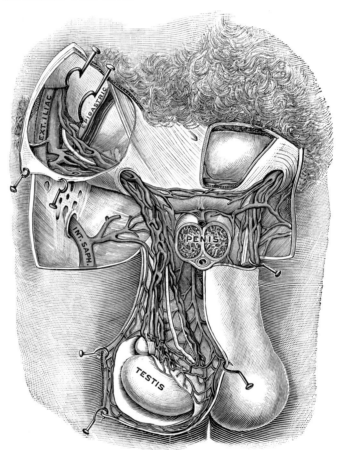

Fig. 580.—Spermatic veins. (Testut.)

The **Hepatic Veins** (*vv. hepaticæ*) commence in the substance of the liver, in the terminations of the portal vein and hepatic artery, and are arranged in two groups, upper and lower. The **upper group** usually consists of three large veins, which converge toward the posterior surface of the liver, and open into the inferior vena cava, while that vessel is situated in the groove on the back part of the liver. The veins of the **lower group** vary in number, and are of small size; they come from the right and caudate lobes. The hepatic veins run singly, and are in direct contact with the hepatic tissue. They are destitute of valves.

THE PORTAL SYSTEM OF VEINS (Fig. 581).

The **portal system** includes all the veins which drain the blood from the abdominal part of the digestive tube (with the exception of the lower part of the rectum) and from the spleen, pancreas, and gall-bladder. From these viscera the blood is conveyed to the liver by the **portal vein**. In the liver this vein ramifies like an artery and ends in capillary-like vessels termed **sinusoids**, from which the blood is conveyed to the inferior vena cava by the hepatic veins. From this it will be seen that the blood of the portal system passes through two sets of minute vessels, viz., (*a*) the capillaries of the digestive tube, spleen, pancreas, and gall-bladder; and (*b*) the sinusoids of the liver. In the adult the portal vein and its tributaries are destitute of valves; in the fetus and for a short time after birth valves can be demonstrated in the tributaries of the portal vein; as a rule they soon atrophy and disappear, but in some subjects they persist in a degenerate form.

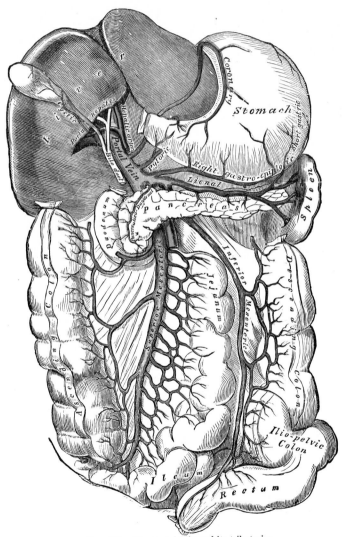

Fig. 581.—The portal vein and its tributaries.

The **portal vein** (*vena portæ*) is about 8 cm. in length, and is formed at the level of the second lumbar vertebra by the junction of the superior mesenteric and lienal veins, the union of these veins taking place in front of the inferior vena cava and behind the neck of the pancreas. It passes upward behind the superior part of the duodenum and then ascends in the right border of the lesser omentum to the right extremity of the porta hepatis, where it divides into a right and a left branch,

44

which accompany the corresponding branches of the hepatic artery into the substance of the liver. In the lesser omentum it is placed behind and between the common bile duct and the hepatic artery, the former lying to the right of the latter. It is surrounded by the hepatic plexus of nerves, and is accompanied by numerous lymphatic vessels and some lymph glands. The **right branch** of the portal vein enters the right lobe of the liver, but before doing so generally receives the cystic vein. The **left branch,** longer but of smaller caliber than the right, crosses the left sagittal fossa, gives branches to the caudate lobe, and then enters the left lobe of the liver. As it crosses the left sagittal fossa it is joined in front by a fibrous cord, the **ligamentum teres** (*obliterated umbilical vein*), and is united to the inferior vena cava by a second fibrous cord. the **ligamentum venosum** (*obliterated ductus venosus*).

Tributaries.—The tributaries of the portal vein are:

Lienal (Splenic).	Pyloric.
Superior Mesenteric.	Cystic.
Coronary.	Parumbilical.

The **Lienal Vein** (*v. lienalis; splenic vein*) *commences* by five or six large branches which return the blood from the spleen. These unite to form a single vessel, which passes from left to right, grooving the upper and back part of the pancreas, below the lienal artery, and ends behind the neck of the pancreas by uniting at a right angle with the superior mesenteric to form the portal vein. The lienal vein is of large size, but is not tortuous like the artery.

Tributaries.—The lineal vein receives the short gastric veins, the left gastro-epiploic vein, the pancreatic veins, and the inferior mesenteric veins.

The **short gastric veins** (*vv. gastricæ breves*),four or five in number, drain the fundus and left part of the greater curvature of the stomach, and pass between the two layers of the gastrolienal ligament to end in the lienal vein or in one of its large tributaries.

The **left gastroepiploic vein** (*v. gastroepiploica sinistra*) receives branches from the antero-superior and postero-inferior surfaces of the stomach and from the greater omentum; it runs from right to left along the greater curvature of the stomach and ends in the commencement of the lienal vein.

The **pancreatic veins** (*vv. pancreaticæ*) consist of several small vessels which drain the body and tail of the pancreas, and open into the trunk of the lienal vein.

The **inferior mesenteric vein** (*v. mesenterica inferior*) returns blood from the rectum and the sigmoid, and descending parts of the colon. It begins in the rectum as the **superior hemorrhoidal vein,** which has its origin in the hemorrhoidal plexus, and through this plexus communicates with the middle and inferior hemorrhoidal veins. The superior hemorrhoidal vein leaves the lesser pelvis and crosses the left common iliac vessels with the superior hemorrhoidal artery, and is continued upward as the inferior mesenteric vein. This vein lies to the left of its artery, and ascends behind the peritoneum and in front of the left Psoas major; it then passes behind the body of the pancreas and opens into the lienal vein; sometimes (10 per cent.) it ends in the angle of union of the lienal and superior mesenteric veins, or drains into the superior mesenteric vein.

Tributaries.—The inferior mesenteric vein receives the **sigmoid veins** from the sigmoid colon and iliac colon, and the **left colic vein** from the descending colon and left colic flexure.

The **Superior Mesenteric Vein** (*v. mesenterica superior*) returns the blood from the small intestine, from the cecum, and from the ascending and transverse portions of the colon. It begins in the right iliac fossa by the union of the veins which drain the terminal part of the ileum, the cecum, and vermiform process, and ascends between the two layers of the mesentery on the right side of the superior mesenteric artery. In its upward course it passes in front of the right ureter, the inferior vena cava, the inferior part of the duodenum, and the lower portion of the head of the pancreas. Behind the neck of the pancreas it unites with the lienal vein to form the portal vein.

Tributaries.—Besides the tributaries which correspond with the branches of the superior mesenteric artery, viz., the **intestinal, ileocolic, right colic,** and **middle colic veins,** the superior mesenteric vein is joined by the right gastroepiploic and pancreaticoduodenal veins.

The **right gastroepiploic vein** (*v. gastroepiploica dextra*) receives branches from the greater omentum and from the lower parts of the antero-superior and postero-inferior surfaces of the stomach; it runs from left to right along the greater curvature of the stomach between the two layers of the greater omentum.

The **pancreaticoduodenal veins** (*vv. pancreaticoduodenales*) accompany their corresponding arteries; the lower of the two frequently joins the right gastroepiploic vein.

The **Coronary Vein** (*v. coronaria ventriculi; gastric vein*) derives tributaries from both surfaces of the stomach; it runs from right to left along the lesser curvature of the stomach, between the two layers of the lesser omentum, to the esophageal opening of the stomach, where it receives some esophageal veins. It then turns backward and passes from left to right behind the omental bursa and ends in the portal vein.

The **Pyloric Vein** is of small size, and runs from left to right along the pyloric portion of the lesser curvature of the stomach, between the two layers of the lesser omentum, to end in the portal vein.

The **Cystic Vein** (*v. cystica*) drains the blood from the gall-bladder, and, accompanying the cystic duct, usually ends in the right branch of the portal vein.

Parumbilical Veins(*vv. parumbilicales*).—In the course of the ligamentum teres of the liver and of the middle umbilical ligament, small veins (*parumbilical*) are found which establish an anastomosis between the veins of the anterior abdominal wall and the portal, hypogastric, and iliac veins. The best marked of these small veins is one which commences at the umbilicus and runs backward and upward in, or on the surface of, the ligamentum teres between the layers of the falciform ligament to end in the left portal vein.

Collateral venous circulation to relieve portal obstruction in the liver is usually effected mainly: (*a*) by communications between the gastric veins and the esophageal veins which empty into the azygos system, and (*b*) by communications between the inferior mesenteric veins and the hemorrhoidal veins that empty into the hypogastric veins. Other possible collaterals which are not of much practical importance are (*c*) the accessory portal system of Sappey, branches of which pass in the round and falciform ligaments to unite with the superior and inferior epigastric, and internal mammary veins, and through the diaphragmatic veins with the azygos; a single large vein, shown to be a parumbilical vein, may pass from the hilus of the liver by the round ligament to the umbilicus, producing there a bunch of prominent varicose veins known as the caput medusæ; and (*d*) the veins of Retzius, which connect the intestinal veins with the inferior vena cava and its retroperitoneal branches.

BIBLIOGRAPHY.

Veins

The function of the vertebral veins and their rôle in the spread of metastases. BATSON, O. V.: 1940. Ann. Surg., Vol. 112, pp. 138–149.

The rôle of the vertebral veins in metastatic processes. BATSON, O. V.: 1942. Ann. Internal Med., Vol. 16, pp. 38–45.

The external jugular vein in American whites and negroes. BROWN, S.: 1941. Am. J. Phys. Anthrop., Vol. 28, pp. 213–226.

The saphenous venous tributaries and related structures in relation to the technique of high ligation. Based chiefly upon a study of 550 anatomical dissections. DASELER, E. H., B. J. ANSON, A. F. REIMANN, and L. E. BEATON: 1946. Surg., Gyn. and Obs., Vol. 82, pp. 53–63.

Applied anatomy of the femoral vein and its tributaries. EDWARDS, E. A., and J. D. ROBUCK, JR.: 1947. Surg., Gyn. and Obs., Vol. 85, pp. 547–557.

A Monograph on Veins. FRANKLIN, K. J.: 1937. Charles C Thomas, Springfield, xxii + 410 pp.

The collateral venous circulation in a case of thrombosis of the inferior vena cava, and its embryological interpretation. KEEN, J. A.: 1941. Brit. J. Surg., Vol. 29, pp. 105–114.

Hereditary variations in the vena cava inferior of the rabbitt. McNUTT, C. W., and P. B. SAWIN: 1943. Am. J. Anat., Vol. 72, pp. 259–289.

The development of the superior caval system in the rat. SCHNEIDER, L. A.: 1938. Anat. Rec., Vol. 71, pp. 265–276.

ANOMALIES AND VARIATIONS

Anomalies of venæ cavæ superiores in an Orang. CHASE, R. E., and C. F. DE GARIS: 1938. Am. J. Phys. Anthrop., Vol. 24, pp. 61–65.

A case of bilateral superior vena cava in an adult. CHOUKE, K. S.: 1939. Anat. Rec., Vol. 74, pp. 151–157.

Report of a case in which all pulmonary veins from both lungs drain into the superior vena cava. CONN, L. C., J. CALDER, J. W. MACGREGOR, and R. F. SHANER: 1942. Anat. Rec., Vol. 83, pp. 335–340.

Report of two unusual venous abnormalities (left postrenal inferior vena cava; postaortic left innominate vein). FRIEDMAN, S. M.: 1945. Anat. Rec., Vol. 92, pp. 71–76.

A multiple anomaly of the great veins and interatrial septum in a human heart. VAN CLEAVE, C. D.: 1931. Anat. Rec., Vol. 50, pp. 45–51.

VALVES

The orientation of venous valves in relation to body surfaces. EDWARDS, E. A.: 1936. Anat. Rec., Vol. 64, pp. 369–385.

The venous valves in thromboangiitis obliterans. EDWARDS, E. A., and J. E.: 1943 Arch. Path., Vol. 35, pp. 242–252.

The origin and development of the venous valves, with particular reference to the saphenous district. KAMPMEIER, O. F., and C. BIRCH: 1927. Am. J. Anat., Vol. 38, pp. 451–499.

THE LYMPHATIC SYSTEM.

THE **lymphatic system** consists of: (1) an extensive capillary network which collects lymph in the various organs and tissues; (2) an elaborate system of collecting vessels which carry the lymph from the lymphatic capillaries to the blood stream, opening into the great veins at the root of the neck; (3) a number of firm rounded bodies called lymph nodes (B. N. A. lymphoglandulæ) which are placed like filters in the paths of the collecting vessels; (4) certain lymphatic organs which resemble the lymph nodes, that is, tonsils and solitary or aggregated lymphatic nodules; (5) the spleen, and (6) the thymus. Another element which might be added is the lymphoid, or, as it is often called, adenoid tissue. It is recognizable only with the aid of a microscope and consists of reticular or areolar connective tissue which contains an accumulation of lymphocytes but lacks the organized

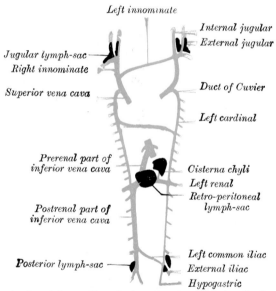

FIG. 582.—Scheme showing relative positions of primary lymph sacs based on the description given by Florence Sabin.

lymphatic nodules. The spleen is generally recognized as a lymphatic organ because it contains lymphatic nodules. The thymus, on the other hand, has been described previously with the ductless glands, but since no evidence of glandular function has been found, and since it is made up principally of lymphoid tissue, it is here classed as a lymphatic organ. The lymphatic capillaries and collecting vessels are lined throughout by a continuous layer of endothelial cells, forming thus a closed system. The lymphatic vessels of the small intestine receive the special designation of **lacteals** or **chyliferous vessels**; they differ in no respect from the lymphatic vessels generally excepting that during the process of digestion they contain a milk-white fluid, the **chyle**.

Development.—The earliest lymphatic endothelium probably arises from venous endothelium as sprouts from several regions of the primitive veins. The first

(693)

sprouts came from the primitive right and left internal jugular veins at their junctions with the subclavians. They grow, branch, and anastomose to form the **jugular lymph sacs.** From these sacs lymphatic capillary plexuses spread to the neck, head, arms, and thorax. The more direct channels of the plexuses enlarge and form the lymphatic vessels. The larger vessels acquire smooth muscular coats with nerve connections, and exhibit contractility. Each jugular sac retains at least one connection with its jugular vein. From the left one the upper part of the thoracic duct develops. At a slightly older stage (8th week) lymphatic sprouts from the primitive vena cava and mesonephric veins form the unpaired **retroperitoneal lymph sac.** From it, lymphatics spread to the abdominal viscera and diaphragm. The sac establishes connections with the cisterna chyli and loses its connections with the veins.

At about the same time another series of sprouts from the primitive veins of the Wolffian bodies forms the **cisterna chyli.** It gives rise to the cisterna chyli and to part of the thoracic duct. It joins that part of the duct which develops from the left jugular sac, and loses all its connections with the veins. At a slightly later stage (8th week) endothelial sprouts are given off from the primitive iliac veins at their junctions with the posterior cardinal veins. They form the paired **posterior lymph sacs.** From these sacs lymphatics spread to the abdominal wall, pelvic region, and legs. They join the cisterna chyli and lose all connections with the veins.

According to this view, all lymphatic endothelium is derived from venous endothelium which it resembles in many respects. An improbable opposing view derives lymphatic endothelium from mesenchymal cells which are supposed to flatten out into endothelium about small isolated accumulations of fluid in the neighborhood of the large primitive veins. These little sacs are supposed to join to form the first lymphatic capillaries and lymph sacs and to acquire secondary connections with the veins. It might be pointed out that this supposed origin of lymphatic endothelium is analogous to the formation of the mesothelium of joint cavities and that true lymphatic endothelium resembles venous endothelium, not mesothelium. Endothelium forms tubes which acquire muscle walls. Mesothelial sacs do neither.

The **primary lymph nodes** begin to develop during the third month in capillary lymphatic plexuses formed out of the large lymph sacs. Secondary lymph nodes develop later, and even after birth, in peripherally located capillary lymphatic plexuses. Lymphocytes are already present in the blood stream and tissues long before lymph nodes begin to appear. The earliest stages are obscure. It seems probable that lymphocytes lodge in special regions of the capillary plexuses and multiply to form larger and larger masses of lymphocytes which become the cortical lymphoid nodules and medullary cords. Parallel with this multiplication of lymphocytes, the surrounding mesenchyme forms a connective tissue capsule from which trabeculæ carrying bloodvessels grow into the lymphoid tissue. In the larger trabeculæ, collagenous fibers are laid down and continued as reticular fibrils into the smaller trabeculæ. The mesenchymal cells of the larger trabeculæ become fibroblasts, those accompanying the reticular fibrils are known as reticular cells. Just what happens to the lymphatic endothelium of the capillary plexus within the developing node is obscure. Some authors believe it forms the cortical and medullary sinuses. Others believe that the endothelial lining becomes incomplete and that the reticular cells are washed by the lymph. With this idea goes the theory that some of the reticular cells round up and become the first lymphocytes of the developing node and that they retain this potency throughout life.

Lymphatic Capillary Plexuses.—The networks which collect lymph from the intercellular fluid may be said to constitute the beginning of the lymphatic system, since from these plexuses arise the lymphatic vessels which conduct the lymph centrally through one or more lymph glands or nodes to the thoracic duct or to the right lymphatic duct. The number, the size, and the richness of the capillary plexuses differ in different regions and organs. Where abundant, they are usually arranged in two or more anastomosing layers. Most capillaries are without valves.

Fig. 583.—Lymph capillaries of the human conjunctiva: *a.* conjunctiva corneæ: *b*, conjunctiva scleroticæ. × 40 dia. (Teichmann.)

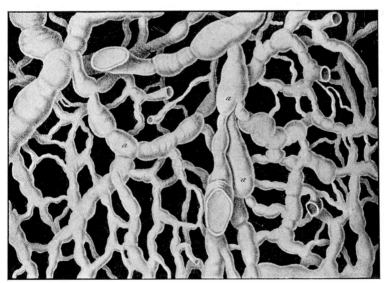

Fig. 584.—Lymph capillaries from the human scrotum, showing also transition from capillaries to the collecting vessels *a. a.* × 20 dia. (Teichmann.)

Lymphatic capillaries are especially abundant in the **dermis** of the skin. They form a continuous network over the entire surface of the body with the exception of the cornea. The dermis has a superficial plexus, without valves, connected by many anastomoses with a somewhat wider coarser deep plexus with a few valves.

The former sends blind ends into the papillæ. The plexuses are especially rich over the palmar surface of the hands and fingers, the plantar surface of the feet and toes, the conjunctiva, the scrotum, the vulva, and around the orifices where the skin becomes continuous with the mucous membranes.

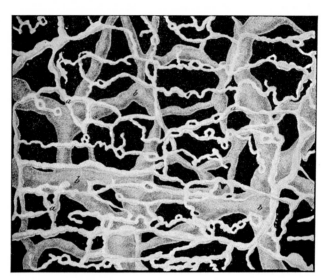

FIG. 585.—Lymph capillaries of the cutis from the inner border of the sole of the human foot. *a, a*, outer layer; *b, b*, inner layer. × 30 dia. (Teichmann.)

Lymphatic capillary plexuses are abundant in the **mucous membranes** of the respiratory and digestive systems. They form a continuous network from the nares and lips to the anus. In most places, there is a subepithelial plexus in the mucosa which anastomoses freely with a coarser plexus in the submucosa. Blind ends extend between the tubular glands of the stomach and into the villi of the intestine. The latter are the lacteals. They have a smooth muscle coat and are contractile.

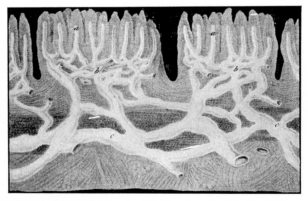

FIG. 586.—Vertical section through human tongue; *a, a*, blind lymph capillaries in the filiform papillæ with the underlying lymphatic plexus. × 45. (Teichmann.)

Those portions of the alimentary canal covered by peritoneum have a subserous capillary plexus beneath the mesothelium which anastomoses with the submucosal set.

The **lungs** have a rich subserous plexus which connects with the deep plexuses within the lungs. The latter accompanies the bronchi and bronchioles. Its capillaries do not extend to the alveoli.

The **salivary glands, pancreas** and **liver** possess deep lymphatic plexuses. They are perilobular and do not extend between the epithelial cells. The gall-bladder, cystic, hepatic, and common bile ducts have rich plexuses in the mucosa. The deep lymphatics of the liver deliver a copious supply of lymph. The liver and gall-bladder have rich subserous plexuses.

The **kidney** has a rich network in the capsule and a deep plexus between the tubules of the parenchyma. The renal pelvis and the ureters have rich networks in the mucosa and muscular layer which are continuous with similar plexuses of the urinary bladder. The male urethra has a dense plexus in the mucosa. The capillaries are especially abundant around the navicular fossa.

The **testis**, epididymis, ductus deferens, seminal vesicles and prostate have superficial capillary plexuses. Both the testis and prostate have deep interstitial plexuses.

The **ovary** has a rich capillary plexus in the parenchyma. Capillaries are absent in the tunica albuginea. The uterine tubes and uterus have mucous and muscular plexuses as well as serous and subserous ones. The vagina has a rich fine-meshed plexus in the mucosa and a coarser one in the muscular layer.

Lymphatic capillary plexuses are abundant beneath the mesothelial lining of the pleural, peritoneal, and pericardial cavities and the joint capsules. The dense connective tissues of tendons, ligaments, and periosteum are richly supplied with plexuses. The **heart** has a rich subepicardial plexus and a subendocardial one. The myocardium has a uniform capillary plexus which anastomoses with both the subendocardial and subepicardial ones. There are no collecting trunks in the myocardium.

Very fine capillary plexuses have been described about the fibers of **skeletal muscle**. Their occurrence in bone and bone marrow is not settled.

No lymphatic capillaries have been found in the central nervous system, the meninges, the eyeball and orbital fat, the cornea, the internal ear, cartilage, subcutaneous tissue, epidermis, and the spleen.

Lymphatic Vessels.—Lymphatic vessels of the first order arise in lymphatic capillary plexuses which they drain. They all enter lymph nodes as afferent vessels. From these nodes, efferent vessels usually pass to one or to a series of lymph nodes before they join the thoracic duct or the right lymphatic duct. Lymphatic vessels frequently anastomose and usually accompany bloodvessels. The larger collecting vessels often extend long distances without change of caliber. The lymphatic vessels are exceedingly delicate, and their coats are so transparent that the fluid they contain is readily seen through them. They are interrupted at intervals by constrictions, which give them a knotted or beaded appearance; these constrictions correspond to the situations of valves in their interior.

The lymphatic vessels are arranged into a **superficial** and a **deep set**. On the surface of the body the **superficial** lymphatic vessels are placed immediately beneath the integument, accompanying the superficial veins; they join the deep lymphatic vessels in certain situations by perforating the deep fascia. In the interior of the body they lie in the submucous areolar tissue, throughout the whole length of the digestive, respiratory, and genito-urinary tracts; and in the subserous tissue of the thoracic and abdominal walls. Plexiform networks of minute lymphatic vessels are found interspersed among the proper elements and bloodvessels of the several tissues; the vessels composing the net-work, as well as the meshes between them, are much larger than those of the capillary plexus. From these net-works small vessels emerge, which pass, either to a neighboring node, or to join some larger lymphatic trunk. The **deep** lymphatic vessels, fewer in number, but larger than the superficial, accompany the deep bloodvessels. Their mode of origin is probably similar to that of the superficial vessels. The lymphatic vessels of any part or organ exceed the veins in number, but in size they are much smaller. Their anastomoses also, especially those of the large trunks, are more frequent, and are effected by vessels equal in diameter to those which they connect, the continuous trunks retaining the same diameter.

Structure of Lymphatic Vessels.—The larger lymphatic vessels are each composed of three coats. The *internal* coat is thin, transparent, slightly elastic, and consists of a layer of elongated endothelial cells with wavy margins by which the contiguous cells are dovetailed into one another; the cells are supported on an elastic membrane. The *middle* coat is composed of smooth muscular and fine elastic fibers, disposed in a transverse direction. The *external* coat consists of connective tissue, intermixed with smooth muscular fibers longitudinally or obliquely disposed; it forms a protective covering to the other coats, and serves to connect the vessel with the neighboring structures. In the smaller vessels there are no muscular or elastic fibers, and the wall consists only of a connective-tissue coat, lined by endothelium. The thoracic duct has a more complex structure than the other lymphatic vessels; it presents a distinct subendothelial layer of branched corpuscles, similar to that found in the arteries; in the middle coat there is, in addition to the muscular and elastic fibers, a layer of connective tissue with its fibers arranged longitudinally. The lymphatic vessels are supplied by nutrient vessels, which are distributed to their outer and middle coats; and here also have been traced many non-medullated nerves in the form of a fine plexus of fibrils.

The valves of the lymphatic vessels are formed of thin layers of fibrous tissue covered on both surfaces by endothelium which presents the same arrangement as on the valves of veins (p. 524). In form the valves are semilunar; they are attached by their convex edges to the wall of the vessel, the concave edges being free and directed along the course of the contained current. Usually two such valves, of equal size, are found opposite one another; but occasionally exceptions occur, especially at or near the anastomoses of lymphatic vessels. Thus, one valve may be of small size and the other increased in proportion.

In the lymphatic vessels the valves are placed at much shorter intervals than in the veins. They are most numerous near the lymph nodes, and are found more frequently in the lymphatic vessels of the neck and upper extremity than in those of the lower extremity. The wall of the lymphatic vessel immediately above the point of attachment of each segment of a valve is expanded into a pouch or sinus which gives to these vessels, when distended, the knotted or beaded appearance already referred to. Valves are wanting in the vessels composing the plexiform net-work in which the lymphatic vessels originate.

The lymph is propelled by contractions of the vessel walls. The valves prevent the backward flow. The segments between the valves contract twelve to eighteen times per minute in the mesenteric lymphatic vessels of the rat.

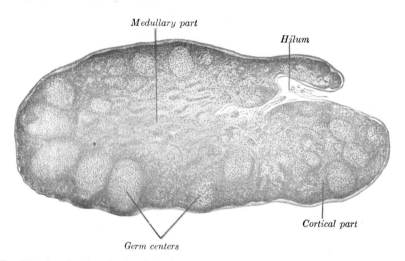

Medullary part

Hilum

Cortical part

Germ centers

Fig. 587.—A section through a lymph gland of a dog. Stained with hematoxylin and eosin. × 34.

Lymph Nodes (*lymphoglandulæ*).—The lymph nodes are small oval or bean-shaped bodies, situated in the course of lymphatic and lacteal vessels so that the lymph and chyle pass through them on their way to the blood. Each generally presents on one side a slight depression—the hilum—through which the bloodvessels enter and leave and efferent lymphatic vessels emerge. Afferent lymphatic vessels enter the organ at various places on the periphery. On section (Fig. 587) a lymph node displays a lighter **cortical** part and a darker **medullary** part. The cortical part is deficient at the hilum. Here the medullary part reaches the surface.

Structure of Lymph Nodes.—A lymph node consists of enormous numbers of **lymphocytes** densely packed into masses that are partially subdivided into a series of cortical nodules and medullary cords by anastomosing connective tissue trabeculæ bordered by lymph sinuses. The **trabeculæ** extend into the node from the connective tissue **capsule** and the hilum. An extensive network of **reticular fibers** extends from the trabeculæ to all parts of the node. Narrow connecting zones just beneath the capsule and bordering the trabeculæ where the lymphocytes are less densely packed are known as the subcapsular, cortical, and medullary **sinuses** (Fig. 588). The afferent vessels open into the subcapsular, and the efferent vessels arise from the medullary sinuses. The lymph flow is retarded by the relatively enormous extent of the sinuses and the great numbers of reticular fibers which cross them in all directions. Numerous reticular cells and macrophages cling to the reticular fibers. Most authors believe that the sinuses are lined by reticular cells and not by lymphatic endothelium.

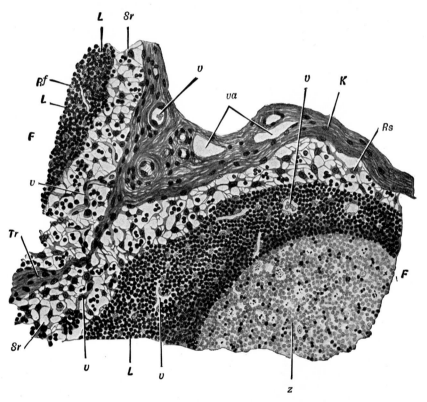

Fig. 588.—Portion of cortex of a lymph node of a dog. *K*, capsule; *Tr*, trabecula; *F*, periphery of follicles with a germinal center; *Z*, *Sr*, subcapsular sinuses; *v*, bloodvessels; *va*, afferent lymphatic vessels; *L*, small lymphocytes; *Rf*, reticular cells in the follicles and *Rs* in the sinus. Hematoxylin-eosin-azure stain. × 187. (Maximow and Bloom, Textbook af Histology, courtesy of W. B. Saunders Company.)

The capsule consists of dense bundles of collagenous fibers, networks of elastic fibers, and a few smooth muscle cells. It is thickened at the hilum. The collagenous fibers are continued into the trabeculæ and seem to be continuous with the reticular fibers of the sinuses and nodules.

Lymphocytes increase by division and enter the lymph. The nodules or follicles in the cortical portion of the gland frequently show, in their centers, areas where karyokinetic figures indicate a division of the lymph corpuscles. These areas are termed **germ centers.** The cells composing them have more abundant protoplasm than the peripheral cells and consist of large and medium-sized lymphocytes.

Bloodvessels enter the hilum; branches traverse the trabeculæ and medullary cords to the cortex. A rich capillary plexus extends throughout the pulp.

Nerves, probably vasomotors, enter the hilum and accompany the bloodvessels.

Hemolymph nodes or **glands** and **hemal nodes** occur in the prevertebral retro-peritoneal and cervical regions, in the neighborhood of the adrenal and renal vessels, along the brim of the pelvis and in the root of the mesentery. They are deep red in color, very small in size, deeply imbedded in fat and few in number. They contain in addition varying amounts of lymphoid tissue blood sinuses.

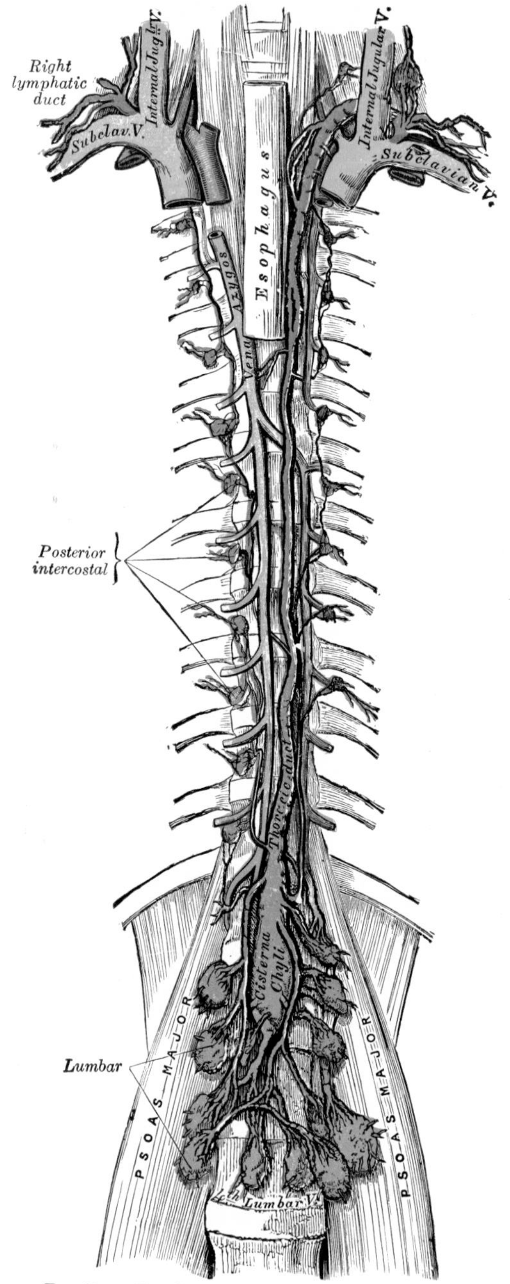

Lymph.—Lymph, found only in the closed lymphatic vessels, is a transparent, colorless, or slightly yellow, watery fluid of specific gravity about 1.015; it closely resembles the blood plasma, but is more dilute. When it is examined under the microscope, leucocytes of the lymphocyte class are found floating in the transparent fluid; they are always increased in number after the passage of the lymph through lymphoid tissue, as in lymph glands. Lymph should be distinguished from "tissue fluid" which is found outside the lymphatic vessels in the tissue spaces.

THE THORACIC DUCT.

The **thoracic duct** (*ductus thoracicus*) (Fig. 589) conveys the greater part of the lymph and chyle into the blood. It is the common trunk of all the lymphatic vessels of the body, excepting those on the right side of the head, neck, and thorax, and right upper extremity, the right lung, right side of the heart, and the convex surface of the liver. In the adult it varies in length from 38 to 45 cm. and extends from the second lumbar vertebra to the root of the neck. It begins in the abdomen by a triangular dilatation, the **cisterna chyli**, which is situated on the front of the body of the second lumbar vertebra, to the right side of and behind the aorta, by the side of the right crus of the diaphragm. It enters the thorax through the aortic hiatus of the diaphragm, and ascends through the posterior mediastinal cavity between the aorta and azygos vein. Behind it in this region are the vertebral column, the right intercostal arteries, and the hemiazygos

Fig. 589.—The thoracic and right lymphatic ducts.

veins as they cross to open into the azygos vein; in front of it are the diaphragm, esophagus, and pericardium, the last being separated from it by a recess of the right pleural cavity. Opposite the fifth thoracic vertebra, it inclines toward the left side, enters the superior mediastinal cavity, and ascends behind the aortic arch and the thoracic part of the left subclavian artery and between the left side of the esophagus and the left pleura, to the upper orifice of the thorax. Passing into the neck it forms an arch which rises about 3 or 4 cm. above the clavicle and crosses anterior to the subclavian artery, the vertebral artery and vein, and the thyrocervical trunk or its branches. It also passes in front of the phrenic nerve and the medial border of the Scalenus anterior, but is separated from these two structures by the prevertebral fascia. In front of it are the left common carotid artery, vagus nerve, and internal jugular vein; it ends by opening into the angle of junction of the left subclavian vein with the left internal jugular vein. The thoracic duct, at its commencement, is about equal in diameter to a goose-quill, but it diminishes considerably in caliber in the middle of the thorax, and is again dilated just before its termination. It is generally flexuous, and constricted at intervals so as to present a varicose appearance. Not infrequently it divides in the middle of its course into two vessels of unequal size which soon reunite, or into several branches which form a plexiform interlacement. It occasionally divides at its upper part into two branches, right and left; the left ending in the usual manner, while the right opens into the right subclavian vein, in connection with the right lymphatic duct. The thoracic duct has several valves; at its termination it is provided with a pair, the free borders of which are turned toward the vein, so as to prevent the passage of venous blood into the duct.

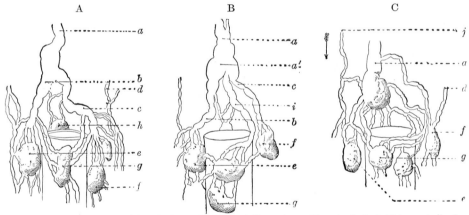

Fig. 590.—Modes of origin of thoracic duct. (Poirier and Charpy.) *a*. Thoracic duct *a'*. Cisterna chyli. *b, c,* Efferent trunks from lateral aortic node. *d*. An efferent vessel which pierces the left crus of the diaphragm. *e, f,* Lateral aortic node. *h*. Retroaortic nodes. *i*. Intestinal trunk. *j*. Descending branch from intercostal lymphatics.

The **cisterna chyli** (*receptaculum chyli*) (Fig. 590) receives the two lumbar lymphatic trunks, right and left, and the intestinal lymphatic trunk. The **lumbar trunks** are formed by the union of the efferent vessels from the lateral aortic lymph glands. They receive the lymph from the lower limbs, from the walls and viscera of the pelvis, from the kidneys and suprarenal nodes and the deep lymphatics of the greater part of the abdominal wall. The **intestinal trunk** receives the lymph from the stomach and intestine, from the pancreas and spleen, and from the lower and front part of the liver.

Tributaries.—Opening into the commencement of the thoracic duct, on either side, is a descending trunk from the posterior intercostal lymph nodes of the lower six or seven intercostal spaces. In the thorax the duct is joined, on either side, by a trunk which drains the upper lumbar lymph nodes and pierces the crus of the diaphragm. It also receives the efferents from the posterior mediastinal lymph glands and from the posterior intercostal lymph nodes of the upper six left spaces. In the neck it is joined by the **left jugular** and **left subclavian trunks,** and sometimes by the **left bronchomediastinal trunk;** the last-named, however, usually opens independently into the junction of the left subclavian and internal jugular veins.

The **right lymphatic duct** (*ductus lymphaticus dexter*) (Fig. 591), about 1.25 cm. in length, courses along the medial border of the Scalenus anterior at the root of the neck and ends in the right subclavian vein, at its angle of junction with the right internal jugular vein. Its orifice is guarded by two semilunar valves, which prevent the passage of venous blood into the duct.

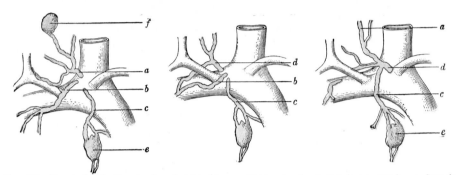

Fig. 591.—Terminal collecting trunks of right side. *a.* Jugular trunk. *b.* Subclavian trunk. *c.* Bronchomediastinal trunk. *d.* Right lymphatic trunk. *e.* Node of internal mammary chain. *f.* Node of deep cervical chain. (Poirier and Charpy.)

Tributaries.—The right lymphatic duct receives the lymph from the right side of the head and neck through the **right jugular trunk**; from the right upper extremity through the **right subclavian trunk**; from the right side of the thorax, right lung, right side of the heart, and part of the convex surface of the liver, through the **right bronchomediastinal trunk**. These three collecting trunks frequently open separately in the angle of union of the two veins.

THE LYMPHATICS OF THE HEAD, FACE, AND NECK.

The Lymph Nodes of the Head (Fig. 592).

The lymph nodes of the head are arranged in the following groups:

Occipital.	Facial.
Posterior Auricular.	Deep Facial.
Anterior Auricular.	Lingual.
Parotid.	Retropharyngeal.

The **occipital nodes** (*lymphoglandulæ occipitales*), one to three in number, are placed on the back of the head close to the margin of the Trapezius and resting on the insertion of the Semispinalis capitis. Their afferent vessels drain the occipital region of the scalp, while their efferents pass to the superior deep cervical nodes.

The **posterior auricular nodes** (*lymphoglandulæ auriculares*; *mastoid nodes*), usually two in number, are situated on the mastoid insertion of the Sternocleidomastoideus, beneath the Auricularis posterior. Their afferent vessels drain the posterior part of the temporoparietal region, the upper part of the cranial surface of the auricula or pinna, and the back of the external acoustic meatus; their efferents pass to the superior deep cervical nodes.

The **anterior auricular nodes** (*lymphoglandulæ auriculares anteriores; superficial parotid or preauricular glands*), from one to three in number, lie immediately in front of the tragus. Their afferents drain the lateral surface of the auricula and the skin of the adjacent part of the temporal region; their efferents pass to the superior deep cervical nodes.

The **parotid nodes** (*lymphoglandulæ parotideæ*), form two groups in relation with the parotid salivary gland, viz., a group imbedded in the substance of the node, and a group of subparotid glands lying on the lateral wall of the pharynx. Occasionally small nodes are found in the subcutaneous tissue over the parotid gland. Their afferent vessels drain the root of the nose, the eyelids, the frontotemporal region, the external acoustic meatus and the tympanic cavity, possibly also the posterior parts of the palate and the floor of the nasal cavity. The efferents of these nodes pass to the superior deep cervical nodes. The afferents of the subparotid nodes drain the nasal part of the pharynx and the posterior parts of the nasal cavities; their efferents pass to the superior deep cervical nodes.

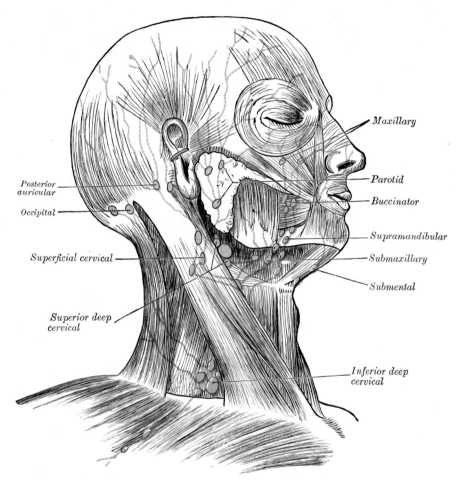

Fig. 592.—Superficial lymph nodes and lymphatic vessels of head and neck.

The **facial nodes** comprise three groups: (*a*) **infraorbital** or **maxillary,** scattered over the infraorbital region from the groove between the nose and cheek to the zygomatic arch; (*b*) **buccinator,** one or more placed on the Buccinator opposite the angle of the mouth; (*c*) **supramandibular,** on the outer surface of the mandible, in front of the Masseter and in contact with the external maxillary artery and anterior facial vein. Their afferent vessels drain the eyelids, the conjunctiva, and the skin and mucous membrane of the nose and cheek; their efferents pass to the submaxillary nodes.

The **deep facial nodes** (*lymphoglandulæ faciales profunda; internal maxillary glands*) are placed beneath the ramus of the mandible, on the outer surface of the Pterygoideus externus, in relation to the internal maxillary artery. Their afferent vessels drain the temporal and infratemporal fossæ and the nasal part of the pharynx their efferents pass to the superior deep cervical nodes.

The **lingual nodes** (*lymphoglandulæ linguales*) are two or three small nodules lying on the Hyoglossus and under the Genioglossus. They form merely glandular substations in the course of the lymphatic vessels of the tongue.

The **retropharyngeal nodes** (Fig. 593), from one to three in number, lie in the buccopharyngeal fascia, behind the upper part of the pharynx and in front of the arch of the atlas, being separated, however, from the latter by the Longus capitis. Their afferents drain the nasal cavities, the nasal part of the pharynx, and the auditory tubes; their efferents pass to the superior deep cervical nodes.

The **lymphatic vessels of the scalp** are divisible into (*a*) those of the frontal region, which terminate in the anterior auricular and parotid nodes; (*b*) those of the temporoparietal region, which end in the parotid and posterior auricular nodes;

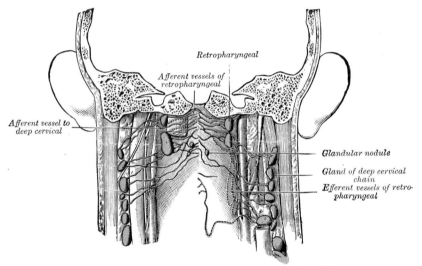

FIG. 593.—Lymphatics and lymph nodes of the pharynx. (Poirier and Charpy.)

and (*c*) those of the occipital region, which terminate partly in the occipital glands and partly in a trunk which runs down along the posterior border of the Sternocleidomastoideus to end in the inferior deep cervical nodes.

The **lymphatic vessels of the auricula and external acoustic meatus** are also divisible into three groups: (*a*) an anterior, from the lateral surface of the auricula and anterior wall of the meatus to the anterior auricular nodes; (*b*) a posterior, from the margin of the auricula, the upper part of its cranial surface, the internal surface and posterior wall of the meatus to the posterior auricular and superior deep cervical nodes; (*c*) an inferior, from the floor of the meatus and from the lobule of the auricula to the superficial and superior deep cervical nodes.

The **lymphatic vessels of the face** (Fig. 594) are more numerous than those of the scalp. Those from the eyelids and conjunctiva terminate partly in the submaxillary but mainly in the parotid nodes. The vessels from the posterior part of the cheek also pass to the parotid nodes, while those from the anterior portion of the cheek, the side of the nose, the upper lip, and the lateral portions of the lower lip end in the submaxillary nodes. The deeper vessels from the temporal and infratemporal fossæ pass to the deep facial and superior deep cervical nodes. The deeper vessels of the cheek and lips end, like the superficial, in the submaxillary nodes. Both superficial and deep vessels of the central part of the lower lip run to the submental nodes.

Lymphatic Vessels of the Nasal Cavities.—Those from the anterior parts of the nasal cavities communicate with the vessels of the integument of the nose and end in the submaxillary nodes; those from the posterior two-thirds of the nasal cavities and from the accessory air sinuses pass partly to the retropharyngeal and partly to the superior deep cervical nodes.

Lymphatic Vessels of the Mouth.—The vessels of the gums pass to the submaxillary nodes; those of the hard palate are continuous in front with those of the upper gum, but pass backward to pierce the Constrictor pharyngis superior and end in the superior deep cervical and subparotid nodes; those of the soft palate pass backward and lateralward and end partly in the retropharyngeal and subparotid, and partly in the superior deep cervical nodes. The vessels of the anterior part of the floor of the mouth pass either directly to the inferior nodes of the superior

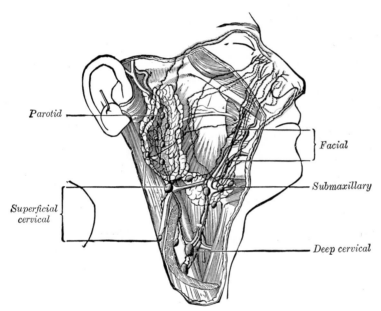

Parotid

Facial

Submaxillary

Superficial cervical

Deep cervical

FIG. 594.—The lymphatics and lymph nodes of the face. (After Küttner.)

deep cervical group, or indirectly through the submental nodes; from the rest of the floor of the mouth the vessels pass to the submaxillary and superior deep cervical nodes.

The **lymphatic vessels of the palatine tonsil,** usually three to five in number, pierce the buccopharyngeal fascia and constrictor pharyngis superior and pass between the Stylohyoideus and internal jugular vein to the uppermost of the superior deep cervical nodes. They end in a node which lies at the side of the posterior belly of the Digastricus, on the internal jugular vein; occasionally one or two additional vessels run to small glands on the lateral side of the vein under cover of the Sternocleidomastoideus.

The **lymphatic vessels of the tongue** (Fig. 595) are drained chiefly into the deep cervical nodes lying between the posterior belly of the Digastricus and the superior belly of the Omohyoideus; one node situated at the bifurcation of the common carotid artery is so intimately associated with these vessels that it is known as the **principal node of the tongue.** The lymphatic vessels of the tongue may be divided

45

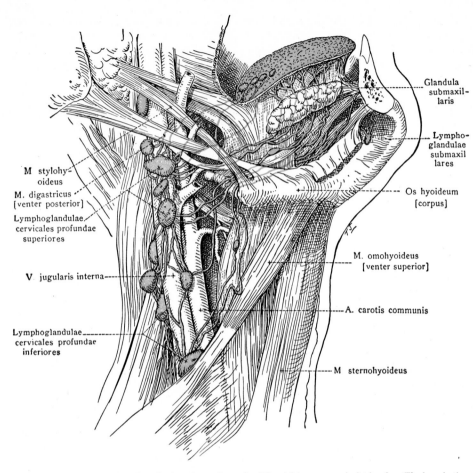

M stylohy-
oideus

M. digastricus
[venter posterior]

Lymphoglandulae
cervicales profundae
superiores

V. jugularis interna

Lymphoglandulae
cervicales profundae
inferiores

Glandula
submaxil-
laris

Lympho-
glandulae
submaxil
lares

Os hyoideum
[corpus]

M. omohyoideus
[venter superior]

A. carotis communis

M sternohyoideus

Fig. 595.—The deep cervical lymphatic nodes and vessels of the right upper cervical triangle. The lymphatic
drainage of the tongue is shown. (Eycleshymer and Jones).

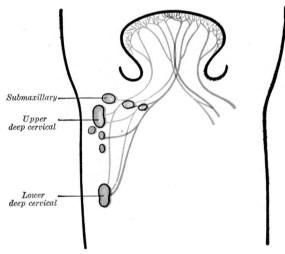

Submaxillary

Upper
deep cervical

Lower
deep cervical

Fig. 596.—A diagram to show the course of the central lymphatic vessels of the tongue to the lymph nodes on both
sides of the neck. (Jamieson and Dobson.)

into four groups: (1) apical, from the tip of the tongue to the suprahyoid nodes and principal node of the tongue; (2) lateral, from the margin of the tongue—some of these pierce the Mylohyoideus to end in the submaxillary nodes, others pass down on the Hyoglossus to the superior deep cervical nodes; (3) basal, from the region of the vallate papillæ to the superior deep cervical nodes; and (4) median, a few of which perforate the Mylohyoideus to reach the submaxillary nodes, while the majority turn around the posterior border of the muscle to enter the superior deep cervical nodes.

The Lymph Nodes of the Neck.

The lymph nodes of the neck include the following groups:

Submaxillary.	Superficial Cervical.
Submental.	Anterior Cervical.

Deep Cervical.

The **submaxillary nodes** (*lymphoglandulæ submaxillares*) (Fig. 594), three to six in number, are placed beneath the body of the mandible in the submaxillary triangle, and rest on the superficial surface of the submaxillary salivary node. One node, the **middle node of Stahr,** which lies on the external maxillary artery as it turns over the mandible, is the most constant of the series; small lymph nodes are sometimes found on the deep surface of the submaxillary salivary nodes. The afferents of the submaxillary nodes drain the medial palpebral commissure, the cheek, the side of the nose, the upper lip, the lateral part of the lower lip, the gums, and the anterior part of the margin of the tongue; efferent vessels from the facial and submental nodes also enter the submaxillary nodes. Their efferent vessels pass to the superior deep cervical nodes.

The **submental** or **suprahyoid nodes** are situated between the anterior bellies of the Digastrici. Their afferents drain the central portions of the lower lip and floor of the mouth and the apex of the tongue; their efferents pass partly to the submaxillary nodes and partly to a node of the deep cervical group situated on the internal jugular vein at the level of the cricoid cartilage.

The **superficial cervical nodes** (*lymphoglandulæ cervicales superficiales*) lie in close relationship with the external jugular vein as it emerges from the parotid gland, and, therefore, superficial to the Sternocleidomastoideus. Their afferents drain the lower parts of the auricula and parotid region, while their efferents pass around the anterior margin of the Sternocleidomastoideus to join the superior deep cervical nodes.

The **anterior cervical nodes** form an irregular and inconstant group on the front of the larynx and trachea. They may be divided into (*a*) a **superficial set,** placed on the anterior jugular vein; (*b*) a **deeper set,** which is further subdivided into prelaryngeal, on the middle cricothyroid ligament, and pretracheal, on the front of the trachea. This deeper set drains the lower part of the larynx, the thyroid node, and the upper part of the trachea; its efferents pass to the lowest of the superior deep cervical nodes.

The **deep cervical nodes** (*lymphoglandulæ cervicales profundæ*) (Figs. 595, 598) are numerous and of large size: they form a chain along the carotid sheath, lying by the side of the pharynx, esophagus, and trachea, and extending from the base of the skull to the root of the neck. They are usually described in two groups: (1) the **superior deep cervical nodes** lying under the Sternocleidomastoideus in close relation with the accessory nerve and the internal jugular vein, some of the nodes lying in front of and others behind the vessel; (2) the **inferior deep cervical nodes** extending beyond the posterior margin of the Sternocleidomastoideus into the supraclavicular triangle, where they are closely related to the brachial plexus and subclavian vein. A few minute **paratracheal nodes** are situated alongside the recurrent nerves on the lateral aspects of the trachea and esophagus. The superior deep cervical nodes drain the occipital portion of the scalp, the auricula, the back of the neck, a considerable part of the tongue, the larynx, thyroid gland, trachea, nasal part of the pharynx, nasal cavities, palate, and esophagus. They receive also the efferent vessels from all the other nodes of the head and neck, except those from the inferior deep cervical nodes. The inferior deep cervical

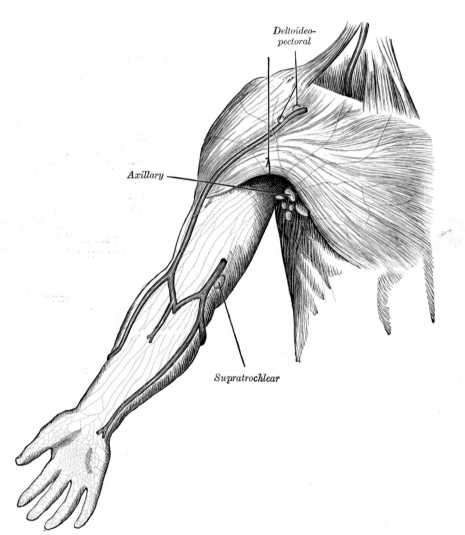

Deltoideo-pectoral

Axillary

Supratrochlear

Fig. 597.—The superficial lymph nodes and lymphatic vessels of the upper extremity.

nodes drain the back of the scalp and neck, the superficial pectoral region, part of the arm (see page 711), and, occasionally, part of the superior surface of the liver. In addition, they receive vessels from the superior deep cervical nodes. The efferents of the superior deep cervical nodes pass partly to the inferior deep cervical nodes and partly to a trunk which unites with the efferent vessel of the inferior deep cervical nodes and forms the **jugular trunk**. On the right side, this trunk ends in the junction of the internal jugular and subclavian veins; on the left side it joins the thoracic duct.

The **lymphatic vessels of the skin and muscles of the neck** pass to the deep cervical nodes. From the upper part of the *pharynx* the lymphatic vessels pass to the retropharyngeal, from the lower part to the deep cervical nodes. From the *larynx*

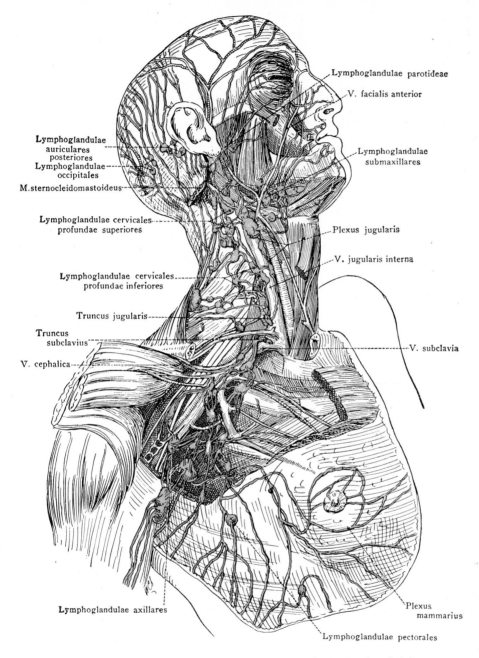

Fig. 598.—The deep lymphatic nodes and vessels of the right side of the head and neck, and of the mammary and axillary regions. (Eycleshymer and Jones.)

two sets of vessels arise, an upper and a lower. The vessels of the upper set pierce the hyothyroid membrane and join the superior deep cervical nodes. Of the lower set, some pierce the conus elasticus and join the pretracheal and prelaryngeal nodes; others run between the cricoid and first tracheal ring and enter the inferior deep cervical nodes. The lymphatic vessels of the *thyroid node* consist of two sets, an upper, which accompanies the superior thyroid artery and enters the superior deep cervical nodes, and a lower, which runs partly to the pretracheal nodes and partly to the small paratracheal nodes which accompany the recurrent nerves. These latter glands receive also the lymphatic vessels from the cervical portion of the trachea.

THE LYMPHATICS OF THE UPPER EXTREMITY.

The Lymph Nodes of the Upper Extremity (Fig. 597).

The lymph nodes of the upper extremity are divided into two sets, **superficial** and **deep**.

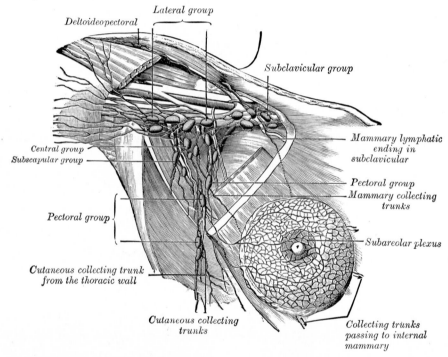

Fig. 599.—Lymphatics of the mamma, and the axillary nodes (semidiagrammatic). (Poirier and Charpy.)

The **superficial lymph nodes** are few and of small size. One or two **supratrochlear nodes** are placed above the medial epicondyle of the humerus, medial to the basilic vein. Their afferents drain the middle, ring, and little fingers, the medial portion of the hand, and the superficial area over the ulnar side of the forearm; these vessels are, however, in free communication with the other lymphatic vessels of the forearm. Their efferents accompany the basilic vein and join the deeper vessels. One or two **deltoideopectoral nodes** are found beside the cephalic vein, between the Pectoralis major and Deltoideus, immediately below the clavicle. They are situated in the course of the external collecting trunks of the arm.

The **deep lymph nodes** are chiefly grouped in the axilla, although a few may be found in the forearm, in the course of the radial, ulnar, and interosseous vessels, and in the arm along the medial side of the brachial artery.

The **Axillary Nodes** (*lymphoglandulæ axillares*) (Fig. 599) are of large size, vary from twenty to thirty in number, and may be arranged in the following groups:

1. A **lateral group** of from four to six glands lies in relation to the medial and posterior aspects of the axillary vein; the afferents of these nodes drain the whole arm with the exception of that portion whose vessels accompany the cephalic vein. The efferent vessels pass partly to the central and subclavicular groups of axillary nodes and partly to the inferior deep cervical nodes.

2. An **anterior** or **pectoral group** consists of four or five nodes along the lower border of the Pectoralis minor, in relation with the lateral thoracic artery. Their afferents drain the skin and muscles of the anterior and lateral thoracic walls, and the central and lateral parts of the mamma; their efferents pass partly to the central and partly to the subclavicular groups of axillary nodes.

3. A **posterior** or **subscapular group** of six or seven nodes is placed along the lower margin of the posterior wall of the axilla in the course of the subscapular artery. The afferents of this group drain the skin and muscles of the lower part of the back of the neck and of the posterior thoracic wall; their efferents pass to the central group of axillary nodes.

4. A **central** or **intermediate group** of three or four large nodes is imbedded in the adipose tissue near the base of the axilla. Its afferents are the efferent vessels of all the preceding groups of axillary nodes; its efferents pass to the subclavicular group.

5. A **medial** or **subclavicular group** of six to twelve nodes is situated partly posterior to the upper portion of the Pectoralis minor and partly above the upper border of this muscle. Its only direct territorial afferents are those which accompany the cephalic vein and one which drains the upper peripheral part of the mamma, but it receives the efferents of all the other axillary nodes. The efferent vessels of the subclavicular group unite to form the **subclavian trunk,** which opens either directly into the junction of the internal jugular and subclavian veins or into the jugular lymphatic trunk; on the left side it may end in the thoracic duct. A few efferents from the subclavicular nodes usually pass to the inferior deep cervical nodes.

The Lymphatic Vessels of the Upper Extremity.

The lymphatic vessels of the upper extremity are divided into two sets, superficial and deep.

The **superficial lymphatic vessels** commence (Fig. 600) in the lymphatic plexus which everywhere pervades the skin; the meshes of the plexus are much finer in the palm and on the flexor aspect of the digits than elsewhere. The digital plexuses are drained by a pair of vessels which run on the sides of each digit, and incline backward to reach the dorsum of the hand. From the dense plexus of the palm, vessels pass in different directions, viz., upward toward the wrist, downward to join the digital vessels, medialward to join the vessels on the ulnar border of the hand, and lateralward to those on the thumb. Several vessels from the central part of the plexus unite to form a trunk, which passes around the metacarpal bone of the index finger to join the vessels on the back of that digit and on the back of the thumb. Running upward in front of and behind the wrist, the lymphatic vessels are collected into radial, median, and ulnar groups, which accompany respectively the cephalic, median, and basilic veins in the forearm. A few of the ulnar lymphatics end in the supratrochlear nodes, but the majority pass directly to the lateral group of axillary nodes. Some of the radial vessels are collected into a trunk which ascends with the cephalic vein to the deltoideopectoral glands; the efferents from this group pass either to the subclavicular axillary glands or to the inferior cervical nodes.

The **deep lymphatic vessels** accompany the deep bloodvessels. In the forearm, they consist of four sets, corresponding with the radial, ulnar, volar, and dorsal interosseous arteries; they communicate at intervals with the superficial lymphatics, and some of them end in the nodes which are occasionally found beside the arteries. In their course upward, a few end in the nodes which lie upon the brachial artery; but most of them pass to the lateral group of axillary nodes.

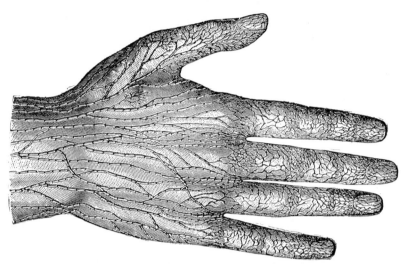

FIG. 600.—Lymphatic vessels of the dorsal surface of the hand. (Sappey.)

THE LYMPHATICS OF THE LOWER EXTREMITY.

The Lymph Nodes of the Lower Extremity.

The lymph glands of the lower extremity consist of the **anterior tibial node** and the **popliteal** and **inguinal nodes.**

The **anterior tibial node** (*lymphoglandula tibialis anterior*) is small and inconstant. It lies on the interosseous membrane in relation to the upper part of the anterior tibial vessels, and constitutes a substation in the course of the anterior tibial lymphatic trunks.

The **popliteal nodes** (*lymphoglandulæ popliteæ*) (Fig. 601), small in size and some six or seven in number, are imbedded in the fat contained in the popliteal fossa. One lies immediately beneath the popliteal fascia, near the terminal part of the small saphenous vein, and drains the region from which this vein derives its tributaries. Another is placed between the popliteal artery and the posterior surface of the knee-joint; it receives the lymphatic vessels from the knee-joint together with those which accompany the genicular arteries. The others lie at the sides of the popliteal vessels, and receive as efferents the trunks which accompany the anterior and posterior tibial vessels. The efferents of the popliteal nodes pass almost entirely alongside the femoral vessels to the deep inguinal nodes, but a few may accompany the great saphenous vein, and end in the nodes of the superficial subinguinal group.

The **inguinal nodes** (*lymphoglandulæ inguinales*) (Fig. 602), from twelve to twenty in number, are situated at the upper part of the femoral triangle. They may be divided into two groups by a horizontal line at the level of the termination of the great saphenous vein; those lying above this line are termed the

superficial inguinal nodes, and those below it the **subinguinal nodes,** the latter group consisting of a *superficial* and a *deep* set.

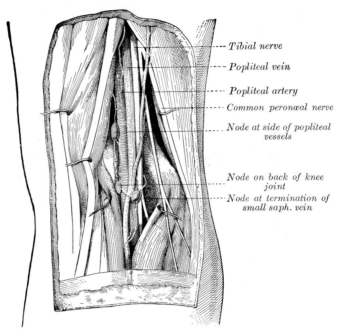

---- *Tibial nerve*

---- *Popliteal vein*

---- *Popliteal artery*

---- *Common peronœal nerve*

---- *Node at side of popliteal vessels*

---- *Node on back of knee joint*

---- *Node at termination of small saph. vein*

Fig. 601.—Lymph nodes of popliteal fossa.   (Poirier and Charpy.)

The **Superficial Inguinal Nodes** form a chain immediately below the inguinal ligament. They receive as afferents lymphatic vessels from the integument of the penis, scrotum, perineum, buttock, and abdomnal wall below the level of the umbilicus.

The **Superficial Subinguinal Nodes** (*lymphoglandulæ subinguinales superficiales*) are placed on either side of the upper part of the great saphenous vein; their efferents consist chiefly of the superficial lymphatic vessels of the lower extremity; but they also receive some of the vessels which drain the integument of the penis, scrotum, perineum, and buttock.

The **Deep Subinguinal Nodes** (*lymphoglandulæ subinguinales profundæ*) vary from one to three in number, and are placed under the fascia lata, on the medial side of the femoral vein. When three are present, the lowest is situated just below the junction of the great saphenous and femoral veins, the middle in the femoral canal, and the highest in the lateral part of the femoral ring. The middle one is the most inconstant of the three, but the highest, the **node of Cloquet or Rosenmüller,** is also frequently absent. They receive as afferents the deep lymphatic trunks which accompany the femoral vessels, the lymphatics from the glans penis vel clitoridis, and also some of the efferents from the superficial subinguinal nodes.

The Lymphatic Vessels of the Lower Extremity.

The lymphatic vessels of the lower extremity consist of two sets, superficial and deep, and in their distribution correspond closely with the veins.

The **superficial lymphatic vessels** lie in the superficial fascia, and are divisible into two groups: a medial, which follows the course of the great saphe-

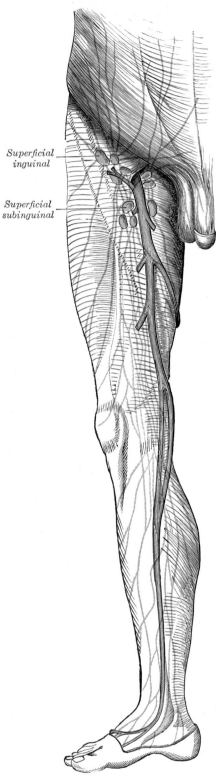

Superficial
inguinal

Superficial
subinguinal

FIG. 602.—The superficial lymph nodes and lymphatic
vessels of the lower extremity.

nous vein, and a lateral, which accompanies the small saphenous vein. The vessels of the **medial group** (Fig. 602) are larger and more numerous than those of the lateral group, and commence on the tibial side and dorsum of the foot; they ascend both in front of and behind the medial malleolus, run up the leg with the great saphenous vein, pass with it behind the medial condyle of the femur, and accompany it to the groin, where they end in the subinguinal group of superficial nodes. The vessels of the **lateral group** *arise* from the fibular side of the foot; some ascend in front of the leg, and, just below the knee, cross the tibia to join the lymphatics on the medial side of the thigh; others pass behind the lateral malleolus, and, accompanying the small saphenous vein, enter the popliteal nodes.

The **deep lymphatic vessels** are few in number, and accompany the deep bloodvessels. In the leg, they consist of three sets, the anterior tibial, posterior tibial, and peroneal, which accompany the corresponding bloodvessels, two or three with each artery; they enter the popliteal lymph nodes.

The deep lymphatic vessels of the gluteal and ischial regions follow the course of the corresponding bloodvessels. Those accompanying the superior gluteal vessels end in a node which lies on the intrapelvic portion of the superior gluteal artery near the upper border of the greater sciatic foramen. Those following the inferior gluteal vessels traverse one or two small nodes which lie below the Piriformis muscle, and end in the hypogastric nodes.

THE LYMPHATICS OF THE ABDOMEN AND PELVIS.

The Lymph Nodes of the Abdomen and Pelvis.

The lymph nodes of the abdomen and pelvis may be divided, from their situations, into (a) **parietal**, lying behind the peritoneum and in close association with the larger bloodvessels; and (b) **visceral**, which are found in relation to the visceral arteries.

The **parietal nodes** (Figs. 603, 604) include the following groups:

External Iliac.	Iliac Circumflex.	⎧ Lateral Aortic.
Common Iliac.	Hypogastric.	Lumbar ⎨ Preaortic.
Epigastric.	Sacral.	⎩ Retroaortic.

The **External Iliac Nodes**, from eight to ten in number, lie along the external iliac vessels. They are arranged in three groups, one on the lateral, another on the medial, and a third on the anterior aspect of the vessels; the third group is, however, sometimes absent. Their principal afferents are derived from the inguinal

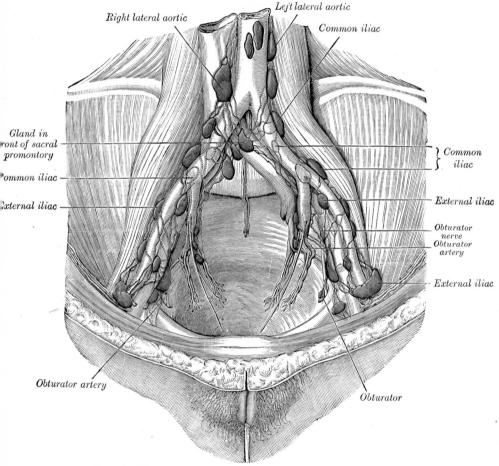

Fig. 603.—The parietal lymph nodes of the pelvis. (Cunéo and Marcille.)

and subinguinal nodes, the deep lymphatics of the abdominal wall below the umbilicus and of the adductor region of the thigh, and the lymphatics from the glans penis vel clitoridis, the membranous urethra, the prostate, the fundus of the bladder, the cervix uteri, and upper part of the vagina.

The **Common Iliac Nodes**, four to six in number, are grouped behind and on the sides of the common iliac artery, one or two being placed below the bifurcation of the aorta, in front of the fifth lumbar vertebra. They drain chiefly the hypogastric and external iliac nodes, and their efferents pass to the lateral aortic nodes.

The **Epigastric Nodes** (*lymphoglandulæ epigastricæ*), three or four in number, are placed alongside the lower portion of the inferior epigastric vessels.

The **Iliac Circumflex Nodes,** two to four in number, are situated along the course of the deep iliac circumflex vessels; they are sometimes absent.

The **Hypogastric Nodes** (*lymphoglandulæ hypogastricæ; internal iliac gland*) (Fig. 604) surround the hypogastric vessels, and receive the lymphatics corresponding to the distribution of the branches of the hypogastric artery, *i. e.,* they receive lymphatics from all the pelvic viscera, from the deeper parts of the perineum, including the membranous and cavernous portions of the urethra, and from the buttock and back of the thigh. An **obturator node** is sometimes seen in the upper part of the obturator foramen.

The **Sacral Nodes** are placed in the concavity of the sacrum, in relation to the middle and lateral sacral arteries; they receive lymphatics from the rectum and posterior wall of the pelvis.

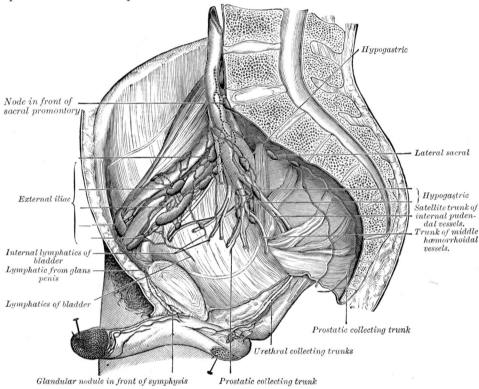

Fig. 604.—Iliopelvic nodes (lateral view). (Cunéo and Marcille.)

The efferents of the hypogastric group end in the common iliac nodes.

The **Lumbar Nodes** (*lymphoglandulæ lumbales*) are very numerous, and consist of right and left lateral aortic, preaortic, and retroaortic groups.

The **right lateral aortic nodes** are situated partly in front of the inferior vena cava, near the termination of the renal vein, and partly behind it on the origin of the Psoas major, and on the right crus of the diaphragm. The **left lateral aortic nodes** form a chain on the left side of the abdominal aorta in front of the origin of the Psoas major and left crus of the diaphragm. The nodes on either side receive (*a*) the efferents of the common iliac glands, (*b*) the lymphatics from the testis in the male and from the ovary, uterine tube, and body of the uterus in the female; (*c*) the lymphatics from the kidney and suprarenal node; and (*d*) the lymphatics draining the lateral abdominal muscles and accompanying the lumbar veins. Most of the efferent vessels of the lateral aortic glands converge to form the **right and left lumbar trunks** which join the cisterna chyli, but some enter the pre- and retroaortic nodes, and others pierce the crura of the diaphragm to join the lower end of the thoracic duct. The **preaortic nodes** lie in front of the aorta, and may be divided into **celiac, superior mesenteric,** and **inferior mesenteric** groups, arranged around the origins of the corresponding arteries. They receive a few vessels from the lateral aortic nodes, but their principal afferents are derived from the viscera supplied by the three arteries with which they are associated. Some of their efferents pass to the retroaortic nodes, but the majority unite to form the **intestinal trunk,** which enters the cisterna chyli. The **retroaortic nodes** are placed below the cisterna chyli, on the bodies of the third and fourth lumbar vertebræ. They receive lymphatic trunks from the lateral and preaortic node, while their efferents end in the cisterna chyli.

The Lymphatic Vessels of the Abdomen and Pelvis.

The lymphatic vessels of the walls of the abdomen and pelvis may be divided into two sets, superficial and deep.

The **superficial vessels** follow the course of the superficial bloodvessels and converge to the superficial inguinal nodes; those derived from the integument of the front of the abdomen below the umbilicus follow the course of the superficial epigastric vessels, and those from the sides of the lumbar part of the abdominal wall pass along the crest of the ilium, with the superficial iliac circumflex vessels. The superficial lymphatic vessels of the gluteal region turn horizontally around the buttock, and join the superficial inguinal and subinguinal nodes.

The **deep vessels** run alongside the principal bloodvessels. Those of the parietes of the pelvis, which accompany the superior and inferior gluteal, and obturator vessels, follow the course of the hypogastric artery, and ultimately join the lateral aortic nodes.

Lymphatic Vessels of the Perineum and External Genitals.—The lymphatic vessels of the perineum, of the integument of the penis, and of the scrotum (or vulva), follow the course of the external pudendal vessels, and end in the superficial inguinal and subinguinal nodes. Those of the glans penis vel clitoridis terminate partly in the deep subinguinal nodes and partly in the external iliac nodes.

The Lymphatic Nodes of the Abdominal and Pelvic Viscera.

The **visceral nodes** are associated with the branches of the celiac, superior and inferior mesenteric arteries. Those related to the branches of the celiac artery form three sets, gastric, hepatic, and pancreaticolienal.

The **Gastric Nodes** (Figs. 605, 606) consist of two sets, **superior** and **inferior**.

The **Superior Gastric Nodes** (*lymphoglandulæ gastricæ superiores*) accompany the left gastric artery and are divisible into three groups, viz.: (*a*) **upper,** on the stem of the artery; (*b*) **lower,** accompanying the descending branches of the artery along the cardiac half of the lesser curvature of the stomach, between the two layers of the lesser omentum; and (*c*) **paracardial** outlying members of the gastric nodes, disposed in a manner comparable to a chain of beads around the neck of the stomach (Jamieson and Dobson[1]). They receive their afferents from the stomach; their efferents pass to the celiac group of preaortic nodes.

The **Inferior Gastric Nodes** (*lymphoglandulæ gastricæ inferiores; right gastro-epiploic glands*), four to seven in number, lie between the two layers of the greater omentum along the pyloric half of the greater curvature of the stomach.

The **Hepatic Nodes** (*lymphoglandulæ hepaticæ*) (Fig. 605), consist of the following groups: (*a*) **hepatic,** on the stem of the hepatic artery, and extending upward

[1] Lancet, April 20 and 27. 1907.

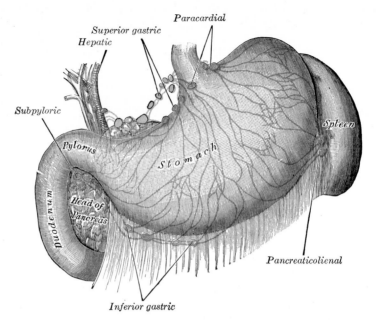

FIG. 605.—Lymphatics of stomach, etc.   (Jamieson and Dobson.)

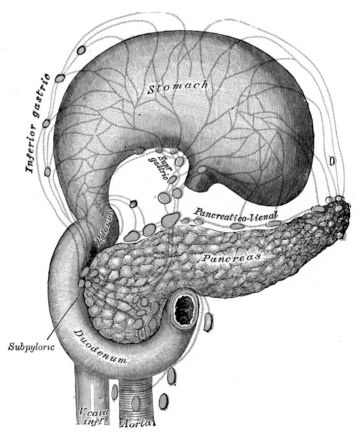

FIG. 606.—Lymphatics of stomach, etc.   The stomach has been turned upward.   (Jamieson and Dobson.)

along the common bile duct, between the two layers of the lesser omentum, as far as the porta hepatis; the **cystic node,** a member of this group, is placed near

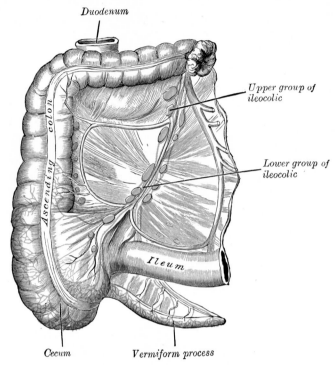

Fig. 607.—The lymphatics of cecum and vermiform process from the front.   (Jamieson and Dobson.)

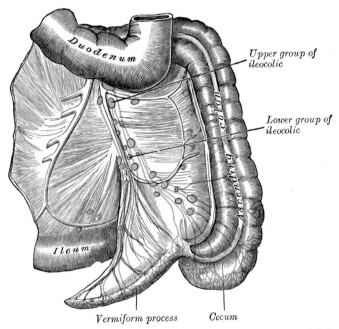

Fig. 608.—The lymphatics of cecum and vermiform process from behind.   (Jamieson and Dobson.)

the neck of the gall-bladder; (*b*) **subpyloric,** four or five in number, in close relation to the bifurcation of the gastroduodenal artery, in the angle between the superior and descending parts of the duodenum; an outlying member of this group is some-times found above the duodenum on the right gastric (pyloric) artery. The nodes of the hepatic chain receive afferents from the stomach, duodenum, liver, gall-bladder, and pancreas; their efferents join the celiac group of preaortic nodes.

The **Pancreaticolienal Nodes** (*lymphoglandulæ pancreaticolienales; splenic glands*) (Fig. 606) accompany the lienal (splenic) artery, and are situated in rela-tion to the posterior surface and upper border of the pancreas; one or two members of this group are found in the gastrolienal ligament (Jamieson and Dobson, *op. cit.*). Their afferents are derived from the stomach, spleen, and pancreas, their efferents join the celiac group of preaortic nodes.

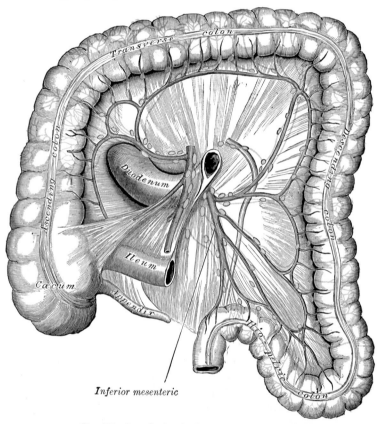

FIG. 609.—Lymphatics of colon. (Jamieson and Dobson.)

The **superior mesenteric nodes** may be divided into three principal groups: mesenteric, ileocolic, and mesocolic.

The **Mesenteric Nodes** (*lymphoglandulæ mesentericæ*) lie between the layers of the mesentery. They vary from one hundred to one hundred and fifty in number, and may be grouped into three sets, viz.: one lying close to the wall of the small intestine, among the terminal twigs of the superior mesenteric artery; a second, in relation to the loops and primary branches of the vessels; and a third along the trunk of the artery.

The **Ileocolic nodes** (Figs. 607, 608), from ten to twenty in number, form a chain around the ileocolic artery, but show a tendency to subdivision into two groups, one near the duodenum and another on the lower part of the trunk of the artery. Where the vessel divides into its terminal branches the chain is broken up into several groups, viz.: (*a*) **ileal**, in relation to the ileal branch of the artery; (*b*) **anterior ileocolic**, usually of three nodes, in the ileocolic fold, near the wall of the cecum; (*c*) **posterior ileocolic**, mostly placed in the angle between the ileum and the colon, but partly lying behind the cecum at its junction with the ascending colon; (*d*) a single node, between the layers of the mesenteriole of the vermiform process; (*e*) **right colic**, along the medial side of the ascending colon.

The **Mesocolic Nodes** (*lymphoglandulæ mesocolicæ*) are numerous, and lie between the layers of the transverse mesocolon, in close relation to the transverse colon; they are best developed in the neighborhood of the right and left colic flexures. One or two small nodes are occasionally seen along the trunk of the right colic artery and others are found in relation to the trunk and branches of the middle colic artery.

The superior mesenteric nodes receive afferents from the jejunum, ileum, cecum, vermiform process, and the ascending and transverse parts of the colon; their efferents pass to the preaortic nodes.

The **inferior mesenteric nodes** (Fig. 609) consist of: (*a*) small nodes on the branches of the left colic and sigmoid arteries; (*b*) a group in the sigmoid mesocolon, around the superior hemorrhoidal artery; and (*c*) a **pararectal** group in contact with the muscular coat of the rectum. They drain the descending, iliac and sigmoid parts of the colon and the upper part of the rectum; their efferents pass to the preaortic nodes.

The Lymphatic Vessels of the Abdominal and Pelvic Viscera.

The lymphatic vessels of the abdominal and pelvic viscera consist of (1) those of the subdiaphragmatic portion of the digestive tube and its associated glands, the liver and pancreas; (2) those of the spleen and suprarenal glands; (3) those of the urinary organs; (4) those of the reproductive organs.

1. The **lymphatic vessels of the subdiaphragmatic portion of the digestive tube** are situated partly in the mucous membrane and partly in the seromuscular coats, but as the former system drains into the latter, the two may be considered as one.

The **Lymphatic Vessels of the Stomach** (Figs. 605, 606) are continuous at the cardiac orifice with those of the esophagus, and at the pylorus with those of the duodenum. They mainly follow the bloodvessels, and may be arranged in four sets. Those of the first set accompany the branches of the left gastric artery, receiving tributaries from a large area on either surface of the stomach, and terminate in the superior gastric nodes. Those of the second set drain the fundus and body of the stomach on the left of a line drawn vertically from the esophagus; they accompany, more or less closely, the short gastric and left gastroepiploic arteries, and end in the pancreaticolienal nodes. The vessels of the third set drain the right portion of the greater curvature as far as the pyloric portion, and end in the inferior gastric nodes, the efferents of which pass to the subpyloric group. Those of the fourth set drain the pyloric portion and pass to the hepatic and subpyloric nodes, and to the superior gastric nodes.

The **Lymphatic Vessels of the Duodenum** consist of an anterior and a posterior set, which open into a series of small **pancreaticoduodenal nodes** on the anterior and posterior aspects of the groove between the head of the pancreas and the duodenum. The efferents of these nodes run in two directions, upward to the hepatic glands and downward to the preaortic nodes around the origin of the superior mesenteric artery.

The **Lymphatic Vessels of the Jejunum and Ileum** are termed **lacteals**, from the

46

milk-white fluid they contain during intestinal digestion. They run between the layers of the mesentery and enter the mesenteric nodes, the efferents of which end in the preaortic nodes.

The **Lymphatic Vessels of the Vermiform Process and Cecum** (Figs. 607, 608) are numerous, since in the wall of this process there is a large amount of adenoid tissue. From the body and tail of the vermiform process eight to fifteen vessels ascend between the layers of the mesenteriole, one or two being interrupted in the node which lies between the layers of this peritoneal fold. They unite to form three or four vessels, which end partly in the lower and partly in the upper nodes of the ileocolic chain. The vessels from the root of the vermiform process and from the cecum consist of an anterior and a posterior group. The anterior vessels pass in front of the cecum, and end in the anterior ileocolic nodes and in the upper and lower glands of the ileocolic chain; the posterior vessels ascend over the back of the cecum and terminate in the posterior ileocolic nodes and in the lower glands of the ileocolic chain.

Lymphatic Vessels of the Colon (Fig. 609).—The lymphatic vessels of the ascending and transverse parts of the colon finally end in the mesenteric nodes, after traversing the right colic and mesocolic nodes. Those of the descending and iliac sigmoid parts of the colon are interrupted by the small nodes on the branches of the left colic and sigmoid arteries, and ultimately end in the preaortic nodes around the origin of the inferior mesenteric artery.

Lymphatic Vessels of the Anus, Anal Canal, and Rectum.—The lymphatics from the **anus** pass forward and end with those of the integument of the perineum and scrotum in the superficial inguinal nodes; those from the **anal canal** accompany the middle and inferior hemorrhoidal arteries, and end in the hypogastric nodes; while the vessels from the **rectum** traverse the pararectal glands and pass to those in the sigmoid mesocolon; the efferents of the latter terminate in the preaortic nodes around the origin of the inferior mesenteric artery.

The **Lymphatic Vessels of the Liver** are divisible into two sets, superficial and deep. The former arise in the subperitoneal areolar tissue over the entire surface of the organ, and may be grouped into (*a*) those on the convex surface, (*b*) those on the inferior surface.

(*a*) On the **convex surface:** The vessels from the back part of this surface reach their terminal nodes by three different routes; the vessels of the middle set, five or six in number, pass through the vena-caval foramen in the diaphragm and end in one or two nodes which are situated around the terminal part of the inferior vena cava; a few vessels from the left side pass backward toward the esophageal hiatus, and terminate in the paracardial group of superior gastric nodes; the vessels from the right side, one or two in number, run on the abdominal surface of the diaphragm, and, after crossing its right crus, end in the preaortic nodes which surround the origin of the celiac artery. From the portions of the right and left lobes adjacent to the falciform ligament, the lymphatic vessels converge to form two trunks, one of which accompanies the inferior vena cava through the diaphragm, and ends in the nodes around the terminal part of this vessel; the other runs downward and forward, and, turning around the anterior sharp margin of the liver, accompanies the upper part of the ligamentum teres, and ends in the upper hepatic nodes. From the anterior surface a few additional vessels turn around the anterior sharp margin to reach the upper hepatic nodes.

(*b*) On the **inferior surface:** The vessels from this surface mostly converge to the porta hepatis, and accompany the deep lymphatics, emerging from the porta to the hepatic nodes; one or two from the posterior parts of the right and caudate lobes accompany the inferior vena cava through the diaphragm, and end in the nodes around the terminal part of this vein.

The deep lymphatics converge to ascending and descending trunks. The ascending trunks accompany the hepatic veins and pass through the diaphragm to end in the nodes around the terminal part of the inferior vena cava. The descending trunks emerge from the porta hepatis, and end in the hepatic nodes.

The **Lymphatic Vessels of the Gall-bladder** pass to the hepatic nodes in the porta hepatis; those of the **common bile duct** to the hepatic nodes alongside the duct and to the upper pancreaticoduodenal nodes.

The **Lymphatic Vessels of the Pancreas** follow the course of its bloodvessels. Most of them enter the pancreaticolienal nodes, but some end in the pancreaticoduodenal nodes, and others in the preaortic nodes near the origin of the superior mesenteric artery. (Fig. 606)

2. The **lymphatic vessels of the spleen** and **suprarenal glands.**

The **Lymphatic Vessels of the Spleen**, both superficial and deep, pass to the pancreaticolienal nodes. (Fig. 605)

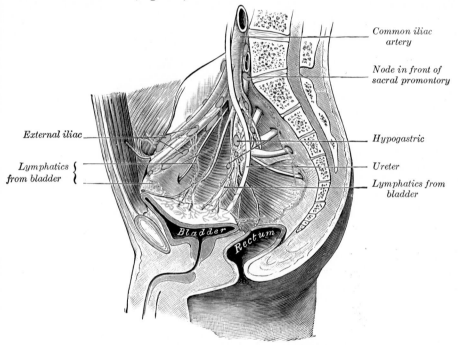

Fig. 610.—Lymphatics of the bladder. (Cunéo and Marcille.)

The **Lymphatic Vessels of the Suprarenal Glands** usually accompany the suprarenal veins, and end in the lateral aortic nodes; occasionally some of them pierce the crura of the diaphragm and end in the nodes of the posterior mediastinum.

3. The **lymphatic vessels of the urinary organs.**

The **Lymphatic Vessels of the Kidney** form three plexuses: one in the substance of the kidney, a second beneath its fibrous capsule, and a third in the perinephric fat; the second and third communicate freely with each other. The vessels from the plexus in the kidney substance converge to form four or five trunks which issue at the hilum. Here they are joined by vessels from the plexus under the capsule, and, following the course of the renal vein, end in the lateral aortic nodes. The perinephric plexus is drained directly into the upper lateral aortic nodes.

The **Lymphatic Vessels of the Ureter** run in different directions. Those from
its upper portion end partly in the efferent vessels of the kidney and partly in the
lateral aortic nodes; those from the portion immediately above the brim of the
lesser pelvis are drained into the common iliac nodes; while the vessels from the
intrapelvic portion of the tube either join the efferents from the bladder, or end
in the hypogastric nodes.

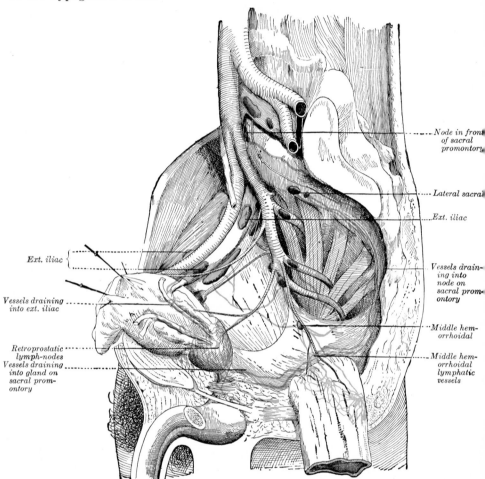

FIG. 611.—Lymphatics of the prostate. (Cunéo and Marcille.)

The **Lymphatic Vessels of the Bladder** (Fig. 610) originate in two plexuses, an
intra- and an extramuscular, it being generally admitted that the mucous membrane is devoid of lymphatics.   The efferent vessels are arranged in two groups,
one from the anterior and another from the posterior surface of the bladder.   The
vessels from the *anterior* surface pass to the external iliac nodes, but in their course
minute nodes are situated.   These minute nodes are arranged in two groups,
an **anterior vesical**, in front of the bladder, and a **lateral vesical**, in relation to the
lateral umbilical ligament.   The vessels from the *posterior* surface pass to the hypogastric, external, and common iliac nodes; those draining the upper part of this
surface traverse the lateral vesical nodes.

The **Lymphatic Vessels of the Prostate** (Fig. 611) terminate chiefly in the hypogastric and sacral nodes, but one trunk from the posterior surface ends in the exter-

nal iliac nodes, and another from the anterior surface joins the vessels which drain the membranous part of the urethra.

Lymphatic Vessels of the Urethra.—The lymphatics of the cavernous portion of the urethra accompany those of the glans penis, and terminate with them in the deep subinguinal and external iliac nodes. Those of the *membranous and prostatic* portions, and those of the whole urethra in the female, pass to the hypogastric nodes.

(4) The **lymphatic vessels of the reproductive organs.**

The **Lymphatic Vessels of the Testes** consist of two sets, superficial and deep, the former commencing on the surface of the tunica vaginalis, the latter in the epididymis and body of the testis. They form from four to eight collecting trunks

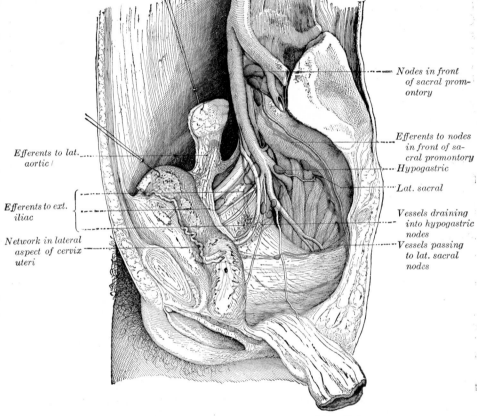

FIG. 612.—Lymphatics of the uterus. (Cunéo and Marcille.)

which ascend with the spermatic veins in the spermatic cord and along the front of the Psoas major to the level where the spermatic vessels cross the ureter and end in the lateral and preaortic groups of lumbar nodes.

The **Lymphatic Vessels of the Ductus Deferens** pass to the external iliac nodes; those of the **vesiculæ seminales** partly to the hypogastric and partly to the external nodes.

The **Lymphatic Vessels of the Ovary** are similar to those of the testis, and ascend with the ovarian artery to the lateral and preaortic nodes.

The **Lymphatic Vessels of the Uterine Tube** pass partly with those of the ovary and partly with those of the uterus.

The **Lymphatic Vessels of the Uterus** (Fig. 612) consist of two sets, superficial and deep, the former being placed beneath the peritoneum, the latter in the substance of the organ. The lymphatics of the cervix uteri run in three directions: transversely to the external iliac nodes, postero-laterally to the hypogastric nodes, and posteriorly to the common iliac nodes. The majority of the vessels of the body and fundus of the uterus pass lateralward in the broad ligaments, and are continued up with the ovarian vessels to the lateral and preaortic nodes; a few, however, run to the external iliac nodes, and one or two to the superficial inguinal nodes. In the unimpregnated uterus the lymphatic vessels are very small, but during gestation they are greatly enlarged.

The **Lymphatic Vessels of the Vagina** are carried in three directions: those of the upper part of the vagina to the external iliac nodes, those of the middle part to the hypogastric nodes, and those of the lower part to the common iliac glands. On the course of the vessels from the middle and lower parts small nodes are situated. Some lymphatic vessels from the lower part of the vagina join those of the vulva and pass to the superficial inguinal nodes. The lymphatics of the vagina anastomose with those of the cervix uteri, vulva, and rectum, but not with those of the bladder.

The **Lymphatic Vessels of the Omentum** accompany the arteries and veins and are richly supplied with valves.

THE LYMPHATICS OF THE THORAX.

The **lymph nodes of the thorax** may be divided into parietal and visceral—the former being situated in the thoracic wall, the latter in relation to the viscera.

The **parietal lymph nodes** include the **sternal, intercostal,** and **diaphragmatic glands.**

1. The **Sternal Nodes** (*lymphoglandulæ sternales; internal mammary glands*) are placed at the anterior ends of the intercostal spaces, by the side of the internal mammary artery. They derive afferents from the mamma, from the deeper structures of the anterior abdominal wall above the level of the umbilicus, from the upper surface of the liver through a small group of nodes which lie behind the xiphoid process, and from the deeper parts of the anterior portion of the thoracic wall. Their efferents usually unite to form a single trunk on either side; this may open directly into the junction of the internal jugular and subclavian veins, or that of the right side may join the right subclavian trunk, and that of the left the thoracic duct.

2. The **Intercostal Nodes** (*lymphoglandulæ intercostales*) occupy the posterior parts of the intercostal spaces, in relation to the intercostal vessels. They receive the deep lymphatics from the postero-lateral aspect of the chest; some of these vessels are interrupted by small lateral intercostal nodes. The efferents of the nodes in the lower four or five spaces unite to form a trunk, which descends and opens either into the cisterna chyli or into the commencement of the thoracic duct. The efferents of the nodes in the upper spaces of the left side end in the thoracic duct; those of the corresponding right spaces, in the right lymphatic duct.

3. The **Diaphragmatic Nodes** lie on the thoracic aspect of the diaphragm, and consist of three sets, anterior, middle, and posterior.

The **anterior set** comprises (*a*) two or three small nodes behind the base of the xiphoid process, which receive afferents from the convex surface of the liver, and (*b*) one or two nodes on either side near the junction of the seventh rib with its cartilage, which receive lymphatic vessels from the front part of the diaphragm. The efferent vessels of the anterior set pass to the sternal nodes.

The **middle set** consists of two or three nodes on either side close to where the phrenic nerves enter the diaphragm. On the right side some of the nodes of this group lie within the fibrous sac of the pericardium, on the front of the termination of the inferior vena cava. The afferents of this set are derived from the middle

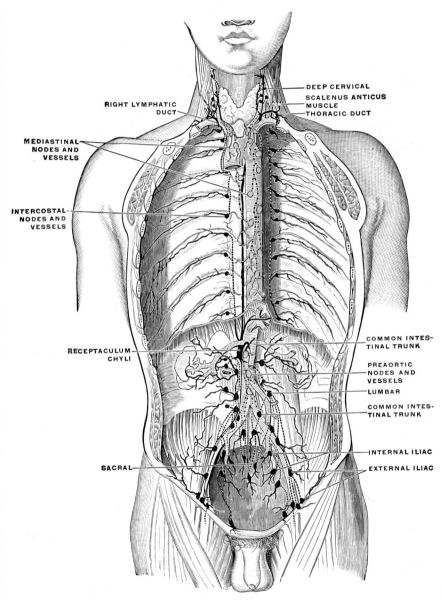

FIG. 613.—Deep lymph nodes and vessels of the thorax and abdomen (diagrammatic). Afferent vessels **are** represented by continuous lines, and efferent and internodular vessels by dotted lines. (Cunningham.)

part of the diaphragm, those on the right side also receiving afferents from the convex surface of the liver. Their efferents pass to the posterior mediastinal nodes.

The **posterior set** consists of a few glands situated on the back of the crura of the diaphragm, and connected on the one hand with the lumbar nodes and on the other with the posterior mediastinal nodes.

The **superficial lymphatic vessels of the thoracic wall** ramify beneath the skin and converge to the axillary nodes. Those over the Trapezius and Latissimus dorsi run forward and unite to form about ten or twelve trunks which end in the subscapular group. Those over the pectoral region, including the vessels from the skin covering the peripheral part of the mamma, run backward, and those over the Serratus anterior upward, to the pectoral group. Others near the lateral margin of the sternum pass inward between the rib cartilages and end in the sternal nodes, while the vessels of opposite sides anastomose across the front of the sternum. A few vessels from the upper part of the pectoral region ascend over the clavicle to the supraclavicular group of cervical nodes.

The **Lymphatic Vessels of the Mamma** originate in a plexus in the interlobular spaces and on the walls of the galactophorous ducts. Those from the central part of the gland pass to an intricate plexus situated beneath the areola, a plexus which receives also the lymphatics from the skin over the central part of the gland and those from the areola and nipple. Its efferents are collected into two trunks which pass to the pectoral group of axillary nodes. The vessels which drain the medial part of the mamma pierce the thoracic wall and end in the sternal nodes, while a vessel has occasionally been seen to emerge from the upper part of the mamma and, piercing the Pectoralis major, terminate in the subclavicular nodes (Fig. 599).

The **deep lymphatic vessels of the thoracic wall** (Fig. 613) consist of:
1. The lymphatics of the muscles which lie on the ribs: most of these end in the axillary nodes, but some from the Pectoralis major pass to the sternal nodes.
2. The intercostal vessels which drain the Intercostales and parietal pleura. Those draining the Intercostales externi run backward and, after receiving the vessels which accompany the posterior branches of the intercostal arteries, end in the intercostal nodes. Those of the Intercostales interni and parietal pleura consist of a single trunk in each space. These trunks run forward in the subpleural tissue and the upper six open separately into the sternal nodes or into the vessels which unite them; those of the lower spaces unite to form a single trunk which terminates in the lowest of the sternal nodes. 3. The **lymphatic vessels of the diaphragm,** which form two plexuses, one on its thoracic and another on its abdominal surface. These plexuses anastomose freely with each other, and are best marked on the parts covered respectively by the pleuræ and peritoneum. That on the thoracic surface communicates with the lymphatics of the costal and mediastinal parts of the pleura, and its efferents consist of three groups: (*a*) anterior, passing to the nodes which lie near the junction of the seventh rib with its cartilage; (*b*) middle, to the nodes on the esophagus and to those around the termination of the inferior vena cava; and (*c*) posterior, to the nodes which surround the aorta at the point where this vessel leaves the thoracic cavity.

The plexus on the abdominal surface is composed of fine vessels, and anastomoses with the lymphatics of the liver and, at the periphery of the diaphragm, with those of the subperitoneal tissue. The efferents from the right half of this plexus terminate partly in a group of nodes on the trunk of the corresponding inferior phrenic artery, while others end in the right lateral aortic nodes. Those from the left half of the plexus pass to the pre- and lateral aortic nodes and to the glands on the terminal portion of the esophagus.

The **visceral lymph nodes** consist of three groups, viz.: **anterior mediastinal, posterior mediastinal,** and **tracheobronchial.**

The **Anterior Mediastinal Nodes** (*lymphoglandulæ mediastinales anteriores*) are placed in the anterior part of the superior mediastinal cavity, in front of the aortic arch and in relation to the innominate veins and the large arterial trunks which arise from the aortic arch. They receive afferents from the thymus and pericardium, and from the sternal nodes; their efferents unite with those of the tracheo-bronchial nodes, to form the right and left bronchomediastinal trunks.

The **Posterior Mediastinal Nodes** (*lymphoglandulæ mediastinales posteriores*) lie behind the pericardium in relation to the esophagus and descending thoracic aorta. Their afferents are derived from the esophagus, the posterior part of the pericardium, the diaphragm, and the convex surface of the liver. Their efferents mostly end in the thoracic duct, but some join the tracheobronchial nodes.

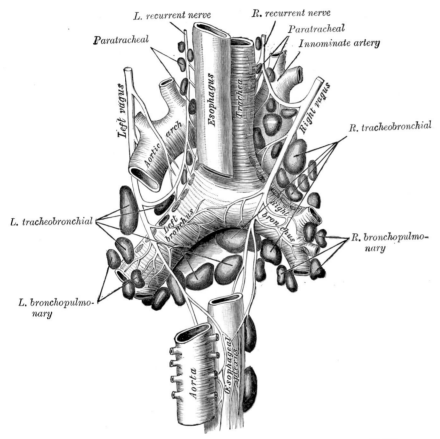

Fig. 614.—The tracheobronchial lymph nodes. (From a figure designed by M. Hallé.)

The **Tracheobronchial Nodes** (Fig. 614) form four main groups: (*a*) **tracheal,** on either side of the trachea; (*b*) **bronchial,** in the angles between the lower part of the trachea and bronchi and in the angle between the two bronchi; (*c*) **broncho-pulmonary,** in the hilum of each lung; and (*d*) **pulmonary,** in the lung substance, on the larger branches of the bronchi. The afferents of the tracheobronchial nodes drain the lungs and bronchi, the thoracic part of the trachea and the heart; some of the efferents of the posterior mediastinal nodes also end in this group. Their efferent vessels ascend upon the trachea and unite with efferents of the internal mammary and anterior mediastinal nodes to form the **right** and **left broncho-mediastinal trunks.** The right bronchomediastinal trunk may join the right lymphatic duct, and the left the thoracic duct, but more frequently they open independently of these ducts into the junction of the internal jugular and subclavian veins of their own side.

In all town dwellers there are continually being swept into these nodes from the bronchi and alveoli large quantities of the dust and black carbonaceous pigment that are so freely inhaled in cities. At first the nodes are moderately enlarged, firm, inky black, and gritty on section; later they enlarge still further, often becoming fibrous from the irritation set up by the minute foreign bodies with which they are crammed, and may break down into a soft slimy mass or may calcify.

The **lymphatic vessels of the thoracic viscera** comprise those of the **heart** and **pericardium, lungs** and **pleura, thymus,** and **esophagus.**

The **Lymphatic Vessels of the Heart** consist of two plexuses: (*a*) deep, immediately under the endocardium; and (*b*) superficial, subjacent to the visceral pericardium. The deep plexus opens into the superficial, the efferents of which form right and left collecting trunks. The **left trunks,** two or three in number, ascend in the anterior longitudinal sulcus, receiving, in their course, vessels from both ventricles. On reaching the coronary sulcus they are joined by a large trunk from the diaphragmatic surface of the heart, and then unite to form a single vessel which ascends between the pulmonary artery and the left atrium and ends in one of the tracheobronchial nodes. The **right trunk** receives its afferents from the right atrium and from the right border and diaphragmatic surface of the right ventricle. It ascends in the posterior longitudinal sulcus and then runs forward in the coronary sulcus, and passes up behind the pulmonary artery, to end in one of the tracheobronchial nodes.

The **Lymphatic Vessels of the Lungs** originate in two plexuses, a superficial and a deep. The superficial plexus is placed beneath the pulmonary pleura. The deep accompanies the branches of the pulmonary vessels and the ramifications of the bronchi. In the case of the larger bronchi the deep plexus consists of two net-works —one, submucous, beneath the mucous membrane, and another, peribronchial, outside the walls of the bronchi. In the smaller bronchi there is but a single plexus, which extends as far as the bronchioles, but fails to reach the alveoli, in the walls of which there are no traces of lymphatic vessels. The superficial efferents turn around the borders of the lungs and the margins of their fissures, and converge to end in some nodes situated at the hilum; the deep efferents are conducted to the hilum along the pulmonary vessels and bronchi, and end in the tracheobronchial nodes. Little or no anastomosis occurs between the superficial and deep lymphatics of the lungs, except in the region of the hilum.

The **Lymphatic Vessels of the Pleura** consist of two sets—one in the visceral and another in the parietal part of the membrane. Those of the visceral pleura drain into the superficial efferents of the lung, while the lymphatics of the parietal pleura have three modes of ending, viz.: (*a*) those of the costal portion join the lymphatics of the Intercostales interni and so reach the sternal glands; (*b*) those of the diaphragmatic part are drained by the efferents of the diaphragm; while (*c*) those of the mediastinal portion terminate in the posterior mediastinal nodes.

The **Lymphatic Vessels of the Thymus** end in the anterior mediastinal, tracheobronchial, and sternal nodes.

The **Lymphatic Vessels of the Esophagus** form a plexus around that tube, and the collecting vessels from the plexus drain into the posterior mediastinal nodes.

THE SPLEEN (LIEN).

The **spleen** is situated principally in the left hypochondriac region, but its superior extremity extends into the epigastric region; it lies between the fundus of the stomach and the diaphragm. It is oblong and flattened, soft, of very friable consistence, highly vascular, and of a dark purplish color. The distinctive function or functions of the spleen are not known. During fetal life and shortly after birth it gives rise to new red blood corpuscles but the evidence that this function is retained in adult life is not satisfactory. It is supposed to be an organ for the destruction of red blood corpuscles and the preparation of new hemoglobin from the iron thus set free.

Development.—The spleen appears about the fifth week as a localized thickening of the mesoderm in the dorsal mesogastrium above the tail of the pancreas. With the change in position of the stomach the spleen is carried to the left, and comes to lie behind the stomach and in contact with the left kidney. The part of the dorsal mesogastrium which intervened between the spleen and the greater curvature of the stomach forms the gastrosplenic ligament.

Relations.—The **diaphragmatic surface** (*facies diaphragmatica; external or phrenic surface*) is convex, smooth, and is directed upward, backward, and to the left, except at its upper end, where it is directed slightly medialward. It is in relation with the under surface of the diaphragm, which separates it from the ninth, tenth, and eleventh ribs of the left side, and the intervening lower border of the left lung and pleura.

The **visceral surface** (Fig. 615) is divided by a ridge into an **anterior** or **gastric** and a **posterior** or **renal** portion.

The **gastric surface** (*facies gastrica*), which is directed forward, upward, and medialward, is broad and concave, and is in contact with the posterior wall of the stomach; and below this with the tail of the pancreas. It presents near its medial border a long fissure, or more frequently a series of depressions termed the **hilum.** This is pierced by several irregular apertures, for the entrance and exit of vessels and nerves.

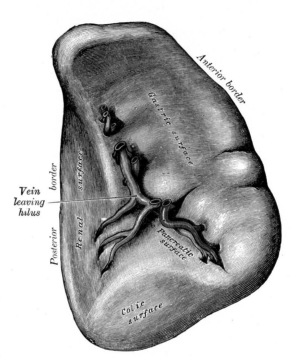

FIG. 615.—The visceral surface of the spleen.

The **renal surface** (*facies renalis*) is directed medialward and downward. It is somewhat flattened, is considerably narrower than the gastric surface, and is in relation with the upper part of the anterior surface of the left kidney and occasionally with the left suprarenal gland.

The **superior extremity** (*extremitas superior*) is directed toward the vertebral column, where it lies on a level with the eleventh thoracic vertebra. The **lower extremity** or **colic surface** (*extremitas inferior*) is flat, triangular in shape, and rests upon the left flexure of the colon and the phrenicocolic ligament, and is generally in contact with the tail of the pancreas. The **anterior border** (*margo anterior*) is free, sharp, and thin, and is often notched, especially below; it separates the diaphragmatic from the gastric surface. The **posterior border** (*margo posterior*), more rounded and blunter than the anterior, separates the renal from the diaphragmatic surface; it corresponds to the lower border of the eleventh rib and lies between the diaphragm and left kidney. The intermediate margin is the ridge which separates the renal and gastric surfaces. The **inferior border** (*internal border*) separates the diaphragmatic from the colic surface.

The spleen is almost entirely surrounded by peritoneum, which is firmly adherent to its capsule. It is held in position by two folds of this membrane. One, the

phrenicolienal ligament, is derived from the peritoneum, where the wall of the general peritoneal cavity comes into contact with the omental bursa between the left kidney and the spleen; the lienal vessels pass between its two layers. The other fold, the **gastrolienal ligament,** is also formed of two layers, derived from the general cavity and the omental respectively, where they meet between the spleen and stomach; the short gastric and left gastroepiploic branches of the lienal artery run between its two layers. The lower end of the spleen is supported by the phrenicocolic ligament.

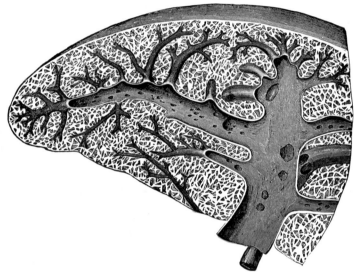

Fig. 616.—Transverse section of the spleen, showing the trabecular tissue and the splenic vein and its tributaries.

The size and weight of the spleen are liable to very extreme variations at different periods of life, in different individuals, and in the same individual under different conditions. *In the adult* it is usually about 12 cm. in length, 7 cm. in breadth, and 3 or 4 cm. in thickness. The spleen increases in weight from 17 grams or less during the first year to 170 grams at twenty years, and then slowly decreases to 122 grams at seventy-six to eighty years. Male spleens weigh more than female ones and spleens from whites weigh more than those from negroes. Variations of weight of adult spleens are 100 to 250 grams, and in extreme cases, 50 to 400 grams. The size of the spleen is increased during and after digestion, and varies according to the state of nutrition of the body, being large in highly fed, and small in starved animals. In malarial fever it becomes much enlarged, weighing occasionally as much as 9 kilos.

Frequently in the neighborhood of the spleen, and especially in the gastrolienal ligament and greater omentum, small nodules of splenic tissue may be found, either isolated or connected to the spleen by thin bands of splenic tissue. They are known as **accessory spleens** (*lien accessorius; supernumerary spleen*). They vary in size from that of a pea to that of a plum.

Structure.—The spleen is invested by two coats: an **external serous** and an **internal fibro-elastic coat.**

The **external** or **serous coat** (*tunica serosa*) is derived from the peritoneum; it is thin, smooth, and in the human subject intimately adherent to the fibroelastic coat. It invests the entire organ, except at the hilum and along the lines of reflection of the phrenicolienal and gastrolienal ligaments.

The **fibroelastic coat** (*tunica albuginea*) invests the organ, and at the hilum is reflected inward upon the vessels in the form of sheaths. From these sheaths, as well as from the inner surface of the fibroelastic coat, numerous small fibrous bands, **trabeculæ** (Fig. 616), are given off in all directions; these uniting, constitute the frame-work of the spleen. The spleen therefore consists of a number of small spaces or **areolæ**, formed by the trabeculæ; in these areolæ is contained the **splenic pulp.**

The fibroelastic coat, the sheaths of the vessels, and the trabeculæ, are composed of white and yellow elastic fibrous tissues, the latter predominating. It is owing to the presence of the elastic tissue that the spleen possesses a considerable amount of elasticity, which allows of the very great variations in size that it presents under certain circumstances. In addition to these constituents of this tunic, there is found in man a small amount of non-striped muscular fiber; and in some mammalia, *e. g.*, dog, pig, and cat, a large amount, so that the trabeculæ appear to consist chiefly of muscular tissue.

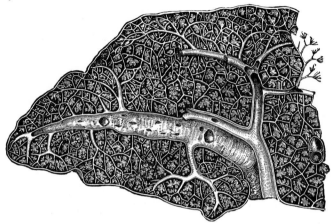

Fig. 617 —Transverse section of the human spleen, showing the distribution of the splenic artery and its branches.

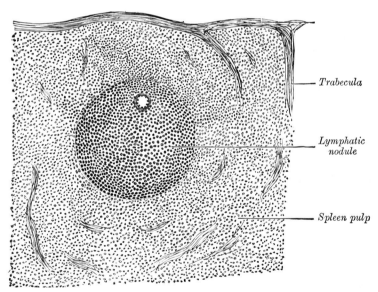

Fig. 618.—Transverse section of a portion of the spleen.

The **splenic pulp** (*pulpa lienis*) is a soft mass of a dark reddish-brown color, resembling grumous blood; it consists of a fine reticulum of fibers, continuous with those of the trabeculæ, to which are applied flat, branching cells. The meshes of the reticulum are filled with blood, and many lymphocytes, polymorphonuclear neutrophiles, and monocytes or macrophages. The latter are often large and contain ingested and partly digested red blood cells and pigment. In the young spleen, giant cells may also be found, each containing numerous nuclei or one compound nucleus Nucleated red-blood corpuscles have also been found in the spleen of young animals.

Bloodvessels of the Spleen.—The **splenic artery** is remarkable for its large size in proportion to the size of the organ, and also for its tortuous course. It divides into six or more branches, which enter the hilum of the spleen and ramify throughout its substance (Fig. 617), receiving sheaths from an involution of the external fibrous tissue. Similar sheaths also invest the nerves and veins. Each of the larger branches of the artery supplies chiefly that region of the organ in which the branch ramifies, having no anastomosis with the majority of the other branches.

Each branch runs in the transverse axis of the organ, from within outward, diminishing in size during its transit, and giving off in its passage smaller branches, some of which pass to the anterior, others to the posterior part. These ultimately leave the trabecular sheaths, and terminate in the proper substance of the spleen in small tufts or pencils of minute arterioles.

Some authors claim that the arterioles are connected with venules by capillaries and that they have a complete endothelial lining. Most authors, however, maintain that the endothelial connections are incomplete. In this open type of circulation the blood moves slowly through the spleen pulp and bathes the reticular network of the sinuses. The flow through the pulp is controlled by rhythmic contractions and relaxations of smooth muscles in the trabeculæ and capsule and by intermittent constriction and relaxation of individual arterioles and groups of them.

The altered coat of the arterioles, consisting of lymphoid tissue, presents here and there thickenings of a spheroidal shape, the **lymphatic nodules** (*Malpighian bodies of the spleen*). These bodies vary in size from about 0.25 mm. to 1 mm. in diameter. They are merely local expansions or hyperplasiæ of the lymphoid tissue, of which the external coat of the smaller arteries of the spleen is formed. They are most frequently found surrounding the arteriole, which thus seems to tunnel them, but occasionally they grow from one side of the vessel only, and present the appearance of a sessile bud growing from the arterial wall. In transverse sections, the artery, in the majority of cases, is found in an eccentric position. These bodies are visible to the naked eye on the surface of a fresh section of the organ, appearing as minute dots of a semiopaque whitish color in the dark substance of the pulp. In minute structure they resemble the lymphoid tissue of lymph nodes, consisting of a delicate reticulum, in the meshes of which lie ordinary lymphocytes (Fig. 618). The reticulum is made up of extremely fine fibrils, and is comparatively open in the center of the corpuscle, becoming closer at its periphery. The cells which it encloses are possessed of ameboid movement. When treated with carmine they become deeply stained, and can be easily distinguished from those of the pulp.

The smaller veins unite to form larger ones; these do not accompany the arteries, but soon enter the trabecular sheaths of the capsule, and by their junction form six or more branches, which emerge from the hilum, and, uniting, constitute the lienal vein, the largest radicle of the portal vein.

The **veins** are remarkable for their numerous anastomoses, while the arteries hardly anastomose at all.

The **lymphatics** are described on page 723.

The **nerves** are derived from the celiac plexus and are chiefly non-medullated. They are distributed to the bloodvessels and to the smooth muscle of the capsule and trabeculæ.

THE THYMUS (Fig. 619).

The thymus of an infant is a prominent organ occupying the upper anterior part of the thorax, but the thymus in an adult of advanced years may be scarcely recognizable because of atrophic changes. During its growth period, it has much of the appearance and texture of a gland, and previously it has been classified as one of the ductless glands, but no glandular function has been established. It is included here among the lymphatic organs because it resembles them structurally in being composed largely of lymphocytes and because its only known function is that of producing lymphocytes.

Development.—The thymus appears in the form of two flask-shaped entodermal diverticula, which arise, one on either side, from the third branchial pouch (Fig. 1158), and extend lateralward and backward into the surrounding mesoderm in front of the ventral aortæ. Here they meet and become joined to one another by connective tissue, but there is never any fusion of the thymus tissue proper. The pharyngeal opening of each diverticulum is soon obliterated, but the neck of the flask persists for some time as a cellular cord. By further proliferation of the cells, buds are formed which become elongated and greatly branched, lose their epithelial character, and become the cellular reticulum which forms the core of the lobules. The lobules remain separated from each other by loose connective tissue and the numerous small lymphocytes which make their appearance probably wander in from the surrounding mesenchyme. As the lobules increase in size, there is a differentiation into a peripheral zone or cortex in which the small lymphocytes are concentrated, and a central medulla in which the cellular reticulum predominates. The thymus attains a weight of 12 to 14 grams before birth, but it does not reach its greatest relative size until the age of two years. It continues to grow until puberty, at which time it reaches its greatest absolute size, weighing about 35 grams.

Anatomy.—The thymus consists of two lateral lobes held in close contact by connective tissue which also encloses the whole organ in a distinct capsule. It is situated partly in the thorax and partly in the neck, extending from the fourth costal cartilage to the lower border of the thyroid gland. In the neck it lies on the front and sides of the trachea, deep to the origins of the Sternohyoidei and Sternothyroidei. In the thorax it occupies the anterior portion of the superior mediastinum (Fig. 962, page 1128); superficial to it is the sternum, and deep to it are the great vessels and the upper part of the fibrous pericardium. The two lobes generally differ in size and shape, the right frequently overlapping the left. It is of a pinkish gray color, soft and lobulated, measuring approximately 5 cm. in length, 4 cm. in width, and 6 mm. in thickness.

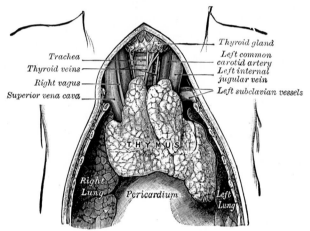

Fig. 619.—The thymus of a full-term fetus; exposed *in situ*.

Structure.—The two lobes are composed of numerous lobules, varying from 0.5 to 2 mm. in diameter, separated from each other by delicate connective tissue, and visible with the unaided eye. With low magnification, two zones of tissue can be seen within each lobule, an outer cortex and an inner medulla. The cortical part is made up almost entirely of small lymphocytes, held in place by reticular tissue composed of reticular (argyrophilic) fibers with relatively few reticular cells. The medullary portion contains much fewer lymphocytes, its reticulum is more cellular, and it contains the characteristic thymic or Hassall's corpuscles. These corpuscles are from 0.03 to 0.1 mm. in diameter; they have a central core of granular cells surrounded by concentric lamellæ of epithelioid cells. Although the lobules appear to be distinct from one another when viewed in a cross section, it has been found by careful study that the medullary tissue forms a continuous system of central stalks and branching cords.

Involution.—After puberty the thymus undergoes involution. Usually this is a gradual process called age involution, but it may be superseded by a rapid accidental involution due to starvation or acute disease. The small lymphocytes of the cortex disappear and the reticular tissue becomes compressed. The disappearing thymic tissue is likely to be replaced by adipose tissue, but the connective tissue capsule may persist, retaining its original shape and approximate size so that, in an older individual, what appears to be a yellowish colored thymus, when sectioned, will reveal only small islands of thymic tissue surrounded by fat.

Function.—No function of the thymus is known except that of producing small lymphocytes, and possibly plasma cells. The association of the organ with the growth of the individual and its involution after sexual maturity have made many investigators attempt to discover some endocrine function, but definite confirmation of claims along these lines is lacking except that its involution and regeneration may be influenced by known endocrine factors.

Vessels and Nerves.—The **arteries** supplying the thymus are derived from the internal mammary, and from the superior and inferior thyroids. The **veins** end in the left innominate vein, and in the thyroid veins. The **lymphatics** end in the anterior mediastinal, tracheobronchial and sternal nodes. The **nerves** are exceedingly minute; they are derived from the vagi and sympathetic. Branches from the descendens hypoglossi and phrenic reach the investing capsule, but do not penetrate into the substance of the gland.

BIBLIOGRAPHY

General and Comprehensive

Lymphatics, Lymph and Lymphoid Tissue. Drinker, C. K., and J. M. Yoffey: 1941. Harvard Univ. Press, Cambridge, ix + 406 pp.

A quantitative study of the lymphoid organs of the albino rat. Kindred, J. E.: 1938. Am. J. Anat., Vol. 62, pp. 453–473.

Anatomy of the Lymphatic System. Rouvière, H. Translated by M. J. Tobias. Edwards Bros., Ann Arbor, ix + 318 pp.

The drainage of particulate matter from the peritoneal cavity by lymphatics. Simer, P. H.: 1944. Anat. Rec., Vol. 88 pp. 175–192.

The effect of removal of a large part of the lymphoid system on the weight of the portion remaining *in situ*. Turner, M. L., and V. E. Hall: 1943. Anat. Rec., Vol. 85, pp. 401–412.

Lymphatic Vessels and Drainage

The lymphatics of the parietal tunica vaginalis propria of man. Allen, L.: 1943. Anat. Rec., Vol. 85, pp. 427–433.

Lymphatic drainage of paranasal sinuses. Dixon, F. W., and N. L. Hoerr: 1944. Laryngoscope, Vol. 54, pp. 165–175.

The morphology of the lymphatics of the mammalian heart. Patek, P. R.: 1939. Am. J. Anat., Vol. 64, pp. 203–249.

Renal lymphatics. Peirce, E. C., 1944. Anat. Rec., Vol. 90, pp. 315–335.

Communication between lymphatic and venous system at renal level in man. Pick, J. W., B. J. Anson, and H. W. Burnett, Jr.: 1944. Quart. Bull., Northwestern Univ. Med. School, Vol. 18, pp. 307–316.

Behavior of lymphatic vessels in the living rat. Webb, R. L., and P. A. Nicoll: 1944. Anat. Rec., Vol. 88, pp. 351–367.

The relation of lymph vessels to omental milk spots. Webb, R. L., and P. H. Simer: 1942. Anat. Rec., Vol. 83, pp. 437–447.

Lymph Nodes

Growth of lymph nodes, thymus, and spleen, and output of thoracic duct lymphocytes in the normal rat. Reinhardt, W.O.: 1946. Anat. Rec., Vol. 94, pp. 197–211.

Spleen

Microscopic observations of the circulatory system of living traumatized spleens, and of dying spleens. Knisely, M. H.: 1936. Anat. Rec., Vol. 65, pp. 131–148.

Postmortem weight of "normal" human spleen at different ages. Krumbhaar, E. B., and S. W. Lippincott: 1939. Am. J. Med. Sci., Vol. 197, pp. 344–358.

Studies on the microscopic anatomy and physiology of living transilluminated mammalian spleens. Mackenzie, D. W., Jr., A. A. Whipple, and M. P. Wintersteiner: 1942. Am. J. Anat., Vol. 68, pp. 397–456.

The variational anatomy of the spleen and splenic artery. Michels, N. A.: 1942. Am. J. Anat., Vol. 70, pp. 21–72.

The guinea-pig spleen. Studies on the structure and connections of the venous sinuses. Snook, T.: 1944. Anat. Rec., Vol. 89, pp. 413–427.

Deep lymphatics of the spleen. Snook, T.: 1946. Anat. Rec., Vol. 94, pp. 43–55.

Thymus

Thymus IV in the pig. Godwin, M. C.: 1943. Anat. Rec., Vol. 85, pp. 229–243.

Regeneration of the involuted thymus after adrenalectomy. Grègoire, C.: 1943. J. Morph., Vol. 72, pp. 239–261.

The morphogenesis and histogenesis of the thymus gland in man. Norris, E. H.: 1938. Carnegie Cont. to Emb., Vol. 27, pp. 191–207.

NEUROLOGY.

THE **Nervous System** is the mechanism concerned with the correlation and integration of various bodily processes, the reactions and adjustments of the organism to its environment, and with conscious life. It may be divided into two parts, **central** and **peripheral**.

The **central nervous system** consists of the **encephalon** or **brain**, contained within the cranium, and the **medulla spinalis** or **spinal cord**, lodged in the vertebral canal; the two portions are continuous with one another at the level of the upper border of the atlas vertebra just above the rootlets of the first cervical nerve.

The **peripheral nervous system** consists of a series of nerves by which the central nervous system is connected with the various tissues of the body. For descriptive purposes these nerves may be arranged in two groups, **cerebrospinal** (*cranial and spinal*) and **autonomic**: the two groups are intimately connected and closely intermingled.

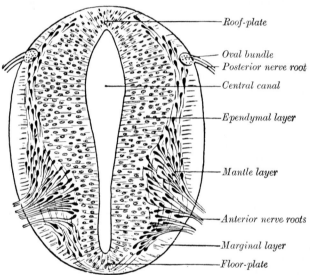

Roof-plate

Oval bundle
Posterior nerve root

Central canal

Ependymal layer

Mantle layer

Anterior nerve roots

Marginal layer

Floor-plate

Fig. 620.—Section of medulla spinalis of a four weeks' embryo. (His.)

DEVELOPMENT OF THE NERVOUS SYSTEM.

The entire nervous system is of ectodermal origin, and its first rudiment is seen in the neural groove and plate which extends along the dorsal aspect of the embryo (Fig. 32). The neural plate curls dorsally until its lateral edges fuse in the mid-dorsal line to form the neural tube. The anterior part of the plate is broad and forms the brain. The narrow posterior part forms the spinal cord. The cavity of the tube forms the ventricles of the brain and the central canal of the spinal cord. Certain of the common malformations of the nervous system can be traced to this very early stage of development. Thus a number of studies in experimental embryology indicate that the failure, to a greater or lesser extent, of the forebrain to develop (resulting in anencephaly, hemianencephaly, cyclopia, etc.) is due to

47

abnormalities in the mesenchymal tissue immediately underlying the rostral end of the neural plate in the very young embryo. If the neural groove fails to close, or having closed, fails to be completely separated from the overlying ectoderm, the development of the supporting bones is also abnormal and spina bifida results.

After formation of the neural tube further development occurs by mitotic division in and near the layer of cells lining the central canal, the **medullary epithelium.** All of the elements in the central nervous system except the microglia and the bloodvessels, are derived from this source. The histogenesis of the different cell types is illustrated in Fig. 621.

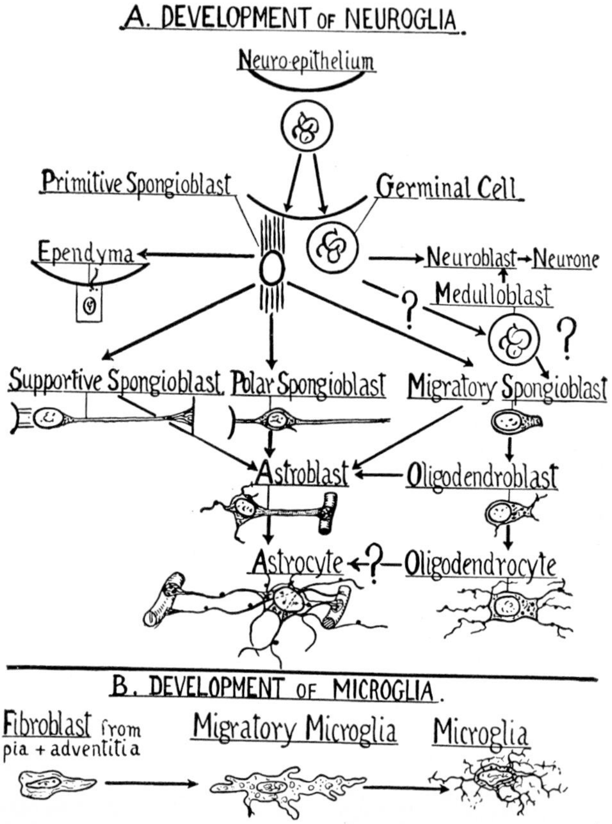

Fig. 621.—Outline of the development of the interstitial cells. Ectodermal development of neuroglia (*A*) above the heavy line; mesodermal development of microglia (*B*) below the line. The supportive spongioblast is formed early in embryonic life; polar spongioblast appears later and the migratory (apolar) spongioblast still later. They are all capable of forming astrocytes as indicated. Oligodendrocytes which appear late in embryonic development are apparently largely formed from migratory spongioblasts. The development of microglia is an entirely separate process due to an immigration of mesodermal cells into the central nervous system about the time of birth in mammals. (Penfield's Cytology and Cellular Pathology of the Nervous System, Courtesy of Paul B. Hoeber, Inc.)

The Medulla Spinalis.—At first the wall of the neural tube is composed of a single layer of columnar ectodermal cells. Soon the side-walls become thickened, while the dorsal and ventral parts remain thin, and are named the **roof-** and **floorplates** (Figs. 620, 623, 624). A transverse section of the tube at this stage presents an oval outline, while its lumen has the appearance of a slit. The cells which constitute the wall of the tube proliferate rapidly, and become arranged in a radiating manner from the central canal. Three layers may now be defined—an internal or ependymal, an intermediate or mantle, and an external or marginal. The **ependymal layer** is ultimately converted into the ependyma of the central canal; the processes of its cells pass outward toward the periphery of the medulla spinalis.

The **marginal layer** is devoid of nuclei, and later forms the supporting framework for the white funiculi of the medulla spinalis. The **mantle layer** represents the whole of the future gray columns of the medulla spinalis; in it the cells are differentiated into two sets, viz., (*a*) **spongioblasts** or **young neuroglia cells**, and (*b*) **germinal cells**, which are the parents of the **neuroblasts** or **young nerve cells** (Fig. 622). The spongioblasts are at first connected to one another by processes of the cells; in these, fibrils are developed, so that as the neuroglial cells become defined they exhibit their characteristic mature appearance with multiple processes proceeding from each cell. The germinal cells are large, round or oval, and first make their appearance between the ependymal cells on the sides of the central canal. They increase rapidly in number, so that by the fourth week they form an almost continuous layer on each side of the tube. No germinal cells are found in the roof- or floor-plates; the roof-plate retains, in certain regions of the brain, its epithelial character; elsewhere, its cells become spongioblasts. By subdivision the germinal cells give rise to the neuroblasts or young nerve cells, which migrate outward from the sides of the central canal into the mantle layer and at the same time become pear-shaped; the tapering part of the cell undergoes still further elongation, and forms the axis-cylinder of the cell.

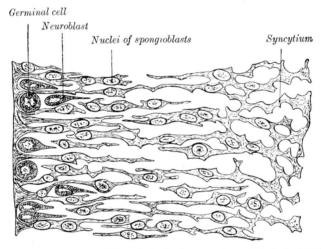

FIG. 622.—Transverse section of the medulla spinalis of a human embryo at the beginning of the fourth week. The left edge of the figure corresponds to the lining of the central canal. (His.)

The lateral walls of the medulla spinalis continue to increase in thickness, and the canal widens out near its dorsal extremity, and assumes a somewhat lozenge-shaped appearance. The widest part of the canal appears as a groove in the lateral wall, known as the **sulcus limitans**, which extends forward into the brain as far as the rostral end of the mesencephalon. This sulcus subdivides the neural tube into a **dorsal** or **alar**, and a **ventral** or **basal lamina** (Figs. 623, 624). The entering, afferent fibers end on cells derived from the former, whereas the outgoing, efferent fibers arise from cells derived from the latter. There are two groups of efferent fibers, those supplying the striped musculature and those to the smooth muscles, bloodvessels and glands. The autonomic cells which give rise to the latter develop in the upper portion of the basal lamina, lateral to the sulcus limitans. At a later stage of development the dorsal part of the central canal in the medulla spinalis is first reduced to a mere slit and then is obliterated by the approximation and fusion of its walls, while the ventral part persists and forms the central canal of the adult stage. The caudal end of the canal exhibits a conical expansion which is known as the **terminal ventricle.**

The ventral part of the mantle layer becomes thickened, and on cross-section appears as a triangular patch between the marginal and ependymal layers. This thickening is the rudiment of the anterior column of gray substance, and contains many neuroblasts, the axis-cylinders of which pass out through the marginal layer and form the anterior roots of the spinal nerves (Figs. 620, 623, 624). The thickening of the mantle layer gradually extends in a dorsal direction, and forms the posterior column of gray substance. The axons of many of the neuroblasts in the alar lamina run forward, and cross in the floor-plate to the opposite side of the medulla spinalis; these form the rudiment of the anterior white commissure.

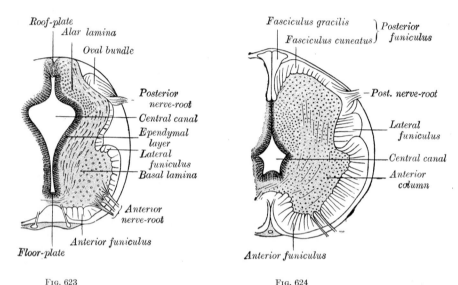

FIG. 623   FIG. 624

FIGS. 623, 624.—Transverse sections through the medullæ spinales of human embryos. (His.) Fig. 623, aged about four and a half weeks. Fig. 624, aged about three months.

The thickening of the walls of the neural tube is not uniform throughout its length, but is greater at the levels of the spinal nerves and is smaller between them. Thus the medulla spinalis develops a segmental appearance, each segment having its own pair of nerves. Further, the relative thickness of the different segments varies roughly in proportion to the size of the nerves. In this regard it is of interest to note that recent studies in experimental embryology indicate that the number of motor nerve cells developing in a given segment is determined to a large extent by the number of muscle fibers to be supplied by the motor nerve from that segment. Later in development, when the long tracts of fibers grow into the marginal layer, the segmental appearance of the medulla spinalis is obliterated.

About the end of the fourth week nerve fibers begin to appear in the marginal layer. The first to develop are the short intersegmental fibers from the neuroblasts in the mantle zone, and the fibers of the dorsal nerve roots which grow into the medulla spinalis from the cells of the spinal ganglia. By the sixth week these dorsal root fibers form a well-defined **oval bundle** in the peripheral part of the alar lamina; this bundle gradually increases in size, and spreading toward the middle line forms the rudiment of the posterior funiculus. The long intersegmental fibers begin to appear about the third month and the cerebrospinal fibers about the fifth month. All nerve fibers are at first destitute of medullary sheaths. Different groups of fibers receive their sheaths at different times—the dorsal and ventral nerve roots about the fifth month, the cerebrospinal fibers after the ninth month.

By the growth of the anterior columns of gray substance, and by the increase in size of the anterior funiculi, a furrow is formed between the lateral halves of the cord anteriorly; this gradually deepens to form the anterior median fissure. The mode of formation of the posterior septum is somewhat uncertain.

Up to the third month of fetal life the medulla spinalis occupies the entire length of the vertebral canal, and the spinal nerves pass outward at right angles to the medulla spinalis. From this time onward, the vertebral column increases in length more rapidly than the medulla spinalis, and the latter, being fixed above through its continuity with the brain, gradually assumes a higher position within the canal. By the sixth month its lower end reaches only as far as the upper end of the sacrum; at birth it is on a level with the third lumbar vertebra, and in the adult with the lower border of the first or upper border of the second lumbar vertebra. A delicate filament, the **filum terminale**, extends from its lower end as far as the coccyx.

The Spinal Nerves.—Each spinal nerve is attached to the medulla spinalis by an anterior or ventral and a posterior or dorsal root.

The fibers of the anterior roots are formed by the axons of the neuroblasts which lie in the ventral part of the mantle layer; these axons grow out through the overlying marginal layer and become grouped to form the anterior nerve root (Fig. 620).

The fibers of the posterior roots are developed from the cells of the spinal ganglia. Before the neural groove is closed to form the neural tube a ridge of ectodermal cells, the **ganglion ridge** or **neural crest** (Fig. 625), appears along the prominent margin of each neural fold. When the folds meet in the middle line the two ganglion ridges fuse and form a wedge-shaped area along the line of closure of the tube. The cells of this area proliferate rapidly opposite the primitive segments and then migrate in a lateral and ventral direction to the sides of the neural tube, where they ultimately form a series of oval-shaped masses, the future spinal ganglia. These ganglia are arranged symmetrically on the two sides of the neural tube and, except in the region of the tail, are equal in number to the primitive segments. The cells of the ganglia, like the cells of the mantle layer, are of two kinds, viz., **spongioblasts** and **neuroblasts**. The spongioblasts develop into sheath cells which, on the one hand, form capsules

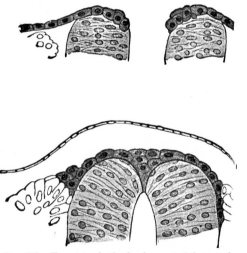

Fig. 625.—Two stages in the development of the neural crest in the human embryo. (Lenhossèk.)

around the cell bodies of the neurons, and on the other, migrate out along the spinal nerves and form the neurilemmal sheaths of the peripheral nerve fibers. The neuroblasts are at first round or oval in shape, but soon assume the form of spindles the extremities of which gradually elongate into central and peripheral processes. The central processes grow medialward into the neural tube and constitute the fibers of the posterior nerve roots, while the peripheral processes grow lateralward to mingle with the fibers of the anterior root in the spinal nerve. As development proceeds the original bipolar form of the cells changes; the two processes become approximated until they ultimately arise from a single stem in a T-shaped manner. Only in the ganglia of the acoustic nerve is the bipolar form retained. More recent observers hold, however, that the T-form is derived from the branching of a single process which grows out from the cell.

In the peripheral growth of the spinal nerves the naked axons grow out first. The tips of the axons are bulbous and show ameboid movement. The factors which control the direction and course of growth are not fully known, but it seems that both chemical tropisms and mechanical factors play a rôle. As the axons proceed peripherally, sheath cells, derived originally from the neural crest, migrate out along the fibers to which they become applied. These cells divide by mitosis, and

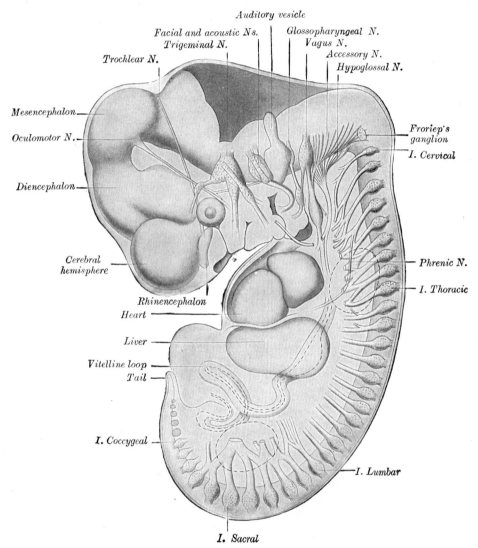

Fig. 626.—Reconstruction of peripheral nerves of a human embyro of 10.2 mm. (After His.) The abducent nerve is not labelled, but is seen passing forward to the eye under the mandibular and maxillary nerves.

the daughter cells extend out along the same fiber, or migrate to a neighboring one. The sheath cells thus come to form the neurilemma, or sheath of Schwann, of the peripheral nerves. Later, myelin develops between the sheath cells and the axon of certain fibers. Both the axon and the sheath cell play a rôle in the formation of myelin, since no myelin forms round a naked axon, nor does myelin form on particular axons (non-myelinated fibers in the adult), although the sheath cells may have been derived from parent cells on well myelinated fibers.

The anterior or ventral and the posterior or dorsal nerve roots join immediately beyond the spinal ganglion to form the **spinal nerve**, which then divides into anterior, posterior, and visceral rami. The anterior and posterior rami proceed directly to their areas of distribution without further association with ganglion cells (Fig. 626). The visceral rami are distributed to the thoracic, abdominal, and pelvic viscera, to reach which they pass through the sympathetic trunk, and many of the fibers form arborizations around the ganglion cells of this trunk. Visceral branches are not given off from all the spinal nerves; they form two groups, viz., (*a*) **thoracico-lumbar**, from the first or second thoracic, to the second or third lumbar nerves; and (*b*) **pelvic**, from the second and third, or third and fourth sacral nerves.

The Brain.—The brain is developed from the expanded anterior part of the wall of the neural tube. By the time the brain plate has fused into a tube, unequal growth in thickness and size together with the development of three flexures enable one to distinguish vaguely different regions which are known as the **hind-brain, mid-brain** and **fore-brain**. The first flexure appears in the region of the mid-brain, and is named the **ventral cephalic flexure** (Fig. 631). By means of it the fore-brain is bent in a ventral direction around the anterior end of the notochord and fore-gut

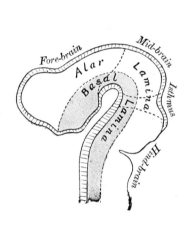

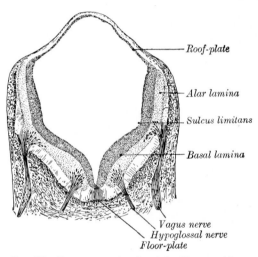

FIG. 627.—Diagram to illustrate the alar and basal laminæ of brain. (His.)

FIG. 628.—Transverse section of medulla oblongata of human embryo. × 32. (Kollmann.)

with the result that the floor of the fore-brain comes to lie almost parallel with that of the hind-brain. The flexure causes the mid-brain to become, for a time, the most prominent part of the brain, since its dorsal surface corresponds with the convexity of the curve. The second bend appears at the junction of the hind-brain and medulla spinalis. This is termed the **cervical flexure** (Fig. 633), and increases from the third to the end of the fifth week, when the hind-brain forms nearly a right angle with the medulla spinalis; after the fifth week erection of the head takes place and the cervical flexure diminishes and disappears. The third bend is named the **pontile flexure** (Fig. 633), because it is found in the region of the future pons Varoli. The lateral wall of the brain-tube, like that of the medulla spinalis is divided by the sulcus limitans into alar, or dorsal, and basal, or ventral, laminæ (Figs. 627, 628). The sulcus limitans is well defined in the hind-brain and mid-brain, but its course in the fore-brain is not definitely known. The nucleus of the oculomotor nerve, lying at the forward end of the mid-brain, is the rostral end of the column of motor cells which innervate striped muscles, and the hypothalamus probably represents the rostral end of the column of autonomic cells. These are the most rostral structures developing from the basal lamina.

The Hind-brain or Rhombencephalon.—The cavity of the hind-brain becomes the fourth ventricle. At the time when the ventral cephalic flexure makes its appearance, the length of the hind-brain exceeds the combined lengths of the other two parts. Immediately behind the mid-brain it exhibits a marked constriction, the **isthmus rhombencephali** (Fig. 631, *Isthmus*), which is best seen when the brain

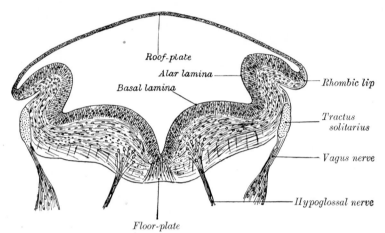

FIG. 629.—Transverse section of medulla oblongata of human embryo. (After His.)

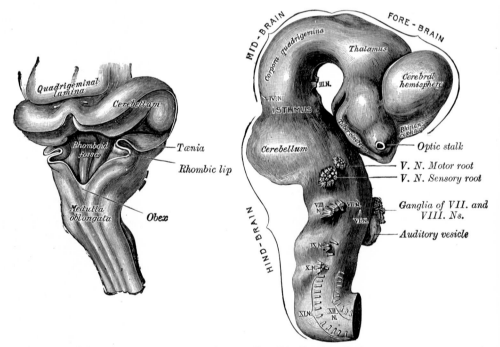

FIG. 630.—Hind-brain of a human embryo of three months—viewed from behind and partly from left side. (From model by His.)

FIG. 631.—Exterior of brain of human embryo of four and a half weeks. (From model by His.)

is viewed from the dorsal aspect. From the isthmus the anterior medullary velum is formed. It is customary to divide the rest of the hind-brain into two parts, viz., an upper, called the **metencephalon**, and a lower, the **myelencephalon**. The cerebellum is developed by a thickening of the roof, and the pons by a thickening in the floor and lateral walls of the metencephalon. The floor and lateral walls of the myelencephalon are thickened to form the medulla oblongata; its roof remains thin, and, retaining to a great extent its epithelial nature, is expanded in a lateral direction. Later, by the growth and backward extension of the cerebellum, the roof is folded inward toward the cavity of the fourth ventricle; it assists in completing the dorsal wall of this cavity, and is also invaginated to form the ependymal covering of its choroid plexuses. Above it is continuous with the posterior medullary velum; below, with the obex and ligulæ.

The early development of the **medulla oblongata** resembles that of the medulla spinalis, but at the same time exhibits interesting modifications. On transverse section the myelencephalon at an early stage is seen to consist of two lateral walls, connected across the middle line by floor- and roof-plates (Figs. 628 and 629). Each lateral wall consists of an alar and a basal lamina, separated by the sulcus limitans. The contained cavity is more or less triangular in outline, the base being formed by the roof-plate, which is thin and greatly expanded transversely. Pear-shaped neuroblasts are developed in the alar and basal laminæ, and their narrow stalks are elongated to form the axis-cylinders of the nerve fibers. The early fundamental pattern of receptor cells in the alar lamina, autonomic cells opposite to the sulcus limitans and motor cells innervating striped musculature in the basal lamina, is similar to that in the medulla spinalis. Opposite the furrow or boundary between the alar and basal laminæ a bundle of nerve fibers attaches itself to the outer surface of the alar lamina. This is named the **tractus solitarius** (Fig. 629), and is formed by the sensory fibers of the glossopharyngeal and vagus nerves. It is the homologue of the **oval bundle** seen in the medulla spinalis, and, like it, is developed by an ingrowth of fibers from the ganglia of the neural crest. At first it is applied to the outer surface of the alar lamina, but it soon becomes buried,

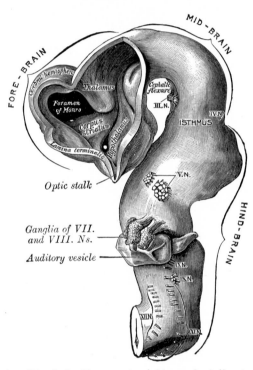

Fig. 632.—Brain of human embryo of four and a half weeks showing interior of fore-brain. (From model by His.)

owing to the growth over it of the neighboring parts. By the fifth week the dorsal part of the alar lamina in the open part of the medulla bends in a lateral direction, to form the **rhombic lip** (Figs. 629, 630). Within a few days this lip becomes applied to, and unites with, the outer surface of the main part of the alar lamina, and so covers in the tractus solitarius and also the spinal root of the trigeminal nerve; the nodulus and flocculus of the cerebellum are developed from the rhombic lip.

Neuroblasts accumulate in the mantle layer; those in the basal lamina correspond with the cells in the anterior gray column of the medulla spinalis, and, like them, give origin to motor nerve fibers; in the medulla oblongata they soon, however, become arranged in groups or nuclei, instead of forming a continuous column. From the alar lamina and its rhombic lip, neuroblasts migrate into the basal lamina, and become aggregated to form the olivary nuclei, while many send their axis-cylinders through the floor-plate to the opposite side, and thus constitute the rudiment of the raphé of the medulla oblongata. By means of this thickening of the ventral portion, the motor nuclei are buried deeply in the interior, and, in the adult, are found close to the rhomboid fossa. This is still further accentuated: (a) by the development of the pyramids, which are formed about the fourth month by the downward growth of the motor fibers from the cerebral cortex; and (b) by the fibers which pass to and from the cerebellum. On the rhomboid fossa a series of six temporary transverse furrows appears; these are termed the **rhombic grooves**. They bear a definite relationship to certain of the cranial nerves; thus, from before backward the first and second grooves overlie the nucleus of the trigeminal; the third, the nucleus of the facial; the fourth, that of the abducent; the fifth, that of the glossopharyngeal; and the sixth, that of the vagus.

The **pons** is developed from the ventro-lateral wall of the metencephalon by a process similar to that which has been described for the medulla oblongata.

The **cerebellum** is developed in the roof of the anterior part of the hind-brain (Figs. 630 to 635). The alar laminæ of this region become thickened to form two lateral plates which soon fuse in the middle line and produce a thick lamina which roofs in the upper part of the cavity of the hind-brain vesicle; this constitutes the rudiment of the cerebellum, the outer surface of which is originally smooth and convex. The fissures of the cerebellum appear first in the vermis and floccular region, and traces of them are found during the third month; the fissures on the cerebellar hemispheres do not appear until the fifth month. The primitive fissures are not developed in the order of their relative size in the adult—thus the horizontal sulcus in the fifth month is merely a shallow groove. The best marked of the early fissures are: (a) **fissura posterolateralis**, the first fissure to develop by the bending over of the rhombic lip, separating the flocculonodular lobe from the corpus cerebelli; (b) the **fissura prima** between the developing culmen and declive; and (c) the **fissura secunda** between the future pyramid and uvula. The flocculus and nodule are developed from the rhombic lip, and are therefore recognizable as separate portions before any of the other cerebellar lobules.

On the ventricular surface of the cerebellar lamina a transverse furrow, the **incisura fastigii**, appears, and deepens to form the tent-like recess of the roof of the fourth ventricle. The rudiment of the cerebellum at first projects in a dorsal direction; but, by the backward growth of the cerebrum, it is folded downward and somewhat flattened, and the thin roof-plate of the fourth ventricle, originally continuous with the posterior border of the cerebellum, is projected inward toward the cavity of the ventricle.

The Mid-brain or Mesencephalon.—The mid-brain (Figs. 631 to 635) exists for a time as a thin-walled cavity of some size, and is separated from the isthmus rhombencephali behind, and from the fore-brain in front, by slight constrictions. Its cavity becomes relatively reduced in diameter, and forms the cerebral aqueduct of the adult brain. Its basal laminæ increase in thickness to form the cerebral peduncles, which are at first of small size, but rapidly enlarge after the fourth month. The neuroblasts of these laminæ are grouped in relation to the sides and floor of the cerebral aqueduct, and very early certain of them are grouped to form the nuclei of the oculomotor and trochlear nerves, with their striped muscle and autonomic components. By a similar thickening process its alar laminæ are developed into the quadrigeminal lamina. It is likely that the cells of the mesencephalic root of the trigeminal nerve are derived from the alar lamina. The dorsal part of the wall for a time undergoes expansion, and presents an internal median furrow and a corresponding external ridge; these, however, disappear, and the latter is replaced by a groove. Subsequently two oblique furrows extend medialward and backward, and the thickened lamina is thus subdivided into the superior and inferior colliculi.

The Fore-brain or Prosencephalon.—A transverse section of the early fore-brain shows the same parts as are displayed in similar sections of the medulla spinalis and medulla oblongata, viz., a pair of thick lateral walls connected by thin floor-and roof-plates. The division into alar and basal laminæ, however, is not clear and whereas certain authors regard the hypothalamus as a derivative of the basal lamina, others maintain that the basal lamina terminates at the mammillary recess and that the whole fore-brain develops from the alar lamina.

At a very early period before the closure of the cranial part of the neural tube, two lateral diverticula, the **optic vesicles,** appear, one on either side of the fore-brain; for a time they communicate with the cavity of the fore-brain by relatively wide openings. The peripheral parts of the vesicles expand, while the proximal parts are reduced to tubular stalks, the **optic stalks.** The optic vesicle gives rise to the retina and the epithelium on the back of the ciliary body and iris; the optic stalk is invaded by nerve fibers to form the optic nerve. The fore-brain then grows

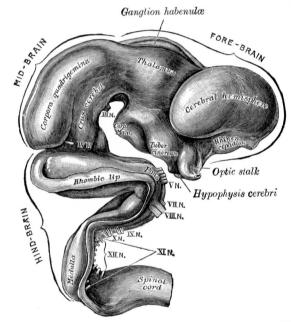

Fig. 633.—Exterior of brain of human embryo of five weeks. (From model by His.)

forward, and from the alar laminæ of this front portion the cerebral hemispheres originate as diverticula which rapidly expand to form two large pouches, one on either side. The cavities of these diverticula are the rudiments of the lateral ventricles; they communicate with the median part of the fore-brain cavity by relatively wide openings, which ultimately form the interventricular foramina. The median portion of the wall of the fore-brain vesicle consists of a thin lamina, the **lamina terminalis** (Figs. 635, 638), which stretches from the interventricular foramen to the recess at the base of the optic stalk. The anterior part of the fore-brain, including the rudiments of the cerebral hemispheres, is named the **telencephalon,** and its posterior portion is termed the **diencephalon;** its cavity is the third ventricle.

The Diencephalon.—From the alar lamina of the diencephalon, the thalamus, metathalamus, and epithalamus are developed. The **thalamus** (Figs. 631 to 635) arises as a thickening which involves the anterior two-thirds of the alar lamina. The two thalami are visible, for a time, on the surface of the brain, but are subsequently hidden by the cerebral hemispheres which grow backward over them.

The thalami extend medialward and gradually narrow the cavity between them into a slit-like aperture which forms the greater part of the third ventricle; their medial surfaces ultimately adhere, in part, to each other, and the **intermediate mass** of the ventricle is developed across the area of contact. The **metathalamus** comprises the geniculate bodies which originate as slight outward bulgings of the alar lamina. In the adult the lateral geniculate body appears as an eminence on the lateral part of the posterior end of the thalamus, while the medial is situated on the lateral aspect of the mid-brain. The **epithalamus** includes the pineal body, the posterior commissure, and the trigonum habenulæ. The pineal body arises as an upward evagination of the roof-plate immediately in front of the mid-brain; this evagination becomes solid with the exception of its proximal part, which persists as the recessus pinealis. In lizards the pineal evagination is elongated into a stalk, and its peripheral extremity is expanded into a vesicle, in which a rudimentary lens and retina are formed; the stalk becomes solid and nerve fibers make their appearance in it, so that in these animals the pineal body forms a rudimentary eye. The posterior commissure is formed by the ingrowth of fibers into the depression behind and below the pineal evagination, and the trigonum habenulæ is developed in front of the pineal recess.

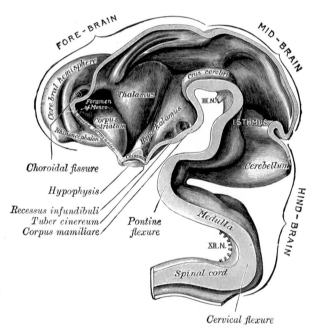

Fig. 634.—Interior of brain of human embryo of five weeks. (From model by His.)

From the ventral part of the wall of the diencephalon are developed the hypothalamus, the optic vesicles and chiasma, and the neurohypophysis. The hypothalamus comprises the mammillary bodies, the tuber cinereum and certain nuclear masses dorsal to the chiasma.

The optic vesicles have already been referred to. Later the optic nerves grow from the eyes along the optic stalk to the brain wall, undergo partial decussation in the optic chiasma and continue as the optic tracts to the lateral geniculate body and the superior colliculus.

The neurohypophysis consists of the median eminence of the tuber cinereum, the infundibular stem and the neural lobe of the hypophysis. It arises as a diverticulum of the floor of the diencephalon; the adenohypophysis is developed from a diverticulum of the ectodermal lining of the stomadeum.

The roof-plate of the diencephalon, in front of the pineal body, remains thin and epithelial in character, and is subsequently invaginated by the choroid plexuses of the third ventricle.

The **telencephalon,** or end-brain, consists of the two lateral diverticula already described and of the rostral end of the neural tube which includes the lamina terminalis. The cavities of the diverticula represent the lateral ventricles, and their walls become thickened to form the nervous matter of the cerebral hemispheres. The dorso-medial parts of the walls of the diverticula, where they are continuous in front with the lamina terminalis and medially with the roof plate of the diencephalon, remain thin and are later invaginated to form the epithelium of the choroid plexuses of the lateral ventricles.

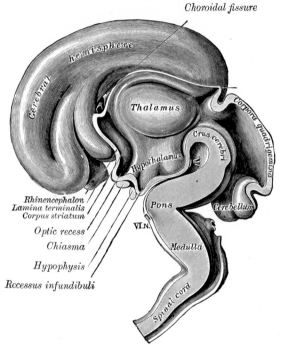

FIG. 635.—Median sagittal section of brain of human embryo of three months. (From model by His.)

The **cerebral hemispheres** develop from the diverticula of the telencephalon (Figs. 631 to 635); they increase rapidly in size and ultimately overlap the structures developed from the mid- and hind-brains. This great expansion of the hemispheres is a characteristic feature of the brains of mammals, and attains its maximum development in the brain of man. Elliott-Smith divides each cerebral hemisphere into three fundamental parts, viz., the **rhinencephalon,** the **corpus striatum,** and the **neopallium.** From that portion of the neural tube between the lamina terminalis and the diverticula of the hemispheres develop certain structures of which the **preoptic area** is best defined.

The **rhinencephalon** (Fig. 635) represents the oldest part of the telencephalon, and forms almost the whole of the hemisphere in fishes, amphibians, and reptiles. In man it is feebly developed in comparison with the rest of the hemisphere, and comprises the following parts, viz., the olfactory lobe (consisting of the olfactory tract and bulb and the trigonum olfactorium), the anterior perforated substance, the septum pellucidum, the subcallosal, supracallosal, and dentate gyri, the fornix, the hippocampus, and the uncus. The rhinencephalon appears as a longitudinal elevation, with a corresponding internal furrow, on the under surface of the hemisphere close to the lamina terminalis; it is separated from the lateral surface of the hemisphere by a furrow, the **external rhinal fissure,** and is continuous behind with that part of the hemisphere, which will ultimately form the anterior end of the temporal lobe. The elevation becomes divided by a groove into an anterior and a posterior part. The anterior grows forward as a hollow stalk the lumen of which is continuous with the anterior part of the ventricular cavity. During the third month the stalk becomes solid and forms the rudiment of the olfactory bulb and tract; a strand of gelatinous tissue in the interior of the bulb indicates the position of the original cavity. From the posterior part the anterior perforated substance and the pyriform lobe are developed; at the beginning of the fourth month the latter forms a curved elevation continuous behind with the medial surface of the temporal lobe, and consisting, from before backward, of the gyrus olfactorius lateralis, gyrus ambiens, and gyrus semilunaris, parts which in the adult brain are represented by the lateral root of the olfactory tract and the uncus. The position and connections of the remaining portions of the rhinencephalon are described with the anatomy of the brain.

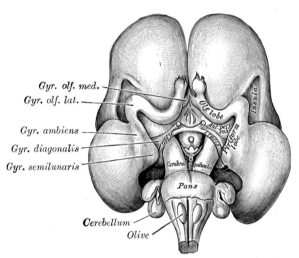

Fig. 636.—Inferior surface of brain of embryo at beginning of fourth month. (From Kollmann.)

The **corpus striatum** (Figs. 632 and 634) appears in the fourth week as a triangular thickening of the floor of the telencephalon between the optic recess and the interventricular foramen, and continuous behind with the thalamic part of the diencephalon. It increases in size, and by the second month is seen as a swelling in the floor of the future lateral ventricle; this swelling reaches as far as the posterior end of the primitive hemisphere, and when this part of the hemisphere grows backward and downward to form the temporal lobe, the posterior part of the corpus striatum is carried into the roof of the inferior horn of the ventricle, where it is seen as the tail of the caudate nucleus in the adult brain. During the fourth and fifth months the corpus striatum becomes incompletely subdivided by the fibers of the internal capsule into two masses, an inner, the **caudate nucleus,** and an outer, the **putamen.** The putamen, together with the **globus pallidus** which adjoins it medially, forms a gray mass which, from its general shape, has been called the **lentiform nucleus.** In front, the corpus striatum is continuous with the anterior perforated substance; laterally it is confluent for a time with that portion of the wall of the ventricle which is developing into the insula, but this continuity is subsequently interrupted by the fibers of the external capsule.

The **neopallium** (Fig. 637) forms the remaining, and by far the greater, part of the cerebral hemisphere. It consists, at an early stage, of a relatively large, more or less hemispherical cavity—the primitive **lateral ventricle**—enclosed by a thin wall from which the cortex of the hemisphere is developed. The vesicle expands in all directions, but more especially upward and backward, so that by the third month the hemispheres cover the diencephalon, by the sixth they overlap the mid-brain, and by the eighth the hind-brain.

The median lamina uniting the two hemispheres does not share in their expansion but remains as the thin roof of the third venticle. Thus the hemispheres are separated by a deep cleft, the forerunner of the longitudinal fissure, and this cleft is occupied by a septum of mesodermal tissue which constitutes the primitive **falx cerebri.** Coincidently with the expansion of the vesicle, its cavity is drawn out into three prolongations which represent the horns of the future lateral ventricle; the hinder end of the vesicle is carried downward and forward and forms the inferior horn; the posterior horn is produced somewhat later, in association with the backward growth of the occipital lobe of the hemisphere. The dorso-

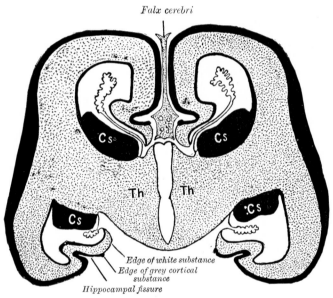

Fig. 637.—Diagrammatic coronal section of brain to show relations of neopallium. (After His.) *Cs.* Corpus striatum *Th.* Thalamus.

medial portion of the vesicle which is immediately continuous with the roof-plate of the neural tube remains thin and of an epithelial character; it is invaginated into the lateral ventricle along the medial wall of the hemisphere. This invagination constitutes the choroidal fissure, and extends from the interventricular foramen to the posterior end of the vesicle. Mesodermal tissue, continuous with that of the primitive falx cerebri, and carrying bloodvessels with it, spreads between the two layers of the invaginated fold and forms the rudiment of the tela choroidea; the margins of the tela become highly vascular and form the choroid plexuses which for some months almost completely fill the ventricular cavities; the tela at the same time invaginates the epithelial roof of the diencephalon to form the choroid plexuses of the third ventricle. By the downward and forward growth of the posterior end of the vesicle to form the temporal lobe the choroidal fissure finally reaches from the interventricular foramen to the extremity of the inferior horn of the ventricle.

Parallel with but above and in front of the choroidal fissure the medial wall of the cerebral vesicle becomes folded outward and gives rise to the **hippocampal** fissure on the medial surface and to a corresponding elevation, the **hippocampus**, within the ventricular cavity. The gray or ganglionic covering of the wall of the vesicle ends at the inferior margin of the fissure in a thickened edge; beneath this the marginal or reticular layer (future white substance) is exposed and its lower thinned edge is continuous with the epithelial invagination covering the choroid plexus (Fig. 637). As a result of the later downward and forward growth of the temporal lobe the hippocampal fissure and the parts associated with it extend from the interventricular foramen to the end of the inferior horn of the ventricle. The thickened edge of gray substance becomes the gyrus dentatus, the fasciola cinerea and the supra- and subcallosal gyri, while the free edge of the white substance forms the fimbria hippocampi and the body and crus of the fornix. The corpus callosum is developed within the arch of the hippocampal fissure, and the upper part of the fissure forms, in the adult brain, the callosal fissure on the medial surface of the hemisphere.

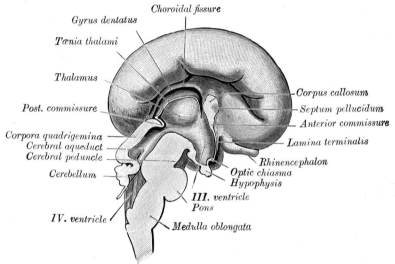

Fig. 638.—Median sagittal section of brain of human embryo of four months. (Marchand.)

The Commissures (Fig. 638).—The development of the posterior commissure has already been referred to (page 748). The great commissures of the hemispheres, viz., the **corpus callosum**, the **fornix**, and **anterior commissures**, arise from the lamina terminalis. About the fourth month a small thickening appears in this lamina, immediately in front of the interventricular foramen. The lower part of this thickening is soon constricted off, and fibers appear in it to form the anterior commissure. The upper part continues to grow with the hemispheres, and is invaded by two sets of fibers. Transverse fibers, extending between the hemispheres, pass into its dorsal part, which is now differentiated as the corpus callosum (in rare cases the corpus callosum is not developed). Into the ventral part longitudinal fibers from the hippocampus pass to the lamina terminalis, and through that structure to the corpora mamillaria; these fibers constitute the fornix. A small portion, lying antero-inferiorly between the corpus callosum and fornix, is not invaded by the commissural fibers; it remains thin, and later a cavity, the cavity of the **septum pellucidum**, forms in its interior.

Fissures and Sulci.—The outer surface of the cerebral hemisphere is at first smooth, but later it exhibits a number of elevations or convolutions, separated from each other by fissures and sulci, most of which make their appearance during the sixth or seventh months of fetal life. The term *fissure* is applied to such grooves as involve the entire thickness of the cerebral wall, and thus produce correspond ing eminences in the ventricular cavity, while the *sulci* affect only the superficial part of the wall, and therefore leave no impressions in the ventricle. The fissures comprise the **choroidal** and **hippocampal** already described, and two others, viz., the **calcarine** and **collateral**, which produce the swellings known respectively as the **calcar avis** and the **collateral eminence** in the ventricular cavity. Of the sulci the following may be referred to, viz., the **central sulcus** (*fissure of Rolando*), which is developed in two parts; the **intraparietal sulcus** in four parts; and the **cingulate sulcus** in two or three parts. The **lateral cerebral** or **Sylvian fissure** differs from all the other fissures in its mode of development. It appears about the third month as a depression, the **Sylvian fossa**, on the lateral surface of the hemisphere (Fig. 639); this fossa corresponds with the position of the corpus striatum, and its floor is moulded to form the insula. The intimate connection which exists between the cortex of the insula and the subjacent corpus striatum prevents this part of the hemisphere wall from expanding at the same rate as the portions which surround it. The neighboring parts of the hemisphere therefore gradually grow over and cover in the insula, and constitute the temporal, parietal, frontal, and orbital opercula of the adult brain.

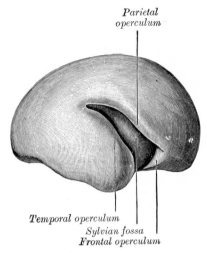

Parietal operculum

Temporal operculum
Sylvian fossa
Frontal operculum

FIG. 639.—Outer surface of cerebral hemisphere of human embryo of about five months.

The frontal and orbital opercula are the last to form, but by the end of the first year after birth the insula is completely submerged by the approximation of the opercula. The fissures separating the opposed margins of the opercula constitute the composite lateral cerebral fissure.

If a section across the wall of the hemisphere about the sixth week be examined microscopically it will be found to consist of a thin marginal or reticular layer, a thick ependymal layer, and a thin intervening mantle layer. Neuroblasts from the ependymal and mantle layers migrate into the deep part of the marginal layer and form the cells of the cerebral cortex. The nerve fibers which form the underlying white substance of the hemispheres consist at first of outgrowths from the cells of the corpora striata and thalami; later the fibers from the cells of the cortex are added. Medullation of these fibers begins about the time of birth and continues until puberty.

The Cranial Nerves.—With the exception of the olfactory, optic, and acoustic nerves, which will be especially considered, the cranial nerves are developed in a similar manner to the spinal nerves (see page 741). The sensory or afferent nerves are derived from the cells of the ganglion rudiments of the neural crest. The central processes of these cells grow into the brain and form the roots of the nerves, while the peripheral processes extend outward and constitute their fibers of distribution (Fig. 626). It has been seen, in considering the development of the medulla oblongata (page 745), that the **tractus solitarius** (Fig. 641), derived from the fibers which grow inward from the ganglion rudiments of the glossopharyngeal and vagus nerves, is the homologue of the **oval bundle** in the cord, which had its origin in the posterior nerve roots. The motor or efferent nerves arise as outgrowths of the neuroblasts situated in the basal laminæ of the mid- and hind-brain. While, however, the spinal motor nerve roots arise in one series from the basal lamina, the cranial motor nerves are grouped into two sets, according as they spring from

48

the medial or lateral parts of the basal lamina. To the former set belong the oculomotor, trochlear, abducent, and hypoglossal nerves; to the latter, the accessory and the motor fibers of the trigeminal, facial, glossopharyngeal, vagus nerves (Figs. 640, 641).

The Autonomic Nervous System.—The primordia of the sympathetic trunks and the prevertebral plexuses arise from cells of cerebrospinal origin which advance peripherally both along the dorsal and ventral roots of the spinal nerves. The vagal parasympathetic plexuses, viz., the pulmonary, the cardiac, and the enteric plexuses, except in the aboral portions of the digestive tube, arise from cells of cerebrospinal origin which migrate peripherally along the vagi. In the more distal portions of the digestive tube the enteric plexuses arise from cells which are derived from the parasympathetic supply in the lower trunk region. The majority of the cells which constitute the primordium of the ciliary ganglion are derived from the semilunar ganglion *via* the ophthalmic nerve. Relatively few are contributed *via* the oculomotor

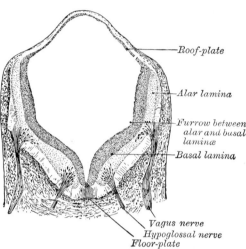

Roof-plate

Alar lamina

Furrow between alar and basal laminæ

Basal lamina

Vagus nerve
Hypoglossal nerve
Floor-plate

FIG. 640.—Transverse section of medulla oblongata of human embryo. × 32. (Kollmann.)

nerve. The cells which enter the primordium of the sphenopalatine ganglion earliest, migrate peripherally along the greater superficial petrosal nerve. The majority of the cells which enter the primordium of this ganglion are derived from the semilunar ganglion *via* the maxillary nerve and its rami. The primordium of the otic ganglion arises at the growing extremity of the lesser superficial petrosal

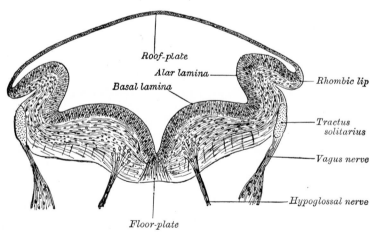

Roof-plate

Alar lamina

Basal lamina

Rhombic lip

Tractus solitarius

Vagus nerve

Hypoglossal nerve

Floor-plate

FIG. 641.—Transverse section of medulla oblongata of human embryo. (After His.)

nerve as an aggregate of cells which advance primarily from the petrosal ganglion. The otic ganglion also receives cells of trigeminal origin *via* the mandibular nerve and its branches. The submaxillary and sublingual ganglia arise on the lingual nerve primarily from cells of trigeminal origin. They probably receive some cells of facial origin *via* the chorda tympani. The smaller parasympathetic ganglia associated with the rami of the glossopharyngeal nerve in the posterior portion of the tongue arise from cells which migrate into the tongue along the glossopharyngeal fibers. The cells which give rise to autonomic neurones are derived both from the cerebrospinal ganglia and the neural tube. Not all of these cells actually migrate as such from the cerebrospinal nervous system. Many of them arise by mitotic division of migrant cells along the paths and in the primordia of the autonomic nervous system.

HISTOLOGY OF THE NERVOUS SYSTEM.

The nervous tissues are composed of **nerve cells** and their various processes, together with a supporting tissue called **neuroglia**, which, however, is found only in the brain and medulla spinalis.

To the naked eye a difference is obvious between certain portions of the brain and medulla spinalis, viz., the **gray substance** and the **white substance**. The **white substance** of nervous tissue is due to the presence of large numbers of myelinated nerve fibers, the myelin sheaths giving the waxy, white color. In the **gray substance** there are few or no myelinated fibers. It consists for the most part of groups of nerve cells with their dendrites as well as large numbers of non-myelinated fibers and the terminations of afferent tracts. Since synaptic relations between one neurone and another occur only on the cell bodies and dendrites, the gray substance may be regarded as the anatomical site of the integrative action of the nervous system. The white substance is the conducting mechanism from one center to another.

Neuroglia.—Neuroglia, the peculiar supporting tissue in which are imbedded the true nervous constituents of the brain and medulla spinalis, consists of two types of cells of ectodermal origin. (1) **Astrocytes**, or macroglia. These are moderately large cells with numerous processes which radiate out from the cell body. In most instances one or more of the processes are attached either to bloodvessels, by expansions known as sucker feet, or to the pia. The marginal astrocytes together with the pia form the **pia-glial membrane**, which invests the brain and spinal cord and accompanies penetrating bloodvessels as a cuff to considerable depths. There are two types of astrocytes, fibrous (Fig. 642, *B*) and protoplasmic (Fig. 642, *A*). The former are found chiefly in the white matter and, with appropriate fixation and staining, appear to contain fibers which run through the protoplasm of the cell body and processes. The protoplasmic astrocytes occur chiefly in the gray matter and their processes branch profusely. The nuclei of the astrocytes are moderately large, oval in shape, and contain scattered chromatin granules, but no nucleolus. (2) **Oligodendrocytes**, or oligodendroglia. These are somewhat smaller than the astrocytes and have fewer processes (Fig. 642, *D*). They are found in close association with smaller bloodvessels, as satellite cells closely applied to large nerve cells, and in rows between bundles of fibers in the white matter. In the latter situation, their processes clasp the nerve fibers. It is thought that the oligodendroglia play a metabolic rôle in the formation and preservation of the myelin sheaths of the nerve fibers in the central nervous system. The nuclei of these cells are round to oval, usually smaller in size but richer in chromatin than the nuclei of the astrocytes. They have no nucleoli.

A third type of cell, the **microgliocyte**, or microglia, is of mesodermal origin and appears to be a modified macrophage (Fig. 642, *C*). It is found diffusely through both the gray and white matter. Normally it is a small cell, with two or more finely branching, feathery processes. The nucleus is small and varies in shape from round to oblong or angular. It stains deeply but contains no nucleolus. The microglia are the scavengers of the nervous system and become actively ameboid and phagocytic in case of injury and death of the other elements. The astrocytes are the repair mechanism and replace lost tissue by forming glial scars.

Neurons or Nerve-cells.—The typical neuron is multipolar and consists of a **cell-body** (perikaryon), with a single **axon** or **axis-cylinder** and several branched processes, the **dendrons** or **dendrites**. Unipolar cells with one axon and no dendrons occur in the cerebrospinal ganglia. Bipolar cells with two axons and no dendrons occur only in the spiral and vestibular ganglia. The nerve cells vary in shape, size and structure. The histological character of a nerve cell is to a certain extent an indication of its function (Figs. 643 and 644). The three types of muscle for example are innervated by three distinct types of nerve cells.

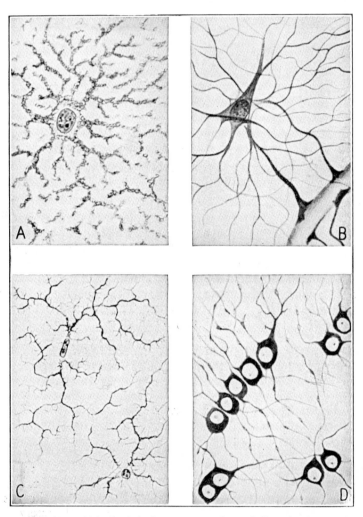

Fig. 642.—Four types of interstitial cells of the human nervous tissue: *A*, Protoplasmic neuroglia cell from the gray substance of the cerebrum. *B*, Neuroglia cell of the fibrous type with pedicles attached to a small vessel, from the white substance. *C*, Microglia cells. *D*, Oligodendroglia cells of the white matter of the brain. (After del Rio-Hortega, from Maximow. Bloom's Textbook of Histology; courtesy of **W. B.** Saunders Company.)

The body of the nerve cells consists of a protoplasmic material, of a reddish or yellowish-brown color, which occasionally presents patches of a deeper tint, caused by the aggregation of pigment granules at one side of the nucleus, as in the substantia nigra and locus cæruleus of the brain. The fixed protoplasm contains peculiar angular granules, which stain deeply with basic dyes, such as methylene blue; these are known as **Nissl granules**. They extend into the dendritic processes but not into the axis-cylinder; the small clear area at the point of exit of the axon in some cell types is termed the **cone of origin**. Elaborate systems of very fine neurofibrils are present in the cell body and its processes in properly fixed and stained preparations. These exist as definite structures in living nerves in certain fish and amphibians, but have not been demonstrated in living mammalian nerves. They probably represent an organization of the molecules constituting the protoplasm of the cell. The neurons are abundantly supplied with mitochondria. The nucleus is, as a rule, a large, well-defined, spherical body, often presenting an intranuclear network, and containing a well-marked nucleolus.

Dendrons or Dendrites.—Neurons usually have several dendrons but some neurons such as those in the cerebrospinal ganglia are without them since the long fiber which conducts impulses toward the cell-body is usually regarded as an axon. Dendrons divide and subdivide into smaller and smaller branches which end nearby. Many short processes or **gemmules** project from them and produce a ragged appearance. They are naked, without myelin or sheath.

Axons or Axis-cylinders.—All nerve-cells possess an axon which is an uninterrupted prolongation of its cytoplasm from cell-body to peripheral termination. They vary greatly in length. Some axons, especially those in the central nervous system, give off collateral branches and all end in terminal arborizations on their end organs or on the dendrons or cell-bodies of one or more neurons. As already noted axons are without Nissl bodies. They are supplied with mitochondria and when properly fixed and stained show fine longitudinal neurofibrils continuous with those in their cell-body. When axons first grow out from the cell-body they are naked; later many develop a sheath except for a short distance at their origin and termination.

Harrison was the first one to demonstrate conclusively that axons grow out from the cell-body and are from their first appearance a part of the neuron. The living mammalian axons do not show neurofibrils.

Nerve-fibers.—All nerve-fibers consist of a single axon, some with and some without sheaths. They may be divided into four classes. (1) **Naked axons** without a sheath of any sort occur in the gray substance of the central nervous system. (2) **Non-medullated** or **gray fibers** with a delicate nucleated neurolemma sheath surrounding the axon, occur in the autonomic system and in the fine afferent fibers of the cerebrospinal nerves. (3) **Myelinated, medullated, or white fibers** without a neurolemma sheath but with an unsegmented myelin sheath make up the white substance of the brain and spinal cord. (4) **Myelinated, medullated or white fibers** with a neurolemma sheath surrounding the myelin sheath make up the bulk of the cerebrospinal nerves. The **myelin** or **medullary sheath**, white substance of Schwann, consists of myelin, a highly refractive, fatty substance which gives the fibers a whitish appearance and stains black with osmic acid. When fixed and stained by particular methods artefacts are produced which give the appearance of a reticular structure or of cones, scales, rings, etc. In the living state no structure can be seen microscopically in the myelin except certain clefts extending diagonally through the wall, known as the incisures of Schmidt-Lantermann. By x-ray analysis, however, it has been demonstrated that the myelin sheath is composed of alternating layers of lipoids and proteins and that the lipoid molecules are radially oriented in the living nerve. The myelin sheath is interrupted at regular intervals by constrictions (nodes of Ranvier) which separates it into internodal segments. In the peripheral nerves the nodes are one to two millimeters apart. In the central nervous system nodes occur rarely and when seen are at a point of bifurcation of a fiber. The myelin sheaths of different sorts of nerve fibers vary greatly in thickness. The non-medullated fibers are only about one-half the diameter of the medullated ones.

The **neurolemma, primitive sheath,** or sheath of Schwann exists only in peripheral nerves. In the central nervous system its function with regard to myelination is thought by some authors to be performed by the oligodendroglia. In living nerves it presents the appearance of a delicate, structureless membrane, but after fixation

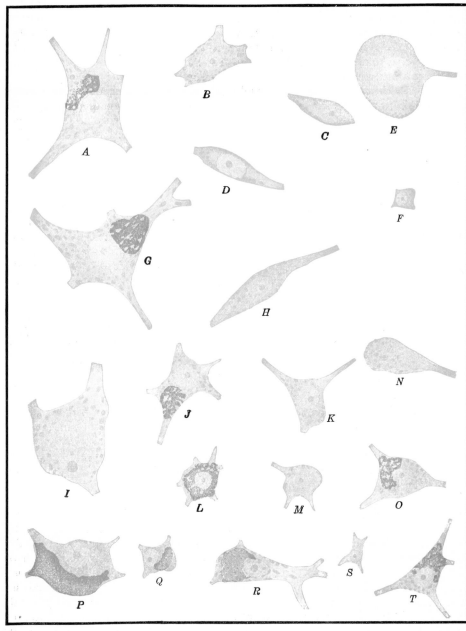

Fig. 643.—Nerve cells from Nissl preparations of the adult human brain and spinal cord that reveal in form and structure their general functional significance. × 500 (Malone). (a to d). Peripheral efferent neurons, (a) cell of medium size with large Nissl granules from hypoglossal nucleus for supply of striated muscle, (b) large cell from the dorsal vagus nucleus, a preganglionic visceral cell probably for the supply of cardiac muscle, (c) small cell from the dorsal vagus nucleus, a preganglionic visceral cell for the supply of smooth muscle, (d) cell from Edinger-Westphal nucleus of the oculomotor nerve, a preganglionic visceral cell for smooth muscle. (e) Peripheral afferent neurons from mesencephalic nucleus of the trigeminal nerve, the cell body, although it has remained within the central nervous system, is a part of the peripheral afferent neurone for muscle sense, this unipolar cell is similar to the large proprioceptive cells of the peripheral afferent ganglia. (f) Exteroceptive reception cell from the peripheral sensory nucleus of the trigeminal nerve. (g and h) Efferent correlation cells, (g) from the reticular formation of the pons, compare with (a), and (h) from the superior olive, an efferent correlation cell for cochlear reactions. (i to o) Proprioceptive correlation cells; the proprioceptive system is functionally and anatomically closely related to the efferent system and this relationship is indicated in the efferent characteristics of the cells of this group; (i) from column of Clarke of spinal cord, (j) from lateral vestibular nucleus, a proprioceptive reception center which is efferent instead of afferent, (k) from lateral reticular nucleus of medulla, (l) from inferior olive, (m) from nuclei pontis, (n) Purkinje cell from cerebellar cortex, (o) from dentate nucleus of cerebellum, (p) from ventral nucleus of the thalamus, (q) from the dorsal portion of lateral nucleus of thalamus, (r) efferent cell from reticular formation of hypothalamus, (s) from caudate nucleus, (t) from the globus pallidus of the lenticular nucleus, the efferent portion of the corpus striatum.

it may appear as a reticulum. It consists of a series of very thin nucleated cells one for each internodal segment. The nuclei are oval and somewhat flattened and situated in depressions in the myelin sheath, surrounded by a small amount of protoplasm. At the nodes of Ranvier the neurolemma dips down and comes in contact with the axon. At these points there is a thickening of the fine connective tissue mesh, sometimes known as the sheath of Henle, which binds the fibers

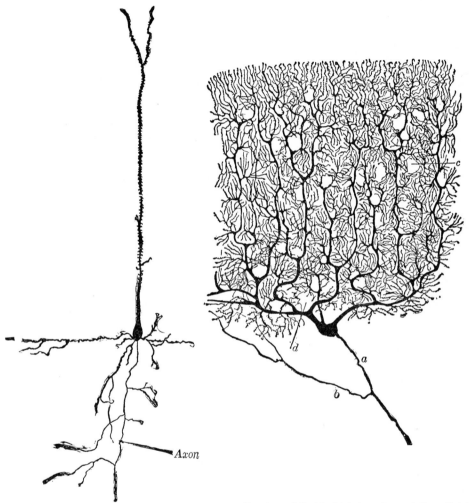

Axon

FIG. 644.—Pyramidal cell from the cerebral cortex of a mouse. (After Ramón y Cajal.)

FIG. 645.—Cell of Purkinje from the cerebellum. Golgi method. (Cajal.) *a*. Axon. *b*. Collateral. *c* and *d* Dendrons.

together into funiculi in the nerve trunk. In myelinated fibers the neurolemma takes part in the formation of myelin. In non-myelinated fibers its function is not known.

Myelination.—Flechsig has shown that the white fibers of the cerebral hemisphere do not all acquire their myelin sheaths at the same period. The process commences in the eighth month of intra-uterine life and involves first the afferent fibers passing to the somesthetic area in the post-central gyrus and the afferent fibers to the hippocampal formation. While the nerve fibers in these areas are receiving their medullary sheaths, the process commences in the afferent fibers leading to the visuosensory and the auditosensory cortical areas. The great, efferent corticospinal pathway does not become myelinated until the second month after birth. Subsequently the fibers of the psychic portions of the motor and somesthetic areas and of the visuo- and auditopsychic areas acquire their sheaths. Last of all, the fibers of the three large association areas (frontal, parietal and temporal) become myelinated and in these areas the process may not be finally completed until the eighteenth year or even later. It would appear that there is considerable individual variation in the age period at which the myelination of the fibers of the association areas is completed.

Structure of the Cerebrospinal Nerves.—The cerebrospinal nerves consist of many nerve fibers bound together into bundles or funiculi of various sizes. Each nerve trunk is surrounded by a connective-tissue sheath, the **epineurium.** Each bundle is covered by an additional individual sheath of connective tissue, the **perineurium** and separated into smaller bundles of various sizes by connective-tissue septa from the perineurium. The nerve fibers are held together and supported by a delicate connective-tissue network (sheath of Henle) continuous with the septa

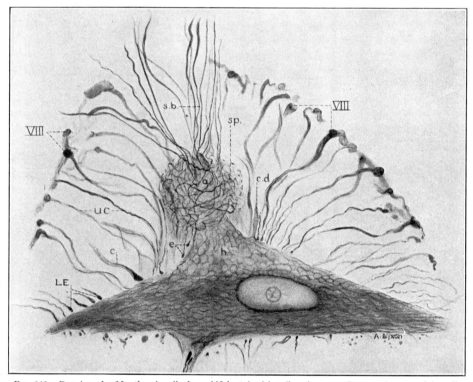

Fig. 646.—Drawing of a Mauthner's cell of a goldfish stained by silver impregnation. *a.* Axon; *c.* club ending; *h.* axon hillock; *e.* small end feet of fine fibers s. b. and s. p. which form a spiral round the axon. *L. E.* Large endings; *u. c.* unmyelinated collaterals from fibers of eighth nerve, VIII. (Bodian, courtesy of Jour. Comp. Neuro.)

and perineurium. Bloodvessels pierce the perineurium and open into elongated capillary plexuses. The epineurium is supplied by myelinated nerve fibers, **nervi nervorum,** which end there in small spheroidal tactile corpuscles, end-bulbs of Krause. They are supposed to be sensory and may be concerned in certain neuralgic pains. The nerve fibers run a spiral course inside the bundles, which results in considerable flexibility. When the nerve trunk is stretched the tension is first taken up by the epineurium.

Groups of nerve fibers frequently pass from one bundle to another within a nerve. Nerves split into branches which frequently join branches of neighboring nerves to form **nerve plexuses.** The individual nerve fibers however do not branch but pass uninterruptedly in nerves and their branches and through the plexuses from center to periphery, until within 1 to 3 centimeters of their end-organs. They then branch a varying number of times, depending on the type of fiber. For instance, a single fiber from an anterior horn cell may divide to supply one hundred and fifty muscle fibers in one muscle, whereas in another muscle the ratio may be one to over four hundred. Plexuses vary in complexity. In the large primary plexuses, cervical, brachial, lumbar and sacral, there is an intricate interlacement so that each nerve leaving the plexus contains fibers from several of the nerves which entered into its formation. Thus the nerve to a muscle may contain fibers from several segments of the spinal cord.

The **autonomic nerves** are constructed in the same manner as the cerebrospinal nerves, but consist mainly of non-medullated fibers, collected in funiculi and enclosed in sheaths of connective tissue. There is, however, in these nerves a certain admixture of medullated fibers. The number of the latter varies in different nerves, and may be estimated by the color of the nerve. Those branches of the autonomic, which present a well-marked gray color, are composed chiefly of non-medullated nerve fibers, intermixed with a few medullated

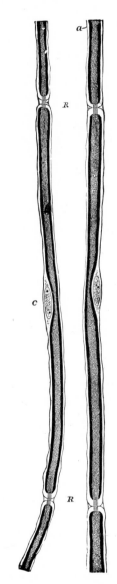

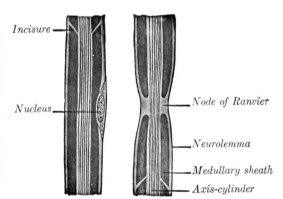

Fig. 647.—Diagram of longitudinal sections of medullated nerve fibers. Osmic acid.

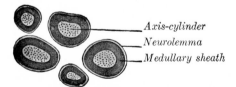

Fig. 648.—Transverse sections of medullated nerve fibers. Osmic acid.

Fig. 649.—Diagram of medullated nerve fibers stained with osmic acid. × 425. (Schäfer.) *R.* Nodes of Ranvier. *a.* Neurolemma. *c.* Nucleus.

fibers; while those of a white color contain many of the latter fibers, and few of the former.

The cerebrospinal and autonomic nerve fibers transmit impulses at rates which vary in different fibers. In general the rates of propagation of the impulses and the electrical potentials which accompany the impulses are roughly proportional to the relative sizes of the fibers. The function of the nerve fibers in the organism taken as a whole depends on where the impulses arise and to what structure they are transmitted, and not on any difference in quality of the impulses. The direction of conduction may be in either direction in a nerve fiber except at its terminations, where conduction is in one direction only, namely from the axon through the synapse to the next nerve cell or through the neuro-muscular ending to the muscle. Thus, in the body the direction of conduction in a nerve depends on its connections. The **sensory**, called also **centripetal**, or **afferent** nerves conduct from peripheral sensory endings to the central nervous system. The **centrifugal** or **efferent** nerves conduct from the central nervous system to striated muscles, smooth muscles, glands, bloodvessels and the heart.

Origins of Nerves.—The origin in some cases is single—that is to say, the whole nerve emerges from the nervous center by a single root; in other instances the nerve arises by two or more roots which come off from different parts of the nerve center, sometimes widely apart from each other, and it often happens, when a nerve arises in this way by two roots, that the functions of these two roots are different; as, for example, in the spinal nerves, each of which arises by two roots, the anterior of which is motor, and the posterior sensory. The point where the nerve root or roots emerge from the surface of the nervous center is named the **superficial or apparent origin,** but the fibers of the nerve can be traced for a certain distance into the substance of the nervous center to some portion of the gray matter, which constitutes the **deep or real origin** of the nerve. The centrifugal or efferent nerve fibers originate in the nerve cells of the gray substance, the axis-cylinder processes of these cells being prolonged to form the fibers. In the case of the centripetal or afferent nerves the fibers grow inward either from nerve cells in the organs of special sense, *e. g.*, the retina, or from nerve cells in the ganglia. Having entered the nerve center they branch and send their ultimate twigs among the cells, without, however, uniting with them.

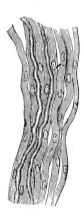

Peripheral Terminations of Nerves. — Nerve fibers terminate peripherally in various ways, and these may be conveniently studied in the sensory and motor nerves respectively. The terminations of the sensory nerves are dealt with in the section on Sense Organs.

Motor nerves can be traced into either unstriped or striped muscular fibers. In the *unstriped* or *involuntary muscles* the nerves are derived from the autonomic and are composed mainly of non-medullated fibers. Near their terminations they divide into numerous branches, which communicate and form intimate plexuses. There are however no fusions of axons or their branches. There is considerable variation in the relationship of these peripheral plexuses to the muscles and glands which the fibers innervate and also in the number and distribution of the ganglion cells which may be associated with them. From these plexuses minute branches are given off which divide and break up into the ultimate fibrillæ of which the nerves are composed. These fibrillæ course between the involuntary muscle cells, and, according to Elischer, terminate on the surfaces of the cells, opposite the nuclei, in minute swellings.

Fig. 650.—A small nervous branch from the sympathetic of a mammal.

In the *striped* or *voluntary muscle* the nerves supplying the muscular fibers are derived from the cerebrospinal nerves, and are composed mainly of medullated fibers. The nerve, after entering the sheath of the muscle, breaks up into fibers or bundles of fibers, which form plexuses, and gradually divide until, as a rule, a single nerve fiber enters a single muscular fiber. Sometimes, however, if the muscular fiber be long, more than one nerve fiber enters it. Within the muscular fiber the nerve terminates in a special expansion, called by Kühne, who first accurately described it, a **motor end-plate** (Fig. 651). The nerve fiber, on approaching the muscular fiber, suddenly loses its medullary sheath, the neurolemma becomes continuous with the sarcolemma of the muscle, and only the axis-cylinder enters the muscular fiber. There it at once spreads out, ramifying like the roots of a tree, immediately beneath the sarcolemma, and becomes imbedded in a layer of granular matter, containing a number of clear, oblong nuclei, the whole constituting an end-plate from which the contractile wave of the muscular fiber is said to start.

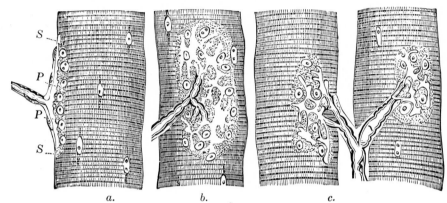

a.   *b.*   *c.*

FIG. 651.—Muscular fibers of *Lacerta viridis* with the terminations of nerves. *a.* Seen in profile. *P, P.* The nerve end-plates. *S, S.* The base of the plate, consisting of a granular mass with nuclei. *b.* The same as seen in looking at a perfectly fresh fiber, the nervous ends being probably still excitable. (The forms of the variously divided plate can hardly be represented in a woodcut by sufficiently delicate and pale contours to reproduce correctly what is seen in nature.) *c.* The same as seen two hours after death from poisoning by curare.

Central Termination of Nerves.—In the central nervous system and in the autonomic-ganglia nerve fibers terminate in endings which are applied to the dendrons or cell bodies, but never to the axons, of other cells. Such a junction may be in the form of one or a group of terminal buttons, or terminal knobs; or it may be a

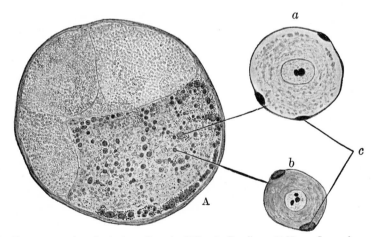

FIG. 652.—Transverse section of spinal ganglion of rabbit. *A.* Ganglion. × 30. *a.* Large clear nerve cell. *b.* Small deeply staining nerve cell. *c.* Nuclei of capsule. × 250. The lines in the center point to the corresponding cells in the ganglion.

thickening of an axon where it comes in contact with a dendron or cell body. Either type of junction is known as a **synapse**. Synapses vary greatly in different parts of the nervous system, sometimes being massive and enveloping as much as two-thirds of the surface of the cell body (as in the acoustic system) more commonly being fine and discrete. There may be as many as a thousand terminal buttons on the cell body and dendrites of an anterior horn cell. There is apparently a single membrane separating the cytoplasm of the axon from that of the cell to which it is attached at the synaptic junction. Although there is still some discussion of the problem, the best recent studies indicate that there is no continuity of the cytoplasm nor of the neurofibrillæ across this membrane. Mitochondria are numerous in both the axon and cell body near the synapse.

Sensory ganglia are found on the posterior roots of the spinal nerves and on the sensory roots of the trigeminal, facial, glossopharyngeal and vagus nerves and on the acoustic and vestibular nerves. They are small aggregations of nerve cells and are traversed by numerous nerve fibers. Each ganglion is invested by a smooth, firm, closely adhering, membranous envelope of dense areolar tissue continuous with the perineurium of the nerves. Numerous septa penetrate the ganglia and carry bloodvessels to supply it. Each nerve cell has a nucleated sheath which is continuous with the neurolemma of its axon. The nerve cells in the ganglia of the spinal nerves are pyriform in shape, and have a single process, the axon, which divides a short distance from the cell, while still in the ganglion, in a T-shaped manner. One branch runs in the posterior root and enters the spinal cord: the larger peripheral branch joins the spinal nerve and runs uninterruptedly to its end organ in the skin or muscle. The larger unipolar neurons have coiled or split axons near the cell-body, but the axon straightens into a single myelinated fiber before it divides. The smaller and more numerous unipolar cells, may or may not have the proximal part of the axon coiled. They have unmyelinated fibers which divide in a T-like manner into a fine central and coarse peripheral branch. The central branches go to the spinal cord and the peripheral ones to the skin, a few to muscle.

Autonomic ganglia consist of multipolar cell-bodies of postganglionic neurons with one axon and several dendrons and of medullated (preganglionic) and non-medullated (postganglionic) fibers which end or traverse or arise in the ganglion. Sheath cells form capsules round the bodies of the ganglion cells, similar to those in the sensory ganglia. In addition, they extend along the dendrons forming what are known as protoplasmic bands or cords, in which little structure is visible. Inside these protoplasmic cords, the preganglionic fibers, having lost their myelin sheaths, end in an extraordinarily dense synaptic relationship with the dendrons of the postganglionic neurons (Fig. 653).

Neuron Theory.—The nerve cell and its processes collectively constitute what is termed a **neuron**, and Waldeyer formulated the theory that the nervous system is built up of numerous neurons, "anatomically and genetically independent of one another." According to this theory (*neuron theory*) the processes of one neuron only come into contact, and are never in direct continuity, with those of other neurons; while impulses are transmitted from one nerve cell to another through these points of contact, the synapses, and thus functional chains or pathways are established. Dendrons never form synapses with the dendrons or cell-bodies of another neuron. Each neuron with its axon and dendrons is a separate cytological and trophic unit. The neurons are the functional units of the nervous system. The **synapse** or **synaptic membrane** seems to allow nervous impulses to pass in one direction only, namely, from the terminals of the axis-cylinder to the dendrons. This theory is based on the following facts, viz.: (1) embryonic nerve cells or neuroblasts are entirely distinct from one another; each neuron is derived from a single embryonic cell, the neuroblast. Harrison observed in tissue cultures the direct outgrowth of the axon from the living cell; (2) when nervous tissues are stained by the Golgi method no continuity is seen even between neighboring neurons; and (3) when degenerative changes occur in nervous tissue, either as the result of disease or experiment, except in particular instances, such as the optic nerve—lateral geniculate body relationship, they never spread from one neuron to another, but are limited to the individual neurons, or groups of neurons, primarily affected. It must, however, be added that within the past few years the validity of the neuron theory has been called in question by certain histologists, who maintain that by the employment of more delicate histological methods, minute fibrils can be followed from one nerve cell into another. Their existence, however, in the living is open to question. Mott and Marinesco made careful examinations of living cells, using even the ultramicroscope and agree that neither Nissl bodies nor neurofibrils are present in the living state. There is also well-established functional evidence for the neuron theory. As more data are accumulated in the future, certain modifications may be necessary, but this theory accounts for the known form and functions of the nervous system better than any other.

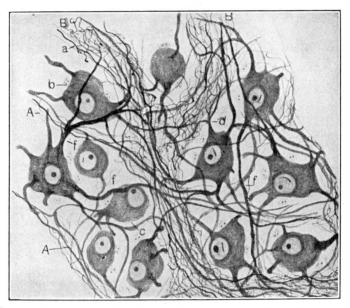

Fig. 653.—A portion of the stellate ganglion of a one and one-half-year-old child. *B*, Stout protoplasmic tract of articulation; *f*, very long primordial dendrite; *d*, very short dendrite; *c*, monopolar sympathetic cell; *a*, preganglionic fibers; *A*, tracts passing through the ganglion. Several of the neurons show intranuclear rods. (deCastro in Penfield's Cytology and Cellular Pathology of the Nervous System, courtesy of Paul B. Hoeber, Inc.)

Degenerative Changes.—Various types of degenerative change occur in neurons due to disease, trauma, senility, etc. Shrinkage and dissolution of cell bodies with consequent degeneration of the axons is a normal phenomenon which starts about the twentieth year and becomes increasingly pronounced with age. Symptoms resulting from such loss of neurons are rarely apparent until after the fifth decade.

Three types of degeneration of neurons have been of value for study of the anatomy of the nervous system. (1) If the cell body is destroyed the axon degenerates, or if an axon is cut that part severed from the cell body degenerates. This is known as **Wallerian degeneration.** Changes occur first at the cut end and progress peripherally. In fishes and amphibians this distal progression is slow and may take days to weeks, but in mammals it is rapid and requires only hours to days, so that at times it appears as though all parts of the severed axon were degenerating simultaneously. There is at first swelling with loss of internal structure. The axon becomes tortuous, then fragmented and soon disappears. The myelin breaks down into globules of fatty material which can be stained by the Marchi method.

This change is at its maximum between two and three weeks. The degenerating myelin is gradually removed by the phagocytic cells. Fat globules, free and intra-cellular, can be found, for as long as three months, in the neighborhood of the degenerated fibers. In the central nervous system, no true regeneration occurs and the lost fibers are replaced by glia, chiefly astrocytes. The scar so formed does not stain by the Weigert method of staining normal myelin sheaths, and when the degenerated fibers form a compact bundle, such as the crossed corticospinal tract, their course can be followed by this method. Since these methods depend on changes in the myelin they have to be supplemented by silver stains on normal material in order to determine the exact termination of the axons.

Attempts to follow degenerating axons by silver and other stains, as well as attempts to identify degenerating synapses after lesions of the axons, have not proved satisfactory.

In peripheral nerves degeneration of the axon and myelin proceeds as described above. The sensory end organs, motor end plates, and striped muscles degenerate more slowly. Smooth muscles and glands undergo certain functional changes. The sheath of Schwann cells at first multiply markedly, and later become indis-tinguishable from connective tissue cells except by their arrangement in rows. Regeneration normally occurs in a manner closely resembling the original develop-ment of the peripheral nerves, though there are liable to be abnormalities in motor and in discriminatory distribution, which persist.

The second type of degeneration important in anatomical investigations is known as **retrograde degeneration.** This term is applied to the changes which occur in the cell body and in the proximal portion of an axon which has been transected. There are wide variations in the extent to which the degeneration may proceed. Many cells show no demonstrable change. In others a condition known as **chro-matolysis** occurs, which consists in fragmentation and loss of the Nissl bodies and in nuclear changes. The nucleus becomes shrunken, irregular, and eccentrically placed, surrounded by a clear zone and the remaining Nissl substance appears in a finely divided, powdery form round the periphery of the cell. Chromatolysis is usually well developed in six to ten days after the lesion, although early changes may be noted in twenty-four hours. In certain cells the condition may remain unchanged for years; other cells rapidly recover; a few types of cells, usually belong-ing to highly specialized systems, proceed to complete degeneration and disappear. In the latter cases the proximal portions of the axons also degenerate. In peripheral nerves retrograde degeneration of the axons usually extends only one or two seg-ments proximal to the injury.

The third type of degeneration is known as **transynaptic.** It occurs only in the cells of certain systems and is probably best illustrated in the case of the visual system. When the optic tract is cut the next neurons in the pathway to the cortex, namely the cells of the lateral geniculate body, undergo chromatolysis which proceeds to disintegration and disappearance.

Retrograde and transynaptic degeneration have been widely used for determining the origins of fibers, both of peripheral nerves and of tracts in the central nervous system, and for studies on the interrelations of various parts of the fore-brain. The methods obviously have their limitations, but with due care give reliable results where they are applicable.

Fasciculi, tracts or **fiber systems** are groups of axons having homologous origin and homologous distribution (as regards their collaterals, subdivisions and ter-minals) and are often named in accordance with their origin and termination, the name of the nucleus or the location of the cell body from which the axon or fiber arises preceding that of the nucleus or location of its termination. A given topo-graphical area seldom represents a pure tract, as in most cases fibers of different systems are mixed.

THE MEDULLA SPINALIS OR SPINAL CORD.

The **medulla spinalis** or **spinal cord** forms the elongated, nearly cylindrical, part of the central nervous system which occupies the upper two-thirds of the vertebral canal. Its average length in the male is about 45 cm., in the female from 42 to 43 cm., while its weight amounts to about 30 gms. It extends from the level of the upper border of the atlas to that of the lower border of the first, or upper border of the second, lumbar vertebra. Above, it is continuous with the brain; below, it ends in a conical extremity, the **conus medullaris**, from the apex of which a delicate filament, the **filum terminale**, descends to the first segment of the coccyx (Fig. 654).

The position of the medulla spinalis varies with the movements of the vertebral column, its lower extremity being drawn slightly upward when the column is flexed. It also varies at different periods of life; up to the third month of fetal life the medulla spinalis is as long as the vertebral canal, but from this stage onward the vertebral column elongates more rapidly than the medulla spinalis, so that by the end of the fifth month the medulla spinalis terminates at the base of the sacrum, and at birth about the third lumbar vertebra.

The medulla spinalis does not fill the part of the vertebral canal in which it lies; it is ensheathed by three protective membranes, separated from each other by two concentric spaces. The three membranes are named from without inward, the **dura mater**, the **arachnoid**, and the **pia mater**. The **dura mater** is a strong, fibrous membrane which forms a wide, tubular sheath; this sheath extends below the termination of the medulla spinalis and ends in a pointed cul-de-sac at the level of the lower border of the second sacral vertebra. The dura mater is separated from the wall of the vertebral canal by the **epidural cavity**, which contains a quantity of loose areolar tissue and a plexus of veins; between the dura mater and the subjacent arachnoid is a capillary interval, the **subdural cavity**, which contains a small quantity of fluid, probably of the nature of lymph. The **arachnoid** is a thin, transparent sheath, separated from the pia mater by a comparatively wide interval, the **subarach-**

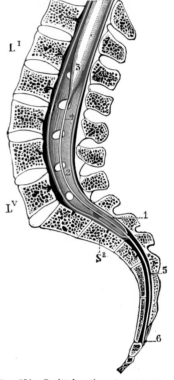

FIG. 654.—Sagittal section of vertebral canal to show the lower end of the medulla spinalis and the filum terminale. *Li, Lv.* First and fifth lumbar vertebræ. *Sii.* Second sacral vertebra. 1. Dura mater. 2. Lower part of tube of dura mater. 3. Lower extremity of medulla spinalis. 4. Intradural, and 5, Extradural portions of filum terminale. 6. Attachment of filum terminale to first segment of coccyx. (Testut.)

noid cavity, which is filled with cerebrospinal fluid. The **pia mater** closely invests the medulla spinalis and sends delicate septa into its substance; a narrow band, the **ligamentum denticulatum**, extends along eack of its lateral surfaces and is attached by a series of pointed processes to the inner surface of the dura mater.

Thirty-one pairs of spinal nerves spring from the medulla spinalis, each nerve having an anterior or ventral, and a posterior or dorsal root, the latter being distinguished by the presence of an oval swelling, the **spinal ganglion**, which contains numerous nerve cells. Each root consists of several bundles of nerve fibers, and at its attachment extends for some distance along the side of the medulla spinalis. The pairs of spinal nerves are grouped as follows: cervical 8, thoracic 12, lumbar

5, sacral 5, coccygeal 1, and, for convenience of description, the medulla spinalis is divided into cervical, thoracic, lumbar and sacral regions, corresponding with the attachments of the different groups of nerves.

Although no trace of transverse segmentation is visible on the surface of the medulla spinalis, it is convenient to regard it as being built up of a series of superimposed **spinal segments** or **neuromeres**, each of which has a length equivalent to the extent of attachment of a pair of spinal nerves. Since the extent of attachment of the successive pairs of nerves varies in different parts, it follows that the spinal segments are of varying lengths; thus,

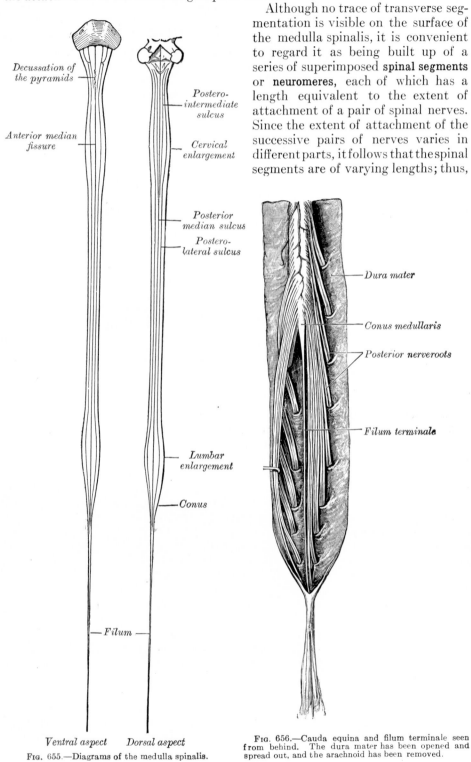

Decussation of the pyramids

Anterior median fissure

Postero-intermediate sulcus

Cervical enlargement

Posterior median sulcus

Postero-lateral sulcus

Lumbar enlargement

Conus

Filum

Ventral aspect   *Dorsal aspect*

Fig. 655.—Diagrams of the medulla spinalis.

Dura mater

Conus medullaris

Posterior nerveroots

Filum terminale

Fig. 656.—Cauda equina and filum terminale seen from behind. The dura mater has been opened and spread out, and the arachnoid has been removed.

in the cervical region they average about 13 mm., in the mid-thoracic region about 26 mm., while in the lumbar and sacral regions they diminish rapidly from about 15 mm. at the level of the first pair of lumbar nerves to about 4 mm. opposite the attachments of the lower sacral nerves.

As a consequence of the relative inequality in the rates of growth of the medulla spinalis and vertebral column, the nerve roots, which in the early embryo passed transversely outward to reach their respective intervertebral foramina, become more and more oblique in direction from above downward, so that the lumbar and sacral nerves descend almost vertically to reach their points of exit. From the appearance these nerves present at their attachment to the medulla spinalis and from their great length they are collectively termed the **cauda equina** (Fig. 656).

The **filum terminale** is about 20 cm. in length, and consists of an upper part, or **filum terminale internum**, 15 cm. in length which is contained within the tubular sheath of dura mater, surrounded by the nerves forming the cauda equina, and a lower part, or **filum terminale externum**, closely invested by, and adherent to, the dura mater; it extends downward from the apex of the tubular sheath and is attached to the back of the first segment of the coccyx. The filum terminale consists mainly of fibrous tissue, continuous above with that of the pia mater. Adhering to its outer surface, however, are a few strands of nerve fibers which probably represent rudimentary second and third coccygeal nerves; further, the central canal of the medulla spinalis extends downward into it for 5 or 6 cm.

Enlargements.—The medulla spinalis is not quite cylindrical, being slightly flattened from before backward; it also presents two swellings or enlargements, an upper or cervical, and a lower or lumbar (Fig. 655).

The **cervical enlargement** is the more pronounced, and corresponds with the attachments of the large nerves which supply the upper limbs. It extends from about the third cervical to the second thoracic vertebra, its maximum circumference (about 38 mm.) being on a level with the attachment of the sixth pair of cervical nerves.

The **lumbar enlargement** gives attachment to the nerves which supply the lower limbs. It commences about the level of the ninth thoracic vertebra, and reaches its maximum circumference, of about 33 mm., opposite the last thoracic vertebra, below which it tapers rapidly into the conus medullaris.

Fissures and Sulci (Fig. 657).—An anterior median fissure and a posterior median sulcus incompletely divide the medulla spinalis into two symmetrical parts, which are joined across the middle line by a commissural band of nervous matter.

The **Anterior Median Fissure** (*fissura mediana anterior*) has an average depth of about 3 mm., but this is increased in the lower part of the medulla spinalis. It contains a double fold of pia mater, and its floor is formed by a transverse band of white substance, the **anterior white commissure**, which is perforated by blood-vessels on their way to or from the central part of the medulla spinalis.

The **Posterior Median Sulcus** (*sulcus medianus posterior*) is very shallow; from it a septum of neuroglia reaches rather more than half-way into the substance of the medulla spinalis; this septum varies in depth from 4 to 6 mm., but diminishes considerably in the lower part of the medulla spinalis.

On either side of the posterior median sulcus, and at a short distance from it, the posterior nerve roots are attached along a vertical furrow named the **postero-lateral sulcus**. The portion of the medulla spinalis which lies between this and the posterior median sulcus is named the **posterior funiculus**. In the cervical and upper thoracic regions this funiculus presents a longitudinal furrow, the **postero-intermediate sulcus**; this marks the position of a septum which extends into the posterior funiculus and subdivides it into two fasciculi—a medial, named the **fasciculus**

49

gracilis (*tract of Goll*); and a lateral, the **fasciculus cuneatus** (*tract of Burdach*) (Fig. 665). The portion of the medulla spinalis which lies in front of the postero-lateral sulcus is termed the **antero-lateral region**. The anterior nerve roots, unlike the posterior, are not attached in linear series, and their position of exit is not marked by a sulcus. They arise by separate bundles which spring from the anterior column of gray substance and, passing forward through the white substance, emerge over an area of some slight width. The most lateral of these bundles is generally taken as a dividing line which separates the antero-lateral region into two parts, viz., an **anterior funiculus**, between the anterior median fissure and the most lateral of the anterior nerve roots; and a **lateral funiculus**, between the exit of these roots and the postero-lateral sulcus. In the upper part of the cervical region a series of nerve roots passes outward through the lateral funiculus of the medulla spinalis; these unite to form the spinal portion of the accessory nerve, which runs upward and enters the cranial cavity through the foramen magnum.

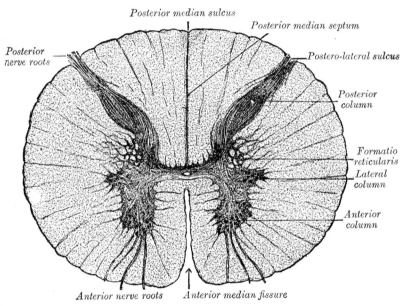

Posterior median sulcus

Posterior median septum

Posterior nerve roots

Postero-lateral sulcus

Posterior column

Formatio reticularis

Lateral column

Anterior column

Anterior nerve roots   *Anterior median fissure*

Fig. 657.—Transverse section of the medulla spinalis in the mid-thoracic region.

The Internal Structure of the Medulla Spinalis.—On examining a transverse section of the medulla spinalis (Fig. 657) it is seen to consist of gray and white nervous substance, the former being enclosed within the latter.

Gray Substance (*substantia grisea centralis*).—The gray substance consists of two symmetrical halves joined across the middle line by a transverse commissure of gray substance, through which runs a minute canal, the **central canal**, just visible to the naked eye. In a transverse section the gray substance presents the appearance of the letter H. An imaginary coronal plane through the central canal serves to divide each crescent into an **anterior** or **ventral**, and a **posterior** or **dorsal column**.

The **Anterior Column** (*columna anterior; anterior cornu*), directed forward, is broad and of a rounded or quadrangular shape. It contains many motor nerve cells. It is separated from the surface of the medulla spinalis by a layer of white substance which is traversed by the bundles of the anterior nerve roots.

In the upper cervical, the thoracic and the **mid-sacral regions**, the gray substance opposite the transverse commissure projects lateralward as a triangular field, which is named the **lateral column** (*columna lateralis; lateral cornu*). It contains many preganglionic cells of the autonomic nervous system.

The **Posterior Column** (*columna posterior; posterior cornu*) is long and slender, and is directed backward and lateralward; it reaches nearly to the postero-lateral sulcus, from which it is separated by a thin layer of white substance, the **tract of Lissauer**. The posterior column cells are concerned with the reception and conduction of sensory impulses entering through the dorsal roots. The posterior apex is capped by a V-shaped or crescentic mass of translucent, gelatinous tissue, termed the **substantia gelatinosa of Rolando**, which contains many small nerve cells. Between the anterior and posterior columns the gray substance extends as a series of processes into the lateral funiculus, to form a net-work called the **formatio reticularis**.

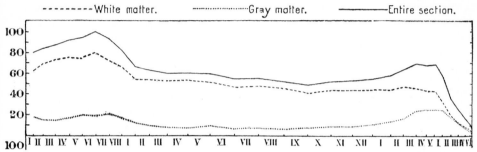

FIG. 658.—Curves showing the sectional area at different levels of the cord. The ordinates show the area in sq. mm (Donaldson and Davis.)

The quantity of gray substance, as well as the form which it presents on transverse section, varies markedly at different levels. In the thoracic region it is small, not only in amount but relatively to the surrounding white substance. In the cervical and lumbar enlargements it is greatly increased: in the latter, and especially in the conus medullaris, its proportion to the white substance is greatest (Fig. 658). In the cervical region its posterior column is comparatively narrow, while its anterior is broad and expanded; in the thoracic region, both columns are attenuated, and the lateral column is evident; in the lumbar enlargement, both are expanded; while in the conus medullaris the gray substance assumes the form of two oval masses, one in each half of the cord, connected together by a broad gray commissure.

The **Central Canal** (*canalis centralis*) runs throughout the entire length of the medulla spinalis. The portion of gray substance in front of the canal is named the **anterior gray commissure**; that behind it, the **posterior gray commissure**. The former is thin, and is in contact anteriorly with the anterior white commissure: it contains a couple of longitudinal veins, one on either side of the middle line. The posterior gray commissure reaches from the central canal to the posterior median septum, and is thinnest in the thoracic region, and thickest in the conus medullaris. The central canal is continued upward through the lower part of the medulla oblongata, and opens into the fourth ventricle of the brain; below, it reaches for a short distance into the filum terminale. In the lower part of the conus medullaris it exhibits a fusiform dilatation, the **terminal ventricle**; this has a vertical measurement of from 8 to 10 mm., is triangular on cross-section with its base directed forward, and tends to undergo obliteration after the age of forty years. It is filled with cerebrospinal fluid, and lined by ciliated, columnar epithelium, outside of which is an encircling band of gelatinous substance, the **substantia gelatinosa centralis**. This gelatinous substance consists mainly of neuroglia, but contains a few nerve cells and fibers; it is traversed by processes from the deep ends of the columnar ciliated cells which line the central canal (Fig. 660).

Structure of the Gray Substance.—The gray substance consists of nerve cells with their dendrites and of an extraordinarily dense interlacement of fine nerve fibers, the whole supported and held together by the neuroglia. The interlacement of nerve fibers is made up of the axons of the cells in the gray matter as they pass out into the white funiculi or into the nerve roots; collaterals from the axons which return into the gray matter; axons of the Golgi type II cells and of the segmental association fibers; terminals and collaterals from fibers in the white substance and posterior roots which turn into the gray substance to end in synaptic relations with the cells. There are relatively few myelinated fibers as the myelin sheaths are lost some distance before the axon terminates. For the most part the neuroglia forms a spongelike mesh of varying density, but over the tips of the posterior horns and round the central canal (Fig. 660) it is more gelatinous in fresh specimens. In general the gray substance may be divided into two major divisions, namely: (1) the motor, consisting of the anterior and lateral horns which develop from the basal laminæ; and (2) the receptor—coördinating, consisting of the posterior horns, which develop from the alar laminæ of the primitive neural tube. Such a separation is useful for a number of purposes, and probably represents the major functional differences, but cannot be regarded as rigorous since there are certain exceptions. There are two characteristic cell types in the ventral or motor division: (1) The **motor** or **anterior horn cells**, which supply the striped musculature; and (2) the **autonomic** or **lateral horn cells**, which give rise to the preganglionic fibers of the thoracic and lumbo-sacral autonomic systems. The axons of these cells make up the anterior roots. The axons of about one in twenty of the anterior horn cells give off collaterals before entering the anterior roots. The collaterals return to ramify in the gray substance of the anterior horn.

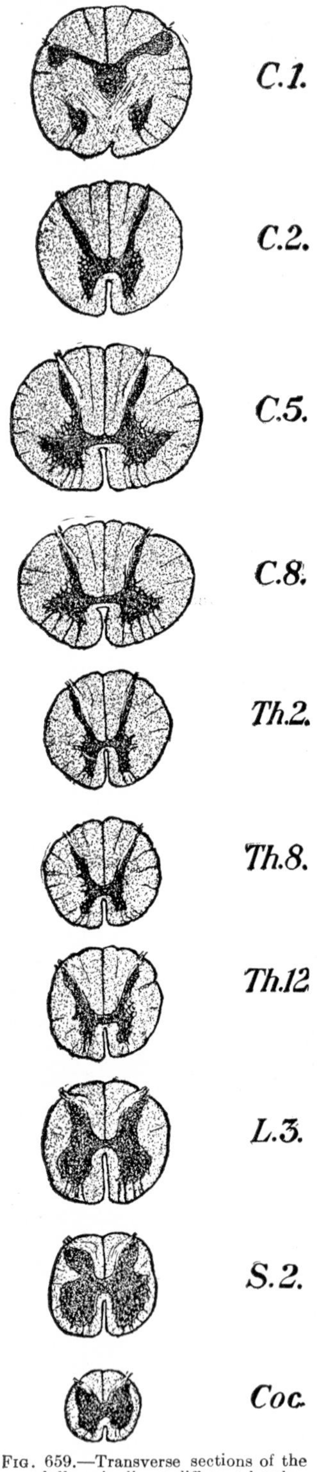

In the posterior horn are a number of different types of cells, many being highly specialized. Some give rise to long fibers which ascend to the thalamus, cerebellum, etc., but the majority give rise to short fibers. Most of the fibers on entering the white matter divide in a T-shaped manner and give ascending and descending branches, and these in turn give off collaterals which reënter and ramify in the gray substance, terminating in synapses on the cell bodies and dendrites of other neurons (Fig. 661). The lengths of the axons vary greatly; some are short and terminate in the same segment in which they arise—**segmental**, others are longer and connect with the adjoining or more distant segments—**intersegmental**. The greater number of these axons terminate on the same side of the spinal cord in

C.1.

C.2.

C.5.

C.8.

Th.2.

Th.8.

Th.12

L.3.

S.2.

Coc.

Fig. 659.—Transverse sections of the medulla spinalis at different levels.

which they arise. Others cross to the opposite side, either through the dorsal and ventral gray commissures or through the anterior white commissure, and are called **crossed, decussating,** or **commissural fibers.** As with the uncrossed fibers, they may make connections in the same, in adjoining, or in more distant segments.

There are in addition throughout the gray substance small nerve cells of the type II of Golgi, *i. e.,* cells whose axons terminate in the same nuclear mass of gray in which the cell body lies.

Taken together with the incoming fibers of the posterior roots, the neurons described above constitute the intrinsic neural mechanisms of the spinal cord. They are responsible for mediating the spinal cord reflexes, both crossed and uncrossed, single and plurisegmental (Fig. 662).

Inasmuch as the motor cells in the spinal cord together with their homologues in the brain stem innervate the effector organs of the body, it is obvious that any activity in any part of the brain must ultimately utilize this motor system in order to gain overt expression. For this reason Sherrington coined the term **the final common path** to indicate the general functional significance of the motor system in its relation to the rest of the brain (Fig. 663).

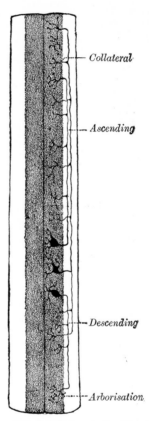

Fig. 661.—Cells of medulla spinalis. Diagram showing in longitudinal section the intersegmental neurons of the medulla spinalis. The gray and white parts correspond respectively to the gray and white substance of the medulla spinalis. (Poirier.)

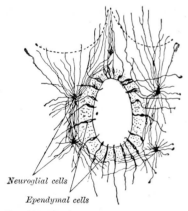

Neuroglial cells

Ependymal cells

Fig. 660.—Section of central canal of medulla spinalis, showing ependymal and neuroglial cells. (v. Lenhossek.)

Nerve Cells in the Anterior Column.—The anterior horn cells are large, polygonal cells with long, branching dendrites, similar in appearance to the cell illustrated in Fig. 643. They are arranged in columnar groups, the muscles which they supply apparently being represented in such groups which extend longitudinally through two to four segments. The exact localization of the cells supplying the individual muscles has not been determined in the human. In general, the trunk musculature is represented medially, the limb musculature laterally, particularly in the cervical and lumbo-sacral enlargements. The columnar groups of cells supplying individual muscles are arranged in larger columns of varying length. A number of studies of the anatomical relationships of these larger columns has been made, that of Bruce,[1] which is summarized below, being one of the more practical

[1] Topographical Atlas of the Spinal Cord, 1901.

for topographical purposes. The **antero-medial column** occupies the medial part of the anterior horn: it is well marked in C4, C5, again from C8 to L4, it diappears in L5 and S1 but is well marked in S2, S3 and S4 (Bruce).[1] Behind it is the **postero-**

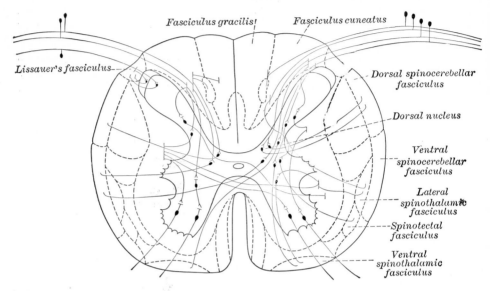

Fasciculus gracilis

Fasciculus cuneatus

Lissauer's fasciculus

Dorsal spinocerebellar fasciculus

Dorsal nucleus

Ventral spinocerebellar fasciculus

Lateral spinothalamic fasciculus

Spinotectal fasciculus

Ventral spinothalamic fasciculus

Fɪɢ. 662.—Diagram showing a few of the connections of afferent (sensory) fibers of the posterior root with the efferent fibers from the ventral column and with the various long ascending fasciculi.

medial column of small cells, which is not represented in L5, S1, S2 nor below S4. Their axons probably supply the muscles of the trunk. In the cervical and lumbar

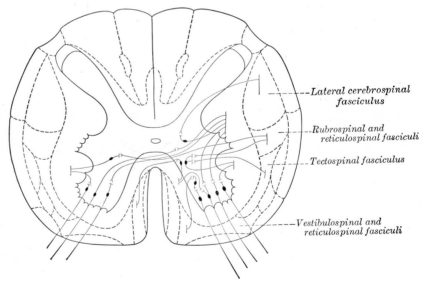

Lateral cerebrospinal fasciculus

Rubrospinal and reticulospinal fasciculi

Tectospinal fasciculus

Vestibulospinal and reticulospinal fasciculi

Fɪɢ. 663.—Diagram showing possible connection of long descending fibers from higher centers with the motor cells of the ventral column through association fibers.

enlargements, where the anterior column is expanded in a lateral direction, the following additional columns are present, viz.: (*a*) **antero-lateral,** which consists

[1] Topographical Atlas of the Spinal Cord, 1901.

of two groups, one in C4, C5, C6 the other in C6, C7, C8 in the cervical enlargement and of a group from L2 to S2 in the lumbo-sacral enlargement; (*b*) **postero-lateral**, in the lower five cervical, lower four lumbar, and upper three sacral segments; (*c*) **post-postero-lateral**, in the last cervical, first thoracic, and upper three sacral segments; and (*d*) a **central**, in the lower four lumbar and upper two sacral segments. These cell groups are evidently related to the nerve roots of the brachial and sacral plexuses and supply fibers to the muscles of the arm and leg.

The peripheral course of the axons extends through the anterior roots and peripheral nerves to the muscles. Each axon divides and subdivides within a few centimeters of its termination, finally ending in motor end plates on a large number of muscle fibers (125 to 400). The contractions of the skeletal muscles are dependent on stimuli from the motor nerve cells of the anterior column which in turn are controlled by impulses coming to them from other parts of the nervous system, either directly through the long tracts or through intercalated neurons of the spinal cord association system. The spinal cord reflexes are mediated through the segmental and intersegmental connections. Volitional control, particularly of fine, precise movements, is lost if the cerebrospinal fasciculus is destroyed. The influences of the cerebellum, of the vestibular mechanism, the reticular substance in the mid- and hind-brain, of the striatum and of other extrapyramidal motor systems of the forebrain are apparently mediated through the rubrospinal and the several vestibulo- and reticulospinal pathways, as well as probably through short neuron chains of the spinal cord association systems. The specific functions of the individual tracts and pathways in the spinal cord have not been definitely determined. The general functions subserved include the following: coördination of move-

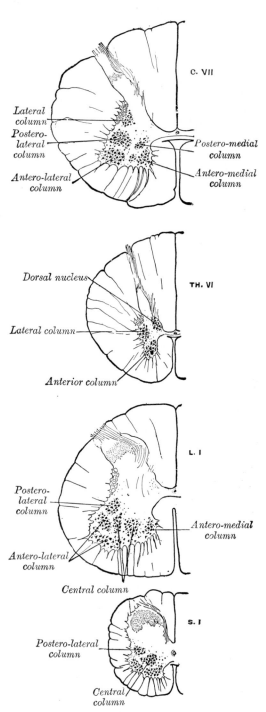

Fig. 664.—Transverse sections of the medulla spinalis at different levels to show the arrangement of the principal cell columns.

ment and posture; equilibratory and antigravity (*i. e.*, standing) reflexes; maintenance of the horizontal position (the "righting reflexes" of Magnus); integration and control of complicated, instinctual behavior patterns. Certain of the connections of these pathways and tracts are illustrated in Figs. 662 and 663.

Nerve Cells in the Lateral Column.—These form a column which is best marked where the lateral gray column is differentiated, viz., in the thoracic region; but it can be traced throughout the entire length of the medulla spinalis in the form of groups of small cells which are situated in the anterior part of the formatio reticularis. In the upper part of the cervical region and lower part of the medulla oblongata as well as in the third and fourth sacral segments this column is again differentiated. In the medulla it is represented by the dorsal nucleus of the vagus and by other groups of autonomic cells extending rostrally parallel with the sulcus limitans. The column terminates with the Edinger-Westphal nucleus in the midbrain. The autonomic motor cells of this column are fusiform or star-shaped and of a medium size, similar to the cells illustrated in Fig. 643, *b, c, d*. The axons pass into the anterior nerve roots and white rami communicantes; they are visceral efferent fibers, **preganglionic fibers of the autonomic system.** The axons of certain other cells of the lateral column pass into the anterior and lateral funiculi, where they become longitudinal.

Nerve Cells in the Posterior Column.—1. The **dorsal nucleus** (*nucleus dorsalis; column of Clarke*) occupies the medial part of the base of the posterior column, and appears on the transverse section as a well-defined oval area. It begins below at the level of the second or third lumbar nerve, and reaches its maximum size opposite the twelfth thoracic nerve. Above the level of the ninth thoracic nerve its size diminishes, and the column ends opposite the last cervical or first thoracic nerve. It is represented, however, in the other regions by scattered cells, which become aggregated to form a **cervical nucleus** opposite the third cervical nerve, and a **sacral nucleus** in the middle and lower part of the sacral region. Its cells are of medium size, and of an oval or pyriform shape (Fig. 639, *i*); their axons pass into the peripheral part of the lateral funiculus of the same side, and there ascend, probably in **dorsal spinocerebellar** (*direct cerebellar*) **fasciculus.** 2. The **nerve cells in the substantia gelatinosa of Rolando** are arranged in three zones: a posterior or marginal, of large angular or fusiform cells; an intermediate, of small fusiform cells; and an anterior, of star-shaped cells. The axons of these cells pass into the lateral and posterior funiculi, and there assume a vertical course. In the anterior zone some Golgi type II cells are found whose short axons ramify in the gray substance. 3. The **substantia reticularis** consists of medium and small cells with strands of non-myelinated fibers extending laterally into the white matter at the base of the posterior horn. It is best developed in the cervical cord and is continuous rostrally with the reticular substance of the medulla. 4. The cells of the body and base of the posterior horn are medium and small sized and in Nissl preparations appear as a group which is known as the **nucleus proprius cornu posterioris,** also called the **posterior basal column.** Scattered through this area and through the reticular substance are occasional cells of somewhat larger size, known as **solitary cells.** The substantia reticularis and nucleus proprius are thought to be the main coördinating centers of the spinal cord. 5. Between the posterior and ventral horns and including the lateral part of the substantia gelatinosa centralis is an area called the **intermediate zone.** It contains scattered fusiform and star-shaped cells. According to some authors, the axons of certain of these leave the cord through the posterior roots, but this observation needs further confirmation. Other authors describe the axons as passing into the lateral columns of the same and opposite sides. The intermediate zone is probably chiefly a coördinating center for autonomic reflexes.

White Substance (*substantia alba*).—The white substance of the medulla spinalis consists of nerve fibers imbedded in a sponge-like net-work of neuroglia, and surrounded by a thin tough layer of neuroglia, the **glial sheath,** which combines with the pia mater to form the **pia-glial membrane.** Both medullated and non-medullated fibers exist in great numbers. The former vary greatly in thickness, the smallest being found in the fasciculus gracilis, the **tract of Lissauer,** and inner part of the lateral funiculus; while the largest are situated in the anterior funiculus, and in the peripheral part of the lateral funiculus. Some of the nerve fibers assume a more or less transverse direction, as for example those which cross from side to side in the anterior white commissure, but the majority pursue a longitudinal course and are divisible into (1) those connecting the medulla spinalis with the brain and conveying impulses to or from the latter, and (2) those which are confined to the medulla spinalis and link together its different segments, *i. e.,* intersegmental or association fibers. The nerve fibers are separated into three topographical funiculi by the posterior and the most lateral of the anterior nerve roots.

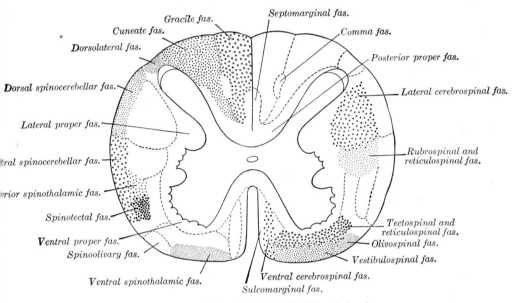

Fig. 665.—Diagram of the principal fasciculi of the spinal cord.

Nerve Fasciculi.—The longitudinal fibers are grouped into bundles or fasciculi, some of which are quite compact and homogeneous, but in most of them, the fibers are considerably scattered and are intermingled with fibers of other origins. Due to this intermingling any diagrammatic representation can at best only indicate the general region in which the tracts run. These are not recognizable from each other in the normal state and their existence has been determined by the following methods: (1) **Wallerian degeneration.** If a bundle of nerve fibers be cut, the portions of the fibers which are separated from their cells rapidly degenerate and become atrophied. Similarly, if a group of nerve cells be destroyed, the fibers arising from them undergo degeneration. Thus if the motor cells of the cerebral cortex be destroyed, or if the fibers arising from these cells be severed, a **descending degeneration** from the seat of injury takes place in the fibers. In the same manner if a spinal ganglion be destroyed, or the fibers which pass from it into the medulla spinalis be cut, an **ascending degeneration** will extend along these fibers. (2) Pathological changes, especially in man, have given important information by causing ascending and descending degenerations. (3) By tracing the development of the nervous system it has been observed that at first the nerve fibers are merely naked axis-cylinders, and that they do not all acquire their medullary sheaths at the same time; hence the fibers can be grouped into different bundles according to the dates at which they receive their medullary sheaths. (4) Various methods of staining nervous tissue are of great value in tracing the course and mode of termination of the axis-cylinder processes.

Anterior Fasciculi.— *Descending Fasciculi.*—The **anterior cerebrospinal** (*fasciculus cerebrospinalis anterior; direct pyramidal tract*) which is usually small, but varies inversely in size with the lateral cerebrospinal fasciculus. It lies close to the anterior median fissure and is present only in the upper part of the medulla spinalis; gradually diminishing in size as it descends, it ends about the middle of the thoracic region. It consists of descending fibers which arise from the large pyramidal cells of the precentral gyrus or motor area of the cerebral hemisphere of the same side which run downward in the medulla spinalis. They are said by some authors to cross in the anterior white commissure at the level in which they terminate and to connect either directly or indirectly (through intermediate neurons in the base of the posterior columns) with the dendrites of the motor cells in the anterior column. They conduct impulses from the precentral gyrus to the motor centers of the cord, and are probably concerned with voluntary movement.

The **direct vestibulospinal fasciculus**, situated chiefly in the marginal part of the funiculus is derived from the cells of Deiters' nucleus, of the same side, *i. e.*, the large celled, lateral vestibular nucleus in the medulla. The fasciculus can be traced to the sacral region. Its terminals and collaterals end either directly or indirectly among the motor cells of the anterior column. This fasciculus is probably concerned with equilibratory and antigravity reflexes.

The **crossed vestibulospinal fasciculus**, from the medial and inferior vestibular nuclei, descends in the sulco-marginal fasciculus.

The **ventral reticulospinal fasciculi, crossed** and **uncrossed** arise from cells in various nuclei of the reticular substance of the medulla and mesencephalon of the opposite and same sides respectively. They have not been adequately studied in the human, but they apparently run in the sulcomarginal and intermingled with the direct vestibulo-spinal and tectospinal fasciculi, finally terminate in the anterior horn. Most of the fibers terminate by the mid-thoracic level, a few continue as far as the sacral.

The **medial longitudinal fasciculus,** which is the main system connecting the vestibular complex and the eye and head turning centers of the brain stem and cervical cord, continues caudalward in the sulcomarginal fasciculus as far as the second or third thoracic segments. It is part of the mechanism coördinating head and eye movements and contains ascending as well as descending fibers.

The **tectospinal fasciculus,** situated partly in the anterior and partly in the lateral funiculus, is mainly derived from the opposite superior colliculus of the mid-brain. The fibers from the superior colliculus cross the median raphé in the fountain decussation of Meynert and descend as the ventral longitudinal bundle in the reticular formation of the brain-stem. Its collaterals and terminals end either directly or indirectly among the motor cells of the anterior column of the same side. Since the superior colliculus is an important visual reflex center, the tectospinal fasciculus is probably concerned with visual reflexes.

Ascending Fasciculi.—The **ventral spinothalamic fasciculus,** situated in the marginal part of the funiculus and intermingled more or less with the vestibulo-spinal fasciculus, is derived from cells in the posterior column or intermediate gray matter of the opposite side. Their axons cross in the anterior commissure. This is a somewhat doubtful fasciculus and its fibers are supposed to end in the thalamus and to conduct certain of the touch impulses.

The remaining anterior fibers constitute what is termed the **anterior proper fasciculus** (*fasciculus anterior proprius; anterior basis bundle*). It consists of (*a*) longitudinal intersegmental fibers which arise from cells in the gray substance, more especially from those of the medial group of the anterior column, and, after a longer or shorter course, reënter the gray substance; (*b*) fibers which cross in the anterior white commissure from the gray substance of the opposite side; (*c*) pathways in the form of long fibers or of neuron chains from autonomic centers in the brainstem to lower centers in the cord.

Lateral Fasciculi.—1. *Descending Fasciculi.*—(*a*) The **lateral cerebrospinal fasciculus** (*fasciculus cerebrospinalis lateralis; crossed pyramidal tract*) extends throughout the entire length of the medulla spinalis, in front of the posterior column and medial to the cerebellospinal. Its fibers arise from the large pyramidal cells of the precentral gyrus or motor area of the cerebral hemisphere of the opposite side. They pass downward in company with those of the anterior cerebrospinal fasciculus through the same side of the brain as that from which they originate, but they cross to the opposite side in the medulla oblongata and descend in the lateral funiculus of the medulla spinalis. The fibers are arranged in concentric layers, those to the arm areas being located most medially, next those to the trunk, and, most peripherally, those to the leg areas of the cord. Some terminate directly on anterior horn cells, but the greater number end on cells, at the base of the posterior column, which in turn link them to the motor cells in the anterior column. In consequence of these interposed neurons the fibers of the cerebrospinal fasciculi correspond not to individual muscles, but to associated groups of muscles. They conduct impulses from the motor cortex to the motor centers of the cord and have to do with voluntary movement.

The pyramidal motor system, consisting of the Betz cells in the motor cortex and their axons which form the ventral and lateral cerebrospinal fasciculi, appears very late philogenetically. In rodents, for example, there are only a few cerebrospinal fibers which run in the posterior columns through the cervical cord. In carnivora the lateral tract is present, but very few fibers reach the lumbosacral region. Ontogenetically this system develops very late and in humans it is not myelinated until some months after birth. The course of the fibers is subject to variation. Usually 70 to 80 per cent. decussate at the caudal end of the medulla, but this varies and occasionally one or the other fasciculus may be entirely absent, all the fibers taking a single course.

In humans the pyramidal system is of very great importance, since lesions of the cells or the fibers result in almost complete paralysis as well as in profound changes in the spinal reflexes. For this reason the pyramidal system and the anterior horn cells are clinically often considered together as the **motor system;** the Betz cells with their axons in the cerebrospinal fasciculi are called the **upper motor neurons,** and the anterior horn cells with their peripherally running axons are the **lower motor neurons.**

The extent to which the fibers of the ventral cerebrospinal fasciculus cross in the cord is open to question. Functional experiments on animals and clinico-pathological studies on humans indicate that, though the influence of the motor cortex is preponderantly contralateral, there is a slight ipsilateral effect. This could either be due to uncrossed connections, or to recrossing of axons of the intercalated neurons.

(*b*) The **rubrospinal fasciculus** (prepyramidal tract) was discovered in lower mammals by von Monakow. In these species it lies on the ventral aspect of the lateral cerebrospinal fasciculus and on transverse section appears as a somewhat triangular area. Its fibers descend, some of them as far as the sacral region, from the mid-brain, where they have their origin in the red nucleus of the tegmentum of the opposite side. Its terminals and collaterals end either directly or indirectly in relation with the motor cells of the anterior column. The rubrospinal fasciculus has not been defined in humans and since the large cells from which it arises in lower mammals do not exist in the human red nucleus, there is some question as to the presence of this tract at all. It is likely that the functions of the red nucleus, which is a way station in the cerebellar coördinating mechanisms, are mediated by some other crossed system, possibly reticulo-spinal.

(c) The **crossed lateral reticulospinal tract** has been described in lower mammals as arising from certain nuclei of the reticular substance of the tegmentum and running just ventral to the rubrospinal fasciculus. It seems likely that such tracts also exist in the human.

(d) The **olivospinal fasciculus** (Helweg) arises in the vicinity of the inferior olivary nucleus in the medulla oblongata, and is seen only in the cervical region of the medulla spinalis, where it forms a small triangular area at the periphery, close to the most lateral of the anterior nerve roots. Its functional significance is unknown.

2. *Ascending Fasciculi.*—(a) The **dorsal spinocerebellar fasciculus** (*fasciculus cerebellospinalis; direct cerebellar tract of Flechsig*) is situated at the periphery of the posterior part of the lateral funiculus, and on transverse section appears as a flattened band reaching as far forward as a line drawn transversely through the central canal. Medially, it is in contact with the lateral cerebrospinal fasciculus, behind, with the fasciculus of Lissauer. It begins about the level of the second or third lumbar nerve, and increasing in size as it ascends, passes to the cortex of the vermis of the cerebellum through the inferior peduncle. Its fibers are generally regarded as being formed by the axons of the cells of the dorsal nucleus (*Clarke's column*) of the same side; they receive their medullary sheaths about the sixth or seventh month of fetal life.

(b) The **ventral spinocerebellar fasciculus** (*Gowers*) skirts the periphery of the lateral funiculus in front of the dorsal spinocerebellar fasciculus. Its fibers come from the same but mostly from the opposite side of the medulla spinalis and cross both in the anterior white commissure and in the gray commissure; they are probably derived from cells of the posterior column and the intermediate portion of the gray matter. The ventral spinocerebellar fasciculus begins about the level of the third pair of lumbar nerves, and can be followed into the medulla oblongata and pons almost to the level of the inferior colliculus where it crosses over the superior peduncle and then passes backward along its medial border to reach the vermis of the cerebellum. In the pons it lies along the lateral edge of the lateral lemniscus. Some of its fibers join the dorsal spinocerebellar fasciculus at the level of the inferior peduncle and pass with them into the cerebellum. Other fibers are said to continue upward in the dorso-lateral part of the tegmentum of the mid-brain probably as far as the thalamus.

The spinocerebellar fasciculi are the only single neuron systems conducting from the spinal cord to the cerebellum. They are philogenetically relatively old, but their specific functions are not known.

(c) The **lateral spinothalamic fasciculus** is supposed to come from cells in the dorsal column and the intermediate gray matter whose axons cross in the anterior commissure to the opposite lateral funiculus where they pass upward on the medial side of the ventral spinocerebellar fasciculus; on reaching the medulla oblongata they continue through the ventro-lateral part of the formatio reticularis and finally terminate in the nucleus ventralis posterolateralis of the thalamus. They are relayed from these to the cerebral cortex. It is supposed to conduct impulses of pain and temperature. The lateral and ventral spinothalamic fasciculi are sometimes termed the **secondary sensory fasciculus** or **spinal lemniscus.**

(d) The **spinotectal fasciculus** arises in the dorsal column of the opposite side but soon crosses and passes upward ventral to the lateral spinothalamic. Its fibers come to lie in the medial portion of the lateral lemniscus and terminate in the superior colliculus of the mid-brain.

(e) The **dorsolateral fasciculus of Lissauer** is a small strand at the tip of the posterior horn, ventral and lateral to the incoming posterior nerve roots. It consists of great numbers of non-myelinated fibers and fewer finely myelinated fibers. The fibers are derived in part from the lateral fascicles of the posterior roots and in part from cells in the posterior horn. The fibers branch into short descending and slightly longer ascending divisions which give off collaterals terminating for the most part in the substantia gelatinosa. The finely myelinated fibers receive their myelin sheaths toward the close of fetal life, *i. e.*, later than the posterior root fibers, and they do not degenerate in locomotor ataxia. They are therefore probably intersegmental.

There is good evidence that pain and reflexes in response to pain are mediated by non-myelinated fibers in the posterior roots and the substantia gelatinosa.

(*f*) The **lateral proper fasciculus** (*fasciculus lateralis proprius; lateral basis bundle*) consists chiefly of intersegmental fibers which arise from cells in the gray substance, and, after a longer or shorter course, reënter the gray substance and ramify in it. These fibers make up a moderately thick layer next to the gray substance. In addition, certain pathways, either long tracts or neuron chains, from autonomic centers in the brainstem to autonomic centers in the cord run in this area, near to the lateral horn.

Posterior Fasciculi.—Ascending fasciculi, viz., the **fasciculus gracilis**, and the **fasciculus cuneatus.** These are separated from each other in the cervical and upper thoracic regions by the postero-intermediate septum, and consist practically entirely of ascending fibers derived from the posterior nerve roots.

The **fasciculus gracilis** (*tract of Goll*) lies next to the posterior median septum, and commences at the lowest limit of the spinal cord (Fig. 666). It increases in size from below upward by the lateral addition of long thin fibers derived from the ascending branches of the medial group of fibers of the posterior nerve roots of the sacral, lumbar and lower thoracic regions. It ascends as far as the medulla oblongata and ends in the nucleus gracilis. Along their course the fibers give off collaterals which enter the gray substance to terminate chiefly in the nucleus proprius and nucleus dorsalis of the posterior horn and also in the anterior horn. Many of the fibers end in this same manner before reaching the nucleus gracilis. It should be noted that the fibers from successive segments are laid down in the tract in successive layers, the fibers from the caudal segments being farther from the gray matter (*i. e.*, closer to the mid-line) and those from the rostral segments closer to the gray matter (Fig. 666).

The **fasciculus cuneatus** (*tract of Burdach*) lies between the fasciculus gracilis and the posterior column. Its fibers, larger than those of the fasciculus gracilis, are mostly derived from the same source, viz., the posterior nerve roots of the thoracic and cervical regions. They give off collaterals and some ascend for only a short distance in the tract, in a manner similar to the fibers of the fasciculus gracilis. The fibers, which reach the medulla oblongata end in the cuneate and accessory cuneate nuclei.

Destruction of the fasciculi gracilis and cuneatus results in loss of discriminatory sensation, such as sense of position of the limbs and of localization on the skin, of muscle tension, of joint movement, of vibration, etc. There are in addition disturbances of muscular coördination, in part due to the loss of the gracile and cuneate afferents to the spinal cord, medullary and cerebellar reflex and coördinating mechanisms.

The **Posterior Proper Fasciculus** (*posterior ground bundle; posterior basis bundle*) arises from cells in the posterior column; their axons bifurcate into ascending and descending branches which occupy the ventral part of the funiculus close to the gray column. They are intersegmental and run for varying distances sending off collaterals and terminals to the gray matter.

Some descending fibers occupy different parts at different levels. In the cervical and upper thoracic regions they appear as a **comma-shaped fasciculus** in the medial part of the fasciculus cuneatus; in the lower thoracic region they form **a dorsal peripheral band** on the posterior surface of the funiculus; in the lumbar region, they are situated by the side of the posterior median septum, and appear on section as a semi-elliptical bundle, which, together with the corresponding bundle of the opposite side, forms the **oval area of Flechsig;** while in the conus medullaris they assume the form of **a triangular strand** in the postero-medial part

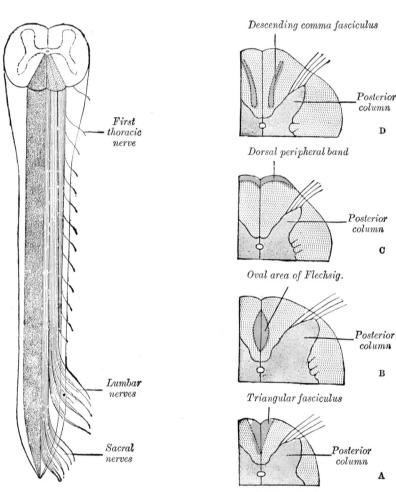

Fig. 666.—Formation of the fasciculus gracilis. Medulla spinalis viewed from behind. To the left, the fasciculus gracilis is shaded. To the right, the drawing shows that the fasciculus gracilis is formed by the long fibers of the posterior roots, and that in this tract the sacral nerves lie next the median plane, the lumbar to their lateral side, and the thoracic still more laterally. (Poirier.)

Fig. 667.—Descending fibers in the posterior funiculi, shown at different levels. *A.* In the conus medullaris. *B.* In the lumbar region. *C.* In the lower thoracic region. *D.* In the upper thoracic region. (After Testut.)

of the fasciculus gracilis. These descending fibers are in part intersegmental in character and derived from cells in the posterior column, in part they consist of the descending branches of the posterior nerve roots. The comma-shaped fasciculus was supposed to belong to the second category, but against this view is the fact that it does not undergo descending degeneration completely when the posterior nerve roots are destroyed.

Roots of the Spinal Nerves.—As already stated, each spinal nerve possesses two roots, an **anterior** and a **posterior,** which are attached to the surface of the medulla spinalis opposite the corresponding column of gray substance (Fig. 668); their fibers become medullated about the fifth month of fetal life.

The **Anterior Nerve Root** (*radix anterior*) consists of efferent fibers, which are the axons of the nerve cells in the ventral part of the anterior and lateral columns. A short distance from their origins, these axons are invested by medullary sheaths and, passing forward, emerge in two or three irregular rows over an area which measures about 3 mm. in width.

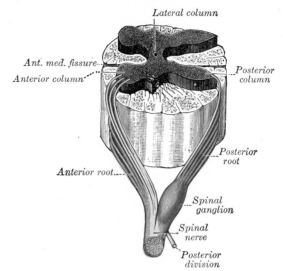

FIG. 668.—A spinal nerve with its anterior and posterior roots.

The **Posterior Root** (*radix posterior*) comprises some six or eight fasciculi, attached in linear series along the postero-lateral sulcus. It consists of afferent fibers which arise from the nerve cells in a spinal ganglion. Each ganglion cell gives off a single fiber which divides in a T-shaped manner into two processes, medial and lateral. The lateral processes extend to the sensory end-organs of the skin, muscles, tendons, joints, etc. (*somatic receptors*), and to the sensory end-organs of the viscera (*visceral receptors*). The medial processes of the ganglion cells grow into the medulla spinalis as the posterior roots of the spinal nerves.

The posterior nerve root enters the medulla spinalis in three chief bundles, medial, intermediate, and lateral. The **medial** strand passes directly into the fasciculus cuneatus: it consists of coarse fibers, which acquire their medullary sheaths about the fifth month of intrauterine life; the **intermediate strand** consists of coarse fibers, which enter the gelatinous substances of Rolando; the **lateral strand** is composed of fine fibers, which assume a longitudinal direction in the tract of Lissauer, and do not acquire their medullary sheaths until after birth.

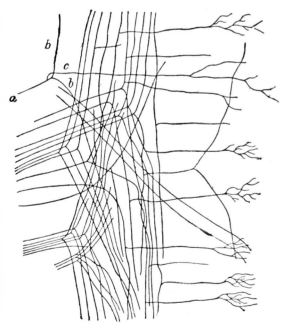

FIG. 669.—Posterior roots entering medulla spinalis and dividing into ascending and descending branches. (Van Gehuchten.) *a*, Stem fiber. *b, b*. Ascending and descending limbs of bifurcation. *c*, Collateral arising from stem fiber.

In addition to these medullated fibers there are great numbers of non-medullated fibers which enter with the lateral bundle. They are more numerous than the myelinated fibers. They arise from the small cells of the spinal ganglia by T-shaped axons similar to the myelinated. They are distributed with the peripheral nerves chiefly to the skin, only a few are found in the nerves to the muscles.

Having entered the medulla spinalis, all the fibers of the posterior nerve roots divide into ascending and descending branches, and these in their turn give off numerous **collaterals** which enter the gray substance (Fig. 669). They are finer than the fibers from which they arise. Some end in the ventral gray column, others in the posterior gray column, the substantia gelatinosa and the dorsal nucleus. All fibers terminate on the entering side. Only second neurons cross through the dorsal commissure to the gray substance of the opposite side. The descending fibers are short, and soon enter the gray substance. The ascending fibers of the **medial strand** are grouped into long, short, and intermediate: the long fibers ascend in the fasciculus cuneatus and fasciculus gracilis as far as the medulla oblongata, where they end by arborizing around the cells of the cuneate and gracile nuclei; the short fibers run upward for a distance of only 5 or 6 mm. and enter the gray substance; while the intermediate fibers, after a somewhat longer course, have a similar destination. All fibers entering the gray substance end by arborizing around its nerve cells or the dendrites of cells, those of intermediate length being especially associated with the cells of the dorsal nucleus.

The **descending fibers of the medial strand** of the posterior roots are short. The shortest terminate immediately in the posterior gray column. The longer ones descend in the comma-shaped fasciculus **(fasciculus interfascicularis)** and in the oval area of Flechsig **(septomarginal fasciculus)**, before entering the posterior gray column.

The **lateral strand** of the posterior root consists mainly of non-medullated fibers which enter the dorso-lateral fasciculus or tract of Lissauer. These divide into short ascending and descending branches.

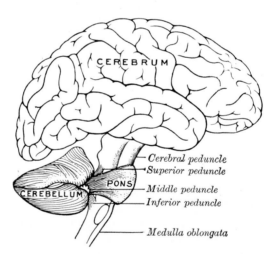

Fig. 670.—Scheme showing the connections of the several parts of the brain. (After Schwalbe.)

THE ENCEPHALON OR BRAIN. (Fig. 670.)

The brain is usually described as consisting of three main divisions, namely: **hind-brain, mid-brain** and **fore-brain.** The hind-brain is usually subdivided into **medulla oblongata, pons** and **cerebellum.** This system of division of the adult brain is conventional and does not accurately represent any fundamental anatomical, developmental, or functional categories.

Weight of the Encephalon.—The average weight of the brain, in the adult male, is about 1380 gms.; that of the female, about 1250 gms. In the male, the maximum weight out of 278 cases was 1840 gms. and the minimum weight 964 gms. The maximum weight of the adult female brain, out of 191 cases, was 1585 gms. and the minimum weight 879 gms. The brain increases rapidly during the first four years of life, and reaches its maximum weight by about the twentieth year. As age advances, the brain decreases slowly in weight; in old age the decrease takes place more rapidly, to the extent of about 28 gms.

The human brain is heavier than that of any of the lower animals, except the elephant and whale. The brain of the former weighs from 3.5 to 5.4 kilogm., and that of a whale, in a specimen 19 metres long, weighed rather more than 6.7 kilogm.

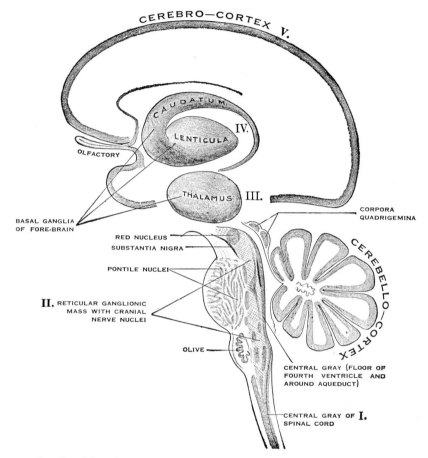

FIG. 671.—Schematic representation of the chief ganglionic categories (I to V). (Spitzka.)

The Medulla Oblongata (Spinal Bulb).

The medulla oblongata extends from the spinal cord to the lower margin of the pons. A plane passing transversely below the pyramidal decussation and above the first pair of cervical nerves corresponds with the upper border of the atlas behind, and the middle of the odontoid process of the axis in front; at this level the medulla oblongata is continuous with the medulla spinalis. Its anterior surface is separated from the basilar part of the occipital bone and the upper part of the odontoid process by the membranes of the brain and the occipito-axial ligaments. Its posterior surface is received into the fossa between the hemispheres of the cerebellum, and the upper portion of it forms the lower part of the floor of the fourth ventricle.

The medulla oblongata is pyramidal in shape, its broad extremity being directed upward toward the pons, while its narrow, lower end is continuous with the medulla

50

spinalis. It measures about 3 cm. in length, about 2 cm. in breadth at its widest part, and about 1.25 cm. in thickness. The central canal of the medulla spinalis is prolonged into its lower half, and then opens into the cavity of the fourth ventricle; the medulla oblongata may therefore be divided into a lower *closed part* containing the central canal, and an upper *open part* corresponding with the lower portion of the fourth ventricle.

The **Anterior Median Fissure** (*fissura mediana anterior; ventral or ventromedian fissure*) contains a fold of pia mater, and extends along the entire length of the medulla oblongata: it ends at the lower border of the pons in a small triangular expansion, termed the **foramen cecum.** Its lower part is interrupted by bundles of fibers which cross obliquely from one side to the other, and constitute the **pyramidal decussation.** Some fibers, termed the **anterior external arcuate fibers,** emerge from the fissure above this decussation and curve lateralward and upward over the surface of the medulla oblongata to join the inferior cerebellar peduncle.

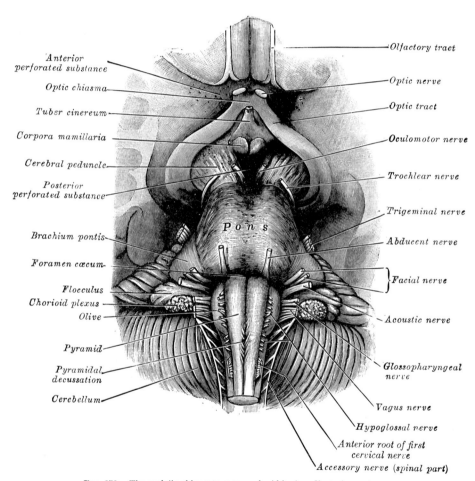

Fig. 672.—The medulla oblongata, pons and mid-brain. Ventral aspect.

The **Posterior Median Fissure** (*fissura mediana posterior; dorsal or dorsomedian fissure*) is a narrow groove; and exists only in the closed part of the medulla oblongata; it becomes gradually shallower from below upward, and finally ends about the middle of the medulla oblongata, where the central canal expands into the cavity of the fourth ventricle.

These two fissures divide the closed part of the medulla oblongata into symmetrical halves, each presenting elongated eminences which, on surface view, are continuous with the funiculi of the medulla spinalis. In the open part, the medulla is similarly divided by the anterior median fissure anteriorly, and by the **median sulcus**, which is a longitudinal groove in the floor of the fourth ventricle, posteriorly. Further subdivisions into gross anatomical areas are demarcated as described below. Further, certain of the cranial nerves pass through the substance of the medulla oblongata, and are attached to its surface in series with the roots of the spinal nerves; thus, the fibers of the hypoglossal nerve represent the upward continuation of the anterior nerve roots, and emerge in linear series from a furrow

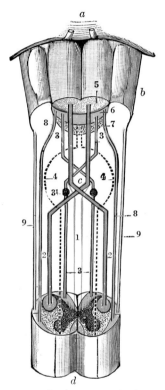

Fig. 673.—Decussation of pyramids. Scheme showing passage of various fasciculi from medulla spinalis to medulla oblongata. *a.* Pons. *b.* Medulla oblongata. *c.* Decussation of the pyramids. *d.* Section of cervical part of medulla spinalis. 1. Anterior cerebrospinal fasciculus (in red). 2. Lateral cerebrospinal fasciculus (in red). 3. Sensory tract (fasciculi gracilis et cuneatus) (in blue). 3′. Gracile and cuneate nuclei. 4. Antero-lateral proper fasciculus (in dotted line). 5. Pyramid. 6. Lemniscus. 7. Medial longitudinal fasciculus. 8. Ventral spinocerebellar fasciculus (in blue). 9. Dorsal spinocerebellar fasciculus (in yellow). (Testut.)

termed the **antero-lateral sulcus.** Similarly, the accessory, vagus, and glossopharyngeal nerves correspond with the posterior nerve roots, and are attached to the bottom of a sulcus named the **postero-lateral sulcus.** Advantage is taken of this arrangement to subdivide each half of the medulla oblongata into three districts, **anterior, middle,** and **posterior.** Although these three districts appear to be directly continuous with the corresponding funiculi of the medulla spinalis, they do not necessarily contain the same fibers, since some of the fasciculi of the medulla spinalis end in the medulla oblongata, while others alter their course in passing through it.

The **anterior district** is named the **pyramid** (*pyramis medullæ oblongatæ*) (Fig. 672) and lies between the anterior median fissure and the antero-lateral sulcus. Its upper end is slightly constricted, and between it and the pons the fibers of the abducent nerve emerge; a little below the pons it becomes enlarged and prominent and finally tapers into the anterior funiculus of the medulla spinalis, with which, at first sight, it appears to be directly continuous.

The two pyramids contain the motor fibers which pass from the brain to the medulla oblongata and medulla spinalis, corticobulbar and corticospinal fibers. When these pyramidal fibers are traced downward it is found that some two-thirds or more of them leave the pyramids in successive bundles, and decussate in the anterior median fissure, forming what is termed the **pyramidal decussation.** Having crossed the middle line, they pass down in the posterior part of the lateral funiculus as the lateral cerebrospinal fasciculus. The remaining fibers—*i. e.,* those which occupy the lateral part of the pyramid—do not cross the middle line, but are carried downward as the anterior cerebrospinal fasciculus (Fig. 673) into the anterior funiculus of the same side.

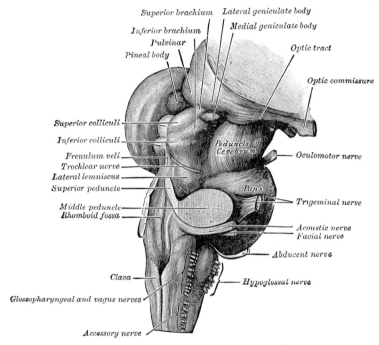

Fig. 674.—Brain-stem postero-lateral view.

The **medial longitudinal fasciculus** is sometimes regarded as the continuation of the anterior proper fasciculus, in that it carries intersegmental connections. It is, however, a highly specialized system.

The **lateral district** (Fig. 674) is limited in front by the antero-lateral sulcus and the roots of the hypoglossal nerve, and behind by the postero-lateral sulcus and the roots of the accessory, vagus, and glossopharyngeal nerves. Its upper part consists of a prominent oval mass which is named the **olive,** while its lower part is of the same width as the lateral funiculus of the medulla spinalis, and appears on the surface to be a direct continuation of it. As a matter of fact, only a portion of the lateral funiculus is continued upward into this district, for the lateral cerebrospinal fasciculus passes into the pyramid of the opposite side, and the dorsal spinocerebellar fasciculus is carried into the inferior peduncle in the posterior district. The ventral spinocerebellar fasciculus is continued upward on the lateral surface of the medulla oblongata in the same relative position it occupies in the spinal cord until it passes under cover of the external arcuate fibers. It passes beneath these fibers just dorsal to the olive and ventral to the roots of the vagus and glossopharyngeal nerves; it continues upward through the pons along the dorso-lateral edge of the lateral lemniscus. The remainder of the lateral funiculus consists chiefly of the lateral proper fasciculus. Most of these fibers dip beneath the olive and disappear from the surface; but a small strand remains superficial to the olive. In a depression at the upper end of this strand is the acoustic nerve.

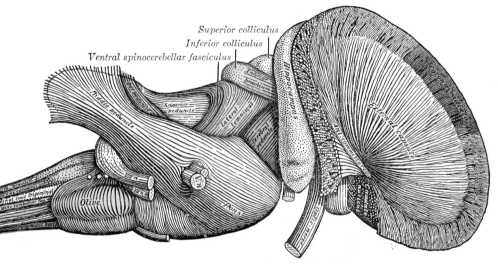

FIG. 675.—Superficial dissection of brain-stem. Lateral view.

The **olive** (*oliva; olivary body*) is situated lateral to the pyramid, from which it is separated by the antero-lateral sulcus, and the fibers of the hypoglossal nerve. Behind, it is separated from the postero-lateral sulcus by the ventral spinocerebellar

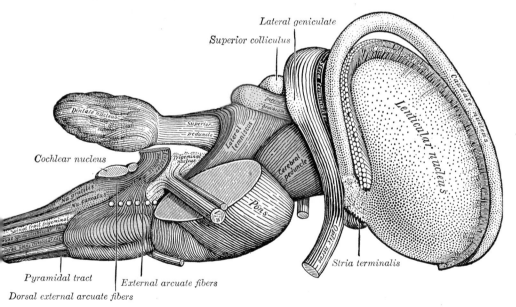

FIG. 676.—Dissection of brain-stem. Lateral view.

fasciculus. In the depression between the upper end of the olive and the pons lies the acoustic nerve. It measures about 1.25 cm. in length, and between its upper end and the pons there is a slight depression from which the roots of the facial nerve emerge. The external arcuate fibers wind across the lower part of the pyramid and olive and enter the inferior peduncle.

The **posterior district** (Fig. 679) lies behind the postero-lateral sulcus and the roots of the accessory, vagus, and the glossopharyngeal nerves, and like the lateral district, is divisible into a lower and an upper portion.

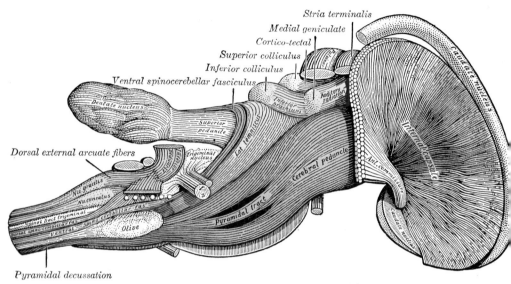

Fig. 677.—Deep dissection of brain-stem. Lateral view.

The **lower part** is limited behind by the posterior median fissure, and consists of the **fasciculus gracilis** and the **fasciculus cuneatus**. The fasciculus gracilis is placed parallel to and along the side of the posterior median fissure, and separated

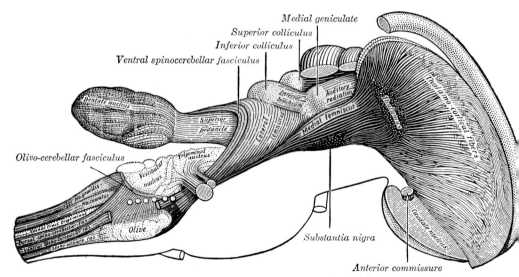

Fig. 678.—Deep dissection of brain-stem. Lateral view.

from the fasciculus cuneatus by the postero-intermediate sulcus and septum. The gracile and cuneate fasciculi are at first vertical in direction; but at the lower part of the rhomboid fossa they diverge from the middle line in a V-shaped manner, and each presents an elongated swelling. That on the fasciculus gracilis is named the **clava**, and is produced by a subjacent nucleus of gray matter, the **nucleus gracilis**; that on the fasciculus cuneatus is termed the **cuneate tubercle**, and is likewise caused by a gray nucleus, named the **nucleus cuneatus**. The fibers of these fasciculi terminate by arborizing around the cells in their respective nuclei. A third elevation, produced by the substantia gelatinosa of Rolando, is present in the lower part of the posterior district of the medulla oblongata. It lies on the lateral aspect of the fasciculus cuneatus, and is separated from the surface of the medulla oblongata by a band of nerve fibers which form the spinal tract (spinal root) of the trigeminal nerve. Narrow below, this elevation gradually expands above, and ends, about 1.25 cm. below the pons, in a tubercle, the **tubercle of Rolando** (*tuber cinereum*).

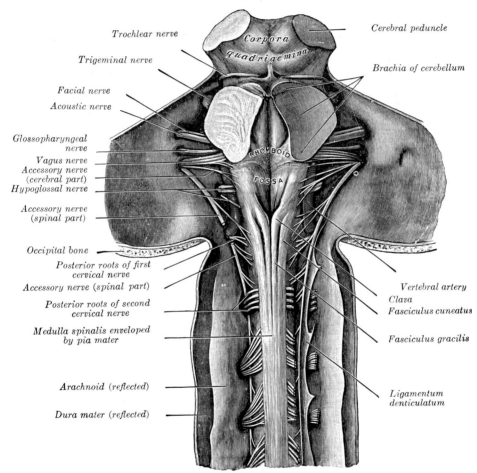

Fig. 679.—The upper part of the medulla spinalis, and the hind- and mid-brains. Exposed from behind.

The **upper part** of the posterior district of the medulla oblongata is occupied by the **inferior cerebellar peduncle**, a thick rope-like strand situated between the lower part of the fourth ventricle and the roots of the glossopharyngeal and vagus nerves. The inferior peduncles connect the medulla spinalis and medulla oblongata with the cerebellum, and are sometimes named the **restiform bodies**. As they pass upward, they diverge from each other, and assist in forming the lower part of the lateral boundaries of the fourth ventricle; higher up, they are directed backward, each passing to the corresponding cerebellar hemisphere. Near their entrance, into the cerebellum they are crossed by several strands of fibers, which run to the median sulcus of the rhomboid fossa, and are named the **striæ medullares.**

Caudal to the striæ medullares the inferior peduncle is partly covered by the corpus pontobulbare (Essick), a thin mass of cells and fibers extending from the pons between the origin of the VII and VIII cranial nerves.

Internal Structure of the Medulla Oblongata.—The medulla rapidly changes in structure above its continuation with the spinal cord just above the origin of the first cervical nerve. The decussation of the corticospinal tracts (pyramids) in the lower closed part of the medulla produces a marked change in the position of the tracts from lateral in the spinal cord to ventral in the medulla and separates part of the ventral gray columns from the central gray matter and the dorsal columns. On the dorsal side of the medulla the fibers of the fasciculus gracilis and fasciculus cuneatus end in enlarged nuclei. From these nuclei (gracile and cuneate) internal arcuate fibers sweep ventrally around the central gray matter separating it from the dorsal column and decussate (decussation of the medial lemniscus) between the central gray matter and the corticospinal tracts. After decussating these fibers turn rostrally in the medial lemnisci, one on either side of the mid-line. Most of the gray substance of the dorsal and ventral gray columns together with new gray matter is traversed and dispersed by the internal arcuate and other fibers and becomes the reticular substance.

The rostral ends of the gracile and cuneate nuclei bend laterally where the central canal opens out into the fourth ventricle and soon end. The central gray matter becomes spread out in the floor of the fourth ventricle.

The structure of the medulla is still further modified by new structures such as the large inferior olives, various new nuclei and by the nuclei and tracts connected with the cranial nerves.

The Cerebrospinal Fasciculi.—The downward course of these fasciculi from the pyramids of the medulla oblongata and their partial decussation have already been described (page 778). In crossing to reach the lateral funiculus of the opposite side, the fibers of the lateral cerebrospinal fasciculi extend backward and pierce through the anterior columns, so that in cross-sections the head of each of these columns appears separated from its base (Figs. 680, 681). The base retains its position in relation to the ventral aspect of the central canal, and, when the latter opens into the fourth ventricle, appears in the rhomboid fossa close to the middle line, where it forms the nuclei of the hypoglossal and abducent nerves; while above the level of the ventricle it exists as the nuclei of the trochlear and oculomotor nerves in relation to the floor of the cerebral aqueduct. The head of the column is pushed lateralward and forms the cranial part of the accessory nucleus, the nucleus ambiguus, the nucleus facialis and the motor trigeminal nucleus. The nucleus ambiguus contributes motor fibers to the vagus and the glossopharyngeal. This continuation of the motor column through the hind- and mid-brain is illustrated in Figs. 689 and 690.

The **fasciculus gracilis** and **fasciculus cuneatus** constitute the posterior sensory fasciculi of the medulla spinalis; they are prolonged upward into the lower part of the medulla oblongata, where they end respectively in the nucleus gracilis and nucleus cuneatus. Many of the fibers end in these nuclei in the closed part of the medulla; the rest are diverted laterally at the level of the open lower part of the fourth ventricle and end there in the upper part of their respective nuclei. Fibers of the fasciculus cuneatus give collaterals to the nucleus cuneatus accessorius, and some of them terminate there. Some collaterals extend forward into the reticular substance of the medulla, but none of the fibers continue directly into the inferior cerebellar peduncle.

The **nucleus gracilis** and **nucleus cuneatus** are covered over by the fibers of the corresponding fasciculi and extend from near the lower end of the medulla to a short distance above the clava. Both are deflected laterally at the level of the

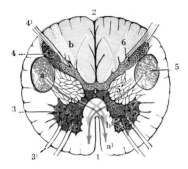

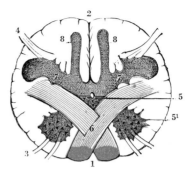

FIG. 680.—Section of the medulla oblongata through the lower part of the decussation of the pyramids. (Testut.) 1. Anterior median fissure. 2. Posterior median sulcus. 3. Anterior column (in red), with 3′, anterior root. 4. Posterior column (in blue), with 4′, posterior roots. 5. Lateral cerebrospinal fasciculus. 6. Posterior funiculus. The red arrow, *a*, *a′*, indicates the course the lateral cerebrospinal fasciculus takes at the level of the decussation of the pyramids; the blue arrow, *b*, *b′*, indicates the course which the sensory fibers take.

FIG. 681.—Section of the medulla oblongata at the level of the decussation of the pyramids. (Testut.) 1. Anterior median fissure. 2. Posterior median sulcus. 3. Motor roots. 4. Sensory roots. 5. Base of the anterior column, from which the head (5′) has been detached by the lateral cerebrospinal fasciculus. 6. Decussation of the lateral cerebrospinal fasciculus. 7. Posterior columns (in blue). 8. Gracile nucleus.

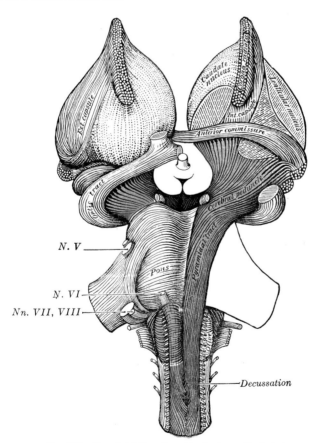

FIG. 682.—Superficial dissection of brain-stem. Ventral view.

lower part of the fourth ventricle. They are composed of small and medium-sized cells around which the fibers of the fasciculus gracilis and fasciculus cuneatus terminate. They produce a slight swelling of the posterior funiculi. From the cells of the nuclei new fibers arise; some of these are supposed to continue as the posterior external arcuate fibers into the inferior peduncle, and through it to the cerebellum, but most of them pass ventrally as the internal arcuate fibers.

The **internal arcuate fibers** sweep ventrally from the gracile and cuneate nuclei around the central gray matter and decussate (decussation of the lemniscus, sensory decussation), across the mid-line. They then turn rostrally on the side opposite their origin to form the medial lemniscus.

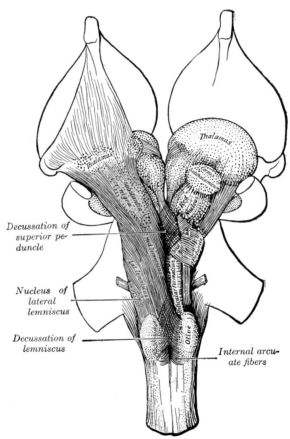

Decussation of superior peduncle

Nucleus of lateral lemniscus

Decussation of lemniscus

Internal arcuate fibers

FIG. 683.—Deep dissection of brain-stem. Ventral view.

The **medial lemniscus** has the shape of a boot in cross-sections through the caudal part of the medulla, occupying the angle between the inferior olive, the median raphé and the pyramid. The fibers run parallel, those from the nucleus gracilis (leg and lower trunk) running in the dorsal part of the bundle, those from the nucleus cuneatus (upper trunk and arm) in the ventral part. Proceeding forward, the band moves slightly dorsally and at the upper end of the inferior olive it swings laterally and then it spreads out into a narrow ribbon lying flat over the upper surface of the pontile nuclei. The leg fibers shift furthest laterally, the arm fibers least, their positions in relation to each other being accurately maintained.

The **lateral** or **accessory cuneate nucleus** (*N. magnocellularis of von Monakow*) lies lateral to the upper end of the nucleus cuneatus and extends forward into the medial margin of the restiform body. It contains large cells and receives collaterals from the fasciculus cuneatus. The axons from its cells are supposed to pass in the inferior cerebellar peduncle to the cerebellum.

The **ventral spinothalamic fasciculus** is deflected dorsally in the lower part of the medulla by the decussation of the corticospinal tracts and continues rostrally just dorsal to the medial lemniscus. Where the medial lemniscus swings laterally, in front of the inferior olives, the ventral spinothalamic tract also turns laterally and so comes to rejoin the lateral spinothalamic tract which it then accompanies to the thalamus.

The **dorso spinocerebellar fasciculus** (*fasciculus cerebellospinalis; direct cerebellar tract*) leaves the lateral district of the medulla oblongata and enters the inferior

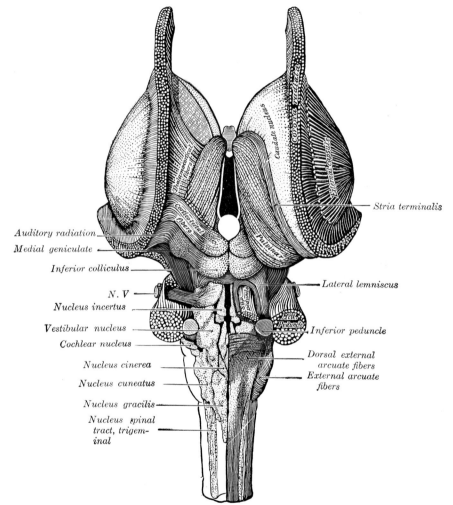

Fig. 684.—Dissection of brain-stem. Dorsal view. The nuclear masses of the medulla are taken from model by Weed, Carnegie Publication, No. 19.

cerebellar peduncle of the same side, through which it is conveyed to the cortex of the vermis cerebelli.

The **ventral spinocerebellar tract** is continued upward on the lateral surface of the medulla in the same relative position it occupies in the spinal cord until it passes beneath the external arcuate fibers. It lies dorsal to the olive, and ventral to the roots of the vagus and glossopharyngeal nerves. It continues upward through the pons along the dorsolateral edge of the lateral lemniscus, turns across the superior cerebellar peduncle to its dorsomedial edge and follows along this to the vermis of the cerebellum.

The **tectospinal tract** descends through the upper part of the medulla between the medial lemniscus and the medial longitudinal fasciculus close to the median plane. In the region of the decussation of the medial lemniscus and the cortico-spinal tract it is diverted to the ventral funiculus.

Fibers which subserve functions similar to those of the intersegmental connections which run in the proper fasciculi of the spinal cord exist in the medulla as small, scattered bundles throughout the reticular substance. Some authors regard the **medial longitudinal fasciculus** as a continuation of the anterior proper fasciculus. It is a highly specialized system and will be referred to later. It appears as a deeply stained bundle of fibers next to the median raphé just under the gray matter of the floor of the fourth ventricle.

Gray Substance of the Medulla Oblongata (Figs. 687, 688).—Due to the fact that the dorsal lips of the primitive neural tube spread apart in the hind-brain the sensory-coördinating mechanisms come to occupy a lateral position in the medulla and pons, instead of a dorsal position as they do in the spinal cord. Autonomic nuclei are found next to the sulcus limitans and the striped muscle motor nuclei form two columns, one close to the mid-line just under the floor of the ventricle, the other in the ventro-lateral part of the reticular substance. The

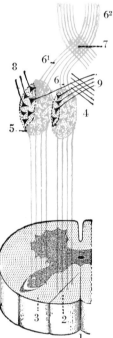

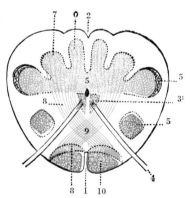

Fig. 685.—Superior terminations of the posterior fasciculi of the medulla spinalis. 1. Posterior median sulcus. 2. Fasciculus gracilis. 3. Fasciculus cuneatus. 4. Gracile nucleus. 5. Cuneate nucleus. 6, 6', 6''. Sensory fibers forming the lemniscus. 7. Sensory decussation. 8. Cerebellar fibers uncrossed (in black). 9. Cerebellar fibers crossed (in black). (Testut.)

Fig. 686.—Transverse section passing through the sensory decussation. (Schematic.) 1. Anterior median fissure. 2. Posterior median sulcus. 3, 3. Head and base of anterior column (in red). 4. Hypoglossal nerve. 5. Bases of posterior columns. 6. Gracile nucleus. 7. Cuneate nucleus. 8, 8. Lemniscus. 9. Sensory decussation. 10. Cerebrospinal fasciculus. (Testut.)

nuclei of the dorsomedial column innervate muscles developing from the head somite, namely the tongue and the extrinsic eye muscles. Those of the ventro-lateral group innervate muscles derived from the branchial arches (laryngeal, pharyngeal, masticator, etc., muscles) or muscles philogenetically derived from the primitive constrictor coli (facial muscles).

In the following description the structures which represent a continuation of the gray columns of the spinal cord into the medulla will be considered first, and the structures more closely related to cerebellar and fore-brain mechanisms later.

1. Motor nuclei. The **hypoglossal nucleus** is situated near the ventrolateral aspect of the central canal in the lower closed part of the medulla; but in the upper part it approaches the rhomboid fossa, where it lies a short distance from the middle

line, under an eminence named the **trigonum hypoglossi** (Fig. 703). Numerous fibers connect the two nuclei, and both nuclei send long dendrons across the midline to the opposite nucleus. The nucleus measures about 2 cm. in length, and consists of large multipolar nerve cells, similar to those in the anterior column of the spinal cord, whose axons constitute the roots of the hypoglossal nerve. These nerve roots leave the ventral side of the nucleus, pass forward between the white reticular formation and the gray reticular formation, some between the inferior olivary nucleus and the medial accessory olivary nucleus, and emerge from the antero-lateral sulcus.

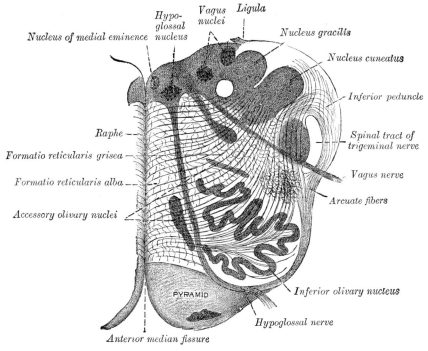

FIG. 687.—Section of the medulla oblongata at about the middle of the olive. (Schwalbe.)

The **nucleus ambiguus** (Figs. 689, 690), the somatic motor nucleus of the glossopharyngeal, vagus and cranial portion of the accessory nerves, is the continuation into the medulla oblongata of the dorso-lateral cell group of the anterior column of the spinal cord. Its large multipolar cells are like those in the anterior column of the cord; they form a slender column in the deep part of the formatio reticularis grisea about midway between the dorsal accessory olive and the nucleus of the spinal tract of the trigeminal. It extends from the level of the decussation of the median fillet to the upper end of the medulla oblongata. Its fibers first pass backward toward the floor of the fourth ventricle and then curve rather abruptly lateralward and ventrally to join the fibers from the dorsal nucleus.

2. Autonomic nuclei. The **dorsal motor nucleus of the vagus** (*nucleus ala cinerea*) (Figs. 689, 691) gives rise to parasympathetic fibers which innervate the heart muscle and smooth muscle. It consists of a long column of cells, dorso-lateral to the hypoglossal nucleus, that extend from the lowest level of the medulla to about the level of the oral pole of the inferior olive. It contains two types of motor cells. The smaller ones give rise to preganglionic fibers to smooth muscle. The larger cells give off preganglionic fibers to the heart muscle (Fig. 643,*b*). They are, as Malone has shown, intermediate in size between the large ventral column cells

supplying skeletal muscle and the small cells supplying preganglionic fibers to smooth muscle. The fibers from the dorsal motor nucleus of the vagus join the motor roots of the vagus and accessory nerves, and are distributed through its branches and plexuses to the thorax and abdomen, where they terminate in ganglia. Postganglionic fibers conduct the impulses to the muscle fibers.

The **nucleus salivatorius** and **nucleus lacrimalis**. Groups of cells of the autonomic type have been described in the upper part of the reticular substance, parallel with the sulcus limitans. These probably represent centers supplying the salivary and lacrimal glands, but they have not been satisfactorily identified.

3. Sensory nuclei. The **substantia gelatinosa trigemini** is a direct rostral continuation of the substantia gelatinosa Rolandi of the spinal cord. It is surrounded laterally by a half moon-shaped bundle of fibers, the spinal tract of the trigeminal nerve. It lies ventral to the inferior and lateral vestibular nuclei and ventro-medial to the restiform body. It is described with the trigeminal nuclei later.

The **nucleus of the tractus solitarius** is a long slender nucleus extending the entire length of the medulla. It lies ventro-lateral to the dorsal motor nucleus. The caudal ends of the two nuclei on the two sides are united dorsal to the central

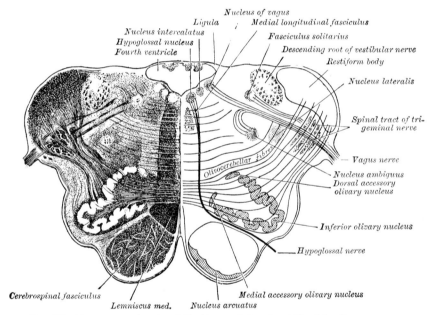

Fig. 688.—Transverse section of medulla oblongata below the middle of the olive.

canal in the closed part of the medulla. The cells of the nucleus partly surround the solitary tract and in part lie among its fibers. The fibers of the facial and glossopharyngeal nerves terminate in the oral end after running but a short distance in the solitary tract. It is especially concerned with the sense of taste. In the larger part of the nucleus terminate the visceral afferent fibers of the vagus after running in the solitary tract for varying distances. Many of the fibers from this nucleus pass to the dorsal motor nucleus.

The **sensory nucleus of the vagus** is a column of cells of the same type as those of the nucleus of the tractus solitarius. It lies dorso-medial to the latter and lateral to the dorsal motor nucleus of the vagus. It receives visceral afferent fibers from the vagus and glossopharyngeal nerves.

The **nuclei of the cochlear and vestibular nerves** are described on pages 806 and 867.

4. The substantia grisia ventriculi quarti (the gray of the floor of the fourth ventricle) is the rostral continuation of the substantia gelatinosa centralis and intermediate zone of the spinal cord, and spreads as a thin layer over the whole floor of the ventricle. Further rostrally it is continuous with the central gray round the aqueduct. It contains small cells, non-myelinated fibers and a few finely myelinated fibers. The most prominent of the latter constitute the **dorsal fasciculus of Schütz**, which runs very superficially to the side of the median sulcus from the hypothalamic region to the level of the dorsal motor nucleus of the vagus.

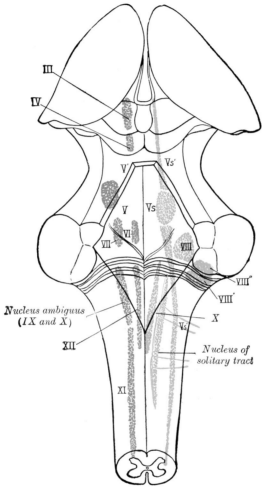

FIG. 689.—The cranial nerve nuclei schematically represented; dorsal view. Motor nuclei in red; sensory in blue (The olfactory and optic centers are not represented.)

A specialized development of the substantia grisia is found at the caudal end of the medulla in the **area postrema** (Wilson). This area contains glia, but no nerve cells, and has a rich capillary bed of a different pattern from that of the surrounding nervous tissue. When vital dyes are injected into an animal, the area postrema, the pars nervosa of the hypophysis including the median eminence, the pineal body, the paraphysis and the supraoptic body are stained, whereas the remainder of the brain and spinal cord remain unstained. The function is unknown.

5. The **substantia reticularis** (Fig. 687) is the continuation of the column of the same name in the spinal cord. Rostrally the column is continued through the

mesencephalon and terminates in the reticular nucleus of the thalamus. The reticulated appearance is due to scattered groups of cells and of intersecting bundles of fibers. Most of the fibers would appear to be short connections between one brain stem center and another, but a number belong to long tracts such as the medial lemniscus, the spinothalamic tracts, the superior spinocerebellar tract, the medial longitudinal fasciculus, the tectospinal tract, the thalamo-olivary tract, etc. The substantia reticularis is made up of a large number of nuclei which have not been adequately studied and of which only a few have been identified in Nissl preparations. The following may be mentioned: the nucleus of Rolla, a group of autonomic cells ventral to the head of the hypoglossal nucleus; the nucleus interfascicularis, large cells scattered between the fascicles of the hypoglossal fibers;

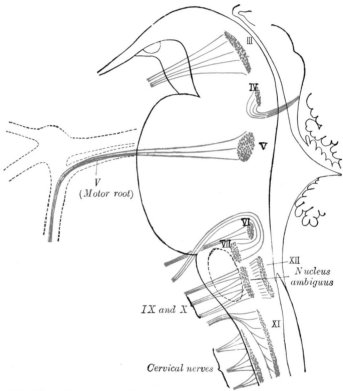

Fig. 690.—Nuclei of origin of cranial motor nerves schematically represented; lateral view.

the nucleus funiculi lateralis, a group of large cells in a layer above the inferior olive. Occasional cells of larger size are scattered through the reticular substance and are sometimes referred to as the nucleus magnocellularis. In general, the medial two-thirds of the reticular substance is associated with the vestibular system (second and third neurons of reflex paths), and the lateral one-third with the trigeminal system. The reticulospinal tracts, referred to before, arise from centers chiefly in the rostral part, and other efferent paths, such as the respiratory pathways, descend into the cord either as long fibers or short neuron chains. The functions of the reticular substance are varied. It apparently contains the neural mechanisms mediating numerous complex reflexes, both of striped muscles and autonomic systems, including respiration and respiratory reflexes, swallowing, crying, movements of the eyes, postural reflexes, as well as many others.

6. Cerebellar systems. The **inferior olivary nuclei** (Fig. 687) are three in number on either side of the middle line, viz., the inferior olivary nucleus, and the medial

and dorsal accessory olivary nuclei; they consist of small, round, yellowish cells and numerous fine nerve fibers. (*a*) The **inferior olivary nucleus** is the largest, and

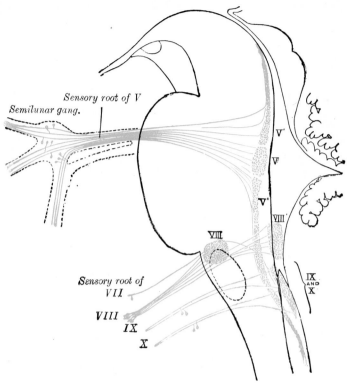

Fig. 691.—Primary terminal nuclei of the afferent (sensory) cranial nerves schematically represented—lateral view. The olfactory and optic centers are not represented.

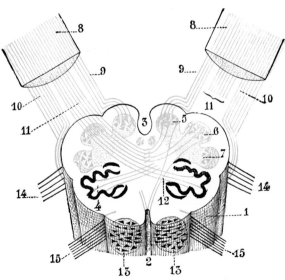

Fig. 692.—Diagram showing the course of the arcuate fibers. (Testut.) 1. Medulla oblongata anterior surface. 2. Anterior median fissure. 3. Fourth ventricle. 4. Inferior olivary nucleus, with the accessory olivary nuclei. 5. Gracile nucleus. 6. Cuneate nucleus. 7. Trigeminal. 8. Inferior peduncles, seen from in front. 9. Posterior external arcuate fibers. 10. Anterior external arcuate fibers. 11. Internal arcuate fibers. 12. Peduncle of inferior olivary nucleus. 13. Nucleus arcuatus. 14. Vagus. 15. Hypoglossal.

51

is situated within the olive. It consists of a gray folded lamina arranged in the form of an incomplete capsule, opening medially by an aperture called the **hilum**; emerging from the hilum are numerous fibers which collectively constitute the **peduncle of the olive.** The axons, **olivocerebellar fibers,** which leave the olivary nucleus pass out through the hilum and decussate with those from the opposite olive in the raphé, then as internal arcuate fibers they pass partly through and partly around the opposite olive and enter the inferior peduncle to be distributed to the cerebellar hemisphere of the opposite side from which they arise. The fibers are smaller than the internal arcuate fibers connected with the medial lemniscus. Fibers passing in the opposite direction from the cerebellum to the olivary nucleus are often described but their existence is doubtful. Much uncertainty also exists in

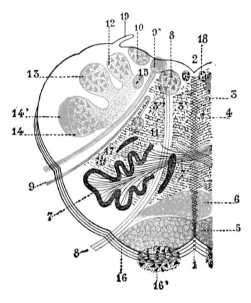

Fig. 693.—The formatio reticularis of the medulla oblongata, shown by a transverse section passing through the middle of the olive. (Testut.) 1. Anterior median fissure. 2. Fourth ventricle. 3. Formatio reticularis, with 3', its internal part (reticularis alba), and 3'', its external part (reticularis grisea). 4. Raphé. 5. Pyramid. 6. Lemniscus. 7. Inferior olivary nucleus with the two accessory olivary nuclei. 8. Hypoglossal nerve, with 8', its nucleus of origin. 9. Vagus nerve, with 9', its nucleus of termination. 10. Lateral dorsal acoustic nucleus. 11. Nucleus ambiguus (nucleus of origin of motor fibers of glossopharyngeal, vagus, and cerebra portion of spinal accessory). 12. Gracilis nucleus. 13. Cuneate nucleus. 14. Head of posterior column, with 14', the lower sensory root of trigeminal nerve. 15. Fasciculus solitarius. 16. Anterior external arcuate fibers, with 16', the nucleus arcuatus. 17. Nucleus lateralis. 18. Nucleus of fasciculus teres. 19. Ligula.

regard to the connections of the olive and the spinal cord. Important connections from structures in the base of the fore-brain and in the mid-brain descend to the olives in the so-called **thalamo-olivary fasciculus** (central tract of the tegmentum). The exact origin of these fibers is unknown. They gather at the rostral part of the mesencephalon to make a broad bundle through the central region of the reticular substance. They extend around the olive as a dense capsule and finally turn into the gray lamina to end in relation to its cells. Many collaterals from the reticular formation and from the pyramids enter the inferior olivary nucleus. Removal of one cerebellar hemisphere is followed by atrophy of the opposite olivary nucleus. (*b*) The **medial accessory olivary nucleus** lies between the inferior olivary nucleus and the pyramid, and forms a curved lamina, the concavity of which is directed laterally. The fibers of the hypoglossal nerve, as they traverse the medulla, pass between the medial accessory and the inferior olivary nuclei. (*c*) The **dorsal accessory olivary nucleus** is the smallest, and appears on transverse section as a curved lamina behind the inferior olivary nucleus.

7. The **nucleus arcuatus** lies superficial to the pyramid in the ventral external

arcuate fibers. It is serially continuous with the nuclei pontis, contains small fusiform cells, around which some of the arcuate fibers end and from which others arise.

Inferior Cerebellar Peduncle (*restiform body*).—The position of the inferior peduncles has already been described (page 791). Each comprises:

(1) Fibers from the **dorsal spinocerebellar fasciculus,** which arise from the dorsal nucleus of the same side of the spinal cord and ascend in the lateral funiculus.

(2) The **olivocerebellar fibers** chiefly from the inferior olivary nucleus of the opposite side together with a few from the nucleus of the same side form the deeper and larger part of the inferior cerebellar peduncle.

(3) Fibers from the arcuate nuclei.

(4) Fibers from the lateral reticular nucleus.

(5) The **posterior external arcuate fibers** take origin in the gracile and cuneate nuclei; they are supposed to pass to the inferior peduncle of the same side. It is uncertain whether fibers are continued directly from the gracile and cuneate fasciculi into the inferior peduncle.

(6) Fibers from the **terminal sensory nuclei** of the cranial nerves, especially the vestibular. Some of the fibers of the vestibular nerve are thought to continue directly into the cerebellum.

(7) According to some authors the nucleus cuneatus accessorius and the nucleus funiculi lateralis also supply fibers to the restiform body.

(8) The existence of fibers in the restiform body from the **cerebellum** (cerebellobulbar, cerebelloölivary, cerebelloreticular) to the medulla is probable.

The Pons (Pons Varoli).

The pons is continuous with the medulla oblongata, but is separated from it in front by a superficial furrow in which the abducent, facial, and acoustic nerves appear. From its superior surface the cerebral peduncles emerge, one on either side of the middle line. Curving around each peduncle, close to the upper surface of the pons, a thin white band, the **tænia pontis,** is frequently seen; it enters the cerebellum between the middle and superior cerebellar peduncles.

Its ventral or anterior surface (*pars basilaris pontis*) is very prominent, markedly convex from side to side, less so from above downward. It consists of transverse fibers arched like a bridge across the middle line, and gathered on either side into a compact mass which forms the **middle cerebellar peduncle.** It rests upon the clivus of the sphenoidal bone, and is limited above and below by well-defined borders. In the middle line is the **sulcus basilaris** for the lodgement of the basilar artery; this sulcus is bounded on either side by an eminence caused by the descent of the cerebrospinal fibers through the substance of the pons. Outside these eminences, near the upper border of the pons, the trigeminal nerves make their exit, each consisting of a smaller, medial, motor root, and a larger, lateral, sensory root; vertical lines drawn immediately beyond the trigeminal nerves may be taken as the boundaries between the ventral surface of the pons and the middle cerebellar peduncle.

Its dorsal or posterior surface (*pars dorsalis pontis*), triangular in shape, is hidden by the cerebellum, and is bounded laterally by the superior cerebellar peduncle; it forms the upper part of the rhomboid fossa, with which it will be described.

Structure (Fig. 694).—Transverse sections of the pons show it to be composed of two parts which differ in appearance and structure: thus, the basilar or ventral portion consists for the most part of fibers arranged in transverse and longitudinal bundles, together with a small amount of gray substance; while the dorsal tegmental portion is a continuation of the reticular formation of the medulla oblongata, and most of its constituents are continued into the tegmentum of the mid-brain.

The **basilar part** of the pons consists of—(a) superficial and deep transverse fibers, (b) longitudinal fasciculi, and (c) gray substance, termed the nuclei pontis which give rise to the transverse fibers.

The **superficial transverse fibers** (*fibræ pontis superficiales*) constitute a rather thick layer on the ventral surface of the pons, and are collected into a large rounded bundle on either side of the middle line. This bundle, with the addition of some transverse fibers from the deeper part of the pons, forms the greater part of the brachium pontis.

The **deep transverse fibers** (*fibræ pontis profundæ*) partly intersect and partly lie on the dorsal aspect of the cerebrospinal fibers. They course to the lateral border of the pons, and form part of the middle peduncle; the further connections of this brachium will be discussed with the anatomy of the cerebellum.

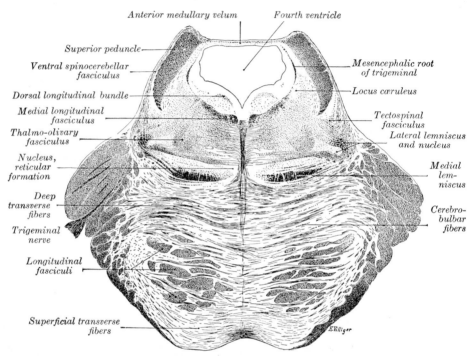

Anterior medullary velum   Fourth ventricle

Superior peduncle

Ventral spinocerebellar fasciculus

Dorsal longitudinal bundle

Medial longitudinal fasciculus

Thalmo-olivary fasciculus

Nucleus, reticular formation

Deep transverse fibers

Trigeminal nerve

Longitudinal fasciculi

Superficial transverse fibers

Mesencephalic root of trigeminal

Locus cæruleus

Tectospinal fasciculus

Lateral lemniscus and nucleus

Medial lemniscus

Cerebro-bulbar fibers

FIG. 694.—Section through upper part of the pons. (Villiger.)

The **longitudinal fasciculi** consist of three groups of fibers which enter the pons through the cerebral peduncles. 1. The **cortico-spinal** tract enters in the middle third of the cerebral peduncle, breaks up into bundles of varying size and becomes compact again at the caudal margin of the pons where it continues caudalward as the pyramid. The fibers give off collaterals to the pontile nuclei on their way through the pons. 2. Certain of the **aberrant pyramidal fibers** (cortico-bulbar fibers) enter the pons through the medial margin of the peduncle and then, turning dorsally, they leave the fascicles of the descending corticofugal fibers, and pass into the tegmentum and finally end in relation to the cells of the cranial motor nerves. They will be referred to again later. 3. The **cortico-pontile** fibers form two main groups: the **fronto-pontile** fibers, which arise from pyramidal cells in the frontal lobe (largely Area 6 of Brodmann), run through the anterior limb of the internal capsule and the medial third of the peduncle; the **parieto-temporo-pontile** fibers, from the parietal and temporal lobes run through the posterior limb and sublenticular portions of the internal capsule and the lateral third of the cerebral peduncle. The cortico-pontile fibers terminate on cells of the pontile nuclei on the same side as the fibers originate. The axons of the pontile cells form the transverse fibers and cross to the opposite side where they ascend to the cerebellum through the brachium pontis. They end in the cortex of the lateral lobes.

The **nuclei pontis** consist of small groups of multipolar nerve cells which are scattered between the bundles of transverse fibers.

The **dorsal or tegmental part** of the pons is chiefly composed of an upward continuation of the reticular formation and gray substance of the medulla oblongata. It consists of transverse and longitudinal fibers and also contains important gray nuclei, and is subdivided by a median raphé, which, however, does not extend into the basilar part, being obliterated by the transverse fibers.

The course through the pons of certain of the long tracts, viz., the medial lemniscus, the ventral and lateral spinothalamic tracts, the ventral spinocerebellar tract, the thalamo-olivary fasciculus, and the medial longitudinal fasciculus, have been described in the section on the medulla oblongata. In addition two other systems are seen here. Certain **aberrant pyramidal** fibers leave the medial margins of the cerebral peduncles in the mid-brain and run caudalward just medial to the medial lemniscus through the pons. Most of them cross, but apparently some remain ipsilateral, and supply the motor nuclei of the fifth, tenth, eleventh and twelfth cranial nerves. The **trapezoid body** is a heavily staining group of transversely oriented fibers in the caudal part of the tegmentum of the pons. It is continuous with the **lateral lemniscus** which proceeds rostrally and slightly laterally, at first dorsal and then lateral to the spinothalamic tracts, to end in the inferior colliculus and medial geniculate. These are parts of the acoustic system and will be referred to later.

The gray columns of the spinal cord and medulla oblongata are continued into the pons where they are represented by the following structures.

1. Motor nuclei. In the dorso-medial column of motor nuclei (Fig. 689) is the **nucleus of the abducent nerve** (*nucleus n. abducentis*). It is situated close to the floor of the ventricle, subjacent to the medial eminence. The cells are of the motor type. The fibers pass forward through the entire thickness of the pons on the medial side of the superior olivary nucleus, and between the lateral fasciculi of the cerebrospinal fibers, and emerge in the furrow between the lower border of the pons and the pyramid of the medulla oblongata.

The **nucleus of the facial nerve** (*nucleus n. facialis*) lies in the ventro-lateral column of motor nuclei. It is situated deeply in the reticular formation of the pons, on the dorsal aspect of the superior olivary nucleus, and the roots of the nerve derived from it pursue a remarkably tortuous course in the substance of the pons. At first they pass backward and medialward until they reach the rhomboid fossa, close to the median sulcus, where they are collected into a round bundle; this passes upward and forward, producing an elevation, the **colliculus facialis,** in the rhomboid fossa, and then takes a sharp bend, and arches lateralward through the substance of the pons to emerge at its lower border in the interval between the olive and the inferior peduncle of the medulla oblongata. The cells, motor in type, are arranged in groups in which the separate facial muscles are represented.

The **motor nucleus of the trigeminal nerve** (*nucleus motorius n. trigemini*) is the most rostral of the ventro-lateral motor nuclei. It is situated in the upper part of the pons, close to its posterior surface and along the line of the lateral margin of the fourth ventricle. It consists of large cells of the motor type. Their axons form the motor root of the trigeminal nerve.

2. No nuclei of the autonomic column have been definitely identified.

3. Sensory nuclei. The **main sensory nucleus of the trigeminal nerve** (*nucleus sensorius n. trigemini*) is situated lateral to the motor nucleus, and beneath the superior cerebellar peduncle. Its cells are of medium and small size. It receives

the ascending branches of the entering trigeminal fibers and its axons cross to the opposite side to join the medial margin of the medial lemniscus and ascend with it to the thalamus. The **substantia gelatinosa trigemini**, or nucleus of the descending tract of the trigeminal nerve, is a direct continuation of the substantia gelatinosa Rolandi of the spinal cord. It receives the descending branches of the trigeminal fibers and its axons cross the mid-line and run forward to the thalamus just medial to the lateral spinothalamic tract. These two nuclei subserve the same functions for the head respectively as the posterior columns and spinothalamic tracts do for the body. The **mesencephalic root** of the trigeminal consists of fibers which arise from cells scattered in a layer over the central gray round the aqueduct. Their axons gather at the ventro-lateral corner of the central gray and descend to pass between the motor and sensory trigeminal nuclei and then join the motor root. They proceed with the motor root to the mandibular branch of the nerve and are thought to be proprioceptive for the muscles of mastication.

The **nuclei of the vestibular nerve** make up a large, roughly diamond-shaped mass of gray which forms a considerable part of the lateral floor and wall of the fourth ventricle in the pons and medulla. The exact subdivisions are not known, but commonly the following nuclei are described: (a) The **superior vestibular nucleus** or **nucleus of Bechterew**, which lies just caudal to the trigeminal motor nucleus in the angle of the floor and lateral wall of the ventricle. It extends dorsally in the wall and is almost continuous with the roof nuclei of the cerebellum. (b) The **medial** (**chief** or **triangular**) **vestibular nucleus** or **nucleus** of **Schwalbe** is the largest and occupies the greater part of the **area acoustica** in the rhomboid fossa. A prolongation of this nucleus extending between the rostral poles of the hypoglossal nucleus and the dorsal motor nucleus of the vagus is known as the **nucleus intercalatus**. The cells of the superior and medial nuclei are small. Many of their axons enter the medial longitudinal fasciculus, others pass to medullary nuclei, particularly the vagus, and still others connect with secondary vestibular centers in the reticular substance, such as the **nucleus prepositus hypoglossi**, which lies between the hypoglossal and abducent nuclei. In addition, there are numerous connections with the cerebellum, particularly from the superior nucleus. (c) The **lateral** (or **magnocellular**) **vestibular nucleus** or **nucleus of Deiters** lies next to the restiform body at the level of entrance of the vestibular nerve. Its cells are large, somewhat resembling the motor type and their axons pass at first medially and then turn caudo-ventrally to form the direct vestibulo-spinal tract. (d) The **inferior vestibular nucleus** or **nucleus of the descending tract of the vestibular nerve** extends from the lateral nucleus almost to the nucleus cuneatus. It lies medial to the restiform body and dorsal to the spinal trigeminal tract. The cells in its lateral portion are large, but medially they are smaller. It contributes fibers to the medial longitudinal fasciculus and gives rise to the crossed vestibulo-spinal tract. There are numerous connections with centers in the reticular substance and it also sends fibers into the restiform body.

The fibers of the vestibular nerves form the caudal halves of the eighth pair of cranial nerves, the cochlear, the rostral halves. The vestibular fibers enter the medulla between the restiform body and spinal tract of the trigeminal and divide into ascending and descending branches. The ascending fibers from the semicircular canals pass to the more rostral part of the medial and to the superior nuclei, those from the maculæ go to the caudal and lateral parts of the medial and to the lateral nuclei. Some authors have described vestibular nerve fibers proceeding directly to the cerebellum. The descending branches of both groups form the descending tract and terminate in its nucleus.

The **nuclei of the cochlear nerve** (*nuclei n. cochlearis*) or **acoustic nuclei** are two in number: (a) the **dorsal cochlear nucleus** forms the tuberculum acusticum on the dorso-lateral surface of the inferior cerebellar peduncle; (b) the **ventral cochlear** nucleus lies on the ventro-lateral aspect of the inferior peduncle at the entrance of the cochlear fibers. On entering, the cochlear fibers divide into two branches, the ascending terminating in the ventral nucleus, the descending in the dorsal. The second neurons pass to the superior olive, the trapezoid body and lateral lemniscus, and are about 60 per cent. crossed. They will be referred to again.

4. The gray of the floor of the fourth ventricle has been described above (p. 806).

5. The **formatio reticularis** of the pons is in general similar in composition and structure to that of the medulla. Just rostral to the motor trigeminal nucleus in the floor of the ventricle is the **locus cæruleus**, a bluish-gray area, which owes its color to the underlying **substantia ferruginea**. The latter consists of a group of deeply pigmented cells which has a specialized, dense capillary bed. This appears to be a secondary trigeminal center of specialized function. Heavy bands of transversely running fibers in the superficial rostral part of the reticular substance are probably interconnections between the trigeminal systems of the two sides.

The Cerebellum.

The cerebellum lies behind the pons and medulla oblongata. It rests on the inferior occipital fossæ, while above it is the tentorium cerebelli, a fold of dura mater which separates it from the tentorial surface of the cerebrum. It is somewhat oval in form, but constricted medially and flattened from above downward, its greatest diameter being from side to side. Its surface is not convoluted like that of the cerebrum, but is traversed by numerous curved furrows or sulci, which vary in depth at different parts, and separate the laminæ of which it is composed. Its average weight in the male is about 150 gms. In the adult the proportion between the cerebellum and cerebrum is about 1 to 8, in the infant about 1 to 20.

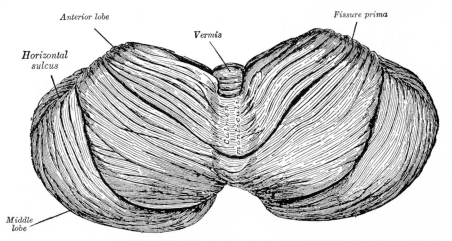

FIG. 695.—Upper surface of the cerebellum. (Schäfer.)

The cerebellum is characterized by a laminated or foliated appearance; it is marked by deep, somewhat curved fissures, which extend for a considerable distance into its substance, and divide it into several lobes. These are further subdivided by shallower sulci, which separate the individual folia or laminæ from each other. Sections across the laminæ show that the folia, though differing in appearance from the convolutions of the cerebrum, are analogous to them, inasmuch as they consist of central white substance covered by gray substance.

The cerebellum is connected to the mid-brain by the superior peduncles, to the pons by the middle peduncles, and to the medulla oblongata by the inferior peduncles.

Subdivisions of the Cerebellum (Figs. 695, 696 and 697).—On gross inspection, the cerebellum is seen to be divided into the two **lateral hemispheres**, and the **vermis** between and partially covered by them. This subdivision is topographically useful,

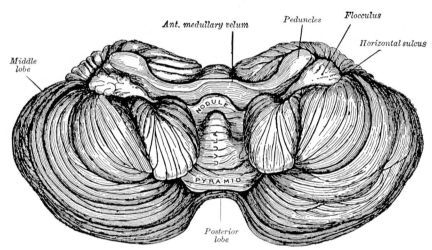

FIG. 696.—Under surface of the cerebellum. (Schäfer.)

but is not fundamental. Studies of the comparative anatomy and embryology of the cerebellum have led to a more basic analysis, as follows:

1. The **flocculonodular lobe**, consisting of the nodulus of the vermis and the flocculi, which are attached one on each side to the nodulus by peduncles containing myelinated fibers.

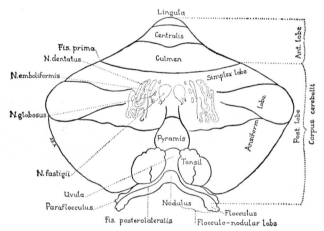

FIG. 697.—Diagrammatic representation of the lobes of the cerebellum redrawn after Larsell with the cerebellar nuclei as illustrated by Jakob projected in dotted lines.

2. The **body of the cerebellum** (**corpus cerebelli**), which is separated from the flocculonodular lobe by the **posterolateral fissure**, the earliest fissure to appear. The corpus is further divided into an **anterior lobe** and a **posterior lobe** by the **fissura prima**, the second fissure to appear and the deepest.

The anterior lobe consists of the lingula, continuous with the anterior medullary velum, and of the central lobule and culmen monticuli with their lateral expansions. The posterior lobe makes up the greater part of the cerebellum and consists of the following parts: (*a*) the **lobus simplex,** immediately behind the primary fissure; (*b*) the **medial lobule** (Ingvar), consisting of the tuber and folium of the vermis; (*c*) the **ansiform lobules,** paired lateral structures which include the remainder of the cerebellar hemispheres and the tonsils; (*d*) the **posteromedian lobule,** a mid-line structure composed of the pyramis and uvula of the vermis. The ansiform lobules are phylogenetically related to the medial lobule. In lower forms, but absent in the human, paired lateral structures, the **paraflocculi,** are found connected by peduncles with the posteromedian lobule.

Internal Structure of the Cerebellum.—The cerebellum consists of an outer layer of gray substance, the cortex, and an inner mass of white substance in which are imbedded four masses of gray substance on each side, the **roof nuclei of the cerebellum.**

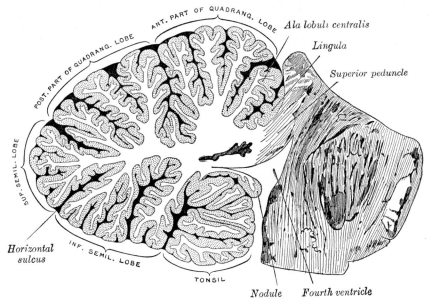

Fig. 698.—Sagitta section of the cerebellum, near the junction of the vermis with the hemisphere. (Schäfer.)

White Substance.—If a sagittal section (Fig. 698) be made through either hemisphere, the interior will be found to consist of a central stem of white substance, in the middle of which is a gray mass, the **dentate nucleus.** From the surface of this central white stem a series of plates is prolonged; these are covered with gray substance and form the laminæ. In consequence of the main branches from the central stem dividing and subdividing, a characteristic appearance, named the **arbor vitæ,** is presented.

The white substance of the cerebellum includes two sets of nerve fibers: (1) **projection fibers,** (2) **fibræ propriæ.**

Projection Fibers.—The cerebellum is connected to the other parts of the brain by three large bundles of projection fibers, viz., to the mid-brain and the thalamus by the superior peduncles, to the pons by the middle peduncles, and to the medulla oblongata and the spinal cord by the inferior peduncles (Fig. 699).

The **superior cerebellar peduncles** (*brachia conjunctiva*) emerge from the upper and medial part of the white substance of the hemispheres and are placed under cover of the upper part of the cerebellum. They enter the lateral walls of the fourth ventricle, being separated dorsally by the anterior medullary velum. As they ascend they sink deeply into the tegmentum, decussate completely in the mesencephalon at the level of the inferior colliculi below the aqueduct of Sylvius and turn upward. The fibers of the superior peduncle are mainly derived from the cells of the dentate nucleus of the cerebellum and emerge from the hilum of this nucleus; others come from the nucleus emboliformis; a few arise from the cells of the nucleus globosus and the nucleus fastigii in the cerebellar white substance. Many of the fibers end in the red nucleus, the reticular substance around this nucleus and in the antero-lateral part of the ventral nucleus of the thalamus. The majority of the fibers of the **ventral spinocerebellar fasciculus** of the medulla spinalis pass to the cerebellum, which they reach by way of the superior peduncle. They terminate in the anterior part of the vermis and in the nucleus fastigii.

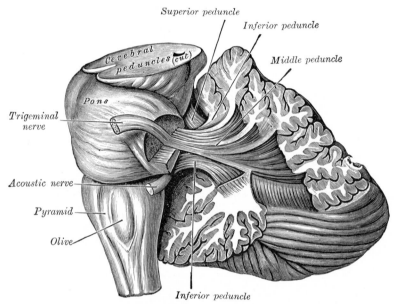

FIG. 699.—Dissection showing the projection fibers of the cerebellum.   (After E. B. Jamieson.)

The **uncinate fasciculus** (hook bundle of Risien Russell) arises in the *nn. fastigii* and *globosus;* 60 to 70 per cent of the fibers promptly decussate just dorsal to the nuclei; the tract runs along the margin of the superior cerebellar peduncle just medial to the ventral spinocerebellar, hooks around the peduncle at the same level as does the ventral spinocerebellar and terminates in the vestibular nuclei and in the reticular substance of the medulla on the same side; only a few fibers cross to the reticular substance on the opposite side.

The **middle cerebellar peduncles** (*brachia pontis*) (Fig. 699) are composed entirely of centripetal fibers, which arise from the cells of the nuclei pontis of the opposite side and end in the cerebellar cortex; the fibers are arranged in three fasciculi, superior, inferior, and deep. The **superior fasciculus**, the most superficial, is derived from the upper transverse fibers of the pons; it is directed backward and lateralward superficial to the other two fasciculi, and is distributed mainly to the lobules on the inferior surface of the cerebellar hemisphere and to the parts of the superior surface adjoining the posterior and lateral margins. The **inferior fasciculus** is formed by the lowest transverse fibers of the pons; it passes under cover of the superior fasciculus and is continued downward and backward more or less parallel with it, to be distributed to the folia on the under surface close to the vermis. The **deep fasciculus** comprises most of the deep transverse fibers of the pons. It is at first covered by the superior and inferior fasciculi, but crosses obliquely and appears on the medial side of the superior, from which it receives a bundle; its fibers spread out and pass to the upper anterior cerebellar folia. The fibers of this fasciculus cover those of the restiform body. Cortico-pontile fibers from the frontal and temporal lobes of the cerebrum end in the nuclei pontis and thus establish a crossed cortico-ponto-cerebellar path.

The **inferior cerebellar peduncles** (*restiform bodies*) pass at first upward and lateral-ward, forming part of the lateral walls of the fourth ventricle, and then bend abruptly backward to enter the cerebellum between the superior and middle peduncles. Each contains the following fasciculi: (1) the dorsal spinocerebellar fasciculus, a proprioceptive path from the dorsal nucleus of the same side of the spinal cord, ending mainly in the superior vermis; (2) the dorsal external arcuate fibers, a proprioceptive path from the gracile and cuneate nuclei of the same side; (3) the olivocerebellar fasciculus from the inferior olivary nuclei, mostly crossed, to the cortex of the hemispheres and the vermis and to the central nuclei; (4) the ventral external arcuate fibers, crossed and uncrossed, from the arcuate and reticular nuclei of the medulla; (5) the vestibulocerebellar fasciculus, a proprioceptive path, derived partly from direct ascending branches of the vestibular nuclei (superior, lateral, inferior and medial, occupying together with fibers from the sensory nuclei of the cranial nerves the *medial segment* of the peduncle, and ends in the cortex of the vermis and in the fastigial nuclei; (6) cerebellar fibers from the roof nuclei to all the vestibular nuclei and to the reticular formation.

The **Fibræ Propriæ** of the cerebellum are of two kinds: (1) **commissural fibers**, which cross the middle line at the anterior and posterior parts of the vermis and connect the opposite halves of the cerebellum; (2) **arcuate or association fibers**, which connect adjacent laminæ with each other.

Gray Substance.—The gray substance of the cerebellum is found in two situations: (1) on the surface, forming the cortex; (2) as independent masses in the interior.

(1) The **gray substance of the cortex** presents a characteristic foliated appearance, due to the series of laminæ which are given off from the central white substance; these in their turn give off secondary laminæ, which are covered by gray substance. Externally, the cortex is covered by pia mater; internally is the medullary center, consisting mainly of nerve fibers.

Microscopic Appearance of the Cortex (Fig. 700).—The cortex consists of two layers, viz., an external gray molecular layer, and an internal rust-colored nuclear layer; between these is an incomplete stratum of cells which are characteristic of the cerebellum, viz., the **cells of Purkinje**.

The **external gray** or **molecular layer** consists of fibers and cells. The nerve fibers are delicate fibrillæ, and are derived from the following sources: (*a*) the dendrites and axon collaterals of Purkinje's cells; (*b*) fibers from cells in the nuclear layer; (*c*) fibers from the central white substance of the cerebellum; (*d*) fibers derived from cells in the molecular layer itself. In addition to these are other fibers, which have a vertical direction, and are the processes of large neuroglia cells, situated in the nuclear layer. They pass outward to the periphery of the gray matter, where they expand into little conical enlargements which form a sort of limiting membrane beneath the pia mater, analogous to the membrana limitans interna in the retina, formed by the sustentacular fibers of Müller.

The **cells of the molecular layer** are small, and are arranged in two strata, an outer and an inner; they all possess branched axons. The cells of the inner layer are termed **basket cells**; their axons run for some distance parallel with the surface of the folium—giving off collaterals which pass in a vertical direction toward the bodies of Purkinje's cells, around which they become enlarged, and form basket-like net-works.

The **cells of Purkinje** form a single stratum of large, flask-shaped cells at the junction of the molecular and nuclear layers, their bases resting against the latter;

in fishes and reptiles they are arranged in several layers. The cells are flattened in a direction transverse to the long axis of the folium, and thus appear broad in sections carried across the folium, and fusiform in sections parallel to the long axis of the folium. From the neck of the flask one or more dendrites arise and pass into the molecular layer, where they subdivide and form an extremely rich arborescence, the various subdivisions of the dendrites being covered by lateral spinelike processes. This arborescence is not circular, but, like the cell, is flattened at right angles to the long axis of the folium; in other words, it does not resemble

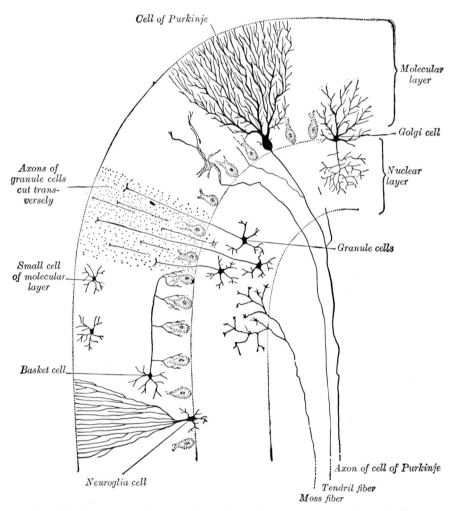

Fig. 700.—Transverse section of a cerebellar folium. (Diagrammatic, after Cajal and Kölliker.)

a round bush, but has been aptly compared by Obersteiner to the branches of a fruit tree trained against a trellis or a wall. Hence, in sections carried across the folium the arborescence is broad and expanded; whereas in those which are parallel to the long axis of the folium, the arborescence, like the cell itself, is seen in profile, and is limited to a narrow area.

From the bottom of the flask-shaped cell the axon arises; this passes through the nuclear layer, and, becoming medullated, is continued as a nerve fiber in the subjacent white substance. As the axon traverses the granular layer it gives off fine collaterals, some of which run back into the molecular layer.

The axons of almost all the Purkinje cells end in the roof nuclei of the cerebellum; those from the anterior, flocculonodular and posteromedian lobes chiefly in the nucleus fastigii; those from the ansiform lobes chiefly in the nucleus dentatus. A few from the flocculonodular lobe pass to the vestibular nuclei of the medulla.

The **internal rust-colored** or **nuclear layer** (Fig. 700) is characterized by containing numerous small nerve cells of a reddish-brown color, together with many nerve fibrils. Most of the cells are nearly spherical and provided with short dendrites which spread out in a spider-like manner in the nuclear layer. Their axons pass outward into the molecular layer, and, bifurcating at right angles, run for some distance parallel with the surface. In the outer part of the nuclear layer are some larger cells, of the type II of Golgi. Their axons undergo frequent division as soon as they leave the nerve cells, and pass into the nuclear layer; while their dendrites ramify chiefly in the molecular layer.

The great majority of the centripetal, or afferent fibers to the cerebellum terminate in the cortex in either the one or the other of two different types of relationship to the cortical cells. (1) Some of the fibers end in the nuclear layer by dividing into numerous branches, on which are to be seen peculiar moss-like appendages;

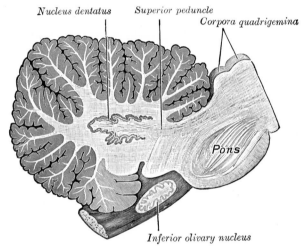

FIG. 701.—Sagittal section through right cerebellar hemisphere. The right olive has also been cut sagittally.

hence they have been termed by Ramón y Cajal the **moss fibers**; they form an arborescence around the cells of the nuclear layer and are said to come mainly from fibers in the inferior peduncle. (2) Other fibers, the **clinging** or **tendril fibers**, derived from the medullary center can be traced into the molecular layer, where their branches cling around the dendrites of Purkinje's cells. They are said to come mainly from fibers of the middle peduncle. Consideration of the connections made by these two types of fibers shows that the mossy fibers would tend to activate a large area of the cortex, whereas the clinging fibers have a very localized effect except as that effect is later spread through the collaterals of the Purkinje cell axons which reënter the cortex.

(2) The **independent centers of gray substance** in the cerebellum are four in number on either side: one is of large size, and is known as the **nucleus dentatus**; the other three, much smaller, are situated near the middle of the cerebellum, and are known as the **nucleus emboliformis, nucleus globosus**, and **nucleus fastigii** (Fig. 697). The cells of these nuclei are medium to moderately large in size, polygonal in shape, with long, branching dendrites. Those of the nucleus dentatus are characterized by a high concentration of iron salts (Fig. 643, ϱ).

The **nucleus dentatus** (Fig. 701) is situated a little to the medial side of the center of the stem of the white substance of the hemisphere. It consists of an irregularly folded lamina, of a grayish-yellow color, containing white fibers, and presenting on its antero-medial aspect an opening, the **hilum**, from which most of the fibers of the superior peduncle emerge (page 809).

The **nucleus emboliformis** lies immediately to the medial side of the nucleus dentatus, and partly covering its hilum. It is an elongated mass, directed antero-posteriorly.

The **nucleus globosus** consists of several small, irregular groups of cells in the white matter between the nucleus emboliformis and the nucleus fastigii. Some authors regard the nuclei emboliformis and globosus as two parts of one mass, called the nucleus interpositus.

The **nucleus fastigii** is somewhat larger than the other two, and is situated close to the middle line at the anterior end of the superior vermis, and immediately over the roof of the fourth ventricle, from which it is separated by a thin layer of white substance.

Function.—The uniform structure of the cerebellar cortex indicates that the influence is of one kind only, and that localization is dependent on the site of origin of the afferents and of the termination of the efferents. For the most part the cerebellar efferents end in centers in the medulla, the mid-brain and the thalamus which are concerned with complex motor responses. It is probable that the function of the cerebellum in general is to coördinate the activity of these motor centers, reinforcing some and inhibiting others, in such a way as to result in smooth and accurate movements. The fact that deficiencies resulting from injuries to the cerebellum are ipsilateral to the lesion is in keeping with the anatomical findings that the main cerebellar systems either do not cross the mid-line, or else cross and then recross to the original side. A more strict localization is still problematical, though there is good evidence that the rostral parts of the body are represented rostrally in the cerebellum and the caudal parts caudally.

The Fourth Ventricle (Ventriculus Quartus).

The fourth ventricle, or cavity of the hind-brain, is situated in front of the cerebellum and behind the pons and upper half of the medulla oblongata. It is lined by ciliated epithelium. Its **superior angle** is on a level with the upper border of the pons, and is continuous with the lower end of the cerebral aqueduct. The **inferior angle** is on a level with the lower end of the olive, and opens into the central canal of the medulla oblongata. On a level with the striæ medullares, the ventricular cavity is prolonged outward in the form of two narrow **lateral recesses**, one on either side; these are situated between the inferior peduncles and the flocculi, and reach as far as the attachments of the glossopharyngeal and vagus nerves.

Lateral Boundaries.—The caudal part of each lateral boundary is constituted by the clava, the fasciculus cuneatus, and the inferior peduncle; the rostral part by the middle and the superior peduncle.

Roof or **Dorsal Wall** (Fig. 702).—The upper portion of the roof is formed by the superior peduncle and the anterior medullary velum; the lower portion, by the posterior medullary velum, the epithelial lining of the ventricle covered by the tela chorioidea inferior, the tæniæ of the fourth ventricle, and the obex.

The **superior peduncles** (page 809), on emerging from the central white substance of the cerebellum, pass upward and forward, forming at first the lateral boundaries of the upper part of the cavity; on approaching the inferior colliculi, they converge, and their medial portions overlap the cavity and form part of its roof.

The **anterior medullary velum** (*velum medullare anterius; valve of Vieussens; superior medullary velum*) is a thin, transparent lamina of white substance, which stretches between the superior cerebellar peduncles; on the dorsal surface of its lower half the folia of the lingula are prolonged. It forms, together with the superior cerebellar peduncles, the roof of the upper part of the fourth ventricle; it is narrow above, where it passes beneath the inferior colliculi, and broader below, where it is continuous with the white substance of the superior vermis. A slightly elevated ridge, the **frænulum veli,** descends upon its upper part from between the inferior colliculi, and on either side of this the trochlear nerve emerges.

The **posterior medullary velum,** a thin sheet of ependymal epithelium and pia mater, forms the roof of the lower part of the fourth ventricle. It extends from the under surface of the cerebellum, near the line of origin of the anterior medullary velum, to the inferior cerebellar peduncles and the clavæ. Its attachment at the lower apex is known as the **obex** and that along the clava and peduncle as the **tænia.** It extends laterally over the peduncle to form a lateral recess. The pia mater covering the ependyma is rich in bloodvessels and is known as the **tela chorioidea.**

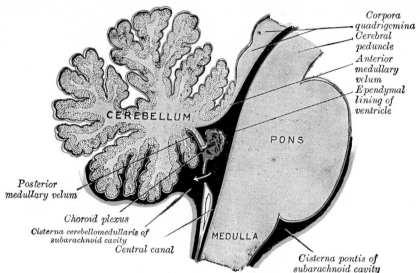

FIG. 702.—Scheme of roof of fourth ventricle. The arrow is in the foramen of Majendie.

Choroid Plexuses.—These consist of two highly vascular inflexions of the tela chorioidea, which invaginate the lower part of the roof of the ventricle and are everywhere covered by the epithelial lining of the cavity. Each consists of a vertical and a horizontal portion: the former lies close to the middle line, and the latter passes into the lateral recess and projects beyond its apex. The vertical parts of the plexuses are distinct from each other, but the horizontal portions are joined in the middle line; and hence the entire structure presents the form of the letter T, the vertical limb of which, however, is double.

Openings in the Roof.—In the roof of the fourth ventricle there are three openings, a medial and two lateral: the **medial aperture** (*foramen Majendii*), is situated immediately above the inferior angle of the ventricle; the **lateral apertures,** (*foramina of Luschka* are found at the extremities of the lateral recesses. By means of these three openings the ventricle communicates with the subarachnoid cavity, and the cerebrospinal fluid can circulate from the one to the other.

Rhomboid Fossa (*fossa rhomboidea; "floor" of the fourth ventricle*) (Fig. 703).— The anterior part of the fourth ventricle is named, from its shape, the **rhomboid fossa,** and its anterior wall, formed by the back of the pons and medulla oblongata, constitutes the floor of the fourth ventricle. It is covered by a thin layer of gray substance continuous with that of the medulla spinalis; superficial to this is a thin lamina of neuroglia which constitutes the ependyma of the ventricle. The fossa consists of three parts, superior, intermediate, and inferior. The **superior part** is triangular in shape and limited laterally by the superior cerebellar peduncle; its apex, directed upward, is continuous with the cerebral aqueduct; its base is represented by an imaginary line at the level of the upper ends of the superior foveæ. The **intermediate** part extends from this level to that of the horizontal portions of the tæniæ of the ventricle; it is narrow above where it is limited laterally by the middle peduncle, but widens below and is prolonged into the lateral recesses of the ventricle. The **inferior** part is triangular, and its downwardly directed apex, named the **calamus scriptorius**, is continuous with the central canal of the closed part of the medulla oblongata.

The rhomboid fossa is divided into symmetrical halves by a **median sulcus** which reaches from the upper to the lower angles of the fossa and is deeper below than above. On either side of this sulcus is an elevation, the **medial eminence,** bounded laterally by a sulcus, the **sulcus limitans.** In the superior part of the fossa the medial eminence has a width equal to that of the corresponding half of the

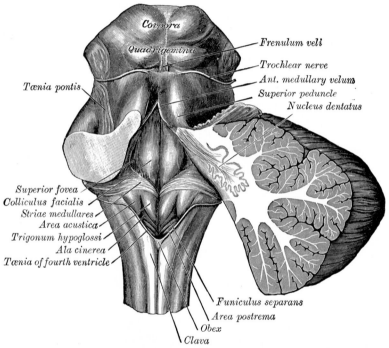

Fig. 703.—Rhomboid fossa.

fossa, but opposite the superior fovea it forms an elongated swelling, the **colliculus facialis,** which overlies the nucleus of the abducent nerve, and is, in part at least, produced by the ascending portion of the root of the facial nerve. In the inferior part of the fossa the medial eminence assumes the form of a triangular area, the **trigonum hypoglossi.** When examined under water with a lens this trigone is seen to consist of a medial and a lateral area separated by a series of oblique furrows; the medial area corresponds with the upper part of the nucleus of the hypoglossal nerve, the lateral with a small nucleus, the **nucleus intercalatus.**

The **sulcus limitans** forms the lateral boundary of the medial eminence. In the superior part of the rhomboid fossa it corresponds with the lateral limit of the fossa and presents a bluish-gray area, the **locus cæruleus,** which owes its color to an underlying patch of deeply pigmented nerve cells, termed the **substantia ferruginea.** At the level of the colliculus facialis the sulcus limitans widens into a flattened depression, the **superior fovea,** and in the inferior part of the fossa appears as a distinct dimple, the **inferior fovea**. Lateral to the foveæ is a rounded elevation named the **area acustica**, which extends into the lateral recess and there forms a feebly marked swelling, the **tuberculum acusticum**. Winding around the inferior peduncle and crossing the area acustica and the medial eminence are a number of white strands, the **striæ medullares**, which disappear into the median sulcus. Below the inferior fovea, and between the trigonum hypoglossi and the lower part of the area acustica is a triangular dark field, the **ala cinerea**, which corresponds to the sensory nucleus of the vagus and glossopharyngeal nerves. The lower end of the ala cinerea is crossed by a narrow translucent ridge, the **funiculus separans**, and between this funiculus and the clava is a small tongue-shaped area, the **area postrema**. On section it is seen that the funiculus separans is formed by a strip of thickened ependyma, and the area postrema by loose, highly vascular, neuroglial tissue containing no nerve cells.

THE MID–BRAIN OR MESENCEPHALON.

The **mid-brain** or **mesencephalon** is the short, constricted segment which connects the pons and cerebellum with the fore-brain. It consists of large ventro-lateral portions, the cerebral peduncles and a dorsal portion, the corpora quadrigemina or tectum. A slender canal, the cerebral aqueduct, passes through the mid-brain and connects the fourth with the third ventricle. Surrounding the aqueduct is the central gray stratum.

The **cerebral peduncles** emerge from the lower surface of the cerebral hemispheres, one on either side, and, converging toward the mid-line as they pass caudalward, enter the upper surface of the pons. The depressed area between them is termed the **interpeduncular fossa**, and consists of a layer of grayish substance, the **posterior perforated substance**, which is pierced by small apertures for the transmission of bloodvessels; its lower part lies on the ventral aspect of the medial portions of the tegmenta, and contains a nucleus named the **interpeduncular ganglion** (page 822); its upper part assists in forming the floor of the third ventricle. The ventral surface of each peduncle is crossed from the medial to the lateral side by the superior cerebellar and

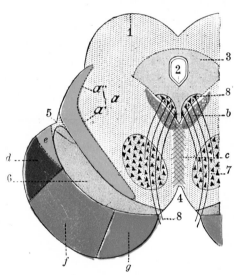

Fig. 704.—Section through mid-brain. (Schematic.) (Testut.) 1. Corpora quadrigemina. 2. Cerebral aqueduct. 3. Central gray stratum. 4. Interpeduncular space. 5. Sulcus lateralis. 6. Substantia nigra. 7. Red nucleus of tegmentum. 8. Oculomotor nerve, with 8', its nucleus of origin. *a.* Lemniscus (in blue) with *a'* the medial lemniscus and *a''* the lateral lemniscus. *b.* Medial longitudinal fasciculus. *c.* Raphé. *d.* Temporo-pontile fibers. *e.* Portion of medial lemniscus, which runs to the lentiform nucleus and insula. *f.* Cerebrospinal fibers. *g.* Frontopontile fibers.

posterior cerebral arteries; its lateral surface is in relation to the gyrus hippocampi of the cerebral hemisphere and is crossed from behind forward by the trochlear nerve. Close to the point of emergence of the peduncle from the cerebral hemisphere, the optic tract winds around its ventro-lateral surface. The medial surface of the peduncle forms the lateral boundary of the interpeduncular fossa, and is marked by a longitudinal furrow, the **oculomotor sulcus**, from which the roots of the oculomotor nerve emerge. On the lateral surface of each peduncle there is a second longitudinal furrow, termed the **lateral sulcus**; the fibers of the lateral lemniscus come close to the surface in this sulcus, and pass backward and upward, to disappear into the inferior colliculus.

52

Structure of the Cerebral Peduncles (Figs. 705, 706).—On transverse section, each peduncle is seen to consist of a dorsal and a ventral part, separated by a deeply pigmented lamina of gray substance, termed the **substantia nigra.**   The dorsal part is named the **tegmentum**; the ventral, the **base** or **crusta**; the two bases are separated

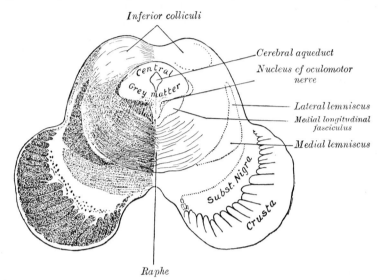

FIG. 705.—Transverse section of mid-brain at level of inferior colliculi.

from each other, but the tegmenta are joined in the median plane by a forward prolongation of the raphé of the pons.   Laterally, the tegmenta are free; dorsally, they blend with the corpora quadrigemina.

The **base** (*basis pedunculi; crusta or pes*) is semilunar on transverse section, and consists almost entirely of longitudinal bundles of efferent fibers, which arise from

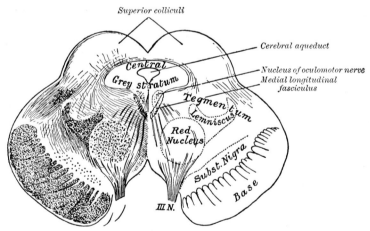

FIG. 706.—Transverse section of mid-brain at level of superior colliculi.

the cells of the cerebral cortex and are grouped into three principal sets, viz., cerebrospinal, fronto-pontile, and temporo-pontile (Fig. 704).   The **cerebrospinal fibers,** derived from the cells of the motor area of the cerebral cortex, occupy the middle three-fifths of the base; they are continued partly to the nuclei of the motor cranial nerves, but mainly into the pyramids of the medulla oblongata. The **fronto-pontile fibers** are situated in the medial fifth of the base; they arise from the cells of the frontal lobe and end in the nuclei of the pons. The **temporo-pontile fibers** are lateral to the cerebrospinal fibers; they originate in the temporal, the parietal and the occipital lobes and are, therefore, sometimes called the parieto-occipito-temporo-pontile fibers. They end in the nuclei pontis. The **cortico-bulbar** fibers, from different areas of the cortex of the cerebral hemispheres, in part accompany the cerebrospinal fibers into the medulla. Others of these fibers form the **aberrant pyramidal tracts** which run in the most medial, most lateral, and in the deepest layers of the crusta. They turn dorsally in groups to pass to the cranial motor nuclei.

The **substantia nigra** (*intercalatum*) is a layer of gray substance containing numerous deeply pigmented, multipolar nerve cells. It is semilunar on transverse section, its concavity being directed toward the tegmentum; from its convexity, prolongations extend between the fibers of the base of the peduncle. Thicker medially than laterally, it reaches from the oculomotor sulcus to the lateral sulcus, and extends from the upper surface of the pons to the subthalamic region. It has two major subdivisions: the **zona compacta**, the layer of gray substance between the crusta and the tegmentum; and the **zona reticulata**, more scattered prolongations of gray substance and cells extending between the bundles of the corticifugal fibers in the crusta. The connections of the cells of the substantia nigra have not been definitely established. It probably receives fibers from the cerebral peduncle, the globus pallidus, the nucleus hypothalamicus (*corpus Luysii*), the colliculi (mainly superior), and from the reticular substance. Some of its efferents run downward in scattered bundles of finely myelinated fibers. Their terminations are unknown. Other efferents enter the crusta and run back towards the hemispheres, probably to terminate in the globus pallidus.

The **tegmentum** is continuous below with the tegmentum of the pons and contains the same columns of gray substance and the continuation of the long fiber tracts met with there, as well as certain additional systems.

In the caudal part of the mid-brain the **lateral lemniscus** turns dorsally close to the surface of the mid-brain and then fans out around the ventrolateral pole of the nucleus of the inferior colliculus. Most of the fibers end there, some continue in the brachium of the inferior colliculus to enter the medial geniculate body. The **ventral** and **lateral spinothalamic tracts**, the **spinotectal tract** and fibers from the substantia gelatinosa trigemini form a compact group close to the lateral surface of the tegmentum, just ventral to the lateral lemniscus. The spinotectal fibers leave the group to enter the deeper layers of the superior colliculus and the other fibers continue into the nucleus ventralis posterolateralis of the thalamus. The **medial lemniscus**, together with the **trigeminal lemniscus** from the main sensory nucleus of the trigeminal, make up a triangular shaped bundle medial to the spinothalamic tracts, at first just lateral to the decussation of the superior cerebellar peduncle and further rostrally, fitting into the angle between the red nucleus and substantia nigra. The fibers continue parallel into the thalamus. The **medial longitudinal fasciculus** occupies the same relative position as in the pons, ventral to the mid-line motor nuclei. Most of its fibers terminate in the nuclei of the trochlear and oculomotor nerves, a few continue forward into the subthalamic region. The **thalamo-olivary fasciculus** is first seen in the reticular substance ventrolateral to the central gray round the aqueduct at the rostral part of the mid-brain. It increases in size and shifts slightly ventrolaterally as it passes caudalward. It can hardly be recognized where its fibers pass between those of the superior cerebellar peduncle at the level of the decussation of the latter. Its origin is not known; the fibers probably arise in several different diencephalic and mesencephalic centers. The **tecto-spinal** tract will be referred to below (page 821). The **rubro-spinal tract** arises in the caudal part of the red nucleus and promptly decussates in the ventral tegmental decussation. It then passes laterally to a position just medial to the spinothalamic tracts and then turns caudalward, through the lateral part of the tegmentum into the lateral column of the spinal cord. The superior cerebellar peduncles enter the tegmentum and decussate, **decussation of the superior cerebellar peduncles,** ventral to the central gray stratum at the level of the inferior colliculus. After decussation the fibers ascend, many end in the red nucleus and the neighboring reticular substance, and others pass through the medial capsule of the red nucleus and continue to the nucleus ventralis lateralis of the thalamus. The latter are accompanied by **reticulo-** and **rubro-thalamic** fibers. This group of afferents to the thalamus run in a position medial and ventral to the medial lemniscus. Other

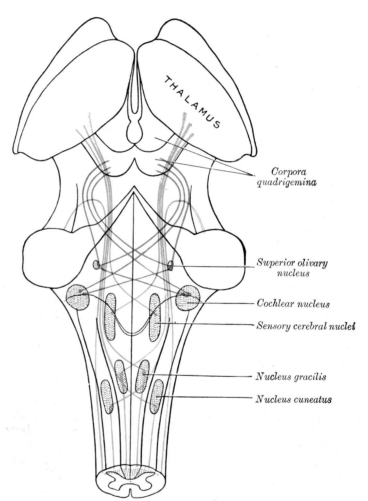

Fig. 707.—Scheme showing the course of the fibers of the lemniscus; medial lemniscus in blue, lateral in red.

reticulo-thalamic fibers run in more scattered fascicles just lateral to the medial lemniscus. **Reticulo-spinal** pathways exist, but their exact origin and course are not known. Other descending tracts from the hypothalamus and from extrapyramidal centers in the diencephalon will be referred to later.

In addition to the decussation of the superior cerebellar peduncles, already described, and the decussation of the tecto-spinal tracts in the dorsal tegmental or fountain decussion of Meynert (page 823) a large number of fibers cross the midline of the tegmentum and make up the ventral tegmental decussation (tegmental decussation of Forel). This extends from the decussation of the superior cerebellar peduncles almost as far forward as the mammillary bodies. The rubro-spinal tract crosses in its caudal part and it contains a number of commissural fibers between the red nuclei. The origins and terminations of most of the fibers, however, are unknown. They probably include crossed connections between centers in the formatio reticularis and descending crossed fibers of extrapyramidal systems.

Rostral to the tegmental decussation of Forel, dorsal and slightly caudal to the mammillary bodies is the supramammillary decussation of Forel. It is at least in part diencephalic, but inasmuch as it consists of fibers which probably interconnect extrapyramidal centers of the mesencephalon and diencephalon it may be considered here. In humans it is not as sharply demarcated from the tegmental decussation of Forel as it is in lower forms and the two are often included in the term the decussation of Forel.

The gray substance of the tegmentum includes continuations of the gray columns of the spinal cord, medulla and pons as well as certain additional structures.

(1) Motor nuclei. The **trochlear nucleus** consists of a compact group of cells near the mid-line, in the dorso-medial margin of the medial longitudinal fasciculus at the level of the inferior colliculus. The cells are large, of the motor type and appear yellowish due to the pigment they contain. Its fibers pass dorso-laterally to swing around the central gray stratum and decussate in the anterior medullary velum. They emerge from the dorsal surface of the brain just caudal to the inferior colliculus.

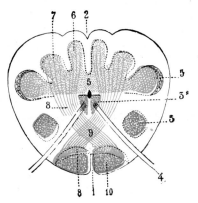

FIG. 708.—Transverse section passing through the sensory decussation. Schematic. (Testut.) 1. Anterior median fissure. 2. Posterior median sulcus. 3, 3′. Head and base of anterior column (in red). 4. Hypoglossal nerve. 5. Bases of posterior column. 6. Gracile nucleus. 7. Cuneate nucleus. 8, 8. Lemniscus. 9. Sensory decussation. 10. Cerebrospinal fasciculus.

The **oculomotor nucleus** lies immediately rostral to the trochlear nucleus. The cells are of the large, motor type and form a column which extends as far as the rostral pole of the superior colliculus. It is not as compact as the trochlear nucleus, the cells being separated by fibers of the medial longitudinal fasciculus. A subdivision of somewhat smaller cells bridges the mid-line and extends from the nucleus of one side to that of the other. This is known as the **nucleus of Perlia** and is supposed to be the center for convergence of the eyes. The two oculomotor nuclei together with the nucleus of Perlia form the shape of the letter H.

(2) Autonomic nuclei. A column of cells of the autonomic type extends as a cap over the trochlear and oculomotor nuclei throughout their extent. It is sometimes called the **dorsal tegmental nucleus**. At its rostral end certain of the cells of this column form a group which bears the name of the **Edinger-Westphal nucleus**. The fibers of the latter pass out with the oculomotor nerve to the ciliary ganglion, from which post-ganglionic fibers go to the pupillo-constrictor muscle.

(3) Sensory nuclei. The **nucleus of the mesencephalic root of the trigeminal nerve** consists of cells, quite similar to those of the sensory type, scattered in groups over the dorsal and lateral surfaces of the central gray stratum. The fibers collect in a small bundle at the ventro-lateral corner of the stratum and run caudalward to the nuclei of the trigeminal where they enter the motor root. They give off collaterals to the motor nucleus. It is thought that they subserve certain proprioceptive functions for the muscles of mastication. Certain authors, however, doubt that they are sensory.

(4) The **stratum griseum centrale** (central gray stratum, central gray round the aqueduct) surrounds the aqueduct and is continuous caudally with the gray of the floor of the fourth ventricle and rostrally with the periventricular system of

the hypothalamus (the substantia grisia ventriculi tertii). It consists of nerve cells of different sizes, mostly small, arranged in a number of groups, and of fibers which for the most part are non-myelinated or finely myelinated. One of the better defined nuclei is the nucleus of Darkschewitz, in the ventrolateral margin of the stratum. This consists of larger cells and is also called the nucleus of the medial longitudinal fasciculus, since it receives connections from and contributes fibers to that bundle. The central gray stratum appears for the most part to be an important autonomic correlation center. The dorsal fasciculus of Schütz, as well as other hypothalamic systems run through it.

(5) The **formatio reticularis mesencephali** (substantia reticulata) is continuous caudally with the formatio reticularis of the pons and rostrally with the reticular nucleus of the thalamus, the zona incerta, and the lateral hypothalamic area. It is sometimes subdivided for topographical purposes into a central nucleus, which lies between the red nuclei; lateral nuclei, lateral to the red nuclei, and dorso-lateral nuclei, ventral to the colliculi. As in the pons and medulla, the reticular substance consists of a number of cell groups with their interconnecting fibers, few of which have been adequately defined. A number of the groups contain pigmented cells, suggestive of a relationship with the nigral and rubral systems. The **nucleus interstitialis of Cajal** consists of moderately large cells in the reticular substance in the angle between the red nucleus and the central gray substance. It is connected with the medial longitudinal fasciculus.

(6) The **nucleus ruber** (red nucleus) is an egg-shaped mass in the anterior part of the tegmentum at the level of the superior colliculus and extending rostrally into the posterior part of the subthalamic region. Its cells are medium to small in size and contain considerable pigment which gives rise to the red color in fresh specimens. This mass probably represents the pars parvocellularis of the red nucleus of lower mammals. The efferent fibers go to several centers, including nuclei of the reticular formation of the same and opposite sides and the nucleus ventralis lateralis of the thalamus (rubro-reticular and rubro-thalamic fibers). The pars magnocellularis of lower mammals, which is the origin of the rubro-spinal tract, is rudimentary in humans and is represented by a few large cells in the reticular formation just caudal to the parvocellular portion described above. The afferents to the red nucleus come chiefly from the superior cerebellar peduncles, the globus pallidus, and the frontal lobe of the cerebral cortex.

The **interpeduncular ganglion** consists of a group of small cells in the ventral part of the tegmentum, forming the lower part of the floor of the interpeduncular fossa. It receives fibers from the habenular ganglia through the retroflex bundle of Meynert (the habenulo-peduncular tract) and its efferents pass into the reticular formation of the tegmentum, but have not been followed further.

The **corpora quadrigemina** (*tectum of the mid-brain*) are four rounded eminences which form the dorsal part of the mid-brain. They are situated above and in front of the anterior medullary velum and superior peduncle, and below and behind the third ventricle and posterior commissure. They are covered by the splenium of the corpus callosum, and are partly overlapped on either side by the medial angle, or **pulvinar,** of the posterior end of the thalamus; on the lateral aspect, under cover of the pulvinar, is an oval eminence, named the **medial geniculate body.** The corpora quadrigemina are arranged in pairs (**superior and inferior colliculi**), and are separated from one another by a crucial sulcus. The longitudinal part of this sulcus expands superiorly to form a slight depression which supports the **pineal body,** a cone-like structure which projects backward from the thalamencephalon and partly obscures the superior colliculi. From the inferior end of the longitudinal sulcus, a white band, termed the **frenulum veli,** is prolonged downward to the anterior medullary velum; on either side of this band the trochlear nerve emerges, and passes forward on the lateral aspect of the cerebral peduncle to reach the base of the brain. The **superior colliculi** are larger and darker in color than the inferior, and are oval in shape. The **inferior colliculi** are hemispherical, and somewhat more prominent than the superior. The superior colliculi are associated with the optic system, the inferior with the auditory system.

The **superior brachium** extends lateralward from the superior colliculus and, passing between the pulvinar and medial geniculate body, is partly continued into an eminence called the **lateral geniculate body,** and partly into the optic tract. It carries fibers from the optic tract and from the occipital lobe of the cortex to the superior colliculus.

The **inferior brachium** passes forward and upward from the inferior colliculus and to the **medial geniculate body.** It carries fibers of the lateral lemniscus and from the inferior colliculus to the **medial geniculate body.** It also contains fibers from the temporal lobe of the cortex to the inferior colliculus.

Structure of the Corpora Quadrigemina.—The **inferior colliculus** (*colliculus inferior; inferior quadrigeminal body; postgemina*) consists of a compact nucleus of gray substance containing medium and small multipolar nerve cells, and more or less completely surrounded by a capsule of white fibers derived from the lateral lemniscus. Most of these fibers end in the gray nucleus of the same side, but some cross the middle line through the commissure of the inferior colliculus and end in that of the opposite side. From the cells of the gray nucleus, fibers pass through the inferior brachium to the medial geniculate body; a second neuron passes from there to the cortex of the temporal lobe; other fibers cross the middle line and end in the opposite colliculus. Scattered large cells lie medial to the main nucleus of the inferior colliculus and give rise to tectobulbar and tectospinal fibers. There are also connections between the inferior colliculus and the substantia nigra, the nuclei of the reticular formation and the pontile nuclei.

The **superior colliculus** (*colliculus superior; superior quadrigeminal body; pregemina*) is covered by a thin stratum (**stratum zonale**) of fine white fibers, the majority of which are derived from the optic tract. Beneath this is the **stratum cinereum,** a cap-like layer of gray substance, thicker in the center than at the circumference, and consisting of numerous small multipolar nerve cells, imbedded in a fine network of nerve fibers. Still deeper is the **stratum opticum,** containing large multipolar nerve cells, separated by numerous nerve fibers which come through the brachium of the superior colliculus and are mainly cortico-tectal fibers from the occipital lobes. There are also fibers from the optic tract and probably from the thalamus and pretectal area. Finally, there is the **stratum lemnisci,** consisting of fibers derived partly from the spinotectal tracts and partly from the cells of the stratum opticum; interspersed among these fibers are many large multipolar nerve cells. There is a large commissural system between the superior colliculi of the two sides, mainly through the commissure of the superior colliculus, partly through the posterior commissure. There are also extensive, fine connections, both medial and lateral, with the reticular formation, the substantia nigra and possibly the pontile nuclei, but the direction of conduction is not known. There are also connections between the caudo-ventral portion of the superior colliculus and the zona incerta. These are probably tecto-incertal as regards conduction.

The **tectospinal** and **tectobulbar fasciculi** arise for the most part from the superior colliculi; some fibers come from the inferior colliculi. The fibers sweep around the central gray matter and decussate (*dorsal tegmental decussation,* fountain decussation of Meynert) in the median raphé ventral to the oculomotor nucleus and the median longitudinal fasciculus. After decussation, the tectospinal fasciculus descends on the ventral aspect of the medial longitudinal fasciculus and somewhat intermingled with it as far as the decussation of the medial lemniscus and the pyramids. In the spinal cord it lies in the ventral funiculus. The tectobulbar fasciculus descends through the reticular formation and gives off collaterals and terminals to the reticular formation, the red nucleus, to the oculomotor, trochlear, abducent and accessory nuclei.

The corpora quadrigemina are larger in the lower animals than in man. In fishes, reptiles, and birds they are hollow, and only two in number (corpora bigemina); they represent the superior colliculi of mammals, and are frequently termed the optic lobes, because of their intimate connection with the optic tracts. In lower mammals the colliculi are apparently important analytical centers. They form parts of neural mechanisms which are capable of mediating complex behavior, such as brightness discrimination, and discrimination between different sounds. In man, however, their functions have not been identified.

The **pretectal area** is represented in man by an ill-defined group of cells between the superior colliculus and the thalamus. In lower forms it is apparently an important reflex center.

The **cerebral aqueduct** (*aqueductus cerebri; aqueduct of Sylvius*) is a narrow canal, about 15 mm. long, situated between the corpora quadrigemina and tegmenta, and connecting the third with the fourth ventricle. Its shape, as seen in transverse section, varies at different levels, being T-shaped, triangular above, and oval in the middle; the central part is slightly dilated, and was named by Retzius the **ventricle of the mid-brain**. It is lined by ependyma and is surrounded by the **central gray stratum**.

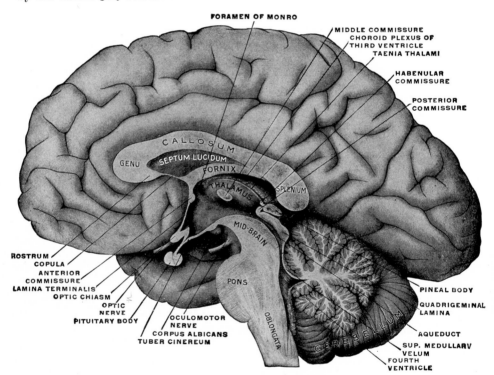

Fig. 709.—Mesal aspect of a brain sectioned in the median sagittal plane.

THE FORE–BRAIN OR PROSENCEPHALON.

The **fore-brain** or **prosencephalon** consists of: (1) the **diencephalon**, corresponding in a large measure to the third ventricle and the structures which bound it; and (2) the **telencephalon**, comprising the largest part of the brain, viz., the cerebral hemispheres; these hemispheres are intimately connected with each other across the middle line by the corpus callosum, and each contains a large cavity, named the lateral ventricle. The lateral ventricles communicate through the interventricular foramen with the third ventricle, but are separated from each other by a medial septum, the **septum pellucidum**; this contains a slit-like cavity, which does not communicate with the ventricles.

The Diencephalon.

The diencephalon is connected above and in front with the cerebral hemispheres; behind with the mid-brain. Its upper surface is concealed by the corpus callosum, and is covered by a fold of pia mater, named the tela chorioidea of the third ventricle; inferiorly it reaches to the base of the brain.

The diencephalon comprises: (1) the **thalamus**; (2) the **metathalamus**; (3) the **epithalamus**; (4) the **subthalamus**; (5) the **hypothalamus**, which includes the **mammillary bodies**, the **tuber cinereum** and the **pars optica**.

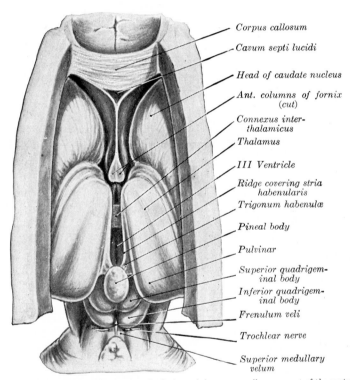

Corpus callosum
Cavum septi lucidi
Head of caudate nucleus
Ant. columns of fornix (cut)
Connexus inter-thalamicus
Thalamus
III Ventricle
Ridge covering stria habenularis
Trigonum habenulæ
Pineal body
Pulvinar
Superior quadrigeminal body
Inferior quadrigeminal body
Frenulum veli
Trochlear nerve
Superior medullary velum

Fig. 710.—The thalami, exposed from above. The trunk and splenium of the corpus callosum, most of the septum lucidum, the body of the fornix, the tela chorioidea with its contained plexuses and the epithelial roof of the third ventricle have all been removed.

The **Thalami** (*optic thalamus*) (Figs. 710, 711) are two large ovoid masses, situated one on either side of the third ventricle and reaching for some distance behind that cavity. Each measures about 4 cm. in length. The anterior extremity is narrow; it lies close to the middle line and forms the posterior boundary of the interventricular foramen. The posterior extremity is expanded, directed backward and lateralward, and overlaps the superior colliculus. Medially it presents an angular prominence, the **pulvinar**, which is continued laterally into an oval swelling, the **lateral geniculate body**, while beneath the pulvinar, but separated from it by the superior brachium, is a second oval swelling, the **medial geniculate body.** The dorsal surface is free, slightly convex, and covered by a layer of white substance, termed the **stratum zonale.** It is separated laterally from the caudate nucleus by a white band, the **stria terminalis,** and by the terminal vein. It is divided into a medial and a lateral portion by an oblique shallow furrow which runs from behind forward and medialward and corresponds with the lateral margin of the fornix; the lateral part forms a portion of the floor of the lateral ventricle, and is covered by the ependymal lining of this cavity; the medial part is covered by the tela chorioidea of the third ventricle. In front, the superior is separated from the medial surface by a salient margin, the **tænia thalami,** along which the epithelial lining of the

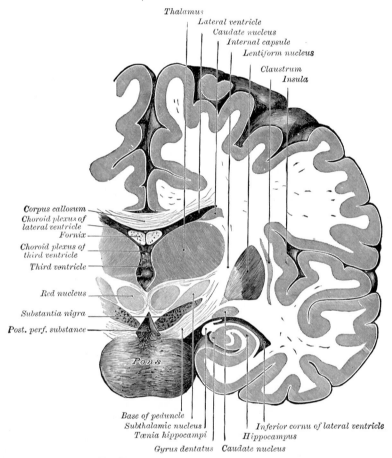

Thalamus
Lateral ventricle
Caudate nucleus
Internal capsule
Lentiform nucleus
Claustrum
Insula

Corpus callosum
Choroid plexus of lateral ventricle
Fornix
Choroid plexus of third ventricle
Third ventricle
Red nucleus
Substantia nigra
Post. perf. substance
Pons

Base of peduncle
Subthalamic nucleus
Tænia hippocampi
Gyrus dentatus   *Caudate nucleus*
Inferior cornu of lateral ventricle
Hippocampus

Fig. 711.—Coronal section of brain immediately in front of pons.

third ventricle is reflected on to the under surface of the tela chorioidea. Behind, it is limited medially by a groove, the **sulcus habenulæ,** which intervenes between it and a small triangular area, termed the **trigonum habenulæ.** The ventral surface rests upon and is continuous with the upward prolongation of the tegmentum (**subthalamic tegmental region**). The medial surface constitutes the upper part of the lateral wall of the third ventricle, and is connected to the corresponding surface of the opposite thalamus by a flattened gray band, the **massa intermedia.** The lateral surface is in contact with a thick band of white substance which forms the occipital part of the internal capsule and separates the thalamus from the lentiform nucleus of the corpus striatum.

Structure.—The thalamus consists chiefly of gray substance, but its upper surface is covered by a layer of white substance, named the **stratum zonale**, and just under its lateral surface by a similar layer termed the **external medullary lamina**. Its gray substance is subdivided into three parts—anterior, medial, and lateral—by a white layer, the **internal medullary lamina**. The nuclei of which the thalamus is composed may be divided into the following groups: (1) Mid-line; (2) Anterior; (3) Medial; (4) Lateral; and (5) Posterior. The following description is based on observations made on monkeys by Walker[1] (Figs. 712 and 713).

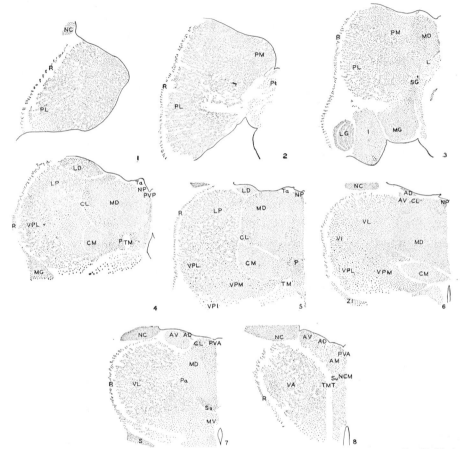

Fig. 712.—*AD*, Nucleus anterodorsalis; *AM*, Nucleus anteromedialis; *AV*, Nucleus anteroventralis; *CL*, Nucleus centralis lateralis; *CM*, Nucleus centrum medianum; *I*, Nucleus pulvinaris inferior; *L*, Nucleus limitans; *LD*, Nucleus lateralis dorsalis; *LG*, Corpus geniculatum laterale; *LP*, Nucleus lateralis posterior; *MD*, Nucleus medialis dorsalis; *MG*, Corpus geniculatum mediale; *MV*, Nucleus medialis ventralis; *NC*, Nucleus caudatus; *NCM*, Nucleus centralis medialis; *NP*, Nucleus parataenialis; *P*, Nucleus parafascicularis; *PA*, Nucleus paracentralis; *PL*, Nucleus pulvinaris lateralis; *PM*, Nucleus pulvinaris medialis; *Pt*, Pretectum; *PVA*, Nucleus periventricularis anterior; *PVP*, Nucleus periventricularis posterior; *R*, Nucleus reticularis; *S*, Corpus subthalamicum; *SG*, Nucleus suprageniculatus; *Su*, Nucleus submedius; *Ta*, Taenia thalami; *TM*, Tractus Meynerti; *VA*, Nucleus ventralis anterior; *VI*, Nucleus ventralis intermedius; *VL*, Nucleus ventralis lateralis; *VPI*, Nucleus ventralis posteroinferior; *VPL*, Nucleus ventralis posterolateralis; *VPM*, Nucleus ventralis posteromedialis; *ZI*, zona incerta. (Walker, The Primate Thalamus, University of Chicago Press.)

1. Mid-line Nuclei.—In about 30 per cent. of human brains there is a **massa intermedia** which bridges the third ventricle and connects the thalami of the two sides. It is composed almost entirely of glia and contains few, if any, nerve cells or fibers, but is probably the homologue of the massive commissural systems of fibers and nuclei of lower forms. In the wall of the ventricle under the ependyma

[1] The Primate Thalamus, University of Chicago Press, Chicago, 1938.

is the **periventricular system** (*substantia grisea ventriculi tertii*), which consists of small cells and fine fibers. It interconnects the thalamus and hypothalamus and is continuous with the central gray round the aqueduct.

2. **Anterior Nuclei.**—This group constitutes the **tubercle of the thalamus** and is formed of the following three nuclei. The **nucleus anterodorsalis** is the most dorsal and consists of medium sized, darkly staining cells. The **nucleus antero-ventralis** lies ventral to the former and the cells stain less deeply. The **nucleus anteromedialis** is ventromedial to the n. anteroventralis, and has similar cells. All three of these nuclei receive connections through the **mammillo-thalamic fas-ciculus (bundle of Vicq d'Azyr)** from the mammillary bodies. This may be regarded as an olfactory projection, as the mammillary bodies receive the fornix which arises

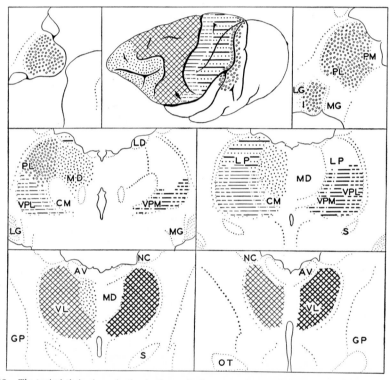

Fig. 713.—The topical thalamic projection to the cerebral cortex (left) and the thalmic termination of the somatic afferent systems (right) as determined by retrograde degeneration of the thalamus following ablation of cortical areas. Similarly marked parts of the thalamus and cerebral cortex have thalamocortical connections. The terminations of the afferent systems are represented as follows: the brachium conjunctivum by heavy cross-hatching, the fibers from the nucleus gracilis by short heavy dashes, the fibers from the nucleus cuneatus by heavy lines, and the ventral trigeminal tract by heavy dots and dashes. (Walker, The Primate Thalamus, University of Chicago Press.)

in the hippocampus. The cortical projections of these nuclei are probably as follows: from the n. anterodorsalis to the retrosplenial portion of the gyrus cinguli; from the n. anteroventralis to the gyrus cinguli just behind the paracentral lobule; and from the n. anteromedialis to the inferior surface of the frontal lobe.

3. **Medial Nuclei.**—The largest nucleus of this group is the **nucleus medialis dorsalis**. It is bounded medially by the periventricular system and on its other sides by the internal medullary lamina. It has two main parts, a ventromedial part of moderately large cells and a larger dorsolateral part of small cells. This nucleus receives many connections from the nuclei of the lateral group and probably from the pretectal and hypothalamic areas. It also receives fibers from the basal olfactory areas via the internal thalamic peduncle. The large-celled ventromedial

portion sends fibers into the periventricular system to the hypothalamus and to the central gray round the aqueduct. The small-celled, dorsolateral part projects to the granular frontal cortex (chiefly to area 9) through the anterior thalamic radiations.

The **nucleus centrum medianum** (the *centre médian of Luys*) is a well defined structure near the caudal end of the thalamus. It is bounded dorsally by the n. medialis dorsalis, and on other sides by a capsule of fibers of the internal medullary lamina. Its connections are poorly known, but it may project to the corpus striatum.

The **intra-lamellar nuclei** consist of groups of cells lying between the fibers of the internal medullary lamina whose axons pass to other thalamic or hypothalamic centers. Their afferent connections are not known.

There are certain other less well defined nuclei in the medial group, the most caudal being the **nucleus parafascicularis**. Its cells are small, darkly stained and they form a compact group round upper part of the habenulo-peduncular tract (the retroflex bundle of Meynert).

4. **Lateral Nuclei.**—This group forms a large mass in front of the pulvinar and between the internal and external medullary laminæ. The boundaries of the separate nuclei of which the group is composed are poorly defined except by methods which show their fiber connections.

The **nucleus ventralis anterior** lies at the rostral pole of the lateral group and is distinctive in that it does not project to the cortex. It probably sends fibers to the striatum.

The **nucleus ventralis lateralis** is a large nucleus, bounded rostrally by the n. ventralis anterior, medially by the internal medullary lamina, laterally by the external medullary lamina and caudally by the n. lateralis dorsalis above and the n. ventralis posterior below. The cells are medium sized. This nucleus receives the dentatorubrothalamic tract from the dentate and red nuclei. It also receives reticulothalamic fibers. The efferent axons go chiefly to the motor area in the precentral gyrus of the cortex (area 4) fewer passing more anteriorly to the premotor area (area 6).

The **nucleus ventralis posterior** is itself composed of several nuclei which together make up the ventral posterior half of the lateral nuclear group. The subdivisions are as follows: 1. The **nucleus ventralis intermedius** forms the anterior part of the nucleus ventralis posterior. 2. The **nucleus ventralis posteromedialis** (*n. semilunaris, n. arcuatus*) forms a half moon-shaped mass around the ventral border of the centrum medianum, and is prominent in myelin stains as it appears pale. The cells are medium sized. This nucleus is the terminus of the ascending trigeminal systems and its axons go to the sensory face areas of the cortex in the lower part of the post-central gyrus. 3. The **nucleus ventralis posterolateralis** is large and lies lateral to the preceding nucleus. The spinothalamic tracts terminate chiefly in this nucleus, though a few fibers go to the lateral part of ventralis posteromedialis. The medial lemniscus also terminates here, the fibers from the n. gracilis more laterally and posteriorly than those from the n. cuneatus. The axons from the cells of the posterolateral ventral nucleus radiate through the posterior limb of the internal capsule to distribute chiefly in the somatosensory areas in the post-central gyrus (areas 3, 1, and 2). Those from the lateral portions of the nucleus pass superiorly to the leg areas, those from the medial part of the nucleus more inferiorly to the arm areas. The fibers from the posteromedial ventral nucleus, already mentioned, lie still further inferior and go to the face areas. 4. The **nucleus ventralis posteroinferior** lies ventral to the posterolateralis and is bounded ventrally by the zona incerta.

In addition to being the diencephalic way-station of the somatic sensory systems, the nucleus ventralis posterior has numerous connections with other neighboring structures, particularly to the lateral and posterior nuclei above it and from the strio-pallidal mechanism lateral to it.

The **nucleus lateralis dorsalis** and the **nucleus lateralis posterior** lie dorsal to the nucleus ventralis posterior and between the pulvinar behind and the nucleus ventralis lateralis in front. These nuclei project to the inferior parietal lobule and to the posterior part of the postcentral gyrus respectively. Their afferents are in part cortico-thalamic fibers from the same areas and in part connections from the posterior ventral nucleus.

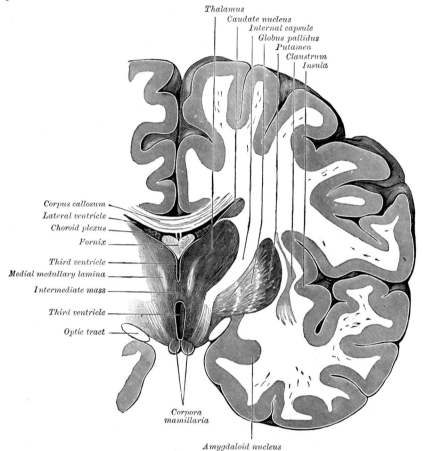

FIG. 714.—Coronal section of brain through intermediate mass of third ventricle.

The **nucleus reticularis** forms a layer of large cells between the external medullary lamina and the internal capsule surrounding the rostral and lateral aspects of the thalamus and metathalamus. Ventrally it is continuous with the zona incerta. The axons from the rostral portions apparently descend, but the lateral and caudal cells project to the same areas of the cortex as do the contiguous thalamic nuclei.

5. **Posterior Nuclei.**—The major nucleus in this group is the **nucleus pulvinaris** (*the pulvinar*), which forms the caudal pole of the thalamus and overhangs the rostral end of the mesencephalon. It may be divided into lateral, medial and inferior parts. It projects to the parietal lobe of the cortex, particularly to the regions contiguous to the somatic sensory, visual and auditory projection areas. It receives fibers from the same cortical zones and also from the diencephalic centers which adjoin it. Together with the nucleus lateralis dorsalis it may be regarded as an association center related to the cortical association centers.

The **Metathalamus** comprises the **geniculate bodies,** (Fig. 715) which are two in number—a **medial** and a **lateral**—on each side.

The **medial geniculate body** (*corpus geniculatum mediale; internal geniculate body*) a small oval tubercle, lies under cover of the pulvinar of the thalamus and on the lateral aspect of the corpora quadrigemina. It consists of a small-celled dorsal and a large-celled ventral nucleus, and receives acoustic fibers from the lateral lemniscus and the inferior colliculus through the brachium of the inferior colliculus and relays these through the auditory radiation to the cortex. The medial geniculate bodies are connected with one another by the commissure of Gudden, which passes through the posterior part of the optic chiasma. The axons of both the small and large cells go forward out of the nuclei and then turn lateralward through the sublenticular part of the internal capsule. They terminate in a well-defined area (areas 41 and 42 of the cortex of the transverse gyri of the superior temporal convolution). A point to point relationship of this part of the cortex to the medial

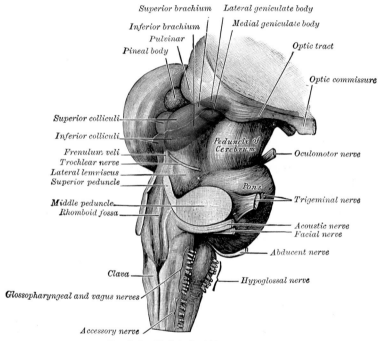

FIG. 715.—Hind- and mid-brains; postero-lateral view.

geniculate body has been demonstrated. The medial geniculate body also receives fibers from this area of the cortex.

The **lateral geniculate body** (*corpus geniculatum laterale; external geniculate body; pregeniculatum*) is an oval elevation on the lateral part of the posterior end of the thalamus and is connected with the superior colliculus by the superior brachium. On section it presents a laminated arrangement consisting of alternate layers of gray and white substance.

Approximately 80 per cent. of the fibers of the optic tract end here, entering the nucleus through its inferior and lateral surfaces. The axons from the nucleus pass forward and then sweep laterally through the retrolenticular portion of the internal capsule to reach the area striata (area 17) of the cortex which surrounds the calcarine fissure.

The **Epithalamus** comprises the **trigonum habenulæ**, the **pineal body,** and the **posterior commissure.**

The **trigonum habenulæ** is a small depressed triangular area situated in front of the superior colliculus and on the lateral aspect of the posterior part of the tænia thalami. It contains the **habenular nucleus**, an olfactory correlation center, which receives fibers from the stria medullaris, a fasciculus which runs with the tænia thalami. The **stria medullaris** contains fibers from the medial basal olfactory areas, the medial fore-brain bundle, the stria terminalis and the fornix. Some of the fibers terminate in the nucleus of the same side; others pass to the habenular nucleus of the opposite side in the **habenular commissure**. The **habenulo-peduncular tract** (*fasciculus retrofexus Meynerti*) arises from cells of the habenular nucleus and passes downward to the interpeduncular ganglion of both sides. This is part of a reflex olfactory pathway.

The **pineal body** (*corpus pineale; epiphysis*) is a small, conical, reddish-gray body which lies in the depression between the superior colliculi. It is placed beneath the splenium of the corpus callosum, but is separated from this by the tela chorioidea of the third ventricle, the lower layer of which envelops it. It measures about 8 mm. in length, and its base, directed forward, is attached by a stalk or peduncle of white substance. The **stalk** of the pineal body divides anteriorly into two laminæ, a dorsal and a ventral, separated from one another by the pineal recess of the third ventricle. The ventral lamina is continuous with the posterior commissure; the dorsal lamina is continuous with the habenular commissure. The pineal body represents the rudiments of a photosensitive organ, the third eye which is present in certain reptiles, and other lower vertebrates. In mammals it consists of specific cells, pineal cells, among which an occasional abortive ganglion cell may be found.

The **posterior commissure** is a rounded band of white fibers crossing the middle line on the dorsal aspect of the upper end of the cerebral aqueduct. Its fibers acquire their medullary sheaths early, but their connections have not been definitely determined. Many are supposed to connect nuclei of the mesencephalic reticular substance of the two sides. Some are probably derived from the posterior part of the thalamus and from the superior colliculus, while others are believed to be continued downward into the medial longitudinal fasciculus.

The **tegmentum diencephali** (subthalamic tegmental region, subthalamus) lies on the ventro-lateral aspect of the thalamus and separates it from the fibers of the internal capsule. The red nucleus and the substantia nigra are prolonged into its lower part. The fibers of the medial lemniscus, on their way to the ventral part of the thalamus, lie first lateral and then dorsolateral to the red nucleus. In front of the red nucleus is a dense mass of longitudinally running fibers, known as the **tegmental field of Forel.** Cells in this area are known as the nucleus of the field of Forel and are a rostral continuation of the reticular column of nuclei. The medial fibers of the field are composed largely of dentato-, rubro and reticulo-thalamic connections. They continue forward to form the field H_1 or thalamic fasciculus of Forel. This enters the medial part of the external medullary lamina and runs through it to terminate in the nucleus ventralis lateralis of the thalamus. The fibers of the lateral part of the tegmental field come largely from the field H_2 of Forel, which lies rostrolaterally. The field H_2 consists principally of the **ansa lenticularis** which comes from the globus pallidus, around and through the rostral part of the peduncle, to the red nucleus and reticular substance.

The **nucleus subthalamicus** (*n. hypothalamicus, corpus Luysii*), a small brownish mass shaped like a cylinder pointed at each end, lies on the dorsal surface of the peduncle dorsolateral to the upper end of the substantia nigra and extends backward as far as the lateral aspect of the red nucleus. It is separated from the lateral nucleus of the thalamus by the zona incerta. The connections of the subthalamic nucleus are obscure. It receives fibers from the globus pallidus and the peduncle, but the course and termination of its efferents are not known. The cells resemble the motor type and are pigmented. Injury to this nucleus results in involuntary flinging movements of the contralateral limbs.

The **zona incerta** consists of cells quite similar to those of the reticular substance. It lies between the n. subthalamicus and the external medullary lamina of the thalamus and extends forward. Caudo-medially it is continuous with the nuclei of the fields of Forel and rostrally and laterally with the reticular nucleus of the thalamus. Its connections, which include fibers from the tectum of the mesencephalon, are poorly known.

The **Hypothalamus** (Figs. 716, 717) includes the structures forming the greater part of the floor of the third ventricle, viz., the **corpora mamillaria, tuber cinereum, infundibulum, hypophysis,** and **optic chiasma.**

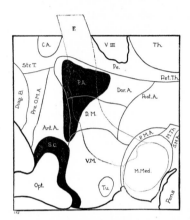

Fig. 716.—Diagrammatic representation of a sagittal section through the middle hypothalamic region. The paraventricular nucleus, most of which lies medial to the level of the section, and the supraoptic nucleus, which extends lateralward, are shown in black. The course of the fornix, which lies at the boundary between the middle and lateral hypothalamic regions is indicated by dotted lines.

Ant. A., anterior hypothalamic area; *C. A.,* anterior commissure; *D. M.,* dorsomedial hypothalamic nucleus; *Diag. B.,* diagonal band of Broca; *Dor. A.,* dorsal hypothalamic area; *F,* fornix; *M. Med.,* medial mammillary nucleus; *M. Th.,* mammillo-thalamic tract; *Opt.,* optic chiasm and tract; *P. A.,* paraventricular nucleus; *Pe.,* periventricular system; *P. M. A.,* premammillary area; *Pons,* pons; *Post. A.,* posterior hypothalamic area; *Pre. O. M. A.,* medial preoptic area; *Ret. th.,* reticular nucleus of thalamus; *S. M. A.,* supramammillary area; *S. O.,* supraoptic nucleus; *Str. T.,* bed nuclei of the stria terminalis; *Th.,* thalamus; *Tu.,* lateral tuberal nuclei; *V. M.,* ventromedial hypothalamic nucleus; *V. III,* third ventricle.

The **mammillary bodies** are two round white masses, each about the size of a small pea, placed side by side below the gray substance of the floor of the third ventricle in front of the posterior perforated substance.

The **tuber cinereum** is a hollow eminence of gray substance situated between the corpora mamillaria behind, and the optic chiasma in front. Laterally it is bounded by the optic tracts and peduncles. From the under surface of the tuber cinereum a hollow conical process, the **infundibulum,** projects downward and forward and is attached to the posterior lobe of the hypophysis. The upper part of the infundibulum, *i. e.,* the portion attached to the floor of the ventricle is broader than the infundibular **stem,** or lower portion, and is known as the **median eminence.** The stem is continuous with the **infundibular process** or **neural lobe** of the hypophysis. The median eminence, the stem and the neural lobe together make up the neurohypophysis. They have a similar structure and function and also a specialized vascular pattern, quite different from nerve tissue. They stain with vital dyes, as do the area postrema and certain other structures, and so may be sharply differentiated from the nerve tissue to which they are attached.

Structure of the Hypothalamus.—Three general areas may be distinguished in the hypothalamus: the periventricular region immediately under the ependyma of the ventricle; a middle region next to it, in which a number of specialized nuclei are found; and a lateral region.

53

The periventricular area is occupied by the **periventricular system**. This consists of small, pale cells and of fine fibers, mostly unmyelinated. It is continuous with the periventricular system of the thalamus dorsally and with the central gray round the aqueduct caudally. It apparently interconnects these structures and also sends fibers caudalward through the dorsal fasciculus of Schütz to nuclei in the pons and medulla.

The middle hypothalmic region is divided into rostral or supraoptic, tuberal or infundibular and caudal or mammillary parts (Fig. 716).

In the rostral part the prominent nuclei are the **nucleus supraopticus** and the **nucleus paraventricularis**. In addition, there is a group of small cells above the chiasm, the **nucleus suprachiasmaticus**, and an area with more diffusely scattered cells, the **anterior hypothalamic area**. The latter is continuous rostrally with the **medial preoptic area** and is bounded caudally by the nuclei of the infundibular region. The **nucleus supraopticus** consists of 50,000 to 70,000 deeply staining, moderately large cells which form a layer over the beginning part of the optic tract, denser in front and behind than over the dorsal surface. There is a very rich capillary bed of particular pattern sharply limited to the extent of the nucleus. The origins of the afferent fibers are not known, other than certain ones from the n. paraventricularis. The efferent axons form the supraoptico-hypophyseal tract to the neuro-hypophysis. The function is concerned with water metabolism. The **nucleus paraventricularis** is a roughly triangular mass of cells extending dorsocaudally, next to the periventricular system, above the n. supraopticus. The cells and capillary bed are similar to those of the latter. An occasional accessory nucleus, with similar cells sometimes is found between these two nuclei. The axons from the ventral half of the paraventricular nucleus form the paraventriculo-hypophyseal tract.

The nuclei in the infundibular region are poorly defined. The most prominent is the nucleus **hypothalamicus ventromedialis**, an oval mass of small, pale cells, lying behind the anterior hypothalamic area and in front of the mammillary bodies. It receives connections from the medial forebrain bundle, from the stria terminalis, from the periventricular system, from the fornix and from the globus pallidus. Certain of its efferents are thought to enter the periventricular system. Above the n. hypothalamicus ventromedialis and between the periventricular system and the fornix lie more scattered cells which have been grouped as the **nucleus hypothalamicus dorsomedialis** and the **dorsal hypothalamic area**. The latter is apparently related to fibers connecting the thalamus and hypothalamus. Caudal to the last mentioned nuclei, and located largely behind the fornix and above the mammillary bodies is the **posterior hypothalamic area**. This is a moderately extensive zone with larger, more deeply staining polygonal cells. It receives fibers from the medial forebrain bundle, the fornix, the periventricular system and probably also from tegmental systems. It is thought to be the main origin of the descending efferent hypothalamic systems which run rather diffusely scattered through the lateral parts of the tegmentum of the pons and medulla. These descending pathways are apparently largely formed by short neuron chains. In the cord they run in the lateral and antero-lateral columns.

The mammillary region contains the mammillary complex and also scattered cells in front of and above the mammillary bodies, the **premammillary area** and the **supramammillary area** respectively. The latter are associated with the fibers of the supramammillary decussation, which apparently interconnects mainly tegmental structures. There are two mammillary nuclei on each side, a medial and a lateral. The **nucleus mamillaris medialis** is an ovoid mass of small cells which constitutes the protuberance of the mammillary body. It has a rather dense lateral division, the cells being more scattered in the medial division. The **nucleus mamillaris lateralis** is smaller, appears triangular in cross-section, and fits into the angle between the lateral margin of the medial nucleus and the base of the brain. Its cells are large, deeply staining and polygonal. In the dorsal part of the nucleus there is a separate group of slightly different cells, the **nucleus intercalatus.** Both the medial and lateral mammillary nuclei receive fibers from the fornix of each side, the crossing fibers decussating just above the mammillary bodies. The white capsule round the bodies is formed of these fibers. They also receive connections from the medial forebrain bundle, from the thalamus and from the **inferior mammillary** peduncle. The last named bundle is small, but well myelinated, and is thought to arise in the deep part of the mesencephalic tegmentum. The fibers run forward

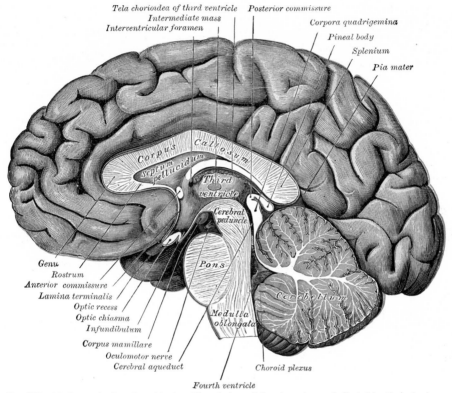

Fig. 717.—Median sagittal section of brain. The relations of the pia mater are indicated by the red color.

and distribute chiefly to both mammillary nuclei, a few continuing on into the hypothalamus. The chief efferents from the mammillary bodies come from both the medial and lateral nuclei and run dorso-rostrally as the **principal mammillary peduncle.** A short distance above the mammillary bodies descending collaterals are given off which pass caudally to an unknown destination, probably the deep part of the mesencephalic tegmentum. This descending bundle is known as the **tractus mamillo-tegmentalis.** The main fibers continue as the **tractus mamillo-thalamicus,** also called the **bundle of Vicq d'Azyr,** to the thalamus where they distribute to all three of the anterior thalamic nuclei.

The **lateral hypothalamic area** is continuous in front with the **lateral preoptic area** and extends caudalward to the level of the mammillary bodies. It consists of medium to large, polygonal, moderately well-staining cells, scattered between the fine fibers of the medial forebrain bundle. As the fibers of this bundle turn into the middle hypothalamic region to terminate in the nuclei there, the lateral hypothalamic area becomes rapidly smaller in its caudal part. The cells of this area resemble those of the motor type and are thought to give rise to descending fibers. There are also connections with tegmental structures laterally. At about mid-way between the infundibulum and mammillary bodies and lying next to the surface of the brain in the lateral hypothalamic area are two to three rounded masses of moderately large cells, quite distinct from the cells of the lateral hypothalamic area. These are the **nuclei tuberis lateralis.** Their connections are not known.

Rostral to the hypothalamus, and of telencephalic origin, are the **medial** and **lateral preoptic areas.** The medial preoptic area is related caudally to the middle region of the hypothalamus and rostrally to the nuclei associated with the stria terminalis, the anterior commissure and the parolfactory areas. The lateral pre-optic area is indistinguishable, except by position, from the lateral hypothalamic area, and contains the medial forebrain bundle. The connections of both these areas are largely with the basal olfactory areas, the hypothalamus and the anterior and medial thalamic nuclei.

Principal Afferent Connections to the Hypothalamus.—1. The **medial forebrain bundle** arises from nuclei in the parolfactory areas and in the anterior perforated substance, as well as from rostro-basal parts of the striatum. It distributes through-out the hypothalamus and some fibers continue to the interpeduncular ganglion and into the tegmentum of the mesencephalon.

2. Thalamo-hypothalamic connections come chiefly by way of the periventricular system and from the medial ends of the internal and external medullary laminæ of the thalamus. There are possibly also such connections through the internal thalamic peduncle, which consists of more or less vertically running fibers between the anterior and medial thalamic nuclei and the basal olfactory areas and medial forebrain bundle.

3. The fornix, arises in the hippocampus and passes chiefly to the mammillary bodies, also to other hypothalamic nuclei and possibly to the tegmentum mesencephali.

4. The stria terminalis arises in the nuclei of the amygdala and follows the tail of the caudate nucleus round the lesser curvature of the lateral ventricle forward to the level of the anterior commissure. Here fibers turn into the hypothalamus of the same and, through the anterior commissure, of the opposite sides.

5. A well myelinated group of fibers comes from the globus pallidus, through the ansa lenticularis, hooks over the fornix and disappears in the region of the nucleus hypothalamicus ventromedialis.

6. The inferior mammillary peduncle, from the tegmentum of the mesencephalon, is small. There are also less well defined connections from the zona incerta and fields of Forel.

Principal Efferent Fibers of the Hypothalamus.—1. Fibers from the whole of the n. supraopticus, from the ventral half of the n. paraventricularis and possibly from nuclei in the tuberal region make up the hypothalamico-hypophyseal tract, which distributes to the neurohypophysis, including the median eminence.

2. Descending systems leave the hypothalamus through the periventricular system to the dorsal fasciculus of Schütz. There are more numerous diffuse systems which leave the posterior part of the hypothalamus to run through the lateral areas of the tegmentum of the mesencephalon, pons and medulla into the lateral and antero-lateral columns of the cord.

3. The mammillo-thalamic and mammillo-tegmental tracts have been referred to already.

Optic Chiasma (*chiasma opticum; optic commissure*).—The optic chiasma is a flattened, somewhat quadrilateral band of fibers, situated at the junction of the floor and anterior wall of the third ventricle. Most of its fibers have their origins in the retina, and reach the chiasma through the optic nerves, which are continuous with its antero-lateral angles. In the chiasma, they undergo a partial decussation

(Fig. 718); the fibers from the nasal half of the retina decussate and enter the optic tract of the opposite side, while the fibers from the temporal half of the retina do not undergo decussation, but pass back into the optic tract of the same side. Occupying the posterior part of the commissure, however, is a very small strand of fibers, the **commissure of Gudden**, which is not derived from the optic nerves; it forms a connecting link between the medial geniculate bodies.

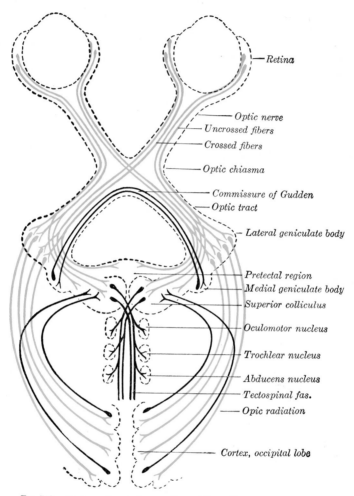

Retina

Optic nerve
Uncrossed fibers
Crossed fibers

Optic chiasma

Commissure of Gudden
Optic tract

Lateral geniculate body

Pretectal region
Medial geniculate body
Superior colliculus

Oculomotor nucleus

Trochlear nucleus

Abducens nucleus
Tectospinal fas.
Opic radiation

Cortex, occipital lobe

Fig. 718.—Diagram of central connections of the optic nerves.

Optic Tracts.—The optic tracts are continued backward and lateralward from the postero-lateral angles of the optic chiasma. Each passes between the anterior perforated substance and the tuber cinereum, and, winding around the ventro-lateral aspect of the cerebral peduncle, divides into a medial and a lateral root. The former comprises the fibers of Gudden's commissure. The lateral root consists mainly of afferent fibers which arise in the retina and undergo partial decussation in the optic chiasma, as described; but it also contains a few fine efferent fibers which have their origins in the brain and their terminations in the retina. When traced backward, approximately four-fifths of the afferent fibers of the lateral root are found to end in the lateral geniculate body, one-fifth in the superior colliculus, and in the pretectal region. Fibers arise from the nerve cells in the lateral geniculate body and pass through the occipital part of the internal capsule, under the name of the **optic radiations**, the **geniculocalcarine tract**, to the cortex of the occipital lobe of the cerebrum, where the **higher** or **cortical visual center** is situated. Some of the fibers of the optic radiations take an opposite course, arising from the cells of the occipital cortex and passing to the lower visual centers.

The **dorsal supraoptic commissures** consist of fibers which cross the mid-line dorso-caudal to the optic chiasma. These commissures are divided into dorsal and ventral parts. The origin and termination of these fibers are not definitely known.

The **Third Ventricle** (*ventriculus tertius*) (Figs. 710, 717).—The third ventricle is a median cleft between the two thalami. Behind, it communicates with the fourth ventricle through the cerebral aqueduct, and in front with the lateral ventricles through the interventricular foramen. Somewhat triangular in shape, with the apex directed backward, it has a **roof**, a **floor**, an **anterior** and a **posterior boundary** and a pair of **lateral walls**.

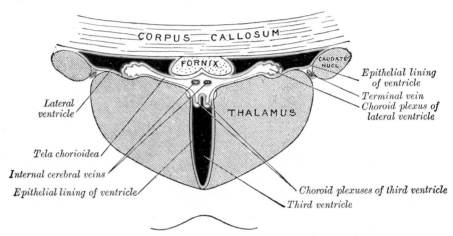

Fig. 719.—Coronal section of lateral and third ventricles. (Diagrammatic.)

The **roof** (Fig. 719) is formed by a layer of epithelium, which stretches between the upper edges of the lateral walls of the cavity and is continuous with the epithelial lining of the ventricle. It is covered by and adherent to a fold of pia mater, named the tela chorioidea of the third ventricle, from the under surface of which a pair of vascular fringed processes, the **choroid plexuses of the third ventricle**, project downward, one on either side of the middle line, and invaginate the epithelial roof into the ventricular cavity.

The **floor** slopes downward and forward and is formed mainly by the structures which constitute the hypothalamus: from before backward these are: the optic chiasma, the tuber cinereum and infundibulum, and the corpora mammillaria. Behind the last, the floor is formed by the interpeduncular fossa and the tegmenta of the cerebral peduncles. The ventricle is prolonged downward as a funnel-shaped recess, the **recessus infundibuli**, into the infundibulum, and to the apex of the latter the hypophysis is attached.

The **anterior boundary** is constituted below by the **lamina terminalis**, a thin layer of gray substance stretching from the upper surface of the optic chiasma to the rostrum of the corpus callosum; above by the columns of the fornix and the anterior commissure. At the junction of the floor and anterior wall, immediately above the optic chiasma, the ventricle presents a small angular recess or diverticulum, the **optic recess**. Between the columns of the fornix, and above the anterior commissure, is a second recess termed the **vulva**. At the junction of the roof and anterior wall of the ventricle, and situated between the thalami behind and the columns of the fornix in front, are the **interventricular foramina** (*foramen of Monro*) through which the third communicates with the lateral ventricles.

The **posterior boundary** is constituted by the pineal body, the posterior commissure and the cerebral aqueduct. A small recess, the **recessus pinealis**, projects into the stalk of the pineal body, while in front of and above the pineal body is a second recess, the **recessus suprapinealis**, consisting of a diverticulum of the epithelium which forms the ventricular roof.

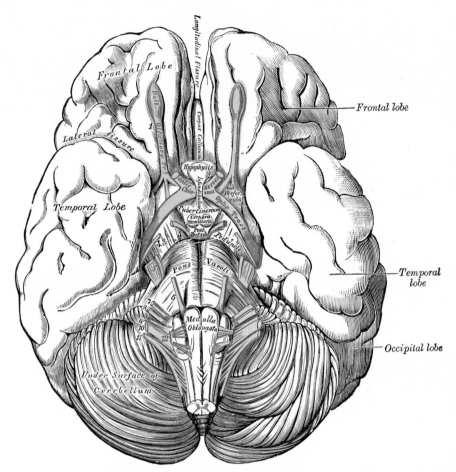

FIG. 720.—Base of brain.

Each **lateral wall** consists of an upper portion formed by the medial surface of the anterior two-thirds of the thalamus, and a lower consisting of an upward continuation of the gray substance of the ventricular floor. They are separated by a furrow, the hypothalamic sulcus, which extends from the interventricular foramen to the cerebral aqueduct. The lateral wall is limited above by the tænia thalami. The columns of the fornix curve downward in front of the interventricular foramen, and then run in the lateral walls of the ventricle, where, at first, they form distinct prominences, but subsequently are lost to sight. The lateral walls are joined to each other across the cavity of the ventricle by a band of gray matter, the **massa intermedia**.

Interpeduncular Fossa (Fig. 720).—This is a somewhat lozenge-shaped area of the base of the brain, limited in front by the optic chiasma, behind by the antero-superior surface of the pons, antero-laterally by the converging optic tracts, and postero-laterally by the diverging cerebral peduncles. The structures contained in it have already been described; from behind forward, they are the posterior perforated substance, corpora mammillaria, tuber cinereum, infundibulum, and hypophysis.

The Telencephalon.

The telencephalon includes: (1) the **cerebral hemispheres** with their cavities, the lateral ventricles; and (2) the **pars optica hypothalami** and the anterior portion of the third ventricle (already described under the diencephalon). As previously stated (see page 749), each cerebral hemisphere may be divided into three fundamental parts, viz., the rhinencephalon, the corpus striatum, and the neopallium. The rhinencephalon, associated with the sense of smell, is the oldest part of the telencephalon, and forms almost the whole of the hemisphere in some of the lower animals, e. g., fishes, amphibians and reptiles. In man it is rudimentary, whereas the neopallium undergoes great development and forms the chief part of the hemisphere.

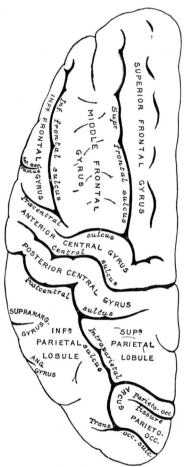

Fig. 721.—Lateral surface of left cerebral hemisphere, viewed from above.

The Cerebral Hemispheres.—The cerebral hemispheres constitute the largest part of the brain, and, when viewed together from above, assume the form of an ovoid mass broader behind than in front, the greatest transverse diameter corresponding with a line connecting the two parietal eminences. The hemispheres are separated medially by a deep cleft, named the **longitudinal cerebral fissure,** and each possesses a central cavity, the lateral ventricle.

The **Longitudinal Cerebral Fissure** (*fissura cerebri longitudinalis; great longitudinal fissure*) contains a sickle-shaped process of dura mater, the **falx cerebri.** It front and behind, the fissure extends from the upper to the under surfaces of the hemispheres and completely separates them, but its middle portion separates them for only about one-half of their vertical extent; for at this part they are connected across the middle line by a great central white commissure, the **corpus callosum.**

In a median sagittal section (Fig. 717) the cut corpus callosum presents the appearance of a broad, arched band. Its thick posterior end, termed the **splenium,** overlaps the mid-brain, but is separated from it by the tela chorioidea of the third ventricle and the pineal body. Its anterior curved end, termed the **genu,** gradually tapers into a thinner portion, the **rostrum,** which is continued downward and backward in front of the anterior commissure to join the lamina terminalis. Arching backward from immediately behind the anterior commissure to the under surface of the splenium is a second white band named the **fornix:** between this and the corpus callosum are the laminæ and cavity of the septum pellucidum.

Surfaces of the Cerebral Hemispheres.—Each hemisphere presents a lateral, medial and inferior surface. These three surfaces are separated from each other by the following borders: (a) supero-medial, between the lateral and medial surfaces; (b) infero-lateral, between the lateral and inferior surfaces; the anterior part of this border separating the lateral from the orbital surface, is known as the superciliary border; (c) medial occipital, separating the medial and tentorial surfaces; and (d) medial orbital, separating the orbital from the medial surface. The anterior end of the hemisphere is named the frontal pole; the posterior, the occipital pole; and the anterior end of the temporal lobe, the temporal pole.

The surfaces of the hemispheres are moulded into a number of irregular eminences, named **gyri** or **convolutions**, and separated by furrows termed **fissures** and **sulci.** The furrows are of two kinds, *complete* and *incomplete.* The former appear early in fetal life, are few in number, and are produced by infoldings of the entire thickness of the brain wall, and give rise to corresponding elevations in the interior of the ventricle. They comprise the hippocampal fissure, and parts of the calcarine and collateral fissures. The incomplete furrows are very numerous, and only indent the subjacent white substance, without producing any corresponding elevations in the ventricular cavity.

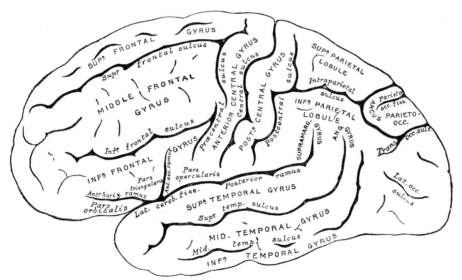

Fig. 722.—Lateral surface of left cerebral hemisphere, viewed from the side.

The gyri and their intervening fissures and the sulci are fairly constant in their arrangement; at the same time they vary within certain limits, not only in different individuals, but on the two hemispheres of the same brain. The convoluted condition of the surface permits of a great increase of the gray matter without the sacrifice of much additional space.

Certain of the fissures and sulci are utilized for the purpose of dividing the hemisphere into lobes, and are therefore termed **interlobular**; included under this category are the lateral cerebral, parieto-occipital, calcarine, and collateral fissures, the central and cingulate sulci, and the sulcus circularis.

The **Lateral Cerebral Fissure** (*fissura cerebri lateralis* [*Sylvii*]; *fissure of Sylvius*) (Fig. 722) is a well-marked cleft on the inferior and lateral surfaces of the hemisphere, and consists of a short stem which divides into three rami. The **stem** is situated on the base of the brain, and commences in a depression at the lateral angle of the anterior perforated substance. From this point it extends between the anterior part of the temporal lobe and the orbital surface of the frontal lobe, and reaches the lateral surface of the hemisphere. Here it divides into three rami: an anterior horizontal, an anterior ascending, and a posterior. The **anterior horizontal ramus** passes forward for about 2.5 cm. into the inferior frontal gyrus, while the **anterior ascending ramus** extends upward into the same convolution for about an equal distance. The **posterior ramus** is the longest; it runs backward and slightly upward for about 7 cm., and ends by an upward inflexion in the parietal lobe.

The **Central Sulcus** (*sulcus centralis* [*Rolandi*]; *fissure of Rolando; central fissure*) (Figs. 721, 722) is situated about the middle of the lateral surface of the hemisphere, and begins in or near the longitudinal cerebral fissure, a little behind its mid-point. It runs sinuously downward and forward, and ends a little above the posterior ramus of the lateral fissure, and about 2.5 cm. behind the anterior ascending ramus of the same fissure. It described two chief curves: a **superior genu** with its concavity directed forward, and an **inferior genu** with its concavity directed backward. The central sulcus forms an angle opening forward of about 70° with the median plane.

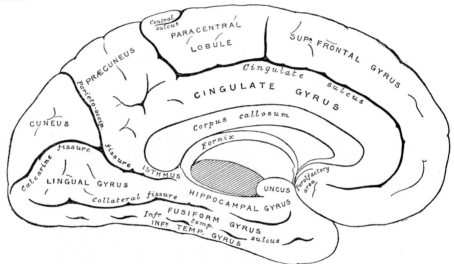

Fig. 723.—Medial surface of left cerebral hemisphere.

The **Parieto-occipital Fissure** (*fissura parieto-occipitalis*).—Only a small part of this fissure is seen on the lateral surface of the hemisphere, its chief part being on the medial surface. The lateral part of the parieto-occipital fissure (Fig. 722) is situated about 5 cm. in front of the occipital pole of the hemisphere, and measures about 1.25 cm. in length. The medial part of the parieto-occipital fissure (Fig. 723) runs downward and forward as a deep cleft on the medial surface of the hemisphere, and joins the calcarine fissure below and behind the posterior end of the corpus callosum. In most cases it contains a submerged gyrus.

The **Calcarine Fissure** (*fissura calcarina*) (Fig. 723) is on the medial surface of the hemisphere. It begins near the occipital pole in two converging rami, and runs forward to a point a little below the splenium of the corpus callosum, where it is joined at an acute angle by the medial part of the parieto-occipital fissure. The anterior part of this fissure gives rise to the prominence of the **calcar avis** in the posterior cornu of the lateral ventricle.

The **Cingulate Sulcus** (*sulcus cinguli; callosomarginal fissure*) (Fig. 723) is on the medial surface of the hemisphere; it begins below the anterior end of the corpus callosum and runs upward and forward nearly parallel to the rostrum of this body and, curving in front of the genu, is continued backward above the corpus callosum, and finally ascends to the supero-medial border of the hemisphere a short distance behind the upper end of the central sulcus. It separates the superior frontal from the cingulate gyrus.

The **Collateral Fissure** (*fissura collateralis*) (Fig. 723) is on the tentorial surface of the hemisphere and extends from near the occipital pole to within a short distance of the temporal pole. Behind, it lies below and lateral to the calcarine fissure, from which it is separated by the lingual gyrus; in front, it is situated between the hippocampal gyrus and the anterior part of the fusiform gyrus.

The **Sulcus Circularis** (*circuminsular fissure*) (Fig. 727) is on the lower and lateral surfaces of the hemisphere: it surrounds the insula and separates it from the frontal, parietal, and temporal lobes.

Lobes of the Hemispheres.—By means of these fissures and sulci, assisted by certain arbitrary lines, each hemisphere is divided into the following lobes: the **frontal**, the **parietal**, the **temporal**, the **occipital**, the **limbic**, and the **insula**.

Frontal Lobe (*lobus frontalis*).—On the lateral surface of the hemisphere this lobe extends from the frontal pole to the central sulcus, the latter separating it from the parietal lobe. Below, it is limited by the posterior ramus of the lateral fissure, which intervenes between it and the central lobe. On the medial surface, it is separated from the cingulate gyrus by the cingulate sulcus; and on the inferior surface, it is bounded behind by the stem of the lateral fissure.

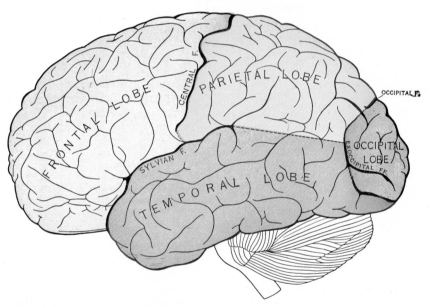

Fig. 724.—Principal fissures and lobes of the cerebrum viewed laterally.

The lateral surface of the frontal lobe (Fig. 722) is traversed by three sulci which divide it into four gyri: the sulci are named the precentral, and the superior and inferior frontal; the gyri are the anterior central, and the superior, middle, and inferior frontal. The **precentral sulcus** runs parallel to the central sulcus, and is usually divided into an upper and a lower part; between it and the central sulcus is the **anterior central gyrus**. From the precentral sulcus, the **superior** and **inferior frontal sulci** run forward and downward, and divide the remainder of the lateral surface of the lobe into three parallel gyri, named, respectively the **superior, middle, and inferior frontal gyri**.

The **anterior central gyrus** (*gyrus centralis anterior; ascending frontal convolution; precentral gyre*) is bounded in front by the precentral sulcus, behind by the central sulcus; it extends from the supero-medial border of the hemisphere to the posterior ramus of the lateral fissure.

The **superior frontal gyrus** (*gyrus frontalis superior; superfrontal gyre*) is situated above the superior frontal sulcus and is continued on to the medial surface of the hemisphere. The portion on the lateral surface of the hemisphere is usually more or less completely subdivided into an upper and a lower part by an antero-posterior sulcus, the **paramedial sulcus**, which, however, is frequently interrupted by bridging gyri.

The **middle frontal gyrus** (*gyrus frontalis medius; medifrontal gyre*), between the superior and inferior frontal sulci, is continuous with the anterior orbital gyrus on the inferior surface of the hemisphere; it is frequently subdivided into two by a horizontal sulcus, the **medial frontal sulcus** of Eberstaller, which ends anteriorly in a wide bifurcation.

The **inferior frontal gyrus** (*gyrus frontalis inferior; subfrontal gyre*) lies below the inferior frontal sulcus, and extends forward from the lower part of the precentral sulcus; it is continuous with the lateral and posterior orbital gyri on the under surface of the lobe. It is subdivided by the anterior horizontal and ascending rami of the lateral fissure into three parts, viz., (1) the **orbital part**, below the anterior horizontal ramus of the fissure; (2) the **triangular part** (*cap of Broca*), between the ascending and horizontal rami; and (3) the **basilar part**, behind the anterior ascending ramus. The left inferior frontal gyrus is, as a rule, more highly developed than the right, and is named the **gyrus of Broca**, from the fact that Broca described it as the center for articulate speech.

The inferior or orbital surface of the frontal lobe is concave, and rests on the orbital plate of the frontal bone (Fig. 725). It is divided into four orbital gyri by a well-marked H-shaped **orbital sulcus**. These are named, from their position, the **medial**, **anterior**, **lateral**, and **posterior orbital gyri**. The medial orbital gyrus presents a well-marked antero-posterior sulcus, the **olfactory sulcus**, for the olfactory tract; the portion medial to this is named the **straight gyrus**, and is continuous with the superior frontal gyrus on the medial surface.

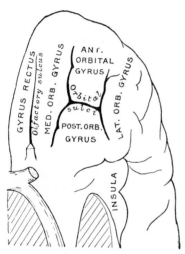

Fig. 725.—Orbital surface of left frontal lobe.

The medial surface of the frontal lobe is occupied by the medial part of the superior frontal gyrus (*marginal gyrus*) (Fig. 723). It lies between the cingulate sulcus and the supero-medial margin of the hemisphere. The posterior part of this gyrus is sometimes marked off by a vertical sulcus, and is distinguished as the **paracentral lobule**, because it is continuous with the anterior and posterior central gyri.

The **cingulate gyrus** (*gyrus cinguli; callosal convolution*) is an arch-shaped convolution, lying in close relation to the superficial surface of the corpus callosum, from which it is separated by a slit-like fissure, the **callosal fissure**. It commences below the rostrum of the corpus callosum, curves around in front of the genu, extends along the upper surface of the body, and finally turns downward behind the splenium, where it is connected by a narrow **isthmus** with the hippocampal gyrus. It is separated from the medial part of the superior frontal gyrus by the cingulate sulcus, and from the precuneus by the subparietal sulcus.

Parietal Lobe (*lobus parietalis*).—The parietal lobe is separated from the frontal lobe by the central sulcus, but its boundaries below and behind are not so definite.

Posteriorly, it is limited by the parieto-occipital fissure, and by a line carried across the hemisphere from the end of this fissure toward the preoccipital notch. Below, it is separated from the temporal lobe by the posterior ramus of the lateral fissure, and by a line carried backward from it to meet the line passing downward to the preoccipital notch.

The lateral surface of the parietal lobe (Fig. 722) is cleft by a well-marked furrow, the **intraparietal sulcus** of Turner, which consists of an oblique and a horizontal portion. The oblique part is named the **postcentral sulcus**, and commences below, about midway between the lower end of the central sulcus and the upturned end of the lateral fissure. It runs upward and backward, parallel to the central sulcus, and is sometimes divided into an *upper* and a *lower* ramus. It forms the hinder limit of the posterior central gyrus.

From about the middle of the postcentral sulcus, or from the upper end of its inferior ramus, the **horizontal portion** of the intraparietal sulcus is carried backward and slightly upward on the parietal lobe, and is prolonged, under the name of the **occipital ramus**, on to the occipital lobe, where it divides into two parts, which form nearly a right angle with the main stem and constitute the **transverse occipital sulcus**. The part of the parietal lobe above the horizontal portion of the intraparietal sulcus is named the **superior parietal lobule**; the part below, the **inferior parietal lobule**.

The **posterior central gyrus** (*gyrus centralis posterior; ascending parietal convolution; postcentral gyre*) extends from the longitudinal fissure above to the posterior ramus of the lateral fissure below. It lies parallel with the anterior central gyrus, with which it is connected below, and also, sometimes, above, the central sulcus.

The **superior parietal lobule** (*lobulus parietalis superior*) is bounded in front by the upper part of the postcentral sulcus, but is usually connected with the posterior central gyrus above the end of the sulcus; behind it is the lateral part of the parieto-occipital fissure, around the end of which it is joined to the occipital lobe by a curved gyrus, the **arcus parieto-occipitalis**; below, it is separated from the inferior parietal lobule by the horizontal portion of the intraparietal sulcus.

The **inferior parietal lobule** (*lobulus parietalis inferior; subparietal district or lobule*) lies below the horizontal portion of the intraparietal sulcus, and behind the lower part of the postcentral sulcus. It is divided from before backward into two gyri. One, the **supramarginal**, arches over the upturned end of the lateral fissure; it is continuous in front with the postcentral gyrus, and behind with the superior temporal gyrus. The second, the **angular,** arches over the posterior end of the superior temporal sulcus, behind which it is continuous with the middle temporal gyrus.

The medial surface of the parietal lobe (Fig. 723) is bounded behind by the medial part of the parieto-occipital fissure; in front, by the posterior end of the cingulate sulcus; and below, it is separated from the cingulate gyrus by the **subparietal sulcus**. It is of small size, and consists of a square-shaped convolution, which is termed the **precuneus or quadrate lobe**.

Occipital Lobe (*lobus occipitalis*).—The occipital lobe is small and pyramidal in shape; it presents three surfaces: **lateral, medial,** and **tentorial**.

The lateral surface is limited in front by the lateral part of the parieto-occipital fissure, and by a line carried from the end of this fissure to the preoccipital notch; it is traversed by the transverse occipital and the lateral occipital sulci. The **transverse occipital sulcus** is continuous with the posterior end of the occipital ramus of the intraparietal sulcus, and runs across the upper part of the lobe, a short distance behind the parieto-occipital fissure. The **lateral occipital sulcus** extends from behind forward, and divides the lateral surface of the occipital lobe into a **superior** and an **inferior gyrus**, which are continuous in front with the parietal and temporal lobes.[1]

---

[1] Elliot Smith has named the lateral occipital sulcus the *sulcus lunatus;* he regards it as the representative, in the human brain, of the "Affenspalte" of the brain of the ape.

The medial surface of the occipital lobe is bounded in front by the medial part of the parieto-occipital fissure, and is traversed by the calcarine fissure, which subdivides it into the cuneus and the lingual gyrus. The cuneus is a wedge-shaped area between the calcarine fissure and the medial part of the parieto-occipital fissure. The **lingual gyrus** lies between the calcarine fissure and the posterior part of the collateral fissure; behind, it reaches the occipital pole; in front, it is continued on to the tentorial surface of the temporal lobe, and joins the hippocampal gyrus.

The tentorial surface of the occipital lobe is limited in front by an imaginary transverse line through the preoccipital notch, and consists of the posterior part of the **fusiform gyrus** (*occipito-temporal convolution*) and the lower part of the lingual gyrus, which are separated from each other by the posterior segment of the collateral fissure.

Temporal Lobe (*lobus temporalis*).—The temporal lobe lies below the lateral fissure. Behind it is limited by a line drawn from the preoccipital notch to the parieto-occipital fissure where it cuts the supramedial margin about 5 cm. in front of the occipital pole. The lateral aspect of the temporal lobe is divided into three parallel gyri by two sulci.

The **superior temporal sulcus** (Fig. 722) runs from before backward across the temporal lobe, some little distance below, but parallel with, the posterior ramus of the lateral fissure; and hence it is often termed the **parallel sulcus**. The **middle temporal sulcus** takes the same direction as the superior, but is situated at a lower level, and is usually subdivided into two or more parts. The **superior temporal gyrus** lies between the posterior ramus of the lateral fissure and the superior temporal sulcus, and is continuous behind with the supramarginal and angular gyri. The **middle temporal gyrus** is placed between the superior and middle temporal sulci, and is joined posteriorly with the angular gyrus. The **inferior temporal gyrus** is placed below the middle temporal sulcus, and is connected behind with the inferior occipital gyrus; it also extends around the infero-lateral border on to the inferior surface of the temporal lobe, where it is limited by the inferior sulcus.

The superior surface forms the lower limit of the lateral fissure and overlaps the insula. On opening out the lateral fissure, three or four gyri will be seen springing from the depth of the hinder end of the fissure, and running obliquely forward and outward on the posterior part of the upper surface of the superior temporal gyrus; these are named the **transverse temporal gyri** (Heschl) (Fig. 726).

The inferior surface is concave, and is continuous posteriorly with the tentorial surface of the occipital lobe. It is traversed by the **inferior temporal sulcus,** which extends from near the occipital pole behind, to within a short distance of the temporal pole in front, but is frequently subdivided by bridging gyri. Lateral to this fissure is the narrow tentorial part of the inferior temporal gyrus, and medial to it the **fusiform gyrus,** which extends from the occipital to the temporal pole; this gyrus is limited medially by the collateral fissure, which separates it from the lingual gyrus behind and from the hippocampal gyrus in front.

The **hippocampal gyrus** (*gyrus hippocampi*) is bounded above by the hippocampal fissure, and below by the anterior part of the collateral fissure. Behind, it is continuous superiorly, through the isthmus, with the cingulate gyrus and inferiorly with the lingual gyrus. Running in the substance of the cingulate and hippocampal gyri, and connecting them together, is a tract of arched fibers, named the **cingulum** (page 867). The anterior extremity of the hippocampal gyrus is recurved in the form of a hook (**uncus**), which is separated from the apex of the temporal lobe by a slight fissure, the **incisura temporalis.** Although superficially continuous with the hippocampal gyrus, the uncus forms morphologically a part of the rhinencephalon.

The **Hippocampal Fissure** (*fissura hippocampi; dentate fissure*) begins immediately behind the splenium of the corpus callosum, and runs forward between the hippocampal and dentate gyri to end in the uncus. It is a complete fissure (page 841), and gives rise to the prominence of the hippocampus in the inferior cornu of the lateral ventricle.

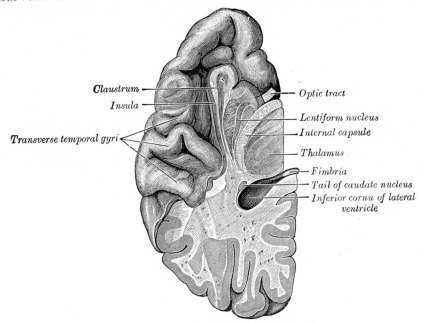

Claustrum
Insula
Transverse temporal gyri
Optic tract
Lentiform nucleus
Internal capsule
Thalamus
Fimbria
Tail of caudate nucleus
Inferior cornu of lateral ventricle

FIG. 726.—Section of brain showing upper surface of temporal lobe.

The **Insula** (*island of Reil; central lobe*) (Fig. 727) lies deeply in the lateral or Sylvian fissure, and can only be seen when the lips of that fissure are widely separated, since it is overlapped and hidden by the gyri which bound the fissure. These gyri are termed the **opercula of the insula**; they are separated from each other

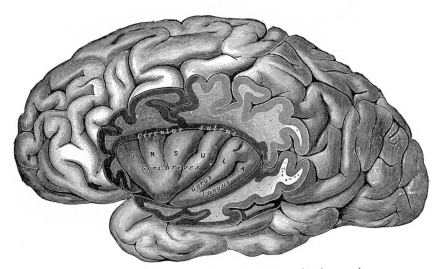

FIG. 727.—The insula of the left side, exposed by removing the opercula.

by the three rami the lateral fissure, and are named the orbital, frontal, fronto-parietal, and temporal opercula. The **orbital operculum** lies below the anterior horizontal ramus of the fissure, the **frontal** between this and the anterior ascending ramus, the **parietal** between the anterior ascending ramus and the upturned end of the posterior ramus, and the **temporal** below the posterior ramus. The frontal operculum is of small size in those cases where the anterior horizontal and ascending rami of the lateral fissure arise from a common stem. The insula is surrounded by a deep **circular sulcus** which separates it from the frontal, parietal, and temporal lobes. When the opercula have been removed, the insula is seen as a triangular eminence, the apex of which is directed toward the anterior perforated substance. It is divided into a larger anterior and a smaller posterior part by a deep sulcus, which runs backward and upward from the apex of the insula. The anterior part is subdivided by shallow sulci into three or four **short gyri,** while the posterior part is formed by one **long gyrus,** which is often bifurcated at its upper end. The cortical gray substance of the insula is continuous with that of the different opercula, while its deep surface corresponds with the lentiform nucleus of the corpus striatum.

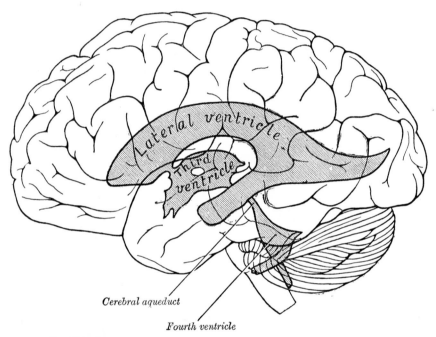

Cerebral aqueduct

Fourth ventricle

Fig. 728.—Scheme showing relations of the ventricles to the surface of the brain.

The **Lateral Ventricles** (*ventriculus lateralis*) (Fig. 728).—The two lateral ventricles are irregular cavities situated in the lower and medial parts of the cerebral hemispheres, one on either side of the middle line. They are separated from each other by a median vertical partition, the **septum pellucidum,** but communicate with the third ventricle and indirectly with each other through the **interventricular foramen.** They are lined by a thin, diaphanous membrane, the **ependyma,** covered by ciliated epithelium, and contain cerebrospinal fluid, which, even in health, may be secreted in considerable amount. Each lateral ventricle consists of a **central part or body,** and three prolongations from it, termed **cornua** (Figs. 729, 730).

The **central part** (*pars centralis ventriculi lateralis; cella*) (Fig. 731) of the lateral ventricle extends from the interventricular foramen to the splenium of the corpus callosum. It is an irregularly curved cavity, triangular on transverse section, with a roof, a floor, and a medial wall. The roof is formed by the under surface of the corpus callosum; the floor by the following parts, enumerated in their order of position, from before backward: the caudate nucleus of the corpus striatum, the stria terminalis and the terminal vein, the lateral portion of the upper surface of the thalamus, the choroid plexus, and the lateral part of the fornix; the medial wall is the posterior part of the septum pellucidum, which separates it from the opposite ventricle.

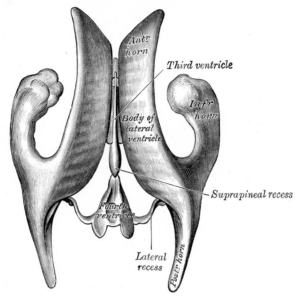

FIG. 729.—Drawing of a cast of the ventricular cavities, viewed from above. (Retzius.)

The **anterior cornu** (*cornu anterius; anterior horn; precornu*) (Fig. 730) passes forward and lateralward, with a slight inclination downward, from the interventricular foramen into the frontal lobe, curving around the anterior end of the caudate nucleus. Its floor is formed by the upper surface of the reflected portion of the corpus callosum, the **rostrum.** It is bounded medially by the anterior portion

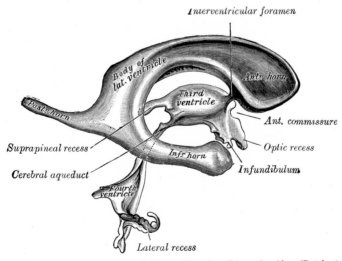

FIG. 730.—Drawing of a cast of the ventricular cavities, viewed from the side. (Retzius.)

of the septum pellucidum, and laterally by the head of the caudate nucleus. Its apex reaches the posterior surface of the genu of the corpus callosum.

The **posterior cornu** (*cornu posterius; postcornu*) (Figs. 731, 732) passes into the occipital lobe, its direction being backward and lateralward, and then medialward.

54

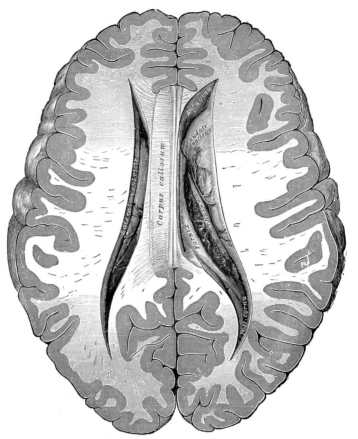

FIG. 731.—Central part and anterior and posterior cornua of lateral ventricles exposed from above.

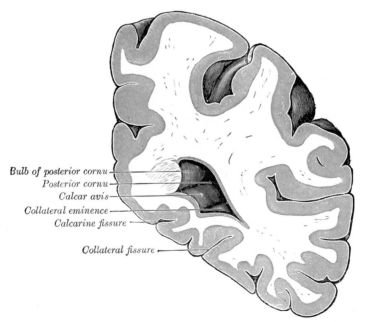

FIG. 732.—Coronal section through posterior cornua of lateral ventricle.

Its roof is formed by the fibers of the corpus callosum passing to the temporal and occipital lobes. On its medial wall is a longitudinal eminence, the **calcar avis** (*hippocampus minor*), which is an involution of the ventricular wall produced by the calcarine fissure. Above this the forceps posterior of the corpus callosum, sweeping around to enter the occipital lobe, causes another projection, termed the

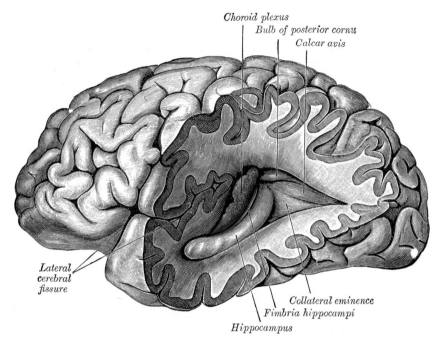

Fig. 733.—Posterior and inferior cornua of left lateral ventricle exposed from the side.

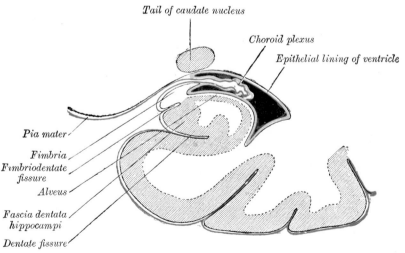

Fig. 734.—Coronal section of inferior horn of lateral ventricle. (Diagrammatic.)

bulb of the posterior cornu. The calcar avis and bulb of the posterior cornu are extremely variable in their degree of development; in some cases they are ill-defined, in others prominent.

The **inferior cornu** (*cornu inferior; descending horn; middle horn; medicornu*) (Fig. 733), the largest of the three, traverses the temporal lobe of the brain, forming in its course a curve around the posterior end of the thalamus. It passes at first backward, lateralward, and downward, and then curves forward to within 2.5 cm. of the apex of the temporal lobe, its direction being fairly well indicated on the surface of the brain by that of the superior temporal sulcus. Its roof is formed chiefly by the inferior surface of the tapetum of the corpus callosum, but the tail of the caudate nucleus and the stria terminalis also extend forward in the roof of the inferior cornu to its extremity; the tail of the caudate nucleus joins the putamen. Its floor presents the following parts: the hippocampus, the fimbria hippocampi, the collateral eminence, and the choroid plexus. When the choroid plexus is removed, a cleft-like opening is left along the medial wall of the inferior cornu; this cleft constitutes the lower part of the choroidal fissure.

Interventricular Foramen (*foramen of Monro*).—Between the columns of the fornix and the anterior ends of the thalami, an oval aperture is present on either side: this is the interventricular foramen, and through it the lateral ventricles communicate with the third ventricle. Behind the epithelial lining of the foramen the choroid plexuses of the lateral ventricles are joined across the middle line.

The **Septum Pellucidum** (*septum lucidum*) (Fig. 717) is a thin, vertically placed partition consisting of two laminæ, separated in the greater part of their extent by a narrow chink or interval, the **cavity of the septum pellucidum.** It is attached, above, to the under surface of the corpus callosum; below, to the anterior part of the fornix behind, and the reflected portion of the corpus callosum in front. It is triangular in form, broad in front and narrow behind; its inferior angle corresponds with the upper part of the anterior commissure. The lateral surface of each lamina takes part in the formation of the medial wall of the body and anterior cornu of the lateral ventricle, and is covered by the ependyma of that cavity.

The **Choroid Plexus of the Lateral Ventricle** (*plexus chorioideus ventriculus lateralis; paraplexus*) (Fig. 735) is a highly vascular, fringe-like process of pia mater, which projects into the ventricular cavity. The plexus, however, is everywhere covered by a layer of epithelium continuous with the epithelial lining of the ventricle. It extends from the interventricular foramen, where it is joined with the plexus of the opposite ventricle, to the end of the inferior cornu. The part in relation to the body of the ventricle forms the vascular fringed margin of a triangular process of pia mater, named the **tela chorioidea of the third ventricle,** and projects from under cover of the lateral edge of the fornix. It lies upon the upper surface of the thalamus, from which the epithelium is reflected over the plexus on to the edge of the fornix (Fig. 719). The portion in relation to the inferior cornu lies in the concavity of the hippocampus and overlaps the fimbria hippocampi: from the lateral edge of the fimbria the epithelium is reflected over the plexus on to the roof of the cornu (Fig. 734). It consists of minute and highly vascular villous processes, each with an afferent and an efferent vessel. The *arteries* of the plexus are: (*a*) the anterior choroidal, a branch of the internal carotid, which enters the plexus at the end of the inferior cornu; and (*b*) the posterior choroidal, one or two small branches of the posterior cerebral, which pass forward under the splenium. The *veins* of the choroid plexus unite to form a tortuous vein, which courses from behind forward to the interventricular foramen and there joins with the terminal vein to form the corresponding internal cerebral vein.

When the choroid plexus is pulled away, the continuity between its epithelial covering and the epithelial lining of the ventricle is severed, and a cleft-like space is produced. This is named the **choroidal fissure;** like the plexus, it extends from the interventricular foramen to the end of the inferior cornu. The upper part of the fissure, *i. e.*, the part nearest the interventricular foramen is situated between the lateral edge of the fornix and the upper surface of the thalamus; farther back at the beginning of the inferior cornu it is between the commencement of the fimbria hippocampi and the posterior end of the thalamus, while in the inferior cornu it lies between the fimbria in the floor and the stria terminalis in the roof of the cornu.

The **tela chorioidea of the third ventricle** (*tela chorioidea ventriculi tertii; velum interpositum*) (Fig. 735) is a double fold of pia mater, triangular in shape, which lies beneath the fornix. The lateral portions of its lower surface rest upon the thalami, while its medial portion is in contact with the epithelial roof of the third ventricle. Its apex is situated at the interventricular foramen; its base corresponds with the splenium of the corpus callosum, and occupies the interval between that structure above and the corpora quadrigemina and pineal body below. This interval, together with the lower portions of the choroidal fissures, is sometimes

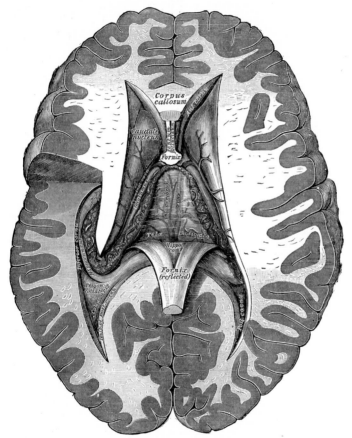

Fig. 735.—Tela chorioidea of the third ventricle, and the choroid plexus of the left lateral ventricle, exposed from above.

spoken of as the **transverse fissure of the brain.** At its base the two layers of the velum separate from each other, and are continuous with the pia mater investing the brain in this region. Its lateral margins are modified to form the highly vascular choroid plexuses of the lateral ventricles. It is supplied by the anterior and posterior choroidal arteries already described. The veins of the tela chorioidea are named the **internal cerebral veins** (*venæ Galeni*); they are two in number, and run backward between its layers, each being formed at the interventricular foramen by the union of the terminal vein with the choroidal vein. The internal cerebral veins unite posteriorly in a single trunk, the **great cerebral vein** (*vena magna Galeni*), which passes backward beneath the splenium and ends in the straight sinus.

Rhinencephalon (Fig. 736).

The rhinencephalon includes all those portions of the cerebrum which are concerned with the reception and conduction of olfactory impressions. In lower vertebrates the rhinencephalon consists of the olfactory lobe and the archipallium, and includes nearly the whole of the fore-brain. In man, however, the archipallium has been so much reduced by the exuberant growth of the neopallium that many of its derivatives are difficult to recognize with the naked eye. They have been relegated to the medial and inferior surfaces; some have become thinned out into a fine sheet by the growth of the corpus callosum, while others have been overgrown and buried by the development of neighboring neopallial areas. The rhinencephalon comprises (1) the **olfactory bulb**, in which the primary olfactory neurons end and the secondary neurones begin, (2) the **olfactory tract**, which conveys the secondary olfactory neurones to (3) the **olfactory trigone**, the **olfactory tubercle** and the **area piriformis**, which give rise to the tertiary olfactory neurones, (4) the **hippocampal formation**, in which the tertiary neurones end, (5) the **paraterminal body**, and (6) the **fornix**, which constitutes the efferent pathway from the hippocampal formation and the archipallium in general.

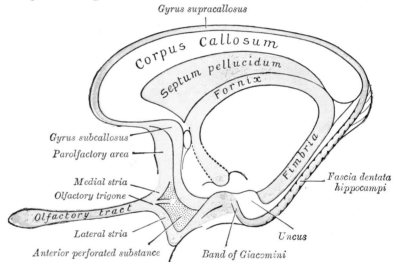

Fig. 736.—Scheme of rhinencephalon.

1. The **Olfactory Bulb** (*bulbus olfactorius*) is an oval, reddish-gray mass which rests on the cribriform plate of the ethmoid. Its under surface receives the olfactory nerves, which pass upward through the cribriform plate from the olfactory region of the nasal cavity. They terminate in glomerular tufts and interlace there with dendritic terminals of the mitral cells. The axons of the mitral cells form the olfactory tract.

2. The **Olfactory Tract** (*tractus olfactorius*), a narrow white band, triangular on coronal section, lies in the olfactory sulcus on the inferior surface of the frontal lobe; it spreads out posteriorly into the olfactory trigone and divides into two striæ, a medial and a lateral. The **lateral olfactory stria** passes laterally at first in the anterior part of the anterior perforated substance where its fibers can usually be detected with the naked eye. They are associated with a narrow band of gray substance, the **lateral olfactory gyrus**, derived from the piriform area but indistinguishable from the gray substance of the anterior perforated substance. On reaching the antero-inferior corner of the insula the stria and its accompanying gyrus bend sharply backward and medially in the floor of the lateral cerebral fossa

and enter the supero-lateral part of the uncus. The **medial olfactory stria** turns medially and ascends on the medial aspect of the hemisphere immediately in front of the paraterminal body, which separates it from the upper end of the lamina terminalis. Like the lateral stria, it is associated with a strip of gray substance, the **medial olfactory gyrus**, indistinguishable from the paraterminal body on naked-eye examination. Together they reach the inferior aspect of the corpus callosum where they become continuous with the subcallosal gyrus.

The olfactory tract contains axons from the mitral cells, secondary neurons, of the olfactory bulb. A few fibers terminate in the olfactory trigone and olfactory tubercle of the anterior perforated substance. Most of the axons pass into the lateral olfactory stria, give off collaterals to the lateral olfactory gyrus and terminate in the uncus and hippocampal gyrus. Some fibers are said to run in the medial olfactory stria to the parolfactory area of Broca, to the subcallosal gyrus and to the septum pellucidum.

Tertiary neurons of the piriform area (olfactory trigone, lateral olfactory gyrus, olfactory tubercle, uncus and anterior part of hippocampal gyrus) send axons to the hippocampus and dentate fascia.

3. (*a*) The **Olfactory Trigone** (*trigonum olfactorium*) is a small triangular area in front of the anterior perforated substance between the diverging olfactory striæ.

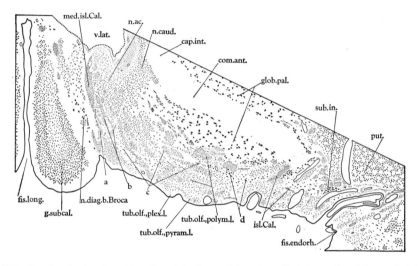

Fig. 737.—Drawing showing the mid-portion of the human tuberculum olfactorium. *Cap. int.*, capsula interna; *com. ant.*, commissura anterior; *d.*, large neurons of polymorph layer; *fis. endorh.*, fissura endorhinalis; *fis. long.*, fissura longitudinalis; *g. subcal.*, gyrus subcallosus; *isl. Cal.*, island of Calleja; *glob. pal.*, globus pallidus; *med. isl. Cal.*, medial island of Calleja; *n. ac.*, nucleus accumbens; *n. caud.*, nucleus caudatus; *n. diag. b. Broca*, nucleus of the diagonal band of Broca; *put.*, putamen; *sub. in.*, substantia innominata; *tub. olf., plex. l.*, tuberculum olfactorium plexiform layer; *tub. olf., polym. l.*, tuberculum olfactorium polymorph layer; *tub. olf., pryam. l.*, tuberculum olfactorium pyramidal layer; *v. lat.*, ventriculus lateralis. (Crosby and Humphrey, Courtesy of Jour. Comp. Neur.)

(*b*) The **olfactory tubercle** (*tuberculum olfactorium*) lies immediately postero-lateral to the olfactory trigone. Very rarely it is visible in the human brain as a small oval elevation in the anterior perforated substance, a depressed area of gray matter, between the olfactory trigone and optic tract. It is pierced by numerous small arteries which run to the basal ganglia.

(*c*) The **anterior perforated substance** (Fig. 737), of which the tuberculum olfactorium forms a part, extends from the olfactory striæ to the optic tract. On the medial, rostral and lateral sides it is continuous, through a transition zone, with the six-layered cortex of the frontal lobe. Caudally it is bounded by: (1) the pyriform area; (2) by the diagonal band of Broca and the preoptic areas; and (3) by the parolfactory nuclei of the paraterminal body. It comes in contact above with the basal parts of the head of the caudate, the putamen and the globus pallidus.

There are numerous connections between them. The internal structure of the anterior perforated area shows three moderately well defined layers: (1) an external molecular layer; (2) a layer of pyramidal cells; and (3) an irregular layer of polymorphic cells. In the third layer two specialized groups of cells are found. Several densely packed groups of small, well stained cells are named **the islands of Calleja.** A band of large cells just under the ventral surface of the globus pallidus is the substantia innominata of Reichert. The **nucleus accumbens** forms the floor of the posterior part of the anterior horn of the lateral ventricle. It lies between the head of the caudate and the anterior perforated substance.

The anterior perforated substance receives fibers from the olfactory striæ. It is the principal origin of the medial forebrain bundle.

(*d*) The **piriform area** includes the anterior part of the **hippocampal gyrus,** the **uncus** and the band of gray substance, the **lateral olfactory gyrus,** which reaches it along with the lateral olfactory stria. The uncus is continuous with the recurved anterior end of the hippocampal gyrus round the anterior end of the hippocampal fissure. Its lower surface cannot be examined until the hippocampal gyrus is removed. It is crossed about its middle by a narrow band of gray substance, continuous at its lateral end with the dentate gyrus, and termed the **banderella of Giacomini.** The portion of the uncus which lies behind the banderella has been termed the **intralimbic gyrus,** and it is morphologically distinct from the part lying anterior to the banderella, which is directly continuous with the hippocampal gyrus.

The **lateral olfactory gyrus** is a strip of gray substance which is associated with the lateral olfactory stria. It cannot be made out in the human brain with the naked eye, but it constitutes an essential part of the piriform area and has already been described with the lateral olfactory stria.

The tertiary olfactory neurons, which arise in the piriform area, proceed at once into the hippocampal formation, but they do not form any composite tract.

4. The **Hippocampal Formation** is formed along the fringe of the pallium on the medial aspect of the hemisphere. It comprises (*a*) the **subcallosal gyrus,** (*b*) the **supracallosal gyrus,** (*c*) the **longitudinal striæ** of the corpus callosum and the **diagonal band** (of Broca), (*d*) the **dentate gyrus,** and (*e*) the **hippocampus.**

The hippocampal formation is laid down in the embryo on the medial wall of the hemisphere, forming an arch immediately outside the arch of the chorioidal fissure. The anterior or upper part of the arch is invaded by the corpus callosum, and the great size of this structure in the human brain reduces the corresponding portion of the hippocampal formation to the mere vestige which is represented by the supra- and subcallosal gyri and the associated longitudinal striæ. The posterior or lower part of the arch is carried downward and forward by the growth of the temporal lobe and so is not affected by the development of the corpus callosum. The **hippocampal fissure** develops in this part of the hippocampal formation, outside the chorioidal fissure, and the strip of cortex which lies between the two fissures forms the dentate gyrus. The cortex at the bottom of the fissure proliferates rapidly and bulges laterally into the cavity of the inferior horn of the ventricle, constituting the hippocampus.

(*a*) The **subcallosal gyrus,** paraterminal body, is the thin sheet of gray substance which covers the under aspect of the rostrum of the corpus callosum and is continuous round the genu with the supracallosal gyrus. Below and behind it is continuous with the gray substance of the medial olfactory gyrus.

(*b*) The **supracallosal gyrus** is the thin sheet of gray substance which covers the upper surface of the corpus callosum and is continuous on each side, round the bottom of the callosal sulcus with the cortex of the gyrus cinguli. It is continuous in front with the subcallosal gyrus and behind with the **fasciola cinerea,** a delicate layer of gray substance which is continuous with the posterior end of the dentate gyrus (Fig. 736).

(*c*) The **medial** and **lateral longitudinal striæ** are two ridges which extend forward on the upper surface of the corpus callosum (Fig. 746). The medial stria lies close to the median plane, but the lateral stria is placed under cover of the gyrus cinguli on the floor of the callosal fissure. They consist of longitudinally running fibers, which sweep round the genu and enter the subcallosal gyrus. From this they emerge as a single band, directed laterally and backward across the anterior perforated substance forming the **diagonal band** (of Broca). They represent the white substance of the vestigial supracallosal gyrus.

(*d*) The **dentate fascia** is a narrow, crenated strip of cortex which lies on the *upper* surface of the hippocampal gyrus, under cover of the fimbria, from which it is separated by the fimbrio-dentate sulcus. The **hippocampal fissure** intervenes between it and the hippocampal gyrus, but except at its anterior end this fissure is not constantly present in the adult human brain. Posteriorly the dentate fascia is prolonged on to the under surface of the splenium of the corpus callosum, as the delicate fasciola cinerea, which in turn becomes continuous with the supracallosal gyrus. Anteriorly, the dentate fascia is continued into the notch of the uncus, and then bends sharply medially across the inferior surface of the uncus. This transverse portion of the dentate fascia is termed the **band of Giacomini**. Unlike the rest of the dentate fascia, the band of Giacomini is smooth and featureless, and it becomes lost on the medial aspect of the uncus.

(*e*) The **hippocampus** is a curved elevation, about 5 cm. long, which extends throughout the entire length of the floor of the inferior cornu of the lateral ventricle. Its anterior or lower extremity is enlarged and is crossed by three or four shallow grooves. The ventricular surface of the hippocampus is covered by a layer of white fibers which constitute the **alveus**, but the great bulk of the elevation is made up of gray substance. Posteriorly, the hippocampus, like the dentate fascia, becomes continuous with the supracallosal gyrus at the splenium of the corpus callosum.

5. The **Paraterminal Body** is the triangular area of the cortex which lies immediately in front of the lamina terminalis. Anteriorly it is limited by the medial olfactory gyrus and stria, and superiorly it becomes continuous with the gray substance of the subcallosal gyrus. Caudo-ventral to the subcallosal gyrus is the **parolfactory area**, consisting of a medial and lateral parolfactory nucleus on each side. These are bounded caudally by the medial preoptic area and by the anterior commissure with its associated nuclei. From the medial parolfactory nucleus a band of large, deeply staining cells and fibers swings ventrally and then laterally and caudally to near the region of the amygdaloid complex. This is the **diagonal band of Broca.**

6. The **Fornix** is the efferent pathway from the cells of the hippocampal formation, and therefore conveys olfactory fibers of the fourth neurones. The fibers of the cells of the dentate fascia and hippocampus pass to the ventricular surface of the latter, on which they form a layer of white substance, termed the **alveus**. The fibers of the alveus converge on the medial aspect of the hippocampus to form the **fimbria,** a flattened band of white fibers which lies above the dentate fascia and immediately below the lower part of the chorioidal fissure. The disposition of the fimbria is variable. It may project above the dentate fascia, with a free medial edge and a lateral border which merges into the alveus, or its free border may be twisted over toward the lateral side, uncovering the dentate fascia. Anteriorly, the fimbria passes into the hook of the uncus (Fig. 738). Traced backward on the floor of the inferior horn of the ventricle, it ascends below the splenium and bends forward above the thalamus, forming the **crus fornicis.** The two **crura** are closely applied to the under surface of the corpus callosum and are connected to one another by a number of transverse fibers which pass between the hippocampal formations of the two hemispheres and form the **hippocampal commissure.** This commissure presents the appearance of a thin, triangular lamina, termed the **psalterium** or **lyra.**

Anteriorly the two crura come together in the median plane and constitute the **body of the fornix,** which is really a symmetrically disposed bilateral structure. The body of the fornix lies above the tela chorioidea and the ependymal roof of the third

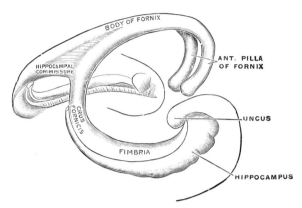

Fig. 738.—Diagram of the fornix. (Spitzka.)

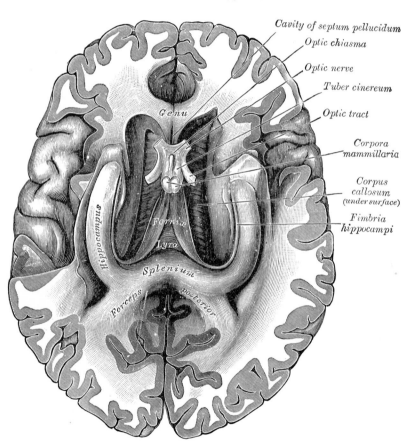

Fig. 739.—The fornix and corpus callosum from below. (From a specimen in the Department of Human Anatomy of the University of Oxford.)

ventricle (Fig. 735) and is attached above to the under surface of the corpus callosum and, more anteriorly, to the lower borders of the laminæ of the septum pellucidum. Laterally, the body of the fornix overlies the medial part of the upper surface of the thalamus and the chorioidal fissure is placed below its free, lateral edge. Through this fissure the chorioidal plexus in the lateral margin of the tela chorioidea thrusts its way into the body of the lateral ventricle (Fig. 731).

Above the interventricular foramen the body of the fornix divides into two *columns* which bend downward and backward, forming the anterior boundary of the interventricular foramen and pass behind the anterior commissure. As they descend, each sinks into the anterior part of the corresponding lateral wall of the third ventricle and reaches the corpus mamillare in which it mainly terminates. Some of the fibers of the fornix system leave the column near the interventricular foramen and run backward, in the stria medullaris thalami, to reach the ganglion habenulæ of the same or the opposite side. Zuckerkandl has described an **olfactory fasciculus** which leaves the column of the fornix and descends in front of the anterior commissure to the base of the brain where it divides into two bundles; one joins the medial olfactory stria; the other joins the subcallosal gyrus and through it reaches the hippocampal gyrus. The fornix is one of the efferent pathways for the archipallium and its fibers, relayed in the corpora mamillaria, pass to the anterior nucleus of the thalamus by the mamillothalamic fasciculus and to the tegmentum of the brain-stem by the mamillotegmental tract.

The **anterior commissure** is a bundle of white fibers which crosses the median plane in front of the columns of the fornix in the anterior wall of the third ventricle. In sagittal section, it is oval in shape, its long diameter being vertical and measuring about 5 mm. Its constituent fiber bundles are twisted like the strands of a rope, and they curve backward and laterally forming a deep groove on the inferior aspect of the anterior part of the corpus striatum. Most of the fibers belong to the rhinencephalon and connect the piriform areas and the amygdalæ of the two sides. Some are thought to belong to the neopallium and can be traced into the temporal lobes where they spread out like the frayed end of a rope so that their precise connections are difficult to determine.

The **hippocampal commissure** forms a thin sheet of transverse fibers which connects the medial edges of the crura of the fornix and is closely applied to the under aspect of the posterior part of the body of the corpus callosum. Its constituent fibers are derived from the pyramidal cells of the hippocampus and traverse the alveus and the fimbria in order to reach the crus. Having crossed the median plane in the commissure, they retrace their course on the opposite side and terminate in the molecular layer of the hippocampus. This commissure therefore functions as the pallial commissure of the rhinencephalon.

Basal Ganglia.

The basal ganglia of the cerebral hemispheres include the **caudate nucleus** and **putamen**, which together form the **corpus striatum**, the **globus pallidus**, the **amygdaloid complex** and the **claustrum**.

The **corpus striatum** derives its name from the striped appearance caused by the white fibers of the internal capsule running between the caudate and putamen, leaving connecting strands of gray between them. The caudate and putamen are continuous rostrally and caudally, and all of the thalamic radiations as well as the descending cortical systems run through the cleft between them.

The **Caudate Nucleus** (*nucleus caudatus; caudatum*) (Figs. 741, 742) is a pear-shaped, highly arched gray mass; its broad extremity, or **head,** is directed forward into the anterior cornu of the lateral ventricle, and is continuous with the anterior perforated substance and with the anterior end of the lentiform nucleus; its narrow end, or **tail,** is directed backward on the lateral side of the thalamus, from which it is separated by the stria terminalis and the terminal vein. It is then continued downward into the roof of the inferior cornu, and ends in the putamen caudal to the amygdala. It is covered by the lining of the ventricle, and crossed by some veins of considerable size. It is separated from the lentiform nucleus, in the greater part of its extent, by a thick lamina of white substance, called the **internal capsule,** but the two portions of the corpus striatum are united in front (Figs. 742, 743, 744). The caudate is composed of numerous small cells, with larger, more deeply staining polygonal cells scattered through it. The basal part of the head of the caudate is closely related to the olfactory areas beneath it, and it is said to contribute fibers to the medial forebrain bundle, some of which may reach the mesencephalon. Afferents to the main part of the head and to the tail come from the cerebral cortex, in part by direct fiber connections, but largely by collaterals from certain of the corticifugal fibers (including the pyramidal tract). The projection of the cortex to the caudate seems to follow a definite pattern. Other afferents apparently come from the medial thalamic nuclei. Most of the efferents

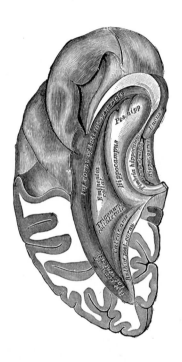

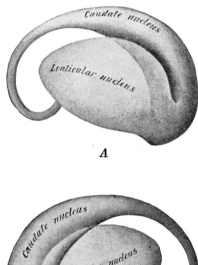

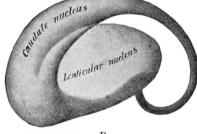

FIG. 740.—Inferior and posterior cornua, viewed from above.

FIG. 741.—Two views of a model of the striatum: *A* lateral aspect; *B,* mesal aspect.

go to the putamen, some to the globus pallidus. There are also fibers directly to the thalamus and others to the mesencephalon.

The **putamen** (Fig. 744) is a thick, convex mass, lying lateral to the internal capsule and globus pallidus and dorsal to the amygdala under the region of the insular cortex. Its cells and connections are similar to those of the caudate, but the projection of the cerebral cortex in this nucleus does not seem to be as precise.

The **globus pallidus** (Fig. 744) lies medial to the putamen, between it and the internal capsule. It is roughly a right-angled triangle on cross section, the perpendicular side adjoining the putamen. There is a lamina of heavily myelinated fibers between the two nuclei and a similar lamina divides the globus pallidus into medial and lateral parts. Smaller, less complete laminæ subdivide each of these again. The cells of the globus pallidus are all large, polygonal, deeply staining, pigmented cells, resembling the motor type. Its afferents come chiefly from the caudate and putamen. Connections ventrally with the olfactory brain are present. Fibers from the substantia nigra have been described ascending to it through the peduncle. Also there is evidence for direct connections from the nuclei gracilis and cuneatus, via the medial lemniscus. Its efferents take three main courses: (1) fine fibers cross the internal capsule to enter the ventral aspect of the thalamus; (2) other fine fibers cross the peduncle to the nucleus subthalamicus, and possibly to the substantia nigra; (3) large fibers leave the tip of the globus pallidus, swing through and round the rostral margin of the peduncle and descend through the field H_2 of Forel as the ansa lenticularis. The latter distributes widely to the red

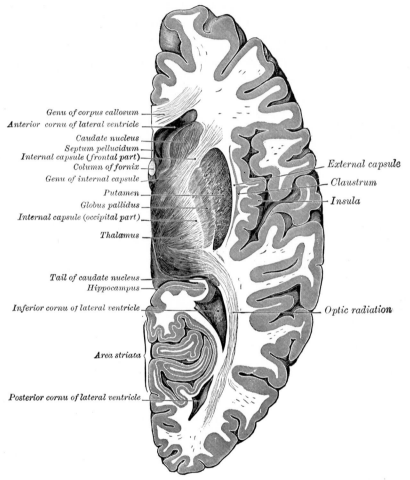

Genu of corpus callosum
Anterior cornu of lateral ventricle
Caudate nucleus
Septum pellucidum
Internal capsule (frontal part)
Column of fornix
Genu of internal capsule
Putamen
Globus pallidus
Internal capsule (occipital part)
Thalamus

External capsule
Claustrum
Insula

Tail of caudate nucleus
Hippocampus
Inferior cornu of lateral ventricle

Optic radiation

Area striata

Posterior cornu of lateral ventricle

FIG. 742.—Horizontal section of right cerebral hemisphere.

nucleus and the nuclei of the mesencephalic reticular formation, few, if any, reaching the pons.

There are no myelinated fibers from the corpus striatum, or globus pallidus to the cortex.

The putamen and globus pallidus were at one time regarded as a single structure and called the **lentiform nucleus.**

The **extrapyramidal motor system**—in certain neurological diseases there are gross disturbances of movement and of posture, although the pyramidal system is found to be intact. The symptoms seen are: (1) involuntary movements, such as chorea, athetosis, torsion spasms, tremors, etc.; and (2) abnormalities in the tonic innervation of muscles, including rigidity, dystonia, etc. In these diseases, lesions have been found in different parts of the basal ganglia, the ventral nuclei of the thalamus, the red nucleus, the nucleus subthalamicus, the substantia nigra, the dentate nucleus of the cerebellum, the inferior olives and the cerebral cortex, or in their connecting fiber systems. For this reason, the corpus striatum, globus pallidus, nucleus subthalamicus, red nucleus and substantia nigra were first grouped under the term "extrapyramidal motor system." Later, the dentate nucleus and inferior olives were added and more recently certain parts of the cerebral cortex have been included by some authors. The latter include areas 6 and 8 of the frontal, area 22 of the temporal, areas 5 and 7 of the parietal and area 19 of the occipital lobes. The efferent pathways to the spinal cord for the extrapyramidal system are the reticulospinal tracts and short neuron chains.

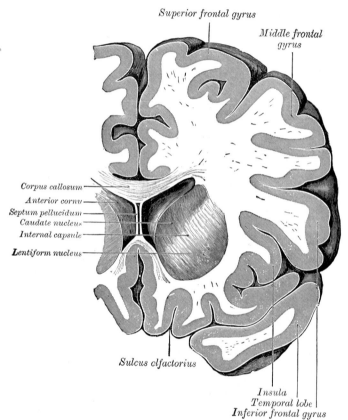

Superior frontal gyrus

Middle frontal gyrus

Corpus callosum
Anterior cornu
Septum pellucidum
Caudate nucleus
Internal capsule
Lentiform nucleus

Sulcus olfactorius

Insula
Temporal lobe
Inferior frontal gyrus

Fig. 743.—Coronal section through anterior cornua of lateral ventricles.

The **stria terminalis** (*tænia semicircularis*) is a narrow band of white substance situated in the depression between the caudate nucleus and the thalamus. Anteriorly, its fibers are partly continued into the stria medullaris to end in the habenular ganglia, some pass over the anterior commissure to the gray substance between the caudate nucleus and septum pellucidum, while the majority turn ventrally into the hypothalamus of the same side, or through the anterior commissure to that of the opposite side. Posteriorly, it is continued into the roof of the inferior cornu of the lateral ventricle, at the extremity of which it enters the nucleus amygdalæ. Superficial to it is a large vein, the **terminal vein** (*vein of the corpus striatum*), which receives numerous tributaries from the corpus striatum and thalamus; it runs forward to the interventricular foramen and there joins with the vein of the choroid plexus to form the corresponding internal cerebral vein. On the surface of the terminal vein is a narrow white band, named the **lamina affixa.**

The **Nucleus Amygdalæ** (*amygdala*) is an ovoid gray mass, situated at the lower end of the roof of the inferior cornu. It consists of a number of well differentiated nuclei which are divided into a baso-lateral group and a cortico-medial group. The calustrum adjoins the dorsal surface of the lateral nuclei. The amygdalæ of the two sides are connected by commissural fibers through the anterior commissure. They receive connections from the medial basal olfactory areas and piriform areas. Efferent fibers form the stria terminalis to the parolfactory areas and hypothalami. In addition, there are apparently striatal and cortical connections.

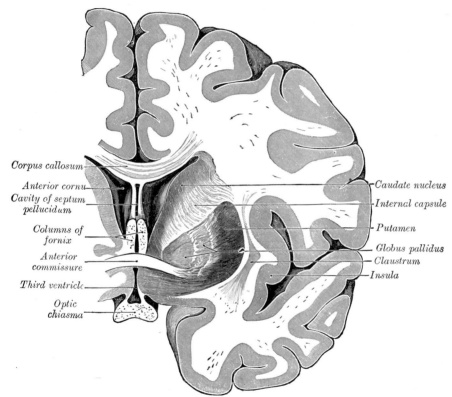

Corpus callosum

Anterior cornu
Cavity of septum
pellucidum

Columns of
fornix
Anterior
commissure

Third ventricle

Optic
chiasma

Caudate nucleus
Internal capsule

Putamen

Globus pallidus
Claustrum
Insula

Fig. 744.—Coronal section of brain through anterior commissure.

The **Claustrum** (Figs. 742, 744) is a thin layer of gray substance, situated on the lateral surface of the external capsule. Its transverse section is triangular, with the apex directed upward. Its medial surface, contiguous to the external capsule, is smooth, but its lateral surface presents ridges and furrows corresponding with the gyri and sulci of the insula, with which it is in close relationship. The claustrum is regarded as a detached portion of the gray substance of the insula, from which it is separated by a layer of white fibers, the **capsula extrema** (*band of Baillarger*). Its cells are small and spindle-shaped, and contain yellow pigment; they are similar to those of the deepest layer of the cortex.

The **Internal Capsule** (*capsula interna*) (Figs. 745, 747) is a flattened band of white fibers, between the lentiform nucleus on the lateral side and the caudate nucleus and thalamus on the medial side. In horizontal section (Fig. 742) it is seen to be somewhat abruptly curved, with its convexity inward; the prominence of the curve is called the **genu**, and projects between the caudate nucleus and the thalamus. The portion in front of the genu, the anterior limb, separates the lentiform from the caudate nucleus; the portion behind the genu, the posterior limb, separates the lentiform nucleus from the thalamus. That part of the posterior limb which curves around the caudal end of the lentiform nucleus is designated as theretrolenticular and the part that lies ventral to the lentiform is the sublenticular part.

The anterior limb of the internal capsule contains: thalamocortical fibers from the lateral nucleus of the thalamus to the frontal lobe; corticothalamic fibers from the frontal lobe to the thalamus; fronto-pontile fibers from the frontal lobe to the nuclei of the pons; probably collaterals from the above tracts to the caudate and putamen; and fibers from the caudate to the putamen. The genu contains in

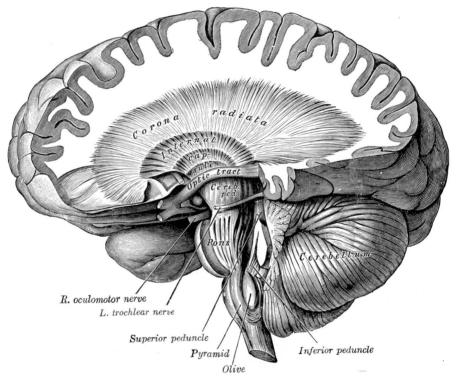

Fig. 745.—Dissection showing the course of the cerebrospinal fibers. (E. B. Jamieson.)

addition to corticothalamic and thalamocortical fibers, corticobulbar fibers to the motor nuclei of the cranial nerves. The adjoining region of the posterior limb contains in addition to corticothalamic and thalamocortical fibers, corticospinal and corticorubral fibers. The corticospinal fibers to the motor nuclei of the muscles of the arm are nearer to the genu than those to the leg. The retrolenticular part contains thalamocortical fibers, sensory fibers from the lateral nucleus of the thalamus to the postcentral gyrus. The sublenticular part contains: the temporopontile fibers from the cortex of the temporal lobe to the pontile nuclei; the auditory radiation from the medial geniculate body to the auditosensory area of the transverse temporal gyrus; the optic radiation (geniculocalcarine tract) from the lateral geniculate body to the visuosensory area of the occipital lobe; fibers from the cortex to the superior colliculus; corticothalamic fibers from the temporal and occipital lobes to the lateral nucleus of the thalamus.

The fibers of the internal capsule radiate widely as they pass to and from the various parts of the cerebral cortex, forming the **corona radiata** (Fig. 745) and intermingling with the fibers of the corpus callosum.

The **External Capsule** (*capsula externa*) (Fig. 742) is a lamina of white substance, situated lateral to the lentiform nucleus, between it and the claustrum, and continuous with the internal capsule below and behind the lentiform nucleus. Its connections are unknown.

Structure of the Cerebral Hemispheres.—The cerebral hemispheres are composed of gray and white substance: the former covers their surface, and is termed the **cortex**; the latter occupies the interior of the hemispheres.

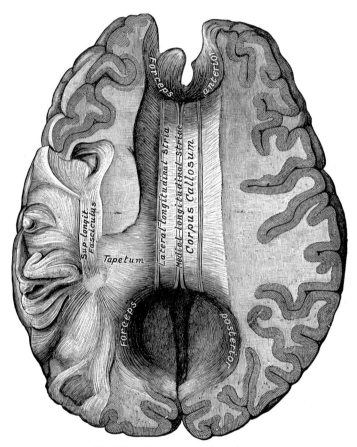

Fig. 746.—Corpus callosum from above.

The **white substance** consists of medullated fibers, varying in size, and arranged in bundles separated by neuroglia. They may be divided, according to their course and connections, into three distinct systems. (1) **Projection fibers** connect the hemisphere with the lower parts of the brain and with the medulla spinalis. (2) **Transverse** or **commissural fibers** unite the two hemispheres. (3) **Association fibers** connect different structures in the same hemisphere; these are, in many instances, collateral branches of the projection fibers, but others are the axons of independent cells.

1. The **projection fibers** consist of efferent and afferent fibers uniting the cortex with the lower parts of the brain and with the medulla spinalis. They pass through the corona radiata to the internal capsule.

2. The **transverse** or **commissural fibers** connect the two hemispheres. They

55

include: (*a*) the *transverse fibers* of the corpus callosum, (*b*) the anterior commissure, (*c*) the posterior commissure, and (*d*) the lyra or hippocampal commissure; the latter have already been described.

The **Corpus Callosum** (Fig. 746) is the great transverse commissure which unites the cerebral hemispheres and roofs in the lateral ventricles. A good conception of

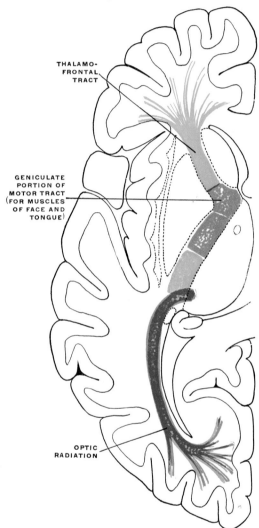

THALAMO-
FRONTAL
TRACT

GENICULATE
PORTION OF
MOTOR TRACT
(FOR MUSCLES
OF FACE AND
TONGUE)

OPTIC
RADIATION

Fig. 746.—Diagram of the tracts in the internal capsule Motor tract red. The sensory tract (blue) is not direct, but formed of neurons receiving impulses from below in the thalamus and transmitting them to the cortex. The optic radiation (occipitothalamic) is shown in violet.

its position and size is obtained by examining a median sagittal section of the brain (Fig. 724), when it is seen to form an arched structure about 10 cm. long. Its anterior end is about 4 cm. from the frontal pole, and its posterior end about 6 cm. from the occipital pole of the hemisphere.

The anterior end is named the **genu,** and is bent downward and backward in front of the septum pellucidum; diminishing rapidly in thickness, it is prolonged backward under the name of the **rostrum,** which is connected below with the lamina terminalis. The anterior cerebral arteries are in contact with the under surface of the rostrum; they then arch over the front of the genu, and are carried backward above the body of the corpus callosum.

The posterior end is termed the **splenium** and constitutes the thickest part of the corpus callosum. It overlaps the tela chorioidea of the third ventricle and the mid-brain, and ends in a thick, convex, free border. A sagittal section of the splenium shows that the posterior end of the corpus callosum is acutely bent forward, the upper and lower parts being applied to each other.

The **superior surface** is convex from before backward, and is about 2.5 cm. wide. Its medial part forms the bottom of the longitudinal fissure, and is in contact posteriorly with the lower border of the falx cerebri. Laterally it is overlapped by the cingulate gyrus, but is separated from it by the slit-like callosal fissure. It is traversed by numerous transverse ridges and furrows, and is covered by a thin layer of gray matter, the **supracallosal gyrus,** which exhibits on either side of the middle line the medial and lateral longitudinal striæ, already described (page 857).

The **inferior surface** is concave, and forms on either side of the middle line the roof of the lateral ventricle. Medially, this surface is attached in front to the septum pellucidum; behind this it is fused with the upper surface of the body of the fornix, while the splenium is in contact with the tela chorioidea.

On either side, the fibers of the corpus callosum radiate in the white substance and pass to the various parts of the cerebral cortex; those curving forward from the genu into the frontal lobe constitute the **forceps anterior,** and those curving backward into the occipital lobe, the **forceps posterior.** Between these two parts is the main body of the fibers which constitute the **tapetum** and extend laterally on either side into the hemispheres, and cover in the central part of the lateral ventricle.

3. The **association fibers** (Fig. 748) unite different parts of the same hemisphere, and are of two kinds: (1) those connecting adjacent gyri, **short association fibers;** (2) those passing between more distant parts, **long association fibers.**

The *short association fibers* lie immediately beneath the gray substance of the cortex of the hemispheres, and connect together adjacent gyri.

The *long association fibers* include the following: (*a*) the uncinate fasciculus; (*b*) the cingulum; (*c*) the superior longitudinal fasciculus; (*d*) the inferior longitudinal fasciculus; (*e*) the perpendicular fasciculus; (*f*) the occipito-frontal fasciculus; and (*g*) the fornix.

(*a*) The *uncinate fasciculus* passes across the bottom of the lateral fissure, and unites the gyri of the frontal lobe with the anterior end of the temporal lobe.

(*b*) The *cingulum* is a band of white matter contained within the cingulate gyrus. Beginning in front at the anterior perforated substance, it passes forward and upward parallel with the rostrum, winds around the genu, runs backward above the corpus callosum, turns around the splenium, and ends in the hippocampal gyrus.

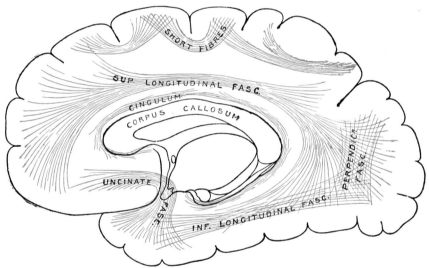

Fig. 748.—Diagram showing principal systems of association fibers in the cerebrum.

(*c*) The *superior longitudinal fasciculus* passes backward from the frontal lobe above the lentiform nucleus and insula; some of its fibers end in the occipital lobe, and others curve downward and forward into the temporal lobe.

(*d*) The *inferior longitudinal fasciculus* connects the temporal and occipital lobes, running along the lateral walls of the inferior and posterior cornua of the lateral ventricle.

(*e*) The *perpendicular fasciculus* runs vertically through the front part of the occipital lobe, and connects the inferior parietal lobule with the fusiform gyrus.

(*f*) The *occipito-frontal fasciculus* passes backward from the frontal lobe, along the lateral border of the caudate nucleus, and on the mesial aspect of the corona radiata; its fibers radiate in a fan-like manner and pass into the occipital and temporal lobes lateral to the posterior and inferior cornua. Déjerine regards the fibers of the tapetum as being derived from this fasciculus, and not from the corpus callosum.

(*g*) The *fornix* connects the hippocampal gyrus with the corpus mamillare and, by means of the thalamomammillary fasciculus, with the thalamus (see page 859). Through the fibers of the hippocampal commissure it probably also unites the opposite hippocampal gyri.

The **gray substance of the hemisphere** is divided into: (1) that of the cerebral cortex, and (2) that of the caudate nucleus, the lentiform nucleus, the claustrum, and the nucleus amygdalæ.

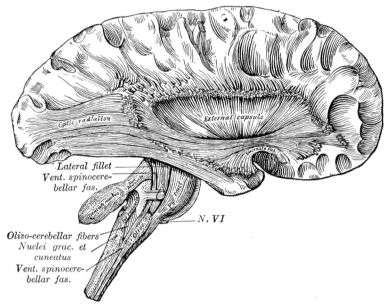

Fig. 749.—Deep dissection of cortex and brain-stem.

Structure of the Cerebral Cortex (Fig. 750).—The cerebral cortex differs in thickness and structure in different parts of the hemisphere. It is thinner in the occipital region than in the anterior and posterior central gyri, and it is also much thinner at the bottom of the sulci than on the top of the gyri. Again, the minute structure of one part differs from that of another part, and areas possessing a specialized type of cortex can be mapped out.

On examining a section of the cortex with a lens, it is seen to consist of alternating white and gray layers thus disposed from the surface inward: (1) a thin layer of white substance; (2) a layer of gray substance; (3) a second white layer (*outer band of Baillarger* or *band of Gennari*); (4) a second gray layer; (5) a third white layer (*inner band of Baillarger*); (6) a third gray layer, which rests on the medullary substance of the gyrus.

The studies of Ramón y Cajal and of R. Lorente de Nó indicate that cortical activity occurs chiefly between cells at different levels in the gray layers and that different parts of the cortex are associated by cells with horizontal axons, cells with axons terminating within the cortex, as well as by short and long association or cortico-cortical fibers.

The general plan of the structure of the parieto-temporo-occipital cortex has been recently described by Lorente de Nó[1] and the following summary is taken from his work. The frontal cortex has not yet been adequately analyzed.

The cortex is divided into six zones or layers on the basis of the distribution of the dendrites of the various types of cells (Figs. 751, 752 and 753).

Layer I, the plexiform layer of Cajal. Horizontal cells (Fig. 753, 22) and cells with short axons. Terminal bushels of the shafts of the deeper pyramid and spindle cells. Final terminations of the thalamo-cortical and cortico-cortical association fibers.

Layer II, small pyramids (Fig. 151, 7). Shafts of deeper pyramids. Numerous collaterals of afferent association fibers and of ascending axons (Fig. 751).

Layer III, small pyramids (Fig. 751, 2, 3,) and cells with short axons (Fig. 753, 23). Similar association fibers as in Layer II, but also a few branches from projection fibers (somato-sensory, visual or auditory).

[1] In "Physiology of the Nervous System," by J. F. Fulton, Oxford University Press, 1938.

Layer IV is subdivided into two strata, IVa and IVb. Both contain star cells (Fig. 751, 5), whose dendrites end in Layer IV, and star pyramids (Fig. 751, 4, 6), characterized by horizontal dendrites in Layer IV, the shaft reaching to Layer I without branches. Cells with short axons (Fig. 753, 24), and with ascending axons (Fig. 753, 20). Layer IV receives the specific projection afferents which break up into a dense fibrillar plexus.

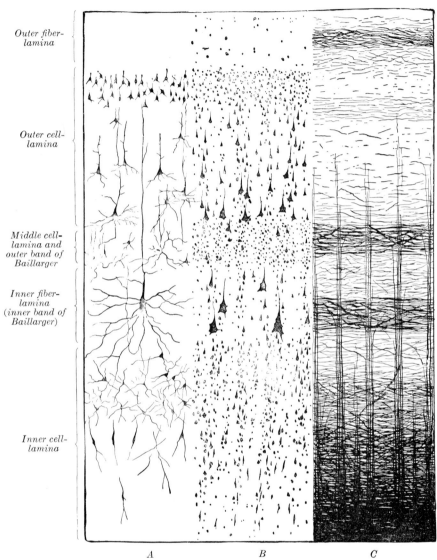

Outer fiber-
lamina

Outer cell-
lamina

Middle cell-
lamina and
outer band of
Baillarger

Inner fiber-
lamina
(inner band of
Baillarger)

Inner cell-
lamina

A   *B*   *C*

Fig. 750.—A diagram showing the layers of cells and fibers in the gray substance of the cortex of the human cerebral hemisphere, according to the histological methods of Golgi, Nissl and Weigert. *A*, Stained by the method of Golgi; *B*, by that of Nissl; *C*, by that of Weigert. (After Brodmann: from Luciani's Physiology, Macmillan & Co., Ltd.)

Layer V is subdivided into three strata, Va, Vb, and Vc, the largest pyramids being Vb. The division between Layers IV and V is definite, but between V and VI is not so sharp. The classical pyramids (Figs. 751, 752, 7, 8, 9) have horizontal dendrites in Layer V only. The shaft extends to Layer I where it terminates in a complicated arborization. Two other types of pyramids are present; medium (Fig. 751, 11), whose shafts terminate and therefore make contacts in Layer IV; and short (Fig. 751, 10), whose shafts terminate in Layer V. Short pyramids are also found in Layer VI (Fig. 751, 12, 13). In addition there are cells with short axons (Fig. 753, 25) and cells with ascending axons (Fig. 753, 19). A few collaterals are given off by the association afferent fibers in this layer.

Fig. 751.—At the left side a diagrammatic Nissl picture of the parietal cortex of the adult mouse stained after Nissl. The cell layers are marked with Roman numerals. Except between IVb and Va there is no sharp boundary between layers. At the center, bodies and dendrites of representative types of cells with descending axons; to avoid complication of the drawing the axons have not been included (see Fig. 752). At the right the main types of cortical afferent fibers. 1, Pyramids of Layer II; 2 and 3, pyramids of Layer III; 4, large star pyramids; 5, star cells; 6, small star pyramids; 7, 8, 9, long deep pyramids; 10, short pyramids; 11, medium pyramids; 12, 13, short pyramids of Layer VIa; 14, long spindles; 15, medium spindles; 16, short spindles; 17, deep star cells; a, b, specific thalamic afferents; c, d, unspecific or pluriareal afferents; e, f, association fibers. The cells have been reproduced from two consecutive sections through the brain of an adult mouse, stained after Golgi-Cox, and the fibers from section through brains of eleven-day old mice stained after Golgi. (Lorente de Nó in Fulton's Phsyiology of the Nervous System, courtesy of Oxford University Press.)

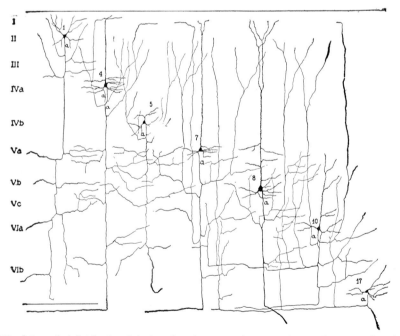

Fig. 752.—Intracortical distribution of the branches of representative types of descending axons. In order not to complicate the drawing, branches have been omitted and others have been drawn shorter than they really are. The numbers on the cells are the same as in Fig. 751. Note that the collateral branches are concentrated in Layers I–III and V–VI. The axons of cells 1 and 5 are entirely distributed within the cortex although in higher mammals, especially in man, they may reach the white substance. The axons of cells 4, 7, 10 and 17 are fibers of association and the axon of cell 8 is a fiber of projection. (Lorente de Nó in Fulton's Physiology of the Nervous System, courtesy of Oxford University Press.)

Layer VI may be subdivided into two strata, VIa and VIb. It contains long spindles (Fig. 751, 14), whose shafts terminate in Layer I; medium spindles (Fig. 751, 15) whose shafts reach Layer IV; and short spindles (Fig. 751, 16) whose shafts end in Layer V. There are also cells whose dendrites are confined to Layer VI (Figs. 751, 752, 17). There are also cells with short axons (Fig. 753, 26) and ascending axons (Fig. 753, 18). The afferent fibers are collaterals of association fibers, which are richer in this layer than in any of the others except II and III.

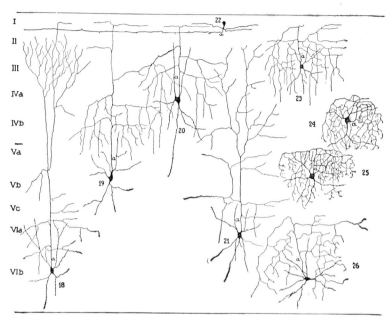

Fig. 753.—The three main types of cells with intracortical axons: 18, 19, 20, 21, cells with ascending axons; 22, cells with horizontal axon; 23, 24, 25, 26, cells with short axons. (Lorente de Nó in Fulton's Physiology of the Nervous System, courtesy of Oxford University Press.)

The different types of descending axons and efferent fibers are illustrated in Fig. 752. Moss of the cells of Layers II, III, and IV have axons which terminate in the cortex, giving off collateralt particularly in Layers V and VI. All of the axons give off collaterals, those from cells in Layers V and VI ascending chiefly to Layers II and III, occasionally to Layer I. A few association fibers come from Layer IV, most from Layers V and VI, the callosal fibers originating in Layers Vc and VIa. The projection fibers come from the large pyramids of Layer Vb.

Several points are of interest. The distribution of the specific projection afferents is quite localized, and many of the cells of the deeper layers cannot be stimulated by these fibers except through intercalated cortical neurons. The dendrite plexuses overlap the boundaries between the layers except that between Layer IV and Layer V, which is sharply demarcated. The ascending axons, recurrent collaterals and association afferents have similar distributions, which suggests that the activity of the cortex is controlled in a similar manner both by its own activity and by the activity of other cortical areas. The interconnections between the cortical layers are such that a cell may be stimulated either directly or through several chains of neurons. The intensity of stimulation is probably proportional to the synaptic area involved and so is related to the density of the dendritic plexus.

The degree of complexity of the cortex is, in large measure, determined by the proportionate number of cells whose axons terminate within the cortex. In the human approximately half the cells are of this type. The human also differs from lower forms in that the recurrent collaterals are larger, longer and more heavily myelinated. They make up the bands of Baillarger to a large extent.

Special Types of Cerebral Cortex.—The researches of Bevan Lewis, Bolton, Campbell, Brodmann, Elliot Smith and the Vogts into cortical structure, the embryological investigations of Flechsig and the experimental work of Sherringron and many others, have shown that the cortex of the cerebral hemispheres can be mapped out into areas which differ from one another in the details of their structure, in the period of the myelination of their efferent fibers and in their functional significance. Brodmann mapped out forty-seven different areas as the result of a histological survey of the cortex using the Nissl method. The Vogts have described over two hundred areas on the basis of differences in the pattern made by the myelinated fibers. Such maps of the cortex are valuable from the standpoint of topography, but have no significance as regards intrinsic function. Certain of the areas are so important from the functional standpoint that, although the structure of the cortex in general has already been described, further reference must be made to these local variations.

The **precentral area** includes the cortex of the precentral (anterior central) gyrus and the posterior portions of the superior, middle and inferior frontal gyri (Campbell). The whole of this area is characterized by the almost complete absence of the granular layer. It is subdivisible into posterior and anterior parts. The posterior part (area 4) does not reach so far forward as the precentral sulcus, and it is characterized by the giant pyramidal cells of Betz which are found in the internal layer of large pyramidal cells. These large cells are more numerous in the upper part of the area, and it has been calculated that their total number is in the neighborhood of 25,000 (Campbell). The whole area shows a great wealth of intracortical fibers, and the molecular layer is unusually dense. Experimental evidence has shown that this area controls the volitional movements of the opposite half of the body, and that the upper end of the precentral gyrus and the adjoining portion of the paracentral lobule control the movements of the lower limb. Below, and in the order given, are found the centers from the trunk, the upper limb, mouth, lips, tongue and larynx. The largest Betz cells (60μ by 25μ) are found in the lower limb area, and the smallest (35μ by 17μ) in the areas associated with the facial and hypoglossal nerves.

Emphasis must be laid on the fact that it is movements and not individual muscles which are represented in the cortex, and in this connection it may be mentioned that whereas the estimated number of motor cells in the anterior column of the spinal medulla is between 250,000 and 300,000, the number of Betz cells is rather less than one-tenth of that figure. It is clear, therefore, that each Betz cell must control the activities of approximately ten anterior column cells.

The anterior part of the precentral area (area 6) resembles the posterior part in every respect, except for the possession of the giant cells of Betz. That the two areas stand in very intimate relationship to one another from the functional standpoint is certain, but the precise relationship is by no means easy to define. Some idea may be conveyed by the statement that, whereas the posterior part of the precentral area is responsible for individual movements, the anterior part is responsible for the control of the orderly series of movements which constitute acts. These two areas are frequently referred to as the **motor** and the **premotor areas.** In front of area 6 is a strip, area 8, electrical stimulation of which evokes conjugate movements of the eyes and of the eyes and head.

The **frontal area** extends from the premotor region to the frontal pole and includes these portions of the frontal lobe which appear on the medial and orbital surfaces. It has been subdivided into frontal and prefrontal areas, but in the present state of knowledge of the functions of this wide area little advantage is to be derived from this subdivision.

Histologically this area differs from the adjoining precentral area in the reappearance of the granular layer and in the diminution of the number of intracortical fibers. The inner layer of large pyramidal cells shows a corresponding reduction in the size and number of its constituent cells. Further, the polymorphous layer is considerably reduced in depth.

In view of the fact that the frontal area is connected to the somesthetic, visual, auditory and other sensory areas by association fibers and to the thalamus by projection fibers, it has been urged that this area of the brain determines the personal reaction of the individual according to the alterations in feeling tone, modified or intensified, as the case may be, by the effects of the past experience, and it is therefore responsible, in a general way, for behavior and conduct. This view receives considerable support from clinical evidence. Lesions of the frontal area, whether cortical or subcortical, commonly result in some alterations in the character of the patient, alterations which may be so slight as to be recognized only by his intimates, or may be so gross as to be obvious to any observer.

The **postcentral area** (areas 3, 1 and 2) occupies all but the lowest part of the postcentral gyrus and is continued over the supero-medial border into the adjoining part of the paracentral lobule. It is divisible into anterior and posterior parts, which show certain differences in structure and play related though distinct parts in the reception and appreciation of somesthetic impressions. The anterior part is characterized by the number of characteristic cells in the outer layer of large pyramidal cells, by the density of the granular layer and by the breadth of the outer band of Baillarger. The largest cells are found in the inner layer of large pyramidal cells, but they are smaller than the giant cells of Betz and they occur discretely instead of in small clusters. In the posterior part the large pyramidal cells are reduced both in size and number, and the granular layer, though rather wider, is not so densely packed with cells.

The postcentral area receives afferent fibers from the thalamus which represent the relays of the somesthetic fibers of the spinal medulla and brain-stem. Both exteroceptive and proprioceptive sensations stream into the postcentral area and receive their full recognition in consciousness. The anterior part of the area may be regarded as the actual receiving area for all varieties of somesthetic sensibility, and the posterior part of the area relates them with past experience and so renders possible their evaluation and discrimination. It is therefore responsible for the tactile element in stereognosis, *i. e.,* the recognition of texture, in its widest sense, without the aid of vision.

The **visual area** of the cortex includes the greater part of the occipital lobe, and is subdivided into the **visuosensory** or **calcarine area** and the **visuopsychic area.**

The **visuosensory area** (area 17) occupies the walls of the posterior part of the calcarine fissure and extends on to the surface of the cuneus above and the lingual gyrus below. Posteriorly, it extends as far as the lunate sulcus, and, depending on the position of that sulcus, the visuosensory area may or may not extend beyond the occipital pole on to the lateral aspect of the hemisphere. Anteriorly, the visuosensory area occupies the floor of the anterior part of the calcarine fissure and the adjoining part of the lingual gyrus. The whole of this area is characterized by the prominent **stria of Gennari** which is quite obvious to the naked eye. Histologically, the visuosensory area presents three distinguishing features. (1) The outer layer of large pyramidal cells contains large stellate cells which replace almost entirely the large pyramidal cells normally found in this position. (2) The outer band of Baillarger is broad and prominent constituting the stria of Gennari. (3) The inner layer of large pyramidal cells contains the solitary cells of Meynert. These are pyramidal in shape, measuring about 30μ, and are arranged in a single widely spaced row.

The visuosensory area is the cortical receiving center for visual impressions. Color, size, form, motion, illumination and transparency are all recognized and determined in this area. The recognition and identification of objects, however, requires the coöperation of the adjoining visuopsychic area.

Owing to the partial decussation of the fibers of the optic nerve, the visuosensory cortex of one hemisphere receives its impressions from the temporal part of the retina of the same side and from the nasal part of the retina of the opposite side. The upper lip of the calcarine fissure is associated with the upper quadrants indicated, and the lower lip with the lower quadrants. The area for the macula is homolateral, but it is uncertain whether it occupies a limited or an extensive region.

The **visuopsychic area** (areas 18 and 19) surrounds the visuosensory area except in its anterior part, where it is restricted to the adjoining lingual and fusiform gyri. The cortex of this area is rather deeper than the cortex of the visuosensory area and is characterized by the stria of Gennari which is just as broad as it is in the visuosensory area, though its edges are not quite so short. Histologically, this area is marked by the number and size of the cells in the outer layer of large pyramidal cells, and by the almost complete absence of large cells from the inner layer of large pyramidal cells.

This area is responsible for the elaboration of visual impressions and their association with past experience, leading to the identification and recognition of objects. The determination of distance and the proper orientation of objects in space is effected by the visuopsychic area. Movements of the eyes can be evoked by stimulation of area 19. This is thought to represent the mechanism for fixation of the eyes on an object even while the head is being rotated in another direction.

The **parietal area** (areas 5, 7, 39 and 40) is situated between the visual area behind and the postcentral area in front, and constitutes one of the three large association areas of the hemisphere. Histologically, this area is characterized by the absence of large elements from the inner and outer layers of large pyramidal cells and by the breadth of the inner band of Baillarger.

Owing to its position relative to the visual, somesthetic and auditory areas, the parietal area is advantageously situated for the purpose of correlating and blending information obtained from these sensory centers. It is through the activities of this part of the brain that accurate knowledge of objects and their significance is obtained and retained.

The **auditory area** of the cortex is associated with the superior temporal gyrus and the transverse temporal gyri (of Heschl). Like the visual area, it can be subdivided into a sensory (areas 41 and 42) and a psychic (area 22) part, the latter adjoining and to a large extent surrounding the former.

The *auditosensory area* (areas 41 and 42) occupies the transverse temporal gyri of Heschl which lie on the floor of the posterior ramus of the lateral fissure (Fig. 762,) and extends for a short distance and over a limited area on to the lateral surface of the superior temporal gyrus. Histologically, this area of the cortex is characterized by the presence of an unusually large number of large pyramidal really giant cells in the outer layer of large pyramidal cells, and by the great number of fibers which are found throughout its whole depth.

Afferent fibers reach the auditosensory area from the medial geniculate body. After traversing the sub-lenticular limb of the internal capsule, these fibers sweep below the posterior part of the lentiform nucleus and form the auditory radiation.

In the auditosensory area auditory impressions reach consciousness as sounds, and their loudness, quality and pitch can be differentiated. The direction from which the sound comes and its character, whether rhythmical or arrhythmical, are also determined by this part of the cortex. The significance and the source of the sound, however, require the adjoining auditopsychic area for their elucidation.

The **auditopsychic area** occupies the whole of the remainder of the superior temporal gyrus. Histologically it can be differentiated from the auditosensory cortex, by the smaller number of giant cells in the outer layer of large pyramidal cells. In this area auditory impressions receive their interpretation and can be differentiated from one another as regards their probable source and origin, by association with past experience.

The large **temporal area** which includes the whole of the middle and inferior temporal gyri, is very similar to the auditopsychic area, in its cortical structure. Lesions of this area are accompanied by a more or less marked disturbance of the auditopsychic functions, but it must be confessed that our knowledge of the functional significance of this large cortical area is very meagre.

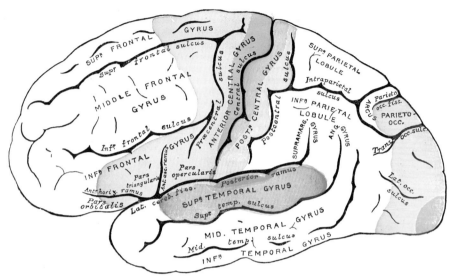

Fig. 754.—Areas of localization on lateral surface of hemisphere. Motor area in red. Area of general sensation in blue. Auditory area in green. Visual area in yellow. The psychic portions are in lighter tints.

The **insular area** comprises the whole of the insula. Histologically two types of cortex are recognizable. The structure of the cortex of the long gyri shows many points of resemblance to that of the temporal area, whereas the cortex of the short gyri is more closely allied to the cortex of the hippocampal gyrus. The functions of this cortical area are quite unknown.

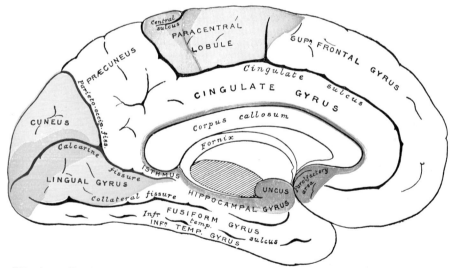

Fig. 755.—Areas of localization on medial surface of hemisphere. Motor area in red. Area of general sensations in blue. Visual area in yellow. Olfactory area in purple. The psychic portions are in lighter tints.

The Structure of the Rhinencephalon.—The laminated arrangement which is characteristic of the cerebral cortex is considerably modified in the rhinencephalon. It is found in a different form in the olfactory bulb, but it is almost unrecognizable in the sub- and supracallosal gyri, and it is archaic in type in the dentate fascia and the hippocampus.

The Olfactory Bulb.—In many animals the olfactory bulb contains a cavity which communicates with the lateral ventricle through a hollow olfactory tract. In man, the walls of the bulb become thickened, the ventral wall more so than the dorsal wall, and the cavity is obliterated, and its site is occupied by a mass of neuroglia. A section through the bulb demonstrates the presence of stratification, and the following layers can be identified: (1) a layer of **olfactory nerve fibers.**—These fibers are the non-medullated axons of the olfactory cells in the nasal mucosa, and they reach the bulb by passing through the lamina cribrosa of the ethmoidal bone. They cover the inferior surface of the bulb and penetrate it to end by forming tuft-like synapses with the dendrites of its mitral cells. (2) **Glomerular layer.**—This layer contains numerous spheroidal bodies, termed glomeruli, formed by the branching and interlacement of one or more olfactory nerve fibers with the descending dendrite of a mitral cell. (3) The **molecular layer.**—This layer consists of a matrix of neuroglia, in which the large, mitral cells form a densely packed stratum. These cells are pyramidal in shape, and from the basal part of each there arises a stout dendrite which descends into the glomerular layer and ends in one of the glomeruli. In addition, the mitral cells give off dendrites which terminate in the molecular layer. Their axons arise from the apices of the cells and proceed upward into the next layer where they turn backward to gain the olfactory tract. (4) **Nerve fiber layer.**—This layer consists chiefly of the medullated axons of the mitral cells; a certain number of efferent fibers are also present, passing to end in the molecular layer. Most of these are derived from the olfactory bulb of the opposite side and cross the median plane in the anterior commissure. (5) **Neuroglial layer.**—A flattened ovoid mass of neuroglia occupies the site of the original cavity of the bulb, and is covered in its dorsal or upper aspect by a thin layer of scattered gray and white substance.

The structure of the anterior perforated substance has been described above.

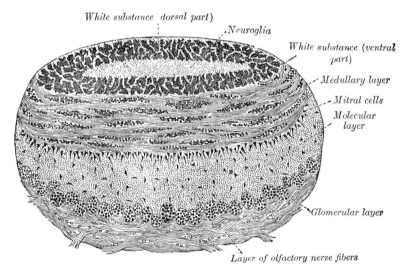

Fig. 756.—Coronal section of olfactory bulb. (Schwalbe.)

The **piriform area** shows a definitely stratified arrangement, which differs in certain respects from the cortex of the neopallium. The molecular layer is unusually broad and contains a large number of tangential fibers. The adjoining layer contains two varieties of cells, each arranged in clumps or cell-nests. The larger cells average 28μ in diameter, are stellate in form and poor in Nissl's bodies. The smaller cells, though pyramidal in form, are smaller than the cells of the layer of small pyramidal cells in the neopallium. The third layer is deep, and the cells which it contains are chiefly pyramidal in shape, and their apices point obliquely to the surface. These cells are especially rich in basal dendrites. The fourth layer is much narrower and contains remarkably few cells, some resembling those of the third layer, while others are small and stellate in shape. The fifth layer is broader and contains cells which resemble the pyramidal elements of the third layer. A sixth, deeper, layer of fusiform cells is also present.

This area receives the olfactory neurones of the second order and gives rise to those of the third order, which proceed to the hippocampal formation.

The **hippocampus** is more primitive in its structure than the piriform area and consists essentially of three layers. It represents a portion of the cortex which has been rolled into the inferior horn of the lateral ventricle and its superficial cortical layer lies in relation to the hippocampal fissure anteriorly and to the dentate fascia posteriorly. The superficial or **molecular layer** is unusually broad and is densely packed with tangential fibers. It is usually described as consisting of a superficial part, the stratum moleculare and a deep part, the stratum lacunosum. This is succeeded by a broad layer of *large pyramidal cells,* which give off long apical dendrites into the molecular layer. Their basal axons run centrally through the succeeding polymorphous layer and pass into the subjacent white substance, which here constitutes the **alveus**. The numerous apical dendrites which are crowded together in the superficial part of this pyramidal layer have given rise to its subdivision into a **stratum radiatum** (or dendritic part) and a **stratum lucidum** (or cellular part). The third layer contains *polymorphous cells* some of which are cells of Martinotti. Here, as elsewhere, they send their axons into the molecular layer. Others are aberrant pyramidal cells, while others, again, send their axons into the pyramidal layer where they end by arborizing around the pyramidal cells.

The white fibers of the alveus cover the polymorphous layer and separate it from the ependyma on the free ventricular surface of the hippocampus.

The **dentate fascia** also consists of three layers, viz., a molecular ayer, a granular layer and a polymorphus layer. The **molecular stratum** is well developed, andl receives the dendrites of the cells of the second layer. These are, for the most part, small granule cells but a number of large pyramidal cells are found among them. The axones of these cells traverse the third, or polymorphous layer, and then enter the adjoining molecular layer of the hippocampus, through which they pass to reach the pyramidal layer, where they terminate by arborizing round the large pyramidal cells. These axons are characterized by small varicosities which are placed on them as they run in the pyramidal layer. The third, or polymorphous layer, contains many Golgi, Type II, cells and many cells which send their axons through the adjoining layers of the hippocampus to reach the alveus.

The curious interlocking which occurs in the region of the hippocampus and the dentate fascia requires explanation. As the hippocampal formation becomes defined, the cells which ultimately form the dentate fascia lie on the fringe of the pallium and immediately adjoin the chorioidal fissure. The constituent cells of the formation proliferate rapidly, and as a result they form an elevation which protrudes into the cavity of the ventricle. The cells which form the intermediate layer of the hippocampus are directly continuous with the granular layer of the neopallium on the one hand and with the intermediate layer of the dentate fascia on the other. As growth proceeds, however, the continuity with the cells of the dentate fascia is broken, and the latter, as seen on transverse section forms an isolated strip which has all the appearance of being inserted, secondarily, into the unfolded cortex of the hippocampus. As a result, the molecular layer of the dentate fascia is in direct contact with the corresponding layer of the hippocampus. The hippocampal fissure, when it is present, intervenes between them. The polymorphous layer of the dentate fascia is in contact with the molecular layer of the hippocampus which has extended over its dorsal aspect.

COMPOSITION AND CENTRAL CONNECTIONS OF THE SPINAL NERVES.

The **typical spinal nerve** consists of **somatic sensory, visceral afferent or sensory, somatic motor** and **autonomic efferent or preganglionic** fibers. The separation of afferent fibers into somatic and visceral is of doubtful significance. The somatic sensory fibers, afferent fibers, arise from cells in the spinal ganglia and are found in all the spinal nerves, except occasionally the first cervical, and conduct impulses of pain, touch and temperature from the surface of the body through the posterior roots to the spinal cord and impulses of muscle sense, tendon sense and joint sense from the deeper structures. The visceral afferent fibers, with cell bodies in the spinal ganglia, conduct sensory impulses from the viscera through the rami communicantes and posterior roots to the spinal cord. They are probably limited to the white rami connected with the spinal nerves in two groups, viz., the first thoracic to the second lumbar and the second sacral to the fourth sacral nerves. The somatic motor fibers, efferent fibers, arise from cells in the anterior column of the spinal cord and pass out through the anterior roots to the voluntary muscles. The autonomic efferent fibers, probably arise from cells in the lateral column or the base of the anterior column and emerge through the anterior roots and white rami communicantes. These are preganglionic fibers which end in various ganglia from which postganglionic fibers conduct the motor impulses to the smooth muscles of the viscera and vessels and secretory impulses to the glands. These fibers are also limited to two regions, the first thoracic to the second lumbar and the second sacral to the fourth sacral nerves.

The afferent fibers which pass into the spinal cord establish various types of connections, some within the cord itself for spinal reflexes, others for reflexes connected with higher centers in the brain, while still others conduct impulses of conscious sensation by a series of neurons to the cerebral cortex.

The Intrinsic Spinal Reflex Paths.—The collaterals and terminals of the ascending and descending branches of the posterior root fibers which leave the fasciculus cuneatus to enter the gray matter of the spinal cord end in various ways. Many end in the dorsal column, some near its apex, in the substance of Rolando, others in the intermediate region between the dorsal and ventral columns, others traverse the whole thickness of the gray matter to reach the ventral column, others end in the dorsal nucleus. All of these collaterals and terminals end in connection with cells or dendrites of cells in the gray columns. The axons of these cells have various destinations, some pass out into the lateral and ventral funiculi and turn upward to reach the brain. Those concerned with the intrinsic spinal reflexes come into relation either directly or indirectly with motor cells in the anterior column. It is very unlikely that either the terminals or collaterals of the dorsal root fibers effect

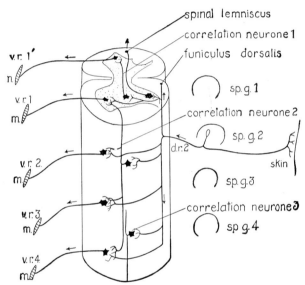

Fig. 757.—Diagram of the spinal cord reflex apparatus. Some of the connections of a single afferent neuron from the skin (*d.r.*2) are indicated; *d.r.*2, dorsal root from second spinal ganglion; *m*, muscles; *sp.g.*1 to *sp.g.*4, spinal ganglia; *v.r.*1′ to *v.r.*4, ventral roots. (After Herrick.)

simple direct connections with the motor cells of the ventral column, there is at least one if not several intercalated neurons in the path. These intercalated or correlation neurons may have short axons that do not pass out of the gray matter or the axons may pass out into the proper fasciculi and extend for varying distances up and down or in both directions giving off collaterals and finally terminating in the gray matter of the same or the opposite side. The shortest fibers of the proper fasciculi lie close to the gray matter, the longest ones are nearer the periphery of the proper fasciculi and are more or less intermingled with the long ascending and descending fasciculi which occupy the more marginal regions of the spinal cord.

Each sensory neuron, with its ascending and descending branches, giving off as it does many collaterals into the gray matter, each one of which may form a synapse with one or several correlation neurons, is thus brought into relation with many correlation neurons and each one of these in turn, with its ascending and descending branches and their numerous collaterals, is brought into relation, either directly or through the intercalation of additional correlation neurons, with great numbers of motor cells in the anterior column. The great complexity of these so-called simple reflex mechanisms, in the least complex portion of the nervous system the spinal cord, renders them extremely difficult of exact analysis.

The association or correlation neurons are concerned not only with the reflex mechanisms of the spinal cord but play an equally important rôle in the transmission of impulses from the higher centers in the brain to the motor neurons of the spinal cord.

The complex mechanisms just described are probably concerned not so much in the contraction of individual muscles as in the complicated action of groups of muscles concerned in the enormous number of movements, which the limbs and trunk exhibit in the course of our daily life.

Sensory Pathways from the Spinal Cord to the Brain.—The posterior root fibers conducting **proprioceptive** impulses to the cerebrum from sensory end-organs (muscle spindles, Pacinian corpuscles) in muscles, tendons and joints, those impulses which have to do with the coördination and adjustment of muscular movements, ascend in the fasciculus gracilis and fasciculus cuneatus to the nucleus gracilis and nucleus cuneatus in the medulla oblongata. In the nucleus gracilis and nucleus cuneatus synaptic relations are found with neurons whose cell bodies are located in these nuclei and whose axons pass by way of the internal arcuate fibers, cross in the raphé to the opposite side in the region between the olives and turn abruptly upward to form the medial lemniscus or medial fillet. The medial fillet passes upward in the ventral part of the formatio reticularis through the medulla oblongata, pons and mid-brain to the nucleus ventralis posterolateralis of the thalamus. Here the terminals form synapses with neurons of the third order whose axons pass through the internal capsule and corona radiata to the somatic sensory area of the cortex in the postcentral gyrus.

Fibers conducting **proprioceptive** impulses to the cerebellum are supposed to pass partly by way of the fasciculus gracilis and fasciculus cuneatus to the nucleus gracilis and nucleus cuneatus, thence neurons of the second order convey the impulses either via the dorsal external arcuate fibers directly into the inferior cerebellar peduncle of the cerebellum or via the ventral external arcuate fibers which are continued from the internal arcuate fibers through the ventral part of the raphé and after crossing the mid-line emerge on the surface of the medulla in the ventral sulcus between the pyramids or in the groove between the pyramid and the olive. They pass over the lateral surface of the medulla and olive to reach the inferior cerebellar peduncle through which they pass to the cerebellum.

Other fibers conducting proprioceptive impulses pass upward in the dorsal spinocerebellar fasciculus, **tract of Flechsig.** They arise from cells in the nucleus dorsalis. The posterior root fibers conducting these impulses pass into the fasciculus cuneatus and the collaterals from them to the nucleus dorsalis are said to come almost exclusively from the middle area of the fasciculus cuneatus. They form by their multiple division baskets about the individual cells of the nucleus dorsalis, each fiber coming in relation with the bodies and dendrites of several cells. The axons of the second order pass into the dorsal spinocerebellar fasciculus of the same side and ascend along the lateral surface of the spinal cord and medulla oblongata until they arrive at the level of the olive, they then curve backward beneath the external arcuate fibers into the inferior peduncle and pass into the cerebellum. Here they give off collaterals to the dentate nucleus and finally terminate in the cortex of the dorsal and superior portion of the vermis on the same side. The fibers lose their myelin sheaths as they enter the gray substance and terminate by end ramifications among the nerve cells and their processes. Some of the fibers are said to end in the nucleus dentatus and the roof nuclei of the cerebellum (the nucleus globosus, nucleus emboliformis and nucleus fastigius) and others pass through them to terminate in the inferior vermis. A few fibers of the dorsal spinocerebellar fasciculus are said not to enter the inferior peduncle but to pass with the ventral spinocerebellar fasciculus. The cerebellar reflex arc is supposed to be completed by the fibers of the superior peduncle which pass from the cerebellum to the red nucleus of the mid-brain where some of their terminals and collaterals form synapses with neurons whose axons descend to the spinal cord in the rubrospinal fasciculus. The terminals and collaterals of this

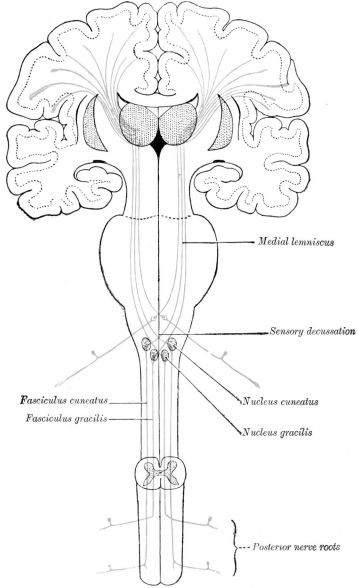

Fig. 758.—The sensory tract. (Modified from Poirier.)

fasciculus end either directly or indirectly about the motor cells in the anterior column.

The ventral spinocerebellar fasciculus (tract of Gowers), since most of its fibers pass to the cerebellum, is also supposed to be concerned in the conduction of proprioceptive impulses. The location of its cells of origin is probably in or near the dorsal nucleus of the opposite side; various other locations are given in the dorsal column. The neurons of the first order whose central fibers enter the fasciculus cuneatus from the dorsal roots send collaterals and terminals to form synapses with these cells. The fibers which come from the opposite gray columns cross some in the white and some in the gray commissure and pass with fibers from the same side through the lateral funiculus to the marginal region ventral to the dorsal spinocerebellar fasciculus. The fasciculus begins about the level of the third lumbar nerve and continues upward on the lateral surface of the spinal cord and medulla oblongata until it passes under cover of the external arcuate fibers. It passes just dorsal to the olive and above this joins the lateral edge of the lateral lemniscus along which it runs, ventral to the roots of the trigeminal nerve; at the level of the motor nucleus of the trigeminal it then crosses over the superior peduncle, turns abruptly backward along its medial border, enters the cerebellum with it and ends in the vermis of the same and the opposite side. Some of its fibers are said to join the dorsal spinocerebellar fasciculus in the medulla oblongata and enter the cerebellum through the inferior peduncle.

The posterior root fibers conducting impulses of **pain** and **temperature** probably terminate in the substantia gelatinosa Rolandi and in the cells immediately below it in the posterior column of the gray matter soon after they enter the spinal cord. The neurons of the second order pass through the anterior commissure to the superficial antero-lateral fasciculus and pass upward in that portion of it known as the lateral spinothalamic fasciculus. This fasciculus lies along the medial side of the ventral spinocerebellar fasciculus. It is stated by some authors that the pain fibers pass upward in the antero-lateral ground bundles. In some of the lower mammals this pathway carries the pain fibers upward by a series of neurons some of which cross to the opposite side, so that in part there is a double path. In man, however, the lateral spinothalamic fasciculus is probably the most important pathway. On reaching the medulla these fibers continue upward through the lateral part of the formatio reticularis, at first in a diffuse layer over the surface of the inferior olives and further forward as a more compact bundle, lateral to the medial lemniscus and ventral to the lateral lemniscus. The fibers terminate in the lateral part of the nucleus ventralis posterolateralis of the thalamus. Neurons of the third order convey impulses of pain and temperature from the thalamus to the somesthetic area in the postcentral gyrus of the cerebrum.

Ranson has shown that the non-medullated fibers of the posterior roots, which turn into Lissauer's tract and ascend or descend for short distances not exceeding one or two segments and finally end in the substantia gelatinosa, are in part at least pain fibers and that the fasciculus of Lissauer and the substantia gelatinosa represent part of the mechanism for reflexes associated with pain conduction and reception while the fibers to the higher centers pass up in the spinothalamic tract.

The fibers of **tactile discrimination** (quantitative touch and pressure, spatial localization, and temporal localization, i. e., vibration sense) pass to the dorsal funiculus with other dorsal root fibers in the medial division and divide into ascending and descending branches. Their cell bodies are in the dorsal root ganglia. The peripheral branch of each axon extends to the skin and underlying tissues. The ascending and descending branches running in the dorsal funiculus give off collaterals and terminals to the dorsal gray column at various levels; some reach the gracile and cuneate nuclei. The axons of the second order follow the same course as that described above (p. 878) for fibers conducting proprioceptive senses.

The fibers for diffuse touch and pressure enter through the posterior roots and terminate with collaterals in the posterior columns of the gray substance. The second neurons cross through the anterior white commissure in the same segment and run rostrally in the ventral spinothalamic fasciculus. This is thought to pass through the medulla at first just dorsal and later lateral to the medial lemniscus.

Its termination in the thalamus and its cortical projection is apparently the same as that of the lateral spinothalamic tract.

The **spinotectal fasciculus** arises from cells in the dorsal gray column. The fibers cross to the opposite side and ascend close together with the lateral spinothalamic fasciculus in the lateral funiculus to the mesencephalon. Here they turn sharply dorsalward and terminate in the deep layers of the superior colliculus, some probably also ending in the inferior colliculus. The **spinoölivary fasciculus** also arises from cells in the dorsal gray column whose axons cross to the opposite side and ascend in the ventral funiculus to the inferior olive.

The **visceral afferent fibers** (splanchnic) have their cell bodies in the spinal ganglia. The peripheral branches pass in the white rami to the sympathetic system and are distributed without interruption to the viscera. The central branches pass with the dorsal roots into the spinal cord.

These visceral afferent fibers presumably divide on entering the spinal cord into ascending and descending branches. Their distribution and termination within the spinal cord differ from those of the peripheral afferents, but have not yet been adequately analyzed. The ascending fibers conveying impulses which give rise to the conscious sensation of pain apparently run with the lateral spinothalamic tracts. There is some evidence that they are both crossed and uncrossed.

The **autonomic efferent fibers** (*splanchnic motor; viscero-motor; preganglionic fibers*) arise from cells in the intermedio-lateral column at the margin of the lateral column. These preganglionic fibers are not distributed throughout the entire series of spinal nerves but are confined to two groups, the thoraco-lumbar, from the first thoracic to the second or third lumbar nerves, and the sacral group, from the second to the fourth sacral nerves. They pass out with the anterior root fibers and through the rami communicantes to end in sympathetic ganglia. The impulses are distributed from cells in these ganglia through postganglionic fibers to the smooth muscles and glands. The thoraco-lumbar outflow and the sacral outflow form two distinct functional groups which are considered more fully under the autonomic system.

COMPOSITION AND CENTRAL CONNECTIONS OF THE CRANIAL NERVES.

The cranial nerves are more varied in their composition than the spinal nerves. Some, for example, contain somatic motor fibers only, others contain the various types of fibers found in the spinal nerves, namely, somatic motor, autonomic efferent, somatic sensory and visceral sensory. In addition there are included the nerves of the special senses, namely, the nerves of smell, sight, hearing, equilibration and taste.

The **Hypoglossal Nerve** (*XII cranial*) contains somatic motor fibers to the muscles of the tongue and sensory fibers from muscle spindles in the tongue; cell bodies unknown. The motor axons arise from cells in the hypoglossal nucleus and pass forward between the white reticular formation and the gray reticular formation to emerge from the antero-lateral sulcus of the medulla. The hypoglossal nuclei of the two sides are connected by many commissural fibers and also by dendrites of motor cells which extend across the mid-line to the opposite nucleus. The hypoglossal nucleus receives either directly or indirectly numerous collaterals and terminals from the contralateral and a few from the ipsilateral aberrant pyramidal tracts (corticobulbar or cerebrobulbar fibers) which convey voluntary motor impulses from the cerebral cortex. Many reflex collaterals enter the nucleus from the secondary sensory paths of the trigeminal and vagus and probably also from the nervus intermedius and the glossopharyngeal. Collaterals from the medial longitudinal fasciculus and the tectobulbar tract are said to pass to the nucleus.

56

The **Accessory Nerve** (*XI*) contains somatic **motor** and **autonomic efferent fibers.**
(1) The **somatic motor fibers.**—The **spinal part** arises from lateral cell groups in the anterior column near its dorso-lateral margin in the upper five or six segments of the cord; its roots pass through the lateral funiculus to the lateral surface of the cord and upward through the foramen magnum. It supplies the Trapezius and Sternocleidomastoideus. The **cranial part** arises from the nucleus ambiguus, the continuation in the medulla oblongata of the lateral cell groups of the anterior column of the spinal cord from which the spinal part has origin. The upper part of the nucleus ambiguus gives motor fibers to the vagus and glossopharyngeal nerves. The cranial part sends its fibers through the vagus to the laryngeal nerves to supply the muscles of the larynx and pharynx. The root fibers of the cranial part of the accessory nerve pass anterior to the spinal tract of the trigeminal, while those of the vagus pass through or dorsal to the trigeminal root, and emerge in line to the postero-lateral sulcus. The nucleus of origin of the spinal part receives either directly or indirectly terminals and collaterals controlling voluntary movements from the pyramidal tracts and also from the aberrant pyramidal tracts. Certain of the latter are uncrossed, since the sternocleidomastoideus muscle turns the head to the opposite side. The nucleus also receives fibers from head-and-eye turning mechanisms through the medial longitudinal fasciculus. It is probable that terminals and collaterals reach the nucleus either directly or indirectly from the rubrospinal and the vestibulospinal tracts. It is also connected indirectly with the spinal somatic sensory nerves by association fibers of the proper fasciculi. The cranial part receives indirectly or directly terminals and collaterals from the opposite aberrant pyramidal tract and from the terminal sensory nuclei of the cranial nerves.
(2) The **visceral efferent fibers** are few in number and arise in the dorsal nucleus of the vagus. Just after the accessory nerve leaves the jugular foramen these fibers pass with the cranial part to the vagus nerve and are distributed with the latter.

The **Vagus Nerve** (*X cranial*) contains somatic sensory, visceral afferent, somatic motor, autonomic efferent and taste fibers. The afferent fibers (somatic sensory, visceral, and taste) have their cells of origin in the jugular ganglion and in the nodosal ganglion (ganglion of the trunk) and on entering the medulla divide into ascending and descending branches as do the sensory fibers of the posterior roots of the spinal nerves after they enter the spinal cord.
(1) The **somatic sensory fibers** are few in number, convey impulses from a limited area of the skin on the back of the ear and posterior part of the external auditory meatus, and probably join the spinal tract of the trigeminal nerve to terminate in its nucleus. Connections are probably established through the central path of the trigeminal with the thalamus and somatic sensory area of the cortex for the conscious recognition of impulses. The descending fibers in the spinal tract of the trigeminal terminating in the nucleus of the tract probably establish relations through connecting neurons with motor nuclei in the anterior column of the spinal cord and with motor nuclei of the medulla.
(2) The **visceral afferent fibers** join the tractus solitarius and terminate in its nucleus. These afferent fibers convey impulses from the heart, the pancreas, and probably from the stomach, esophagus and respiratory tract. Their terminals in the sensory nucleus and in the nucleus of the tractus solitarius come into relation with neurons whose axons probably make connections with centers in the reticular substance. Such centers include the respiratory center at the caudal end of the medulla, vaso-pressor and vaso-depressor centers, etc. From such centers pathways descend to the spinal cord. There are probably connections also to the dorsal motor nucleus of the vagus.
(3) **Taste fibers** conducting impulses from the epiglottis and larynx are supposed

to pass in the vagus and to join the tractus solitarius, finally terminating in the nucleus of the tractus solitarius. It is not certain that this nucleus represents the primary terminal center for taste and some authors maintain that the taste fibers terminate in the sensory nucleus. The secondary ascending pathways from the primary gustatory nucleus to the cortex as well as the location of the cortical center for taste are unknown. There is evidence that the second neurons cross the mid-line, run forward and enter the ventro-medial part of the thalamus. A gustatory center has been described near the anterior end of the temporal lobe. The nucleus of the tractus solitarius is connected with motor centers of the pons, medulla and spinal cord for the reactions of mastication and deglutition.

(4) **Somatic motor fibers** to the cross striated muscles of the pharynx and larynx arise in the nucleus ambiguus. This nucleus undoubtedly receives either directly or indirectly collaterals or terminals from the opposite aberrant pyramidal tract controlling the voluntary movements of the pharynx and larynx. The reflex pathways conveying impulses from the terminal sensory nuclei are unknown, but probably form part of the intricate maze of fibers constituting the reticular formation.

(5) **Autonomic efferent fibers** arise from cells in the dorsal nucleus (nucleus of the ala cinerea). These are preganglionic fibers and all terminate in ganglia in or near the various organs. From these ganglia postganglionic fibers are distributed, *i. e.*, motor fibers to the esophagus, stomach, small intestine, gall-bladder, and to the lungs; inhibitory fibers to the heart; secretory fibers to the stomach and pancreas. The dorsal nucleus not only receives terminals of visceral afferent fibers for reflexes but undoubtedly receives terminals and collaterals from many other sources, but the exact pathways are at present unknown. Many come from the vestibular nuclei. In addition there are connections from the hypothalamus, some of which probably come through the dorsal fasciculus of Schütz, others through tracts scattered in the reticular substance.

The **Glossopharyngeal Nerve** (*I X cranial*) is similar to the vagus nerve as regards its central connections and is usually described with it. It contains somatic sensory, visceral afferent, taste, somatic motor and autonomic efferent fibers. The afferent sensory fibers arise from cells in the superior ganglion and in the petrosal ganglion. The same uncertainty exists concerning the nuclei of termination and nuclei of origin of the various components as for the vagus.

(1) The **somatic sensory fibers** are few in number. Some are distributed with the auricular branch of the vagus to the external ear; others probably pass to the pharynx and fauces. They are supposed to join the spinal tract of the trigeminal and terminate in its nucleus. The connections are similar to those of the somatic sensory fibers of the vagus.

(2) **Visceral afferent fibers** from the pharynx and middle ear are supposed to terminate in the nucleus of the tractus solitarius. Connections are probably established with motor nuclei concerned in chewing and swallowing; very little is known however, about the connections with other parts of the brain.

(3) **Taste fibers** from the tongue probably terminate in the nucleus of the tractus solitarius. These fibers together with similar fibers from the facial (nervus intermedius) and the vagus are supposed to form the tractus solitarius and terminate in its nucleus. The central connections have been considered under the vagus.

(4) **Somatic motor fibers** to the Stylopharyngeus muscle arise in the upper end of the nucleus ambiguus. The existence of these fibers in the roots of the glossopharyngeal is uncertain, as there are other paths by which such fibers might reach the glossopharyngeal from the vagus. The sources of impulses passing to the nucleus ambiguus are considered under the vagus.

(5) **Autonomic efferent fibers** (*motor and secretory fibers*) arise from the dorsal motor nucleus. Some authors believe that the secretory fibers to the parotid gland arise from a distinct nucleus, the salivatory nucleus, situated near the dorsal

nucleus. The preganglionic fibers from this nucleus terminate in the otic ganglion; the postganglionic fibers from the otic ganglion pass to the parotid gland.

The **Acoustic Nerve** (*VIII cranial*) consists of two distinct nerves the **cochlear nerve**, the nerve of hearing, and the **vestibular nerve**, the nerve of equilibration.

The **Cochlear Nerve** arises from bipolar cells in the spiral ganglion of the cochlea; the peripheral fibers end in the organ of Corti, the central fibers bifurcate as they enter the **cochlear nuclei**; the short ascending branches end in the ventral cochlear nucleus; the longer descending branches terminate in the dorsal cochlear nucleus. The terminations of the fibers is very orderly, different parts of the cochlea being represented in different parts of the cochlear nuclei. Each branch of the entering fibers gives off many collaterals, usually about 50. In most cases one, and not more than three, of these collaterals ends in a giant synapse which makes contact with as much as two-thirds of the area of the cell body of the second neuron.

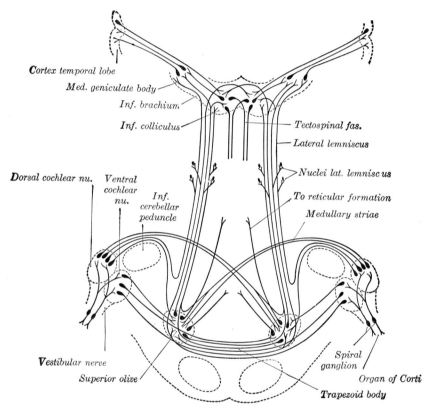

Fig. 759.—Connections of cochlear nerve.

The **dorsal cochlear nucleus** forms a projection on the dorsal and lateral aspect of the inferior cerebellar peduncle, the acoustic tubercle. Axons of the second order from its large fusiform cells pass over the peduncle and cross the floor of the fourth ventricle as the **striæ medullaris acousticæ**. These fibers run under the gray of the floor of the ventricle, through the upper margin of the reticular substance. Many of them cross in the median raphé, sink into the reticular formation and join the trapezoid body or the lateral lemniscus or terminate in the superior olivary nucleus on the side opposite their origin. They pass upward in the lateral lemniscus and end by terminals and collaterals in the nuclei of the lateral lemniscus, in the inferior colliculus and in the medial geniculate body. Some of the fibers in the striæ medullares do not cross the mid-line but dip into the reticular formation and end in the superior olivary nucleus of the same side or join the lateral lemniscus and pass upward in it to end by terminals and collaterals in the nuclei of the lateral lemniscus, in the inferior colliculus and in the medial geniculate body of the same side. The fibers of the striæ medullares are not visible on the floor of the rhomboid fossa. The **ventral cochlear nucleus** is ventral but continuous with the dorsal cochlear nucleus. Axons of the second order from its cells pass horizontally in the trapezoid body; here some of them end in the superior olivary nucleus of the same side; others cross the midline and end in the superior olivary nucleus of the opposite side or pass by these nuclei, giving off collaterals to them, and join the lateral lemniscus. They are distributed with fibers from the dorsal cochlear nucleus to the nuclei of the lateral lemniscus and to the inferior colliculus by collaterals and terminals. Other fibers from the ventral cochlear nucleus pass dorsal to the inferior peduncle and then dip into the substance of the pons to join the trapezoid body or the superior olivary nucleus of the same side.

The **trapezoid body** consists of horizontal fibers in the ventral part of the formatio reticularis of the lower part of the pons behind its deep transverse fibers and the pyramid bundles. The axons come from the dorsal and ventral portions of the cochlear nucleus. After crossing the raphé, where they decussate with those from the opposite side, they turn upward to form the lateral lemniscus. Fibers from the striæ medullares contribute to the trapezoid body, in addition it sends terminals or collaterals to and receives axons from the superior olivary nucleus.

The **superior olivary nucleus** consists of three small masses of gray matter situated on the dorso-lateral aspect of the trapezoid body just above the inferior olive. It receives terminals and collaterals from the cochlear nuclei of the same and the opposite side. From its fusiform cells axons of the third order pass dorsally, as the **peduncle of the superior olive**, and cross the mid-line ventral to the nucleus of the abducens. Their termination is not known. These axons form reflex pathways. The majority of axons of the third order, after giving off collaterals to the nucleus itself, join the lateral lemniscus of the same side and end in the inferior colliculus and the medial geniculate body by terminals or collaterals, or cross in the trapezoid body to the opposite lateral lemniscus to terminate in the inferior colliculus and medial geniculate body.

The **lateral lemniscus** (*lateral fillet*), the continuation upward of the central path of hearing, consists of fibers which come from the cochlear nuclei of the same and the opposite side by way of the trapezoid body and from the olivary nuclei. It lies in the ventral or ventro-lateral part of the reticular formation of the pons, at first ventral then lateral to the median fillet. Above the pons these ascending fibers come to the surface at the side of the reticular formation in the trigonum lemnisci and are covered by a layer of ependyma. On reaching the level of the inferior colliculus the dorsal fibers which overlie the superior peduncle decussate in the velum medullare anterius with similar fibers of the opposite side. Numerous small masses of cells are scattered along the path of the lateral lemniscus above the superior olivary nucleus and constitute **lower and upper nuclei of the lateral lemniscus.** They are supplied with many collaterals and possibly terminals from the fibers of the lemniscus. The axons of the lower nucleus of the lateral lemniscus, which arise from the larger stellate or spindle-shaped cells, with long, smooth, much branched dendrites, are said by some authors to join the lateral lemniscus, but according to Cajal they pass medially toward the raphé; their termination is unknown. The cells of the upper nucleus of the lateral lemniscus are more scattered. The same uncertainty exists in regard to their termination.

The fibers of the lateral lemniscus end by terminals or collaterals in the inferior colliculus and the medial geniculate body. A few of the fibers are said to pass by the inferior colliculus to terminate in the middle portion of the stratum griseum of the superior colliculus, and are probably concerned with reflex movements of the eyes depending on acoustic stimuli.

The **inferior colliculi** (*lower or posterior quadrigeminal bodies*) are important auditory reflex centers. Each consists of a compact nucleus of gray matter covered by a superficial white layer from the lateral lemniscus and separated from the central gray matter about the aqueduct by a thin, deep, white layer. Many of the fibers which appear in the superficial white layer ascend through the **inferior brachium** to the medial geniculate body. The inferior (quadrigeminal) brachium also contains fibers of the third order which arise from cells in the inferior colliculus and pass to the medial geniculate body. There are in addition fibers from the cerebral cortex to the inferior colliculus. Others mainly from large cells in the dorso-mesial part of the nucleus pass through the deep white layer into the tegmentum of the same and the opposite side and descend. Their termination is unknown, but they probably constitute an auditory reflex path to the lower motor centers, perhaps descending into the spinal cord with the tectospinal fasciculus. Other axons are said to descend in the lateral lemniscus to the various nuclei in the auditory path (Held) and probably to motor nuclei of the medulla and spinal cord.

The **medial geniculate body** receives terminals and collaterals from the dorsal and ventral cochlear nuclei and from the superior olive. They ascend in the lateral lemniscus (the central auditory path) and the inferior brachium. It also receives large numbers of axons from the inferior colliculus of the same side and a few from the opposite side. They pass with the preceding in the inferior brachium. It is thus a station in the central auditory path. A large proportion of its axons pass forward beneath the optic tract to join the corona radiata and then sweep backward and lateralward as the auditory radiation to terminate in the cortex of the superior temporal gyrus. V. Monakow holds that Golgi cells type II are interpolated between the terminations of the incoming fibers to the medial geniculate body and the cells located there which give rise to the fibers of the auditory radiation. The medial geniculate bodies are united by the long slender **commissure of Gudden**. These fibers join the optic tract as it passes over the edge of the medial geniculate and passes through the posterior part of the optic chiasma. It is probably a commissure connected with the auditory system.

The **Vestibular Nerve** (*vestibular root, VIII cranial*) arises from the bipolar cells in the vestibular ganglion (Scarpa's ganglion). The peripheral fibers end in the semicircular canals, the saccule and the utricle, the end-organs concerned with mechanism for the maintenance of bodily equilibrium. The central fibers enter the medulla oblongata and pass between the inferior cerebellar peduncle and the spinal tract of the trigeminal. They bifurcate into ascending and descending branches as do the dorsal root fibers of all the spinal nerves and all afferent cranial nerves. The descending branches constitute the descending or spinal root of the vestibular nerve and they terminate on the cells of the associated nucleus. The ascending branches pass to the medial (Schwalbe's) nucleus, to the lateral (Deiters's) nucleus, to the superior (Bechterew's) nucleus and a few through the inferior peduncle of the cerebellum to the nucleus fastigii and to the vermis. The fibers from ganglion cells which innervate the ampullæ of the semicircular canals have a different distribution centrally to those from cells which innervate the macula utriculi and the macula sacculi. The ascending branches of the former pass to the superior and to the rostral portions of the medial nuclei. Those from the macular fibers end in the lateral nucleus and in the caudal parts of the medial nucleus. In addition to the fibers from the vestibular nerve, the vestibular nuclei receive connections from the cerebellar nuclei of the same and the opposite sides directly and through the hook bundle of Russel. A few fibers from the cerebellar cortex terminate here and numerous interconnections with the reticular substance also exist.

The **medial vestibular nucleus** (*dorsal, triangular, principal or Schwalbe's nucleus*) is a large mass of small cells in the floor of the fourth ventricle under the area acustica, located partly in the medulla and partly in the pons. The striæ medullares cross the upper part of it. It is separated from the median plane by the nucleus prepositus hypoglossi. The connections of the medial nucleus are widespread through the medulla and pons, to various nuclei of the reticular formation, to the other cranial nerve motor nuclei and to autonomic centers and nuclei. It contributes many fibers to the medial longitudinal fasciculus of both sides. These fibers bifurcate into ascending and descending branches.

The **superior vestibular nucleus** (*Bechterew's nucleus*) forms the rostro-lateral part of the vestibular complex and extends up into the lateral wall of the ventricle towards the cerebellum. Its cells are small and similar to those of the medial nucleus. The superior nucleus is particularly associated with the nuclei, the vermis and the flocculo-nodular lobe of the cerebellum. It contributes crossed ascending fibers to the medial longitudinal fasciculus.

The **lateral vestibular nucleus** (*Deiter's nucleus*) lies between the medial nucleus and the restiform body. Its cells are large, polygonal in shape and stain deeply. The axons run at first medially into the reticular formation and then turn caudalward. As they descend they shift to a more ventral position and in the spinal cord they constitute the direct vestibulo-spinal tract. This is apparently the chief anti-gravity mechanism of the nervous system. Collaterals from the axons ascend through the inferior cerebellar peduncle into the cerebellum where they terminate principally in the anterior and posterior parts of the vermis.

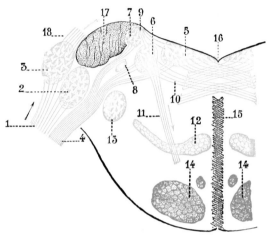

Fig. 760.—Terminal nuclei of the vestibular nerve, with their upper connections. (Schematic.) 1. Cochlear nerve, with its two nuclei. 2. Accessory nucleus. 3. Tuberculum acusticum. 4. Vestibular nerve. 5. Internal nucleus. 6. Nucleus of Deiters. 7. Nucleus of Bechterew. 8. Inferior or descending root of acoustic. 9. Ascending cerebellar fibers. 10. Fibers going to raphé. 11. Fibers taking an oblique course. 12. Lemniscus. 13. Inferior sensory root of trigeminal. 14. Cerebrospinal fasciculus. 15. Raphé. 16. Fourth ventricle. 17. Inferior peduncle. 18. Origin of striæ medullares. (Testut.)

The **nucleus of the descending or spinal root of the vestibular nerve** (inferior vestibular nucleus) extends from the level of the entrance of the nerve almost to the rostral pole of the nucleus cuneatus. It consists of large, medium and small cells. This nucleus also has widespread connections through the medulla and pons, particularly with nuclei of the reticular formation. It contributes large fibers to the medial longitudinal fasciculus of both sides. The fibers bifurcate into ascending and descending branches. Certain of the descending fibers form the crossed vestibulo-spinal tract which runs in the sulco-marginal fasciculus in the cord.

The **Facial Nerve** (*VII cranial*) consists of somatic sensory, visceral afferent, taste, somatic motor and sympathetic efferent fibers. The afferent or sensory fibers arise from cells in the geniculate ganglion. This portion of the nerve is often described as the nervus intermedius.

(1) The **somatic sensory fibers** are few in number and convey sensory impulses from the middle ear region. Their existence has not been fully confirmed. Their central termination is likewise uncertain, it is possible that they join the spinal tract of the trigeminal as do the somatic sensory fibers of the vagus and glossopharyngeal.

(2) The **visceral afferent fibers** are likewise few in number and of unknown termination.

(3) **Taste fibers** convey impulses from the anterior two-thirds of the tongue via the chorda tympani. They are supposed to join the tractus solitarius and terminate in its nucleus. The central connections of this nucleus have already been considered.

(4) **Somatic motor fibers**, supplying the muscles derived from the hyoid arch, arise from the large multipolar cells of the nucleus of the facial nerve. This nucleus is serially homologous with the nucleus ambiguus and lateral part of the anterior column of the spinal cord. The various facial muscles are represented in separate small groups of cells in the nucleus. Those cells which innervate the muscles of the lower face receive connections from the aberrant pyramidal system which are entirely crossed. The cells innervating the musculature of the upper face receive fibers from both cerebral hemispheres. Numerous connections from medullary reflex mechanisms and from other motor systems also are present. Some of the more complicated of these have to do with emotional expression. There are important reflex connections from the substantia gelatinosa trigemini.

(5) **Autonomic efferent fibers** (*preganglionic fibers*) arise according to some authors from the small cells of the facial nucleus, or according to others from a special nucleus near the sulcus limitans, dorsomedial to the facial nucleus. This is sometimes called the **superior salivatory nucleus**. These preganglionic fibers are distributed partly via the chorda tympani and lingual nerves to the submaxillary ganglion, thence by postganglionic (vasodilator) fibers to the submaxillary and sublingual glands. Some of the preganglionic fibers pass to the sphenopalatine ganglion via the great superficial petrosal nerve.

The **Abducens Nerve** (*VI cranial*) contains somatic motor fibers only which supply the lateral rectus muscle of the eye. The fibers arise from the nucleus of the abducens nerve and pass ventrally through the formatio reticularis of the pons to emerge in the transverse groove between the caudal edge of the pons and the pyramid. The nucleus is serially homologous with the nuclei of the trochlear and oculomotor above and with the hypoglossal and medial part of the anterior column of the spinal cord below. It is situated close to the floor of the fourth ventricle, just above the level of the striæ medullares. Voluntary impulses from the cerebral cortex are conducted by the aberrant pyramidal tract fibers. These fibers probably terminate in relation with association neurons which control the coördinated action of all the eye muscles. This association and coördination mechanism is interposed between the terminals and collaterals of the voluntary fibers and the neurons within the nuclei of origin of the motor fibers to the eye muscles. The fibers of the medial longitudinal fasciculus play an important rôle in the coördination of turning movements of the eyes, head, neck and shoulders. Many of these fibers originate in the vestibular nuclei, others interconnect the motor nuclei, others are contributed by the nucleus of Darkschewitz, by the interstitial nucleus of Cajal and by various nuclei of the reticular formation. Some of the fibers of the medial longitudinal fasciculus extend forward into the hypothalamus and posterior part of the thalamus. The abducens nucleus probably receives collaterals and terminals from the ventral longitudinal bundle (tectospinal fasciculus); fibers which have their origin in the superior colliculus, the primary visual center, and are concerned with visual reflexes. Others probably come from the reflex auditory center in the inferior colliculus and from other sensory nuclei of the brain-stem.

The **Trigeminal Nerve** (*V cranial*) contains somatic motor and somatic sensory fibers. The motor fibers arise in the motor nucleus of the trigeminal and pass ventro-laterally through the pons to supply the muscles of mastication. The sensory fibers arise from the unipolar cells of the semilunar ganglion; the peripheral branches of the T-shaped fibers are distributed to the face and anterior two-thirds of the head; the central fibers pass into the pons with the motor root and bifurcate into ascending and descending branches which terminate in the sensory nuclei of the trigeminal.

The **motor nucleus** of the trigeminal is situated in the upper part of the pons beneath the lateral angle of the fourth ventricle. It is serially homologous with the facial nucleus and the nucleus ambiguus (motor nucleus of the vagus and glossopharyngeal) which belong to the motor nuclei of the lateral somatic group. The axons arise from large pigmented multipolar cells. The motor nucleus receives reflex collaterals and terminals, (1) from the terminal nucleus of the trigeminal of the same and a few from the opposite side, via the central sensory tract (trigeminothalamic tract); (2) from the mesencephalic root of the trigeminal; (3) from nuclei in the formatio reticularis. It also receives collaterals and terminals from the aberrant pyramidal tracts of both sides, but more from the opposite side, for voluntary movements. There is probably a connecting or association neuron interposed between these fibers and the motor neurons.

The **terminal sensory nucleus** consists of an enlarged upper end, the **main sensory nucleus,** and a long more slender descending portion which passes down through the pons and medulla to become continuous with the substantia gelatinosa of the spinal cord. This descending portion consists mainly of substantia gelatinosa and is called the **nucleus of the spinal tract of the trigeminal nerve.**

The **main sensory nucleus** lies lateral to the motor nucleus beneath the superior peduncle. The main sensory nucleus is primarily for discriminative sense and the spinal tract is primarily for pain and temperature. The former receives the short ascending branches of the sensory root. The descending branches which form the **tractus spinalis** pass down through the pons and medulla on the lateral side of the **nucleus of the tractus spinalis,** in which they end by collaterals and terminals, into the spinal cord on the level of the second cervical segment. It decreases rapidly in size as it descends. At first it is located between the emergent part of the facial nerve and the vestibular nerve, then between the nucleus of the facial nerve and the inferior peduncle. Lower down in the upper part of the medulla it lies beneath the inferior peduncle and is broken up into bundles by the olivocerebellar fibers and the roots of the ninth and tenth cranial nerves. Finally it comes to the surface of the medulla under the tubercle of Rolando and continues in this position lateral to the fasciculus cuneatus as far as the upper part of the cervical region, where it disappears.

The cells of the main sensory nucleus are of large and medium size and send their axons to the opposite side of the brainstem where they form two tracts, a ventral and a dorsal. The former, sometimes called the **trigeminal lemniscus,** consists of well myelinated fibers which join with the medial lemniscus, forming a band on its dorso-medial margin. They run forward through the mesencephalon in this position. The other tract runs forward through the dorsal part of the reticular substance just ventro-lateral to the central gray round the aqueduct. Both tracts terminate in the nucleus ventralis posteromedialis of the thalamus. From here another neuron goes to the face area of the post-central region of the cortex (Fig. 754). There are also supposed to be some uncrossed trigemino-thalamic fibers.

The second neurons from the substantia gelatinosa trigemini cross to the opposite side through the reticular substance and join the medial margin of the lateral spino-thalamic tract. They run forward with it and terminate also in the nucleus ventralis posteromedialis thalami.

In addition to these projection tracts there are numerous connections from the sensory trigeminal nuclei to the motor nuclei of the medulla and pons. The lateral third of the reticular formation is particularly related to the trigeminal system and contains many secondary and tertiary centers. There are numerous commissural fibers of this system in the rostral part of the pons.

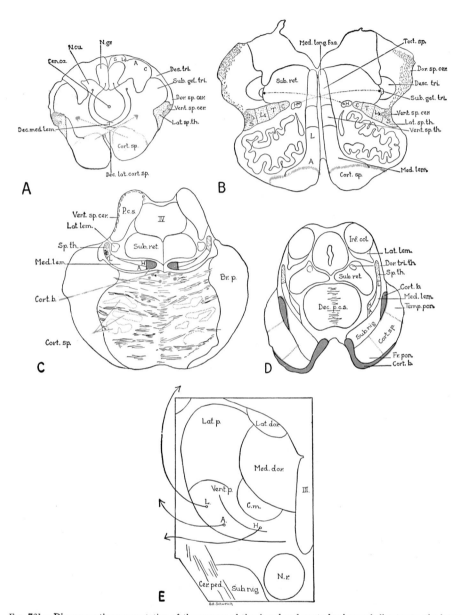

FIG. 761.—Diagrammatic representation of the courses of the dorsal and ventral spinocerebellar tracts, the lateral spinothalamic tract, the medial lemniscus, the trigeminothalamic tracts, the corticospinal and corticobulbar tracts through the brain-stem. The outline of the sections and the courses of the spinocerebellar and lateral spinothalamic tracts are taken from preparations by Schwartz and O'Leary. The diagrams are otherwise after Walker and Déjerine.

    A. Through the caudal end of the medulla.
    B. Through the middle of the medulla.
    C. Through the rostral margin of the pons.
    D. Through the inferior colliculus.
    E. Through the posterior part of the thalamus.

    A, arm fibers; *Br.p.*, brachium pontis; *C*, cervical fibers, *C.m.*, nucleus centrum medianum thalami; *Cen.ca.* central canal; *Cer.ped.*, cerebral peduncle; *Cort. b.*, corticobulbar tracts; *Cort.sp.*, corticospinal tract; *Dec. lat. cort.sp.*, decussation of the lateral corticospinal tract; *Dec.med.lem.*, descussation of the medial lemniscus; *Dec.p.c.s.*, decussation of the superior cerebellar peduncle; *Des.tri.*, descending root of the trigeminal; *Dor.sp.cer.*, dorsal spinocerebellar tract; *Dor.tri.th.*, dorsal trigeminothalamic tract; *Fr.po.n*, frontopontile fibers; *H.*, head (trigeminal) fibers; *Inf.col.*, inferior colliculus; *L.*, leg fibers; *L¹*, lumbar fibers; *Lat.dor.*, nucleus lateralis dorsalis thalami; *Lat.lem.*, lateral lemniscus; *Lat.p.*, nucleus lateralis posterior thalami; *Lat.sp.th.*, lateral spinothalamic tract; *Med.dor.*, nucleus medialis dorsalis thalami; *Med.lem.*, medial lemniscus; *Med.long.fas.*, medial longitudinal fasciculus; *N.cu.*, nucleus cuneatus; *N.gr.*, nucleus gracilis; *N.r.*, red nucleus; *P.c.s.*, superior cerebellar peduncle; *S*, sacral fibers; *sp.th.*, spinothalamic tracts; *Sub.gel.tri.*, substantia gelatinosa trigemini; *Sub.nig.*, substantia nigra; *Sub.ret.*, reticular substance; *Tect.sp.*, tectospinal tract; *Temp.pon.*, temporopontile fibers; *Vent.p.*, nucleus ventralis posterolateralis thalami; *Vent.sp.cer.*, ventral spinocerebellar tract; *Vent.sp.th.*, ventral spinothalamic tract.

The somatic sensory fibers of the vagus, the glossopharyngeal and the facial nerves probably end in the nucleus of the descending tract of the trigeminal and their cortical impulses are probably carried up in the central sensory path of the trigeminal.

The **mesencephalic root** (*descending root of the trigeminal*) arises from unipolar cells arranged in scattered groups in a column at the lateral edge of the central gray matter surrounding the upper end of the fourth ventricle and the cerebral aqueduct. There has been considerable controversy as to the functional nature of the mesencephalic root. The cells develop from the alar lamina and are sensory in type. The axons give off collaterals to the motor nucleus and then join the motor root to pass into the mandibular branch of the trigeminal nerve. It is now thought they are proprioceptive for the muscles of mastication.

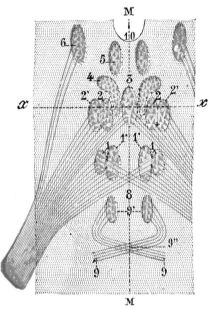

Fig. 762.—Figure showing the different groups of cells, which constitute, according to Perlia the nucleus or origin of the oculomotor nerve. 1. Posterior dorsal nucleus. 1′. Posterior ventral nucleus. 2. Anterior dorsal nucleus. 2′. Anterior ventral nucleus. 3. Central nucleus. 4. Nucleus of Edinger and Westphal. 5. Antero-internal nucleus. 6. Antero-external nucleus. 8. Crossed fibers. 9. Trochlear nerve, with 9′, its nucleus of origin, and 9″, its decussation. 10. Third ventricle. *M, M.* Median line. (Testut.)

The **Trochlear Nerve** (*IV cranial*) contains somatic motor fibers only to the superior oblique muscle of the eye and afferent fibers from the muscle spindles. Its nucleus of origin, **trochlear nucleus**, is a small, oval mass situated in the ventral part of the central gray matter of the cerebral aqueduct at the level of the upper part of the inferior colliculus. The axons from the nucleus pass downward in the tegmentum toward the pons, but turn abruptly dorsalward before reaching it, and pass into the superior medullary velum, in which they cross horizontally, to decussate with the nerve of the opposite side, and emerge from the surface of the velum, immediately behind the inferior colliculus. The nuclei of the two sides are separated by the raphé through which dendrites extend from one nucleus to the other. They receive many collaterals and terminals from the medial longitudinal fasciculus which lies on the ventral side of the nucleus.

The **Oculomotor Nerve** (*III cranial*) contains somatic motor fibers to the Obliquus inferior, Rectus inferior, Rectus superior, Levator palpebræ superioris and Rectus medialis muscles, afferent fibers from the muscle spindles and autonomic efferent fibers (preganglionic fibers) to the ciliary ganglion. The postganglionic fibers connected with these supply the ciliary muscle and the sphincter of the iris. The axons arise from the nucleus of the oculomotor nerve and pass in bundles through the medial longitudinal fasciculus, the tegmentum, the red nucleus and the medial margin of the substantia nigra in a series of curves and finally emerge from the oculomotor sulcus on the medial side of the cerebral peduncle.

The **oculomotor nucleus** lies in the gray substance of the floor of the cerebral aqueduct subjacent to the superior colliculus and extends in front of the aqueduct a short distance into the floor of the third ventricle. The inferior end is continuous with the trochlear nucleus. It is from 6 to 10 mm. in length. It is intimately related to the medial longitudinal bundle which lies against its ventro-lateral aspect and many of its cells lie among the fibers of the posterior longitudinal bundle. The nucleus of the oculomotor nerve contains several groups of cells which differ in size and send their axons each to a separate muscle. The representation of the muscles from rostral to caudal in the nucleus is as follows: Levator palpebræ superioris, Rectus superior, Obliquus inferior, Rectus medialis, Rectus inferior. The last is in contact with the trochlear nucleus which supplies the Obliquus superior. At about the middle of the nucleus, adjacent to the representation of the Rectus medialis, is a mid-line group of cells, the nucleus of Perlia. It is probably concerned with convergence of the eyes, its fibers passing to the motor nuclei lying lateral to it.

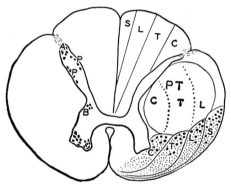

Fig. 763.—Semischematic drawing to show on the left side the cell groups of the posterior horn, and on the right side the arrangement of the spinothalamic and other tracts in the lower cervical region. The heavy dots represent fibers concerned with temperature; the medium-sized dots, fibers mediating pain, and the fine dots, fibers carrying touch and pressure impulses. Note the overlapping and topical arrangement of the fibers. A, apical group of large ganglion cells of the posterior horn; B, basal group of large ganglion cells of the posterior horn; C, fibers from the cervical segment of the spinal cord; L, fibers from the lumbar segment of the spinal cord; P, pericornual groups of large ganglion cells of the posterior horn; PT, tractus pyramidalis; S, fibers from the sacral segment of the spinal cord, and T, fibers from the thoracic segment of the spinal cord. (Walker, courtesy of Arch. Neur. and Psych.)

The fibers from the cerebral cortex controlling eye movements arise chiefly from area 8, for voluntary movement, and from the upper part of area 19, for fixation of gaze in response to a visual stimulus. Other fibers appear to come from parts of the parietal and temporal lobes. They leave the peduncles in the rostral part of the mesencephalon. It is doubtful whether many of them pass directly to the eye-muscle nuclei. Most apparently terminate in nuclei of the reticular substance where conjugate movements of the eyes are integrated. A center for conjugate lateral deviation of gaze lies close to the abducens nucleus, and one for conjugate upward deviation of gaze apparently lies dorso-lateral to the oculomotor nucleus. From such centers connections pass to the eye-muscle nuclei both directly and through the medial longitudinal fasciculus. The last mentioned fasciculus also carries the following types of connections: from the vestibular nuclei, crossed and uncrossed; from various nuclei of the reticular formation; interconnections between the eye-muscle and head and neck-turning nuclei, and from proprioceptive systems in the cervical cord. Connections from the tectum of the mesencephalon are also present.

The **autonomic nuclei** associated with the oculomotor and trochlear nuclei form a column in the ventral part of the stratum griseum centrale. The rostral end of this column is termed the **Edinger-Westphal** nucleus. Its fibers enter the oculomotor nerve and end in the ciliary ganglion. The postganglionics innervate the sphincter of the pupil.

The **Optic Nerve** (*II cranial*) (Fig. 718) consists chiefly of coarse fibers which arise from the ganglionic layer of the retina. The majority constitute the third neuron in the series composing the visual path. A number of fibers pass in the optic nerve from the retina to the primary centers and are concerned in the pupillary reflexes. There are in addition a few fibers which pass from the brain to the retina; they are supposed to control chemical changes in the retina and the movements of the pigment cells and cones. Each optic nerve has, according to Arey and Bickel, about 1,250,000 fibers.

In the **optic chiasma** the fibers from the medial half of each retina cross to enter the opposite optic tract, while the fibers from the lateral half of each retina pass into the optic tract of the same side. The fibers from the macula lutea make up the temporal half of the optic disc, but in the nerve they soon take a central position with the fibers from the peripheral retinal quadrants arranged around them. At the chiasma the medial macular fibers cross in the center, the upper nasal quadrant fibers above and the lower below. There is some clinical evidence that the whole fovea is bilaterally represented in the cortex, but the anatomical mechanism for this is not known. The temporal fibers do not cross. Thus the fibers from the right half of each retina pass to the right hemisphere, from the left half to the left hemisphere. Approximately 60 per cent. of the fibers cross. The optic tract is attached to the tuber cinereum and lamina terminalis and also to the cerebral peduncle as it crosses obliquely over its under surface. These are not functional connections. A small band of fibers from the medial geniculate body joins the optic tract as the latter passes over it and crosses to the opposite tract and medial geniculate body in the posterior part of the chiasma. This is the commissure of Gudden and is connected with the auditory system.

Most of the fibers of the **optic tract** terminate in the lateral geniculate body; some pass through the superior brachium to the superior colliculus, and others pass to the pretectal region. These end-stations are often called the **primary visual centers.**

The **pretectal region,** immediately in front of the superior colliculus, receives fibers from the optic tract. Neurons of the pretectal region send axons ventrally around the central gray matter of the upper and of the mid-brain to the nucleus of Edinger-Westphal, the autonomic efferent part of the III nucleus. Its visceral efferent fibers pass in the oculomotor nerve to the ciliary ganglion. Postganglionic fibers run from it to the iris.

The **lateral geniculate body** of the metathalamus consists of medium-sized pigmented nerve cells arranged in several layers. The projection of the retina on the lateral geniculate body is illustrated in Figure 764.

The outermost lamina of the geniculate receives fibers from the contra-lateral eye, the next lamina from the ipsi-lateral, the third from the contra-lateral, and so on alternately. The axons from the cells of the lateral geniculate body leave its dorso-rostral surface, run forward and then sweep lateralward through the retrolenticular portion of the internal capsule to form the **geniculocalcarine fasciculus.** Some of the fibers make a detour over the temporal horn of the ventricle before turning back to the occipital lobe. They pass backward and medially to terminate in the visuosensory cortex (area striata, or area 17) in the immediate neighborhood of the calcarine fissure of the occipital lobe. The projection of the lateral geniculate in the area striata is illustrated in Figure 764. This center is connected with the one in the opposite side by commissural fibers which course in the optic radiation and the splenium of the corpus callosum. Association fibers connect it with other

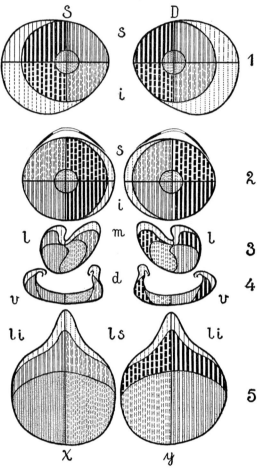

FIG. 764.—Diagrammatic illustrations of the projection of the various quadrants of the visual fields. Left (*S*) and right (*D*) sides of the visual fields and of the afferent visual apparatus. Number 1 represents both fields of vision with their upper (*s*) and lower (*i*), nasal and temporal halves; the smaller inner circles represent the "central" or macular portions (their relative size in comparison with the perimacular portion is somewhat exaggerated); the large circles represent the peri- or extramacular portions of the binocular visual fields; the outermost lightly shaded sickle-shaped zones represent the monocular portions of the visual fields. Number 2 represents left and right retinæ with their upper (*s*) and lower (*i*), nasal and temporal halves; smaller and larger circles and the monocular portions as above. Number 3 represents a schematic cross section through the left and right geniculate bodies; their internal margins (*m*) close to the thalamus; their external margins (*l*); their concave contours in the figure facing upward represent their ventral margins. Number 4 represents cross sections through the left and right visual radiation (external sagittal strata of the parieto-occipital lobes); their dorsal horizontal branches (*d*), their ventral horizontal branches (*v*), with perpendicular or vertical branches (in the figure horizontal) connecting both horizontal branches. Number 5 represents the left and right visual projection cortex, the area striata of Elliot Smith, field 17 of Brodmann, each subdivided into an upper (*ls*) and a lower half (*li*) corresponding with the upper and lower lips of the calcarine fissures. The dividing lines, vertical in the figure, and terminating at the letters *x* and *y*, correspond in their upper parts to the bottom of the calcarine fissures and to the horizontal meridians of both visual fields dividing the upper from the lower extramacular quadrants; in their lower parts (lower in the figure) these lines correspond to horizontal meridians dividing the upper from lower macular quadrants. The points where these lines reach the posterior limits of both striate areas, marked by the letters *x* and *y* in the figure, correspond to both points of fixation in the visual fields. The vertical lines or meridians dividing the left from the right homonymous halves of the macular portion of the visual fields correspond to the posterior (lower in the figure) circumference of the striate areas close to the letters *x* and *y*. (Polyak, University of California Press, 1932.)

regions of the cortex of the same side, and there are also fibers from the striate area back to the geniculate body.

The **superior colliculus** receives fibers from the optic tract through the superior brachium. Most of the fibers from the superior brachium pass into the **stratum** opticum (upper gray-white layer). Some of these turn upward into the gray cap, while others terminate among the cells of this layer. There is a point to point relationship between the retina and superior colliculus similar to that between the retina and the lateral geniculate. Since the superior colliculi in lower forms appear to be highly complex analytical centers we should expect to find them receiving fibers from other sensory paths. Many fibers pass to the superior colliculus from the spinotectal fasciculus, bringing the superior colliculus into relation with the sensory fibers of the spinal cord. Fibers from the central sensory path of the trigeminal probably pass with these. The superior colliculus is intimately connected with the central auditory path (the **lateral lemniscus**), as part of its fibers pass the inferior colliculus and terminate in the superior colliculus. They are probably concerned with reflex movements of the eyes, depending on auditory stimuli. It receives fibers from the visual cortex through the cortico-tectal radiations which run with the optic radiations. The superior colliculus is said to receive fibers from the stria medullaris thalamus of the opposite side which pass through the commissura habenulæ and turn back to the roof of the mid-brain. By this path both the primary and cortical olfactory centers are also brought into relation with the eye-muscle reflex apparatus.

The descending efferent fibers arise from large cells in the stratum opticum and stratum lemnisci and pass around the ventral aspect of the central gray matter where most of them cross the mid-line in the dorsal tegmental decussation (fountain decussation of Meynert) and then turn downward to form the **tectobulbar and tectospinal fasciculi**. This bundle runs down partly through the red nucleus, in the formatio reticularis, ventral to the medial longitudinal fasciculus of the mid-brain, pons and medulla oblongata into the ventral funiculus of the spinal cord, where it is known as the **tectospinal fasciculus**. From the tectospinal and tectobulbar fasciculi collaterals are given off to the nuclei of the eye muscles, the oculomotor, the trochlear and the abducens and many collaterals pass to the red nucleus. The fibers of the tectospinal tract end by collaterals and terminals either directly or indirectly among the motor cells in the ventral column of the spinal cord.

The superior colliculus receives fibers from the visual sensory area of the occipital cortex; they pass in the optic radiation. Probably no fibers pass from the superior colliculus to the visual sensory cortex.

The pupillary reflex path consists of special fibers in the optic nerve and tract which pass caudal to the lateral geniculate body in the superior brachium and end in one or another of several nuclei lying just medial to the caudal pole of the lateral geniculate. From here another neuron passes to the Edinger-Westphal nuclei of both sides.

The **Olfactory Nerves** (*I cranial*) or **nerves of smell** arise from spindle-shaped bipolar cells in the surface epithelium of the olfactory region of the nasal cavity. The non-medullated axons pass upward in groups through numerous foramina in the cribriform plate to the olfactory bulb; here several fibers, each ending in a tuft of terminal filaments, come into relation with the brush-like end of a single dendrite from a mitral cell. This interlacing gives rise to the olfactory glomeruli of the bulb. The termination of several or many olfactory fibers in a single glomerulus where they form synapses with the dendrites of one or two mitral cells provides for the summation of stimuli in the mitral cells and accounts in part at least for the detection by the olfactory organs of very dilute solutions. Lateral arborizations of the dendrites of the mitral cells and the connection of neighboring glomeruli by the axons of small cells of the glomeruli and the return of impulses of the mitral cells by collaterals either directly or through the interpolation of granule cells to the dendrites of the mitral cells reinforce the discharge of the mitral cells along their axons. The axons turn abruptly backward in the deep fiber layer of the bulb to form the olfactory tract. The olfactory tract is continued into the olfactory trigone, just in front of the anterior perforated substance. The axons of the mitral cells on reaching the olfactory trigone separate into three bundles, the **lateral olfactory stria**, the **medial olfactory stria** and the **intermedial olfactory stria**.

The **lateral olfactory striæ** curve lateralward, a few of the fibers end in the olfactory trigone and the antero-lateral portion of the anterior perforated substance. Most of the fibers, however, pass into the uncus, the anterior end of the hippocampal gyrus, and there end in the complicated cortex of the hippocampal gyri. The lateral striæ more or less disappear as they cross the antero-lateral region of the anterior perforated substance.

The greater mass of the fibers of the olfactory tract pass into the lateral stria. Numerous collaterals are given into the plexiform layer of the subfrontal cortex, over which the striæ pass on their way to the uncus, where they intermingle with the apical dendrons of the medium-sized and small pyramidal cells of the pyramidal layer of this subfrontal or frontal olfactory cortex. The axons give rise to projection fibers which take an antero-posterior direction to the lateral hypothalamic area sending collaterals and terminal branches to the stria medullaris and others toward the thalamus. Some of the fibers extend farther back and reach the tegmentum of the mesencephalon.

Most of the fibers of the lateral olfactory stria pass to the hippocampal region of the cortex, especially to the gyrus hippocampi, which may be regarded as the main ending place of the secondary olfactory path derived from axons of the mitral cells.

The **intermediate olfactory striæ**, more important than the medial striæ in man, are visible macroscopically and terminate in the anterior perforated substance; a few are said to continue to the uncus.

The trigonum olfactorium, anterior perforated substance and the adjoining part of the septum pellucidum are important primary olfactory centers, especially for olfactory reflexes; in these centers terminate many axons from the mitral cells of the olfactory bulb. In addition the gray substance of the olfactory tract and the gyrus subcallosus receive terminals of the mitral cells.

The pathways from these centers to lower centers in the brain-stem and spinal cord are only partially known. The most direct path, the **medial forebrain bundle** (*basal olfactory bundle of Wallenburg*), is supposed to arise from cells in the gray substance of the olfactory tract, the olfactory trigone, the anterior perforated substance and the adjoining part of the septum pellucidum. The fibers are said to pass direct to the tuber cinereum, to the corpus mamillare and to the brainstem. The fibers which enter the mammillary body probably come into relation with cells whose axons give rise to the **fasciculus mamillotegmentalis** (*mamillotegmental bundle of Gudden*) which is supposed to end in the gray substance of the tegmentum.

Some of the fibers of the medial olfactory stria came into relation with cells in the parolfactory area of Broca and in the anterior perforated substance, whose axons course in the medullary stria of the thalamus. As the axons pass through the lower part of the septum pellucidum they are joined by other fibers whose cells receive impulses from the mitral cells. These fibers of the medullary stria end for the most part in the habenular nucleus of the same side, some, however, cross in the habenular commissure to the habenular nucleus of the opposite side. A few fibers of the medullary stria are said to pass by the habenular nucleus to the roof of the mid-brain, especially the superior colliculus.

The ganglion of the habenulæ located in the trigonum habenulæ just in front of the superior colliculus contains a mesial nucleus with small cells and a lateral nucleus with larger cells. The axons of these cells are grouped together in a bundle, the **fasciculus retroflexus of Meynert**, which passes ventrally medial to the red nucleus and terminates in a small medial ganglion in the substantia perforata posterior, immediately in front of the pons, called the **interpeduncular ganglion**.

The **interpeduncular ganglion** has rather large nerve cells whose axons curve backward and downward, to end partly in the dorsal tegmental nucleus and surrounding gray substance where they come into relation with association neurons and the dorsal longitudinal bundle of Schütz.

The majority of the axons that arise from the mitral cells of the olfactory bulb and course in the olfactory tract course in the lateral olfactory stria to the uncus and hippocampal gyrus, and terminate in the cortex. Other fibers probably pass to the uncus and hippocampal gyrus from the primary olfactory centers in the trigonum and anterior perforated substance. The gyrus hippocampus is continued through the isthmus into the gyrus cinguli which passes over the corpus callosum to the area parolfactoria. The cortical portions of these gyri are connected together by a thick association bundle, the **cingulum,** that lies buried in the depth of the gyrus cinguli extending forward to the parolfactory area and backward into the hippocampal region. The axons from the gyrus cinguli pass into the cingulum, many of them bifurcate, the anterior branches together with the axons which run in that direction are traceable as far forward as the anterior part of the septum pellucidum and the anterior end of the corpus striatum, where some of them are incorporated with projection fibers passing toward the internal capsule. The branches and axons which pass backward terminate partly in the hippocampus, the dentate gyrus and hippocampal gyrus. Shorter association fibers connect various sections of the gyrus fornicatus (cingulate gyrus, isthmus, and hippocampal gyrus) and these with other regions of the cortex. These gyri constitute the cortical center for smell.

The **dentate gyrus** which may be considered as a modified part of the hippocampus is partially separated from the gyrus hippocampus by the hippocampal fissure and from the fimbria by the fimbrio-dentate sulcus; it is intimately connected with the hippocampal gyrus and the hippocampus. When followed backward the dentate gyrus separates from the fimbria at the splenium, loses its incisions and knobs, and as the fasciola cinerea passes over the splenium onto the dorsal surface of the corpus callosum and spreads out into a thin layer of gray substance known as the **indusium,** which can be traced forward around the genu of the corpus callosum into the gyrus subcallosus. The white matter of the indusium known as the **medial longitudinal striæ** (*nerves of Lancisi*) and the **lateral longitudinal striæ,** are related to the indusium somewhat as the cingulum is to the gyrus cinguli. Axons from the indusium pass into the longitudinal striæ, some running forward and others backward while some after entering the medial longitudinal stria, pierce the corpus callosum to join the fornix. Some of the fibers which pass forward extend around the front of the corpus callosum and the anterior commissure, then curve downward, according to Cajal, to enter the corpus striatum where they join the olfactory projection path. Other fibers are said to arise in the parolfactory area and the **gyrus subcallosus** and course backward in the longitudinal striæ to the dentate gyrus and the hippocampal region. The indusium is usually considered as a rudimentary part of the rhinencephalon.

The **olfactory projection fibers** which arise from the pyramid cells of the uncus and hippocampus and from the polymorphic cells of the dentate gyrus form a dense stratum on the ventricular surface, especially on the hippocampus, called the **alveus.** These fibers pass over into the fimbria and are continued into the **fornix.** About one-fourth of all the fibers of the fimbria are large projection fibers, the other three-fourths consist of fine commissural fibers which pass from the hippocampus of one side through the fimbria and **hippocampal commissure** (*ventral psalterium or lyre*), to the fimbria and hippocampus of the opposite side where they penetrate the pyramidal layer and terminate in the stratum radiatum. The fibers which course in the fornix pass forward and downward into the corpora mamillaria where numerous collaterals are given off and many terminate. A few of the fibers in the fornix, however, pass through the corpora, cross the middle line and turn downward in the reticular formation. As the fornix passes beneath the corpus callosum it receives fibers from the longitudinal striæ of the indusium and from the cingulum; these are the perforating fibers of the fornix which pass through the corpus callosum and course in the fornix toward the mammillary body. As the fornix passes the anterior end of the thalamus a few fibers are given off to the stria medullaris of the thalamus and turn back in the stria to the habenular ganglion of the same and the opposite side, having probably the same relation that the reflex fibers have which arise from the primary centers and course in the stria medullaris of the thalamus. The fornix also contributes a few fibers to the hypothalamic nuclei as it passes through the hypothalamus.

The mammillary bodies receive collaterals and terminals then from the cortical centers via the fornix and other collaterals and terminals are received directly from the primary centers through the medial forebrain bundle. According to Cajal fibers also reach the mammillary body through the peduncle of the corpus mamillare from the tegmentum. The fornix probably brings the cortical centers into relation with the reflex path that runs from the primary centers to the mammillary body and the tuber cinereum.

The **principal mammillary peduncle** arises from cells in both the medial and lateral nuclei of the mammillary body. The axons divide into two branches just above the mammillary bodies; the coarser branches pass into the anterior nucleus of the thalamus as the bundle of Vicq d'Azyr, the finer branches pass downward as the mamillotegmental bundle of Gudden. The bundle of Vicq d'Azyr spreads out fan-like as it terminates in the anterior nuclei of the thalamus. The axons from these nuclei form part of the thalamocortical system.

The mamillotegmental bundle has already been considered under the olfactory reflex paths.

The **amygdaloid nuclei** and the **stria terminalis** (*tænia semicircularis*) probably belong to the central olfactory apparatus. The amygdaloid nuclei are interconnected with the basal olfactory areas, the pyriform areas, the striatum and with the cortex of the temporal lobe. The amygdalæ of the two sides are connected together through the anterior commissure. The stria terminalis arises in the amygdaloid nuclei and runs round the lesser curvature of the lateral ventricle, just medial to the tail of the caudate. At the level of the inter-ventricular foramen it bends ventrally and medially. Separate components then pass to the parolfactory area, to the habenular ganglia (through the stria medullaris), and to the hypothalamus of the same side and of the opposite side (through the anterior commissure).

PATHWAYS FROM THE BRAIN TO THE SPINAL CORD.

The descending fasciculi which convey impulses from the higher centers to the spinal cord and located in the lateral and ventral funiculi.

The **Motor Tract** (Figs. 762 and 765), conveying voluntary impulses, arises from the pyramid cells situated in the motor area of the cortex, the anterior central and the posterior portions of the frontal gyri and the paracentral lobule. The fibers are at first somewhat widely diffused, but as they descend through the corona radiata they gradually approach each other, and pass between the lentiform nucleus and thalamus, in the genu and anterior two-thirds of the occipital part of the internal capsule; those in the genu are named the **geniculate fibers,** while the remainder constitute the **cerebrospinal fibers;** proceeding downward they enter the middle three-fifths of the base of the cerebral peduncle. The geniculate fibers cross the middle line, and end by arborizing around the cells of the motor nuclei of the cranial nerves. The cerebrospinal fibers are continued downward into the pyramids of the medulla oblongata, and the transit of the fibers from the medulla oblongata is effected by two paths. The fibers nearest to the anterior median fissure cross the middle line, forming the **decussation of the pyramids,** and descend in the opposite side of the medulla spinalis, as the **lateral cerebrospinal fasciculus** (*crossed*

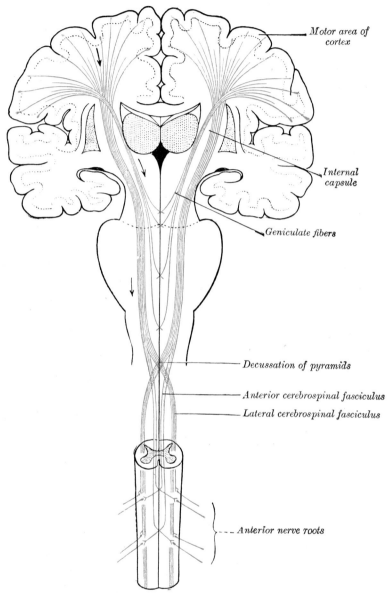

Motor area of cortex

Internal capsule

Geniculate fibers

Decussation of pyramids

Anterior cerebrospinal fasciculus

Lateral cerebrospinal fasciculus

Anterior nerve roots

Fɪɢ. 765.—The motor tract. (Modified from Poirier.)

pyramidal tract). Throughout the length of the medulla spinalis fibers from this column pass into the gray substance, to terminate either directly or indirectly around the motor cells of the anterior column. The more laterally placed portion of the tract does not decussate in the medulla oblongata, but descends as the **anterior cerebrospinal fasciculus** (*direct pyramidal tract*); these fibers, however, end in the anterior gray column of the opposite side of the medulla spinalis by passing across in the anterior white commissure. There is considerable variation in the extent to which decussation takes place in the medulla oblongata; about two-thirds or three-fourths of the fibers usually decussate in the medulla oblongata and the remainder in the medulla spinalis. A few fibers of both the lateral and anterior tracts remain uncrossed and terminate on the same side of the cord.

The axons of the motor cells in the anterior column pass out as the fibers of the anterior roots of the spinal nerves, along which the impulses are conducted to the muscles of the trunk and limbs.

From this it will be seen that the great majority of the fibers of the motor tract pass to the nuclei of the motor nerves on the opposite side of the brain or medulla spinalis, a fact which explains why a lesion involving the motor area of one side causes paralysis of the muscles of the opposite side of the body. Further, it will be seen that there is a break in the continuity of the motor chain; in the case of the cranial nerves this break occurs in the nuclei of these nerves; and in the case of the spinal nerves, in the anterior gray column of the medulla spinalis. For clinical purposes it is convenient to emphasize this break and divide the motor tract into two portions: (1) a series of **upper motor neurons** which comprises the motor cells in the cortex and their descending fibers down to the nuclei of the motor nerves; (2) a series of **lower motor neurons** which includes the cells of the nuclei of the motor cerebral nerves or the cells of the anterior columns of the medulla spinalis and their axis-cylinder processes to the periphery.

The small **rubrospinal fasciculus** arises from a few large cells in the caudal pole of the red nucleus. The fibers cross the raphé of the mid-brain in the decussation of Forel and descend in the formatio reticularis of the pons and medulla and as they pass into the spinal cord come to lie in a position ventral to the crossed pyramidal tracts in the lateral funiculus. The rubrospinal fibers end either directly or indirectly by terminals and collaterals about the motor cells in the anterior column on the side opposite from their origin in the red nucleus. A few are said to pass down on the same side. Since the red nucleus is intimately related to the cerebellum by terminals and collaterals of the superior peduncle which arises in the dentate nucleus of the cerebellum, the rubrospinal fasciculus is supposed to be concerned with cerebellar reflexes, complex motor coördinations necessary in locomotion and equilibrium. The afferent paths concerned in these reflexes have already been partly considered, namely, the dorsal and ventral spinocerebellar fasciculi, and probably some of the fibers of the posterior funiculi which reach the cerebellum by the inferior peduncle.

The **tectospinal fasciculus** arises from the superior colliculus of the roof (tectum) of the mid-brain. The axons come from large cells in the stratum opticum and stratum lemnisci and sweep ventrally around the central gray matter of the aqueduct, cross the raphé in the fountain decussation of Meynert and turn downward in the tegmentum. Some of the fibers do not cross in the raphé but pass down on the same side; it is uncertain whether they come from the superior colliculus of the same side or arch over the aqueduct from the colliculus of the opposite side. The tectospinal fasciculus passes down through the tegmentum and reticular formation of the pons and medulla oblongata ventral to the medial longitudinal bundle. In the medulla the two bundles are more or less intermingled The tectospinal fasciculus splits into a medial tectospinal fasciculus which continues into the ventral funiculus of the cord and a smaller lateral tectospinal fasciculus which runs with the rubrospinal tract. Some of the fibers of the tectospinal fasciculus pass through the red nucleus giving off collaterals to it; others are given off to the motor nuclei of the cranial nerves and in the spinal cord they terminate either directly or indirectly by terminals and collaterals among the nuclei of the anterior column. Since the superior colliculus is an important optic reflex center, this tract is probably concerned in optic reflexes, and possibly also with auditory reflexes, since some of the fibers of the central auditory path, the lateral lemniscus, terminate in the superior colliculus.

The **direct vestibulospinal fasciculus** (*part of the anterior marginal fasciculus or Loewenthal's tract*) situated chiefly in the marginal part of the anterior funiculus is derived from the cells of the lateral nucleus of the vestibular nerve. It descends in the ventral funiculus of the spinal cord. The vestibulospinal fasciculus is concerned with equilibratory reflexes. Its terminals and collaterals end about the motor cells in the anterior column. It extends to the sacral region of the cord. Its fibers are intermingled with the ascending spinothalamic fasciculus, with the anterior proper fasciculus and laterally with the tectospinal fasciculus. Its fibers are uncrossed.

The **pontospinal fasciculus** (*Bechterew*) arises from the cells in the reticular formation of the pons from the same and the opposite side and is associated in the brainstem with the ventral longitudinal bundle. In the cord it is intermingled with the fibers of the vestibulospinal fasciculus in the anterior funiculus. Not much is known about this tract.

There are other reticulo-spinal fasciculi which arise in various nuclei of the reticular substance. Some are crossed, some uncrossed, and in the cord they run in the sulco-marginal fasciculus, in the anterior columns close to the direct vestibulospinal fasciculus and in the lateral columns close to the rubrospinal fasciculus.

MENINGES OF THE BRAIN AND MEDULLA SPINALIS.

The brain and medulla spinalis are enclosed within three membranes. These are named from without inward: the **dura mater,** the **arachnoid,** and the **pia mater.**

The Dura Mater.

The **dura mater** is a thick and dense inelastic membrane. The portion which encloses the brain differs in several essential particulars from that which surrounds the medulla spinalis, and therefore it is necessary to describe them separately; but at the same time it must be distinctly understood that the two form one complete membrane, and are continuous with each other at the foramen magnum.

The **Cranial Dura Mater** (*dura mater encephali; dura of the brain*) lines the interior of the skull, and serves the twofold purpose of an internal periosteum to the bones, and a membrane for the protection of the brain. It is composed of two layers, an inner or meningeal and an outer or endosteal, closely connected together, except in certain situations, where, as already described (page 661), they separate to form sinuses for the passage of venous blood. Its outer surface is rough and fibrillated, and adheres closely to the inner surfaces of the bones, the adhesions being most marked opposite the sutures and at the base of the skull its inner surface is smooth and lined by a layer of mesothelium. It sends inward four processes which divide the cavity of the skull into a series of freely communicating compartments, for the lodgment and protection of the different parts of the brain; and it is prolonged to the outer surface of the skull, through the various foramina which exist at the base, and thus becomes continuous with the pericranium; its fibrous layer forms sheaths for the nerves which pass through these apertures. Around the margin of the foramen magnum it is closely adherent to the bone, and is continuous with the spinal dura mater.

Processes.—The processes of the cranial dura mater, which projects into the cavity of the skull, are formed by reduplications of the inner or meningeal layer of the membrane, and are four in number: the **falx cerebri**, the **tentorium cerebelli**, the **falx cerebelli**, and the **diaphragma sellæ**.

The **falx cerebri** (Fig. 558), so named from its sickle-like form, is a strong, arched process which descends vertically in the longitudinal fissure between the cerebral hemispheres. It is narrow in front, where it is attached to the crista galli of the ethmoid; and broad behind, where it is connected with the upper surface of the tentorium cerebelli. Its upper margin is convex, and attached to the inner surface of the skull in the middle line, as far back as the internal occipital protuberance; it contains the superior sagittal sinus. Its lower margin is free and concave, and contains the inferior sagittal sinus.

The **tentorium cerebelli** is an arched lamina, elevated in the middle, and inclining downward toward the circumference. It covers the superior surface of the cerebellum, and supports the occipital lobes of the brain. Its anterior border is free and concave, and bounds a large oval opening, the **incisura tentorii**, for the transmission of the cerebral peduncles. It is attached, behind, by its convex border, to the transverse ridges upon the inner surface of the occipital bone, and there encloses the transverse sinuses; in front, to the superior angle of the petrous part of the temporal bone on either side, enclosing the superior petrosal sinuses. At the apex of the petrous part of the temporal bone the free and attached borders meet, and, crossing one another, are continued forward to be fixed to the anterior and posterior clinoid processes respectively. To the middle line of its upper surface the posterior border of the falx cerebri is attached, the straight sinus being placed at their line of junction.

The **falx cerebelli** is a small triangular process of dura mater, received into the posterior cerebellar notch. Its base is attached, above, to the under and back part of the tentorium; its posterior margin, to the lower division of the vertical crest on the inner surface of the occipital bone. As it descends, it sometimes divides into two smaller folds, which are lost on the sides of the foramen magnum.

The **diaphragma sellæ** is a small circular horizontal fold, which roofs in the sella turcica and almost completely covers the hypophysis; a small central opening transmits the infundibulum.

Structure.—The cranial dura mater consists of white fibrous tissue and elastic fibers arranged in flattened laminæ which are imperfectly separated by lacunar spaces and bloodvessels into two layers, **endosteal** and **meningeal**. The **endosteal layer** is the internal periosteum for the cranial bones, and contains the bloodvessels for their supply. At the margin of the foramen magnum it is continuous with the periosteum lining the vertebral canal. The **meningeal or supporting layer** is lined on its inner surface by a layer of nucleated flattened mesothelium, similar to that found on serous membranes.

The **arteries** of the dura mater are very numerous. Those in the anterior fossa are the anterior meningeal branches of the anterior and posterior ethmoidal and internal carotid, and a branch from the middle meningeal. Those in the middle fossa are the middle and accessory meningeal of the internal maxillary; a branch from the ascending pharyngeal, which enters the skull through the foramen lacerum; branches from the internal carotid, and a recurrent branch from the lacrimal. Those in the posterior fossa are meningeal branches from the occipital, one entering the skull through the jugular foramen, and another through the mastoid foramen; the posterior meningeal from the vertebral; occasional meningeal branches from the ascending pharyngeal, entering the skull through the jugular foramen and hypoglossal canal; and a branch from the middle meningeal.

The **veins** returning the blood from the cranial dura mater anastomose with the diploic veins and end in the various sinuses. Many of the meningeal veins do not open directly into the sinuses, but indirectly through a series of ampullæ, termed **venous lacunæ**. These are found on either side of the superior sagittal sinus, especially near its middle portion, and are often invaginated by arachnoid granulations; they also exist near the transverse and straight sinuses. They communicate with the underlying cerebral veins, and also with the diploic and emissary veins.

The **nerves** of the cranial dura mater are filaments from the semilunar ganglion, from the ophthalmic, maxillary, mandibular, vagus, and hypoglossal nerves, and from the sympathetic.

The **Spinal Dura Mater** (*dura mater spinalis; spinal dura*) (Fig. 766) forms a loose sheath around the medulla spinalis, and represents only the inner or meningeal layer of the cranial dura mater; the outer or endosteal layer ceases at the foramen magnum, its place being taken by the periosteum lining the vertebral canal. The spinal dura mater is separated from the arachnoid by a potential cavity, the **subdural cavity**; the two membranes are, in fact, in contact with each other, except where they are separated by a minute quantity of fluid, which serves to moisten the apposed surfaces. It is separated from the wall of the vertebral canal by a space, the **epidural space**, which contains a quantity of loose areolar tissue and a plexus of veins; the situation of these veins between the dura mater and the periosteum of the vertebræ corresponds therefore to that of the cranial sinuses between the meningeal and endosteal layers of the cranial dura mater. The spinal dura mater is attached to the circumference of the foramen magnum, and to the second and third cervical vertebræ; it is also connected to the posterior longitudinal ligament, especially near the lower end of the vertebral canal, by fibrous slips. The subdural cavity ends at the lower border of the second sacral vertebra; below this level the dura mater closely invests the filum terminale and descends to the back of the coccyx, where it blends with the periosteum. The sheath of dura mater is much larger than is necessary for the accommodation of its contents, and its size is greater in the cervical and lumbar regions than in

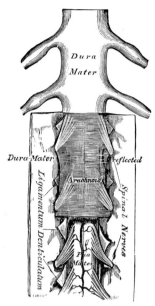

FIG. 766.—The medulla spinalis and its membranes.

the thoracic. On each side may be seen the double openings which transmit the two roots of the corresponding spinal nerve, the dura mater being continued in the form of tubular prolongations on them as they pass through the intervertebral foramina. These prolongations are short in the upper part of the vertebral column, but gradually become longer below, forming a number of tubes of fibrous membrane, which enclose the lower spinal nerves and are contained in the vertebral canal.

Structure.—The spinal dura mater resembles in structure the meningeal or supporting layer of the cranial dura mater, consisting of white fibrous and elastic tissue arranged in bands or lamellæ which, for the most part, are parallel with one another and have a longitudinal arrangement. Its internal surface is smooth and covered by a layer of mesothelium. It is sparingly supplied with bloodvessels, and a few nerves have been traced into it.

The Arachnoid.

The **arachnoid** is a delicate membrane enveloping the brain and medulla spinalis and lying between the pia mater internally and the dura mater externally; it is separated from the pia mater by the subarachnoid cavity, which is filled with cerebrospinal fluid.

The **Cranial Part** (*arachnoidea encephali*) of the arachnoid invests the brain loosely, and does not dip into the sulci between the gyri, nor into the fissures, with the exception of the longitudinal. On the upper surface of the brain the arachnoid is thin and transparent; at the base it is thicker, and slightly opaque toward the central part, where it extends across between the two temporal lobes in front of the pons, so as to leave a considerable interval between it and the brain.

The **Spinal Part** (*arachnoidea spinalis*) of the arachnoid is a thin, delicate, tubular membrane loosely investing the medulla spinalis. *Above*, it is continuous with the cranial arachnoid; *below*, it widens out and invests the cauda equina and the nerves proceeding from it. It is separated from the dura mater by the **subdural space**, but here and there this space is traversed by isolated connective-tissue trabeculæ, which are most numerous on the posterior surface of the medulla spinalis.

The arachnoid surrounds the cranial and spinal nerves, and encloses them in loose sheaths as far as their points of exit from the skull and vertebral canal.

Structure.—The arachnoid consists of bundles of white fibrous and elastic tissue intimately blended together. Its outer surface is covered with a layer of low cuboidal mesothelium. The inner surface and the trabeculæ are likewise covered by a somewhat low type of cuboidal meso-thelium which in places are flattened to a pavement type. Vessels of considerable size, but few in number, and, according to Bochdalek, a rich plexus of nerves derived from the motor root of the trigeminal, the facial, and the accessory nerves, are found in the arachnoid.

The **Subarachnoid Cavity** (*cavum subarachnoideale; subarachnoid space*) is the interval between the arachnoid and pia mater. It is occupied by a spongy tissue consisting of trabeculæ of delicate connective tissue, and intercommunicating channels in which the subarachnoid fluid is contained. This cavity is small on the surface of the hemispheres of the brain; on the summit of each gyrus the pia mater and the arachnoid are in close contact; but in the sulci between the gyri, triangular spaces are left, in which the subarachnoid trabecular tissue is found, for the pia mater dips into the sulci, whereas the arachnoid bridges across them from gyrus to gyrus. At certain parts of the base of the brain, the arachnoid is separated from the pia mater by wide intervals, which communicate freely with each other and are named **subarachnoid cisternæ**; in these the subarachnoid tissue is less abundant.

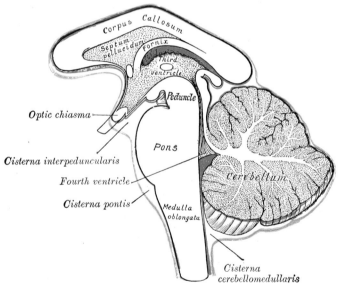

Fig. 767.—Diagram showing the positions of the three principal subarachnoid cisternæ.

Subarachnoid Cisternæ (*cisternæ subarachnoidales*) (Fig. 768).—The **cisterna cerebellomedullaris** (*cisterna magna*) is triangular on sagittal section, and results from the arachnoid bridging over the interval between the medulla oblongata and the under surfaces of the hemispheres of the cerebellum; it is continuous with the subarachnoid cavity of the medulla spinalis at the level of the foramen magnum. The **cisterna pontis** is a considerable space on the ventral aspect of the pons. It contains the basilar artery, and is continuous behind with the subarachnoid cavity of the medulla spinalis, and with the cisterna cerebellomedullaris; and n front of the pons with the cisterna interpeduncularis. The **cisterna interpeduncularis** (*cisterna basalis*) is a wide cavity where the arachnoid extends across between the two temporal lobes. It encloses the cerebral peduncles and the structures contained in the interpeduncular fossa, and contains the arterial circle of Willis. In front, the cisterna interpeduncularis extends forward across the optic chiasma, forming the **cisterna chiasmatis,** and on to the upper surface of the corpus callosum, for the arachnoid stretches across from one cerebral hemisphere to the other immediately beneath the free border of the falx cerebri, and thus leaves a space in which the anterior cerebral arteries are contained. The **cisterna fossæ cerebri lateralis** is formed in front of either temporal lobe by the arachnoid bridging across the lateral fissure. This cavity contains the middle cerebral artery. The **cisterna venæ magnæ cerebri** occupies the interval between the splenium of the corpus callosum and the superior surface of the cerebellum; it extends between the layers of the tela chorioidea of the third ventricle and contains the great cerebral vein.

The subarachnoid cavity communicates with the general ventricular cavity of the brain by three openings; one, the **foramen of Majendie,** is in the middle line at the inferior part of the roof of the fourth ventricle; the other two are at the extremities of the lateral recesses of that ventricle, behind the upper roots of the glossopharyngeal nerves and are known as the **foramina of Luschka.** It is still somewhat uncertain whether these foramina are actual openings or merely modified areas of the inferior velum which permit the passage of the cerebrospinal fluid from the ventricle into the subarachnoid spaces as through a permeable membrane.

The spinal part of the subarachnoid cavity is a very wide interval, and is the largest at the lower part of the vertebral canal, where the arachnoid encloses the nerves which form the cauda equina. Above, it is continuous with the cranial subarachnoid cavity; below, it ends at the level of the lower border of the second sacral vertebra. It is partially divided by a longitudinal septum, the **subarachnoid septum,** which connects the arachnoid with the pia mater opposite the posterior median sulcus of the medulla spinalis, and forms a partition, incomplete and cribriform above, but more perfect in the thoracic region. The spinal subarachnoid cavity is further subdivided by the **ligamentum denticulatum,** (Fig. 766) which will be described with the pia mater.

The cerebrospinal fluid is a clear limpid fluid, having a saltish taste, and a slightly alkaline reaction. According to Lassaigne, it consists of 98.5 parts of water, the remaining 1.5 per cent, being solid matters, animal and saline. It varies in quantity, being most abundant in old persons. and is quickly secreted.

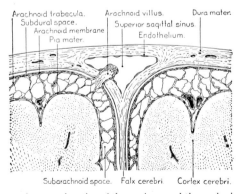

FIG. 768.— Schematic diagram of a coronal section of the meninges and the cerebral cortex, showing the relation of an arachnoid villus to the dural venous sinus. (Weed, Am. J. Anat.; courtesy of Wistar Institute.)

The **Arachnoid Villi** (*granulationes arachnoideales; glandulæ Pacchioni; Pacchionian bodies*) (Fig. 767) are small, fleshy-looking elevations, usually collected into clusters of variable size, which are present upon the outer surface of the dura mater, in the vicinity of the superior sagittal sinus, and in some other situations. Upon laying open the sagittal sinus and the venous lacunæ on either side of it villi will be found protruding into its interior. They are not seen in infancy, and very rarely until the third year. They are usually found after the seventh year; and from this period they increase in number and size as age advances. They are not glandular in structure, but are enlarged normal villi of the arachnoid. As they grow they push the thinned dura mater before them, and cause absorption of the bone from pressure, and so produce the pits or depressions on the inner wall of the calvarium.

Structure.—An arachnoidal villus represents an invasion of the dura by the arachnoid membrane, the latter penetrates the dura in such a manner that the arachnoid mesothelial cells come to lie directly beneath the vascular endothelium of the great dural sinuses. It consists of the following parts: (1) In the interior is a core of subarachnoid tissue, continuous with the meshwork of the general subarachnoid tissue through a narrow pedicle, by which the villus is attached to the arachnoid. (2) Around this tissue is a layer of arachnoid membrane, limiting and enclosing the subarachnoid tissue. (3) Outside this is the thinned wall of the lacuna, which is separated from the arachnoid by a potential space which corresponds to and is continuous with the subdural cavity. (4) And finally, if the villus projects into the sagittal sinus, it will be covered by the greatly thinned wall of the sinus which may consist merely of endothelium. It will be seen, therefore, that fluid injected into the subarachnoid cavity will find its way into these villi, and it has been found experimentally that it passes from the villi into the venous sinuses into which they project.

The Pia Mater.

The **pia mater** is a vascular membrane, consisting of a minute plexus of blood-vessels, held together by an extremely fine areolar tissue and covered by a reflexion

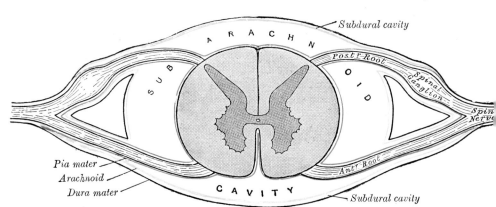

Fig. 769.—Diagrammatic transverse section of the medulla spinalis and its membranes.

of the mesothelial cells from the arachnoid trabeculæ. It is an incomplete membrane, absent probably at the foramen of Majendie and the two foramina of Luschka and perforated in a peculiar manner by all the bloodvessels as they enter or leave the nervous system. In the perivascular spaces, the pia apparently enters as a mesothelial lining of the outer surface of the space; a variable distance from the exterior these cells become unrecognizable and are apparently lacking, replaced by neuroglia elements. The inner walls of these perivascular spaces seem likewise covered for a certain distance by the mesothelial cells, reflected with the vessels from the arachnoid covering of these vascular channels as they traverse the subarachnoid spaces.

The **Cranial Pia Mater** (*pia mater encephali; pia of the brain*) invests the entire surface of the brain, dips between the cerebral gyri and cerebellar laminæ, and is invaginated to form the tela chorioidea of the third ventricle, and the choroid plexuses of the lateral and third ventricles (pages 852 and 853); as it passes over the roof of the fourth ventricle, it forms the tela chorioidea and the choroid plexuses of this ventricle. On the cerebellum the membrane is more delicate; the vessels from its deep surface are shorter, and its relations to the cortex are not so intimate.

The **Spinal Pia Mater** (*pia mater spinalis; pia of the cord*) (Figs. 766, 769) is thicker, firmer, and less vascular than the cranial pia mater: this is due to the fact that it consists of two layers, the outer or additional one being composed of bundles of connective-tissue fibers, arranged for the most part longitudinally. Between the layers are cleft-like spaces which communicate with the subarachnoid cavity, and a number of bloodvessels which are enclosed in perivascular lymphatic sheaths. The spinal pia mater covers the entire surface of the medulla spinalis, and is very intimately adherent to it; in front it sends a process backward into the anterior fissure. A longitudinal fibrous band, called the **linea splendens**, extends along the middle line of the anterior surface; and a somewhat similar band, the **ligamentum denticulatum**, is situated on either side. Below the conus medullaris, the pia mater is continued as a long, slender filament (**filum terminale**), which descends through the center of the mass of nerves forming the cauda equina. It blends with the dura mater at the level of the lower border of the second sacral vertebra, and extends downward as far as the base of the coccyx, where it fuses with the periosteum. It assists in maintaining the medulla spinalis in its position during the movements of the trunk, and is, from this circumstance, called the **central ligament** of the medulla spinalis.

The pia mater forms sheaths for the cranial and spinal nerves; these sheaths are closely connected with the nerves, and blend with their common membranous investments.

The **ligamentum denticulatum** (*dentate ligament*) (Fig. 766) is a narrow fibrous band situated on either side of the medulla spinalis throughout its entire length, and separating the anterior from the posterior nerve roots. Its medial border is continuous with the pia mater at the side of the medulla spinalis. Its lateral border presents a series of triangular tooth-like processes, the points of which are fixed at intervals to the dura mater. These processes are twenty-one in number, on either side, the first being attached to the dura mater, opposite the margin of the foramen magnum, between the vertebral artery and the hypoglossal nerve; and the last near the lower end of the medulla spinalis.

THE CEREBROSPINAL FLUID.[1]

The cerebrospinal fluid, for the most part elaborated by the choroid plexuses, is poured into the cerebral ventricles which are lined by smooth ependyma. That portion of the fluid formed in the lateral ventricles escapes by the foramen of Monro into the third ventricle and thence by the aqueduct into the fourth ventricle. Likewise an ascending current of fluid apparently occurs in the central canal of the spinal cord; this, representing a possible product of the ependyma, may be added to the intraventricular supply. From the fourth ventricle the fluid is poured into the subarachnoid spaces through the medial foramen of Majendie and the two lateral foramina of Luschka. There is no evidence that functional communications between the cerebral ventricles and the subarachnoid spaces exist in any region except from the fourth ventricle.

In addition to the elaboration of the cerebrospinal fluid by the choroid plexuses, there seems fairly well established a second source of the fluid from the nervous system itself. The bloodvessels that enter and leave the brain are surrounded by perivascular channels. It seems most likely that the outer wall of these channels is

[1] Weed, L. H., Anat. Record, 1917, vol. **12**; Am. Jour. Anat., 1923, vol. **31**.

lined by a continuation inward of the pial mesothelium while the inner wall is probably derived from the mesothelial covering of the vessels, which are thus protected throughout the subarachnoid spaces. These mesothelial cells continue inward only a short distance, neuroglia cells probably replacing on the outer surface the mesothelial elements. Through these perivascular channels there is probably a small amount of fluid flowing from nerve cell to subarachnoid space. The chemical differences between the subarachnoid fluid (product of choroid plexuses and perivascular system) and the ventricular fluid (product of choroid plexuses alone) indicate that some of the products of nerve metabolism are poured into the subarachnoid space.

The absorption of the cerebrospinal fluid is a dual process, being chiefly a rapid drainage through the arachnoid villi into the great dural sinuses, and, in small part, a slow escape into the true lymphatic vessels, by way of an abundant but indirect perineural course.

In general the arachnoid channels are equipped as fluid retainers with unquestionable powers of diffusion or absorption in regard to certain elements in the normal cerebrospinal fluid, deriving in this way a cellular nutrition.

The subdural space (between arachnoid and dura) is usually considered to be a part of the cerebrospinal channels. It is a very small space, the two limiting surfaces being separated by merely a capillary layer of fluid. Whether this fluid is exactly similar to the cerebrospinal fluid is very difficult to ascertain. Likewise our knowledge of the connections between the subdural and subarachnoid spaces is hardly definite. In some ways the subdural space may be likened to a serous cavity. The inner surface of the dura is covered by flattened polygonal mesothelial cells but the outer surface of the arachnoid is covered by somewhat cuboidal mesothelium. The fluid of the subdural space has probably a local origin from the cells lining it.

BIBLIOGRAPHY

CENTRAL NERVOUS SYSTEM

The weights of the brain and of its parts, of the spinal cord and of the eyeballs in the adult cat. LATIMER, H. B.: 1938. J. Comp. Neur. ,Vol. 68, pp. 395–404.

The brain of the giant panda (Ailuropoda melanoleuca). METTLER, F. A., and L. J. Goss: 1946. J. Comp. Neur., Vol. 84, pp. 1–9.

Certain phylogenetic anatomical relations of localizing significance for the mammalian central nervous system. WOODBURNE, R. T.: 1939. J. Comp. Neur., Vol. 71, pp. 215–257.

SPINAL CORD

Studies on the motor cells of the spinal cord. I. Distribution in the normal human cord. II. Distribution in the normal human fetal cord. ELLIOTT, H. C.: 1942–3. Am. J. Anat., Vol. 70, pp. 95–117, and Vol. 72, pp. 29–38.

The human pyramidal tract. XV. A study of axons in selected cases with congenital cerebral malformations. LASSEK, A. M.: 1946. J. Comp. Neur., Vol. 85, pp. 477–483.

The nuclear masses in the cervical spinal cord of Macaca mulatta. REED, A. F.: 1940. J. Comp. Neur., Vol. 72, pp. 187–206.

Intramedullary sensory type ganglion cells in the spinal cord of human embryos. YOUNGSTROM, K. A.: 1944. J. Comp. Neur., Vol. 81, pp. 47–53.

MEDULLA AND MESENCEPHALON

The nuclear pattern of the non-tectal portions of the midbrain and isthmus in the dog and cat. BROWN, J. O.: 1943. J. Comp. Neur., Vol. 78, pp. 365–405.

The pretectal region of the rabbit's brain. KUHLENBECK, H., and R. N. MILLER: 1942. J. Comp. Neur., Vol. 76, pp. 323–365.

The olivary peduncle and other fiber projections of the superior olivary complex. RASMUSSEN, G. L.: 1946. J. Comp. Neur., Vol. 84, pp. 141–219.

The mammalian midbrain and isthmus regions. Part II. The fiber connections. A. The relations of the tegmentum of the midbrain with the basal ganglia in Macaca mulatta. WOODBURNE, R. T., E. C. CROSBY, and R. E. McCOTTER: 1946. J. Comp. Neur., Vol. 85, pp. 67–92.

Diencephalon

The efferent fibers of the thalamus of Macacus rhesus. II. The anterior nuclei, medial nuclei, pulvinar, and additional studies on the ventral nuclei. Crouch, R. L.: 1940. J. Comp. Neur., Vol. 72, pp. 177–186.

The capillary beds of the paraventricular and supra-optic nuclei of the hypothalamus. Finley, K. H.: 1939. J. Comp. Neur., Vol. 71, pp. 1–19.

The stria terminalis, longitudinal association bundle and precommissural fornix fibers in the cat. Fox, C. A.: 1943. J. Comp. Neur., Vol. 79, pp. 277–295.

The lateral geniculate complex of the platyrrhine monkey, Cebus fatuellus. Harman, P. J., and O. C. Solnitzky: 1944. J. Comp. Neur., Vol. 81, pp. 227–247.

The thalamus of the chimpanzee. IV. Thalamic projections to the cerebral cortex. Walker, A. E.: 1938. J. Anat., Vol. 73, pp. 37–93.

Telencephalon

Certain basal telencephalic centers in the cat. Fox, C. A.: 1940. J. Comp. Neur., Vol. 72, pp. 1–62.

On the significance of fissuration of the isocortex. Harman, P. J.: 1947. J. Comp. Neur., Vol. 87, pp. 161–168.

The nuclear pattern and fiber connections of certain basal telencephalic centers in the Macaque. Lauer, E. W.: 1945. J. Comp. Neur., Vol. 82, pp. 215–254.

The course of efferent fibers from the human premotor cortex. Minckler, J., R. M. Klemme, and D. B. Minckler: 1944. J. Comp. Neur., Vol. 81, pp. 259–277.

Analysis of potential sources in the optic lobe of duck and goose. O'Leary, J. L., and G. H. Bishop: 1943. J. Cell. and Comp. Physiol., Vol. 22, pp. 73–87.

Reciprocal connections of the striatum and pallidum in the brain of Pithecus (Macacus) rhesus. Papez, J. W.: 1938. J. Comp. Neur., Vol. 69, pp. 329–349.

Cytoarchitecture of individual parietal areas in the monkey (Macaca mulatta) and the distribution of the efferent fibers. Peele, T. L.: 1942. J. Comp. Neur., Vol. 77, pp. 693–737.

The extent of recurrent geniculo-calcarine fibers (loop of Archambault and Meyer) as demonstrated by gross brain dissection. Rasmussen, A. T.: 1943. Anat. Rec., Vol. 85, pp. 277–284.

Experiments on the corpus striatum and rhinencephalon. Rioch, D. McK., and C. Brenner: 1938. J. Comp. Neur., Vol. 68, pp. 491–507.

A comparative study of the central and peripheral sectors of the visual cortex in primates, with observations on the lateral geniculate body. Solnitzky, O., and P. J. Harman: 1946. J. Comp. Neur., Vol. 85, pp. 313–419.

Thalamic connections of the frontal cortex of the cat. Waller, W. H.: 1940. J. Comp. Neur., Vol. 73, pp. 117–138.

Neurones

The chromatin content of nerve cells in man and in the mouse with special regard to the rôle of the nucleolus: Observations in normal and malnourished specimens. Andrew, W., and N. V. Andrew: 1942. J. Comp. Neur., Vol. 76, pp. 423–433.

Intracentral and peripheral factors in the differentiation of motor neurons in transplanted lumbosacral spinal cords of chick embryos. Bueker, E. D.: 1943. J. Exp. Zool., Vol. 93, pp. 99–129.

Decrease in human neurones with age. Gardner, E.: 1940. Anat. Rec., Vol. 77, pp. 529–536.

Cytological studies by the Altmann-Gersh freezing-drying method. III. The preexistence of neurofibrillæ and their disposition in the nerve fiber. IV. The structure of the myelin sheath of nerve fibers. Hoerr, N. L.: 1936. Anat. Rec., Vol. 66, pp. 81–90 and 91–95.

Reactive, regressive, and regenerative processes of neurons, cultivated *in vitro* and injured with micromanipulator. Levi, G., and H. Meyer: 1945. J. Exp. Zool., Vol. 99, pp. 141–181.

Transynaptic effect of neonatal axon section on bouton appearance about somatic motor cells. Schadewald, M. A.: 1942. J. Comp. Neur., Vol. 77, pp. 739–746.

Chromatolysis and recovery of efferent neurons. Turner, R. S.: 1943. J. Comp. Neur., Vol. 79, pp. 73–78.

Neuroglia and Meninges

Morphological similarity of neuroglia fibers to fibers of other connective tissues. Andrew, W., and C. T. Ashworth: 1944. Am. J. Anat., Vol. 75, pp. 329–367.

Studies on the cytogenesis of microglia and their relation to cells of the reticulo-endothelial system. Dougherty, T. F.: 1944. Am. J. Anat., Vol. 74, pp. 61–95.

The perivascular spaces of the mammalian brain. Patek, P. R.: 1944. Anat. Rec., Vol. 88, pp. 1–24.

A note on the occurrence of transverse fibrous bands in the spinal dural sac of man. Seybold W. D.: 1940. Anat. Rec., Vol. 76, pp. 55–63.

Embryology

The behavior of the neural crest in the forebrain region of Amblystoma. BAKER, R. C., and G. O. GRAVES: 1939. J. Comp. Neur., Vol. 71, pp. 389–415.

The origin of the neural crest. CONEL, J. L.: 1942. J. Comp. Neur., Vol. 76, pp. 191–215.

Neuroembryology. DETWILER, S. R.: 1936. Macmillan, New York, X + 218 pp.

Neural fold derivatives in the Amphibia: Pigment cells, spinal ganglia and Rohon-Beard cells. DuSHANE, G. P.: 1938. J. Exp. Zool., Vol. 78, pp. 485, 503.

An iconometrographic representation of the growth of the central nervous system in man. Part I. The spinal cord. Part II. The brain. GRENELL, R. G., and R. E. SCAMMON: 1943. J. Comp. Neur., Vol. 79, pp. 329–354.

The development of the nucleus dorsalis (Clarke's column). HOGG, I. D.: 1944. J. Comp. Neur., Vol. 81, pp. 69–95.

Primitive neurons in the embryonic human central nervous system. HUMPHREY, T.: 1944. J. Comp. Neur., Vol. 81, pp. 1–45.

The development of the forebrain of the American water snake (Natrix sipedon). WARNER, F. J.: 1946. J. Comp. Neur., Vol. 84, pp. 385–418.

Development of the human mesencephalic trigeminal root and related neurons. WINDLE, W. F., and J. E. FITZGERALD: 1942. J. Comp. Neur., Vol. 77, pp. 597–608.

THE PERIPHERAL NERVOUS SYSTEM.

THE CRANIAL NERVES (NERVI CEREBRALES; CEREBRAL NERVES).

There are twelve pairs of cranial nerves; they are attached to the brain and are transmitted through foramina in the base of the cranium. The different pairs are named from before backward as follows:

1st. Olfactory.	5th. Trigeminal.	9th. Glossopharyngeal.
2d. Optic.	6th. Abducent.	10th. Vagus.
3d. Oculomotor.	7th. Facial.	11th. Accessory.
4th. Trochlear.	8th. Acoustic.	12th. Hypoglossal.

The **nervus terminalis,** discovered long after the other cranial nerves, originates from the cerebral hemisphere in the region of the medial olfactory stria, and passes along with the olfactory nerves to reach the nasal septum. The cells of origin, the exact termination and the function of the fibers in this nerve are not well established.[1]

THE OLFACTORY NERVES (NN. OLFACTORII; FIRST NERVE) (Fig. 770).

The **olfactory nerves** or **nerves of smell** are distributed to the mucous membrane of the olfactory region of the nasal cavity: this region comprises the superior nasal concha, and the corresponding part of the nasal septum. The nerves originate from the central or deep processes of the olfactory cells of the nasal mucous membrane. They form a plexiform net-work in the mucous membrane, and are then collected into about twenty branches, which pierce the cribriform plate of the ethmoid bone in two groups, a **lateral** and a **medial group,** and end in the glomeruli

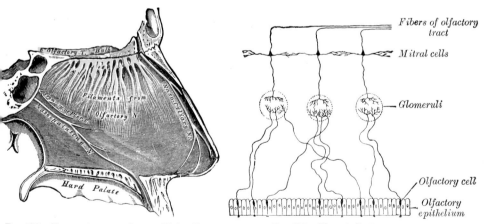

Fig. 770.—Nerves of septum of nose. Right side.

Fig. 771.—Plan of olfactory neurons.

of the olfactory bulb (Fig. 771). Each branch receives tubular sheaths from the dura mater, arachnoid, and pia mater, the first being lost in the periosteum of the nose, the last two in the neurilemma of the nerve.

[1] In a recent paper, Pearson, A. A. (The Development of the Nervus Terminalis in Man, Jour. Comp. Neurol., 1941, 75, 39–66) states, "The consensus is that the nervus terminalis is functional in mammals and that there are sensory and autonomic components."

The olfactory nerves are non-medullated, and consist of axis-cylinders surrounded by nucleated sheaths, in which, however, there are fewer nuclei than are found in the sheaths of ordinary non-medullated nerve fibers.

The olfactory center in the cortex is generally associated with the rhinencephalon (page 854).

The olfactory nerves are developed from the cells of the ectoderm which lines the olfactory pits; these cells undergo proliferation and give rise to what are termed the **olfactory cells** of the nose. The axons of the olfactory cells grow into the overlying olfactory bulb and form the olfactory nerves.

THE OPTIC NERVE (N. OPTICUS; SECOND NERVE) (Fig. 772).

The **optic nerve**, or **nerve of sight**, consists mainly of fibers derived from the ganglionic cells of the retina. These axons terminate in arborizations around the

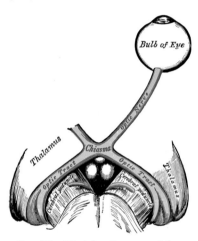

cells in the lateral geniculate body, pretectal region, and superior colliculus which constitute the lower or primary visual centers. From the cells of the lateral geniculate body fibers pass to the cortical visual center, situated in the cuneus and in the neighborhood of the calcarine fissure. The work of Arey has shown that the optic nerve contains efferent fibers which pass to the retina.

The optic nerve is peculiar in that its fibers and ganglion cells are probably third in the series of neurons from the receptors to the brain and in that its fibers do not have neurilemmal sheaths. In the light of its embryological development and its structure, the optic nerve corresponds to a tract of fibers within the brain rather than to the other cranial nerves. Its fibers pass backward and medialward through the orbit and optic foramen to the optic chiasma where they partially decussate. The mixed fibers from the two nerves are continued in the optic tracts, the **primary visual centers of the brain.**

FIG. 772.—The left optic nerve and the optic tracts.

The orbital portion of the optic nerve is from 20 mm. to 30 mm. in length and has a slightly sinuous course to allow for movements of the eyeball. It is invested by an outer sheath of dura mater and an inner sheath from the arachnoid and pia mater which are attached to the sclera around the area where the nerve fibers pierce the choroid and sclera of the bulb. A little behind the bulb of the eye the central artery of the retina with its accompanying vein perforates the optic nerve, and runs within it to the retina. As the nerve enters the optic foramen its dural sheath becomes continuous with that lining the orbit and the optic foramen. In the optic foramen the ophthalmic artery lies below and to its outer side. The intracranial portion of the optic nerve is about 10 mm. in length.

The **Optic Chiasma** (*chiasma opticum*), somewhat quadrilateral in form, rests upon the tuberculum sellæ and on the anterior part of the diaphragma sellæ. It is in relation, *above*, with the lamina terminalis; *behind*, with the tuber cinereum; on *either side*, with the anterior perforated substance. Within the chiasma, the optic nerves undergo a partial decussation. The fibers forming the medial part of each tract and posterior part of the chiasma have no connection with the optic nerves. They simply cross in the chiasma, and form the **commissure of Gudden.** The remaining and principal part of the chiasma consists of two sets of fibers, crossed and uncrossed. The **crossed fibers** which are the more numerous, occupy the central part of the chiasma, and pass from the optic nerve of one side to the optic tract of the other, decussating in the chiasma with similar fibers of the opposite optic nerve. The **uncrossed fibers** occupy the lateral part of the chiasma, and pass from the nerve of one side into the tract of the same side. Congenital absence is rare.

The fibers of the optic nerve which are to cross tend to occupy the medial side of the nerve and those that do not cross have a more lateral position. In the optic tract, the fibers are much more intermingled.[1]

The Optic Tract (Fig. 718), passes backward and outward from the optic chiasma over the tuber cinereum and anterior perforated substance to the cerebral peduncle and winds obliquely across its under surface. Its fibers terminate in the lateral geniculate body, the pretectal region and the superior colliculus. It is adherent to the tuber cinereum and the cerebral peduncle as it passes over them. In the region of the lateral geniculate body it splits into two bands, the lateral and medial roots. The medial and smaller one is a part of the commissure of Gudden, whose fibers have been described as terminating in the medial geniculate body. Indications from recent work point to other terminations.

From its mode of development, and from its structure, the optic nerve must be regarded as a prolongation of the brain substance, rather than as an ordinary cerebrospinal nerve. As it passes from the brain it receives sheaths from the three cerebral membranes, a perineural sheath from the pia mater, an intermediate sheath from the arachnoid, and an outer sheath from the dura mater, which is also connected with the periosteum as it passes through the optic foramen. These sheaths are separated from each other by cavities which communicate with the subdural and subarachnoid cavities respectively. The innermost or perineural sheath sends a process around the arteria centralis retinæ into the interior of the nerve, and enters intimately into its structure. No neurilemmal sheaths are present about the nerve fibers but neurogliar elements are to be found.

THE OCULOMOTOR NERVE (N. OCULOMOTORIUS; THIRD NERVE)
(Figs. 773, 774, 775).

The **oculomotor nerve** supplies somatic motor fibers to the levator palpebræ superioris and all the ocular muscles, except the Obliquus superior and Rectus lateralis; it also supplies through its connections with the ciliary ganglion, parasympathetic motor fibers to the Sphincter pupillæ and the Ciliaris muscles.

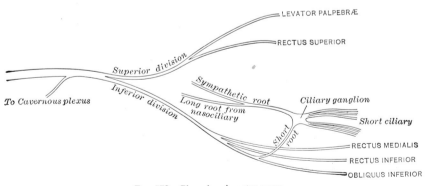

Fig. 778.—Plan of oculomotor nerve.

The fibers of the oculomotor nerve arise from a nucleus which lies in the gray substance of the floor of the cerebral aqueduct and extends in front of the aqueduct for a short distance into the floor of the third ventricle. From this nucleus the fibers pass forward through the tegmentum, the red nucleus, and the medial part

---

[1] The anatomical relations of the optic nerve and its components have been reviewed and described by L. L. Mayer (The Optic Pathway, Archives of Ophthalmology, 1940, **23**, 382–394).

of the substantia nigra, forming a series of curves with a lateral convexity, and emerge from the oculomotor sulcus on the medial side of the cerebral peduncle.

The nucleus of the oculomotor nerve, considered from a physiological standpoint, can be subdivided into several smaller groups of cells, each group controlling a particular muscle. (See page 890.)

On emerging from the brain, the nerve is invested with a sheath of pia mater, and enclosed in a prolongation from the arachnoid. It passes between the superior cerebellar and posterior cerebral arteries, and then pierces the dura mater in front of and lateral to the posterior clinoid process, passing between the free and attached borders of the tentorium cerebelli. It runs along the lateral wall of the cavernous sinus, above the other orbital nerves, receiving in its course one or two filaments from the cavernous plexus of the sympathetic, and a communicating branch from the ophthalmic division of the trigeminal. It then divides into two branches, which enter the orbit through the superior orbital fissure, between the two heads of the Rectus lateralis. Here the nerve is placed below the trochlear nerve and the frontal and lacrimal branches of the ophthalmic nerve, while the nasociliary nerve is placed between its two rami.

The **superior ramus**, the smaller, passes medialward over the optic nerve, and supplies the Rectus superior and Levator palpebræ superioris. The **inferior ramus**, the larger, divides into three branches. One passes beneath the optic nerve to the Rectus medialis; another, to the Rectus inferior; the third and longest runs forward between the Recti inferior and lateralis to the Obliquus inferior. From the last a short thick branch is given off to the lower part of the ciliary ganglion, and forms its **short root**. All these branches enter the muscles on their ocular surfaces, with the exception of the nerve to the Obliquus inferior, which enters the muscle at its posterior border.

THE TROCHLEAR NERVE (N. TROCHLEARIS; FOURTH NERVE) (Fig. 774).

The **trochlear nerve**, the smallest of the cranial nerves, supplies the Obliquus superior oculi.

It *arises* from a nucleus (the trochlear nucleus) situated in the floor of the cerebral aqueduct, opposite the upper part of the inferior colliculus. From its origin it runs downward through the tegmentum, and then turns backward into the upper part of the anterior medullary velum. Here it decussates with its fellow of the opposite side and emerges from the surface of the velum at the side of the frenulum veli, immediately behind the inferior colliculus.

The nerve is directed across the superior cerebellar peduncle, and then winds forward around the cerebral peduncle, immediately above the pons, pierces the dura mater in the free border of the tentorium cerebelli, just behind, and lateral to, the posterior clinoid process, and passes forward in the lateral wall of the cavernous sinus, between the oculomotor nerve and the ophthalmic division of the trigeminal. It crosses the oculomotor nerve, and enters the orbit through the superior orbital fissure. It now becomes superior to all the nerves, and lies medial to the frontal nerve. In the orbit it passes medialward, above the origin of the Levator palpebræ superioris, and finally enters the orbital surface of the Obliquus superior.

In the lateral wall of the cavernous sinus the trochlear nerve forms communications with the ophthalmic divisions of the trigeminal and with the cavernous plexus of the sympathetic. In the superior orbital fissure it occasionally gives off a branch to the lacrimal nerve. It gives off a recurrent branch which passes backward between the layers of the tentorium cerebelli and divides into two or three filaments which may be traced as far as the wall of the transverse sinus.

THE TRIGEMINAL NERVE (N. TRIGEMINUS; FIFTH OR TRIFACIAL NERVE).

The **trigeminal nerve** is the largest cranial nerve and is the great sensory nerve of the superficial and deep portions of the head and face, and the motor nerve of the muscles of mastication. It emerges from the side of the pons, near its upper border, by a small motor and a large sensory root—the former being situated in front of and medial to the latter. In the posterior cranial fossa, the roots course forward and through the dura under the region where the tentorium cerebelli joins the petrous portion of the temporal bone.

Motor Root.—The fibers of the motor root *arise* from two nuclei, a superior and an inferior. The **superior or mesencephalic nucleus** consists of a strand of cells occupying the whole length of the lateral portion of the gray substance of the cerebral aqueduct. The **inferior or motor nucleus** is situated in the upper part of the pons, close to its dorsal surface, and along the line of the lateral margin of the rhomboid fossa. The fibers from the superior nucleus constitute the **mesencephalic root**: they descend through the mid-brain, and, entering the pons, join with the fibers from the lower nucleus, and the motor root, thus formed, passes forward through the pons to its point of emergence.

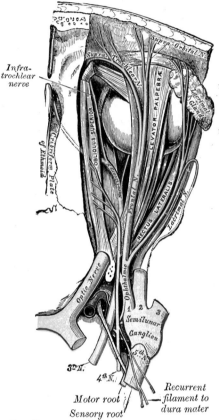

The work of Corbin and Harrison (Function of Mesencephalic Root of Fifth Cranial Nerve, Jour. Neurophysiol., 1940, **3**, 423–435) demonstrates conclusively that the mesencephalic root of the fifth cranial nerve of the cat mediates sensory impulses when the masticator muscles are stretched and when pressure is applied to the teeth and hard palate. This root in man probably is sensory and conducts proprioceptive impulses.

Sensory Root.—The fibers of the sensory root *arise* from the cells of the semilunar ganglion which lies in a cavity of the dura mater near the apex of the petrous part of the temporal bone. They pass backward below the superior petrosal sinus and tentorium cerebelli, and, entering the pons, divide into upper and lower roots.

FIG. 774.—Nerves of the orbit. Seen from above.

The upper root ends partly in a nucleus (the main sensory nucleus) which is situated in the pons lateral to the lower motor nucleus; the lower root descends through the pons and medulla oblongata so far as the upper part of the substantia gelatinosa of Rolando. This lower root is sometimes named the **spinal root** of the nerve and its fibers terminate in the nucleus of the spinal tract of the trigeminal nerve. Medullation of the fibers of the sensory root begins about the fifth month of fetal life, but the majority of its fibers are not medullated until the third month after birth.

The **Semilunar Ganglion** (*ganglion semilunare* [*Gasseri*]; *Gasserian ganglion*) occupies a cavity (*cavum Meckelii*) in the dura mater covering the trigeminal impression near the apex of the petrous part of the temporal bone. It is somewhat crescentic in shape, with its convexity directed forward: medially, it is in relation with the internal carotid artery and the posterior part of the cavernous sinus. The motor root runs in front of and medial to the sensory root, and passes beneath the ganglion; it leaves the skull through the foramen ovale, and, immediately below this foramen, joins the mandibular nerve. The greater superficial petrosal nerve also lies underneath the ganglion.

The ganglion receives, on its medial side, filaments from the carotid plexus of the sympathetic. It gives off minute branches to the tentorium cerebelli, and to the dura mater in the middle fossa of the cranium. From its convex border, which is directed forward and lateralward, three large nerves proceed, viz., the **ophthalmic, maxillary,** and **mandibular.** The ophthalmic and maxillary consist of sensory fibers; the mandibular is joined outside the cranium by the motor root.

Associated with the three divisions of the trigeminal nerve are four small ganglia. The **ciliary ganglion** is connected with the ophthalmic nerve; the **sphenopalatine ganglion** with the maxillary nerve; and the **otic** and **submaxillary ganglia** with the mandibular nerve. All four receive sensory filaments from the trigeminal, and autonomic filaments from various sources; these filaments are called the **roots of the ganglia.**

The **Ophthalmic Nerve** (*n. ophthalmicus*) (Figs. 774, 775), or first division of the trigeminal, is a sensory nerve. It supplies branches to the cornea, ciliary body, and iris; to the lacrimal gland and conjunctiva; to the part of the mucous membrane of the nasal cavity and some of the sinuses; and to the skin of the eyelids, eyebrow, forehead, and nose. It is the smallest of the three divisions of the trigeminal, and *arises* from the upper part of the semilunar ganglion as a short, flattened band, about 2.5 cm. long, which passes forward along the lateral wall of the cavernous sinus, below the oculomotor and trochlear nerves; just before entering the orbit, through the superior orbital fissure, it divides into three branches, **lacrimal, frontal,** and **nasociliary.**

The ophthalmic nerve is joined by filaments from the cavernous plexus of the sympathetic, and communicates with the oculomotor, trochlear, and abducent nerves; it gives off a recurrent filament which passes between the layers of the tentorium.

The **Lacrimal Nerve** (*n. lacrimalis*) is the smallest of the three branches of the ophthalmic. It sometimes receives a filament from the trochlear nerve, but this is possibly derived from the branch which goes from the ophthalmic to the trochlear nerve. It passes forward in a separate tube of dura mater, and enters the orbit through the narrowest part of the superior orbital fissure. In the orbit it runs along the upper border of the Rectus lateralis, with the lacrimal artery, and communicates with the zygomatic branch of the maxillary nerve. It enters the lacrimal gland and gives off several filaments, which supply the gland and the conjunctiva. Finally it pierces the orbital septum, and ends in the skin of the upper eyelid, joining with filaments of the facial nerve. The lacrimal nerve is occasionally absent, and its place is then taken by the zygomaticotemporal branch of the maxillary. Sometimes the latter branch is absent, and a continuation of the lacrimal is substituted for it.

The lacrimal nerve contains postganglionic parasympathetic fibers destined to the lacrimal gland. Their cells of origin are in the sphenopalatine ganglion and they pass in the maxillary nerve, its zygomatic ramus and the zygomatico-temporal which anastomoses with the lacrimal nerve. (Kuntz, 1934, p. 282.)

The **Frontal Nerve** (*n. frontalis*) is the largest branch of the ophthalmic, and may be regarded, both from its size and direction, as the continuation of the nerve. It enters the orbit through the superior orbital fissure, and runs forward between

ne Levator palpebræ superioris and the periosteum. Midway between the apex
nd base of the orbit it divides into two branches, **supratrochlear** and **supraorbital**.
The **supratrochlear nerve** (*n. supratrochlearis*), the smaller of the two, passes
bove the pulley of the Obliquus superior, and gives off a descending filament, to
in the infratrochlear branch of the nasociliary nerve. It then escapes from the
rbit between the pulley of the Obliquus superior and the supraorbital foramen,
rves up on to the forehead close to the bone, ascends beneath the Corrugator
nd Frontalis, and dividing into branches which pierce these muscles, it supplies
ne skin of the lower part of the forehead close to the middle line and sends
aments to the conjunctiva and skin of the upper eyelid.

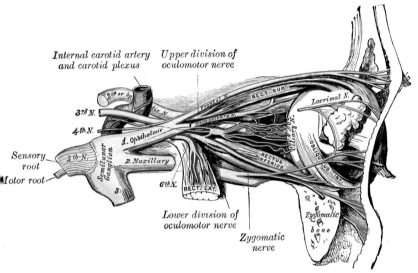

FIG. 775.—Nerves of the orbit, and the ciliary ganglion. Side view.

The **supraorbital nerve** (*n. supraorbitalis*) passes through the supraorbital foramen,
nd gives off, in this situation, palpebral filaments to the upper eyelid. It then
scends upon the forehead, and ends in two branches, a medial and a lateral,
which supply the integument of the scalp, reaching nearly as far back as the lamboidal suture; they are at first situated beneath the Frontalis, the medial branch
erforating the muscle, the lateral branch the galea aponeurotica. Both branches
upply small twigs to the pericranium.

The **Nasociliary Nerve** (*n. nasociliaris; nasal nerve*) is intermediate in size between
ne frontal and lacrimal, and is more deeply placed. It enters the orbit between
ne two heads of the Rectus lateralis, and between the superior and inferior rami
f the oculomotor nerve. It passes across the optic nerve and runs obliquely
eneath the Rectus superior and Obliquus superior, to the medial wall of the orbital
avity. Here it passes through the anterior ethmoidal foramen, and, entering
ne cavity of the cranium, traverses a shallow groove on the lateral margin of the
ront part of the cribriform plate of the ethmoid bone, and runs down, through
slit at the side of the crista galli, into the nasal cavity. It supplies **internal
asal branches** to the mucous membrane of the front part of the septum and lateral
vall of the nasal cavity. Finally, it emerges, as the **external nasal branch**, between
ne lower border of the nasal bone and the lateral nasal cartilage, and, passing
own beneath the Nasalis muscle, supplies the skin of the ala and apex of the nose.

The nasociliary nerve gives off the following branches, viz.: the **long root of the
iliary ganglion**, the **long ciliary**, the **infratrochlear**, and the **ethmoidal nerves**.

The **long root of the ciliary ganglion** (*radix longa ganglii ciliaris*) usually arise from the nasociliary between the two heads of the Rectus lateralis. It passe forward on the lateral side of the optic nerve, and enters the postero-superior ang of the ciliary ganglion; it is sometimes joined by a filament from the cavernou plexus of the sympathetic, or from the superior ramus of the trochlear nerve.

The **long ciliary nerves** (*nn. ciliares longi*), two or three in number, are given o from the nasociliary, as it crosses the optic nerve. They accompany the shor ciliary nerves from the ciliary ganglion, pierce the posterior part of the sclera and running forward between it and the choroid, are distributed to the iris an cornea. In addition to afferent fibers, the long ciliary nerves probably contai sympathetic fibers from the superior cervical ganglion to the Dilatator pupill muscle.

The **infratrochlear nerve** (*n. infratrochlearis*) is given off from the nasociliar just before it enters the anterior ethmoidal foramen. It runs forward along th upper border of the Rectus medialis, and is joined, near the pulley of the Obliquu superior, by a filament from the supratrochlear nerve. It then passes to th medial angle of the eye, and supplies the skin of the eyelids and side of the nose the conjunctiva, lacrimal sac, and caruncula lacrimalis.

The **ethmoidal branches** (*nn. ethmoidales*) supply the ethmoidal cells; the posterio branch leaves the orbital cavity through the posterior ethmoidal foramen and give some filaments to the sphenoidal sinus.

The Ciliary Ganglion (*ophthalmic or lenticular ganglion*) (Figs. 773, 775).—Th ciliary ganglion is a small, sympathetic ganglion, of a reddish-gray color, and abou the size of a pin's head; it is situated at the back part of the orbit, in some loos fat between the optic nerve and the Rectus lateralis muscle, lying generally on th lateral side of the ophthalmic artery.

Its **roots** are three in number, and enter its posterior border. One, the lon or sensory root, is derived from the nasociliary nerve, and joins its postero-superio angle. The second, the short or motor root, is a thick nerve (occasionally divide into two parts) derived from the branch of the oculomotor nerve to the Obliquu inferior, and connected with the postero-inferior angle of the ganglion. The moto root contains parasympathetic efferent fibers (preganglionic fibers) from th Edinger-Westphal nucleus of the third nerve in the mid-brain to the ciliary ganglion Here they form synapses with neurons whose fibers (postganglionic) pass to th Ciliary muscle and to the Sphincter muscle of the pupil. The third, the sympa thetic root, is a slender filament from the cavernous plexus of the sympathetic it is frequently blended with the long root. The cells of origin of fibers in th sympathetic root are situated in the superior cervical sympathetic ganglion According to Tiedemann, the ciliary ganglion receives a twig of communicatio from the sphenopalatine ganglion.

Its **branches** are the **short ciliary nerves**. These are delicate filaments, from si to ten in number, which *arise* from the forepart of the ganglion in two bundle connected with its superior and inferior angles; the lower bundle is the larger They run forward with the ciliary arteries in a wavy course, one set above and th other below the optic nerve, and are accompanied by the long ciliary nerves from the nasociliary. They pierce the sclera at the back part of the bulb of the eye, pas forward in delicate grooves on the inner surface of the sclera, and are distribute to the Ciliaris muscle, iris, and cornea. Tiedemann has described a small branc as penetrating the optic nerve with the arteria centralis retinæ.

The **Maxillary Nerve** (*n. maxillaris; superior maxillary nerve*) (Figs. 776, 777 782), or second division of the trigeminal, is a sensory nerve. It is intermediate both in position and size, between the ophthalmic and mandibular. It begins a the middle of the semilunar ganglion as a flattened plexiform band, and, passin horizontally forward, it leaves the skull through the foramen rotundum, where it becomes more cylindrical in form, and firmer in texture. It then crosses the pterygopalatine fossa, inclines lateralward on the back of the maxilla, and enters the orbit through the inferior orbital fissure; it traverses the infraorbital groove and canal in the floor of the orbit, and appears upon the face at the infraorbital foramen. At its termination, the nerve lies beneath the Quadratus labii superioris, and divides into a leash of branches which spread out upon the side of the nose, the lower eyelid, and the upper lip, joining with filaments of the facial nerve.

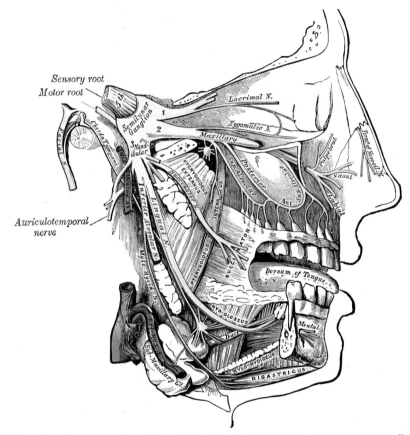

Fig. 776.—Distribution of the maxillary and mandibular nerves, and the submaxillary ganglion.

Branches.—Its branches may be divided into four groups, according as they are given off in the **cranium**, in the **pterygopalatine fossa**, in the **infraorbital canal**, or on the **face**.

In the Cranium	Middle meningeal.
In the Pterygopalatine Fossa .	{ Zygomatic. Sphenopalatine. Posterior superior alveolar.
In the Infraorbital Canal . .	{ Anterior superior alveolar. Middle superior alveolar.
On the Face	{ Inferior palpebral. External nasal. Superior labial.

The **Middle Meningeal Nerve** (*n. meningeus medius; meningeal or dural branch*) is given off from the maxillary nerve directly after its origin from the semilunar ganglion; it accompanies the middle meningeal artery and supplies the dura mater.

The **Zygomatic Nerve** (*n. zygomaticus; temporomalar nerve; orbital nerve*) *arises* in the pterygopalatine fossa, enters the orbit by the inferior orbital fissure, and divides at the back of that cavity into two branches, **zygomaticotemporal** and **zygomaticofacial**.

The **zygomaticotemporal branch** (*ramus zygomaticotemporalis; temporal branch*) runs along the lateral wall of the orbit in a groove in the zygomatic bone, receives a branch of communication from the lacrimal, and, passing through a foramen in the zygomatic bone, enters the temporal fossa. It ascends between the bone, and substance of the Temporalis muscle, pierces the temporal fascia about 2.5 cm. above the zygomatic arch, and is distributed to the skin of the side of the forehead, and communicates with the facial nerve and with the auriculotemporal branch of the mandibular nerve. As it pierces the temporal fascia, it gives off a slender twig, which runs between the two layers of the fascia to the lateral angle of the orbit.

The **zygomaticofacial branch** (*ramus zygomaticofacialis; malar branch*) passes along the infero-lateral angle of the orbit, emerges upon the face through a foramen in the zygomatic bone, and, perforating the Orbicularis oculi, supplies the skin on the prominence of the cheek. It joins with the facial nerve and with the inferior palpebral branches of the maxillary.

The **Sphenopalatine Branches** (*nn. sphenopalatini*), two in number, descend to the sphenopalatine ganglion.

The **Posterior Superior Alveolar Branches** (*rami alveolares superiores posteriores; posterior superior dental branches*) *arise* from the trunk of the nerve just before it enters the infraorbital groove; they are generally two in number, but sometimes arise by a single trunk. They descend on the tuberosity of the maxilla and give off several twigs to the gums and neighboring parts of the mucous membrane of the cheek. They then enter the posterior alveolar canals on the infratemporal surface of the maxilla, and, passing from behind forward in the substance of the bone, communicate with the middle superior alveolar nerve, and give off branches to the lining membrane of the maxillary sinus and three twigs to each molar tooth; these twigs enter the foramina at the apices of the roots of the teeth.

The **Middle Superior Alveolar Branch** (*ramus alveolaris superior medius; middle superior dental branch*), is given off from the nerve in the posterior part of the infraorbital canal, and runs downward and forward in a canal in the lateral wall of the maxillary sinus to supply the two premolar teeth. It forms a superior dental plexus with the anterior and posterior superior alveolar branches.

The **Anterior Superior Alveolar Branch** (*ramus alveolaris superior anteriores; anterior superior dental branch*), of considerable size, is given off from the nerve just before its exit from the infraorbital foramen; it descends in a canal in the anterior wall of the maxillary sinus, and divides into branches which supply the incisor and canine teeth. It communicates with the middle superior alveolar branch, and gives off a **nasal branch**, which passes through a minute canal in the lateral wall of the inferior meatus, and supplies the mucous membrane of the anterior part of the inferior meatus and the floor of the nasal cavity, communicating with the nasal branches from the sphenopalatine ganglion.

The **Inferior Palpebral Branches** (*rami palpebrales inferiores; palpebral branches*) (Fig. 776) ascend behind the Orbicularis oculi. They supply the skin and conjunctiva of the lower eyelid, joining at the lateral angle of the orbit with the facial and zygomatico-facial nerves.

The **External Nasal Branches** (*rami nasales externi*) (Fig. 776) supply the skin of the side of the nose and of the septum mobile nasi, and join with the terminal twigs of the nasociliary nerve.

The **Superior Labial Branches** (*rami labiales superiores; labial branches*) (Fig. 776), the largest and most numerous, descend behind the Quadratus labii superioris, and are distributed to the skin of the upper lip, the mucous membrane of the mouth, and labial glands. They are joined, immediately beneath the orbit, by filaments from the facial nerve, forming with them the **infraorbital plexus.**

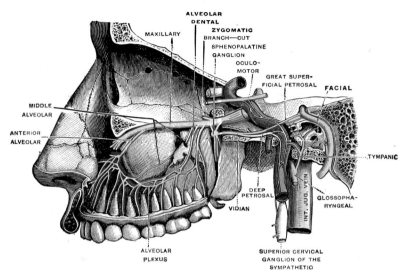

Fig. 777.—Alveolar branches of superior maxillary nerve and sphenopalatine ganglion. (Testut.)

Sphenopalatine Ganglion (*ganglion of Meckel*) (Fig. 778).—The sphenopalatine ganglion, the largest of the sympathetic ganglia associated with the branches of the trigeminal nerve, is deeply placed in the pterygopalatine fossa, close to the sphenopalatine foramen. It is triangular or heart-shaped, of a reddish-gray color, and is situated just below the maxillary nerve as it crosses the fossa. It receives a sensory, a motor (parasympathetic), and a sympathetic root.

Its **sensory root** is derived from two sphenopalatine branches of the maxillary nerve; their fibers, for the most part, pass directly into the palatine nerves; a few, however, enter the ganglion, constituting its sensory root. Its **motor root** is probably derived from the nervus intermedius through the greater superficial petrosal nerve and consists in part of parasympathetic efferent (preganglionic) fibers from the medulla. In the sphenopalatine ganglion they form synapses with neurons whose postganglionic axons, vasomotor and secretory fibers are distributed with the deep branches of the trigeminal to the mucous membrane of the lacrimal gland, nose, soft palate, tonsils, uvula, roof of the mouth, upper lip and gums, and to the upper part of the pharynx. Its **sympathetic root** is derived from the carotid plexus through the deep petrosal nerve and contains postganglionic fibers with cells of origin in the superior cervical sympathetic ganglion. These two nerves join to form the nerve of the pterygoid canal before their entrance into the ganglion.

The **greater superficial petrosal nerve** (*n. petrosus superficialis major; large superficial petrosal nerve*) is given off from the genicular ganglion of the facial nerve; it passes through the hiatus of the facial canal, enters the cranial cavity, and runs forward beneath the dura mater in a groove on the anterior surface of the petrous portion of the temporal bone. It then enters the cartilaginous substance which fills the foramen lacerum, and joining with the deep petrosal branch forms the nerve of the pterygoid canal.

The **deep petrosal nerve** (*n. petrosus profundus; large deep petrosal nerve*) is given off from the carotid plexus, and runs through the carotid canal lateral to the internal carotid artery. It then enters the cartilaginous substance which fills the foramen lacerum, and joins with the greater superficial petrosal nerve to form the nerve of the pterygoid canal.

The **nerve of the pterygoid canal** (*n. canalis pterygoidei [Vidii]; Vidian nerve*), formed by the junction of the two preceding nerves in the cartilaginous substance which fills the foramen lacerum, passes forward, through the pterygoid canal, with the corresponding artery, and is joined by a small ascending **sphenoidal branch** from the otic ganglion. Finally, it enters the pterygopalatine fossa, and joins the posterior angle of the sphenopalatine ganglion.

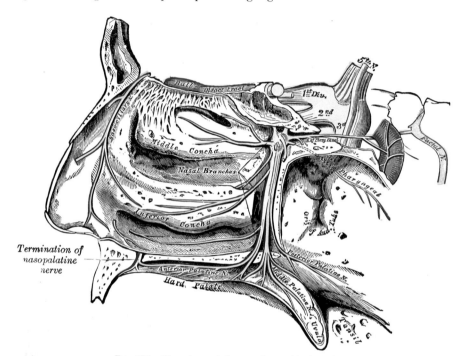

Fig. 778.—The sphenopalatine ganglion and its branches.

Branches of Distribution.—These are divisible into four groups, viz., **orbital, palatine, posterior superior nasal,** and **pharyngeal.**

The **orbital branches** (*rami orbitales; ascending branches*) are two or three delicate filaments, which enter the orbit by the inferior orbital fissure, and supply the periosteum. According to Luschka, some filaments pass through foramina in the fronto-ethmoidal suture to supply the mucous membrane of the posterior ethmoidal and sphenoidal sinuses.

The **palatine nerves** (*nn. palatini; descending branches*) are distributed to the roof of the mouth, soft palate, tonsil, and lining membrane of the nasal cavity. Most of their fibers are derived from the sphenopalatine branches of the maxillary nerve. They are three in number: **anterior, middle,** and **posterior.**

The **anterior palatine nerve** (*n. palatinus anterior*) descends through the pterygo-palatine canal, emerges upon the hard palate through the greater palatine foramen, and passes forward in a groove in the hard palate, nearly as far as the incisor teeth. It supplies the gums, the mucous membrane and glands of the hard palate, and, communicates in front with the terminal filaments of the nasopalatine nerve. While in the pterygopalatine canal, it gives off **posterior inferior nasal branches** which enter the nasal cavity through openings in the palatine bone, and ramify over the inferior nasal concha and middle and inferior meatuses; at its exit from the canal, a palatine branch is distributed to both surfaces of the soft palate.

The **middle palatine nerve** (*n. palatinus medius*) emerges through one of the minor palatine canals and distributes branches to the uvula, tonsil, and soft palate. It is occasionally wanting.

The **posterior palatine nerve** (*n. palatinus posterior*) descends through the pterygo-palatine canal, and emerges by a separate opening behind the greater palatine foramen; it supplies the soft palate, tonsil, and uvula. The middle and posterior palatine join with the tonsillar branches of the glossopharyngeal to form a plexus (**circulus tonsillaris**) around the tonsil.

The **posterior superior nasal branches** (*rami nasales posteriores superiores*) are distributed to the septum and lateral wall of the nasal fossa. They enter the posterior part of the nasal cavity by the sphenopalatine foramen and supply the mucous membrane covering the superior and middle nasal conchæ, the lining of the posterior ethmoidal cells, and the posterior part of the septum. One branch, longer and larger than the others, is named the **nasopalatine nerve**. It enters the nasal cavity through the sphenopalatine foramen, passes across the roof of the nasal cavity below the orifice of the sphenoidal sinus to reach the septum, and then runs obliquely downward and forward between the periosteum and mucous membrane of the lower part of the septum. It descends to the roof of the mouth through the incisive canal and communicates with the corresponding nerve of the opposite side and with the anterior palatine nerve. It furnishes a few filaments to the mucous membrane of the nasal septum.

The **pharyngeal nerve** (*pterygopalatine nerve*) is a small branch *arising* from the posterior part of the ganglion. It passes through the pharyngeal canal with the pharyngeal branch of the internal maxillary artery, and is distributed to the mucous membrane of the nasal part of the pharynx, behind the auditory tube.

The **mandibular nerve** (*n. mandibularis; inferior maxillary nerve*) (Figs. 776, 779, 780, 782) supplies the teeth and gums of the mandible, the skin of the temporal region, the auricula, the lower lip, the lower part of the face, and the muscles of mastication; it also supplies the mucous membrane of the anterior two-thirds of the tongue. It is the largest of the three divisions of the fifth, and is made up of two roots: a large, **sensory root** proceeding from the inferior angle of the semilunar ganglion, and a small **motor root** (the motor part of the trigeminal), which passes beneath the ganglion, and unites with the sensory root, just after its exit through the foramen ovale. The main trunk of the mandibular nerve separates into two large divisions, an anterior and a posterior, but immediately beneath the base of the skull before this division takes place, it gives off from its medial side a recurrent branch (nervus spinosus) and the nerve to the pterygoideus internus. The **nervus spinosus** (*recurrent or meningeal branch*) enters the skull through the foramen spinosum with the middle meningeal artery. It divides into two branches, anterior and posterior, which accompany the main divisions of the artery and supply the dura mater; the posterior branch also supplies the mucous lining of the mastoid cells; the anterior communicates with the meningeal branch of the maxillary nerve. The **internal pterygoid nerve** (*n. pterygoideus internus*) is a slender branch, which enters the deep surface of the muscle; it gives off one or two filaments to the otic ganglion.

The *anterior and smaller division* of the mandibular nerve receives nearly the whole of the fibers of the motor root of the nerve, and supplies the muscles of mastication and the skin and mucous membrane of the cheek. Its branches are the **masseteric, deep temporal, buccinator,** and **external pterygoid.**

The **Masseteric Nerve** (*n. massetericus*) passes lateralward, above the Pterygoideus externus, in front of the temporomandibular articulation, and behind the tendon of the Temporalis; it crosses the mandibular notch with the masseteric artery, to the deep surface of the Masseter, in which it ramifies nearly as far as its anterior border.　It gives a filament to the temporomandibular joint.

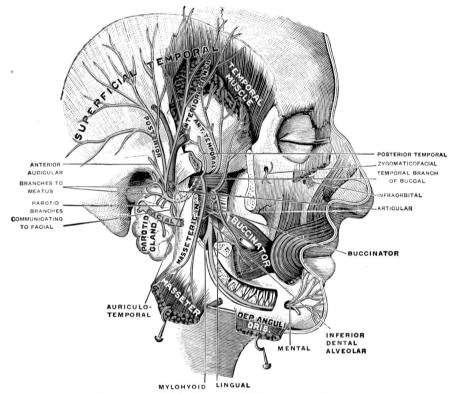

Fig. 779.—Mandibular division of the trifacial nerve.　(Testut.)

The **Deep Temporal Nerves** (*nn. temporales profundi*) are two in number, anterior and posterior.　They pass above the upper border of the Pterygoideus externus and enter the deep surface of the Temporalis.　The **posterior branch,** of small size, is placed at the back of the temporal fossa, and sometimes arises in common with the masseteric nerve.　The **anterior branch** is frequently given off from the buccinator nerve, and then turns upward over the upper head of the Pterygoideus externus. Frequently a third or intermediate branch is present.

The **Buccinator Nerve** (*n. buccinatorus; long buccal nerve*) passes forward between the two heads of the Pterygoideus externus, and downward beneath or through the lower part of the Temporalis; it emerges from under the anterior border of the Masseter, ramifies on the surface of the Buccinator, and unites with the buccal branches of the facial nerve.　It supplies a branch to the Pterygoideus externus during its passage through that muscle, and may give off the anterior deep temporal nerve.　The buccinator nerve supplies the skin over the Buccinator, and the mucous membrane lining its inner surface.

External Pterygoid Nerve (*n. pterygoideus externus*).—The nerve to the Pterygoideus externus frequently *arises* in conjunction with the buccinator nerve, but it may be given off separately from the anterior division of the mandibular nerve.　It enters the deep surface of the muscle.

The *posterior and larger division* of the mandibular nerve is for the most part sensory, but receives a few filaments from the motor root.　It divides into **auriculotemporal, lingual,** and **inferior alveolar nerves.**

The **Auriculotemporal Nerve** (*n. auriculotemporalis*) generally *arises* by two roots, between which the middle meningeal artery ascends (Fig. 781). It runs backward beneath the Pterygoideus externus to the medial side of the neck of the mandible. It then turns upward with the superficial temporal artery, between the auricula and condyle of the mandible, under cover of the parotid gland; escaping from beneath the gland, it ascends over the zygomatic arch, and divides into superficial temporal branches(Fig.788).

The **branches of communication** of the auriculotemporal nerve are with the facial nerve and with the otic ganglion. The branches to the facial, usually two in number,

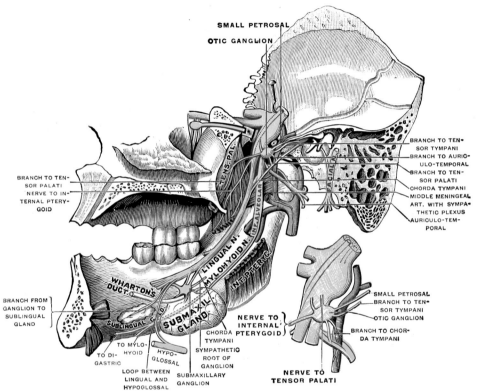

FIG. 780.—Mandibular division of trifacial nerve, seen from the middle line. The small figure is an enlarged view of the otic ganglion. (Testut.)

pass forward from behind the neck of the mandible and join the facial nerve at the posterior border of the Masseter. The filaments to the otic ganglion are derived from the roots of the auriculotemporal nerve close to their origin (Fig. 781).

Its **branches of distribution** are:

Anterior auricular.	Articular.
Branches to the external acoustic meatus.	Parotid.
Superficial temporal.	

The **anterior auricular branches** (*nn. auriculares anteriores*) are usually two in number; they supply the front of the upper part of the auricula, being distributed principally to the skin covering the front of the helix and tragus.

The **branches to the external acoustic meatus** (*n. meatus auditorii externi*), two in number, enter the meatus between its bony and cartilaginous portions and supply the skin lining it; the upper one sends a filament to the tympanic membrane.

The **articular branches** consist of one or two twigs which enter the posterior part of the temporomandibular joint.

The **parotid branches** (*rami parotidei*) supply the parotid gland.

The **superficial temporal branches** (*rami temporales superficiales*) accompany the superficial temporal artery to the vertex of the skull; they supply the skin of the temporal region and communicate with the facial and zygomaticotemporal nerves.

The **Lingual Nerve** (*n. lingualis*) (Fig. 776) supplies the mucous membrane of the anterior two-thirds of the tongue. It lies at first beneath the Pterygoideus externus, medial to and in front of the inferior alveolar nerve, and is occasionally joined to this nerve by a branch which may cross the internal maxillary artery. The chorda tympani also joins it at an acute angle in this situation. The nerve then passes between the Pterygoideus internus and the ramus of the mandible, and crosses obliquely to the side of the tongue over the Constrictor pharyngis superior and Styloglossus, and then between the Hyoglossus and deep part of the submaxillary gland; it finally runs across the duct of the submaxillary gland, and along the tongue to its tip, lying immediately beneath the mucous membrane.

Its **branches of communication** are with the facial (through the chorda tympani), the inferior alveolar and hypoglossal nerves, and the submaxillary ganglion. The branches to the submaxillary ganglion are two or three in number; those connected with the hypoglossal nerve form a plexus at the anterior margin of the Hyoglossus.

Its **branches of distribution** supply the sublingual gland, the mucous membrane of the mouth, the gums, and the mucous membrane of the anterior two-thirds of the tongue; the terminal filaments communicate, at the tip of the tongue, with the hypoglossal nerve.

The **Inferior Alveolar Nerve** (*n. alveolaris inferior; inferior dental nerve*) (Figs. 779, 780) is the largest branch of the mandibular nerve. It descends with the inferior alveolar artery, at first beneath the Pterygoideus externus, and then between the sphenomandibular ligament and the ramus of the mandible to the mandibular foramen. It then passes forward in the mandibular canal, beneath the teeth, as far as the mental foramen, where it divides into two terminal branches, incisive and mental.

The branches of the inferior alveolar nerve are the **mylohyoid, dental, incisive, and mental.**

The **mylohyoid nerve** (*n. mylohyoideus*) is derived from the inferior alveolar just before it enters the mandibular foramen. It descends in a groove on the deep surface of the ramus of the mandible, and reaching the under surface of the Mylohyoideus supplies this muscle and the anterior belly of the Digastricus.

The **dental branches** supply the molar and premolar teeth. They correspond in number to the roots of those teeth; each nerve entering the orifice at the point of the root, and supplying the pulp of the tooth; above the alveolar nerve they form an **inferior dental plexus.**

The **incisive branch** is continued onward within the bone, and supplies the canine and incisor teeth.

The **mental nerve** (*n. mentalis*) emerges at the mental foramen, and divides beneath the Triangularis muscle into three branches; one descends to the skin of the chin, and two ascend to the skin and mucous membrane of the lower lip; these branches communicate freely with the facial nerve.

Two small ganglia, the **otic** and the **submaxillary,** are connected with the mandibular nerve.

Otic Ganglion (*ganglion oticum*) (Figs. 780, 781).—The otic ganglion is a small, oval-shaped, flattened ganglion of a reddish-gray color, situated immediately below the foramen ovale; it lies on the medial surface of the mandibular nerve, and surrounds the origin of the nerve to the Pterygoideus internus. It is in relation, *laterally,* with the trunk of the mandibular nerve at the point where the motor and sensory roots join; *medially,* with the cartilaginous part of the auditory tube, and the origin of the Tensor veli palatini; *posteriorly,* with the middle meningeal artery.

Branches of Communication.—It is connected by two or three short filaments with the nerve to the Pterygoideus internus, from which it may obtain a motor (parasympathetic) and possibly a sensory root. It communicates with the glosso-pharyngeal and facial nerves, through the lesser superficial petrosal nerve continued from the tympanic plexus, and through this nerve it probably receives a root from the glossopharyngeal and a motor root from the facial; its sympathetic root consists of a filament from the plexus surrounding the middle meningeal artery. The fibers from the glossopharyngeal which pass to the otic ganglion in the smaller superficial petrosal are supposed to be parasympathetic efferent (preganglionic) fibers from the dorsal nucleus or inferior salivatory nucleus of the medulla. Fibers (postganglionic) from cells in the otic ganglion with which parasympathetic preganglionic fibers form synapses pass with the auriculotemporal nerve to the parotid gland. A slender filament (sphenoidal) ascends from it to the nerve of the Pterygoid canal, and a small branch connects it with the chorda tympani.

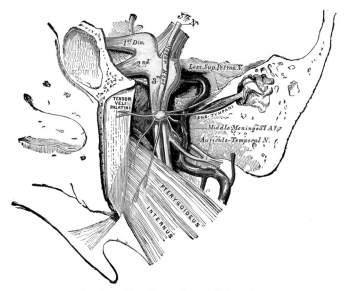

Fig. 781.—The otic ganglion and its branches.

Its **branches of distribution** are: a filament to the Tensor tympani, and one to the Tensor veli palatini. The former passes backward, lateral to the auditory tube; the latter arises from the ganglion, near the origin of the nerve to the Pterygoideus internus, and is directed forward. The motor fibers to these muscles have their cells of origin in the brain stem (probably in the motor nucleus of the trigeminal nerve), pass to the otic ganglion by way of a branch from the nerve to the Pterygoideus internus, and then through the ganglion without synapses into its branches of distribution.

Submaxillary Ganglion (*ganglion submaxillare*) (Figs. 776, 780).—The submaxillary ganglion is of small size and is fusiform in shape. It is situated above the deep portion of the submaxillary gland, on the hyoglossus, near the posterior border of the Mylohyoideus, and is connected by filaments with the lower border of the lingual nerve. It is suspended from the lingual nerve by two filaments which join the anterior and posterior parts of the ganglion. Through the posterior of these it receives a branch from the chorda tympani nerve which runs in the sheath of the lingual; these are parasympathetic efferent (preganglionic) fibers from the facial nucleus or the superior salivatory nucleus of the medulla oblongata that terminate in the submaxillary ganglion. The postganglionic fibers pass to the submaxillary gland; it communicates with the sympathetic by filaments from the sympathetic plexus around the external maxillary artery.

Its **branches of distribution** are five or six in number; they *arise* from the lower part of the ganglion, and supply the mucous membrane of the mouth and the duct of the submaxillary gland, some being lost in the submaxillary gland. The branch of communication from the lingual to the forepart of the ganglion is by some regarded as a branch of distribution, through which filaments pass from the ganglion to the lingual nerve, and by it are conveyed to the sublingual gland and the tongue.

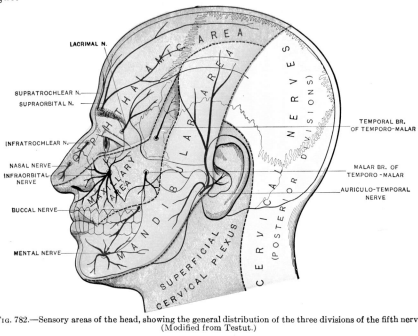

LACRIMAL N.

SUPRATROCHLEAR N.
SUPRAORBITAL N.

INFRATROCHLEAR N.

NASAL NERVE
INFRAORBITAL NERVE

BUCCAL NERVE

MENTAL NERVE

TEMPORAL BR. OF TEMPORO-MALAR

MALAR BR. OF TEMPORO-MALAR

AURICULO-TEMPORAL NERVE

Fig. 782.—Sensory areas of the head, showing the general distribution of the three divisions of the fifth nerve. (Modified from Testut.)

Referred Pain in the Distribution of the Trigeminal Nerve.—Pains referred to various branches of the trigeminal nerve are of very frequent occurrence, and should always lead to a careful examination in order to discover a local cause. As a general rule the diffusion of pain over the various branches of the nerve is at first confined to one only of the main divisions, and the search for the causative lesion should always commence with a thorough examination of all those parts which are supplied by that division; although in severe cases pain may radiate over the branches of the other main divisions. The commonest example of this condition is the neuralgia which is so often associated with dental caries—here, although the tooth itself may not appear to be painful, the most distressing referred pains may be experienced, and these are at once relieved by treatment directed to the affected tooth.

Many other examples of reference of pain could be quoted, but it will be sufficient to mention the more common ones. Dealing with the ophthalmic nerve, severe supraorbital pain is commonly associated with acute glaucoma or with disease of the frontal or ethmoidal air cells. Malignant growths or empyema of the maxillary antrum, or unhealthy conditions about the inferior conchæ or the septum of the nose, are often found giving rise to "second division" neuralgia, and should be always looked for in the absence of dental disease in the maxilla.

It is on the mandibular nerve, however, that some of the most striking references are seen. It is quite common to meet with patients who complain of pain in the ear, in whom there is no sign of aural disease, and the cause is usually to be found in a carious tooth in the mandible. Moreover, with an ulcer or cancer of the tongue, often the first pain to be experienced is one which radiates to the ear and temporal fossa, over the distribution of the auriculotemporal nerve.

In these few examples of referred pain in the distribution of the trigeminal nerve, there has been an error of localization of the exact site from which the pain impulses have arisen. This misinterpretation may be due to a failure of attaching proper "local sign" to pain impulses as they are brought by way of nerve fibers from the different distributions into the neuron-pool of the nucleus of the spinal tract of the trigeminal nerve.

THE ABDUCENT NERVE (N. ABDUCENS; SIXTH NERVE) (Fig. 775).

The **abducent nerve** supplies the Rectus lateralis oculi.

Its fibers arise from a small nucleus (the nucleus of the abducent nerve) situated in the upper part of the rhomboid fossa, close to the middle line and beneath the colliculus facialis. They pass downward and forward through the pons, and emerge in the furrow between the lower border of the pons and the upper end of the pyramid of the medulla oblongata.

From the nucleus of the sixth nerve, fibers are said to pass through the medial longitudinal fasciculus to terminate in the nucleus of the oculomotor nerve. Such internuncial neurons may serve in the proper coördination of the activity of the Rectus lateralis and the Rectus medialis of the two sides (Fig. 783).

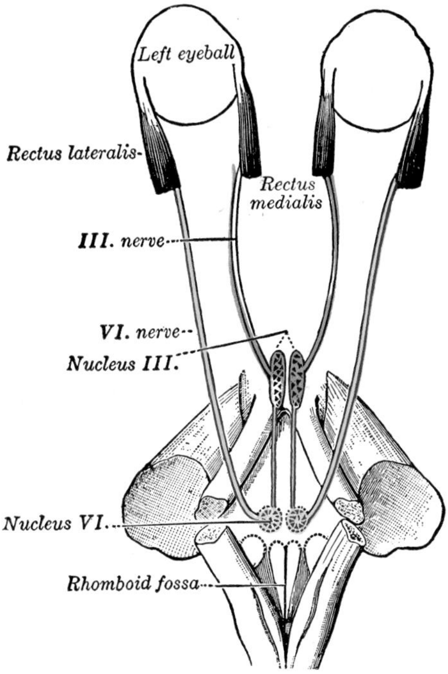

The nerve pierces the dura mater on the dorsum sellæ of the sphenoid, runs through a notch in the bone below the posterior clinoid process, and passes forward through the cavernous sinus, on the lateral side of the internal carotid artery. It enters the orbit through the superior orbital fissure, above the ophthalmic vein, from which it is separated by a lamina of dura mater. It then passes between the two heads of the Rectus lateralis, and enters the ocular surface of that muscle. The abducent nerve is joined by several filaments from the carotid and cavernous plexuses, and by one from the ophthalmic nerve.

FIG. 783.—Figure showing the mode of innervation of the Recti medialis and lateralis of the eye (modified after Duval and Laborde).

The oculomotor, trochlear, ophthalmic, and abducent nerves bear certain relations to each other in the cavernous sinus, at the superior orbital fissure, and in the cavity of the orbit, as follows:

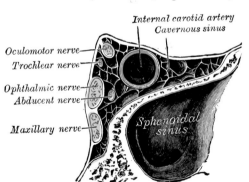

FIG. 784.—Oblique section through the right cavernous sinus.

In the **cavernous sinus** (Fig. 784), the oculomotor, trochlear, and ophthalmic nerves are placed in the lateral wall of the sinus, in the order given, from above downward. The abducent nerve lies at the lateral side of the internal carotid artery. As these nerves pass forward to the superior orbital fissure, the oculomotor and ophthalmic divide into branches, and the abducent nerve approaches the others; so that their relative positions are considerably changed.

In the **superior orbital fissure** (Fig. 785), the trochlear nerve and the frontal and lacrimal divisions of the ophthalmic lie in this order from the medial to the lateral side upon the same plane; they enter the cavity of the orbit above the muscles. The remaining nerves enter the orbit between the two heads of the Rectus lateralis.

The superior division of the oculomotor is the highest of these; beneath this lies the nasociliary branch of the ophthalmic; then the inferior division of the oculomotor; and the abducent lowest of all.

In the **orbit**, the trochlear, frontal, and lacrimal nerves lie immediately beneath the periosteum, the trochlear nerve resting on the Obliquus superior, the frontal on the Levator palpebræ superioris, and the lacrimal on the Rectus lateralis

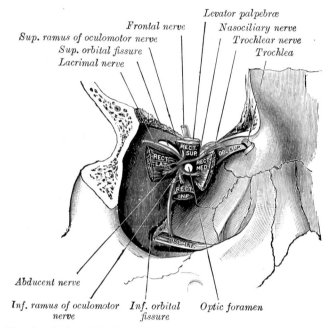

Fig.785—Dissection showing origins of right ocular muscles, and nerves entering by the superior orbital fissure.

The superior division of the oculomotor nerve lies immediately beneath the Rectus superior, while the nasociliary nerve crosses the optic nerve to reach the medial wall of the orbit. Beneath these is the optic nerve, surrounded in front by the ciliary nerves, and having the ciliary ganglion on its lateral side, between it and the Rectus lateralis. Below the optic nerve are the inferior division of the oculomotor, and the abducent, the latter lying on the medial surface of the Rectus lateralis.

THE FACIAL NERVE (N. FACIALIS; SEVENTH NERVE) (Figs. 786, 788).

The **facial nerve** consists of a motor and a sensory part, the latter being frequently described under the name of the **nervus intermedius** (*pars intermedii of Wrisberg*) (Fig. 786). The two parts emerge at the lower border of the pons in the recess between the olive and the inferior peduncle, the motor part being the more medial, immediately to the lateral side of the sensory part is the acoustic nerve.

The motor part supplies somatic motor fibers to the muscles of the face, scalp, and auricle, the Buccinator and Platysma, the Stapedius, the Stylohyoideus, and posterior belly of the Digastricus; it also contains some autonomic motor fibers which constitute the vasodilator and secretory nerves of the submaxillary and sublingual glands, and are conveyed through the chorda tympani nerve. these are preganglionic fibers of the parasympathetic system with cells of origin probably in the Nucleus Salivatorius Superior and terminate in the submaxillary ganglion and small ganglia in the hilum of the submaxillary gland. From these ganglia postganglionic fibers are conveyed to these glands. The sensory part is made up of fibers with cells of origin in the genicular ganglion. This contains the fibers of taste for the anterior two-thirds of the tongue with central terminations in the Nucleus of the Tractus Solitarius and a few somatic sensory fibers from the middle ear region with central terminations in the Nucleus of the Spinal Tract of the Trigeminal Nerve. A few visceral (splanchnic) afferent fibers are also present.

The **motor root** *arises* from a nucleus (motor nucleus of the facial nerve) which lies deeply in the reticular formation of the lower part of the pons. This nucleus is situated above the nucleus ambiguus, behind the superior olivary nucleus, and medial to the spinal tract of the trigeminal nerve. From this origin the fibers pursue a curved course in the substance of the pons. They first pass backward and medialward toward the rhomboid fossa, and, reaching the posterior end of the nucleus of the abducent nerve, run upward close to the middle line beneath the colliculus facialis. At the anterior end of the nucleus of the abducent nerve they

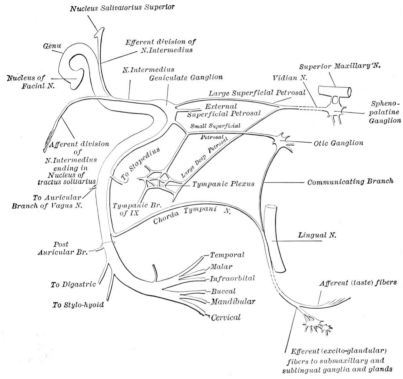

Fig. 786.—Plan of the facial and intermediate nerves and their communication with other nerves.

make a second bend, and run downward and forward through the pons to their point of emergence between the olive and the inferior peduncle. The portion of the facial nerve which curves around the nucleus of the abducent nerve is called the genu (genu internum radicis nervi facialis).

The **sensory root** *arises* from the genicular ganglion, which is situated on the geniculum of the facial nerve in the facial canal, behind the hiatus of the canal. The cells of this ganglion are unipolar, and the single process divides in a T-shaped manner into central and peripheral branches. The central branches leave the trunk of the facial nerve in the internal acoustic meatus, and form the sensory root; the peripheral branches are continued into the various branches of distribution of the facial nerve. Entering the brain at the lower border of the pons between the motor root and the acoustic nerve, the fibers of the sensory root pass into the substance of the medulla oblongata and end mainly in the nucleus of the tractus solitarius. Fibers of somatic sensibility which course in the facial nerve probably terminate in the nucleus of the spinal tract of the trigeminal nerve.

From their superficial attachments to the brain, the two roots of the facial nerve pass lateralward and forward with the acoustic nerve to the internal acoustic meatus. In the meatus the motor root lies in a groove on the upper and anterior surface of the acoustic nerve, the sensory root being placed between them.

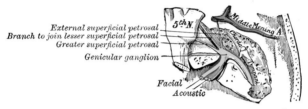

FIG. 787.—The course and connections of the facial nerve in the temporal bone.

At the bottom of the meatus, the facial nerve enters the facial canal, which it traverses to its termination at the stylomastoid foramen. It is at first directed lateralward between the cochlea and vestibule toward the medial wall of the tympanic cavity; it then bends suddenly backward and arches downward behind the tympanic cavity to the stylomastoid foramen. The point where it changes its direction is named the **geniculum**; it presents a reddish gangliform swelling, the **genicular ganglion** (*ganglion geniculi; geniculate ganglion; nucleus of the sensory root of the nerve*) (Fig. 787). On emerging from the stylomastoid foramen, the facial nerve runs forward in the substance of the parotid gland, crosses the external carotid artery, and divides behind the ramus of the mandible into branches, from which numerous offsets are distributed over the side of the head, face, and upper part of the neck, supplying the superficial muscles in these regions. The branches and their offsets unite to form the **parotid plexus.**

Branches of Communication.—The functional significance of many of the branches of communication of the facial nerve is unknown. They may be arranged as follows

In the internal acoustic meatus	With the acoustic nerve.
At the genicular ganglion .	With the sphenopalatine ganglion by the greater superficial petrosal nerve. With the otic ganglion by a branch which joins the lesser superficial petrosal nerve. With the sympathetic on the middle meningeal artery.
In the facial canal . . .	With the auricular branch of the vagus.
At its exit from the stylo-mastoid foramen . . .	With the glossopharyngeal. With the vagus. With the great auricular. With the auriculotemporal.
Behind the ear . . .	With the lesser occipital.
On the face	With the trigeminal.
In the neck	With the cutaneous cervical.

In the internal acoustic meatus some minute filaments pass from the facial to the acoustic nerve.

The **greater superficial petrosal nerve** (*large superficial petrosal nerve*) *arises* from the genicular ganglion, and consists chiefly of sensory branches which are distributed to the mucous membrane of the soft palate; but it contains the preganglionic fibers which form the motor root of the sphenopalatine ganglion. It passes forward through the hiatus of the facial canal, and runs in a sulcus on the anterior surface of the petrous portion of the temporal bone beneath the semilunar ganglion, to the foramen lacerum.

It receives a twig from the tympanic plexus, and in the foramen is joined by the deep petrosal, from the sympathetic plexus on the internal carotid artery, to form the nerve of the pterygoid canal which passes forward through the pterygoid canal and ends in the sphenopalatine ganglion. The genicular ganglion is connected with the otic ganglion by a branch which joins the lesser superficial petrosal nerve, and also with the sympathetic filaments accompanying the middle meningeal artery. According to Arnold, a twig passes back from the ganglion to the acoustic nerve. Just before the facial nerve emerges from the stylomastoid foramen, it generally receives a twig from the auricular branch of the vagus.

After its exit from the stylomastoid foramen, the facial nerve sends a twig to the glossopharyngeal, and communicates with the auricular branch of the vagus, with the great auricular nerve of the cervical plexus, with the auriculotemporal nerve in the parotid gland, and with the lesser occipital behind the ear; on the face with the terminal branches of the trigeminal, and in the neck with the cutaneous cervical nerve.

Branches of Distribution.—The branches of distribution (Fig. 786) of the facial nerve may be thus arranged:

Within the facial canal .	{ Nerve to the Stapedius muscle. { Chorda tympani.
At its exit from the stylo-mastoid foramen . .	{ Posterior auricular. { Digastric. { Stylohyoid.
On the face	{ Temporal. { Zygomatic. { Buccal. { Mandibular. { Cervical.

The **Nerve to the Stapedius** (*n. stapedius; tympanic branch*) *arises* opposite the pyramidal eminence (page 1073); it passes through a small canal in this eminence to reach the muscle.

The **Chorda Tympani Nerve** is given off from the facial as it passes downward behind the tympanic cavity, about 6 mm. from the stylomastoid foramen. It runs upward and forward in a canal, and enters the tympanic cavity, through an aperture (**iter chordæ posterius**) on its posterior wall, close to the medial surface of the posterior border of the tympanic membrane and on a level with the upper end of the manubrium of the malleus. It traverses the tympanic cavity, between the fibrous and mucous layers of the tympanic membrane, crosses the manubrium of the malleus, and emerges from the cavity through a foramen situated at the inner end of the petrotympanic fissure, and named the **iter chordæ anterius** (*canal of Huguier*). It then descends between the Pterygoideus externus and internus on the medial surface of the spina angularis of the sphenoid, which it sometimes grooves, and joins, at an acute angle, the posterior border of the lingual nerve. It contains efferent preganglionic fibers with cells of origin in the Nucleus Salivatorius Superior. These pass in the facial and chorda tympani nerves to terminate about postganglionic neurons in the submaxillary ganglion (and in the substance of the glands), and axons of the latter are distributed to the submaxillary and sublingual glands. The majority of its fibers are afferent, and are continued onward through the muscular substance of the tongue to the mucous membrane covering its anterior two-thirds; they constitute the nerve of taste for this portion of the tongue. Before uniting with the lingual nerve the chorda tympani is joined by a small branch from the otic ganglion.

The **Posterior Auricular Nerve** (*n. auricularis posterior*) *arises* close to the stylo-mastoid foramen, and runs upward in front of the mastoid process; here it is joined by a filament from the auricular branch of the vagus, and communicates with the posterior branch of the great auricular, and with the lesser occipital. As it ascends between the external acoustic meatus and mastoid process it divides into auricular and occipital branches. The **auricular branch** supplies the Auricularis posterior and the intrinsic muscles on the cranial surface of the auricula. The **occipital branch**, the larger, passes backward along the superior nuchal line of the occipital bone, and supplies the Occipitalis.

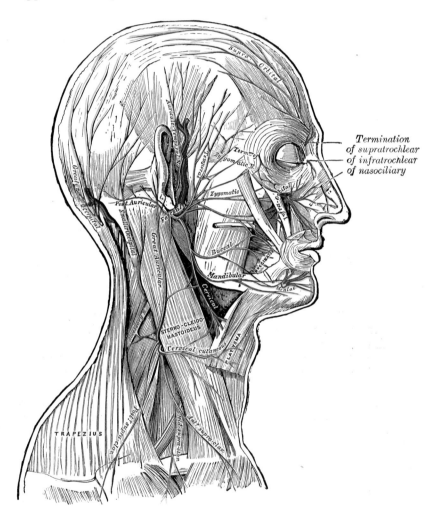

Fig. 788.—The nerves of the scalp, face, and side of neck.

The **Digastric Branch** (*ramus digastricus*) *arises* close to the stylomastoid foramen and divides into several filaments, which supply the posterior belly of the Digastricus; one of these filaments joins the glossopharyngeal nerve.

The **Stylohyoid Branch** (*ramus stylohyoideus*) frequently *arises* in conjunction with the digastric branch; it is long and slender, and enters the Stylohyoideus about its middle.

The **Temporal Branches** (*rami temporales*) cross the zygomatic arch to the temporal region, supplying the Auriculares anterior and superior, and joining with the zygomaticotemporal branch of the maxillary, and with the auriculotemporal branch of the mandibular. The more anterior branches supply the Frontalis, the Orbicularis oculi, and the Corrugator, and join the supraorbital and lacrimal branches of the ophthalmic.

The **Zygomatic Branches** (*rami zygomatici; malar branches*) run across the zygomatic bone to the lateral angle of the orbit, where they supply the Orbicularis oculi, and join with filaments from the lacrimal nerve and the zygomaticofacial branch of the maxillary nerve.

The **Buccal Branches** (*rami buccales; infraorbital branches*), of larger size than the rest, pass horizontally forward to be distributed below the orbit and around the mouth. The **superficial branches** run beneath the skin and above the superficial muscles of the face, which they supply: some are distributed to the Procerus, joining at the medial angle of the orbit with the infratrochlear and nasociliary branches of the ophthalmic. The **deep branches** pass beneath the Zygomaticus and the Quadratus labii superioris, supplying them and forming an **infraorbital plexus** with the infraorbital branch of the maxillary nerve. These branches also supply the small muscles of the nose. The lower deep branches supply the Buccinator and Orbicularis oris, and join with filaments of the buccinator branch of the mandibular nerve.

The **Mandibular Branch** (*ramus marginalis mandibulæ*) passes forward beneath the Platysma and Triangularis, supplying the muscles of the lower lip and chin, and communicating with the mental branch of the inferior alveolar nerve.

The **Cervical Branch** (*ramus colli*) runs forward beneath the Platysma, and forms a series of arches across the side of the neck over the suprahyoid region. One branch descends to join the cervical cutaneous nerve from the cervical plexus; others supply the Platysma.

THE ACOUSTIC NERVE (EIGHTH NERVE) (Figs. 787).

The **Acoustic Nerve** consists of two distinct sets of fibers, the **Cochlear** and **Vestibular Nerves**, which differ in their peripheral endings, central connections, functions, and time of medullation. These two portions of the acoustic nerve are joined in a common trunk as it enters the internal auditory meatus, where the Facial Nerve is found on its upper and anterior surface. Centrally, the acoustic nerve divides into a lateral (cochlear) root and a medial (vestibular) root. As it passes distally in the internal auditory meatus, it divides into the various branches which are distributed to the receptor areas in the membranous labyrinth. (Figs. 915–921.) Both divisions of this nerve are sensory and the fibers arise from bipolar ganglion cells.

Cochlear Nerve.—The cochlear nerve or root, the **nerve of hearing**, arises from bipolar cells in the spiral ganglion of the cochlea, situated near the inner edge of the osseous spiral lamina. The peripheral fibers pass to the organ of Corti. (Figs. 928–931, 923.) The central ones pass down the modiolus and then through the foramina of the tractus spiralis foraminosus or through the foramen centrale into the lateral or outer end of the internal auditory meatus. The nerve passes along the internal auditory meatus with the vestibular nerve and across the subarachnoid space, just above the flocculus, almost directly medialward toward the inferior peduncle to terminate in the cochlear nuclei.

The cochlear nerve is placed lateral to the vestibular root. Its fibers end in two nuclei: one, the **ventral cochlear nucleus**, lies immediately in front of the inferior cerebellar peduncle; the other, the dorsal cochlear nucleus, **tuberculum acusticum**, somewhat lateral to it.

Vestibular Nerve.—The vestibular nerve or root, the **nerve of equilibration**, arises from bipolar cells in the vestibular ganglion, **ganglion of Scarpa**, which is situated in the upper part of the outer end of the internal auditory meatus. The peripheral fibers divide into three branches: the superior branch passes through the foramina in the area vestibularis superior and ends in the utricle and in the ampullæ of the superior and lateral semicircular ducts; the fibers of the inferior branch traverse the foramina in the area vestibularis inferior and end in the saccule; the posterior branch runs through the foramen singulare and supplies the ampulla of the posterior semicircular duct.

THE GLOSSOPHARYNGEAL NERVE (N. GLOSSOPHARYNGEUS; NINTH NERVE) (Figs. 789, 790).

The **glossopharyngeal nerve** contains both motor and sensory fibers, and is distributed, as its name implies, to the tongue and pharynx. It is the nerve of ordinary sensation to the mucous membrane of the pharynx, fauces, and palatine tonsil, and the nerve of taste to the posterior part of the tongue. It is attached by three or four filaments to the upper part of the medulla oblongata, in the groove between the olive and the inferior peduncle.

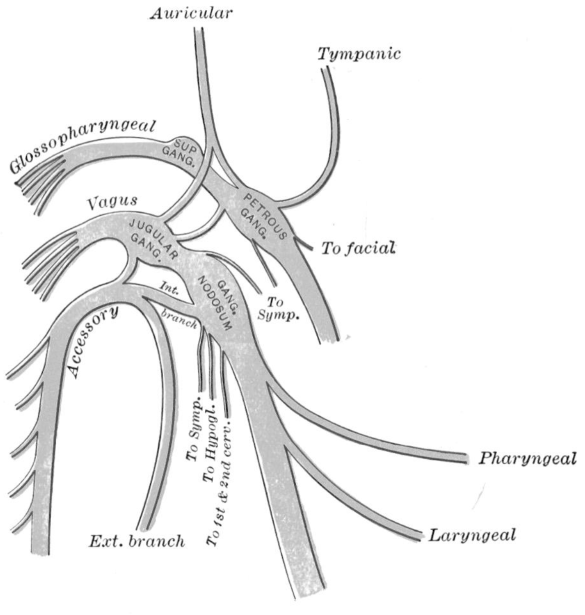

FIG. 789.—Plan of upper portions of glossopharyngeal, vagus, and accessory nerves.

The **sensory fibers** *arise* from the cells of the superior and petrous ganglia, which are situated on the trunk of the nerve, and will be presently described. When traced into the medulla, some of the sensory fibers, probably visceral afferent, end by arborizing around the cells of the upper part of a nucleus which lies beneath the ala cinerea in the lower part of the rhomboid fossa. Many of the fibers, probably the **taste fibers**, contribute to form a strand, named the **fasciculus solitarius**, which descends in the medulla oblongata. Associated with this strand are numerous nerve cells (the nucleus of the tractus solitarius) and around these the fibers of the fasciculus end. The **somatic sensory fibers**, few in number, are said to join the spinal tract of the trigeminal nerve.

The **somatic motor fibers** spring from the cells of the **nucleus ambiguus**, which lies some distance from the surface of the rhomboid fossa in the lateral part of the medulla and is continuous below with the anterior gray column of the medulla spinalis. From this nucleus the fibers are first directed backward, and then they bend forward and lateralward to join the fibers of the sensory root. The nucleus ambiguus gives origin to the motor branches of the glossopharyngeal and vagus nerves, and to the cranial part of the accessory nerve which are distributed to striped muscle.

The **parasympathetic efferent fibers** from the nucleus beneath the ala cinerea, the dorsal nucleus, are probably both preganglionic motor fibers (*i. e.*, they carry impulses which activate postganglionic neurons distributed to smooth muscle) and preganglionic secretory fibers of the autonomic system. The secretory fibers pass to the otic ganglion which contains postganglionic neurons distributed to the parotid gland. Some authors describe these fibers as arising from a distinct nucleus, the inferior salivatory nucleus, which lies near the dorsal nucleus.

From the medulla oblongata, the glossopharyngeal nerve passes lateralward across the flocculus, and leaves the skull through the central part of the jugular foramen, in a separate sheath of the dura mater, lateral to and in front of the vagus and accessory nerves (Fig. 790). In its passage through the jugular foramen, it grooves the lower border of the petrous part of the temporal bone; and, at its exit from the skull, passes forward between the internal jugular vein and internal carotid artery; it descends in front of the latter vessel, and beneath the styloid process and the muscles connected with it, to the lower border of the Stylopharyngeus. It then curves forward, forming an arch on the side of the neck and lying upon the Stylopharyngeus and Constrictor pharyngis medius. Thence it passes under cover of the Hyoglossus, and is finally distributed to the palatine tonsil, the mucous membrane of the fauces and base of the tongue, and the mucous glands of the mouth.

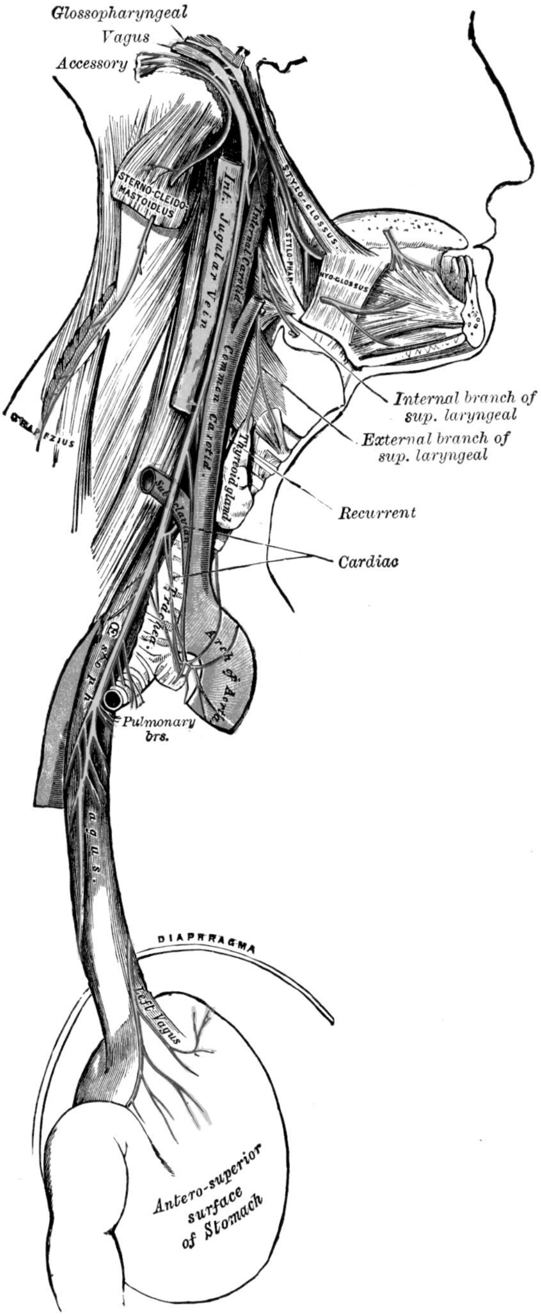

In passing through the jugular foramen, the nerve presents two ganglia, the **superior** and the **petrous** (Fig. 789).

The **Superior Ganglion** (*ganglion superius; jugular ganglion*) is situated in the upper part of the groove in which the nerve is lodged during its passage through the jugular foramen. It is very small, may be absent,

Fig. 790.—Course and distribution of the glossopharyngeal, vagus. and accessory nerves.

and is usually regarded as a detached portion of the petrous ganglion.

The **Petrous Ganglion** (*ganglion petrosum; inferior ganglion*) is larger than the superior and is situated in a depression in the lower border of the petrous portion of the temporal bone.

Branches of Communication.—The glossopharyngeal nerve communicates with the vagus, sympathetic, and facial.

The branches to the vagus are two filaments which *arise* from the petrous ganglion, one passing to the auricular branch, and the other to the jugular ganglion, of the vagus. The petrous ganglion is connected by a filament with the superior cervical ganglion of the sympathetic. The branch of communication with the facial perforates the posterior belly of the Digastricus. It *arises* from the trunk of the glossopharyngeal below the petrous ganglion, and joins the facial just after the exit of that nerve from the stylomastoid foramen.

Branches of Distribution.—The branches of distribution of the glossopharyngeal are: the **tympanic, carotid, pharyngeal, muscular, tonsillar, and lingual.**

The **Tympanic Nerve** (*n. tympanicus; nerve of Jacobson*) *arises* from the petrous ganglion, and ascends to the tympanic cavity through a small canal on the under surface of the petrous portion of the temporal bone on the ridge which separates the carotid canal from the jugular fossa. In the tympanic cavity it divides into branches which form the **tympanic plexus** and are contained in grooves upon the surface of the promontory. This plexus gives off: (1) the lesser superficial petrosal nerve; (2) a branch to join the greater superficial petrosal nerve; and (3) branches to the tympanic cavity, all of which will be described in connection with the anatomy of the middle ear.

The **Carotid Branches** (*n. caroticotympanicus superior* and *n. caroticotympanicus inferior*) descend along the trunk of the internal carotid artery as far as its origin, communicating with the pharyngeal branch of the vagus, and with branches of the sympathetic. It terminates in the carotid sinus and conveys impulses from special pressure end-organs in the sinus to the medulla. It is concerned with the regulation of blood-pressure and is known to physiologists as the carotid sinus nerve.

The **Pharyngeal Branches** (*rami pharyngei*) are three or four filaments which unite, opposite the Constrictor pharyngis medius, with the pharyngeal branches of the vagus and sympathetic, to form the **pharyngeal plexus**; branches from this plexus perforate the muscular coat of the pharynx and supply its muscles and mucous membrane.

The **Muscular Branch** (*ramus stylopharyngeus*) is distributed to the Stylopharyngeus.

The **Tonsillar Branches** (*rami tonsillares*) supply the palatine tonsil, forming around it a plexus from which filaments are distributed to the soft palate and fauces, where they communicate with the palatine nerves.

The **Lingual Branches** (*rami linguales*) are two in number; one supplies the papillæ vallatæ and the mucous membrane covering the base of the tongue; the other supplies the mucous membrane and follicular glands of the posterior part of the tongue, and communicates with the lingual nerve.

THE VAGUS NERVE (N. VAGUS; TENTH NERVE; PNEUMOGASTRIC NERVE) (Figs. 789, 790).

The **vagus nerve** is composed of visceral sensory and motor (parasympathetic preganglionic), and somatic motor and sensory fibers, and has a more extensive course and distribution than any of the other cranial nerves, since it passes through the neck and thorax to the abdomen.

The vagus is attached by eight or ten filaments to the medulla oblongata in the groove between the olive and the inferior peduncle, below the glossopharyngeal. The **sensory fibers** *arise* from the cells of the jugular ganglion and ganglion nodosum of the nerve, and, when traced into the medulla oblongata mostly end by arborizing around the cells of the inferior part of a nucleus which lies beneath the ala cinerea in the lower part of the rhomboid fossa. These are the visceral afferent fibers. Some of the sensory fibers of the glossopharyngeal nerve have been seen to end in the upper part of this nucleus. A few of the sensory fibers of the vagus, probably **taste fibers**, descend in the fasciculus solitarius and end around its cells. The **somatic sensory fibers**, few in number, from the posterior part of the external auditory meatus and the back of the ear, probably join the spinal tract of the trigeminal as it descends in the medulla. The **somatic motor fibers** *arise* from the cells of the nucleus ambiguus, already referred to in connection with the motor root of the glossopharyngeal nerve.

The **parasympathetic efferent fibers** arise from the dorsal nucleus of the vagus. They are preganglionic fibers to the thoracic and abdominal viscera, *i. e.*, motor fibers to the bronchial tree, inhibitory (possibly also accelerator) fibers to the heart, motor fibers to the esophagus, stomach, small intestine and gall passages, and secretory fibers to the stomach and pancreas. They end in small ganglia in or near the organ. Postganglionic fibers carry the impulses to the end-organ.

The filaments of the nerve unite, and form a flat cord, which passes beneath the flocculus to the jugular foramen, through which it leaves the cranium. In emerging through this opening, the vagus is accompanied by and contained in the same sheath of dura mater with the accessory nerve, a septum separating them from the glossopharyngeal which lies in front In this situation the vagus presents a well-marked ganglionic enlargement, which is called the **jugular ganglion** (*ganglion of the root*); to it the accessory nerve is connected by one or two filaments. After its exit from the jugular foramen the vagus is joined by the cranial portion of the accessory nerve, and enlarges into a second gangliform swelling, called the **ganglion nodosum** (*ganglion of the trunk*); through this the fibers of the cranial portion of the accessory pass without interruption, being principally distributed to the pharyngeal and superior laryngeal branches of the vagus, but some of its fibers descend in the trunk of the vagus, to be distributed with the recurrent nerve.

The vagus nerve passes vertically down the neck within the carotid sheath, lying between the internal jugular vein and internal carotid artery as far as the upper border of the thyroid cartilage, and then between the same vein and the common carotid artery to the root of the neck. The further course of the nerve differs on the two sides of the body.

On the *right side*, the nerve passes across the subclavian artery between it and the right innominate vein, and descends by the side of the trachea to the back of the root of the lung, where it spreads out in the **posterior pulmonary plexus**. From the lower part of this plexus two cords descend on the esophagus, and divide to form, with branches from the opposite nerve, the **esophageal plexus**. Below, these branches are collected into a single cord, which runs along the back of the esophagus enters the abdomen, and is distributed to the postero-inferior surface of the stomach, joining the left side of the celiac plexus, and sending filaments to the lienal plexus.

On the *left side*, the vagus enters the thorax between the left carotid and subclavian arteries, behind the left innominate vein. It crosses the left side of the arch of the aorta, and descends behind the root of the left lung, forming there the **posterior pulmonary plexus**. From this it runs along the anterior surface of the esophagus, where it unites with the nerve of the right side in the **esophageal plexus**, and is continued to the stomach, distributing branches over its antero-superior surface; some of these extend over the fundus, and others along the lesser curvature. Filaments from these branches enter the lesser omentum, and join the hepatic plexus.

The **Jugular Ganglion** (*ganglion jugulare; ganglion of the root*) is of a grayish color, spherical in form, about 4 mm. in diameter.

Branches of Communication.—This ganglion is connected by several delicate filaments to the cranial portion of the accessory nerve; it also communicates by a twig with the petrous ganglion of the glossopharyngeal, with the facial nerve by means of its auricular branch, and with the sympathetic by means of an ascending filament from the superior cervical ganglion.

The **Ganglion Nodosum** (*ganglion of the trunk; inferior ganglion*) is cylindrical in form, of a reddish color, and 2.5 cm. in length. Passing through it is the cranial portion of the accessory nerve, which blends with the vagus below the ganglion.

Branches of Communication.—This ganglion is connected with the hypoglossal, the superior cervical ganglion of the sympathetic, and the loop between the first and second cervical nerves.

Branches of Distribution.—The branches of distribution of the vagus are:

In the Jugular Fossa	{ Meningeal. { Auricular.
In the Neck	⎧ Pharyngeal. ⎪ Superior laryngeal. ⎨ Recurrent. ⎩ Superior cardiac.
In the Thorax	⎧ Inferior cardiac. ⎪ Anterior bronchial. ⎨ Posterior bronchial. ⎩ Esophageal.
In the Abdomen	⎧ Gastric. ⎨ Celiac. ⎩ Hepatic.

The **Meningeal Branch** (*ramus meningeus; dural branch*) is a recurrent filament given off from the jugular ganglion; it is distributed to the dura mater in the posterior fossa of the base of the skull.

The **Auricular Branch** (*ramus auricularis; nerve of Arnold*) runs from the jugular ganglion, and is joined soon after its origin by a filament from the petrous ganglion of the glossopharyngeal; it passes behind the internal jugular vein, and enters the mastoid canaliculus on the lateral wall of the jugular fossa. Traversing the substance of the temporal bone, it crosses the facial canal about 4 mm. above the stylomastoid foramen, and here it gives off an ascending branch which joins the facial nerve. The nerve reaches the surface by passing through the tympanomastoid fissure between the mastoid process and the tympanic part of the temporal bone, and divides into two branches: one joins the posterior auricular nerve, the other is distributed to the skin of the back of the auricula and to the posterior part of the external acoustic meatus.

The **Pharyngeal Branch** (*ramus pharyngeus*), the principal motor nerve of the pharynx, runs from the upper part of the ganglion nodosum, and consists principally of filaments from the cranial portion of the accessory nerve. It passes across the internal carotid artery to the upper border of the Constrictor pharyngis medius, where it divides into numerous filaments, which join with branches from the glossopharyngeal, sympathetic, and external laryngeal to form the **pharyngeal plexus.** From the plexus, branches are distributed to the muscles and mucous membrane of the pharynx and the muscles of the soft palate, except the Tensor veli palatini. A minute filament descends and joins the hypoglossal nerve as it winds around the occipital artery.

The **Superior Laryngeal Nerve** (*n. laryngeus superior*) larger than the preceding, runs from the middle of the ganglion nodosum and in its course receives a branch from the superior cervical ganglion of the sympathetic. It descends, by the side of the pharynx, behind the internal carotid artery, and divides into two branches, **external** and **internal.**

The **external branch** (*ramus externus*), the smaller, descends on the larynx, beneath the Sternothyreoideus, to supply the Cricothyreoideus. It gives branches to the pharyngeal plexus and the Constrictor pharyngis inferior, and communicates with the superior cardiac nerve, behind the common carotid artery.

The **internal branch** (*ramus internus*) descends to the hyothyroid membrane, pierces it in company with the superior laryngeal artery, and is distributed to the mucous membrane of the larynx. Of these branches some are distributed to the epiglottis, the base of the tongue, and the epiglottic glands; others pass backward, in the aryepiglottic fold, to supply the mucous membrane surrounding the entrance of the larynx, and that lining the cavity of the larynx as low down as the vocal folds. A filament descends beneath the mucous membrane on the inner surface of the thyroid cartilage and joins the recurrent nerve.

The **Recurrent Nerve** (*n. recurrens; inferior or recurrent laryngeal nerve*) *arises*, on the *right side*, in front of the subclavian artery; winds from before backward around that vessel, and ascends obliquely to the side of the trachea behind the common carotid artery, and either in front of or behind the inferior thyroid artery. On the *left* side, it *arises* on the left of the arch of the aorta, and winds below the aorta at the point where the ligamentum arteriosum is attached, and then ascends to the side of the trachea. The nerve on either side ascends in the groove between the trachea and esophagus, passes under the lower border of the Constrictor pharyngis inferior, and enters the larynx behind the articulation of the inferior cornu of the thyroid cartilage with the cricoid; it is distributed to all the muscles of the larynx, excepting the Cricothyreoideus. It communicates with the internal branch of the superior laryngeal nerve, and gives off a few filaments to the mucous membrane of the lower part of the larynx.

As the recurrent nerve hooks around the subclavian artery or aorta, it gives off several cardiac filaments to the deep part of the cardiac plexus. As it ascends in the neck it gives off branches, more numerous on the left than on the right side, to the mucous membrane and muscular coat of the esophagus; branches to the mucous membrane and muscular fibers of the trachea; and some pharyngeal filaments to the Constrictor pharyngis inferior.

The **Superior Cardiac Branches** (*rami cardiaci superiores; cervical cardiac branches*), two or three in number, *arise* from the vagus, at the upper and lower parts of the neck.

The **upper branches** are small, and communicate with the cardiac branches of the sympathetic. They can be traced to the deep part of the cardiac plexus.

The **lower branch** *arises* at the root of the neck, just above the first rib. That from the right vagus passes in front or by the side of the innominate artery, and proceeds to the deep part of the cardiac plexus; that from the left runs down across the left side of the arch of the aorta, and joins the superficial part of the cardiac plexus.

The **Inferior Cardiac Branches** (*rami cardiaci inferiores; thoracic cardiac branches*), on the right side, *arise* from the trunk of the vagus as it lies by the side of the trachea, and from its recurrent nerve; on the left side from the recurrent nerve only; passing inward, they end in the deep part of the cardiac plexus. (Fig. 840)

The **Anterior Bronchial Branches** (*rami bronchiales anteriores; anterior or ventral pulmonary branches*), two or three in number, and of small size, are distributed on the anterior surface of the root of the lung. They join with filaments from the sympathetic, and form the **anterior pulmonary plexus.**

The **Posterior Bronchial Branches** (*rami bronchiales posteriores; posterior or dorsal* *pulmonary branches*), more numerous and larger than the anterior, are distributed on the posterior surface of the root of the lung; they are joined by filaments from the third and fourth (sometimes also from the first and second) thoracic ganglia of the sympathetic trunk, and form the **posterior pulmonary plexus**. Branches from this plexus accompany the ramifications of the bronchi through the substance of the lung.

The **Esophageal Branches** (*rami œsophagei*) are given off both above and below the bronchial branches; the lower are numerous and larger than the upper. They form, together with the branches from the opposite nerve, the **esophageal plexus**. From this plexus filaments are distributed to the back of the pericardium.

The **Gastric Branches** (*rami gastrici*) are distributed to the stomach. The right vagus forms the **posterior gastric plexus** on the postero-inferior surface of the stomach and the left the **anterior gastric plexus** on the antero-superior surface.

The **Celiac Branches** (*rami cœliaci*) are mainly derived from the right vagus: they join the celiac plexus and through it supply branches to the pancreas, spleen, kidneys, suprarenal bodies, and intestine.

The **Hepatic Branches** (*rami hepatici*) *arise* from the left vagus: they join the hepatic plexus and through it are conveyed to the liver.

THE ACCESSORY NERVE (N. ACCESSORIUS; ELEVENTH NERVE; SPINAL ACCESSORY NERVE) (Figs. 788, 789, 790, 801).

The **accessory nerve** consists of two parts: a **cranial** and a **spinal**.

The **Cranial Part** (*ramus internus; accessory portion*) is the smaller of the two. Its fibers *arise* from the cells of the **nucleus ambiguus** and emerge as four or five delicate rootlets from the side of the medulla oblongata, below the roots of the vagus. It runs lateralward to the jugular foramen, where it interchanges fibers with the spinal portion or becomes united to it for a short distance; here it is also connected by one or two filaments with the jugular ganglion of the vagus. It then passes through the jugular foramen, separates from the spinal portion and is continued over the surface of the ganglion nodosum of the vagus, to the surface of which it is adherent, and is distributed principally to the pharyngeal and superior laryngeal branches of the vagus. Through the pharyngeal branch it probably supplies the Musculus uvulæ and Levator veli palatini. Some few filaments from it are continued into the trunk of the vagus below the ganglion, to be distributed with the recurrent nerve.

The **Spinal Part** (*ramus externus; spinal portion*) is firm in texture, and its fibers *arise* from the motor cells in the lateral part of the anterior column of the gray substance of the medulla spinalis as low as the fifth cervical nerve. Passing through the lateral funiculus of the medulla spinalis, they emerge on its surface and unite to form a single trunk, which ascends between the ligamentum denticulatum and the posterior roots of the spinal nerves, enters the skull through the foramen magnum, and is then directed to the jugular foramen, through which it passes, lying in the same sheath of dura mater as the vagus, but separated from it by a fold of the arachnoid. In the jugular foramen, it receives one or two filaments from the cranial part of the nerve, or else joins it for a short distance and then separates from it again. At its exit from the jugular foramen, it runs backward in front of the internal jugular vein in 66.6 per cent. of cases, and behind in it 33.3 per cent. (Tandler). The nerve then descends obliquely behind the Digastricus and Stylohyoideus to the upper part of the Sternocleidomastoideus; it pierces this muscle, and courses obliquely across the posterior triangle of the neck, to end in the deep surface of the Trapezius. As it traverses the Sternocleidomastoideus it gives several filaments to the muscle, and joins with branches from the second cervical nerve.

n the posterior triangle it unites with the second and third cervical nerves, while
eneath the Trapezius it forms a plexus with the third and fourth cervical nerves,
nd from this plexus fibers are distributed to the muscle.[1]

THE HYPOGLOSSAL NERVE (N. HYPOGLOSSUS; TWELFTH NERVE)
(Figs. 791, 792).

The **hypoglossal nerve** is the motor nerve of the tongue.

Its fibers *arise* from the cells of the **hypoglossal nucleus**, which is an upward
rolongation of the base of the anterior column of gray substance of the medulla
pinalis. This nucleus is about 2 cm. in length, and its upper part is subjacent
o the **trigonum hypoglossi**, or lower portion of the medial eminence of the rhom-

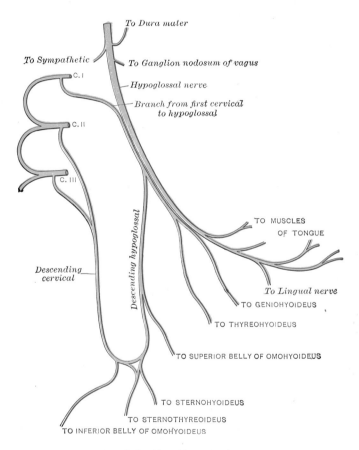

Fig. 791.—Plan of hypoglossal nerve.

oid fossa (page 797). The lower part of the nucleus extends downward into the
losed part of the medulla oblongata, and there lies in relation to the ventro-lateral
spect of the central canal. The fibers run forward through the medulla oblongata,
nd emerge in the antero-lateral sulcus between the pyramid and the olive.

The rootlets of this nerve are collected into two bundles, which perforate the
ura mater separately, opposite the hypoglossal canal in the occipital bone, and

[1] Experimental work by Corbin and Harrison (The Sensory Innervation of the Spinal Accessory and Tongue Mus-
llature in the Rhesus Monkey, Brain, 1939, **62**, 191–197) indicates that in the monkey, "the anastomotic branches
etween the upper cervical ventral rami and the accessory nerve carry sensory fibers only." These fibers arise in the
ervical dorsal root ganglia and probably carry proprioceptive impulses from the muscles which receive somatic motor
nervation from the accessory nerve.

unite together after their passage through it; in some cases the canal is divided into two by a small bony spicule. The nerve descends almost vertically to a point corresponding with the angle of the mandible. It is at first deeply seated beneath the internal carotid artery and internal jugular vein, and intimately connected with the vagus nerve; it then passes forward between the vein and artery, and lower down in the neck becomes superficial below the Digastricus. The nerve then loops around the occipital artery, and crosses the external carotid and lingual arteries below the tendon of the Digastricus. It passes beneath the tendon of the Digastricus, the Stylohyoideus, and the Mylohyoideus, lying between the last-named muscle and the Hyoglossus, and communicates at the anterior border of the Hyo-

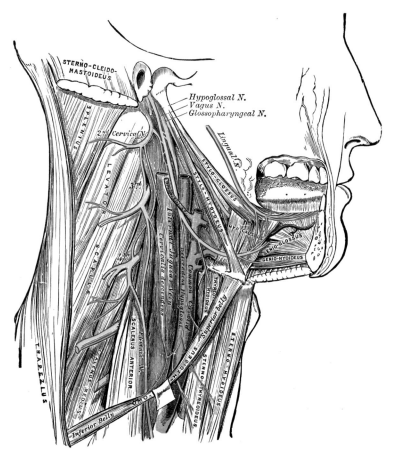

Fig. 792.—Hypoglossal nerve, cervical plexus, and their branches.

glossus with the lingual nerve; it is then continued forward in the fibers of the Genioglossus as far as the tip of the tongue, distributing branches to its muscular substance.

Branches of Communication.—Its branches of communication are, with the

Vagus.	First and second cervical nerves.
Sympathetic.	Lingual.

The communications with the vagus take place close to the skull, numerous filaments passing between the hypoglossal and the ganglion nodosum of the vagus through the mass of connective tissue which unites the two nerves. As the nerve winds around the occipital artery it gives off a filament to the pharyngeal plexus.

The communication with the sympathetic takes place opposite the atlas by branches derived from the superior cervical ganglion, and in the same situation the nerve is joined by a filament derived from the loop connecting the first and second cervical nerves.

The communications with the lingual take place near the anterior border of the Hyoglossus by numerous filaments which ascend upon the muscle.

Branches of Distribution.—The branches of distribution of the hypoglossal nerve are:

Meningeal.	Thyrohyoid.
Descending.	Muscular.

Of these branches, the meningeal, descending, thyrohyoid, and the muscular twig to the Geniohyoideus, are probably derived mainly from the branch which passes from the loop between the first and second cervical to join the hypoglossal (Figs. 791, 792, 801).

Meningeal Branches (*dural branches*). —As the hypoglossal nerve passes through the hypoglossal canal it gives off, according to Luschka, several filaments to the dura mater in the posterior fossa of the skull.

The **Descending Ramus** (*ramus descendens; descendens hypoglossi*), long and slender, quits the hypoglossal where it turns around the occipital artery and descends in front of or in the sheath of the carotid vessels; it gives a branch to the superior belly of the Omohyoideus, and then joins the communicantes cervicales from the second and third cervical nerves just below the middle of the neck, to form a loop, the **ansa hypoglossi**. From the convexity of this loop branches pass to supply the Sternohyoideus, the Sternothyreoideus, and the inferior belly of the Omohyoideus. According to Arnold, another filament descends in front of the vessels into the thorax, and joins the cardiac and phrenic nerves.

Fig.. 793—A portion of the spinal cord, showing its right lateral surface. The dura is opened and arranged to show the nerve roots. (Testut.)

The **Thyrohyoid Branch** (*ramus thyreohyoideus*) *arises* from the hypoglossal near the posterior border of the hyoglossus; it runs obliquely across the greater cornu of the hyoid bone, and supplies the Thyreohyoideus muscle.

The **Muscular Branches** are distributed to the Styloglossus, Hyoglossus, Geniohyoideus, and Genioglossus. At the under surface of the tongue numerous slender branches pass upward into the substance of the organ to supply its intrinsic muscles. The hypoglossal nerve as it enters the tongue musculature probably contains sensory fibers with cells of origin in the first (if present) and second cervical dorsal root ganglia.

60

THE SPINAL NERVES (NERVI SPINALES).

The **spinal nerves** spring from the medulla spinalis, and are transmitted through the intervertebral foramina. They number thirty-one pairs, which are grouped as follows: Cervical, 8; Thoracic, 12; Lumbar, 5; Sacral, 5; Coccygeal, 1.

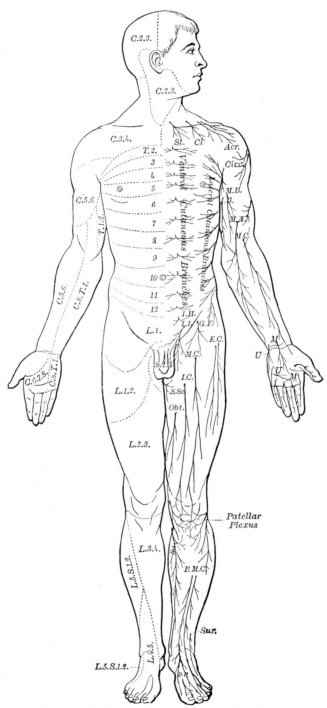

Fig. 794.—Distribution of cutaneous nerves. Ventral aspect.

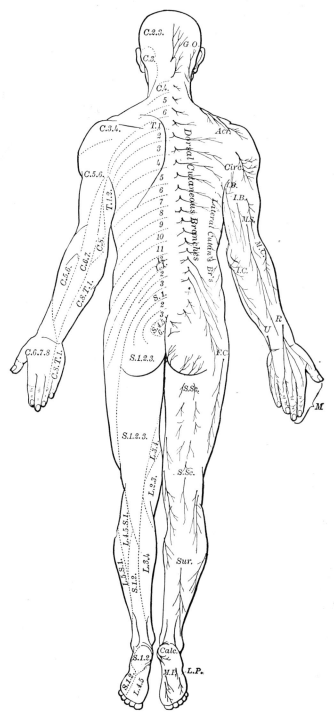

Fig. 795.—Distribution of cutaneous nerves. Dorsal aspect.

Figs 794 and 795 (and others like them) show areas of skin supplied by each of the dorsal root ganglia is diagrammatic. The work of Sherrington has demonstrated that the "sensory root field" of a particular dorsal root ganglion overlaps that of the zones or "dermatomes" supplied by the ganglion above and below (Fig. 799). In fact fibers carrying different modalities, *i. e.*, pain and touch, vary in the amount of this overlap. This interesting subject is discussed by Fulton, J. F. (Physiology of the Nervous System, Oxford University Press, New York, 1938, see pages 34–38).

The **first cervical nerve** emerges from the vertebral canal between the occipital bone and the atlas, and is therefore called the **suboccipital nerve;** the eighth issues between the seventh cervical and first thoracic vertebræ.

Nerve Roots.—Each nerve is attached to the medulla spinalis by two roots, an **anterior** or **ventral**, and a **posterior** or **dorsal**, the latter being characterized by the presence of a ganglion, the **spinal ganglion.**

The **Anterior Root** (*radix anterior; ventral root*) emerges from the anterior surface of the medulla spinalis as a number of rootlets or filaments (*fila radicularia*), which coalesce to form two bundles near the intervertebral foramen.

The **Posterior Root** (*radix posterior; dorsal root*) is larger than the anterior owing to the greater size and number of its rootlets; these are attached along the postero-lateral furrow of the medulla spinalis and unite to form two bundles which join the spinal ganglion. The posterior root of the first cervical nerve is exceptional in that it is smaller than the anterior; it is occasionally wanting.

The **Spinal Ganglia** (*ganglion spinale*) are collections of nerve cells on the posterior roots of the spinal nerves. Each ganglion is oval in shape, reddish in color, and its size bears a proportion to that of the nerve root on which it is situated; it is bifid medially where it is joined by the two bundles of the posterior nerve root. The ganglia are usually placed in the intervertebral foramina, immediately outside the points where the nerve roots perforate the dura mater, but there are exceptions to this rule; thus the ganglia of the first and second cervical nerves lie on the vertebral arches of the atlas and axis respectively, those of the sacral nerves are inside the vertebral canal, while that on the posterior root of the coccygeal nerve is placed within the sheath of dura mater.

The ganglia of the first cervical nerve may be absent, while small *aberrant ganglia* consisting of groups of nerve cells are sometimes found on the posterior roots between the spinal ganglia and the medulla spinalis.

Each nerve root receives a covering from the pia mater, and is loosely invested by the arachnoid, the latter being prolonged as far as the points where the roots pierce the dura mater. The two roots pierce the dura mater separately, each receiving a sheath from this membrane; where the roots join to form the spinal nerve this sheath is continuous with the epineurium of the nerve.

Size and Direction.—The roots of the upper four *cervical* nerves are small, those of the lower four are large. The posterior roots of the cervical nerves bear a proportion to the anterior of three to one, which is greater than in the other regions; their individual filaments are also larger than those of the anterior roots. The posterior root of the first cervical is an exception to this rule, being smaller than the anterior root; in eight per cent. of cases it is wanting. The roots of the first and second cervical nerves are short, and run nearly horizontally to their points of exit from the vertebral canal. From the second to the eighth cervical they are directed obliquely downward, the obliquity and length of the roots successively increasing; the distance, however, between the level of attachment of any of these roots to the medulla spinalis and the points of exit of the corresponding nerves never exceeds the depth of one vertebra.

The roots of the *thoracic* nerves, with the exception of the first, are small, and the posterior only slightly exceed the anterior in size. They increase successively in length, from above downward, and in the lower part of the thoracic region descend in contact with the medulla spinalis for a distance equal to the height of at least two vertebræ before they emerge from the vertebral canal.

The roots of the lower *lumbar* and upper *sacral* nerves are the largest, and their individual filaments the most numerous of all the spinal nerves, while the roots of the *coccygeal* nerve are the smallest.

The roots of the lumbar, sacral, and coccygeal nerves run vertically downward to their respective exits, and as the medulla spinalis ends near the lower border of the first lumbar vertebra it follows that the length of the successive roots must rapidly increase. The term **cauda equina** is applied to this collection of nerve roots.

From the description given it will be seen that the largest nerve roots, and consequently the largest spinal nerves, are attached to the cervical and lumbar swellings of the medulla spinalis; these nerves are distributed to the upper and lower limbs.

Connections with Sympathetic and Parasympathetic.[1]—Immediately beyond the spinal ganglion, the anterior and posterior nerve roots unite to form the **spinal nerve** which emerges through the intervertebral foramen. Each spinal nerve receives a branch (**gray ramus communicans**) from the adjacent ganglion of the sympathetic trunk, while the thoracic, and the first and second lumbar nerves

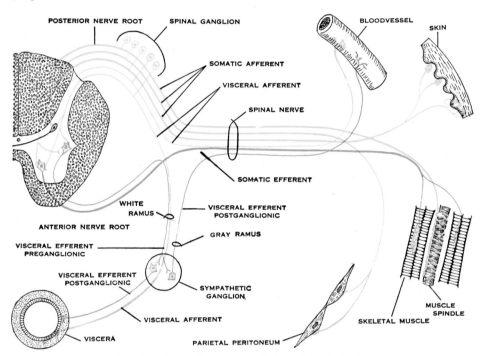

Fɪɢ. 796.—Scheme showing structure of a typical spinal nerve.

(sometimes third and even fourth lumbar) each contribute a branch (**white ramus communicans**) to the adjoining sympathetic ganglion. The second, third, and fourth sacral nerves also supply white rami, parasympathetic fibers; these, however, are not connected with the ganglia of the sympathetic trunk, but run directly into the pelvic plexuses of the sympathetic and end in small ganglia on the pelvic viscera.

Structure.—A typical spinal nerve contains **somatic efferent fibers, autonomic (efferent) fibers and afferent (sensory) fibers.**

1. The **somatic efferent fibers** are motor. They originate in the cells of the anterior column of the medulla spinalis, and run outward through the anterior nerve roots to the spinal nerve. They convey impulses to the striped muscles, and are continuous from their origin to their peripheral distribution.

[1] The terms sympathetic and parasympathetic are of importance as terms to delineate structural relations in the visceral nervous system. However, the physiologist now uses the terms adrenergic and cholinergic to denote the function of the various visceral efferent fibers (See: Connon, W. B., and Rosenblueth, A.: Autonomic Neuro-effector Systems, The Macmillan Co., New York, 1937). The postganglionic fibers in the thoracolumbar (sympathetic) outflow may be adrenergic or cholinergic; those in the sacral (parasympathetic), cholinergic and possibly adrenergic.

2. The **autonomic fibers** are all efferent, and convey impulses to glands and to smooth and cardiac muscle. The preganglionic fibers arise from cells in the lateral column of the spinal cord. There are two distinct groups of autonomic fibers, the sympathetic and the parasympathetic. The **sympathetic fibers** are conveyed through the anterior nerve roots of the thoracic and upper three lumbar nerves, the **thoracolumbar outflow.** They pass in the white rami communicantes to the sympathetic trunk; here they may end by forming synapses around its cells, or may run through the ganglion to end in another of the ganglia of the sympathetic trunk, or in a more distally placed ganglion in one of the sympathetic plexuses. In all cases they end by forming synapses around other nerve cells. From the cells of the ganglia of the sympathetic trunk other fibers, postganglionic fibers, take origin; some of these run through the gray rami communicantes to join the spinal nerves, along which they are carried to the bloodvessels, glands and smooth muscle of the trunk and limbs, while others pass to the viscera via visceral branches of the sympathetic trunk. Some of the visceral branches also contain preganglionic fibers which have coursed through the sympathetic trunk on their way to terminate about postganglionic neurons of collateral ganglia. Postganglionic fibers arise from the latter and pass to structures in the viscera in various branches of the plexuses.

The **parasympathetic fibers** or **sacral outflow** are efferent fibers, preganglionic fibers, which also originate in the lateral column of the spinal cord, and are conveyed through the anterior nerve roots of the second, third and fourth sacral nerves and their white rami communicantes. They do not enter the sympathetic trunk but pass in the pelvic nerves and through the pelvic plexus to end in small ganglia in or on the walls of the pelvic viscera. Postganglionic fibers are distributed in the walls of the viscera to the end-organs, smooth muscle, glands, etc.

The **afferent (sensory) fibers** convey impulses from the body to the central nervous system. They originate in the unipolar nerve cells of the spinal ganglia. The single axon divides into a peripheral and a central branch. The central fibers enter the spinal cord in the posterior nerve roots. The peripheral fibers join the anterior roots to form the spinal nerves and are distributed without interruption to sensory end-organs in the skin, muscle, tendons, viscera, etc. The afferent fibers from the skin, muscle, etc., are known as **somatic afferent fibers.** Those to the viscera pass in the white rami communicantes, join the autonomic fibers, and are distributed with them, but without interruption, to the sensory end-organs in the viscera. The afferent fibers from the viscera are known as **visceral** (splanchnic) **afferent fibers.**

Divisions.—After emerging from the intervertebral foramen, each spinal nerve gives off a small **meningeal branch** which reënters the vertebral canal through the intervertebral foramen and supplies the vertebræ and their ligaments, and the bloodvessels of the medulla spinalis and its membranes. The spinal nerve then splits into a **posterior** or **dorsal,** and an **anterior** or **ventral ramus,** each receiving fibers from both nerve roots.

POSTERIOR RAMI OF THE SPINAL NERVES (RAMI POSTERIORES).

The **posterior rami** are, as a rule, smaller than the anterior. They are directed backward, and, with the exceptions of those of the first cervical, the fourth and fifth sacral, and the coccygeal, divide into medial and lateral branches for the supply of the muscles and skin (Figs. 815, 797, 798) of the posterior part of the trunk.

The Cervical Nerves (Nn. Cervicales).

The **posterior ramus of the suboccipital or first cervical nerve** is larger than the anterior division, and emerges above the posterior arch of the atlas and beneath the vertebral artery. It enters the suboccipital triangle and supplies the muscles which bound this triangle, viz., the Rectus capitis posterior major, and the Obliqui superior and inferior; it gives branches also to the Rectus capitis posterior minor and the Semispinalis capitis. A filament from the branch to the Obliquus inferior joins the posterior ramus of the second cervical nerve.

The nerve occasionally gives off a cutaneous branch which accompanies the occipital artery to the scalp, and communicates with the greater and lesser occipital nerves.

The **posterior ramus of the second cervical nerve** is much larger than the anterior ramus, and is the greatest of all the cervical posterior rami. It emerges between the posterior arch of the atlas and the lamina of the axis, below the Obliquus inferior. It supplies a twig to this muscle, receives a communicating filament from the posterior ramus of the first cervical, and then divides into a large medial and a small lateral branch.

The **medial branch** (*ramus medialis; internal branch*), called from its size and distribution the **greater occipital nerve** (*n. occipitalis major; great occipital nerve*), ascends obliquely between the Obliquus inferior and the Semispinalis capitis, and pierces the latter muscle and the Trapezius near their attachments to the occipital bone (Fig. 797). It is then joined by a filament from the medial branch of the posterior division of the third cervical, and, ascending on the back of the head with the occipital artery, divides into branches which communicate with the lesser occipital nerve and supply the skin of the scalp as far forward as the vertex of the skull. It gives off muscular branches to the Semispinalis capitis, and occasionally a twig to the back of the auricula. The **lateral branch** (*ramus lateralis; external*

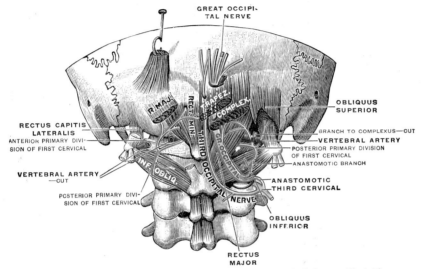

FIG. 797.—Posterior primary divisions of the upper three cervical nerves. (Testut.)

branch) supplies filaments to the Splenius, Longissimus capitis, and Semispinalis capitis, and is often joined by the corresponding branch of the third cervical.

The **posterior ramus of the third cervical** is intermediate in size between those of the second and fourth. Its **medial branch** runs between the Semispinalis capitis and cervicis, and, piercing the Splenius and Trapezius, ends in the skin. While under the Trapezius it gives off a branch called the **third occipital nerve**, which pierces the Trapezius and ends in the skin of the lower part of the back of the head (Fig. 797). It lies medial to the greater occipital and communicates with it. The **lateral branch** often joins that of the second cervical.

The posterior division of the suboccipital, and the medial branches of the posterior division of the second and third cervical nerves are sometimes joined by communicating loops to form the *posterior cervical plexus* (Cruveilhier).

The **posterior rami of the lower five cervical nerves** divide into medial and lateral branches. The **medial branches** of the fourth and fifth run between the Semispinales cervicis and capitis, and, having reached the spinous processes, pierce the Splenius and Trapezius to end in the skin (Fig. 798). Sometimes the branch of the fifth fails to reach the skin. Those of the lower three nerves are small, and end in the Semispinales cervicis and capitis, Multifidus, and Interspinales. The **lateral branches** of the lower five nerves supply the Iliocostalis cervicis, Longissimus cervicis, and Longissimus capitis.

The Thoracic Nerves (Nn. Thoracales).

The **medial branches** (*ramus medialis; internal branch*) of the **posterior rami of the upper six thoracic nerves** run between the Semispinalis dorsi and Multifidus,

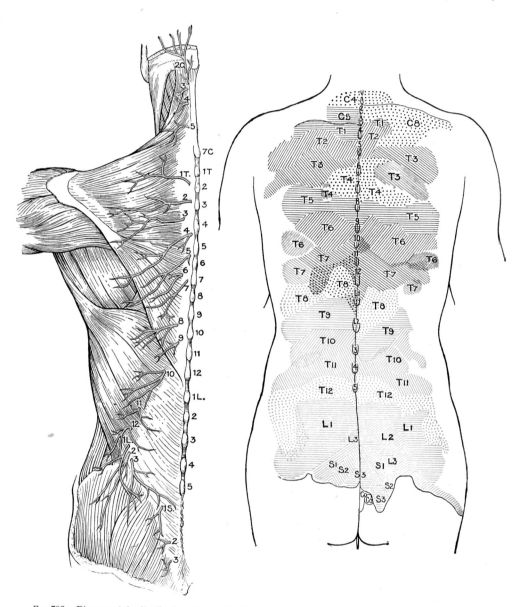

FIG. 798.—Diagram of the distribution of the cutaneous branches of the posterior divisions of the spinal nerves.

FIG. 799.—Areas of distribution of the cutaneous branches of the posterior divisions of the spinal nerves. The areas of the media branches are in black, those of the lateral in red. (H. M. Johnston.)

which they supply; they then pierce the Rhomboidei and Trapezius, and reach the skin by the sides of the spinous processes (Fig. 798). The medial branches of the **lower six** are distributed chiefly to the Multifidus and Longissimus dorsi, occasionally they give off filaments to the skin near the middle line.

The **lateral branches** (*ramus lateralis; external branch*) increase in size from above downward. They run through or beneath the Longissimus dorsi to the interval between it and the Iliocostales, and supply these muscles; the lower five or six also give off cutaneous branches which pierce the Serratus posterior inferior and Latissimus dorsi in a line with the angles of the ribs (Fig. 798). The lateral branches of a variable number of the upper thoracic nerves also give filaments to the skin. The lateral branch of the twelfth thoracic, after sending a filament medialward along the iliac crest, passes downward to the skin of the buttock.

The medial cutaneous branches of the posterior rami of the thoracic nerves descend for some distance close to the spinous processes before reaching the skin, while the lateral branches travel downward for a considerable distance—it may be as much as the breadth of four ribs—before they become superficial; the branch from the twelfth thoracic, for instance, reaches the skin only a little way above the iliac crest.

The Lumbar Nerves (Nn. Lumbales).

The **medial branches** of the **posterior rami of the lumbar nerves** run close to the articular processes of the vertebræ and end in the Multifidus.

The **lateral branches** supply the Sacrospinalis. The upper three give off cutaneous nerves which pierce the aponeurosis of the Latissimus dorsi at the lateral border of the Sacrospinalis and descend across the posterior part of the iliac crest to the skin of the buttock (Fig. 798), some of their twigs running as far as the level of the greater trochanter.

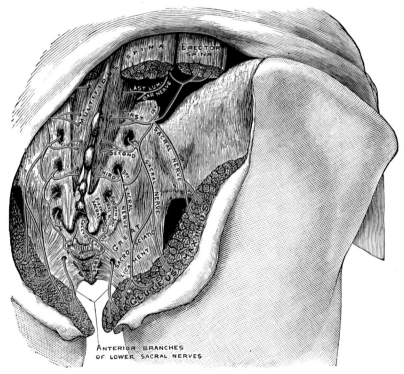

Fig. 800.—The posterior divisions of the sacral nerves.

The Sacral Nerves (Nn. Sacrales).

The **posterior rami of the sacral nerves** (*rami posteriores*) (Fig. 800) are small, and diminish in size from above downward; they emerge, except the last, through the posterior sacral foramina. The *upper three* are covered at their points of exit by the Multifidus, and divide into medial and lateral branches.

The **medial branches** are small, and end in the Multifidus.

The **lateral branches** join with one another and with the lateral branches of the posterior divisions of the last lumbar and fourth sacral to form loops on the dorsal surface of the sacrum. From these loops branches run to the dorsal surface of the sacrotuberous ligament and form a second series of loops under the Glutæus maximus. From this second series cutaneous branches, two or three in number, pierce the Glutæus maximus along a line drawn from the posterior superior iliac spine to the tip of the coccyx; they supply the skin over the posterior part of the buttock.

The posterior rami of the *lower two* sacral nerves are small and lie below the Multifidus. They do not divide into medial and lateral branches, but unite with each other and with the posterior rami of the coccygeal nerve to form loops on the back of the sacrum; filaments from these loops supply the skin over the coccyx.

The Coccygeal Nerve (N. Coccygeus).

The **posterior ramus of the coccygeal nerve** (*ramus posterior*) does not divide into a medial and a lateral branch, but receives, as already stated, a communicating branch from the last sacral; it is distributed to the skin over the back of the coccyx.

ANTERIOR RAMI OF THE SPINAL NERVES (RAMI ANTERIORES).

The **anterior rami of the spinal nerves** supply the antero-lateral parts of the trunk, and the limbs; they are for the most part larger than the posterior rami. In the thoracic region they run independently of one another, but in the cervical, lumbar, and sacral regions they unite near their origins to form plexuses.

The Cervical Nerves (Nn. Cervicales).

The anterior rami of the cervical nerves, with the exception of the first, pass outward between the Intertransversarii anterior and posterior, lying on the grooved upper surfaces of the transverse processes of the vertebræ. The **anterior ramus of the first** or **suboccipital nerve** issues from the vertebral canal above the posterior arch of the atlas and runs forward around the lateral aspect of its superior articular process, medial to the vertebral artery. In most cases it descends medial to and in front of the Rectus capitis lateralis, but occasionally it pierces the muscle.

The anterior rami of the **upper four cervical nerves** unite to form the **cervical plexus,** and each receives a gray ramus communicans from the superior cervical ganglion of the sympathetic trunk. Those of the **lower four cervical,** together with the greater part of the first thoracic, form the **brachial plexus.** They each receive a gray ramus communicans, those for the fifth and sixth being derived from the middle, and those for the seventh and eighth from the lowest, cervical ganglion of the sympathetic trunk.

The Cervical Plexus (*plexus cervicalis*) (Fig. 801).—The cervical plexus is formed by the anterior rami of the upper four cervical nerves; each nerve, except the first, divides into an upper and a lower branch, and the branches unite to form three loops. The plexus is situated opposite the upper four cervical vertebræ, in front of the Levator scapulæ and Scalenus medius, and covered by the Sternocleidomastoideus.

Its branches are divided into two groups, **superficial and deep,** and are here given in tabular form; the figures following the names indicate the nerves from which the different branches take origin:

Superficial		{	Smaller occipital . . . . . . 2, C.			
			Great auricular . . . . 2, 3, C.			
			Cutaneous cervical . . . . . 2, 3, C.			
			Supraclavicular . . . . . . 3, 4, C.			

Deep	{ Internal	{	Communicating {	With hypoglossal . 1, 2, C.
				" vagus . . . 1, 2, C.
				" sympathetic . 1, 2, 3, 4, C.
			Muscular . . {	Rectus capitis lateralis 1, C.
				Rectus capitis anterior 1, 2, C.
				Longus capitis . . 1, 2, 3, C.
				Communicantes cervi-
				cales . . . 2, 3, C.
				Phrenic . . . 3, 4, 5, C.
	External	{	Communicating with accessory . . . 2, 3, 4, C.	
			Muscular . . {	Sternocleidomastoideus 2, C.
				Trapezius . . . 3, 4, C.
				Levator scapulæ . . 3, 4, C.
				Scalenus medius . 3, 4, C.

Superficial Branches of the Cervical Plexus (Figs. 782, 802).—The **Smaller Occipital Nerve** (*n. occipitalis minor; small occipital nerve*) *arises* from the second cervical nerve, sometimes also from the third; it curves around and ascends along the posterior border of the Sternocleidomastoideus. Near the cranium it perforates the deep fascia, and is continued upward along the side of the head behind the auricula, supplying the skin and communicating with the greater occipital, the great auricular, and the posterior auricular branch of the facial. The smaller occipital varies in size, and is sometimes duplicated.

It gives off an **auricular branch**, which supplies the skin of the upper and back part of the auricula, communicating with the mastoid branch of the great auricular. This branch is occasionally derived from the greater occipital nerve.

The **Great Auricular Nerve** (*n. auricularis magnus*) is the largest of the ascending branches. It arises from the second and third cervical nerves, winds around the posterior border of the Sternocleidomastoideus, and, after perforating the deep fascia, ascends upon that muscle beneath the Platysma to the parotid gland, where it divides into an anterior and a posterior branch.

The **anterior branch** (*ramus anterior; facial branch*) is distributed to the skin of the face over the parotid gland, and communicates in the substance of the gland with the facial nerve.

The **posterior branch** (*ramus posterior; mastoid branch*) supplies the skin over the mastoid process and on the back of the auricula, except at its upper part; a filament pierces the auricula to reach its lateral surface, where it is distributed to the lobule and lower part of the concha. The posterior branch communicates with the smaller occipital, the auricular branch of the vagus, and the posterior auricular branch of the facial.

The **Cutaneous Cervical** (*n. cutaneus colli; superficial or transverse cervical nerve*) *arises* from the second and third cervical nerves, turns around the posterior border of the Sternocleidomastoideus about its middle, and, passing obliquely forward beneath the external jugular vein to the anterior border of the muscle, it perforates the deep cervical fascia, and divides beneath the Platysma into ascending and descending branches, which are distributed to the antero-lateral parts of the neck.

The **ascending branches** (*rami superiores*) pass upward to the submaxillary region, and form a plexus with the cervical branch of the facial nerve beneath the Platysma;

others pierce that muscle, and are distributed to the skin of the upper and front part of the neck.

The **descending branches** (*rami inferiores*) pierce the Platysma, and are distributed to the skin of the side and front of the neck, as low as the sternum.

The **Supraclavicular Nerves** (*nn. supraclaviculares; descending branches*) *arise* from the third and fourth cervical nerves; they emerge beneath the posterior border of the Sternocleidomastoideus, and descend in the posterior triangle of the neck beneath the Platysma and deep cervical fascia. Near the clavicle they perforate the fascia and Platysma to become cutaneous, and are arranged, according to their position, into three groups—**anterior, middle** and **posterior.**

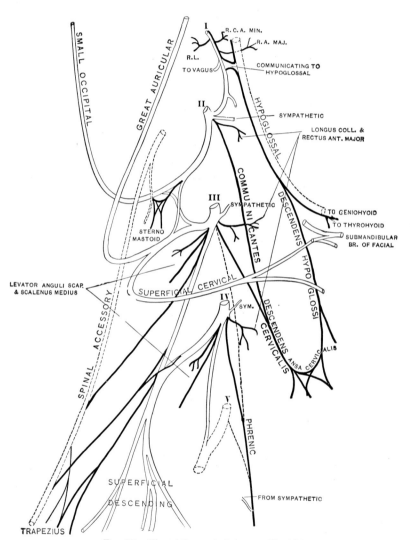

Fig. 801.—Plan of the cervical plexus. (Gerrish.)

The **anterior supraclavicular nerves** (*nn. supraclaviculares anteriores; suprasternal nerves*) cross obliquely over the external jugular vein and the clavicular and sternal heads of the Sternocleidomastoideus, and supply the skin as far as the middle line. They furnish one or two filaments to the sternoclavicular joint.

The **middle supraclavicular nerves** (*nn. supraclaviculares medii; supraclavicular* *nerves*) cross the clavicle, and supply the skin over the Pectoralis major and Deltoideus, communicating with the cutaneous branches of the upper intercostal nerves.

The **posterior supraclavicular nerves** (*nn. supraclaviculares posteriores; supra-acromial nerves*) pass obliquely across the outer surface of the Trapezius and the acromion, and supply the skin of the upper and posterior parts of the shoulder.

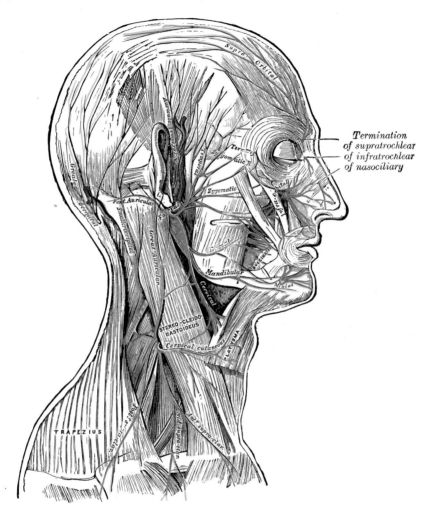

FIG. 802.—The nerves of the scalp, face, and side of neck.

Deep Branches of the Cervical Plexus. INTERNAL SERIES.—The **Communicating Branches** consist of several filaments, which pass from the loop between the first and second cervical nerves to the vagus, hypoglossal,[1] and sympathetic. The branch to the hypoglossal ultimately leaves that nerve as a series of branches, viz., the descending ramus, the nerve to the Thyreohyoideus and the nerve, to the Geniohyoideus. A communicating branch also passes from the fourth to the fifth cervical, while each of the first four cervical nerves receives a gray ramus communicans from the superior cervical ganglion of the sympathetic.

Muscular Branches supply the Longus capitis, Rectus capitis anterior, and Rectus capitis lateralis.

The **Communicantes Cervicales** (*communicantes hypoglossi*) (Fig. 801) consist

---

[1] By this communication, these cervical nerves probably contribute sensory fibers to the hypoglossal nerve.

usually of two filaments, one derived from the second, and the other from the third cervical. These filaments join to form the **descendens cervicalis**, which passes downward on the lateral side of the internal jugular vein, crosses in front of the vein a little below the middle of the neck, and forms a loop (**ansa hypoglossi**) with the descending ramus of the hypoglossal in front of the sheath of the carotid vessels. Occasionally, the loop is formed within the sheath.

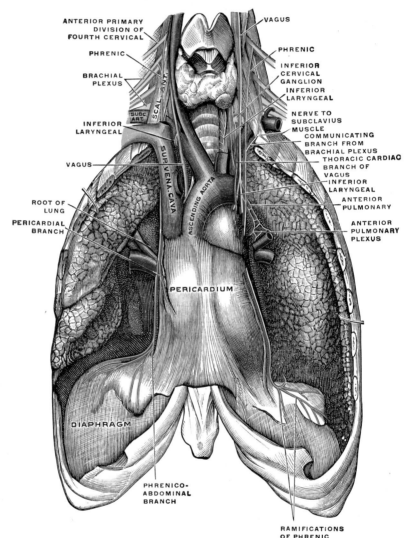

FIG. 803.—The phrenic nerve and its relations with the vagus nerve.

The **Phrenic Nerve** (*n. phrenicus; internal respiratory nerve of Bell*) contains motor and sensory fibers in the proportion of about two to one.[1] It *arises* chiefly from the fourth cervical nerve, but receives a branch from the third and another from the fifth; the fibers from the fifth occasionally come through the nerve to the Subclavius. It descends to the root of the neck, running obliquely across the front of the Scalenus anterior, and beneath the Sternocleidomastoideus, the inferior

[1] The sensory fibers in the phrenic nerve are of importance in the interpretation of the pain which is caused by stimulation of receptors in the central portion of the diaphragmatic pleura and peritoneum. Such stimulation does not cause pain which is localized to the area of stimulation but one that is referred to the tip of the shoulder. (See Hinsey, J. C., and Phillips, R. A.: Observations upon Diaphragmatic Sensation, Jour. Neuro-physiol., 1940, **3**, 175–181.

belly of the Omohyoideus, and the transverse cervical and transverse scapular vessels. It next passes in front of the first part of the subclavian artery, between it and the subclavian vein, and, as it enters the thorax, crosses the internal mammary artery near its origin. Within the thorax, it descends nearly vertically in front of the root of the lung, and then between the pericardium and the mediastinal pleura, to the diaphragm, where it divides into branches, which pierce that muscle, and are distributed to its under surface. In the thorax it is accompanied by the pericardiacophrenic branch of the internal mammary artery.

The two phrenic nerves differ in their length, and also in their relations at the upper part of the thorax.

The **right nerve** is situated more deeply, and is shorter and more vertical in direction than the left; it lies lateral to the right innominate vein and superior vena cava.

The **left nerve** is rather longer than the right, from the inclination of the heart to the left side, and from the diaphragm being lower on this than on the right side. At the root of the neck it is crossed by the thoracic duct; in the superior mediastinum it lies between the left common carotid and left subclavian arteries, and crosses superficial to the vagus on the left side of the arch of the aorta.

Each nerve supplies filaments to the pericardium and pleura, and at the root of the neck is joined by a filament from the sympathetic, and, occasionally, by one from the ansa hypoglossi. Branches have been described as passing to the peritoneum.

From the *right nerve*, one or two filaments pass to join in a small **phrenic ganglion** with phrenic branches of the celiac plexus; and branches from this ganglion are distributed to the falciform and coronary ligaments of the liver, the suprarenal gland, inferior vena cava, and right atrium. From the *left nerve*, filaments pass to join the phrenic branches of the celiac plexus, but without any ganglionic enlargement; and a twig is distributed to the left suprarenal gland.

Deep Branches of the Cervical Plexus. EXTERNAL SERIES.—**Communicating Branches.**—The external series of deep branches of the cervical plexus communicates with the accessory nerve, in the substance of the Sternocleidomastoideus, in the posterior triangle, and beneath the Trapezius.[1]

Muscular Branches are distributed to the Sternocleidomastoideus, Trapezius, Levator scapulæ, and Scalenus medius.

The branch for the Sternocleidomastoideus is derived from the second cervical; the Trapezius and Levator scapulæ receive branches from the third and fourth. The Scalenus medius receives twigs either from the third or fourth, or occasionally from both.

The Brachial Plexus (*plexus brachialis*) (Figs. 804, 805).—The brachial plexus is formed by the union of the anterior rami of the lower four cervical nerves and the greater part of the anterior division of the first thoracic nerve; the fourth cervical usually gives a branch to the fifth cervical, and the first thoracic frequently receives one from the second thoracic. The plexus extends from the lower part of the side of the neck to the axilla. The nerves which form it are nearly equal in size, but their mode of communication is subject to some variation (Kerr). The following is, however, the most constant arrangement. The fifth and sixth cervical unite soon after their exit from the intervertebral foramina to form a trunk. The eighth cervical and first thoracic also unite to form one trunk, while the seventh cervical runs out alone. Three trunks—upper, middle, and lower—are thus formed, and, as they pass beneath the clavicle, each splits into an **anterior** and a **posterior division.**[2] The anterior divisions of the upper and middle trunks unite to form a cord,

---

[1] See reference to work of Corbin and Harrison, Footnote, p. 943.
[2] The posterior division of the lower trunk is very much smaller than the others, and is frequently derived entirely from the eighth cervical nerve.

which is situated on the lateral side of the second part of the axillary artery, and is called the **lateral cord** or **fasciculus of the plexus**. The anterior division of the lower trunk passes down on the medial side of the axillary artery, and forms the

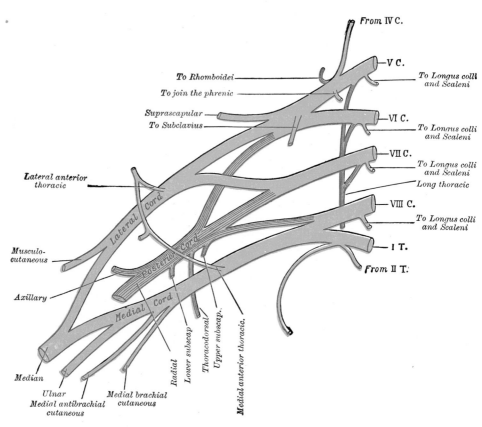

To Rhomboidei

To join the phrenic

Suprascapular

To Subclavius

Lateral anterior thoracic

Musculo-cutaneous

Axillary

Lateral Cord

Posterior Cord

Medial Cord

Median

Ulnar

Medial antibrachial cutaneous

Medial brachial cutaneous

Radial

Lower subscap

Thoracodorsal

Upper subscap.

Medial anterior thoracic.

From IV C.

V C.

To Longus colli and Scaleni

VI C.

To Longus colli and Scaleni

VII C.

To Longus colli and Scaleni

Long thoracic

VIII C.

To Longus colli and Scaleni

I T.

From II T.

Fig. 804.—Plan of brachial plexus.

medial cord or **fasciculus of the brachial plexus.** The posterior divisions of all three trunks unite to form the **posterior cord** or **fasciculus of the plexus,** which is situated behind the second portion of the axillary artery.

Relations.—*In the neck,* the brachial plexus lies in the posterior triangle, being covered by the skin, Platysma, and deep fascia; it is crossed by the supraclavicular nerves, the inferior belly of the Omohyoideus, the external jugular vein, and the transverse cervical artery. It emerges between the Scaleni anterior and medius; its upper part lies above the third part of the subclavian artery, while the trunk formed by the union of the eighth cervical and first thoracic is placed behind the artery; the plexus next passes behind the clavicle, the Subclavius, and the transverse scapular vessels, and lies upon the first digitation of the Serratus anterior, and the Subscapularis. *In the axilla* it is placed lateral to the first portion of the axillary artery; it surrounds the second part of the artery, one cord lying medial to it, one lateral to it, and one behind it; at the lower part of the axilla it gives off its terminal branches to the upper limb.

Branches of Communication.—Close to their exit from the intervertebral foramina the fifth and sixth cervical nerves each receive a gray ramus communicans from the middle cervical ganglion of the sympathetic trunk, and the seventh and eighth cervical similar twigs from the inferior ganglion. The first thoracic nerve receives a gray ramus from, and contributes a white ramus to, the first thoracic ganglion. On the Scalenus anterior the phrenic nerve is joined by a branch from the fifth cervical.

Branches of Distribution.—The branches of distribution of the brachial plexus may be arranged into two groups, viz., those given off above and those below the clavicle.

SUPRACLAVICULAR BRANCHES.

Dorsal scapular	5 C.
Suprascapular	5, 6 C.
Nerve to Subclavius	5, 6 C.
Long thoracic	5, 6, 7 C.
To Longus colli and Scaleni	5, 6, 7, 8 C.

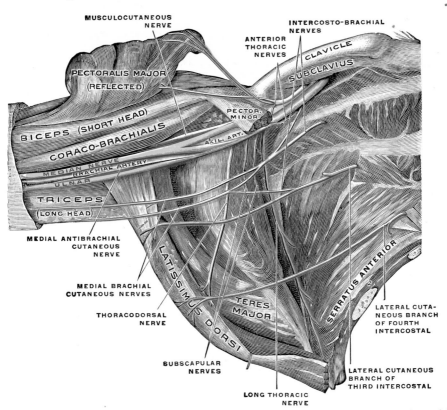

FIG. 805.—The right brachial plexus (infraclavicular portion) in the axillary fossa; viewed from below and in front. The Pectoralis major and minor muscles have been in large part removed; their attachments have been reflected. (Spalteholz.)

The **Dorsal Scapular Nerve** (*n. dorsalis scapulæ; nerve to the Rhomboidei; posterior scapular nerve*) *arises* from the fifth cervical, pierces the Scalenus medius, passes beneath the Levator scapulæ, to which it occasionally gives a twig, and ends in the Rhomboidei.

The **Suprascapular** (*n. suprascapularis*) (Figs. 806, 814) *arises* from the trunk formed by the union of the fifth and sixth cervical nerves. It runs lateralward beneath the Trapezius and the Omohyoideus, and enters the supraspinatous fossa through the suprascapular notch, below the superior transverse scapular ligament; it then passes beneath the Supraspinatus, and curves around the lateral border of the spine of the scapula to the infraspinatous fossa. In the supraspinatous fossa it gives off two branches to the Supraspinatus muscle, and an articular filament to the shoulder-joint; and in the infraspinatous fossa it gives off two branches to the Infraspinatous muscle, besides some filaments to the shoulder-joint and scapula.

The **Nerve to the Subclavius** (*n. subclavius*) is a small filament, which *arises* from the point of junction of the fifth and sixth cervical nerves; it descends to the muscle in front of the third part of the subclavian artery and the lower trunk of the plexus, and is usually connected by a filament with the phrenic nerve.

The **Long Thoracic Nerve** (*n. thoracalis longus; external respiratory nerve of Bell; posterior thoracic nerve*) (Figs. 805, 812) supplies the Serratus anterior. It usually *arises* by three roots from the fifth, sixth, and seventh cervical nerves; but the root from the seventh nerve may be absent. The roots from the fifth and sixth nerves pierce the Scalenus medius, while that from the seventh passes in front of the muscle. The nerve descends behind the brachial plexus and the axillary vessels, resting on the outer surface of the Serratus anterior. It extends along the side of the thorax to the lower border of that muscle, supplying filaments to each of its digitations.

The branches for the Longus colli and Scaleni arise from the lower four cervical nerves at their exit from the intervertebral foramina.

INFRACLAVICULAR BRANCHES.

The infraclavicular branches (Fig. 805) are derived from the three cords of the brachial plexus, but the fasciculi of the nerves may be traced through the plexus to the spinal nerves from which they originate. They are as follows:

Lateral cord .	Musculocutaneous . . .	5, 6, 7 C.
	Lateral anterior thoracic . .	5, 6, 7 C.
	Lateral head of median . . .	6, 7 C.
Medial cord .	Medial anterior thoracic . .	
	Medial antibrachial cutaneous .	
	Medial brachial cutaneous .	8 C, 1 **T.**
	Ulnar	
	Medial head of median . . .	
Posterior cord .	Upper subscapular	5, 6 C.
	Lower subscapular	5, 6 C.
	Thoracodorsal	5, 6, 7 C.
	Axillary	5, 6 C.
	Radial	5, 6, 7, 8 C, 1 T.

The **Anterior Thoracic Nerves** (*nn. thoracales anteriores*) (Fig. 812) supply the Pectorales major and minor.

The **lateral anterior thoracic** (*fasciculus lateralis*) the larger of the two, *arises* from the lateral cord of the brachial plexus, and through it from the fifth, sixth, and seventh cervical nerves. It passes across the axillary artery and vein, pierces the coracoclavicular fascia, and is distributed to the deep surface of the Pectoralis major. It sends a filament to join the medial anterior thoracic and form with it a loop in front of the first part of the axillary artery.

The **medial anterior thoracic** (*fasciculus medialis*) *arises* from the medial cord of the plexus and through it from the eighth cervical and first thoracic. It passes behind the first part of the axillary artery, curves forward between the axillary artery and vein, and unites in front of the artery with a filament from the lateral nerve. It then enters the deep surface of the Pectoralis minor, where it divides into a number of branches, which supply the muscle. Two or three branches pierce the muscle and end in the Pectoralis major.

The **Subscapular Nerves** (*nn. subscapulares*) (Fig. 805), two in number, spring from the posterior cord of the plexus and through it from the fifth and sixth cervical nerves.

The **upper subscapular** (*short subscapular*), the smaller enters the upper part of the Subscapularis, and is frequently represented by two branches.

The **lower subscapular** supplies the lower part of the Subscapularis, and ends in the Teres major; the latter muscle is sometimes supplied by a separate branch

The **Thoracodorsal Nerve** (*n. thoracodorsalis; middle or long subscapular nerve*) (Fig. 805), a branch of the posterior cord of the plexus, derives its fibers from the fifth, sixth, and seventh cervical nerves; it follows the course of the subscapular artery, along the posterior wall of the axilla to the Latissimus dorsi, in which it may be traced as far as the lower border of the muscle.

The **Axillary Nerve** (*n. axillaris; circumflex nerve*) (Figs. 804, 806) *arises* from the posterior cord of the brachial plexus, and its fibers are derived from the fifth and sixth cervical nerves. It lies at first behind the axillary artery, and in front of the

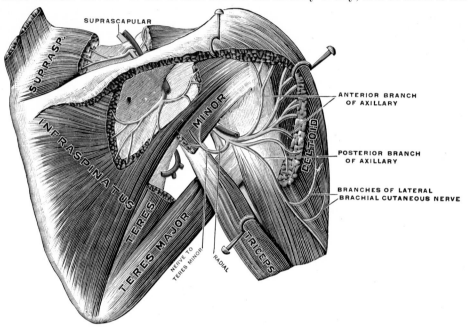

Fig. 806.—Suprascapular and axillary nerves of right side, seen from behind. (Testut.)

Subscapularis, and passes downward to the lower border of that muscle. It then winds backward, in company with the posterior humeral circumflex artery, through a quadrilateral space bounded above by the Subscapularis and Teres minor, below by the Teres major, medially by the long head of the Triceps brachii, and laterally by the surgical neck of the humerus, and divides into an anterior and a posterior branch.

The **anterior branch** (*upper branch*) winds around the surgical neck of the humerus, beneath the Deltoideus, with the posterior humeral circumflex vessels, as far as the anterior border of that muscle, supplying it, and giving off a few small cutaneous branches, which pierce the muscle and ramify in the skin covering its lower part.

The **posterior branch** (*lower branch*) supplies the Teres minor and the posterior part of the Deltoideus; upon the branch to the Teres minor an oval enlargement (pseudoganglion) usually exists. The posterior branch then pierces the deep fascia and is continued as the **lateral brachial cutaneous nerve,** which sweeps around the posterior border of the Deltoideus and supplies the skin over the lower two-thirds of the posterior part of this muscle, as well as that covering the long head of the Triceps brachii (Figs. 807–810).

The trunk of the axillary nerve gives off an articular filament which enters the shoulder-joint below the Subscapularis.

The **Musculocutaneous Nerve** (*n. musculocutaneus*) (Fig. 812) *arises* from the lateral cord of the brachial plexus, opposite the lower border of the Pectoralis minor, its fibers being derived from the fifth, sixth, and seventh cervical nerves. It pierces the Coracobrachialis muscle and passes obliquely between the Biceps brachii and the Brachialis, to the lateral side of the arm; a little above the elbow

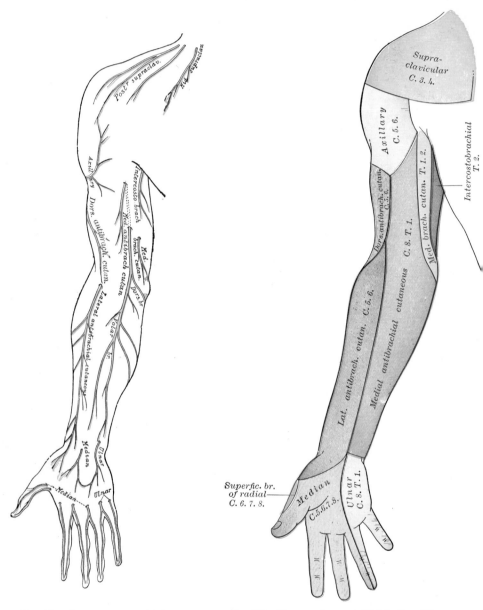

FIG. 807.—Cutaneous nerves of right upper extremity. Anterior view.

FIG. 808.—Diagram of segmental distribution of the cutaneous nerves of the right upper extremity. Anterior view.

it pierces the deep fascia lateral to the tendon of the Biceps brachii and is continued into the forearm as the **lateral antibrachial cutaneous nerve.** In its course through the arm it supplies the Coracobrachialis, Biceps brachii, and the greater part of the Brachialis. The branch to the Coracobrachialis is given off from the nerve close to its origin, and in some instances as a separate filament from the lateral cord of the plexus; it is derived from the seventh cervical nerve. The branches to the Biceps brachii and Brachialis are given off after the musculocutaneous has pierced the Coracobrachialis; that supplying the Brachialis gives a filament to the elbow-joint. The nerve also sends a small branch to the bone, which enters the nutrient foramen with the accompanying artery.

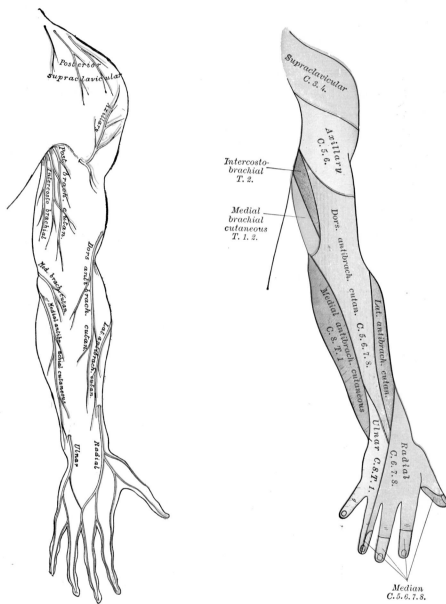

Fig. 809.—Cutaneous nerves of right upper extremity. Posterior view.

Fig. 810.—Diagram of segmental distribution of the cutaneous nerves of the right upper extremity. Posterior view.

The **lateral antibrachial cutaneous nerve** (*n. cutaneus antibrachii lateralis; cutaneous branch of musculocutaneous nerve*) passes behind the cephalic vein, and divides, opposite the elbow-joint, into a volar and a dorsal branch (Figs. 807–810).

The **volar branch** (*ramus volaris; anterior branch*) descends along the radial border of the forearm to the wrist, and supplies the skin over the lateral half of its volar surface. At the wrist-joint it is placed in front of the radial artery, and some filaments, piercing the deep fascia, accompany that vessel to the dorsal surface of the carpus. The nerve then passes downward to the ball of the thumb, where it ends in cutaneous filaments. It communicates with the superficial branch of the radial nerve, and with the palmar cutaneous branch of the median nerve.

The **dorsal branch** (*ramus dorsalis; posterior branch*) descends, along the dorsal surface of the radial side of the forearm to the wrist. It supplies the skin of the lower two-thirds of the dorso-lateral surface of the forearm, communicating with the superficial branch of the radial nerve and the dorsal antibrachial cutaneous branch of the radial.

The musculocutaneous nerve presents frequent irregularities. It may adhere for some distance to the median and then pass outward, beneath the Biceps brachii, instead of through the Coracobrachialis. Some of the fibers of the median may run for some distance in the musculocutaneous and then leave it to join their proper trunk; less frequently the reverse is the case, and the median sends a branch to join the musculocutaneous. The nerve may pass under the Coracobrachialis or through the Biceps brachii. Occasionally it gives a filament to the Pronator teres, and it supplies the dorsal surface of the thumb when the superficial branch of the radial nerve is absent.

The **Medial Antibrachial Cutaneous Nerve** (*n. cutaneus antibrachii medialis; internal cutaneous nerve*) (Fig. 812) *arises* from the medial cord of the brachial plexus. It derives its fibers from the eighth cervical and first thoracic nerves, and at its commencement is placed medial to the axillary artery. It gives off, near the axilla, a filament, which pierces the fascia and supplies the integument covering the Biceps brachii, nearly as far as the elbow. The nerve then runs down the ulnar side of the arm medial to the brachial artery, pierces the deep fascia with the basilic vein, about the middle of the arm, and divides into a volar and an ulnar branch.

The **volar branch** (*ramus volaris; anterior branch*), the larger, passes usually in front of, but occasionally behind, the vena mediana cubiti (*median basilic vein*). It then descends on the front of the ulnar side of the forearm, distributing filaments to the skin as far as the wrist, and communicating with the palmar cutaneous branch of the ulnar nerve (Figs. 807, 808).

The **ulnar branch** (*ramus ulnaris; posterior branch*) passes obliquely downward on the medial side of the basilic vein, in front of the medial epicondyle of the humerus, to the back of the forearm, and descends on its ulnar side as far as the wrist, distributing filaments to the skin. It communicates with the medial brachial cutaneous, the dorsal antibrachial cutaneous branch of the radial, and the dorsal branch of the ulnar (Figs. 809, 810).

The **Medial Brachial Cutaneous Nerve** (*n. cutaneus brachii medialis; lesser internal cutaneous nerve; nerve of Wrisberg*) is distributed to the skin on the ulnar side of the arm (Figs. 805, 807, 809). It is the smallest branch of the brachial plexus, and *arising* from the medial cord, receives its fibers from the eighth cervical and first thoracic nerves. It passes through the axilla, at first lying behind, and then medial to the axillary vein, and communicates with the intercostobrachial nerve. It descends along the medial side of the brachial artery to the middle of the arm, where it pierces the deep fascia, and is distributed to the skin of the back of the lower third of the arm, extending as far as the elbow, where some filaments are lost in the skin in front of the medial epicondyle, and others over the olecranon. It communicates with the ulnar branch of the medial antibrachial cutaneous nerve.

In some cases the medial brachial cutaneous and intercostobrachial are connected by two or three filaments, which form a plexus in the axilla. In other cases the intercostobrachial is of large size, and takes the place of the medial brachial cutaneous, receiving merely a filament of communication from the brachial plexus, which represents the latter nerve; in a few cases, this filament is wanting.

The **Median Nerve** (*n. medianus*) (Fig. 812) extends along the middle of the arm and forearm to the hand. It *arises* by two roots, one from the lateral and one from the medial cord of the brachial plexus; these embrace the lower part of the axillary artery, uniting either in front of or lateral to that vessel. Its fibers are derived from the sixth, seventh, and eighth cervical and first thoracic nerves. As it descends through the arm, it lies at first lateral to the brachial artery; about the level of the insertion of the Coracobrachialis it crosses the artery, usually in front of, but occasionally behind it, and lies on its medial side at the bend of the elbow, where it is situated behind the lacertus fibrosus (*bicipital fascia*), and is separated from the elbow-joint by the Brachialis. **In the forearm** it passes between the two heads of the Pronator teres and crosses the ulnar artery, but is separated from this vessel by the deep head of the Pronator teres. It descends beneath the Flexor digitorum sublimis, lying on the Flexor digitorum profundus, to within 5 cm. of the transverse carpal ligament; here it becomes more superficial, and is situated between the tendons of the Flexor digitorum sublimis and Flexor carpi radialis. In this situation it lies behind, and rather to the radial side of, the tendon of the Palmaris longus, and is covered by the skin and fascia. It then passes behind the transverse carpal ligament into the palm of the hand. In its course through the forearm it is accompanied by the median artery, a branch of the volar interosseous artery.

Branches.—With the exception of the nerve to the Pronator teres, which sometimes arises above the elbow-joint, the median nerve gives off no branches in the arm. As it passes in front of the elbow, it supplies one or two twigs to the joint.

In the forearm its branches are: **muscular, volar interosseous,** and **palmar.**

The **muscular branches** (*rami musculares*) are derived from the nerve near the elbow and supply all the superficial muscles on the front of the forearm, except the Flexor carpi ulnaris.

The **volar interosseous nerve** (*n. interosseus* [*antibrachii*] *volaris; anterior interosseous nerve*) (Fig. 812) supplies the deep muscles on the front of the forearm, except the ulnar half of the Flexor digitorum profundus. It accompanies the volar interosseous artery along the front of the interosseous membrane, in the interval between the Flexor pollicis longus and Flexor digitorum profundus, supplying the whole of the former and the radial half of the latter, and ending below in the Pronator quadratus and wrist-joint.

The **palmar branch** (*ramus cutaneus palmaris n. mediani*) (Figs. 811, 812) of the median nerve *arises* at the lower part of the forearm. It pierces the volar carpal ligament, and divides into a lateral and a medial branch; the lateral branch supplies the skin over the ball of the thumb, and communicates with the volar branch of the lateral antebrachial cutaneous nerve; the medial branch supplies the skin of the palm and communicates with the palmar cutaneous branch of the ulnar.

In the palm of the hand the median nerve is covered by the skin and the palmar aponeurosis, and rests on the tendons of the Flexor muscles (Figs. 811, 813). Immediately after emerging from under the transverse carpal ligament the nerve becomes enlarged and flattened and splits into a smaller, lateral, and a larger, medial portion. The **lateral portion** supplies a short, stout branch to certain of the muscles of the ball of the thumb, viz., the Abductor brevis, the Opponens, and the superficial head of the Flexor brevis, and then divides into three **proper volar digital nerves**; two of these supply the sides of the thumb, while the third gives a twig to the first Lumbricalis and is distributed to the radial side of the index finger (Figs. 807, 808, 810). The **medial portion** of the nerve divides into two **common volar digital nerves.** The first of these gives a twig to the second Lumbricalis and runs toward the cleft between the index and middle fingers, where it divides into two proper digital nerves for the adjoining sides of these digits; the second runs toward the cleft between the middle and ring fingers, and splits into two proper digital nerves for the adjoining sides of these digits; it communicates with a branch from the ulnar nerve and sometimes sends a twig to the third Lumbricalis.

Each proper digital nerve, opposite the base of the first phalanx, gives off a dorsal branch which joins the dorsal digital nerve from the superficial branch of the radial nerve, and supplies the integument on the dorsal aspect of the last phalanx (Fig. 810). At the end of the digit, the proper digital nerve divides into two branches, one of which supplies the pulp of the finger, the other ramifies around

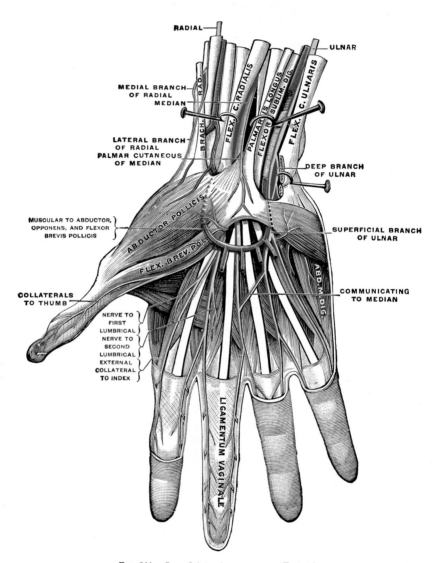

FIG. 811.—Superficial palmar nerves. (Testut.)

and beneath the nail. The proper digital nerves, as they run along the fingers, are placed superficial to the corresponding arteries.

The **Ulnar Nerve** (*n. ulnaris*) (Fig. 812) is placed along the medial side of the limb, and is distributed to the muscles and skin of the forearm and hand. It *arises* from the medial cord of the brachial plexus, derives its fibers from the eighth cervical and first thoracic nerves, and is distributed to the muscles and skin of the forearm and hand (Figs. 808, 810). It is smaller than the median, and lies at first behind it, but diverges from it in its course down the arm. At its origin it lies

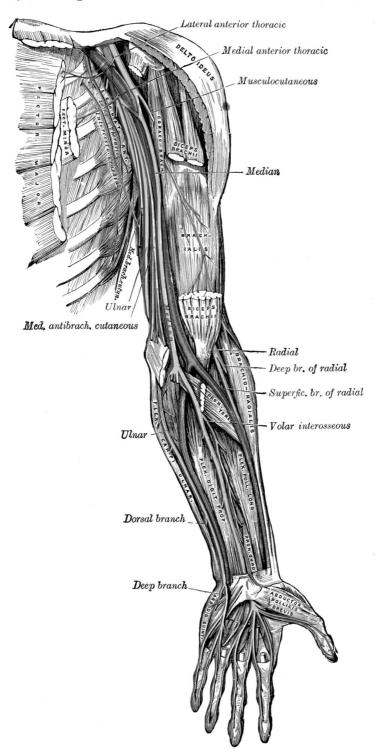

Fig. 812.—Nerves of the left upper extremity.

medial to the axillary artery, and bears the same relation to the brachial artery as far as the middle of the arm. Here it pierces the medial intermuscular septum, runs obliquely across the medial head of the Triceps brachii, and descends to the groove between the medial epicondyle and the olecranon, accompanied by the superior ulnar collateral artery. **At the elbow,** it rests upon the back of the medial

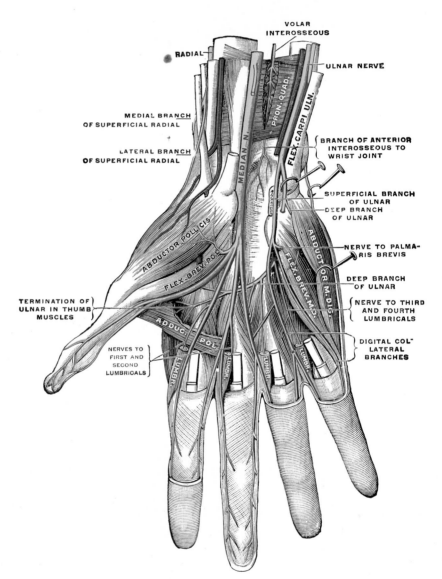

VOLAR INTEROSSEOUS

RADIAL

ULNAR NERVE

MEDIAL BRANCH OF SUPERFICIAL RADIAL

LATERAL BRANCH OF SUPERFICIAL RADIAL

PRON. QUAD.

FLEX. CARPI ULN.

MEDIAN N.

BRANCH OF ANTERIOR INTEROSSEOUS TO WRIST JOINT

SUPERFICIAL BRANCH OF ULNAR

DEEP BRANCH OF ULNAR

ABDUCTOR POLLICIS

FLEX. BREV. POL.

ABDUCTOR M. DIG.

FLEX. BREV. M. D.

NERVE TO PALMARIS BREVIS

DEEP BRANCH OF ULNAR

TERMINATION OF ULNAR IN THUMB MUSCLES

ADDUC. POL.

NERVE TO THIRD AND FOURTH LUMBRICALS

NERVES TO FIRST AND SECOND LUMBRICALS

LUMBR.

LUMBR.

LUMBR.

LUMBR.

DIGITAL COLLATERAL BRANCHES

F IG . 813.—Deep palmar nerves. (Testut.)

epicondyle, and enters the forearm between the two heads of the Flexor carpi ulnaris. **In the forearm,** it descends along the ulnar side, lying upon the Flexor digitorum profundus; its upper half is covered by the Flexor carpi ulnaris, its lower half lies on the lateral side of the muscle, covered by the integument and fascia. In the upper third of the forearm, it is separated from the ulnar artery by a considerable interval, but in the rest of its extent lies close to the medial side of the artery. About 5 cm. above the wrist it ends by dividing into a dorsal and a volar branch.

The branches of the ulnar nerve are: **articular** to the elbow-joint, **muscular**, **palmar cutaneous**, **dorsal**, and **volar**.

The **articular branches** to the elbow-joint are several small filaments which *arise* from the nerve as it lies in the groove between the medial epicondyle and olecranon.

The **muscular branches** (*rami musculares*) two in number, *arise* near the elbow: one supplies the Flexor carpi ulnaris; the other, the ulnar half of the Flexor digitorum profundus.

The **palmar cutaneous branch** (*ramus cutaneus palmaris*) arises about the middle of the forearm, and descends on the ulnar artery, giving off some filaments to the vessel. It perforates the volar carpal ligament and ends in the skin of the palm, communicating with the palmar branch of the median nerve.

The **dorsal branch** (*ramus dorsalis manus*) arises about 5 cm. above the wrist; it passes backward beneath the Flexor carpi ulnaris, perforates the deep fascia, and, running along the ulnar side of the back of the wrist and hand, divides into two dorsal digital branches; one supplies the ulnar side of the little finger; the other, the adjacent sides of the little and ring fingers. It' also sends a twig to join that given by the superficial branch of the radial nerve for the adjoining sides of the middle and ring fingers, and assists in supplying them. A branch is distributed to the metacarpal region of the hand, communicating with a twig of the superficial branch of the radial nerve (Fig. 809).

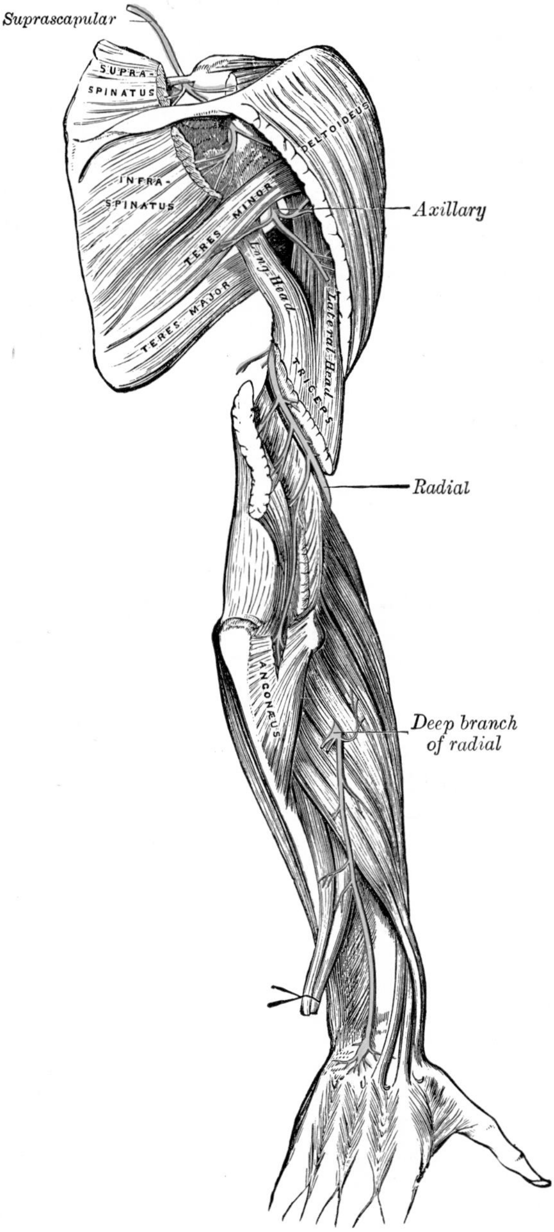

On the little finger the dorsal digital branches extend only as far as the base of the terminal phalanx, and on the ring finger as far as the base of the second phalanx; the more distal parts

FIG. 814.—The suprascapular, axillary, and radial nerves.

of these digits are supplied by dorsal branches derived from the proper volar digital branches of the ulnar nerve.

The **volar branch** (*ramus volaris manus*) crosses the transverse carpal ligament on the lateral side of the pisiform bone, medial to and a little behind the ulnar artery. It ends by dividing into a superficial and a deep branch (Fig. 813).

The **superficial branch** (*ramus superficialis* [*n. ulnaris*]) supplies the Palmaris brevis, and the skin on the ulnar side of the hand, and divides into a proper volar digital branch for the ulnar side of the little finger, and a common volar digital branch which gives a communicating twig to the median nerve and divides into two proper digital nerves for the adjoining sides of the little and ring fingers (Fig. 807). The proper digital branches are distributed to the fingers in the same manner as those of the median.

The **deep branch** (*ramus profundus*) accompanied by the deep branch of the ulnar artery, passes between the Abductor digiti quinti and Flexor digiti quinti brevis; it then perforates the Opponens digiti quinti and follows the course of the deep volar arch beneath the Flexor tendons. At its origin it supplies the three short muscles of the little finger. As it crosses the deep part of the hand, it supplies all the Interossei and the third and fourth Lumbricales; it ends by supplying the Adductores pollicis and the medial head of the Flexor pollicis brevis. It also sends articular filaments to the wrist-joint.

It has been pointed out that the ulnar part of the Flexor digitorum profundus is supplied by the ulnar nerve; the third and fourth Lumbricales, which are connected with the tendons of this part of the muscle, are supplied by the same nerve. In like manner the lateral part of the Flexor digitorum profundus and the first and second Lumbricales are supplied by the median nerve; the third Lumbricalis frequently receives an additional twig from the median nerve.

The **Radial Nerve** (*n. radialis; musculospiral nerve*) (Fig. 814), the largest branch of the brachial plexus, is the continuation of the posterior cord of the plexus. Its fibers are derived from the fifth, sixth, seventh, and eighth cervical nerves. It descends behind the third part of the axillary artery and the upper part of the brachial artery, and in front of the tendons of the Latissimus dorsi and Teres major. It then winds around from the medial to the lateral side of the humerus in a groove with the a. profunda brachii, between the medial and lateral heads of the Triceps brachii. It pierces the lateral intermuscular septum, and passes between the Brachialis and Brachioradialis to the front of the lateral epicondyle, where it divides into a superficial and a deep branch (Fig. 812).

The **branches** of the radial nerve are:

Muscular.	Superficial.
Cutaneous.	Deep.

The **muscular branches** (*rami musculares*) supply the Triceps brachii, Anconæus. Brachioradialis, Extensor carpi radialis longus, and Brachialis, and are grouped as medial, posterior, and lateral.

The medial muscular branches supply the medial and long heads of the Triceps brachii. That to the medial head is a long, slender filament, which lies close to the ulnar nerve as far as the lower third of the arm, and is therefore frequently spoken of as the **ulnar collateral nerve.**

The posterior muscular branch, of large size, *arises* from the nerve in the groove between the Triceps brachii and the humerus. It divides into filaments, which supply the medial and lateral heads of the Triceps brachii and the Anconæus muscles. The branch for the latter muscle is a long, slender filament, which descends in the substance of the medial head of the Triceps brachii.

The lateral muscular branches supply the Brachioradialis, Extensor carpi radialis longus, and the lateral part of the Brachialis.

The **cutaneous branches** are two in number, the posterior brachial cutaneous and the dorsal antibrachial cutaneous.

The **posterior brachial cutaneous nerve** (*n. cutaneus brachii posterior; internal cutaneous branch of musculospiral*) (Fig. 809) *arises* in the axilla, with the medial muscular branch. It is of small size, and passes through the axilla to the medial side of the area supplying the skin on its dorsal surface nearly as far as the olecranon. In its course it crosses behind, and communicates with, the intercostobrachial.

The **dorsal antibrachial cutaneous nerve** (*n. cutaneus antibrachii dorsalis; external cutaneous branch of musculospiral*) (Figs. 807–810) *perforates* the lateral head of the Triceps brachii at its attachment to the humerus. The **upper** and smaller branch of the nerve passes to the front of the elbow, lying close to the cephalic vein, and supplies the skin of the lower half of the arm (Fig. 807). The **lower** branch pierces the deep fascia below the insertion of the Deltoideus, and descends along the lateral side of the arm and elbow, and then along the back of the forearm to the wrist, supplying the skin in its course, and joining, near its termination, with the dorsal branch of the lateral antibrachial cutaneous nerve (Fig. 809).

The **Superficial Branch of the Radial Nerve** (*ramus superficialis nervi radialis* passes along the front of the radial side of the forearm to the commencement of its lower third. It lies at first slightly lateral to the radial artery, concealed beneath the Brachioradialis. In the middle third of the forearm, it lies behind the same muscle, close to the lateral side of the artery. It quits the artery about 7 cm. above the wrist, passes beneath the tendon of the Brachioradialis, and, piercing the deep fascia, divides into two branches (Figs. 809, 811, 813).

The lateral branch, the smaller, supplies the skin of the radial side and ball of the thumb, joining with the volar branch of the lateral antibrachial cutaneous nerve.

The medial branch communicates, above the wrist, with the dorsal branch of the lateral antibrachial cutaneous, and, on the back of the hand, with the dorsal branch of the ulnar nerve. It then divides into four digital nerves, which are distributed as follows: the first supplies the ulnar side of the thumb; the second, the radial side of the index finger; the third, the adjoining sides of the index and middle fingers; the fourth communicates with a filament from the dorsal branch of the ulnar nerve, and supplies the adjacent sides of the middle and ring fingers.

The **Deep Branch of the Radial Nerve** (*n. interosseus dorsalis; dorsal or posterior interosseous nerve*) (Fig. 814) winds to the back of the forearm around the lateral side of the radius between the two planes of fibers of the Supinator, and is prolonged downward between the superficial and deep layers of muscles, to the middle of the forearm. Considerably diminished in size, it descends, as the **dorsal interosseous nerve,** on the interosseous membrane, in front of the Extensor pollicis longus, to the back of the carpus, where it presents a gangliform enlargement from which filaments are distributed to the ligaments and articulations of the carpus. It supplies all the muscles on the radial side and dorsal surface of the forearm, excepting the Anconæus, Brachioradialis, and Extensor carpi radialis longus.

The Thoracic Nerves (Nn. Thoracales).

The **anterior rami of the thoracic nerves** (*rami anteriores; ventral divisions*) (Fig. 794) are twelve in number on either side. Eleven of them are situated between the ribs, and are therefore termed **intercostal**; the twelfth lies below the last rib. Each nerve is connected with the adjoining ganglion of the sympathetic trunk by a gray and a white ramus communicans. The intercostal nerves are distributed chiefly to the parietes of the thorax and abdomen, and differ from the anterior divisions of the other spinal nerves, in that each pursues an independent course, *i. e.*, there is no plexus formation. The first two nerves supply fibers to the upper limb in addition to their thoracic branches; the next four are limited in their distribution to the parietes of the thorax; the lower five supply the parietes of the thorax and abdomen. The twelfth thoracic is distributed to the abdominal wall and the skin of the buttock.

The First Thoracic Nerve.—The anterior ramus of the first thoracic nerve divides into two branches: one, the larger, leaves the thorax in front of the neck of the first rib, and enters the brachial plexus; the other and smaller branch, the **first intercostal nerve,** runs along the first intercostal space, and ends on the front of the chest as the first anterior cutaneous branch of the thorax. Occasionally this anterior cutaneous branch is wanting. The first intercostal nerve as a rule gives off no lateral cutaneous branch; but sometimes it sends a small branch to communicate with the intercostobrachial. From the second thoracic nerve it frequently receives a connecting twig, which ascends over the neck of the second rib.

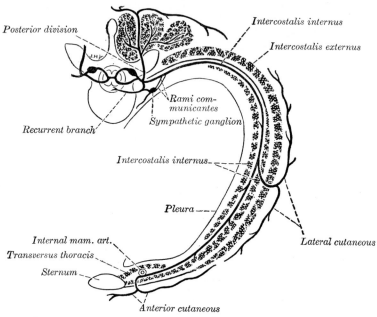

Posterior division

Intercostalis internus

Intercostalis externus

Rami communicantes

Recurrent branch

Sympathetic ganglion

Intercostalis internus

Pleura

Lateral cutaneous

Internal mam. art.

Transversus thoracis

Sternum

Anterior cutaneous

Fig. 815.—Diagram of the course and branches of a typical intercostal nerve.

The Upper Thoracic Nerves (*nn. intercostales*).—The anterior rami of the second, third, fourth, fifth, and sixth thoracic nerves, and the small branch from the first thoracic, are confined to the parietes of the thorax, and are named **thoracic intercostal nerves.** They pass forward (Fig. 815) in the intercostal spaces below the intercostal vessels. At the back of the chest they lie between the pleura and the posterior intercostal membranes as far as the angles of the ribs. From the angle to the middle of the ribs, they pass between the Intercostales interni and the posterior intercostal membranes. They then enter the substance of the Intercostales interni, and, running amidst their fibers as far as the costal cartilages, they gain the inner surfaces of the muscles and lie between them and the pleura. Near the sternum, they cross in front of the internal mammary artery and Transversus thoracis muscle, pierce the Intercostales interni, the anterior intercostal membranes, and Pectoralis major, and supply the integument of the front of the thorax and over the mamma, forming the anterior cutaneous branches of the thorax(Fig. 794); the branch from the second nerve unites with the anterior supraclavicular nerves of the cervical plexus.

Branches.—Numerous slender muscular filaments supply the Intercostales, the Subcostales, the Levatores costarum, the Serratus posterior superior, and the Transversus thoracis. At the front of the thorax some of these branches cross the costal cartilages from one intercostal space to another.

Lateral cutaneous branches (*rami cutanei laterales*) (Figs. 816, 817) are derived from the intercostal nerves, about midway between the vertebræ and sternum; they pierce the Intercostales externi and Serratus anterior, and divide into anterior and posterior branches. The **anterior branches** run forward to the side and the fore-part of the chest, supplying the skin and the mamma; those of the fifth and sixth nerves supply the upper digitations of the Obliquus externus abdominis. The **posterior branches** run backward, and supply the skin over the scapula and Latissimus dorsi.

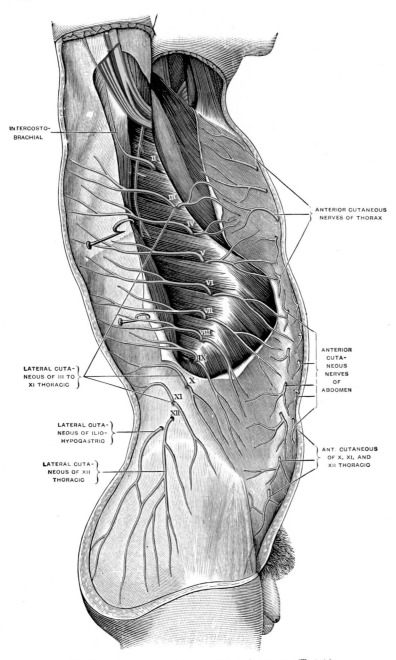

INTERCOSTO-BRACHIAL

ANTERIOR CUTANEOUS NERVES OF THORAX

ANTERIOR CUTANEOUS NERVES OF ABDOMEN

LATERAL CUTA-NEOUS OF III TO XI THORACIC

LATERAL CUTA-NEOUS OF ILIO-HYPOGASTRIC

LATERAL CUTA-NEOUS OF XII THORACIC

ANT. CUTANEOUS OF X, XI, AND XII THORACIC

FIG. 816.—Cutaneous distribution of thoracic nerves. (Testut.)

The lateral cutaneous branch of the second intercostal nerve does not divide, like the others, into an anterior and a posterior branch; it is named the **intercosto-**

brachial nerve (Figs. 812, 816, 817). It pierces the Intercostalis externus and the Serratus anterior, crosses the axilla to the medial side of the arm, and joins with a filament from the medial brachial cutaneous nerve. It then pierces the fascia, and supplies the skin of the upper half of the medial and posterior part of the arm,

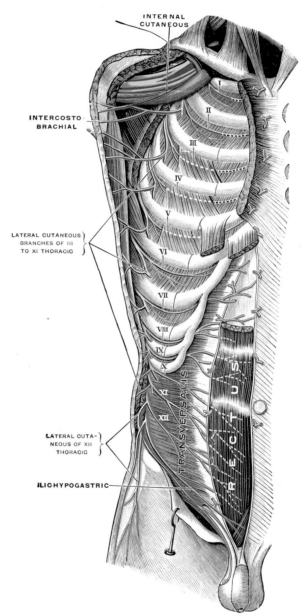

Fig. 817.—Intercostal nerves, the superficial muscles having been removed. (Testut.)

communicating with the posterior brachial cutaneous branch of the radial nerve. The size of the intercostobrachial nerve is in inverse proportion to that of the medial brachial cutaneous nerve. A second intercostobrachial nerve is frequently given off from the lateral cutaneous branch of the third intercostal; it supplies filaments to the axilla and medial side of the arm.

The Lower Thoracic Nerves.—The anterior divisions of the seventh, eighth, ninth, tenth, and eleventh thoracic nerves are continued anteriorly from the intercostal spaces into the abdominal wall; hence they are named **thoracicoabdominal intercostal nerves.** They have the same arrangement as the upper ones as far as the anterior ends of the intercostal spaces, where they pass behind the costal cartilages, and between the Obliquus internus and Transversus abdominis, to the sheath of the Rectus abdominis, which they perforate. They supply the Rectus abdominis and end as the **anterior cutaneous branches** of the abdomen; they supply the skin of the front of the abdomen (Fig. 794). The lower intercostal nerves supply the Intercostales and abdominal muscles; the last three send branches to the Serratus posterior inferior. About the middle of their course they give off **lateral cutaneous branches.** These pierce the Intercostales externi and the Obliquus externus abdominis, in the same line as the lateral cutaneous branches of the upper thoracic nerves, and divide into anterior and posterior branches, which are distributed to the skin of the abdomen and back; the anterior branches supply the digitations of the Obliquus externus abdominis, and extend downward and forward nearly as far as the margin of the Rectus abdominis; the posterior branches pass backward to supply the skin over the Latissimus dorsi.

The anterior division of the **twelfth thoracic nerve** is larger than the others; it runs along the lower border of the twelfth rib, often gives a communicating branch to the first lumbar nerve, and passes under the lateral lumbocostal arch. It then runs in front of the Quadratus lumborum, perforates the Transversus, and passes forward between it and the Obliquus internus to be distributed in the same manner as the lower intercostal nerves. It communicates with the iliohypogastric nerve of the lumbar plexus, and gives a branch to the Pyramidalis. The **lateral cutaneous branch** of the last thoracic nerve is large, and does not divide into an anterior and a posterior branch. It perforates the Obliqui internus and externus, descends over the iliac crest in front of the lateral cutaneous branch of the iliohypogastric (Figs. 816, 817), and is distributed to the skin of the front part of the gluteal region, some of its filaments extending as low as the greater trochanter.

The Lumbosacral Plexus (Plexus Lumbosacralis).

The anterior rami of the lumbar, sacral, and coccygeal nerves form the lumbosacral plexus, the first lumbar nerve being frequently joined by a branch from the twelfth thoracic. For descriptive purposes this plexus is usually divided into three parts—the **lumbar, sacral,** and **pudendal plexuses.**

The Lumbar Nerves (Nn. Lumbales).

The **anterior rami of the lumbar nerves** (*rami anteriores*) increase in size from above downward. They are joined, near their origins, by *gray rami communicantes* from the lumbar ganglia of the sympathetic trunk. These rami consist of long, slender branches which accompany the lumbar arteries around the sides of the vertebral bodies, beneath the Psoas major. Their arrangement is somewhat irregular: one ganglion may give rami to two lumbar nerves, or one lumbar nerve may receive rami from two ganglia. The first and second, and sometimes the third and fourth lumbar nerves are each connected with the lumbar part of the sympathetic trunk by a *white ramus communicans*.

The nerves pass obliquely outward behind the Psoas major, or between its fasciculi, distributing filaments to it and the Quadratus lumborum. The first three and the greater part of the fourth are connected together in this situation by anastomotic loops, and form the **lumbar plexus.** The smaller part of the fourth joins with the fifth to form the **lumbosacral trunk,** which assists in the formation

62

of the sacral plexus. The fourth nerve is named the **nervus furcalis**, from the fact that it is subdivided between the two plexuses.[1]

The Lumbar Plexus[2] (*plexus lumbalis*) (Figs. 818, 819, 820).—The lumbar plexus is formed by the loops of communication between the anterior rami of the first three and the greater part of the fourth lumbar nerves; the first lumbar often receives a branch from the last thoracic nerve. It is situated in the posterior part of the Psoas major, in front of the transverse processes of the lumbar vertebræ.

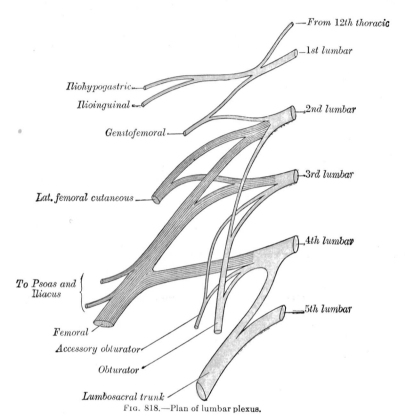

Fig. 818.—Plan of lumbar plexus.

The mode in which the plexus is arranged varies in different subjects. It differs from the brachial plexus in not forming an intricate interlacement, but the several nerves of distribution *arise* from one or more of the spinal nerves, in the following manner: the first lumbar nerve, frequently supplemented by a twig from the last thoracic, splits into an upper and lower branch; the upper and larger branch divides into the iliohypogastric and ilioinguinal nerves; the lower and smaller branch unites with a branch of the second lumbar to form the genitofemoral nerve. The remainder of the second nerve, and the third and fourth nerves, divide into ventral and dorsal divisions. The ventral division of the second unites with the ventral divisions of the third and fourth nerves to form the obturator nerve. The dorsal divisions of the second and third nerves divide into two branches, a smaller branch from each uniting to form the lateral femoral cutaneous nerve, and a larger branch from each joining with the dorsal division of the fourth nerve to form the femoral

---

[1] In most cases the fourth lumbar is the *nervus furcalis;* but this arrangement is frequently departed from. The third is occasionally the lowest nerve which enters the lumbar plexus, giving at the same time some fibers to the sacral plexus, and thus forming the nervus furcalis; or both the third and fourth may be furcal nerves. When this occurs, the plexus is termed *high* or *prefixed.* More frequently the fifth nerve is divided between the lumbar and sacral plexuses, and constitutes the nervus furcalis; and when this takes place, the plexus is distinguished as a *low* or *postfixed* plexus. These variations necessarily produce corresponding modifications in the sacral plexus.

[2] Bardeen, Amer. Jour. Anat., 1907, vol. **6**.

nerve. The accessory obturator, when it exists, is formed by the union of two small branches given off from the third and fourth nerves.

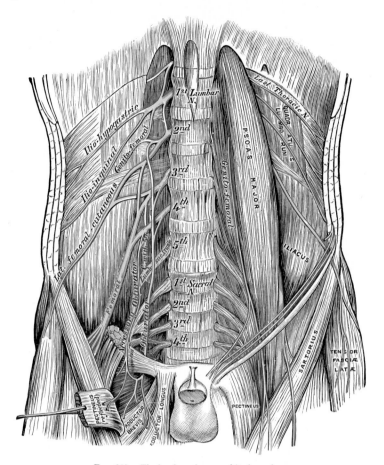

Fig. 819.—The lumbar plexus and its branches.

The **branches** of the lumbar plexus may therefore be arranged as follows:

Iliohypogastric	. . . .	1 L.
Ilioinguinal	. . . .	1 L.
Genitofemoral	. . . .	1, 2 L.
		Dorsal divisions.
Lateral femoral cutaneous	. . . . .	2, 3 L.
Femoral	. . . .	2, 3, 4 L.
		Ventral divisions.
Obturator	. . . .	2, 3, 4 L.
Accessory obturator	. . . . . .	3, 4 L.

The **Iliohypogastric Nerve** (*n. iliohypogastricus*) (Fig. 820) *arises* from the first lumbar nerve. It emerges from the upper part of the lateral border of the Psoas major, and crosses obliquely in front of the Quadratus lumborum to the iliac crest. It then perforates the posterior part of the Transversus abdominis, near the crest of the ilium, and divides between that muscle and the Obliquus internus abdominis into a **lateral** and an **anterior cutaneous branch** (Fig. 817).

The **lateral cutaneous branch** (*ramus cutaneus lateralis; iliac branch*) pierces the Obliqui internus and externus immediately above the iliac crest, and is distributed to the skin of the gluteal region, behind the lateral cutaneous branch of the last thoracic nerve (Figs. 816, 826); the size of this branch bears an inverse proportion to that of the lateral cutaneous branch of the last thoracic nerve.

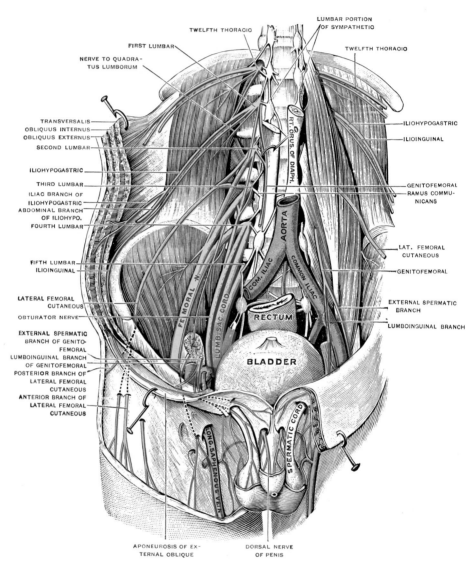

FIG. 820.—Deep and superficial dissection of the lumbar plexus. (Testut.)

The **anterior cutaneous branch** (*ramus cutaneus anterior; hypogastric branch*) (Figs. 817, 821) continues onward between the Obliquus internus and Transversus. It then pierces the Obliquus internus, becomes cutaneous by perforating the aponeurosis of the Obliquus externus about 2.5 cm. above the subcutaneous inguinal ring, and is distributed to the skin of the hypogastric region (Fig. 794).

The iliohypogastric nerve communicates with the last thoracic and ilioinguinal nerves.

The **Ilioinguinal Nerve** (*n. ilioinguinalis*) (Fig. 820), smaller than the preceding, *arises* with it from the first lumbar nerve. It emerges from the lateral border of the Psoas major just below the iliohypogastric, and, passing obliquely across the Quadratus lumborum and Iliacus, perforates the Transversus abdominis, near the

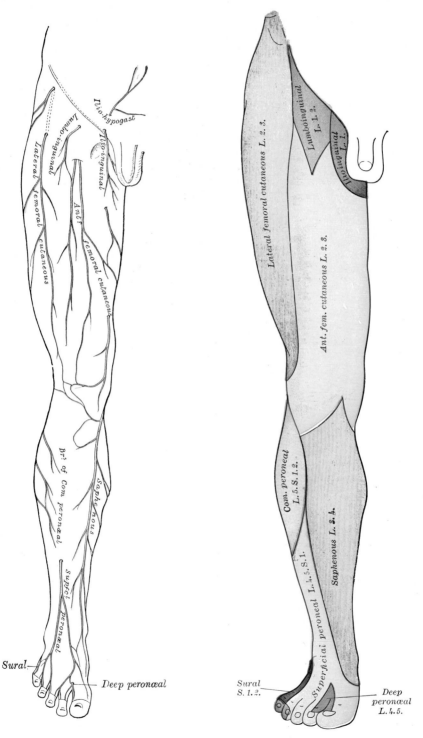

FIG. 821.—Cutaneous nerves of right lower extremity. Front view.

FIG. 822.—Diagram of segmental distribution of the cutaneous nerves of the right lower extremity. Front view.

anterior part of the iliac crest, and communicates with the iliohypogastric nerve between the Transversus and the Obliquus internus. The nerve then pierces the Obliquus internus, distributing filaments to it, and, accompanying the spermatic cord through the subcutaneous inguinal ring, is distributed to the skin of the upper and medial part of the thigh, to the skin over the root of the penis and upper part of the scrotum in the male (Fig. 822), and to the skin covering the mons pubis and labium majus in the female. The size of this nerve is in inverse proportion to that of the iliohypogastric. Occasionally it is very small, and ends by joining the ilio-hypogastric; in such cases, a branch from the iliohypogastric takes the place of the ilioinguinal, or the latter nerve may be altogether absent.

The **Genitofemoral Nerve** (*n. genitofemoralis; genitocrural nerve*) (Figs. 819, 820) *arises* from the first and second lumbar nerves. It passes obliquely through the substance of the Psoas major, and emerges from its medial border, close to the vertebral column, opposite the fibrocartilage between the third and fourth lumbar vertebræ; it then descends on the surface of the Psoas major, under cover of the peritoneum, and divides into the external spermatic and lumboinguinal nerves. Occasionally these two nerves emerge separately through the substance of the Psoas.

The **external spermatic nerve** (*n. spermaticus externus; genital branch of genito-femoral*) passes outward on the Psoas major, and pierces the fascia transversalis, or passes through the abdominal inguinal ring; it then descends behind the spermatic cord to the scrotum, supplies the Cremaster, and gives a few filaments to the skin of the scrotum. In the female, it accompanies the round ligament of the uterus, and is lost upon it.

The **lumboinguinal nerve** (*n. lumboinguinalis; femoral or crural branch of genito-femoral*) descends on the external iliac artery, sending a few filaments around it, and, passing beneath the inguinal ligament, enters the sheath of the femoral vessels, lying superficial and lateral to the femoral artery. It pierces the anterior layer of the sheath of the vessels and the fascia lata, and supplies the skin of the anterior surface of the upper part of the thigh (Figs. 821, 822). On the front of the thigh it communicates with the anterior cutaneous branches of the femoral nerve. A few filaments from the lumboinguinal nerve may be traced to the femoral artery.

The **Lateral Femoral Cutaneous Nerve** (*n. cutaneus femoralis lateralis; external cutaneous nerve*) (Figs. 819, 820) *arises* from the dorsal divisions of the second and third lumbar nerves. It emerges from the lateral border of the Psoas major about its middle, and crosses the Iliacus obliquely, toward the anterior superior iliac spine. It then passes under the inguinal ligament and over the Sartorius muscle into the thigh, where it divides into two branches, an **anterior** and a **posterior** (Fig. 821).

The **anterior branch** becomes superficial about 10 cm. below the inguinal ligament, and divides into branches which are distributed to the skin of the anterior and lateral parts of the thigh, as far as the knee (Fig. 822). The terminal filaments of this nerve frequently communicate with the anterior cutaneous branches of the femoral nerve, and with the infrapatellar branch of the saphenous nerve, forming with them the **patellar plexus** (Fig. 794).

The **posterior branch** pierces the fascia lata, and subdivides into filaments which pass backward across the lateral and posterior surfaces of the thigh, supplying the skin from the level of the greater trochanter to the middle of the thigh (Fig. 827).

The **Obturator Nerve** (*n. obturatorius*) (Fig. 819) *arises* from the ventral divisions of the second, third, and fourth lumbar nerves; the branch from the third is the largest, while that from the second is often very small. It descends through the fibers of the Psoas major, and emerges from its medial border near the brim of the pelvis; it then passes behind the common iliac vessels, and on the lateral side of the hypogastric vessels and ureter; it runs along the lateral wall of the lesser pelvis, above and in front of the obturator vessels (Fig. 833), to the upper part of the obturator foramen. Here it enters the thigh, and divides into an anterior and a posterior branch, which are separated at first by some of the fibers of the Obturator externus, and lower down by the Adductor brevis.

The **anterior branch** (*ramus anterior*) (Fig. 823) leaves the pelvis in front of the Obturator externus and descends in front of the Adductor brevis, and behind the Pectineus and Adductor longus; at the lower border of the latter muscle it communicates with the anterior cutaneous and saphenous branches of the femoral nerve, forming a kind of plexus. It then descends upon the femoral artery, to which it is finally distributed. Near the obturator foramen the nerve gives off an articular branch to the hip-joint. Behind the Pectineus, it distributes branches to the Adductor longus and Gracilis, and usually to the Adductor brevis, and in rare cases to the Pectineus; it receives a communicating branch from the accessory obturator nerve when that nerve is present.

Occasionally the communicating branch to the anterior cutaneous and saphenous branches of the femoral is continued down, as a cutaneous branch, to the thigh and leg. When this is so, it emerges from beneath the lower border of the Adductor longus, descends along the posterior margin of the Sartorius to the medial side of the knee, where it pierces the deep fascia, communicates with the saphenous nerve, and is distributed to the skin of the tibial side of the leg as low down as its middle.

The **posterior branch** (*ramus posterior*) pierces the anterior part of the Obturator externus, and supplies this muscle; it then passes behind the Adductor brevis on the front of the Adductor magnus, where it divides into numerous muscular branches which are distributed to the Adductor magnus and the Adductor

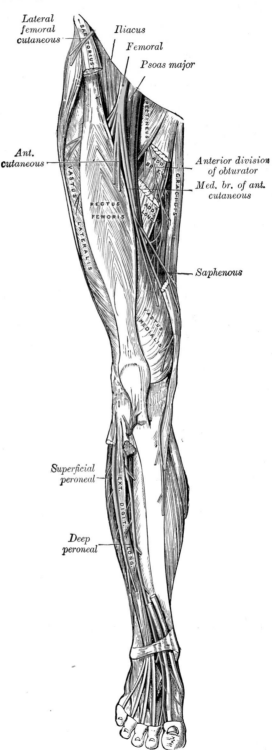

FIG. 823.—Nerves of the right lower extremity   Front view.

brevis when the latter does not receive a branch from the anterior division of the nerve. It usually gives off an articular filament to the knee-joint.

The **articular branch for the knee-joint** is sometimes absent; it either perforates the lower part of the Adductor magnus, or passes through the opening which transmits the femoral artery, and enters the popliteal fossa; it then descends upon the popliteal artery, as far as the back part of the knee-joint, where it perforates the oblique popliteal ligament, and is distributed to the synovial membrane. It gives filaments to the popliteal artery.

The **Accessory Obturator Nerve** (*n. obturatorius accessorius*) (Fig. 819) is present in about 29 per cent. of cases. It is of small size, and *arises* from the ventral divisions of the third and fourth lumbar nerves. It descends along the medial border of the Psoas major, crosses the superior ramus of the pubis, and passes under the Pectineus, where it divides into numerous branches. One of these supplies the Pectineus, penetrating its deep surface, another is distributed to the hip-joint; while a third communicates with the anterior branch of the obturator nerve. Occasionally the accessory obturator nerve is very small and is lost in the capsule of the hip-joint. When it is absent, the hip-joint receives two branches from the obturator nerve.

The **Femoral Nerve** (*n. femoralis; anterior crural nerve*) (Figs. 819, 820, 823), the largest branch of the lumbar plexus, *arises* from the dorsal divisions of the second, third, and fourth lumbar nerves. It descends through the fibers of the Psoas major, emerging from the muscle at the lower part of its lateral border, and passes down between it and the Iliacus, behind the iliac fascia; it then runs beneath the inguinal ligament, into the thigh, and splits into an anterior and a posterior division. Under the inguinal ligament, it is separated from the femoral artery by a portion of the Psoas major.

Within the abdomen the femoral nerve gives off small branches to the Iliacus, and a branch which is distributed upon the upper part of the femoral artery; the latter branch may arise in the thigh.

In the thigh the anterior division of the femoral nerve gives off anterior cutaneous and muscular branches. The anterior cutaneous branches comprise the intermediate and medial cutaneous nerves (Fig. 821).

The **intermediate cutaneous nerve** (*ramus cutaneus anterior; middle cutaneous nerve*) pierces the fascia lata (and generally the Sartorius) about 7.5 cm. below the inguinal ligament, and divides into two branches which descend in immediate proximity along the forepart of the thigh, to supply the skin as low as the front of the knee. Here they communicate with the medial cutaneous nerve and the infrapatellar branch of the saphenous, to form the patellar plexus. In the upper part of the thigh the lateral branch of the intermediate cutaneous communicates with the lumboinguinal branch of the genitofemoral nerve.

The **medial cutaneous nerve** (*ramus cutaneus anterior; internal cutaneous nerve*) passes obliquely across the upper part of the sheath of the femoral artery, and divides in front, or at the medial side of that vessel, into two branches, an anterior and a posterior. The **anterior branch** runs downward on the Sartorius, perforates the fascia lata at the lower third of the thigh, and divides into two branches: one supplies the integument as low down as the medial side of the knee; the other crosses to the lateral side of the patella, communicating in its course with the infrapatellar branch of the saphenous nerve. The **posterior branch** descends along the medial border of the Sartorius muscle to the knee, where it pierces the fascia lata, communicates with the saphenous nerve, and gives off several cutaneous branches. It then passes down to supply the integument of the medial side of the leg. Beneath the fascia lata, at the lower border of the Adductor longus, it joins to form a plexiform net-work (**subsartorial plexus**) with branches of the saphenous and obturator nerves. When the communicating branch from the obturator nerve is large and continued to the integument of the leg, the posterior branch of the medial cutaneous is small, and terminates in the plexus, occasionally giving off a few cutaneous filaments. The medial cutaneous nerve, before dividing, gives off a few filaments, which pierce the fascia lata, to supply the integument of the medial side of the thigh, accompanying the long saphenous vein. One of these filaments passes through the saphenous opening; a second becomes subcutaneous about the middle of the thigh; a third pierces the fascia at its lower third.

MUSCULAR BRANCHES (*rami musculares*).—The **nerve to the Pectineus** *arises* immediately below the inguinal ligament, and passes behind the femoral sheath to enter the anterior surface of the muscle; it is often duplicated. The **nerve to the Sartorius** *arises* in common with the intermediate cutaneous.

The posterior division of the femoral nerve gives off the saphenous nerve, and muscular and articular branches.

The **Saphenous Nerve** (*n. saphenus; long or internal saphenous nerve*) (Figs. 821–823, 826) is the largest cutaneous branch of the femoral nerve. It approaches the femoral artery where this vessel passes beneath the Sartorius, and lies in front of it, behind the aponeurotic covering of the adductor canal, as far as the opening in the lower part of the Adductor magnus. Here it quits the artery, and emerges from behind the lower edge of the aponeurotic covering of the canal; it descends vertically along the medial side of the knee behind the Sartorius, pierces the fascia lata, between the tendons of the Sartorius and Gracilis, and becomes subcutaneous. The nerve then passes along the tibial side of the leg, accompanied by the great saphenous vein, descends behind the medial border of the tibia, and, at the lower third of the leg, divides into two branches: one continues its course along the margin of the tibia, and ends at the ankle; the other passes in front of the ankle, and is distributed to the skin on the medial side of the foot, as far as the ball of the great toe, communicating with the medial branch of the superficial peroneal nerve.

BRANCHES.—The saphenous nerve, about the middle of the thigh, gives off a branch which joins the subsartorial plexus.

At the medial side of the knee it gives off a large **infrapatellar branch,** which pierces the Sartorius and fascia lata, and is distributed to the skin in front of the patella. This nerve communicates above the knee with the anterior cutaneous branches of the femoral nerve; below the knee, with other branches of the saphenous; and, on the lateral side of the joint, with branches of the lateral femoral cutaneous nerve, forming a plexiform net-work, the **plexus patellæ.** The infrapatellar branch is occasionally small, and ends by joining the anterior cutaneous branches of the femoral, which supply its place in front of the knee.

Below the knee, the branches of the saphenous nerve are distributed to the skin of the front and medial side of the leg, communicating with the cutaneous branches of the femoral, or with filaments from the obturator nerve.

The **muscular branches** supply the four parts of the Quadriceps femoris (Fig. 823). The branch to the Rectus femoris enters the upper part of the deep surface of the muscle, and supplies a filament to the hip-joint. The branch to the Vastus lateralis, of large size, accompanies the descending branch of the lateral femoral circumflex artery to the lower part of the muscle. It gives off an articular filament to the knee-joint. The branch to the Vastus medialis descends lateral to the femoral vessels in company with the saphenous nerve. It enters the muscle about its middle, and gives off a filament, which can usually be traced downward, on the surface of the muscle, to the knee-joint. The branches to the Vastus intermedius, two or three in number, enter the anterior surface of the muscle about the middle of the thigh; a filament from one of these descends through the muscle to the Articularis genu and the knee-joint. The **articular branch to the hip-joint** is derived from the nerve to the Rectus femoris.

The **articular branches to the knee-joint** are three in number. One, a long slender filament, is derived from the nerve to the Vastus lateralis; it penetrates the capsule of the joint on its anterior aspect. Another, derived from the nerve to the Vastus medialis, can usually be traced downward on the surface of this muscle to near the joint; it then penetrates the muscular fibers, and accompanies the articular branch of the highest genicular artery, pierces the medial side of the articular capsule, and supplies the synovial membrane. The third branch is derived from the nerve to the Vastus intermedius.

The Sacral and Coccygeal Nerves (Nn. Sacrales et Coccygeus).

The **anterior rami of the sacral and coccygeal nerves** (*rami anteriores*) form the sacral and pudendal plexuses. The anterior rami of the upper four sacral nerves enter the pelvis through the anterior sacral foramina, that of the fifth between the sacrum and coccyx, while that of the coccygeal nerve curves forward below the rudimentary transverse process of the first piece of the coccyx. The first and second sacral nerves are large; the third, fourth, and fifth diminish progressively from above downward. Each receives a gray ramus communicans from the corresponding ganglion of the sympathetic trunk, while from the third and frequently from the second and the fourth sacral nerves, a white ramus communicans is given to the pelvic plexuses of the sympathetic.

The Sacral Plexus (*plexus sacralis*) (Fig. 824).—The sacral plexus is formed by the lumbosacral trunk, the anterior ramus of the first, and portions of the anterior rami of the second and third sacral nerves.

The lumbosacral trunk comprises the whole of the anterior ramus of the fifth and a part of that of the fourth lumbar nerve; it appears at the medial margin of the Psoas major and runs downward over the pelvic brim to join the first sacral nerve. The anterior ramus of the third sacral nerve divides into an upper and a lower branch, the former entering the sacral and the latter the pudendal plexus.

The nerves forming the sacral plexus converge toward the lower part of the greater sciatic foramen, and unite to form a flattened band, from the anterior and posterior surfaces of which several branches arise. The band itself is continued as the **sciatic nerve**, which splits on the back of the thigh into the **tibial** and **common peroneal nerves**; these two nerves sometimes arise separately from the plexus, and in all cases their independence can be shown by dissection.

Relations.—The sacral plexus lies on the back of the pelvis between the Piriformis and the pelvic fascia (Fig. 825); in front of it are the hypogastric vessels, the ureter and the sigmoid colon. The superior gluteal vessels run between the lumbosacral trunk and the first sacral nerve, and the inferior gluteal vessels between the second and third sacral nerves.

All the nerves entering the plexus, with the exception of the third sacral, split into ventral and dorsal divisions, and the nerves arising from these are as follows:

	Ventral divisions.	Dorsal divisions.
Nerve to Quadratus femoris and Gemellus inferior	4, 5 L, 1 S.	
Nerve to Obturator internus and Gemellus superior	5 L, 1, 2 S.	
Nerve to Piriformis		(1) 2 S.
Superior gluteal		4, 5 L, 1 S.
Inferior gluteal		5 L, 1, 2 S.
Posterior femoral cutaneous	2, 3 S . . .	1, 2 S.
Sciatic { Tibial . . .	4, 5 L, 1, 2, 3 S.	
{ Common peroneal		4, 5 L, 1, 2 S.

The **Nerve to the Quadratus Femoris and Gemellus Inferior** *arises* from the ventral divisions of the fourth and fifth lumbar and first sacral nerves: it leaves the pelvis through the greater sciatic foramen, below the Piriformis, and runs down in front of the sciatic nerve, the Gemelli, and the tendon of the Obturator internus, and enters the anterior surfaces of the muscles; it gives an articular branch to the hip-joint.

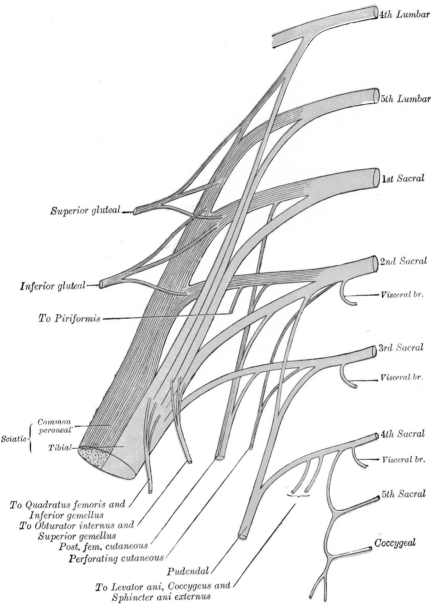

Superior gluteal

Inferior gluteal

To Piriformis

Sciatic { *Common peroneal* *Tibial*

To Quadratus femoris and Inferior gemellus
To Obturator internus and Superior gemellus
Post. fem. cutaneous
Perforating cutaneous
Pudendal
To Levator ani, Coccygeus and Sphincter ani externus

4th Lumbar

5th Lumbar

1st Sacral

2nd Sacral
Visceral br.

3rd Sacral
Visceral br.

4th Sacral
Visceral br.

5th Sacral

Coccygeal

Fig. 824.—Plan of sacral and coccygeal plexuses.

The **Nerve to the Obturator Internus and Gemellus Superior** *arises* from the ventral divisions of the fifth lumbar and first and second sacral nerves. It leaves the pelvis through the greater sciatic foramen below the Piriformis, and gives off the branch to the Gemellus superior, which enters the upper part of the posterior surface of the muscle. It then crosses the ischial spine, reënters the pelvis through the lesser sciatic foramen, and pierces the pelvic surface of the Obturator internus.

The **Nerve to the Piriformis** *arises* from the dorsal division of the second sacral nerve, or the dorsal divisions of the first and second sacral nerves, and enters the anterior surface of the muscle; this nerve may be double.

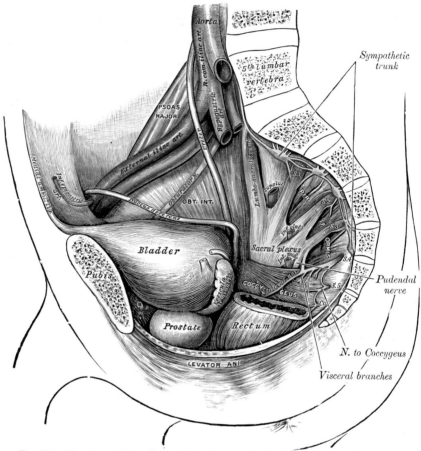

Fig. 825.—Dissection of side wall of pelvis showing sacral and pudendal plexuses. (Testut.

The **Superior Gluteal Nerve** (*n. glutæus superior*) (Fig. 828) *arises* from the dorsal divisions of the fourth and fifth lumbar and first sacral nerves: it leaves the pelvis through the greater sciatic foramen above the Piriformis, accompanied by the superior gluteal vessels, and divides into a superior and an inferior branch. The **superior branch** accompanies the upper branch of the deep division of the superior gluteal artery and ends in the Glutæus minimus. The **inferior branch** runs with the lower branch of the deep division of the superior gluteal artery across the Glutæus minimus; it gives filaments to the Glutæi medius and minimus, and ends in the Tensor fasciæ latæ.

The **Inferior Gluteal Nerve** (*n. glutæus inferior*) *arises* from the dorsal divisions of the fifth lumbar and first and second sacral nerves: it leaves the pelvis through the greater sciatic foramen, below the Piriformis, and divides into branches which enter the deep surface of the Glutæus maximus.

The **Posterior Femoral Cutaneous Nerve** (*n. cutaneus femoralis posterior; small sciatic nerve*) (Figs. 826, 827, 828) is distributed to the skin of the perineum and posterior surface of the thigh and leg. It *arises* partly from the dorsal divisions of the first and second, and from the ventral divisions of the second and third sacral nerves, and issues from the pelvis through the greater sciatic foramen below the Piriformis. It then descends beneath the Glutæus maximus with the inferior gluteal

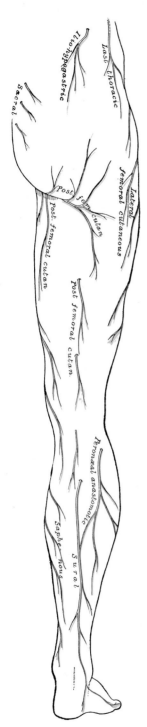

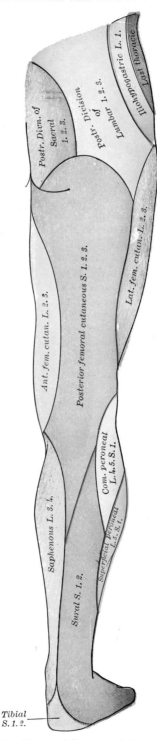

FIG. 826.—Cutaneous nerves of right lower extremity. Posterior view.

FIG. 827.—Diagram of the segmental distribution of the cutaneous nerves of the right lower extremity. Posterior view.

artery, and runs down the back of the thigh beneath the fascia lata, and over the long head of the Biceps femoris to the back of the knee; here it pierces the deep fascia and accompanies the small saphenous vein to about the middle of the back of the leg, its terminal twigs communicating with the sural nerve.

Its branches are all cutaneous, and are distributed to the gluteal region, the perineum, and the back of the thigh and leg.

The **gluteal branches** (*nn. clunium inferiores*), three or four in number, turn upward around the lower border of the Glutæus maximus, and supply the skin covering the lower and lateral part of that muscle.

The **perineal branches** (*rami perineales*) are distributed to the skin at the upper and medial side of the thigh. One long perineal branch, **inferior pudendal** (*long scrotal nerve*) (Fig. 833), curves forward below and in front of the ischial tuberosity, pierces the fascia lata, and runs forward beneath the superficial fascia of the perineum to the skin of the scrotum in the male, and of the labium majus in the female. It communicates with the inferior hemorrhoidal and posterior scrotal nerves.

The **branches to the back of the thigh and leg** consist of numerous filaments derived from both sides of the nerve, and distributed to the skin covering the back and medial side of the thigh, the popliteal fossa, and the upper part of the back of the leg (Fig. 826).

The **Sciatic** (*n. ischiadicus; great sciatic nerve*) (Fig. 828) supplies nearly the whole of the skin of the leg, the muscles of the back of the thigh, and those of the leg and foot. It is the largest nerve in the body, measuring 2 cm. in breadth, and is the continuation of the flattened band of the sacral plexus. It passes out of the pelvis through the greater sciatic foramen, below the Piriformis muscle. It descends between the greater trochanter of the femur and the tuberosity of the ischium, and along the back of the thigh to about its lower third, where it divides into two large branches, the tibial and common peroneal nerves. This division may take place at any point between the sacral plexus and the lower third of the thigh. When it occurs at the plexus, the common peroneal nerve usually pierces the Piriformis.

In the upper part of its course the nerve rests upon the posterior surface of the ischium, the nerve to the Quadratus femoris, the Obturator internus and Gemelli, and the Quadratus femoris; it is accompanied by the posterior femoral cutaneous nerve and the inferior gluteal artery, and is covered by the Glutæus maximus. Lower down, it lies upon the Adductor magnus, and is crossed obliquely by the long head of the Biceps femoris.

The nerve gives off articular and muscular branches.

The **articular branches** (*rami articulares*) *arise* from the upper part of the nerve and supply the hip-joint, perforating the posterior part of its capsule; they are sometimes derived from the sacral plexus.

The **muscular branches** (*rami musculares*) are distributed to the Biceps femoris, Semitendinosus, Semimembranosus, and Adductor magnus. The nerve to the short head of the Biceps femoris comes from the common peroneal part of the sciatic, while the other muscular branches *arise* from the tibial portion, as may be seen in those cases where there is a high division of the sciatic nerve.

The **Tibial Nerve** (*n. tibialis; internal popliteal nerve*) (Fig. 828) the larger of the two terminal branches of the sciatic, *arises* from the anterior branches of the fourth and fifth lumbar and first, second, and third sacral nerves. It descends along the back of the thigh and through the middle of the popliteal fossa, to the lower part of the Popliteus muscle, where it passes with the popliteal artery beneath the arch of the Soleus. It then runs along the back of the leg with the posterior tibial vessels to the interval between the medial malleolus and the heel, where it divides beneath the laciniate ligament into the medial and lateral plantar nerves. In the thigh it is overlapped by the hamstring muscles above, and then becomes more superficial, and lies lateral to, and some distance from, the popliteal vessels;

opposite the knee-joint, it is in close relation with these vessels, and crosses to the medial side of the artery. In the leg it is covered in the upper part of its course by the muscles of the calf; lower down by the skin, the superficial and deep fasciæ. It is placed on the deep muscles, and lies at first to the medial side of the posterior tibial artery, but soon crosses that vessel and descends on its lateral side as far as the ankle. In the lower third of the leg it runs parallel with the medial margin of the tendo calcaneus.

The **branches** of this nerve are: articular, muscular, medial sural cutaneous, medial calcaneal, medial and lateral plantar.

Articular branches (*rami articulares*), usually three in number, supply the knee-joint; two of these accompany the superior and inferior medial genicular arteries; and a third, the middle genicular artery. Just above the bifurcation of the nerve an articular branch is given off to the ankle-joint.

Muscular branches (*rami musculares*), four or five in number, *arise* from the nerve as it lies between the two heads of the Gastrocnemius muscle; they supply that muscle, and the Plantaris, Soleus, and Popliteus. The branch for the Popliteus turns around the lower border and is distributed to the deep surface of the muscle. Lower down, muscular branches *arise* separately or by a common trunk and supply the Soleus, Tibialis posterior, Flexor digitorum longus, and Flexor hallucis longus; the branch to the last muscle accompanies the peroneal artery; that to the Soleus enters the deep surface of the muscle.

The **medial sural cutaneous nerve** (*n. cutaneous suræ medialis; n. communicans tibialis*) descends between the two heads of the Gastrocnemius, and, about the middle of the back of the leg, pierces the deep fascia, and unites with the anastomotic ramus of the common peroneal to form the sural nerve (Fig. 826).

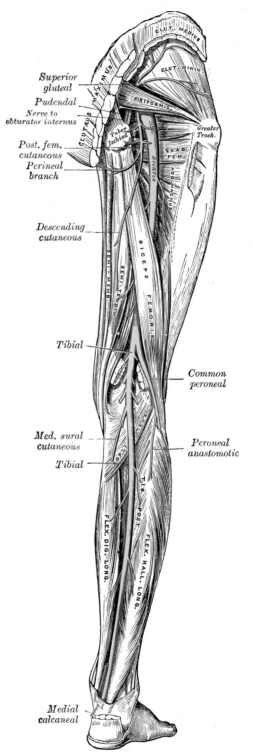

FIG. 828.—Nerves of the right lower extremity.[1]
Posterior view.

[1] N. B.—In this diagram the medial sural cutaneous and peroneal anastomotic are not in their normal position. They have been displaced by the removal of the superficial muscles.

The **sural nerve** (*n. suralis; short saphenous nerve*), formed by the junction of the medial sural cutaneous with the peroneal anastomotic branch, passes downward near the lateral margin of the tendo calcaneus, lying close to the small saphenous vein, to the interval between the lateral malleolus and the calcaneus. It runs forward below the lateral malleolus, and is continued as the **lateral dorsal cutaneous nerve** along the lateral side of the foot and little toe (Fig. 832), communicating on the dorsum of the foot with the intermediate dorsal cutaneous nerve, a branch of the superficial peroneal. In the leg, its branches communicate with those of the posterior femoral cutaneous.

The **medial calcaneal branches** (*rami calcanei mediales; internal calcaneal branches*) (Fig. 828) perforate the laciniate ligament, and supply the skin of the heel and medial side of the sole of the foot.

The **medial plantar nerve** (*n. plantaris medialis; internal plantar nerve*) (Fig. 829), the larger of the two terminal divisions of the tibial nerve, accompanies the medial plantar artery. From its origin under the laciniate ligament it passes under cover of the Abductor hallucis, and, appearing between this muscle and the Flexor digitorum brevis, gives off a proper digital plantar nerve and finally divides opposite the bases of the metatarsal bones into three common digital plantar nerves.

BRANCHES.—The branches of the medial plantar nerve are: (1) **cutaneous,** (2) **muscular**, (3) **articular**, (4) a **proper digital nerve** to the medial side of the great toe, and (5) three **common digital nerves**.

The **cutaneous branches** pierce the plantar aponeurosis between the Abductor hallucis and the Flexor digitorum brevis and are distributed to the skin of the sole of the foot (Fig. 830).

The **muscular branches** supply the Abductor hallucis, the Flexor digitorum brevis, the Flexor hallucis brevis, and the first Lumbricalis; those for the Abductor hallucis and Flexor digitorum brevis arise from the trunk of the nerve near its origin and enter the deep surfaces of the muscles; the branch of the Flexor hallucis brevis springs from the proper digital nerve to the medial side of the great toe, and that for the first Lumbricalis from the first common digital nerve.

The **articular branches** supply the articulations of the tarsus and metatarsus.

The **proper digital nerve of the great toe** (*nn. digitales plantares proprii; plantar digital branches*) supplies the Flexor hallucis brevis and the skin on the medial side of the great toe.

The **three common digital nerves** (*nn. digitales plantares communes*) pass between the divisions of the plantar aponeurosis, and each splits into two proper digital nerves—those of the first common digital nerve supply the adjacent sides of the great and second toes; those of the second, the adjacent sides of the second and third toes; and those of the third, the adjacent sides of the third and fourth toes. The third common digital nerve receives a communicating branch from the lateral plantar nerve; the first gives a twig to the first Lumbricalis. Each proper digital nerve gives off cutaneous and articular filaments; and opposite the last phalanx sends upward a dorsal branch, which supplies the structures around the nail, the continuation of the nerve being distributed to the ball of the toe. It will be observed that these digital nerves are similar in their distribution to those of the median nerve in the hand.

The **Lateral Plantar Nerve** (*n. plantaris lateralis; external plantar nerve*) (Figs. 829, 830) supplies the skin of the fifth toe and lateral half of the fourth, as well as most of the deep muscles, its distribution being similar to that of the ulnar nerve in the hand. It passes obliquely forward with the lateral plantar artery to the lateral side of the foot, lying between the Flexor digitorum brevis and Quadratus plantæ; and, in the interval between the former muscle and the Abductor digiti quinti, divides into a superficial and a deep branch. Before its division, it supplies the Quadratus plantæ and Abductor digiti quinti.

The **superficial branch** (*ramus superficialis*) splits into a proper and a common digital nerve; the proper digital nerve supplies the lateral side of the little toe, the Flexor digiti quinti brevis, and the two Interossei of the fourth intermetatarsal space; the common digital nerve communicates with the third common digital branch of the medial plantar nerve and divides into two proper digital nerves which supply the adjoining sides of the fourth and fifth toes.

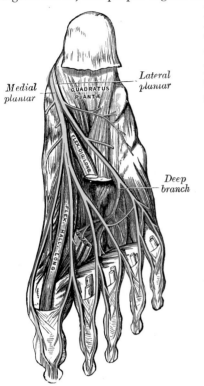

FIG. 829.—The plantar nerves.

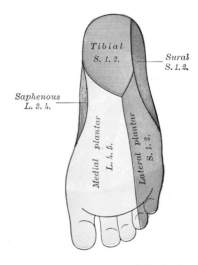

FIG. 830.—Diagram of the segmental distribution of the cutaneous nerves of the sole of the foot.

The **deep branch** (*ramus profundus; muscular branch*) accompanies the lateral plantar artery on the deep surface of the tendons of the Flexor muscles and the Adductor hallucis, and supplies all the Interossei (except those in the fourth metatarsal space), the second, third, and fourth Lumbricales, and the Adductor hallucis.

The **Common Peroneal Nerve** (*n. peronæus communis; external popliteal nerve; peroneal nerve*) (Fig. 828), about one-half the size of the tibial, is derived from the dorsal branches of the fourth and fifth lumbar and the first and second sacral nerves. It descends obliquely along the lateral side of the popliteal fossa to the head of the fibula, close to the medial margin of the Biceps femoris muscle. It lies between the tendon of the Biceps femoris and lateral head of the Gastrocnemius muscle, winds around the neck of the fibula, between the Peronæus longus and the bone, and divides beneath the muscle into the superficial and deep peroneal nerves. Previous to its division it gives off articular and lateral sural cutaneous nerves.

The **articular branches** (*rami articulares*) are three in number; two of these accompany the superior and inferior lateral genicular arteries to the knee; the upper one occasionally *arises* from the trunk of the sciatic nerve. The third (*recurrent*) articular nerve is given off at the point of division of the common peroneal nerve; it ascends with the anterior recurrent tibial artery through the Tibialis anterior to the front of the knee.

The **lateral sural cutaneous nerve** (*n. cutaneus suræ lateralis; lateral cutaneous branch*) supplies the skin on the posterior and lateral surfaces of the leg (Fig. 827); one branch, the **peroneal anastomotic** (*n. communicans fibularis*) (Figs. 826, 828), *arises* near the head of the fibula, crosses the lateral head of the Gastrocnemius to

63

the middle of the leg, and joins with the medial sural cutaneous to form the sural nerve. The peroneal anastomotic is occasionally continued down as a separate branch as far as the heel.

The **Deep Peroneal Nerve** (*n. peronæus profundus; anterior tibial nerve*) (Figs. 823, 831) begins at the bifurcation of the common peroneal nerve, between the fibula and upper part of the Peronæus longus, passes obliquely forward beneath the Extensor digitorum longus to the front of the interosseous membrane, and comes into relation with the anterior tibial artery above the middle of the leg; it then descends with the artery to the front of the ankle-joint, where it divides into a lateral and a medial terminal branch. It lies at first on the lateral side of the anterior tibial artery, then in front of it, and again on its lateral side at the ankle-joint.

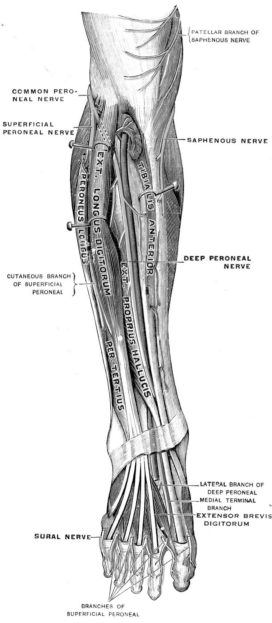

In the leg, the deep peroneal nerve supplies **muscular branches** to the Tibialis anterior, Extensor digitorum longus, Peronæus tertius, and Extensor hallucis proprius, and an **articular branch** to the ankle-joint.

The **lateral terminal branch** (*external or tarsal branch*) passes across the tarsus, beneath the Extensor digitorum brevis, and, having become enlarged like the dorsal interosseous nerve at the wrist, supplies the Extensor digitorum brevis. From the enlargement three minute **interosseous branches** are given off, which supply the tarsal joints and the metatarsophalangeal joints of the second, third, and fourth toes. The first of these sends a filament to the second Interosseus dorsalis muscle.

The **medial terminal branch** (*internal branch*) accompanies the dorsalis pedis artery along the dorsum of the foot, and, at the first interosseous space, divides into two **dorsal digital nerves** (*nn. digitales dorsales hallucis lateralis et digiti secundi medialis*) (Figs. 821, 822, 832) which supply the adjacent sides of the great and second toes, communicating with the medial dorsal cutaneous branch of the superficial peroneal nerve. Before it divides it gives off to the first space an **interosseous branch** which supplies

FIG. 831.—Deep nerves of the front of the leg. (Testut.)

Image labels: PATELLAR BRANCH OF SAPHENOUS NERVE; COMMON PERONEAL NERVE; SUPERFICIAL PERONEAL NERVE; SAPHENOUS NERVE; EXT. PERONEUS LONGUS DIGITORUM LONGUS; TIBIALIS ANTERIOR; EXT. PROPRIUS HALLUCIS; PER. TERTIUS; DEEP PERONEAL NERVE; CUTANEOUS BRANCH OF SUPERFICIAL PERONEAL; LATERAL BRANCH OF DEEP PERONEAL; MEDIAL TERMINAL BRANCH; EXTENSOR BREVIS DIGITORUM; SURAL NERVE; BRANCHES OF SUPERFICIAL PERONEAL the metatarsophalangeal joint of the great toe and sends a filament to the first Interosseous dorsalis muscle.

The **Superficial Peroneal Nerve** (*n. peronæus superficialis; musculocutaneous nerve*) (Figs. 823, 831, 832) supplies the Peronei longus and brevis and the skin over the greater part of the dorsum of the foot. It passes forward between the Peronæi and the Extensor digitorum longus, pierces the deep fascia at the lower third of the leg, and divides into a medial and an intermediate dorsal cutaneous nerve. In its course between the muscles, the nerve gives off muscular branches to the Peronæi longus and brevis, and cutaneous filaments to the integument of the lower part of the leg.

The **medial dorsal cutaneous nerve** (*n. cutaneus dorsalis medialis; internal dorsal cutaneous branch*) (Figs. 821, 822) passes in front of the ankle-joint, and divides into two dorsal **digital branches,** one of which supplies the medial side of the great toe, the other, the adjacent side of the second and third toes. It also supplies the integument of the medial side of the foot and ankle, and communicates with the saphenous nerve, and with the deep peroneal nerve (Fig. 831).

The **intermediate dorsal cutaneous nerve** (*n. cutaneus dorsalis intermedius; external dorsal cutaneous branch*), the smaller, passes along the lateral part of the dorsum of the foot, and divides into **dorsal digital branches,** which supply the contiguous sides of the third and fourth, and of the fourth and fifth toes. It also supplies the skin of the lateral side of the foot and ankle, and communicates with the sural nerve (Fig. 832). The branches of the

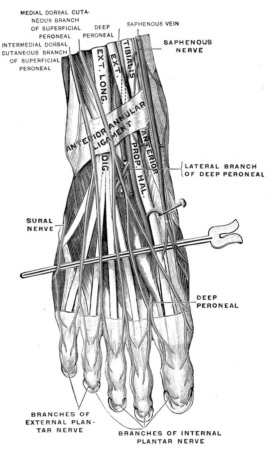

Fig. 832.—Nerves of the dorsum of the foot. (Testut.)

superficial peroneal nerve supply the skin of the dorsal surfaces of all the toes excepting the lateral side of the little toe, and the adjoining sides of the great and second toes, the former being supplied by the lateral dorsal cutaneous nerve from the sural nerve, and the latter by the medial branch of the deep peroneal nerve (Figs. 821, 822). Frequently some of the lateral branches of the superficial peroneal are absent, and their places are then taken by branches of the sural nerve.

The **Perforating Cutaneous Nerve** (*n. clunium inferior medialis*) usually *arises* from the posterior surface of the second and third sacral nerves. It pierces the lower part of the sacrotuberous ligament, and winding around the inferior border of the Glutæus maximus supplies the skin covering the medial and lower parts of that muscle.

The perforating cutaneous nerve may arise from the pudendal or it may be absent; in the latter case its place may be taken by a branch from the posterior femoral cutaneous nerve or by a branch from the third and fourth, or fourth and fifth, sacral nerves.

The **Pudendal Plexus** (*plexus pudendus*) (Figs. 824, 833) is formed generally by the anterior branches of the second, third, and fourth sacral nerves, but it is subject to variations so that it may include branches of the first or fifth sacral nerves. It is located in the back of the pelvis in front of the lower portion of the Piriformis and is sometimes considered as a portion of the sacral plexus. From it are derived Visceral Branches, Muscular Branches and the Pudendal Nerve.

The **Visceral Branches** (*rami viscerales*) arise from the third and fourth, and sometimes from the second sacral nerves. They contain visceral afferent and preganglionic visceral (parasympathetic) efferent fibers which mediate impulses from and to the pelvic viscera. They participate with fibers from the hypogastric plexus and from visceral branches of sacral chain ganglia in the formation of the pelvic plexuses, in the branches of which they are distributed to the various pelvic viscera, i. e., to the rectum in the middle hemorrhoidal plexus, to the bladder in the vesical plexus, to male reproductive organs in the prostatic plexus, and to the female reproductive tract in the vaginal and uterine plexuses.

The **Muscular Branches** are derived mainly from the fourth sacral (sometimes also from the third and fifth sacral), and supply the Levator ani, Coccygeus, and Sphincter ani externus. The branches to the Levator ani and Coccygeus enter their pelvic surfaces; that to the Sphincter ani externus (perineal branch) reaches the ischiorectal fossa by piercing the Coccygeus or by passing between it and the Levator ani. Cutaneous filaments from this branch supply the skin between the anus and the coccyx.

The **Pudendal Nerve** (*n. pudendus; internal pudic nerve*) (Fig. 833) derives its fibers from the ventral branches of the second, third, and fourth sacral nerves. It passes between the Piriformis and Coccygeus muscles and leaves the pelvis through the lower part of the greater sciatic foramen. It then crosses the spine of the ischium, and reënters the pelvis through the lesser sciatic foramen. It accompanies the internal pudendal vessels upward and forward along the lateral wall of the ischiorectal fossa, being contained in a sheath of the obturator fascia termed **Alcock's canal,** and divides into two terminal branches, viz., the **perineal nerve,** and the **dorsal nerve of the penis** or **clitoris.** Before its division it gives off the **inferior hemorrhoidal nerve.**

The **inferior hemorrhoidal nerve** (*n. hæmorrhoidalis inferior*) occasionally *arises* directly from the sacral plexus; it crosses the ischiorectal fossa, with the inferior hemorrhoidal vessels, toward the anal canal and the lower end of the rectum, and is distributed to the Sphincter ani externus and to the integument around the anus. Branches of this nerve communicate with the perineal branch of the posterior femoral cutaneous and with the posterior scrotal nerves at the forepart of the perineum.

The **perineal nerve** (*n. perinei*), the inferior and larger of the two terminal branches of the pudendal, is situated below the internal pudendal artery. It accompanies the perineal artery and divides into **posterior scrotal** (or **labial**) and **muscular branches.**

The **posterior scrotal (or labial) branches** (*nn. scrotales (or labiales) posteriores: superficial peroneal nerves*) are two in number, medial and lateral. They pierce the fascia of the urogenital diaphragm, and run forward along the lateral part of the urethral triangle in company with the posterior scrotal branches of the perineal artery; they are distributed to the skin of the scrotum and communicate with the perineal branch of the posterior femoral cutaneous nerve. These nerves supply the labium majus in the female.

The **muscular branches** are distributed to the Transversus perinæi superficialis, Bulbocavernous, Ischiocavernous, Transversus perinæi profundus and Sphincter urethræ membranaceæ. A branch, the **nerve to the bulb** (Fig. 833), given off from the nerve to the Bulbocavernosus, pierces this muscle, and supplies the corpus cavernosum urethræ, ending in the mucous membrane of the urethra.

The **dorsal nerve of the penis** (*n. dorsalis penis*) is the deepest division of the pudendal nerve; it accompanies the internal pudendal artery along the ramus of the
ischium; it then runs forward along the margin of the inferior ramus of the pubis,
between the superior and inferior layers of the fascia of the urogenital diaphram.

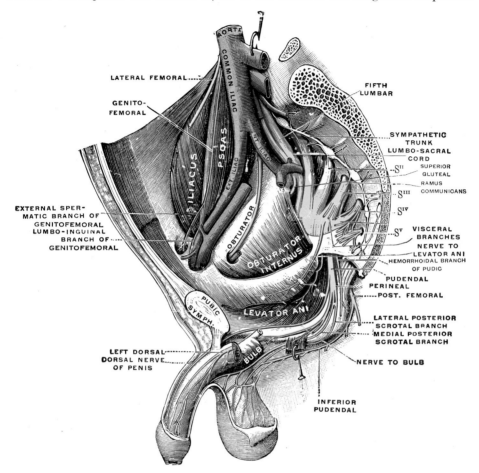

FIG. 833.—Sacral plexus of the right side. (Testut.

Piercing the inferior layer it gives a branch to the corpus cavernosum penis, and
passes forward, in company with the dorsal artery of the penis, between the layers
of the suspensory ligament, on to the dorsum of the penis, and ends on the glans
penis. In the female this nerve is very small, and supplies the **clitoris** (*n. dorsalis
clitoridis*).

The **Coccygeal Plexus** (*plexus coccygeus*) (Fig. 824).—The fifth sacral nerve receives a communicating filament from the fourth, and unites with the coccygeal
nerve to form the coccygeal plexus. From this plexus, the Anococcygeal Nerves
take origin; they consist of a few fine filaments which pierce the sacrotuberous
ligament to supply the skin in the region of the coccyx (Fig. 799).

THE AUTONOMIC NERVOUS SYSTEM.

The **autonomic nervous system** (Fig. 834) innervates all the smooth muscles and
the various glands of the body, and the striated muscle of the heart. It is made
up of efferent fibers and may be divided into two systems, the craniosacral (para-

sympathetics) and the thoracolumbar (sympathetics).   Various viscera and organs receive a double autonomic innervation, one from the craniosacral and one from

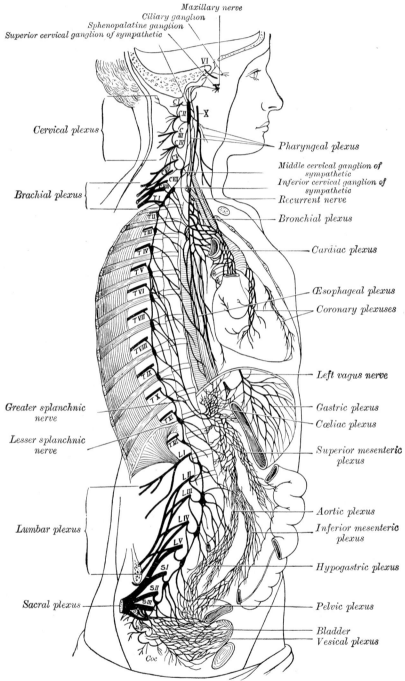

FIG. 834.—The right sympathetic chain and its connections with the thoracic, abdominal, and pelvic plexuses. (After Schwalbe.)

the thoracolumbar division.   The **preganglionic**, efferent fibers of both systems arise from nerve cells in the central nervous system.   These preganglionic fibers end in peripheral ganglia and from these ganglia **postganglionic** fibers are distributed to bloodvessels, viscera, glands, heart, etc. The preganglionic fibers of the craniosacral system leave the central nervous system with the oculomotor, the facial, the glossopharyngeal and the vagus nerves, the cranial outflow, and with the second, third and fourth sacral nerves, the sacral outflow. The craniosacral outflow is separated from the thoracolumbar outflow by intervals where no preganglionic fibers exist. The preganglionic fibers of the thoracolumbar system leave the spinal cord in the anterior nerve roots of the thoracic and the first two or three lumbar nerves.

The **visceral afferent** or **sensory fibers** which conduct impulses from the viscera to the central nervous system have their cell bodies in the cerebrospinal ganglia as do the somatic afferent fibers. The distinction between somatic and visceral afferent fibers is one of peripheral distribution rather than one of fundamental anatomical or physiological significance. The visceral afferent fibers are not strictly a part of the autonomic system, although they course along with the autonomic fibers in different portions of the visceral nervous system.

The cranial and sacral outflows are grouped together owing to the resemblance between the reactions produced by stimulating them and by the effects of certain drugs. Furthermore they are morphologically similar in that their postganglionic neurons are situated in the wall of the viscus innervated, or nearby in most instances. When injected intravenously in very small doses, acetyl-choline produces similar effects as the stimulation of the craniosacral outflow. Introduction of adrenaline elicits effects similar to those produced by stimulation of the thoracolumbar outflow. However the term cholinergic is now used to denote fibers whose activity elicits effects similar to those of acetyl-choline and adrenergic for fibers which on stimulation produce responses like those caused by adrenaline. Preganglionic fibers in the autonomic system are said to be cholinergic, while the postganglionic fibers in the thoracolumbar outflow may be adrenergic or cholinergic; those in the craniosacral outflow, cholinergic and possibly adrenergic. (See footnote, page 949.)

Much of our present knowledge of the autonomic nervous system has been acquired through application of various drugs, especially nicotine which paralyses the connections or synapses between the preganglionic and postganglionic fibers. When it is injected into the general circulation in proper doses, all such synapses are paralyzed; when it is applied locally on a ganglion only the synapses occurring in that particular ganglion are paralyzed.

Langley,[1] who has made most important contributions to the knowledge of this field, adopted a widely-accepted terminology in which he used the term autonomic for the efferent innervation of the viscera. Various terms have been introduced such as involuntary nervous system[2] and vegetative nervous system.[3] Considerable confusion in terminology has arisen. Ranson (1939) and others use the term visceral nervous system to denote an aggregation of ganglia, nerves and plexuses through which the viscera, glands, heart and bloodvessels, and smooth muscle, wherever it occurs, receive their innervation. It has sensory (visceral afferent) and motor (visceral efferent) components, is under the control of integrating mechanisms in the central nervous system, influences and is influenced by the cerebrospinal nervous system. Enteric components are those relatively unknown nervous structures which have been thought to subserve local reflexes in the viscera, i. e., myenteric reflexes in the wall of the gastrointestinal tract which have been described as still being present after section of all the extrinsic nerves.

Langley.	Meyer and Gottlieb [3]
Autonomic nervous system.	Vegetative nervous system.
Parasympathetics.	Autonomic.
Tectal autonomics.	Cranial autonomics.
Bulbar autonomics	
Sacral autonomics.	Sacral autonomics.
Sympathetic.	Sympathetic.
Thoracic autonomic.	
Enteric.	Enteric.

[1] Schäfer, Textbook of Physiology, 1900.
[2] Gaskell, W. H., The Involuntary Nervous System, London, 1916.
[3] Die Experimentelle Pharmakologie, 1910

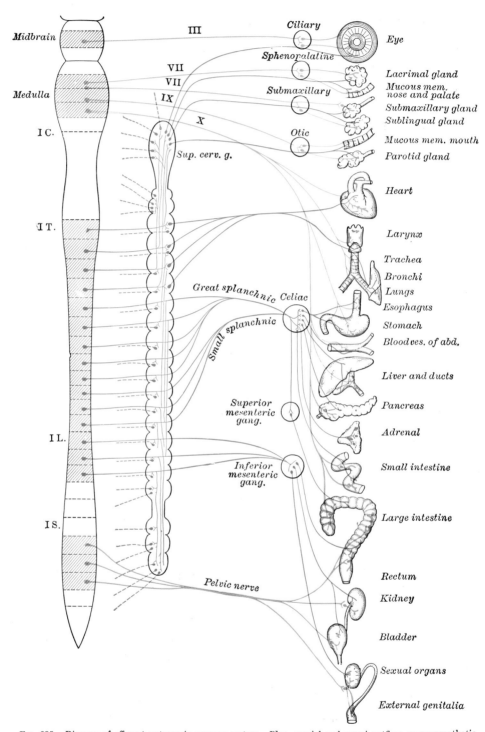

FIG. 835.—Diagram of efferent autonomic nervous system. Blue, cranial and sacral outflow, parasympathetic Red, thoracolumbar outflow, sympathetic. ------, Postganglionic fibers to spinal and cranial nerves to supply vaso-motors to head, trunk and limbs, motor fibers to smooth muscles of skin and fibers to sweat glands. (Modified after Meyer and Gottlieb.) This is only a diagram and does not accurately portray all of the details of distribution.

Visceral Nervous System (major sympathetic system; plexiform nervous system; systema nervorum sympatheticum; vegetative nervous system; involuntary nervous system)

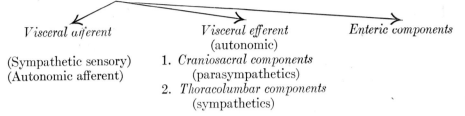

Visceral afferent

(Sympathetic sensory)
(Autonomic afferent)

Visceral efferent
(autonomic)
1. *Craniosacral components*
     (parasympathetics)
2. *Thoracolumbar components*
     (sympathetics)

Enteric components

THE CRANIAL OUTFLOW (PARASYMPATHETICS).

The **cranial outflow (parasympathetics)** includes efferent fibers in the oculomotor, facial, glossopharyngeal and vagus nerves, and nuclei in the mid-brain and medulla oblongata.

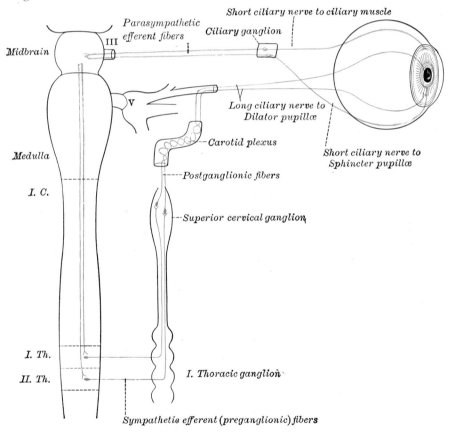

FIG. 836.—Autonomic connections of the ciliary and superior cervical ganglia.

The **Visceral Efferent Fibers of the Oculomotor Nerve** arise from cells in the Edinger-Westphal nucleus located in the anterior part of the oculomotor nucleus in the tegmentum of the mid-brain. These preganglionic fibers run with the third nerve into the orbit and pass to the ciliary ganglion where they terminate by forming synapses with autonomic motor neurons whose axons, postganglionic fibers, proceed as the short ciliary nerves to the eyeball. Here they supply motor fibers to the Ciliaris muscle and the Sphincter pupillæ muscle (Figs. 775, 836).

The **Visceral Efferent Fibers of the Facial Nerve** arise from the superior salivatory nucleus, consisting of cells scattered in the reticular formation, dorso-medial to the facial nucleus. These preganglionic fibers are distributed partly through the chorda tympani and lingual nerves to the submaxillary ganglion, where they terminate about the cell bodies of neurons whose axons as postganglionic fibers conduct secretory and vasodilator impulses to the submaxillary and sublingual glands. Other preganglionic fibers of the facial nerve pass via the great superficial

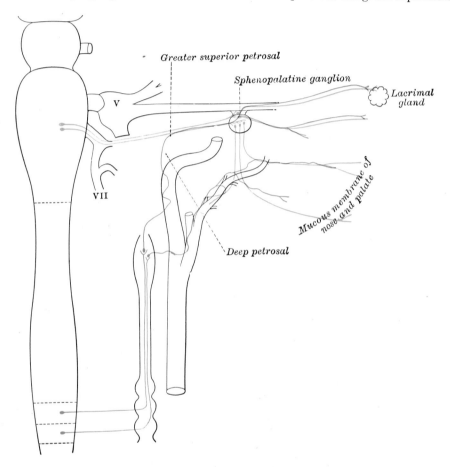

Fɪɢ. 837.—Autonomic connections of the sphenopalatine and superior cervical ganglia.

petrosal nerve to the sphenopalatine ganglion where they form synapses with neurons whose postganglionic fibers are distributed with the superior maxillary nerve as vasodilator and secretory fibers to the mucous membrane of the nose, soft palate, tonsils, uvula, roof of the mouth, upper lips and gums, lacrimal, parotid, and orbital glands (Figs. 837, 838).

The **Visceral Efferent Fibers of the Glossopharyngeal Nerve** arise in the inferior salivatory nucleus, situated near the dorsal nucleus. These preganglionic fibers probably pass into the tympanic branch of the glossopharyngeal and then with the small superficial petrosal nerve to the otic ganglion. Postganglionic fibers, vasodilator and secretory fibers are distributed to the parotid gland, to the mucous membrane and its glands on the tongue, the floor of the mouth, and the lower gums (Fig. 839).

Visceral Afferent Fibers of the Glossopharyngeal whose cells of origin lie in the superior or inferior ganglion of the trunk are supposed to terminate in the dorsal nucleus. Very little is known of the peripheral distribution of these fibers.

The **Visceral Efferent Fibers of the Vagus Nerve** arise in the dorsal nucleus of the vagus. These preganglionic fibers are all supposed to end in ganglia situated in or near the organs supplied by the vagus. The fibers to the heart terminate in the small ganglia of the heart wall, especially the atrium, from which postganglionic

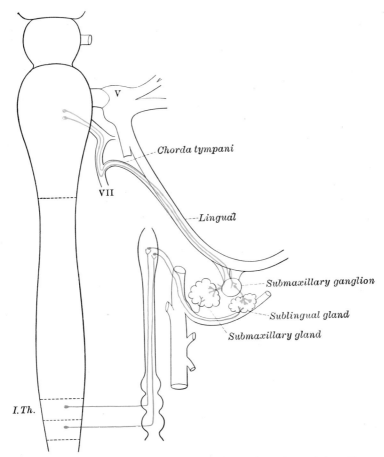

Fig. 838.—Autonomic connections of the submaxillary and superior cervical ganglia.

fibers are distributed to the musculature. The preganglionic motor fibers to the esophagus, the stomach, the small intestine, and the greater part of the large intestine are supposed to terminate in the myenteric (Auerbach) and submucous (Meissner) plexuses, from which postganglionic fibers are distributed to the smooth muscles and glands of these organs. Other fibers pass to the smooth muscles of the bronchial tree and to the gall-bladder and its ducts. In addition the vagus is believed to contain secretory fibers to the stomach and pancreas. It probably contains many other efferent fibers than those enumerated above. Although the vagus efferent pathways to the heart are mainly inhibitory, animal experiments indicate that accelerator fibers may also be present.

Visceral Afferent Fibers of the Vagus, whose cells of origin lie in the jugular ganglion and mainly in the ganglion nodosum, probably terminate in the dorsal nucleus of the medulla oblongata or, according to some authors, in the nucleus of the tractus solitarius. Peripherally the fibers accompany the visceral efferent fibers to the various organs which they supply.

THE SACRAL OUTFLOW (PARASYMPATHETICS).

The **Sacral Visceral Efferent Fibers** leave the spinal cord with the anterior roots of the second, third and fourth sacral nerves. These small medullated preganglionic fibers pass in the visceral branches of the pudendal plexus through the pelvic plexus and its branches to small ganglia on (or near) the pelvic viscera from which postganglionic fibers are distributed to the viscera. Motor fibers pass to the smooth muscle of the descending colon, rectum, anus and bladder. Vasodilators are distributed to these organs and to the external genitalia, while inhibitory fibers probably pass to the smooth muscles of the external genitalia. **Afferent visceral fibers** conduct impulses from the pelvic viscera to the second, third and fourth sacral nerves. Their cells of origin lie in the spinal ganglia.

THE THORACOLUMBAR OUTFLOW (SYMPATHETICS).

The **thoracolumbar visceral efferent fibers** arise from the dorso-lateral region of the anterior column of the gray matter of the spinal cord and pass with the anterior roots of all the thoracic and the upper two or three lumbar spinal nerves. These preganglionic fibers enter the white rami communicantes and proceed to the sympathetic trunk where many of them end in its ganglia, others pass to the prevertebral plexuses and terminate in its collateral ganglia. After entering the sympathetic trunk, the preganglionic fibers may terminate in the ganglion at the level of entrance or they may pass to ganglia above or below in the trunk. In the upper thoracic trunk, many of them pass upward, in the lower thoracic and lumbar portion most of them go downward and in the mid-thoracic portion, they may pass both up and down. One preganglionic fiber may give collaterals to postganglionic neurons in several of the chain ganglia and may terminate about as many as 15 or 20 postganglionic neurons. The postganglionic fibers have a wide distribution.

The **vasoconstrictor fibers** to the bloodvessels of the skin of the trunk and limbs, for example, leave the spinal cord as preganglionic fibers in all the thoracic and the upper two or three lumbar spinal nerves and terminate in the ganglia of the sympathetic trunk, either in the ganglion directly connected with its ramus or in neighboring ganglia. Postganglionic fibers arise in these ganglia, pass through gray rami communicantes to all the spinal nerves, and are distributed with their cutaneous branches, ultimately leaving these branches to join the small arteries. The postganglionic fibers do not necessarily return to the same spinal nerves which contain the corresponding preganglionic fibers. The vasoconstrictor fibers to the head come from the upper thoracic nerves, the preganglionic fibers end in the superior cervical ganglion. The postganglionic fibers pass through the internal carotid nerve and branch from it to join the sensory branches of the various cranial nerves, especially the trigeminal nerve; other fibers to the deep structures and the salivary glands probably accompany the arteries.

The postganglionic vasoconstrictor fibers to the bloodvessels of the abdominal viscera arise in the prevertebral or collateral ganglia in which terminate many preganglionic fibers. Vasoconstrictor fibers to the pelvic viscera arise from cells in the inferior mesenteric ganglia (in man the ganglion cells are scattered in a network around the proximal portion of the inferior mesenteric artery) and possibly also in the pelvic plexus.

The pilomotor fibers to the hairs and the motor fibers to the sweat glands apparently have a distribution similar to that of the vasoconstrictors of the skin.

Vasoconstrictor centers have been located by the physiologists in the hypothalamus and in the medulla oblongata. Axons from cells at higher levels descend in the spinal cord to terminate about cell bodies of the preganglionic neurons located in the posterolateral portion of the anterior column of the thoracic and upper lumbar region.[1]

The motor supply to the dilatator pupillæ muscle of the eye comes from preganglionic sympathetic fibers which leave the spinal cord with the anterior roots of the upper (mainly first and second) thoracic nerves. These fibers pass to the sympathetic trunk through the white rami communicantes and terminate in the superior cervical ganglion. Postganglionic fibers from the superior cervical ganglion pass through the internal carotid nerve and the ophthalmic division of the trigeminal nerve to the orbit where the long ciliary nerves conduct the impulses to the eyeball and the dilatator pupillæ muscle. Accessory pathways for the postganglionic fibers may be present. The cell bodies of these preganglionic fibers are connected with fibers which descend from higher levels in the brain stem. Interruption of these descending pathways or of the pre-

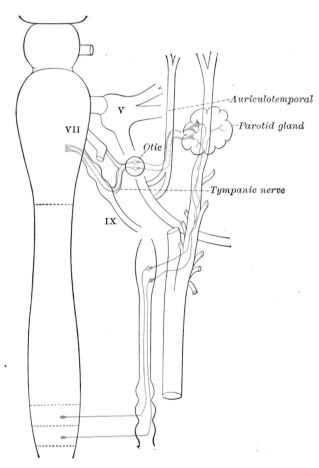

Fig. 839.—Autonomic connections of the otic and superior cervical ganglia.

or postganglionic pathways connected with the upper cervical chain causes a combination of symptoms known as Horner's syndrome. These have been described as a sinking of the eyeball into the orbit (enophthalmus), constriction of the pupil (myosis), drooping of the eyelid (ptosis), vasodilatation and absence of sweating on the side of the lesion. These symptoms are due to an absence of tonic impulses via the thoracolumbar visceral efferent (sympathetic) pathways. (See Fulton, J. F.: Physiology of the Nervous System, Oxford University Press, New York, 2nd Ed., 1943, pp. 201–203.)

Other postganglionic fibers from the superior cervical ganglion are distributed as secretory fibers to the salivary glands, the lacrimal glands and to the small glands of the mucous membrane of the nose, mouth and pharynx.

[1] Magoun, H. W.: Descending Connections from the Hypothalamus, Res. Pbl. Assn. Nerv. and Ment. Dis., 1940, **20**, 270–285.

The thoracolumbar outflow supplies accelerator nerves to the heart. The preganglionic visceral efferent fibers emerge from the spinal cord in the anterior roots of the upper five or six thoracic nerves and pass with the white rami to the sympathetic trunk and its chain ganglia. Some of the preganglionic fibers terminate about postganglionic neurons in the upper thoracic and inferior cervical ganglia, while others course in the ansa subclavia to reach the middle and superior cervical sympathetic ganglia. The postganglionic fibers pass from the cervical portion of the trunk via its cardiac nerves, while others traverse the visceral cardiac branches from the upper thoracic trunk.

Vasomotor and sudomotor pathways to the bloodvessels and sweat glands of the hand consist of preganglionic fibers leaving the spinal cord from the second through the ninth thoracic levels via anterior roots and white rami into and up the sympathetic trunk, and of postganglionic neurons in the inferior cervical and the first (and possibly second and third) thoracic chain ganglia. The preganglionic fibers join appropriate spinal nerves via gray rami.

Preganglionic fibers to the smooth musculature of the stomach, the small intestine and most of the large intestine emerge in the anterior roots of the lower six or seven thoracic and upper lumbar nerves. These fibers pass through the white rami and sympathetic trunk and are conveyed by the splanchnic nerves and visceral branches of the lumbar sympathetic trunk to the prevertebral plexus where they terminate in the collateral ganglia. From the celiac and superior mesenteric ganglia postganglionic fibers are distributed to the stomach, the small intestine and most of the large intestine. Inhibitory fibers to the descending colon, the rectum and Internal sphincter ani are probably postganglionic fibers from the inferior mesenteric ganglion.

The thoracolumbar sympathetics are characterized by the presence of numerous ganglia which may be divided into two groups, **central** and **collateral.**

The **central ganglia** are arranged in two vertical rows, one on either side of the middle line, situated partly in front and partly at the sides of the vertebral column. Each ganglion is joined by intervening nervous cords to adjacent ganglia so that two chains, the **sympathetic trunks,** are formed. The **collateral ganglia** are found in connection with three great **prevertebral plexuses,** placed within the thorax, abdomen, and pelvis respectively.

The **sympathetic trunks** (*truncus sympathicus; gangliated cord*) extend from the base of the skull to the coccyx. The cephalic end of each is continued upward through the carotid canal into the skull, and forms a plexus on the internal carotid artery; the caudal ends of the trunks converge and end in a single ganglion, the **ganglion impar,** placed in front of the coccyx. The ganglia of each trunk are distinguished as **cervical, thoracic, lumbar,** and **sacral** and, except in the neck, they closely correspond in number to the vertebræ. There may be variation in their number but in general they are arranged as follows:

Cervical portion	3 ganglia
Thoracic "	10 or 11 "
Lumbar "	4 "
Sacral "	4 or 5 "

In the neck the ganglia lie in front of the transverse processes of the vertebræ; **in the thoracic region** in front of the heads of the ribs; **in the lumbar region** on the sides of the vertebral bodies; and **in the sacral region** in front of the sacrum.

Connections with the Spinal Nerves.—Communications are established between the sympathetic and spinal nerves through what are known as the **gray** and **white rami communicantes** (Fig. 796); the gray rami convey sympathetic fibers into the spinal nerves and the white rami transmit spinal fibers into the sympathetic. Each spinal nerve receives a gray ramus communicans from the sympathetic trunk, but white rami are not supplied by all the spinal nerves. White rami are derived from the first thoracic to the second or third or fourth lumbar nerves inclusive. In addition there are visceral branches which run from the second, third, and fourth sacral nerves directly to the pelvic plexuses of the sympathetic.[1]

---

[1] Attention should be called to variations in the arrangement of the rami. White and gray rami may be completely fused. A white ramus may contain some postganglionic fibers and a gray ramus may contain a few visceral preganglionic and afferent fibers.

The fibers which reach the sympathetic through the white rami communicantes are mainly medullated; those which spring from the cells of the sympathetic ganglia are almost entirely non-medullated. However some postganglionic fibers may be medullated. (The sympathetic nerves consist of efferent and afferent fibers, the origin and course of which are described on page 950).

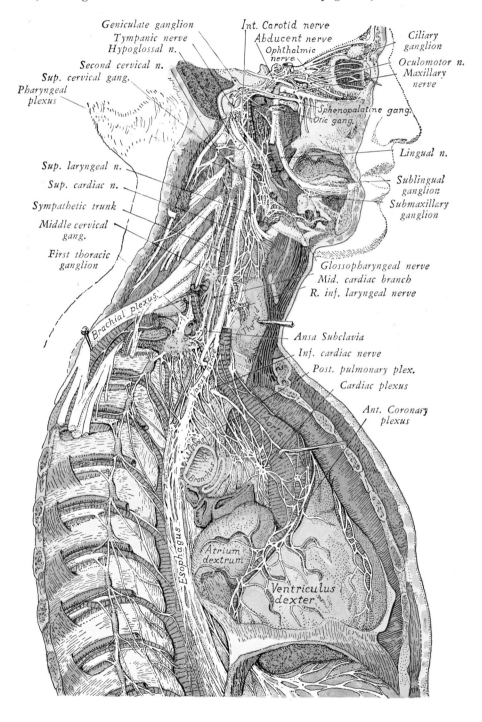

Fig. 840.—Cephalic, cervical, and thoracic portions of the sympathetic nervous system. (After Hirschfeld by J. G. Cowell.)

Some of the visceral afferent fibers which course along with the thoracolumbar outflow are of great importance in the mediation and reference of visceral pain. For example, visceral afferent fibers from the heart enter the sympathetic trunk in the middle and inferior cardiac nerves and in the visceral cardiac branches of the upper thoracic sympathetic trunk. These fibers then enter the first five or six thoracic white rami, pass through the corresponding posterior root ganglia where they have cells of origin and then into the spinal cord with the posterior roots. Cardiac pain may be referred into the dermatomes supplied by somatic afferent fibers entering these segments, *i. e.*, down the ulnar surface of the arm, into the axilla, and precordial region.[1]

The **three great gangliated plexuses** (*collateral ganglia*) are situated in front of the vertebral column in the thoracic, abdominal, and pelvic regions, and are named, respectively, the **cardiac**, the **solar** or **epigastric**, and the **hypogastric plexuses**. They consist of collections of nerves and ganglia; the nerves being derived from the sympathetic trunks and from the cerebrospinal nerves. They distribute branches to the viscera.

Development.—The ganglion cells of the sympathetic system are derived from the cells of the neural crests. As these crests move forward along the sides of the neural tube and become segmented off to form the spinal ganglia, certain cells detach themselves from the ventral margins of the crests and migrate toward the sides of the aorta, where some of them are grouped to form the ganglia of the sympathetic trunks, while others undergo a further migration and form the ganglia of the prevertebral and visceral plexuses. Experiments, some of them recent, indicate that sympathetic ganglia are derived from the ventral portion of the neural tube rather than from the neural crest.[2] The ciliary, sphenopalatine, otic, and submaxillary ganglia which are found on the branches of the trigeminal nerve are formed by groups of cells which have migrated from the part of the neural crest which gives rise to the semilunar ganglion. Some of the cells of the ciliary ganglion are said to migrate from the neural tube along the oculomotor nerve.

THE CEPHALIC PORTION OF THE SYMPATHETIC SYSTEM (PARS CEPHALICA S. SYMPATHICI).

The **cephalic portion** of the sympathetic system begins as the **internal carotid nerve**, which appears to be a direct prolongation of the superior cervical ganglion and contains postganglionic fibers which arise therein. It is soft in texture, and of a reddish color. It ascends by the side of the internal carotid artery, and, entering the carotid canal in the temporal bone, divides into two branches, which lie one on the lateral and the other on the medial side of that vessel.

The **lateral branch**, the larger of the two, distributes filaments to the internal carotid artery, and forms the **internal carotid plexus**.

The **medial branch** also distributes filaments to the internal carotid artery, and, continuing onward, forms the **cavernous plexus**.

The **internal carotid plexus** (*plexus caroticus internus; carotid plexus*) is situated on the lateral side of the internal carotid artery, and in the plexus there occasionally exists a small gangliform swelling, the **carotid ganglion**, on the under surface of the artery. The internal carotid plexus communicates with the semilunar ganglion, the abducent nerve, and the sphenopalatine ganglion; it distributes filaments to the wall of the carotid artery, and also communicates with the tympanic branch of the glossopharyngeal nerve.

The communicating branches with the abducent nerve consist of one or two filaments which join that nerve as it lies upon the lateral side of the internal carotid artery. The communication with the sphenopalatine ganglion is effected by a branch, the **deep petrosal**, given off from the plexus on the lateral side of the artery;

[1] For details see: Livingston, W. K.: The Clinical Aspects of Visceral Neurology, Charles C Thomas, Springfield, Ill., 1935. White, J. C.: The Autonomic Nervous System, The Macmillan Co., New York, 1935. Hinsey, J. C.: The Anatomical Relation of the Sympathetic System to Visceral Sensation, Res. Pbl. Assn. Nerv. and Ment. Dis., 1934, **15**, 105–180.
[2] Jones, D. S.: Further Studies on the Origin of Sympathetic Ganglia in the Chick Embryo, Anat. Rec., 1941, **79**, 7–15.

this branch passes through the cartilage filling up the foramen lacerum, and joins the greater superficial petrosal to form the nerve of the pterygoid canal (*Vidian nerve*), which passes through the pterygoid canal to the sphenopalatine ganglion. The communication with the tympanic branch of the glossopharyngeal nerve is effected by the **caroticotympanic,** which may consist of two or three delicate filaments.

The **cavernous plexus** (*plexus cavernosus*) is situated below and medial to that part of the internal carotid artery which is placed by the side of the sella turcica in the cavernous sinus, and is formed chiefly by the medial division of the internal carotid nerve. It communicates with the oculomotor, the trochlear, the ophthalmic and the abducent nerves, and with the ciliary ganglion, and distributes filaments to the wall of the internal carotid artery. The branch of communication with the oculomotor nerve joins that nerve at its point of division; the branch to the trochlear nerve joins it as it lies on the lateral wall of the cavernous sinus; other filaments are connected with the under surface of the ophthalmic nerve; and a second filament joins the abducent nerve.

The **filaments of connection** with the ciliary ganglion *arise* from the anterior part of the cavernous plexus and enter the orbit through the superior orbital fissure; they may join the nasociliary branch of the ophthalmic nerve, or be continued forward as a separate branch.

The **terminal filaments** from the internal carotid and cavernous plexuses are prolonged as plexuses around the anterior and middle cerebral arteries and the ophthalmic artery; along the former vessels, they may be traced to the pia mater; along the latter, into the orbit, where they accompany each of the branches of the vessel. The filaments prolonged on to the anterior communicating artery connect the sympathetic nerves of the right and left sides.

THE CERVICAL PORTION OF THE SYMPATHETIC SYSTEM (PARS CERVICALIS S. SYMPATHICI).

The **cervical portion** of the sympathetic trunk consists of three ganglia, distinguished, according to their positions, as the **superior, middle,** and **inferior ganglia,** connected by intervening cords (Fig. 841). This portion receives no white rami communicantes from the cervical spinal nerves; its spinal fibers are derived from the white rami of the upper thoracic nerves, and enter the corresponding thoracic ganglia of the sympathetic trunk, through which they ascend into the neck. The spinal components consist of preganglionic and visceral afferent fibers. The visceral afferent fibers have their cells of origin in the thoracic dorsal root ganglia. It is probable that few, if any of these afferent fibers, pass in the trunk above the middle cervical ganglion. The cervical trunk may contain a few postganglionic fibers with cells of origin in the cervical sympathetic ganglia.

The **superior cervical ganglion** (*ganglion cervicale superius*), the largest of the three, is placed opposite the second and third cervical vertebræ. It is of a reddish-gray color, and usually fusiform in shape; sometimes broad and flattened, and occasionally constricted at intervals; it is believed to be formed by the coalescence of four ganglia, corresponding to the upper four cervical nerves. It is in relation, in *front,* with the sheath of the internal carotid artery and internal jugular vein; *behind,* with the Longus capitis muscle.

In addition to the internal carotid nerve which has been described (page 1008), its **branches** may be divided into **inferior, lateral, medial,** and **anterior.**

The **Inferior Branch** communicates with the middle cervical ganglion.

The **Lateral Branches** (*external branches*) consist of gray rami communicantes to the upper four cervical nerves and to certain of the cranial nerves. Sometimes the branch to the fourth cervical nerve may come from the trunk connecting the upper and middle cervical ganglia. The branches to the cranial nerves consist of delicate filaments, which run to the ganglion nodosum of the vagus, and to the hypoglossal nerve. A filament, the **jugular nerve**, passes upward to the base of the skull, and divides to join the petrous ganglion of the glossopharyngeal, and the jugular ganglion of the vagus.

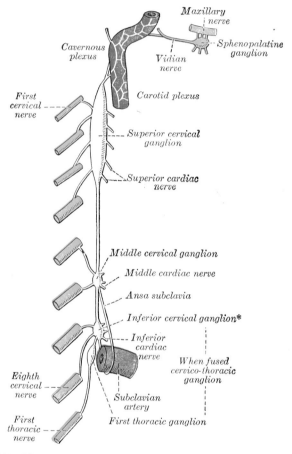

FIG. 841.—Diagram of the cervical sympathetic. (Modified after Testut.)

The **Medial Branches** (*internal branches*) are peripheral, and are the **larnygopharyngeal branches** and the **superior cardiac nerve**.

The **laryngopharyngeal branches** (*rami laryngopharyngei*) pass to the side of the pharynx, where they join with branches from the glossopharyngeal, vagus, and external laryngeal nerves to form the **pharyngeal plexus**.

The **superior cardiac nerve** (*n. cardiacus superior*) *arises* by two or more branches from the superior cervical ganglion, and occasionally receives a filament from the trunk between the superior and middle cervical ganglia. It runs down the neck behind the common carotid artery, and in front of the Longus colli muscle; and

---

* The inferior cervical ganglion may be fused with the first thoracic ganglion to form the cervicothoracic (stellate) ganglion. In man, such a fusion may be found in fifty per cent or more of the cases. The term "stellate" has been used to denote various ganglia but it is most commonly applied to the fused inferior cervical and first thoracic ganglia. Although it has not been officially recognized, cervicothoracic ganglion seems to be the best term to apply to the fused inferior cervical and first thoracic ganglia. Sheehan has described the variations which may occur in this structure (Sheehan, D.: On the Innervation of the Blood vessels of the Upper Extremity; Some Anatomical Considerations, Brit. Jour. Surg., 1933, **20**, 412–424).

crosses in front of the inferior thyroid artery, and recurrent nerve. The course of the nerves on the two sides then differ. The **right nerve**, at the root of the neck, passes either in front of or behind the subclavian artery, and along the innominate artery to the back of the arch of the aorta, where it joins the deep part of the cardiac plexus. It is connected with other branches of the sympathetic; about the middle of the neck it receives filaments from the external laryngeal nerve; lower down, one or two twigs from the vagus; and as it enters the thorax it is joined by a filament from the recurrent nerve. Filaments from the nerve communicate with the thyroid branches from the middle cervical ganglion. The **left nerve**, in the thorax, runs in front of the left common carotid artery and across the left side of the arch of the aorta, to the superficial part of the cardiac plexus.

The **Anterior Branches** (*nn. carotici externi*) ramify upon the common carotid artery and upon the external carotid artery and its branches, forming around each a delicate plexus, on the nerves composing which small ganglia are occasionally found. The plexuses accompanying some of these arteries have important communications with other nerves. That surrounding the external maxillary artery communicates with the submaxillary ganglion by a filament; and that accompanying the middle meningeal artery sends an offset to the otic ganglion, and a second, the **external petrosal nerve**, to the genicular ganglion of the facial nerve.

The **middle cervical ganglion** (*ganglion cervicale medium*) is the smallest of the three cervical ganglia, and is occasionally wanting. It is placed opposite the sixth cervical vertebra, usually in front of, or close to, the inferior thyroid artery. It is probably formed by the coalescence of two ganglia corresponding to the fifth and sixth cervical nerves.

It sends gray rami communicantes to the fifth and sixth cervical nerves, and gives off the middle cardiac nerve.

The **Middle Cardiac Nerve** (*n. cardiacus medius; great cardiac nerve*), the largest of the three cardiac nerves, *arises* from the middle cervical ganglion, or from the trunk between the middle and inferior ganglia. On the right side it descends behind the common carotid artery, and at the root of the neck runs either in front of or behind the subclavian artery; it then descends on the trachea, receives a few filaments from the recurrent nerve, and joins the right half of the deep part of the cardiac plexus. In the neck, it communicates with the superior cardiac and recurrent nerves. On the left side, the middle cardiac nerve enters the chest between the left carotid and subclavian arteries, and joins the left half of the deep part of the cardiac plexus.

The **inferior cervical ganglion** (*ganglion cervicale inferius*) is situated between the base of the transverse process of the last cervical vertebra and the neck of the first rib, on the medial side of the costocervical artery. Its form is irregular; it is larger in size than the preceding, and is frequently fused with the first thoracic ganglion to form the cervicothoracic (stellate) ganglion. It is probably formed by the coalescence of two ganglia which correspond to the seventh and eighth cervical nerves. It is connected to the middle cervical ganglion by two or more cords, one of which forms a loop around the subclavian artery and supplies offsets to it. This loop is named the **ansa subclavia** (*Vieussenii*).

The ganglion sends gray rami communicantes to the seventh and eighth cervical nerves.

It gives off the inferior cardiac nerve, and offsets to bloodvessels.

The **inferior cardiac nerve** (*n. cardiacus inferior*) *arises* from either the inferior cervical or the first thoracic ganglion. It descends behind the subclavian artery and along the front of the trachea, to join the deep part of the cardiac plexus. It communicates freely behind the subclavian artery with the recurrent nerve and the middle cardiac nerve. The cardiac nerves which arise from the cervical sympathetic trunk contain postganglionic fibers with cells of origin in the cervical chain ganglia. In addition, in the middle and inferior cardiac nerves, there are visceral afferent fibers with cells of origin in the upper thoracic posterior root ganglia; these fibers constitute a portion of the pain pathway from the heart.

The **offsets to bloodvessels** form plexuses on the subclavian artery and its branches. The plexus on the vertebral artery is continued on to the basilar, posterior cerebral, and cerebellar arteries. The plexus on the inferior thyroid artery accompanies the artery to the thyroid gland, and communicates with the recurrent and external laryngeal nerves, with the superior cardiac nerve, and with the plexus on the common carotid artery.

THE THORACIC PORTION OF THE SYMPATHETIC SYSTEM (PARS THORACALIS S. SYMPATHICI) (Fig. 840).

The thoracic portion of the sympathetic trunk consists of a series of ganglia, which usually correspond in number to that of the vertebræ; but, on account of the occasional coalescence of two ganglia, their number is uncertain. The thoracic ganglia rest against the heads of the ribs, and are covered by the costal pleura; the last two, however, are more anterior than the rest, and are placed on the sides of the bodies of the eleventh and twelfth thoracic vertebræ. The ganglia are small in size, and of a grayish color. The first, larger than the others, is of an elongated form, and frequently blended with the inferior cervical ganglion to form the cervicothoracic (stellate) ganglion. They are connected together by the intervening portions of the trunk.

Two rami communicantes, a white and a gray, connect each ganglion with its corresponding spinal nerve.

The visceral *branches from the upper five ganglia* are very small; they supply filaments to the thoracic aorta and its branches and some terminate in the cardiac plexus. Twigs from the second, third, and fourth ganglia enter the posterior pulmonary plexus. These visceral branches contain postganglionic fibers with cells of origin in the chain ganglia and visceral afferent fibers with cells of origin in the posterior root ganglia of the upper thoracic spinal nerves. Some of these visceral afferent fibers conduct pain impulses from the heart.

THE SPLANCHNIC NERVES. Fig. (840)

The visceral branches from the lower seven ganglia are large, and white in color; they distribute filaments to the aorta, and unite to form the greater, the lesser, and the lowest splanchnic nerves. Although these visceral branches which unite to form the splanchnic nerves appear to originate in the chain ganglia, it should be emphasized that to a large extent they contain preganglionic fibers with cells of origin in the thoracic spinal cord and visceral afferent fibers from cells in the thoracic posterior root ganglia. These preganglionic visceral efferent and visceral afferent fibers enter the thoracic sympathetic trunk in the white rami and pass without synapses into the visceral branches which make up the splanchnic nerves. The preganglionic fibers terminate about postganglionic neurons in the collateral ganglia (*i. e.*, celiac and aorticorenal). The splanchnic nerves contain a few postganglionic fibers that arise in neurons in the thoracic chain ganglia and pass through the celiac plexus without further synapses to reach effectors in the viscera.

The visceral afferent fibers in the splanchnic nerves pass through the celiac plexus to terminate in receptors in the viscera. These fibers are both myelinated and unmyelinated. Some of them mediate pain impulses from the abdominal viscera (*i. e.*, stomach, small intestines, gall-bladder).

The **greater splanchnic nerve** (*n. splanchnicus major; great splanchnic nerve*) is white in color, firm in texture, and of a considerable size; it is formed by branches from the fifth to the ninth or tenth thoracic ganglia, but the fibers in the higher roots may be traced upward in the sympathetic trunk. It descends obliquely on the bodies of the vertebræ, perforates the crus of the diaphragm, and ends in the celiac ganglion. A ganglion (**ganglion splanchnicum**) exists on this nerve opposite the eleventh or twelfth thoracic vertebra. This contains postganglionic neurons which have not migrated as far distally as those found in the celiac ganglion.

The **lesser splanchnic nerve** (*n. splanchnicus minor*) is formed by filaments from the ninth and tenth, and sometimes the eleventh thoracic ganglia, and from the cord between them. It pierces the diaphragm with the preceding nerve, and joins the aorticorenal ganglion.

The **lowest splanchnic nerve** (*n. splanchnicus imus; least splanchnic nerve*) arises from the last thoracic ganglion, and, piercing the diaphragm, ends in the renal plexus.

THE ABDOMINAL PORTION OF THE SYMPATHETIC SYSTEM (PARS ABDOMINALIS S. SYMPATHICI; LUMBAR PORTION OF GANGLIATED CORD) (Fig. 842).

The abdominal portion of the sympathetic trunk is situated in front of the vertebral column, along the medial margin of the Psoas major. It consists usually of four lumbar ganglia, connected together by interganglionic cords. It is continuous above with the thoracic portion beneath the medial lumbocostal arch, and below with the pelvic portion behind the common iliac artery. The ganglia are of small size, and placed much nearer the median line than are the thoracic ganglia.

Gray rami communicantes pass from all the ganglia to the lumbar spinal nerves. The first and second, and sometimes the third and fourth lumbar nerves send white rami communicantes to the corresponding ganglia. The rami communicantes are of considerable length, and accompany the lumbar arteries around the sides of the bodies of the vertebræ, passing beneath the fibrous arches from which some of the fibers of the Psoas major arise.

Of the **branches of distribution**, some pass in front of the aorta, and join the aortic plexus; others descend in front of the common iliac arteries, and assist in forming the hypogastric plexus. These visceral branches are sometimes called inferior or lumbar splanchnic nerves. They probably contain visceral afferent, postganglionic and preganglionic fibers. The preganglionic fibers terminate about postganglionic neurons in the celiac and inferior mesenteric (probably also pelvic) plexuses.

THE PELVIC PORTION OF THE SYMPATHETIC SYSTEM (PARS PELVINA S. SYMPATHICI). (Fig.844, 845)

The pelvic portion of each sympathetic trunk is situated in front of the sacrum, medial to the anterior sacral foramina. It consists of four or five small sacral ganglia, connected together by interganglionic cords, and continuous above with the abdominal portion. Below, the two pelvic sympathetic trunks converge, and end on the front of the coccyx in a small ganglion, the **ganglion impar.**

Gray rami communicantes pass from the ganglia to the sacral and coccygeal nerves. No white rami communicantes are given to this part of the gangliated cord. The preganglionic fibers to the sacral sympathetic ganglia enter the sympathetic trunk in the lower thoracic and lumbar white rami and course downward in it.

The **branches of distribution** communicate on the front of the sacrum with the corresponding branches from the opposite side; some, from the first two ganglia, pass to join the pelvic plexus, and others form a plexus, which accompanies the middle sacral artery and sends filaments to the **glomus coccygeum** (*coccygeal body*).

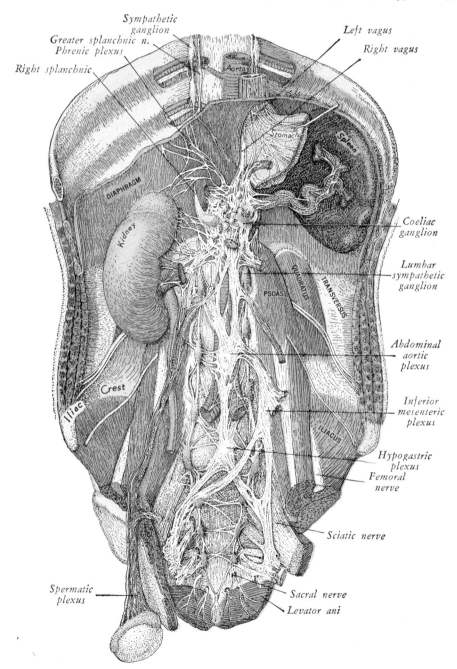

FIG. 842.—Abdominal portion of the sympathetic system. (After Hirschfeld by J. G. Cowell.)

THE GREAT PLEXUSES OF THE SYMPATHETIC SYSTEM.

The great plexuses of the sympathetic are aggregations of nerves and ganglia, situated in the thoracic, abdominal, and pelvic cavities, and named the **cardiac**, celiac, and **hypogastric plexuses**. They contain visceral afferent and visceral efferent fibers of both the thoracolumbar and craniosacral outflows. From the plexuses branches are given to the thoracic, abdominal, and pelvic viscera.

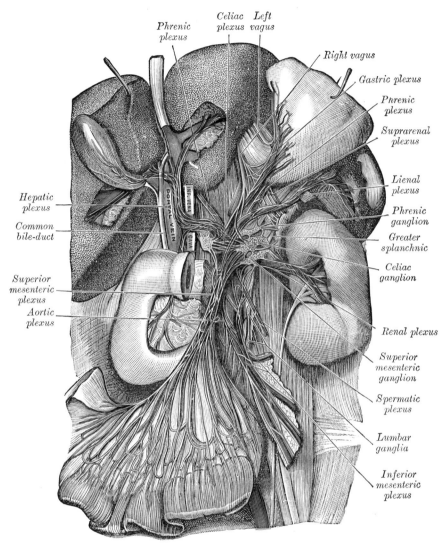

Fig. 843.—The celiac ganglia with the sympathetic plexuses of the abdominal viscera radiating from the ganglia (Toldt.)

The Cardiac Plexus (Plexus Cardiacus) (Fig. 840).

The **cardiac plexus** is situated at the base of the heart, and is divided into a **superficial part**, which lies in the concavity of the aortic arch, and a **deep part**, between the aortic arch and the trachea. The two parts are, however, closely connected.

The **superficial part of the cardiac plexus** lies beneath the arch of the aorta, in front of the right pulmonary artery. It is formed by the superior cardiac branch of the left sympathetic and the lower superior cervical cardiac branch of the left vagus. A small ganglion, the **cardiac ganglion of Wrisberg**, is occasionally found connected with these nerves at their point of junction. This ganglion, when present, is situated immediately beneath the arch of the aorta, on the right side of the ligamentum arteriosum. It probably contains postganglionic parasympathetic neurons which receive impulses from preganglionic fibers in the vagus. The superficial part of the cardiac plexus gives branches (*a*) to the deep part of the plexus; (*b*) to the anterior coronary plexus; and (*c*) to the left anterior pulmonary plexus.

The **deep part of the cardiac plexus** is situated in front of the bifurcation of the trachea, above the point of division of the pulmonary artery, and behind the aortic arch. It is formed by the cardiac nerves derived from the cervical ganglia of the sympathetic, and the cardiac branches of the vagus and recurrent nerves. The only cardiac nerves which do not enter into the formation of the deep part of the cardiac plexus are the superior cardiac nerve of the left sympathetic, and the lower of the two superior cervical cardiac branches from the left vagus, which pass to the superficial part of the plexus.

The branches from the **right half** of the deep part of the cardiac plexus pass, some in front of, and others behind, the right pulmonary artery; the former, the more numerous, transmit a few filaments to the anterior pulmonary plexus, and are then continued onward to form part of the anterior coronary plexus; those behind the pulmonary artery distribute a few filaments to the right atrium, and are then continued onward to form part of the posterior coronary plexus.

The **left half** of the deep part of the plexus is connected with the superficial part of the cardiac plexus, and gives filaments to the left atrium, and to the anterior pulmonary plexus, and is then continued to form the greater part of the posterior coronary plexus.

The **Posterior Coronary Plexus** (*plexus coronarius posterior; left coronary plexus*) is larger than the anterior, and accompanies the left coronary artery; it is chiefly formed by filaments prolonged from the left half of the deep part of the cardiac plexus, and by a few from the right half. It gives branches to the left atrium and ventricle.

The **Anterior Coronary Plexus** (*plexus coronarius anterior; right coronary plexus*) is formed partly from the superficial and partly from the deep parts of the cardiac plexus. It accompanies the right coronary artery, and gives branches to the right atrium and ventricle.

The Celiac Plexus (Plexus Cœliacus; Solar Plexus) (Figs. 834, 843).

The **celiac plexus,** the largest of the three sympathetic plexuses, is situated at the level of the upper part of the first lumbar vertebra and is composed of two large ganglia, the **celiac ganglia,** and a dense net-work of nerve fibers uniting them together. It surrounds the celiac artery and the root of the superior mesenteric artery. It lies behind the stomach and the omental bursa, in front of the crura of the diaphragm and the commencement of the abdominal aorta, and between the suprarenal glands. The plexus and the ganglia receive the greater and lesser splanchnic nerves of both sides and some filaments from the right vagus, and give off numerous secondary plexuses along the neighboring arteries.

The **Celiac Ganglia** (*ganglia cœliaca; semilunar ganglia*) are two large irregularly-shaped masses having the appearance of lymph nodes and placed one on either side of the middle line in front of the crura of the diaphragm close to the suprarenal glands, that on the right side being placed behind the inferior vena cava. The upper part of each ganglion is joined by the greater splanchnic nerve, while the lower part, which is segmented off and named the **aorticorenal ganglion,** receives the lesser splanchnic nerve and gives off the greater part of the renal plexus. These ganglia contain postganglionic neurons which receive impulses from preganglionic visceral efferent fibers in the splanchnic nerves.

The secondary plexuses springing from or connected with the celiac plexus are the

Phrenic.	Superior gastric.	Spermatic.
Hepatic.	Suprarenal.	Superior mesenteric.
Lienal.	Renal.	Abdominal aortic.

The **phrenic plexus** (*plexus phrenicus*) accompanies the inferior phrenic artery to the diaphragm, some filaments passing to the suprarenal gland. It *arises* from the upper part of the celiac ganglion, and is larger on the right than on the left side. It receives one or two branches from the phrenic nerve. At the point of junction of the right phrenic plexus with the phrenic nerve is a small ganglion (**ganglion phrenicum**). This plexus distributes branches to the inferior vena cava, and to the suprarenal and hepatic plexuses.

The **hepatic plexus** (*plexus hepaticus*), the largest offset from the celiac plexus, receives filaments from the left vagus and right phrenic nerves. It accompanies the hepatic artery, ramifying upon its branches, and upon those of the portal vein in the substance of the liver. Branches from this plexus accompany all the divisions of the hepatic artery. A considerable plexus accompanies the gastroduodenal artery and is continued as the **inferior gastric plexus** on the right gastroepiploic artery along the greater curvature of the stomach, where it unites with offshoots from the lienal plexus.

The **lienal plexus** (*plexus lienalis; splenic plexus*) is formed by branches from the celiac plexus, the left celiac ganglion, and from the right vagus nerve. It accompanies the lienal artery to the spleen, giving off, in its course, subsidiary plexuses along the various branches of the artery.

The **superior gastric plexus** (*plexus gastricus superior; gastric or coronary plexus*) accompanies the left gastric artery along the lesser curvature of the stomach, and joins with branches from the left vagus.

The **suprarenal plexus** (*plexus suprarenalis*) is formed by branches from the celiac plexus, from the celiac ganglion, and from the phrenic and greater splanchnic nerves, a ganglion being formed at the point of junction with the latter nerve. The plexus supplies the suprarenal gland, being distributed chiefly to its medullary portion; its branches are remarkable for their large size in comparison with that of the organ they supply.

The **renal plexus** (*plexus renalis*) is formed by filaments from the celiac plexus, the aorticorenal ganglion, and the aortic plexus. It is joined also by the smallest splanchnic nerve. The nerves from these sources, fifteen or twenty in number, have a few ganglia developed upon them. They accompany the branches of the renal artery into the kidney; some filaments are distributed to the spermatic plexus and, on the right side, to the inferior vena cava.

The **spermatic plexus** (*plexus spermaticus*) is derived from the renal plexus, receiving branches from the aortic plexus. It accompanies the internal spermatic artery to the testis. In the female, the **ovarian plexus** (*plexus arteriæ ovaricæ*) *arises* from the renal plexus, and is distributed to the ovary, and fundus of the uterus.

The **superior mesenteric plexus** (*plexus mesentericus superior*) is a continuation of the lower part of the celiac plexus, receiving a branch from the junction of the right vagus nerve with the plexus. It surrounds the superior mesenteric artery, accompanies it into the mesentery, and divides into a number of secondary plexuses, which are distributed to all the parts supplied by the artery, viz., pancreatic branches to the pancreas; intestinal branches to the small intestine; and ileocolic, right colic, and middle colic branches, which supply the corresponding parts of the large intestine. The nerves composing this plexus are white in color and firm in texture; in the upper part of the plexus close to the origin of the superior mesenteric artery is a ganglion (**ganglion mesentericum superius**).

The **abdominal aortic plexus** (*plexus aorticus abdominalis; aortic plexus*) is formed by branches derived, on either side, from the celiac plexus and ganglia, and receives filaments from some of the lumbar ganglia. It is situated upon the sides and front of

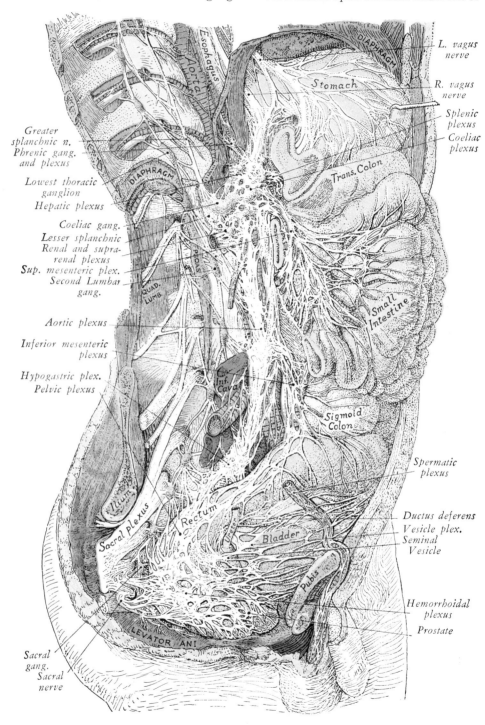

Fig. 844.—Abdominal and pelvic sympathetic system, including plexuses and ganglia. Male. (After Hirschfeld by J. G. Cowell.)

the aorta, between the origins of the superior and inferior mesenteric arteries. From this plexus arise part of the spermatic, the inferior mesenteric, and the hypogastric plexuses; it also distributes filaments to the inferior vena cava.

The **inferior mesenteric plexus** (*plexus mesentericus inferior*) is derived chiefly from the aortic plexus. It surrounds the inferior mesenteric artery, and divides into a number of secondary plexuses, which are distributed to all the parts supplied by the artery, viz., the **left colic** and **sigmoid plexuses**, which supply the descending and sigmoid parts of the colon; and the **superior hemorrhoidal plexus**, which supplies the rectum and joins in the pelvis with branches from the pelvic plexuses.

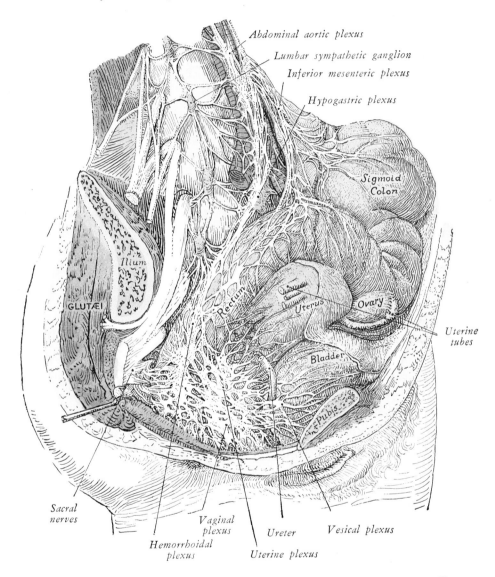

Fig. 845.—Abdominal and pelvic sympathetic system. Female. (After Hirschfeld by J. G. Cowell.)

The Hypogastric Plexus (Plexus Hypogastricus) (Fig. 844, 845).

The **hypogastric plexus** is situated in front of the last lumbar vertebra and the promontory of the sacrum, between the two common iliac arteries, and is formed by the union of numerous filaments, which descend on either side from the aortic plexus, and from the lumbar ganglia; it divides, below, into two lateral portions which are named the **pelvic plexuses**. The hypogastric plexus contains visceral efferent and afferent fibers of the thoracolumbar outflow. The visceral afferent fibers enter the spinal cord in the lower thoracic and upper lumbar dorsal roots. Some of these afferent fibers are important in pain conduction from the pelvic viscera.

The Pelvic Plexuses (Fig. 844).—The pelvic plexuses supply the viscera of the pelvic cavity, and are situated at the sides of the rectum in the male, and at the sides of the rectum and vagina in the female. They are formed on either side by a continuation of the hypogastric plexus, by the sacral visceral efferent and afferent fibers from the second, third, and fourth sacral nerves, and by a few filaments from the first two sacral ganglia. At the points of junction of these nerves small ganglia are found. From these plexuses numerous branches are distributed to the viscera of the pelvis. They accompany the branches of the hypogastric artery.

The **Middle Hemorrhoidal Plexus** (*plexus hæmorrhoidalis medius*) *arises* from the upper part of the pelvic plexus. It supplies the rectum, and joins with branches of the superior hemorrhoidal plexus.

The **Vesical Plexus** (*plexus vesicalis*) *arises* from the forepart of the pelvic plexus. The nerves composing it are numerous, accompany the vesical arteries, and are distributed to the sides and fundus of the bladder. Numerous filaments also pass to the vesiculæ seminales and ductus deferentes; those accompanying the ductus deferens join, on the spermatic cord, with branches from the spermatic plexus.

The **Prostatic Plexus** (*plexus prostaticus*) is continued from the lower part of the pelvic plexus. The nerves composing it are of large size. They are distributed to the prostate vesiculæ seminales and the corpora cavernosa of the penis and urethra. The nerves supplying the corpora cavernosa consist of two sets, the lesser and greater cavernous nerves, which arise from the forepart of the prostatic plexus, and, after joining with branches from the pudendal nerve, pass forward beneath the pubic arch.

The **lesser cavernous nerves** (*nn. cavernosi penis minores; small cavernous nerves*) perforate the fibrous covering of the penis, near its root.

The **greater cavernous nerve** (*n. cavernosus penis major; large cavernous plexus*) passes forward along the dorsum of the penis, joins with the dorsal nerve of the penis, and is distributed to the corpora cavernosa.

The **Vaginal Plexus** (Fig. 845) *arises* from the lower part of the pelvic plexus. It is distributed to the walls of the vagina, to the erectile tissue of the vestibule, and to the clitoris.

The **Uterine Plexus** accompanies the uterine artery to the side of the uterus, between the layers of the broad ligament; it communicates with the ovarian plexus.

BIBLIOGRAPHY

PERIPHERAL NERVOUS SYSTEM

CRANIAL NERVES

The oculomotor nucleus in the human fetus. PEARSON, A. A.: 1944. J. Comp. Neur., Vol. 80 pp. 47–63.

The trochlear nerve in human fetuses. PEARSON, A. A.: 1943. J. Comp. Neur., Vol. 78, pp. 29–43.

The distribution of myelinated afferent fibers in the branches of the cat's facial nerve. BRUESCH, S. R.: 1944. J. Comp. Neur., Vol. 81, pp. 169–191.

The sensory and motor axons of the chorda tympani. FOLEY, J. O.: 1945. Proc. Soc. Exp. Biol. and Med., Vol. 60, pp. 262–267.

The ratio of nerve fibers to nerve cells in the geniculate ganglion. FOLEY, J. O., H. R. PEPPER, and W. H. KESSLER: 1946. J. Comp. Neur., Vol. 85, pp. 141–148.

Development of the afferent components of the facial, glossopharyngeal and vagus nerves in the rabbit embryo. KIMMEL, D. L.: 1941. J. Comp. Neur., Vol. 74, pp. 447–471.

The surgical anatomy of the facial nerve with special reference to the parotid gland. McCORMACK, L. J., E. W. CAULDWELL, and B. J. ANSON: 1945. Surg., Gyn., and Obs., Vol. 80, pp. 620–630.

The development of the motor nuclei of the facial nerve in man. PEARSON, A. A.: 1946. J. Comp. Neur., Vol. 85, pp. 461–476.

Surgical anatomy of the carotid sinus nerve. SHEEHAN, D., J. H. MULHOLLAND, and B. SHAFIROFF: 1941. Anat. Rec., Vol. 80, pp. 431–442.

Quantitative studies of the vagus nerve in the cat. DuBois, F. S., and J. O. FOLEY: 1937. J.-Comp. Neur., Vol. 67, pp. 69–87.

The intramedullary course of afferent fibers of the vagus nerve in the cat. INGRAM, W. R., and E. A. DAWKINS: 1945. J. Comp. Neur., Vol. 82, pp. 157–168.

The origin of the vagi and the parasympathetic ganglion cells of the viscera of the chick. JONES, D. S.: 1942. Anat. Rec., Vol. 82, pp. 185–197.

The relations of the inferior laryngeal nerve to the inferior thyroid artery. REED, A. F.: 1943. Anat. Rec., Vol. 85, pp. 17–23.

Proprioceptive components of cranial nerves. The spinal accessory nerve. CORBIN, K. B., and F. HARRISON: 1938. J. Comp. Neur., Vol. 69, pp. 315–328.

The hypoglossal complex of vertebrates. BARNARD, J. W.: 1940. J. Comp. Neur., Vol. 72, pp. 489–524.

The hypoglossal nerve in human embryos. PEARSON, A. A.: 1939. J. Comp. Neur., Vol. 71, pp. 21–39.

SPINAL NERVES

The relation of the sciatic nerve and of its subdivisions to the piriformis muscle. BEATON, L. E., and B. J. ANSON: 1937. Anat. Rec., Vol. 70, pp. 1–5.

Further determinations of the numbers of fibers and cells in the dorsal roots and ganglia of the cat. DUNCAN, D., and L. L. KEYSER: 1938. J. Comp. Neur., Vol. 68, pp. 479–490.

The dermatomes in man. FOERSTER, O.: 1933. Brain, Vol. 56, pp. 1–39.

Sensory nerves and associated structures in the skin of human fetuses of 8 to 14 weeks of menstrual age correlated with functional capability. HOGG, I. D.: 1941. J. Comp. Neur., Vol. 75, pp. 371–410.

Neurosurgical interpretation of dermatome hypalgesia with herniation of the lumbar intervertebral disc. KEEGAN, J. J.: 1944. J. Bone and Joint Surg., Vol. 26, pp. 238–248.

Brachialgia. A manifestation of various lesions. NACHLAS, I. W.: 1944. J. Bone and Joint Surg., Vol. 26, pp. 177–184.

Metrical and non-metrical features of the muscular branches of the radial, ulnar, median, and sciatic nerves. SUNDERLAND, S., *et al.:* 1946. J. Comp. Neur., Vol. 85, pp. 93–111, 113–125, 191–203, 205–222.

AUTONOMIC NERVES

The pelvic autonomic nerves in the male. ASHLEY, F. L., and B. J. ANSON: 1946. Surg., Gyn. and Obs., Vol. 82, pp. 598–608.

The distribution of sympathetic nerve fibers to the hind limb of the cat. BURNS, B. I.: 1935. J. Comp. Neur., Vol. 61, pp. 191–219.

Nerve fibers within the cranio-pharyngeal canal. DRAGER, G. A.: 1944. Anat. Rec., Vol. 88, pp. 235–243.

Variations in the formation of the splanchnic nerves in man. EDWARDS, L. F., and R. C. BAKER: 1940. Anat. Rec., Vol. 77, pp. 335–342.

The components of the cervical sympathetic trunk with special reference to its accessory cells and ganglia. FOLEY, J. O.: 1945. J. Comp. Neur., Vol. 82, pp. 77–91.

Operative technique of thoracolumbar sympathectomy. HINTON, J. W. and J. W. Lord, Jr. 1946. Surg., Gyn and Obs., Vol. 83, pp. 643–646.

Regeneration of pre- and postganglionic fibers following sympathectomy of the upper extremity. KIRGIS, H. D., and E. A. OHLER: 1944. Ann. Surg., Vol. 119, pp. 201–210.

The components of the upper thoracic sympathetic nerves. SACCOMANNO, G.: 1943. J. Comp. Neur., Vol. 79, pp. 355–378.

The surgical anatomy of the superior hypogastric plexus, with report of 150 personal dissections. WEINSTEIN, B. B.: 1942. Surg., Gyn. and Obs., Vol. 74, pp. 245–255.

An experimental analysis of the inferior mesenteric plexus. HARRIS, A. J.: 1943. J. Comp. Neur., Vol. 79, pp. 1–17.

PLEXUS

An experimental study of spinal nerve segmentation in amblystoma with reference to the plurisegmental contribution to the brachial plexus. DETWILER, S. R.: 1934. J. Exp. Zool., Vol. 67, pp. 395–441.

The anatomy of (A) the lumbosacral nerve plexus—its relation to variations of vertebral segmentation, and (B), the posterior sacral nerve plexus. HORWITZ, M. T.: 1939. Anat. Rec., Vol. 74, pp. 91–107.

The brachial plexus of nerves in man, the variations in its formation and branches. KERR, A. T.: 1918. Am. J. Anat., Vol. 23, pp. 285–395.

Comparative studies upon the morphology and distribution of the brachial plexus. MILLER, R. A.: 1934. Am. J. Anat., Vol. 54, pp. 143–175.

Observations upon the arrangement of the axillary artery and brachial plexus. MILLER, R. A.: 1939. Am. J. Anat., Vol. 64, pp. 143–163.

Comparative studies upon the origin and development of the brachial plexus. MILLER, R. A., and S. R. DETWILER: 1936. Anat. Rec., Vol. 65, pp. 273–292.

Human brachial plexus united into a single cord. SINGER, E.: 1933. Anat. Rec., Vol. 55, pp. 411–419.

The innervation of the pharynx in the rhesus monkey, and the formation of the pharyngeal plexus in primates. SPRAGUE, J. M.: 1944. Anat. Rec., Vol. 90, pp. 197–208.

GANGLIA

Sympathetic ganglion cell changes in adrenalectomized animals. BURNS, B. I., J. D. REESE, and A. H. SELLMANN: 1937. Proc. Soc. Exp. Biol. and Med., Vol. 36, pp. 261–266.

A study of the weight of the coeliac ganglion and its relationship to essential hypertension. CANTOR, M. O.: 1942. Ann. Surg., Vol. 115, pp. 400–412.

The development of spinal ganglia following transplantation of the spinal cord with or without somites. DETWILER, S. R. : 1935. Anat. Rec., Vol. 61, pp. 441–455.

The origin of the ciliary ganglia in the chick embryo. JONES, D. S.: 1945. Anat. Rec., Vol. 92, pp. 441–447.

The structural organization of the celiac ganglia. KUNTZ, A.: 1938. J. Comp. Neur., Vol. 69, pp. 1–12.

The number of ganglion cells in the dorsal root ganglia of the second and third cervical nerves in human fetuses of various ages. MCKINNISS, M. E.: 1936. Anat. Rec., Vol. 65, pp. 255–259.

Studies on living spinal ganglion cells. MURNAGHAN, D. P.: 1941. Anat. Rec., Vol. 81, pp. 183–203.

Morphological alterations in the Gasserian ganglion cells and their association with senescence in man. TRUEX, R. C.: 1940. Am. J. Path., Vol. 16, pp. 255–268.

Degenerate *versus* multipolar neurons in sensory ganglia. TRUEX, R. C.: 1941. Am. J. Path., Vol. 17, pp. 211–218.

NERVE ENDINGS

Development of the neuromuscular spindle in human fetuses. CUAJUNCO, F.: 1940. Carnegie Cont. Emb., Vol. 28, pp. 95–128.

Development of the human motor end plate. CUAJUNCO, F.: 1942. Carnegie Cont. Emb., Vol. 30, pp. 127–152.

The development of the aortic arch bodies in the cat. HAMMOND, W. S.: 1941. Am. J. Anat., Vol. 69, pp. 265–293.

The origin of the nerve fibers to the glomus aorticum of the cat. HOLLINSHEAD, W. H.: 1939. J. Comp. Neur., Vol. 71, 417–426.

The innervation of the supracardial bodies in the cat. HOLLINSHEAD, W. H.: 1940. J. Comp. Neur., Vol. 73, pp. 37–48.

Chemoreceptors in the abdomen. HOLLINSHEAD, W. H.: 1941. J. Comp. Neur., Vol. 74, pp. 269–285.

Distribution of the aortic nerve fibers and the epithelioid bodies (supracardial 'paraganglia') in the dog. NONIDEZ, J. F.: 1937. Anat. Rec., Vol. 69, pp. 299–317.

BLOOD SUPPLY

The blood supply of nerves. I. Historical review. ADAMS, W. E.: 1942. J. Anat., Vol. 76, pp. 323–341.

Studies on the blood vessels of the human Gasserian ganglion. BERGMANN, L.: 1942. Anat. Rec., Vol. 82, pp. 609–629.

The blood vessels of human celiac ganglia and changes in their vascular pattern associated with age. BERGMANN, L.: 1943. Anat. Rec., Vol. 85, pp. 117–133.

A note on the blood supply of the supracardial bodies in the kitten. HOLLINSHEAD, W. H.: 1940. Anat. Rec., Vol. 76, pp. 283–289.

EXPERIMENTAL EMBRYOLOGY AND CYTOLOGY

Microscopic studies on the regeneration of medullated nerves in the living mammal. CLARK, E. R., and E. L.: 1947. Am. J. Anat., Vol. 81, pp. 233–268.

Application of vital dyes to the study of sheath cell origin. DETWILER, S. R.: 1937. Proc. Soc. Exp. Biol. and Med., Vol. 37, pp. 380–382; J. Exp. Zool., Vol. 81, pp. 415–435.

In vitro control of growing chick nerve fibers by applied electric currents. MARSH, G., and H. W. BEAMS: 1946. J. Cell. and Comp. Physiol., Vol. 27, pp. 139–157.

Characteristics of human Schwann cells *in vitro*. MURRAY, M. R., and A. P. STOUT: 1942. Anat. Rec., Vol. 84, pp. 275–293.

Adult human sympathetic ganglion cells cultivated *in vitro*. MURRAY, M. R., and A. P. STOUT: 1947. Am. J. Anat., Vol. 80, pp. 225–273.

Depletions and abnormalities in the cervical sympathetic system of the chick following extirpation of neural crest. YNTEMA, C. L., and W. S. HAMMOND: 1945. J. Exp. Zool., Vol. 100, pp. 237–263.

THE ORGANS OF THE SENSES.

THE organs of the senses may be divided into (*a*) those of the special senses of taste, smell, sight, and hearing, and (*b*) those associated with the **general sensations** of heat, cold, pain, pressure, etc.

THE PERIPHERAL ORGANS OF THE SPECIAL SENSES.

THE ORGAN OF TASTE (ORGANON GUSTUS).

The **peripheral gustatory** or **taste organs** consist of certain modified epithelial cells arranged in flask-shaped groups termed **gustatory calyculi** (*taste-buds*), which are found on the tongue and adjacent parts. They occupy nests in the stratified epithelium, and are present in large numbers on the sides of the papillæ vallatæ (Fig. 846), and to a less extent on their opposed walls. They are also found on the fungiform papillæ over the back part and sides of the tongue, and in the general epithelial covering of the same areas. They are very plen-

Vallum

Fossa

Taste-bud

Serous gland

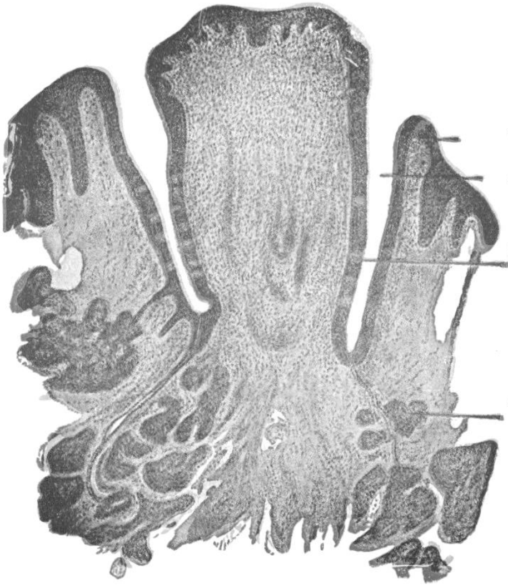

FIG. 846.—A vertical section through a human papilla vallata. Stained with hematoxylin and eosin.   × 15.

FIG. 487.—A section through a taste-bud from the human tongue. Stained with hematoxylin and eosin.   × 450.

tiful over the fimbriæ linguæ, and are also present on the under surface of the soft palate, and on the posterior surface of the epiglottis. The number of taste buds per papilla vallata decreases slightly during adult life from about 245 to 208, and rapidly in extreme old age to about 88.

Structure.—Each taste-bud is flask-like in shape (Fig. 847), its broad base resting on the corium, and its neck opening by an orifice, the **gustatory pore,** between the cells of the epithelium. The bud is formed by two kinds of cells: supporting cells and gustatory cells. The **supporting cells** are mostly arranged like the staves of a cask, and form an outer envelope for the bud. Some, however, are found in the interior of the bud between the gustatory cells. The **gustatory cells** occupy the central portion of the bud; they are spindle-shaped, and each possesses a large spherical nucleus near the middle of the cell. The peripheral end of the cell terminates at the gustatory pore in a fine hair-like filament, the **gustatory hair.** The central process passes toward the deep extremity of the bud, and there ends in single or bifurcated varicosities. The nerve fibrils after losing their medullary sheaths enter the taste-bud, and end in fine extremities between the gustatory cells; other nerve fibrils ramify between the supporting cells and terminate in fine extremities; these, however, are believed to be nerves of ordinary sensation and not gustatory.

(1023)

Nerves of Taste.—The chorda tympani nerve, derived from the sensory root of the facial, is the nerve of taste for the anterior two-thirds of the tongue; the nerve for the posterior third is the glossopharyngeal.

THE ORGAN OF SMELL (ORGANON OLFACTUS; THE NOSE).

The **peripheral olfactory organ** or **organ of smell** consists of two parts: an outer, the **external nose**, which projects from the center of the face; and an internal, the **nasal cavity**, which is divided by a septum into **right** and **left nasal chambers.**

The External Nose (Nasus Externus; Outer Nose).

The **external nose** is pyramidal in form, and its upper angle or **root** is connected directly with the forehead; its free angle is termed the **apex.** The two elliptical orifices, the **nares,** are separated from each other by an antero-posterior septum, the **columna.** The margins of the nares are provided with a number of stiff hairs, or **vibrissæ,** which arrest the passage of foreign substances carried with the current of air intended for respiration. The lateral surfaces of the nose form by their union in the middle line, the **dorsum nasi,** the direction of which varies considerably in different individuals; the upper part of the dorsum is supported by the nasal bones, and is named the **bridge.** The lateral surface ends below in a rounded eminence, the **ala nasi.**

Structure.—The frame-work of the external nose is composed of bones and cartilages; it is covered by the integument, and lined by mucous membrane.

The **bony frame-work** occupies the upper part of the organ; it consists of the nasal bones, and the frontal processes of the maxillæ.

The **cartilaginous frame-work** (*cartilagines nasi*) consists of five large pieces, viz., the **cartilage of the septum,** the **two lateral** and the **two greater alar cartilages,** and several smaller pieces the **lesser alar cartilages** (Figs. 848, 849, 850). The varius cartilages are connected to each other and to the bones by a tough fibrous membrane.

The **cartilage of the septum** (*cartilago septi nasi*) is somewhat quadrilateral in form, thicker at its margins than at its center, and completes the separation between the nasal cavities in front. Its anterior margin, thickest above,is connected with the nasal bones, and is continuous with the anterior margins of the lateral cartilages; below, it is connected to the medial crura of the greater alar cartilages by fibrous tissue. Its posterior margin is connected with the perpendicular plate of the ethmoid; its inferior margin with the vomer and the palatine processes of the maxillæ.

It may be prolonged backward (especially in children) as a narrow process, the **sphenoidal process,** for some distance between the vomer and perpendicular plate of the ethmoid. The septal cartilage does not reach as far as the lowest part of the nasal septum. This is formed by the medial crura of the greater alar cartilages and by the skin; it is freely movable, and hence is termed the **septum mobile nasi.**

The **lateral cartilage** (*cartilago nasi lateralis; upper lateral cartilage*) is situated below the inferior margin of the nasal bone, and is flattened, and triangular in shape. Its anterior margin is thicker than the posterior, and is continuous above with the cartilage of the septum, but separated from it below by a narrow fissure; its superior margin is attached to the nasal bone and the frontal process of the maxilla; its inferior margin is connected by fibrous tissue with the greater alar cartilage.

The **greater alar cartilage** (*cartilago alaris major; lower lateral cartilage*) is a thin, flexible plate, situated immediately below the preceding, and bent upon itself in such a manner as to form the medial and lateral walls of the naris of its own side. The portion which forms the **medial wall** (*crus mediale*) is loosely connected with the corresponding portion of the opposite cartilage, the two forming, together with the thickened integument and subjacent tissue, the **septum mobile nasi.** The part which forms the **lateral wall** (*crus laterale*) is curved to correspond with the ala of the nose; it is oval and flattened, narrow behind, where it is connected with the frontal process of the maxilla by a tough fibrous membrane, in which are found three or four small cartilaginous plates, the **lesser alar cartilages** (*cartilagines alares minores; sesamoid cartilages*). Above, it is connected by fibrous tissue to the lateral cartilage and front part of the cartilage of the septum; below, it falls short of the margin of the naris, the ala being completed by fatty and fibrous tissue covered by skin. In front, the greater alar cartilages are separated by a notch which corresponds with the apex of the nose.

The **muscles** acting on the external nose have been described in the section on Myology.

The **integument** of the dorsum and sides of the nose is thin, and loosely connected with the subjacent parts; but over the tip and alæ it is thicker and more firmly adherent, and is furnished with a large number of sebaceous follicles, the orifices of which are usually very distinct.

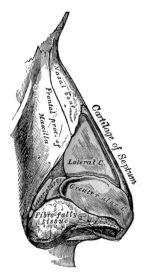

Fɪɢ. 848.—Cartilages of the nose. Side view.

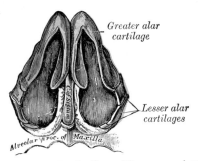

Fɪɢ. 849.—Cartilages of the nose, seen from below.

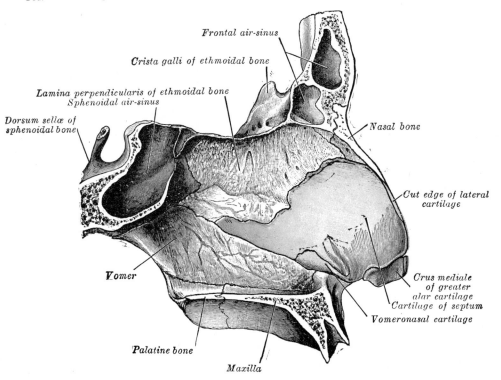

Fɪɢ. 850.—Bones and cartilages of septum of nose. Right side.

The **arteries** of the external nose are the alar and septal branches of the external maxillary, which supply the alæ and septum; the dorsum and sides being supplied from the dorsal nasal branch of the ophthalmic and the infraorbital branch of the internal maxillary. The **veins** end in the anterior facial and ophthalmic veins.

The **nerves** for the muscles of the nose are derived from the facial, while the skin receives branches from the infratrochlear and nasociliary branches of the ophthalmic, and from the infraorbital of the maxillary.

65

The Nasal Cavity (Cavum Nasi; Nasal Fossa).

The nasal chambers are situated one on either side of the median plane. They open in front through the nares, and communicate behind through the choanæ with the nasal part of the pharynx. The **nares** are somewhat pear-shaped apertures, each measuring about 2.5 cm. antero-posteriorly and 1.25 cm. transversely at its widest part. The **choanæ** are two oval openings each measuring 2.5 cm. in the vertical, and 1.25 cm. in the transverse direction in a well-developed adult skull.

For the description of the bony boundaries of the nasal cavities, see page 123.

Inside the aperture of the nostril is a slight dilatation, the **vestibule,** bounded laterally by the ala and lateral crus of the greater alar cartilage, and medially by the medial crus of the same cartilage. It is lined by skin containing hairs and sebaceous glands, and extends as a small recess toward the apex of the nose. Each nasal cavity, above and behind the vestibule, is divided into two parts: an **olfactory region,** consisting of the superior nasal concha and the opposed part of the septum, and a **respiratory region,** which comprises the rest of the cavity.

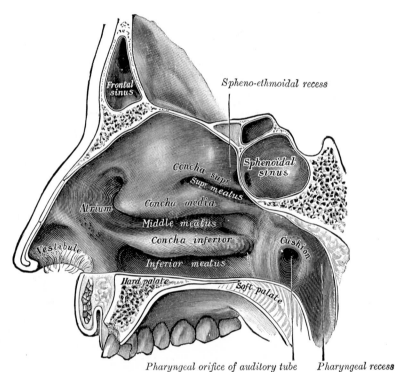

Fig. 851.—Lateral wall of nasal cavity.

Lateral Wall (Figs. 851, 852).—On the lateral wall are the **superior, middle,** and **inferior nasal conchæ,** and below and lateral to each concha is the corresponding nasal passage or meatus. Above the superior concha is a narrow recess, the **sphenoethmoidal recess,** into which the sphenoidal sinus opens. The **superior meatus** is a short oblique passage extending about half-way along the upper border of the middle concha; the posterior ethmoidal cells open into the front part of this meatus. The **middle meatus** is below and lateral to the middle concha, and is continued anteriorly into a shallow depression, situated above the vestibule and named the **atrium** of the middle meatus. By raising or removing the middle concha the lateral wall of this meatus is fully displayed. On it is a rounded elevation, the **bulla ethmoidalis,** and below and in front of this is a curved cleft, the **hiatus semilunaris.**

The **bulla ethmoidalis** is caused by the bulging of the middle ethmoidal cells which open on or immediately above it, and the size of the bulla varies with that of its contained cells.

The **hiatus semilunaris** is bounded inferiorly by the sharp concave margin of the **uncinate process** of the ethmoid bone, and leads into a curved channel, the **infundibulum,** bounded above by the bulla ethmoidalis and below by the lateral surface of the uncinate process of the ethmoid. The anterior ethmoidal cells open into the front part of the infundibulum, and this in slightly over 50 per cent. of subjects is directly continuous with the frontonasal duct or passage leading from the frontal air sinus; but when the anterior end of the uncinate process fuses with the front part of the bulla, this continuity is interrupted and the frontonasal duct then opens directly into the anterior end of the middle meatus.

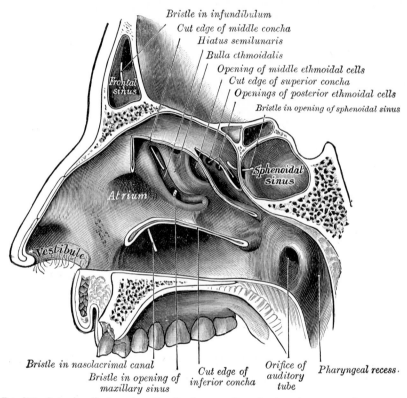

Bristle in infundibulum
Cut edge of middle concha
Hiatus semilunaris
Bulla ethmoidalis
Opening of middle ethmoidal cells
Cut edge of superior concha
Openings of posterior ethmoidal cells
Bristle in opening of sphenoidal sinus

Frontal sinus
Sphenoidal sinus
Atrium
Vestibule

Bristle in nasolacrimal canal
Bristle in opening of maxillary sinus
Cut edge of inferior concha
Orifice of auditory tube
Pharyngeal recess.

Fɪɢ. 852.—Lateral wall of nasal cavity; the three nasal conchæ have been removed.

Below the bulla ethmoidalis, and partly hidden by the inferior end of the uncinate process, is the **ostium maxillare,** or opening from the maxillary sinus; in a frontal section this opening is seen to be placed near the roof of the sinus. An accessory opening from the sinus is frequently present below the posterior end of the middle nasal concha. The **inferior meatus** is below and lateral to the inferior nasal concha; the nasolacrimal duct opens into this meatus under cover of the anterior part of the inferior concha.

Medial Wall (Fig. 850).—The medial wall or septum is frequently more or less deflected from the median plane, thus lessening the size of one nasal cavity and increasing that of the other; ridges or spurs of bone growing into one or other cavity from the septum are also sometimes present. Immediately over the incisive canal at the lower edge of the cartilage of the septum a depression, the **nasopalatine recess,** is seen. In the septum close to this recess a minute orifice may be discerned; it leads backward into a blind pouch, the rudimentary **vomeronasal organ of Jacobson,** which is supported by a strip of cartilage, the **vomeronasal cartilage.** This organ is well-developed in many of the lower animals, where it apparently plays a part in the sense of smell, since it is supplied by twigs of the olfactory nerve and lined by epithelium similar to that in the olfactory region of the nose.

The **roof** of the nasal cavity is narrow from side to side, except at its posterior part, and may be divided, from behind forward, into sphenoidal, ethmoidal, and frontonasal parts, after the bones which form it.

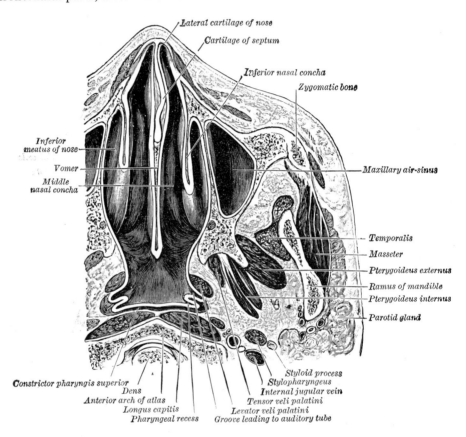

Fig. 853.—Transverse section through the anterior part of the head at a level just below the apex of the dens (odontoid process). Viewed from below.

The **floor** is concave from side to side and almost horizontal antero-posteriorly; its anterior three-fourths are formed by the palatine process of the maxilla, its posterior fourth by the horizontal process of the palatine bone. In its antero-medial part, directly over the incisive foramen, a small depression, the **nasopalatine recess,** is sometimes seen; it points downward and forward and occupies the position of a canal which connected the nasal with the buccal cavity in early fetal life.

The Mucous Membrane (*membrana mucosa nasi*).—The nasal mucous membrane lines the nasal cavities, and is intimately adherent to the periosteum or perichondrium. It is continuous with the skin through the nares, and with the mucous membrane of the nasal part of the pharynx through the choanæ. From the nasal cavity its continuity with the conjunctiva may be traced, through the nasolacrimal and lacrimal ducts; and with the frontal, ethmoidal, sphenoidal, and maxillary sinuses, through the several openings in the meatuses. The mucous membrane is thickest, and most vascular, over the nasal conchæ. It is also thick over the septum; but it is very thin in the meatuses on the floor of the nasal cavities, and in the various sinuses.

Owing to the thickness of the greater part of this membrane, the nasal cavities are much narrower, and the middle and inferior nasal conchæ appear larger and more prominent than in the skeleton; also the various apertures communicating with the meatuses are considerably narrowed.

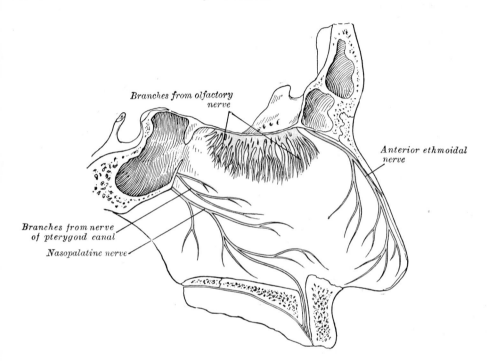

Fig. 854.—The nerves of the right side of the septum of the nose.

Structure of the Mucous Membrane (Fig. 855).—The epithelium covering the mucous membrane differs in its character according to the functions of the part of the nose in which it is found. In the **respiratory region** it is columnar and ciliated Interspersed among the columnar cells are goblet or mucin cells, while between their bases are found smaller pyramidal cells. Beneath the epithelium and its basement membrane is a fibrous layer infiltrated with lymph corpuscles, so as to form in many parts a diffuse lymphoid tissue, and under this a nearly continuous layer of small and larger glands, some mucous and some serous, the ducts of which open upon the surface. In the **olfactory region** the mucous membrane is yellowish in color and the epithelial cells are columnar and non-ciliated; they are of two kinds, supporting cells and olfactory cells. The **supporting cells** contain oval nuclei, which are situated in the deeper parts of the cells and constitute the zone of oval nuclei; the superficial part of each cell is columnar, and contains granules of yellow pigment, while its deep part is prolonged as a delicate process which ramifies and communicates with similar processes from neighboring cells, so as to form a net-work in the mucous membrane. Lying between the deep processes of the supporting cells are a number of bipolar nerve cells, the **olfactory cells,** each consisting of a small amount of granular protoplasm with a large spherical nucleus, and possessing two processes—a superficial one which runs between the columnar epithelial cells, and projects on the surface of the mucous membrane as a fine, hair-like process, the **olfactory hair**; the other or deep process runs inward, is frequently beaded, and is continued as the axon of an olfactory nerve fiber. Beneath the epithelium, and extending through the thickness of the mucous membrane, is a layer of tubular, often branched, glands, the **glands of Bowman,** identical in structure with serous glands. The epithelial cells of the nose, fauces and respiratory passages play an important role in the maintenance of an equable tempera-ture, by the moisture with which they keep the surface always slightly lubricated.

Vessels and Nerves.—The **arteries** of the nasal cavities are the anterior and posterior eth-moidal branches of the ophthalmic, which supply the ethmoidal cells, frontal sinuses, and roof of the nose; the sphenopalatine branch of the internal maxillary, which supplies the mucous membrane covering the conchæ, the meatuses and septum; the septal branch of the superior labial of the external maxillary; the infraorbital and alveolar branches of the internal maxillary, which supply the lining membrane of the maxillary sinus; and the pharyngeal branch of the same artery, distributed to the sphenoidal sinus. The ramifications of these vessels form a close plexiform net-work, beneath and in the substance of the mucous membrane.

The **veins** form a close cavernous plexus beneath the mucous membrane. This plexus is especi-ally well-marked over the lower part of the septum and over the middle and inferior conchæ. Some

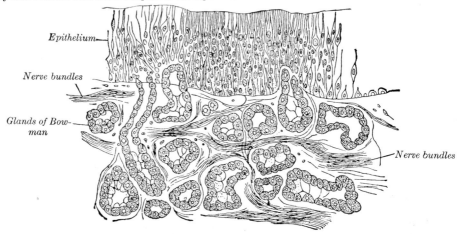

Fig. 855.—Section of the olfactory mucous membrane. (Cadiat.)

of the veins open into the sphenopalatine vein; others join the anterior facial vein; some accom-pany the ethmoidal arteries, and end in the ophthalmic veins; and, lastly, a few communicate with the veins on the orbital surface of the frontal lobe of the brain, through the foramina in the cribriform plate of the ethmoid bone; when the foramen cecum is patent it transmits a vein to the superior sagittal sinus.

The **lymphatics** have already been described (page 705).

The **nerves** of ordinary sensation are: the nasociliary branch of the ophthalmic, filaments from the anterior alveolar branch of the maxillary, the nerve of the pterygoid canal, the nasopalatine, the anterior palatine, and nasal branches of the sphenopalatine ganglion.

The nasociliary branch of the ophthalmic distributes filaments to the forepart of the septum and lateral wall of the nasal cavity. Filaments from the anterior alveolar nerve supply the inferior meatus and inferior concha. The nerve of the pterygoid canal supplies the upper and back part of the septum, and superior concha; and the upper nasal branches from the sphenopalatine gang-lion have a similar distribution. The nasopalatine nerve supplies the middle of the septum. The anterior palatine nerve supplies the lower nasal branches to the middle and inferior conchæ.

The *olfactory*, the special nerve of the sense of smell, is distributed to the olfactory region Its fibers arise from the bipolar olfactory cells and are destitute of medullary sheaths. They unite in fasciculi which form a plexus beneath the mucous membrane and then ascend in grooves or canals in the ethmoid bone; they pass into the skull through the foramina in the cribriform plate of the ethmoid and enter the under surface of the olfactory bulb, in which they ramify and form synapses with the dendrites of the mitral cells (Fig. 771).

The Accessory Sinuses of the Nose (Sinus Paranasales) (Figs. 851, 852, 856.)

The **accessory sinuses** or **air cells of the nose** are the **frontal, ethmoidal, sphe-noidal,** and **maxillary;** they vary in size and form in different individuals, and are lined by ciliated mucous membrane directly continuous with that of the nasal cavities.

The **Frontal Sinuses** (*sinus frontales*), situated behind the superciliary arches, are rarely symmetrical, and the septum between them frequently deviates to one or other side of the middle line. Their average measurements are as follows: height, 3 cm.; breadth, 2.5 cm.; depth from before backward, 2.5 cm. Each opens into the anterior part of the corresponding middle meatus of the nose through the frontonasal duct which traverses the anterior part of the labyrinth of the ethmoid. Absent at birth, they are generally fairly well developed between the seventh and eighth years, but only reach their full size after puberty.

The **Ethmoidal Air Cells** (*cellulæ ethmoidales*) consist of numerous thin-walled cavities situated in the ethmoidal labyrinth and completed by the frontal, maxilla, lacrimal, sphenoidal, and palatine. They lie between the upper parts of the nasal cavities and the orbits, and are separated from these cavities by thin bony laminæ. On either side they are arranged in three groups, **anterior, middle,** and **posterior.** The anterior and middle groups open into the middle meatus of the

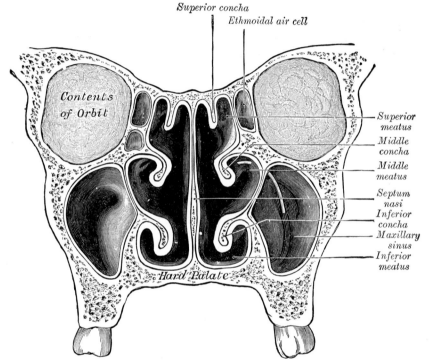

FIG. 856.—Coronal section of nasal cavities.

nose, the former by way of the infundibulum, the latter on or above the bulla ethmoidalis. The posterior cells open into the superior meatus under cover of the superior nasal concha; sometimes one or more opens into the sphenoidal sinus. The ethmoidal cells begin to develop during fetal life.

The **Sphenoidal Sinuses** (*sinus sphenoidales*) (Fig. 852) contained within the body of the sphenoid vary in size and shape, owing to the lateral displacement of the intervening septum they are rarely symmetrical. The following are their average measurements: vertical height, 2.2 cm.; transverse breadth, 2 cm.; antero-posterior depth, 2.2 cm. When exceptionally large they may extend into the roots of the pterygoid processes or great wings, and may invade the basilar part of the occipital bone. Each sinus communicates with the sphenoethmoidal recess by means of an aperture in the upper part of its anterior wall. They are present as minute cavities at birth, but their main development takes place after puberty.

The **Maxillary Sinus** (*sinus maxillaris; antrum of Highmore*), the largest of the accessory sinuses of the nose, is a pyramidal cavity in the body of the maxilla.

Its base is formed by the lateral wall of the nasal cavity, and its apex extends into the zygomatic process. Its roof or orbital wall is frequently ridged by the infra-orbital canal, while its floor is formed by the alveolar process and is usually $\frac{1}{2}$ to 10 mm. below the level of the floor of the nose; projecting into the floor are several conical elevations corresponding with the roots of the first and second molar teeth, and in some cases the floor is perforated by one or more of these roots. The size of the sinus varies in different skulls, and even on the two sides of the same skull. The adult capacity varies from 9.5 c.c. to 20 c.c., average about 14.75 c.c. The following measurements are those of an average-sized sinus: vertical height opposite the first molar tooth, 3.75 cm.; transverse breadth, 2.5 cm.; antero-posterior depth, 3 cm. In the antero-superior part of its base is an opening through which it communicates with the lower part of the hiatus semilunaris; a second orifice is frequently seen in, or immediately behind, the hiatus. The maxillary sinus appears as a shallow groove on the medial surface of the bone about the fourth month of fetal life, but does not reach its full size until after the second dentition.[1] At birth it measures about 7 mm. in the dorso-ventral direction and at twenty months about 20 mm.[2]

THE ORGAN OF SIGHT (ORGANON VISUS; THE EYE).

The **bulb of the eye** (*bulbus oculi; eyeball*), or **organ of sight**, is contained in the cavity of the orbit, where it is protected from injury and moved by the ocular muscles. Associated with it are certain accessory structures, viz., the muscles, fasciæ, eyebrows, eyelids, conjunctiva, and lacrimal apparatus.

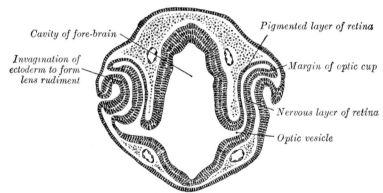

Cavity of fore-brain

Invagination of ectoderm to form lens rudiment

Pigmented layer of retina

Margin of optic cup

Nervous layer of retina

Optic vesicle

Fɪɢ. 857.—Transverse section of head of chick embryo of forty-eight hours' incubation. (Duval.)

The bulb of the eye is imbedded in the fat of the orbit, but is separated from it by a thin membranous sac, the fascia bulbi (page 1054). It is composed of segments of two spheres of different sizes. The anterior segment is one of a small sphere; it is transparent, and forms about one-sixth of the bulb. It is more prominent than the posterior segment, which is one of a larger sphere, and is opaque, and forms about five-sixths of the bulb. The term **anterior pole** is applied to the central point of the anterior curvature of the bulb, and that of **posterior pole** to the central point of its posterior curvature; a line joining the two poles forms the **optic axis**. The axes of the two bulbs are nearly parallel, and therefore do not correspond to the axes of the orbits, which are directed forward and lateralward. The optic nerves follow the direction of the axes of the orbits, and are therefore not parallel; each

---

[1] The various measurements of the accessory sinuses of the nose are based on those given by Aldren Turner in his Accessory Sinuses of the Nose.
[2] Schaeffer, J. P., Am. Jour. Anat., 1910, vol. **10**.

enters its eyeball 3 mm. to the nasal side and a little below the level of the posterior pole. The bulb measures rather more in its transverse and antero-posterior diameters than in its vertical diameter, the former amounting to about 24 mm., the latter to about 23.5 mm.; in the female all three diameters are rather less than in the male;

its antero-posterior diameter at birth is about 17.5 mm., and at puberty from 20 to 21 mm.

Development.—The retina and optic nerve come from the forebrain; the lens from the overlying ectoderm; and the accessory structures from the mesenchyme. The eyes begin to develop as a pair of diverticula from the lateral aspects of the fore-brain. These diverticula make their appearance before the closure of the anterior end of the neural tube; after the closure of the tube they are known as the **optic vesicles.** They project toward the sides of the head, and the peripheral part of each expands to

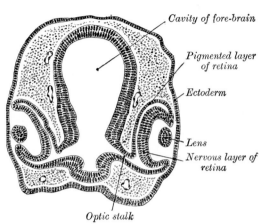

Fig. 858.—Transverse section of head of chick embryo of fifty-two hours' incubation. (Duval.)

form a hollow bulb, while the proximal part remains narrow and constitutes the **optic stalk.** The optic vesicle comes in contact with and adheres to the ectoderm; here the latter thickens, invaginates, becomes severed from the ectoderm, and forms the **lens vesicle.** At the same time the optic vesicle invaginates to form the **optic cup.** Its two layers are continuous with each other at the cup margin, which ultimately overlaps the front of the lens and reaches as far forward as the future aperture

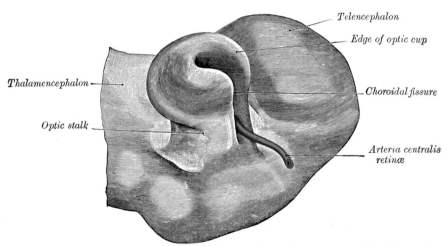

Fig. 859.—Optic cup and choroidal fissure seen from below, from a human embryo of about four weeks. (Kollmann.)

of the pupil (Figs. 857, 858). The invagination also involves the postero-inferior surface of the vesicle and the optic stalk. It produces the **choroidal fissure** of the optic cup and optic stalk (Fig. 859). Mesenchyme and the retinal bloodvessels (hyaloid artery) grow into the fissure. The fissure closes during the seventh week and the two-layered optic cup and optic stalk become complete. Sometimes the choroidal fissure persists, and when this occurs the choroid and iris in the region of the fissure remain undeveloped, giving rise to the condition known as *coloboma* of the choroid or iris.

The **retina** is developed from the optic cup. The outer stratum of the cup persists as a single layer of cells which assume a columnar shape, acquire pigment, and form the pigmented layer of the retina; the pigment first appears in the cells near the edge of the cup. The cells of the inner stratum proliferate and form a layer of considerable thickness from which the nervous elements and the sustentacular fibers of the retina are developed. In that portion of the cup which overlaps the lens the inner stratum is not differentiated into nervous elements, but forms a layer of columnar cells which is applied to the pigmented layer, and these two strata form the **pars ciliaris** and **pars iridica retinæ**.

The cells of the inner or retinal layer of the optic cup become differentiated into spongioblasts and germinal cells, and the latter by their subdivisions give rise to neuroblasts. From the spongioblasts the sustentacular fibers of Müller, the outer and inner limiting membranes, together with the groundwork of the molecular layers of the retina are formed. The neuroblasts become arranged to form the ganglionic and nuclear layers. The layer of rods and cones is first developed in the central part of the optic cup, and from there gradually extends toward the cup margin. All the layers of the retina are completed by the eighth month of fetal life.

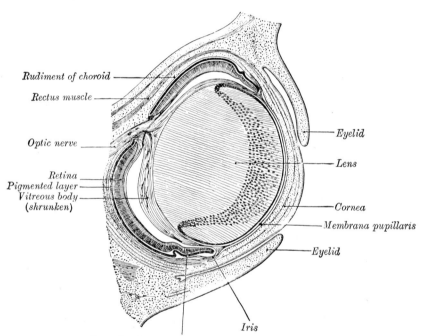

Pars ciliaris and pars iridica retinæ

FIG. 860.—Horizontal section through the eye of an eighteen days' embryo rabbit. × 30. (Kölliker.)

The optic stalk is converted into the **optic nerve** by the obliteration of its cavity and the growth of nerve fibers into it. Most of these fibers are centripetal, and grow backward into the optic stalk from the nerve cells of the retina, but a few extend in the opposite direction and are derived from nerve cells in the brain. The fibers of the optic nerve receive their medullary sheaths about the tenth week after birth. The **optic chiasma** is formed by the meeting and partial decussation of the fibers of the two optic nerves. Behind the chiasma the fibers grow backward as the optic tracts to the thalami and mid-brain.

The **crystalline lens** is developed from the lens vesicle, which recedes within the margin of the cup, and becomes separated from the overlying ectoderm by mesoderm. The cells forming the posterior wall of the vesicle lengthen and are converted into the lens fibers, which grow forward and fill up the cavity of the vesicle (Fig. 860). The cells forming the anterior wall retain their cellular character, and form the epithelium on the anterior surface of the adult lens.

The Hyaloid Artery.—A capillary net continuous with the primitive choroid net enters the choroid fissure. As the fissure closes, connections with the choroid net are all cut off except at the edge of the cup. The vessel enclosed in the optic stalk is the hyaloid artery. Its branches surround the deep surface of the lens and drain into the choroid net at the margin of the cup. As the vitreous body increases, the hyaloid supplies branches to it. By the second month the lens is invested by a vascular mesodermal capsule, the **capsula vasculosa lentis;** the bloodvessels supplying the posterior part of this capsule are derived from the hyaloid artery; those for the anterior part from the anterior ciliary arteries; the portion of the capsule which covers the front of the lens is named the **pupillary membrane.** By the sixth month all the vessels of the capsule are atrophied except the hyaloid artery, which disappears during the ninth month; the position of this artery is indicated in the adult by the hyaloid canal, which reaches from the optic disk to the posterior surface of the lens. With the loss of its bloodvessels the capsula vasculosa lentis disappears, but sometimes the pupillary membrane persists at birth, giving rise to the condition termed *congenital atresia of the pupil.*

The Central Artery of the Retina.—By the fourth month branches of the hyaloid artery and veins which have developed during the third month begin to spread out in the retina and reach the ora serrata by the eighth month. After atrophy of the vitreous part of the hyaloid vessels, the proximal part in the optic nerve and retina becomes the central artery of the retina.

The **choroid** is analogous to the pia-arachnoid of the brain and spinal cord. It develops from mesenchyme between the sclera (dura) and the optic cup (an extension of the brain wall). The mesenchyme is invaded by capillaries, from the ciliary vessels. They form a rich plexus over the outer surface of the optic cup and connect in the pupillary region with the hyaloid capillary plexus. The mesenchyme forms a loose network of multipolar and pigmented cells and white fibrils, partially separated by mesothelial-lined, fluid-containing spaces.

Canal of Schlemm (*sinus venosus scleræ*) and the circular vessels of the iris develop from the anterior extension of the choroid plexus. The former is analogous to a venous sinus of the dura mater; the anterior chamber to the subarachnoid spaces. The drainage of aqueous humor via the pectinate villi into the canal of Schlemm is analogous to the drainage of the subarachnoid fluid via the arachnoid villi into the dural sinuses.

The **vitreous body** develops between the lens and the optic cup as the two structures become separated. Some authors believe that at the beginning, the retina, and perhaps the lens also, play rôles in the formation of the vitreous body; others believe that the retina plays the sole rôle; and still others, that both retina and invading mesenchyme are involved. Fixed and stained preparations show throughout the vitreous body a delicate network of fibrils continuous with the long processes of stellate mesenchyme cells and with the retina. Later the fibrils are limited to the ciliary region where they are supposed to form the **zonula ciliaris.**

The **sclera** is derived from the mesenchyme surrounding the optic cup. A dense layer of white or collagenous fibers, continuous with the sheath of the optic nerve, is formed by the fibroblasts. The sclera is analogous to the dura mater.

Most of the **cornea** is derived from mesenchyme which invades the region between the lens and ectoderm. The overlying ectoderm becomes the corneal epithelial. The endothelial (mesothelial) layer comes from mesenchyme cells which line the corneal side of the cleft (anterior chamber) which develops between the cornea and pupillary membrane. The factors responsible for the transparency of the cornea are unknown.

The **anterior chamber** of the eye appears as a cleft in the mesoderm separating the lens from the overlying ectoderm. The layer of mesoderm in front of the cleft forms the substantia propria of the cornea, that behind the cleft the stroma of the iris and the pupillary membrane.

The fibers of the **ciliary muscle** are derived from the mesoderm, but those of the Sphincter and Dilatator pupillæ are of ectodermal origin, being developed from the cells of the pupillary part of the optic cup.

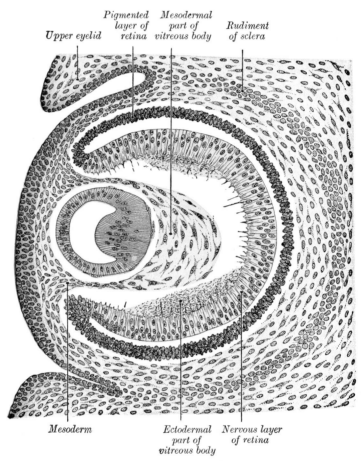

Fig. 861.—Sagittal section of eye of human embryo of six weeks. (Kollmann.)

The **eyelids** are formed as small cutaneous folds (Figs. 860, 861), which about the middle of the third month come together and unite in front of the cornea. They remain united until about the end of the sixth month.

The **lacrimal sac** and **nasolacrimal duct** result from a thickening of the ectoderm in the groove, **nasoöptic furrow,** between the lateral nasal and maxillary processes. This thickening forms a solid cord of cells which sinks into the mesoderm; during the third month the central cells of the cord break down, and a lumen, the nasolacrimal duct, is established. The lacrimal ducts arise as buds from the upper part of the cord of cells and secondarily establish openings (*puncta lacrimalia*) on the margins of the lids. The **epithelium** of the cornea and conjunctiva, and that which lines the ducts and alveoli of the lacrimal gland, are of ectodermal origin, as are also the **eyelashes** and the lining cells of the glands which open on the lid-margins.

The Tunics of the Eye (Fig. 862).

From without inward the three tunics are: (1) A fibrous tunic, consisting of the **sclera** behind and the **cornea** in front; (2) a vascular pigmented tunic, comprising, from behind forward, the **choroid, ciliary body,** and **iris**; and (3) a nervous tunic, the **retina**.

The Fibrous Tunic (*tunica fibrosa oculi*).—The sclera and cornea (Fig. 862) form the fibrous tunic of the bulb of the eye; the sclera is opaque, and constitutes the posterior five-sixths of the tunic; the cornea is transparent, and forms the anterior sixth.

The Sclera.—The sclera has received its name from its extreme density and hardness; it is a firm, unyielding membrane, serving to maintain the form of the bulb. It is much thicker behind than in front; the thickness of its posterior part is 1 mm. Its **external surface** is of white color, and is in contact with the inner surface of the fascia of the bulb; it is quite smooth, except at the points where the Recti and Obliqui are inserted into it; its anterior part is covered by the conjunctival mem-

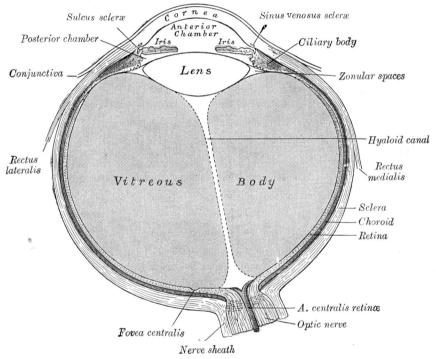

Fig. 862.—Horizontal section of the eyeball.

brane; the rest of the surface is separated from the fascia bulbi (capsule of Tenor) by very loose connective tissue containing mesothelial-lined, fluid-containing spaces (spaces of Tenon) of capillary dimensions. This permits rotation of the eyeball within the fascia bulbi. Its **inner surface** is brown in color and marked by grooves, in which the ciliary nerves and vessels are lodged; it is loosely attached to the pigmented lamina suprachoroidea of the choroid. Behind it is pierced by the optic nerve, and is continuous through the fibrous sheath of this nerve with the dura mater. Where the optic nerve passes through the sclera, the latter forms a thin cribriform lamina, the **lamina cribrosa scleræ**; the minute orifices in this lamina serve for the transmission of the nervous filaments, and the fibrous septa dividing them from one another are continuous with the membranous processes which separate the bundles of nerve fibers. One of these openings, larger than the rest, occupies the center of the lamina; it transmits the central artery and vein of the retina. Around the entrance of the optic nerve are numerous small apertures for the transmission of the ciliary vessels and nerves, and about mid-way between this entrance and the sclero-corneal junction are four or five large apertures for the transmission of veins (**venæ vorticosæ**). In front, the sclera is directly continuous with the cornea, the oblique line of union being termed the **sclero-corneal junction.**

Near the sclero-corneal junction the inner surface of the sclera projects to form a circular ridge, the **scleral spur.** To it is attached the ciliary muscle and the iris. In front of this ridge there is a circular depression, the scleral sulcus, crossed by trabecular tissue which separates the angle of the anterior chamber from the sinus venosus scleræ (canal of Schlemm). The spaces of the trabecular tissue (spaces of Fontana) connect on one side with the anterior chamber of the eye and on the other with the pectinate villi. The aqueous humor filters through the walls of the villi into the sinus venosus scleræ.

Structure.—The sclera is formed of white fibrous tissue intermixed with fine elastic fibers; flattened connective-tissue corpuscles, some of which are pigmented, are contained in cell spaces between the fibers. The fibers are aggregated into bundles, which are arranged chiefly in a longitudinal direction. Its *vessels* are not numerous, the capillaries being of small size, uniting at long and wide intervals. Its *nerves* are derived from the ciliary nerves, but their exact mode of ending is not known.

The Cornea.—The cornea is the projecting transparent part of the external tunic, and forms the anterior sixth of the surface of the bulb. It is almost circular in outline, occasionally a little broader in the transverse than in the vertical direction. It is convex anteriorly and projects like a dome in front of the sclera. Its degree of curvature varies in different individuals, and in the same individual at different periods of life, being more pronounced in youth than in advanced life. The cornea is dense and of uniform thickness throughout; its posterior surface is perfectly circular in outline, and exceeds the anterior surface slightly in diameter. Immediately in front of the sclero-corneal junction the cornea bulges inward as a thickened rim.

Structure (Fig. 863).—The cornea consists of five layers, viz.: (1) the **corneal epithelium**, continuous with that of the conjunctiva; (2) the **anterior lamina**; (3) the **substantia propria**; (4) the **posterior lamina**; and (5) the **endothelium** (mesothelium) of the anterior chamber.

The **corneal epithelium** (*epithelium corneæ; anterior layer*) covers the front of the cornea and consists of several layers of cells. The cells of the deepest layer are columnar; then follow two or three layers of polyhedral cells, the majority of which are prickle cells similar to those found in the stratum mucosum of the cuticle. Lastly, there are three or four layers of squamous cells, with flattened nuclei.

The **substantia propria** is fibrous, tough, unyielding, and perfectly transparent. It is composed of about sixty flattened lamellæ, superimposed one on another. These lamellæ are made up of bundles of modified connective tissue, the fibers of which are directly continuous with those of the sclera. The fibers of each lamella are for the most part parallel with one another, but at right angles to those of adjacent lamellæ. Fibers, however, frequently pass from one lamella to the next. The lamellæ are connected with each other by an interstitial cement substance, in which are spaces, the **corneal spaces.** These are stellate in shape and communicate with one another by numerous offsets. Each contains a cell, the **corneal corpuscle**, a modified fibroblast, resembling in form the space in which it is lodged, but not entirely filling it.

The **anterior lamina** (*lamina elastica anterior; anterior limiting layer; Bowman's membrane*) consists of extremely closely interwoven fibrils, similar to those found in the substantia propria, but contains no corneal corpuscles. It may be regarded as a condensed part of the substantia propria

The **posterior elastic lamina** (*lamina elastica posterior; membrane of Descemet; membrane of Demours*) covers the posterior surface of the substantia propria, and is an elastic, transparent homogeneous membrane, of extreme thinness, which is not rendered opaque by either water, alcohol, or acids. When stripped from the substantia propria it curls up, or rolls upon itself with the attached surface innermost.

At the margin of the cornea the posterior elastic lamina breaks up into fibers which form the trabecular tissue already described. Some of the fibers of this trabecular tissue are continued into the substance of the iris, forming the **pectinate ligament of the iris**; while others are connected with the forepart of the sclera and choroid.

The endothelium of the anterior chamber (*endothelium cameræ anterioris; posterior layer; corneal endothelium*).—This is a mesothelial, not an endothelial layer. It covers the posterior surface of the elastic lamina, is reflected on to the front of the iris, and also lines the spaces of the angle of the iris; it consists of a single stratum of polygonal, flattened, nucleated cells.

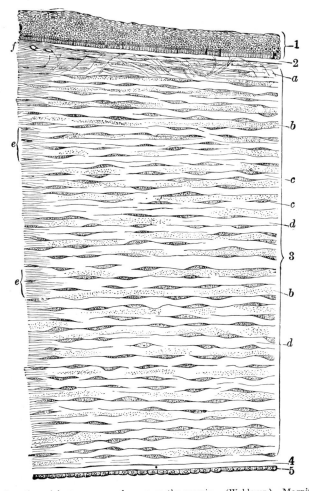

Fig. 863.—Vertical section of human cornea from near the margin. (Waldeyer.) Magnified. 1. Epithelium. 2. Anterior lamina. 3. Substantia propria. 4. Posterior elastic lamina. 5. Endothelium of the anterior chamber. a. Oblique fibers in the anterior layer of the substantia propria. b. Lamellæ the fibers of which are cut across, producing a dotted appearance. c. Corneal corpuscles appearing fusiform in section. d. Lamellæ the fibers of which are cut longitudinally. e. Transition to the sclera, with more distinct fibrillation, and surmounted by a thicker epithelium. f. Small bloodvessels cut across near the margin of the cornea.

Vessels and Nerves.—The cornea is a non-vascular structure; the capillary vessels ending in loops at its circumference are derived from the anterior ciliary arteries. Lymphatic vessels have not yet been demonstrated in it, but are represented by the channels in which the bundles of nerves run; these channels are lined by an endothelium. The **nerves** are numerous and are derived from the ciliary nerves. Around the periphery of the cornea they form an *annular plexus*, from which fibers enter the substantia propria. They lose their medullary sheaths and ramify throughout its substance in a delicate net-work, and their terminal filaments form a firm and closer plexus on the surface of the cornea proper, beneath the epithelium. This is termed the *subepithelial plexus*, and from it fibrils are given off which ramify between the epithelial cells, forming an *intraepithelial plexus*.

The Vascular Tunic (*tunica vasculosa oculi; uvea*) (Figs. 864, 865, 866).—The vascular tunic of the eye is formed from behind forward by the choroid, the ciliary body, and the iris.

The choroid invests the posterior five-sixths of the bulb, and extends as far forward as the ora serrata of the retina. The ciliary body connects the choroid to the circumference of the iris. The iris is a circular diaphragm behind the cornea, and presents near its center a rounded aperture, the **pupil**.

The Choroid (*chorioidea*).—The choroid

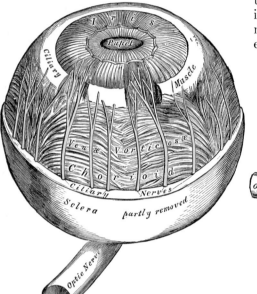

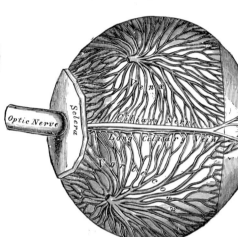

Fig. 864.—The choroid and iris. (Enlarged.)   Fig. 865.—The veins of the choroid. (Enlarged.)

is a thin, highly vascular membrane, of a dark brown or chocolate color, investing the posterior five-sixths of the globe; it is pierced behind by the optic nerve, and in this situation is firmly adherent to the sclera. It is thicker behind than

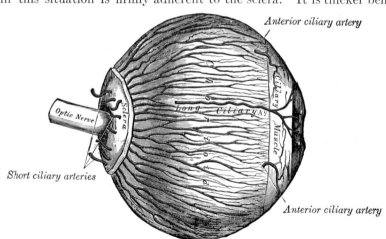

Fig. 866.—The arteries of the choroid and iris. The greater part of the sclera has been removed. (Enlarged.)

in front. Its outer surface is loosely connected by the lamina suprachorioidea with the sclera; its inner surface is attached to the pigmented layer of the retina.

Structure.—The choroid consists mainly of a dense capillary plexus, and of small arteries and veins carrying blood to and returning it from this plexus. On its external surface is a thin membrane, the **lamina suprachorioidea,** composed of delicate non-vascular lamellæ—each lamella consisting of a net-work of fine elastic fibers among which are branched pigment cells. The potential spaces between the lamellæ are lined by mesothelium, and open freely into the perichoroidal space.

Internal to this lamina is the **choroid proper,** consisting of two layers: an outer, composed of small arteries and veins, with pigment cells interspersed between them; and an inner, consisting of a capillary plexus. The **outer layer** (*lamina vasculosa*) consists, in part, of the larger branches of the short ciliary arteries which run forward between the veins, before they bend inward to end in the capillaries, but is formed principally of veins, named, from their arrangement, the **venæ vorticosæ.** They converge to four or five equidistant trunks, which pierce the sclera about midway between the sclero-corneal junction and the entrance of the optic nerve. Interspersed between the vessels are dark star-shaped pigment cells, the processes of which, communicating with those of neighboring cells, form a delicate net-work or stroma, which toward the inner surface of the choroid loses its pigmentary character. The **inner layer** (*lamina choriocapillaris*) consists of an exceedingly fine capillary plexus, formed by the short ciliary vessels; the net-work is closer and finer in the posterior than in the anterior part of the choroid.

About 1.25 cm. behind the cornea its meshes become larger, and are continuous with those of the ciliary processes. These two laminæ are connected by a **stratum intermedium** consisting of fine elastic fibers. On the inner surface of the lamina choriocapillaris is a very thin, structureless, or faintly fibrous membrane, called the **lamina basalis;** it is closely connected with the stroma of the choroid, and separates it from the pigmentary layer of the retina.

One of the functions of the choroid is to provide nutrition for the retina, and to convey vessels and nerves to the ciliary body and iris.

Tapetum.—This name is applied to the outer and posterior part of the choroid, which in many animals presents an iridescent appearance.

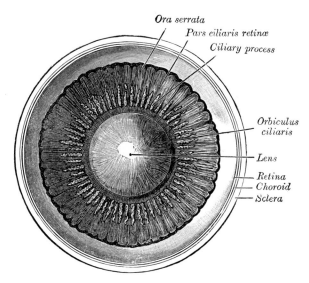

Fig. 867.—Interior of anterior half of bulb of eye.

The Ciliary Body (*corpus ciliary*).—The ciliary body extends from the ora serrata of the retina to the outer edge of the iris and the sclero-corneal junction. It consists of the thickened vascular tunic of the eye and the ciliary muscle. Its inner surface is covered by the thin, pigmented ciliary part of the retina. The suspensory ligament of the lens is attached to the ciliary body. The ciliary body comprises two zones, the orbiculus ciliaris and the ciliary processes (Fig. 867).

The **orbiculus ciliaris** is 4 mm. wide and extends from the ora serrata to the ciliary processes. Its thickness increases as it approaches the ciliary processes owing to the increase in thickness of the ciliary muscle. The choroid layer is

66

thicker here than over the optical part of the retina. Its inner surface presents numerous small radial ridges.

The **ciliary processes** (*processus ciliares*) are formed by the inward folding of the various layers of the choroid, *i. e.*, the choroid proper and the lamina basalis, and are received between corresponding foldings of the suspensory ligament of the lens. They are arranged in a circle, and form a sort of frill behind the iris, around the

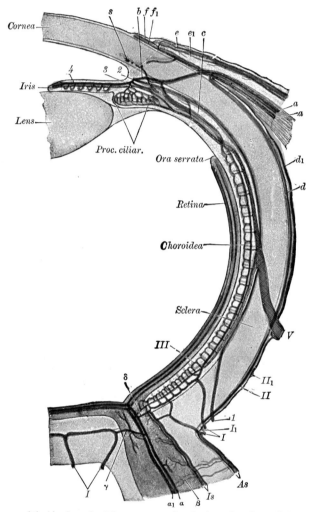

Fig. 868.—Diagram of the bloodvessels of the eye, as seen in a horizontal section.   (Leber, after Stöhr.)
Course of vasa centralia retinæ: *a*. Arteria.   *a.*[1] Vena centralis retinæ.   B. Anastomosis with vessels of outer coats.   Anastomosis with branches of short posterior ciliary arteries.   D. Anastomosis with chorioideal vessels.
Course of vasa ciliar. postic. brev.: I. Arteriæ, and I[1]. Venæ ciliar. postic. brev.   II. Episcleral arrery.   II[1]. Episcleral vein.   III. Capillaries of lamina choriocapillaris.
Course of vasa ciliar. postic. long.: 1. a. ciliar. post. longa.   2. Circulus iridis major cut across.   3. Branches to ciliary body.   4. Branches to iris.
Course of vasa ciliar. ant.: *a*. Arteria.   *a*[1]. Vena ciliar. ant.   *b*. Junction with the circulus iridis major.   *c*. Junction with lamina choriocapill.   *d*. Arterial, and *d*[1]. Venous episcleral branches.   *e*. Arterial, and *e*[1]. Venous branches to conjunctiva scleræ.   *f*. Arterial, and *f*[1]. Venous branches to corneal border.   *V*. Vena vorticosa.   *S*. Transverse section of sinus venosus scleræ.

margin of the lens (Fig. 867). They vary from sixty to eighty in number, lie side by side, and may be divided into large and small; the former are about 2.5 mm. in length, and the latter, consisting of about one-third of the entire number, are situated in spaces between them, but without regular arrangement. They are attached by their periphery to three or four of the ridges of the orbiculus ciliaris, and are continuous with the layers of the choroid: their opposite extremities are free and rounded, and are directed toward the posterior chamber of the eyeball and circumference of the lens. In front, they are continuous with the periphery of the iris. Their posterior surfaces are connected with the suspensory ligament of the lens.

Structure.—The ciliary processes (Fig. 867) are similar in structure to the choroid, but the vessels are larger, and have chiefly a longitudinal direction. Their posterior surfaces are covered by a bilaminar layer of black pigment cells, which is continued forward from the retina, and is named the **pars ciliaris retinæ.** In the stroma of the ciliary processes there are also stellate pigment cells, but these are not so numerous as in the choroid itself.

The **Ciliaris muscle** (*m. ciliaris; ciliary muscle*) consists of unstriped fibers; it forms a grayish, semitransparent, circular band, about 3 mm. broad, on the outer surface of the forepart of the choroid. It is thickest in front, and consists of two sets of fibers, **meridional** and **circular.** The meridional fibers, much the more numerous, arise from the posterior margin of the scleral spur; they run backward, and are attached to the ciliary processes and orbiculus ciliaris. The circular fibers are internal to the meridional ones, and in a meridional section appear as a triangular zone behind the filtration angle and close to the circumference of the iris. They are well-developed in hypermetropic, but are rudimentary or absent in myopic eyes. The Ciliaris muscle is the chief agent in accommodation, *i. e.,* in adjusting the eye to the vision of near objects. When it contracts it draws forward the ciliary processes, relaxes the suspensory ligament of the lens, and thus allows the lens to become more convex.

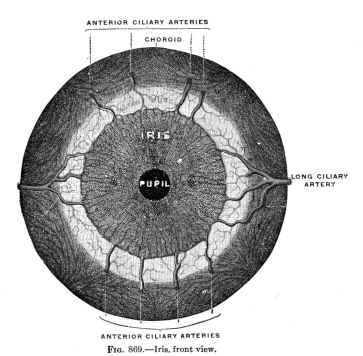

Fig. 869.—Iris, front view.

The Iris.—The iris has received its name from its various colors in different individuals. It is a thin, circular, contractile disk, suspended in the aqueous humor between the cornea and lens, and perforated a little to the nasal side of its center by a circular aperture, the **pupil.** By its periphery it is continuous with the ciliary body, and is also connected with the posterior elastic lamina of the cornea by means of the pectinate ligament; its surfaces are flattened, and look forward and backward, the anterior toward the cornea, the posterior toward the ciliary processes and lens. The iris divides the space between the lens and the cornea into an anterior and a posterior chamber. The **anterior chamber** of the eye is bounded in front by the posterior surface of the cornea; behind by the front of the iris and the central part of the lens. The **posterior chamber** is a narrow chink behind the peripheral part of the iris, and in front of the suspensory ligament of the lens and the ciliary processes. In the adult the two chambers communicate through the pupil, but in the fetus up to the seventh month they are separated by the *membrana pupillaris*.

Structure.—The iris is composed of the following structures:

1. In front is a layer of flattened mesothelial cells placed on a delicate hyaline basement membrane. This layer is continuous with the mesothelium covering the posterior elastic lamina of the cornea, and in individuals with dark-colored irides the cells contain pigment granules.

2. The **stroma** (*stroma iridis*) of the iris consists of fibers and cells. The former are made up of delicate bundles of fibrous tissue; a few fibers at the circumference of the iris have a circular direction; but the majority radiate toward the pupil, forming by their interlacement, delicate meshes, in which the vessels and nerves are contained. Interspersed between the bundles of connective tissue are numerous branched cells with fine processes. In dark eyes many of them contain pigment granules, but in blue eyes and the eyes of albinos they are unpigmented.

3. The **muscular fibers** are involuntary, and consist of circular and radiating fibers. The **circular fibers** form the Sphincter pupillæ; they are arranged in a narrow band about 1 mm. in width which surrounds the margin of the pupil toward the posterior surface of the iris; those near the free margin are closely aggregated; those near the periphery of the band are somewhat separated and form incomplete circles. The **radiating fibers** form the Dilatator pupillæ; they converge from the circumference toward the center, and blend with the circular fibers near the margin of the pupil.

4. The posterior surface of the iris is of a deep purple tint, being covered by two layers of pigmented columnar epithelium, continuous at the periphery of the iris with the pars ciliaris retinæ. This pigmented epithelium is named the **pars iridica retinæ.**

The color of the iris is produced by the reflection of light from dark pigment cells underlying a translucent tissue, and is therefore determined by the amount of the pigment and its distribution throughout the texture of the iris. The number and the situation of the pigment cells differ in different irides. In the albino pigment is absent; in the various shades of blue eyes the pigment cells are confined to the posterior surface of the iris, whereas in gray, brown, and black eyes pigment is found also in the cells of the stroma and in those of the endothelium on the front of the iris.

The iris may be absent, either in part or altogether as a congenital condition, and in some instances the pupillary membrane may remain persistent, though it is rarely complete. Again, the iris may be the seat of a malformation, termed *coloboma*, which consists in a deficiency or cleft, clearly due in a great number of cases to an arrest in development. In these cases the cleft is found at the lower aspect, extending directly downward from the pupil, and the gap frequently extends through the choroid to the porus opticus. In some rarer cases the gap is found in other parts of the iris, and is not then associated with any deficiency of the choroid.

Vessels and Nerves.—The **arteries of the iris** are derived from the long and anterior ciliary arteries, and from the vessels of the ciliary processes (see p. 576). Each of the two long ciliary arteries, having reached the attached margin of the iris, divides into an upper and lower branch; these anastomose with corresponding branches from the opposite side and thus encircle the iris; into this vascular circle (*circulus arteriosus major*) the anterior ciliary arteries pour their blood, and from it vessels converge to the free margin of the iris, and there communicate and form a second circle (*circulus arteriosus minor*) (Figs. 868 and 869).

The **nerves of the choroid and iris** are the long and short ciliary; the former being branches of the nasociliary nerve, the latter of the ciliary ganglion. They pierce the sclera around the entrance of the optic nerve, run forward in the perichoroidal space, and supply the bloodvessels of the choroid. After reaching the iris they form a plexus around its attached margin; from this are derived non-medullated fibers which end in the Sphincter and Dilatator pupillæ; their exact mode of termination has not been ascertained. Other fibers from the plexus end in a net-work on the anterior surface of the iris. The fibers derived through the motor root of the ciliary ganglion from the oculomotor nerve, supply the Sphincter, while those derived from the sympathetic supply the Dilatator.

Membrana Pupillaris.—In the fetus, the pupil is closed by a delicate vascular membrane, the **membrana pupillaris,** which divides the space in which the iris is suspended into two distinct chambers. The vessels of this membrane are partly derived from those of the margin of the iris and partly from those of the capsule of the lens; they have a looped arrangement, and converge toward each other without anastomosing. About the sixth month the membrane begins to disappear by absorption from the center toward the circumference, and at birth only a few fragments are present; in exceptional cases it persists.

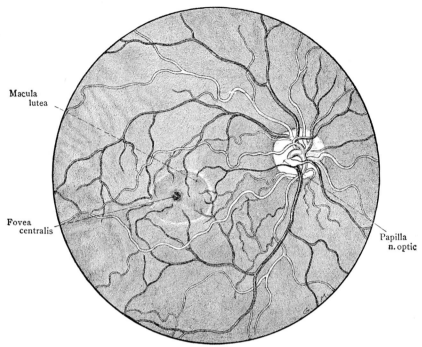

FIG. 870.—Interior of posterior half of right eye as viewed from in front. The distribution of blood vessels is shown (veins darker than arteries) and their relation to the optic disc. The area of most acute vision, the macula lutea, is shown. (Eycleshymer and Jones.)

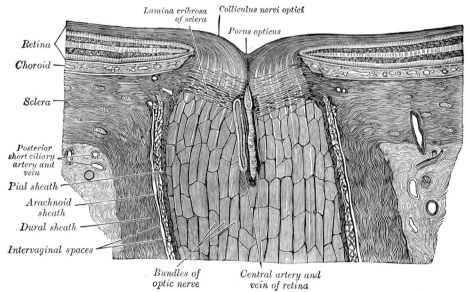

FIG. 871.—The terminal portion of the optic nerve and its entrance into the eyeball, in horizontal section. (Toldt.)

The Retina (*tunica interna*).—The retina is a delicate nervous membrane, upon which the images of external objects are received. Its outer surface is in contact with the choroid; its inner with the vitreous body. Behind, it is continuous with the optic nerve; it gradually diminishes in thickness from behind forward, and extends nearly as far as the ciliary body, where it appears to end in a jagged margin, the **ora serrata**. Here the nervous tissues of the retina end, but a thin prolongation of the membrane extends forward over the back of the ciliary processes and iris, forming the **pars ciliaris retinæ** and **pars iridica retinæ** already referred to. This forward prolongation consists of the pigmentary layer of the retina together with a stratum of columnar epithelium. The retina is soft, semitransparent, and of a purple tint in the fresh state, owing to the presence of a coloring material named **rhodopsin** or **visual purple**; but it soon becomes clouded, opaque, and bleached when exposed to sunlight. Exactly in the center of the posterior part of the retina, corresponding to the axis of the eye, and at a point in which the sense of vision is most perfect, is an oval yellowish area, the **macula lutea**; in the macula is a central depression, the **fovea centralis** (Fig. 870). At the fovea centralis the retina is exceedingly thin, and the dark color of the choroid is distinctly seen through it. About 3 mm. to the nasal side of the macula lutæ is the entrance of the optic nerve (*optic disk*), the circumference of which is slightly raised to form an eminence (*colliculus nervi optici*) (Fig. 871); the arteria centralis retinæ pierces the center of the disk. This is the only part of the surface of the retina which is insensitive to light, and it is termed the **blind spot.**

Structure (Figs. 872, 873).—The retina consists of an outer pigmented layer and an inner nervous stratum or retina proper.

The **pigmented layer** consists of a single stratum of cells. When viewed from the outer surface these cells are smooth and hexagonal in shape; when seen in section each cell consists of an outer non-pigmented part containing a large oval nucleus and an inner pigmented portion which extends as a series of straight thread-like processes between the rods, this being especially the case when the eye is exposed to light. In the eyes of albinos the cells of this layer are destitute of pigment.

Retina Proper.—The nervous structures of the retina proper are supported by a series of nonnervous or sustentacular fibers, and, when examined microscopically by means of sections made perpendicularly to the surface of the retina, are found to consist of seven layers, named from within outward as follows:

1. Stratum opticum.
2. Ganglionic layer.
3. Inner plexiform layer.
4. Inner nuclear layer, or layer of inner granules.
5. Outer plexiform layer.
6. Outer nuclear layer, or layer of outer granules.
7. Layer of rods and cones.

1. The **stratum opticum** or **layer of nerve fibers** is formed by the expansion of the fibers of the optic nerve; it is thickest near the porus opticus, gradually diminishing toward the ora serrata.

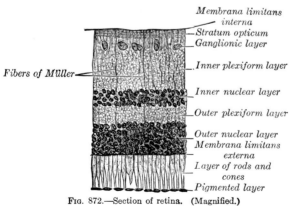

Membrana limitans
interna
Stratum opticum
Ganglionic layer

Inner plexiform layer

Fibers of Müller

Inner nuclear layer

Outer plexiform layer

Outer nuclear layer
Membrana limitans
externa
Layer of rods and
cones
Pigmented layer

Fig. 872.—Section of retina. (Magnified.)

As the nerve fibers pass through the lamina cribrosa scleræ they lose their medullary sheaths and are continued onward through the choroid and retina as simple axis-cylinders. When they reach the internal surface of the retina they radiate from their point of entrance over this surface grouped in bundles, and in many places arranged in plexuses. Most of the fibers are centripetal, and are the direct continuations of the axis-cylinder processes of the cells of the ganglionic layer, but a few of them are centrifugal and ramify in the inner plexiform and inner nuclear layers, where they end in enlarged extremities.

2. The **ganglionic layer** consists of a single layer of large ganglion cells, except in the macula lutea, where there are several strata. The cells are somewhat flask-shaped; the rounded internal surface of each resting on the stratum opticum, and sending off an axon which is prolonged into it. From the opposite end numerous dendrites extend into the inner plexiform layer, where

they branch and form flattened arborizations at different levels. The ganglion cells vary much in size, and the dendrites of the smaller ones as a rule arborize in the inner plexiform layer as soon as they enter it; while those of the larger cells ramify close to the inner nuclear layer.

3. The **inner plexiform layer** is made up of a dense reticulum of minute fibrils formed by the interlacement of the dendrites of the ganglion cells with those of the cells of the inner nuclear layer; within this reticulum a few branched spongioblasts are sometimes imbedded.

4. The **inner nuclear layer** or **layer of inner granules** is made up of a number of closely packed cells, of which there are three varieties, viz.: bipolar cells, horizontal cells, and amacrine cells.

The **bipolar cells,** by far the most numerous, are round or oval in shape, and each is prolonged into an inner and an outer process. They are divisible into rod bipolars and cone bipolars. The inner processes of the **rod bipolars** run through the inner plexiform layer and arborize around the bodies of the cells of the ganglionic layer; their outer processes end in the outer plexiform layer in tufts of fibrils around the button-like ends of the inner processes of the rod granules. The inner processes of the **cone bipolars** ramify in the inner plexiform layer in contact with the dendrites of the ganglionic cells.

The **horizontal cells** lie in the outer part of the inner nuclear layer and possess somewhat flattened cell bodies. Their dendrites divide into numerous branches in the outer plexiform layer, while their axons run horizontally for some distance and finally ramify in the same layer.

The **amacrine cells** are placed in the inner part of the inner nuclear layer, and are so named because they have not yet been shown to possess axis-cylinder processes. Their dendrites undergo extensive ramification in the inner plexiform layer.

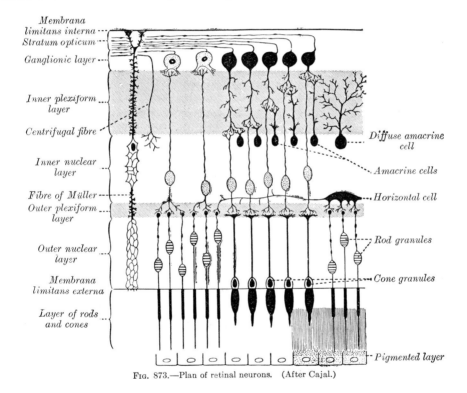

FIG. 873.—Plan of retinal neurons. (After Cajal.)

5. The **outer plexiform layer** is much thinner than the inner; but, like it, consists of a dense net-work of minute fibrils derived from the processes of the horizontal cells of the preceding layer, and the outer processes of the rod and cone bipolar granules, which ramify in it, forming arborizations around the enlarged ends of the rod fibers and with the branched foot plates of the cone fibers.

6. The **outer nuclear layer** or **layer of outer granules,** like the inner nuclear layer, contains several strata of oval nuclear bodies; they are of two kinds, viz.: rod and cone granules, so named on account of their being respectively connected with the rods and cones of the next layer. The **rod granules** are much the more numerous, and are placed at different levels throughout the layer. Their nuclei present a peculiar cross-striped appearance, and prolonged from either extremity of each cell is a fine process; the outer process is continuous with a single rod of the layer of rods and cones; the inner ends in the outer plexiform layer in an enlarged extremity, and

is imbedded in the tuft into which the outer processes of the rod bipolar cells break up. In its course it presents numerous varicosities. The **cone granules**, fewer in number than the rod granules, are placed close to the membrana limitans externa, through which they are continuous with the cones of the layer of rods and cones. They do not present any cross-striation, but contain a pyriform nucleus, which almost completely fills the cell. From the inner extremity of the granule a thick process passes into the outer plexiform layer, and there expands into a pyramidal enlargement or foot plate, from which are given off numerous fine fibrils, that come in contact with the outer processes of the cone bipolars.

7. **The Layer of Rods and Cones** (*Jacob's membrane*).—The elements composing this layer are of two kinds, **rods** and **cones**, the former being much more numerous than the latter except in the macula lutea. The **rods** are cylindrical, of nearly uniform thickness, and are arranged perpendicularly to the surface. Each rod consists of two segments, an outer and inner, of about equal lengths. The segments differ from each other as regards refraction and in their behavior toward coloring reagents; the inner segment is stained by carmine, iodine, etc.; the outer segment is not stained by these reagents, but is colored yellowish brown by osmic acid. The outer segment is marked by transverse striæ, and tends to break up into a number of thin disks superimposed on one another; it also exhibits faint longitudinal markings. The deeper part of the inner segment is indistinctly granular; its more superficial part presents a longitudinal striation, being composed of fine, bright, highly refracting fibrils. The visual purple or rhodopsin is found only in the outer segments.

The **cones** are conical or flask-shaped, their broad ends resting upon the membrana limitans externa, the narrow-pointed extremity being turned to the choroid. Like the rods, each is made up of two segments, outer and inner; the outer segment is a short conical process, which, like the outer segment of the rod, exhibits transverse striæ. The inner segment resembles the inner segment of the rods in structure, presenting a superficial striated and deep granular part, but differs from it in size and shape, being bulged out laterally and flask-shaped. The chemical and optical characters of the two portions are identical with those of the rods.

Supporting Frame-work of the Retina.—The nervous layers of the retina are connected together by a supporting frame-work, formed by the **sustentacular fibers of Müller**; these fibers pass through all the nervous layers, except that of the rods and cones. Each begins on the inner surface of the retina by an expanded, often forked base, which sometimes contains a spheroidal body staining deeply with hematoxylin, the edges of the bases of adjoining fibers being united to form the **membrana limitans interna**. As the fibers pass through the nerve fiber and ganglionic layers they give off a few lateral branches; in the inner nuclear layer they give off numerous lateral processes for the support of the bipolar cells, while in the outer nuclear layer they form a network around the rod- and cone-fibrils, and unite to form the **membrana limitans externa** at the bases of the rods and cones. At the level of the inner nuclear layer each sustentacular fiber contains a clear oval nucleus.

Macula Lutea and Fovea Centralis.—In the macula lutea the nerve fibers are wanting as a continuous layer, the ganglionic layer consists of several strata of cells, there are no rods, but only cones, which are longer and narrower than in other parts, and in the outer nuclear layer there are only cone-granules, the processes of which are very long and arranged in curved lines. In the fovea centralis the only parts present are (1) the cones; (2) the outer nuclear layer, the cone-fibers of which are almost horizontal in direction; (3) an exceedingly thin inner plexiform layer. The pigmented layer is thicker and its pigment more pronounced than elsewhere. The color of the macula seems to imbue all the layers except that of the rods and cones; it is of a rich yellow, deepest toward the center of the macula, and does not appear to be due to pigment cells, but simply to a staining of the constituent parts.

At the **ora serrata** the nervous layers of the retina end abruptly, and the retina is continued onward as a single layer of columnar cells covered by the pigmented layer. This double layer is known as the **pars ciliaris retinæ**, and can be traced forward from the ciliary processes on to the back of the iris, where it is termed the **pars iridica retinæ**.

The **arteria centralis retinæ** (Fig. 870) and its accompanying vein pierce the optic nerve, and enter the bulb of the eye through the porus opticus. The artery immediately bifurcates into an upper and a lower branch, and each of these again divides into a medial or nasal and a lateral or temporal branch, which at first run between the hyaloid membrane and the nervous layer; but they soon enter the latter, and pass forward, dividing dichotomously. From these branches a minute capillary plexus is given off, which does not extend beyond the inner nuclear layer. The macula receives two small branches (superior and inferior macular arteries) from the temporal branches and small twigs directly from the central artery; these do not, however, reach as far as the fovea centralis, which has no bloodvessels. The branches of the arteria centralis retinæ do not anastomose with each other—in other words they are terminal arteries. In the fetus, a small vessel, the arteria hyaloidea, passes forward as a continuation of the arteria centralis retinæ through the vitreous humor to the posterior surface of the capsule of the lens.

The Refracting Media.

The refracting media are four, viz.:

The Cornea (see page 1038).   Aqueous humor.   Vitreous body.   Crystalline lens.

The Aqueous Humor (*humor aqueus*).—The aqueous humor fills the anterior and posterior chambers of the eyeball. It is small in quantity, has an alkaline reaction, and consists mainly of water, less than one-fiftieth of its weight being solid matter, chiefly chloride of sodium. The aqueous humor is secreted by the ciliary processes. The fluid passes through the posterior chamber and the pupil into the anterior chamber. From the angle of the anterior chamber it passes into the spaces of Fontana to the pectinate villi through which it is filtered into the venous canal of Schlemm.

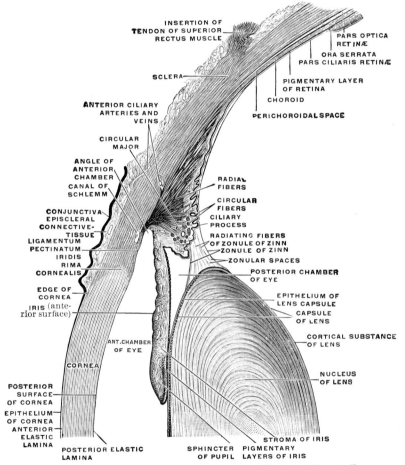

Fig. 874.—The upper half of a sagittal section through the front of the eyeball.

The **Vitreous Body** (*corpus vitreum*) fills the concavity of the pars optica retinæ to which it is firmly adherent especially at the ora serrata. It is hollowed in front for the lens. It is transparent, semigelatinous, and consists of water (99 per cent.), salts, and albumen. Some indications of the hyaloid canal, between the optic nerve and lens may persist.

No bloodvessels penetrate the vitreous body, so that its nutrition must be carried on by vessels of the retina and ciliary processes, situated upon its exterior.

The **Zonula Ciliaris** (*zonule of Zinn, suspensory ligament of the lens*) consists of a series of straight fibrils which radiate from the ciliary body to the lens. It is attached to the capsule of the lens a short distance in front of its equator. Scattered and delicate fibers are also attached to the region of the equator itself. This ligament retains the lens in position, and is relaxed by the contraction of the meridional fibers of the Ciliaris muscle, so that the lens is allowed to become more convex. Behind the suspensory ligament there is a sacculated canal, the **spatia zonularia** (*canal of Petit*), which encircles the equator of the lens; it can be easily inflated through a fine blowpipe inserted under the suspensory ligament.

The Crystalline Lens (*lens crystallina*). — The crystalline lens, enclosed in its capsule, is situated immediately behind the iris, in front of the vitreous body, and encircled by the ciliary processes, which slightly overlap its margin.

FIG. 875.—The crystalline lens, hardened and divided. (Enlarged.)

A.   B.

FIG. 876. — Diagram to show the direction and arrangement of the radiating lines on the front and back of the fetal lens. A. From the front. B. From the back.

1   2   3

FIG. 877.—Profile views of the lens at different periods of life. 1. In the fetus. 2. In adult life. 3. In old age.

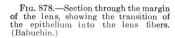

FIG. 878.—Section through the margin of the lens, showing the transition of the epithelium into the lens fibers. (Babuchin.)

The **capsule of the lens** (*capsula lentis*) is a transparent, structureless membrane which closely surrounds the lens, and is thicker in front than behind. It is brittle but highly elastic, and when ruptured the edges roll up with the outer surface innermost. It rests, behind, in the hyaloid fossa in the forepart of the vitreous body; in front, it is in contact with the free border of the iris, but recedes from it at the circumference, thus forming the posterior chamber of the eye; it is retained in its position chiefly by the suspensory ligament of the lens, already described.

The **lens** is a transparent, biconvex body, the convexity of its anterior being less than that of its posterior surface. The central points of these surfaces are termed respectively the **anterior** and **posterior poles**; a line connecting the poles constitutes the **axis** of the lens, while the marginal circumference is termed the **equator.**

Structure.—The lens is made up of soft cortical substance and a firm, central part, the **nucleus** (Fig. 875). Faint lines (*radii lentis*) radiate from the poles to the equator. In the adult there may be six or more of these lines, but in the fetus they are only three in number and diverge from each other at angles of 120° (Fig. 876); on the anterior surface one line ascends vertically and the other two diverge downward; on the posterior surface one ray descends vertically and the other two diverge upward. They correspond with the free edges of an equal number of septa composed of an amorphous substance, which dip into the substance of the lens. When the lens has been hardened it is seen to consist of a series of concentrically arranged laminæ, each of which is interrupted at the septa referred to. Each lamina is built up of a number of hexagonal, ribbon-like lens fibers, the edges of which are more or less serrated—the serrations fitting between those of neighboring fibers, while the ends of the fibers come into apposition at the septa. The fibers run in a curved manner from the septa on the anterior surface to those on the posterior surface. No fibers pass from pole to pole; they are arranged in such a way that those which begin near the pole on one surface of the lens end near the peripheral extremity of the plane on the other, and *vice versa*. The fibers of the outer layers of the lens are nucleated, and together form a nuclear layer, most distinct toward the equator. The anterior surface of the lens is covered by a layer of transparent, columnar, nucleated epithelium. At the equator the cells become elongated, and their gradual transition into lens fibers can be traced (Fig. 878).

In the fetus, the lens is nearly spherical, and has a slightly reddish tint; it is soft and breaks down readily on the slightest pressure. A small branch from the arteria centralis retinæ runs forward, as already mentioned, through the vitreous body to the posterior part of the capsule of the lens, where its branches radiate and form a plexiform network, which covers the posterior surface of the capsule, and they are continuous around the margin of the capsule with the vessels of the pupillary membrane, and with those of the iris. **In the adult,** the lens is colorless, transparent, firm in texture, and devoid of vessels. **In old age** it becomes flattened on both surfaces, slightly opaque, of an amber tint, and increased in density (Fig. 877).

Vessels and Nerves.—The **arteries** of the bulb of the eye are the long, short, and anterior ciliary arteries, and the arteria centralis retinæ. They have already been described (see p. 575).

The **ciliary veins** are seen on the outer surface of the choroid, and are named, from their arrangement, the *venæ vorticosæ;* they converge to four or five equidistant trunks which pierce the sclera midway between the sclero-corneal junction and the porus opticus. Another set of veins accompanies the anterior ciliary arteries. All of these veins open into the ophthalmic veins.

The **ciliary nerves** are derived from the nasociliary nerve and from the ciliary ganglion.

The Accessory Organs of the Eye (Organa Oculi Accessoria).

The accessory organs of the eye include the **ocular muscles,** the **fasciæ,** the **eyebrows,** the **eyelids,** the **conjunctiva,** and the **lacrimal apparatus.**

The Ocular Muscles (*musculi oculi*).—The ocular muscles are the:

Levator palpebræ superioris.	Rectus medialis.
Rectus superior.	Rectus lateralis.
Rectus inferior.	Obliquus superior.

Obliquus inferior.

The **Levator palpebræ superioris** (Fig. 879) is thin, flat, and triangular in shape. It *arises* from the under surface of the small wing of the sphenoid, above and in front of the optic foramen, from which it is separated by the origin of the Rectus superior. At its origin, it is narrow and tendinous, but soon becomes broad and fleshy, and ends anteriorly in a wide aponeurosis which splits into three lamellæ. The superficial lamella blends with the upper part of the orbital septum, and is prolonged forward above the superior tarsus to the palpebral part of the Orbicularis oculi, and to the deep surface of the skin of the upper eyelid. The middle lamella, largely made up of non-striped muscular fibers, is inserted into the upper margin of the superior tarsus, while the deepest lamella blends with an expansion from the sheath of the Rectus superior and with it is attached to the superior fornix of the conjunctiva.

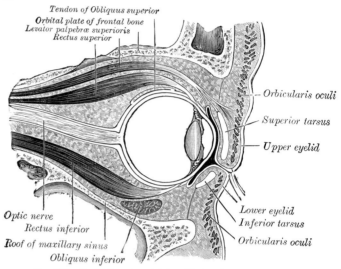

Fig. 879.—Sagittal section of right orbital cavity.

Whitnall[1] has pointed out that the upper part of the sheath of the Levator palpebræ becomes thickened in front and forms, above the anterior part of the muscle, a transverse ligamentous band which is attached to the sides of the orbital cavity. On the medial side it is mainly fixed to the pulley of the Obliquus superior, but some fibers are attached to the bone behind the pulley and a slip passes forward and bridges over the supraorbital notch; on the lateral side it is fixed to the capsule of the lacrimal gland and to the frontal bone. In front of the transverse ligament-

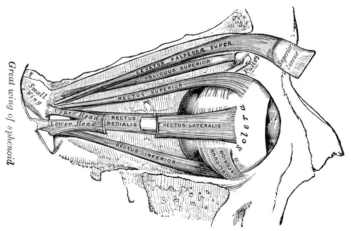

Fig. 880.—Muscles of the right orbit.

ous band the sheath is continued over the aponeurosis of the Levator palpebræ, as a thin connective-tissue layer which is fixed to the upper orbital margin immediatly behind the attachment of the orbital septum. When the Levator palpebræ contracts, the lateral and medial parts of the ligamentous band are stretched and check the action of the muscle; the retraction of the upper eyelid is checked also by the orbital septum coming into contact with the transverse part of the ligamentous band.

[1] Journal of Anatomy and Physiology, vol. 45.

The four **Recti** (Fig. 880) *arise* from a fibrous ring (*annulus tendineus communis*) which surrounds the upper, medial, and lower margins of the optic foramen and encircles the optic nerve (Fig. 881). The ring is completed by a tendinous bridge prolonged over the lower and medial part of the superior orbital fissure and attached to a tubercle on the margin of the great wing of the sphenoid, bounding the fissure. Two specialized parts of this fibrous ring may be made out: a lower, the **ligament** or **tendon of Zinn**, which gives origin to the Rectus inferior, part of the Rectus medialis, and the lower head of origin of the Rectus lateralis; and an upper, which gives origin to the Rectus superior, the rest of the Rectus medialis, and the upper

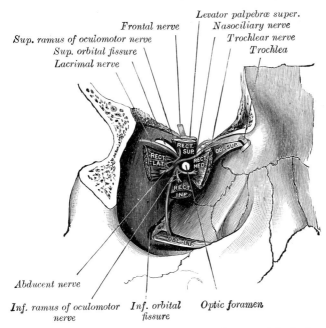

Levator palpebræ super.
Frontal nerve
Nasociliary nerve
Sup. ramus of oculomotor nerve
Trochlear nerve
Sup. orbital fissure
Trochlea
Lacrimal nerve

Abducent nerve

Inf. ramus of oculomotor nerve   *Inf. orbital fissure*   *Optic foramen*

Fig. 881.—Dissection showing origins of right ocular muscles, and nerves entering by the superior orbital fissure.

head of the Rectus lateralis. This upper band is sometimes termed the **superior tendon of Lockwood**. Each muscle passes forward in the position implied by its name, to be inserted by a tendinous expansion into the sclera, about 6 mm. from the margin of the cornea. Between the two heads of the Rectus lateralis is a narrow interval, through which pass the two divisions of the oculomotor nerve, the naso-ciliary nerve, the abducent nerve, and the ophthalmic vein. Although these muscles present a common origin and are inserted in a similar manner into the sclera, there are certain differences to be observed in them as regards their length and breadth. The Rectus medialis is the broadest, the Rectus lateralis the longest, and the Rectus superior the thinnest and narrowest.

The **Obliquus oculi superior** (*superior oblique*) is a fusiform muscle, placed at the upper and medial side of the orbit. It *arises* immediately above the margin of the optic foramen, above and medial to the origin of the Rectus superior, and, passing forward, ends in a rounded tendon, which plays in a fibrocartilaginous ring or pulley attached to the trochlear fovea of the frontal bone. The contiguous surfaces of the tendon and ring are lined by a delicate mucous sheath, and enclosed in a thin fibrous investment. The tendon is reflected backward, lateralward, and downward beneath the Rectus superior to the lateral part of the bulb of the eye, and is inserted into the sclera, behind the equator of the eyeball, the insertion of the muscle lying between the Rectus superior and Rectus lateralis.

The **Obliquus oculi inferior** (*inferior oblique*) is a thin, narrow muscle, placed near the anterior margin of the floor of the orbit. It *arises* from the orbital surface of the maxilla, lateral to the lacrimal groove. Passing lateralward, backward, and upward, at first between the Rectus inferior and the floor of the orbit, and then between the bulb of the eye and the Rectus lateralis, it is inserted into the lateral part of the sclera between the Rectus superior and Rectus lateralis, near to, but somewhat behind the insertion of the Obliquus superior.

Nerves.—The Levator palpebræ superioris, Obliquus inferior, and the Recti superior, inferior, and medialis are supplied by the oculomotor nerve; the Obliquus superior, by the trochlear nerve; the Rectus lateralis, by the abducent nerve.

Actions.—The Levator palpebræ *raises* the upper eyelid, and is the direct antagonist of the Orbicularis oculi. The four Recti are attached to the bulb of the eye in such a manner that, acting singly, they will turn its corneal surface either upward, downward, medialward, or lateralward, as expressed by their names. The movement produced by the Rectus superior or Rectus inferior is not quite a simple one, for inasmuch as each passes obliquely lateralward and forward to the bulb of the eye, the elevation or depression of the cornea is accompanied by a certain deviation medialward, with a slight amount of rotation. These latter movements are corrected by the Obliqui, the Obliquus inferior correcting the medial deviation caused by the Rectus superior and the Obliquus superior that caused by the Rectus inferior. The contraction of the Rectus lateralis or Rectus medialis, on the other hand, produces a purely horizontal movement. If any two neighboring Recti of one eye act together they carry the globe of the eye in the diagonal of these directions, viz., upward and medialward, upward and lateralward, downward and medialward, or downward and lateralward. Sometimes the corresponding Recti of the two eyes act in unison, and at other times the opposite Recti act together. Thus, in turning the eyes to the right, the Rectus lateralis of the right eye will act in unison with the Rectus medialis of the left eye; but if both eyes are directed to an object in the middle line at a short distance, the two Recti mediales will act in unison. The movement of circumduction, as in looking around a room, is performed by the successive actions of the four Recti. The Obliqui rotate the eyeball on its antero-posterior axis, the superior directing the cornea downward and lateralward, and the inferior directing it upward and lateralward; these movements are required for the correct viewing of an object when the head is moved laterally, as from shoulder to shoulder, in order that the picture may fall in all respects on the same part of the retina of either eye.

A layer of non-striped muscle, the **Orbitalis muscle** of H. Müller, may be seen bridging across the inferior orbital fissure.

The **Fascia Bulbi** (*capsule of Tenon*) is a thin membrane which envelops the eyeball from the optic nerve to the ciliary region, separating it from the orbital fat and forming a socket in which it plays. Its inner surface is smooth, and is separated from the outer surface of the sclera by the **periscleral space**. This space is continuous with the subdural and subarachnoid cavities, and is traversed by delicate bands of connective tissue which extend between the fascia and the sclera. The fascia is perforated behind by the ciliary vessels and nerves, and fuses with the sheath of the optic nerve and with the sclera around the entrance of the optic nerve. In front it blends with the ocular conjunctiva, and with it is attached to the ciliary region of the eyeball. It is perforated by the tendons of the ocular muscles, and is reflected backward on each as a tubular sheath. The sheath of the Obliquus superior is carried as far as the fibrous pulley of that muscle; that on the Obliquus inferior reaches as far as the floor of the orbit, to which it gives off a slip. The sheaths on the Recti are gradually lost in the perimysium, but they give off important expansions. The expansion from the Rectus superior blends with the tendon of the Levator palpebræ; that of the Rectus inferior is attached to the inferior tarsus. The expansions from the sheaths of the Recti medialis and lateralis are strong, especially that from the latter muscle, and are attached to the lacrimal and zygomatic bones respectively. As they probably check the actions of these two Recti they have been named the **medial** and **lateral check ligaments**. Lockwood has described a thickening of the lower part of the fascia bulbi, which he has named the **suspensory ligament of the eye**. It is slung like a hammock below the eyeball, being expanded in the center, and narrow at its extremities which are attached to the zygomatic and lacrimal bones respectively.

The Periorbita forms the periosteum of the orbit. It is loosely connected to the bones and can be readily separated from them. Behind, it is united with the dura mater by processes which pass through the optic foramen and superior orbital fissure, and with the sheath of the optic nerve. In front, it is connected with the periosteum at the margin of the orbit, and sends off a process which assists in forming the **orbital septum**. From it two processes are given off; one to enclose the lacrimal gland, the other to hold the pulley of the Obliquus superior in position.

The **Eyebrows** (*supercilia*) are two arched eminences of integument, which surmount the upper circumference of the orbits, and support numerous short, thick hairs, directed obliquely on the surface. The eyebrows consist of thickened integument, connected beneath with the Orbicularis oculi, Corrugator, and Frontalis muscles.

The **Eyelids** (*palpebræ*) are two thin, movable folds, placed in front of the eye, protecting it from injury by their closure. The upper eyelid is the larger, and the more movable of the two, and is furnished with an elevator muscle, the Levator palpebræ superioris. When the eyelids are open, an elliptical space, the palpebral **fissure** (*rima palpebrarum*), is left between their margins, the angles of which correspond to the junctions of the upper and lower eyelids, and are called the **palpebral commissures** or **canthi**.

The **lateral palpebral commissure** (*commissura palpebrarum lateralis; external canthus*) is more acute than the medial, and the eyelids here lie in close contact with the bulb of the eye: but the **medial palpebral commissure** (*commissura palpebrarum medialis; internal canthus*) is prolonged for a short distance toward the nose, and the two eyelids are separated by a triangular space, the **lacus lacrimalis** (Fig. 882). At the basal angles of the lacus lacrimalis, on the margin of each eyelid, is a small conical elevation, the **lacrimal papilla**, the apex of which is pierced by a small orifice, the **punctum lacrimale**, the commencement of the lacrimal duct.

The **eyelashes** (*cilia*) are attached to the free edges of the eyelids; they are short, thick, curved hairs, arranged in a double or triple row: those of the upper eyelid, more numerous and longer than those of the lower, curve upward; those of the lower eyelid curve downward, so that they do not interlace in closing the lids. Near the attachment of the eyelashes are the openings of a number of glands, the **ciliary glands**, arranged in several rows close to the free margin of the lid; they are regarded as enlarged and modified sudoriferous glands.

Structure of the Eyelids.—The eyelids are composed of the following structures taken in their order from without inward: integument, areolar tissue, fibers of the Orbicularis oculi, tarsus, orbital septum, tarsal glands and conjunctiva. The upper eyelid has, in addition, the aponeurosis of the Levator palpebræ superioris (Fig. 884).

The **integument** is extremely thin, and continuous at the margins of the eyelids with the conjunctiva.

The **subcutaneous areolar tissue** is very lax and delicate, and seldom contains any fat.

The **palpebral fibers of the Orbicularis oculi** are thin, pale in color, and possess an involuntary as well as a voluntary action.

The **tarsi** (*tarsal plates*) (Fig. 884) are two thin, elongated plates of dense connective tissue. about 2.5 cm. in length; one is placed in each eyelid, and contributes to its form and support, The **superior tarsus** (*tarsus superior; superior tarsal plate*), the larger, is of a semilunar form, about 10 mm. in breadth at the center, and gradually narrowing toward its extremities. To the anterior surface of this plate the aponeurosis of the Levator palpebræ superioris is attached The **inferior tarsus** (*tarsus inferior; inferior tarsal plate*), the smaller, is thin, elliptical in form. and has a vertical diameter of about 5 mm. The free or ciliary margins of these plates are thick and straight. The attached or orbital margins are connected to the circumference of the orbit by the orbital septum. The lateral angles are attached to the zygomatic bone by the lateral palpebral raphé. The medial angles of the two plates end at the lacus lacrimalis, and are attached to the frontal process of the maxilla by the medial palpebral ligament (page 355).

The **orbital septum** (*septum orbitale; palpebral ligament*) is a membranous sheet, attached to the edge of the orbit, where it is continuous with the periorbita. In the upper eyelid it blends

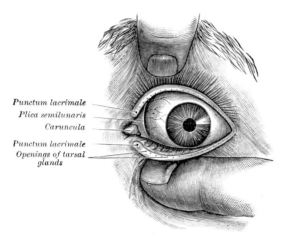

Punctum lacrimale
Plica semilunaris
Caruncula
Punctum lacrimale
Openings of tarsal glands

Fig. 882.—Front of left eye with eyelids separated to show medial canthus.

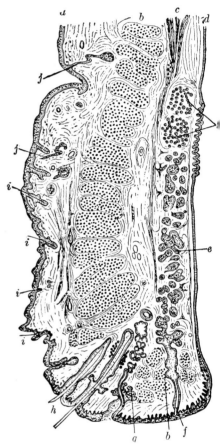

Fig. 883.—Sagittal section through the upper eyelid. (After Waldeyer.) *a.* Skin. *b* Orbicularis oculi. *b′.* Marginal fasciculus of Orbicularis (ciliary bundle). *c.* Levator palpebræ. *d.* Conjunctiva. *e.* Tarsus. *f.* Tarsal gland. *g.* Sebaceous gland. *h.* Eyelashes. *i.* Small hairs of skin. *j,* Sweat glands. *k.* Posterior tarsal glands.

by its peripheral circumference with the tendon of the Levator palpebræ superioris and the superior tarsus, in the lower eyelid with the inferior tarsus. Medially it is thin, and, becoming separated from the medial palpebral ligament, is fixed to the lacrimal bone immediately behind the lacrimal sac. The septum is perforated by the vessels and nerves which pass from the orbital cavity to the face and scalp. The eyelids are richly supplied with blood.

The **Tarsal Glands** (*glandulæ tarsales* [*Meibomi*]; *Meibomian glands*) (Fig. 885). —The tarsal glands are situated upon the inner surfaces of the eyelids, between the tarsi and conjunctiva, and may be distinctly seen through the latter on everting the eyelids, presenting an appearance like parallel strings of pearls. There are about thirty in the upper eyelid, and somewhat fewer in the lower. They are imbedded in grooves in the inner surfaces of the tarsi, and correspond in length with the breadth of these plates; they are, consequently, longer in the upper than in the lower eyelid. Their ducts open on the free magins of the lids by minute foramina.

Structure.—The tarsal glands are modified sebaceous glands, each consisting of a single straight tube or follicle, with numerous small lateral diverticula. The tubes are supported by a basement membrane, and are lined at their mouths by stratified epithelium; the deeper parts of the tubes and the lateral offshoots are lined by a layer of polyhedral cells.

The **conjunctiva** is the mucous membrane of the eye. It lines the inner surfaces of the eyelids or palpebræ, and is reflected over the forepart of the sclera and cornea.

The **Palpebral Portion** (*tunica conjunctiva palpebrarum*) is thick, opaque, highly vascular, and covered with numerous papillæ, its deeper part presenting a considerable amount of lymphoid tissue. At the margins of the lids it becomes continuous with the lining membrane of the ducts of the tarsal glands, and, through the lacrimal ducts, with the lining membrane of the lacrimal sac and nasolacrimal

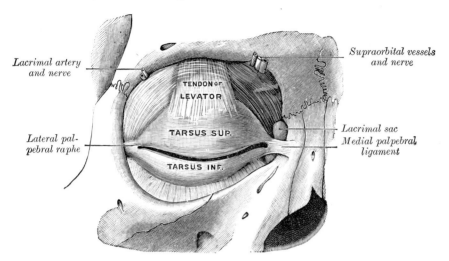

Lacrimal artery and nerve

Supraorbital vessels and nerve

TENDON OF LEVATOR

Lateral palpebral raphe

TARSUS SUP.

TARSUS INF.

Lacrimal sac Medial palpebral ligament

FIG. 884.—The tarsi and their ligaments. Right eye; front view.

duct. At the lateral angle of the upper eyelid the ducts of the lacrimal gland open on its free surface; and at the medial angle it forms a semilunar fold, the **plica semilunaris**. The line of reflection of the conjunctiva from the upper eyelid on to the bulb of the eye is named the **superior fornix**, and that from the lower lid the **inferior fornix**.

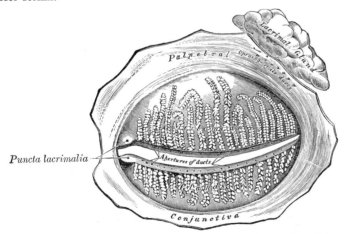

Palpebral Opening of tarsal duct

Lacrimal Gland

Puncta lacrimalia

Apertures of ducts

Conjunctiva

FIG. 885.—The tarsal glands, etc., seen from the inner surface of the eyelids.

The **Bulbar Portion** (*tunica conjunctiva bulbi*).—Upon the *sclera* the conjunctiva is loosely connected to the bulb of the eye; it is thin, transparent, destitute of papillæ, and only slightly vascular. Upon the *cornea*, the conjunctiva consists only of epithelium, constituting the epithelium of the cornea, already described (see page 1038). *Lymphatics* arise in the conjunctiva in a delicate zone around the cornea, and run to the ocular conjunctiva.

67

In and near the fornices, but more plentiful in the upper than in the lower eyelid, a number of convoluted tubular glands open on the surface of the conjunctiva. Other glands, analogous to lymphoid follicles, and called by Henle **trachoma glands,** are found in the conjunctiva, and, according to Strohmeyer, are chiefly situated near the medial palpebral commissure. They were first described by Brush, in his description of Peyer's patches of the small intestine, as "identical structures existing in the under eyelid of the ox."

The **caruncula lacrimalis** is a small, reddish, conical-shaped body, situated at the medial palpebral commissure, and filling up the **lacus lacrimalis.** It consists of a small island of skin containing sebaceous and sudoriferous glands, and is the source of the whitish secretion which constantly collects in this region. A few slender hairs are attached to its surface. Lateral to the caruncula is a slight semilunar fold of conjunctiva, the concavity of which is directed toward the cornea; it is called the **plica semilunaris.** Müller found smooth muscular fibers in this fold; in some of the domesticated animals it contains a thin plate of cartilage.

The nerves in the conjunctiva are numerous and form rich plexuses. According to Krause they terminate in a peculiar form of tactile corpuscle, which he terms "terminal bulbs."

The **Lacrimal Apparatus** (*apparatus lacrimalis*) (Fig. 886) consists of (*a*) the **lacrimal gland,** which secretes the tears, and its excretory ducts, which convey the fluid to the surface of the eye; (*b*) the **lacrimal ducts,** the **lacrimal sac,** and the **naso-lacrimal duct,** by which the fluid is conveyed into the cavity of the nose.

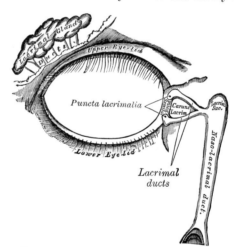

Fig. 886.—The lacrimal apparatus. Right side.

The Lacrimal Gland (*glandula lacrimalis*).—The lacrimal gland is lodged in the lacrimal fossa, on the medial side of the zygomatic process of the frontal bone. It is of an oval form, about the size and shape of an almond, and consists of two portions, described as the superior and inferior lacrimal glands. The **superior lacrimal gland** is connected to the periosteum of the orbit by a few fibrous bands, and rests upon the tendons of the Recti superioris and lateralis, which separate it from the bulb of the eye. The **inferior lacrimal gland** is separated from the superior by a fibrous septum, and projects into the back part of the upper eyelid, where its deep surface is related to the conjunctiva. The ducts of the glands, from six to twelve in number, run obliquely beneath the conjunctiva for a short distance, and open along the upper and lateral half of the superior conjunctival fornix.

Structures of the Lacrimal Gland.—In structure and general appearance the lacrimal resembles the serous salivary glands.

The Lacrimal Ducts (*ductus lacrimalis; lacrimal canals*).—The lacrimal ducts, one in each eyelid, commence at minute orifices, termed **puncta lacrimalia**, on the summits of the **papillæ lacrimales**, seen on the margins of the lids at the lateral

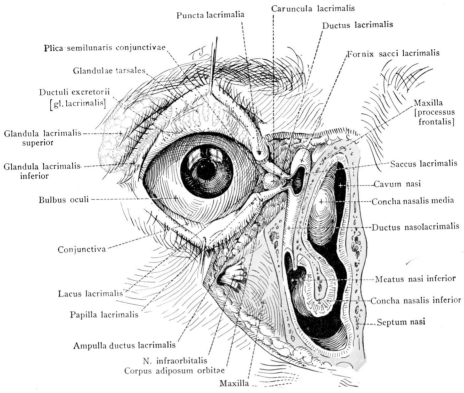

Fig. 887.—Topography of the lacrimal apparatus. The lacrimal and tarsal glands are shown in blue. The nose and a portion of the face have been cut away. Eycleshymer and Jones

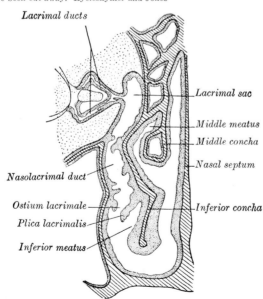

Fig. 888.—Sketch from a frontal section through the right nasal cavity, viewed from the front, to show the relation of the lacrimal passages to the maxillary and ethmoidal sinuses, and the inferior nasal conchæ. The mucous membrane is colored. (After Gerard, 1907).[1]

[1] Whitnall, Anatomy of the Human Orbit, Oxford Medical Publications.

extremity of the lacus lacrimalis. The **superior duct**, the smaller and shorter of the two, at first ascends, and then bends at an acute angle, and passes medialward and downward to the lacrimal sac. The **inferior duct** at first descends, and then runs almost horizontally to the lacrimal sac. At the angles they are dilated into **ampullæ**; their walls are dense in structure and their mucous lining is covered by stratified squamous epithelium, placed on a basement membrane. Outside the latter is a layer of striped muscle, continuous with the lacrimal part of the Orbicularis oculi; at the base of each lacrimal papilla the muscular fibers are circularly arranged and form a kind of sphincter.

The Lacrimal Sac (*saccus lacrimalis*).—The lacrimal sac is the upper dilated end of the nasolacrimal duct, and is lodged in a deep groove formed by the lacrimal bone and frontal process of the maxilla. It is oval in form and measures from 12 to 15 mm. in length; its upper end is closed and rounded; its lower is continued into the nasolacrimal duct. Its superficial surface is covered by a fibrous expansion derived from the medial palpebral ligament, and its deep surface is crossed by the lacrimal part of the Orbicularis oculi (page 355), which is attached to the crest on the lacrimal bone.

Structure.—The lacrimal sac consists of a fibrous elastic coat, lined internally by mucous membrane: the latter is continuous, through the lacrimal ducts, with the conjunctiva, and through the nasolacrimal duct with the mucous membrane of the nasal cavity.

The **Nasolacrimal Duct** (*ductus nasolacrimalis; nasal duct*).—The nasolacrimal duct is a membranous canal, about 18 mm. in length, which extends from the lower part of the lacrimal sac to the inferior meatus of the nose, where it ends by a somewhat expanded orifice, provided with an imperfect valve, the **plica lacrimalis** (*Hasneri*), formed by a fold of the mucous membrane. It is contained in an osseous canal, formed by the maxilla, the lacrimal bone, and the inferior nasal concha; it is narrower in the middle than at either end, and is directed downward, backward, and a little lateralward. The mucous lining of the lacrimal sac and nasolacrimal duct is covered with columnar epithelium, which in places is ciliated.

THE ORGAN OF HEARING (ORGANON AUDITUS; THE EAR).

The ear, or **organ of hearing**, is divisible into three parts: the **external ear**, the **middle ear** or **tympanic cavity**, and the **internal ear** or **labyrinth**.

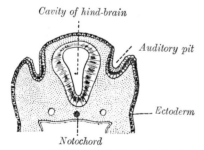

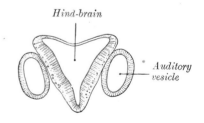

Fig. 889.—Section through the head of a human embryo, about twelve days old, in the region of the hind-brain. (Kollmann.)

Fig. 890.—Section through hind-brain and auditory vesicles of an embryo more advanced than that of Fig. 889. (After His.)

The Development of the Ear.—The first rudiment of the internal ear appears shortly after that of the eye, in the form of a patch of thickened ectoderm, the **auditory plate**, over the region of the hind-brain. The auditory plate becomes depressed and converted into the **auditory pit** (Fig. 889). The mouth of the pit is then closed, and thus a shut sac, the **auditory vesicle**, is formed (Fig. 890); from it the epithelial lining of the membranous labyrinth is derived. The vesicle becomes pear-shaped, and the neck of the flask is obliterated (Fig. 891). From the vesicle certain diverticula are given off which form the various parts of the membranous labyrinth. One from the middle part forms the ductus and saccus endolymphaticus, another from the anterior end gradually elongates, and, forming a tube coiled on itself, becomes the cochlear duct, the vestibular extremity of which is subsequently constricted to form the canalis reuniens. Three others appear as disk-like evaginations on the surface of the vesicle; the central parts of the walls of the disks coalesce and disappear, while the peripheral portions persist to form the semicircular ducts; of these the superior is the first and the lateral the last to be completed (Fig. 893). The central part of the vesicle represents the membranous vestibule, and is subdivided by a constriction into a smaller ventral part, the saccule, and a larger dorsal and posterior part, the utricle. This subdivision is effected by a fold which extends deeply into the proximal part of the ductus endolymphaticus, with the result that the utricle and saccule ultimately communicate with each other by means of a Y-shaped canal. The saccule opens into the cochlear duct, through the canalis reuniens, and the semicircular ducts communcate with the utricle.

The mesodermal tissue surrounding the various parts of the epithelial labyrinth is converted into a cartilaginous ear-capsule, and this is finally ossified to form the bony labyrinth. Between the cartilaginous capsule and the epithelial structures is a stratum of mesodermal tissue which is differentiated into three layers, viz., an outer, forming the periosteal lining of the bony labyrinth; an inner, in direct contact with the epithelial structures; and an intermediate, consisting of gelatinous tissue: by the absorption of this latter tissue the perilymphatic spaces are developed. The modiolus and osseous spiral lamina of the cochlea are not preformed in cartilage but are ossified directly from connective tissue.

The **middle ear** and **auditory tube** are developed from the first pharyngeal pouch. The entodermal lining of the dorsal end of this pouch is in contact with the ectoderm of the corresponding pharyngeal groove; by the extension of the mesoderm between these two layers the tympanic membrane is formed. During the sixth or seventh month the tympanic antrum appears as an upward and backward expansion of the tympanic cavity. With regard to the exact mode of development of the ossicles of the middle ear there is some difference of opinion. The view generally held is that the **malleus** is developed from the proximal end of the mandibular (Meckel's) cartilage (Fig. 41), the **incus** in the proximal end of the mandibular arch, and that the **stapes** is formed from the proximal end of the hyoid arch. The malleus, with the exception of its anterior process is ossified from a single center which appears near the neck of the bone; the anterior process is ossified separately in membrane and joins the main part of the bone about the sixth month of fetal life. The incus is ossified from one center which appears in the upper part of its long crus and ultimately extends into its lenticular process. The stapes first appears as a ring (*annulus stapedius*) encircling a small vessel, the stapedial artery, which subsequently undergoes atrophy; it is ossified from a single center which appears in its base.

The **external acoustic meatus** is developed from the first branchial groove. The lower part of this groove extends inward as a funnel-shaped tube (primary meatus) from which the cartilaginous portion and a small part of the roof of the osseous portion of the meatus are developed. From the lower part of the funnel-shaped tube an epithelial lamina extends downward and inward along the inferior wall of the primitive tympanic cavity; by the splitting of this lamina the inner part of the meatus (secondary meatus) is produced, while the inner portion of the lamina forms the cutaneous stratum of the tympanic membrane. The **auricula** or **pinna** is developed by the gradual differentiation of tubercles which appear around the margin of the first branchial groove. The rudiment of the **acoustic nerve** appears

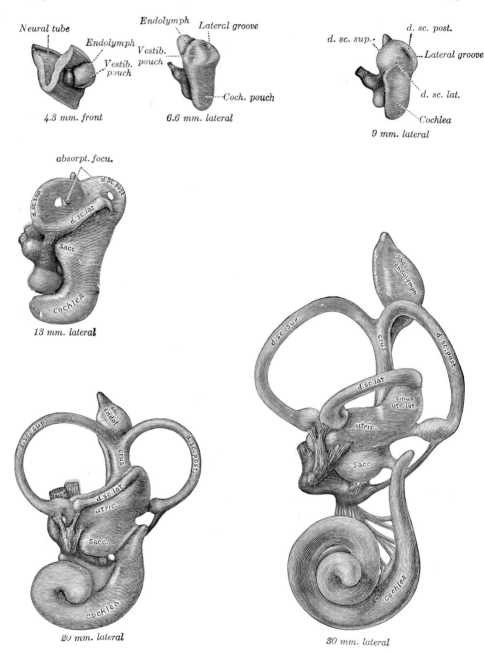

Fig. 891.—Lateral views of membranous labyrinth and acoustic complex. × 25 dia. (Streeter.) *absorpt. focu,* area of wall where absorption is complete; *amp.,* ampulla membranacea; *crus,* crus commune; *d. sc. lat.,* ductus semicircularis laleralis; *d. sc. post.,* ductus semicircularis posterior; *d. sc. sup.,* ductus semicircular superior; *coch. or cochlea,* ductus cochltaris; *duct. endolymph,* ductus endolymphaticus; *d. reuniens,* ductus reuniens Henseni: *endol. or endolymphs* sppendix enedolymphaticus; *rec. utr.,* recessus utriculi; *sacc.,* sacculus; *sac. endol.,* saccus endolymphaticus; *sinus utr. lat.* sinus utriculi lateralis; *utric.,* utriculus; *vestib. p.,* vestibular pouch.

about the end of the third week as a group of ganglion cells closely applied to the cephalic edge of the auditory vesicle. Whether these cells are derived from the ectoderm adjoining the auditory vesicle, or have migrated from the wall of the neural tube, is as yet uncertain. The ganglion gradually splits into two parts, the **vestibular ganglion** and the **spiral ganglion**. The peripheral branches of the

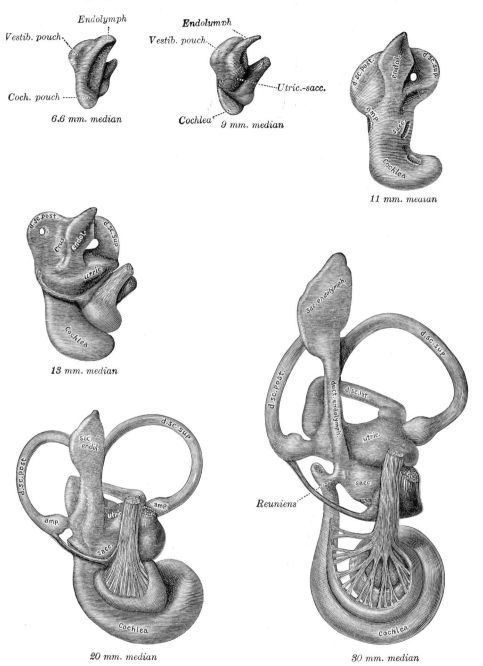

FIG. 892.—Median views of membranous labyrinth and acoustic complex in human embryos. × 25 dia. (Streeter)

vestibular ganglion pass in two divisions, the pars superior giving rami to the superior ampulla of the superior semicircular duct, to the lateral ampulla and to the utricle; and the pars inferior giving rami to the saccule and the posterior ampulla. The proximal fibers of the vestibular ganglion form the vestibular nerve; the proximal fibers of the spiral ganglion form the cochlear nerve.

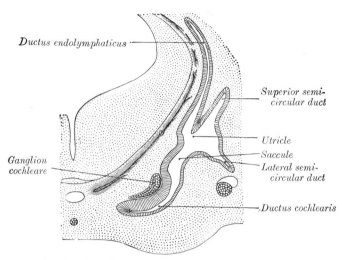

FIG. 893.—Transverse section through head of fetal sheep, in the region of the labyrinth. × 30. (After Boettcher.)

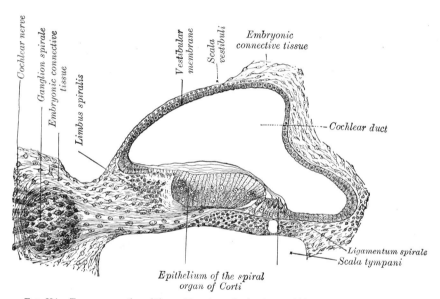

FIG. 894.—Transverse section of the cochlear duct of a fetal cat. (After Boettcher and Ayres.)

The External Ear.

The **external ear** consists of the expanded portion named the **auricula** or **pinna**, and the **external acoustic meatus**. The former projects from the side of the head and serves to collect the vibrations of the air by which sound is produced; the latter leads inward from the bottom of the auricula and conducts the vibrations to the tympanic cavity.

The **Auricula** or **Pinna** (Fig. 895) is of an ovoid form, with its larger end directed upward. Its lateral surface is irregularly concave, directed slightly forward, and presents numerous eminences and depressions to which names have been assigned.

The prominent rim of the auricula is called the **helix**; where the helix turns downward behind, a small tubercle, the **auricular tubercle of Darwin**, is frequently seen; this tubercle is very evident about the sixth month of fetal life when the whole auricula has a close resemblance to that of some of the adult monkeys. Another

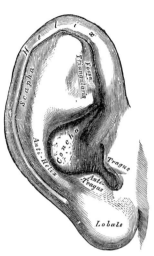

FIG. 895.—The auricula. Lateral surface.

curved prominence, parallel with and in front of the helix, is called the **antihelix**; this divides above into two crura, between which is a triangular depression, the **fossa triangularis**. The narrow curved depression between the helix and the antihelix is called the **scapha**; the antihelix describes a curve around a deep, capacious cavity, the **concha**, which is partially divided into two parts by the **crus** or commencement of the helix; the upper part is termed the **cymba conchæ**, the lower part the **cavum conchæ**. In front of the concha, and projecting backward over the meatus, is a small pointed eminence, the **tragus**, so called from its being generally covered on its under surface with a tuft of hair, resembling a goat's beard. Opposite the tragus, and separated from it by the **intertragic notch**, is a small tubercle, the **antitragus**. Below this is the **lobule**, composed of tough areolar and adipose tissues, and wanting the firmness and elasticity of the rest of the auricula.

The cranial surface of the auricula presents elevations which correspond to the depressions on its lateral surface and after which they are named, *e. g.*, **eminentia conchæ, eminentia triangularis**, etc.

Structure.—The auricula is composed of a thin plate of yellow fibrocartilage, covered with integument, and connected to the surrounding parts by ligaments and muscles; and to the commencement of the external acoustic meatus by fibrous tissue.

The **skin** is thin, closely adherent to the cartilage, and covered with fine hairs furnished with sebaceous glands, which are most numerous in the concha and scaphoid fossa. On the tragus and antitragus the hairs are strong and numerous. The skin of the auricula is continuous with that lining the external acoustic meatus.

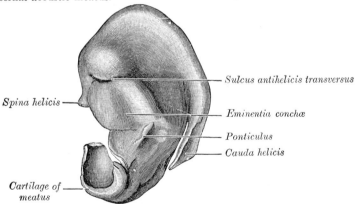

FIG. 896.—Cranial surface of cartilage of right auricula.

The **cartilage of the auricula** (*cartilage auriculæ; cartilage of the pinna*) (Figs. 896, 897) consists of a single piece; it gives form to this part of the ear, and upon its surface are found the eminences and depressions above described. It is absent from the lobule; it is deficient, also, between the tragus and beginning of the helix, the gap being filled up by dense fibrous tissue. At the front part of the auricula, where the helix bends upward, is a small projection of cartilage, called the *spina helicis*, while in the lower part of the helix the cartilage is prolonged downward as a tail-like process, the **cauda helicis**; this is separated from the antihelix by a fissure, the fissura antitragohelicina. The cranial aspect of the cartilage exhibits a transverse furrow, the sulcus antihelicis transversus, which corresponds with the inferior crus of the antihelix and separates the eminentia conchæ from the eminentia triangularis. The eminentia conchæ is crossed by a vertical ridge (*ponticulus*), which gives attachment to the Auricularis posterior muscle. In the cartilage of the auricula are two fissures, one behind the crus helicis and another in the tragus

The ligaments of the auricula (*ligamenti auricularia* [*Valsalva*]; *ligaments of the pinna*) consist of two sets: (1) extrinsic, connecting it to the side of the head; (2) intrinsic, connecting various parts of its cartilage together.

The extrinsic ligaments are two in number, anterior and posterior. The *anterior ligament* extends from the tragus and spina helicis to the root of the zygomatic process of the temporal bone. The *posterior ligament* passes from the posterior surface of the concha to the outer surface of the mastoid process.

The chief intrinsic ligaments are: (*a*) a strong fibrous band, stretching from the tragus to the commencement of the helix, completing the meatus in front, and partly encircling the boundary of the concha; and (*b*) a band between the antihelix and the cauda helicis. Other less important bands are found on the cranial surface of the pinna.

The muscles of the auricula (Fig. 897) consist of two sets: (1) the extrinsic, which connect it with the skull and scalp and move the auricula as a whole; and (2) the intrinsic, which extend from one part of the auricle to another.

The extrinsic muscles are the Auriculares anterior, superior, and posterior.

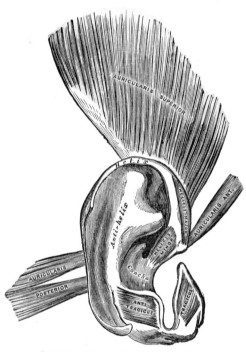

The *Auricularis anterior* (*Attrahens aurem*), the smallest of the three, is thin, fan-shaped, and its fibers are pale and indistinct. It *arises* from the lateral edge of the galea aponeurotica, and its fibers converge to be inserted into a projection on the front of the helix.

The *Auricularis superior* (*Attolens aurem*), the largest of the three, is thin and fan-shaped. Its fibers *arise* from the galea aponeurotica, and converge to be inserted by a thin, flattened tendon into the upper part of the cranial surface of the auricula.

The *Auricularis posterior* (*Retrahens aurem*) consists of two or three fleshy fasciculi, which *arise* from the mastoid portion of the temporal bone by short aponeurotic fibers. They are inserted into the lower part of the cranial surface of the concha.

Actions.—In man, these muscles possess very little action: the Auricularis anterior draws the auricula forward and upward; the Auricularis superior slightly raises it; and the Auricularis posterior draws it backward.

The *intrinsic* muscles are the:

Fig. 897.—The muscles of the auricula.

Helicis major.	Antitragicus.
Helicis minor.	Transversus auriculæ.
Tragicus.	Obliquus auriculæ.

The *Helicis major* is a narrow vertical band situated upon the anterior margin of the helix. It *arises* below, from the spina helicis, and is inserted into the anterior border of the helix, just where it is about to curve backward.

The *Helicis minor* is an oblique fasciculus, covering the crus helicis.

The *Tragicus* is a short, flattened vertical band on the lateral surface of the tragus.

The *Antitragicus arises* from the outer part of the antitragus, and is inserted into the cauda helicis and antihelix.

The *Transversus auriculæ* is placed on the cranial surface of the pinna. It consists of scattered fibers, partly tendinous and partly muscular, extending from the eminentia conchæ to the prominence corresponding with the scapha.

The *Obliquus auriculæ*, also on the cranial surface, consists of a few fibers extending from the upper and back part of the concha to the convexity immediately above it.

Nerves.—The Auriculares anterior and superior and the intrinsic muscles on the lateral surface are supplied by the temporal branch of the facial nerve, the Auricularis posterior and the intrinsic muscles on the cranial surface by the posterior auricular branch of the same nerve.

The **arteries of the auricula** are the posterior auricular from the external carotid, the anterior auricular from the superficial temporal, and a branch from the occipital artery.

The **veins** accompany the corresponding arteries.

Thr **sensory nerves** are: the great auricular, from the cervical plexus; the auricular branch of the vagus; the auriculotemporal branch of the mandibular nerve; and the lesser occipital from the cervical plexus.

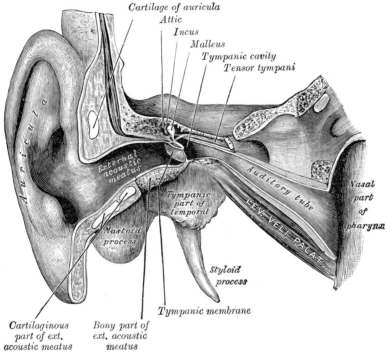

FIG. 898.—External and middle ear, opened from the front.   Right side.

The **External Acoustic Meatus** (*meatus acusticus externus; external auditory canal or meatus*) extends from the bottom of the concha to the tympanic membrane (Figs. 898, 899). It is about 4 cm. in length if measured from the tragus; from the bottom of the concha its length is about 2.5 cm. It forms an S-shaped curve, and is directed at first inward, forward, and slightly upward (*pars externa*); it then passes inward and backward (*pars media*), and lastly is carried inward, forward, and slightly downward (*pars interna*). It is an oval cylindrical canal, the greatest diameter being directed downward and backward at the external orifice, but nearly horizontally at the inner end. It presents two constrictions, one near the inner end of the cartilaginous portion, and another, the **isthmus**, in the osseous portion, about 2 cm. from the bottom of the concha. The tympanic membrane, which closes the inner end of the meatus, is obliquely directed; in consequence of this the floor and anterior wall of the meatus are longer than the roof and posterior wall.

The external acoustic meatus is formed partly by cartilage and membrane, and partly by bone, and is lined by skin.

The **cartilaginous portion** (*meatus acusticus externus cartilagineus*) is about 8 mm. in length; it is continuous with the cartilage of the auricula, and firmly attached to the circumference of the auditory process of the temporal bone. The cartilage is deficient at the upper and back part of the meatus, its place being supplied by fibrous membrane; two or three deep fissures are present in the anterior part of the cartilage.

The **osseous portion** (*meatus acusticus externus osseus*) is about 16 mm. in length, and is narrower than the cartilaginous portion. It is directed inward and a little forward, forming in its course a slight curve the convexity of which is upward and backward. Its inner end is smaller than the outer, and sloped, the anterior wall projecting beyond the posterior for about 4 mm.; it is marked, except at its upper part, by a narrow groove, the **tympanic sulcus**, in which the circumference of the tympanic membrane is attached. Its outer end is dilated and rough in the greater part of its circumference, for the attachment of the cartilage of the auricula. The front and lower parts of the osseous portion are formed by a curved plate of bone, the tympanic part of the temporal, which, in the fetus, exists as a separate ring (**annulus tympanicus**,) incomplete at its upper part (page 151).

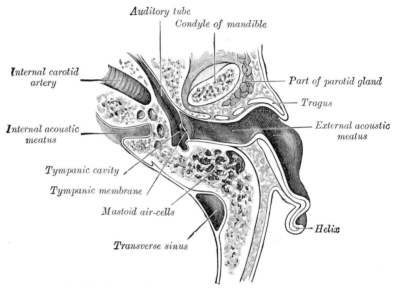

FIG. 899.—Horizontal section through left ear; upper half of section.

The **skin** lining the meatus is very thin; adheres closely to the cartilaginous and osseous portions of the tube, and covers the outer surface of the tympanic membrane. After maceration, the thin pouch of epidermis, when withdrawn, preserves the form of the meatus. In the thick subcutaneous tissue of the cartilaginous part of the meatus are numerous ceruminous glands, which secrete the ear-wax; their structure resembles that of the sudoriferous glands.

Relations of the Meatus.—In front of the osseous part is the condyle of the mandible, which however, is frequently separated from the cartilaginous part by a portion of the parotid gland. The movements of the jaw influence to some extent the lumen of this latter portion. Behind the osseous part are the mastoid air cells, separated from the meatus by a thin layer of bone.

The **arteries** supplying the meatus are branches from the posterior auricular, internal maxillary, and temporal.

The **nerves** are chiefly derived from the auriculotemporal branch of the mandibular nerve and the auricular branch of the vagus.

The Middle Ear or Tympanic Cavity (Cavum Tympani; Drum; Tympanum).

The **middle ear or tympanic cavity** is an irregular, laterally compressed space within the temporal bone. It is filled with air, which is conveyed to it from the nasal part of the pharynx through the auditory tube. It contains a chain of movable bones, which connect its lateral to its medial wall, and serve to convey the vibrations communicated to the tympanic membrane across the cavity to the internal ear.

The tympanic cavity consists of two parts: the **tympanic cavity proper**, opposite the tympanic membrane, and the **attic** or **epitympanic recess**, above the level of the membrane; the latter contains the upper half of the malleus and the greater part of the incus. Including the attic, the vertical and antero-posterior diameters of the cavity are each about 15 mm. The transverse diameter measures about 6 mm. above and 4 mm. below; opposite the center of the tympanic membrane it is only about 2 mm. The tympanic cavity is bounded laterally by the tympanic membrane; medially, by the lateral wall of the internal ear; it communicates, behind, with the tympanic antrum and through it with the mastoid air cells, and in front with the auditory tube (Fig. 898).

The **Tegmental Wall** or **Roof** (*paries tegmentalis*) is formed by a thin plate of bone, the **tegmen tympani**, which separates the cranial and tympanic cavities. It is situated on the anterior surface of the petrous portion of the temporal bone close to its angle of junction with the squama temporalis; it is prolonged backward so as to roof in the tympanic antrum, and forward to cover in the semicanal for the Tensor tympani muscle. Its lateral edge corresponds with the remains of the petrosquamous suture.

The **Jugular Wall** or **Floor** (*paries jugularis*) is narrow, and consists of a thin plate of bone (**fundus tympani**) which separates the tympanic cavity from the jugular fossa. It presents, near the labyrinthic wall, a small aperture for the passage of the tympanic branch of the glossopharyngeal nerve.

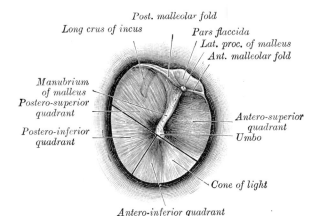

Fig. 900.—Right tympanic membrane as seen through a speculum.

The **Membranous** or **Lateral Wall** (*paries membranacea; outer wall*) is formed mainly by the tympanic membrane, partly by the ring of bone into which this membrane is inserted. This ring of bone is incomplete at its upper part, forming a notch (**notch of Rivinus**), close to which are three small apertures: the **iter chordæ posterius**, the **petrotympanic fissure**, and the **iter chordæ anterius**.

The **iter chordæ posterius** (*apertura tympanica canaliculi chordæ*) is situated in the angle of junction between the mastoid and membranous wall of the tympanic cavity immediately behind the tympanic membrane and on a level with the upper end of the manubrium of the malleus; it leads into a minute canal, which descends in front of the canal for the facial nerve, and ends in that canal near the stylomastoid foramen. Through it the chorda tympani nerve enters the tympanic cavity.

The **petrotympanic fissure** (*fissura petrotympanica; Glaserian fissure*) opens just above and in front of the ring of bone into which the tympanic membrane is inserted; in this situation it is a mere slit about 2 mm. in length. It lodges the anterior process and anterior ligament of the malleus, and gives passage to the anterior tympanic branch of the internal maxillary artery.

The **iter chordæ anterius** (*canal of Huguier*) is placed at the medial end of the petrotympanic fissure; through it the chorda tympani nerve leaves the tympanic cavity.

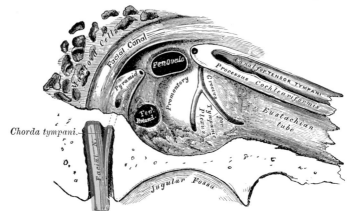

FIG. 901.—View of the inner wall of the tympanum (enlarged.)

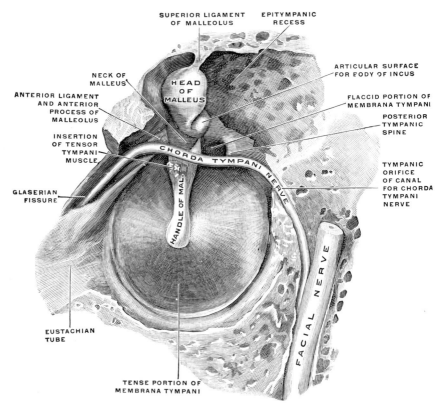

FIG. 902.—The right membrana tympani with the hammer and the chorda tympani, viewed from within, from behind and from above. (Spalteholz.)

The **Tympanic Membrane** (*membrana tympani*) (Figs. 900, 902) separates the tympanic cavity from the bottom of the external acoustic meatus. It is a thin, semitransparent membrane, nearly oval in form, somewhat broader above than below, and directed very obliquely downward and inward so as to form an angle of about fifty-five degrees with the floor of the meatus. Its longest diameter is downward and forward, and measures from 9 to 10 mm.; its shortest diameter measures from 8 to 9 mm. The greater part of its circumference is thickened, and forms a **fibrocartilaginous ring** which is fixed in the **tympanic sulcus** at the inner end of the meatus. This sulcus is deficient superiorly at the notch of Rivinus, and from the ends of this notch two bands, the **anterior** and **posterior malleolar folds**, are prolonged to the lateral process of the malleus. The small, somewhat triangular part of the membrane situated above these folds is lax and thin, and is named the **pars flaccida**; in it a small orifice is sometimes seen. The manubrium of the malleus is firmly attached to the medial surface of the membrane as far as its center, which it draws toward the tympanic cavity; the lateral surface of the membrane is thus concave, and the most depressed part of this concavity is named the **umbo**.

Structure.—The tympanic membrane is composed of three strata: a **lateral** (*cutaneous*), an **intermediate** (*fibrous*), and a **medial** (*mucous*). The **cutaneous stratum** is derived from the integument lining the meatus. The **fibrous stratum** consists of two layers: a radiate stratum, the fibers of which diverge from the manubrium of the malleus, and a circular stratum, the fibers of which are plentiful around the circumference but sparse and scattered near the center of the membrane. Branched or dendritic fibers, as pointed out by Grüber, are also present, especially in the posterior half of the membrane.

Vessels and Nerves.—The **arteries** of the tympanic membrane are derived from the deep auricular branch of the internal maxillary, which ramifies beneath the cutaneous stratum; and from the stylomastoid branch of the posterior auricular, and tympanic branch of the internal maxillary, which are distributed on the mucous surface. The superficial **veins** open into the external jugular; those on the deep surface drain partly into the transverse sinus and veins of the dura mater, and partly into a plexus on the auditory tube. The membrane receives its chief **nerve supply** from the auriculotemporal branch of the mandibular; the auricular branch of the vagus, and the tympanic branch of the glossopharyngeal also supply it.[1]

The **Labyrinthic** or **Medial Wall** (*paries labyrinthica; inner wall*) (Fig. 903) is vertical in direction, and presents for examination the **fenestræ vestibuli** and **cochleæ**, the **promontory**, and the **prominence of the facial canal**.

The **fenestra vestibuli** (*fenestra ovalis*) is a reniform opening leading from the tympanic cavity into the vestibule of the internal ear; its long diameter is horizontal, and its convex border is upward. In the recent state it is occupied by the base of the stapes, the circumference of which is fixed by the annular ligament to the margin of the foramen.

The **fenestra cochleæ** (*fenestra rotunda*) is situated below and a little behind the fenestra vestibuli, from which it is separated by a rounded elevation, the **promontory**. It is placed at the bottom of a funnel-shaped depression and, in the macerated bone, leads into the cochlea of the internal ear; in the fresh state it is closed by a membrane, the **secondary tympanic membrane**, which is concave toward the tympanic cavity, convex toward the cochlea. This membrane consists of three layers: an external, or mucous, derived from the mucous lining of the tympanic cavity; an internal, from the lining membrane of the cochlea; and an intermediate, or fibrous layer.

The **promontory** (*promontorium*) is a rounded hollow prominence, formed by the projection outward of the first turn of the cochlea; it is placed between the fenestræ, and is furrowed on its surface by small grooves, for the lodgment of branches of the tympanic plexus. A minute spicule of bone frequently connects the promontory to the pyramidal eminence.

The **prominence of the facial canal** (*prominentia canalis facialis; prominence of aqueduct of Fallopius*) indicates the position of the bony canal in which the facial nerve is contained; this canal traverses the labyrinthic wall of the tympanic cavity above the fenestra vestibuli, and behind that opening curves nearly vertically downward along the mastoid wall.

The **Mastoid** or **Posterior Wall** (*paries mastoidea*) is wider above than below, and

---

[1]Wilson, J. G., American Journal of Anatomy, 1911, vol. **11**.

presents for examination the **entrance to the tympanic antrum,** the **pyramidal eminence,** and the **fossa incudis.**

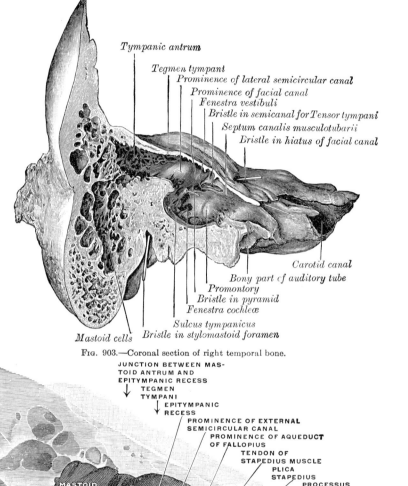

Fig. 903.—Coronal section of right temporal bone.

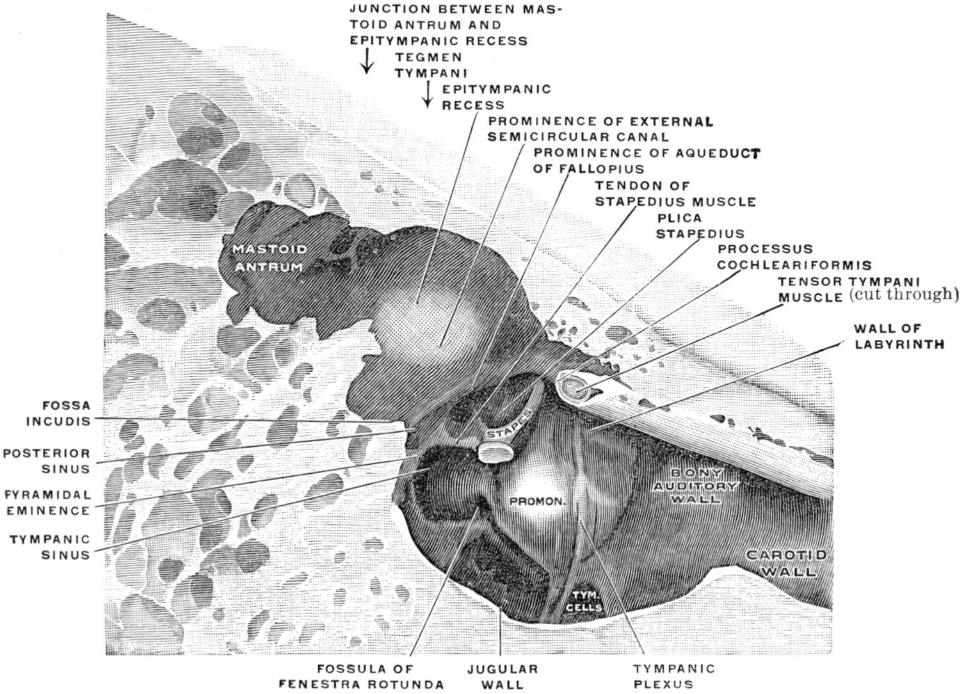

Fig. 904.—The medial wall and part of the posterior and anterior walls of the right tympanic cavity, lateral view. (Spalteholz.)

The **entrance to the antrum** is a large irregular aperture, which leads backward from the epitympanic recess into a considerable air space, named the **tympanic** or **mastoid antrum** (see page 147). The antrum communicates behind and below with the **mastoid air cells**, which vary considerably in number, size, and form; the antrum and mastoid air cells are lined by mucous membrane, continuous with that lining the tympanic cavity. On the medial wall of the entrance to the antrum is a rounded eminence, situated above and behind the prominence of the facial canal; it corresponds with the position of the ampullated ends of the superior and lateral semicircular canals.

The **pyramidal eminence** (*eminentia pyramidalis; pyramid*) is situated immediately behind the fenestra vestibuli, and in front of the vertical portion of the facial canal; it is hollow, and contains the Stapedius muscle; its summit projects forward toward the fenestra vestibuli, and is pierced by a small aperture which transmits the tendon of the muscle. The cavity in the pyramidal eminence is prolonged downward and backward in front of the facial canal, and communicates with is by a minute aperture which transmits a twig from the facial nerve to the Stapedius muscle.

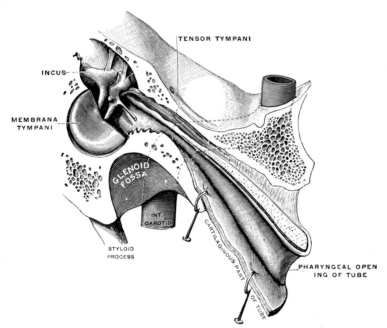

FIG. 905.—Auditory tube, laid open by a cut in its long axis. (Testut.)

The **fossa incudis** is a small depression in the lower and back part of the epitympanic recess; it lodges the short crus of the incus.

The **Carotid** or **Anterior Wall** (*paries carotica*) is wider above than below; it corresponds with the carotid canal, from which it is separated by a thin plate of bone perforated by the tympanic branch of the internal carotid artery, and by the deep petrosal nerve which connects the sympathetic plexus on the internal carotid artery with the tympanic plexus on the promontory. At the upper part of the anterior wall are the orifice of the semicanal for the Tensor tympani muscle and the tympanic orifice of the auditory tube, separated from each other by a thin horizontal plate of bone, the **septum canalis musculotubarii**. These canals run from the tympanic cavity forward and downward to the retiring angle between the squama and the petrous portion of the temporal bone.

The **semicanal for the Tensor tympani** (*semicanalis m. tensoris tympani*) is the superior and the smaller of the two; it is cylindrical and lies beneath the tegmen tympani. It extends on to the labyrinthic wall of the tympanic cavity and ends immediately above the fenestra vestibuli.

The **septum canalis musculotubarii** (*processus cochleariformis*) passes backward below this semicanal, forming its lateral wall and floor; it expands above the anterior end of the fenestra vestibuli and terminates there by curving laterally so as to form a pulley over which the tendon of the muscle passes.

The **Auditory Tube** (*tuba auditiva; Eustachian tube*) is the channel through which the tympanic cavity communicates with the nasal part of the pharynx. Its length is about 36 mm., and its direction is downward, forward, and medialward, forming an angle of about 45 degrees with the sagittal plane and one of from 30 to 40 degrees with the horizontal plane. It is formed partly of bone, partly of cartilage and fibrous tissue (Figs. 898, 905).

The **osseous portion** (*pars osseo tubæ auditivæ*) is about 12 mm. in length. It begins in the carotid wall of the tympanic cavity, below the septum canalis musculotubarii, and, gradually narrowing, ends at the angle of junction of the squama and the petrous portion of the temporal bone, its extremity presenting a jagged margin which serves for the attachment of the cartilaginous portion.

The **cartilaginous portion** (*pars cartilaginea tubæ auditivæ*), about 24 mm. in length, is formed of a triangular plate of elastic fibrocartilage, the apex of which is attached to the margin of the medial end of the osseous portion of the tube, while its base lies directly under the mucous membrane of the nasal part of the pharynx, where it forms an elevation, the **torus tubarius** or **cushion**, behind the pharyngeal orifice of the tube. The upper edge of the cartilage is curled upon itself, being bent laterally so as to present on transverse section the appearance of a hook; a groove or furrow is thus produced, which is open below and laterally, and this part of the canal is completed by fibrous membrane. The cartilage lies in a groove between the petrous part of the temporal and the great wing of the sphenoid; this groove ends opposite the middle of the medial pterygoid plate. The cartilaginous and bony portions of the tube are not in the same plane, the former inclining downward a little more than the latter. The diameter of the tube is not uniform throughout, being greatest at the pharyngeal orifice, least at the junction of the bony and cartilaginous portions, and again increased toward the tympanic cavity; the narrowest part of the tube is termed the **isthmus**. The position and relations of the pharyngeal orifice are described with the nasal part of the pharynx. The mucous membrane of the tube is continuous in front with that of the nasal part of the pharynx, and behind with that of the tympanic cavity; it is covered with ciliated epithelium and is thin in the osseous portion, while in the cartilaginous portion it contains many mucous glands and near the pharyngeal orifice a considerable amount of adenoid tissue, which has been named by Gerlach the **tube tonsil**. The tube is opened during deglutition by the Salpingopharyngeus and Dilatator tubæ. The latter arises from the hook of the cartilage and from the membranous part of the tube, and blends below with the Tensor veli palatini.

The Auditory Ossicles (Ossicula Auditus).

The tympanic cavity contains a chain of three movable ossicles, the **malleus**, **incus**, and **stapes**. The first is attached to the tympanic membrane, the last to the circumference of the fenestra vestibuli, the incus being placed between and connected to both by delicate articulations.

The **Malleus** (Fig. 906), so named from its fancied resemblance to a hammer, consists of a **head**, **neck**, and three processes, viz., the **manubrium**, the **anterior** and **lateral processes**.

The **head** (*capitulum mallei*) is the large upper extremity of the bone; it is oval in shape, and articulates posteriorly with the incus, being free in the rest of its extent. The facet for articulation with the incus is constricted near the middle, and consists of an upper larger and lower smaller part, which form nearly a right angle with each other. Opposite the constriction the lower margin of the facet projects in the form of a process, the **cog-tooth** or **spur of the malleus.**

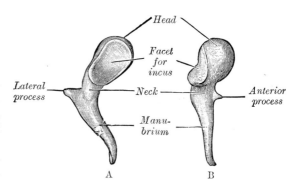

FIG. 906.—Left malleus. *A.* From behind. *B.* From within.

The **neck** (*collum mallei*) is the narrow contracted part just beneath the head; below it, is a a prominence, to which the various processes are attached.

The **manubrium mallei** (*handle*) is connected by its lateral margin with the tympanic membrane. It is directed downward, medialward, and backward; it decreases in size toward its free end, which is curved slightly forward, and flattened transversely. On its medial side, near its upper end, is a slight projection, into which the tendon of the Tensor tympani is inserted.

The **anterior process** (*processus anterior [Folii]; processus gracilis*) is a delicate spicule, which springs from the eminence below the neck and is directed forward to the petrotympanic fissure, to which it is connected by ligamentous fibers. In the fetus this is the longest process of the malleus, and is in direct continuity with the cartilage of Meckel.

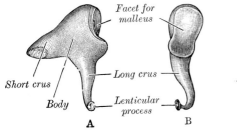

FIG. 907.—Left incus. *A.* From within. *B.* From the front.

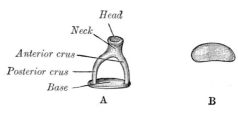

FIG. 908.—*A.* Left stapes. *B.* Base of stapes, medial surface.

The **lateral process** (*processus lateralis; processus brevis*) is a slight conical projection, which springs from the root of the manubrium; it is directed laterally, and is attached to the upper part of the tympanic membrane and, by means of the anterior and posterior malleolar folds, to the extremities of the notch of Rivinus.

The **Incus** (Fig. 907) has received its name from its supposed resemblance to an anvil, but it is more like a premolar tooth, with two roots, which differ in length, and are widely separated from each other. It consists of a **body** and **two crura.**

The **body** (*corpus incudis*) is somewhat cubical but compressed transversely. On its anterior surface is a deeply concavo-convex facet, which articulates with the head of the malleus.

The two crura diverge from one another nearly at right angles.

The **short crus** (*crus breve; short process*), somewhat conical in shape, projects almost horizontally backward, and is attached to the **fossa incudis**, in the lower and back part of the epitympanic recess.

The **long crus** (*crus longum; long process*) descends nearly vertically behind and parallel to the manubrium of the malleus, and, bending medialward, ends in a rounded projection, the **lenticular process**, which is tipped with cartilage, and articulates with the head of the stapes.

The **Stapes** (Fig. 908), so called from its resemblance to a stirrup, consists of a **head, neck, two crura,** and a **base.**

The **head** (*capitulum stapedis*) presents a depression, which is covered by cartilage, and articulates with the lenticular process of the incus.

The **neck**, the constricted part of the bone succeeding the head, gives insertion to the tendon of the Stapedius muscle.

The **two crura** (*crus anterius and crus posterius*) diverge from the neck and are connected at their ends by a flattened oval plate, the **base** (*basis stapedis*), which forms the foot-plate of the stirrup and is fixed to the margin of the fenestra vestibuli by a ring of ligamentous fibers. Of the two crura the anterior is shorter and less curved than the posterior.

Articulations of the Auditory Ossicles (*articulationes ossiculorum auditus*).— The incudomalleolar joint is a saddle-shaped diarthrosis; it is surrounded by an articular capsule, and the joint cavity is incompletely divided into two by a wedge-shaped articular disk or meniscus. The incudostapedial joint is an enarthrosis, surrounded by an articular capsule; some observers have described an articular disk or meniscus in this joint; others regard the joint as a syndesmosis.

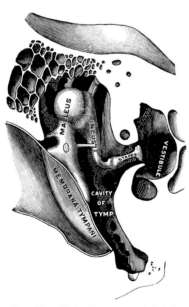

Ligaments of the Ossicles (*ligamenta ossiculorum auditus*).—The ossicles are connected with the walls of the tympanic cavity by ligaments: three for the malleus, and one each for the incus and stapes.

The **anterior ligament of the malleus** (*lig. mallei anterius*) is attached by one end to the neck of the malleus, just above the anterior process, and by the other to the anterior wall of the tympanic cavity, close to the petrotympanic fissure, some of its fibers being prolonged through the fissure to reach the spina angularis of the sphenoid.

The **superior ligament of the malleus** (*lig. mallei superius*) is a delicate, round bundle which descends from the roof of the epitympanic recess to the head of the malleus.

The **lateral ligament of the malleus** (*lig. mallei laterale; external ligament of the malleus*) is a triangular band passing from the posterior part of the notch of Rivinus to the head of the malleus. Helmholtz described the anterior ligament and the posterior part of the lateral ligament as forming together the **axis ligament** around which the malleus rotates.

The **posterior ligament of the incus** (*lig. incudis posterius*) is a short, thick band connecting the end of the short crus of the incus to the fossa incudis.

A **superior ligament of the incus** (*lig. incudis superius*) has been described, but it is little more than a fold of mucous membrane.

The vestibular surface and the circumference of the base of the stapes are covered with hyaline cartilage; that encircling the base is attached to the margin of the fenestra vestibuli by a fibrous ring, the **annular ligament of the base of the stapes** (*lig. annulare baseos stapedis*).

The **Muscles of the Tympanic Cavity** (*musculi ossiculorum auditus*) are the Tensor tympani and Stapedius.

The **Tensor tympani**, the larger, is contained in the bony canal above the osseous portion of the auditory tube, from which it is separated by the septum canalis musculotubarii. It *arises* from the cartilaginous portion of the auditory tube and the adjoining part of the great wing of the sphenoid, as well as from the osseous canal in which it is contained. Passing backward through the canal, it ends in a slender tendon which enters the tympanic cavity, makes a sharp bend around the extremity of the septum, and is inserted into the manubrium of the malleus, near its root. It is supplied by a branch of the mandibular nerve through the otic ganglion.

The **Stapedius** *arises* from the wall of a conical cavity, hollowed out of the interior of the pyramidal eminence; its tendon emerges from the orifice at the apex of the eminence, and, passing forward, is inserted into the posterior surface of the neck of the stapes. It is supplied by a branch of the facial nerve.

Actions.—The Tensor tympani draws the tympanic membrane medialward, and thus increases its tension. The Stapedius pulls the head of the stapes backward and thus causes the base of the bone to rotate on a vertical axis drawn through its own center; the back part of the base is pressed inward toward the vestibule, while the forepart is withdrawn from it. By the action of the muscle the tension of the fluid within the internal ear is probably increased.

The **Mucous Membrane of the Tympanic Cavity** is continuous with that of the pharynx, through the auditory tube. It invests the auditory ossicles, and the muscles and nerves contained in the tympanic cavity; forms the medial layer of the tympanic membrane, and the lateral layer of the secondary tympanic membrane, and is reflected into the tympanic antrum and mastoid cells, which it lines throughout. It forms several vascular folds, which extend from the walls of the tympanic cavity to the ossicles; of these, one descends from the roof of the cavity to the head of the malleus and upper margin of the body of the incus, a second invests the Stapedius muscle: other folds invest the chorda tympani nerve and the Tensor tympani muscle. These folds separate off pouch-like cavities, and give the interior of the tympanum a somewhat honey-combed appearance. One of these pouches, the **pouch of Prussak**, is well-marked and lies between the neck of the malleus and the membrana flaccida. Two other recesses may be mentioned: they are formed by the mucous membrane which envelops the chorda tympani nerve and are situated, one in front of, and the other behind the manubrium of the malleus; they are named the **anterior** and **posterior recesses of Troltsch.** In the tympanic cavity this membrane is pale, thin, slightly vascular, and covered for the most part with columnar ciliated epithelium, but over the pyramidal eminence, ossicles, and tympanic membrane it possesses a flattened non-ciliated epithelium. In the tympanic antrum and mastoid cells its epithelium is also non-ciliated. In the osseous portion of the auditory tube the membrane is thin; but in the cartilaginous portion it is very thick, highly vascular, and provided with numerous mucous glands; the epithelium which lines the tube is columnar and ciliated.

Vessels and Nerves.—The **arteries** are six in number. Two of them are larger than the others, viz., the tympanic branch of the internal maxillary, which supplies the tympanic membrane; and the stylomastoid branch of the posterior auricular, which supplies the back part of the tympanic cavity and mastoid cells. The smaller arteries are—the petrosal branch of the middle meningeal, which enters through the hiatus of the facial canal; a branch from the ascending pharyngeal, and another from the artery of the pterygoid canal, which accompany the auditory tube; and the tympanic branch from the internal carotid, given off in the carotid canal and perforating the thin anterior wall of the tympanic cavity. The **veins** terminate in the pterygoid plexus and the superior petrosal sinus. The **nerves** constitute the tympanic plexus, which ramifies upon the surface of the promontory. The plexus is formed by (1) the tympanic branch of the glossopharyngeal; (2) the caroticotympanic nerves; (3) the smaller superficial petrosal nerve; and (4) a branch which joins the greater superficial petrosal.

The **tympanic branch of the glossopharyngeal** (*Jacobson's nerve*) enters the tympanic cavity by an aperture in its floor close to the labyrinthic wall, and divides into branches which ramify on the promontory and enter into the formation of the tympanic plexus. The **superior and inferior caroticotympanic nerves** from the carotid plexus of the sympathetic pass through the wall of the carotid canal, and join the branches of the tympanic branch of the glossopharyngeal. The branch to the greater superficial petrosal passes through an opening on the labyrinthic wall, in front of the fenestra vestibuli. The **smaller superficial petrosal nerve,** from the otic ganglion, passes backward through a foramen in the middle fossa of the base of the skull (sometimes through the foramen ovale), and enters the anterior surface of the petrous part of the temporal bone through a small aperture, situated lateral to the hiatus of the facial canal; it courses downward through the bone, past the genicular ganglion of the facial nerve, receiving a connecting filament from it, and enters the tympanic cavity, where it communicates with the tympanic branch of the glossopharyngeal, and assists in forming the tympanic plexus.

The **branches of distribution** of the tympanic plexus are supplied to the mucous membrane of the tympanic cavity; a branch passes to the fenestra vestibuli, another to the fenestra cochleæ, and a third to the auditory tube. The smaller superficial petrosal may be looked upon as the continuation of the tympanic branch of the glossopharyngeal through the plexus to the otic ganglion.

In addition to the tympanic plexus there are the nerves supplying the muscles. The Tensor tympani is supplied by a branch from the mandibular through the otic ganglion, and the Stapedius by a branch from the facial.

The **chorda tympani nerve** crosses the tympanic cavity. It is given off from the sensory part of the facial, about 6 mm. before the nerve emerges from the stylomastoid foramen. It runs from below upward and forward in a canal, and enters the tympanic cavity through the iter chordæ posterius, and becomes invested with mucous membrane. It traverses the tympanic cavity, crossing medial to the tympanic membrane and over the upper part of the manubrium of the malleus to the carotid wall, where it emerges through the iter chordæ anterius (*canal of Huguier*).

The Internal Ear or Labyrinth (Auris Interna).

The **internal ear** is the essential part of the organ of hearing, receiving the ultimate distribution of the auditory nerve. It is called the **labyrinth**, from the complexity of its shape, and consists of two parts: the **osseous labyrinth**, a series of cavities within the petrous part of the temporal bone, and the **membranous labyrinth**, a series of communicating membranous sacs and ducts, contained within the bony cavities.

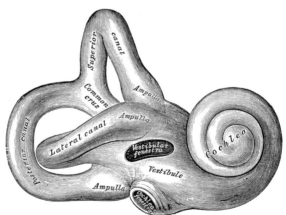

Fig. 910.—Right osseous labyrinth. Lateral view.

The **Osseous Labyrinth** (*labyrinthus osseus*) (Figs. 910, 911).—The osseous labyrinth consists of three parts: the **vestibule, semicircular canals, and cochlea.** These are cavities hollowed out of the substance of the bone, and lined by periosteum; they contain a clear fluid, the **perilymph,** in which the membranous labyrinth is situated.

The **Vestibule** (*vestibulum*).—The vestibule is the central part of the osseous labyrinth, and is situated medial to the tympanic cavity, behind the cochlea, and in front of the semicircular canals. It is somewhat ovoid in shape, but flattened transversely; it measures about 5 mm. from before backward, the same from above downward, and about 3 mm. across. In its *lateral* or *tympanic wall* is the **fenestra vestibuli,** closed, in the fresh state, by the base of the stapes and annular ligament. On its *medial wall*, at the forepart, is a small circular depression, the **recessus** sphæricus, which is perforated, at its anterior and inferior part, by several minute holes (**macula cribrosa media**) for the passage of filaments of the acoustic nerve to the saccule; and behind this depression is an oblique ridge, the **crista vestibuli,** the anterior end of which is named the **pyramid of the vestibule.** This ridge bifurcates below to enclose a small depression, the **fossa cochlearis,** which is perforated by a number of holes for the passage of filaments of the acoustic nerve which supply the vestibular end of the ductus cochlearis. At the hinder part of the medial wall is the orifice of the **aquæductus vestibuli,** which extends to the posterior surface of the petrous portion of the temporal bone. It transmits a small vein, and contains a tubular prolongation of the membranous labyrinth, the **ductus endolymphaticus,** which ends in a cul-de-sac between the layers of the dura mater within the cranial cavity. On the *upper wall* or *roof* is a transversely oval depression, the **recessus ellipticus,** separated from the recessus sphæricus by the crista vestibuli already mentioned. The pyramid and adjoining part of the recessus ellipticus are perforated by a number of holes (**macula cribrosa superior**). The apertures in the pyramid transmit the nerves to the utricle; those in the recessus ellipticus the nerves to the ampullæ of the superior and lateral semicircular ducts. *Behind* are the five orifices of the semicircular canals. In *front* is an elliptical opening, which communicates with the scala vestibuli of the cochlea.

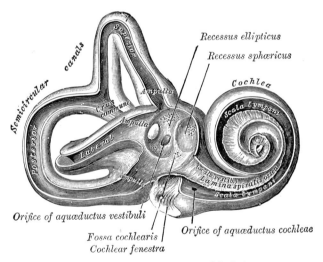

Fig. 911.—Interior of right osseous labyrinth.

The Bony Semicircular Canals (*canales semicirculares ossei*).—The bony semicircular canals are three in number, **superior, posterior,** and **lateral,** and are situated above and behind the vestibule. They are unequal in length, compressed from side to side, and each describes the greater part of a circle. Each measures about 0.8 mm. in diameter, and presents a dilatation at one end, called the **ampulla,** which measures more than twice the diameter of the tube. They open into the vestibule by five orifices, one of the apertures being common to two of the canals.

The **superior semicircular canal** (*canalis semicircularis superior*), 15 to 20 mm. in length, is vertical in direction, and is placed transversely to the long axis of the petrous portion of the temporal bone, on the anterior surface of which its arch forms a round projection. It describes about two-thirds of a circle. Its lateral extremity is ampullated, and opens into the upper part of the vestibule; the opposite end joins with the upper part of the posterior canal to form the **crus commune,** which opens into the upper and medial part of the vestibule.

The **posterior semicircular canal** (*canalis semicircularis posterior*), also vertical, is directed backward, nearly parallel to the posterior surface of the petrous bone; it is the longest of the three, measuring from 18 to 22 mm.; its lower or ampullated end opens into the lower and back part of the vestibule, its upper into the crus commune already mentioned.

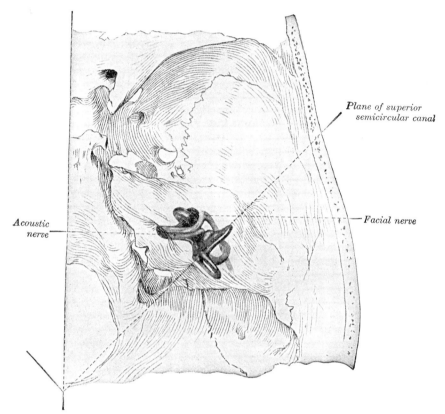

Plane of superior semicircular canal

Acoustic nerve

Facial nerve

FIG. 912.—Position of the right bony labyrinth of the ear in the skull, viewed from above. The temporal bone is considered transparent and the labyrinth drawn in from a corrosion preparation. (Spalteholz.)

The **lateral** or **horizontal canal** (*canalis semicircularis lateralis; external semicircular canal*) is the shortest of the three. It measures from 12 to 15 mm., and its arch is directed horizontally backward and lateralward; thus each semicircular canal stands at right angles to the other two. Its ampullated end corresponds to the upper and lateral angle of the vestibule, just above the fenestra vestibuli, where it opens close to the ampullated end of the superior canal; its opposite end opens at the upper and back part of the vestibule. The lateral canal of one ear is very nearly in the same plane as that of the other; while the superior canal of one ear is nearly parallel to the posterior canal of the other.

The **Cochlea** (Figs. 910, 911).—The cochlea bears some resemblance to a common snail-shell; it forms the anterior part of the labyrinth, is conical in form, and placed almost horizontally in front of the vestibule; its **apex** (*cupula*) is directed forward and lateralward, with a slight inclination downward, toward the upper and front part of the labyrinthic wall of the tympanic cavity; its **base** corresponds with the bottom of the internal acoustic meatus, and is perforated by numerous apertures for the passage of the cochlear division of the acoustic nerve. It measures about 5 mm. from base to apex, and its breadth across the base is about 9 mm. It consists of a conical shaped central axis, the **modiolus**; of a canal, the inner wall of which is formed by the central axis, wound spirally around it for two turns and three-quarters, from the base to the apex; and of a delicate lamina, the **osseous spiral lamina,** which projects from the modiolus, and, following the windings of the canal, partially subdivides it into two. In the recent state a membrane, the **basilar membrane,** stretches from the free border of this lamina to the outer wall of the bony cochlea and completely separates the canal into two passages, which, however, communicate with each other at the apex of the modiolus by a small opening, named the **helicotrema.**

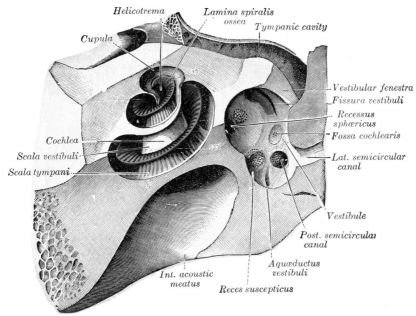

Fig. 913.—The cochlea and vestibule, viewed from above. All the hard parts which form the roof of the internal ear have been removed with the saw.

The **modiolus** is the conical central axis or pillar of the cochlea. Its base is broad, and appears at the bottom of the internal acoustic meatus, where it corresponds with the area cochleæ; it is perforated by numerous orifices, which transmit filaments of the cochlear division of the acoustic nerve; the nerves for the first turn and a half pass through the foramina of the tractus spiralis foraminosus; those for the apical turn, through the foramen centrale. The canals of the tractus spiralis foraminosus pass up through the modiolus and successively bend outward to reach the attached margin of the lamina spiralis ossea. Here they become enlarged, and by their apposition form the **spiral canal of the modiolus,** which follows the course of the attached margin of the osseous spiral lamina and lodges the **spiral ganglion** (*ganglion of Corti*). The foramen centrale is continued into a canal which runs up the middle of the modiolus to its apex. The modiolus diminishes rapidly in size in the second and succeeding coil.

The bony canal of the cochlea takes two turns and three-quarters around the modiolus. It is about 30 mm. in length, and diminishes gradually in diameter from the base to the summit, where it terminates in the **cupula,** which forms the apex of the cochlea. The beginning of this canal is about 3 mm. in diameter; it diverges from the modiolus toward the tympanic cavity and vestibule, and presents three openings. One, the **fenestra cochleæ,** communicates with the tympanic cavity—in the fresh state this aperture is closed by the **secondary tympanic** membrane; another, of an elliptical form, opens into the vestibule. The third is the aperture of the aquæductus cochleæ, leading to a minute funnel-shaped canal, which opens on the inferior surface of the petrous part of the temporal bone and transmits a small vein, and also forms a communication between the subarachnoid cavity and the scala tympani.

The **osseous spiral lamina** (*lamina spiralis ossea*) is a bony shelf or ledge which projects from the modiolus into the interior of the canal, and, like the canal, takes two- and three-quarter turns around the modiolus. It reaches about half-way toward the outer wall of the tube, and partially divides its cavity into two passages or scalæ, of which the upper is named the **scala vestibuli**, while the lower is termed the **scala tympani**. Near the summit of the cochlea the lamina ends in a hook-shaped process, the **hamulus laminæ spiralis**; this assists in forming the boundary of a small opening, the **helicotrema**, through which the two scalæ communicate with each other. From the spiral canal of the modiolus numerous canals pass outward through the osseous spiral lamina as far as its free edge. In the lower part of the first turn a second bony lamina, the **secondary spiral lamina**, projects inward from the outer wall of the bony tube; it does not, however, reach the primary osseous spiral lamina, so that if viewed from the vestibule a narrow fissure, the **vestibule fissure**, is seen between them.

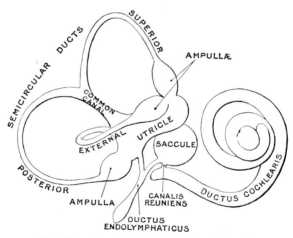

Fig. 914.—The membranous labyrinth.   (Enlarged.)

The *osseous labyrinth* is lined by an exceedingly thin fibro-serous membrane; its attached surface is rough and fibrous, and closely adherent to the bone; its free surface is smooth and pale, covered with a layer of epithelium, and secretes a thin, limpid fluid, the **perilymph**. A delicate tubular process of this membrane is prolonged along the aqueduct of the cochlea to the inner surface of the dura mater.

The **Membranous Labyrinth** (*labyrinthus membranaceus*) (Figs. 914, 915, 916).—The membranous labyrinth is lodged within the bony cavities just described, and has the same general form as these; it is, however, considerably smaller, and is partly separated from the bony walls by a quantity of fluid, the **perilymph**. In certain places it is fixed to the walls of the cavity. The membranous labyrinth contains fluid, the **endolymph**, and on its walls the ramifications of the acoustic nerve are distributed.

Within the osseous vestibule the membranous labyrinth does not quite preserve the form of the bony cavity, but consists of two membranous sacs, the **utricle**, and the **saccule**.

The Utricle (*utriculus*).—The utricle, the larger of the two, is of an oblong form, compressed transversely, and occupies the upper and back part of the vestibule, lying in contact with the recessus ellipticus and the part below it. That portion which is lodged in the recess forms a sort of pouch or cul-de-sac, the floor and anterior wall of which are thickened, and form the **macula acustica utriculi**, which receives the utricular filaments of the acoustic nerve. The cavity of the utricle communicates behind with the semicircular ducts by five orifices. From its anterior wall is given off the **ductus utriculosaccularis**, which opens into the ductus endolymphaticus.

The Saccule (*sacculus*).—The saccule is the smaller of the two vestibular sacs; it is globular in form, and lies in the recessus sphæricus near the opening of the scala vestibuli of the cochlea. Its anterior part exhibits an oval thickening, the **macula acustica sacculi**, to which are distributed the saccular filaments of the acoustic nerve. Its cavity does not directly communicate with that of the utricle. From the posterior wall a canal, the **ductus endolymphaticus**, is given off; this duct is joined by the ductus utriculosaccularis, and then passes along the aquæductus vestibuli and ends in a blind pouch (**saccus endolymphaticus**) on the posterior surface of the petrous portion of the temporal bone, where it is in contact with the dura mater. From the lower part of the saccule a short tube, the **canalis reuniens of Hensen**, passes downward and opens into the ductus cochlearis near its vestibular extremity (Fig. 914).

The Semicircular Ducts (*ductus semicirculares; membranous semicircular canals*), (Figs. 915, 916).—The semicircular ducts are about one-fourth of the diameter of the osseous canals, but in number, shape, and general form they are precisely similar, and each presents at one end an ampulla. They open by five orifices into the utricle, one opening being common to the medial end of the superior and the upper end of the posterior duct. In the ampullæ the wall is thickened, and projects into the cavity as a fiddle-shaped, transversely placed elevation, the **septum transversum**, in which the nerves end.

The utricle, saccule, and semicircular ducts are held in position by numerous fibrous bands which stretch across the space between them and the bony walls.

Structure (Fig. 917).—The walls of the utricle, saccule, and semicircular ducts consist of three layers. The *outer layer* is a loose and flocculent structure, apparently composed of ordinary fibrous tissue containing bloodvessels and some pigment-cells. The *middle layer*, thicker and more transparent, forms a homogeneous membrana propria, and presents on its internal surface, especially in the semicircular ducts, numerous papilliform projections, which, on the addition of acetic acid, exhibit an appearance of longitudinal fibrillation. The *inner layer* is formed of polygonal nucleated epithelial cells. In the maculæ of the utricle and saccule, and in the transverse septa of the ampullæ of the semicircular ducts, the middle coat is thickened and the epithelium is columnar, and consists of **supporting cells** and **hair cells**. The former are fusiform, and their deep ends are attached to the membrana propria, while their free extremities are united to form a thin cuticle. The hair cells are flask-shaped, and their deep, rounded ends do not reach the membrana propria, but lie between the supporting cells. The deep part of each contains a large nucleus, while its more superficial part is granular and pigmented. The free end is surmounted by a long, tapering, hair-like filament, which projects into the cavity. The filaments of the acoustic nerve enter these parts, and having pierced the outer and middle layers, they lose their medullary sheaths, and their axis-cylinders ramify between the hair cells.

Two small rounded bodies termed **otoconia**, each consisting of a mass of minute crystalline grains of carbonate of lime, held together in a mesh of gelatinous tissue, are suspended in the endolymph in contact with the free ends of the hairs projecting from the maculæ. According to Bowman, a calcareous material is also sparingly scattered in the cells lining the ampullæ of the semicircular ducts.

The Ductus Cochlearis (*membranous cochlea; scala media*).—The ductus cochlearis consists of a spirally arranged tube enclosed in the bony canal of the cochlea and lying along its outer wall.

As already stated, the osseous spiral lamina extends only part of the distance between the modiolus and the outer wall of the cochlea, while the **basilar membrane**

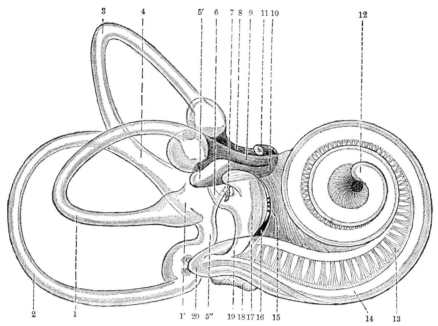

Fig. 915.—Right human membranous labyrinth, removed from its bony enclosure and viewed from the antero-lateral aspect. (G. Retzius.)

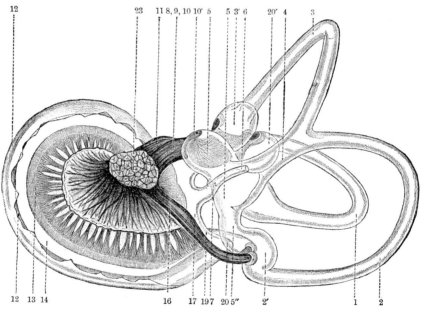

Fig. 916.—The same from the postero-medial aspect. 1. Lateral semicircular canal; 1′, its ampulla; 2. Posterior canal; 2′, its ampulla. 3. Superior canal; 3′, its ampulla. 4. Conjoined limb of superior and posterior canals (*sinus utriculi superior*). 5. Utricle. 5′. Recessus utriculi. 5″. Sinus utriculi posterior. 6. Ductus endolymphaticus. 7. Canalis utriculosaccularis. 8. Nerve to ampulla of superior canal. 9. Nerve to ampulla of lateral canal 10. Nerve to recessus utriculi (in Fig. 915, the three branches appear conjoined). 10′. Ending of nerve in recessus utriculi. 11. Facial nerve. 12. Lagena cochleæ. 13. Nerve of cochlea within spiral lamina. 14. Basilar membrane. 15. Nerve fibers to macula of saccule. 16. Nerve to ampulla of posterior canal. 17. Saccule. 18. Secondary membrane of tympanum. 19. Canalis reuniens. 20. Vestibular end of ductus cochlearis. 23. Section of the facial and acoustic nerves within internal acoustic meatus the separation between them is not apparent in the section). (G. Retzius.)

stretches from its free edge to the outer wall of the cochlea, and completes the roof of the scala tympani. A second and more delicate membrane, the **vestibular membrane** (*Reissneri*) extends from the thickened periosteum covering the osseous spiral lamina to the outer wall of the cochlea, where it is attached at some little distance above the outer edge of the basilar membrane. A canal is thus shut off between the scala tympani below and the scala vestibuli above; this is the **ductus cochlearis or scala media** (Fig. 918). It is triangular on transverse section, its roof being formed by the vestibular membrane, its outer wall by the periosteum lining the bony canal, and its floor by the membrana basilaris and the outer part of the lamina spiralis ossea. Its extremities are closed; the upper is termed the **lagena** and is attached to the cupula at the upper part of the helicotrema; the lower is lodged in the recessus cochlearis of the vestibule. Near the lower end the ductus cochlearis is brought into continuity with the saccule by a narrow, short canal, the **canalis reuniens of Hensen** (Fig. 914). On the membrana basilaris is situated

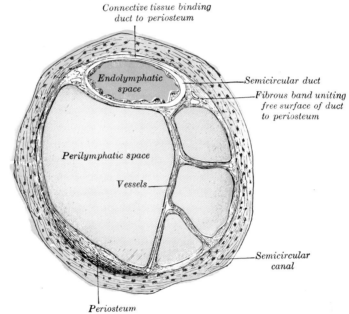

FIG. 917.—Transverse section of a human semicircular canal and duct (after Rüdinger).

the spiral organ of Corti. The vestibular membrane is thin and homogeneous, and is covered on its upper and under surfaces by a layer of epithelium. The periosteum, forming the outer wall of the ductus cochlearis, is greatly thickened and altered in character, and is called the **spiral ligament**. It projects inward below as a triangular prominence, the **basilar crest**, which gives attachment to the outer edge of the basilar membrane; immediately above the crest is a concavity, the **sulcus spiralis externus.** The upper portion of the spiral ligament contains numerous capillary loops and small bloodvessels, and is termed the **stria vascularis.**

The osseous spiral lamina consists of two plates of bone, and between these are the canals for the transmission of the filaments of the acoustic nerve. On the upper plate of that part of the lamina which is outside the vestibular membrane, the periosteum is thickened to form the **limbus laminæ spiralis** (Fig. 919), this ends externally in a concavity, the **sulcus spiralis internus**, which represents, on section, the form of the letter C; the upper part, formed by the overhanging extremity of the limbus, is named the **vestibular lip;** the lower part, prolonged and tapering, is called the **tympanic lip,** and is perforated by numerous foramina for the passage of the cochlear nerves. The upper surface of the vestibular lip is intersected at right angles by a number of furrows, between which are numerous elevations; these present the appearance of teeth along the free surface and margin of the lip, and have been

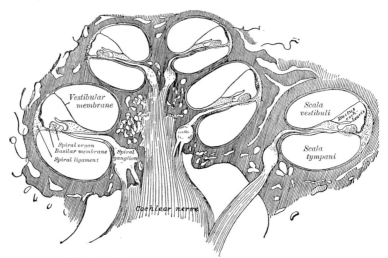

Fig. 918.—Diagrammatic longitudinal section of the cochlea.

named by Huschke the **auditory teeth** (Fig. 920). The limbus is covered by a layer of what appears to be squamous epithelium, but the deeper parts of the cells with their contained nuclei occupy the intervals between the elevations and between the auditory teeth. This layer of epithelium is continuous on the one hand with that lining the sulcus spiralis internus, and on the other with that covering the under surface of the vestibular membrane.

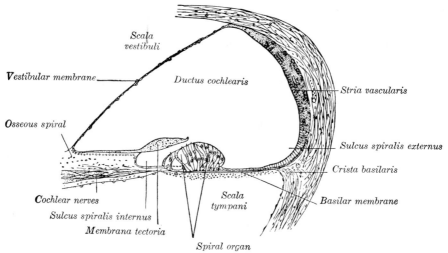

Fig. 919.—A transverse section through the middle coil of the ductus cochlearis. (Retzius).

Basilar Membrane.—The basilar membrane stretches from the tympanic lip of the osseous spiral lamina to the basilar crest and consists of two parts, an inner and an outer. The inner is thin, and is named the **zona arcuata:** it supports the spiral organ of Corti. The outer is thicker and striated, and is termed the **zona pectinata**. The under surface of the membrane is covered by a layer of vascular connective tissue; one of the vessels in this tissue is somewhat larger than the rest, and is named the **vas spirale**; it lies below Corti's tunnel.

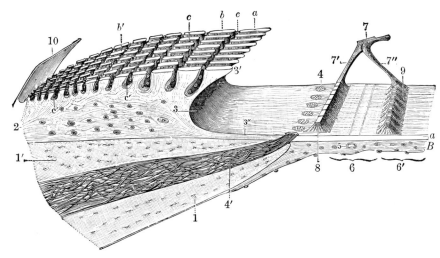

FIG. 920.—Limbus laminæ spiralis and membrana basilaris. (Schematic.) **1, 1′.** Upper and lower lamellæ of the lamina spiralis ossea. **2.** Limbus laminæ spiralis, with *a*, the teeth of the first row; *b*, *b′*, the auditory teeth of the other rows; *c*, *c′*, the interdental grooves and the cells which are lodged in them. **3.** Sulcus spiralis internus, with 3′, its labium vestibulare, and 3″, its labium tympanicum. **4.** Foramina nervosa, giving passage to the nerves from the ganglion spirale or ganglion of Corti. **5.** Vas spirale. **6.** Zona arcuata, and 6′, zona pectinata of the basilar membrane, with *a*, its hyaline layer, *B*, its connective-tissue layer. **7.** Arch of spiral organ, with 7′, its inner rod, and 7″, its outer rod. **8.** Feet of the internal rods, from which the cells are removed. **9.** Feet of the external rods. **10.** Vestibular membrane, at its origin. (Testut.)

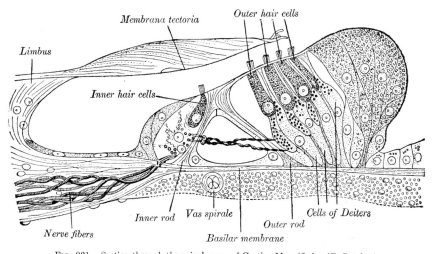

FIG. 921.—Section through the spiral organ of Corti. Magnified. (G. Retzius.)

The **spiral organ of Corti** (*organon spirale [Corti]; organ of Corti*) (Figs. 921, 922) is composed of a series of epithelial structures placed upon the inner part of the basilar membrane. The average length is 31.5 mm. The more central of these structures are two rows of rod-like bodies, the **inner and outer rods** or **pillars of Corti.** The bases of the rods are supported on the basilar membrane, those of the inner row at some distance from those of the outer; the two rows incline toward each other and, coming into contact above, enclose between them and the basilar membrane a triangular tunnel, the **tunnel of Corti.** On the inner side of the inner rods is a single row of hair cells, and on the outer side of the outer rods three or four rows of similar cells, together with certain supporting cells termed the cells of Deiters and Hensen. The free ends of the outer hair cells occupy a series of apertures in a net-like membrane, the **reticular membrane,** and the entire organ is covered by the tectorial membrane.

Rods of Corti.—Each of these consists of a base or foot-plate, and elongated part or body, and an upper end or head; the body of each rod is finely striated, but in the head there is an oval non-striated portion which stains deeply with carmine. Occupying the angles between the rods and the basilar membrane are nucleated cells which partly envelop the rods and extend on to the floor of Corti's tunnel; these may be looked upon as the undifferentiated parts of the cells from which the rods have been formed.

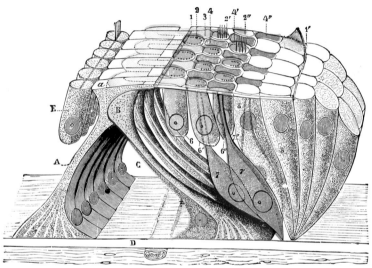

Fig. 922.—The lamina reticularis and subjacent structures. (Schematic.) *A.* Internal rod of Corti, with *a,* its plate. *B.* External rod (in yellow). *C* Tunnel of Corti. *D.* Membrana basilaris. *E.* Inner hair cells. 1, 1′. Internal and external borders of the membrana reticularis. 2, 2′, 2″. The three rows of circular holes (in blue). 3. First row of phalanges (in yellow). 4, 4′, 4″. Second, third, and fourth rows of phalanges (in red). 6, 6′, 6″. The three rows of outer hair cells (in blue). 7, 7′, 7″. Cells of Deiters. 8. Cells of Hensen and Claudius. (Testut.)

The **inner rods** number nearly 6000, and their bases rest on the basilar membrane close to the tympanic lip of the sulcus spiralis internus. The shaft or body of each is sinuously curved and forms an angle of about 60 degrees with the basilar membrane. The head resembles the proximal end of the ulna and presents a deep concavity which accommodates a convexity on the head of the outer rod. The head-plate, or portion overhanging the concavity, overlaps the head-plate of the outer rod.

The **outer rods,** nearly 4000 in number, are longer and more obliquely set than the inner, forming with the basilar membrane an angle of about 40 degrees. Their heads are convex internally; they fit into the concavities on the heads of the inner rods and are continued outward as thin flattened plates, termed **phalangeal processes,** which unite with the phalangeal processes of Deiters' cells to form the reticular membrane.

Hair Cells.—The hair cells are short columnar cells; their free ends are on a level with the heads of Corti's rods, and each is surmounted by about twenty hair-like processes arranged in the form of a crescent with its concavity directed inward. The deep ends of the cells reach about half-way along Corti's rods, and each contains a large nucleus; in contact with the deep ends of the hair cells are the terminal filaments of the cochlear division of the acoustic nerve. The *inner* hair cells, about 3500 in number, are arranged in a single row on the medial side of the inner rods, and their diameters being greater than those of the rods it follows that each hair cell is supported by more than one rod. The free ends of the inner hair cells are encircled by a cuticular membrane which is fixed to the heads of the inner rods. Adjoining the inner hair cells are one or two rows of columnar supporting cells, which, in turn, are continuous with the cubical cells lining the sulcus spiralis internus The *outer* hair cells number about 12,000, and are nearly twice as long as the inner. In the basal coil of the cochlea they are arranged in three regular rows; in the apical coil, in four, somewhat irregular, rows. The studies of Crowe, Guild and Polvogt show that the receptors for high tones are located in the basal turn of the cochlea.

Between the rows of the outer hair cells are rows of supporting cells, called the **cells of Deiters;** their expanded bases are planted on the basilar membrane, while the opposite end of each presents a clubbed extremity or **phalangeal process.** Immediately to the outer side of Deiters' cells are five or six rows of columnar cells, the **supporting cells of Hensen.** Their bases are narrow, while their upper parts are expanded and form a rounded elevation on the floor of the ductus cochlearis. The columnar cells lying outside Hensen's cells are termed the **cells of Claudius.** A space exists between the outer rods of Corti and the adjacent hair cells; this is called the **space of Nuel.**

The **reticular lamina** (Fig. 921) is a delicate frame-work perforated by rounded holes which are occupied by the free ends of the outer hair cells. It extends from the heads of the outer rods of Corti to the external row of the outer hair cells, and is formed by several rows of "minute fiddle-shaped cuticular structures," called **phalanges,** between which are circular apertures containing the free ends of the hair cells. The inner most row of phalanges consists of the phalangeal processes of the outer rods of Corti; the outer rows are formed by the modified free ends of Deiters' cells.

Covering the sulcus spiralis internus and the spiral organ of Corti is the **tectorial membrane,** which is attached to the limbus laminæ spiralis close to the inner edge of the vestibular membrane. Its inner part is thin and overlies the auditory teeth of Huschke; its outer part is thick, and along its lower surface, opposite the inner hair cells, is a clear band, named **Hensen's stripe,** due to the intercrossing of its fibers. The lateral margin of the membrane is much thinner. Hardesty considers the tectorial membrane as the vibrating mechanism in the cochlea. It is inconceivably delicate and flexible; far more sensitively flexible in the transverse than in the longitudinal direction and the readiness with which it bends when touched is beyond description. It is ectodermal in origin. It consists of fine colorless fibers embedded in a transparent matrix (the matrix may be a variety of soft keratin), of a soft collagenous, semisolid character with marked adhesiveness. The general transverse direction of the fibers inclines from the radius of the cochlea toward the apex.

The **acoustic nerve** (*n. acusticus; auditory nerve or nerve of hearing*) divides near the bottom of the internal acoustic meatus into an anterior or cochlear and a posterior or vestibular branch.

The **vestibular nerve** (*n. vestibularis*) supplies the utricle, the saccule, and the ampullæ of the semicircular ducts. On the trunk of the nerve, within the internal acoustic meatus, is a ganglion, the **vestibular ganglion** (*ganglion of Scarpa*); the fibers of the nerve arise from the cells of this ganglion. On the distal side of the ganglion the nerve splits into a superior, an inferior, and a posterior branch. The filaments of the *superior branch* are transmitted through the foramina in the area vestibularis superior, and end in the macula of the utricle and in the ampullæ of the superior and lateral semicircular ducts; those of the *inferior branch* traverse the foramina in the area vestibularis inferior, and end in the macula of the saccule.

The *posterior branch* runs through the foramen singulare at the postero-inferior part of the bottom of the meatus and divides into filaments for the supply of the ampulla of the posterior semicircular duct.

The **cochlear nerve** (*n. cochlearis*) divides into numerous filaments at the base of the modiolus; those for the basal and middle coils pass through the foramina in the tractus spiralis foraminosis, those for the apical coil through the canalis centralis, and the nerves bend outward to pass between the lamellæ of the osseous spiral lamina. Occupying the spiral canal of the modiolus is the **spiral ganglion of the cochlea** (*ganglion of Corti*) (Fig. 918), consisting of bipolar nerve cells, which constitute the cells of origin of this nerve. Reaching the outer edge of the osseous spiral lamina, the fibers of the nerve pass through the foramina in the tympanic lip; some end by arborizing around the bases of the inner hair cells, while others pass

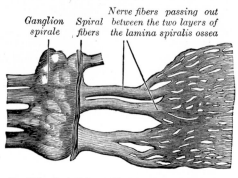

Ganglion   Spiral   *Nerve fibers passing out*
spirale   , *fibers*   *between the two layers of*
                      the lamina spiralis ossea

Fɪɢ. 923.—Part of the cochlear division of the acoustic nerve, highly magnified. (Henle.)

between Corti's rods and across the tunnel, to end in a similar manner in relation to the outer hair cells. The cochlear nerve gives off a vestibular branch to supply the vestibular end of the ductus cochlearis; the filaments of this branch pass through the foramina in the fossa cochlearis (page 1079).

Vessels.—The **arteries of the labyrinth** are the internal auditory, from the basilar, and the stylomastoid, from the posterior auricular. The internal auditory artery divides at the bottom of the internal acoustic meatus into two branches: cochlear and vestibular. The cochlear branch subdivides into twelve or fourteen twigs, which traverse the canals in the modiolus, and are distributed, in the form of a capillary net-work, in the lamina spiralis and basilar membrane. The vestibular branches are distributed to the utricle, saccule, and semicircular ducts.

The **veins** of the vestibule and semicircular canals accompany the arteries, and, receiving those of the cochlea at the base of the modiolus, unite to form the internal auditory veins which end in the posterior part of the superior petrosal sinus or in the transverse sinus.

PERIPHERAL TERMINATIONS OF NERVES OF GENERAL SENSATIONS.

The peripheral terminations of the nerves, receptors, associated with general sensations, *i. e.*, the muscular sense and the senses of heat, cold, pain, and pressure, are widely distributed throughout the body. These nerves may end *free* among the tissue elements, or in *special end-organs* where the terminal nerve filaments are enclosed in capsules.

Free nerve-endings occur chiefly in the epidermis and in the epithelium covering certain mucous membranes; they are well seen also in the stratified squamous epithelium of the cornea, and are also found in the root-sheaths and papillæ of the hairs, and around the bodies of the sudoriferous glands. When the nerve fiber approaches its termination, the medullary sheath suddenly disappears, leaving only the axis-cylinder surrounded by the neurolemma. After a time the fiber loses its neurolemma, and consists only of an axis-cylinder, which can be seen, in preparations stained with chloride of gold, to be made up of fine varicose fibrillæ. Finally, the axis-cylinder breaks up into its constituent fibrillæ which often present regular varicosities and anastomose with one another, and end in small knobs or disks between the epithelial cells.

Under this heading may be classed the **tactile disks** described by Merkel as occurring in the epidermis of the pig's snout, where the fibrillæ of the axis-cylinder end in cup-shaped disks in apposition with large epithelial cells.

The **special end-organs** exhibit great variety in size and shape, but have one feature in common, viz., the terminal nerve fibrillæ are enveloped by a capsule. Included in this group are the end-bulbs of Krause, the corpuscles of Grandry, of Pacini, of Golgi and Mazzoni, of Wagner and Meissner, and the neurotendinous and neuromuscular spindles.

The **end-bulbs of Krause** (Fig. 924) are minute cylindrical or oval bodies, consisting of a capsule formed by the expansion of the connective-tissue sheath of a medullated fiber, and containing a soft semifluid core in which the axis-cylinder terminates either in a bulbous extremity or in a coiled-up plexiform mass. End-bulbs are found in the conjunctiva of the eye (where they are spheroidal in shape in man, but cylindrical in most other animals), in the mucous membrane of the lips and tongue, and in the epineurium of nerve trunks. They are also found in the penis and the clitoris, and have received the name of **genital corpuscles;** in these situations they have a mulberry-like appearance, being constricted by connective-tissue septa into from two to six knob-like masses. In the synovial membranes of certain joints, *e. g.*, those of the fingers, rounded or oval end-bulbs occur, and are designated **articular end-bulbs.**

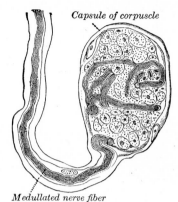

Capsule of corpuscle

Medullated nerve fiber

Fɪɢ. 924.—End-bulb of Krause.   (Klein.)

The **tactile corpuscles of Grandry** occur in the papillæ of the beak and tongue of birds. Each consists of a capsule composed of a very delicate, nucleated membrane, and contains two or more granular, somewhat flattened cells; between these cells the axis-cylinder ends in flattened disks.

The **Pacinian corpuscles** (Fig. 925) are found in the subcutaneous tissue on the nerves of the palm of the hand and sole of the foot and in the genital organs of both sexes; they also occur in connection with the nerves of the joints, and in some other situations, as in the mesentery and pancreas of the cat and along the tibia of the rabbit. Each of these corpuscles is attached to and encloses the termination of a single nerve fiber. The corpuscle, which is perfectly visible to the naked eye (and which can be most easily demonstrated in the mesentery of a cat), consists of a number of lamellæ or capsules arranged more or less concentrically around a central clear space, in which the nerve fiber is contained. Each lamella is composed of bundles of fine connective-tissue fibers, and is lined on its inner surface by a single layer of flattened epithelioid cells. The central clear space, which is elon-

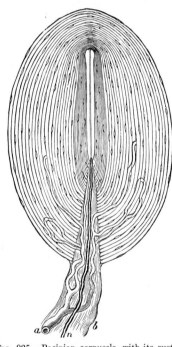

Fɪɢ. 925.—Pacinian corpuscle, with its system of capsules and central cavity. *a.* Arterial twig, ending in capillaries, which form loops in some of the intercapsular spaces, and one penetrates to the central capsule. *b.* The fibrous tissue of the stalk. *n.* Nerve tube advancing to the central capsule, there losing its white matter, and stretching along the axis to the opposite end, where it ends by a tuberculated enlargement.

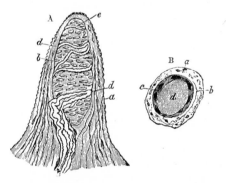

Fɪɢ. 926.—Papilla of the hand, treated with acetic acid. Magnified 350 times. *A.* Side view of a papilla of the hand. *a.* Cortical layer. *b.* Tactile corpuscle. *c.* Small nerve of the papilla, with neurolemma. *d.* Its two nervous fibers running with spiral coils around the tactile corpuscle. *e.* Apparent termination of one of these fibers. *B.* A tactile papilla seen from above so as to show its transverse section. *a.* Cortical layer. *b.* Nerve fiber. *c.* Outer layer of the tactile body, with nuclei. *d.* Clear interior substance.

gated or cylindrical in shape, is filled with a transparent core, in the middle of which the axis-cylinder traverses the space to near its distal extremity, where it ends in one or more small knobs. Todd and Bowman have described minute arteries as entering by the sides of the nerves and forming capillary loops in the intercapsular spaces, and even penetrating into the central space.

Herbst has described a nerve-ending somewhat similar to the Pacinian corpuscle, in the mucous membrane of the tongue of the duck, and in some other situations. It differs, however, from the Pacinian corpuscle, in being smaller, in its capsules being more closely approximated, and especially in the fact that the axis-cylinder in the central clear space is coated with a continuous row of nuclei. These bodies are known as the **corpuscles of Herbst.**

The **corpuscles of Golgi and Mazzoni** are found in the subcutaneous tissue of the pulp of the fingers. They differ from Pacinian corpuscles in that their capsules are thinner, their contained cores thicker, and in the latter the axis-cylinders ramify more extensively and end in flat expansions.

The **tactile corpuscles of Wagner and Meissner** (Fig. 926) are oval-shaped bodies. Each is enveloped by a connective-tissue capsule, and imperfect membranous septa derived from this penetrate the interior. The axis-cylinder passes through the capsule, and after making several spiral turns around the body of the corpuscle ends in small globular or pyriform enlargements. These tactile corpuscles occur in the papillæ of the corium of the hand and foot, the front of the forearm, the skin of the lips, the mucous membrane of the tip of the tongue, the palpebral conjunctiva, and the skin of the mammary papilla.

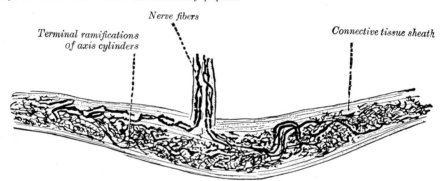

Terminal ramifications of axis cylinders   *Nerve fibers*   *Connective tissue sheath*

FIG. 927.—Nerve ending of Ruffini. (After A. Ruffini.)

Corpuscles of Ruffini.—Ruffini described a special variety of nerve-ending in the subcutaneous tissue of the human finger (Fig. 927); they are principally situated at the junction of the corium with the subcutaneous tissue. They are oval in shape, and consist of strong connective-tissue sheaths, inside which the nerve fibers divide into numerous branches, which show varicosities and end in small free knobs.

The **neurotendinous spindles** (*organs of Golgi*) are chiefly found near the junctions of tendons and muscles. Each is enclosed in a capsule which contains a number of enlarged tendon fasciculi (*intrafusal fasciculi*). One or more nerve fibers perforate the side of the capsule and lose their medullary sheaths; the axis-cylinders subdivide and end between the tendon fibers in irregular disks or varicosities (Fig. 928).

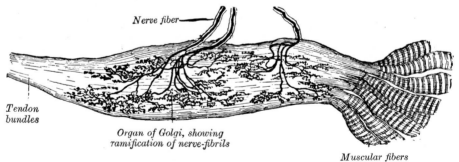

Nerve fiber

Tendon bundles

Organ of Golgi, showing ramification of nerve-fibrils

Muscular fibers

FIG. 928.—Organ of Golgi (neurotendinous spindle) from the human tendo calcaneus. (After Ciaccio.)

The **neuromuscular spindles** are present in the majority of voluntary muscles, and consist of small bundles of peculiar muscular fibers (*intrafusal fibers*), embryonic in type, invested by capsules, within which nerve fibers, experimentally shown to be sensory in origin, terminate. These neuromuscular spindles vary in length from 0.8 mm. to 5 mm., and have a distinctly fusiform appearance. The large medullated nerve fibers passing to the end-organ are from one to three or four in number; entering the fibrous capsule, they divide several times, and, losing their medullary sheaths, ultimately end in naked axis-cylinders encircling the intrafusal fibers by flattened expansions, or irregular ovoid or rounded disks (Fig. 930). Neuromuscular spindles have not yet been demonstrated in the tongue muscles, and only a few exist in the ocular muscles.

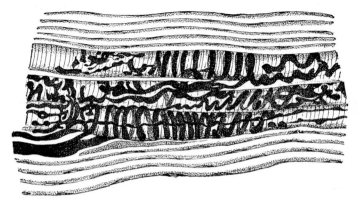

Fig. 929.—Middle third of a terminal plaque in the muscle spindle of an adult cat. (After Ruffini.)

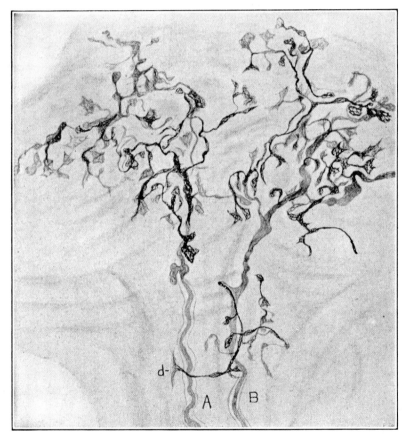

Fig. 930.—Receptor, Type II, of human carotid sinus. *A, B,* afferent medullated fibers to glossopharyngeal nerve. (De Castro, Travaux du Laboratoire de Recherches Biologiques de l'Universite de Madrid.)

Visceral Receptors.—Medullated afferent fibers from the viscera, lungs, digestive tract, heart, liver, pancreas, kidneys, etc., presumably convey impulses from receptors located in those organs. The receptors in the carotid sinus, the aorta, the glomus aorticum and the glomus caroticum have been extensively studied during the past few years.

Carotid sinus, a slight enlargement of the beginning of the internal carotid artery contains in its walls elaborate receptors, carotid receptors. The afferent fibers join the carotid branch of the glossopharyngeal nerve.

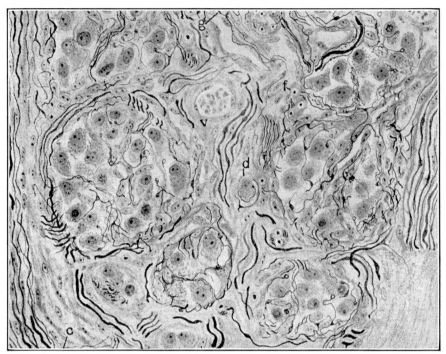

Fig. 931.—Human carotid glomus showing nerve endings and fibers among epithelioid cells. (De Castro, Travaux du Laboratoire de Recherches Bibliogiques de l'Universite de Madrid.)

Aortic Receptors.—Receptors similar to those in the carotid sinus are located in the wall of the aortic arch proximal to the origin of the left subclavian artery and in the wall of the right subclavian artery and adjoining part of the innominate artery. The afferent fibers run (in the aortic (depressor) nerve) to the vagus.

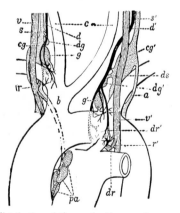

Fig. 932.—Diagram showing the distribution of the aortic (depressor) nerves (*d, d′*), the position of the aortic glomi (*g, ′g*), and the paraganglion aorticum supracardiale (*pa*). Based on a transverse series of a newborn rabbit. *a*, ansa subclavia; *b*, innominate artery; *c*, common carotids; *cg, cg′*, inferior cervical ganglion; *dg, dγ′*, ganglion at the junction of sympathetic rami with the aortic nerve; *ds*, ramus of sympathetic joining the aortic nerve; *r, r′*, recurrent nerve; *s, s′*, cervical sympathetic trunk; *v, v′*, vagus. (Nonidez, Am. J. Anat.; courtesy of Wistar Institute.)

The **glomus caroticum** (carotid body) is situated behind the common carotid artery at the bifurcation into external and internal carotid arteries. They are reddish-brown in color, oval in shape and about 5 mm. in length. Each body is invested with a fibrous capsule and consists largely of masses of epithelioid cells arranged in cords and richly supplied with special nerve endings (chemoreceptors). The afferent fibers from these end-organs join the carotid branch of the glossopharyngeal nerve. Sympathetic nerve fibers from plexus on the carotid artery are distributed throughout the organ but are not concerned with the specific reactions.

Glomus Aorticum (Aortic Bodies).—The structure and function of the glomus aorticum is essentially the same as that of the glomus caroticum. The aortic glomi have been carefully studied in mammals and presumably these findings will apply to man. The right glomus is situated in the angle at the junction of the right subclavian and right common carotid arteries. It receives a branch directly from the subclavian artery. The left aortic glomus is situated in the angle between the left subclavian artery and the aorta. It receives a branch directly from the aorta or the subclavian artery. Each consists of special epithelioid cells grouped in cords and is richly supplied with receptors which appear to respond to chemical changes in the blood hence have been termed chemoreceptors. The afferent fibers from these endings join the aortic nerve a branch of vagus.

Sympathetic nerve fibers from the inferior cervical ganglion join the aortic nerves and enter the aortic bodies but they are probably not concerned with the specific functions of those bodies.

Function.—The aortic and carotid receptors respond to mechanical (blood-pressure) stimuli and are concerned with the regulation of both circulation and respiration. It seems probable that the receptors in the glomi respond to chemical stimuli and are primarily concerned with the regulation of respiration.

BIBLIOGRAPHY

NOSE

The lymphatic drainage of the paranasal sinuses. DIXON, F. W., and N. L. HOERR: 1944. Laryngoscope, Vol. 54, pp. 165–175.

Development of the bridge of the nose. GOLDSTEIN, M. S.: 1939. Am. J. Phys. Anthrop., Vol. 25, pp. 101–117.

Lymphatic pathways from the nose. LARSELL, O., and R. A. FENTON: 1936. Arch. Otolaryngol., Vol. 24, pp. 696–713.

The Nose, Paranasal Sinuses, Nasolacrimal Passageways, and Olfactory Organ in Man. SCHAEFFER, J. P.: 1920. Blakiston, Phila., xxii 370 pp.

EYE

The problem of cyclopia. ADELMANN, H. B.: 1936. Quart. Rev. Biol., Vol. 11. pp. 284–304.

Superficial lymphatics of human eyelids observed by injection **in vivo**. BURCH, G. E.: 1939. Anat. Rec., Vol. 73, pp. 443–446.

Vertebrate photoreceptors. DETWILER, S. R.: 1938. Yale J. Biol. and Med., Vol. 10, pp. 485–512.

On the role of chemical factors in retinal photomechanical responses. DETWILER, S. R.: 1945. Am. J. Anat., Vol. 77, pp. 117–157.

Intra-coelomic grafts of the eye primordium of the chick. JOY, E. A.: 1939. Anat. Rec., Vol. 74, pp. 461–485.

Reflex control of the ciliary muscle. KUNTZ, A., C. A. RICHINS, and E. J. CASEY: 1946. J. Neurophysiol., Vol. 9, pp. 445–451.

Developmental Abnormalities of the Eye. MANN, I.: 1937. Cambridge Univ. Press, London, xi 444 pp.

An **in vitro** analysis of the organization of the eye-forming area in the early chick blastoderm. SPRATT, N. T., JR.: 1940. J. Exp. Zool., Vol. 85, pp. 171–209.

Return of vision in eyes exchanged between adult salamanders of different species. STONE, L. S., and F. S. ELLISON: 1945. J. Exp. Zool., Vol. 100, pp. 217–227.

EAR

The development of the auditory ossicles and associated structures in man. ANSON, B. J., and T. H. BAST: 1946. Ann. Otol., Rhin. and Laryng., Vol. 55, pp. 467–494.

Origin and distribution of air cells in the temporal bone. BAST, T. H., and H. B. FORESTER: 1939. Arch. Otolaryngol., Vol. 30, pp. 183–205.

The eustachian tube. A review of its descriptive, microscopic, topographic and clinical anatomy. GRAVES, G. O., and L. F. EDWARDS: 1944. Arch. Otolaryngol., Vol. 39, pp. 359–397.

Storage of trypan blue in the internal ear of the rat. SPECTOR, B.: 1944. Anat. Rec., Vol. 88, pp. 83–89.

THE COMMON INTEGUMENT (SKIN).

THE integument (Fig. 933) covers the body and protects the deeper tissues from injury, from drying and from invasion by foreign organisms; it contains the peripheral endings of many of the sensory nerves; it plays an important part in the regulation of the body temperature, and has also limited excretory and absorbing powers. It consists principally of a layer of dense connective tissue, named the **corium** or **cutis vera**, and an external covering of epithelium, termed the **epidermis** or **cuticle**. On the surface of the former layer are sensitive and **vascular papillæ**; within, or beneath it, are certain organs with special functions: namely, the **sudoriferous** and **sebaceous glands**, and the **hair follicles**.

Development.—The epidermis and its appendages, consisting of the hairs, nails, sebaceous and sweat glands, are developed from the ectoderm, while the corium or true skin is of mesodermal origin. About the fifth week the epidermis consists of two layers of cells, the deeper one corresponding to the rete mucosum. The subcutaneous fat appears about the fourth month, and the papillæ of the true skin about the sixth. A considerable desquamation of epidermis takes place during fetal life, and this desquamated epidermis, mixed with sebaceous secretion, constitutes the **vernix caseosa**, with which the skin is smeared during the last three months of fetal life. The nails are formed at the third month, and begin to project from the epidermis about the sixth. The hairs appear between the third and fourth months in the form of solid downgrowths of the deeper layer of the epidermis, the growing extremities of which become inverted by papillary projections from the corium. The central cells of the solid downgrowths undergo alteration to form the hair, while the peripheral cells are retained to form the lining cells of the hair-follicle. About the fifth month the fetal hairs (**lanugo**) appear, first on the head and then on the other parts; they drop off after birth, and give place to the permanent hairs. The cellular structures of the sudoriferous and sebaceous glands are formed from the ectoderm, while the connective tissue and bloodvessels are derived from the mesoderm. All the sweat-glands are fully formed at birth; they begin to develop as early as the fourth month.

Structure.—The **epidermis, cuticle, or scarf skin** is non-vascular, and consists of stratified epithelium, and is accurately moulded on the papillary layer of the corium. It varies in thickness in different parts. In some situations, as in the palms of the hands and soles of the feet, it is thick, hard, and horny in texture. This may be in a measure due to the fact that these parts are exposed to intermittent pressure, but that this is not the only cause is proved by the fact that the condition exists to a very considerable extent at birth. The more superficial layers of cells, called the **horny layer** (*stratum corneum*), may be separated by maceration from a deeper stratum, which is called the **stratum mucosum**, and which consists of several layers of differently shaped cells. The free surface of the epidermis is marked by a net-work of linear furrows of variable size, dividing the surface into a number of polygonal or lozenge-shaped areas. Some of these furrows are large, as opposite the flexures of the joints, and correspond to the folds in the corium produced by movements. In other situations, as upon the back of the hand, they are exceedingly fine, and intersect one another at various angles. Upon the palmar surfaces of the hands and fingers, and upon the soles of the feet, the epidermal ridges are very distinct, and are disposed in curves; they depend upon the large size and peculiar arrangements of the papillæ upon which the epidermis is placed. The function of these ridges is primarily to increase resistance between contact surfaces for the purpose of preventing slipping whether in walking or prehension. The direction of the ridges is at right angles with the force that tends to produce slipping or to the resultant of such forces when these forces vary in direction. In each individual the lines on the tips of the fingers and thumbs form distinct patterns unlike those of

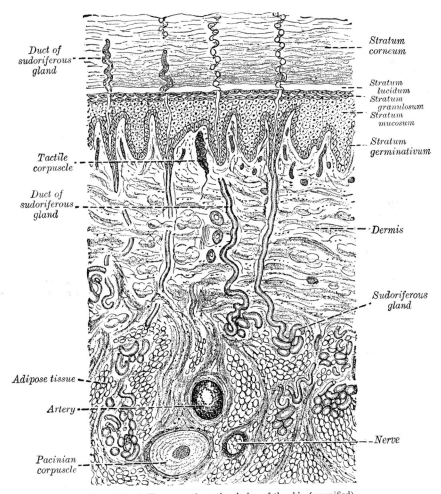

Fig. 933.—A diagrammatic sectional view of the skin (magnified).

any other person. A method of determining the identity of a criminal is based on this fact, impressions ("finger-prints") of these lines being made on paper covered with soot, or on white paper after first covering the fingers with ink. The deep surface of the epidermis is accurately moulded upon the papillary layer of the corium, the papillæ being covered by a basement membrane; so that when the epidermis is removed by maceration, it presents on its under surface a number of pits or depressions corresponding to the papillæ, and ridges corresponding to the intervals between them. Fine tubular prolongations are continued from this layer into the ducts of the sudoriferous and sebaceous glands.

The epidermis consists of stratified squamous epithelium which is arranged in four layers from within outward as follows: (*a*) **stratum mucosum**, (*b*) **stratum granulosum**, (*c*) **stratum lucidum**, and (*d*) **stratum corneum**.

The **stratum mucosum** (*mucous layer*) is composed of several layers of cells; those of the deepest layer are columnar in shape and placed perpendicularly on the surface of the basement membrane, to which they are attached by toothed extremities; this deepest layer is sometimes termed the **stratum germinativum**; the succeeding strata consist of cells of a more rounded or polyhedral form, the contents of which are soft, opaque, granular, and soluble in acetic acid. These are known as prickle cells because of the bridges by which they are connected to one another. They contain fine fibrils which are continuous across the connecting processes with corresponding fibrils in adjacent cells. Between the bridges are fine intercellular clefts serving for the passage of lymph, and in these lymph corpuscles or pigment granules may be found.

The **stratum granulosum** comprises two or three layers of flattened cells which contain granules of *eleidin*, a substance readily stained by hematoxylin or carmine, and probably an intermediate substance in the formation of keratin. They are supposed to be cells in a transitional stage between the protoplasmic cells of the stratum mucosum and the horny cells of the superficial layers.

The **stratum lucidum** appears in section as a homogeneous or dimly striated membrane, composed of closely packed cells in which traces of flattened nuclei may be found, and in which minute granules of a substance named *keratohyalin* are present.

The **stratum corneum** (*horny layer*) consists of several layers of horny epithelial scales in which no nuclei are discernible, and which are unaffected by acetic acid, the protoplasm having become changed into horny material or **keratin**. According to Ranvier they contain granules of a material which has the characteristics of beeswax.

The black color of the skin in the negro, and the tawny color among some of the white races, is due to the presence of pigment in the cells of the epidermis. This pigment is more especially distinct in the cells of the stratum mucosum, and is similar to that found in the cells of the pigmentary layer of the retina. As the cells approach the surface and desiccate, the color becomes partially lost; the disappearance of the pigment from the superficial layers of the epidermis is, however, difficult to explain.

The pigment (**melanin**) consists of dark brown or black granules of very small size, closely packed together within the cells, but not involving the nucleus.

The main purpose served by the epidermis is that of protection, as the surface is worn away new cells are supplied and thus the true skin, the vessels and nerves which it contains are defended from damage.

The **Corium, Cutis Vera, Dermis,** or **True Skin** is tough, flexible, and elastic. It varies in thickness in different parts of the body. Thus it is very thick in the palms of the hands and soles of the feet; thicker on the dorsal aspect of the body than on the ventral, and on the lateral than on the medial sides of the limbs. In the eyelids, scrotum, and penis it is exceedingly thin and delicate.

It consists of felted connective tissue, with a varying amount of elastic fibers and numerous bloodvessels, lymphatics, and nerves. The connective tissue is arranged in two layers: a **deeper** or **reticular**, and a **superficial** or **papillary**.

Smooth muscle cells are found in the corium and the subcutaneous layers of the scrotum, penis, labia majora, and nipples. In the mammary papilla, the smooth muscle cells are disposed in circular bands and radiating bundles, arranged in superimposed laminæ. In parts of the skin where there are hairs, discrete bundles of smooth muscle called the Arrectores pilorum are attached in the superficial layers of the corium and near the base of each hair follicle.

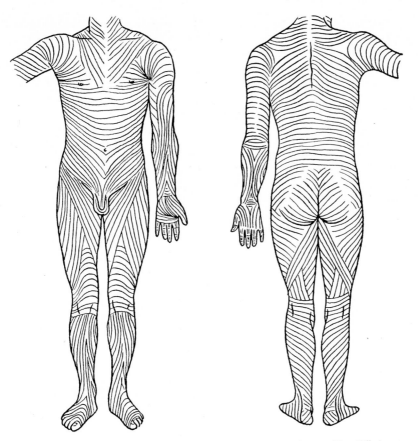

Fig. 934.—Cleavage lines (Langer's lines) of the skin. Trunk and extremities. (Eller).

The **papillary layer** (*stratum papillare; superficial layer; corpus papillare of the corium*) consists of numerous small, highly sensitive, and vascular eminences, the **papillæ,** which rise perpendicularly from its surface. The papillæ are minute conical eminences, having rounded or blunted extremities, occasionally divided into two or more parts, and are received into corresponding pits on the under surface of the cuticle. On the general surface of the body, more especially in parts endowed with slight sensibility, they are few in number, and exceedingly minute; but in some situations, as upon the palmar surfaces of the hands and fingers, and upon the plantar surfaces of the feet and toes, they are long, of large size, closely aggregated together, and arranged in parallel curved lines, forming the elevated ridges seen on the free surface of the epidermis. Each ridge contains two rows of papillæ, between which the ducts of the sudoriferous glands pass out-

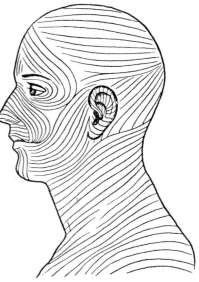

Fig. 935.—Cleavage lines (Langer's lines) of the skin. Head and neck (Eller).

ward to open on the summit of the ridge.   Each papilla consists of very small and closely interlacing bundles of finely fibrillated tissue, with a few elastic fibers; within this tissue is a capillary loop, and in some papillæ, especially in the palms of the hand and the fingers, there are tactile corpuscles.

The **reticular layer** (*stratum reticulare*; *deep layer*) consists of fibro-elastic connective tissue, composed chiefly of collagenous bundles, but containing yellow elastic fibers in varying number in different parts of the body.   The cells it contains are principally fibroblasts and histiocytes, but other types may be found.   Near the papillary layer the collagenous bundles are small and compactly arranged; in the deeper layers they are larger and coarser and between their meshes are sweat glands, sebaceous glands, hair shafts or follicles, and small collections of fat cells. The deep surface of the reticular layer merges with the adipose tissue of the subcutaneous superficial fascia (tela subcutanea).

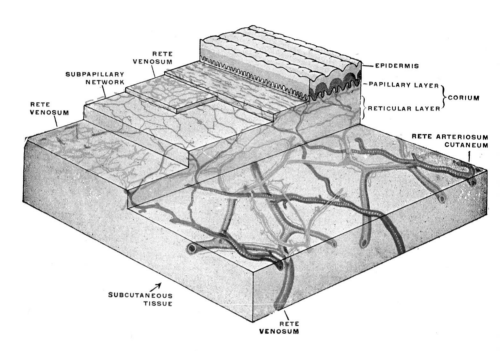

Fig. 936.—The distribution of the bloodvessels in the skin of the sole of the foot.   (Spalteholz)

Cleavage Lines of the Skin (*Langer's lines*).—When a penetrating wound is made with a sharp conical instrument it does not leave a round hole in the skin, as might be expected, but a slit such as would be expected from a flat blade.   Maps of the directions of these slits from puncture wounds over all parts of the body have been made from dissecting room material (Fig. 934).   These maps indicate that there are definite lines of **tension** or **cleavage lines** within the skin which are characteristic for each part of the body.   In microscopic sections cut parallel with these lines, most of the collagenous bundles of the reticular layer are cut longitudinally, while in sections cut across the lines, the bundles are in cross section.   The cleavage lines correspond closely with the crease lines on the surface of the skin in most parts of the body.   The pattern of the cleavage lines, according to Cox (1941) varies with body configuration, but is constant for individuals of similar build, regardless of age.   There are limited areas of the body in which the orientation of the bundles is irregular and confused. The cleavage lines are of particular interest to the surgeon because an incision parallel to the lines heals with a fine linear scar while an incision across the lines may set up irregular tensions which result in an unsightly scar.

The **arteries** supplying the skin form a net-work in the subcutaneous tissue, and from this net-work branches are given off to supply the sudoriferous glands, the hair follicles, and the fat. Other branches unite in a plexus immediately beneath the corium; from this plexus, fine capillary vessels pass into the papillæ, forming, in the smaller ones, a single capillary loop, but in the larger, a more or less convoluted vessel. The **lymphatic vessels** of the skin form two net-works, superficial and deep, which communicate with each other and with those of the subcutaneous tissue by oblique branches.

The **nerves** of the skin terminate partly in the epidermis and partly in the corium; their different modes of ending are described on pages 1099 to 1092.

THE APPENDAGES OF THE SKIN.

The appendages of the skin are the **nails,** the **hairs,** and the **sudoriferous** and **sebaceous glands** with their ducts.

The **Nails** (*ungues*) (Fig. 937) are flattened, elastic structures of a horny texture, placed upon the dorsal surfaces of the terminal phalanges of the fingers and toes. Each nail is convex on its outer surface, concave within, and is implanted by a portion, called the **root,** into a groove in the skin; the exposed portion is called the **body,** and the distal extremity the **free edge.** The nail is firmly adherent to the corium, being accurately moulded upon its surface; the part beneath the body and root of the nail is called the **nail matrix,** because from it the nail is produced. Under the greater part of the body of the nail, the matrix is thick, and raised into a series of longitudinal ridges which are very vascular, and the color is seen through the transparent tissue. Near the root of the nail, the papillæ are smaller, less vascular, and have no regular arrangement, and here the tissue of the nail is not firmly adherent to the connective-tissue stratum but only in contact with it; hence this portion is of a whiter color, and is called the **lunula** on account of its shape.

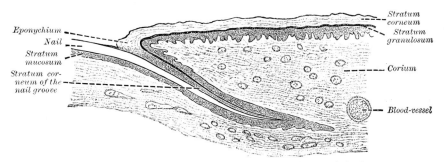

Fig. 937.—Longitudinal section through nail and its nail groove (sulcus).

The cuticle as it passes forward on the dorsal surface of the finger or toe is attached to the surface of the nail a little in advance of its root; at the extremity of the finger it is connected with the under surface of the nail a little behind its free edge. The cuticle and the horny substance of the nail (both epidermic structures) are thus directly continuous with each other. The superficial, horny part of the nail consists of a greatly thickened stratum lucidum, the stratum corneum forming merely the thin cuticular fold (**eponychium**) which overlaps the lunula; the deeper part consists of the stratum mucosum. The cells in contact with the papillæ of the matrix are columnar in form and arranged perpendicularly to the surface; those which succeed them are of a rounded or polygonal form, the more superficial ones becoming broad, thin, and flattened, and so closely packed as to make the limits of the cells very indistinct. The nails grow in length by the proliferation of the cells of the stratum mucosum at the root of the nail, and in thickness from that part of the stratum mucosum which underlies the lunula.

Hairs (*pili*) are found on nearly every part of the surface of the body, but are absent from the palms of the hands, the soles of the feet, the dorsal surfaces of the terminal phalanges, the glans penis, the inner surface of the prepuce, and the inner surfaces of the labia. They vary much in length, thickness, and color in different parts of the body and in different races of mankind. In some parts, as in the skin of the eyelids, they are so short as not to project beyond the follicles containing them; in others, as upon the scalp, they are of considerable length; again, in other parts, as the eyelashes, the hairs of the pubic region, and the whiskers and beard, they are remarkable for their thickness. Straight hairs are stronger than curly hairs, and present on transverse section a cylindrical or oval outline; curly hairs, on the other hand, are flattened. A hair consists of a **root**, the part implanted in the skin; and a **shaft** or **scapus**, the portion projecting from the surface.

The **root of the hair** (*radix pili*) ends in an enlargement, the **hair bulb**, which is whiter in color and softer in texture than the shaft, and is lodged in a follicular involution of the epidermis called the **hair follicle** (Fig. 938). When the hair is of

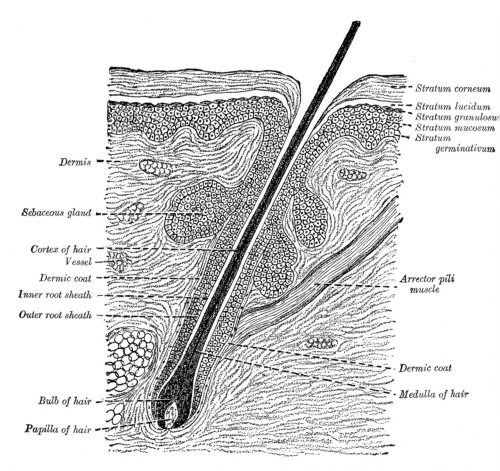

Fig. 938.—Section of skin, showing the epidermis and dermis; a hair in its follicle; the Arrector pili muscle; sebaceous glands.

considerable length the follicle extends into the subcutaneous cellular tissue. The hair follicle commences on the surface of the skin with a funnel-shaped opening, and passes inward in an oblique or curved direction—the latter in curly hairs—to become dilated at its deep extremity, where it corresponds with the hair bulb. Opening into the follicle, near its free extremity, are the ducts of one or more sebaceous glands. At the bottom of each hair follicle is a small conical, vascular eminence or papilla, similar in every respect to those found upon the surface of the skin; it is continuous with the dermic layer of the follicle, and is supplied with nerve fibrils. The hair follicle consists of two coats—an **outer** or **dermic,** and an **inner** or **epidermic.**

The **outer** or **dermic coat** is formed mainly of fibrous tissue; it is continuous with the corium, is highly vascular, and supplied by numerous minute nervous filaments. It consists of three layers (Fig. 939). The most internal is a hyaline basement membrane, which is well-marked in the larger hair follicles, but is not very distinct in the follicles of minute hairs; it is limited to the deeper part of the

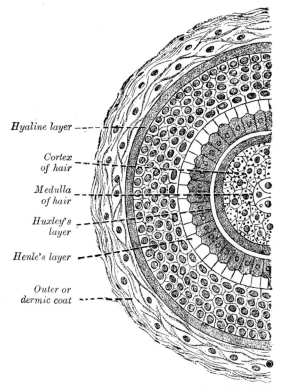

Hyaline layer

Cortex of hair

Medulla of hair

Huxley's layer

Henle's layer

Outer or dermic coat

FIG. 939.—Transverse section of hair follicle.

follicle. Outside this is a compact layer of fibers and spindle-shaped cells arranged circularly around the follicle; this layer extends from the bottom of the follicle as high as the entrance of the ducts of the sebaceous glands. Externally is a thick layer of connective tissue, arranged in longitudinal bundles, forming a more open texture and corresponding to the reticular part of the corium; in this are contained the bloodvessels and nerves.

The **inner** or **epidermic coat** is closely adherent to the root of the hair, and consists of two strata named respectively the **outer** and **inner root sheaths;** the former of these corresponds with the stratum mucosum of the epidermis, and resembles it in the rounded form and soft character of its cells; at the bottom of the hair follicle these cells become continuous with those of the root of the hair. The inner root sheath consists of (1) a delicate cuticle next the hair, composed of a single layer of imbricated scales with atrophied nuclei; (2) one or two layers of horny, flattened, nucleated cells, known as **Huxley's layer;** and (3) a single layer of cubical cells with clear flattened nuclei, called **Henle's layer.**

The hair bulb is moulded over the papilla and composed of polyhedral epithelial cells, which as they pass upward into the root of the hair become elongated and spindle-shaped, except some in the center which remain polyhedral. Some of these latter cells contain pigment granules which give rise to the color of the hair. It occasionally happens that these pigment granules completely fill the cells in the center of the bulb; this gives rise to the dark tract of pigment often found, of greater or less length, in the axis of the hair.

The **shaft of the hair** (*scapus pili*) consists, from within outward, of three parts, the medulla, the cortex, and the cuticle. The **medulla** is usually wanting in the fine hairs covering the surface of the body, and commonly in those of the head. It is more opaque and deeper colored than the cortex when viewed by transmitted light; but when viewed by reflected light it is white. It is composed of rows of polyhedral cells, containing granules of eleidin and frequently air spaces. The **cortex** constitutes the chief part of the shaft; its cells are elongated and united to form flattened fusiform fibers which contain pigment granules in dark hair, and air in white hair. The **cuticle** consists of a single layer of flat scales which overlap one another from below upward.

Connected with the hair follicles are minute bundles of involuntary muscular fibers, termed the **Arrectores pilorum.** They *arise* from the superficial layer of the corium, and are inserted into the hair follicle, below the entrance of the duct of the sebaceous gland. They are placed on the side toward which the hair slopes, and by their action diminish the obliquity of the follicle and elevate the hair (Fig. 938). The sebaceous gland is situated in the angle which the Arrector muscle forms with the superficial portion of the hair follicle, and contraction of the muscle thus tends to squeeze the sebaceous secretion out from the duct of the gland.

The **Sebaceous Glands** (*glandulæ sebaceæ*) are small, sacculated, glandular organs, lodged in the substance of the corium. They are found in most parts of the skin, but are especially abundant in the scalp and face; they are also very numerous around the apertures of the anus, nose, mouth, and external ear, but are wanting in the palms of the hands and soles of the feet. Each gland consists of a single duct, more or less capacious, which emerges from a cluster of oval or flask-shaped alveoli which vary from two to five in number, but in some instances there may be as many as twenty. Each alveolus is composed of a transparent basement membrane, enclosing a number of epithelial cells. The outer or marginal cells are small and polyhedral, and are continuous with the cells lining the duct. The remainder of the alveolus is filled with larger cells, containing fat, except in the center, where the cells have become broken up, leaving a cavity filled with their débris and a mass of fatty matter, which constitutes the **sebum cutaneum.** The ducts open most frequently into the hair follicles, but occasionally upon the general surface, as in the labia minora and the free margin of the lips. On the nose and face the glands are of large size, distinctly lobulated, and often become much enlarged from the accumulation of pent-up secretion. The tarsal glands of the eyelids are elongated sebaceous glands with numerous lateral diverticula.

The **Sudoriferous** or **Sweat Glands** (*glandulæ sudoriferæ*) are found in almost every part of the skin, and are situated in small pits on the under surface of the corium, or, more frequently, in the subcutaneous areolar tissue, surrounded by a quantity of adipose tissue. Each consists of a single tube, the deep part of which is rolled into an oval or spherical ball, named the **body** of the gland, while the superficial part, or **duct**, traverses the corium and cuticle and opens on the surface of the skin by a funnel-shaped aperture. In the superficial layers of the corium the duct is straight, but in the deeper layers it is convoluted or even twisted; where the epidermis is thick, as in the palms of the hands and soles of the feet, the part of the duct which passes through it is spirally coiled. The size of the glands varies. They are especially large in those regions where the amount of perspiration is great, as in the axillæ, where they form a thin, mammillated layer of a reddish color, which corresponds exactly to the situation of the hair in this region; they are large also in the groin. Their number varies. They are very plentiful on the palms of the hands, and on the soles of the feet, where the orifices of the ducts are exceedingly regular, and open on the curved ridges; they are least numerous in the neck and back. On the palm there are about 370 per square centimeter; on the back of the hand about 200; forehead 175, breast, abdomen and forearm 155, and on the leg and back from 60 to 80 per square centimeter. Krause estimates the total number at about 2,000,000. The average number of sweat glands per square centimeter of skin area in various races as shown by the fingers is as follows:[1]

American (white)	558.2
American (negro)	597.2
Filipino	653.6
Moro	684.4
Negrito (adult)	709.2
Hindu	738.2
Negrito (youth)	950.0

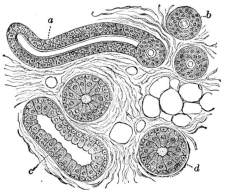

Fig. 940.—Body of a sudoriferous-gland cut in various directions. *a.* Longitudinal section of the proximal part of the coiled tube. *b.* Transverse section of the same. *c.* Longitudinal section of the distal part of the coiled tube. *d.* Transverse section of the same. (Klein and Noble Smith.)

They are absent in the deeper portion of the external auditory meatus, the prepuce and the glans penis. The tube, both in the body of the gland and in the duct consists of two layers—an outer, of fine **areolar tissue**, and an inner of **epithelium** (Fig. 940). The outer layer is thin and is continuous with the superficial stratum of the corium. In the body of the gland the epithelium consists of a single layer of cubical cells, between the deep ends of which the basement membrane is a layer of longitudinally or obliquely arranged non-striped muscular fibers. The ducts are destitute of muscular fibers and are composed of a basement membrane lined by two or three layers of polyhedral cells; the lumen of the duct is coated by a thin cuticle.

[1] Clark and Lhamon, Anatomical Record, 1917, vol. **12.**

When the epidermis is carefully removed from the surface of the corium, the ducts may be pulled out from the corium in the form of short, thread-like processes. The ceruminous glands of the external acoustic meatus, the ciliary glands at the margins of the eyelids, the circumanal glands and probably the mammary glands are modified sudoriferous glands. The average quantity of sweat secreted in twenty-four hours varies from 700 to 900 grams.

BIBLIOGRAPHY

INTEGUMENT

Localization of maximum cell division in epidermis. COWDRY, E. V., and H. C. THOMPSON, JR.: 1944. Anat. Rec., Vol. 88, pp. 403–409.

The cleavage lines of the skin. Cox, H. T.: 1941. Brit. J. Surg., Vol. 29, pp. 234–240.

Finger prints correlated with handedness. CUMMINS, H.: 1940. Am. J. Phys. Anthrop., Vol. 26, pp. 151–166.

The breadths of the epidermal ridges on the finger tips and palms: A study of variation. CUMMINS, H., W. J. WAITS, and J. T. McQUITTY: 1941. Am. J. Anat., Vol. 68, pp. 127–150.

The pigments and color of living human skin. EDWARDS, E. A., and S. Q. DUNTLEY: 1939. Am. J. Anat., Vol. 65, pp. 1–33.

Pigment cell migration in mouse epidermis. REED, S. C., and J. M. HENDERSON: 1940. J. Exp. Zool., Vol. 85, pp. 409–418.

HAIR

Hair growth and sebaceous glands in skin transplanted under the skin and into the peritoneal cavity in the rat. BUTCHER, E. O.: 1946. Anat. Rec., Vol. 96, pp. 101–109.

Male hormone stimulation is prerequisite and an incitant in common baldness. HAMILTON, J. B.: 1942. Am. J. Anat., Vol. 71, pp. 451–480.

Glycogen and phosphatase in the developing hair. JOHNSON, P. L., and G. BEVELANDER: 1946. Anat. Rec., Vol. 95, pp. 193–199.

A review of the classifications of hairs. TROTTER, M.: 1938. Am. J. Phys. Anthrop., Vol. 24, pp. 105–126.

Classifications of hair color. TROTTER, M.: 1939. Am. J. Phys. Anthrop., Vol. 25, pp. 237–260.

NAILS

The significance of the lunula of the nail. BURROWS, M. T.: 1917. Anat. Rec., Vol. 12, pp. 161–166.

THE RESPIRATORY APPARATUS.

(APPARATUS RESPIRATORIUS; RESPIRATORY SYSTEM).

THE respiratory apparatus consists of the **larynx, trachea, bronchi, lungs,** and **pleuræ.**

Development.—The rudiment of the respiratory organs appears as a median longitudinal groove in the ventral wall of the pharynx. The groove deepens and its lips fuse to form a septum which grows from below upward and converts the groove into a tube, the **laryngo-tracheal tube** (Fig. 941), the cephalic

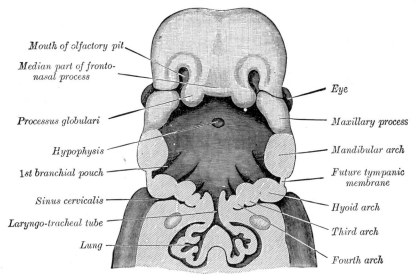

Mouth of olfactory pit

Median part of fronto-nasal process

Processus globulari

Hypophysis

1st branchial pouch

Sinus cervicalis

Laryngo-tracheal tube

Lung

Eye

Maxillary process

Mandibular arch

Future tympanic membrane

Hyoid arch

Third arch

Fourth arch

FIG. 941.—The head and neck of a human embryo thirty-two days old, seen from the ventral surface. The floor of the mouth and pharynx have been removed. (His.)

end of which opens into the pharynx by a slit-like aperture formed by the persistent anterior part of the groove. The tube is lined by entoderm from which the epithelial lining of the respiratory tract is developed. The cephalic part of the tube becomes the larynx, and its next succeeding part the trachea, while from its caudal end two lateral outgrowths, the right and left **lung buds,** arise, and from them the bronchi and lungs are developed. The first rudiment of the larynx consists of two **arytenoid swellings,** which appear, one on either side of the cephalic end of the laryngo-tracheal groove, and are continuous in front of the groove with a transverse ridge **(furcula of His)** which lies between the ventral ends of the third branchial arches and from which the epiglottis is subsequently developed (Figs. 974, 975). After the separation of the trachea from the esophagus the arytenoid swellings come into contact with one another and with the back of the epiglottis, and the entrance to the larynx assumes the form of a T-shaped cleft, the margins of the cleft adhere to one another and the laryngeal entrance is for a time occluded. The mesodermal

(1107)

wall of the tube becomes condensed to form the cartilages of the larynx and trachea. The arytenoid swellings are differentiated into the arytenoid and corniculate cartilages, and the folds joining them to the epiglottis form the aryepiglottic folds in which the cuneiform cartilages are developed as derivatives of the epiglottis. The thyroid cartilage appears as two lateral plates, each chondrified from two centers and united in the mid-ventral line by membrane in which an additional center of chondrification develops. The cricoid cartilage arises from two cartilaginous centers, which soon unite ventrally and gradually extend and ultimately fuse on the dorsal aspect of the tube.

J. Ernest Frazer[1] has made an important investigation on the development of the larynx and the following are his main conclusions:

The opening of the pulmonary diverticulum lies between the two fifth arch masses and behind a "central mass" in the middle line—the proximal end of the diverticulum is compressed between the fifth arch masses. The fifth arch is joined by the fourth to form a "lateral mass" on each side of the opening, and these "lateral masses" grow forward and overlap the central mass and so form a secondary transverse cavity, which is really a part of the cavity of the pharynx. The two parts of the cavity of the larynx are separated in the adult by a line drawn back along the vocal fold and then upward along the border of the arytenoid eminence to the interarytenoid notch. The arytenoid and cricoid are developed in the fifth arch mass. The thyroid is primarily a fourth arch derivative, and if it has a fifth arch element this is a later addition. The epiglottis is derived from the "central mass," and has a third arch element in its oral and upper aspect; the arch value of the "central mass" is doubtful.

Fig. 942.—Lung buds from a human embryo of about four weeks, showing commencing lobulations (His.)

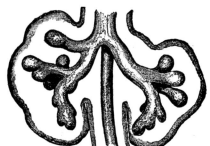

Fig. 943.—Lungs of a human embryo more advanced in development. (His.)

The right and left lung buds grow out behind the ducts of Cuvier, and are at first symmetrical, but their ends soon become lobulated, three lobules appearing on the right, and two on the left; these subdivisions are the early indications of the corresponding lobes of the lungs (Figs. 942, 943). The buds undergo further subdivision and ramification, and ultimately end in minute expanded extremities—the infundibula of the lung. After the sixth month the air-sacs begin to make their appearance on the infundibula in the form of minute pouches. The pulmonary arteries are derived from the sixth aortic arches. During the course of their development the lungs migrate in a caudal direction, so that by the time of birth the bifurcation of the trachea is opposite the fourth thoracic vertebra. As the lungs grow they project into that part of the celom which will ultimately form the pleural cavities, and the superficial layer of the mesoderm enveloping the lung rudiment expands on the growing lung and is converted into the pulmonary pleura.

THE LARYNX.

The **larynx** or **organ of voice** is placed at the upper part of the air passage. It is situated between the trachea and the root of the tongue, at the upper and forepart of the neck, where it presents a considerable projection in the middle line. It forms the lower part of the anterior wall of the pharynx, and is covered

[1] Journal of Anatomy and Physiology, vol. 44.

behind by the mucous lining of that cavity; on either side of it lie the great vessels of the neck. Its vertical extent corresponds to the fourth, fifth, and sixth cervical vertebræ, but it is placed somewhat higher in the female and also during childhood. Symington found that in infants between six and twelve months of age the tip of the epiglottis was a little above the level of the fibrocartilage between the odontoid process and body of the axis, and that between infancy and adult life the larynx descends for a distance equal to two vertebral bodies and two intervertebral fibrocartilages. According to Sappey the average measurements of the adult larynx are as follows:

	In males.	In females.
Length	44 mm.	36 mm.
Transverse diameter	43 "	41 "
Antero-posterior diameter . . .	36 "	26 "
Circumference	136 "	112 "

Until puberty the larynx of the male differs little in size from that of the female. In the female its increase after puberty is only slight; in the male it undergoes considerable increase; all the cartilages are enlarged and the thyroid cartilage becomes prominent in the middle line of the neck, while the length of the rima glottidis is nearly doubled.

The larynx is broad above, where it presents the form of a triangular box flattened behind and at the sides, and bounded in front by a prominent vertical ridge. Below, it is narrow and cylindrical. It is composed of cartilages, which are connected together by ligaments and moved by numerous muscles. It is lined by mucous membrane continuous above with that of the pharynx and below with that of the trachea.

The **Cartilages of the Larynx** (*cartilagines laryngis*) (Fig. 944) are nine in number, three single and three paired, as follows:

Thyroid.
Cricoid.
Two Arytenoid.

Two Corniculate.
Two Cuneiform.
Epiglottis.

The **Thyroid Cartilage** (*cartilago thyreoidea*) is the largest cartilage of the larynx. It consists of two laminæ the anterior borders of which are fused with each other at an acute angle in the middle line of the neck, and form a subcutaneous projection named the **laryngeal prominence** (Adam's apple). This prominence is most distinct at its upper part, and is larger in the male than in the female. Immediately above it the laminæ are separated by a V-shaped notch, the **superior thyroid notch.** The laminæ are irregularly quadrilateral in shape, and their posterior angles are prolonged into processes termed the **superior** and **inferior cornua.**

On the *outer surface* of each lamina an **oblique line** runs downward and forward from the superior thyroid tubercle situated near the root of the superior cornu, to the inferior thyroid tubercle on the lower border. This line gives attachment to the Sternothyreoideus, Thyreohyoideus, and Constrictor pharyngis inferior. The *inner surface* is smooth; above and behind, it is slightly concave and covered by mucous membrane. In front, in the angle formed by the junction of the laminæ, are attached the stem of the epiglottis, the ventricular and vocal ligaments, the Thyreoarytænoidei, Thyreoepiglottici and Vocales muscles, and the thyroepiglottic ligament. The *upper border* is concave behind and convex in front; it gives attachment to the corresponding half of the hyothyroid membrane. The *lower border* is concave behind, and nearly straight in front, the two parts being separated by the inferior thyroid tubercle. A small part of it in and near the middle line is connected to the cricoid cartilage by the middle cricothyroid ligament. The *posterior border,* thick and rounded, receives the insertions of the Stylopharyngeus and Pharyngo-palatinus. It ends above, in the superior cornu, and below, in the inferior cornu.

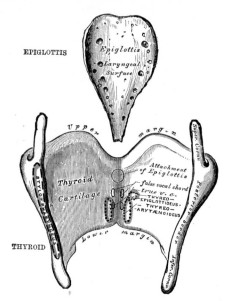

EPIGLOTTIS

THYROID

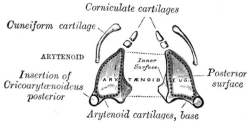

Corniculate cartilages

Cuneiform cartilage

ARYTENOID

Insertion of Cricoarytænoideus posterior

Posterior surface

Arytenoid cartilages, base

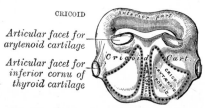

CRICOID

Articular facet for arytenoid cartilage

Articular facet for inferior cornu of thyroid cartilage

FIG. 944.—The cartilages of the larynx. Posterior view.

The **superior cornu** is long and narrow, directed upward, backward, and medialward, and ends in a conical extremity, which gives attachment to the lateral hyothyroid ligament. The **inferior cornu** is short and thick; it is directed downward, with a slight inclination forward and medialward, and presents, on the medial side of its tip, a small oval articular facet for articulation with the side of the cricoid cartilage.

During infancy the laminæ of the thyroid cartilage are joined to each other by a narrow, lozenge-shaped strip, named the **intrathyroid cartilage**. This strip extends from the upper to the lower border of the cartilage in the middle line, and is distinguished from the laminæ by being more transparent and more flexible.

The **Cricoid Cartilage** (*cartilago cricoidea*) is smaller, but thicker and stronger than the thyroid, and forms the lower and posterior parts of the wall of the larynx. It consists of two parts: a **posterior quadrate lamina**, and a narrow **anterior arch**, one-fourth or one-fifth of the depth of the lamina.

The **lamina** (*lamina cartilaginis cricoideæ; posterior portion*) is deep and broad, and measures from above downward about 2 or 3 cm.; on its posterior surface, in the middle line, is a vertical ridge to the lower part of which are attached the longitudinal fibers of the esophagus; and on either side of this a broad depression for the Cricoarytænoideus posterior.

The **arch** (*arcus cartilaginis cricoideæ; anterior portion*) is narrow and convex, and measures vertically from 5 to 7 mm.; it affords attachment externally in front and at the sides to the Cricothyreiodei, and behind, to part of the Constrictor pharyngis inferior.

On either side, at the junction of the lamina with the arch, is a small round articular surface, for articulation with the inferior cornu of the thyroid cartilage.

The lower border of the cricoid cartilage is horizontal, and connected to the highest ring of the trachea by the cricotracheal ligament. The upper border runs obliquely upward and backward, owing to the great depth of the lamina. It gives attachment, in front, to the middle cricothyroid ligament; at the side, to the conus elasticus and the Cricoarytænoidei laterales; behind, it presents, in the middle, a shallow notch, and on either side of this is a smooth, oval, convex surface, directed upward and lateralward, for articulation with the base of an arytenoid cartilage. The inner surface of the cricoid cartilage is smooth, and lined by mucous membrane.

The **Arytenoid Cartilages** (*cartilagines arytænoideæ*) are two in number, and situated at the upper border of the lamina of the cricoid cartilage, at the back of the larynx. Each is pyramidal in form, and has three surfaces, a base, and an apex.

The posterior surface is triangular, smooth, concave, and gives attachment to the Arytænoidei obliquus and transversus. The antero-lateral surface is somewhat convex and rough. On it, near the apex of the cartilage, is a rounded elevation (**colliculus**) from which a ridge (**crista arcuata**) curves at first backward and then downward and forward to the vocal process. The lower part of this crest intervenes between two depressions or **foveæ**, an upper, triangular, and a lower oblong in shape; the latter gives attachment to the Vocalis muscle. The medial surface is narrow, smooth, and flattened, covered by mucous membrane, and forms the lateral bound-

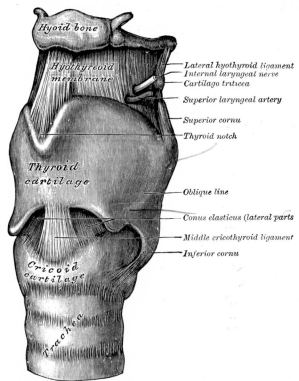

Fig. 945.—The ligaments of the larynx. Antero-lateral view.

ary of the intercartilaginous part of the rima glottidis. The base of each cartilage is broad, and on it is a concave smooth surface, for articulation with the cricoid cartilage. Its lateral angle is short, rounded, and prominent; it projects backward and lateralward, and is termed the **muscular process**; it gives insertion to the Cricoarytænoideus posterior behind, and to the Cricoarytænoideus lateralis in front. Its anterior angle, also prominent, but more pointed, projects horizontally forward; it gives attachment to the vocal ligament, and is called the **vocal process** (Fig. 947).

The **apex** of each cartilage is pointed, curved backward and medialward, and surmounted by a small conical, cartilaginous nodule, the **corniculate cartilage**.

The **Corniculate Cartilages** (*cartilagines corniculatæ; cartilages of Santorini*) are two small conical nodules consisting of yellow elastic cartilage, which articulate with the summits of the arytenoid cartilages and serve to prolong them backward and medialward. They are situated in the posterior parts of the aryepiglottic folds of mucous membrane, and are sometimes fused with the arytenoid cartilages.

The **Cuneiform Cartilages** (*cartilagines cuneiformes; cartilages of Wrisberg*) are two small, elongated pieces of yellow elastic cartilage, placed one on either side, in the aryepiglottic fold, where they give rise to small whitish elevations on the surface of the mucous membrane, just in front of the arytenoid cartilages.

The **Epiglottis** (*cartilago epiglottica*) is a thin lamella of fibrocartilage of a yellowish color, shaped like a leaf, and projecting obliquely upward behind the root of the tongue, in front of the entrance to the larynx. The free extremity is broad and rounded; the attached part or stem is long, narrow, and connected by the **thyroepiglottic ligament** to the angle formed by the two laminæ of the thyroid cartilage, a short distance below the superior thyroid notch. The lower part of its anterior surface is connected to the upper border of the body of the hyoid bone by an elastic ligamentous band, the **hyoepiglottic ligament.**

The **anterior or lingual surface** is curved forward, and covered on its upper, free part by mucous membrane which is reflected on to the sides and root of the tongue, forming a median and two lateral **glossoepiglottic folds**; the lateral folds are partly attached to the wall of the pharynx. The depressions between the epiglottis and the root of the tongue, on either side of the median fold, are named the **valleculæ** (Fig. 949). The lower part of the anterior surface lies behind the hyoid bone, the hyothyroid membrane, and upper part of the thyroid cartilage, but is separated from these structures by a mass of fatty tissue.

The **posterior or laryngeal surface** is smooth, concave from side to side, concavo-convex from above downward; its lower part projects backward as an elevation, the **tubercle or cushion.** When the mucous membrane is removed, the surface of the cartilage is seen to be indented by a number of small pits, in which mucous glands are lodged. To its sides the aryepiglottic folds are attached.

Structure.—The corniculate and cuneiform cartilages, the epiglottis, and the apices of the arytenoids at first consist of hyaline cartilage, but later elastic fibers are deposited in the matrix, converting them into yellow fibrocartilage, which shows little tendency to calcification. The thyroid, cricoid, and the greater part of the arytenoids consist of hyaline cartilage, and become more or less ossified as age advances. Ossification commences about the twenty-fifth year in the thyroid cartilage, and somewhat later in the cricoid and arytenoids; by the sixty-fifth year these cartilages may be completely converted into bone.

Ligaments.—The ligaments of the larynx (Figs. 945, 946) are **extrinsic,** *i. e.,* those connecting the thyroid cartilage and epiglottis with the hyoid bone, and the cricoid cartilage with the trachea; and **intrinsic,** those which connect the several cartilages of the larynx to each other.

Extrinsic Ligaments.—The ligaments connecting the thyroid cartilage with the hyoid bone are the hyothyroid membrane, and a middle and two lateral hyothyroid ligaments.

The **Hyothyroid Membrane** (*membrana hyothyreoidea; thyrohyoid membrane*) is a broad, fibro-elastic layer, attached below to the upper border of the thyroid cartilage and to the front of its superior cornu, and above to the upper margin of the posterior surface of the body and greater cornua of the hyoid bone, thus passing behind the posterior surface of the body of the hyoid, and being separated from it by a mucous bursa, which facilitates the upward movement of the larynx during deglutition. Its middle thicker part is termed the **middle hyothyroid ligament** (*ligamentum hyothyreoideum medium; middle thyrohyoid ligament*), its lateral thinner portions are pierced by the superior laryngeal vessels and the internal branch of the superior laryngeal nerve. Its anterior surface is in relation with the Thyreohyoideus, Sternohyoideus, and Omohyoideus, and with the body of the hyoid bone.

The **Lateral Hyothyroid Ligament** (*ligamentum hyothyreoideum laterale; lateral thyrohyoid ligament*) is a round elastic cord, which forms the posterior border of the hyothyroid membrane and passes between the tip of the superior cornu of the thyroid cartilage and the extremity of the greater cornu of the hyoid bone. A small cartilaginous nodule (*cartilago triticea*), sometimes bony, is frequently found in it.

The **Epiglottis** is connected with the hyoid bone by an elastic band, the **hyo-epiglottic ligament** (*ligamentum hyoepiglotticum*), which extends from the anterior surface of the epiglottis to the upper border of the body of the hyoid bone. The glossoepiglottic folds of mucous membrane (page 1112) may also be considered as extrinsic ligaments of the epiglottis.

The **Cricotracheal Ligament** (*ligamentum cricotracheale*) connects the cricoid cartilage with the first ring of the trachea. It resembles the fibrous membrane which connects the cartilaginous rings of the trachea to each other.

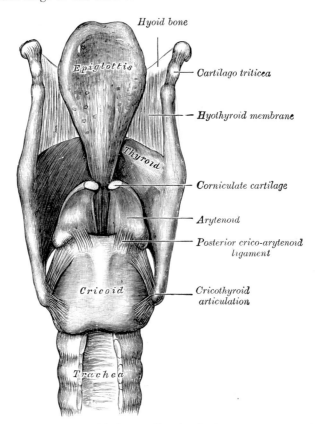

Hyoid bone

Epiglottis

Cartilago triticea

Hyothyroid membrane

Thyroid

Corniculate cartilage

Arytenoid

Posterior crico-arytenoid ligament

Cricoid

Cricothyroid articulation

Trachea

Fig. 946.—Ligaments of the larynx. Posterior view.

Intrinsic Ligaments.—Beneath the mucous membrane of the larynx is a broad sheet of fibrous tissue containing many elastic fibers, and termed the **elastic membrane of the larynx**. It is subdivided on either side by the interval between the ventricular and vocal ligaments, the upper portion extends between the arytenoid cartilage and the epiglottis and is often poorly defined; the lower part is a well-marked membrane forming, with its fellow of the opposite side, the conus elasticus which connects the thyroid, cricoid, and arytenoid cartilages to one another. In addition the joints between the individual cartilages are provided with ligaments.

The **Conus Elasticus** (*cricothyroid membrane*) is composed mainly of yellow elastic tissue. It consists of an anterior and two lateral portions. The **anterior part** or **middle cricothyroid ligament** (*ligamentum cricothyreoideum medium: central part of* *cricothyroid membrane*) is thick and strong, narrow above and broad below. It connects together the front parts of the contiguous margins of the thyroid and cricoid cartilages. It is overlapped on either side by the Cricothyreoideus, but between these is subcutaneous; it is crossed horizontally by a small anastomotic arterial arch, formed by the junction of the two cricothyroid arteries, branches of which pierce it. The **lateral portions** are thinner and lie close under the mucous membrane of the larynx; they extend from the superior border of the cricoid cartilage to the inferior margin of the vocal ligaments, with which they are continuous. These ligaments may therefore be regarded as the free borders of the lateral portions of the conus elasticus, and extend from the vocal processes of the arytenoid cartilages to the angle of the thyroid cartilage about midway between its upper and lower borders.

An **articular capsule**, strengthened posteriorly by a well-marked fibrous band, encloses the articulation of the inferior cornu of the thyroid with the cricoid cartilage on either side.

Each arytenoid cartilage is connected to the cricoid by a capsule and a posterior cricoarytenoid ligament. The **capsule** (*capsula articularis cricoarytenoidea*) is thin and loose, and is attached to the margins of the articular surfaces. The **posterior cricoarytenoid ligament** (*ligamentum cricoarytenoideum posterius*) extends from the cricoid to the medial and back part of the base of the arytenoid.

The **thyroepiglottic ligament** (*ligamentum thyreoepiglotticum*) is a long, slender, elastic cord which connects the stem of the epiglottis with the angle of the thyroid cartilage, immediately beneath the superior thyroid notch, above the attachment of the ventricular ligaments.

Movements.—The articulation between the inferior cornu of the thyroid cartilage and the cricoid cartilage on either side is a diarthrodial one, and permits of rotatory and gliding movements. The rotatory movement is one in which the cricoid cartilage rotates upon the inferior cornua of the thyroid cartilage around an axis passing transversely through both joints. The gliding movement consists in a limited shifting of the cricoid on the thyroid in different directions.

The articulation between the arytenoid cartilages and the cricoid is also a diarthrodial one, and permits of two varieties of movement: one is a rotation of the arytenoid on a vertical axis, whereby the vocal process is moved lateralward or medialward, and the rima glottidis increased or diminished; the other is a gliding movement, and allows the arytenoid cartilages to approach or recede from each other; from the direction and slope of the articular surfaces lateral gliding is accompanied by a forward and downward movement. The two movements of gliding and rotation are associated, the medial gliding being connected with medialward rotation, and the lateral gliding with lateralward rotation. The posterior cricoarytenoid ligaments limit the forward movement of the arytenoid cartilages on the cricoid.

Interior of the Larynx (Figs. 947, 948).—The **cavity of the larynx** (*cavum laryngis*) extends from the laryngeal entrance to the lower border of the cricoid cartilage where it is continuous with that of the trachea. It is divided into two parts by the projection of the vocal folds, between which is a narrow triangular fissure or chink, the **rima glottidis**. The portion of the cavity of the larynx above the vocal folds is called the **vestibule**; it is wide and triangular in shape, its base or anterior wall presenting, however, about its center the backward projection of the tubercle of the epiglottis. It contains the ventricular folds, and between these and the vocal folds are the **ventricles of the larynx**. The portion below the vocal folds is at first of an elliptical form, but lower down it widens out, assumes a circular form, and is continuous with the tube of the trachea.

The **entrance of the larynx** (Fig. 949) is a triangular opening, wide in front, narrow behind, and sloping obliquely downward and backward. It is bounded, in front, by the epiglottis; behind, by the apices of the arytenoid cartilages, the corniculate cartilages, and the interarytenoid notch; and on either side, by a fold of mucous membrane, enclosing ligamentous and muscular fibers, stretched between the side of the epiglottis and the apex of the arytenoid cartilage; this is the **aryepiglottic**

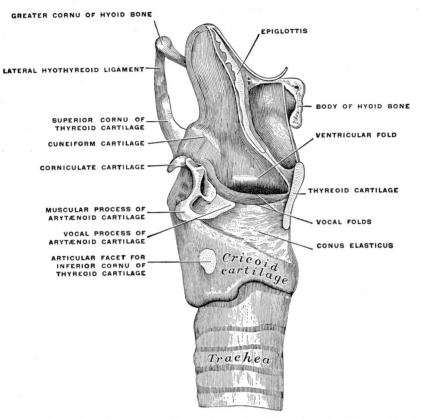

GREATER CORNU OF HYOID BONE

EPIGLOTTIS

LATERAL HYOTHYREOID LIGAMENT

BODY OF HYOID BONE

SUPERIOR CORNU OF THYREOID CARTILAGE

CUNEIFORM CARTILAGE

VENTRICULAR FOLD

CORNICULATE CARTILAGE

THYREOID CARTILAGE

MUSCULAR PROCESS OF ARYTÆNOID CARTILAGE

VOCAL FOLDS

VOCAL PROCESS OF ARYTÆNOID CARTILAGE

CONUS ELASTICUS

ARTICULAR FACET FOR INFERIOR CORNU OF THYREOID CARTILAGE

Cricoid cartilage

Trachea

Fig. 947.—A dissection to show the right half of the conus elasticus. The right lamina of the thyroid cartilage and the subjacent muscles have been removed.

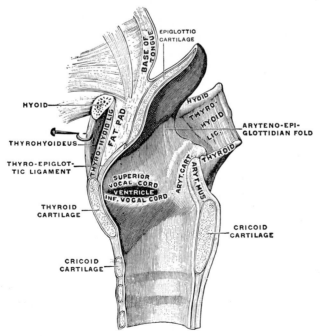

EPIGLOTTIC CARTILAGE

BASE OF TONGUE

HYOID

HYOID

THYRO-HYOID LIG.

THYROHYOIDEUS

ARYTENO-EPI-GLOTTIDIAN FOLD

THYRO-EPIGLOT-TIC LIGAMENT

THYROID

FAT PAD

ARYT. CART.

ARYT. MUS.

SUPERIOR VOCAL CORD

VENTRICLE

INF. VOCAL CORD

THYROID CARTILAGE

CRICOID CARTILAGE

CRICOID CARTILAGE

Fig. 948.—Sagittal section of larynx, right half. (Testut.)

fold, on the posterior part of the margin of which the cuneiform cartilage forms a more or less distinct whitish prominence, the **cuneiform tubercle.**

The **Ventricular Folds** (*plicæ ventriculares; superior or false vocal cords*) are two thick folds of mucous membrane, each enclosing a narrow band of fibrous tissue, the **ventricular ligament** which is attached in front to the angle of the thyroid cartilage immediately below the attachment of the epiglottis, and behind to the antero-lateral surface of the arytenoid cartilage, a short distance above the vocal process. The lower border of this ligament, enclosed in mucous membrane, forms a free crescentic margin, which constitutes the upper boundary of the ventricle of the larynx.

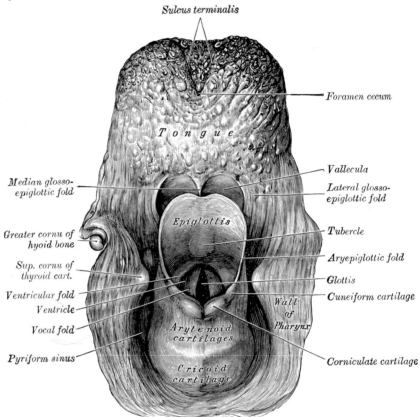

FIG. 949.—The entrance to the larynx, viewed from behind.

The **Vocal Folds** (*plicæ vocales; inferior or true vocal cords*) are concerned in the production of sound, and enclose two strong bands, named the **vocal ligaments** (*ligamenta vocales; inferior thyroarytenoid*). Each ligament consists of a band of yellow elastic tissue, attached in front to the angle of the thyroid cartilage, and behind to the vocal process of the arytenoid. Its lower border is continuous with the thin lateral part of the conus elasticus. Its upper border forms the lower boundary of the ventricle of the larynx. Laterally, the Vocalis muscle lies parallel with it. It is covered medially by mucous membrane, which is extremely thin and closely adherent to its surface.

The **Ventricle of the Larynx** (*ventriculus laryngis* [*Morgagnii*]; *laryngeal sinus*) is a fusiform fossa, situated between the ventricular and vocal folds on either side, and extending nearly their entire length. The fossa is bounded, *above*, by the free crescentic edge of the ventricular fold; *below*, by the straight margin of the vocal fold; *laterally*, by the mucous membrane covering the corresponding Thyreoary-tænoideus. The anterior part of the ventricle leads up by a narrow opening into a cecal pouch of mucous membrane of variable size called the **appendix.**

The **appendix of the laryngeal ventricle** (*appendix ventriculi laryngis; laryngeal saccule*) is a membranous sac, placed between the ventricular fold and the inner surface of the thyroid cartilage, occasionally extending as far as its upper border or even higher; it is conical in form, and curved slightly backward. On the surface of its mucous membrane are the openings of sixty or seventy mucous glands, which are lodged in the submucous areolar tissue. This sac is enclosed in a fibrous capsule, continuous below with the ventricular ligament. Its medial surface is covered by a few delicate muscular fasciculi, which *arise* from the apex of the arytenoid cartilage and become lost in the aryepiglottic fold of mucous membrane; laterally it is separated from the thyroid cartilage by the Thyreoepiglotticus. These muscles compress the sac, and express the secretion it contains upon the vocal folds to lubricate their surfaces.

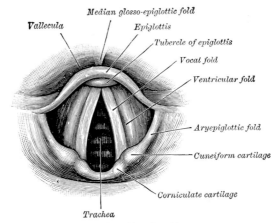

FIG. 950.—Laryngoscopic view of interior of larynx.

The **Rima Glottidis** (Fig. 950) is the elongated fissure or chink between the vocal folds in front, and the bases and vocal processes of the arytenoid cartilages behind. It is therefore subdivided into a larger anterior intramembranous part (*glottis vocalis*), which measures about three-fifths of the length of the entire aperture, and a posterior intercartilaginous part (*glottis respiratoria*). Posteriorly it is limited by the mucous membrane passing between the arytenoid cartilages. The rima glottidis is the narrowest part of the cavity of the larynx, and its level corresponds with the bases of the arytenoid cartilages. Its length, in the male, is about 23 mm.; in the female from 17 to 18 mm. The width and shape of the rima glottidis vary with the movements of the vocal folds and arytenoid cartilages during respiration and phonation. In the condition of rest, *i. e.*, when these structures are uninfluenced by muscular action, as in quiet respiration, the intermembranous part is triangular, with its apex in front and its base behind—the latter being represented by a line, about 8 mm. long, connecting the anterior ends of the vocal processes, while the medial surfaces of the arytenoids are parallel to each other, and hence the intercartilaginous part is rectangular. During extreme adduction of the vocal folds, as in the emission of a high note, the intermembranous part is reduced to a linear slit by the apposition of the vocal folds, while the intercartilaginous part is triangular, its apex corresponding to the anterior ends of the vocal processes of the arytenoids, which are approximated by the medial rotation of the cartilages. Conversely in extreme abduction of the vocal folds, as in forced inspiration, the arytenoids and their vocal processes are rotated lateralward, and the intercartilaginous part is triangular in shape but with its apex directed backward. In this condition the entire glottis is somewhat lozenge-shaped, the sides of the intramembranous part diverging from before backward, those of the intercartilaginous part diverging from behind forward—the widest part of the aperture corresponding with the attachments of the vocal folds to the vocal processes.

Muscles.—The muscles of the larynx are *extrinsic*, passing between the larynx and parts around—these have been described in the section on Myology; and *intrinsic*, confined entirely to the larynx.

The intrinsic muscles are:

Cricothyreoideus.	Cricoarytænoideus lateralis.
Cricoarytænoideus posterior.	Arytænoideus.
	Thyroarytænoideus.

The **Cricothyreoideus** (*Cricothyroid*) (Fig. 951), triangular in form, *arises* from the front and lateral part of the cricoid cartilage; its fibers diverge, and are arranged in two groups. The lower fibers constitute a **pars obliqua** and slant backward and lateralward to the anterior border of the inferior cornu; the anterior fibers, forming a **pars recta**, run upward, backward, and lateralward to the posterior part of the lower border of the lamina of the thyroid cartilage.

The medial borders of the two muscles are separated by a triangular interval, occupied by the middle cricothyroid ligament.

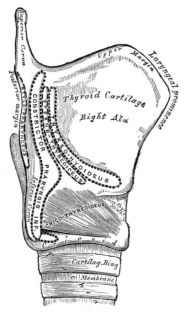

FIG. 951.—Side view of the larynx, showing muscular attachments.

The **Cricoarytænoideus posterior** (*posterior cricoarytenoid*) (Fig. 952) *arises* from the broad depression on the corresponding half of the posterior surface of the lamina of the cricoid cartilage; its fibers run upward and lateralward, and converge to be *inserted* into the back of the muscular process of the arytenoid cartilage. The uppermost fibers are nearly horizontal, the middle oblique, and the lowest almost vertical.

The **Cricoarytænoideus lateralis** (*lateral cricoarytenoid*) (Fig. 953) is smaller than the preceding, and of an oblong form. It *arises* from the upper border of the arch of the cricoid cartilage, and, passing obliquely upward and backward, is inserted into the front of the muscular process of the arytenoid cartilage.

The **Arytænoideus** (Fig. 952) is a single muscle, filling up the posterior concave surfaces of the arytenoid cartilages. It *arises* from the posterior surface and lateral border of one arytenoid cartilage, and is inserted into the corresponding parts of the opposite cartilage. It consists of oblique and transverse parts. The **Arytænoideus obliquus**, the more superficial, forms two fasciculi, which pass from the base of one cartilage to the apex of the opposite one, and therefore cross each other like the limbs of the letter X; a few fibers are continued around the lateral margin of the cartilage, and are prolonged into the aryepiglottic fold; they are sometimes described as a separate muscle, the **Aryepiglotticus**. The **Arytænoideus transversus** crosses transversely between the two cartilages.

The **Thyreoarytænoideus** (*Thyroarytenoid*) (Figs. 953, 954) is a broad, thin, muscle which lies parallel with and lateral to the vocal fold, and supports the wall

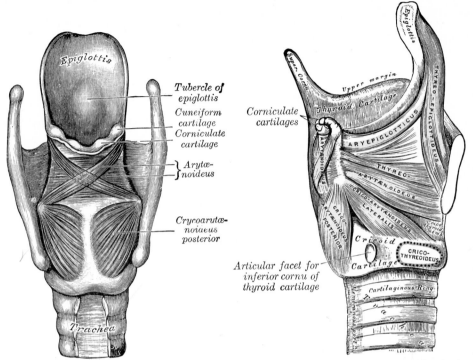

FIG. 952.—Muscles of larynx. Posterior view.

FIG. 953 —Muscles of larynx. Side view. Right lamina of thyroid cartilage removed.

of the ventricle and its appendix. It *arises in front* from the lower half of the angle of the thyroid cartilage, and from the middle cricothyroid ligament. Its fibers pass backward and lateralward, to be *inserted* into the base and anterior surface of the arytenoid cartilage. The lower and deeper fibers of the muscle can be differentiated as a triangular band which is inserted into the vocal process of the arytenoid cartilage, and into the adjacent portion of its anterior surface; it is termed the **Vocalis**, and lies parallel with the vocal ligament, to which it is adherent.

A considerable number of the fibers of the Thyreoarytænoideus are prolonged into the aryepiglottic fold, where some of them become lost, while others are continued to the margin of the epiglottis.

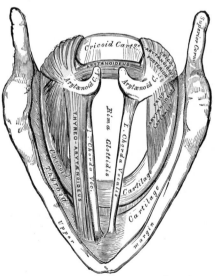

FIG. 954.—Muscles of the larynx, seen from above. (Enlarged.)

They have received a distinctive name, **Thyreoepiglotticus**, and are sometimes described as a separate muscle. A few fibers extend along the wall of the ventricle from the lateral wall of the arytenoid cartilage to the side of the epiglottis and constitute the **Ventricularis** muscle.

Actions.—In considering the actions of the muscles of the larynx, they may be conveniently divided into two groups, viz.: 1. Those which open and close the glottis. 2. Those which regulate the degree of tension of the vocal folds.

The *Cricoarytænoidei posteriores* separate the vocal folds, and, consequently, open the glottis, by rotating the arytenoid cartilages outward around a vertical axis passing through the cricoarytenoid joints; so that their vocal processes and the vocal folds attached to them become widely separated.

The *Cricoarytænoidei laterales* close the glottis by rotating the arytenoid cartilages inward, so as to approximate their vocal processes.

The *Arytænoideus* approximates the arytenoid cartilages, and thus closes the opening of the glottis, especially at its back part.

The *Cricothyreoidei* produce tension and elongation of the vocal folds by drawing up the arch of the cricoid cartilage and tilting back the upper border of its lamina; the distance between the vocal processes and the angle of the thyroid is thus increased, and the folds are consequently elongated.

The *Thyreoarytænoidei*, consisting of two parts having different attachments and different directions, are rather complicated as regards their action. Their main use is to draw the arytenoid cartilages forward toward the thyroid, and thus shorten and relax the vocal folds. Their lateral portions rotate the arytenoid cartilage inward, and thus narrow the rima glottidis by bringing the two vocal folds together. Certain minute fibers of the vocalis division, inserting obliquely upon the vocal ligament and designated as the aryvocalis muscle, are considered by Strong to be chiefly responsible for the control of pitch, through their ability to regulate the length of the vibrating part of the vocal folds.

The manner in which the entrance of the larynx is closed during deglutition is referred to on page 1182.

Mucous Membrane.—The mucous membrane of the larynx is continuous above with that lining the mouth and pharynx, and is prolonged through the trachea and bronchi into the lungs. It lines the posterior surface and the upper part of the anterior surface of the epiglottis, to which it is closely adherent, and forms the aryepiglottic folds which bound the entrance of the larynx. It lines the whole of the cavity of the larynx; forms, by its reduplication, the chief part of the ventricular fold, and, from the ventricle, is continued into the ventricular appendix. It is then reflected over the vocal ligament, where it is thin, and very intimately adherent; covers the inner surface of the conus elasticus and cricoid cartilage; and is ultimately continuous with the lining membrane of the trachea. The anterior surface and the upper half of the posterior surface of the epiglottis, the upper part of the aryepiglottic folds and the vocal folds are covered by stratified squamous epithelium; all the rest of the laryngeal mucous membrane is covered by columnar ciliated cells, but patches of stratified squamous epithelium are found in the mucous membrane above the glottis.

Glands.—The mucous membrane of the larynx is furnished with numerous mucous secreting glands, the orifices of which are found in nearly every part; they are very plentiful upon the epiglottis, being lodged in little pits in its substance; they are also found in large numbers along the margin of the aryepiglottic fold, in front of the arytenoid cartilages, where they are termed the **arytenoid glands.** They exist also in large numbers in the ventricular appendages. None are found on the free edges of the vocal folds.

Vessels and Nerves.—The chief **arteries** of the larynx are the laryngeal branches derived from the superior and inferior thyroid. The **veins** accompany the arteries; those accompanying the superior laryngeal artery join the superior thyroid vein which opens into the internal jugular vein; while those accompanying the inferior laryngeal artery join the inferior thyroid vein which opens into the innominate vein. The **lymphatic vessels** consist of two sets, superior and inferior. The former accompany the superior laryngeal artery and pierce the hyothyroid membrane, to end in the nodes situated near the bifurcation of the common carotid artery. Of the latter, some pass through the middle cricothyroid ligament and open into nodes lying in front of that ligament or in front of the upper part of the trachea, while others pass to the deep cervical nodes and to the nodes accompanying the inferior thyroid artery. The **nerves** are derived from the internal and external branches of the superior laryngeal nerve, from the recurrent nerve, and from the sympathetic. The internal laryngeal branch is sensory. It enters the larynx by piercing the posterior part of the hyothyroid membrane above the superior laryngeal vessels, and divides into a branch which is distributed to both surfaces of the epiglottis, a second to the aryepiglottic fold, and a third, the largest, which supplies the mucous membrane over the back of the larynx and communicates with the recurrent nerve. The external laryngeal branch supplies the Cricothyreoideus. The recurrent nerve passes upward beneath the lower border of the Constrictor pharyngis inferior immediately behind the cricothyroid joint. It supplies all the muscles of the larynx except the Cricothyreoideus. The sensory branches of the laryngeal nerves form subepithelial plexuses, from which fibers pass to end between the cells covering the mucous membrane.

Over the posterior surface of the epiglottis, in the aryepiglottic folds, and less regularly in some other parts, taste-buds, similar to those in the tongue, are found.

THE TRACHEA AND BRONCHI (Figs. 955, 956).

The **trachea** or **windpipe** is a cartilaginous and membranous tube, extending from the lower part of the larynx, on a level with the sixth cervical vertebra, to the upper border of the fifth thoracic vertebra, where it divides into the two bronchi, one for each lung. The trachea is nearly but not quite cylindrical, being flattened posteriorly; it measures about 11 cm. in length; its diameter, from side to side, is from 2 to 2.5 cm., being always greater in the male than in the female. In the child the trachea is smaller, more deeply placed, and more movable than in the adult.

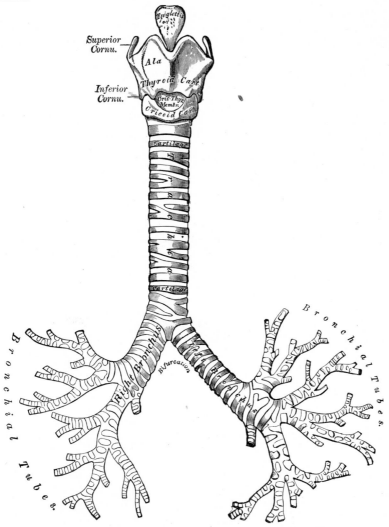

FIG. 955.—Front view of cartilages of larynx, trachea, and bronchi.

Relations.—The *anterior surface* of the trachea is convex, and covered, **in the neck,** from above downward, by the isthmus of the thyroid gland, the inferior thyroid veins, the arteria thyroidea ima (when that vessel exists), the Sternothyreoideus and Sternohyoideus muscles, the cervical fascia, and, more superficially, by the anastomosing branches between the anterior jugular veins; **in the thorax,** it is covered from before backward by the manubrium sterni, the remains of the thymus, the left innominate vein, the aortic arch, the innominate and left common carotid arteries, and the deep cardiac plexus. Posteriorly it is in contact with the esophagus. *Laterally,* **in the neck,** it is in relation with the common carotid arteries, the right and left lobes of the thyroid gland, the inferior thyroid arteries, and the recurrent nerves; **in the thorax,** it lies in the superior mediastinum, and is in relation on the right side with the pleura and right vagus, and near the root of the neck with the innominate artery; on its left side are the left recurrent nerve, the aortic arch, and the left common carotid and subclavian arteries.

The **Right Broncus** (*bronchus dexter*) is wider, shorter, and less abrupt in its divergence from the trachea than the left. It is about 2.5 cm. long and enters the right lung nearly opposite the fifth thoracic vertebra. The azygos vein arches over it and the pulmonary artery lies at first inferior and then ventral to it. It gives rise to three subsidiary bronchi, one to each of the lobes. The superior lobe bronchus comes off above the pulmonary artery and was called by Aeby, therefore, the **eparterial bronchus.** The bronchi to the middle and inferior lobes separate below the pulmonary artery and are accordingly hyparterial in position.

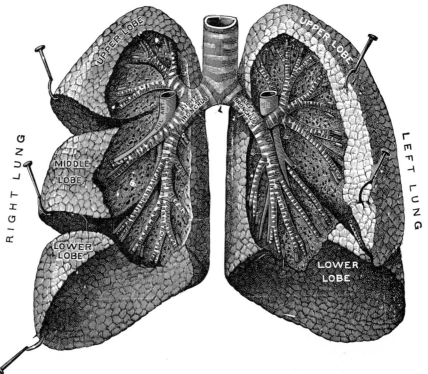

Fig. 956.—Bronchi and bronchioles. The lungs have been widely separated and tissue cut away to expose the air-tubes
(Testut.)

The **right superior lobe bronchus** divides into three branches named, according to the bronchopulmonary segments which they enter, the bronchus for the apical segment, for the posterior segment, and for the anterior segment. The **right middle lobe bronchus** divides into two branches, the bronchus for the lateral and for the medial segments. The **right inferior lobe bronchus** first gives off the bronchus to the superior segment, and then divides into four bronchi for the basal segments, the medial basal, anterior basal, lateral basal, and posterior basal segments.

The **Left Bronchus** (*bronchus sinister*) is smaller in caliber but about twice as long as the right (5 cm.). It passes under the aortic arch, and crosses ventral to the esophagus, thoracic duct, and descending aorta. It is superior to the pulmonary artery at first, then dorsal, and finally passes inferior to the artery before it divides into the bronchi for the superior and inferior lobes. Both lobar bronchi, therefore, are hyparterial in position.

The **left superior lobe bronchus** divides into two branches, one of which is distributed to a portion of the left lung corresponding to the right superior lobe, the other to a portion corresponding to the right middle lobe. These two branches are called the superior division and inferior division bronchi to differentiate them from segmental bronchi. The *superior division bronchus* of the left superior lobe divides into branches for the apical-posterior segment and the anterior segment. The *inferior division bronchus* divides into bronchi for the superior and inferior segments. The **left inferior lobe bronchus** gives off first the bronchus for the superior segment and then divides into three branches for basal segments, the anterior-medial basal, lateral basal, and posterior basal segments.

The picture seen through a bronchoscope may be reproduced if a section is made across the trachea and a bird's eye view taken of its interior (Fig. 957). At the bottom of the trachea, the septum which separates the two bronchi is visible as a spur (in bronchoscopic terminology) and is named in this case the carina.

The **carina** is placed to the left of the middle line and the right bronchus appears as a more direct continuation of the trachea than the left. Because of this asymetry and because the right bronchus is larger in diameter than the left, foreign bodies which enter the trachea have a tendency to drop into the right bronchus rather than the left.

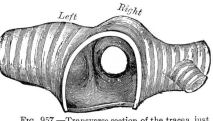

FIG. 957.—Transverse section of the tracea ,just above its bifurcation, with a bird's-eye view of the interior

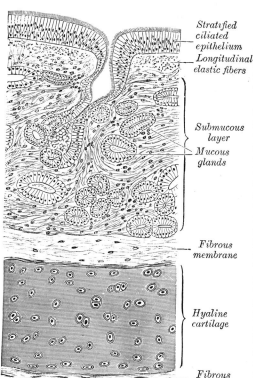

Stratified ciliated epithelium
Longitudinal elastic fibers
Submucous layer
Mucous glands
Fibrous membrane
Hyaline cartilage
Fibrous membrane

FIG. 958.—Transverse section of trachea.

Structure (Fig. 958).—The trachea and extrapulmonary bronchi are composed of imperfect rings of hyaline cartilage, fibrous tissue, muscular fibers, mucous membrane, and glands.

The **cartilages** of the trachea vary from sixteen to twenty in number: each forms an imperfect ring, which occupies the anterior two-thirds or so of the circumference of the trachea, being deficient behind, where the tube is completed by fibrous tissue and unstriped muscular fibers. The cartilages are placed horizontally above each other, separated by narrow intervals. They measure about 4 mm. in depth and 1 mm. in thickness. Their outer surfaces are flattened in a vertical direction, but the internal are convex, the cartilages being thicker in the middle than at the margins. Two or more of the cartilages often unite, partially or completely, and they are sometimes bifurcated at their extremities. They are highly elastic, but may become calcified in advanced life. In the right bronchus the cartilages vary in number from six to eight; in the left, from nine to twelve. They are shorter and narrower than those of the trachea, but have the same shapeand arrangement. The peculiar tracheal cartilages are the first and the last (Fig. 955).

The **first cartilage** is broader than the rest, and often divided at one end; it is connected by the cricotracheal ligament with the lower border of the cricoid cartilage, with which, or with the succeeding cartilage, it is sometimes blended.

The **last cartilage** is thick and broad in the middle, in consequence of its lower border being prolonged into a triangular hook-shaped process, which curves downward and backward between the two bronchi. It ends on each side in an imperfect ring, which encloses the commencement of the bronchus. The cartilage above the last is somewhat broader than the others at its center.

The Fibrous Membrane.—The cartilages are enclosed in an elastic fibrous membrane, which consists of two layers; one, the thicker, passing over the outer surface of the ring, the other over the inner surface: at the upper and lower margins of the cartilages the two layers blend together to form a single membrane, which connects the rings one with another. They are thus invested by the membrane. In the space behind, between the ends of the rings, the membrane forms a single layer.

The **muscular tissue** consists of two layers of non-striated muscle, longitudinal and transverse. The **longitudinal fibers** are external, and consist of a few scattered bundles. The **transverse fibers** (Trachealis muscle) are arranged internally in branching and anastomosing bands which extend more or less transversely between the ends of the cartilage.

Mucous Membrane.—The mucous membrane is continuous above with that of the larynx, and below with that of the bronchi. It consists of areolar and lymphoid tissue, and presents a well-marked basement membrane, supporting a stratified epithelium, the surface layer of which is columnar and ciliated, while the deeper layers are composed of oval or rounded cells. Beneath the basement membrane there is a distinct layer of longitudinal elastic fibers with a small amount of intervening areolar tissue. The submucous layer is composed of a loose mesh-work of connective tissue, containing large bloodvessels, nerves, and mucous glands; the ducts of the latter pierce the overlying layers and open on the surface (Fig. 958).

Vessels and Nerves.—The trachea is supplied with blood by the inferior thyroid **arteries**. The **veins** end in the thyroid venous plexus. The **nerves** are derived from the vagus and the recurrent nerves, and from the sympathetic; they are distributed to the Trachealis muscles and between the epithelial cells.

THE PLEURÆ.

Each lung is invested by an exceedingly delicate serous membrane, the **pleura** which is arranged in the form of a closed invaginated sac. A portion of the serous membrane covers the surface of the lung and dips into the fissures between its lobes; it is called the **pulmonary pleura.** The rest of the membrane lines the inner surface of the chest wall, covers the diaphragm, and is reflected over the structures; occupying the middle of the thorax; this portion is termed the **parietal pleura.** The two layers are continuous with one another around and below the root of the lung; in health they are in actual contact with one another, but the potential space between them is known as the **pleural cavity.** When the lung collapses or when air or fluid collects between the two layers the cavity becomes apparent. The right and left pleural sacs are entirely separate from one another; between them are all the thoracic viscera except the lungs, and they only touch each other for a short distance in front, opposite the second and third pieces of the sternum; the interval between the two sacs is termed the mediastinum.

Different portions of the parietal pleura have received special names which indicate their position: thus, that portion which lines the inner surfaces of the ribs and Intercostales is the **costal pleura;** that clothing the convex surface of the diaphragm is the **diaphragmatic pleura;** that which rises into the neck, over the summit of the lung, is the **cupula of the pleura** (*cervical pleura*); and that which is applied to the other thoracic viscera is the **mediastinal pleura.**

Reflections of the Pleura (Figs. 959, 960).—Commencing at the sternum, the pleura passes lateralward, lines the inner surfaces of the costal cartilages, ribs, and Intercostales, and at the back part of the thorax passes over the sympathetic trunk and its branches, and is reflected upon the sides of the bodies of the vertebræ, where it is separated by a narrow interval, the **posterior mediastinum,** from the opposite pleura. From the vertebral column the pleura passes to the side of the pericardium, which it covers to a slight extent; it then covers the back part of the root of the lung, from the lower border of which a triangular sheet descends vertically toward the diaphragm. This sheet is the posterior layer of a wide fold, known as the **pulmonary ligament**. From the back of the lung root, the pleura may be traced over the costal surface of the lung, the apex and base, and also over the sides of the fissures between the lobes, on to its mediastinal surface and the front part of its root. It is continued from the lower margin of the root as the anterior layer of the pulmonary ligament, and from this it is reflected on to the pericardium (**pericardial pleura**), and from it to the back of the sternum. Above the level of the root of the lung, however, the mediastinal pleura passes uninterruptedly from the vertebral column to the sternum over the structures in the superior mediastinum. *Below*, it covers the upper surface of the diaphragm and extends, in front, as low as the costal cartilage of the seventh rib; at the side of the chest, to the lower border of the tenth rib on the left side and to the upper border of the

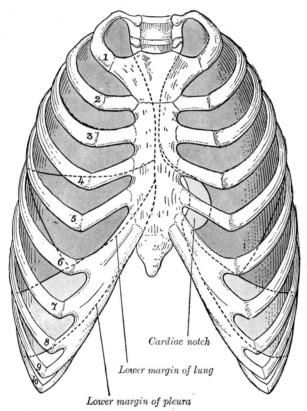

Cardiac notch

Lower margin of lung

Lower margin of pleura

Fɪɢ. 959.—Front view of thorax, showing the relations of the pleuræ and lungs to the chest wall. Phrenicocostal and costomediastinal sinus in blue; lungs in purple.

same rib on the right side; and *behind*, it reaches as low as the twelfth rib, and sometimes even to the transverse process of the first lumbar vertebra. *Above*, its cupula projects through the superior opening of the thorax into the neck, extending from 2.5 to 5 cm. above the sternal end of the first rib; this portion of the sac is strengthened by a dome-like expansion of fascia (**Sibson's fascia**), attached in front to the inner border of the first rib, and behind to the anterior border of the transverse process of the seventh cervical vertebra. This is covered and strengthened by a few spreading muscular fibers derived from the Scaleni.

In the front of the chest, where the parietal pleura is reflected backward to the pericardium, the two pleural sacs are in contact for a short distance. At the upper part of the chest, behind the manubrium, they are separated by an angular interval; the line of reflection being represented by a line drawn from the sternoclavicular articulation to the mid-point of the junction of the manubrium with the body of the sternum. From this point the two pleuræ descend in close contact to the level of the fourth costal cartilages, and the line of reflection on the right side is continued downward in nearly a straight line to the xiphoid process, and then turns lateralward, while on the left side the line of reflection diverges lateralward and is continued downward, close to the left border of the sternum, as far as the sixth costal cartilage. The inferior limit of the pleura is on a considerably lower level than the corresponding limit of the lung, but does not extend to the attachment of the diaphragm, so that below the line of reflection of the pleura from the chest wall on to the diaphragm the latter is in direct contact with the rib cartilages and the Intercostales interni. Moreover, in ordinary inspiration the thin inferior margin of the lung does not extend as low as the line of the pleural reflection, with the result that the costal and diaphragmatic pleuræ are here in contact, the intervening narrow slit being termed the **phrenicocostal sinus.** A similar condition exists behind the sternum and rib cartilages, where the anterior thin margin of the lung falls short of the line of pleural reflection, and where the slit-like cavity between the two layers of pleura forms what is called the **costomediastinal sinus.**

The line along which the right pleura is reflected from the chest-wall to the diaphragm starts in front, immediately below the seventh sternocostal joint, and runs downward and backward behind the seventh costal cartilage so as to cross the tenth rib in the mid-axillary line, from which it is prolonged to the spinous process of the twelfth thoracic vertebra. The reflection of the left pleura follows at first the ascending part of the sixth costal cartilage, and in the rest of its course is slightly lower than that of the right side.

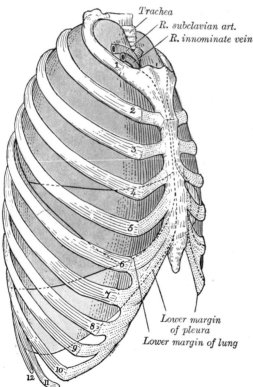

Trachea
R. subclavian art.
R. innominate vein

1
2
3
4
5
6
7
8
9
10
12

Lower margin of pleura
Lower margin of lung

Fig. 960.—Lateral view of thorax; showing the relations of the pleuræ and lungs to the chest wall. Phrenicocostal and costomediastinal sinus in blue; lungs in purple.

The free surface of the pleura is smooth, polished, and moistened by a serous fluid; its attached surface is intimately adherent to the lung, and to the pulmonary vessels as they emerge from the pericardium; it is also adherent to the upper surface of the diaphragm: throughout the rest of its extent it is easily separable from the adjacent parts.

The right pleural sac is shorter, wider, and reaches higher in the neck than the left.

Pulmonary Ligament (*ligamentum pulmonale; ligamentum latum pulmonis*).—From the above description it will be seen that the root of the lung is covered in front above, and behind by pleura, and that at its lower border the investing layers come into contact. Here they form a sort of mesenteric fold, the pulmonary ligament, which extends between the lower part of the mediastinal surface of the lung and the pericardium. Just above the diaphragm the ligament ends in a free falciform border. It serves to retain the lower part of the lung in position.

Structure of Pleura.—Like other serous membranes, the pleura is covered by a single layer of flattened mesothelial cells resting upon a delicate basement membrane, beneath which lies a stroma of collagenous tissue containing several prominent net-works of yellow elastic fibers. Bloodvessels, lymphatics, and nerves are distributed in the substance of the pleura.

Vessels and Nerves.—The **arteries of the pleura** are derived from the intercostal, internal mammary, musculophrenic, thymic, pericardiac, pulmonary, and bronchial vessels. The **veins** correspond to the arteries. The **lymphatics** are described on page 730. The **nerves** of the parietal pleura are derived from the phrenic, intercostal, vagus and sympathetic nerves; those of the pulmonary pleura from the vagus and sympathetic through the pulmonary plexuses at the hilus of the lung. Kölliker states that nerves accompany the ramifications of the bronchial arteries in the pulmonary pleura.

THE MEDIASTINUM.

The **mediastinum** is interposed as a septum, the **mediastinal septum** (*septum mediastinale*), in the median portion of the thorax, separating the pleural sacs of the two lungs (Figs. 569 and 522). It extends from the sternum ventrally to the vertebral column dorsally and comprises all the thoracic viscera, except the lungs and pleuræ, imbedded in a thickening and expansion of the subserous fascia of the

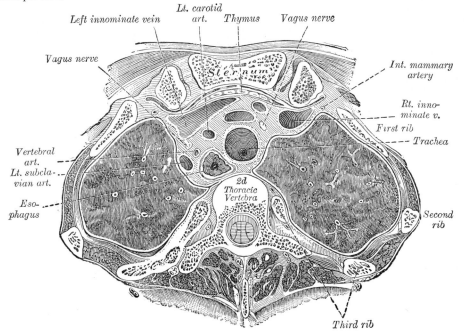

Fig. 961.—Transverse section through the upper margin of the second thoracic vertebra. (Braune.)

thorax. It is divided arbitrarily, for the purposes of description, into upper and lower parts, at the upper level of the pericardium, by a plane which extends from the sternal angle to the lower border of the fourth thoracic vertebra. The upper part is named the **superior mediastinum**; the lower part is again subdivided into three parts: the **anterior mediastinum**, in front of the pericardium; the **middle mediastinum**, containing the pericardium; and the **posterior mediastinum**, behind the pericardium.

The **superior mediastinum** (Fig. 961) is bounded above, by the superior aperture of the thorax; below, by the plane of the superior limit of the pericardium; ventrally, by the manubrium; dorsally, by the upper four thoracic vertebræ; and laterally, by the mediastinal pleuræ of the two lungs. It contains the origins of the Sterno-hyoidei and Sternothyreoidei and the lower ends of the Longi colli; the aortic arch; the innominate artery and the thoracic portions of the left common carotid and the left subclavian arteries; the innominate veins and the upper half of the superior vena cava; the left highest intercostal vein; the vagus, cardiac, phrenic, and left recurrent nerves; the trachea, esophagus, and thoracic duct; the remains of the thymus, and some lymph nodes.

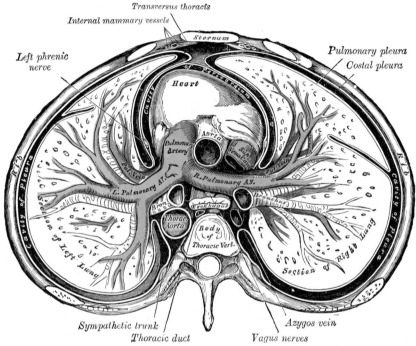

Fig. 962.--A transverse section of the thorax, showing the contents of the middle and the posterior mediastinum The pleural and pericardial cavities are exaggerated since normally there is no space between parietal and viscera pleura and between pericardium and heart.

The **anterior mediastinum** (Fig. 962) is bounded ventrally by the body of the sternum and, because of the position of the heart, the left Transversus thoracis muscle and parts of the fourth, fifth, sixth, and seventh costal cartilages. It is bounded dorsally by the parietal pericardium and extends downward as far as the diaphragm. Besides a few lymph nodes and vessels, it contains only a thin layer of subserous fascia which is separated from the endothoracic or deep fascia superiorly by a fascial cleft, but there is a firm attachment in its lower part which forms the pericardio-sternal ligament.

The **middle mediastinum** (Fig. 962) is the broadest part of the interpleural septum. It contains the heart enclosed in the pericardium, the ascending aorta, the lower half of the superior vena cava with the azygos vein opening into it, the pulmonary artery dividing into its two branches, the right and left pulmonary veins, and the phrenic nerves.

The **posterior mediastinum** (Fig. 962) is an irregularly shaped mass running parallel with the vertebral column, and because of the slope of the diaphragm, extends caudally beyond the pericardium. It is bounded ventrally, by the pericardium and, more caudally, by the diaphragm; dorsally, by the vertebral column from the lower border of the fourth to the twelfth thoracic vertebra; and on either side, by the mediastinal pleuræ. It contains the thoracic part of the descending aorta, the azygos and hemiazygos veins, the vagus and splanchnic nerves, the bifurcation of the trachea and the two bronchi, the esophagus, the thoracic duct, and many large lymph nodes.

The bifurcation of the trachea, the two bronchi, and the roots of the two lungs are included in the middle mediastinum by some authorities.

THE LUNGS (PULMONES).

The **lungs** are the essential organs of respiration; they are two in number, placed one on either side within the thorax, and separated from each other by the heart and other contents of the mediastinum (Figs. 963, 964). The substance of the lung is

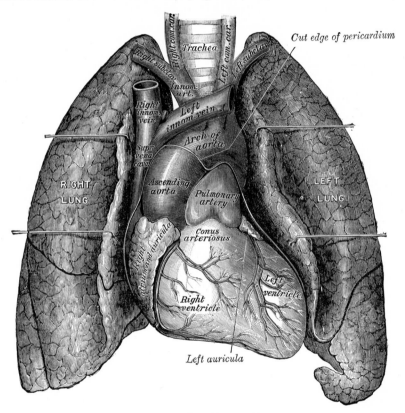

Fig. 963.—Front view of heart and lungs.

of a light, porous, spongy texture; it floats in water, and crepitates when handled, owing to the presence of air in the alveoli; it is also highly elastic; hence the retracted state of these organs when they are removed from the closed cavity of the thorax. The surface is smooth, shining, and marked out into numerous polyhedral areas, indicating the lobules of the organ: each of these areas is crossed by numerous lighter lines.

At birth the lungs are pinkish-white in color; in adult life the color is a dark slaty-gray, mottled in patches, and as age advances, this mottling assumes a black color. The coloring matter consists of granules of a carbonaceous substance deposited in the areolar tissue near the surface of the organ. It increases in quantity as age advances, and is more abundant in males than in females. As a rule, the posterior border of the lung is darker than the anterior.

The right lung usually weighs about 625 gm., the left 567 gm., but much variation is met with according to the amount of blood or serous fluid they may contain. The lungs are heavier in the male than in the female, their proportion to the body being, in the former, as 1 to 37, in the latter as 1 to 43. The vital capacity, the quantity of air that can be exhaled by the deepest expiration after making the deepest inspiration varies greatly with the individual; an average for an adult man is 3700 cc. The total volume of the fully expanded lungs is about 6500 cc., this includes both tissues and contained air. The tidal air, the amount of air breathed in or out during quiet respiration is about 500 cc. for the adult man. Various calculations indicate that the total epithelial area of the respiratory and non-respiratory surfaces during ordinary deep inspiration of the adult is not greater than 70 square meters.

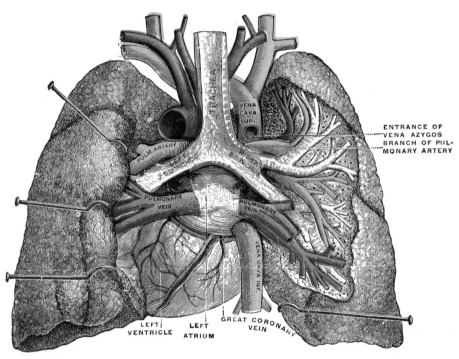

Fig. 964.—Pulmonary vessels, seen in a dorsal view of the heart and lungs. The lungs have been pulled away from the median line, and a part of the right lung has been cut away to display the air-ducts and blood vessels. (Testut.)

Each lung is conical in shape, and presents for examination an **apex**, a **base**, three **borders**, and two **surfaces**.

The **apex** (*apex pulmonis*) is rounded, and extends into the root of the neck, reaching from 2.5 to 4 cm. above the level of the sternal end of the first rib. A sulcus produced by the subclavian artery as it curves in front of the pleura runs upward and lateralward immediately below the apex.

The **base** (*basis pulmonis*) is broad, concave, and rests upon the convex surface of the diaphragm, which separates the right lung from the right lobe of the liver, and the left lung from the left lobe of the liver, the stomach, and the spleen. Since the diaphragm extends higher on the right than on the left side, the concavity on the base of the right lung is deeper than that on the left. Laterally and behind, the base is bounded by a thin, sharp margin which projects for some distance into the phrenicocostal sinus of the pleura, between the lower ribs and the costal attachment of the diaphragm. The base of the lung descends during inspiration and ascends during expiration.

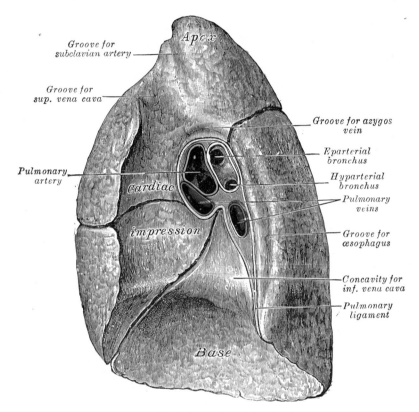

Fig. 965.—Mediastinal surface of right lung.

Surfaces.—The **costal surface** (*facies costalis; external or thoracic surface*) is smooth, convex, of considerable extent, and corresponds to the form of the cavity of the chest, being deeper behind than in front. It is in contact with the costal pleura, and presents, in specimens which have been hardened *in situ*, slight grooves corresponding with the overlying ribs.

The **mediastinal surface** (*facies mediastinalis; inner surface*) is in contact with the mediastinal pleura. It presents a deep concavity, the **cardiac impression,** which accommodates the pericardium; this is larger and deeper on the left than on the right lung, on account of the heart projecting farther to the left than to the right side of the median plane. Above and behind this concavity is a triangular depression named the **hilum**, through which the structures which form the root of the lung enter and leave. These structures are invested by pleura, which, below the hilum and behind the pericardial impression, forms the pulmonary ligament. On the *right* lung (Fig. 965), immediately above the hilum, is an arched furrow which accommodates the azygos vein; while running upward, and then arching lateralward some little distance below the apex, is a wide groove for the superior vena cava and right innominate vein; behind this, and nearer the apex, is a furrow for the subclavian artery. Behind the hilum and the attachment of the pulmonary ligament is a vertical groove for the esophagus; this groove becomes less distinct below, owing to the inclination of the lower part of the esophagus to the left of the middle line. In front and to the right of the lower part of the esophageal groove is a deep concavity for the extrapericardiac portion of the thoracic part of the inferior vena cava. On the *left* lung (Fig. 966), immediately above the hilum, is a well-marked curved furrow produced by the aortic arch, and running upward from this toward the apex is a groove accommodating the left subclavian artery; a slight impression in front of the latter and close to the margin of the lung lodges the left innominate vein. Behind the hilum and pulmonary ligament is a vertical furrow produced by the descending aorta, and in front of this, near the base of the lung, the lower part of the esophagus causes a shallow impression.

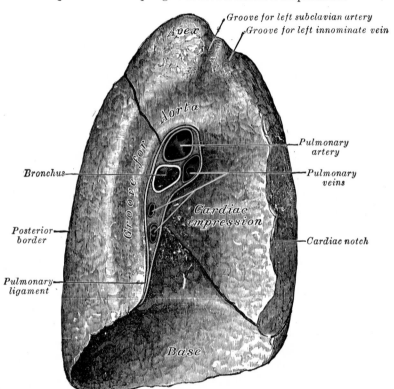

Fig. 966.—Mediastinal surface of left lung.

Borders.—The **inferior border** (*margo inferior*) is thin and sharp where it separates the base from the costal surface and extends into the phrenicocostal sinus; medially where it divides the base from the mediastinal surface it is blunt and rounded.

The **posterior border** (*margo posterior*) is broad and rounded, and is received into the deep concavity on either side of the vertebral column. It is much longer than the anterior border, and projects, below, into the phrenicocostal sinus.

The **anterior border** (*margo anterior*) is thin and sharp, and overlaps the front of the pericardium. The anterior border of the *right* lung is almost vertical, and projects into the costomediastinal sinus; that of the *left* presents, below, an angular notch, the **cardiac notch**, in which the pericardium is exposed. Opposite this notch the anterior margin of the left lung is situated some little distance lateral to the line of reflection of the corresponding part of the pleura.

Fissures and Lobes of the Lungs.—The **left lung** is divided into two lobes, an upper and a lower, by an interlobar fissure, which extends from the costal to the mediastinal surface of the lung both above and below the hilum. As seen on the surface, this fissure begins on the mediastinal surface of the lung at the upper and posterior part of the hilum, and runs backward and upward to the posterior border, which it crosses at a point about 6 cm. below the apex. It then extends downward and forward over the costal surface, and reaches the lower border a little behind its anterior extremity, and its further course can be followed upward and backward across the mediastinal surface as far as the lower part of the hilum. The **superior lobe** lies above and in front of this fissure, and includes the apex, the anterior border, and a considerable part of the costal surface and the greater part of the mediastinal surface of the lung. The **inferior lobe,** the larger of the two, is situated below and behind the fissure, and comprises almost the whole of the base, a large portion of the costal surface, and the greater part of the posterior border.

The **right lung** is divided into three lobes, superior, middle, and inferior, by two interlobar fissures. One of these separates the inferior from the middle and superior lobes, and corresponds closely with the fissure in the left lung. Its direction is, however, more vertical, and it cuts the lower border about 7.5 cm. behind its anterior extremity. The other fissure separates the superior from the middle lobe. It begins in the previous fissure near the posterior border of the lung, and, running horizontally forward, cuts the anterior border on a level with the sternal end of the fourth costal cartilage; on the mediastinal surface it may be traced backward to the hilum. The **middle lobe,** the smallest lobe of the right lung, is wedge-shaped, and includes the lower part of the anterior border and the anterior part of the base of the lung.

The right lung, although shorter by 2.5 cm. than the left, in consequence of the diaphragm rising higher on the right side to accommodate the liver, is broader, owing to the inclination of the heart to the left side; its total capacity is greater and it weighs more than the left lung.

Further Subdivision of the Lung. — The importance of certain smaller units of structure of the lungs, called bronchopulmonary segments, has been emphasized by the thoracic surgeon, bronchoscopist, and radiologist. In order to interpret these units correctly, one should give particular attention to the concept that the lung is fundamentally the aggregate of all the branchings of the bronchus. According to this concept, a bronchopulmonary segment would be that portion of the lung to which any particular bronchus is distributed and the term might conceivably be applied to the lobule, supplied by its lobular bronchus. In actual practice, however, it is customary to restrict the term bronchopulmonary segment to the portion of the lung supplied by the direct branches of the lobar bronchi (and of the division bronchi in the case of the left superior lobe). These segments are as definite as the lobes and their relative extent and position can be demonstrated by introducing different colored gelatin into their bronchi. It is possible, in many cases, to follow the delicate connective tissue between them and dissect them apart. Another demonstration of their fundamental nature is given by the fact that the majority of extra fissures follow the planes of separation between the segments.

The Bronchopulmonary Segments (Fig. 967).—The bronchopulmonary segments are named according to their positions in the lobes and the bronchus to each is named after its segment. The right superior lobe has three segments, an apical, a posterior, and an anterior segment. The right middle lobe has a lateral and a medial segment. The right inferior lobe has a superior and four basal segments, the medial basal, anterior basal, lateral basal, and posterior basal segments. The left superior lobe is first separated into two divisions, the superior division corresponding to the right superior lobe and an inferior division, corresponding to the right middle lobe. The superior division of the left superior lobe has an apical-

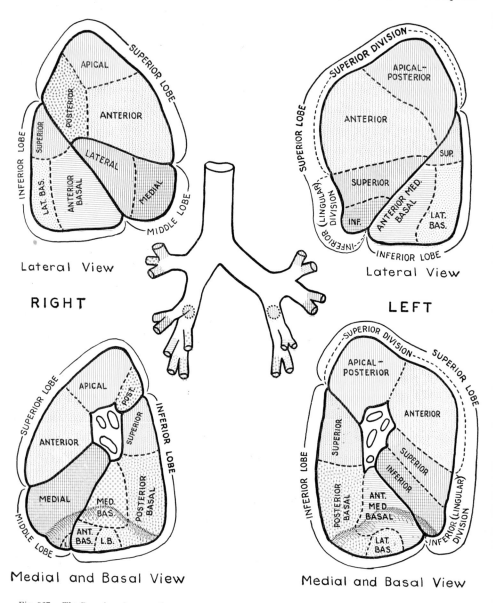

Fig. 967.—The Bronchopulmonary Segments. The segmental branches of the bronchi are shown in corresponding colors. (After J.F. Huber by W.B. Stewart)

posterior and an anterior segment. The inferior division of the left superior lobe has a superior and an inferior segment. The left inferior lobe has a superior and three basal segments, the anterior-medial basal, lateral basal, and posterior basal segments.

Right Lung			Left Lung		
LOBES	SEGMENTS		LOBES		SEGMENTS
Superior	Apical Posterior Anterior		Superior	Superior Division	Apical-posterior Anterior
Middle	Lateral Medial			Inferior (Lingular) Division	Superior Inferior
Inferior	Superior Medial Basal Anterior Basal Lateral Basal Posterior Basal		Inferior	Superior Anterior-medial Basal Lateral Basal Posterior Basal	

Variations.—The branching of the lobar bronchi to form segmental bronchi is reasonably constant, according to Huber (1947). The superior lobe bronchus is somewhat more constant than the inferior lobe bronchus. In approximately 95 per cent of the specimens, it is possible to identify three segmental bronchi coming from the right superior lobe bronchus, although in some of these cases, two segmental bronchi may seem to arise from a very short common stem. The size of the lung segment supplied by a particular bronchus may be larger or smaller than expected, even when the branching appears at first glance to follow the usual pattern, because it may have exchanged a smaller branch bronchus with an adjacent segmental bronchus. In the case of the lower lobe bronchus, the superior and the medial basal segmental bronchi are about as constant as the branches in the superior lobe, but there is more variation in the anterior basal, lateral basal, and posterior basal segments. In somewhat less than 50 per cent of the specimens, branches come from the posterior aspect of the inferior lobe bronchus between the superior segmental and the basal segmental bronchi, or from the stem below the anterior basal segmental bronchus.

The Root of the Lung (*radix pulmonis*) (Figs. 965, 966) is formed by the bronchus, pulmonary artery, pulmonary veins, bronchial arteries and veins, pulmonary plexuses of nerves, lymphatic vessels, and bronchial lymph nodes. These structures are all imbedded in mediastinal connective tissue and the entire mass is encircled by a reflection of the pleura. It corresponds to the hilum, which is near the center of the mediastinal surface of the lung, dorsal to the cardiac impression and closer to the posterior than the anterior border. The root of the right lung lies dorsal to the superior vena cava and the right atrium, and the azygos vein arches over it (Fig. 569). The root of the left lung is ventral to the descending aorta and inferior to the aortic arch (Fig. 522). The phrenic nerve, the pericardiophrenic artery and vein, and the anterior pulmonary plexus of nerves are ventral, while the vagus nerve and its posterior pulmonary plexus are dorsal to the root of the lung on both sides. Below the root of each lung, the reflection of the pleura from mediastinum to lung is prolonged downward toward the diaphragm as the pulmonary ligament (page 1126).

The chief structures of the roots of both lungs have a similar relation to each other in a dorso-ventral direction, but there is a difference in their superior and inferior relations on the two sides. Thus the pulmonary veins are ventral, the bronchi dorsal, and the pulmonary arteries between, on both sides. On the right side, the superior lobe bronchus is superior, the pulmonary artery is slightly lower, next are the bronchi to the middle and inferior lobes, and most inferior is the pulmonary vein (Fig. 965). On the left side, the pulmonary artery is superior, the pulmonary veins inferior, and the bronchus between (Fig. 966).

Structure.—The lungs are composed of an external serous coat, a subserous areolar tissue and the pulmonary substance or parenchyma.

The **serous coat** is the pulmonary pleura (page 1124); it is thin, transparent, and invests the entire organ as far as the root.

The **subserous areolar tissue** contains a large proportion of elastic fibers; it invests the entire surface of the lung, and extends inward between the lobules.

The **parenchyma** is composed of secondary lobules which, although closely connected together by an interlobular areolar tissue, are quite distinct from one another, and may be teased asunder without much difficulty in the fetus. The secondary lobules vary in size; those on the surface are large, of pyramidal form, the base turned toward the surface; those in the interior smaller, and of various forms. Each secondary lobule is composed of several primary lobules, the anatomical units of the lung. The primary lobule consists of an alveolar duct, the air spaces connected with it and their blood vessels, lymphatics and nerves (Fig. 968).

The **intrapulmonary bronchi** divide and subdivide throughout the entire organ, the smallest subdivisions constituting the lobular bronchioles. The *larger divisions* consist of: (1) an outer coat of fibrous tissue in which are found at intervals irregular plates of hyaline cartilage, most developed at the points of division; (2) internal to the fibrous coat, an interlacing net-work of circularly disposed smooth muscle fibers, the bronchial muscle; and (3) most internally, the mucous membrane, lined by columnar ciliated epithelium resting on a basement membrane.

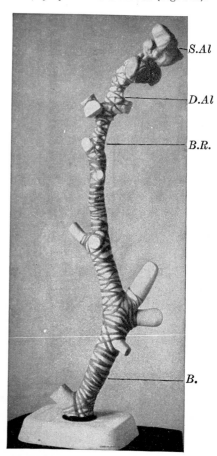

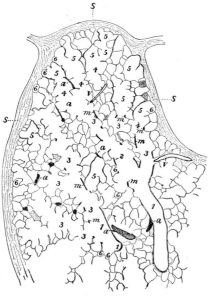

Fig. 968.—Part of a secondary lobule from the depth of a human lung, showing parts of several primary lobules. 1, bronchiole; 2, respiratory bronchiole; 3, alveolar duct; 4, atria; 5, alveolar sac; 6, alveolus or air cell; *m,* smooth muscle; *a,* branch pulmonary artery; *v,* branch pulmonary vein; *s,* septum between secondary lobules. Camera drawing of one 50 μ section. × 20 diameters. (Miller, Jour. Morph.)

Fig. 969.—View of a reconstructon, from a dog's lung, of the musculature of a non-cartilaginous bronchiolus (lobular bronchiole), 0.565 mm. in diameter, its branches, and its termination in a primary lobule of which only a single alveolar sac is shown completely reconstructed. *B,* bronchiolus; *B.R.,* bronchiolus respiratorius; *D.Al.,* ductulus alveolaris; *S.Al.,* sacculus alveolaris. × 125 and reduced to 8. (Miller, The Lung, courtesy of Charles C Thomas.)

The corium of the mucous membrane contains numerous elastic fibers running longitudinally, and a certain amount of lymphoid tissue; it also contains the ducts of mucous glands, the acini of which lie in the fibrous coat. In the **lobular bronchioles** (terminal bronchioles) the ciliated epithelial cells become cuboidal in shape, and cartilage plates cease to exist when the diameter of the bronchiole reaches about 1 mm. Branching and anastomosing bands of smooth muscle fibers, continuous with those of the intrapulmonary bronchi, invest the bronchiole and its subdivisions to the point of junction between alveolar duct and atrium (Fig. 969).

Each bronchiole, according to Miller, divides into two or more **respiratory bronchioles,** with scattered alveoli, and each of these again divides into several **alveolar ducts,** with a greater number of alveoli connected with them. Each alveolar duct is connected with a variable number of irregularly spherical spaces, which also possess alveoli, the **atria.** With each atrium a variable number (2–5) of **alveolar sacs** are connected which bear on all parts of their circumference **alveoli** or air sacs. Willson claims there is no "spherical space" or "atrium" such as described by Miller.

The **alveoli** are lined by a delicate layer of simple squamous epithelium, the cells of which are united at their edges by cement substance. Between the squames are here and there smaller, polygonal, nucleated cells. Outside the epithelial lining is a little delicate connective tissue containing numerous elastic fibers and a close net-work of blood capillaries, and forming a common wall to adjacent alveoli. Josselyn claims that the epithelial lining of the respiratory bronchioles probably ends abruptly at the mouths of the alveolar ducts and alveoli and that the alveoli are lined by naked capillaries resting on a membrane composed of reticular and elastic fibers and a homogenous transparent ground substance.

The fetal lung resembles a gland in that the alveoli have a small lumen and are lined by cubical epithelium. After the first respiration the alveoli become distended, and the epithelium takes on the characters described above.

Bloodvessels (Fig. 970).—The lung receives two sets of bloodvessels; one derived from the pulmonary artery and serving for respiratory or functional circulation, one derived from the bronchial arteries and furnishing nutritive supply to the lung tissue, including the walls of the pulmonary vessels.

A single **pulmonary artery** conveys the venous blood to each lung; it divides into branches which accompany the bronchi, coursing chiefly along their posterior surface. The bronchopulmonary segments are supplied by main intrasegmental branches of the pulmonary arteries, which are single, for the most part, but which may arise as common trunks for adjacent segments (Boyden, 1945). The artery for one segment is likely to supply small branches to the neighboring segments. Distal to the alveolar duct branches are distributed to each atrium, from which arise smaller radicles terminating in a dense capillary net-work in the walls of the alveoli.

These **pulmonary capillaries** form the richest capillary net-work in the body, the meshes of which are smaller than the vessels themselves. These plexuses lie immediately beneath the lining epithelium in the walls of the alveoli, of which they form a part; the net-work forming a single layer, which is usually common to two or more adjacent alveoli. The arteries of neighboring lobules are independent of each other, but the veins freely anastomose.

The **pulmonary veins,** of which there are usually two for each lung, have their chief origin in the pulmonary capillaries of the alveoli, twenty-five or more capillary loops intervening between the arterial and venous radicles. Other origins consist of capillary net-works within the pleura, and in the walls of the atria, alveolar ducts, and bronchioles. These venous radicles coalesce into larger branches which run through the substance of the lung, independently of the pulmonary arteries and bronchi. The veins are usually intersegmental in position and drain the blood from adjacent parts of two neighboring bronchopulmonary segments. After freely communicating with other branches they form large vessels, which ultimately come into relation with the arteries and bronchial tubes, and accompany them to the hilum of the organ. Finally they open into the left atrium of the heart, conveying oxygenated blood to be distributed to all parts of the body by the aorta.

The **bronchial arteries** supply blood for the nutrition of the lung; the right lung usually receives a single artery and the left lung two. They are derived from the ventral side of the upper part of the thoracic aorta or from the upper aortic intercostal arteries. Some are distributed to the bronchial glands and to the walls of the bronchi and pulmonary vessels; those supplying the bronchi extending as far as the respiratory bronchioles, where they form capillary plexuses which unite with similar plexuses formed by the pulmonary artery, both of which give rise to small venous trunks forming one of the sources of the pulmonary vein. Others are distributed in the interlobular areolar tissue, and end partly in the deep, partly in the superficial, bronchial veins. Lastly, some ramify upon the surface of the lung, beneath the pleura, where they form a capillary network.

The **bronchial vein** is formed at the root of the lung, receiving superficial and deep veins from a limited area about the hilum; the larger part of the blood supplied by the bronchial arteries being returned by the pulmonary veins. It ends on the right side in the azygos vein, and on the left side in the highest intercostal or in the accessory hemiazygos vein.

The **lymphatics** are described on page 730.

Nerves.—The lungs are supplied from the anterior and posterior pulmonary plexuses, formed chiefly by branches from the sympathetic and vagus. The filaments from these plexuses accompany the bronchial tubes, supplying efferent fibers to the bronchial muscle and afferent fibers to the bronchial mucous membrane and probably to the alveoli of the lung. Small ganglia are found upon these nerves.

72

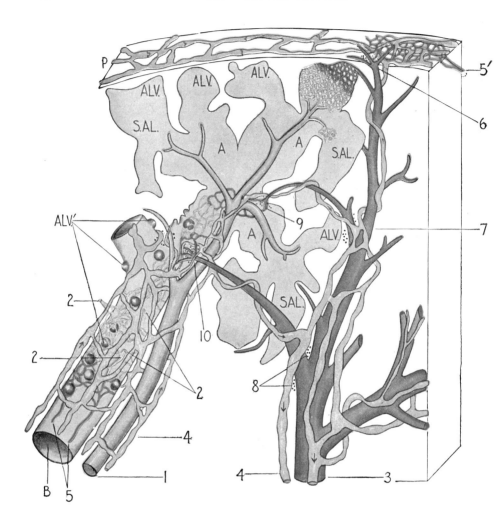

Fig. 970.—General scheme of a primary lobule, showing the subdivisions of (B) a respiratory bronchiole into two alveolar ducts; and the atria (A), alveolar sacs (S.AL.) and alveoli (ALV.) of one of these ducts. ALV,[1] alveoli scattered along the bronchioles; P, pleura; 1, pulmonary artery, dividing into smaller radicles for each atrium, one of which terminates in a capillary plexus on the wall of an alveolus; 2, its branches to the respiratory bronchiole and alveolar duct; 3, pulmonary vein with its tributaries from the pleura (6), capillary plexus of alveolus, and wall of the atrium (9) and alveolar duct (10); 4, lymphatics; dotted areas at 7, 8, 9 and 10, indicating areas of lymphoid tissue; 5, bronchial arteries terminating in a plexus on the wall of the bronchiole; 5[1], bronchial artery terminating in pleura. (Miller, The Lung, courtesy of Charles C Thomas.)

BIBLIOGRAPHY

LARYNX

The laryngeal sacs of an infant and an adult gorilla. MILLER, R. A.: 1941. Am. J. Anat., Vol. 69, pp. 1–17.

The mechanism of laryngeal pitch. STRONG, L. H.: 1935. Anat. Rec., Vol. 63, pp. 13–28.

TRACHEA AND BRONCHI

Anatomic-roentgenological analysis of the normal hilar shadow. HERRNHEISER, G.: 1942. Am. J. Roentgenol., Vol. 48, pp. 595–612.

The musculature of the bronchi and lungs. MACKLIN, C. C.: 1929. Physiol. Rev., Vol. 9, pp. 1–60.

LUNGS AND THORAX

A study of the histological structure of the respiratory portion of the lungs of aquatic mammals. BÉLANGER, L. F.: 1940. Am. J. Anat., Vol. 67, pp. 437–469.

Evidence of an epithelial lining in the labyrinth of the avian lung. BREMER, J. L.: 1939. Anat. Rec., Vol. 73, pp. 497–513.

A critique of the theories of pulmonary evolution in the mammalia. HUNTINGTON, G. S.: 1920. Am. J. Anat., Vol. 27, pp. 99–201.

The dynamic concept of thoracic topography: A critical review of present day teaching of visceral anatomy. LACHMAN, E.: 1946. Am. J. Roentgenol., Vol. 56, pp. 419–440.

The Lung. MILLER, W. S.: 1937. Charles C Thomas, Springfield, xiv + 209 pp.

A thoracic window for observation of the lung in a living animal. TERRY, R. J.: 1939. Science, Vol. 90, pp. 43–44.

BRONCHOPULMONARY SEGMENTS

Segments and blood-vessels of the lungs. APPLETON, A. B.: 1944. Lancet, Vol. 2, pp. 592–594.

The intrahilar and related segmental anatomy of the lung. BOYDEN, E. A.: 1945. Surgery, Vol. 18, pp. 706–731.

An analysis of variations in the bronchopulmonary segments of the left upper lobes of fifty lungs. BOYDEN, E. A., and J. F. HARTMANN: 1946. Am. J. Anat., Vol. 79, pp. 321–360.

The level of the interlobar fissures of the lungs. BROCK, R. C.: 1942. Guy's Hosp. Rep., Vol. 91 pp. 140–146.

Lung lobation in rhesus monkey, compared with man. CHASE, R. E.: 1942. Am. J. Phys. Anthrop., Vol. 29, pp. 267–286.

Correlated applied anatomy of the bronchial tree and lungs with a system of nomenclature. JACKSON, C. L., and J. F. HUBER: 1943. Dis. of the Chest, Vol. 9, pp. 319–326.

The origin and significance of the megakaryocytes of the lungs. JORDAN, H. E.: 1940. Anat. Rec., Vol. 77, pp. 91–101.

EMBRYOLOGY AND GROWTH

Embryonic development of the respiratory portion of the pig's lung. CLEMENTS, L. P.: 1938. Anat. Rec., Vol. 70, pp. 575–595.

Factors affecting the postnatal growth of the lung. COHN, R.: 1939. Anat. Rec., Vol. 75, pp. 195–205.

NERVES AND BLOOD VESSELS

Relation of the volume of pulmonary circulation to respiration at birth. ABEL, S., and W. F. WINDLE: 1939. Anat. Rec., Vol. 75, pp. 451–464.

The afferent and parasympathetic innervation of the lungs and trachea of the dog. ELFTMAN, A. G.: 1943. Am. J. Anat., Vol. 72, pp. 1–27.

The ganglia, plexuses and nerve-terminations of the mammalian lung and pleura pulmonalis. LARSELL, O.: 1922. J. Comp. Neur., Vol. 35, pp. 97–132.

The pathways for nervous reflexes from the parenchyma of the lung. RASMUSSEN, A. T.: 1926. Am. Rev. Tuberc., Vol. 13, pp. 545–549.

PLEURA

Pleuro-peritoneal membrane and bursa infracardiaca. BREMER, J. L.: 1943. Anat. Rec., Vol. 87, pp. 311–319.

A comparison of the posterior boundaries of lungs and pleura as demonstrated on the cadaver and on the roentgenogram of the living. LACHMAN, E.: 1942. Anat. Rec., Vol. 83, pp. 521–542.

The costomediastinal border of the left pleura in the precordial area. WOODBURNE, R. T.: 1947. Anat. Rec., Vol. 97, pp. 197–210.

THE DIGESTIVE APPARATUS.

(APPARATUS DIGESTORIUS; ORGANS OF DIGESTION.)

THE apparatus for the digestion of the food consists of the **digestive tube** and of certain **accessory organs.**

The **Digestive Tube** (*alimentary canal*) is a musculomembranous tube, about 9 meters long, extending from the mouth to the anus, and lined throughout its entire extent by mucous membrane. It has received different names in the various parts of its course: at its commencement is the **mouth**, where provision is made for the mechanical division of the food (*mastication*), and for its admixture with a fluid secreted by the salivary glands (*insalivation*); beyond this are the organs of deglutition, the **pharynx** and the **esophagus**, which convey the food into the **stomach**, in which it is stored for a time and in which also the first stages of the digestive process take place; the stomach is followed by the **small intestine**, which is divided for purposes of description into three parts, the **duodenum**, the **jejunum**, and **ileum**. In the small intestine the process of digestion is completed and the resulting products are absorbed into the blood and lacteal vessels. Finally the small intestine ends in the **large intestine**, which is made up of **cecum, colon, rectum,** and **anal canal**, the last terminating on the surface of the body at the **anus**.

The accessory organs are the **teeth**, for purposes of mastication; the three pairs of **salivary glands**—the **parotid, submaxillary,** and **sublingual**—the secretion from which mixes with the food in the mouth and converts it into a bolus and acts chemically on one of its constituents; the **liver** and **pancreas**, two large glands in the abdomen, the secretions of which, in addition to that of numerous minute glands in the walls of the alimentary canal, assist in the process of digestion.

The Development of the Digestive Tube.—The primitive digestive tube consists of two parts, viz.: (1) the **fore-gut**, within the cephalic flexure, and dorsal to the heart; and (2) the **hind-gut**, within the caudal flexure (Fig. 971). Between these is the wide opening of the yolk-sac, which is gradually narrowed and reduced to a small foramen leading into the vitelline duct. At first the fore-gut and hind-gut end blindly. The anterior end of the fore-gut is separated from the stomodeum by the buccopharyngeal membrane (Fig. 971); the hind-gut ends in the cloaca, which is closed by the cloacal membrane.

The Mouth.—The mouth is developed partly from the stomodeum, and partly from the floor of the anterior portion of the fore-gut. By the growth of the head and of the embryo, and the formation of the cephalic flexure, the pericardial area and the buccopharyngeal membrane come to lie on the ventral surface of the embryo. With the further expansion of the brain, and the forward bulging of the pericardium, the buccopharyngeal membrane is depressed between these two prominences. This depression constitutes the **stomodeum** (Fig. 971). It is lined by ectoderm, and is separated from the anterior end of the fore-gut by the buccopharyngeal membrane. This membrane is devoid of mesoderm, being formed by the apposition of the stomodeal ectoderm with the fore-gut entoderm; at the end of the third week it disappears, and thus a communication is established between the mouth and the future pharynx. No trace of the membrane is found in the adult; and the communication just mentioned must not be confused with the permanent isthmus faucium. The lips, teeth, and gums are formed from the walls of the stomodeum, but the tongue is developed in the floor of the pharynx.

The visceral arches extend in a ventral direction between the stomodeum and the pericardium; and with the completion of the mandibular arch and the formation

(1141)

of the maxillary processes, the mouth assumes the appearance of a pentagonal orifice. The orifice is bounded in front by the fronto-nasal process, behind by the

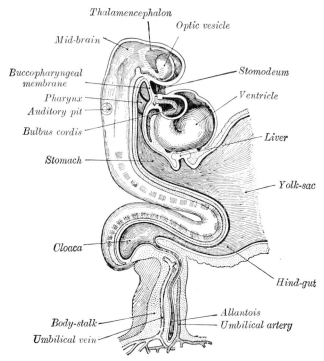

FIG. 971.—Human embryo about fifteen days old. Brain and heart represented from right side. Digestive tube and yolk sac in median section. (After His.)

mandibular arch, and laterally by the maxillary processes (Fig. 972). With the inward growth and fusion of the palatine processes (Figs. 48, 49), the stomodeum

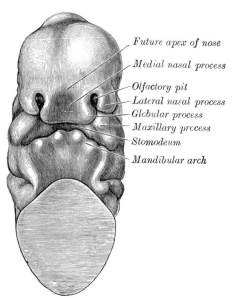

FIG. 972.—Head end of human embryo of about thirty to thirty-one days. (From model by Peters.)

is divided into an upper nasal, and a lower buccal part. Along the free margins of the processes bounding the mouth cavity a shallow groove appears; this is termed the **primary labial groove**, and from the bottom of it a downgrowth of ectoderm takes place into the underlying mesoderm. The central cells of the ectodermal downgrowth degenerate and a **secondary labial groove** is formed; by the deepening of this, the lips and cheeks are separated from the alveolar processes of the maxillæ and mandible.

The Salivary Glands. — The salivary glands arise as buds from the epithelial lining of the mouth; the parotid appears during the fourth week in the angle between the maxillary process and the mandibular arch; the submaxillary appears in the sixth week, and the sublingual during the ninth week in the hollow between the tongue and the mandibular arch.

The Tongue (Figs. 973 to 975).—The tongue is developed in the floor of the pharynx, and consists of an anterior or buccal and a posterior or pharyngeal part which are separated in the adult by the V-shaped sulcus terminalis. During the third week there appears, immediately behind the ventral ends of the two halves of the mandibular arch, a rounded swelling named the **tuberculum impar**, which was described by His as undergoing enlargement to form the buccal part of the tongue. More recent researches, however, show that this part of the tongue is

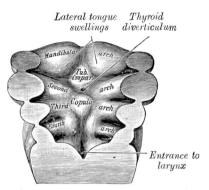

Fig. 973.—Floor of pharynx of human embryo about twenty-six days old. (From model by Peters.)

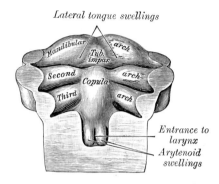

Fig. 974.—Floor of pharynx of human embryo of about the end of the fourth week. (From model by Peters.)

mainly, if not entirely, developed from a pair of lateral swellings which rise from the inner surface of the mandibular arch and meet in the middle line. The tuberculum impar is said to form the central part of the tongue immediately in front of the foramen cecum, but Hammar insists that it is purely a transitory structure and forms no part of the adult tongue. From the ventral ends of the fourth arch there arises a second and larger elevation, in the center of which is a median groove or furrow. This elevation was named by His the **furcula,** and is at first separated from the tuberculum impar by a depression, but later by a ridge, the **copula,** formed by the forward growth and fusion of the ventral ends of the second and third arches. The posterior or pharyngeal part of the tongue is developed from the copula, which extends forward in the form of a V, so as to embrace between its two limbs the buccal part of the tongue. At the apex of the V a pit-like invagination occurs, to form the thyroid gland, and this depression is represented in the adult by the **foramen cecum** of the

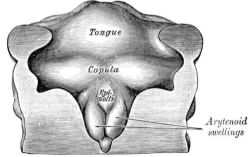

Fig. 975.—Floor of pharynx of human embryo about thirty days old. (From model by Peters.)

tongue. In the adult the union of the anterior and posterior parts of the tongue is marked by the V-shaped sulcus terminalis, the apex of which is at the foramen cecum, while the two limbs run lateralward and forward, parallel to, but a little behind, the vallate papillæ.

The Palatine Tonsils.—The palatine tonsils are developed from the dorsal angles of the second branchial pouches. The entoderm which lines these pouches grows in the form of a number of solid buds into the surrounding mesoderm. These buds become hollowed out by the degeneration and casting off of their central cells, and by this means the tonsillar crypts are formed. Lymphoid cells accumulate around the crypts, and become grouped to form the lymphoid follicles; the latter, however, are not well-defined until after birth.

The Further Development of the Digestive Tube.—The upper part of the fore-gut becomes dilated to form the pharynx (Fig. 971), in relation to which the branchial

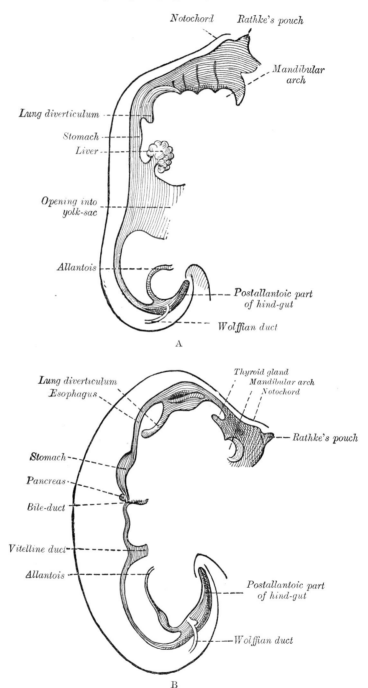

Fig. 976.—Sketches in profile of two stages in the development of the human digestive tube. (His.)
A × 30.   *B* × 20.

arches are developed (see page 45); the succeeding part remains tubular, and with the descent of the stomach is elongated to form the esophagus. About the fourth week a fusiform dilatation, the future stomach, makes its appearance, and beyond this the gut opens freely into the yolk-sac (Fig. 976, *A* and *B*). The opening is at

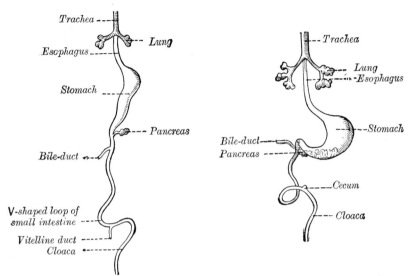

FIG. 977.—Front view of two successive stages in the development of the digestive tube. (His.)

first wide, but is gradually narrowed into a tubular stalk, the **yolk-stalk** or **vitelline duct**. Between the stomach and the mouth of the yolk-sac the liver diverticulum appears. From the stomach to the rectum the alimentary canal is attached to the notochord by a band of mesoderm, from which the common mesentery of the gut is subsequently developed. The stomach has an additional attachment, viz.,

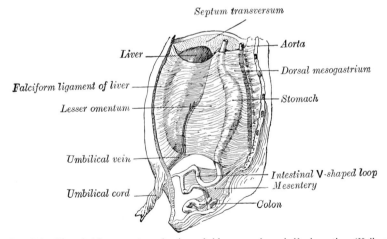

FIG. 978.—The primitive mesentery of a six weeks' human embryo, half schematic. (Kollmann.)

to the ventral abdominal wall as far as the umbilicus by the septum transversum. The cephalic portion of the septum takes part in the formation of the diaphragm, while the caudal portion into which the liver grows forms the **ventral mesogastrium** (Fig. 978). The stomach undergoes a further dilatation, and its two curvatures can be recognized (Figs. 976, *B*, and 977), the greater directed toward the vertebral column and the lesser toward the anterior wall of the abdomen, while its two surfaces look to the right and left respectively. Behind the stomach the gut undergoes great elongation, and forms a V-shaped loop which projects downward and forward; from the bend or angle of the loop the vitelline duct passes to the umbilicus (Fig. 977). For a time a considerable part of the loop extends beyond the abdominal cavity into the umbilical cord, but by the end of the third month it is withdrawn within the cavity. With the lengthening of the tube, the mesoderm, which attaches it to the future vertebral column and carries the bloodvessels for the supply of the gut, is thinned and drawn out to form the **posterior common mesentery.** The portion of this mesentery attached to the greater curvature of the stomach is named the **dorsal mesogastrium,** and the part which suspends the colon is termed the **mesocolon** (Fig. 979). About the sixth week a diverticulum

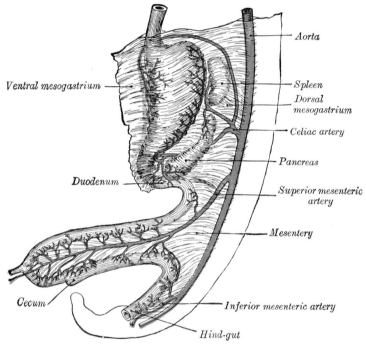

Fig. 979.—Abdominal part of digestive tube and its attachment to the primitive or common mesentery. Human embryo of six weeks. (After Toldt.)

of the gut appears just behind the opening of the vitelline duct, and indicates the future cecum and vermiform process. The part of the loop on the distal side of the cecal diverticulum increases in diameter and forms the future ascending and transverse portions of the large intestine. Until the fifth month the cecal diverticulum has a uniform caliber, but from this time onward its distal part remains rudimentary and forms the vermiform process, while its proximal part expands to form the cecum. Changes also take place in the shape and position of the stomach. Its dorsal part or greater curvature, to which the dorsal mesogastrium is attached, grows much more rapidly than its ventral part or lesser curvature to which the ventral mesogastrium is fixed. Further, the greater curvature is carried downward and to the left, so that the right surface of the stomach is now directed backward and the left surface forward (Fig. 980), a change in position which explains why the left vagus nerve is found on the front, and the right vagus on the back of the stomach. The dorsal mesogastrium being attached to the greater curvature must necessarily follow its movements, and hence it becomes greatly elongated and drawn lateralward and ventralward from the vertebral column, and, as in the case of the stomach, the right surfaces of both the dorsal and ventral mesogastria are now directed backward, and the left forward. In this way a pouch, the **bursa omentalis,** is formed behind the stomach, and this increases in size as the digestive tube undergoes further development; the entrance to the pouch constitutes the future **foramen epiploicum** or **foramen of Winslow.** The duodenum is developed from that part of the tube which immediately succeeds the stomach;

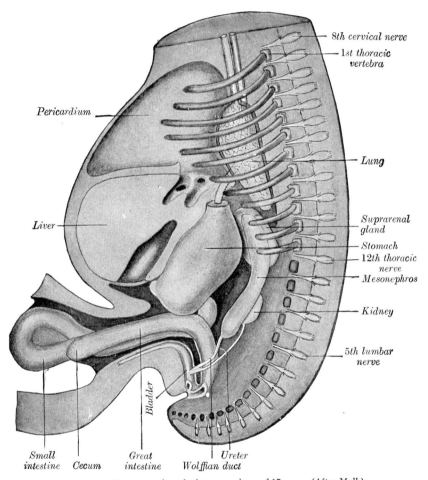

Fig. 980.—Reconstruction of a human embryo of 17 mm. (After Mall.)

it undergoes little elongation, being more or less fixed in position by the liver and pancreas, which arise as diverticula from it. The duodenum is at first suspended by a mesentery, and projects forward in the form of a loop. The loop and its mesentery are subsequently displaced by the transverse colon, so that the right surface of the duodenal mesentery is directed backward, and, adhering to the parietal peritoneum, is lost. The remainder of the digestive tube becomes greatly elongated, and as a consequence the tube is coiled on itself, and this elongation demands a corresponding increase in the width of the intestinal attachment of the mesentery, which becomes folded.

At this stage the small and large intestines are attached to the vertebral column by a common mesentery, the coils of the small intestine falling to the right of the middle line, while the large intestine lies on the left side[1] (Fig. 981).

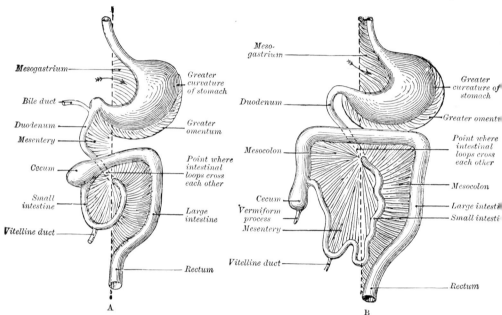

FIG. 981.—Diagrams to illustrate two stages in the development of the digestive tube and its mesentery. The arrow indicates the entrance to the bursa omentalis.

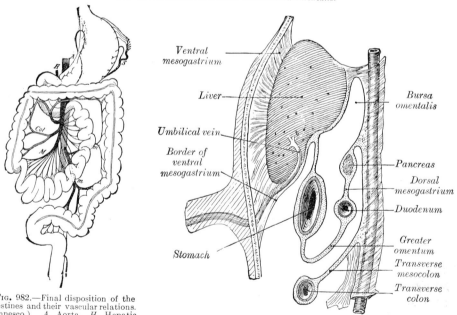

FIG. 982.—Final disposition of the intestines and their vascular relations. (Jonnesco.) A. Aorta. H. Hepatic artery. M, Col. Branches of superior mesenteric artery. m, m'. Branches of inferior mesenteric artery. S. Splenic artery.

FIG. 983.—Schematic figure of the bursa omentalis, etc. Human embryo of eight weeks. (Kollmann.)

[1] Sometimes this condition persists throughout life, and it is then found that the duodenum does not cross from the right to the left side of the vertebral column, but lies entirely on the right side of the median plane, where it is continued into the jejunum; the arteries to the small intestine (aa. intestinales) also arise from the right instead of the left side of the superior mesenteric artery.

The gut is now rotated upon itself, so that the large intestine is carried over in front of the small intestine, and the cecum is placed immediately below the liver; about the sixth month the cecum descends into the right iliac fossa, and the large intestine forms an arch consisting of the ascending, transverse, and descending portions of the colon—the transverse portion crossing in front of the duodenum and lying just below the greater curvature of the stomach; within this arch the coils of the small intestine are disposed (Fig. 982). Sometimes the downward progress of the cecum is arrested, so that in the adult it may be found lying imme-diately below the liver instead of in the right iliac region.

Further changes take place in the bursa omentalis and in the common mesentery, and give rise to the peritoneal relations seen in the adult. The bursa omentalis, which at first reaches only as far as the greater curvature of the stomach, grows downward to form the greater omentum, and this downward extension lies in front of the transverse colon and the coils of the small intestine (Fig. 983). Above, before the pleuro-peritoneal opening is closed, the bursa omentalis sends up a diverticulum on either side of the esophagus; the left diverticulum soon disappears, but the right is constricted off and persists in most adults as a small sac lying within the thorax

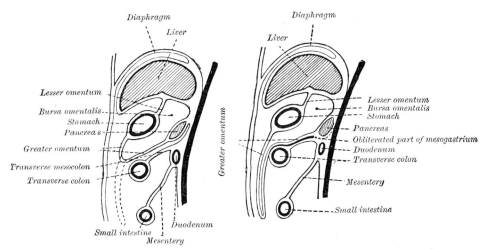

Fig. 984.—Diagrams to illustrate the development of the greater omentum and transverse mesocolon.

on the right side of the lower end of the esophagus. The anterior layer of the transverse mesocolon is at first distinct from the posterior layer of the greater omentum, but ultimately the two blend, and hence the greater omentum appears as if attached to the transverse colon (Fig. 984). The mesenteries of the ascending and descending parts of the colon disappear in the majority of cases, while that of the small intestine assumes the oblique attachment characteristic of its adult condition.

The lesser omentum is formed, as indicated above, by a thinning of the meso-derm or **ventral mesogastrium,** which attaches the stomach and duodenum to the anterior abdominal wall. By the subsequent growth of the liver this leaf of mesoderm is divided into two parts, viz., the lesser omentum between the stomach and liver, and the falciform and coronary ligaments between the liver and the abdominal wall and diaphragm (Fig. 983).

The Rectum and Anal Canal.—The hind-gut is at first prolonged backward into the body-stalk as the tube of the allantois; but, with the growth and flexure of the tail-end of the embryo, the body-stalk, with its contained allantoic tube, is carried forward to the ventral aspect of the body, and consequently a bend is formed at the junction of the hind-gut and allantois. This bend becomes dilated into a pouch, which constitutes the **entodermal cloaca**; into its dorsal part the hind-gut opens, and from its ventral part the allantois passes forward. At a later stage the Wolffian and Müllerian ducts open into its ventral portion. The cloaca is, for a time, shut off from the exterior by a membrane, the **cloacal membrane**, formed by the apposition of the ectoderm and entoderm, and reaching, at first, as far forward as the future umbilicus. Behind the umbilicus, however, the mesoderm subsequently

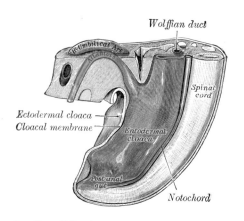

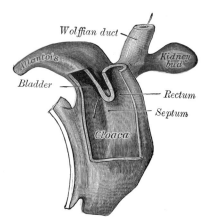

Fig. 985.—Tail end of human embryo from fifteen to eighteen days old. (From model by Keibel.)

Fig. 986.—Cloaca of human embryo from twenty-five to twenty-seven days old. (From model by Keibel.)

extends to form the lower part of the abdominal wall and symphysis pubis. By the growth of the surrounding tissues the cloacal membrane comes to lie at the bottom of a depression, which is lined by ectoderm and named the **ectodermal cloaca** (Fig. 985).

The entodermal cloaca is divided into a dorsal and a ventral part by means of a partition, the **urorectal septum** (Fig. 986), which grows downward from the ridge

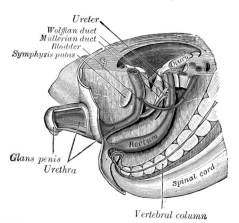

Fig. 987.—Tail end of human embryo, from eight and a half to nine weeks old. (From model by Keibel.)

separating the allantoic from the cloacal opening of the intestine and ultimately fuses with the cloacal membrane and divides it into an anal and a urogenital part. The dorsal part of the cloaca forms the rectum, and the anterior part forms the urogenital sinus and bladder. For a time a communication named the **cloacal duct** exists between the two parts of the cloaca below the urorectal septum; this duct occasionally persists as a passage between the rectum and urethra. The anal canal is formed by an invagination of the ectoderm behind the urorectal septum. This invagination is termed the **proctodeum**, and it meets with the entoderm of the hind-gut and forms with it the **anal membrane**. By the absorption of this membrane the anal canal becomes continuous with the rectum (Fig. 987). A small part of the hind-gut projects backward beyond the anal membrane; it is named the **post-anal gut** (Fig. 985), and usually becomes obliterated and disappears.

THE MOUTH (CAVUM ORIS; ORAL OR BUCCAL CAVITY).

The **cavity of the mouth** is placed at the commencement of the digestive tube (Fig. 989); it is a nearly oval-shaped cavity which consists of two parts: an outer, smaller portion, the **vestibule**, and an inner, larger part, the **mouth cavity proper**.

The **Vestibule** (*vestibulum oris*) is a slit-like space, bounded externally by the lips and cheeks; internally by the gums and teeth. It communicates with the surface of the body by the **rima** or **orifice of the mouth**. Above and below, it is limited by the reflection of the mucous membrane from the lips and cheeks to the gum covering the upper and lower alveolar arch respectively. It receives the

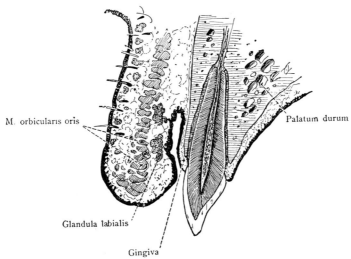

M. orbicularis oris

Palatum durum

Glandula labialis

Gingiva

Fig. 988.—Section through lip and tooth. (Eycleshymer and Jones).

secretion from the parotid salivary glands, and communicates, when the jaws are closed, with the mouth cavity proper by an aperture on either side behind the wisdom teeth, and by narrow clefts between opposing teeth.

The **Mouth Cavity Proper** (*cavum oris proprium*) (Fig. 1008) is bounded laterally and in front by the alveolar arches with their contained teeth; behind, it communicates with the pharynx by a constricted aperture termed the **isthmus faucium**. It is roofed in by the hard and soft palates, while the greater part of the floor is formed by the tongue, the remainder by the reflection of the mucous membrane from the sides and under surface of the tongue to the gum lining the inner aspect of the mandible. It receives the secretion from the submaxillary and sublingual salivary glands.

Structure.—The **mucous membrane** lining the mouth is continuous with the integument at the free margin of the lips, and with the mucous lining of the pharynx behind; it is of a rose-pink tinge during life, and very thick where it overlies the hard parts bounding the cavity. It is covered by stratified squamous epithelium.

The **Lips** (*labia oris*) (Fig. 988), the two fleshy folds which surround the rima or orifice of the mouth, are formed externally of integument and internally of mucous membrane, between which are found the Orbicularis oris muscle, the labial vessels,

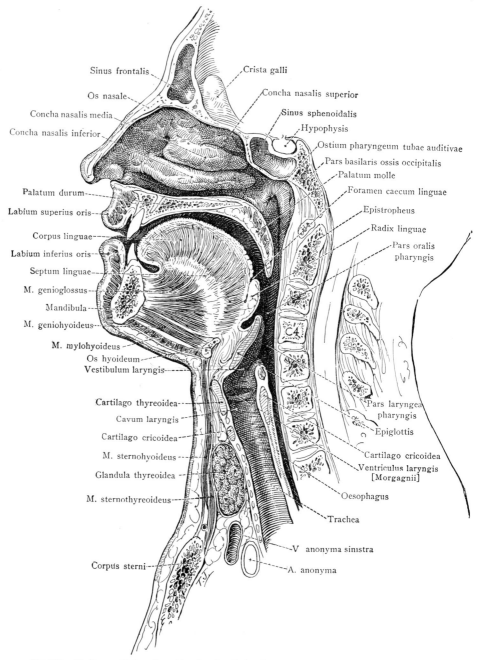

Fig. 989.—Median sagittal section of head and neck showing nasal, pharyngeal, and laryngeal cavities. (Eycleshymer and Jones).

some nerves, areolar tissue, and fat, and numerous small labial glands. The inner surface of each lip is connected in the middle line to the corresponding gum by a fold of mucous membrane, the **frenulum**—the upper being the larger.

The **Labial Glands** (*glandulæ labiales*) are situated between the mucous membrane and the Orbicularis oris, around the orifice of the mouth. They are circular in form and about the size of small peas; their ducts open by minute orifices upon the mucous membrane. In structure they resemble the salivary glands.

The **Cheeks** (*buccæ*) form the sides of the face, and are continuous in front with the lips. They are composed externally of integument; internally of mucous membrane; and between the two of a muscular stratum, besides a large quantity of fat, areolar tissue, vessels, nerves, and buccal glands.

Structure.—The **mucous membrane** lining the cheek is reflected above and below upon the gums, and is continuous behind with the lining membrane of the soft palate. Opposite the second molar tooth of the maxilla is a papilla, on the summit of which is the aperture of the parotid duct. The principal muscle of the cheek is the Buccinator; but other muscles enter into its formation, viz., the Zygomaticus, Risorius, and Platysma.

The *buccal glands* are placed between the mucous membrane and Buccinator muscle: they are similar in structure to the labial glands, but smaller. About five, of a larger size than the rest, are placed between the Masseter and Buccinator muscles around the distal extremity of the parotid duct; their ducts open in the mouth opposite the last molar tooth. They are called **molar glands.**

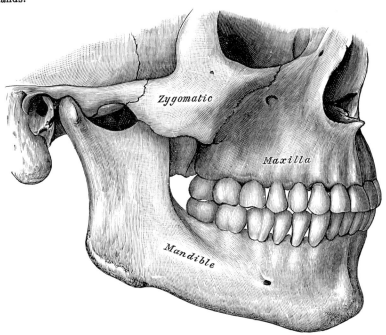

Fig. 990.—Side view of the teeth and jaws.

The **Gums** (*gingivæ*) are composed of dense fibrous tissue, closely connected to the periosteum of the alveolar processes, and surrounding the necks of the teeth. They are covered by smooth and vascular mucous membrane, which is remarkable for its limited sensibility. Around the necks of the teeth this membrane presents numerous fine papillæ, and is reflected into the alveoli, where it is continuous with the periosteal membrane lining these cavities.

The **Palate** (*palatum*) forms the roof of the mouth; it consists of two portions, the **hard palate** in front, the **soft palate** behind.

The **Hard Palate** (*palatum durum*) (Fig. 989) forms the roof of the mouth and separates the oral and nasal cavities. It is bounded in front and at the sides by the alveolar arches and gums; behind, it is continuous with the soft palate. Its bony support, formed by the palatine process of the maxilla and the horizontal part of

73

the palatine bone (Fig. 991), is covered by a dense structure, formed by the periosteum and mucous membrane of the mouth, which are intimately adherent. Along the middle line is a linear raphé, which ends anteriorly in a small papilla corresponding with the incisive canal. On either side and in front of the raphé the mucous membrane is thick, pale in color, and corrugated; behind, it is thin, smooth, and of a deeper color; it is covered with stratified squamous epithelium, and furnished with numerous palatal glands, which lie between the mucous membrane and the surface of the bone.

The **Soft Palate** (*palatum molle*) (Fig. 989) is a movable fold, suspended from the posterior border of the hard palate. It consists of a fold of mucous membrane enclosing muscular fibers, an aponeurosis, vessels, nerves, lymphoid tissue, and mucous glands. These are described on page 1177. When elevated, as in swallowing and in suckling, it completely separates the nasal cavity and nasopharynx from the posterior part of the oral cavity and the oral portion of the pharynx (Fig. 989).

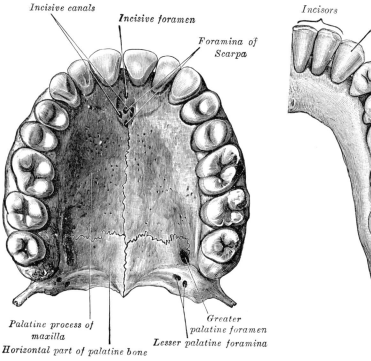

Fig. 991.—Permanent teeth of upper dental arch, seen from below.

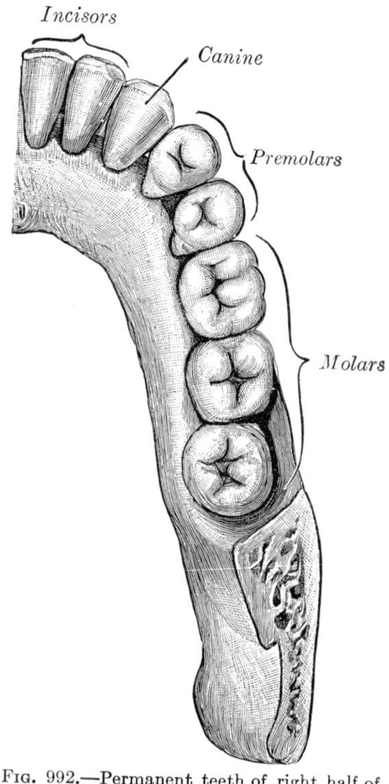

Fig. 992.—Permanent teeth of right half of lower dental arch, seen from above.

When occupying its usual position, *i. e.*, relaxed and pendent, its anterior surface is concave, continuous with the roof of the mouth, and marked by a median raphé. Its posterior surface is convex, and continuous with the mucous membrane covering the floor of the nasal cavities. Its upper border is attached to the posterior margin of the hard palate, and its sides are blended with the pharynx. Its lower border is free. Its lower portion, which hangs like a curtain between the mouth and pharynx is termed the **palatine velum.**

Hanging from the middle of its lower border is a small, conical, pendulous process, the **palatine uvula;** and arching lateralward and downward from the base of the uvula on either side are two curved folds of mucous membrane, containing muscular fibers, called the **arches** or **pillars of the fauces.**

The Teeth (*dentes*) (Figs. 990 to 996).—Man is provided with two sets of teeth, which make their appearance at different periods of life. Those of the first set appear in childhood, and are called the **deciduous** or **milk teeth**. Those of the second set, which also appear at an early period, may continue until old age, and are named **permanent**.

The **deciduous teeth** are twenty in number: four incisors, two canines, and four molars, in each jaw.

The **permanent teeth** are thirty-two in number: four incisors, two canines, four premolars, and six molars, in each jaw.

The dental formulæ may be represented as follows:

Deciduous Teeth.

	mol.	can.	in.	in.	can.	mol.	
Upper jaw	2	1	2	2	1	2	
Lower jaw	2	1	2	2	1	2	} Total 20

Permanent Teeth.

	mol.	pr. mol.	can.	in.	in.	can.	pr. mol.	mol.	
Upper jaw . . .	3	2	1	2	2	1	2	3	
Lower jaw . . .	3	2	1	2	2	1	2	3	} Total 32

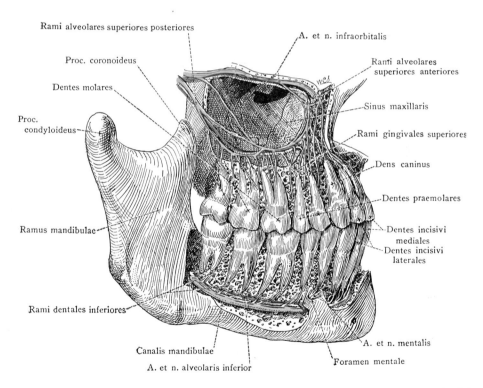

FIG. 993. — The permanent teeth, viewed from the right. The external layer of bone has been partly removed and the maxillary sinus has been opened. (Eycleshymer and Jones).

General Characteristics. — Each tooth consists of three portions: the **crown**, projecting above the gum; the **root**, imbedded in the alveolus; and the **neck**, the constricted portion between the crown and root.

The roots of the teeth are firmly implanted in depressions within the alveoli; these depressions are lined with periosteum which invests the tooth as far as the neck. At the margins of the alveoli, the periosteum is continuous with the fibrous structure of the gums.

In consequence of the curve of the dental arch, terms such as anterior and posterior, as applied to the teeth, are misleading and confusing. Special terms are therefore used to indicate the different surfaces of a tooth: the surface directed toward the lips or cheek is known as the **labial** or **buccal surface;** that directed

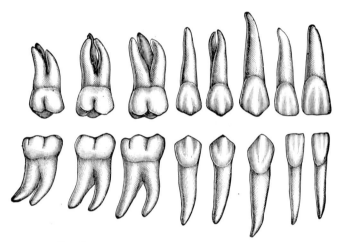

Fig. 994.—Permanent teeth.   Right side.   (Burchard.)

toward the tongue is described as the **lingual surface;** those surfaces which touch neighboring teeth are termed **surfaces of contact.** In the case of the incisor and canine teeth the surfaces of contact are medial and lateral; in the premolar and molar teeth they are anterior and posterior.

The superior dental arch is larger than the inferior, so that in the normal condition the teeth in the maxillæ slightly overlap those of the mandible both in front and at the sides. Since the upper central incisors are wider than the lower, the other teeth in the upper arch are thrown somewhat distally, and the two sets do not quite correspond to each other when the mouth is closed: thus the upper canine tooth rests partly on the lower canine and partly on the first premolar, and the cusps of the upper molar teeth lie behind the corresponding cusps of the lower molar teeth. The two series, however, end at nearly the same point behind; this is mainly because the molars in the upper arch are the smaller.

The Permanent Teeth (*dentes permanentes*) (Figs. 993, 994).—The **Incisors** (*dentes incisivi; incisive or cutting teeth*) are so named from their presenting a sharp cutting edge, adapted for biting the food. They are eight in number, and form the four front teeth in each dental arch.

The **crown** is directed vertically, and is chisel-shaped, being bevelled at the expense of its lingual surface, so as to present a sharp horizontal cutting edge, which, before being subjected to attrition, presents three small prominent points separated by two slight notches. It is convex, smooth, and highly polished on its labial surface; concave on its lingual surface, where, in the teeth of the upper arch, it is frequently marked by an inverted V-shaped eminence, situated near the gum. This is known as the **basal ridge** or **cingulum.** The **neck** is constricted. The **root** is long, single, conical, transversely flattened, thicker in front than behind, and slightly grooved on either side in the longitudinal direction.

The **upper incisors** are larger and stronger than the lower, and are directed obliquely downward and forward. The central ones are larger than the lateral, and their roots are more rounded.

The **lower incisors** are smaller than the upper: the central ones are smaller than the lateral, and are the smallest of all the incisors. They are placed vertically and are somewhat bevelled in front, where they have been worn down by contact with the overlapping edge of the upper teeth. The cingulum is absent.

The **Canine Teeth** (*dentes canini*) are four in number, two in the upper, and two in the lower arch, one being placed laterally to each lateral incisor. They are larger and stronger than the incisors, and their roots sink deeply into the bones, and cause well-marked prominences upon the surface.

The **crown** is large and conical, very convex on its labial surface, a little hollowed and uneven on its lingual surface, and tapering to a blunted point or cusp, which projects beyond the level of the other teeth. The **root** is single, but longer and thicker than that of the incisors, conical in form, compressed laterally, and marked by a slight groove on each side.

The **upper canine teeth** (popularly called *eye teeth*) are larger and longer than the lower, and usually present a distinct basal ridge.

The **lower canine teeth** (popularly called *stomach teeth*) are placed nearer the middle line than the upper, so that their summits correspond to the intervals between the upper canines and the lateral incisors.

The **Premolars** or **Bicuspid teeth** (*dentes præmolares*) are eight in number, four in each arch. They are situated lateral to and behind the canine teeth, and are smaller and shorter than they.

The **crown** is compressed antero-posteriorly, and surmounted by two pyramidal eminences or cusps, a labial and a lingual, separated by a groove; hence their name **bicuspid**. Of the two cusps the labial is the larger and more prominent. The **neck** is oval. The **root** is generally single, compressed, and presents in front and behind a deep groove, which indicates a tendency in the root to become double. The apex is generally bifid.

The **upper premolars** are larger, and present a greater tendency to the division of their roots than the lower; this is especially the case in the first upper premolar.

The **Molar Teeth** (*dentes molares*) are the largest of the permanent set, and their broad crowns are adapted for grinding and pounding the food. They are twelve in number; six in each arch, three being placed posterior to each of the second premolars.

The **crown** of each is nearly cubical in form, convex on its buccal and lingual surfaces, flattened on its surfaces of contact; it is surmounted by four or five tubercles, or cusps, separated from each other by a crucial depression; hence the molars are sometimes termed **multicuspids**. The **neck** is distinct, large, and rounded.

Upper Molars.—As a rule the first is the largest, and the third the smallest of the upper molars. The crown of the first has usually four tubercles; that of the second, three or four; that of the third, three. Each upper molar has three roots, and of these two are buccal and nearly parallel to one another; the third is lingual and diverges from the others as it runs upward. The roots of the third molar (*dens serotinus* or *wisdom-tooth*) are more or less fused together.

Lower Molars.—The lower molars are larger than the upper. On the crown of the first there are usually five tubercles; on those of the second and third, four or five. Each lower molar has two roots, an anterior, nearly vertical, and a posterior, directed obliquely backward; both roots are grooved longitudinally, indicating a tendency to division. The two roots of the third molar (*dens serotinus* or *wisdom tooth*) are more or less united.

The Deciduous Teeth (*dentes decidui; temporary or milk teeth*) (Fig. 995).—The deciduous are smaller than, but, generally speaking, resemble in form, the teeth which bear the same names in the permanent set. The hinder of the two molars is the largest of all the deciduous teeth, and is succeeded by the first molar. The first upper molar has only three cusps—two labial, one lingual; the second upper molar has four cusps. The first lower molar has four cusps; the second lower molar has five. The roots of the deciduous molars are smaller and more divergent than those of the permanent molars, but in other respects bear a strong resemblance to them.

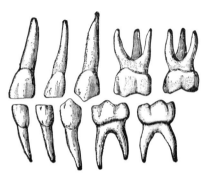

Fig. 995.—Deciduous teeth. Left side.

Structure of the Teeth.— On making a vertical section of a tooth (Figs. 996, 997), a cavity will be found in the interior of the crown and the center of each root; it opens by a minute orifice at the extremity of the latter. This is called the **pulp cavity**, and contains the **dental pulp**, a loose connective tissue richly supplied with vessels and nerves, which enter the cavity through the

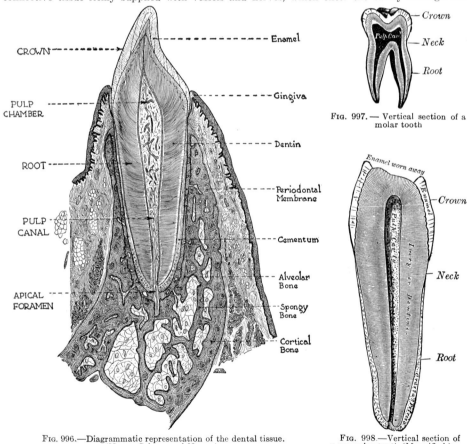

Fig. 996.—Diagrammatic representation of the dental tissue.
(Noyes, Schour and Noyes.)

Fig. 997. — Vertical section of a molar tooth

Fig. 998.—Vertical section of a premolar tooth.(Magnified.)

small aperture at the point of each root. Some of the cells of the pulp are arranged as a layer on the wall of the pulp cavity; they are named the **odontoblasts of Waldeyer,** and during the development of the tooth, are columnar in shape, but later on, after the dentin is fully formed, they become flattened and resemble osteoblasts. Each has two fine processes, the outer one passing into a dental canaliculus, the inner being continuous with the processes of the connective-tissue cells of the pulp matrix.

The solid portion of the tooth consists of (1) the **ivory** or **dentin**, which forms the bulk of the tooth; (2) the **enamel**, which covers the exposed part of the crown; and (3) a thin layer of bone, the **cement** or **crusta petrosa**, which is disposed on the surface of the root.

The **dentin** (*substantia eburnea; ivory*) (Fig. 998) forms the principal mass of a tooth. It is a modification of osseous tissue, from which it differs, however, in structure. On microscopic examination is seen to consist of a number of minute wavy and branching tubes, the **dental canaliculi**, imbedded in a dense homogeneous substance, the **matrix**.

The **dental canaliculi** (*dentinal tubules*) (Fig. 999) are placed parallel with one another, and open at their inner ends into the pulp cavity. In their course to the periphery they present two or three curves, and are twisted on themselves in a spiral direction. These canaliculi vary in direction: thus in a tooth of the mandible they are vertical in the upper portion of the crown, becoming oblique and then horizontal in the neck and upper part of the root, while toward the lower part of the root they are inclined downward. In their course they divide and subdivide dichotomously, and, especially in the root, give off minute branches, which join together in loops in the matrix, or end blindly. Near the periphery of the dentin, the finer ramifications of the canaliculi terminate imperceptibly by free ends. The dental canaliculi have definite walls, consisting of an elastic homogeneous membrane, the **dentinal sheath of Neumann,** which resists the action of acids; they contain slender cylindrical prolongations of the odontoblasts, first described by Tomes, and named **Tomes' fibers** or **dentinal fibers.**

The **matrix** (*intertubular dentin*) is translucent, and contains the chief part of the earthy matter of the dentin. In it are a number of fine fibrils, which are continuous with the fibrils of the dental pulp. After the earthy matter has been removed by steeping a tooth in weak acid, the animal basis remaining may be torn into laminæ which run parallel with the pulp cavity, across the direction of the tubes. A section of dry dentin often displays a series of some-what parallel lines—the **incremental lines of Salter.** These lines are composed of imperfectly calcified dentin arranged in layers. In consequence of the imperfection in the calcifying process, little irregular cavities are left, termed **interglobular spaces** (Fig. 999). Normally a series of these spaces is found toward the outer surface of the dentin, where they form a layer which is sometimes known as the **granular layer.** They have received their name from the fact that they are surrounded by minute nodules or globules of dentin. Other curved lines may be seen parallel to the surface. These are the **lines of Schreger,** and are due to the optical effect of simultaneous curvature of the dentinal fibers.

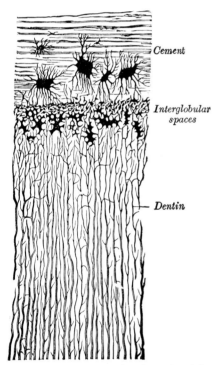

Fig. 999.—Transverse section of a portion of the root of a canine tooth. × 300.

Chemical Composition.—According to Berzelius and von Bibra, dentin consists of 28 parts of animal and 72 parts of earthy matter. The organic matter is a sclero-protein containing an abundance of tyrosin. The earthy matter consists of phosphate of lime, carbonate of lime, a trace of fluoride of calcium, phosphate of magnesium, and other salts.

The **enamel** (*substantia adamantina*) is the hardest and most compact part of the tooth, and forms a thin crust over the exposed part of the crown, as far as the commencement of the root. It is thickest on the grinding surface of the crown, until worn away by attrition, and becomes thinner toward the neck. It consists of minute hexagonal rods or columns termed **enamel fibers** or **enamel prisms** (*prismata adamantina*). They lie parallel with one another, resting by one extremity upon the dentin, which presents a number of minute depressions for their reception; and forming the free surface of the crown by the other extremity. The columns are directed vertically on the summit of the crown, horizontally at the sides; they are about 4μ in diameter, and pursue a more or less wavy course. Each column is a six-sided prism and presents numerous dark transverse shadings; these shadings are probably due to the manner in which the columns are developed in successive stages, producing shallow constrictions, as will be subsequently explained. Another series of lines, having a brown appearance, the **parallel**

(Labels in figure: Cement, Interglobular spaces, Dentin)

striæ or **colored lines of Retzius,** is seen on section. According to Ebner, they are produced by air in the interprismatic spaces; others believe that they are the result of true pigmentation.

Numerous minute interstices intervene between the enamel fibers near their dentinal ends, a provision calculated to allow of the permeation of fluids from the dental canaliculi into the substance of the enamel.

Chemical Composition.—According to von Bibra, enamel consists of 96.5 per cent. of earthy matter, and 3.5 per cent. of animal matter. The earthy matter consists of phosphate of lime, with traces of fluoride of calcium, carbonate of lime, phosphate of magnesium, and other salts. According to Tomes, the enamel contains the merest trace of organic matter.

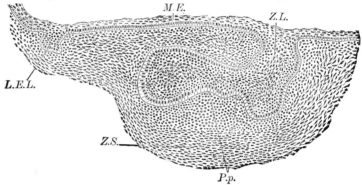

Fig. 1000. — Sagittal section through the first lower deciduous molar of a human embryo 30 mm. long. (Röse.) × 100. *L.E.L.* Labiodental lamina, here separated from the dental lamina. *Z.L.* Placed over the shallow dental furrow, points to the dental lamina, which is spread out below to form the enamel germ of the future tooth. *P.p* Bicuspidate papilla, capped by the enamel germ. *Z.S.* Condensed tissue forming dental sac. *M.E.* Mouth epithelium.

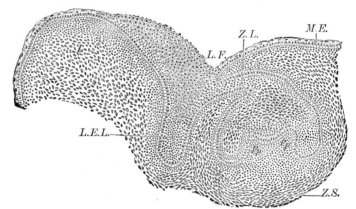

Fig. 1001.—Similar section through the canine tooth of an embryo 40 mm. long. (Röse.) × 100 *L.F.* Labiodental furrow. The other lettering as in Fig. 1000.

The **crusta petrosa** or **cement** (*substantia ossea*) is disposed as a thin layer on the roots of the teeth, from the termination of the enamel to the apex of each root, where it is usually very thick. In structure and chemical composition it resembles bone. It contains, sparingly, the lacunæ and canaliculi which characterize true bone; the lacunæ placed near the surface receive the canaliculi radiating from the side of the lacunæ toward the periodontal membrane; and those more deeply placed join with the adjacent dental canaliculi. In the thicker portions of the crusta petrosa, the lamellæ and Haversian canals peculiar to bone are also found.

As age advances, the cement increases in thickness, and gives rise to those bony growths or exostoses so common in the teeth of the aged; the pulp cavity also becomes partially filled up by a hard substance, intermediate in structure between dentin and bone (*osteodentin,* Owen; *secondary dentin,* Tomes). It appears to be formed by a slow conversion of the dental pulp, which shrinks, or even disappears

Development of the Teeth (Figs. 1000 to 1003).—In describing the development of the teeth the mode of formation of the deciduous teeth must first be considered, and then that of the permanent series.

Development of the Deciduous Teeth.—The development of the deciduous teeth begins about the sixth week of fetal life as a thickening of the epithelium along the line of the future jaw, the thickening being due to a rapid multiplication of the more deeply situated epithelial cells. As the cells multiply they extend into the subjacent mesoderm, and thus form a ridge or strand of cells imbedded in mesoderm. About the seventh week a longitudinal splitting or cleavage of this strand of cells takes place, and it becomes divided into two strands; the separation begins in front and extends laterally, the process occupying four or five weeks. Of the two strands thus formed, the **labial** forms the **labiodental lamina**; while the other, the **lingual,** is the ridge of cells in connection with which the teeth, both deciduous and permanent, are developed. Hence it is known as the **dental lamina** or **common dental germ.** It forms a flat band of cells, which grows into the substance of the embryonic jaw, at first horizontally inward, and then, as the teeth develop, vertically, *i. e.,* upward in the upper jaw, and downward in the lower jaw. While still maintaining a horizontal direction it has two edges —an *attached edge,* continuous with the epithelium lining the mouth, and a *free edge,* projecting inward, and imbedded in the mesodermal tissue of the embryonic jaw. Along its line of attachment to the buccal epithelium is a shallow groove, the **dental furrow.**

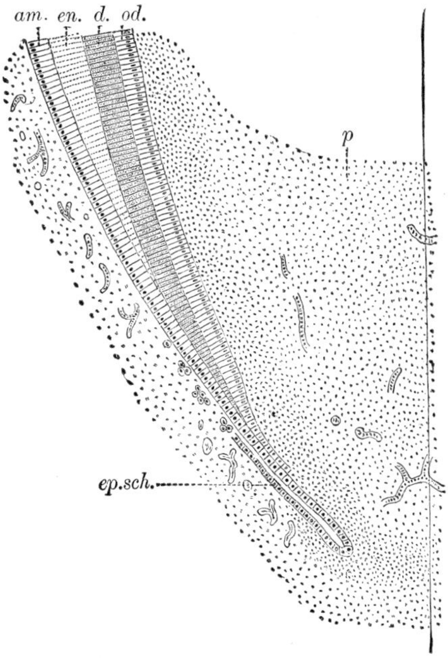

FIG. 1002.—Longitudinal section of the lower part of a growing tooth, showing the extension of the layer of ameloblasts beyond the crown to mark off the limit of formation of the dentin of the root. (Röse.) *am.* Ameloblasts, continuous below with *ep.sch.,* the epithelial sheath of Hertwig. *d.* Dentin. *en.* Enamel. *od.* Odontoblasts. *p.* Pulp.

About the ninth week the dental lamina begins to develop enlargements along its free border. These are ten in number in each jaw, and each corresponds to a future deciduous tooth. They consist of masses of epithelial cells; and the cells of the deeper part—that is, the part farthest from the margin of the jaw—increase rapidly and spread out in all directions. Each mass thus comes to assume a club shape, connected with the general epithelial lining of the mouth by a narrow neck, embraced by mesoderm. They are now known as **special dental germs.** After a time the lower expanded portion inclines outward, so as to form an angle with the superficial constricted portion, which is sometimes known as the neck of the special dental germ. About the tenth week the mesodermal tissue beneath these special dental germs becomes differentiated into papillæ; these grow upward, and come in contact with the epithelial cells of the special dental germs, which become folded over them like a hood or cap. There is, then, at this stage a papilla (or papillæ) which has already begun to assume somewhat the shape of the crown of the future tooth, and from which the dentin and pulp of the tooth are formed, surmounted by a dome or cap of epithelial cells from which the enamel is derived.

In the meantime, while these changes have been going on, the dental lamina has been extending backward behind the special dental germ corresponding to the second deciduous molar tooth, and at about the seventeenth week it presents an enlargement, the special dental germ, for the first permanent molar, soon followed by the formation of a papilla in the mesodermal tissue for the same tooth. This is followed, about the sixth month after birth, by a further extension backward of the dental lamina, with the formation of another enlargement and its corresponding papilla for the second molar. And finally the process is repeated for the third molar, its papilla appearing about the fifth year of life.

After the formation of the special dental germs, the dental lamina undergoes atrophic changes and becomes cribriform, except on the lingual and lateral aspects of each of the special germs of the temporary teeth, where it undergoes a local thickening forming the special dental germ of each of the successional permanent teeth—*i. e.,* the ten anterior ones in each jaw. Here the same process goes on as has been described in connection with those of the deciduous teeth: that is, they recede into the substance of the gum behind the germs of the deciduous teeth. As they recede they become club-shaped, form expansions at their distal extremities, and finally meet papillæ, which have been formed in the mesoderm, just in the same manner as was the case in the deciduous teeth. The apex of each papilla indents the dental germ, which encloses it, and, forming a cap for it, becomes converted into the enamel, while the papilla forms the dentin and pulp of the permanent tooth.

The special dental germs consist at first of rounded or polyhedral epithelial cells; after the formation of the papillæ, these cells undergo a differentiation into three layers. Those which are in immediate contact with the papilla become elongated, and form a layer of well-marked columnar epithelium coating the papilla. They are the cells which form the enamel fibers, and are therefore termed **enamel cells** or **ameloblasts.** The cells of the outer layer of the special dental germ, which are in contact with the inner surface of the dental sac, presently to be described, are much shorter, cubical in form, and are named the **external enamel epithelium.** All the intermediate round cells of the dental germ between these two layers undergo a peculiar change. They become stellate in shape and develop processes, which unite to form a net-work into which fluid is secreted; this has the appearance of a jelly, and to it the name of enamel pulp is given. This transformed special dental germ is now known under the name of **enamel organ** (Fig. 1003).

While these changes are going on, a sac is formed around each enamel organ from the surrounding mesodermal tissue. This is known as the **dental sac,** and is a vascular membrane of connective tissue. It grows up from below, and thus encloses the whole tooth germ; as it grows it causes the neck of the enamel organ to atrophy and disappear; so that all communication between the enamel organ and the superficial epithelium is cut off. At this stage there are vascular papillæ surmounted by caps of epithelial cells, the whole being surrounded by membranous sacs.

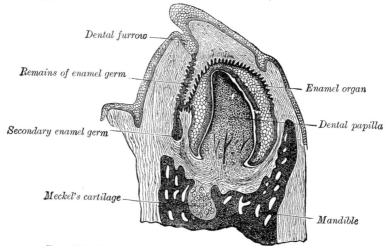

Fig. 1003.—Vertical section of the mandible of an early human fetus. × 25.

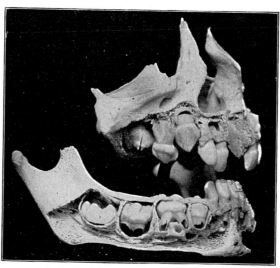

Fig. 1004.—Maxillæ at about one year. (Noyes.)

Formation of the Enamel.—The enamel is formed exclusively from the enamel cells or ameloblasts of the special dental germ, either by direct calcification of the columnar cells, which become elongated into the hexagonal rods of the enamel; or, as is more generally believed, as a secretion from the ameloblasts, within which calcareous matter is subsequently deposited.

The process begins at the apex of each cusp, at the ends of the enamel cells in contact with the dental papilla. Here a fine globular deposit takes place, being apparently shed from the end of the ameloblasts. It is known by the name of the **enamel droplet,** and resembles keratin in its resistance to the action of mineral acids. This droplet then becomes fibrous and calcifies and forms the first layer of the enamel; a second droplet now appears and calcifies, and so on; successive droplets of keratin-like material are shed from the ameloblasts and form successive layers of enamel, the ameloblasts gradually receding as each layer is produced, until at the termination of the process they have almost disappeared. The intermediate cells of the enamel pulp atrophy and disappear, so that the newly formed calcified material and the external enamel epithelium come into apposition. This latter layer, however, soon disappears on the emergence of the tooth beyond the gum. After its disappearance the crown of the tooth is still covered by a distinct membrane, which persists for some time. This is known as the **cuticula dentis,** or **Nasmyth's membrane,** and is believed to be the last-formed layer of enamel derived from the ameloblasts, which has not become calcified. It forms a horny layer, which may be separated from the subjacent calcified mass by the action of strong acids. It is marked by the hexagonal impressions of the enamel prisms, and, when stained by nitrate of silver, shows the characteristic appearance of epithelium.

Formation of the Dentin.—While these changes are taking place in the epithelium to form the enamel, contemporaneous changes occurring in the differentiated mesoderm of the dental papillæ result in the formation of the dentin. As before stated, the first germs of the dentin are the papillæ, corresponding in number to the teeth, formed from the soft mesodermal tissue which bounds the depressions containing the special enamel germs. The papillæ grow upward into the enamel germs and become covered by them, both being enclosed in a vascular connective tissue, the **dental sac,** in the manner above described. Each papilla then constitutes the formative pulp from which the dentin and permanent pulp are developed; it consists of rounded cells and is very vascular, and soon begins to assume the shape of the future tooth. The next step is the appearance of the **odontoblasts,** which have a relation to the development of the teeth similar to that of the osteoblasts to the formation of bone. They are formed from the cells

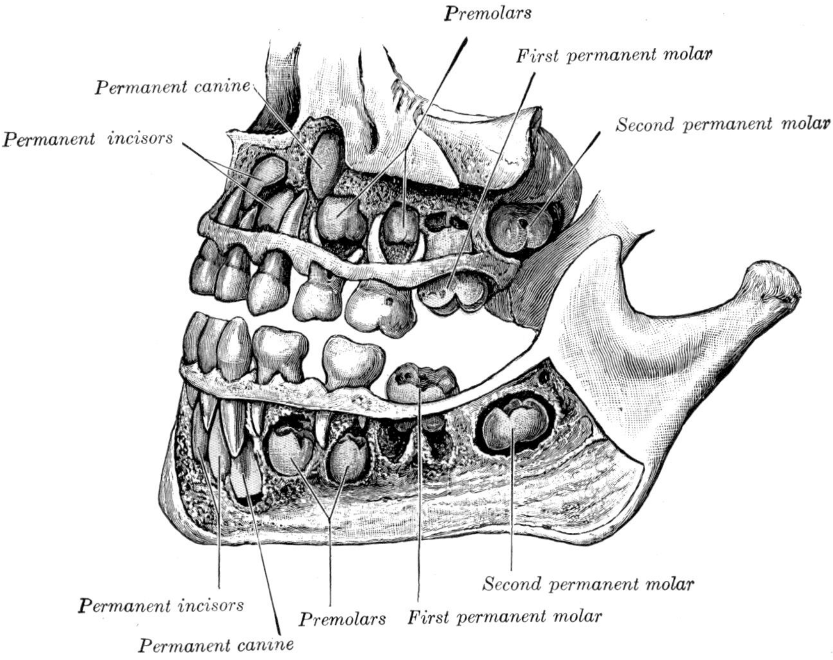

FIG. 1005.—The teeth of a child aged about seven years. The permanent teeth are colored *blue.*

of the periphery of the papilla—that is to say, from the cells in immediate contact with the ameloblasts of the special dental germ. These cells become elongated, one end of the elongated cell resting against the epithelium of the special dental germs, the other being tapered and oftened branched. By the direct transformation of the peripheral ends of these cells, or by a secretion from them, a layer of uncalcified matrix (**prodentin**) is formed which caps the cusp or cusps, if there are more than one, of the papillæ. This matrix becomes fibrillated, and in it islets of calcification make their appearance, and coalescing give rise to a continuous layer of calcified material which covers each cusp and constitutes the first layer of dentin. The odontoblasts, having thus formed the first layer, retire toward the center of the papilla, and, as they do so, produce successive layers of dentin from their peripheral extremities—that is to say, they form the dentinal matrix in which calcification subsequently takes place. As they thus recede from the periphery of the papilla, they leave behind them filamentous processes of cell protoplasm, provided with finer side processes; these are surrounded by calcified material, and thus form the dental canaliculi, and, by their side branches, the anastomosing canaliculi: the processes of protoplasm contained within them constitute the **dentinal fibers** (*Tomes' fibers*). In this way the entire thickness of the dentin is developed, each canaliculus being completed throughout its whole length by a single odontoblast. The central part of the papilla does not undergo calcification, but persists as the pulp of the tooth. In this process of formation of dentin it has been shown that an uncalcified matrix is first developed, and that in this matrix islets of calcification appear which subsequently blend together to form a cap to each cusp: in like manner successive layers are produced, which ultimately become blended with each other. In certain places this blending is not complete, portions of the matrix remaining uncalcified between the successive layers; this gives rise to little spaces, which are the interglobular spaces alluded to above.

Formation of the Cement.—The root of the tooth begins to be formed shortly before the crown emerges through the gum, but is not completed until some time afterward. It is produced by a downgrowth of the epithelium of the dental germ, which extends almost as far as the situation of the apex of the future root, and determines the form of this portion of the tooth. This fold of epithelium is known as the **epithelial sheath**, and on its papillary surface odontoblasts appear, which in turn form dentin, so that the dentin formation is identical in the crown and root of the tooth. After the dentin of the root has been developed, the vascular tissues of the dental sac begin to break through the epithelial sheath, and spread over the surface of the root as a layer of bone-forming material. In this osteoblasts make their appearance, and the process of ossification goes on in identically the same manner as in the ordinary intramembranous ossification of bone. In this way the cement is formed, and consists of ordinary bone containing canaliculi and lacunæ.

Formation of the Alveoli.—About the fourteenth week of embryonic life the dental lamina becomes enclosed in a trough or groove of mesodermal tissue, which at first is common to all the dental germs, but subsequently becomes divided by bony septa into loculi, each loculus containing the special dental germ of a deciduous tooth and its corresponding permanent tooth. After birth each cavity becomes subdivided, so as to form separate loculi (the future alveoli) for the deciduous tooth and its corresponding permanent tooth. Although at one time the whole of the growing tooth is contained in the cavity of the alveolus, the latter never completely encloses it, since there is always an aperture over the top of the crown filled by soft tissue, by which the dental sac is connected with the surface of the gum, and which in the permanent teeth is called the **gubernaculum dentis**.

Development of the Permanent Teeth.—The permanent teeth as regards their development may be divided into two sets: (1) those which replace the deciduous teeth, and which, like them, are ten in number in each jaw: these are the **successional permanent teeth;** and (2) those which have no deciduous predecessors, but are superadded distal to the temporary dental series. These are three in number on either side in each jaw, and are termed **superadded permanent teeth.** They are the three molars of the permanent set, the molars of the deciduous set being replaced by the premolars of the permanent set. The development of the successional permanent teeth—the ten anterior ones in either jaw—has already been indicated. During their development the permanent teeth, enclosed in their sacs, come to be placed on the lingual side of the deciduous teeth and more distant from the margin of the future gum, and, as already stated, are separated from them by bony partitions. As the crown of the permanent tooth grows, absorption of these bony partitions and of the root of the deciduous tooth takes place, through the agency of **osteoclasts,** which appear at this time, and finally nothing but the crown of the deciduous tooth remains. This is shed or removed, and the permanent tooth takes its place.

The superadded permanent teeth are developed in the manner already described, by extensions backward of the posterior part of the dental lamina in each jaw.

Eruption of the Teeth.—When the calcification of the different tissues of the tooth is sufficiently advanced to enable it to bear the pressure to which it will be afterward subjected, eruption takes place, the tooth making its way through the gum. The gum is absorbed by the pressure of the crown of the tooth against it, which is itself pressed up by the increasing size of the root. At the same time the septa between the dental sacs ossify, and constitute the alveoli; these firmly embrace the necks of the teeth, and afford them a solid basis of support.

The eruption of the deciduous teeth commences about the seventh month after birth, and is completed about the end of the second year, the teeth of the lower jaw preceding those of the upper.

The following, according to C. S. Tomes, are the most usual times of eruption:

Lower central incisors	6 to 9 months.
Upper incisors	8 to 10 months.
Lower lateral incisors and first molars . .	15 to 21 months.
Canines	16 to 20 months.
Second molars	20 to 24 months.

There are, however, considerable variations in these times; thus, according to Holt:

At the age of 1	year	a child should have	6	teeth.
" "	$1\frac{1}{2}$ years	"	"	12	"
" "	2	"	"	16	"
" "	$2\frac{1}{2}$	"	"	20	"

Calcification of the permanent teeth proceeds in the following order in the lower jaw (in the upper jaw it takes place a little later): the first molar, soon after birth; the central and lateral incisors, and the canine, about six months after birth; the premolars, at the second year, or a little later; the second molar, about the end of the second year; the third molar, about the twelfth year.

The eruption of the permanent teeth takes place at the following periods, the teeth of the lower jaw preceding those of the upper by short intervals:

First molars	6th year.
Two central incisors	7th year.
Two lateral incisors	8th year.
First premolars	9th year.
Second premolars	10th year.
Canines	11th to 12th year.
Second molars	12th to 13th year.
Third molars	17th to 25th year.

Toward the sixth year, before the shedding of the deciduous teeth begins, there are twenty-four teeth in each jaw, viz., the ten deciduous teeth and the crowns of all the permanent teeth except the third molars.

The Tongue (*lingua*).—The tongue is the principal organ of the sense of taste, and an important organ of speech; it also assists in the mastication and deglutition of the food. It is situated in the floor of the mouth, within the curve of the body of the mandible.

Its **Root** (*radix linguæ; base*) is directed backward, and connected with the hyoid bone by the Hyoglossi and Genioglossi muscles and the hyoglossal membrane; with the epiglottis by three folds (*glossoepiglottic*) of mucous membrane; with the soft palate by the glossopalatine arches; and with the pharynx by the Constrictores pharyngis superiores and the mucous membrane.

Its **Apex** (*apex linguæ; tip*), thin and narrow, is directed forward against the lingual surfaces of the lower incisor teeth.

Its **Inferior Surface** (*facies inferior linguæ; under surface*) (Fig. 1006) is connected with the mandible by the Genioglossi; the mucous membrane is reflected from it to the lingual surface of the gum and on to the floor of the mouth, where, in the middle line, it is elevated into a distinct vertical fold, the **frenulum linguæ.** On either side lateral to the frenulum is a slight fold of the mucous membrane, the **plica fimbriata,** the free edge of which occasionally exhibits a series of fringe-like processes.

The apex of the tongue, part of the inferior surface, the sides, and dorsum are free.

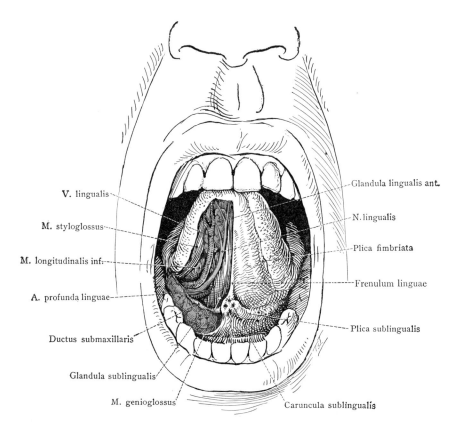

Fig. 1006.—The inferior surface of the tongue, with the right side dissected to show the blood vessels, nerve and salivary glands (Eycleshymer and Jones).

The **Dorsum of the Tongue** (*dorsum linguæ*) (Fig. 1007) is convex and marked by a **median sulcus,** which divides it into symmetrical halves; this sulcus ends behind, about 2.5 cm. from the root of the organ, in a depression, the **foramen cecum,** from which a shallow groove, the **sulcus terminalis,** runs lateralward and forward on either side to the margin of the tongue. The part of the dorsum of the tongue in front of this groove, forming about two-thirds of its surface, looks upward, and is rough and covered with papillæ; the posterior third looks backward, and is smoother, and contains numerous muciparous glands and lymph follicles (**lingual tonsil**). The foramen cecum is the remains of the upper part of the **thyroglossal duct** or diverticulum from which the thyroid gland is developed; the pyramidal lobe of the thyroid gland indicates the position of the lower part of the duct.

The **Papillæ of the Tongue** (Fig. 1007) are projections of the corium. They are thickly distributed over the anterior two-thirds of its dorsum, giving to this surface its characteristic roughness. The varieties of papillæ met with are the **papillæ vallatæ, papillæ fungiformes, papillæ filiformes,** and **papillæ simplices.**

The **papillæ vallatæ** (*circumvallate papillæ*) (Fig. 846) are of large size, and vary from eight to twelve in number. They are situated on the dorsum of the tongue immediately in front of the foramen cecum and sulcus terminalis, forming a row on either side; the two rows run backward and medialward, and meet in the middle line, like the limbs of the letter V inverted. Each papilla consists of a projection of mucous membrane from 1 to 2 mm. wide, attached to the bottom of a circular depression of the mucous membrane; the margin of the depression is elevated to

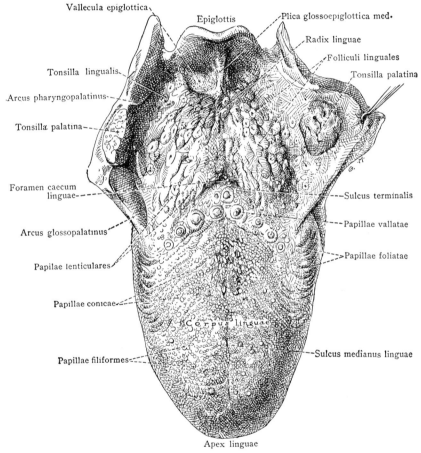

Fig. 1007.—The dorsum of the tongue. (Eycleshymer and Jones).

form a wall (*vallum*), and between this and the papilla is a circular sulcus termed the fossa. The papilla is shaped like a truncated cone, the smaller end being directed downward and attached to the tongue, the broader part or base projecting a little above the surface of the tongue and being studded with numerous small secondary papillæ and covered by stratified squamous epithelium.

The **papillæ fungiformes** (*fungiform papillæ*) (Fig. 1010), more numerous than the preceding, are found chiefly at the sides and apex, but are scattered irregularly and sparingly over the dorsum. They are easily recognized, among the other papillæ, by their large size, rounded eminences, and deep red color. They are narrow at their attachment to the tongue, but broad and rounded at their free extremities, and covered with secondary papillæ.

The **papillæ filiformes** (*filiform or conical papillæ*) (Fig. 1010) cover the anterior two-thirds of the dorsum. They are very minute, filiform in shape, and arranged in lines parallel with the two rows of the papillæ vallatæ, excepting at the apex of the organ, where their direction is transverse. Projecting from their apices are numerous filamentous processes, or secondary papillæ; these are of a whitish

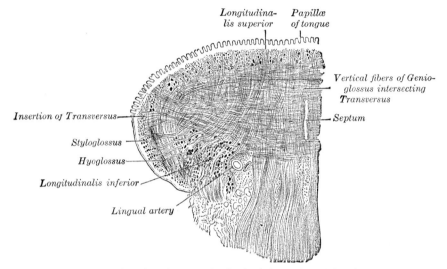

FIG. 1008.—Coronal section of tongue, showing intrinsic muscles. (Altered from Krause.)

tint owing to the thickness and density of the epithelium of which they are composed, which has here undergone a peculiar modification, the cells having become cornified and elongated into dense, imbricated, brush-like processes. They contain also a number of elastic fibers, which render them firmer and more elastic than the papillæ of mucous membrane generally. The larger and longer papillæ of this group are sometimes termed **papillæ conicæ.**

The **papillæ simplices** are similar to those of the skin, and cover the whole of the mucous membrane of the tongue, as well as the larger papillæ. They consist of closely set microscopic elevations of the corium, each containing a capillary loop, covered by a layer of epithelium.

Muscles of the Tongue.—The tongue is divided into lateral halves by a median fibrous septum which extends throughout its entire length and is fixed below to the hyoid bone. In either half there are two sets of muscles, extrinsic and intrinsic; the former have their origins outside the tongue, the latter are contained entirely within it.

The **extrinsic muscles** (Fig. 1009) are:

Genioglossus.	Chondroglossus.
Hyoglossus.	Styloglossus.
Glossopalatinus.[1]	

The **Genioglossus** (*Geniohyoglossus*) is a flat triangular muscle close to and parallel with the median plane, its apex corresponding with its point of origin from the mandible, its base with its insertion into the tongue and hyoid bone. It *arises*

---

[1] The *Glossopalatinus* (*Palatoglossus*), although one of the muscles of the tongue, is more closely associated with the soft palate both in situation and function; it has consequently been described with the muscles of that structure (pp. 1181).

by a short tendon from the superior mental spine on the inner surface of the symphysis menti, immediately above the Geniohyoideus, and from this point spreads

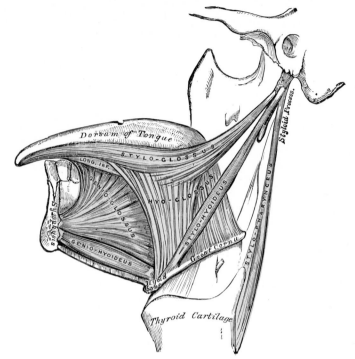

Fig. 1009.—Extrinsic muscles of the tongue. Left side.

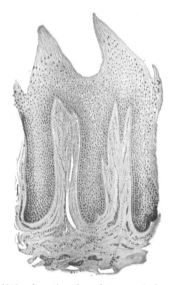

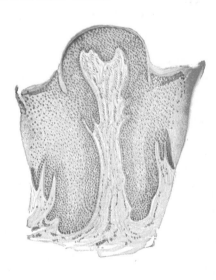

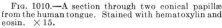

Fig. 1010.—A section through two conical papillæ from the human tongue. Stained with hematoxylin and eosin. × 15.

Fig. 1011.—A section through a fungiform papilla from the human tongue. Stained with hematoxylin and eosin. × 15.

out in a fan-like form. The inferior fibers extend downward, to be attached by a thin aponeurosis to the upper part of the body of the hyoid bone, a few passing between the Hyoglossus and Chondroglossus to blend with the Constrictores

74

pharyngis; the middle fibers pass backward, and the superior ones upward and forward, to enter the whole length of the under surface of the tongue, from the root to the apex. The muscles of opposite sides are separated at their insertions by the median fibrous septum of the tongue; in front, they are more or less blended owing to the decussation of fasciculi in the median plane.

The **Hyoglossus**, thin and quadrilateral, *arises* from the side of the body and from the whole length of the greater cornu of the hyoid bone, and passes almost vertically upward to enter the side of the tongue, between the Styloglossus and Longitudinalis inferior. The fibers arising from the body of the hyoid bone overlap those from the greater cornu.

The **Chondroglossus** is sometimes described as a part of the Hyoglossus, but is separated from it by fibers of the Genioglossus, which pass to the side of the pharynx. It is about 2 cm. long, and *arises* from the medial side and base of the lesser cornu and contiguous portion of the body of the hyoid bone. and passes directly upward to blend with the intrinsic muscular fibers of the tongue, between the Hyoglossus and Genioglossus.

A small slip of muscular fibers is occasionally found, arising from the cartilago triticea in the lateral hyothyroid ligament and entering the tongue with the hindermost fibers of the Hyoglossus.

The **Styloglossus**, the shortest and smallest of the three styloid muscles, *arises* from the anterior and lateral surfaces of the styloid process, near its apex, and from the stylomandibular ligament. Passing downward and forward between the internal and external carotid arteries, it divides upon the side of the tongue into two portions: one, longitudinal, enters the side of the tongue near its dorsal surface, blending with the fibers of the Longitudinalis inferior in front of the Hyoglossus; the other, oblique, overlaps the Hyoglossus and decussates with its fibers.

The **intrinsic muscles** (Fig. 1009) are:

Longitudinalis superior.	Transversus.
Longitudinalis inferior.	Verticalis.

The **Longitudinalis linguæ superior** (*Superior lingualis*) is a thin stratum of oblique and longitudinal fibers immediately underlying the mucous membrane on the dorsum of the tongue. It *arises* from the submucous fibrous layer close to the epiglottis and from the median fibrous septum, and runs forward to the edges of the tongue.

The **Longitudinalis linguæ inferior** (*Inferior lingualis*) is a narrow band situated on the under surface of the tongue between the Genioglossus and Hyoglossus. It extends from the root to the apex of the tongue: behind, some of its fibers are connected with the body of the hyoid bone; in front it blends with the fibers of the Styloglossus.

The **Transversus linguæ** (*Transverse lingualis*) consists of fibers which *arise* from the median fibrous septum and pass lateralward to be inserted into the submucous fibrous tissue at the sides of the tongue.

The **Verticalis linguæ** (*Vertical lingualis*) is found only at the borders of the forepart of the tongue. Its fibers extend from the upper to the under surface of the organ.

The median fibrous septum of the tongue is very complete, so that the anastomosis between the two lingual arteries is not very free.

Nerves.—The muscles of the tongue described above are supplied by the hypoglossal nerve.

Actions.—The movements of the tongue, although numerous and complicated, may be understood by carefully considering the direction of the fibers of its muscles. The Genioglossi, by means of their posterior fibers, draw the root of the tongue forward, and protrude the apex from the mouth. The anterior fibers draw the tongue back into the mouth. The two muscles acting in their entirety draw the tongue downward, so as to make its superior surface concave from side to side, forming a channel along which fluids may pass toward the pharynx, as in sucking. The Hyoglossi depress the tongue, and draw down its sides. The Styloglossi draw the tongue upward and backward. The Glossopalatini draw the root of the tongue upward. The intrinsic muscles are mainly concerned in altering the shape of the tongue, whereby it becomes shortened, narrowed, or curved in different directions; thus, the Longitudinalis superior and inferior tend to shorten the tongue, but the former, in addition, turn the tip and sides upward so as to render the dorsum concave, while the latter pull the tip downward and render the dorsum convex. The Transversus narrows and elongates the tongue, and the Verticalis flattens and broadens it. The complex arrangement of the muscular fibers of the tongue, and the various directions in which they run, give to this organ the power of assuming the forms necessary for the enunciation of the different consonantal sounds; and Macalister states "there is reason to believe that the musculature of the tongue varies in different races owing to the hereditary practice and habitual use of certain motions required for enunciating the several vernacular languages."

Structure of the Tongue.—The tongue is partly invested by mucous membrane and a submucous fibrous layer.

The **mucous membrane** (*tunica mucosa linguæ*) differs in different parts. That covering the under surface of the organ is thin, smooth, and identical in structure with that lining the rest of the oral cavity. The mucous membrane of the dorsum of the tongue behind the foramen cecum and sulcus terminalis is thick and freely movable over the subjacent parts. It contains a large number of lymphoid follicles, which together constitute what is sometimes termed the **lingual tonsil** (Fig. 1007). Each follicle forms a rounded eminence, the center of which is perforated by a minute orifice leading into a funnel-shaped cavity or recess; around this recess are grouped numerous oval or rounded nodules of lymphoid tissue, each enveloped by a capsule derived from the submucosa, while opening into the bottom of the recesses are also seen the ducts of mucous glands. The mucous membrane on the anterior part of the dorsum of the tongue is thin, intimately adherent to the muscular tissue, and presents numerous minute surface eminences, the **papillæ** of the tongue. It consists of a layer of connective tissue, the **corium** or **mucosa**, covered with epithelium. (Fig. 1010, 1011.)

The epithelium is of the stratified squamous variety, similar to but much thinner than that of the skin: and each papilla has a separate investment from root to summit. The deepest cells may sometimes be detached as a separate layer, corresponding to the rete mucosum, but they never contain coloring matter.

The **corium** consists of a dense felt-work of fibrous connective tissue, with numerous elastic fibers, firmly connected with the fibrous tissue forming the septa between the muscular bundles of the tongue. It contains the ramifications of the numerous vessels and nerves from which the papillæ are supplied, large plexuses of lymphatic vessels, and the glands of the tongue.

Structure of the Papillæ.—The papillæ apparently resemble in structure those of the cutis, consisting of cone-shaped projections of connective tissue, covered with a thick layer of stratified squamous epithelium, and containing one or more capillary loops among which nerves are distributed in great abundance. If the epithelium be removed, it will be found that they are not simple elevations like the papillæ of the skin, for the surface of each is studded with minute conical processes which form secondary papillæ. In the papillæ vallatæ, the nerves are numerous and of large size; in the papillæ fungiformes they are also numerous, and end in a plexiform net-work, from which brush-like branches proceed; in the papillæ filiformes, their mode of termination is uncertain.

Glands of the Tongue.—The tongue is provided with mucous and serous glands.

The **mucous glands** are similar in structure to the labial and buccal glands. They are found especially at the back part behind the vallate papillæ, but are also present at the apex and marginal parts. In this connection the anterior lingual glands (Blandin or Nuhn) require special notice. They are situated on the under surface of the apex of the tongue (Fig. 1006), one on either side of the frenulum, where they are covered by a fasciculus of muscular fibers derived from the Styloglossus and Longitudinalis inferior. They are from 12 to 25 mm. long, and about 8 mm. broad, and each opens by three or four ducts on the under surface of the apex.

The **serous glands** occur only at the back of the tongue in the neighborhood of the taste-buds, their ducts opening for the most part into the fossæ of the vallate papillæ. These glands are racemose, the duct of each branching into several minute ducts, which end in alveoli, lined by a single layer of more or less columnar epithelium. Their secretion is of a watery nature, and probably assists in the distribution of the substance to be tasted over the taste area. (Ebner.)

The **septum** consists of a vertical layer of fibrous tissue, extending throughout the entire length of the median plane of the tongue, though not quite reaching the dorsum. It is thicker behind than in front, and occasionally contains a small fibrocartilage, about 6 mm. in length. It is well displayed by making a vertical section across the organ.

The **hyoglossal membrane** is a strong fibrous lamina, which connects the under surface of the root of the tongue to the body of the hyoid bone. This membrane receives, in front, some of the fibers of the Geinoglossi.

Taste-buds, the end-organs of the gustatory sense, are scattered over the mucous membrane of the mouth and tongue at irregular intervals. They occur especially in the sides of the vallate papillæ. They are described under the organs of the senses (page 1023).

Vessels and Nerves.—The main **artery** of the tongue is the lingual branch of the external carotid, but the external maxillary and ascending pharyngeal also give branches to it. The **veins** open into the internal jugular.

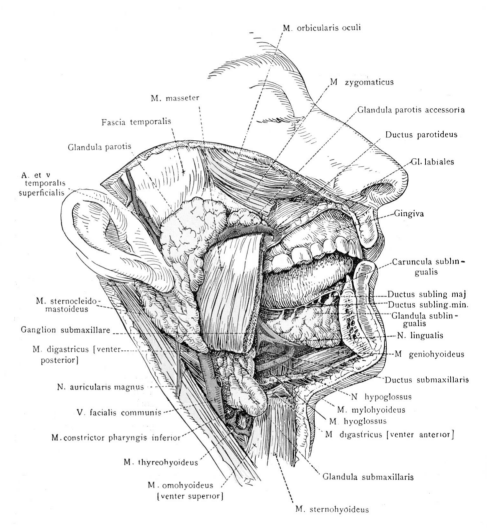

Fig. 1012.   The salivary glands in a dissection of the right side of the face.   (Eycleshymer and Jones**).**

The **lymphatics of the tongue** have been described on page 705.

The **sensory nerves of the tongue** are: (1) the lingual branch of the mandibular, which is distributed to the papillæ at the forepart and sides of the tongue, and forms the nerve of ordinary sensibility for its anterior two-thirds; (2) the chorda tympani branch of the facial, which runs in the sheath of the lingual, and is generally regarded as the nerve of taste for the anterior two-thirds; this nerve is a continuation of the sensory root of the facial (*nervus intermedius*); (3) the lingual branch of the glossopharyngeal, which is distributed to the mucous membrane at the base and sides of the tongue, and to the papillæ vallatæ, and which supplies both gustatory filaments and fibers of general sensation to this region; (4) the superior laryngeal, which sends some fine branches to the root near the epiglottis.

The Salivary Glands (Fig. 1012).—Three pairs of large salivary glands communicate with the mouth, and pour their secretion into its cavity; they are the **parotid**, **submaxillary**, and **sublingual**.

Parotid Gland (*glandula parotis*).—The parotid gland (Figs. 1013, 1014), the largest of the three, varies in weight from 14 to 28 gm. It lies upon the side of the face,

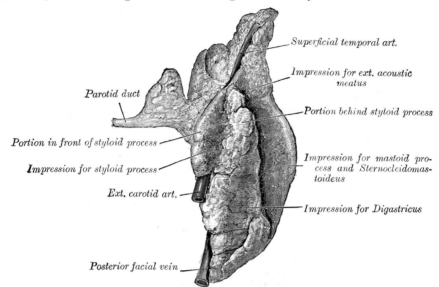

Fig. 1013.—Right parotid gland. Posterior and deep aspects.

immediately below and in front of the external ear. The main portion of the gland is superficial, somewhat flattened and quadrilateral in form, and is placed between the ramus of the mandible in front and the mastoid process and Sternocleido-

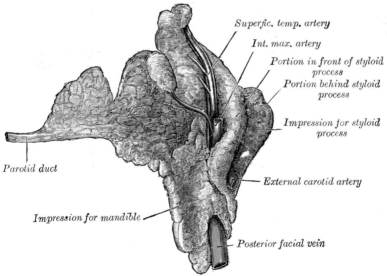

Fig 1014.—Right parotid gland. Deep and anterior aspects.

mastoideus behind, overlapping, however, both boundaries. Above, it is broad and reaches nearly to the zygomatic arch; below, it tapers somewhat to about the level of a line joining the tip of the mastoid process to the angle of the mandible.

The remainder of the gland is irregularly wedge-shaped, and extends deeply inward toward the pharyngeal wall.

The gland is enclosed within a capsule continuous with the deep cervical fascia; the layer covering the superficial surface is dense and closely adherent to the gland; a portion of the fascia, attached to the styloid process and the angle of the mandible, is thickened to form the stylomandibular ligament which intervenes between the parotid and submaxillary glands.

The **anterior surface** of the gland is moulded on the posterior border of the ramus of the mandible, clothed by the Pterygoideus internus and Masseter. The inner lip of the groove dips, for a short distance, between the two Pterygoid muscles, while the outer lip extends for some distance over the superficial surface of the Masseter; a small portion of this lip immediately below the zygomatic arch is usually detached, and is named the **accessory part** (*socia parotidis*) of the gland.

The **posterior surface** is grooved longitudinally and abuts against the external acoustic meatus, the mastoid process, and the anterior border of the Sterno-cleidomastoideus.

The **superficial surface**, slightly lobulated, is covered by the integument, the superficial fascia containing the facial branches of the great auricular nerve and some small lymph glands, and the fascia which forms the capsule of the gland.

The **deep surface** extends inward by means of two processes, one of which lies on the Digastricus, styloid process, and the styloid group of muscles, and projects under the mastoid process and Sternocleidomastoideus; the other is situated in front of the styloid process, and sometimes passes into the posterior part of the mandibular fossa behind the temporomandibular joint. The deep surface is in contact with the internal and external carotid arteries, the internal jugular vein, and the vagus and glossopharyngeal nerves.

The gland is separated from the pharyngeal wall by some loose connective tissue.

Structures within the Gland.—The *external carotid artery* lies at first on the deep surface, and then in the substance of the gland. The artery gives off its *posterior auricular* branch which emerges from the gland behind; it then divides into its terminal branches, the *internal maxillary* and *superficial temporal;* the former runs forward deep to the neck of the mandible; the latter runs upward across the zygo-matic arch and gives off its *transverse facial* branch which emerges from the front of the gland. Superficial to the arteries are the *superficial temporal* and *internal maxillary veins,* uniting to form the *posterior facial* vein; in the lower part of the gland this vein splits into anterior and posterior divisions. The anterior division emerges from the gland and unites with the anterior facial to form the *common facial* vein; the posterior unites in the gland with the posterior auricular to form the *external jugular* vein. On a still more superficial plane is the facial nerve, the branches of which emerge from the borders of the gland. Branches of the *great auricular nerve* pierce the gland to join the facial, while the *auriculotemporal nerve* issues from the upper part of the gland.

The **parotid duct** (*ductus parotideus; Stensen's duct*) is about 7 cm. long. It begins by numerous branches from the anterior part of the gland, crosses the Masse-ter, and at the anterior border of this muscle turns inward nearly at a right angle, passes through the corpus adiposum of the cheek and pierces the Buccinator; it then runs for a short distance obliquely forward between the Buccinator and mucous membrane of the mouth, and opens upon the oral surface of the cheek by a small orifice, opposite the second upper molar tooth. While crossing the Masseter, it receives the duct of the accessory portion; in this position it lies between the branches of the facial nerve; the accessory part of the gland and the transverse facial artery are above it.

Structure.—The parotid duct is dense, its wall being of considerable thickness; its canal is about the size of a crow-quill, but at its orifice on the oral surface of the cheek its lumen is greatly reduced in size. It consists of a thick external fibrous coat which contains contractile fibers, and of an internal or mucous coat lined with short columnar epithelium.

Vessels and Nerves.—The **arteries** supplying the parotid gland are derived from the external carotid, and from the branches given off by that vessel in or near its substance. The **veins** empty themselves into the external jugular, through some of its tributaries. The **lymphatics** end in the superficial and deep cervical lymph nodes, passing in their course through two or three nodes, placed on the surface and in the substance of the parotid. The **nerves** are derived from the plexus of the sympathetic on the external carotid artery, and from the auriculotemporal nerve. The fibers from the latter nerve are cranial parasympathetics derived from the glosso-pharyngeal, and possibly from the facial, through the otic ganglion. The sympathetic fibers are regarded as chiefly vasoconstrictors, the parasympathetic fibers as secretory.

Submaxillary Gland (*glandula submaxillaris*).— The submaxillary gland (Fig. 1022) is irregular in form and about the size of a walnut. A considerable part of it is situated in the submaxillary triangle, reaching forward to the anterior belly of the Digastricus and backward to the stylomandibular ligament, which intervenes between it and the parotid gland. Above, it extends under cover of the body of the mandible; below, it usually overlaps the intermediate tendon of the Digastricus and the insertion of the Stylohyoideus, while from its deep surface a tongue-like *deep process* extends forward above the Mylohyoideus muscle.

Its **superficial surface** consists of an upper and a lower part. The **upper part** is directed outward, and lies partly against the submaxillary depression on the inner surface of the body of the mandible, and partly on the Pterygoideus internus. The **lower part** is directed downward and outward, and is covered by the skin, superficial fascia, Platysma, and deep cervical fascia; it is crossed by the anterior facial vein and by filaments of the facial nerve; in contact with it, near the mandible, are the submaxillary lymph nodes.

The **deep surface** is in relation with the Mylohyoideus, Hyoglossus, Styloglossus, Stylohyoideus, and posterior belly of the Digastricus; in contact with it are the mylohyoid nerve and the mylohyoid and submental vessels.

The external maxillary artery is imbedded in a groove in the posterior border of the gland.

The **deep process** of the gland extends forward between the Mylohyoideus below and externally, and the Hyoglossus and Styloglossus internally; above it is the lingual nerve and submaxillary ganglion; below it the hypoglossal nerve and its accompanying vein.

The **submaxillary duct** (*ductus submaxillaris; Wharton's duct*) is about 5 cm. long, and its wall is much thinner than that of the parotid duct. It begins by numerous branches from the deep surface of the gland, and runs forward between the Mylohyoideus and the Hyoglossus and Genioglossus, then between the sublingual gland and the Genioglossus, and opens by a narrow orifice on the summit of a small papilla, at the side of the frenulum linguæ. On the Hyoglossus it lies between the lingual and hypoglossal nerves, but at the anterior border of the muscle it is crossed laterally by the lingual nerve; the terminal branches of the lingual nerve ascend on its medial side.

Vessels and Nerves.—The **arteries** supplying the submaxillary gland are branches of the external maxillary and lingual. Its **veins** follow the course of the arteries. The **nerves** are derived from the sympathetic, through a plexus of fibers extending along the external maxillary artery from the carotid plexus; and from cranial parasympathetic fibers of the facial, and perhaps the glossopharyngeal, which pass via the chorda tympani and submaxillary ganglion.

Sublingual Gland (*glandula sublingualis*).—The sublingual gland (Fig. 1014) is the smallest of the three glands. It is situated beneath the mucous membrane of the floor of the mouth, at the side of the frenulum linguæ, in contact with the sublingual depression on the inner surface of the mandible, close to the symphysis.

It is narrow, flattened, shaped somewhat like an almond, and weighs nearly 2 gm. It is in relation, *above*, with the mucous membrane; *below*, with the Mylohyoideus; *behind*, with the deep part of the submaxillary gland; *laterally*, with the mandible; and *medially*, with the Genioglossus, from which it is separated by the lingual nerve and the submaxillary duct. Its excretory ducts are from eight to twenty in number. Of the **smaller sublingual ducts** (*ducts of Rivinus*), some join the submaxillary duct; others open separately into the mouth, on the elevated crest of mucous membrane (*plica sublingualis*), caused by the projection of the gland, on either side of the frenulum linguæ. One or more join to form the **larger sublingual duct** (*duct of Bartholin*), which opens into the submaxillary duct.

Vessels and Nerves.—The sublingual gland is supplied with blood from the sublingual and submental arteries. Its nerves are derived in a manner similar to those of the submaxillary gland.

Structure of the Salivary Glands.—The salivary glands are compound racemose glands consisting of numerous lobes, which are made up of smaller lobules, connected together by dense areolar tissue, vessels, and ducts. Each lobule consists of the ramifications of a single duct, the branches ending in dilated ends or alveoli on which the capillaries are distributed. The alveoli are enclosed by a basement membrane, which is continuous with the membrana propria of the duct and consists of a net-work of branched and flattened nucleated cells.

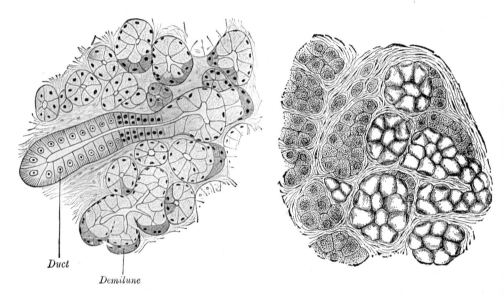

Duct

Demilune

FIG. 1015.—Section of submaxillary gland of kitten. Duct semidiagrammatic. × 200.

FIG. 1016.—Human submaxillary gland. (R. Heidenhain.) At the right is a group of mucous alveoli; at the left a group of serous alveoli.

The alveoli of the salivary glands are of two kinds, which differ in the appearance of their secreting cells, in their size, and in the nature of their secretion. (1) The mucous variety secretes a viscid fluid, which contains mucin; (2) the serous variety secretes a thinner and more watery fluid. The sublingual gland consists of mucous, the parotid of serous alveoli. The submaxillary contains both mucous and serous alveoli, the latter, however, preponderating.

The cells in the **mucous alveoli** are columnar in shape. In the fresh condition they contain large granules of mucinogen. In hardened preparations a delicate protoplasmic net-work is seen, and the cells are clear and transparent. The nucleus is usually situated near the basement membrane, and is flattened.

In some alveoli are seen peculiar crescentic bodies, lying between the cells and the membrana propria. They are termed the **crescents of Gianuzzi**, or the **demilunes of Heidenhain** (Fig. 1015), and are composed of polyhedral granular cells, which Heidenhain regards as young epithelial cells destined to supply the place of those salivary cells which have undergone disintegration. This view, however, is not accepted by Klein. Fine canaliculi pass between the mucus-secreting cells to reach the demilunes and even penetrate the cells forming these structures.

In the **serous alveoli** the cells almost completely fill the cavity, so that there is hardly any lumen perceptible; they contain secretory granules imbedded in a closely reticulated protoplasm (Fig. 1016). The cells are more cubical than those of the mucous type; the nucleus of each is spherical and placed near the center of the cell, and the granules are smaller.

Both mucous and serous cells vary in appearance according to whether the gland is in a resting condition or has been recently active. In the former case the cells are large and contain many secretory granules; in the latter case they are shrunken and contain few granules, chiefly collected at the inner ends of the cells. The granules are best seen in fresh preparations.

The ducts are lined at their origins by epithelium which differs little from the pavement form. As the ducts enlarge, the epithelial cells change to the columnar type, and the part of the cell next the basement membrane is finely striated.

The lobules of the salivary glands are richly supplied with bloodvessels which form a dense net-work in the interalveolar spaces. Fine plexuses of nerves are also found in the interlobular tissue. The nerve fibrils pierce the basement membrane of the alveoli, and end in branched varicose filaments between the secreting cells. In the hilum of the submaxillary gland there is a collection of nerve cells termed **Langley's ganglion.**

Accessory Glands.—Besides the salivary glands proper, numerous other glands are found in the mouth. Many of these glands are found at the posterior part of the dorsum of the tongue behind the vallate papillæ, and also along its margins as far forward as the apex. Others lie around and in the palatine tonsil between its crypts, and large numbers are present in the soft palate, the lips, and cheeks. These glands are of the same structure as the larger salivary glands, and are of the mucous or mixed type.

THE FAUCES.

The aperture by which the mouth communicates with the pharynx is called the **isthmus faucium.** (Fig. 1017). It is bounded, above, by the soft palate; below, by the dorsum of the tongue; and on either side, by the glossopalatine arch.

The **glossopalatine arch** (*arcus glossopalatinus; anterior pillar of fauces*) on either side runs downward, lateralward, and forward to the side of the base of the tongue, and is formed by the projection of the Glossopalatinus with its covering mucous membrane.

The **pharyngopalatine arch** (*arcus pharyngopalatinus; posterior pillar of fauces*) is larger and projects farther toward the middle line than the anterior; it runs downward, lateralward, and backward to the side of the pharynx, and is formed by the projection of the Pharyngopalatinus, covered by mucous membrane. On either side the two arches are separated below by a triangular interval, in which the palatine tonsil is lodged.

The **Palatine Tonsils** (*tonsillæ palatinæ; tonsil,* (Figs. 1017, 1018) are two prominent masses situated one on either side between the glossopalatine and pharyngopalatine arches. Each tonsil consists fundamentally of an aggregation of lymphatic tissue underlying the mucous membrane between the palatine arches. The lymphatic mass, however, does not completely fill the interval between the two arches, so that a small depression, the **supratonsillar fossa,** exists at the upper part of the interval. Further, the tonsil extends for a variable distance under cover of the glossopalatine arch, and is here covered by a reduplication of mucous membrane; the upper part of this fold reaches across the supratonsillar fossa, between the two arches, as a thin fold sometimes termed the **plica semilunaris;** the remainder of the fold is called the **plica triangularis.** Between the plica triangularis and the surface of the tonsil is a space known as the **tonsillar sinus;** in many cases, however, this sinus is obliterated by its walls becoming adherent. From this description it will be apparent that a portion of the tonsil is below the level of the surrounding mucous membrane, *i. e.,* is imbedded, while the remainder projects as the visible tonsil. In the child the tonsils are relatively (and frequently absolutely) larger than in the adult, and about one-third of the tonsil is imbedded. After puberty the imbedded portion diminishes considerably in size and the tonsil assumes a disk-like form, flattened from side to side; the shape and size of the tonsil, however, vary considerably in different individuals.

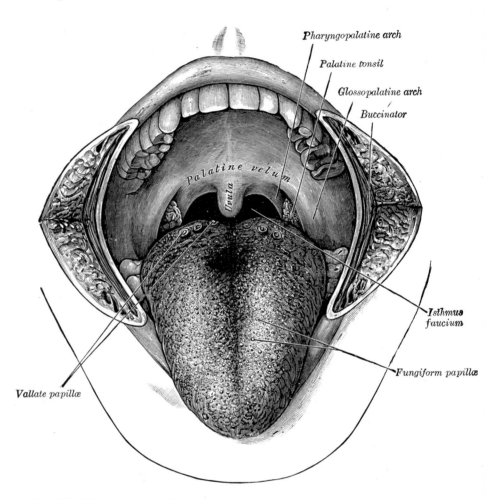

FIG. 1017.—The mouth cavity. The cheeks have been slit transversely and the tongue pulled forward.

The **medial surface** of the tonsil is free except anteriorly, where it is covered by the plica triangularis; it presents from twelve to fifteen orifices leading into **crypts** or recesses (*fossulæ tonsillares*) which may branch and extend deeply into the tonsillar substance.

The **lateral** or **deep surface** is adherent to a fibrous capsule which is continued into the plica triangularis. It is separated from the inner surface of the Constrictor pharyngis superior usually by some loose connective tissue; this muscle intervenes between the tonsil and the external maxillary artery with its tonsillar and ascending palatine branches. The internal carotid artery lies behind and lateral to the tonsil at a distance of 20 to 25 mm. from it.

The tonsils form part of a circular band of lymphatic tissue which guards the opening into the digestive and respiratory tubes (Fig. 1018). The anterior part of the ring is formed by the submucous lymphatic collections (**lingual tonsil**) on the posterior part of the tongue; the lateral portions consist of the palatine tonsils and the lymphatic collections in the vicinity of the auditory tubes, while the ring is completed behind by the pharyngeal tonsil on the posterior wall of the pharynx. In the intervals between these main masses are smaller collections of lymphoid tissue.

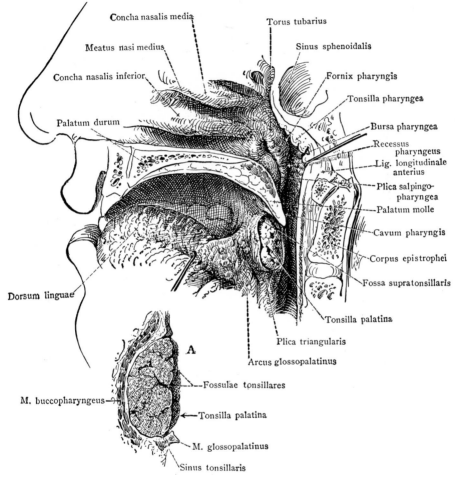

FIG. 1018. The oral and nasal pharynx in median sagittal section, showing palatine and pharyngeal tonsils. A. Detail of palatine tonsil in frontal section. (Eycleshymer and Jones).

Structure (Fig. 1019).—Stratified squamous epithelium, like that of the palate and oral pharynx, covers the free surface of the tonsil and extends down into its substance to form the lining of the crypts. Each **crypt** is surrounded by a layer of lymphatic tissue containing numerous scattered lymphatic nodules whose germinal centers are especially prominent in children and young adults. A thin connnective tissue capsule, derived from the submucosa of the pharynx, encloses the whole tonsil and sends delicate septa in between the lymphatic tissue layers surrounding the crypts. The epithelium of the crypts is so invaded by leucocytes in many places that it is scarcely distinguishable from the lymphatic tissue. Polymorphonuclear leucocytes from the blood as well as lymphocytes penetrate the epithelium, and when they are found as free swimming cells in the saliva, they are known as *salivary corpuscles*. Small mucous glands occur in the submucosa about the tonsil but their ducts, as a rule, do not open into the crypts.

Vessels and Nerves.—The **arteries** supplying the tonsil are the dorsalis linguæ from the lingual, the ascending palatine and tonsillar from the external maxillary, the ascending pharyngeal from the external carotid, the descending palatine branch of the internal maxillary, and a twig from the small meningeal.

The **veins** end in the tonsillar plexus, on the lateral side of the tonsil.

The **lymphatic vessels**, beginning in the dense network of capillaries surrounding the lymphatic tissue, penetrate the pharyngeal wall (page 705) and pass to the deep cervical nodes. The largest of these nodes, lying beside the posterior belly of the Digastricus, is especially associated with the tonsil and is easily palpated when the latter is inflamed.

The **nerves** are derived from the middle and posterior palatine branches of the maxillary, and from the glossopharyngeal.

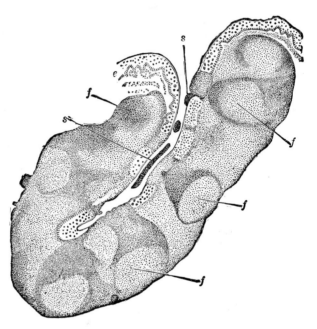

Fig. 1019.—Section through one of the crypts of the tonsil. (Stöhr.) Magnified. *e.* Stratified epithelium of general surface, continued into crypt. *f, f.* Nodules of lymphoid tissue—opposite each nodule numbers of lymph cells are passing into or through the epithelium. *s, s.* Cells which have thus escaped to mix with the saliva as salivary corpuscles.

Palatine Aponeurosis.—Attached to the posterior border of the hard palate is a thin, firm fibrous lamella which supports the muscles and gives strength to the soft palate. It is thicker above than below, where it becomes very thin and difficult to define. Laterally it is continuous with the pharyngeal aponeurosis.

Muscles of the Palate.—The muscles of the palate (Fig. 1020) are:

Levator veli palatini.   Glossopalatinus.
Tensor veli palatini.   Pharyngopalatinus.
Musculus uvulæ.

The **Levator veli palatini** (*Levator palati*) is a thick, rounded muscle situated lateral to the choanæ. It *arises* from the under surface of the apex of the petrous part of the temporal bone and from the medial lamina of the cartilage of the auditory tube. After passing above the upper concave margin of the Constrictor pharyngis superior it spreads out in the palatine velum, its fibers extending obliquely downward and medialward to the middle line, where they blend with those of the opposite side.

The **Tensor veli palatini** (*Tensor palati*) is a broad, thin, ribbon-like muscle placed lateral to the Levator veli palatini. It *arises* by a flat lamella from the scaphoid fossa at the base of the medial pterygoid plate, from the spina angularis of the sphenoid and from the lateral wall of the cartilage of the auditory tube. Descending vertically between the medial pterygoid plate and the Pterygoideus internus it ends in a tendon which winds around the pterygoid hamulus, being retained in this situation by some of the fibers of origin of the Pterygoideus internus. Between the tendon and the hamulus is a small bursa. The tendon then passes medialward and is *inserted* into the palatine aponeurosis and into the surface behind the transverse ridge on the horizontal part of the palatine bone.

The **Musculus uvulæ** (*Azygos uvulæ*) *arises* from the posterior nasal spine of the palatine bones and from the palatine aponeurosis; it descends to be inserted into the uvula.

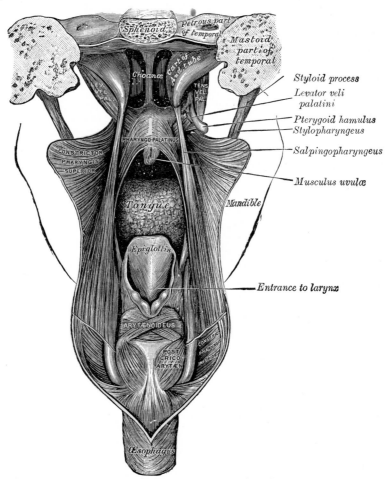

Fig. 1020.—Dissection of the muscles of the palate from behind.

The **Glossopalatinus** (*Palatoglossus*) is a small fleshy fasciculus, narrower in the middle than at either end, forming, with the mucous membrane covering its surface, the glossopalatine arch. It *arises* from the anterior surface of the soft palate, where it is continuous with the muscle of the opposite side, and passing downward, forward, and lateralward in front of the palatine tonsil, is inserted into the side of the tongue, some of its fibers spreading over the dorsum, and others passing deeply into the substance of the organ to intermingle with the Transversus linguæ.

The **Pharyngopalatinus** (*Palatopharyngeus*) is a long, fleshy fasciculus narrower in the middle than at either end, forming, with the mucous membrane covering its surface, the pharyngopalatine arch. It is separated from the Glossopalatinus by an angular interval, in which the palatine tonsil is lodged. It *arises* from the soft palate, where it is divided into two fasciculi by the Levator veli palatini and Musculus uvulæ. The **posterior fasciculus** lies in contact with the mucous membrane, and joins with that of the opposite muscle in the middle line; the **anterior fasciculus**, the thicker, lies in the soft palate between the Levator and Tensor, and joins in the middle line the corresponding part of the opposite muscle. Passing lateralward and downward behind the palatine tonsil, the Pharyngopalatinus joins the Stylopharyngeus, and is inserted with that muscle into the posterior border of the thyroid cartilage, some of its fibers being lost on the side of the pharynx and others passing across the middle line posteriorly, to decussate with the muscle of the opposite side.

Nerves.—The Tensor veli palatini is supplied by a branch of the fifth cranial nerve; the remaining muscles of this group are in all probability supplied by the bulbar portion of the accessory nerve through the pharyngeal plexus.[1]

Actions.—During the *first stage* of deglutition, the bolus of food is driven back into the fauces by the pressure of the tongue against the hard palate, the base of the tongue being, at the same time, retracted, and the larynx raised with the pharynx. During the second stage the entrance to the larynx is closed by the drawing forward of the arytenoid cartilages toward the cushion of the epiglottis—a movement produced by the contraction of the Thyreoarytænoidei, the Arytænoidei, and the Arytænoepiglottidei.

After leaving the tongue the bolus passes on to the posterior or laryngeal surface of the epiglottis, and glides along this for a certain distance; then the Glossopalatini, the constrictors of the fauces, contract behind it; the palatine velum is slightly raised by the Levator veli palatini, and made tense by the Tensor veli palatini; and the Pharyngopalatini, by their contraction, pull the pharynx upward over the bolus, and come nearly together, the uvula filling up the slight interval between them. By these means the food is prevented from passing into the nasal part of the pharynx; at the same time, the Pharyngopalatini form an inclined plane, directed obliquely downward and backward along the under surface of which the bolus descends into the lower part of the pharynx. The Salpingopharyngei raise the upper and lateral parts of the pharynx—*i. e.*, those parts which are above the points where the Stylopharyngei are attached to the pharynx.

Mucous Membrane.—The *mucous membrane of the soft palate* is thin, and covered with stratified squamous epithelium on both surfaces, excepting near the pharyngeal ostium of the auditory tube, where it is columnar and ciliated. According to Klein, the mucous membrane on the nasal surface of the soft palate in the fetus is covered throughout by columnar ciliated epithelium, which subsequently becomes squamous except at its free margin. Beneath the mucous membrane on the oral surface of the soft palate is a considerable amount of adenoid tissue. The palatine glands form a continuous layer on its posterior surface and around the uvula.

Vessels and Nerves.—The **arteries** supplying the palate are the descending palatine branch of the internal maxillary, the ascending palatine branch of the external maxillary, and the palatine branch of the ascending pharyngeal. The **veins** end chiefly in the pterygoid and tonsillar plexuses. The **lymphatic vessels** pass to the deep cervical nodes. The **sensory nerves** are derived from the palatine and nasopalatine nerves and from the glossopharyngeal.

THE PHARYNX.

The **pharynx** is that part of the digestive tube which is placed behind the nasal cavities, mouth, and larynx. It is a musculomembranous tube, somewhat conical in form, with the base upward, and the apex downward, extending from the under surface of the skull to the level of the cricoid cartilage in front, and that of the sixth cervical vertebra behind.

The cavity of the pharynx is about 12.5 cm. long, and broader in the transverse than in the antero-posterior diameter. Its greatest breadth is immediately below the base of the skull, where it projects on either side, behind the pharyngeal ostium

---

[1] "The Innervation of the Soft Palate," by Aldren Turner, Journal of Anatomy and Physiology, **23,** 523. The Innervation of the Tensor Veli Palatini Muscles, A. R. Rich, Johns Hopkins Hosp. Bull., 1920, vol. **31.**

of the auditory tube, as the **pharyngeal recess** (*fossa of Rosenmüller*); its narrowest
point is at its termination in the esophagus. It is limited, *above*, by the body
of the sphenoid and basilar part of the occipital bone; *below*, it is continuous with
the esophagus; *posteriorly*, it is connected by loose areolar tissue with the cervical
portion of the vertebral column, and the prevertebral fascia covering the Longus
colli and Longus capitis muscles; *anteriorly*, it is incomplete, and is attached in

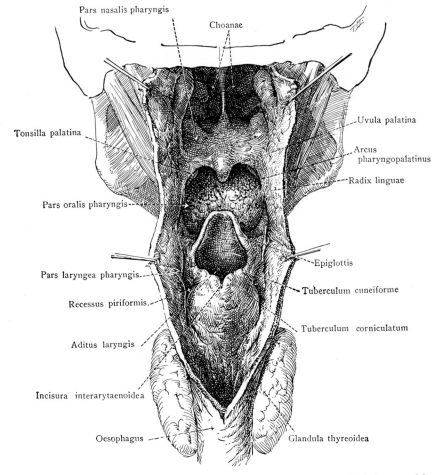

FIG. 1021. The pharynx viewed through a median incision of its posterior wall. (Eycleshymer and Jones).

succession to the medial pterygoid plate, pterygomandibular raphé, mandible,
tongue, hyoid bone, and thyroid and cricoid cartilages; *laterally*, it is connected to
the styloid processes and their muscles, and is in contact with the common and
internal carotid arteries, the internal jugular veins, the glossopharyngeal, vagus,
and hypoglossal nerves, and the sympathetic trunks, and above with small parts
of the Pterygoidei interni. Seven cavities communicate with it, viz., the two
nasal cavities, the two tympanic cavities, the mouth, the larynx, and the esophagus.
The cavity of the pharynx may be subdivided from above downward into three
parts: **nasal, oral,** and **laryngeal** (Fig. 989).

The **Nasal Part of the Pharynx** (*pars nasalis pharyngis; nasopharynx*) lies behind
the nose and above the level of the soft palate: it differs from the oral and laryngeal parts of the pharynx in that its cavity always remains patent. In front (Fig.

1021) it communicates through the choanæ with the nasal cavities. On its lateral wall is the **pharyngeal ostium of the auditory tube,** somewhat triangular in shape, and bounded behind by a firm prominence, the **torus** or **cushion,** caused by the

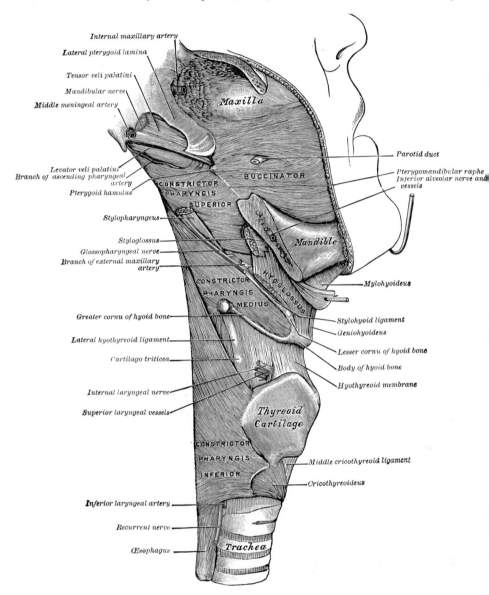

Fig. 1022.—The Buccinator and muscles of the pharynx.

medial end of the cartilage of the tube which elevates the mucous membrane. A vertical fold of mucous membrane, the **salpingopharyngeal fold,** stretches from the lower part of the torus; it contains the Salpingopharyngeus muscle. A second and smaller fold, the **salpingopalatine fold,** stretches from the upper part of the torus to the palate. Behind the ostium of the auditory tube is a deep recess, the **pharyn-**

geal recess (*fossa of Rosenmuller*) (Fig. 1018). On the posterior wall is a promi-nence produced by lymphatic tissue, which is known as the **pharyngeal tonsil**; during childhood it is likely to be hypertrophied into a considerable mass when it is called **adenoids** (Fig. 1018). Above the pharyngeal tonsil, in the middle line, an irregular flask-shaped depression of the mucous membrane sometimes extends up as far as the basilar process of the occipital bone; it is known as the **pharyngeal bursa.**

The **Oral Part of the Pharynx** (*pars oralis pharyngis*) reaches from the soft palate to the level of the hyoid bone. It opens anteriorly, through the isthmus faucium, into the mouth, while in its lateral wall, between the two palatine arches, is the **palatine tonsil.**

The **Laryngeal Part of the Pharynx** (*pars laryngea pharyngis*) reaches from the hyoid bone to the lower border of the cricoid cartilage, where it is continuous with the esophagus. In front it presents the triangular entrance of the larynx, the base of which is directed forward and is formed by the epiglottis, while its lateral boun-daries are constituted by the aryepiglottic folds. On either side of the laryngeal orifice is a recess, termed the **sinus piriformis**, which is bounded medially by the aryepiglottic fold, laterally by the thyroid cartilage and hyothyroid membrane.

Muscles of the Pharynx.—The muscles of the pharynx (Fig. 1022) are:

Constrictor inferior.	Stylopharyngeus.
Constrictor medius.	Salpingopharyngeus.
Constrictor superior.	Pharyngopalatinus.[1]

The **Constrictor pharyngis inferior** (*Inferior constrictor*) (Figs. 1022, 1023), the thickest of the three constrictors, *arises* from the sides of the cricoid and thyroid cartilage. From the cricoid cartilage it arises in the interval between the Cricothyreoideus in front, and the articular facet for the inferior cornu of the thyroid cartilage behind. On the thyroid cartilage it arises from the oblique line on the side of the lamina, from the surface behind this nearly as far as the posterior border and from the inferior cornu. From these origins the fibers spread backward and medialward to be *inserted* with the muscle of the opposite side into the fibrous raphé in the posterior median line of the pharynx. The inferior fibers are horizontal and con-tinuous with the circular fibers of the esophagus; the rest ascend, increasing in obliquity, and overlap the Constrictor medius.

The **Constrictor pharyngis medius** (*Middle constrictor*) (Figs. 1022, 1023) is a fan-shaped muscle, smaller than the preceding. It *arises* from the whole length of the upper border of the greater cornu of the hyoid bone, from the lesser cornu, and from the stylohyoid ligament. The fibers diverge from their origin: the lower ones descend beneath the Constrictor inferior, the middle fibers pass transversely, and the upper fibers ascend and overlap the Constrictor superior. It is *inserted* into the posterior median fibrous raphé, blending in the middle line with the muscle of the opposite side.

The **Constrictor pharyngis superior** (*Superior constrictor*) (Figs. 1022, 1023) is a quadrilateral muscle, thinner and paler than the other two. It *arises* from the lower third of the posterior margin of the medial pterygoid plate and its hamulus, from the pterygomandibular raphé, from the alveolar process of the mandible above the posterior end of the mylohyoid line, and by a few fibers from the side of the tongue. The fibers curve backward to be inserted into the median raphé, being also prolonged by means of an aponeurosis to the pharyngeal spine on the basilar part of the occipital bone. The superior fibers arch beneath the Levator veli palatini and the auditory tube. The interval between the upper border of the muscle and the base of the skull is closed by the pharyngeal aponeurosis, and is known as the **sinus of Morgagni.**

---

[1] The Pharyngopalatinus is described with the muscles of the palate (p. 1181).

The **Stylopharyngeus** (Fig. 1009) is a long, slender muscle, cylindrical above, flattened below. It *arises* from the medial side of the base of the styloid process, passes downward along the side of the pharynx between the Constrictores superior and medius, and spreads out beneath the mucous membrane. Some of its fibers are lost in the Constrictor muscles, while others, joining with the Pharyngopalatinus, are inserted into the posterior border of the thyroid cartilage. The glossopharyngeal nerve runs on the lateral side of this muscle, and crosses over it to reach the tongue.

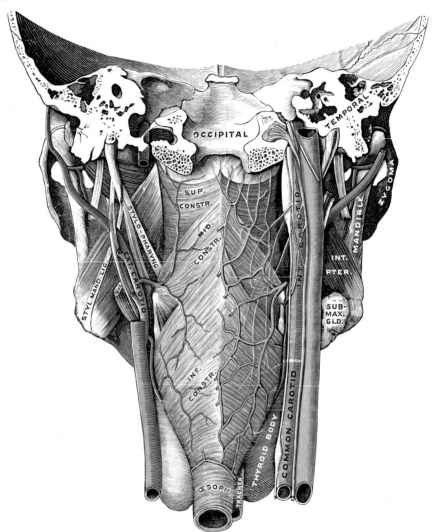

Fig. 1023.—Muscles of the pharynx, viewed from behind, together with the associated vessels and nerves. (Modified after Testut.)

The **Salpingopharyngeus** (Fig. 1020) *arises* from the inferior part of the auditory tube near its orifice; it passes downward and blends with the posterior fasciculus of the Pharyngopalatinus.

Nerves.—The Constrictores and Salpingopharyngeus are supplied by branches from the pharyngeal plexus, the Constrictor inferior by additional branches from the external laryngeal and recurrent nerves, and the Stylopharyngeus by the glossopharyngeal nerve.

Actions.—When deglutition is about to be performed, the pharynx is drawn upward and dilated in different directions, to receive the food propelled into it from the mouth. The Stylopharyngei, which are much farther removed from one another at their origin than at their insertion, draw the sides of the pharynx upward and lateralward, and so increase its transverse diameter; its breadth in the antero-posterior direction is increased by the larynx and tongue being carried forward in their ascent. As soon as the bolus of food is received in the pharynx, the elevator muscles relax, the pharynx descends, and the Constrictores contract upon the bolus, and convey it downward into the esophagus.

Structure.—The pharynx is composed of three coats: **mucous, fibrous, and muscular.**

The **pharyngeal aponeurosis**, or **fibrous coat,** is situated between the mucous and muscular layers. It is thick above where the muscular fibers are wanting, and is firmly connected to the basilar portion of the occipital and the petrous portions of the temporal bones. As it descends it diminishes in thickness, and is gradually lost. It is strengthened posteriorly by a strong fibrous band, which is attached above to the pharyngeal spine on the under surface of the basilar portion of the occipital bone, and passes downward, forming a median raphé, which gives attachment to the Constrictores pharyngis.

The **mucous coat** is continuous with that lining, the nasal cavities, the mouth, the auditory tubes, and the larynx. In the nasal part of the pharynx it is covered by columnar ciliated epithelium; in the oral and laryngeal portions the epithelium is stratified squamous. Beneath the mucous membrane are found racemose mucous glands; they are especially numerous at the upper part of the pharynx around the orifices of the auditory tubes.

THE ESOPHAGUS (Fig. 1024).

The **esophagus or gullet** is a muscular canal, about 23 to 25 cm. long, extending from the pharynx to the stomach. It begins in the neck at the lower border of the cricoid cartilage, opposite the sixth cervical vertebra, descends along the front of the vertebral column, through the superior and posterior mediastina, passes through the diaphragm, and, entering the abdomen, ends at the cardiac orifice of the stomach, opposite the eleventh thoracic vertebra. The general direction of the esophagus is vertical; but it presents two slight curves in its course. At its commencement it is placed in the middle line; but it inclines to the left side as far as the root of the neck, gradually passes to the middle line again at the level of the fifth thoracic vertebra, and finally deviates to the left as it passes forward to the esophageal hiatus in the diaphragm. The esophagus also presents antero-posterior flexures corresponding to the curvatures of the cervical and thoracic portions of the vertebral column. It is the narrowest part of the digestive tube, and is most contracted at its commencement, and at the point where it passes through the diaphragm.

Relations.—The **cervical portion** of the esophagus is in relation, *in front*, with the trachea; and at the lower part of the neck, where it projects to the left side, with the thyroid gland; *behind*, it rests upon the vertebral column and Longus colli muscles; *on either side* it is in relation with the common carotid artery (especially the left, as it inclines to that side), and parts of the lobes of the thyroid gland; the recurrent nerves ascend between it and the trachea; to its left side is the thoracic duct.

The **thoracic portion** of the esophagus is at first situated in the superior mediastinum between the trachea and the vertebral column, a little to the left of the median line. It then passes behind and to the right of the aortic arch, and descends in the posterior mediastinum along the right side of the descending aorta, then runs in front and a little to the left of the aorta, and enters the abdomen through the diaphragm at the level of the tenth thoracic vertebra. Just before it perforates the diaphragm it presents a distinct dilatation. It is in relation, *in front*, with the trachea, the left bronchus, the pericardium, and the diaphragm; *behind*, it rests upon the vertebral column, the Longus colli muscles, the right aortic intercostal arteries, the thoracic duct, and the hemiazygos veins; and below, near the diaphragm, upon the front of the aorta. On its *left* side, in the superior mediastinum, are the terminal part of the aortic arch, the left subclavian artery, the thoracic duct, and left pleura, while running upward in the angle between it and the trachea is the left recurrent nerve; below, it is in relation with the descending thoracic aorta. On its *right* side are the right pleura, and the azygos vein which it overlaps. Below the roots of the lungs the vagi descend in close contact with it, the right nerve passing down behind, and the left nerve in front of it; the two nerves uniting to form a plexus around the tube.

In the lower part of the posterior mediastinum the thoracic duct lies to the right side of the esophagus; higher up, it is placed behind it, and, crossing about the level of the fourth thoracic vertebra, is continued upward on its left side.

The **abdominal portion** of the esophagus lies in the esophageal groove on the posterior surface of the left lobe of the liver. It measures about 1.25 cm. in length, and only its front and left aspects are covered by peritoneum. It is somewhat conical with its base applied to the upper orifice of the stomach, and is known as the **antrum cardiacum.**

Structure (Fig. 1025).—The esophagus has four coats: an **external** or **fibrous,** a **muscular,** a **submucous** or **areolar,** and an **internal** or **mucous** coat.

The **muscular coat** (*tunica muscularis*) is composed of two planes of considerable thickness: an external of longitudinal and an internal of circular fibers.

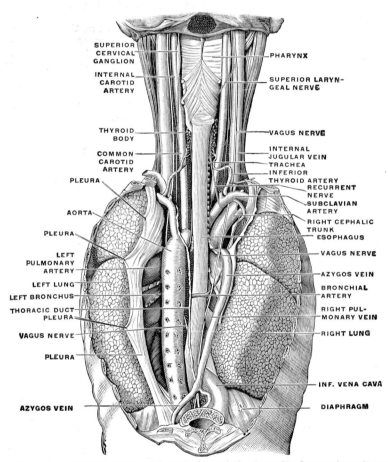

Fig. 1024.—The position and relation of the esophagus in the cervical region and in the posterior mediastinum. Seen from behind. (Poirier and Charpy.)

The *longitudinal fibers* are arranged, at the commencement of the tube, in three fasciculi: one in front, which is attached to the vertical ridge on the posterior surface of the lamina of the cricoid cartilage; and one at either side, which is continuous with the muscular fibers of the pharynx: as they descend they blend together, and form a uniform layer, which covers the outer surface of the tube.

Accessory slips of muscular fibers pass between the esophagus and the left pleura, where the latter covers the thoracic aorta, or the root of the left bronchus, or the back of the pericardium.

The *circular fibers* are continuous above with the Constrictor pharyngis inferior; their direction is transverse at the upper and lower parts of the tube, but oblique in the intermediate part.

The muscular fibers in the upper part of the esophagus are of a red color, and consist chiefly of skeletal muscle; the intermediate part is mixed and the lower part with rare exceptions contains only smooth muscle.

The **areolar** or **submucous coat** (*tela submucosa*) connects loosely the mucous and muscular coats. It contains blood vessels, nerves, and mucous glands.

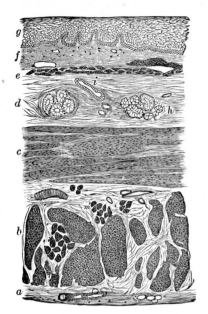

FIG. 1025.—Section of the human esophagus. (From a drawing by V. Horsley.) Moderately magnified. The section is transverse and from near the middle of the gullet. *a.* Fibrous covering. *b.* Divided fibers of longitudinal muscular coat. *c.* Transverse muscular fibers. *d.* Submucous or areolar layer. *e.* Muscularis mucosæ. *f.* Mucous membrane, with vessels and part of a lymphoid nodule. *g.* Stratified epithelial lining. *h.* Mucous gland. *i.* Gland duct. *m'.* Striated muscular fibers cut across.

The **mucous coat** (*tunica mucosa*) is thick, of a reddish color above, and pale below. It is disposed in longitudinal folds, which disappear on distension of the tube. Its surface is studded with minute papillæ, and it is covered throughout with a thick layer of stratified squamous epithelium. Beneath the mucous membrane, between it and the areolar coat, is a layer of longitudinally arranged non-striped muscular fibers. This is the **muscularis mucosæ.** At the commencement of the esophagus it is absent, or only represented by a few scattered bundles; lower down it forms a considerable stratum. The **esophageal glands** (*glandulæ œsophageæ*) are small compound racemose glands of the mucous type: they are lodged in the submucous tissue, and each opens upon the surface by a long excretory duct.

Vessels and Nerves.—The **arteries** supplying the esophagus are derived from the inferior thyroid branch of the thyrocervical trunk, from the descending thoracic aorta, from the bronchial arteries, from the left gastric branch of the celiac artery, and from the left inferior phrenic of the abdominal aorta. They have for the most part a longitudinal direction.

The **veins** end in the inferior thyroid, azygos, hemiazygos, and gastric veins, thereby forming a connection between the portal and systemic venous systems (see p. 691).

The **nerves** are derived from the recurrent vagus, supplying the striated musculature of the organ, and from the vagus and sympathetic trunks which supply fibers to the smooth musculature; these cranial parasympathetic and sympathetic fibers form plexuses between the two layers of the muscular coat, and in the submucosa, as in the stomach and intestines.

THE ABDOMEN.

The **abdomen** is the largest cavity in the body. It is of an oval shape, the extremities of the oval being directed upward and downward. The upper boundary is formed by the **diaphragm** which extends as a dome over the abdomen, so that the cavity extends high into the bony thorax, reaching on the right side, in the mammary line, to the upper border of the fifth rib; on the left side it falls below this level by about 2.5 cm. The lower boundary is formed principally by the Levator ani and Coccygeus or the **diaphragm of the pelvis.** In order to facilitate description, it is artificially divided into two parts: an upper and larger part, the **abdomen proper;** and a lower and smaller part, the **pelvis,** the limit between them being marked by the superior aperture of the lesser pelvis.

The **abdomen proper** differs from the other great cavities of the body in being bounded for the most part by muscles and fasciæ, so that it can vary in capacity and shape according to the condition of the viscera which it contains; but, in addition to this, the abdomen varies in form and extent with age and sex. In the adult male, with moderate distension of the viscera, it is oval in shape, but at the same time flattened from before backward. In the adult female, with a fully developed pelvis, it is ovoid with the narrower pole upward, and in young children it is also ovoid but with the narrower pole downward.

Boundaries.—It is bounded *in front* and *at the sides* by the abdominal muscles and the Iliacus muscles; *behind* by the vertebral column and the Psoas and Quadratus lumborum muscles; *above* by the diaphragm; *below* by the plane of the superior aperture of the lesser pelvis. The muscles forming the boundaries of the cavity are lined upon their inner surfaces by transversalis fascia.

The abdomen contains the greater part of the digestive tube; some of the accessory organs to digestion, viz., the liver and pancreas; the spleen, the kidneys, and the suprarenal glands. Most of these structures, as well as the wall of the cavity in which they are contained, are more or less covered by an extensive and complicated serous membrane, the **peritoneum.**

The Apertures in the Walls of the Abdomen.—The apertures in the walls of the abdomen, for the transmission of structures to or from it, are, *in front*, the **umbilical,** for the transmission of the umbilical vessels, the allantois, and vitelline duct in the fetus; *above*, the **vena caval opening,** for the transmission of the inferior vena cava, the **aortic hiatus,** for the passage of the aorta, azygos vein, and thoracic duct, and the **esophageal hiatus,** for the esophagus and vagi. *Below*, there are two apertures on either side: one for the passage of the femoral vessels and lumbo-inguinal nerve, and the other for the transmission of the spermatic cord in the male, and the round ligament of the uterus in the female.

Regions.—For convenience of description, the abdomen is artificially divided into nine regions by two horizontal and two sagittal planes, indicated by lines drawn on the surface of the body (Fig. 1206). Of the horizontal planes the upper or **transpyloric** is indicated by a line midway between the jugular notch and the symphysis pubis, the lower by a line midway between the transpyloric and the symphysis pubis. The latter is the **intertubercular plane**; its level corresponds with the prominent tubercle on the iliac crest about 5 cm. behind the anterior superior iliac spine. By means of these planes the abdomen is divided into three zones, the **subcostal, umbilical,** and **hypogastric zones.** Each of these is further subdivided into three regions by the two sagittal planes, which pass vertically through points half-way between the anterior superior iliac spines and the symphysis pubis.

The middle region of the upper zone is called the **epigastric**; and the two lateral regions, the **right** and **left hypochondriac.** The central region of the middle zone is the **umbilical**; and the two lateral regions, the **right** and **left lumbar.** The middle region of the lower zone is the **hypogastric or pubic region**; and the lateral regions are the **right** and **left iliac or inguinal** (Fig. 1206).

The **pelvis** is that portion of the abdominal cavity which lies below and behind a plane passing through the promontory of the sacrum, lineæ terminales of the hip bones, and the pubic crests. It is bounded behind by the sacrum, coccyx, Piriformes, and the sacrospinous and sacrotuberous ligaments; in front and laterally by the pubes and ischia and Obturatores interni; above it is continuous with the abdomen proper; below it is closed by the Levatores ani and Coccygei and the urogenital diaphragm. The pelvis contains the urinary bladder, the sigmoid colon and rectum, a few coils of the small intestine, and some of the generative organs.

When the anterior abdominal wall is removed (Fig. 1026), the viscera are partly exposed as follows: above and to the right side is the liver, situated chiefly under the shelter of the right ribs and their cartilages, but extending across the middle line and reaching for some distance below the level of the xiphoid process. To the left of the liver is the stomach, from the lower border of which an apron-like fold of peritoneum, the **greater omentum,** descends for a varying distance, and obscures, to a greater or lesser extent, the other viscera. Below it, however, some of the coils of the small intestine can generally be seen, while in the right and left iliac regions respectively the cecum and the iliac colon are partly exposed. The bladder occupies the anterior part of the pelvis, and, if distended, will project above the symphysis pubis; the rectum lies in the concavity of the sacrum, but is usually obscured by the coils of the small intestine. The sigmoid colon lies between the rectum and the bladder.

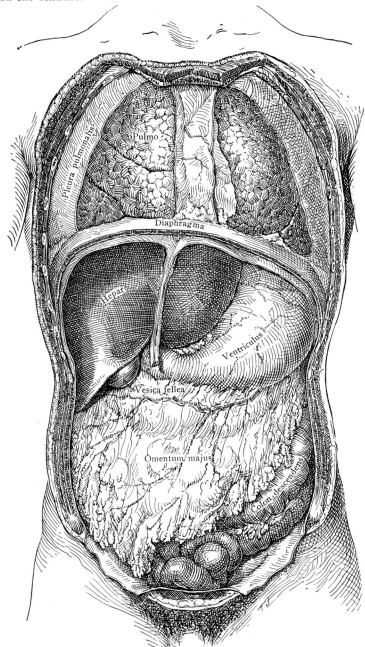

Fig. 1026.   Ventral view of the thoracic and abdominal viscera in position after removal of the anterior thoracic and abdominal walls.   (Eycleshymer and Jones.)

When the stomach is followed from left to right (Fig. 1027) it is seen to be continuous with the first part of the small intestine, or duodenum, the point being marked by a thickened ring, the pyloric valve. The duodenum passes toward the under surface of the liver, and then, curving downward, is lost to sight. If, however, the greater omentum be thrown upward over the chest (Fig. 1028), the

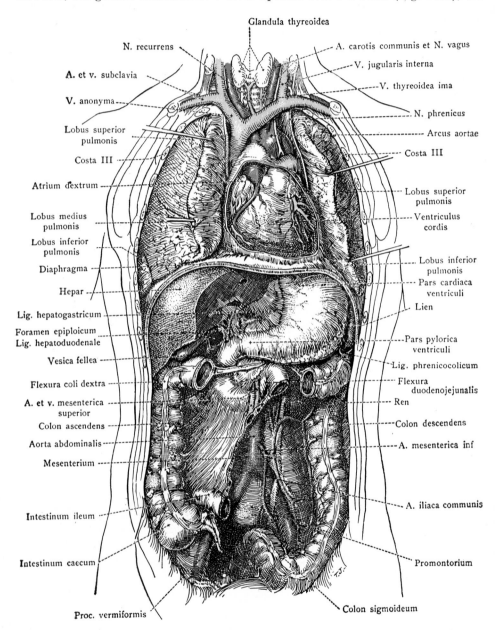

Glandula thyreoidea

N. recurrens

A. carotis communis et N. vagus

V. jugularis interna

A. et v. subclavia

V. thyreoidea ima

V. anonyma

N. phrenicus

Lobus superior pulmonis

Arcus aortae

Costa III

Costa III

Atrium dextrum

Lobus superior pulmonis

Lobus medius pulmonis

Ventriculus cordis

Lobus inferior pulmonis

Lobus inferior pulmonis

Diaphragma

Pars cardiaca ventriculi

Hepar

Lien

Lig. hepatogastricum

Foramen epiploicum
Lig. hepatoduodenale

Pars pylorica ventriculi

Vesica fellea

Lig. phrenicocolicum

Flexura coli dextra

Flexura duodenojejunalis

A. et v. mesenterica superior

Ren

Colon ascendens

Colon descendens

Aorta abdominalis

A. mesenterica inf

Mesenterium

Intestinum ileum

A. iliaca communis

Intestinum caecum

Promontorium

Proc. vermiformis

Colon sigmoideum

FIG. 1027. Ventral view of the thoracic and abdominal viscera partially dissected. The anterior pleuræ and pericardium have been removed; the structures at the root of the neck dissected. The left lobe of the liver, the greater omentum, transverse colon, jejunum and ileum have been removed. (Eycleshymer and Jones.)

inferior part of the duodenum will be observed passing across the vertebral column toward the left side, where it becomes continuous with the coils of the jejunum and ileum. These measure some 6 meters in length, and if followed downward the ileum will be seen to end in the right iliac fossa by opening into the cecum, the commencement of the large intestine. From the cecum the large intestine takes an arched course, passing at first upward on the right side, then across the middle

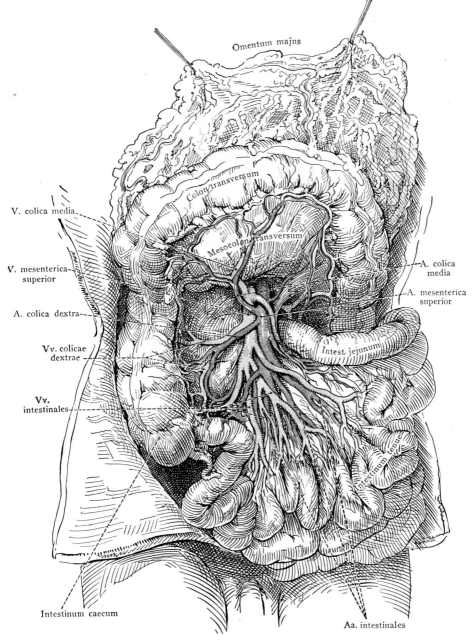

Fig. 1028. Small and large intestines with their mesenteries and blood vessels viewed after the greater omentum has been drawn upward over the chest. (Eycleshymer and Jones.)

line and downward on the left side, forming the ascending, transverse, and descending colon. In the pelvis it assumes the form of a loop, the sigmoid colon, and ends in the rectum.

The spleen (*lien*) lies behind the stomach in the left hypochondriac region (Fig. 1027), and may be in part exposed by pulling the stomach over toward the right side.

The smooth and glistening appearance of the internal surface of the abdominal wall and of the exposed viscera is due to the serous membrane, or **peritoneum**.

The Peritoneum (Tunica Serosa).

The peritoneum is the largest serous membrane in the body, and consists, in the male, of a closed sac, a part of which is applied against the abdominal parietes, while the remainder is reflected over the contained viscera. In the female the peritoneum is not a closed sac, since the free ends of the uterine tubes open directly

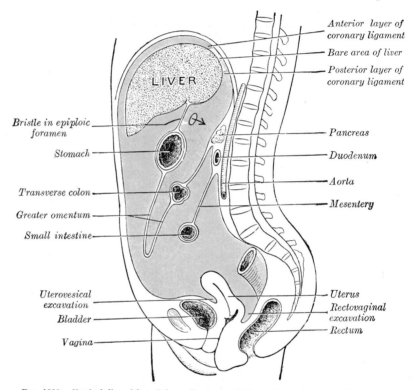

Fig. 1029.—Vertical disposition of the peritoneum. Main cavity, red; omental bursa, blue.

into the peritoneal cavity. The part which lines the abdominal wall is named the **parietal peritoneum**; that which is reflected over the contained viscera constitutes the **visceral peritoneum**. The *free surface* of the membrane is a smooth layer of flattened mesothelium, lubricated by a small quantity of serous fluid, which allows the viscera to glide freely against the wall of the cavity or upon each other with the least possible friction. The *attached* surface is connected to the viscera and inner surface of the parietes by means of areolar tissue, termed the **subserous fascia**. The parietal portion is separated by a fascial cleft from the transversalis fascia lining of the abdomen and pelvis, but is more closely adherent to the under surface of the diaphragm, and also in the middle line of the abdomen.

The space between the parietal and visceral layers of the peritoneum is named the **peritoneal cavity**; but under normal conditions this cavity is merely a potential one, since the parietal and visceral layers are in contact. The peritoneal cavity gives off a large diverticulum, the **omental bursa,** which is situated behind the stomach and adjoining structures; the neck of communication between the cavity and the bursa is termed the **epiploic foramen** (*foramen of Winslow*). (Fig. 1027) Formerly the main portion of the cavity was described as the greater, and the omental bursa as the lesser sac.

The peritoneum differs from the other serous membranes of the body in presenting a much more complex arrangement, and one that can be clearly understood

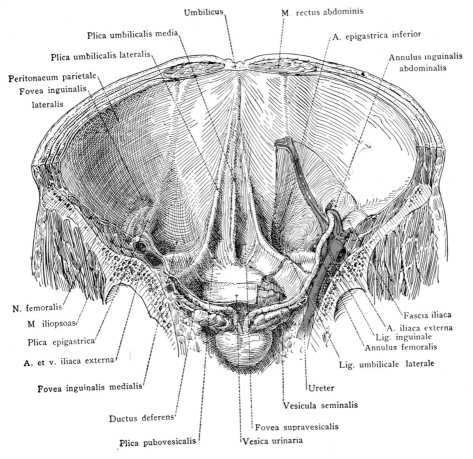

FIG. 1030.—The lower portion of the anterior abdominal wall, viewed from within. The pertioneum has been partially removed from the right side. (Eycleshymer and Jones.)

only by following the changes which take place in the digestive tube during its development (pages 1144 to 1149).

To trace the membrane from one viscus to another, and from the viscera to the parietes, it is necessary to follow its continuity in the vertical and horizontal directions, and it will be found simpler to describe the main portion of the cavity and the omental bursa separately.

Vertical Disposition of the main Peritoneal Cavity (*greater sac*) (Fig. 1029). It is convenient to trace this from the back of the abdominal wall at the level of the umbilicus. On following the peritoneum upward from this level it is seen to be reflected around a fibrous cord, the **ligamentum teres** (*obliterated umbilical vein*), which reaches from the umbilicus to the under surface of the liver. This reflection forms a somewhat triangular fold, the **falciform ligament of the liver,** attaching the upper and anterior surfaces of the liver to the diaphragm and abdominal wall (Figs. 1071 to 1073.) With the exception of the line of attachment of this ligament the peritoneum covers the whole of the under surface of the anterior part of the diaphragm, and is continued from it on to the upper surface of the right lobe of the liver as the **anterior layer of the coronary ligament** and on to the upper surface of the left lobe as the **anterior layer of the left triangular ligament** of the liver. Covering upper and anterior surfaces of the liver, it is continued around its sharp margin on to the under surface, where it presents the following relations: (*a*) It covers the under surface of the right lobe and is reflected from the back part of this on to the right suprarenal gland and upper extremity of the right kidney, forming in this situation the **posterior layer of the coronary ligament;** a special fold, the **hepatorenal ligament** is frequently present between the inferior surface of the liver and the front of the kidney. From the kidney it is carried downward to the duodenum and right colic flexure and medialward in front of the inferior vena cava, where it is continuous with the posterior wall of the omental bursa. Between the two layers of the coronary ligament there is a large triangular surface of the liver devoid of peritoneal covering; this is named the **bare area** of the liver, and is attached to the diaphragm by areolar tissue. Toward the right margin of the liver the two layers of the coronary ligament gradually approach each other, and ultimately fuse to form a small triangular fold connecting the right lobe of the liver to the diaphragm, and named the **right triangular ligament** of the liver. The apex of the triangular bare area corresponds with the point of meeting of the two layers of the coronary ligament, its base with the fossa for the inferior vena cava. (*b*) It covers the lower surface of the quadrate lobe, the under and lateral surfaces of the gall-bladder, and the under surface and posterior border of the left lobe; it is then reflected from the upper surface of the left lobe to the diaphragm as the **inferior layer of the left triangular ligament,** and from the porta of the liver and the fossa for the ductus venosus to the lesser curvature of the stomach and the first 2.5 cm. of the duodenum as the anterior layer of the **hepatogastric** and **hepatoduodenal ligaments,** which together constitute the **lesser omentum.** If this layer of the lesser omentum be followed to the right it will be found to turn around the hepatic artery, bile duct, and portal vein, and become continuous with the anterior wall of the omental bursa, forming a free folded edge of peritoneum. Traced downward, it covers the antero-superior surface of the stomach and the commencement of the duodenum, and is carried down into a large free fold, known as the **gastrocolic ligament** or **greater omentum.** Reaching the free margin of this fold, it is reflected upward to cover the under and posterior surfaces of the transverse colon, and thence to the posterior abdominal wall as the inferior layer of the **transverse mesocolon.** It reaches the abdominal wall at the head and anterior border of the pancreas, is then carried down over the lower part of the head and over the inferior surface of the pancreas on the superior mesenteric vessels, and thence to the small intestine as the anterior layer of the **mesentery.** It encircles the intestine, and subsequently may be traced, as the posterior layer of the mesentery, upward and backward to the abdominal wall. From this it sweeps down over the aorta into the pelvis, where it invests the sigmoid colon, its reduplication forming the **sigmoid mesocolon.** Leaving first the sides and then the front of the rectum, it is reflected on to the seminal vesicles and fundus of the urinary bladder and, after covering the upper surface of that viscus, is carried along the medial and lateral umbilical ligaments (Fig. 1030) on to the back of the abdominal wall to the level from which a start was made.

Between the rectum and the bladder it forms, in the male, a pouch, the **recto-**

vesical excavation, the bottom of which is slightly below the level of the upper-ends of the vesiculæ seminales—*i. e.*, about 7.5 cm. from the orifice of the anus. When the bladder is distended, the peritoneum is carried up with the expanded viscus so that a considerable part of the anterior surface of the latter lies directly against the abdominal wall without the intervention of peritoneal membrane (*pre-vesical space of Retzius*). In the female the peritoneum is reflected from the rectum over the posterior vaginal fornix to the cervix and body of the uterus, forming the rectouterine excavation (*pouch of Douglas*). It is continued over the intestinal surface and fundus of the uterus on to its vesical surface, which it covers as far as the junction of the body and cervix uteri, and then to the bladder, forming here a second, but shallower, pouch, the vesicouterine excavation. It is also reflected from the sides of the uterus to the lateral walls of the pelvis as two expanded folds, the broad ligaments of the uterus, in the free margin of each of which is the uterine tube.

Vertical Disposition of the Omental Bursa (*lesser peritoneal sac*) (Fig. 1029).—A start may be made in this case on the posterior abdominal wall at the anterior border of the pancreas. From this region the peritoneum may be followed upward over the pancreas on to the inferior surface of the diaphragm, and thence on to the caudate lobe and caudate process of the liver to the fossa from the ductus venosus

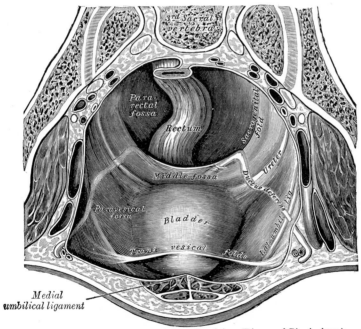

Fig. 1031.—The peritoneum of the male pelvis. (Dixon and Birmingham.)

and the porta of the liver. Traced to the right, it is continuous over the inferior vena cava with the posterior wall of the main cavity. From the liver it is carried downward to the lesser curvature of the stomach and the commencement of the duodenum as the posterior layer of the lesser omentum, and is continuous on the right, around the hepatic artery, bile duct, and portal vein, with the anterior layer of this omentum. The posterior layer of the lesser omentum is carried down as a covering for the postero-inferior surfaces of the stomach and commencement of the duodenum, and is continued downward as the deep layer of the gastrocolic ligament or greater omentum. From the free margin of this fold it is reflected upward on itself to the anterior and superior surfaces of the transverse colon, and thence as the superior layer of the transverse mesocolon to the anterior border of the pancreas, the level from which a start was made. It will be seen that the loop formed by the wall of the omental bursa below the transverse colon follows, and is closely applied to, the deep surface of that formed by the peritoneum of the main cavity, and that the greater omentum or large fold of peritoneum which hangs in front of the small intestine therefore consists of four layers, two anterior and two posterior separated by the potential cavity of the omental bursa.

Horizontal Disposition of the Peritoneum.—Below the transverse colon the arrangement is simple, as it includes only the main cavity; above the level of the transverse colon it is more complicated on account of the existence of the omental bursa. Below the transverse colon it may be considered in the two regions, viz., in the **pelvis** and in the **abdomen proper.**

(1) **In the Pelvis.**—The peritoneum here follows closely the surfaces of the pelvic viscera and the inequalities of the pelvic walls, and presents important differences in the two sexes. (*a*) **In the male** (Fig. 1031) it encircles the sigmoid colon, from which it is reflected to the posterior wall of the pelvis as a fold, the **sigmoid mesocolon.** It then leaves the sides and, finally, the front of the rectum, and is continued on to the upper ends of the seminal vesicles and the bladder; on either side of the rectum it forms a fossa, the **pararectal fossa,** which varies in size with the distension of the rectum. In front of the rectum the peritoneum forms the rectovesical excavation, which is limited laterally by peritoneal folds extending from the sides of the bladder to the rectum and sacrum. These folds are known from their position as the **rectovesical** or **sacrogenital folds.** The peritoneum of the anterior pelvic wall covers the superior surface of the bladder, and on either side of this viscus forms a depression, termed the **paravesical fossa,** which is limited laterally by the fold of peritoneum covering the ductus deferens. The size of this fossa is dependent on the state of distension of the bladder; when the bladder is empty, a variable fold of peritoneum, the **plica vesicalis transversa,** divides the fossa into two portions. On the peritoneum between the paravesical and pararectal fossæ the only elevations are those produced by the ureters and the hypogastric vessels. (*b*) **In the female,** pararectal and paravesical fossæ similar to those in the male are present: the lateral limit of the paravesical fossa is the peritoneum investing the round ligament of the uterus. The rectovesical excavation is, however, divided by the uterus and vagina into a small anterior vesicouterine and a large, deep, posterior rectouterine excavation. The sacrogenital folds form the margins of the latter, and are continued on to the back of the uterus to form a transverse fold, the **torus uterinus.** The broad ligaments extend from the sides of the uterus to the lateral walls of the pelvis; they contain in their free margins the uterine tubes, and in their posterior layers the ovaries. Below, the broad ligaments are continuous with the peritoneum on the lateral walls of the pelvis. On the lateral pelvic wall behind the attachment of the broad ligament, in the angle between the elevations produced by the diverging hypogastric and external iliac vessels is a slight fossa, the **ovarian fossa,** in which the ovary normally lies.

(2) **In the Lower Abdomen** (Fig. 1032).—Starting from the linea alba, below the level of the transverse colon, and tracing the continuity of the peritoneum in a horizontal direction to the right, the membrane covers the inner surface of the abdominal wall almost as far as the lateral border of the Quadratus lumborum; it encloses the cecum and vermiform process, and is reflected over the sides and front of the ascending colon; it may then be traced over the duodenum, Psoas major, and inferior vena cava toward the middle line, whence it passes along the mesenteric vessels to invest the small intestine, and back again to the large vessels in front of the vertebral column, forming the **mesentery,** between the layers of which

are contained the mesenteric bloodvessels, nerves, lacteals, and lymph nodes. It is then continued over the left Psoas; it covers the sides and front of the descending colon, and, reaching the abdominal wall, is carried on it to the middle line.

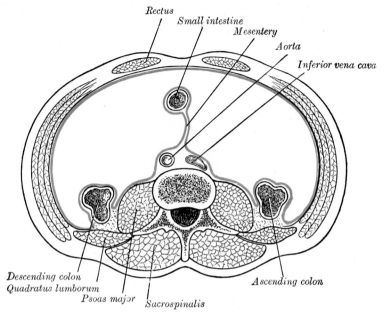

Fig. 1032.—Horizontal disposition of the peritoneum in the lower part of the abdomen.

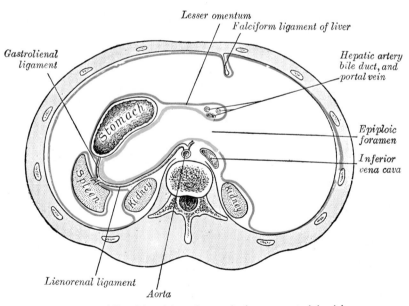

Fig. 1033.—Horizontal disposition of the peritoneum in the upper part of the abdomen.

(3) **In the Upper Abdomen** (Fig. 1033).—Above the transverse colon the omental bursa is superadded to the general sac, and the communication of the two cavities with one another through the epiploic foramen can be demonstrated.

(*a*) **Main Cavity.**—Commencing on the posterior abdominal wall at the inferior vena cava, the peritoneum may be followed to the right over the front of the suprarenal gland and upper part of the right kidney on to the antero-lateral abdominal wall. From the middle line of the anterior wall a backwardly directed fold encircles the obliterated umbilical vein and forms the falciform ligament of the liver. Continuing to the left, the peritoneum lines the antero-lateral

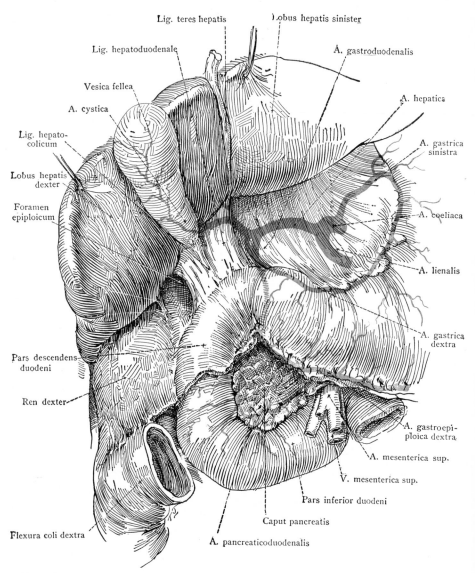

Fig. 1034.—The epiploic foramen (of Winslow) and neighboring structures . (Eycleshymer and Jones.)

abdominal wall and covers the lateral part of the front of the left kidney, and is reflected to the posterior border of the hilus of the spleen as the posterior layer of the **lienorenal ligament.** It can then be traced around the surface of the spleen to the front of the hilum, and thence to the cardiac end of the greater curvature of the stomach as the anterior layer of the **gastrolienal ligament.** It covers the antero-superior surfaces of the stomach and commencement of the duodenum, and extends up from the lesser curvature of the stomach to the liver as the anterior layer of the lesser omentum.

(*b*) **Omental Bursa** (*bursa omentalis; lesser peritoneal sac*).—On the posterior abdominal wall the peritoneum of the general cavity is continuous with that of the omental bursa in front of the inferior vena cava. Starting from here, the bursa may be traced across the aorta and over the medial part of the front of the left kidney and diaphragm to the hilum of the spleen as the anterior layer of the lienorenal ligament. From the spleen it is reflected to the stomach as the posterior layer of the gastrolienal ligament. It covers the postero-inferior surfaces of the stomach and commencement of the duodenum, and extends upward to the liver as the posterior layer of the lesser omentum; the right margin of this layer is continuous around the hepatic artery, bile duct, and portal vein, with the wall of the general cavity.

The **epiploic foramen** (*foramen epiploicum; foramen of Winslow*) is the passage of communication between the general cavity and the omental bursa. It is bounded *in front* by the free border of the lesser omentum, with the common bile duct, hepatic artery, and portal vein between its two layers; *behind* by the peritoneum covering the inferior vena cava; *above* by the peritoneum on the caudate process of the liver; and *below* by the peritoneum covering the commencement of the duodenum and the hepatic artery, the latter passing forward below the foramen before ascending between the two layers of the lesser omentum.

The boundaries of the *omental bursa* will now be evident. It is bounded *in front*, from above downward, by the caudate lobe of the liver, the lesser omentum, the stomach, and the greater omentum. *Behind*, it is limited, from below upward, by the greater omentum, the transverse colon, the transverse mesocolon, the upper surface of the pancreas, the left suprarenal gland, and the upper end of the left kidney. To the right of the esophageal opening of the stomach it is formed by that part of the diaphragm which supports the caudate lobe of the liver. *Laterally*, the bursa extends from the epiploic foramen to the hilum of the spleen, where it is limited by the phrenicolienal and gastrolienal ligaments.

The omental bursa, therefore, consists of a series of pouches or recesses to which the following terms are applied: (1) the **vestibule,** a narrow channel continued from the epiploic foramen, over the head of the pancreas to the **gastropancreatic fold**; this fold extends from the omental tuberosity of the pancreas to the right side of the fundus of the stomach, and contains the left gastric artery and coronary vein; (2) the **superior omental recess**, between the caudate lobe of the liver and the diaphragm; (3) the **lienal recess**, between the spleen and the stomach; (4) the **inferior omental recess**, which comprises the remainder of the bursa.

In the fetus the bursa reaches as low as the free margin of the greater omentum, but in the adult its vertical extent is usually more limited owing to adhesions between the layers of the omentum. During a considerable part of fetal life the transverse colon is suspended from the posterior abdominal wall by a mesentery of its own, the two posterior layers of the greater omentum passing at this stage in front of the colon. This condition occasionally persists throughout life, but as a rule adhesion occurs between the mesentery of the transverse colon and the posterior layer of the greater omentum, with the result that the colon appears to receive its peritoneal covering by the splitting of the two posterior layers of the latter fold. In the adult the omental bursa intervenes between the stomach and the structures on which that viscus lies, and performs therefore the functions of a serous bursa for the stomach.

Numerous peritoneal folds extend between the various organs or connect them to the parietes; they serve to hold the viscera in position, and, at the same time, enclose the vessels and nerves proceeding to them. They are grouped under the three headings of **ligaments, omenta,** and **mesenteries.**

The **ligaments** will be described with their respective organs.

There are two **omenta,** the lesser and the greater.

The **lesser omentum** (*omentum minus; small omentum; gastrohepatic omentum*) is the duplicature which extends to the liver from the lesser curvature of the stomach and the commencement of the duodenum. It is extremely thin, and is continuous with the two layers of peritoneum which cover respectively the antero-superior and postero-inferior surfaces of the stomach and first part of the duodenum. When these two layers reach the lesser curvature of the stomach and the upper border of the duodenum, they join together and ascend as a double fold to the porta of the liver; to the left of the porta the fold is attached to the bottom of the fossa for the ductus venosus, along which it is carried to the diaphragm, where the two layers separate to embrace the end of the esophagus. At the right border of the omentum the two layers are continuous, and form a free margin which constitutes the anterior boundary of the epiploic foramen. The portion of the lesser omentum extending between the liver and stomach is termed the **hepatogastric ligament,** while that between the liver and duodenum is the **hepatoduodenal ligament.** Between the two layers of the lesser omentum, close to the right free margin, are the hepatic artery, the common bile duct, the portal vein, lymphatics, and the hepatic plexus of nerves—all these structures being enclosed in a **fibrous capsule** (*Glisson's capsule*). Between the layers of the lesser omentum, where they are attached to the stomach, run the right and left gastric vessels.

The **greater omentum** (*omentum maius; great omentum; gastrocolic omentum*) is the largest peritoneal fold. It consists of a double sheet of peritoneum, folded on itself so that it is made up of four layers. The two layers which descend from the stomach and commencement of the duodenum pass in front of the small intestines, sometimes as low down as the pelvis; they then turn upon themselves, and ascend again as far as the transverse colon, where they separate and enclose that part of the intestine. These individual layers may be easily demonstrated in the young subject, but in the adult they are more or less inseparably blended. The left border of the greater omentum is continuous with the gastrolienal ligament; its right border extends as far as the commencement of the duodenum. The greater omentum is usually thin, presents a cribriform appearance, and always contains some adipose tissue, which in fat people accumulates in considerable quantity. Between its two anterior layers, a short distance from the greater curvature of the stomach, is the anastomosis between the right and left gastroepiploic vessels.

The **mesenteries** are: the **mesentery proper,** the **transverse mesocolon,** and the **sigmoid mesocolon.** In addition to these there are sometimes present an ascending and a descending mesocolon.

The **mesentery proper** (*mesenterium*) is the broad, fan-shaped fold of peritoneum which connects the convolutions of the jejunum and ileum with the posterior wall of the abdomen. Its **root**—the part connected with the structures in front of the vertebral column—is narrow, about 15 cm. long, and is directed obliquely from the duodenojejunal flexure at the left side of the second lumbar vertebra to the right sacroiliac articulation (Fig. 1035). Its **intestinal border** is about 6 metres long; and here the two layers separate to enclose the intestine, and form its peritoneal coat. It is narrow above, but widens rapidly to about 20 cm., and is thrown into numerous plaits or folds. It suspends the small intestine, and contains between its layers the intestinal branches of the superior mesenteric artery, with their accompanying veins and plexuses of nerves, the lacteal vessels, and mesenteric lymph nodes.

The **transverse mesocolon** (*mesocolon transversum*) is a broad fold, which connects the transverse colon to the posterior wall of the abdomen. It is continuous with the two posterior layers of the greater omentum, which, after separating to surround the transverse colon, join behind it, and are continued backward to the vertebral column, where they diverge in front of the anterior border of the pancreas. This fold contains between its layers the vessels which supply the transverse colon.

The **sigmoid mesocolon** (*mesocolon sigmoideum*) is the fold of peritoneum which retains the sigmoid colon in connection with the pelvic wall. Its line of attachment

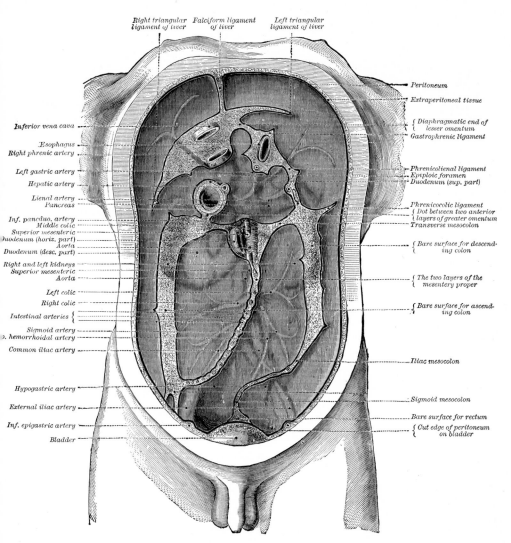

FIG. 1035.—Diagram devised by Delépine to show the lines along which the peritoneum leaves the wall of the abdomen to invest the viscera.

forms a V-shaped curve, the apex of the curve being placed about the point of division of the left common iliac artery. The curve begins on the medial side of the left Psoas major, and runs upward and backward to the apex, from which it bends sharply downward, and ends in the median plane at the level of the third sacral vertebra. The sigmoid and superior hemorrhoidal vessels run between the two layers of this fold.

In most cases the peritoneum covers only the front and sides of the ascending and descending parts of the colon. Sometimes, however, these are surrounded by the serous membrane and attached to the posterior abdominal wall by an ascending and a descending mesocolon respectively. A fold of peritoneum, the **phrenicocclic ligament,** is continued from the left colic flexure to the diaphragm opposite the tenth and eleventh ribs; it passes below and serves to support the spleen, and therefore has received the name of **sustentaculum lienis.**

The **appendices epiploicæ** are small pouches of the peritoneum filled with fat and situated along the colon and upper part of the rectum. They are chiefly appended to the transverse and sigmoid parts of the colon.

Peritoneal Recesses or Fossæ (*retroperitoneal fossæ*).—In certain parts of the abdominal cavity there are recesses of peritoneum forming culs-de-sac or pouches, which are of surgical interest in connection with the possibility of the occurrence of "retroperitoneal" herniæ. The largest of these is the omental bursa (already described), but several others, of smaller size, require mention, and may be divided into three groups, viz.: **duodenal, cecal,** and **intersigmoid.**

1. **Duodenal Fossæ** (Figs. 1036, 1037).—Three are fairly constant, viz.: (*a*) The **inferior duodenal fossa,** present in about 75 per cent. of bodies, is situated opposite the third lumbar vertebra on the left side of the ascending portion of the duodenum. Its opening is directed upward, and is bounded by a thin sharp fold of peritoneum.

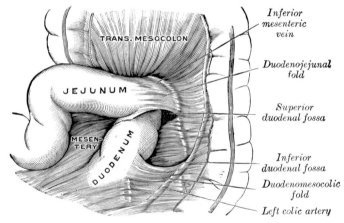

FIG. 1036.—Superior and inferior duodenal fossæ. (Poirier and Charpy.)

The tip of the index finger introduced into the fossa under the fold passes some little distance behind the ascending portion of the duodenum. (*b*) The **superior duodenal fossa,** present in about 50 per cent. of bodies, often coexists with the inferior one, and its orifice looks downward. It lies on the left of the ascending portion of the duodenum, in front of the second lumbar vertebra, and behind a sickle-shaped fold of peritoneum, the **duodenojejunal fold,** and has a depth of about 2 cm. (*c*) The **duodenojejunal fossa** exists in about 20 per cent. of bodies. It is bounded above by the pancreas, to the right by the aorta, and to the left by the kidney; beneath is the left renal vein. It has a depth of from 2 to 3 cm., and its orifice, directed downward and to the right, is nearly circular and will admit the tip of the little finger. (*d*) The **paraduodenal fossa,** rarely found, lies a short distance to the left of the ascending portion of the duodenum behind a peritoneal fold which contains the ascending branch of the left colic artery. (*e*) The **retroduodenal fossa,** only occasionally present, lies behind the horizontal and ascending parts of the duodenum and in front of the aorta.

2. **Cecal Fossæ** (*pericecal folds or fossæ*).—There are three principal pouches

or recesses in the neighborhood of the cecum (Figs. 1038 to 1040): (*a*) The **superior ileocecal fossa** is formed by a fold of peritoneum, arching over the branch of the ileocolic artery which supplies the ileocolic junction. The fossa is a narrow chink

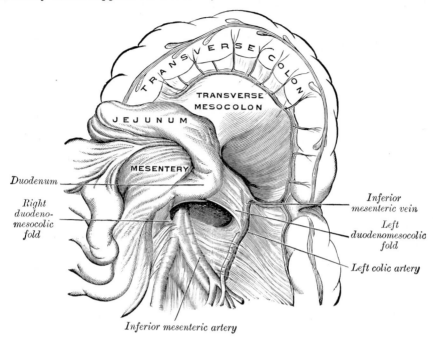

FIG. 1037.—Duodenojejunal fossa. (Poirier and Charpy.)

situated between the mesentery of the small intestine, the ileum, and the small portion of the cecum behind. (*b*) The **inferior ileocecal fossa** is situated behind the angle of junction of the ileum and cecum. It is formed by the **ileocecal fold** of peritoneum (*bloodless fold of Treves*), the upper border of which is fixed to the ileum,

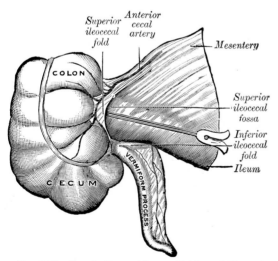

FIG. 1038.—Superior ileocecal fossa. (Poirier and Charpy.)

opposite its mesenteric attachment, while the lower border, passing over the ileocecal junction, joins the mesenteriole of the vermiform process, and sometimes the process itself. Between this fold and the mesenteriole of the vermiform process is the inferior ileocecal fossa. It is bounded above by the posterior surface of the ileum and the mesentery; in front and below by the ileocecal fold, and behind by the upper part of the mesenteriole of the vermiform process. (*c*) The **cecal fossa** is situated immediately behind the cecum, which has to be raised to bring it into view. It varies much in size and extent. In some cases it is sufficiently large to admit the index finger, and extends upward behind the ascending colon in the direction of the kidney; in others it is merely a shallow depression. It is bounded on the right by the cecal fold, which is attached by one edge to the abdominal wall from the lower border of the kidney to the iliac fossa and by the other to the postero-lateral aspect of the colon. In some instances additional fossae, the retrocecal fossae, are present.

3. The **intersigmoid fossa** (*recessus intersigmoideus*) is constant in the fetus and during infancy, but disappears in a certain percentage of cases as age advances

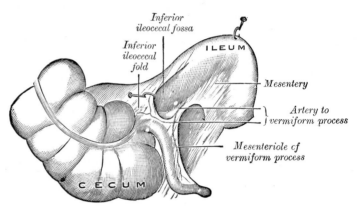

Fig. 1039.—Inferior ileocecal fossa. The cecum and ascending colon have been drawn lateralward and downward the ileum upward and backward, and the vermiform process downward. (Poirier and Charpy.)

When the sigmoid colon is drawn upward, the left surface of the sigmoid mesocolon is exposed, and on it will be seen a funnel-shaped recess of the peritoneum, lying on the external iliac vessels, in the interspace between the Psoas and Iliacus muscles.

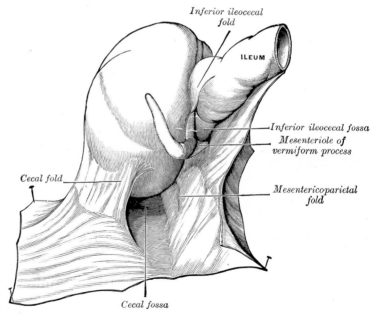

Fig. 1040.—The cecal fossa. The ileum and cecum are drawn backward and upward. (Souligoux.)

This is the orifice leading to the intersigmoid fossa, which lies behind the sigmoid mesocolon, and in front of the parietal peritoneum. The fossa varies in size; in some instances it is a mere dimple, whereas in others it will admit the whole of the index finger.

The Stomach (Ventriculus; Gaster).

The **stomach** is the most dilated part of the digestive tube, and is situated between the end of the esophagus and the beginning of the small intestine. It lies in the epigastric, umbilical, and left hypochondriac regions of the abdomen, and occupies a recess bounded by the upper abdominal viscera, and completed in front and on the left side by the anterior abdominal wall and the diaphragm.

The **shape and position** of the stomach are so greatly modified by changes within itself and in the surrounding viscera that no one form can be described as typical. The chief modifications are determined by (1) the amount of the stomach contents, (2) the stage which the digestive process has reached, (3) the degree of development of the gastric musculature, and (4) the condition of the adjacent intestines. It is, however, possible by comparing a series of stomachs to determine certain markings more or less common to all (Figs. 1041, 1042).

Openings.—The opening by which the esophagus communicates with the stomach is known as the **cardiac orifice,** and is situated on the left of the middle line at the level of the tenth thoracic vertebra. The short abdominal portion of the esophagus (*antrum cardiacum*) is conical in shape and curved sharply to the left

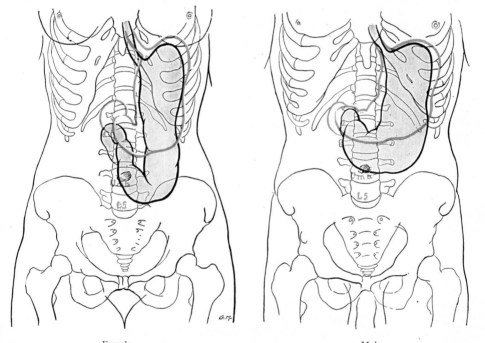

Female   Male
Fig. 1041. Average position of the stomach based on X-ray studies. Standing position in black; reclining position in red. (Eycleshymer and Jones.)

the base of the cone being continuous with the cardiac orifice of the stomach. The right margin of the esophagus is continuous with the lesser curvature of the stomach, while the left margin joins the greater curvature at an acute angle, termed the **incisura cardiaca.**

The **pyloric orifice** communicates with the duodenum, and its position is usually indicated on the surface of the stomach by a circular groove, the **duodenopyloric constriction.** This orifice lies to the right of the middle line at the level of the upper border of the first lumbar vertebra.

Curvatures.—The **lesser curvature** (*curvatura ventriculi minor*) (Fig. 1043), extending between the cardiac and pyloric orifices, forms the right or concave border of the stomach. It descends as a continuation of the right margin of the esophagus in front of the fibers of the right crus of the diaphragm, and then, turning to the right, it crosses the first lumbar vertebra and ends at the pylorus. Nearer its pyloric than its cardiac end is a well-marked notch, the **incisura angularis** (Fig. 1042), which varies somewhat in position with the state of distension; it serves to separate the stomach into a right and a left portion. The lesser curvature gives attachment to the hepatogastric ligament which contains the left gastric artery and the right gastric branch of the hepatic artery.

The **greater curvature** (*curvatura ventriculi major*) is directed mainly forward, and is four or five times as long as the lesser curvature. Starting from the cardiac orifice at the incisura cardiaca, it forms an arch backward, upward, and to the left; the highest point of the convexity is on a level with the sixth left costal cartilage From this level it may be followed downward and forward, with a slight convexity to the left as low as the cartilage of the ninth rib; it then turns to the right, to the end of the pylorus. Directly opposite the incisura angularis of the lesser curvature the greater curvature presents a dilatation, which is the **pyloric vestibule**; this dilatation is limited on the right by a slight groove, the **sulcus intermedius**, which is about 2.5 cm. from the pyloric valve. The portion between the sulcus intermedius and the pyloric valve is termed the **pyloric antrum**. At its commencement the greater curvature is covered by peritoneum continuous with that covering the front of the organ. The left part of the curvature gives attachment to the gastro-lienal ligament, the anterior portion to the greater omentum.

Surfaces.—When the stomach is in the contracted condition, its surfaces are directed upward and downward respectively, but when the viscus is distended they are directed forward, and backward. They may therefore be described as antero-superior and postero-inferior.

Antero-superior Surface.—The left half of this surface is in contact with the diaphragm, which separates it from the base of the left lung, the heart, and the seventh, eighth, and ninth ribs, and intercostal spaces of the left side. The right half is in relation with the left and quadrate lobes of the liver and with the anterior abdominal wall. When the stomach is empty, the transverse colon may lie on the front part of this surface. The whole surface is covered by peritoneum.

The **Postero-inferior Surface** is in relation with the diaphragm, the spleen, the left suprarenal gland, the upper part of the front of the left kidney, the anterior surface of the pancreas, the left colic flexure, and the upper layer of the transverse mesocolon. These structures form a shallow bed, the **stomach bed**, on which the viscus rests. The transverse mesocolon separates the stomach from the duodeno-jejunal flexure and small intestine. The postero-inferior surface is covered by peritoneum, except over a small area close to the cardiac orifice; this area is limited by the lines of attachment of the **gastrophrenic ligament**, and lies in apposition with the diaphragm, and frequently with the upper portion of the left supra-renal gland.

Component Parts of the Stomach.—A plane passing through the incisura angularis on the lesser curvature and the left limit of the opposed dilatation on the greater curvature divides the stomach into a left portion or body and a right or **pyloric portion**. The superior portion of the body is known as the **fundus**, and is marked off from the remainder of the body by a plane passing horizontally through the cardiac orifice. The pyloric portion is divided by a plane through the sulcus inter-medius at right angles to the long axis of this portion; the part to the right of this plane is the **pyloric antrum** (Fig. 1042).

If the stomach be examined during the process of digestion it will be found divided by a muscular constriction into a large dilated left portion, and a narrow contracted tubular right portion. The constriction is in the body of the stomach, and does not follow any of the anato-mical landmarks; indeed, it shifts gradually toward the left as digestion progresses, *i. e.*, more of the body is gradually absorbed into the tubular part.

Position of the Stomach.—The position of the stomach varies with the posture, with the amount of the stomach contents and with the condition of the intestines on which it rests.

According to Moody, radiographs of the normal erect living body show the ordinary range of variation of the most caudal part of the greater curvature to be from 7.3 cm. above to 13.5 cm. below the interiliac line in males and from 6.5 cm. above to 13.7 cm. below the line in females. It is below the interiliac line in 74.4 per cent. of males and in 87 per cent. of females. With the body horizontal the most caudal part of the greater curvature is in males 16.5 cm. above to 7.3 cm. below the interiliac line and in females 15.5 cm. above to 8.4 cm. below the line. The most common position in the erect male (26 per cent.) is 2.6 cm. to 5 cm. below and in the horizontal male (22.4 per cent.) 2.5 cm. to 5 cm. above the interiliac line. In the erect female the most common position (22.4 per cent.) is 5 cm. to 7.5 cm. below and in the horizontal female (24 per cent.) 2.5 cm. to 5 cm. above the interiliac line.

The position of the pylorus in the erect living body of the male varies from 14.5 cm. above to 8 cm. below and in the female from 15 cm. above to 2.5 cm. below the interiliac line. The range of position in regard to the sagittal axis of the erect body varies in males from 8.8 cm. to the right to 2 cm. to the left of the axis. In 84 per cent. it is to the right of the axis. In females the position ranges from 6 cm. to the right to 2.6 cm. to the left of the sagittal axis, In 89.5 per cent. it is to the right. The most common position in both males and females is from 2.5 cm. to 5 cm. to the right.

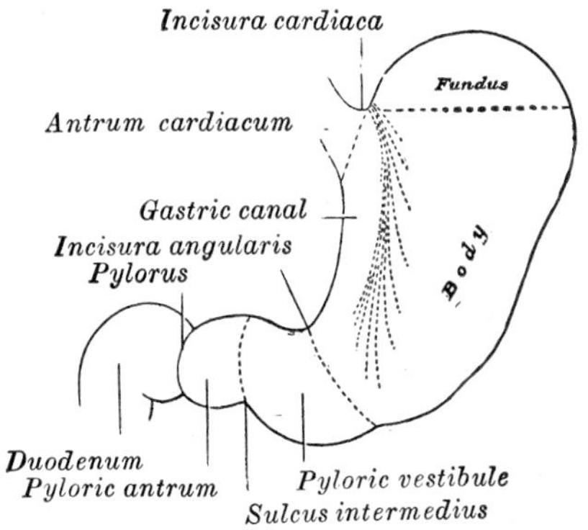

FIG. 1042.—Diagram showing the subdivisions of the human stomach. (F. T. Lewis.)

Interior of the Stomach.—When examined after death, the stomach is usually fixed at some temporary stage of the digestive process. A common form is that shown in Fig. 1043. If the viscus be laid open by a section through the plane of its two curvatures. it is seen to consist of two segments: (*a*) a large globular portion on the left and (*b*) a narrow tubular part on the right. These correspond to the clinical subdivisions of fundus and pyloric portions already described, and are separated by a constriction which indents the body and greater curvature, but does not involve the lesser curvature. To the left of the cardiac orifice is the incisura cardiaca: the projection of this notch into the cavity of the stomach increases as the organ distends, and has been supposed to act as a valve preventing regurgitation into the esophagus. In the pyloric portion are seen: (*a*) the elevation corresponding to the incisura angularis, and (*b*) the circular projection from the duodenopyloric constriction which forms the pyloric valve; the separation of the pyloric antrum from the rest of the pyloric part is scarcely indicated.

The **pyloric valve** (*valvula pylori*) is a muscular ring formed by a thickening of the circular layer of the muscular coat. Some of the deeper longitudinal fibers turn in and interlace with the circular fibers of the valve.

Structure.—The wall of the stomach consists of four coats: **serous, muscular, areolar,** and **mucous,** together with vessels and nerves.

The **serous coat** (*tunica serosa*) is derived from the peritoneum, and covers the entire surface of the organ, excepting along the greater and lesser curvatures at the points of attachment of the greater and lesser omenta; here the two layers of peritoneum leave a small triangular space, along which the nutrient vessels and nerves pass. On the posterior surface of the stomach, close to the cardiac orifice, there is also a small area uncovered by peritoneum, where the organ is in contact with the under surface of the diaphragm.

The **muscular coat** (*tunica muscularis*) (Figs. 1044, 1045) is situated immediately beneath the serous covering, with which it is closely connected. It consists of three sets of smooth muscle fibers: longitudinal, circular and oblique.

The *longitudinal fibers* (*stratum longitudinale*) are the most superficial, and are arranged in two sets. The first set consists of fibers continuous with the longitudinal fibers of the esophagus; they radiate in a stellate manner from the cardiac orifice and are practically all lost before the pyloric portion is reached. The second set commences on the body of the stomach and passes to the right, its fibers becoming more thickly distributed as they approach the pylorus. Some of the more superficial fibers of this set pass on to the duodenum, but the deeper fibers dip inward and interlace with the circular fibers of the pyloric valve.

The *circular fibers* (*stratum circulare*) form a uniform layer over the whole extent of the stomach beneath the longitudinal fibers. At the pylorus they are most abundant, and are aggregated into a circular ring, which projects into the lumen, and forms, with the fold of mucous membrane covering its surface, the **pyloric valve.** They are continuous with the circular fibers of the esophagus, but are sharply marked off from the circular fibers of the duodenum.

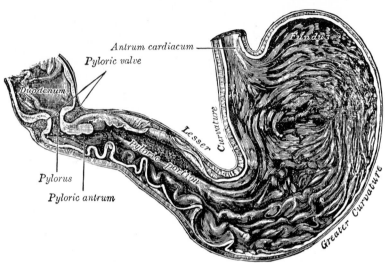

Fig. 1043.—Interior of the stomach.

The *oblique fibers* (*fibræ obliquæ*) internal to the circular layer, are limited chiefly to the cardiac end of the stomach, where they are disposed as a thick uniform layer, covering both surfaces, some passing obliquely from left to right, others from right to left, around the cardiac end.

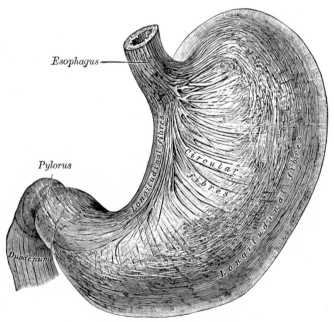

Fig. 1044.—The longitudinal and circular muscular fibers of the stomach, viewed from above and in front. (Spalteholz)

The **areolar** or **submucous coat** (*tela submucosa*) consists of a loose, areolar tissue, connecting the mucous and muscular layers.

The **mucous membrane** (*tunica mucosa*) is thick and its surface is smooth, soft, and velvety. In the fresh state it is of a pinkish tinge at the pyloric end, and of a red or reddish-brown color over the rest of its surface. In infancy it is of a brighter hue, the vascular redness being more marked. It is thin at the cardiac extremity, but thicker toward the pylorus. During the contracted state of the organ it is thrown into numerous plaits or rugæ, which, for the most part, have a longitudinal direction, and are most marked toward the pyloric end of the stomach, and along the greater curvature (Fig. 1043). These folds are entirely obliterated when the organ becomes distended.

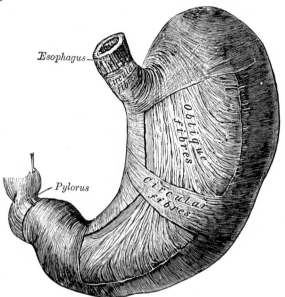

Fig. 1045.—The oblique muscular fibers of the stomach, viewed from above and in front. (Spalteholz.)

Structure of the Mucous Membrane.—When examined with a lens, the inner surface of the mucous membrane presents a peculiar honeycomb appearance from being covered with small shallow depressions or alveoli, of a polygonal or hexagonal form, which vary from 0.12 to 0.25

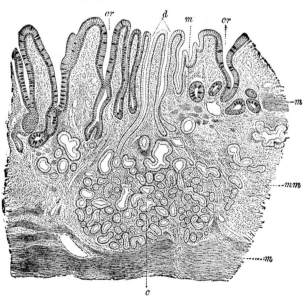

Fig. 1046.—Section of mucous membrane of human stomach, near the cardiac orifice. (v. Ebner, after J. Schaffer.) × 45. *c.* Cardiac glands. *d.* Their ducts. *cr.* Gland similar to the intestinal glands, with goblet cells. *mm.* Mucous membrane. *m.* Muscularis mucosæ. *m′.* Muscular tissue within the mucous membrane.

mm. in diameter. These are the ducts of the gastric glands, and at the bottom of each may be seen one or more minute orifices, the openings of the gland tubes. The surface of the mucous membrane is covered by a single layer of columnar epithelium with occasional goblet cells. This epithelium commences very abruptly at the cardiac orifice, where there is a sudden transition from the stratified epithelium of the esophagus. The epithelial lining of the gland ducts is of the same character and is continuous with the general epithelial lining of the stomach (Fig. 1048).

The Gastric Glands.—The gastric glands are of three kinds: (a) **pyloric,** (b) **cardiac,** and (c) **fundus** or **oxyntic glands.** They are tubular in character, and are formed of a delicate basement membrane, consisting of flattened transparent endothelial cells lined by epithelium. The **pyloric glands** (Fig. 1047) are found in the pyloric portion of the stomach. They consist of two or three short closed tubes opening into a common duct or mouth. These tubes are wavy, and are about one-half the length of the duct. The duct is lined by columnar cells, continuous with the epithelium lining the surface of the mucous membrane of the stomach, the tubes by shorter and more cubical cells which are finely granular. The **cardiac glands** (Fig. 1046), few in number, occur close to the cardiac orifice. They are of two kinds: (1) simple tubular glands resembling those of the pyloric end of the stomach, but with short ducts; (2) compound racemose glands resembling the duodenal glands. The **fundus glands** (Fig. 1048) are found in the body and fundus of the stomach; they are simple tubes, two or more of which open into a single duct. The duct, however, in these glands is shorter than in the pyloric variety, sometimes not amounting to more than one-sixth of the whole length of the gland; it is lined throughout by columnar epithelium. The gland tubes are straight and parallel to each

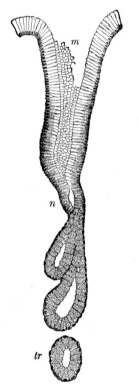

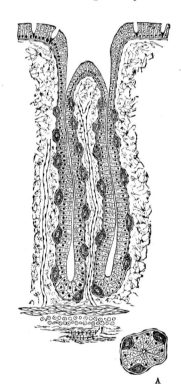

FIG. 1047.—A pyloric gland, from a section of the dog's stomach. (Ebstein.) *m.* Mouth. *n.* Neck. *tr.* A deep portion of a tubule cut transversely.

FIG. 1048.—A fundus gland. *A.* Transverse section of gland.

other. At the point where they open into the duct, which is termed the neck, the epithelium alters, and consists of short columnar or polyhedral, granular cells, which almost fill the tube, so that the lumen becomes suddenly constricted and is continued down as a very fine channel. They are known as the **chief** or **central cells** of the glands. Between these cells and the basement membrane, larger oval cells, which stain deeply with eosin, are found; these cells are studded throughout the tube at intervals, giving it a beaded or varicose appearance. These are known as the **parietal** or **oxyntic cells,** and they are connected with the lumen by fine channels which run into their substance. Between the glands the mucous membrane consists of a connective-tissue frame-work, with lymphoid tissue. In places, this latter tissue, especially in early life, is collected into little masses, which to a certain extent resemble the solitary nodules of the intestine, and are termed the **lenticular glands** of the stomach. They are not, however, so distinctly circumscribed as the solitary nodules. Beneath the mucous membrane, and between it and the submucous coat, is a thin stratum of involuntary muscular fiber (*muscularis mucosæ*), which in some parts consists only of a single longitudinal layer; in others of two layers, an inner circular and an outer longitudinal.

Vessels and Nerves.—The arteries supplying the stomach are: the left gastric, the right gastric and right gastroepiploic branches of the hepatic, and the left gastroepiploic and short gastric branches of the lienal. They supply the muscular coat, ramify in the submucous coat, and are finally distributed to the mucous membrane. The arrangement of the vessels in the mucous membrane is somewhat peculiar. The arteries break up at the base of the gastric tubules into a plexus of fine capillaries which run upward between the tubules, anastomosing with each other, and ending in a plexus of larger capillaries, which surround the mouths of the tubes, and also form hexagonal meshes around the ducts. From these the **veins** arise, and pursue a straight course downward, between the tubules, to the submucous tissue; they end either in the lienal and superior mesenteric veins, or directly in the portal vein. The **lymphatics** are numerous: they consist of a superficial and a deep set, and pass to the lymph nodes found along the two curvatures of the organ (page) **717.** The **nerves** are the terminal branches of the right and left vagi, the former usually being distributed upon the back, and the latter upon the front part of the organ; and numerous sympathetic fibers arising chiefly from the various subdivisions of the celiac plexus and accompanying the different bloodvessels to the organ. According to Mitchell[1], small sympathetic filaments may also arise directly from the phrenic and splanchnic trunks. Nerve plexuses are found in the submucous coat and between the layers of the muscular coat as in the intestine. From these plexuses fibrils are distributed to the muscular tissue and the mucous membrane.

The Small Intestine (Intestinum Tenue).

The **small intestine** is a convoluted tube, extending from the pylorus to the colic valve, where it ends in the large intestine It is about 7 metres long,[2] and gradually diminishes in size from its commencement to its termination. It is contained in the central and lower part of the abdominal cavity, and is surrounded above and at the sides by the large intestine; a portion of it extends below the superior aperture of the pelvis and lies in front of the rectum. It is in relation, in front, with the greater omentum and abdominal parietes, and is connected to the vertebral column by a fold of peritoneum, the **mesentery.** The small intestine is divisible into three portions: the **duodenum,** the **jejunum,** and the **ileum.**

The **Duodenum** (Fig. 1049) has received its name from being about equal in length to the breadth of twelve fingers (25 cm.). It is the shortest, the widest, and the most fixed part of the small intestine, and has no mesentery, being only partially covered by peritoneum. Its course presents a remarkable curve, somewhat of the shape of an imperfect circle, so that its termination is not far removed from its starting-point.

In the adult the course of the duodenum is as follows: commencing at the pylorus it passes backward, upward, and to the right, beneath the quadrate lobe of the liver to the neck of the gall-bladder, varying slightly in direction according to the degree of distension of the stomach: it then takes a sharp curve and descends along the right margin of the head of the pancreas, for a variable distance, generally to the level of the upper border of the body of the fourth lumbar vertebra. It now takes a second bend, and passes from right to left across the vertebral column, having a slight inclination upward; and on the left side of the vertebral column it ascends for about 2.5 cm., and then ends opposite the second lumbar vertebra in the jejunum. As it unites with the jejunum it turns abruptly forward, forming the **duodenojejunal flexure.** From the above description it will be seen that the duodenum may be divided into four portions: **superior, descending, horizontal,** and **ascending.**

Relations.—The **superior portion** (*pars superior; first portion*) is about 5 cm. long.

[1] Jour. Anat., 1940, vol. 75.
[2] Treves states that, in one hundred cases, the average length of the small intestine in the adult male was 22 feet 6 inches, and in the adult female 23 feet 4 inches: but that it varies very much, the extremes in the male being 31 feet 10 inches, and 15 feet 6 inches. He states that in the adult the length of the bowel is independent of age, height, and weight.

Beginning at the pylorus, it ends at the neck of the gall-bladder. It is the most movable of the four portions. It is almost completely covered by peritoneum, but a small part of its posterior surface near the neck of the gall-bladder and the inferior vena cava is uncovered; the upper border of its first half has the hepatoduodenal

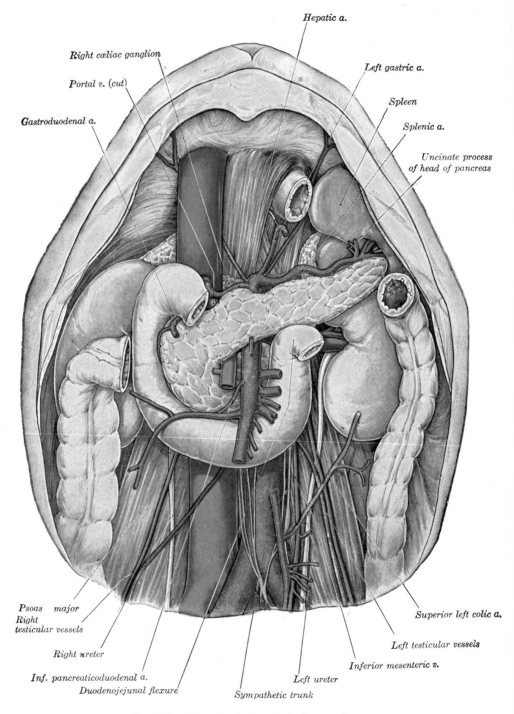

Fɪɢ. 1049.—A dissection to show the duodenum and pancreas.

ligament attached to it, while to the lower border of the same segment the greater omentum is connected. It is in such close relation with the gall-bladder that it is usually found to be stained by bile after death, especially on its anterior surface. It is in relation above and in front with the quadrate lobe of the liver and the gall-bladder; behind with the gastroduodenal artery, the common bile duct, and the portal vein; and below and behind with the head and neck of the pancreas.

The **descending portion** (*pars descendens; second portion*) is from 7 to 10 cm. long, and extends from the neck of the gall-bladder, on a level with the first lumbar vertebra, along the right side of the vertebral column as low as the upper border of the body of the fourth lumbar vertebra. It is crossed in its middle third by the transverse colon, the posterior surface of which is uncovered by peritoneum and is connected

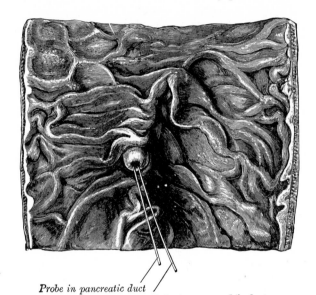

Probe in pancreatic duct

Probe in common bile-duct

Fig. 1050.—Interior of the descending portion of the duodenum, showing bile papilla.

to the duodenum by a small quantity of connective tissue. The supra- and infra-colic portions are covered in front by peritoneum, the infracolic part by the right leaf of the mesentery. Posteriorly the descending portion of the duodenum is not covered by peritoneum. The descending portion is in relation, in front, from above downward, with the duodenal impression on the right lobe of the liver, the transverse colon, and the small intestine; behind, it has a variable relation to the front of the right kidney in the neighborhood of the hilum, and is connected to it by loose areolar tissue; the renal vessels, the inferior vena cava, and the Psoas below, are also behind it. At its medial side is the head of the pancreas, and the common bile duct; to its lateral side is the right colic flexure. The common bile duct and the pancreatic duct together perforate the medial side of this portion of the intestine obliquely (Figs. 1050 and 1086), some 7 to 10 cm. below the pylorus; the accessory pancreatic duct sometimes pierces it about 2 cm. above and slightly in front of these.

The **horizontal portion** (*pars horizontalis; third or preaortic or transverse portion*) is from 5 to 7.5 cm. long. It begins at the right side of the upper border of the fourth lumbar vertebra and passes from right to left, with a slight inclination upward, in front of the great vessels and crura of the diaphragm, and ends in the ascending portion in front of the abdominal aorta. It is crossed by the superior mesenteric vessels and the mesentery. Its front surface is covered by peritoneum, except near the middle line, where it is crossed by the superior mesenteric vessels. Its posterior surface is uncovered by peritoneum, except toward its left extremity, where the posterior layer of the mesentery may sometimes be found covering it to a variable extent. This surface rests upon the right crus of the diaphragm, the inferior vena cava, and the aorta. The upper surface is in relation with the head of the pancreas.

The **ascending portion** (*pars ascendens; fourth portion*) of the duodenum is about 2.5 cm. long. It ascends on the left side of the aorta, as far as the level of the upper border of the second lumbar vertebra, where it turns abruptly forward to become the jejunum, forming the **duodenojejunal flexure.** It lies in front of the left Psoas major and left renal vessels, and is covered in front, and partly at the sides, by peritoneum continuous with the left portion of the mesentery.

The superior part of the duodenum, as stated above, is somewhat movable, but the rest is practically fixed, and is bound down to neighboring viscera and the posterior abdominal wall by the peritoneum. In addition to this, the duodeno-jejunal flexure is held in place by a fibrous and muscular band, the **ligament of Treitz** (*Musculus suspensorius duodeni*). This structure commences in the connective tissue around the celiac artery and left crus of the diaphragm, and passes downward to be inserted into the superior border of the duodenojejunal curve and a part of the ascending duodenum, and from this it is continued into the mesentery. It possesses, according to Treitz, smooth muscular fibers mixed with the fibrous tissue of which it is principally made up. It is of little importance as a muscle, but acts as a suspensory ligament.

Vessels and Nerves.—The **arteries** supplying the duodenum are the right gastric and superior pancreaticoduodenal branches of the hepatic, and the inferior pancreaticoduodenal branch of the superior mesenteric. The **veins** end in the lienal and superior mesenteric. The **nerves** are derived from the cœliac plexus.

Jejunum and Ileum.—The remainder of the small intestine from the end of the duodenum is named **jejunum** and **ileum**; the former term being given to the upper two-fifths and the latter to the lower three-fifths. There is no morphological line of distinction between the two, and the division is arbitrary; but at the same time the character of the intestine gradually undergoes a change from the commencement of the jejunum to the end of the ileum, so that a portion of the bowel taken from these two situations would present characteristic and marked differences. These are briefly as follows:

The **Jejunum** (*intestinum jejunum*) is wider, its diameter being about 4 cm., and is thicker, more vascular, and of a deeper color than the ileum, so that a given length weighs more. The circular folds (*valvulæ conniventes*) of its mucous membrane are large and thickly set, and its villi are larger than in the ileum. The aggregated lymph nodules are almost absent in the upper part of the jejunum, and in the lower part are less frequently found than in the ileum, and are smaller and tend to assume a circular form. By grasping the jejunum between the finger and thumb the circular folds can be felt through the walls of the gut; these being absent in the lower part of the ileum, it is possible in this way to distinguish the upper from the lower part of the small intestine.

The **Ileum** (*intestinum ileum*) is narrow, its diameter being 3.75 cm., and its coats thinner and less vascular than those of the jejunum. It possesses but few circular folds, and they are small and disappear entirely toward its lower end, but aggregated lymph nodules (Peyer's patches) are larger and more numerous. The jejunum for the most part occupies the umbilical and left iliac regions, while the ileum occupies chiefly the umbilical, hypogastric, right iliac, and pelvic regions. The terminal part of the ileum usually lies in the pelvis, from which it ascends over the right Psoas and right iliac vessels; it ends in the right iliac fossa by opening into the medial side of the commencement of the large intestine. The jejunum and ileum are attached to the posterior abdominal wall by an extensive fold of peritoneum, the **mesentery,** which allows the freest motion, so that each coil can accommodate itself to changes in form and position. The mesentery is fan-shaped: its posterior border or root, about 15 cm. long, is attached to the posterior abdominal wall from the left side of the body of the second lumbar vertebra to the right sacro-iliac articulation, crossing successively the horizontal part of the duodenum, the aorta, the inferior vena cava, the ureter, and right Psoas muscle (Fig. 1035). Its breadth between its vertebral and intestinal borders averages about 20 cm., and is greater in the middle than at its upper and lower ends. According to Lockwood it tends to increase in breadth as age advances. Between the two layers of which it is composed are contained bloodvessels, nerves, lacteals, and lymph glands, together with a variable amount of fat.

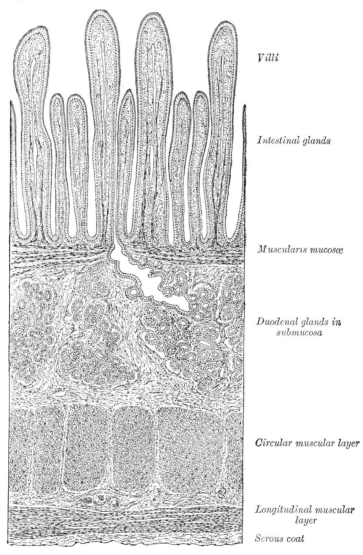

Villi

Intestinal glands

Muscularis mucosœ

Duodenal glands in submucosa

Circular muscular layer

Longitudinal muscular layer

Serous coat

Fig. 1051.—Section of duodenum of cat. (After Schäfer.) × 60.

Meckel's Diverticulum (*diverticulum ilei*).—This consists of a pouch which projects from the lower part of the ileum in about 2 per cent. of subjects. Its average position is about 1 meter above the colic valve, and its average length about 5 cm. Its caliber is generally similar to that of the ileum, and its blind extremity may be free or may be connected with the abdominal wall or with some other portion of the intestine by a fibrous band. It represents the remains of the proximal part of the vitelline duct, the duct of communication between the yolk-sac and the

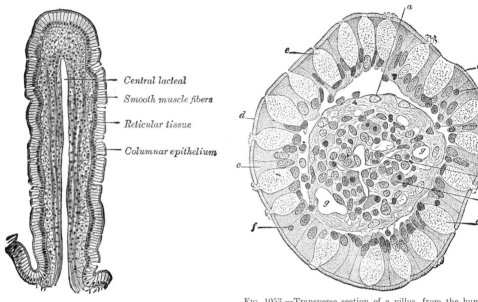

Fig. 1052.—Vertical section of a villus from the dog's small intestine. × 80.

Fig. 1053.—Transverse section of a villus, from the human intestine. (v. Ebner.) × 350. *a.* Basement membrane, here somewhat shrunken away from the epithelium. *b.* Lacteal. *c.* Columnar epithelium. *d.* Its striated border. *e.* Goblet cells. *f.* Leucocytes in epithelium. *f'.* Leucocytes below epithelium. *g.* Bloodvessels. *h.* Muscle cells cut across.

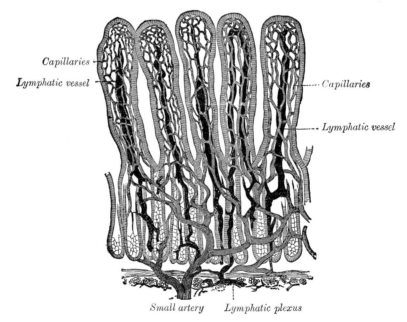

Fig. 1054.—Villi of small intestine, showing bloodvessels and lymphatic vessels. (Cadiat.)

primitive digestive tube in early fetal life.

Structure.—The wall of the small intestine (Fig. 1051) is composed of four coats: **serous, muscular, areolar,** and **mucous.**

The **serous coat** (*tunica serosa*) is derived from the peritoneum. The superior portion of the duodenum is almost completely surrounded by this membrane near its pyloric end, but is only covered in front at the other extremity; the descending portion is covered by it in front, except where it is carried off by the transverse colon; and the inferior portion lies behind the peritoneum which passes over it without being closely incorporated with the other coats of this part of the intestine, and is separated from it in and near the middle line by the superior mesenteric vessels. The rest of the small intestine is surrounded by the peritoneum, excepting along its attached or mesenteric border; here a space is left for the vessels and nerves to pass to the gut.

The **muscular coat** (*tunica muscularis*) consists of two layers of unstriped fibers: an external, longitudinal, and an internal, circular layer. The *longitudinal fibers* are thinly scattered over the surface of the intestine, and are more distinct along its free border. The *circular fibers* form a thick, uniform layer, and are composed of plain muscle cells of considerable length. The muscular coat is thicker at the upper than at the lower part of the small intestine.

The **areolar** or **submucous coat** (*tela submucosa*) connects together the mucous and muscular layers. It consists of loose, filamentous areolar tissue containing blood vessels, lymphatics, and nerves. It is the strongest layer of the intestine.

The **mucous membrane** (*tunica mucosa*) is thick and highly vascular at the upper part of the small intestine, but somewhat paler and thinner below. It consists of the following structures: next the areolar or submucous coat is a double layer of unstriped muscular fibers, outer longitudinal and inner circular, the **muscularis mucosæ**; internal to this is a quantity of retiform tissue, enclosing in its meshes lymph corpuscles, and in this the bloodvessels and nerves ramify; lastly, a basement membrane, supporting a single layer of epithelial cells, which throughout the intestine are columnar in character. The cells are granular in appearance, and each possesses a clear oval nucleus. At their superficial or unattached ends they present a distinct layer of highly refracting material, marked by vertical striæ, the **striated border**.

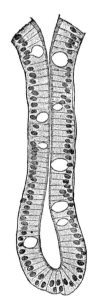

FIG. 1055.—An intestinal gland from the human intestine. (Flemming.)

The mucous membrane presents for examination the following structures, contained within it or belonging to it:

Circular folds.	Intestinal glands.
Villi.	Solitary lymphatic nodules.
Duodenal glands.	Aggregated lymphatic nodules.

The **circular folds** (*plicæ circulares* [*Kerkringi*]; *valvulæ conniventes; valves of Kerkring*) are large valvular flaps projecting into the lumen of the bowel. They are composed of reduplications of the mucous membrane, the two layers of the fold being bound together by submucous tissue; unlike the folds in the stomach, they are permanent, and are not obliterated when the intestine is distended. The majority extend transversely around the cylinder of the intestine for about one-half or two-thirds of its circumference, but some form complete circles, and others have a spiral direction; the latter usually extend a little more than once around the bowel, but occasionally two or three times. The larger folds are about 8 mm. in depth at their broadest part; but the greater number are of smaller size. The larger and smaller folds alternate with each other. They are not found at the commencement of the duodenum, but begin to appear about 2.5 or 5 cm. beyond the pylorus. In the lower part of the descending portion, below the point where the bile and pancreatic ducts enter the intestine, they are very large and closely approximated. In the horizontal and ascending portions of the duodenum and upper half of the jejunum they are large and numerous, but from this point, down to the middle of the ileum, they diminish considerably in size. In the lower part of the ileum they almost entirely disappear; hence the comparative thinness of this portion of the intestine, as compared with the duodenum and jejunum. The circular folds retard the passage of the food along the intestines, and afford an increased surface for absorption.

The **intestinal villi** (*villi intestinales*) are highly vascular processes, projecting from the mucous membrane of the small intestine throughout its whole extent, and giving to its surface a velvety appearance. They are largest and most numerous in the duodenum and jejunum, and become fewer and smaller in the ileum.

Structure of the villi (Figs. 1052, 1053).—The essential parts of a villus are: the lacteal vessel, the bloodvessels, the epithelium, the basement membrane, and the musculart issue of the mucosa, all being supported and held together by retiform lymphoid tissue.

The *lacteals* are in some cases double, and in some animals multiple, but usually there is a single vessel. Situated in the axis of the villus, each commences by dilated cecal extremities near to, but not quite at, the summit of the villus. The walls are composed of a single layer of endothelial cells.

The *muscular fibers* are derived from the muscularis mucosæ, and are arranged in longitudinal bundles around the lacteal vessel, extending from the base to the summit of the villus, and giving off, laterally, individual muscle cells, which are enclosed by the reticulum, and by it are attached to the basement-membrane and to the lacteal.

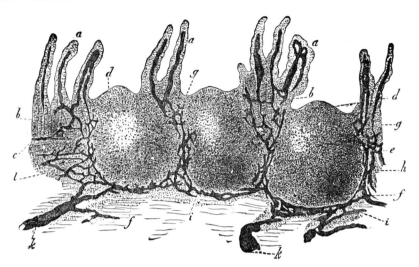

FIG. 1056.—Vertical section of a human aggregated lymphatic nodule, injected through its lymphatic canals. *a*, Villi with their chyle passages. *b*. Intestinal glands. *c*. Muscularis mucosæ. *d*. Cupola or apex of solitary nodule. *e*. Mesial zone of nodule. *f*. Base of nodule. *g*. Points of exit of the lacteals from the villi, and entrance into the true mucous membrane. *h*. Retiform arrangement of the lymphatics in the mesial zone. *i*. Course of the latter at the base of the nodule. *k*. Confluence of the lymphatics opening into the vessels of the submucous tissue. *l*. Follicular tissue of the latter.

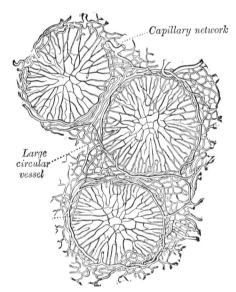

FIG. 1057.—Transverse section through the equatorial plane of three aggregated lymphatic nodules from the rabbit.

The *bloodvessels* (Fig. 1054) form a plexus under the basement membrane, and are enclosed in the reticular tissue.

These structures are surrounded by the *basement membrane*, which is made up of a stratum of endothelial cells, and upon this is placed a layer of *columnar epithelium*, the characteristics of which have been described. The *retiform tissue* forms a net-work (Fig. 1053) in the meshes of which a number of leucocytes are found.

The **intestinal glands** (*glandulæ intestinales* [*Lieberkühni*]; *crypts of Lieberkühn*) (Fig. 1055) are found in considerable numbers over every part of the mucous membrane of the small intestine. They consist of minute tubular depressions of the mucous membrane, arranged perpendicularly to the surface, upon which they open by small circular apertures. They may be seen with the aid of a lens, their orifices appearing as minute dots scattered between the villi. Their walls are thin, consisting of a basement membrane lined by columnar epithelium, and covered on their exterior by capillary vessels.

The **duodenal glands** (*glandulæ duodenales* [*Brunneri*]; *Brunner's glands*) are limited to the duodenum (Fig. 1051), and are found in the submucous areolar tissue. They are largest and most numerous near the pylorus, forming an almost complete layer in the superior portion and upper half of the descending portions of the duodenum. They then begin to diminish in number, and practically disappear at the junction of the duodenum and jejunum. They are small compound acinotubular glands consisting of a number of alveoli lined by short columnar epithelium and opening by a single duct on the inner surface of the intestine.

The **solitary lymphatic nodules** (*noduli lymphatici solitarii; solitary glands*) are found scattered throughout the mucous membrane of the small intestine, but are most numerous in the lower part of the ileum. Their free surfaces are covered with rudimentary villi, except at the summits, and each gland is surrounded by the openings of the intestinal glands. Each consists of a dense interlacing retiform tissue closely packed with lymph-corpuscles, and permeated with an abundant capillary network. The interspaces of the retiform tissue are continuous with larger lymph spaces which surround the gland, through which they communicate with the lacteal system. They are situated partly in the submucous tissue, partly in the mucous membrane, where they form slight projections of its epithelial layer (see Fig. 1069).

The **aggregated lymphatic nodules** (*noduli lymphatici aggregati; Peyer's patches; Peyer's glands; agminated follicles; tonsillæ intestinales*) (Fig. 1056) form circular or oval patches, from twenty to thirty in number, and varying in length from 2 to 10 cm. They are largest and most numerous in the ileum. In the lower part of the jejunum they are small, circular, and few in number. They are occasionally seen in the duodenum. They are placed lengthwise in the intestine, and are situated in the portion of the tube most distant from the attachment of the mesentery. Each patch is formed of a group of solitary lymphatic nodules covered with mucous membrane, but the patches do not, as a rule, possess villi on their free surfaces. They are best marked in the young subject, become indistinct in middle age, and sometimes disappear altogether in advanced life. They are freely supplied with bloodvessels (Fig. 1057), which form an abundant plexus around each follicle and give off fine branches permeating the lymphoid tissue in the interior of the follicle. The lymphatic plexuses are especially abundant around these patches.

Vessels and Nerves.—The jejunum and ileum are supplied by the **superior mesenteric artery,** the intestinal branches of which, having reached the attached border of the bowel, run between the serous and muscular coats, with frequent inosculations to the free border, where they also anastomose with other branches running around the opposite surface of the gut. From these vessels numerous branches are given off, which pierce the muscular coat, supplying it and forming an intricate plexus in the submucous tissue. From this plexus minute vessels pass to the glands and villi of the mucous membrane. The **veins** have a course and arrangement similar to that of

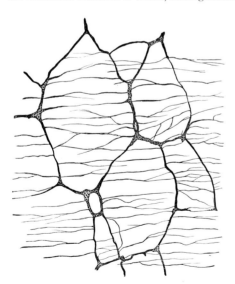

FIG. 1058.—The myenteric plexus from the rabbit. × 50.

FIG. 1059.—The plexus of the submucosa from the rabbit. ×50.

the arteries. The **lymphatics** of the small intestine (lacteals) are arranged in two sets, those of the mucous membrane and those of the muscular coat. The lymphatics of the villi commence in these structures in the manner described above. They form an intricate plexus in the mucous and submucous tissue, being joined by the lymphatics from the lymph spaces at the bases of the solitary nodules, and from this pass to larger vessels at the mesenteric border of the gut. The lymphatics of the muscular coat are situated to a great extent between the two layers of muscular fibers, where they form a close plexus; throughout their course they communicate freely with the lymphatics from the mucous membrane, and empty themselves in the same manner as these into the origins of the lacteal vessels at the attached border of the gut.

The **nerves** of the small intestines are derived from the plexuses of sympathetic nerves around the superior mesenteric artery, representing cranial parasympathetic fibers of the vagus and post-ganglionic sympathetic fibers from the celiac plexus. From this source they run to the **myenteric plexus** (*Auerbach's plexus*) (Fig. 1058) of nerves and ganglia situated between the circular and longitudinal muscular fibers from which the nervous branches are distributed to the muscular coats of the intestine. From this a secondary plexus, the **plexus of the submucosa** (*Meissner's plexus*) (Fig. 1059) is derived, and is formed by branches which have perforated the circular muscular fibers. This plexus lies in the submucous coat of the intestine; it also contains ganglia from which nerve fibers pass to the muscularis mucosæ and to the mucous membrane. The nerve bundles of the submucous plexus are finer than those of the myenteric plexus.

The Large Intestine (Intestinum Crassum).

The **large intestine** extends from the end of the ileum to the anus. It is about 1.5 meters long, being one-fifth of the whole extent of the intestinal canal. Its caliber is largest at its commencement at the cecum, and gradually diminishes as far as the rectum, where there is a dilatation of considerable size just above the anal canal. It differs from the small intestine in its greater caliber, its more fixed position, its sacculated form, and in possessing certain appendages to its external coat, the **appendices epiploicæ**. Further, its longitudinal muscular fibers do not form a continuous layer around the gut, but are arranged in three **longitudinal bands or tæniæ**. The large intestine, in its course, describes an arch which surrounds the convolutions of the small intestine. It commences in the right iliac region, in a dilated part, the **cecum**. It ascends through the right lumbar and hypochondriac regions to the under surface of the liver; it here takes a bend, the **right colic flexure**, to the left and passes transversely across the abdomen on the confines of the epigastric and umbilical regions, to the left hypochondriac region; it then bends again, the **left colic flexure**, and descends through the left lumbar and iliac regions to the pelvis, where it forms a bend called the **sigmoid flexure**; from this it is continued along the posterior wall of the pelvis to the anus. The large intestine is divided into the **cecum, colon, rectum**, and **anal canal**.

The **Cecum** (*intestinum cæcum*) (Fig. 1060), the commencement of the large intestine, is the large blind pouch situated below the colic valve. Its blind end is directed downward, and its open end upward, communicating directly with the colon, of which this blind pouch appears to be the beginning or head, and hence the old name of **caput cæcum coli** was applied to it. Its size is variously estimated by different authors, but on an average it may be said to be 6.25 cm. in length and 7.5 in breadth. It is situated in the right iliac fossa, above the lateral half of the inguinal ligament: it rests on the Iliacus and Psoas major, and usually lies in contact with the anterior abdominal wall, but the greater omentum and, if the cecum be empty, some coils of small intestine may lie in front of it. According to Moody the common position of the cecum in the erect living body is not in the right iliac fossa but in the cavity of the true pelvis. As a rule, it is entirely enveloped by peritoneum, but in a certain number of cases (5 per cent., Berry) the peritoneal covering is not complete, so that the upper part of the posterior surface is uncovered and connected to the iliac fascia by connective tissue. The cecum lies quite free in the abdominal cavity and enjoys a considerable amount of movement, so that it may become herniated down the right inguinal canal, and has occasionally been found in an inguinal hernia on the left side. The cecum varies in shape, but, according to Treves, in man it may be classified under one of four types. In early fetal life it is short, conical, and broad at the base, with its apex turned upward and medialward toward the ileocolic junction. It then resembles the cecum of some monkeys, *e. g.*, mangabey monkey. As the fetus grows the cecum increases in length more than in breadth, so that it forms a longer tube than in the primitive form and without the broad base, but with the same inclination of the apex toward the ileocolic junction. This form is seen in other monkeys, *e. g.*, the spider monkey. As development goes on, the lower part of the tube ceases to grow and the upper part becomes greatly increased, so that at birth there is a narrow tube, the vermiform process, hanging from a conical projection. the cecum. This is the infantile form, and as it persists throughout life in about 2 per cent. of cases, it is regarded by Treves as the *first* of his four types of human ceca. The cecum is conical and the appendix rises from its apex. The three longitudinal bands start from the appendix and are equidistant from each other. In the second type, the conical cecum has become quadrate by the growing out of a saccule on either side of the anterior longitudinal band. These saccules are of equal size, and the appendix arises from between them, instead of from the apex of a cone. This type is found in about 3 per cent. of cases. The *third* type is the normal type of man. Here the two saccules, which in the second type were uniform, have grown at unequal rates: the right with greater rapidity than the left. In consequence of this an apparently new apex has been formed by the growing downward of the right saccule, and the original apex, with the appendix attached, is pushed over to the left toward the ileocolic junction. The three longitudinal bands still start from the base of the vermiform process, but they are now no longer equidistant from each other, because the right saccule has grown between the anterior and postero-lateral bands, pushing them over to the left. This type occurs in about 90 per cent. of cases. The *fourth* type is merely an exaggerated condition of the third; the right saccule is still larger, and at the same time the left saccule has become atrophied, so that the original apex of the cecum, with the vermiform process, is close to the ileocolic junction, and the anterior band courses medialward to the same situation. This type is present in about 4 per cent. of cases.

The **Appendix** or **Vermiform Process** (*processus vermiformis*) (Fig. 1060) is a long, narrow, worm-shaped tube, which starts from what was originally the apex of the cecum, and may pass in one of several directions: upward behind the cecum; to the left behind the ileum and mesentery; or downward into the lesser pelvis. It varies from 2 to 20 cm. in length, its average being about 8.3 cm. It is retained in position by a fold of peritoneum (mesenteriole), derived from the left leaf of the mesentery. This fold, in the majority of cases, is more or less triangular in shape, and as a rule extends along the entire length of the tube. Between its two layers and close to its free margin lies the appendicular artery (Fig. 1060). The canal of the vermiform process is small, extends throughout the whole length of the tube, and communicates with the cecum by an orifice which is placed below and behind the ileocecal opening. It is sometimes guarded by a semilunar valve formed by a fold of mucous membrane, but this is by no means constant.

Structure.—The coats of the vermiform process are the same as those of the intestine: serous muscular, submucous, and mucous. The **serous coat** forms a complete investment for the tube, except along the narrow line of attachment of its mesenteriole in its proximal two-thirds. The *longitudinal muscular fibers* do not form three bands as in the greater part of the large intestine, but invest the whole organ, except at one or two points where both the longitudinal and circular fibers are deficient so that the peritoneal and submucous coats are contiguous over small areas.

The *circular muscle fibers* form a much thicker layer than the longitudinal fibers, and are separated from them by a small amount of connective tissue. The **submucous coat** is well marked, and contains a large number of masses of lymphoid tissue which cause the mucous membrane to bulge into the lumen and so render the latter of small size and irregular shape. The **mucous membrane** is lined by columnar epithelium and resembles that of the rest of the large intestine, but the intestinal glands are fewer in number (Fig. 1061).

The Colic Valve (*valvula coli; ileocecal valve*) (Fig. 1062).—The lower end of the ileum ends by opening into the medial and back part of the large intestine, at the point of junction of the cecum with the colon. The opening is guarded by a valve, consisting of two segments or lips, which project into the lumen of the large intes-

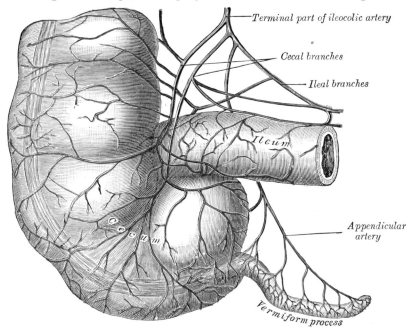

Terminal part of ileocolic artery

Cecal branches

Ileal branches

Ileum

Appendicular artery

Cecum

Vermiform process

Fig. 1060.—The cecum and appendix, with their arteries.

tine. If the intestine has been inflated and dried, the lips are of a semilunar shape. The upper one, nearly horizontal in direction, is attached by its convex border to the line of junction of the ileum with the colon; the lower lip, which is longer

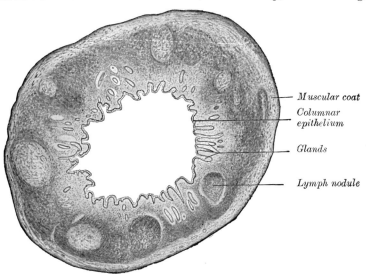

Muscular coat

Columnar epithelium

Glands

Lymph nodule

Fig. 1061.—Transverse section of human appeudix × 20.

and more concave, is attached to the line of junction of the ileum with the cecum. At the ends of the aperture the two segments of the valve coalesce, and are continued as narrow membranous ridges around the canal for a short distance, forming the

frenula of the valve. The left or anterior end of the aperture is rounded; the right or posterior is narrow and pointed. In the fresh condition, or in specimens which have been hardened *in situ*, the lips project as thick cushion-like folds into the lumen of the large gut, while the opening between them may present the appearance of a slit or may be somewhat oval in shape.

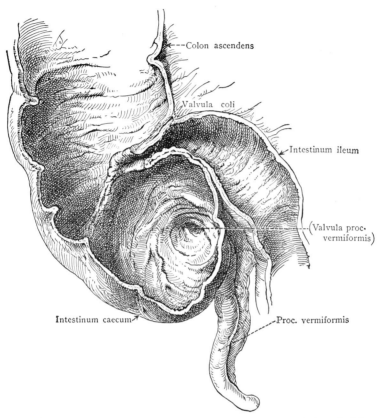

Fig. 1062.—The cecum, colic valve, and appendix vermiformis, with anterior wall of terminal ileum and cecum removed. (Eycleshymer and Jones.)

Each lip of the valve is formed by a reduplication of the mucous membrane and of the circular muscular fibers of the intestine, the longitudinal fibers and peritoneum being continued uninterruptedly from the small to the large intestine.

The surfaces of the valve directed toward the ileum are covered with villi, and present the characteristic structure of the mucous membrane of the small intestine; while those turned toward the large intestine are destitute of villi, and marked with the orifices of the numerous tubular glands peculiar to the mucous membrane of the large intestine. These differences in structure continue as far as the free margins of the valve. It is generally maintained that this valve prevents reflux from the cecum into the ileum, but in all probability it acts as a sphincter around the end of the ileum and prevents the contents of the ileum from passing too quickly into the cecum.

The **Colon** is divided into four parts: the **ascending, transverse, descending,** and **sigmoid.**

The **Ascending Colon** (*colon ascendens*) is smaller in caliber than the cecum, with which it is continuous. It passes upward, from its commencement at the cecum, opposite the colic valve, to the under surface of the right lobe of the liver, on the right of the gall-bladder, where it is lodged in a shallow depression, the **colic impression**; here it bends abruptly forward and to the left, forming the **right colic** (*hepatic*) **flexure** (Fig. 1027). It is retained in contact with the posterior wall of the abdomen by the peritoneum, which covers its anterior surface and sides, its posterior surface being connected by loose areolar tissue with the Iliacus, Quadratus lumborum, aponeurotic origin of Transversus abdominis, and with the front of the lower and lateral part of the right kidney. Sometimes the peritoneum completely invests it, and forms a distinct but narrow mesocolon.[1] It is in relation, in front, with the convolutions of the ileum and the abdominal parietes.

The **Transverse Colon** (*colon transversum*) the longest and most movable part of the colon, passes with a downward convexity from the right hypochondriac region across the abdomen, opposite the confines of the epigastric and umbilical zones, into the left hypochondriac region, where it curves sharply on itself beneath the lower end of the spleen, forming the **left colic** (*splenic*) **flexure**. In the erect posture the most caudal part is in the majority of males from 7.5 cm. to 10 cm. below the interiliac line and in the majority of females from 10 cm. to 12.5 cm. below the line. (Moody.) It is almost completely invested by peritoneum, and is connected to the inferior border of the pancreas by a large and wide duplicature of that membrane, the **transverse mesocolon**. It is in relation, by its upper surface, with the liver and gall-bladder, the greater curvature of the stomach, and the lower end of the spleen; by its under surface, with the small intestine; by its anterior surface, with the anterior layers of the greater omentum and the abdominal parietes; its posterior surface is in relation from right to left with the descending portion of the duodenum, the head of the pancreas, and some of the convolutions of the jejunum and ileum.

The **left colic** or **splenic flexure** (Fig. 1027) is situated at the junction of the transverse and descending parts of the colon, and is in relation with the lower end of the spleen and the tail of the pancreas; the flexure is so acute that the end of the transverse colon usually lies in contact with the front of the descending colon. It lies at a higher level than, and on a plane posterior to, the right colic flexure, and is attached to the diaphragm, opposite the tenth and eleventh ribs, by a peritoneal fold, named the **phrenicocolic ligament**, which assists in supporting the lower end of the spleen (see page 1204). Its position varies greatly.

The **Descending Colon**[2] (*colon descendens*) passes downward through the left hypochondriac and lumbar regions along the lateral border of the left kidney. At the lower end of the kidney it turns medialward toward the lateral border of the Psoas, and then descends, in the angle between Psoas and Quadratus lumborum, to the crest of the ilium, where it ends in the iliac colon. The peritoneum covers its anterior surface and sides, while its posterior surface is connected by areolar tissue with the lower and lateral part of the left kidney, the aponeurotic origin of the Transversus abdominis, and the Quadratus lumborum (Fig. 1049). It is smaller in caliber and more deeply placed than the ascending colon, and is more frequently covered with peritoneum on its posterior surface than the ascending colon (Treves). In front of it are some coils of small intestine.

The **Iliac Colon** (Fig. 1049) is situated in the left iliac fossa, and is about 12 to 15 cm. long. It begins at the level of the iliac crest, where it is continuous with the descending colon, and ends in the sigmoid colon at the superior aperture of the lesser pelvis. It curves downward and medialward in front of the Iliacus and Psoas,

---

[1] Treves states that, after a careful examination of one hundred subjects, he found that in fifty-two there was neither an ascending nor a descending mesocolon. In twenty-two there was a descending mesocolon, but no trace of a corresponding fold on the other side. In fourteen subjects there was a mesocolon to both the ascending and the descending segments of the bowel; while in the remaining twelve there was an ascending mesocolon, but no corresponding fold on the left side. It follows, therefore, that in performing lumbar colotomy a mesocolon may be expected upon the left side in 36 per cent. of all cases, and on the right in 26 per cent.—The Anatomy of the Intestinal Canal and Peritoneum in Man, 1885, p. 55.

[2] In the Basle nomenclature the descending colon is the portion between the left colic flexure and the superior aperture of the lesser pelvis; it is, however, convenient to describe its lowest part as the iliac colon.

and, as a rule, is covered by peritoneum on its sides and anterior surface only.

The **Sigmoid Colon** (*colon sigmoideum; pelvic colon; sigmoid flexure*) (Fig. 1063) forms a loop which averages about 40 cm. in length, and normally lies within the pelvis, but on account of its freedom of movement it is liable to be displaced into the abdominal cavity. It begins at the superior aperture of the lesser pelvis, where it is continuous with the iliac colon, and passes transversely across the front of the sacrum to the right side of the pelvis; it then curves on itself and turns toward the left to reach the middle line at the level of the third piece of the sacrum, where it bends downward and ends in the rectum. It is completely surrounded by peritoneum, which forms a mesentery (**sigmoid mesocolon**), which diminishes in length from the center toward the ends of the loop, where it disappears, so that the loop is fixed at its junctions with the iliac colon and rectum, but enjoys a considerable range of movement in its central portion. *Behind* the sigmoid colon are the external iliac vessels, the left Piriformis, and left sacral plexus of nerves; in *front*

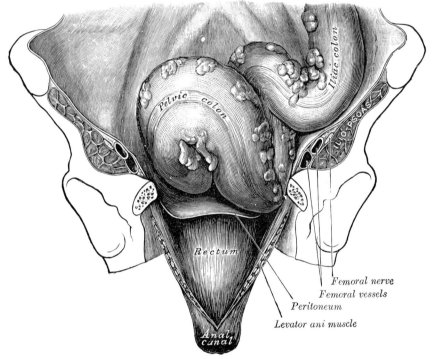

Fig. 1063.—Iliac colon, sigmoid or pelvic colon, and rectum seen from the front, after removal of pubic bones and bladder.

it is separated from the bladder in the male, and the uterus in the female, by some coils of the small intestine.

The **Rectum** (*intestinum rectum*) (Fig. 1064) is continuous above with the sigmoid colon, while below it ends in the anal canal. From its origin at the level of the third sacral vertebra it passes downward, lying in the sacrococcygeal curve, and extends for about 2.5 cm. in front of, and a little below, the tip of the coccyx, as far as the apex of the prostate. It then bends sharply backward into the anal canal. It therefore presents two antero-posterior curves: an upper, with its convexity backward, and a lower, with its convexity forward. Two lateral curves are also described, one to the right opposite the junction of the third and fourth sacral vertebræ, and the other to the left, opposite the left sacrococcygeal articulation;

they are, however, of little importance. The rectum is about 12 cm. long, and at its commencement its caliber is similar to that of the sigmoid colon, but near its termination it is dilated to form the **rectal ampulla**. The rectum has no sacculations comparable to those of the colon, but when the lower part of the rectum is contracted, its mucous membrane is thrown into a number of folds, which are longitudinal in direction and are effaced by the distension of the gut. Besides these there are certain permanent transverse folds, of a semilunar shape, known as **Houston's**

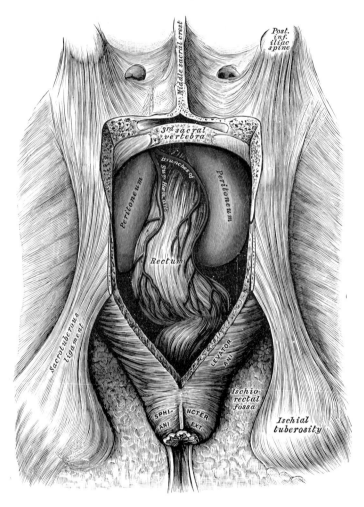

Fig. 1064.—The posterior aspect of the rectum exposed by removing the lower part of the sacrum and the coccyx.

valves (Fig. 1065). They are usually three in number; sometimes a fourth is found, and occasionally only two are present. One is situated near the commencement of the rectum, on the right side; a second, about 3 cm. below the first; extends inward from the left side of the tube; a third, the largest and most constant, projects backward from the forepart of the rectum, opposite the fundus of the urinary bladder. When a fourth is present, it is situated nearly 2.5 cm. above the anus on the left and posterior wall of the tube. These folds are about 12 mm. in width, and contain some of the circular fibers of the gut. In the empty state of the intestine they overlap each other, as Houston remarks, so effectually as to require considerable maneuvering to conduct a bougie or the finger along the canal.

Their use seems to be, "to support the weight of fecal matter, and prevent its urging toward the anus, where its presence always excites a sensation demanding its discharge.[1]

The peritoneum is related to the upper two-thirds of the rectum, covering at first its front and sides, but lower down its front only; from the latter it is reflected on to the seminal vesicles in the male and the posterior vaginal wall in the female.

The level at which the peritoneum leaves the anterior wall of the rectum to be reflected on to the viscus in front of it is of considerable importance from a surgical point of view, in connection with the removal of the lower part of the rectum. It is higher in the male than in the female. In the former the height of the recto-vesical excavation is about 7.5 cm., *i. e.*, the height to which an ordinary index finger can reach from the anus. In the female the height of the rectouterine excavation is about 5.5 cm. from the anal orifice. The rectum is surrounded by a dense tube of fascia loosely attached to the rectal wall by areolar tissue in order to allow distension.

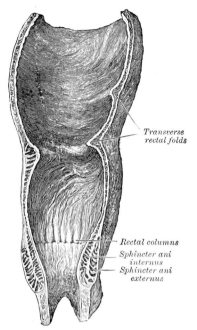

Transverse rectal folds

Rectal columns
Sphincter ani internus
Sphincter ani externus

Fig. 1065.—Coronal section of rectum and anal canal.

Relations of the Rectum.—The upper part of the rectum is in relation, *behind*, with the superior hemorrhoidal vessels, the left Piriformis, and left sacral plexus of nerves, which separate it from the pelvic surfaces of the sacral vertebræ; in its lower part it lies directly on the sacrum, coccyx, and Levatores ani, a dense fascia alone intervening; *in front*, it is separated above, in the male, from the fundus of the bladder; in the female, from the intestinal surface of the uterus and its appendages, by some convolutions of the small intestine, and frequently by the sigmoid colon; *below*, it is in relation in the male with the triangular portion of the fundus of the bladder, the vesiculæ seminales, and ductus deferentes, and more anteriorly with the posterior surface of the prostate; in the female, with the posterior wall of the vagina.

The **Anal Canal** (*pars analis recti*) (Figs. 1066, 1067, 1068), or terminal portion of the large intestine, begins at the level of the apex of the prostate, is directed downward and backward, and ends at the anus. It forms an angle with the lower part of the rectum, and measures from 2.5 to 4 cm. in length. It has no peritoneal covering, but is invested by the Sphincter ani internus, supported by the Levatores ani, and surrounded at its termination by the Sphincter ani externus. In the empty condition it presents the appearance of an antero-posterior longitudinal slit. Behind it is a mass of muscular and fibrous tissue, the **anococcygeal body** (Symington); in front of it, in the male, but separated by the perineal center from it, are the membranous portion and bulb of the urethra, and the fascia of the urogenital diaphragm; and in the female it is separated from the lower end of the vagina by a mass of muscular and fibrous tissue, named the **perineal body**.

The lumen of the anal canal presents, in its upper half, a number of vertical folds, produced by an infolding of the mucous membrane and some of the muscular tissue. They are known as the **rectal columns** [*Morgagni*] (Fig. 1070), and are

[1] Paterson ("The Form of the Rectum," Journal of Anatomy and Physiology, vol. **43**) utilizes the third fold for the purpose of dividing the rectum into an upper and a lower portion; he considers the latter "to be just as much a duct as the narrower anal canal below," and maintains that, under normal conditions, it does not contain feces except during the act of defecation.

separated from one another by furrows (**rectal sinuses**), which end below in small valve-like folds, termed **anal valves**, which join together the lower ends of the rectal columns.

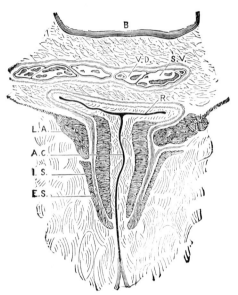

Fig. 1066.—Coronal section through the anal canal. (Symington.) *B.* Cavity of urinary bladder. *V.D.* Ductus deferens. *S.V.* Seminal vesicle. *R.* Second part of rectum. *A.C.* Anal canal. *L.A.* Levator ani. *I.S.* Sphincter ani internus. *E.S.* Sphincter ani externus.

Structure of the Colon.—The large intestine has four coats: **serous, muscular, areolar,** and **mucous.**

The **serous coat** (*tunica serosa*) is derived from the peritoneum, and invests the different portions of the large intestine to a variable extent. The cecum is completely covered by the serous membrane, except in about 5 per cent. of cases where the upper part of the posterior surface is uncovered. The ascending, descending, and iliac parts of the colon are usually covered only in front and at the sides; a variable amount of the posterior surface is uncovered. The transverse colon is almost completely invested, the parts corresponding to the attachment of the greater omentum and transverse mesocolon being alone excepted. The sigmoid colon is entirely surrounded.

The rectum is covered above on its anterior surface and sides; below, on its anterior aspect only; the anal canal is entirely devoid of any serous covering. In the course of the colon the peritoneal coat is thrown into a number of small projections filled with fat, called **appendices epiploicæ.** They are most numerous on the transverse colon.

The **muscular coat** (*tunica muscularis*) consists of an external longitudinal, and an internal circular, layer of non-striped muscular fibers.

The *longitudinal fibers* do not form a continuous layer over the whole surface of the large intestine. In the cecum and colon they are especially collected into three flat longitudinal bands (*tænæi coli*), each of about 12 mm. in width; one, the posterior, is placed along the attached border of the intestine; the anterior, the largest, corresponds along the arch of the colon to the

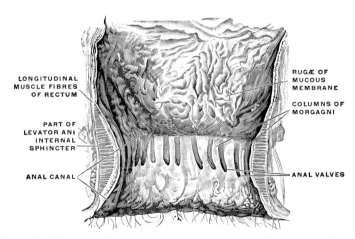

Fig. 1067.—The interior of the anal canal and lower part of the rectum, showing the columns of Morgagni and the anal valves between their lower ends. The columns were more numerous in the specimen than usual. (Cunningham.)

attachment of the greater omentum, but is in front in the ascending, descending, and iliac parts of the colon, and in the sigmoid colon; the third, or lateral band, is found on the medial side of the ascending and descending parts of the colon, and on the under aspect of the transverse colon. These bands are shorter than the other coats of the intestine, and serve to produce the *haustra* which are characteristic of the cecum and colon; accordingly, when they are dissected off, the tube can be lengthened, and its sacculated character disappears. In the sigmoid colon the longitudinal fibers become more scattered; and around the rectum they spread out and form

MUCOUS MEMBRANE

DILATATION OF VEINS

COLUMNS OF MORGAGNI

VALVE OF MORGAGNI

HILTON'S WHITE LINE

SKIN

MUSCULAR **WALL** OF RECTUM

INTERNAL HEMOR-RHOIDAL PLEXUS

DILATATION OF VEIN

COMMUNICATION BE-TWEEN INTERNAL AND EXTERNAL HEMOR-RHOIDAL PLEXUS

INTERNAL SPHINCTER

EXTERNAL SPHINCTER

LONGITUDINAL TENDINOUS FIBRES

SUBCUTANEOUS CELLULAR TISSUE

Fig. 1068.—Inner wall of the lower end of the rectum and anus. On the right the mucous membrane has been removed to show the dilatation of the veins and how they pass through the muscular wall to anastomose with the external hemorrhoidal plexus. (Luschka.)

a layer, which completely encircles this portion of the gut, but is thicker on the anterior and posterior surfaces, where it forms two bands, than on the lateral surfaces. In addition, two bands of plain muscular tissue arise from the second and third coccygeal vertebræ, and pass

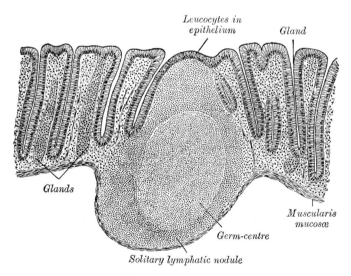

Leucocytes in epithelium

Gland

Glands

Germ-centre

Solitary lymphatic nodule

Muscularis mucosæ

Fig. 1069.—Section of mucous membrane of human rectum. (Sobotta.) × 60.

downward and forward to blend with the longitudinal muscular fibers on the posterior wall of the anal canal. These are known as the **Rectococcygeal muscles.**

The *circular fibers* form a thin layer over the cecum and colon, being especially accumulated in the intervals between the sacculi; in the rectum they form a thick layer, and in the anal canal they become numerous, and constitute the Sphincter ani internus.

The **areolar coat** (*tela submucosa; submucous coat*) connects the muscular and mucous layers closely together.

The **mucous membrane** (*tunica mucosa*) in the cecum and colon, is pale, smooth, destitute of villi, and raised into numerous crescentic folds which correspond to the intervals between the sacculi. In the rectum it is thicker, of a darker color, more vascular, and connected loosely to the muscular coat, as in the esophagus.

As in the small intestine, the mucous membrane (Fig. 1069) consists of a muscular layer, the muscularis mucosæ; a quantity of retiform tissue in which the vessels ramify; a basement membrane and epithelium which is of the columnar variety, and resembles the epithelium found in the small intestine. The mucous membrane of the large intestine presents for examination glands and solitary lymphatic nodules.

The glands of the large intestine are minute tubular prolongations of the mucous membrane arranged perpendicularly, side by side, over its entire surface; they are longer, more numerous, and placed in much closer apposition than those of the small intestine; and they open by minute rounded orifices upon the surface, giving it a cribriform appearance. Each gland is lined by short columnar epithelium and contains numerous goblet cells.

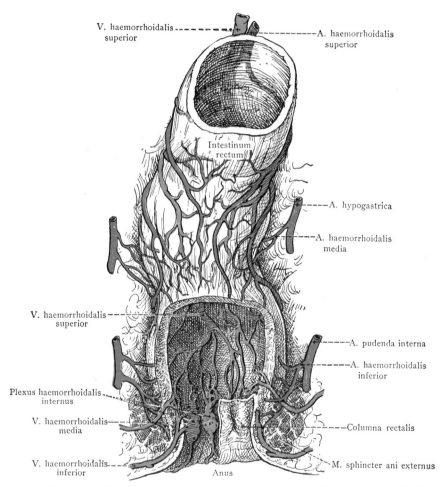

FIG. 1070.—The blood supply of the rectum. A portion of the anterior wall has been cut away to show the rectal columns and the internal hæmorrhoidal plexus. (Eycleshymer and Jones.)

The **solitary lymphatic nodules** (*noduli lymphatic solitarii*) (Fig. 1069) of the large intestine are most abundant in the cecum and vermiform process, but are irregularly scattered also over the rest of the intestine. They are similar to those of the small intestine.

Vessels and Nerves (Fig. 1070).—The **arteries** supplying the colon are derived from the colic and sigmoid branches of the mesenteric arteries. They give off large branches, which ramify between and supply the muscular coats, and after dividing into small vessels in the submucous tissue, pass to the mucous membrane. The rectum is supplied by the superior hemorrhoidal branch of the inferior mesenteric, and the anal canal by the middle hemorrhoidal from the hypogastric, and the inferior hemorrhoidal from the internal pudendal artery. The superior hemorrhoidal, the continuation of the inferior mesenteric, divides into two branches, which run down either side of the rectum to within about 12.5 cm. of the anus; they here split up into about six branches, which pierce the muscular coat and descend between it and the mucous membrane in a longitudinal direction, parallel with each other as far as the Sphincter ani internus, where they anastomose with the other hemorrhoidal arteries and form a series of loops around the anus. The **veins** of the rectum commence in a plexus of vessels which surrounds the anal canal. In the vessels forming this plexus are smaller saccular dilatations just within the margin of the anus; from the plexus about six vessels of considerable size are given off. These ascend between the muscular and mucous coats for about 12.5 cm., running parallel to each other; they then pierce the muscular coat (Fig. 1068), and unite to form a single trunk, the superior hemorrhoidal vein. This arrangement is termed the **hemorrhoidal plexus;** it communicates with the tributaries of the middle and inferior hemorrhoidal veins, at its commencement, and thus a communication is established between the systemic and portal circulations. The **lymphatics** of the large intestine are described on page 722. The **nerves** to that region of the colon supplied by the superior mesenteric artery are derived in the same manner as those for the small intestine; those to the more distal portions of the colon, and to the rectum, are derived from sympathetic and sacral parasympathetic fibers through the inferior mesenteric and hypogastric plexuses (see pages 1019, 1020). They are distributed in a similar way to those found in the small intestine.

The Liver (Hepar).

The **liver,** the largest gland in the body, is situated in the upper and right parts of the abdominal cavity, occupying almost the whole of the right hypochondrium, the greater part of the epigastrium, and not uncommonly extending into the left hypochondrium as far as the mammillary line. In the male it weighs from 1.4 to 1.6 kilogm., in the female from 1.2 to 1.4 kilogm. It is relatively much larger in the fetus than in the adult, constituting, in the former, about one-eighteenth, and in the latter about one thirty-sixth of the entire body weight. Its greatest transverse measurement is from 20 to 22.5 cm. Vertically, near its lateral or right surface, it measures about 15 to 17.5 cm., while its greatest antero-posterior diameter is on a level with the upper end of the right kidney, and is from 10 to 12.5 cm. Opposite the vertebral column its measurement from before backward is reduced to about 7.5 cm. Its consistence is that of a soft solid; it is friable, easily lacerated and highly vascular; its color is a dark reddish-brown, and its specific gravity is 1.05.

When hardened *in situ,* it presents the appearance of a wedge, the base of which is directed to the right and the thin edge toward the left. Symington describes its shape as that "of a right-angled triangular prism with the right angle rounded off."

The **superior surface** (*facies superior*) (Fig. 1071) comprises a part of both lobes, and, as a whole, is convex, and fits under the vault of the diaphragm which in front separates it on the right from the sixth to the tenth ribs and their cartilages, and on the left from the seventh and eighth costal cartilages. Its middle part lies behind the xiphoid process, and, in the angle between the diverging rib cartilage of opposite sides, is in contact with the abdominal wall. Behind this the diaphragm separates the liver from the lower part of the lungs and pleuræ, the heart and pericardium and the right costal arches from the seventh to the eleventh inclusive. It is completely covered by peritoneum except along the line of attachment of the falciform ligament.

The **inferior surface** (*facies inferior; visceral surface*) (Figs. 1072, 1073), is uneven, concave, directed downward, backward, and to the left, and is in relation with the stomach and duodenum, the right colic flexure, and the right kidney and suprarenal gland. The surface is almost completely invested by peritoneum; the only parts devoid of this covering are where the gall-bladder is attached to the liver, and at the porta hepatis where the two layers of the lesser omentum are separated from each other by the bloodvessels and ducts of the liver. The inferior surface of the left lobe presents behind and to the left the **gastric impression,** moulded over the antero-superior surface of the stomach, and to the right of this a rounded eminence, the **tuber omentale,** which fits into the concavity of the lesser curvature of the stomach and lies in front of the anterior layer of the lesser omentum. The under surface of the right lobe is divided into two unequal portions by the fossa for the gall-bladder; the portion to the left, the smaller of the two, is the **quadrate lobe,** and is in relation with the pyloric end of the stomach, the superior portion of the duodenum, and the transverse colon. The portion of the under surface of

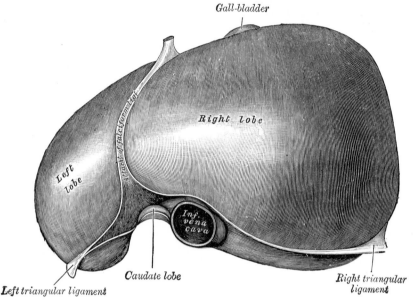

FIG. 1071.—The superior surface of the liver. (From model by His.)

the right lobe to the right of the fossa for the gall-bladder presents two impressions, one situated behind the other, and separated by a ridge. The anterior of these two impressions, the **colic impression,** is shallow and is produced by the right colic flexure; the posterior, the **renal impression,** is deeper and is occupied by the upper part of the right kidney and lower part of the right suprarenal gland. Medial to the renal impression is a third and slightly marked impression, lying between it and the neck of the gall-bladder. This is caused by the descending portion of the duodenum, and is known as the **duodenal impression.** Just in front of the inferior vena cava is a narrow strip of liver tissue, the **caudate process,** which connects the right inferior angle of the caudate lobe to the under surface of the right lobe. It forms the upper boundary of the epiploic foramen of the peritoneum.

The **posterior surface** (*facies posterior*) (Fig. 1073) is rounded and broad behind the right lobe, but narrow on the left. Over a large part of its extent it is not covered by peritoneum; this uncovered portion is about 7.5 cm. broad at its widest part, and is in direct contact with the diaphragm. It is marked off from the upper surface by the line of reflection of the upper layer of the coronary ligament, and from the under surface by the line of reflection of the lower layer of the coronary ligament. The central part of the posterior surface presents a deep concavity which is moulded on the vertebral column and crura of the diaphragm. To the right of this the inferior vena cava is lodged in its fossa between the uncovered area and the caudate lobe. Close to the right of this fossa and immediately above the renal impression is a small triangular depressed area, the **suprarenal impression,** the greater part of which is devoid of peritoneum; it lodges the right suprarenal gland. To the left of the inferior vena cava is the **caudate lobe,** which lies between the fossa for the vena cava and the fossa for the ductus venosus. Its lower end

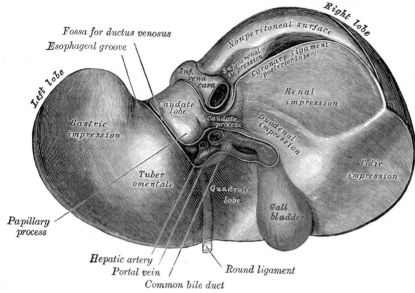

Fig. 1072.—Inferior surface of the liver. (From model by His.)

projects and forms part of the posterior boundary of the porta; on the right, it is connected with the under surface of the right lobe of the liver by the **caudate process,** and on the left it presents an elevation, the **papillary process.** Its posterior

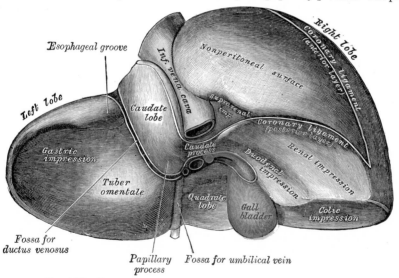

Fig. 1073.—Posterior and inferior surfaces of the liver. (From model by His.)

surface rests upon the diaphragm, being separated from it merely by the upper part of the omental bursa. To the left of the fossa for the ductus venosus is a groove in which lies the antrum cardiacum of the esophagus.

The **anterior border** (*margo anterior*) is thin and sharp, and marked opposite the attachment of the falciform ligament by a deep notch, the **umbilical notch,** and opposite the cartilage of the ninth rib by a second notch for the fundus of the gall-bladder. In adult males this border generally corresponds with the lower margin of the thorax in the right mammillary line; but in women and children it usually projects below the ribs. In the erect position it often extends below the interiliac line.

The **left extremity of the liver** is thin and flattened from above downward.

Fossæ.—The **left sagittal fossa** (*fossa sagittalis sinistra; longitudinal fissure*) is a deep groove, which extends from the notch on the anterior margin of the liver to the upper border of the posterior surface of the organ; it separates the right and left lobes. The porta joins it, at right angles, and divides it into two parts. The anterior part, or **fossa for the umbilical vein**, lodges the umbilical vein in the fetus, and its remains (the ligamentum teres) in the adult; it lies between the quadrate lobe and the left lobe of the liver, and is often partially bridged over by a prolongation of the hepatic substance, the **pons hepatis**. The posterior part, or **fossa for the ductus venosus**, lies between the left lobe and the caudate lobe; it lodges in the fetus, the ductus venosus, and in the adult a slender fibrous cord, the **ligamentum venosum**, the obliterated remains of that vessel.

The **porta or transverse fissure** (*porta hepatis*) is a short but deep fissure, about 5 cm. long, extending transversely across the under surface of the left portion of the right lobe, nearer its posterior surface than its anterior border. It joins nearly at right angles with the left sagittal fossa, and separates the quadrate lobe in front from the caudate lobe and process behind. It transmits the portal vein, the hepatic artery and nerves, and the hepatic duct and lymphatics. The hepatic duct lies in front and to the right, the hepatic artery to the left, and the portal vein behind and between the duct and artery.

The **fossa for the gall-bladder** (*fossa vesicæ felleæ*) is a shallow, oblong fossa, placed on the under surface of the right lobe, parallel with the left sagittal fossa. It extends from the anterior free margin of the liver, which is notched by it, to the right extremity of the porta.

The **fossa for the inferior vena cava** (*fossa venæ cavæ*) is a short deep depression, occasionally a complete canal in consequence of the substance of the liver surrounding the vena cava. It extends obliquely upward on the posterior surface between the caudate lobe and the bare area of the liver, and is separated from the porta by the caudate process. On slitting open the inferior vena cava the orifices of the hepatic veins will be seen opening into this vessel at its upper part, after perforating the floor of this fossa.

Lobes.—The **right lobe** (*lobus hepatis dexter*) is much larger than the left; the proportion between them being as six to one. It occupies the right hypochondrium, and is separated from the left lobe on its upper surface by the falciform ligament; on its under and posterior surfaces by the left sagittal fossa; and in front by the umbilical notch. It is of a somewhat quadrilateral form, its under and posterior surfaces being marked by three fossæ: the porta and the fossæ for the gall-bladder and inferior vena cava, which separate its left part into two smaller lobes; the **quadrate** and **caudate lobes.** The impressions on the right lobe have already been described.

The **quadrate lobe** (*lobus quadratus*) is situated on the under surface of the right lobe, bounded in front by the anterior margin of the liver; behind by the porta; on the right, by the fossa for the gall-bladder; and on the left, by the fossa for the umbilical vein. It is oblong in shape, its antero-posterior diameter being greater than its transverse.

The **caudate lobe** (*lobus caudatus; Spigelian lobe*) is situated upon the posterior surface of the right lobe of the liver, opposite the tenth and eleventh thoracic vertebræ. It is bounded, below, by the porta; on the right, by the fossa for the inferior vena cava; and, on the left, by the fossa for the ductus venosus. It looks backward, being nearly vertical in position; it is longer from above downward than from side to side, and is somewhat concave in the transverse direction. The **caudate process** is a small elevation of the hepatic substance extending obliquely lateralward, from the lower extremity of the caudate lobe to the under surface of the right lobe. It is situated behind the porta, and separates the fossa for the gall-bladder from the commencement of the fossa for the inferior vena cava.

The **left lobe** (*lobus hepatis sinister*) is smaller and more flattened than the right. It is situated in the epigastric and left hypochondriac regions. Its upper surface is slightly convex and is moulded on to the diaphragm; its under surface presents the gastric impression and omental tuberosity, already referred to on page 1234.

Ligaments.—The liver is connected to the under surface of the diaphragm and to the anterior wall of the abdomen by five ligaments; four of these—the **falciform**, the **coronary**, and the two **lateral**—are peritoneal folds; the fifth, the **round ligament**, is a fibrous cord, the obliterated umbilical vein. The liver is also attached to the lesser curvature of the stomach by the hepatogastric and to the duodenum by the hepatoduodenal ligament (see page 1202).

The **falciform ligament** (*ligamentum falciforme hepatis*) is a broad and thin antero-posterior peritoneal fold, falciform in shape, its base being directed downward and backward, its apex upward and backward. It is situated in an antero-posterior plane, but lies obliquely so that one surface faces forward and is in contact with the peritoneum behind the right Rectus and the diaphragm, while the other is directed backward and is in contact with the left lobe of the liver. It is attached by its left margin to the under surface of the diaphragm, and the posterior surface of the sheath of the right Rectus as low down as the umbilicus; by its right margin it extends from the notch on the anterior margin of the liver, as far back as the posterior surface. It is composed of two layers of peritoneum closely united together. Its base or free edge contains between its layers the round ligament and the parumbilical veins.

The **coronary ligament** (*ligamentum coronarium hepatis*) consists of an anterior and a posterior layer. The *anterior layer* is formed by the reflection of the peritoneum from the upper margin of the bare area of the liver to the under surface of the diaphragm, and is continuous with the right layer of the falciform ligament. The *posterior layer* is reflected from the lower margin of the bare area on to the right kidney and suprarenal gland, and is termed the **hepatorenal ligament.**

The **triangular ligaments** (*lateral ligaments*) are two in number, right and left. The **right triangular ligament** (*ligamentum triangulare dextrum*) is situated at the right extremity of the bare area, and is a small fold which passes to the diaphragm, being formed by the apposition of the anterior and posterior layers of the coronary ligament. The **left triangular ligament** (*ligamentum triangulare sinistrum*) is a fold of some considerable size, which connects the posterior part of the upper surface of the left lobe to the diaphragm; its anterior layer is continuous with the left layer of the falciform ligament.

The **round ligament** (*ligamentum teres hepatis*) is a fibrous cord resulting from the obliteration of the umbilical vein. It ascends from the umbilicus, in the free margin of the falciform ligament, to the umbilical notch of the liver, from which it may be traced in its proper fossa on the inferior surface of the liver to the porta, where it becomes continuous with the *ligamentum venosum.*

Fixation of the Liver.—Several factors contribute to maintain the liver in place. The attachments of the liver to the diaphragm by the coronary and tri-angular ligaments and the intervening connective tissue of the uncovered area, together with the intimate connection of the inferior vena cava by the connective tissue and hepatic veins would hold up the posterior part of the liver. The lax falciform ligament certainly gives no support though it probably limits lateral displacement.

The Functions of the Liver.—The functions of the liver are the excretion of bile, the internal excretion of urea, the formation of glycogen, and probably also of fibrinogen. Bile consists partly of waste products and partly of digestive secretions which aid in the absorbtion of fat. The bile pigments are derived from the hemoglobin of decrepit red blood cells which are taken up and digested by the macrophages, so abundantly distributed throughout the body, especially in the spleen, lymph nodes, liver (Kupffer cells), subcutaneous tissue, etc. The hemoglobin is converted by the macrophages into bilirubin and biliverdin. These substances are then taken up by the liver and excreted in the bile. Various other substances such as bile acids, lecithin and cholesterin are also excreted by the liver in the bile. *Urea* is apparently formed by the liver and given off into the blood. *Glycogen* is also formed by the liver cells from the carbohydrates and to a less extent from proteins brought to them by the blood, especially that in the portal vein. The glycogen is stored in the liver until needed by other tissues of the body. It is then converted into dextrose and secreted into the blood stream.

Development.—The liver arises in the form of a diverticulum or hollow outgrowth from the ventral surface of that portion of the gut which afterward becomes the descending part of the duodenum (Fig. 1074). This diverticulum is lined by entoderm, and grows upward and forward into the septum transversum, a mass of mesoderm between the vitelline duct and the pericardial cavity, and there gives off two solid buds of cells which represent the right and the left lobes of the liver.

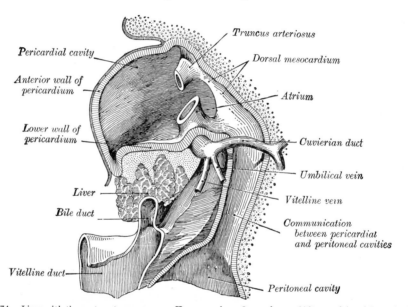

FIG. 1074.—Liver with the septum transversum. Human embryo 3 mm. long. (After model and figure by His.)

The solid buds of cells grow into columns or cylinders, termed the **hepatic cylinders,** which branch and anastomose to form a close meshwork. This network invades the vitelline and umbilical veins, and breaks up these vessels into a series of capillary-like vessels termed **sinusoids** (Minot), which ramify in the meshes of the cellular network and ultimately form the venous capillaries of the liver (see page 515). By the continued growth and ramification of the hepatic cylinders the mass of the liver is gradually formed. The original diverticulum from the duodenum forms the common bile-duct, and from this the cystic duct and gall-bladder arise as a solid outgrowth which later acquires a lumen. The opening of the common duct is at first in the ventral wall of the duodenum; later, owing to the rotation of the gut, the opening is carried to the left and then dorsalward to the position it occupies in the adult.

As the liver undergoes enlargement, both it and the ventral mesogastrium of the fore-gut are gradually differentiated from the septum transversum; and from the under surface of the latter the liver projects downward into the abdominal cavity. By the growth of the liver the ventral mesogastrium is divided into two parts, of which the anterior forms the falciform and coronary ligaments, and the posterior the lesser omentum. About the third month the liver almost fills the abdominal cavity, and its left lobe is nearly as large as its right. From this period the relative development of the liver is less active, more especially that of the left lobe, which actually undergoes some degeneration and becomes smaller than the right; but up to the end of fetal life the liver remains relatively larger than in the adult.

Vessels and Nerves.—The vessels connected with the liver are: the **hepatic artery,** the **portal vein,** and the **hepatic veins.**

The **hepatic artery** and **portal vein,** accompanied by numerous nerves, ascend to the porta, between the layers of the lesser omentum. The *bile duct* and the lymphatic vessels descend from the porta between the layers of the same omentum. The relative positions of the three structures are as follows: the bile duct lies to the right, the hepatic artery to the left, and the portal vein behind and between the other two. They are enveloped in a loose areolar tissue, the **fibrous capsule of Glisson,** which accompanies the vessels in their course through the portal canals in the interior of the organ (Fig. 1076).

The **hepatic veins** (Fig. 1075) convey the blood from the liver, and are described on page 688. They have very little cellular investment, and what there is binds their parietes closely to the walls of the canals through which they run; so that, on section of the organ, they remain widely open and are solitary, and may be easily distinguished from the branches of the portal vein, which are more or less collapsed, and always accompanied by an artery and duct.

The **lymphatic vessels** of the liver are described under the lymphatic system.

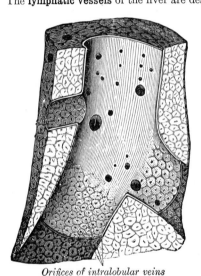

Orifices of intralobular veins

Fig. 1075.—Longitudinal section of a hepatic vein. (After Kiernan.)

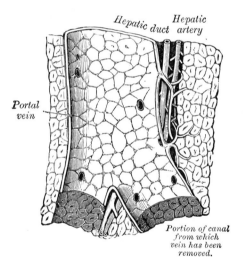

Portion of canal from which vein has been removed.

Fig. 1076.—Longitudinal section of a small portal vein and canal. (After Kiernan.)

The **nerves** of the liver, are derived from the right and left vagus and the celiac plexuses of the sympathetic. The fibers form plexuses along the hepatic artery and portal vein, enter the porta, and accompany the vessels and ducts to the interlobular spaces. The hepatic vessels are said to receive only sympathetic fibers; while both sympathetic and parasympathetic fibers are distributed to the walls of the bile ducts and gall bladder, where they form plexuses similar to the enteric plexuses of the intestinal wall.

Structure of the Liver.—The substance of the liver is composed of lobules, held together by an extremely fine areolar tissue, in which ramify the portal vein, hepatic ducts, hepatic artery, hepatic veins, lymphatics, and nerves; the whole being invested by a serous and a fibrous coat.

The **serous coat** (*tunica serosa*) is derived from the peritoneum, and invests the greater part of the surface of the organ. It is intimately adherent to the fibrous coat.

The **fibrous coat** (*capsula fibrosa* [*Glissoni*]; *areolar coat*) lies beneath the serous investment, and covers the entire surface of the organ. It is difficult of demonstration, excepting where the serous coat is deficient. At the porta it is continuous with the fibrous capsule of Glisson, and on the surface of the organ with the areolar tissue separating the lobules.

The **lobules** (*lobuli hepatis*) form the chief mass of the hepatic substance; they may be seen either on the surface of the organ, or by making a section through the gland, as small granular bodies, about the size of a millet-seed, measuring from 1 to 2.5 mm. in diameter. In the human subject their outlines are very irregular; but in some of the lower animals (for example, the pig) they are well-defined, and, when divided transversely, have polygonal outlines. The bases of the lobules are clustered around the smallest radicles (*sublobular*) of the hepatic veins, to which each is connected (Fig. 1075) by means of a small branch which issues from the center of the lobule (*intralobular*). The remaining part of the surface of each lobule is imperfectly isolated from the surrounding lobules by a thin stratum of areolar tissue, in which is contained a

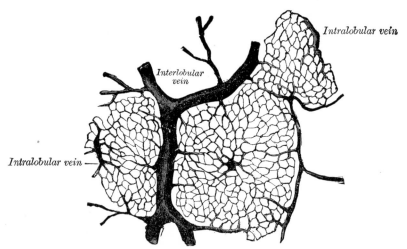

Fig. 1077.—Section of injected liver (dog).

plexus of vessels, the **interlobular plexus** (Fig. 1077), and ducts. In some animals, as the pig, the lobules are completely isolated from one another by the interlobular areolar tissue (Fig. 1078).

If one of the sublobular veins be laid open, the bases of the lobules may be seen through the thin wall of the vein on which they rest, arranged in a form resembling a tesselated pave-

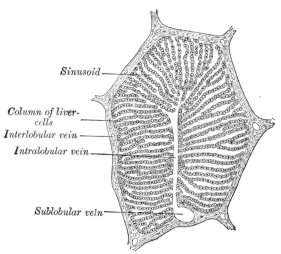

Fig. 1078.—A single lobule of the liver of a pig. × 60.

ment, the center of each polygonal space presenting a minute aperture, the mouth of an intralobular vein (Fig. 1076).

Microscopic Appearance (Fig. 1078).—Each lobule consists of a mass of cells, **hepatic cells,** arranged in irregular radiating columns between which are the blood channels (*sinusoids*).

Between the cells are also the minute bile capillaries. Therefore, in the lobule there are all the essentials of a secreting gland; that is to say: (1) **cells**, by which the secretion is formed; (2) **bloodvessels**, in close relation with the cells, containing the blood from which the secretion is derived; (3) **ducts**, by which the secretion, when formed, is carried away.

1. The *hepatic cells* are polyhedral in form. They vary in size from 12 to 25μ in diameter. They contain one or sometimes two distinct nuclei. The nucleus exhibits an intranuclear network and one or two refractile nucleoli. The cells usually contain granules; some of which are protoplasmic, while others consist of glycogen, fat, or an iron compound. In the lower vertebrates, *e. g.*, frog, the cells are arranged in tubes with the bile duct forming the lumen and bloodvessels externally. According to Delépine, evidences of this arrangement can be found in the human liver.

2. *The Bloodvessels.*—The blood in the capillary plexus around the liver cells is brought to the liver principally by the portal vein, but also to a certain extent by the hepatic artery.

The **hepatic artery**, entering the liver at the porta with the portal vein and hepatic duct, ramifies with these vessels through the portal canals. It gives off **vaginal branches**, which ramify in the fibrous capsule of Glisson, and appear to be destined chiefly for the nutrition of the coats of the vessels and ducts. It also gives off **capsular branches**, which reach the surface of the organ, ending in its fibrous coat in stellate plexuses. Finally, it gives off **interlobular branches**, which form a plexus outside each lobule, to supply the walls of the interlobular veins and the accompanying bile ducts. From these plexuses capillaries join directly with the sinusoids of the liver lobule at its periphery.

The **portal vein** also enters at the porta, and runs through the portal canals (Fig. 1079), enclosed in Glisson's capsule, dividing in its course into branches, which finally break up in the interlobular spaces, into the **interlobular plexus**, which give off portal venules, these divide into small branches and twigs as they pass to the surfaces of the lobules to join directly the hepatic sinusoids.

Hepatic sinusoids are large richly anastomosing modified capillary channels lying between the cords of liver cells. They traverse the liver lobule from its periphery to the intralobular or central vein. At the periphery of the lobule they connect with interlobular branches of the portal vein an hepatic artery. Thus all the blood which enters the liver passes through the sinusoids to the central veins. The sinusoids are lined by modified endothelium and contain many macrophages (v. Kupffer cells) attached to their walls.

Hepatic Veins.—At the center of the lobule, the sinusoids empty into one vein, of considerable size, which runs down the center of the lobule from apex to base, and is called the **intralobular** or **central vein**. At the base of the lobule this vein opens directly into the **sublobular vein**, with which the lobule is connected. The sublobular veins unite to form larger and larger trunks, and end at last in the hepatic veins, these converge to form three large trunks which open into the inferior vena cava while that vessel is situated in its fossa on the posterior surface of the liver.

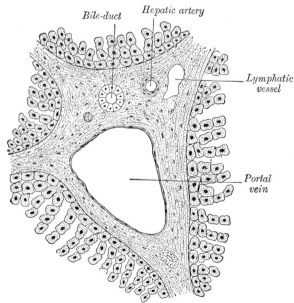

The **bile ducts** commence by little passages in the liver cells which communicate with canaliculi termed **intercellular biliary passages** (*bile capillaries*). These passages are merely little channels or spaces left between the contiguous surfaces of two cells, or in the angle where three or more liver cells meet (Fig. 1080), and they are

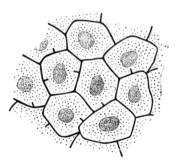

FIG. 1079.—Section across portal canal of pig. × 250.

FIG. 1080.—Bile capillaries of rabbit shown by Golgi's method. × 450.

always separated from the blood capillaries by at least half the width of a liver cell. The channels thus formed radiate to the circumference of the lobule, and open into the interlobular bile ducts which run in Glisson's capsule, accompanying the portal vein and hepatic artery. (Fig. 1079). These join with other ducts to form two main trunks, which leave the liver at the transverse fissure, and by their union form the **hepatic duct.**

3. *Structure of the Ducts.*—The walls of the biliary ducts consist of a connective-tissue coat, in which are muscle cells, arranged both circularly and longitudinally, and an epithelial layer, consisting of short columnar cells resting on a distinct basement membrane.

Excretory Apparatus of the Liver.—The excretory apparatus of the liver consists of (1) the **hepatic duct,** formed by the junction of the two main ducts, which pass out of the liver at the porta; (2) the **gall-bladder,** which serves as a reservoir for the bile; (3) the **cystic duct,** or the duct of the gall-bladder; and (4) the **common bile duct,** formed by the junction of the hepatic and cystic ducts.

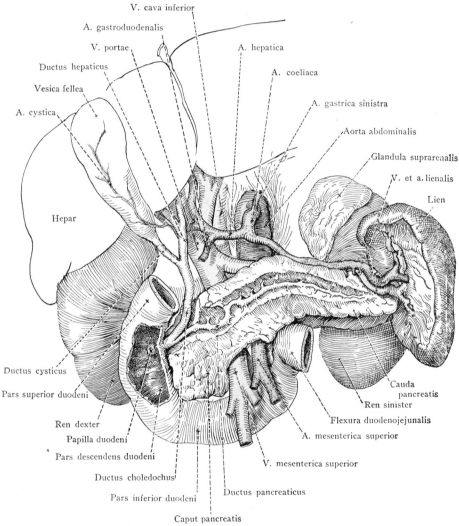

Fig. 1081.—The gall bladder, bile ducts, and neighboring structures. (Eycleshymer and Jones.)

The Hepatic Duct (*ductus hepaticus*) (Fig. 1081).—Two main trunks of nearly equal size issue from the liver at the porta, one from the right, the other from the left lobe; these unite to form the hepatic duct, which passes downward and to the right for about 4 cm., between the layers of the lesser omentum, where it is joined at an acute angle by the cystic duct, and so forms the common bile duct. The hepatic duct is accompanied by the hepatic artery and portal vein.

The **Gall-bladder** (*vesica fellea*) (Fig. 1082).—The gall-bladder is a conical or pear-shaped musculomembranous sac, lodged in a fossa on the under surface of the right lobe of the liver, and extending from near the right extremity of the porta to the anterior border of the organ. It is from 7 to 10 cm. in length, 2.5 cm. in breadth at its widest part, and holds from 30 to 35 c.c. It is divided into a fundus, body, and neck. The **fundus**, or broad extremity, is directed downward, forward, and to the right, and projects beyond the anterior border of the liver; the **body** and **neck** are directed upward and backward to the left. The upper surface of the gall-bladder is attached to the liver by connective tissue and vessels. The under surface is covered by peritoneum, which is reflected on to it from the surface of the liver. Occasionally the whole of the organ is invested by the serous membrane, and is then connected to the liver by a kind of mesentery.

Relations.—The **body** is in relation, by its upper surface, with the liver; by its under surface, with the commencement of the transverse colon; and farther back usually with the upper end of the descending portion of the duodenum, but sometimes with the superior portion of the duodenum or pyloric end of the stomach. The **fundus** is completely invested by peritoneum; it is in relation, in front, with the abdominal parietes, immediately below the ninth costal cartilage; behind with the transverse colon. The **neck** is narrow, and curves upon itself like the letter S; at its point of connection with the cystic duct it presents a well-marked constriction.

Structure (Fig. 1083).—The gall-bladder consists of three coats: **serous, fibromuscular,** and **mucous.**

The **external** or **serous coat** (*tunica serosa vesicæ felleæ*) is derived from the peritoneum; it completely invests the fundus, but covers the body and neck only on their under surfaces.

The **fibromuscular coat** (*tunica muscularis vesicæ felleæ*), a thin but strong layer forming the framework of the sac, consists of dense fibrous tissue, which interlaces in all directions, and is mixed with plain muscular fibers, disposed chiefly in a longitudinal direction, a few running transversely.

The **internal** or **mucous coat** (*tunica mucosa vesicæ felleæ*) is loosely connected with the fibrous layer. It is generally of a yellowish-brown color, and is elevated into minute rugæ. Opposite the neck of the gall-bladder the mucous membrane projects inward in the form of oblique ridges or folds, forming a sort of spiral valve.

The mucous membrane is continuous through the hepatic duct with the mucous membrane lining the ducts of the liver, and through the common bile duct with the mucous membrane of the duodenum. It is covered with columnar epithelium, and secretes mucin; in some animals it secretes a nucleoprotein instead of mucin.

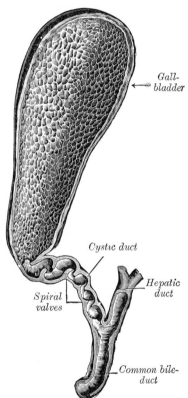

Fig. 1082.—The gall-bladder and bile ducts laid open. (Spalteholz.)

Vessels and Nerves.—The **arteries** to the gall bladder are derived from the cystic artery; its **veins** drain into liver capillaries and into the portal vein. The **lymphatics** are described under the lymphatic system. The **nerves** are described on page 1239.

The **Cystic Duct** (*ductus cysticus*).—The cystic duct about 4 cm. long, runs backward, downward, and to the left from the neck of the gall-bladder, and joins the hepatic duct to form the common bile duct. The mucous membrane lining its interior is thrown into a series of crescentic folds, from five to twelve in number, similar to those found in the neck of the gall-bladder. They project into the duct in regular succession, and are directed obliquely around the tube, presenting much the appearance of a continuous spiral valve. They constitute the "spiral valve of Heister," which are found only in primates and represent a device to prevent distension or collapse of the cystic duct with changing pressures in the gall bladder or common duct, associated with the assumption of an erect posture. When the duct is distended, the spaces between the folds are dilated, so as to give to its exterior a twisted appearance.

The **Common Bile Duct** (*ductus choledochus*) (Fig. 1082).—The common bile duct is formed by the junction of the cystic and hepatic ducts; it is about 7.5 cm. long, and of the diameter of a goose-quill.

It descends along the right border of the lesser omentum behind the superior portion of the duodenum, in front of the portal vein, and to the right of the hepatic artery; it then runs in a groove near the right border of the posterior surface of the head of the pancreas; here it is situated in front of the inferior vena cava, and is occasionally completely imbedded in the pancreatic substance. At its termination it lies for a short distance along the right side of the terminal part of the pancreatic duct and passes with it obliquely between the mucous and muscular coats. The two ducts unite and open by a common orifice upon the summit of the **duodenal papilla** (Fig. 1081), situated at the medial side of the descending portion of the duodenum, a little below its middle and about 7 to 10 cm. from the pylorus (Fig. 1086). The short tube formed by the union of the two ducts is dilated into an ampulla, the **ampulla of Vater**.

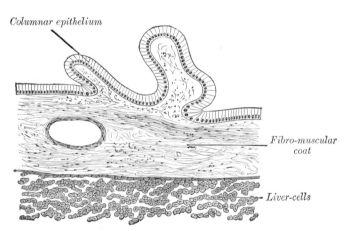

Fig. 1083.—Transverse section of gall-bladder.

Structure.—The coats of the large biliary ducts are an **external** or **fibrous,** and an **internal** or **mucous.** The **fibrous coat** is composed of strong fibroareolar tissue, with a certain amount of muscular tissue, arranged, for the most part, in a circular manner around the duct. The **mucous coat** is continuous with the lining membrane of the hepatic ducts and gall-bladder, and also with that of the duodenum; and, like the mucous membrane of these structures, its epithelium is of the columnar variety. It is provided with numerous mucous glands, which are lobulated and open by minute orifices scattered irregularly in the larger ducts.

The Pancreas (Fig. 1086).

The **pancreas** is a compound racemose gland, analogous in its structures to the salivary glands, though softer and less compactly arranged than those organs. Its secretion, the **pancreatic juice,** carried by the pancreatic duct to the duodenum, is an important digestive fluid. In addition the pancreas has an important internal secretion, elaborated by the cells of Langerhans, which is taken up by the blood stream and is concerned with sugar metabolism. It is long and irregularly prismatic in shape; its right extremity, being broad, is called the **head,** and is connected to the main portion of the organ, or **body**, by a slight constriction, the **neck**; while its left extremity gradually tapers to form the **tail**. It is situated transversely across the posterior wall of the abdomen, at the back of the epigastric and left hypochondriac regions. Its length varies from 12.5 to 15 cm.; its weight is in the female 84.88 to 14.95 grams. and in the male 90.41 to 16.08 grams.

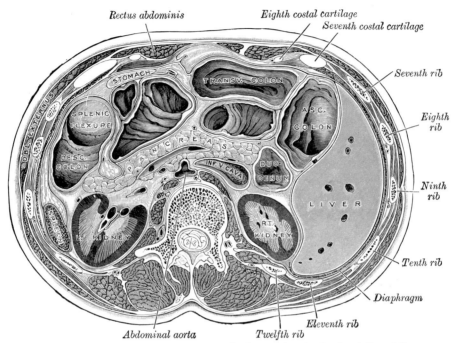

Fig. 1084.—Transverse section through the middle of the first lumbar vertebra, showing the relations of the pancreas (Braune.)

Relations.—The **Head** (*caput pancreatis*) is flattened from before backward, and is lodged within the curve of the duodenum. Its upper border is overlapped by the superior part of the duodenum and its lower overlaps the horizontal part; its right and left borders overlap in front of, and insinuate themselves behind, the descending and ascending parts of the duodenum respectively. The angle of junction of the lower and left lateral borders forms a prolongation, termed the **uncinate process**. In the groove between the duodenum and the right lateral and lower borders in front are the anastomosing superior and inferior pancreaticoduodenal arteries (Fig. 1049); the common bile duct descends behind, close to the right border, to its termination in the descending part of the duodenum.

Anterior Surface.—The greater part of the right half of this surface is in contact with the transverse colon, only areolar tissue intervening. From its upper part the **neck** springs, its right limit being marked by a groove for the gastroduodenal artery. The lower part of the right half, below the transverse colon, is covered by peritoneum continuous with the inferior layer of the transverse mesocolon, and is in contact with the coils of the small intestine. The superior mesenteric artery passes down in front of the left half across the uncinate process; the superior mesenteric vein runs upward on the right side of the artery and, behind the neck, joins with the lienal vein to form the portal vein (Fig. 1085).

Posterior Surface.—The posterior surface is in relation with the inferior vena cava, the common bile duct, the renal veins, the right crus of the diaphragm, and the aorta.

The **Neck** springs from the right upper portion of the front of the head. It is about 2.5 cm. long, and is directed at first upward and forward, and then upward and to the left to join the body; it is somewhat flattened from above downward and backward. Its antero-superior surface supports the pylorus; its postero-inferior surface is in relation with the commencement of the portal vein; on the right it is grooved by the gastroduodenal artery.

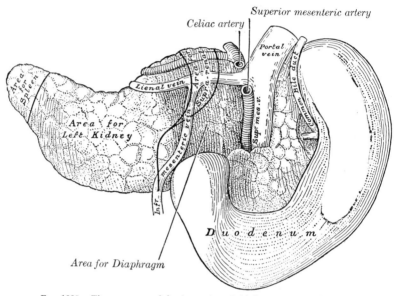

Fig. 1085.—The pancreas and duodenum from behind. (From model by His.)

The **Body** (*corpus pancreatis*) is somewhat prismatic in shape, and has three surfaces: anterior, posterior, and inferior.

The **anterior surface** (*facies anterior*) is somewhat concave; and is directed forward and upward: it is covered by the postero-inferior surface of the stomach which rests upon it, the two organs being separated by the omental bursa. Where it joins the neck there is a well-marked prominence, the **tuber omentale**, which abuts against the posterior surface of the lesser omentum.

The **posterior surface** (*facies posterior*) is devoid of peritoneum, and is in contact with the aorta, the lienal vein, the left kidney and its vessels, the left suprarenal gland, the origin of the superior mesenteric artery, and the crura of the diaphragm.

The **inferior surface** (*facies inferior*) is narrow on the right but broader on the left, and is covered by peritoneum; it lies upon the duodenojejunal flexure and on some coils of the jejunum; its left extremity rests on the left colic flexure.

The **superior border** (*margo superior*) is blunt and flat to the right; narrow and sharp to the left, near the tail. It commences on the right in the omental tuberosity, and is in relation with the celiac artery, from which the hepatic artery courses to the right just above the gland, while the lienal artery runs toward the left in a groove along this border.

The **anterior border** (*margo anterior*) separates the anterior from the inferior surface, and along this border the two layers of the transverse mesocolon diverge from one another; one passing upward over the anterior surface, the other backward over the inferior surface.

The **inferior border** (*margo inferior*) separates the posterior from the inferior surface; the superior mesenteric vessels emerge under its right extremity.

The **Tail** (*cauda pancreatis*) is narrow; it extends to the left as far as the lower part of the gastric surface of the spleen, lying in the phrenicolienal ligament, and it is in contact with the left colic flexure.

Birmingham described the body of the pancreas as projecting forward as a prominent ridge into the abdominal cavity and forming part of a shelf on which the stomach lies. "The portion of the pancreas to the left of the middle line has a very considerable antero-posterior thickness; as a result the anterior surface is of considerable extent; it looks strongly upward, and forms a large and important part of the shelf. As the pancreas extends to the left toward the spleen it crosses the upper part of the kidney, and is so moulded on to it that the top of the kidney forms an extension inward and backward of the upper surface of the pancreas and extends the bed in this direction. On the other hand, the extremity of the pancreas comes in contact with the spleen in such a way that the plane of its upper surface runs with little interruption upward and backward into the concave gastric surface of the spleen, which completes the bed behind and to the left, and, running upward, forms a partial cap for the wide end of the stomach.[1]

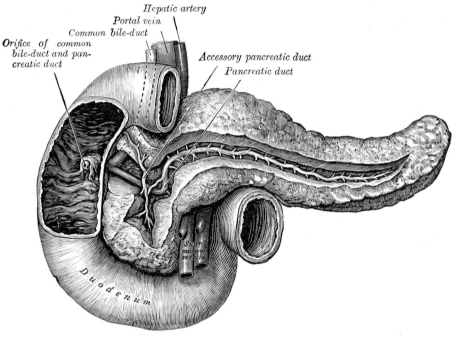

Fig. 1086.—The pancreatic duct.

The **Pancreatic Duct** (*ductus pancreaticus* [*Wirsungi*]; *duct of Wirsung*) extends transversely from left to right through the substance of the pancreas (Fig. 1086). It commences by the junction of the small ducts of the lobules situated in the tail of the pancreas, and, running from left to right through the body, it receives the ducts of the various lobules composing the gland. Considerably augmented in size, it reaches the neck, and turning downward, backward, and to the right, it comes into relation with the common bile duct, which lies to its right side; leaving the head of the gland, it passes very obliquely through the muscular and mucous coats of the duodenum, and ends by an orifice common to it and the common bile duct upon the summit of the duodenal papilla, situated at the medial side of the descending portion

[1] Journal of Anatomy and Physiology, pt. 1, vol. **31**, 102.

of the duodenum, 7.5 to 10 cm. below the pylorus. The pancreatic duct, near the duodenum, is about the size of an ordinary quill. Sometimes the pancreatic duct and the common bile duct open separately into the duodenum. Frequently there is an additional duct, which is given off from the pancreatic duct in the neck of the pancreas and opens into the duodenum about 2.5 cm. above the duodenal papilla. It receives the ducts from the lower part of the head, and is known as the **accessory pancreatic duct** (*duct of Santorini*).

Development (Figs. 1087, 1088).—The pancreas is developed in two parts, a dorsal and a ventral. The former arises as a diverticulum from the dorsal aspect of the duodenum a short distance above the hepatic diverticulum, and, growing upward and backward into the dorsal mesogastrium, forms a part of the head and uncinate process and the whole of the body and tail of the pancreas. The ventral

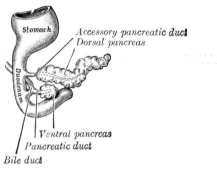

Fig. 1087.—Pancreas of a human embryo of five weeks. (Kollmann.)

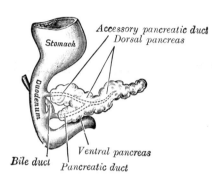

Fig. 1088.—Pancreas of a human embryo at end of sixth week. (Kollmann.)

part appears in the form of a diverticulum from the primitive bile-duct and forms the remainder of the head and uncinate process of the pancreas. The duct of the dorsal part (**accessory pancreatic duct**) therefore opens independently into the duodenum, while that of the ventral part (**pancreatic duct**) opens with the common bile-duct. About the sixth week the two parts of the pancreas meet and fuse and a communication is established between their ducts. After this has occurred the terminal part of the accessory duct, *i. e.*, the part between the duodenum and the point of meeting of the two ducts, undergoes little or no enlargement, while the pancreatic duct increases in size and forms the main duct of the gland. The opening of the accessory duct into the duodenum is sometimes obliterated, and even when it remains patent it is probable that the whole of the pancreatic secretion is conveyed through the pancreatic duct.

At first the pancreas is directed upward and backward between the two layers of the dorsal mesogastrium, which give to it a complete peritoneal investment, and its surfaces look to the right and left. With the change in the position of the stomach the dorsal mesogastrium is drawn downward and to the left, and the right side of the pancreas is directed backward and the left forward. The right surface becomes applied to the posterior abdominal wall, and the peritoneum which covered it undergoes absorption; and thus, in the adult, the gland appears to lie behind the peritoneal cavity.

Structure (Fig. 1089).—In structure, the pancreas resembles the salivary glands. It differs from them, however, in certain particulars, and is looser and softer in its texture. It is not enclosed in a distinct capsule, but is surrounded by areolar tissue, which dips into its interior and connects together the various lobules of which it is composed. Each lobule, like the lobules of the salivary glands, consists of one of the ultimate ramifications of the main duct, ending in a number of cecal pouches or alveoli, which are tubular and somewhat convoluted. The minute ducts connected with the alveoli are narrow and lined with flattened cells. The alveoli are almost completely filled with secreting cells, so that scarcely any lumen is visible. In some animals spindle-shaped cells occupy the center of the alveolus and are known as the **centro-acinar cells of Langerhans.** These are prolongations of the terminal ducts. The true secreting cells which line the wall of the alveolus are very characteristic. They are columnar in shape and present two zones: an outer one, clear and finely striated next the basement membrane, and an inner granular one next the lumen. In hardened specimens the outer zone stains deeply with various dyes, whereas the inner zone stains slightly. During activity the granular zone gradually diminishes in size, and when exhausted is only seen as a small area next to the lumen. During the resting stages it gradually increases until it forms nearly three-fourths of the cell. In some of the secreting cells of the pancreas is a spherical mass, staining more easily than the rest of the cell; this is termed the **paranucleus,** and is believed to be an extension from the nucleus. Between the alveoli are to be found small groups of cells which are termed **interalveolar cell islets** (*islands of Langerhans*). The cells of these stain lightly with hematoxylin or carmine, and are more or less polyhedral in shape, forming a net-work in which ramify many capillaries. There are two main types of cell in the islets, distinguished as A-cells

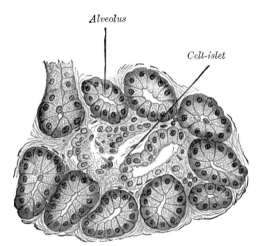

Alveolus

Cell-islet

Fig. 1089.—Section of pancreas of dog. × 250.

and B-cells according to the special staining reactions of the granules they contain. The cell islets produce the internal secretion (insulin) of the pancreas which is necessary for carbohydrate metabolism.

The walls of the pancreatic duct are thin, consisting of two coats, an external fibrous and an internal mucous; the latter is smooth, and furnished near its termination with a few scattered follicles.

Vessels and Nerves. — The **arteries** of the pancreas are derived from the lienal, and the pancreaticoduodenal branches of the hepatic and superior mesenteric. Its **veins** open into the lienal and superior mesenteric veins. Its **lymphatics** are described on page 723. Its **nerves** are filaments from the lienal plexus, representing cranial parasympathetics of the vagus and sympathetic fibers from the celiac plexus.

BIBLIOGRAPHY

DIGESTIVE SYSTEM

EMBRYOLOGY AND ABNORMALITIES

Anomalies of intestinal rotation; their embryology and surgical aspects. DOTT, N. M.: 1923. Brit. J. Surg., Vol. 11, pp. 251–286.

The early looping of the alimentary canal in the mammalian and human foetus and the mechanisms assumed to be active in this process. ENBOM, G.: 1939. Anat. Rec., Vol. 75, pp. 409–414.

Meckel's diverticulum. HARBIN, R. M.: 1930. Surg., Gyn. and Obs., Vol. 51, pp. 863–868.

The development of gut and its derivatives from the mesectoderm and mesentoderm of early chick blastoderms. HUNT, T. E.: 1937. Anat. Rec., Vol. 68, pp. 349–369.

The origin of entodermal cells from the primitive streak of the chick embryo. HUNT, T. E.: 1937. Anat. Rec., Vol. 68, pp 449-459.

The development of the gastro-intestinal tract of the rat. I and II. KAMMERAAD, A.: 1942.

J. Morph., Vol. 70, pp. 323–351 and J. Exp. Zool., Vol. 91, pp. 45–63.

Omphalocele. Anatomical and clinical considerations. SPECHT, N. W., and E. H. SHRYOCK: 1943. Surg., Gyn. and Obs., Vol. 77, pp. 319–325.

Partial inversion of the duodenum. VON BONIN, G.: 1944. Anat. Rec., Vol. 89, pp. 71–73.

MOUTH

The development of tooth germs in vitro. GLADSTONE, S.: 1935. J. Anat., Vol. 70, pp. 260–266.

Variation of the diastemata in the dentition of the anthropoid apes and its significance for the origin of man. MONTAGU, M. F. ASHLEY: 1943. Am. J. Phys. Anthrop., Vol. 1, pp. 325–353.

Pigment studies on the incisor teeth of vitamin E deficient rats of the Long-Evans strain. TELFORD, I. R.: 1946. Proc. Soc. Exp. Biol. & Med., Vol. 63, pp. 89–91.

PHARYNX AND ESOPHAGUS

A radiological study of deglutition. JOHNSTONE, A. S.: 1942. J. Anat., Vol. 77, pp. 97–100.

Afferent nerve endings in the ganglia of the intermuscular plexus of the dog's oesophagus. NONIDEZ, J. F.: 1946. J. Comp. Neur., Vol. 85, pp. 177–189.

The innervation of the pharynx in the rhesus monkey, and the formation of the pharyngeal plexus in primates. SPRAGUE, J. M.: 1944. Anat. Rec., Vol. 90, pp. 197–208.

STOMACH

The distribution of the chief or pepsin-forming cells in the gastric mucosa of the cat. BOWIE, D. J.: 1940. Anat. Rec., Vol. 78, pp. 9–17.

A note on the argentaffin cells of the gastric mucosa of the rat. DAWSON, A. B.: 1944. Anat. Rec., Vol. 89, pp. 287–294.

Sensory endings on gastric muscle. LANGWORTHY, O. R., and L. ORTEGA: 1943. J. Comp. Neur., Vol. 79, pp. 425–430.

A note on the relatively high number of argentaffin cells in the mucosa of the human stomach. SHARPLES, W.: 1945. Anat. Rec., Vol. 91, pp. 237–243.

SMALL INTESTINE

The arterial supply of the small intestine. BEATON, L. E., and B. J. ANSON: 1942. Quart. Bull., Northwestern U. Med. School, Vol. 16, pp. 114–122.

The position and mobility of the duodenum in the living subject. FRIEDMAN, S. M.: 1946. Am. J. Anat., Vol. 79, pp. 147–165.

The suspensory muscle of the duodenum. HALEY, J. C., and J. K. PEDEN: 1943. Am. J. Surg., Vol. 59, pp. 546–550.

The blood vessels of the jejunum and ileum: A comparative study of man and certain laboratory animals. NOER, R. J.: 1943. Am. J. Anat., Vol. 73, pp. 293–334.

On the mechanism of active absorption from the intestine. PETERS, H. C., and M. B. VISSCHER: 1939. J. Cell. & Comp. Physiol., Vol. 13, pp. 51–67.

The number of nerve cells in the myenteric and submucous plexuses of the small intestine of the cat. SAUER, M. E., and C. T. RUMBLE: 1946. Anat. Rec., Vol. 96, pp. 373–381.

CAECUM AND APPENDIX

Gross variations in the ileocecal valve. A study of the factors underlying incompetency. BUIRGE, R. E.: 1943. Anat. Rec., Vol. 86, pp. 373–385.

The arterial supply of the vermiform appendix. SHAH, M. A., and M. SHAH: 1946. Anat. Rec., Vol. 95, pp. 457–460.

LIVER

The basophilic bodies in hepatic cells. DEANE, H. W.: 1946. Am. J. Anat., Vol. 78, pp. 227–243.

On the origin of the cells lining the liver sinusoids in the cat and the rat. HAMMOND, W. S.: 1939. Am. J. Anat., Vol. 65, pp. 199–227.

An anatomical consideration of the structures in the hepatic pedicle. LANDER, H. H., R. Y. LYMAN, and B. J. ANSON: 1941. Quart. Bull., Northwestern U. Med. School, Vol. 15, pp. 103–109.

Effect of muscular exercise on the fat content of the liver. SELYE. H.: 1939. Anat. Rec., Vol. 73, pp. 391–400.

A study of the nucleus in the normal and hyperplastic liver of the rat. SULKIN, N. M.: 1943. Am. J. Anat., Vol. 73, pp. 107–125.

The intrahepatic circulation of blood. (Quartz-rod transillumination). WAKIM, K. G., and F. C. MANN: 1942. Anat. Rec., Vol. 82, pp. 233–253.

A morphological and experimental study of the intranuclear crystals in the hepatic cells of the dog. WEATHERFORD, H. L.: 1938. Anat. Rec., Vol. 71, pp. 413–446.

BILE DUCTS AND GALL BLADDER

The innervation of the biliary system. ALEXANDER, W. F.: 1940. J. Comp. Neur., Vol. 72, pp. 357–370.

Congenital variations of the extrahepatic biliary tract. Boyden, E. A.: 1944. Minnesota Med., Vol. 27, pp. 932–933.

A study of certain cells observed in the gall-bladder mucosa of cats. Dawson, H. L.: 1943. Anat. Rec., Vol. 85, pp. 135–155.

A simian, deeply cleft, bilobed gall-bladder with a "phrygian cap". Kirkman, H.: 1946. Anat. Rec., Vol. 95, pp. 423–447.

An acidophil lining in bile capillaries. Morton, T. H.: 1939. Anat. Rec., Vol. 73, pp. 359–371.

The blood supply and innervation of the choledochoduodenal junction in the cat. Schulze, J. W., and E. A. Boyden: 1943. Anat. Rec., Vol. 86, pp. 15–39.

Pancreas

Histological observations upon an adult human pancreas (autofluorescence, fat and pigment). Grafflin, A. L.: 1940. Anat. Rec., Vol. 78, pp. 207–214.

The arterial blood supply of the pancreas. Pierson, J. M.: 1943. Surg., Gyn. & Obs., Vol. 77, pp. 426–432.

The innervation of the pancreas. Richins, C. A.: 1945. J. Comp. Neur., Vol. 83, pp. 223–236.

The pancreas of snakes. Thomas, T. B.: 1942. Anat. Rec., Vol. 82, pp. 327–345.

Pancreatic Islets

Studies on the cells of the pancreatic islets. Gomori, G.: 1939. Anat. Rec., Vol. 74, pp. 439–459.

The origin and differentiation of the alpha and beta cells in the pancreatic islets of the rat. Hard, W. L.: 1944. Am. J. Anat., Vol. 75, pp. 369–403.

Studies on the amphibian digestive system. III. The origin and development of pancreatic islands in certain species of anura. Janes, R. G.: 1938. J. Morph., Vol. 62, pp. 375–391.

Changes in the islets of Langerhans of the albino rat induced by insulin administration. Latta, J. S., and H. T. Harvey: 1942. Anat. Rec., Vol. 82, pp. 281–295.

Peritoneum

Reaction of the rat peritoneum to acid colloidal pigments. Baillif, R. N.: 1946. Proc. Soc. Exp. Biol. & Med., Vol. 62, pp. 264–269.

Structure of the intestinal peritoneum in man. Baron, M. A.: 1941. Am. J. Anat., Vol. 69, pp. 439–495.

The Anatomy of the Human Peritoneum and Abdominal Cavity. Huntington, G. S.: 1903. Lea Brothers & Co., Phila., vii & 292 pp.

Peritoneal Fossae and Retroperitoneal Hernia

Mechanism, symptoms and treatment of hernia into descending mesocolon (left duodenal hernia); plea for change in nomenclature. Callander, C. L., G. Y. Rusk, and A. Nemir: 1935. Surg., Gyn. & Obs., Vol. 60, pp. 1052–1071.

Intra-abdominal hernia. Hansmann, G. H., and S. A. Morton: 1939. Arch. Surg., Vol. 39, pp. 973–986.

On retro-peritoneal hernia with report on literature. Short, A. R.: 1925. Brit. J. Surg., Vol. 12, pp. 456–465.

A case of right duodenal hernia. Gushue-Taylor, G., and R. Hayward: 1942. Anat. Rec., Vol. 83, pp. 389–399.

Intra-abdominal hernia—Review of 39 cases in which treatment was surgical. Mayo, C. W., L. K. Stalker, and J. M. Miller: 1941. Ann. Surg., Vol. 114; pp.875—885.

A Mesenteric pouch hernia simulating paraduodenal hernia. McCarty, R. B., and A. J, Present: 1944. Surg., Gyn. and Obs., Vol. 78, pp. 643—648.

THE UROGENITAL SYSTEM.

(APPARATUS UROGENITALIS; UROGENITAL ORGANS).

THE urogenital apparatus consists of (*a*) the **urinary organs** for the formation and discharge of the urine, and (*b*) the **genital organs**, which are concerned with the process of reproduction.

DEVELOPMENT OF THE URINARY AND GENERATIVE ORGANS.

The urogenital glands and ducts are developed from the intermediate cell-mass which is situated between the primitive segments and the lateral plates of mesoderm. The permanent organs of the adult are preceded by structures which,

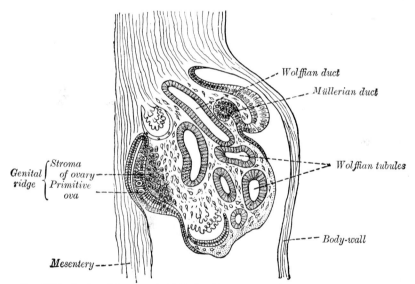

Fig. 1090.—Section of the urogenital fold of a chick embryo of the fourth day. (Waldeyer.)

with the exception of the ducts, disappear almost entirely before the end of fetal life. These paired structures are: the **pronephros**, the **mesonephros**, and the **Wolffian** and **Müllerian ducts**. The pronephros disappears very early. The structural elements of the mesonephros almost entirely degenerate, but in their place the genital gland develops. The Wolffian duct remains as the duct of the male genital gland, the Müllerian as that of the female. The final kidney is a new organ, the metanephros.

The Pronephros and Wolffian Duct.—In the outer part of the intermediate cell-mass, immediately under the ectoderm, in the region from the fifth cervical to the third thoracic segments, a series of short evaginations from each segment grows dorso-laterally and caudally, fusing successively from before backward to form the **pronephric duct**. This continues to grow caudally until it opens into the ventral part of the cloaca; beyond the pronephros it is termed the **Wolffian duct**.

The original evaginations form a series of transverse tubules each of which communicates by means of a funnel-shaped ciliated opening with the celomic cavity,

(1253)

and in the course of each duct a glomerulus also is developed. A secondary glomerulus is formed ventral to each of these, and the complete group constitutes the **pronephros**. The pronephros undergoes rapid atrophy and disappears in 4 mm. embryos except for the pronephric ducts which persist as the excretory ducts of the succeeding kidneys, the mesonephroi.

The Mesonephros, Müllerian Duct, and Genital Gland.—On the medial side of the Wolffian duct, from the sixth cervical to the third lumbar segments, a series of tubules, the **Wolffian tubules** (Fig. 1090), is developed; at a later stage in development they increase in number by outgrowths from the original tubules. These tubules first appear as solid masses of cells, which later develop lumena; one end grows toward and finally opens into the Wolffian duct, the other dilates and is invaginated by a tuft of capillary bloodvessels to form a glomerulus. The tubules collectively constitute the **mesonephros** or **Wolffian body** (Figs. 980, 1091). By the fifth or sixth week this body forms an elongated spindle-shaped structure, termed

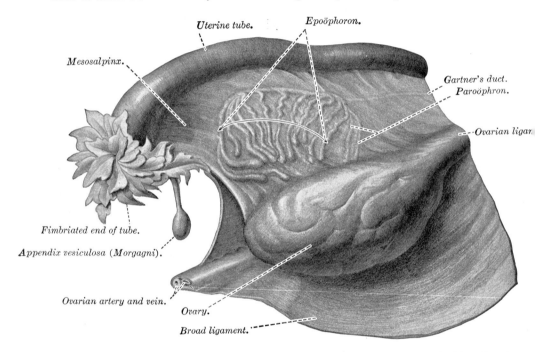

FIG. 1091.—Broad ligament of adult, showing remains of the Wolffian body and duct. (Modified from Farre.)

the **urogenital fold** (Fig. 1090), which projects into the celomic cavity at the side of the dorsal mesentery, reaching from the septum transversum in front to the fifth lumbar segment behind. The reproductive glands develop in the urogenital folds. The Wolffian bodies are the permanent kidneys in fishes and amphibians, but in reptiles, birds, and mammals, they atrophy and for the most part disappear coincidentally with the development of the permanent kidneys. The atrophy begins during the sixth or seventh week and rapidly proceeds, so that by the beginning of the fourth month only the ducts and a few of the tubules remain.

In the male the Wolffian duct persists, and forms the epididymis, the ductus deferens and the ejaculatory duct, while the seminal vesicle arises during the third month as a lateral diverticulum from its caudal end. A large part of the cephalic portion of the mesonephros atrophies and disappears, but a few tubules may persist as the appendix of the epididymis vestigial structures which end blindly. From the remainder of the anterior tubules the efferent ducts of the testis form.

The posterior tubules are represented by the ductuli aberrantes, and by the paradidymis (Fig. 1092, *C*).

In the female the Wolffian bodies and ducts atrophy. The remains of the Wolffian tubules may be roughly divided into three groups. One group of tubules from the cranial portion of the mesonephros or Wolffian body persists and produces one or more **vesicular appendices** in the fringes of the uterine tube. The middle and largest group, together with a segment of the mesonephric (Wolffian) duct persist as the **epoöphoron** or **organ of Rosenmüller**. Persistent portions of the Wolffian duct are known as **Gartner's ducts**. These may exist as part of the epoöphoron or as isolated segments as far as the hymen. The third and most caudal group of remaining mesonephric ducts constitutes the paroöphoron, which usually disappears completely before the adult stage. Any one of these vestigial tubules which persists in the adult as a stalked vesicle is called an hydatid (Fig. 1092, *B*).

The Müllerian Ducts.—Shortly after the formation of the Wolffian ducts a second pair of ducts is developed; these are named the **Müllerian ducts**. Each arises on the lateral aspect of the corresponding Wolffian duct as a tubular invagination of the cells lining the celom (Fig. 1090). The orifice of the invagination remains patent, and undergoes enlargement and modification to form the abdominal ostium of the uterine tube. The ducts pass backward lateral to the Wolffian ducts, but toward the posterior end of the embryo they cross to the medial side of these ducts, and thus come to lie side by side between and behind the latter—the four ducts forming what is termed the **genital cord** (Fig. 1093). The Müllerian ducts end in an epithelial elevation, the **Müllerian eminence**, on the ventral part of the cloaca between the orifices of the Wolffian ducts; at a later date they open into the cloaca in this situation.

In the male the Müllerian ducts atrophy, but traces of their cephalic ends are represented by the **appendices testis** (*hydatids of Morgagni*), while their caudal portions fuse to form the utriculus in the floor of the prostatic portion of the urethra (Fig. 1092, *C*).

In the female the Müllerian ducts persist and undergo further development. The portions which lie in the genital core fuse to form the uterus and vagina; the parts in front of this cord remain separate, and each forms the corresponding uterine tube—the abdominal ostium of which is developed from the anterior extremity of the original tubular invagination from the celom (Fig. 1092 *B*,). The fusion of the Müllerian ducts begins in the third month, and the septum formed by their fused medial walls disappears from below upward. Entodermal epithelium of the urogenital sinus invades the region where the vagina forms, replacing the Müllerian epithelium almost entirely, and for a time the vagina is represented by a solid rod of epithelial cells, but in fetuses of five months the lumen reappears. About the fifth month an annular constriction marks the position of the neck of the uterus, and after the sixth month the walls of the uterus begin to thicken. A ring-like outgrowth of epithelium occurs at the lower end of the uterus and marks the future vaginal fornices. The hymen arises at the site of the Müllerian eminence. It represents the separation between vagina and urogenital sinus.

Genital Glands.—The first appearance of the genital gland is essentially the same in the two sexes, and consists in a thickening of the epithelial layer which lines the peritoneal cavity on the medial side of the urogenital fold (Fig. 1090). The thick plate of epithelium pushes the mesoderm before it and forms a distinct projection. This is termed the **genital ridge** (Fig. 1090), and from it the testis in the male and the ovary in the female are developed. At first the mesonephros and genital ridge are suspended by a common mesentery, but as the embryo grows the genital ridge gradually becomes pinched off from the mesonephros, with which it is at first continuous, though it still remains connected to the remnant of this body by a fold of peritoneum, the **mesorchium** or **mesovarium** (Fig.

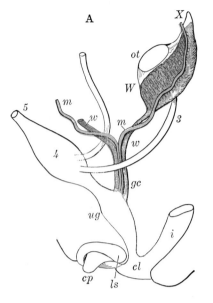

Fig. 1092.—Diagrams to show the development of male and female generative organs from a common type. (Allen Thomson.)

A.—Diagram of the primitive urogenital organs in the embryo previous to sexual distinction. 3. Ureter. 4. Urinary bladder. 5. Urachus. *cl*. Cloaca. *cp*. Elevation which becomes clitoris or penis. *i*. Lower part of the intestine. *ls*. Fold of integument from which the labia majora or scrotum are formed. *m, m*. Right and left Müllerian ducts uniting together and running with the Wolffian ducts in *gc*, the genital cord. *ot*. The genital ridge from which either the ovary or testis is formed. *ug*. Sinus urogenitalis. *W*. Left Wolffian body. *w, w*. Right and left Wolffian ducts.

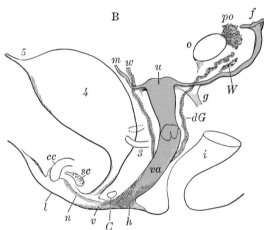

B.—Diagram of the female type of sexual organs. *C*. Greater vestibular gland, and immediately above it the urethra. *cc*. Corpus cavernosum clitoridis. *dG*. Remains of the left Wolffian duct, such as give rise to the duct of Gärtner, represented by dotted lines; that of the right side is marked *w*. *f*. The abdominal opening of the left uterine tube. *g*. Round ligament, corresponding to gubernaculum. *h*. Situation of the hymen. *i*. Lower part of the intestine. *l*. Labium major. *n*. Labium minus. *o*. The left ovary. *po*. Epoöphoron. *sc*. Corpus cavernosum urethrae. *u*. Uterus. The uterine tube of the right side is marked *m*. *v*. Vulva. *va*. Vagina. *W*. Scattered remains of Wolffian tubes near it (paraoöphoron of Waldeyer).

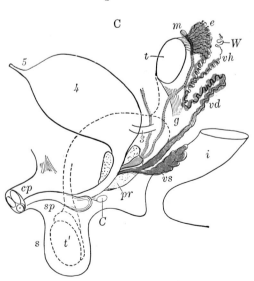

C.—Diagram of the male type of sexual organs. *C*. Bulbo-urethral gland of one side. *cp*. Corpora cavernosa penis cut short. *e*. Caput epididymis. *g*. The gubernaculum. *i*. Lower part of the intestine. *m*. Müllerian duct, the upper part of which remains as the hydatid of Morgagni; the lower part, represented by a dotted line descending to the prostatic utricle, constitutes the occasionally existing cornu and tube of the uterus masculinus. *pr*. The prostate. *s*. Scrotum. *sp*. Corpus cavernosum urethrae. *t*. Testis in the place of its original formation. *t'*, together with the dotted lines above, indicates the direction in which the testis and epididymis descend from the abdomen into the scrotum. *vd*. Ductus deferens. *vh*. Ductus aberrans. *vs*. The vesicula seminalis. *W*. Scattered remains of the Wolffian body, constituting the organ of Giraldès, or the paradidymis of Waldeyer.

1094). About the seventh week the distinction of sex in the genital ridge begins to be perceptible.

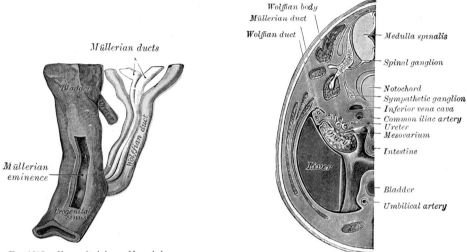

FIG. 1093.—Urogenital sinus of female human embryo eight and a half to nine weeks old. (From model by Keibel.)

FIG. 1094.—Transverse section of human embryo eight and a half to nine weeks old. (From model by Keibel.)

The Ovary.—The ovary, thus formed from the genital ridge, is at first a mass of cells derived from the celomic epithelium; later the mass is differentiated into a central part or medulla (Fig. 1095) covered by a surface layer, the **germinal**

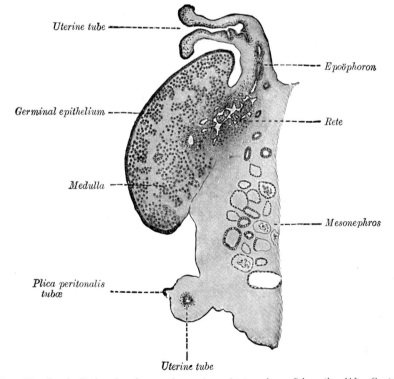

FIG. 1095.—Longitudinal section of ovary of cat embryo of 9.4 cm. long. Schematic. (After Cœrt.)

epithelium. Between the cells of the germinal epithelium a number of larger cells, the **primitive ova,** are found. These are carried into the subjacent stroma by bud-like ingrowths (**genital cords**) of the germinal epithelium (Fig. 1096). The surface epithelium ultimately forms the permanent epithelial covering of this Organ; it soon loses its connection with the central mass, and a tunica albuginea oevelops between them. The ova are chiefly derived from the cells of the central mass; these are separated from one another by the growth of connective tissue in an irregular manner; each ovum acquires a covering of connective tissue (follicle) cells, and in this way the rudiments of the ovarian follicles are formed.

Primordial germ cells are according to some authors set aside at a very early age from the somatic cells. They are first recognized in the yolk sac. Later they migrate through the mesentery into the primitive germinal epithelium to be carried into the gonad with the sex cords and later develop either into ova or sperm cells. Some authors deny their existence while others claim they all degenerate and take no part in formation of the adult sex cells.

The Testis.—The testis is developed in much the same way as the ovary. Like the ovary, in its earliest stages it consists of a central mass of epithelium covered by a surface epithelium. In the central mass a series of cords appear (Fig. 1097), and the periphery of the mass is converted into the tunica albuginea, thus excluding the surface epithelium from any part in the formation of the tissue of the testis. The cords of the central mass run together toward the future hilum and form a net-work which ultimately becomes the rete testis. From the cords the seminiferous tubules are developed, and between them connective tissue septa extend. The seminiferous tubules become connected with outgrowths from the Wolffian body, which, as before mentioned, form the efferent ducts of the testis.

Descent of the Testes.—The testes, at an early period of fetal life, are placed at the back part of the abdominal cavity, behind the peritoneum, and each is attached by a peritoneal fold, the **mesorchium**, to the mesonephros. From the front of the mesonephros a fold of peritoneum termed the **inguinal fold** grows forward to meet and fuse with a peritoneal fold, the **inguinal crest**, which grows backward from the anterolateral abdominal wall. The testis thus acquires an indirect connection with the anterior abdominal wall; and at the same time a portion of the peritoneal cavity lateral to these fused folds is marked off as the future saccus vagi-

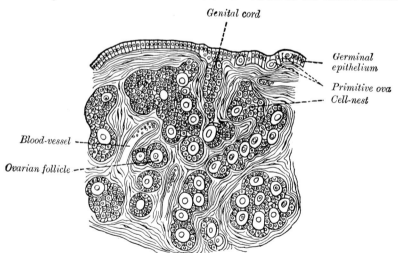

Fig. 1096.—Section of the ovary of a newly born child. (Waldeyer.)

nalis. In the inguinal crest a peculiar structure, the **gubernaculum testis**, makes its appearance. This is at first a slender band, extending from that part of the skin of the groin which afterward forms the scrotum through the inguinal canal to the body and epididymis of the testis. As development advances, the peritoneum enclosing the gubernaculum forms two folds, one above the testis and the other below it. The one above the testis is the **plica vascularis,** and contains ultimately the internal spermatic vessels; the one below, the **plica gubernatrix,** contains the lower part of the gubernaculum, which has now grown into a thick cord; it ends below at the abdominal inguinal ring in a tube of peritoneum, the **saccus vaginalis,** which protrudes itself down the inguinal canal. By the fifth month the lower part of the gubernaculum has become a thick cord, while the upper part has disappeared. The lower part now consists of a central core of unstriped muscle fiber, and outside this of a firm layer of striped elements, connected, behind the peritoneum, with the abdominal wall. The main portion of the gubernaculum is attached to the skin at the point where the scrotum develops and as the pouch forms most of the lower end of the gubernaculum is carried with it; other bands extend to the medial side of the thigh and to the perineum. The tube of peritoneum constituting the saccus vaginalis projects itself downward into the inguinal canal, and emerges at the subcutaneous inguinal ring, pushing

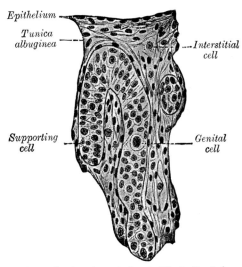

Fig. 1097.—Section of a genital cord of the testis of a human embryo 3.5 cm. long. (Felix and Bühler.)

before it a part of the Obliquus internus and the fascia of the Obliquus externus, which form respectively the Cremaster muscle and the intercrural fascia. It forms a gradually elongating pouch, which eventually reaches the bottom of the scrotum, and behind this pouch the testis descends. Since the growth of the gubernaculum is not commensurate with the growth of the body of the fetus, the latter increasing more rapidly in relative length, it has been assumed that this prevents cephalad

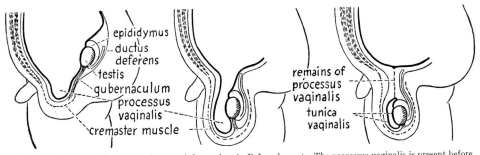

Fig. 1098.—Diagram illustrating descent of the testis: *A.* Before descent. The processus vaginalis is present before descent begins, the testis lying behind the peritoneum. *B.* Descent nearly complete but processsus vaginalis not obliterated. *C.* Processus vaginalis obliterated except for the terminal portion, which persists as the tunica vaginalis of the adult.

displacement of the testis. In addition the gubernaculum may actually shorten, in which case it might exert traction on the testis and tend to displace it toward the scrotum. Occasionally the testis fails to descend or the descent is incomplete, a condition known as cryptorchidism. In such cases administration of an extract of the pituitary gland may cause the testis to occupy its normal position. This would seem to indicate that the descent may to some extent be under hormonal control. By the end of the eighth month the testis has reached the scrotum, preceded by the saccus vaginalis, which communicates by its upper extremity with the peritoneal cavity. Just before birth the upper part of the saccus vaginalis normally becomes closed, and this obliteration extends gradually downward to within a short distance of the testis. The process of peritoneum surrounding the testis is now entirely cut off from the general peritoneal cavity and constitutes the tunica vaginalis.

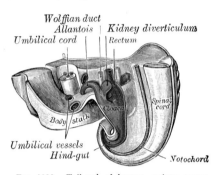

FIG. 1099.—Tail end of human embryo twenty-five to twenty-nine days old. (From model by Keibel.)

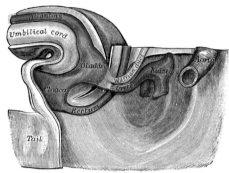

FIG. 1100.—Tail end of human embryo thirty-two to thirty-three days old. (From model by Keibel.)

Descent of the Ovaries.—In the female there is also a gubernaculum, which effects a considerable change in the position of the ovary, though not so extensive a change as in that of the testis. The gubernaculum in the female lies in contact with the fundus of the uterus and acquires adhesions to this organ, thus the ovary is prevented from descending below this level. The part of the gubernaculum between the ovary and the uterus becomes ultimately the proper ligament of the ovary, while the part between the uterus and the labium majus forms the round ligament of the uterus. A pouch of peritoneum analogous to the saccus vaginalis in the male accompanies it along the inguinal canal: it is called the **canal of Nuck**. In rare cases the gubernaculum may fail to develop adhesions to the uterus, and then the ovary descends through the inguinal canal into the labium majus, and under these circumstances its position resembles that of the testis.

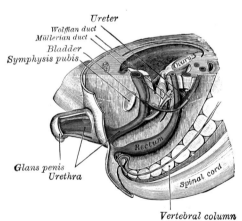

FIG. 1101.—Tail end of human embryo; from eight and a half to nine weeks old. (From model by Keibel.)

The Metanephros and the Permanent Kidney.—The rudiments of the permanent kidneys make their appearance about the end of the first or the beginning of the second month. Each kidney has a two-fold origin, part arising from the metanephros, and part as a diverticulum from the hind-end of the Wolffian duct, close to where the latter opens into the cloaca (Figs. 1099, 1100). The metanephros arises in the intermediate cell mass, caudal to the mesonephros, which it resembles in structure. The diverticulum from the Wolffian duct grows dorsally and cephalad along the posterior abdominal wall, where its blind extremity expands and subsequently divides into several buds, which form the rudiments of the pelvis and calyces of the kidney; by continued growth and subdivision it gives rise to the collecting tubules of the kidney. The proximal portion of the diverticulum becomes the ureter. The secretory tubules are developed from the metanephros, which is moulded over the growing end of the diverticulum from the Wolffian duct. The tubules of the metanephros, unlike those of the pronephros and mesonephros, do not open into the Wolffian duct. One end expands to form a glomerulus, while the rest of the tubule rapidly elongates to form the convoluted and straight tubules, the loops of Henle, and the connecting tubules; these last join and establish communications with the collecting tubules derived from the ultimate ramifications of the diverticulum from the Wolffian duct. The mesoderm around the tubules becomes condensed to form the connective tissue of the kidney. The ureter opens at first into the hind-end of the Wolffian duct; after the sixth week it separates from the Wolffian duct, and opens independently into the part of the cloaca which ultimately becomes the bladder (Figs. 1101, 1102).

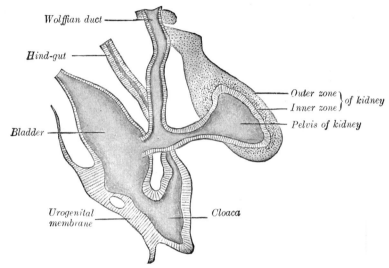

Fig. 1102.—Primitive kidney and bladder, from a reconstruction. (After Schreiner.)

The secretory tubules of the kidney become arranged into pyramidal masses or lobules (Fig. 1103), and the lobulated condition of the kidneys exists for some time after birth, while traces of it may be found even in the adult. The kidney of the ox and many other animals remains lobulated throughout life.

The Urinary Bladder.—The bladder is formed partly from the entodermal cloaca and partly from the ends of the Wolffian ducts; the allantois takes no share in its formation. After the separation of the rectum from the dorsal part of the cloaca (p. 1150), the ventral part becomes subdivided into three portions: (1) an anterior **vesico-urethral portion,** continuous with the allantois—into this portion the Wolffian ducts open; (2) an intermediate narrow channel, the **pelvic portion;** and (3) a posterior **phallic portion,** closed externally by the urogenital membrane (Fig. 1102). The second and third parts together constitute the **urogenital sinus.** The vesico-urethral portion absorbs the ends of the Wolffian ducts and the associated ends of the renal diverticula, and these give rise to the trigone of the bladder and part of the prostatic urethra. The remainder of the vesico-urethral portion forms the body of the bladder and part of the prostatic urethra; its apex is prolonged to the umbilicus as a narrow canal, which later is obliterated and becomes the middle umbilical ligament (urachus).

The Prostate.—The prostate arises between the third and fourth months as a series of solid diverticula from the epithelium lining the urogenital sinus and vesico-urethral part of the cloaca. These buds arise in five distinct groups, grow rapidly in length and soon acquire lumena. Eventually the prostatic urethra and ejaculatory ducts are embedded in a five-lobed gland the parts of which are called the median, anterior, posterior and lateral lobes. The lateral lobes are the largest. There are no distinct dividing lines between the parts of the formed gland, and the divisions are important only because of their individual peculiarities in disease processes. **Skene's ducts** in the female urethra are regarded as the homologues of the prostatic glands.

The **bulbo–urethral glands of Cowper** in the male, and **greater vestibular glands of Bartholin** in the female, also arise as diverticula from the epithelial lining of the urogenital sinus.

The External Organs of Generation (Fig. 1104).—As already stated (page 1150), the cloacal membrane, composed of ectoderm and entoderm, originally reaches from the umbilicus to the tail. The mesoderm extends to the midventral line for some distance behind the umbilicus, and forms the lower part of the abdominal wall; it ends below in a prominent swelling, the **cloacal tubercle.** Behind this tubercle the urogenital part of the cloacal membrane separates the ingrowing sheets of mesoderm.

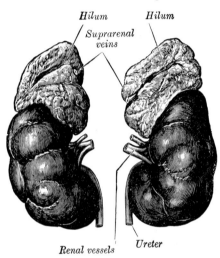

Hilum   Hilum

Suprarenal veins

Renal vessels   Ureter

FIG. 1103.—The kidneys and suprarenal glands of a new-born child. Anterior aspect.

The first rudiment of the penis (or clitoris) is a structure termed the **phallus**; it is derived from the phallic portion of the cloaca which has extended on to the end and sides of the under surface of the cloacal tubercle. The terminal part of the phallus representing the future glans becomes solid; the remainder, which is hollow, is converted into a longitudinal groove by the absorption of the urogenital membrane.

In the female a deep groove forms around the phallus and separates it from the rest of the cloacal tubercle, which is now termed the **genital tubercle.** The sides of the genital tubercle grow backward as the **genital swellings**, which ultimately form the labia majora; the tubercle itself becomes the mons pubis. The labia minora arise by the continued growth of the lips of the groove on the under surface of the phallus; the remainder of the phallus forms the clitoris.

In the male the early changes are similar, but the pelvic portion of the cloaca undergoes much greater development, pushing before it the phallic portion. The genital swellings extend around between the pelvic portion and the anus, and form a scrotal area; during the changes associated with the descent of the testes this area is drawn out to form the scrotal sacs. The penis is developed from the phallus. As in the female, the urogenital membrane undergoes absorption, forming a channel on the under surface of the phallus; this channel extends only as far forward as the corona glandis.

The **corpora cavernosa** of the penis (or clitoris) and of the urethra arise from the mesodermal tissue in the phallus; they are at first dense structures, but later vascular spaces appear in them, and they gradually become cavernous.

The **prepuce** in both sexes is formed by the growth of a solid plate of ectoderm into the superficial part of the phallus; on coronal section this plate presents the shape of a horseshoe. By the breaking down of its more centrally situated cells the plate is split into two lamellæ, and a cutaneous fold, the prepuce, is liberated and forms a hood over the glans. Adherent prepuce is not an adhesion really, but a hindered central desquamation.

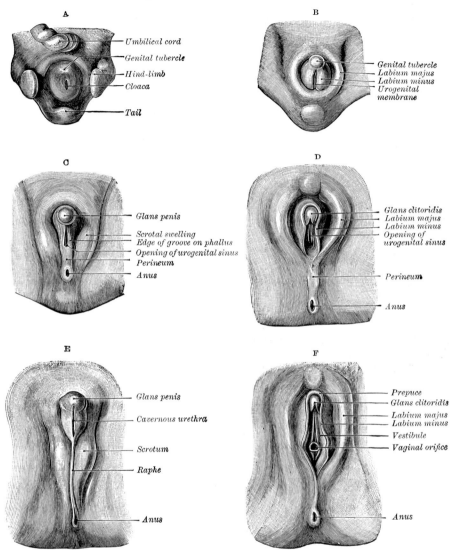

Fig. 1104.—Stages in the development of the external sexual organs in the male and female. (Drawn from the Ecker-Ziegler models.)

The Urethra.—As already described, in both sexes the phallic portion of the cloaca extends on to the under surface of the cloacal tubercle as far forward as the apex. At the apex the walls of the phallic portion come together and fuse, the lumen is obliterated, and a solid plate, the **urethral plate**, is formed. The remainder of the phallic portion is for a time tubular, and then, by the absorption of the urogenital membrane, it establishes a communication with the exterior; this opening is the **primitive urogenital ostium**, and it extends forward to the corona glandis.

In the female this condition is largely retained; the portion of the groove on the clitoris broadens out while the body of the clitoris enlarges, and thus the adult urethral opening is situated behind the base of the clitoris.

In the male, by the greater growth of the pelvic portion of the cloaca a longer urethra is formed, and the primitive ostium is carried forward with the phallus, but it still ends at the corona glandis. Later it closes from behind forward. Meanwhile the urethral plate of the glans breaks down centrally to form a median groove continuous with the primitive ostium. This groove also closes from behind forward, so that the external urethral opening is shifted forward to the end of the glans.

THE URINARY ORGANS.

The urinary organs comprise the **kidneys**, which produce the urine, the **ureters**, or ducts, which convey urine to the **urinary bladder**, where it is for a time retained; and the **urethra**, through which it is discharged from the body.

The Kidneys (Renes).

The **kidneys** are situated in the posterior part of the abdomen, one on either side of the vertebral column, behind the peritoneum, and surrounded by a mass of fat and loose areolar tissue. Their upper extremities are on a level with the upper border of the twelfth thoracic vertebra, their lower extremities on a level with the third lumbar. The right kidney is usually slightly lower than the left, probably due to the presence of the liver. The long axis of each kidney is directed downward and lateralward; the transverse axis backward and lateralward.

Each kidney is about 11.25 cm. in length, 5 to 7.5 cm. in breadth, and rather more than 2.5 cm. in thickness. The left is somewhat longer, and narrower, than the right. The weight of the kidney in the adult male varies from 125 to 170 gm., in the adult female from 115 to 155 gm. The combined weight of the two kidneys in proportion to that of the body is about 1 to 240. The kidneys in the new-born are about three times as large in proportion to the body weight as in the adult.

The kidney has a characteristic form, and presents for examination two surfaces, two borders, and an upper and lower extremity.

Relations.—The **anterior surface** (*facies anterior*) (Fig. 1108) of each kidney is convex, and looks forward and lateralward. Its relations to adjacent viscera differ so completely on the two sides that separate descriptions are necessary.

Anterior Surface of Right Kidney.—A narrow portion at the upper extremity is in relation with the right suprarenal gland. A large area just below this and involving about three-fourths of the surface, lies in the renal impression on the inferior surface of the liver, and a narrow but somewhat variable area near the medial border is in contact with the descending part of the duodenum. The lower part of the anterior surface is in contact laterally with the right colic flexure, and medially, as a rule, with the small intestine. The areas in relation with the liver and small intestine are covered by peritoneum; the suprarenal, duodenal, and colic areas are devoid of peritoneum.

Anterior Surface of Left Kidney.—A small area along the upper part of the medial border is in relation with the left suprarenal gland, and close to the lateral border is a long strip in contact with the renal impression on the spleen. A somewhat quadrilateral field, about the middle of the anterior surface, marks the site of contact with the body of the pancreas, on the deep surface of which are the lienal vessels. Above this is a small triangular portion, between the suprarenal and splenic areas, in contact with the postero-inferior surface of the stomach. Below the pancreatic area the lateral part is in relation with the left colic flexure, the medial with the small intestine. The areas in contact with the stomach and spleen are covered by the peritoneum of the omental bursa, while that in relation to the small intestine is covered by the peritoneum of the general cavity; behind the latter are some branches of the left colic vessels. The suprarenal, pancreatic, and colic areas are devoid of peritoneum.

The **Posterior Surface** (*facies posterior*) (Fig 1109). — The posterior surface of each kidney is directed backward and medialward. It is imbedded in areolar

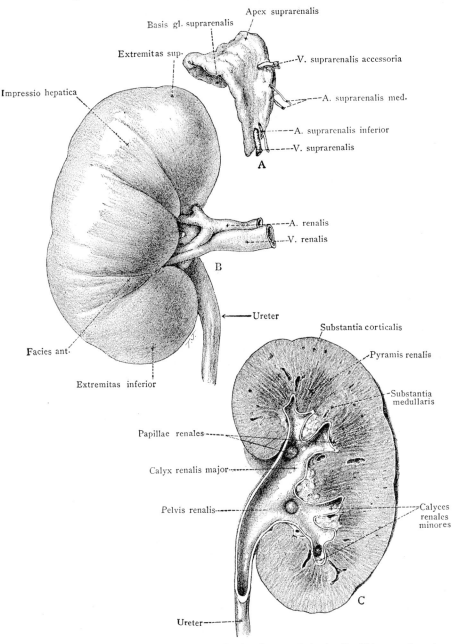

Apex suprarenalis

Basis gl. suprarenalis

Extremitas sup.

- - -V. suprarenalis accessoria

Impressio hepatica

- - -A. suprarenalis med.

- - -A. suprarenalis inferior

- - -V. suprarenalis

A

- - -A. renalis

- - -V. renalis

B

←— Ureter

Substantia corticalis

Pyramis renalis

Substantia medullaris

Facies ant.

Extremitas inferior

Papillae renales - - -

Calyx renalis major - - -

Pelvis renalis - - -

Calyces renales minores

C

Ureter - - -

Fig. 1105.—The right kidney and suprarenal gland. A.—Suprarenal gland. B.—Kidney, surface view. C.—Kidney, longitudinal section showing pelvis. (Eycleshymer and Jones.)

and fatty tissue and entirely devoid of peritoneal covering. It lies upon the diaphragm, the medial and lateral lumbocostal arches, the Psoas major, the Quadratus lumborum, and the tendon of the Transversus abdominis, the subcostal, and one or two of the upper lumbar arteries, and the last thoracic, iliohypogastric, and ilioinguinal nerves. The superior extremity of the right kidney rests upon the twelfth rib, the left usually on the eleventh and twelfth. The diaphragm separates the kidney from the pleura, which dips down to form the phrenicocostal sinus, but

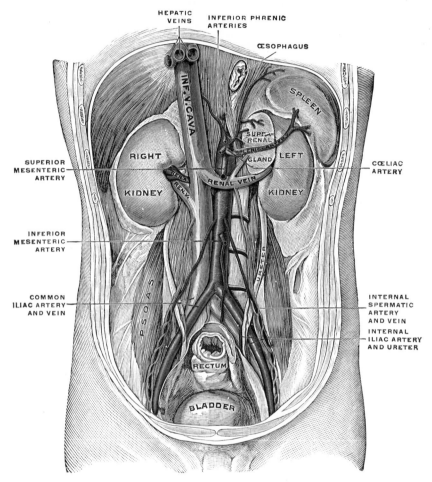

Fig. 1106.—Posterior abdominal wall, after removal of the peritoneum, showing kidneys, suprarenal capsules, and great vessels. (Corning.)

frequently the muscular fibers of the diaphragm are defective or absent over a triangular area immediately above the lateral lumbocostal arch, and when this is the case the perinephric areolar tissue is in contact with the diaphragmatic pleura.

Borders.—The **lateral border** (*margo lateralis; external border*) is convex, and is directed toward the postero-lateral wall of the abdomen. On the left side it is in contact at its upper part, with the spleen.

The **medial border** (*margo medialis; internal border*) is concave in the center and convex toward either extremity; it is directed forward and a little downward. Its central part presents a deep longitudinal fissure, bounded by prominent overhanging anterior and posterior lips. This fissure is named the **hilum**, and transmits the vessels, nerves, and ureter. Above the hilum the medial border is in relation with the suprarenal gland; below the hilum, with the ureter.

Extremities.—The **superior extremity** (*extremitas superior*) is thick and rounded, and is nearer the median line than the lower; it is surmounted by the suprarenal gland, which covers also a small portion of the anterior surface.

The **inferior extremity** (*extremitas inferior*) is smaller and thinner than the superior and farther from the median line. It extends to within 5 cm. of the iliac crest.

The relative position of the main structures in the hilum is as follows: the vein is in front, the artery in the middle, and the ureter behind and directed downward. Frequently, however, branches of both artery and vein are placed behind the ureter.

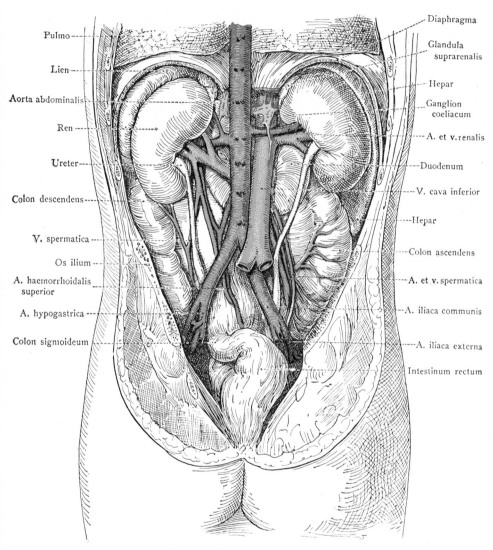

Fig. 1107.—Dissection of abdominal viscera, dorsal view showing relations of the kidneys. After Corning's Topographischen Anatomie in (Eycleshymer and Jones.)

Renal Fascia (*fascia renalis*) (Figs. 1110, 1113).—The kidney and its vessels are imbedded in a mass of fatty tissue, termed the adipose capsule or *perirenal fat*, which is thickest at the margins of the kidney and is prolonged through the hilum into the renal sinus. The kidney and the adipose capsule together are enclosed in a specialized lamination of the subserous fascia called the renal fascia. It occupies a position between the internal investing layer of deep fascia (transversalis, endoabdominal fascia) and the stratum of subserous fascia associated with the intestine and its blood vessels (Fig. 1111). In forming the renal fascia, the subserous fascia of the lateral abdominal wall splits into two fibrous lamellæ near the lateral border of the kidney (Fig. 1113). Both lamellæ extend medially, the anterior one over

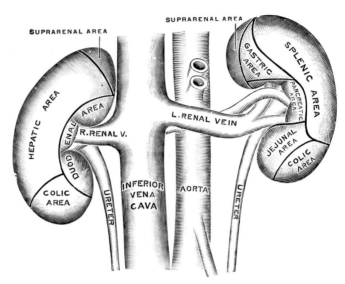

Fig. 1108.—The anterior surfaces of the kidneys, showing the areas of contact of neighboring viscera.

the ventral surface of the kidney, the posterior one over the dorsal surface. The anterior lamella continues over the renal vessels and aorta to join the similar mem-

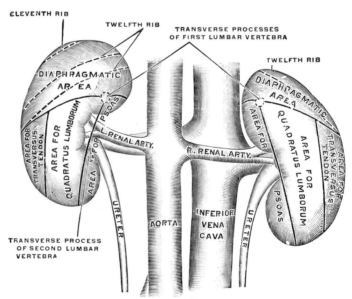

Fig. 1109.—The posterior surfaces of the kidneys, showing areas of relation to the parietes.

brane of the other side. The posterior lamella also continues across the middle line but lies deep to the aorta, and is there more adherent to the underlying deep fascia than in the region of the kidney. The renal fascia is connected to the fibrous tunic of the kidney by numerous trabeculæ, which traverse the adipose capsule, and are strongest near the lower end of the organ. Behind the fascia renalis is a considerable quantity of fat, which constitutes the *paranephric body* (*pararenal fat*).

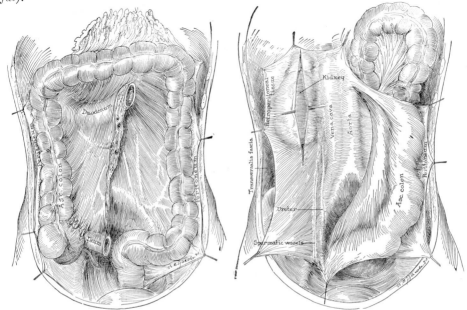

FIG. 1110.—Visceral and parietal peritoneum associated with large intestine. Small intestine and mesentery removed.

FIG. 1111.—Peritoneum associated with ascending colon dissected free and displaced to expose the deeper stratum of subserous fascia associated with kidney and great vessels.

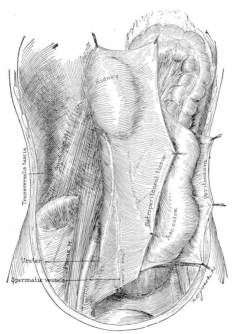

FIG. 1112.—Deeper stratum of subserous fascia dissected free and displaced to expose the transversalisa fascia. Tobin, courtesy of Anat. Record.

Fixation of the Kidney.—The kidneys are not rigidly fixed to the abdominal wall and, since they are in contact with the diaphragm, move with it during respiration. They are held in position by the renal fascia described above and by the large renal arteries and veins. That the adipose capsule and the paranephric fat body play an important part in holding the kidney in position is indicated by the occurrence of a condition called movable kidney in emaciated individuals (see page 1275).

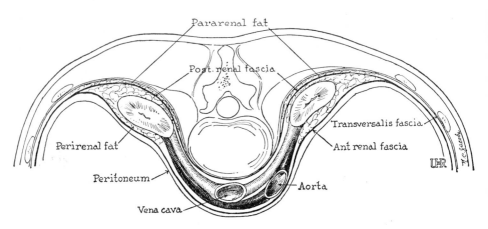

FIG. 1113.—Transverse section, showing relations of renal fascia.   (Tobin, courtesy of Anat. Record.)

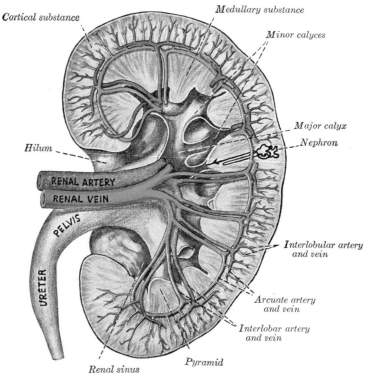

FIG. 1114.—Diagram of a vertical section through the kidney. Nephron and bloodvessels greatly enlarged.

General Structure of the Kidney.—The kidney is invested by a fibrous tunic or capsule which forms a firm, smooth covering to the organ. The tunic can be easily stripped off, but in doing so numerous fine processes of connective tissue and

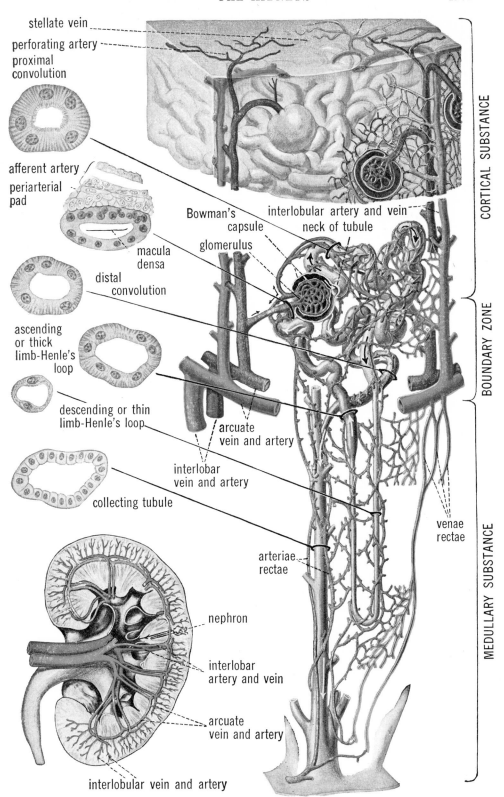

stellate vein

perforating artery

proximal convolution

afferent artery

periarterial pad

macula densa

distal convolution

ascending or thick limb-Henle's loop

descending or thin limb-Henle's loop

collecting tubule

Bowman's capsule

glomerulus

interlobular artery and vein

neck of tubule

arcuate vein and artery

interlobar vein and artery

arteriae rectae

nephron

interlobar artery and vein

arcuate vein and artery

interlobular vein and artery

venae rectae

CORTICAL SUBSTANCE

BOUNDARY ZONE

MEDULLARY SUBSTANCE

Fig. 1115.—Diagram of a portion of kidney lobule illustrating a nephron, typical histological sections of the various divisions of a nephron, and the disposition of the renal vessels. The section of the collecting tubule is reproduced at a lower magnification than the divisions of the nephron.

small bloodvessels are torn through. When the capsule is stripped off, the surface of the kidney is found to be smooth and of a deep red color. In infants fissures extending for some depth may be seen on the surface of the organ, a remnant of the lobular construction of the gland. If a vertical section of the kidney be made from its convex to its concave border, it will be seen that the hilum expands into a central cavity, the **renal sinus**, this contains the upper part of the renal pelvis and the calyces, surrounded by some fat in which are imbedded the branches of the renal vessels and nerves. The renal sinus is lined by a prolongation of the fibrous tunic, which is continuous with the covering of the pelvis of the kidney around the lips of the hilum. The **minor renal calyces**, from four to thirteen in number, are cup-shaped tubes, each of which embraces usually one but occasionally two or more of the renal papillæ; they unite to form two or three short tubes, the major calyces, and these in turn join to form a funnel-shaped sac, the **renal pelvis**. Spirally arranged muscles surround the calyces which may have a milking action on these tubes, thereby aiding the flow of urine into the renal pelvis. As the pelvis leaves the renal sinus it diminishes rapidly in caliber and merges insensibly into the ureter, the excretory duct of the kidney.

The kidney is composed of an internal **medullary** and an external **cortical substance**.

The **medullary substance** (*substantia medullaris*) consists of a series of striated conical masses, termed the **renal pyramids**. They vary from eight to eighteen in number and have their bases directed toward the circumference of the kidney, while their apices converge toward the renal sinus, where they form prominent papillæ projecting into the lumina of the minor calyces.

The **cortical substance** (*substantia corticalis*) is reddish brown in color and soft and granular in consistence. It lies immediately beneath the fibrous tunic, arches over the bases of the pyramids, and dips in between adjacent pyramids toward the renal sinus. The parts dipping in between the pyramids are named the **renal columns** (Bertini), while the portions which connect the renal columns to each other and intervene between the bases of the pyramids and the fibrous tunic are called the **cortical arches** (Fig. 1114). If the cortex be examined with a lens, it will be seen to consist of a series of lighter-colored, conical areas, termed the radiate part, and a darker colored intervening substance, which from the complexity of its structure is named the convoluted part. The rays gradually taper toward the circumference of the kidney, and consist of a series of outward prolongations from the base of each renal pyramid.

Minute Anatomy.—The **renal tubules** (Fig. 1115), of which the kidney is for the most part made up, commence in the cortical substance, and after pursuing a very circuitous course through the cortical and medullary substances, finally end at the apices of the renal pyramids by open mouths, so that the fluid which they contain is emptied, through the calyces, into the pelvis of the kidney. If the surface of one of the papillæ be examined with a lens, it will be seen to be studded over with minute openings, the orifices of the renal tubules, from sixteen to twenty in number, and if pressure be made on a fresh kidney, urine will be seen to exude from these orifices. The tubules commence in the cortex and renal columns as the **renal corpuscles** or **Malpighian bodies**. They are small rounded masses, deep red in color, varying in size, but averaging about 0.2 mm. in diameter. Each of these bodies is composed of two parts: a central glomerulus of vessels, and a double walled membranous envelope, the **glomerular capsule** (*capsule of Bowman*), which is the invaginated-pouch-like commencement of a renal tubule.

The **glomerulus** is a tuft of non-anastomosing capillaries, among which there is a scanty amount of connective tissue. This capillary tuft is derived from an arteriole, the *afferent vessel*, which enters the capsule, generally at a point opposite to that at which the capsule joins the tubule. (Fig. 1115.) Upon entering the capsule the afferent arteriole divides into from 2 to 10 primary branches, which in turn subdivide into about 50 capillary loops which generally do not anastomose. These loops are from 300 to 500μ in length. The capillaries join to form the afferent arteriole, which leaves Bowman's capsule adjacent to the afferent vessel, the latter generally being the larger of the two. The total surface area of the capillaries of all glomeruli is about 1 square meter. For a variable distance before the afferent arteriole enters the glomerulus the muscle cells of the media adjacent to the distal convolution of its own nephron are modified, appearing as relatively large afibrillar cells. This structure is said to present evidence of glandular activity. At times it appears partially to invest the artery in a nest-like group of cells embedded in a delicate fibrillar network. It is variously known as the **juxtaglomerular apparatus** (Goormagtigh), the **polkissen** (Zimmerman) and the **periarterial pad** (Edwards). Its exact function has not been determined; neither is it known whether or not all afferent arteries contain it, but it is common in man. The efferent arteriole has only circular, smooth muscle fibers in its wall, which may be a means of regulating glomerular blood pressure. The **Malpighian** or **Bowman's capsule,** which surrounds the glomerulus, consists of a double-walled sac. The outer wall (parietal layer) is continuous with the inner wall (visceral layer) at the points of entrance and exit of the afferent and efferent vessels respectively. The cavity between the two layers is continuous with the lumen of the proximal convoluted tubule. The parietal layer is smooth. The visceral layer covers the glomerulus and dips in between the capillary loops, almost completely surrounding each one. Both layers of the capsule consist of flattened epithelial cells which have a basement membrane. This covers the outer surface of the parietal layer and is continuous with that of the tubule cells. The basement membrane of the visceral layer is in contact with the glomerular capillaries. Microdissection experiments of living glomeruli show them to lie in a gelatinous matrix. The walls of the capillaries, the overlying cells of the visceral layer of the capsule and the gelatinous matrix are now thought to constitute a filter mechanism through which non-protein constituents of the blood plasma can enter the tubule.

A **renal tubule,** beginning with the capsule of Bowman as it surrounds the glomerulus and ending where the tubule joins the excretory duct or collecting tubule, constitutes a **nephron**— the structural and functional unit of the kidney. There are about 1,250,000 of these units in each kidney.

A tubule presents during its course, many changes in shape and direction, and is contained partly in the medullary and partly in the cortical substance. At its junction with the glomerular capsule it exhibits a somewhat constricted portion, which is termed the **neck.** Beyond this the tubule becomes convoluted, and pursues a considerable course in the cortical substance constituting the **proximal convoluted tube.** The convolutions disappear as the tube approaches the medullary substance in a more or less spiral manner. Throughout this portion of its course the renal tubule is contained entirely in the cortical substance, and presents a fairly uniform caliber. It now enters the medullary substance, suddenly becomes much smaller, quite straight, and dips down for a variable depth into the pyramids, constituting the thin or **descending limb of Henle's loop.** Bending on itself, it forms what is termed the **loop of Henle** and ascending it becomes suddenly enlarged, forming the thick or **ascending limb of Henle's loop,** which enters the cortical substance where it again becomes dilated, and tortuous. It is now called the **distal convoluted tubule.** The terminal part of the ascending limb of Henle's loop crosses in contact with or sometimes lies parallel to the afferent arteriole of its own glomerulus. The turns of the distal convoluted tubule into which it merges lie among the coils of the proximal portion of the nephron and terminate in a narrow part which enters a collecting tubule.

The **straight** or **collecting tubes** commence in the radiate part of the cortex, where they receive the curved ends of the distal convoluted tubules. They unite at short intervals with one another, the resulting tubes presenting a considerable increase in caliber, so that a series of comparatively large tubes passes from the bases of the rays into the renal pyramids. In the medulla the tubes of each pyramid converge to join a central tube (*duct of Bellini*) which finally opens on the summit of one of the papillæ; the contents of the tube are therefore discharged into one of the minor calyces.

Structure of the Renal Tubules.—The various parts of the nephron present quite different cellular appearances and these appearances vary depending upon the functional state of the cells. The proximal convoluted tubule is about 14 mm. long and 59μ in diameter. It is composed of one layer of large cuboidal cells with central spherical nuclei. The cells dovetail laterally with one another and the lateral cell limits are rarely seen. The distal ends of the cells bulge into the lumen and are covered by a brush border. The cytoplasm is abundant and coarsely granular. Parallel striations in the cytoplasm perpendicular to the basement membrane are due to mitochondria.

The transition between the epithelium of the proximal convoluted tubule and the thin segment is abrupt. The thin segment may be absent in nephrons beginning near the surface of the kidney. It is composed of squamous cells with pale-staining cytoplasm and flattened nuclei. The epithelial change from the descending limb to the ascending or thick limb is also quite abrupt. The cells become cuboidal and deeper-staining, with perpendicular striations in the basal parts but without distinct cell boundaries or brush borders. At about the junction of the ascending limb with the distal convoluted tubule the nephron comes into contact with the "Polkissen" of its own afferent arteriole. Here the epithelium of the tubule is greatly modified, having high cells and crowded nuclei. This constitutes the **macula densa** or epithelial plaque, the function of which is unknown. Transition to the tortuous distal convoluted tubule is gradual. This segment of the nephron is about 5 mm. long and 35μ in diameter. The cells are lower and the lumen larger than in the proximal tubule. They do not have a brush border and the boundaries are fairly distinct. The distal convoluted tubule merges into a short connecting segment which joins the collecting or excretory tubule.

The collecting tubules have a typical epithelium which is quite different from that in the various portions of the nephron. In the smallest tubes the cells are cuboidal and distinctly outlined with round nuclei and clear cytoplasm. As the tubules become larger the cells are higher, finally becoming tall columnar in the ducts of Bellini. The columnar epithelium becomes continuous with the cells covering the surface of the papillæ.

The length of the nephron varies from 30 to 38 mm., while the length of the collecting tubules is estimated at from 20 to 22 mm.

The Renal Bloodvessels.—The kidney is plentifully supplied with blood by the renal artery, a large branch of the abdominal aorta. Before entering the kidney substance the number and disposition of the branches of the renal artery exhibit great variation. In most cases the renal artery divides into two primary branches, a larger anterior and a smaller posterior. The anterior branch supplies exclusively the anterior or ventral half of the organ and the posterior supplies the posterior or dorsal part. Therefore there is a line (Bröedel's line) in the long axis of the lateral border of the kidney which passes between the two main arterial divisions and in which there are no large vessels, a feature which is utilized to minimize hemorrhage when nephrotomy is done. The primary branches subdivide and diverge until they come to lie on the anterior and posterior aspects respectively of the calyces. Further subdivisions occur which enter the kidney substance and run between the pyramids. These are known as **interlobar arteries.** When these vessels reach the corticomedullary zone they make more or less well defined arches over the bases of the pyramids and are then called **arcuate arteries.** These vessels give off a series of branches called **interlobular** arteries. The interlobular arteries and the terminal parts of the arcuate vessels run vertically and nearly parallel towards the cortex and periphery of the kidney. The interlobular arteries may terminate as (1) an afferent glomerular artery to one or more glomeruli; (2) in a capillary plexus around the convoluted tubules in the cortices without relation to the glomerulus, therefore a nutrient artery, and (3) as a perforating capsular vessel. Divisions classified under (2) must be regarded as exceptional. The most important and numerous branches of the interlobular arteries are the afferent glomerular vessels. These break up into capillary loops, the glomerulus, within Bowman's capsule. The loops unite to form the efferent arteriole. The efferent glomerular vessel forms a plexus about the convoluted tubule and part of Henle's loop and sends one or more branches toward the pelvis, the **arteria recta,** which supplies the collecting tubules and loops of Henle. The arteriæ rectæ are derived chiefly from the efferent arterioles of glomeruli located in the boundary zone. They are frequently known as **arteriæ rectæ spuriæ** to distinguish them from a few straight vessels arising directly from the arcuate or interlobular arteries without relation to glomeruli and hence called **arteriæ rectæ veræ.** It is likely that the so-called arteriæ rectæ veræ were once derived from an efferent glomerular vessel but that the glomerulus atrophied, thus giving them the appearance of true nutrient branches from the arcuate or interlobular arteries. No arteriæ rectæ are derived from the vessels of the cortical zone. It has not been determined whether or not there are anastomoses between the capillaries of adjacent nephrons. However, there is free anastomosis between the branches of the arteriæ rectæ. The arteriæ rectæ or straight arteries surround the limbs of Henle and pass down between the straight collecting tubules, where they form terminal plexuses around the tubes. This plexus drains into the **venæ rectæ** which in turn carry the blood to the interlobular veins, thence into the arcuate veins, then into the interlobar veins and finally into the renal veins, which discharge into the inferior vena cava. It will be noted that the chief renal arteries have counterparts in the venous system. All veins from the dorsal half of the kidney cross to the ventral half between the minor calyces to join the ventral collecting veins before leaving the kidney. Whatever arterial anastomoses there are within the kidney occur post glomerular, the renal arteries and their branches therefore being terminal as far as the arteriæ rectæ. An exception to this condition is found in cases in which arterio-venous anastomoses have been described. These connections have been found in three locations; between the arteries and veins of the sinus renalis, between the subcapsular vessels and between the interlobular arteries and veins. In the latter position particularly arterial blood could reach the tubules of the nephron by retrograde flow through the veins. The constancy with which this type of anastomosis occurs or its rôle in the circulation of the kidney has not been accurately determined. Anastomosis between veins is very rich. The perforating capsular vessels, the terminations of interlobular arteries, form connections with non-renal vessels in the fat which surrounds the kidney. They frequently drain into the subcapsular or **stellate veins,** which in turn drain into the interlobular veins.

The **lymphatics** of the kidney are described on page 723.

Nerves of the Kidney.—The nerves of the kidney, although small, are about fifteen in number. They have small ganglia developed upon them, and are derived from the renal plexus, which is formed by branches from the celiac plexus, the lower and outer part of the celiac ganglion and aortic plexus, and from the lesser and lowest splanchnic nerves. They communicate with the spermatic plexus, a circumstance which may explain the occurrence of pain in the testis in affections of the kidney. They accompany the renal artery and its branches, and are distributed to the bloodvessels and to the cells of the urinary tubules.

Connective Tissue (*intertubular stroma*). — Although the tubules and vessels are closely packed, a small amount of connective tissue, continuous with the fibrous tunic, binds them firmly together and supports the bloodvessels, lymphatics, and nerves.

Variations.—Malformations of the kidney are not uncommon. There may be an entire absence of one kidney, but, according to Morris, the number of these cases is "excessively small": or there may be congenital atrophy of one kidney, when the kidney is very small, but usually healthy in structure. These cases are of great importance, and must be duly taken into account when nephrectomy is contemplated. A more common malformation is where the two kidneys are fused together. They may be joined together only at their lower ends by means of a thick mass of renal tissue, so as to form a horseshoe-shaped body, or they may be completely united, forming a disk-like kidney, from which two ureters descend into the bladder. These fused kidneys are generally situated in the middle line of the abdomen, but may be displaced as well. In some mammals, *e. g.*, ox and bear, the kidney consists of a number of distinct lobules; this lobulated condition is characteristic of the kidney of the human fetus, and traces of it may persist in the adult. Sometimes the pelvis is duplicated, while a double ureter is not very uncommon. In some rare instances a third kidney may be present.

One or both kidneys may be misplaced as a congenital condition, and remain fixed in this abnormal position. They are then very often misshapen. They may be situated higher, though this is very uncommon, or lower than normal or removed farther from the vertebral column than usual; or they may be displaced into the iliac fossa, over the sacroiliac joint, on to the promontory of the sacrum, or into the pelvis between the rectum and bladder or by the side of the uterus. In these latter cases they may give rise to very serious trouble. The kidney may also be displaced as a congenital condition, but may not be fixed; it is then known as a *floating kidney*. It is believed to be due to the fact that the kidney is completely enveloped by peritoneum which then passes backward to the vertebral column as a double layer, forming a mesonephron which permits movement. The kidney may also be misplaced as an acquired condition; in these cases the kidney is mobile in the tissues by which it is surrounded, moving with the capsule in the perinephric tissues. This condition is known as *movable kidney*, and is more common in the female than in the male. It occurs in badly nourished people, or in those who have become emaciated from any cause. It must not be confounded with the *floating kidney*, which is a congenital condition due to the development of a mesonephron. The two conditions cannot, however, be distinguished until the abdomen is opened or the kidney explored from the loin. Accessory renal arteries entering one or another or both poles of the kidney instead of at the hilum are fairly common.

The Ureters.

The **ureters** are the two tubes which convey the urine from the kidneys to the urinary bladder. Each commences within the sinus of the corresponding kidney as a number of short cup-shaped tubes, termed **calyces**, which encircle the renal papillæ. Since a single calyx may enclose more than one papilla the calyces are generally fewer in number than the pyramids—the former varying from seven to thirteen, the latter from eight to eighteen. The calyces join to form two or three short tubes, and these unite to form a funnel-shaped dilatation, wide above and narrow below, named the **renal pelvis,** which is situated partly inside and partly outside the renal sinus. It is usually placed on a level with the spinous process of the first lumbar vertebra.

The **Ureter Proper** varies in length from 28 to 34 cm., the right being about 1 cm. shorter than the left. It is a thick-walled narrow tube which is directly continuous near the lower end of the kidney with the tapering extremity of the renal pelvis. It is not of uniform caliber, varying from 1 mm. to 1 cm. in diameter. It runs downward and medialward on the Psoas major muscle and, entering the pelvic cavity, finally opens into the fundus of the bladder.

The **abdominal part** (*pars abdominalis*) lies behind the peritoneum on the medial part of the Psoas major imbedded in the subserous fascia, and is crossed obliquely by the internal spermatic vessels. It enters the pelvic cavity by crossing either the termination of the common, or the commencement of the external, iliac vessels.

At its origin the *right* ureter is usually covered by the descending part of the duodenum, and in its course downward lies to the right of the inferior vena cava, and is crossed by the right colic and ileocolic vessels, while near the superior aperture of the pelvis it passes behind the lower part of the mesentery and the terminal part of the ileum. The *left* ureter is crossed by the left colic vessels, and near the superior aperture of the pelvis passes behind the sigmoid colon and its mesentery.

The **pelvic part** (*pars pelvina*) runs at first downward on the lateral wall of the pelvic cavity, along the anterior border of the greater sciatic notch and under cover of the peritoneum. It lies in front of the hypogastric artery medial to the obturator nerve and the obturator, inferior vesical, and middle hemorrhoidal arteries. Opposite the lower part of the greater sciatic foramen it inclines medialward, and reaches the lateral angle of the bladder, where it is situated in front of the upper end of the seminal vesicle, here the ductus deferens crosses to its medial side, and the vesical veins surround it. Finally, the ureters run obliquely for about 2 cm. through the wall of the bladder and open by slit-like apertures into the cavity of the viscus at the lateral angles of the trigone. When the bladder is distended the openings of the ureters are about 5 cm. apart, but when it is empty and contracted the distance between them is diminished by one-half. Owing to their oblique course through the coats of the bladder, the upper and lower walls of the terminal portions of the ureters become closely applied to each other when the viscus is distended, and, acting as valves, prevent regurgitation of urine from the bladder. There are three points in the course of the ureter where it normally undergoes constriction: (1) at the ureteropelvic junction, average diameter 2 mm.; (2) at the place where it crosses the iliac vessels, 4 mm., and (3) where it joins the bladder, 1 to 5 mm. Between these points the abdominal ureter averages 10 mm. in diameter and the pelvic ureter 5 mm.

In the **female**, the ureter forms, as it lies in relation to the wall of the pelvis, the posterior boundary of a shallow depression named the **ovarian fossa**, in which the ovary is situated. It then runs medialward and forward on the lateral aspect of the cervix uteri and upper part of the vagina to reach the fundus of the bladder. In this part of its course it is accompanied for about 2.5 cm. by the uterine artery, which then crosses over the ureter and ascends between the two layers of the broad ligament. The ureter is distant about 2 cm. from the side of the cervix of the uterus.

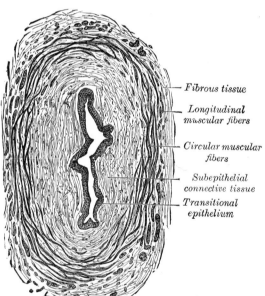

Fibrous tissue

Longitudinal muscular fibers

Circular muscular fibers

Subepithelial connective tissue

Transitional epithelium

Fig. 1116.—Transverse section of ureter.

Structure (Fig. 1116).—The ureter is composed of three coats: **fibrous, muscular,** and **mucous coats.**

The **fibrous coat** (*tunica adventitia*) is continuous at one end with the fibrous tunic of the kidney on the floor of the sinus; while at the other it is lost in the fibrous structure of the bladder.

In the renal pelvis the **muscular coat** (*tunica muscularis*) consists of two layers, longitudinal and circular: the longitudinal fibers become lost upon the sides of the papillæ at the extremities of the calyces; the circular fibers may be traced surrounding the medullary substance in the same situation. In the ureter proper the muscular fibers are very distinct, and are arranged in three layers: an external longitudinal, a middle circular, and an internal, less distinct than the other two, but having a general longitudinal direction. According to Kölliker this internal layer is found only in the neighborhood of the bladder.

The **mucous coat** (*tunica mucosa*) is smooth, presenting only a few longitudinal folds which become effaced by distension. It is continuous with the mucous membrane of the bladder below, while it is prolonged over the papillæ of the kidney above. Its epithelium is of a transitional character, and resembles that found in the bladder (see Fig. 1123). It consists of several layers of cells, of which the innermost—that is to say, the cells in contact with the urine—are somewhat flattened, with concavities on their deep surfaces into which the rounded ends of the cells of the second layer fit. These, the intermediate cells, more or less resemble columnar epithelium, and are pear-shaped, with rounded internal extremities which fit into the concavities of the cells of the first layer, and narrow external extremities which are wedged in between the cells of the third layer. The external or third layer consists of conical or oval cells varying in number in different parts, and presenting processes which extend down into the basement membrane. Beneath the epithelium, and separating it from the muscular coats, is a dense layer of fibrous tissue containing many elastic fibers.

Vessels and Nerves.—The **arteries** supplying the ureter are branches from the renal, internal spermatic, hypogastric, and inferior vesical.

The **nerves** are derived from the inferior mesenteric, spermatic, and pelvic plexuses. The lower one-third of the ureter contains nerve cells which are probably incorporated in vagus efferent chains. The afferent supply of the ureter is contained in the eleventh and twelfth thoracic and first lumbar nerves. The vagus supply to the ureter probably also has afferent components.

Variations.—The upper portion of the ureter is sometimes double; more rarely it is double the greater part of its extent, or even completely so. In such cases there are two openings into the bladder. Asymmetry in these variations is common.

The Urinary Bladder (Vesica Urinaria; Bladder) (Fig. 1117).

The **urinary bladder** is a musculomembranous sac which acts as a reservoir for the urine; and as its size, position, and relations vary according to the amount

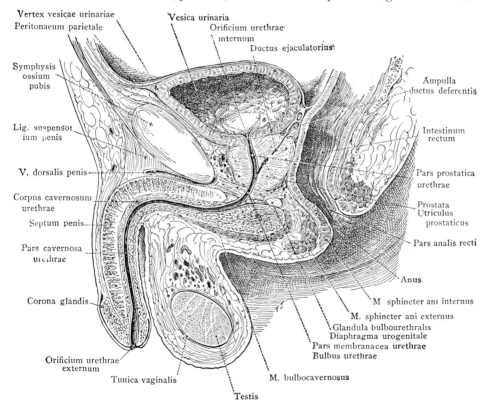

Fig. 1117.—Median sagittal section through male pelvis, viewed from left side. (Eycleshymer and Jones.)

of fluid it contains, it is necessary to study it as it appears (*a*) when *empty*, and (*b*) when *distended*. In both conditions the position of the bladder varies with the condition of the rectum, being pushed upward and forward when the rectum is distended.

The Empty Bladder.—When hardened *in situ*, the empty bladder has the form of a flattened tetrahedron, with its vertex tilted forward. It presents a fundus, a vertex, a superior and an inferior surface. The **fundus** (Fig. 1136) is triangular in shape, and is directed downward and backward toward the rectum, from which it is separated by the rectovesical fascia, the vesiculæ seminales, and the terminal portions of the ductus deferentes. The **vertex** is directed forward toward the upper part of the symphysis pubis, and from it the middle umbilical ligament is continued upward on the back of the anterior abdominal wall to the umbilicus. The peritoneum is carried by it from the vertex of the bladder on to the abdominal wall to form the middle umbilical fold. The **superior surface** is triangular, bounded on either side by a lateral border which separates it from the inferior surface, and

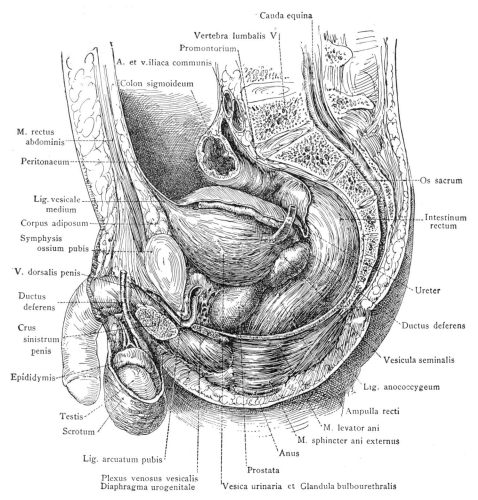

Fig. 1118.—Male pelvic organs and perineum seen from left side after removal of left pelvic wall. Bladder and rectum moderately distended. (Eycleshymer and Jones.)

behind by a posterior border, represented by a line joining the two ureters, which intervenes between it and the fundus. The lateral borders extend from the ureters to the vertex, and from them the peritoneum is carried to the walls of the pelvis. On either side of the bladder the peritoneum shows a depression, named the **para-**

vesical fossa (Fig. 1031). The superior surface is directed upward, is covered by peritoneum, and is in relation with the sigmoid colon and some of the coils of the small intestine. When the bladder is empty and firmly contracted, this surface is convex and the lateral and posterior borders are rounded; whereas if the bladder be relaxed it is concave, and the interior of the viscus, as seen in a median sagittal section, presents the appearance of a V-shaped slit with a shorter posterior and a longer anterior limb—the apex of the V corresponding with the internal orifice of the urethra. The **inferior surface** is directed downward and is uncovered by peritoneum. It may be divided into a posterior or prostatic area and two infero-lateral surfaces. The prostatic area is somewhat triangular: it rests upon and is in direct continuity with the base of the prostate; and from it the urethra emerges. The infero-lateral portion of the inferior surface is directed downward and lateralward and is separated from the symphysis pubis by the prevesical fascial cleft (cavum Retzii).

When the bladder is empty it is placed entirely within the pelvis, below the level of the obliterated hypogastric arteries, and below the level of those portions of the ductus deferentes which are in contact with the lateral wall of the pelvis; after they cross the ureters the ductus deferentes come into contact with the fundus of the bladder. As the viscus fills, its fundus, being more or less fixed, is only slightly depressed; while its superior surface gradually rises into the abdominal cavity, carrying with it its peritoneal covering, and at the same time rounding off the posterior and lateral borders.

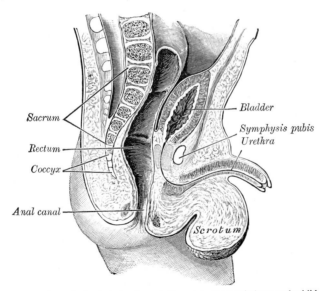

FIG. 1119.—Sagittal section through the pelvis of a newly born male child.

The Distended Bladder.—When the bladder is moderately full it contains about 0.5 liter and assumes an oval form; the long diameter of the oval measures about 12 cm. and is directed upward and forward. In this condition it presents a postero-superior, an antero-inferior, and two lateral surfaces, a fundus and a summit. The **postero-superior surface** is directed upward and backward, and is covered by peritoneum: behind, it is separated from the rectum by the rectovesical excavation, while its anterior part is in contact with the coils of the small intestine. The **antero-inferior surface** is devoid of peritoneum, and rests, below, against the pubic bones, above which it is in contact with the back of the anterior abdominal wall. The lower parts of the lateral surfaces are destitute of peritoneum, and are in contact with the lateral walls of the pelvis. The line of peritoneal reflection from the lateral surface is raised to the level of the obliterated hypogastric artery. The **fundus** undergoes little alteration in position, being only slightly lowered. It exhibits, however, a narrow triangular area, which is separated from the rectum merely by the rectovesical fascia. This area is bounded below by the prostate, above by the rectovesical fold of peritoneum, and laterally by the ductus deferentes. The ductus deferentes frequently come in contact with each other above the prostate, and under such circumstances the lower part of the triangular area is obliterated. The line of reflection of the peritoneum from the rectum to the bladder appears to undergo little or no change when the latter is distended; it is situated about 10 cm. from the anus. The **summit** is directed upward and forward above the point of attachment of the middle umbilical ligament, and hence the peritoneum which follows the ligament, forms a pouch of varying depth between the summit of the bladder, and the anterior abdominal wall.

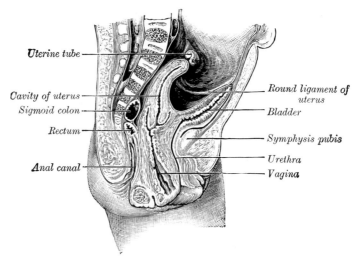

Fig. 1120.—Sagittal section through the pelvis of a newly born female child.

The Bladder in the Child (Figs. 1119, 1120).—In the newborn child the internal urethral orifice is at the level of the upper border of the symphysis pubis; the bladder therefore lies relatively at a much higher level in the infant than in the adult. Its anterior surface "is in contact with about the lower two-thirds of that part of the abdominal wall which lies between the symphysis pubis and the umbilicus" (Symington[1]). Its fundus is clothed with peritoneum as far as the level of the internal orifice of the urethra. Although the bladder of the infant is usually described as an abdominal organ, Symington has pointed out that only about one-half of it lies above the plane of the superior aperture of the pelvis. Disse maintains that the internal urethral orifice sinks rapidly during the first three years, and then more slowly until the ninth year, after which it remains stationary until puberty, when it again slowly descends and reaches its adult position.

The Female Bladder (Fig. 1121).—In the female, the bladder is in relation behind with the uterus and the upper part of the vagina. It is separated from the anterior surface of the body of the uterus by the vesicouterine excavation, but below the level of this excavation it is connected to the front of the cervix uteri and the upper part of the anterior wall of the vagina by areolar tissue. When the bladder is empty the uterus rests upon its superior surface. The female bladder is said by some to be more capacious than that of the male, but probably the opposite is the case.

[1] The Anatomy of the Child.

Ligaments.—The bladder is held in position by ligamentous attachments at its inferior portion or base, that is, near the exit of the urethra, and at the vertex. The remainder of the wall, enclosed in subserous fascia, is free to move during the expansion and contraction of filling and emptying.

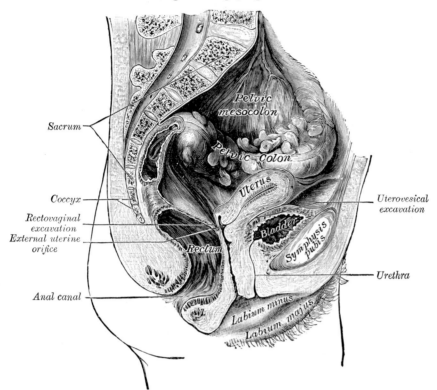

Fɪɢ. 1121.—Median sagittal section of female pelvis.

The base of the bladder is attached to the internal investing layer of deep fascia on the pubic bone by strong fibrous bands which may contain muscle fibers, the **Pubovesicales.** In the male, because the prostate is firmly bound to the bladder in this region, these attachments are between the prostate and pubic bone rather than directly to the bladder, and are named the **medial** and **lateral puboprostatic ligaments** (see page 415). In the female the attachments are directly between bladder and pubis and are therefore called the **pubovesical ligaments.**

The base of the bladder is secured posteriorly to the sides of the rectum and the sacrum by condensations of the subserous fascia underlying the sacrogenital folds. They are called the **rectovesical ligaments**, or, since they may contain smooth muscle bundles, the **Rectovesicales** muscles.

The **middle umbilical ligament** is a fibrous or fibromuscular cord, the remains of the urachus (page 1261), which extends from the vertex of the bladder to the umbilicus. It is broad at its attachment to the bladder and becomes narrow as it nears the umbilicus.

In addition to these fibrous or true ligaments, there are a series of folds, where the peritoneum is reflected from the bladder to the abdominal wall, called **false ligaments of the bladder.** Anteriorly there are three folds: the **middle umbilical fold** on the middle umbilical ligament, and two **lateral umbilical folds** on the obliterated hypogastric arteries. The reflections of the peritoneum on to the side wall of the pelvis form the **lateral false ligaments**, while the **sacrogenital folds** constitute **posterior false ligaments.**

81

Interior of the Bladder (Fig. 1122). The mucous membrane lining the bladder is, over the greater part of the viscus, loosely attached to the muscular coat, and appears wrinkled or folded when the bladder is contracted: in the distended condition of the bladder the folds are effaced. Over a small triangular area, termed the **trigonum vesicæ,** immediately above and behind the internal orifice of the urethra, the mucous membrane is firmly bound to the muscular coat, and is always smooth. The anterior angle of the trigonum vesicæ is formed by the internal orifice of the

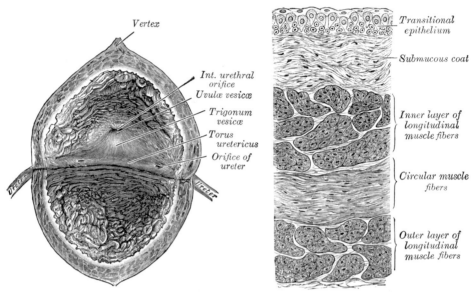

FIG. 1122.—The interior of bladder.

FIG. 1123.—Vertical section of bladder wall.

urethra: its postero-lateral angles by the orifices of the ureters. Stretching behind the latter openings is a slightly curved ridge, the **torus uretericus,** forming the base of the trigone and produced by an underlying bundle of non-striped muscular fibers. The lateral parts of this ridge extend beyond the openings of the ureters, and are named the **plicæ uretericæ;** they are produced by the terminal portions of the ureters as they traverse obliquely the bladder wall. When the bladder is illuminated the torus uretericus appears as a pale band and forms an important guide during the operation of introducing a catheter into the ureter.

The **orifices of the ureters** are placed at the postero-lateral angles of the trigonum vesicæ, and are usually slit-like in form. In the contracted bladder they are about 2.5 cm. apart and about the same distance from the internal urethral orifice; in the distended viscus these measurements may be increased to about 5 cm.

The **internal urethral orifice** is placed at the apex of the trigonum vesicæ, in the most dependent part of the bladder, and is usually somewhat crescentic in form; the mucous membrane immediately behind it presents a slight elevation, the **uvula vesicæ,** caused by the middle lobe of the prostate.

Structure (Fig. 1123).—The bladder is composed of the four coats: **serous, muscular, sub-mucous,** and **mucous coats.**

The **serous coat** (*tunica serosa*) is a partial one, and is derived from the peritoneum. It invests the superior surface and the upper parts of the lateral surfaces, and is reflected from these on to the abdominal and pelvic walls.

The **muscular coat** (*tunica muscularis*) consists of three layers of unstriped muscular fibers: an external layer, composed of fibers having for the most part a longitudinal arrangement; a middle layer, in which the fibers are arranged, more or less, in a circular manner; and an internal layer, in which the fibers have a general longitudinal arrangement (Fig. 1124).

The *fibers of the external layer* arise from the posterior surface of the body of the pubis in both sexes (*musculi pubovesicales*), and in the male from the adjacent part of the prostate and its capsule. They pass, in a more or less longitudinal manner, up the inferior surface of the bladder, over its vertex, and then descend along its fundus to become attached to the prostate in the male, and to the front of the vagina in the female. At the sides of the bladder the fibers are arranged obliquely and intersect one another. This layer has been named the **Detrusor urinæ muscle.**

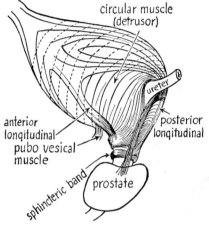

FIG. 1124.—Diagram of the muscles of the bladder (after McCrea).

The *fibers of the middle circular layer* are very thinly and irregularly scattered on the body of the organ, and, although to some extent placed transversely to the long axis of the bladder, are for the most part arranged obliquely. Toward the lower part of the bladder, around the internal urethral orifice, they are disposed in a thick circular layer, forming the **Sphincter vesicæ,** which is continuous with the muscular fibers of the prostate.

The *internal longitudinal layer* is thin, and its fasciculi have a reticular arrangement, but with a tendency to assume for the most part a longitudinal direction. Two bands of oblique fibers, originating behind the orifices of the ureters, converge to the back part of the prostate, and are inserted by means of a fibrous process, into the middle lobe of that organ. They are the **muscles of the ureters,** described by Sir C. Bell, who supposed that during the contraction of the bladder they serve to retain the oblique direction of the ureters, and so prevent the reflux of the urine into them.

The **submucous coat** (*tela submucosa*) consists of a layer of areolar tissue, connecting together the muscular and mucous coats, and intimately united to the latter.

The **mucous coat** (*tunica mucosa*) is thin, smooth, and of a pale rose color. It is continuous above through the ureters with the lining membrane of the renal tubules, and below with that of the urethra. The loose texture of the submucous layer allows the mucous coat to be thrown into folds or *rugæ* when the bladder is empty. Over the trigonum vesicæ the mucous membrane is closely attached to the muscular coat, and is not thrown into folds, but is smooth and flat. The epithelium covering it is of the transitional variety, consisting of a superficial layer of polyhedral flattened cells, each with one, two, or three nuclei; beneath these is a stratum of large club-shaped cells, with their narrow extremities directed downward and wedged in between smaller spindle-shaped cells, containing oval nuclei (Fig. 1124). The epithelium varies according as the bladder is distended or contracted. In the former condition the superficial cells are flattened and those of the other layers are shortened; in the latter they present the appearance described above. There are no true glands in the mucous membrane of the bladder, though certain mucous follicles which exist, especially near the neck of the bladder, have been regarded as such.

Vessels and Nerves.—The **arteries** supplying the bladder are the superior, middle, and inferior vesical, derived from the anterior trunk of the hypogastric. The obturator and inferior gluteal arteries also supply small visceral branches to the bladder, and in the female additional branches are derived from the uterine and vaginal arteries.

The **veins** form a complicated plexus on the inferior surface, and fundus near the prostate, and end in the hypogastric veins.

The **lymphatics** are described on page 724.

The **nerves** of the bladder are (1) fine medullated fibers from the third and fourth sacral nerves, and (2) non-medullated fibers from the hypogastric plexus. They are connected with ganglia in the outer and submucous coats and are finally distributed, all as non-medullated fibers, to the muscular layer and epithelial lining of the viscus.

Variations.—A defect of development, in which the bladder is implicated, is known under the name of *extroversion of the bladder*. In this condition the lower part of the abdominal wall and the anterior wall of the bladder are wanting, so that the fundus of the bladder presents on the abdominal surface, and is pushed forward by the pressure of the viscera within the abdomen, forming a red vascular tumor on which the openings of the ureters are visible. The penis, except the glans, is rudimentary and is cleft on its dorsal surface, exposing the floor of the urethra, a condition known as *epsipadias*. The pelvic bones are also arrested in development.

The Male Urethra (Urethra Virilis) (Fig. 1125).

The **male urethra** extends from the internal urethral orifice in the urinary bladder to the external urethral orifice at the end of the penis. It presents a double curve in the ordinary relaxed state of the penis (Fig. 1117).

Its length varies from 17.5 to 20 cm.; and it is divided into three portions, the **prostatic, membranous,** and **cavernous,** the structure and relations of which are essentially different. Except during the passage of the urine or semen, the greater part of the urethral canal is a mere transverse cleft or slit, with its upper and under surfaces in contact; at the external orifice the slit is vertical, in the membranous portion irregular or stellate, and in the prostatic portion somewhat arched.

The **prostatic portion** (*pars prostatica*), the widest and most dilatable part of the canal, is about 3 cm. long, It runs almost vertically through the prostate from its base to its apex, lying nearer its anterior than its posterior surface; the form of the canal is spindle-shaped, being wider in the middle than at either extremity, and narrowest below, where it joins the membranous portion. A transverse section of the canal as it lies in the prostate is horseshoe-shaped, with the convexity directed forward.

Upon the posterior wall or floor is a narrow longitudinal ridge, the **urethral crest** (*verumontanum*), formed by an elevation of the mucous membrane and its subjacent tissue. It is from 15 to 17 mm. in length, and about 3 mm. in height. On

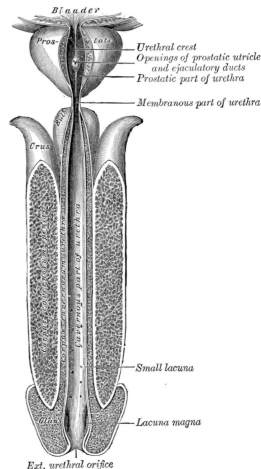

Fig. 1125.—The male urethra laid open on its anterior (upper) surface.

either side of the crest is a slightly depressed fossa, the **prostatic sinus,** the floor of which is perforated by numerous apertures, the **orifices of the prostatic ducts** from the lateral lobes of the prostate; the ducts of the middle lobe open behind the crest. At the forepart of the urethral crest, below its summit, is a median elevation, the **colliculus seminalis,** upon or within the margins of which are the orifices of the prostatic utricle and the slit-like openings of the ejaculatory ducts. The **prostatic utricle** (*sinus pocularis*) forms a cul-de-sac about 6 mm. long, which runs upward and backward in the substance of the prostate behind the middle lobe. Its walls are composed of fibrous tissue, muscular fibers, and mucous membrane, and numerous small glands open on its inner surface. It was called by Weber the **uterus masculinus,** from its being developed from the united lower ends of the atrophied Müllerian ducts, and therefore homologous with the uterus and vagina in the female.

The **membranous portion** (*pars membranacea*) is the shortest, least dilatable, and, with the exception of the external orifice, the narrowest part of the canal. It extends downward and forward, with a slight anterior concavity, between the apex of the prostate and the bulb of the urethra, perforating the urogenital diaphragm about 2.5 cm. below and behind the pubic symphysis. The hinder part of the urethral bulb lies in apposition with the superficial layer of the urogenital diaphragm, but its upper portion diverges somewhat from this fascia: the anterior wall of the membranous urethra is thus prolonged for a short distance in front of the urogenital diaphragm; it measures about 2 cm. in length, while the posterior wall which is between the two fasciæ of the diaphragm is only 1.25 cm. long.

The membranous portion of the urethra is completely surrounded by the fibers of the Sphincter urethræ membranaceæ. In front of it the deep dorsal vein of the penis enters the pelvis between the transverse ligament of the pelvis and the arcuate pubic ligament; on either side near its termination are the bulbourethral glands.

The **cavernous portion** (*pars cavernosa; penile or spongy portion*) is the longest part of the urethra, and is contained in the corpus cavernosum urethræ. It is about 15 cm. long, and extends from the termination of the membranous portion to the external urethral orifice. Commencing below the superficial layer of the urogenital diaphragm it passes forward and upward to the front of the symphysis pubis; and then, in the flaccid condition of the penis, it bends downward and forward. It is narrow, and of uniform size in the body of the penis, measuring about 6 mm. in diameter; it is dilated behind, within the bulb, and again anteriorly within the glans penis, where it forms the **fossa navicularis urethræ**.

The **external urethral orifice** (*orificium urethræ externum; meatus urinarius*) is the most contracted part of the urethra; it is a vertical slit, about 6 mm. long, bounded on either side by two small labia.

The lining membrane of the urethra, especially on the floor of the cavernous portion, presents the orifices of numerous mucous glands and follicles situated in the submucous tissue, and named the **urethral glands** (*Littré*). Besides these there are a number of small pit-like recesses, or **lacunæ**, of varying sizes. Their orifices are directed forward, so that they may easily intercept the point of a catheter in its passage along the canal. One of these lacunæ, larger than the rest, is situated on the upper surface of the fossa navicularis; it is called the **lacuna magna**. The bulbo-urethral glands open into the cavernous portion about 2.5 cm. in front of the inferior fascia of the urogenital diaphragm.

Structure.—The urethra is composed of mucous membrane, supported by a submucous tissue which connects it with the various structures through which it passes.

The **mucous coat** forms part of the genito-urinary mucous membrane. It is continuous with the mucous membrane of the bladder, ureters, and kidneys; externally, with the integument covering the glans penis; and is prolonged into the ducts of the glands which open into the urethra, viz., the bulbo-urethral glands and the prostate; and into the ductus deferentes and vesiculæ seminales, through the ejaculatory ducts. In the cavernous and membranous portions the mucous membrane is arranged in longitudinal folds when the tube is empty. Small papillæ are found upon it, near the external urethral orifice; its epithelial lining is of the columnar variety except near the external orifice, where it is squamous and stratified.

The submucosa has a characteristic structure. It is composed of a thick stroma of connective tissue very rich in elastic fibers. These fibers connect freely with the spongy tissue of the penis which prevents ready removal of the mucosa in this region. However, in the membranous and prostatic portions, which change but little during erection, the urethra is quite free and may on dissection be stripped readily.

Congenital defects of the urethra occur occasionally. The one most frequently met with is where there is a cleft on the floor of the urethra owing to an arrest of union in the middle line. This is known as *hypospadias,* and the cleft may vary in extent. The simplest and by far the most common form is where the deficiency is confined to the glans penis. The urethra ends at the point where the extremity of the prepuce joins the body of the penis, in a small valve-like opening. The prepuce is also cleft on its under surface and forms a sort of hood over the glans.

There is a depression on the glans in the position of the normal meatus. This condition produces no disability and requires no treatment. In more severe cases the cavernous portion of the urethra is cleft throughout its entire length, and the opening of the urethra is at the point of junction of the penis and scrotum. The under surface of the penis in the middle line presents a furrow lined by a moist mucous membrane, on either side of which is often more or less dense fibrous tissue stretching from the glans to the opening of the urethra, which prevents complete erection taking place. Great discomfort is induced during micturition, and sexual connection is impossible. The condition may be remedied by a series of plastic operations. The worst form of this condition is where the urethra is deficient as far back as the perineum, and the scrotum is cleft. The penis is small and bound down between the two halves of the scrotum, so as to resemble an hypertrophied clitoris. The testes are often retained. The condition of parts, therefore, very much resembles the external organs of generation of the female, and many children the victims of this malformation have been brought up as girls. The halves of the scrotum, deficient of testes, resemble the labia, the cleft between them looks like the orifice of the vagina, and the diminutive penis is taken for an enlarged clitoris. There is no remedy for this condition.

A much more uncommon form of malformation is where there is an apparent deficiency of the upper wall of the urethra; this is named *epispadias*. The deficiency may vary in extent; when it is complete the condition is associated with extroversion of the bladder. In less extensive cases, where there is no extroversion, there is an infundibuliform opening into the bladder. The penis is usually dwarfed and turned upward, so that the glans lies over the opening. Congenital stricture is also occasionally met with, and in such cases multiple strictures may be present throughout the whole length of the cavernous portion.

The Female Urethra (Urethra Muliebris) (Fig. 1121).

The **female urethra** is a narrow membranous canal, about 4 cm. long, extending from the internal to the external urethral orifice. It is placed behind the symphysis pubis, imbedded in the anterior wall of the vagina, and its direction is obliquely downward and forward; it is slightly curved with the concavity directed forward. Its diameter when undilated is about 6 mm. It perforates the fasciæ of the urogenital diaphragm, and its external orifice is situated directly in front of the vaginal opening and about 2.5 cm. behind the glans clitoridis. The lining membrane is thrown into longitudinal folds, one of which, placed along the floor of the canal, is termed the **urethral crest**. Many small urethral glands open into the urethra. The largest of these are the paraurethral glands (Skene) the ducts of which open just within the urethral orifice.

Structure.—The urethra consists of three coats: **muscular, erectile,** and **mucous.**

The **muscular coat** is continuous with that of the bladder; it extends the whole length of the tube, and consists of circular fibers. In addition to this, between the superior and inferior fasciæ of the urogenital diaphragm, the female urethra is surrounded by the Sphincter urethræ membranaceæ, as in the male.

A **thin layer of spongy erectile tissue,** containing a plexus of large veins, intermixed with bundles of unstriped muscular fibers, lies immediately beneath the mucous coat.

The **mucous coat** is pale; it is continuous externally with that of the vulva, and internally with that of the bladder. It is lined by stratified squamous epithelium, which becomes transitional near the bladder. Its external orifice is surrounded by a few mucous follicles.

THE MALE GENITAL ORGANS (ORGANA GENITALIA VIRILIA).

The male genitals include the **testes,** the **ductus deferentes,** the **vesiculæ seminales,** the **ejaculatory ducts,** and the **penis,** together with the following accessory structures, viz., the **prostate** and the **bulbourethral glands.**

The Testes and Their Coverings (Figs. 1126, 1127, 1128).

The **testes** are two glandular organs, which produce the semen; they are suspended in the scrotum by the spermatic cords. At an early period of fetal life the testes are contained in the abdominal cavity, behind the peritoneum. Before birth they descend to the inguinal canal, along which they pass with the spermatic cord, and, emerging at the subcutaneous inguinal ring, descend into the scrotum, becoming invested in their course by coverings derived from the serous, muscular, and fibrous layers of the abdominal parietes, as well as by the scrotum.

The **coverings of the testes** are, the

Skin $\left.\right\}$ Scrotum
Dartos tunic
External spermatic fascia.

Cremasteric layer
Internal spermatic fascia.
Tunica vaginalis.

The **Scrotum** is a cutaneous pouch which contains the testes and parts of the spermatic cords. It is divided on its surface into two lateral portions by a ridge

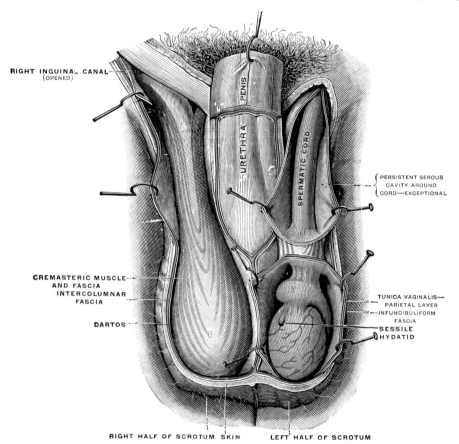

RIGHT INGUINAL CANAL (OPENED)

PENIS

URETHRA

SPERMATIC CORD

PERSISTENT SEROUS CAVITY AROUND CORD—EXCEPTIONAL

CREMASTERIC MUSCLE AND FASCIA

INTERCOLUMNAR FASCIA

DARTOS

TUNICA VAGINALIS— PARIETAL LAYER

INFUNDIBULIFORM FASCIA

SESSILE HYDATID

RIGHT HALF OF SCROTUM SKIN   LEFT HALF OF SCROTUM

Fig. 1126—The scrotum. On the left side the cavity of the tunica vaginalis has been opened; on the right side only the layers superficial to the Cremaster have been removed. (Testut)

or **raphé,** which is continued forward to the under surface of the penis, and backward, along the middle line of the perineum to the anus. Of these two lateral portions the left hangs lower than the right, to correspond with the greater length of the left spermatic cord. Its external aspect varies under different circumstances: thus, under the influence of warmth, and in old and debilitated persons, it becomes elongated and flaccid; but, under the influence of cold, and in the young and robust, it is short, corrugated, and closely applied to the testes.

The scrotum consists of two layers, the **integument** and the **dartos tunic.**

The **Integument** is very thin, of a brownish color, and generally thrown into folds or rugæ. It is provided with sebaceous follicles, the secretion of which has a peculiar odor, and is beset with thinly scattered, crisp hairs, the roots of which are seen through the skin.

The **Dartos Tunic** (*tunica dartos*) contains a thin layer of non-striped muscular fibers, continuous, around the base of the scrotum, with the two layers of the superficial fascia of the groin and the perineum; it sends inward a septum, which divides the scrotal pouch into two cavities for the testes, and extends between the raphé and the under surface of the penis, as far as its root.

The dartos tunic is closely united to the skin externally, but is separated from the subjacent parts by a distinct fascial cleft, upon which it glides with the greatest facility.   It contains no fat and is highly vascular.

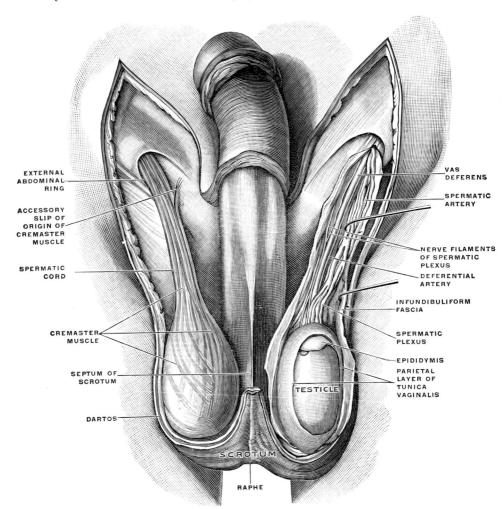

EXTERNAL ABDOMINAL RING

ACCESSORY SLIP OF ORIGIN OF CREMASTER MUSCLE

SPERMATIC CORD

CREMASTER MUSCLE

SEPTUM OF SCROTUM

DARTOS

VAS DEFERENS

SPERMATIC ARTERY

NERVE FILAMENTS OF SPERMATIC PLEXUS

DEFERENTIAL ARTERY

INFUNDIBULIFORM FASCIA

SPERMATIC PLEXUS

EPIDIDYMIS

PARIETAL LAYER OF TUNICA VAGINALIS

TESTICLE

SCROTUM

RAPHE

Fig. 1127 — The scrotum.   The penis has been turned upward, and the anterior wall of the scrotum has been removed. On the right side, the spermatic cord, the infundibuliform fascia, and the Cremaster muscles are displayed; on the left side, the infundibuliform fascia has been divided by a longitudinal incision passing along the front of the cord and the testicle, and a portion of the parietal layer of the tunica vaginalis has been removed to display the testicle and a portion of the head of the epididymis, which are covered by the visceral layer of the tunica vaginalis.   (Toldt.)

The **Tunica Vaginalis** is described with the testes.

The **External Spermatic Facia** (*intercrural or intercolumnar fascia*) is a thin membrane prolonged downward over the cord and testis.   It is continuous, at the subcutaneous inguinal ring, with the deep fascia covering the aponeurosis of the Obliquus externus abdominis (fascia innominata of Gallaudet) and is therefore part of the external investing fascia of the body.   It is separated from the enclosing dartos by a fascial cleft (page 397).

The **Cremasteric Layer** consists of the scattered bundles of the Cremaster connected into a continuous membrane by the cremateric fascia. It forms the *middle spermatic layer* and corresponds to the Obliquus internus abdominis and its fasciæ (page 398).

The **Internal Spermatic Fascia** (*infundibuliform fascia; tunica vaginalis communis*) is a thin membrane, often difficult to separate from the preceding, but more easily separated from the cord and testis which it encloses. It is continuous at the internal inguinal ring with the transversalis fascia (page 404).

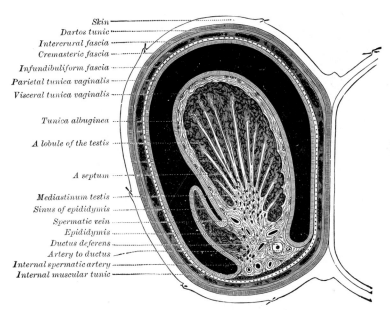

Skin
Dartos tunic
Intercrural fascia
Cremasteric fascia
Infundibuliform fascia
Parietal tunica vaginalis
Visceral tunica vaginalis
Tunica albuginea
A lobule of the testis
A septum
Mediastinum testis
Sinus of epididymis
Spermatic vein
Epididymis
Ductus deferens
Artery to ductus
Internal spermatic artery
Internal muscular tunic

Fig. 1128.—Transverse section through the left side of the scrotum and the left testis. The sac of the tunica vaginalis is represented in a distended condition. (Diagrammatic.) (Delépine.)

Vessels and Nerves.—The **arteries** supplying the coverings of the testes are: the superficial and deep external pudendal branches of the femoral, the superficial perineal branch of the internal pudendal, and the cremasteric branch from the inferior epigastric. The **veins** follow the course of the corresponding arteries. The **lymphatics** end in the inguinal lymph nodes. The **nerves** are the ilioinguinal and lumboinguinal branches of the lumbar plexus, the two superficial perineal branches of the internal pudendal nerve, and the pudendal branch of the posterior femoral cutaneous nerve.

The **Inguinal Canal** (*canalis inguinalis*) is described on page 406.

The **Spermatic Cord** (*funiculus spermaticus*) (Fig. 1129) extends from the abdominal inguinal ring, where the structures of which it is composed converge, to the back part of the testis. In the abdominal wall the cord passes obliquely along the inguinal canal, lying at first beneath the Obliquus internus, and upon the fascia transversalis; but nearer the pubis, it rests upon the inguinal and lacunar ligaments, having the aponeurosis of the Obliquus externus in front of it, and the inguinal falx behind it. It then escapes at the subcutaneous ring, and descends nearly vertically into the scrotum. The left cord is rather longer than the right, consequently the left testis hangs somewhat lower than the right.

Structure of the Spermatic Cord.—The spermatic cord is composed of arteries, veins, lymphatics, nerves, and the excretory duct of the testis. These structures are connected together by the **innermost spermatic fascia** which is continuous with the subserous fascia of the abdomen at the internal inguinal ring, and are invested by the layers brought down by the testis in its descent.

The **arteries of the cord** are: the internal and external spermatics; and the artery to the ductus deferens.

The *internal spermatic artery*, a branch of the abdominal aorta, escapes from the abdomen at the abdominal inguinal ring, and accompanies the other constituents of the spermatic cord along the inguinal canal and through the subcutaneous inguinal ring into the scrotum. It then descends to the testis, and, becoming tortuous, divides into several branches, two or three of which accompany the ductus deferens and supply the epididymis, anastomosing with the artery of the ductus deferens: the others supply the substance of the testis.

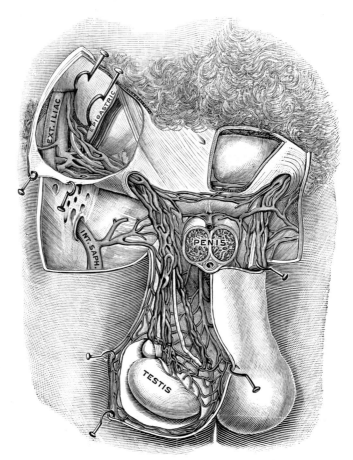

Fig. 1129.—Spermatic veins and spermatic cord.   (Testut.)

The *external spermatic artery* is a branch of the inferior epigastric artery. It accompanies the spermatic cord and supplies the coverings of the cord, anastomosing with the internal spermatic artery.

The *artery of the ductus deferens*, a branch of the superior vesical, is a long, slender vessel, which accompanies the ductus deferens, ramifying upon its coats, and anastomosing with the internal spermatic artery near the testis.

The **spermatic veins** (Fig. 1129) emerge from the back of the testis, and receive tributaries from the epididymis: they unite and form a convoluted plexus, the **plexus pampiniformis**, which forms the chief mass of the cord; the vessels composing this plexus are very numerous, and ascend along the cord in front of the ductus deferens; below the subcutaneous inguinal ring they unite to form three or four veins, which pass along the inguinal canal, and, entering the abdomen through the abdominal inguinal ring, coalesce to form two veins. These again unite to form a single vein, which opens on the right side into the inferior vena cava, at an acute angle, and on the left side into the left renal vein, at a right angle.

The **lymphatic vessels** are described on page 725.

The **nerves** are the spermatic plexus from the sympathetic, joined by filaments from the **pelvic plexus** which accompany the artery of the ductus deferens.

The scrotum forms an admirable covering for the protection of the testes. These bodies, lying suspended and loose in the cavity of the scrotum and surrounded by serous membrane, are capable of great mobility, and can therefore easily slip about within the scrotum and thus avoid injuries from blows or squeezes. The skin of the scrotum is very elastic and capable of great distension, and on account of the looseness and amount of subcutaneous tissue, the scrotum becomes greatly enlarged in cases of edema, to which this part is especially liable as a result of its dependent position.

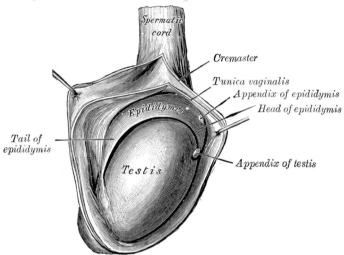

Fig. 1130.—The right testis, exposed by laying open the tunica vaginalis.

The **Testes** are suspended in the scrotum by the spermatic cords. They average 4 to 5 cm. in length, 2.5 cm. in breadth, and 3 cm. in the antero-posterior diameter.

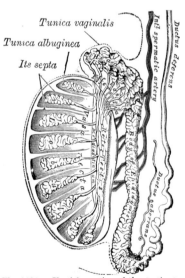

Fig. 1131 — Verticle section of the testis, to show the arrangement of the ducts.

The weight of one gland varies from 10.5 to 14 gm. Each testis is of an oval form (Fig. 1130), compressed laterally, and having an oblique position in the scrotum; the upper extremity is directed forward and a little lateralward; the lower, backward and a little medialward; the anterior convex border looks forward and downward, the posterior or straight border, to which the cord is attached, backward and upward.

The anterior border and lateral surfaces, as well as both extremities of the organ, are convex, free, smooth, and invested by the visceral layer of the tunica vaginalis. The posterior border, to which the cord is attached, receives only a partial investment from that membrane. Lying upon the lateral edge of this posterior border is a long, narrow, flattened body, named the **epididymis.**

The **epididymis** consists of a central portion or **body;** an upper enlarged extremity, the **head** (*globus maior*); and a lower pointed extremity, the **tail** (*globus minor*), which is continuous with the ductus deferens, the **duct of the testis.** The head is intimately connected with the upper end of the testis by means of the efferent ductules of the gland; the tail is connected with the lower end by cellular tissue, and a reflection of the tunica vaginalis. The lateral surface, head and tail of the epididymis are free and covered by the serous membrane; the body is also completely invested by it, excepting along its posterior border; while between the body and the testis is a pouch, named the **sinus of the epididymis** (*digital fossa*). The epididymis is connected to the back of the testis by a fold of the serous membrane.

Appendages of the Testis and Epididymis.—On the upper extremity of the testis, just beneath the head of the epididymis, is a minute oval, sessile body, the **appendix of the testis** (*hydatid of Morgagni*); it is the remnant of the upper end of the Müllerian duct. On the head of the epididymis is a second small stalked appendage (sometimes duplicated); it is named the **appendix of the epididymis** (*pedunculated hydatid*), and is usually regarded as a detached efferent duct.

The testis is invested by three tunics: the **tunica vaginalis, tunica albuginea,** and **tunica vasculosa.**

The **Tunica Vaginalis** (*tunica vaginalis propria testis*) is the serous covering of the testis. It is a pouch of serous membrane, derived from the saccus vaginalis of the peritoneum, which in the fetus preceded the descent of the testis from the abdomen into the scrotum. After its descent, that portion of the pouch which extends from the abdominal inguinal ring to near the upper part of the gland becomes obliterated; the lower portion remains as a closed sac, which invests the testis, and may be described as consisting of a **visceral** and a **parietal lamina.**

The **visceral lamina** (*lamina visceralis*) covers the greater part of the testis and epididymis, connecting the latter to the testis by means of a distinct fold. From the posterior border of the gland it is reflected on to the internal surface of the scrotal coverings.

The **parietal lamina** (lamina parietalis) is more extensive than the visceral, extending upward for some distance in front and on the medial side of the cord, and reaching below the testis. The inner surface of the tunica vaginalis is smooth, and covered by a layer of mesothelial cells. The interval between the visceral and parietal laminæ constitutes the cavity of the tunica vaginalis.

The obliterated portion of the saccus vaginalis may generally be seen as a fibrocellular thread lying in the loose areolar tissue around the spermatic cord; sometimes this may be traced as a distinct band from the upper end of the inguinal canal, where it is connected with the peritoneum, down to the tunica vaginalis; sometimes it gradually becomes lost on the spermatic cord. Occasionally no trace of it can be detected. In some cases it happens that the pouch of peritoneum does not become obliterated, but the sac of the peritoneum communicates with the tunica vaginalis. This may give rise to one of the varieties of oblique inguinal hernia (page 1295). In other cases the pouch may contract, but not become entirely obliterated; it then forms a minute canal leading from the peritoneum to the tunica vaginalis.

The **Tunica Albuginea** is the fibrous covering of the testis. It is a dense membrane, of a bluish-white color, composed of bundles of white fibrous tissue which interlace in every direction. It is covered by the tunica vaginalis, except at the points of attachment of the epididymis to the testis, and along its posterior border, where the spermatic vessels enter the gland. It is applied to the tunica vasculosa over the glandular substance of the testis, and, at its posterior border, is reflected into the interior of the gland, forming an incomplete vertical septum, called the **mediastinum testis** (*corpus Highmori*).

The **mediastinum testis** extends from the upper to near the lower extremity of the gland, and is wider above than below. From its front and sides numerous imperfect septa (*trabeculæ*) are given off, which radiate toward the surface of the organ, and are attached to the tunica albuginea. They divide the interior of the organ into a number of incomplete spaces which are somewhat cone-shaped, being broad at their bases at the surface of the gland, and becoming narrower as they converge to the mediastinum. The mediastinum supports the vessels and duct of the testis in their passage to and from the substance of the gland.

The **Tunica Vasculosa** is the vascular layer of the testis, consisting of a plexus of bloodvessels, held together by delicate areolar tissue. It clothes the inner surface of the tunica albuginea and the different septa in the interior of the gland, and therefore forms an internal investment to all the spaces of which the gland is composed.

Structure.—The glandular structure of the testis consists of numerous lobules. Their number, in a single testis, is estimated by Berres at 250, and by Krause at 400. They differ in size according to their position, those in the middle of the gland being larger and longer. The lobules (Fig. 1131) are conical in shape, the base being directed toward the circumference of the organ, the apex toward the mediastinum. Each lobule is contained in one of the intervals between the fibrous septa which extend between the mediastinum testis and the tunica albuiginea, and consists of from one to three, or more, minute convoluted tubes, the **tubuli seminiferi.**

The tubules may be separately unravelled, by careful dissection under water, and may be seen to commence either by free cecal ends or by anastomotic loops. They are supported by loose connective tissue which contains here and there groups of "interstitial cells" containing yellow pigment granules. The total number of tubules is estimated by Lauth at 840, and the average length of each is 70 to 80 cm. Their diameter varies from 0.12 to 0.3 mm. The tubules are pale in color in early life, but in old age they acquire a deep yellow tinge from containing much fatty matter. Each tubule consists of a basement layer formed of laminated connective tissue containing numerous elastic fibers with flattened cells between the layers and covered externally by a layer of flattened epithelioid cells. Within the basement membrane are epithelial eclls arranged in several irregular layers, which are not always clearly separated, but which may be ar: ranged in three different groups (Fig. 1133). Among these cells may be seen the **spermatozoa** in different stages of development. (1) Lining the basement membrane and forming the outer zone is a layer of cubical cells, with small nuclei; some of these enlarge to become **spermatogonia.** The nuclei of some of the spermatogonia may be seen to be in process of indirect division (*karyokineses*, page 19), and in consequence of this daughter cells are formed, which constitute the second zone. (2) Within this first layer is to be seen a number of larger polyhedral cells, with clear nuclei, arranged in two or three layers; these are the **intermediate cells** or **spermatocytes.** Most of these cells are in a condition of karyokinetic division, and the cells which

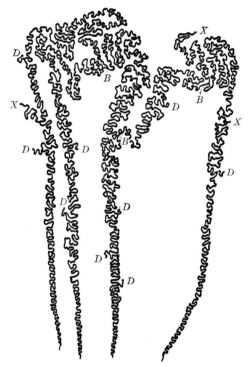

Fig. 1132.— Four seminiferous tubules from human testis showing anastomosing loops. *B*, branching or fork; *D*, diverticulum; *X*, broken end. (Johnson, Anat. Rec.. 1934; courtesy of Wistar Institute.)

result from this division form those of the next layer, the **spermatoblasts or spermatids.** (3) The third layer of cells consists of the spermatoblasts or spermatids, and each of these, without further subdivision, becomes a **spermatozoön.** The spermatids are small polyhedral cells, the nucleus of each of which contains half the usual number of chromosomes. In addition to these three layers of cells others are seen, which are termed the **supporting cells** (*cells of Sertoli*). They are elongated and columnar, and project inward from the basement membrane toward the lumen of the tube. As development of the spermatozoa proceeds the latter group themselves around the inner extremities of the supporting cells. The nuclear portion of the spermatid, which is partly imbedded in the supporting cell, is differentiated to form the head of the spermatozoön, while part of the cell protoplasm forms the middle piece and the tail is produced by an outgrowth from the double centriole of the cell. Ultimately the heads are liberated and the spermatozoa are set free. The structure of the spermatozoa is described on page 22.

In the apices of the lobules, the tubules become less convoluted, assume a nearly straight course, and unite together to form from twenty to thirty larger ducts, of about 0.5 mm. in diameter, and these, from their straight course, are called **tubuli recti** (Fig. 1131).

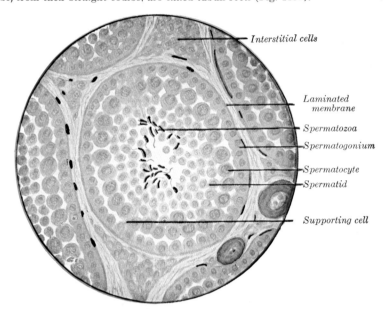

Fɪɢ. 1133.—Transverse section through a part of a human testis. Stained with hematoxylin and eosin.   × 350.

The **tubuli recti** enter the fibrous tissue of the mediastinum, and pass upward and backward, forming, in their ascent, a close net-work of anastomosing tubes which are merely channels in the fibrous stroma, lined by flattened epithelium, and having no proper walls; this constitutes the

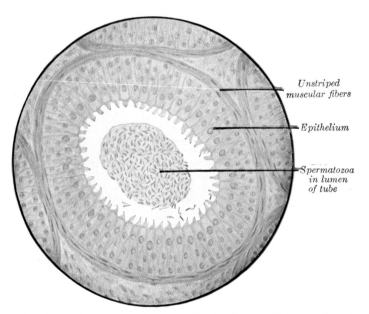

Fɪɢ. 1134.—Transverse section through the tube of the human epididymis. Stained with hematoxylin and eosin.   × 350.

rete testis. At the upper end of the mediastinum, the vessels of the rete testis terminate in from twelve to fifteen or twenty ducts, the **ductuli efferentes;** they perforate the tunica albuginea, and carry the seminal fluid from the testis to the epididymis. Their course is at first straight;

they then become enlarged, and exceedingly convoluted, and form a series of conical masses, the **coni vasculosi,** which together constitute the head of the epididymis. Each cone consists of a single convoluted duct, from 15 to 20 cm. in length, the diameter of which gradually decreases from the testis to the epididymis. Opposite the bases of the cones the efferent vessels open at narrow intervals into a single duct, which constitutes, by its complex convolutions, the body and tail of the epididymis. When the convolutions of this tube are unravelled, it measures upward of 6 meters in length; it increases in diameter and thickness as it approaches the ductus deferens. The convolutions are held together by fine areolar tissue, and by bands of fibrous tissue.

The tubuli recti have very thin walls; like the channels of the rete testis they are lined by a single layer of flattened epithelium. The ductuli efferentes and the tube of the epididymis have walls of considerable thickness, on account of the presence in them of muscular tissue, which is principally arranged in a circular manner. These tubes are lined by columnar ciliated epithelium (Fig. 1134).

Variations.—The testis, developed in the lumbar region, may be arrested or delayed in its transit to the scrotum (*cryptorchism*). It may be retained in the abdomen; or it may be arrested at the abdominal inguinal ring, or in the inguinal canal; or it may just pass out of the subcutaneous inguinal ring without finding its way to the bottom of the scrotum. When retained in the abdomen it gives rise to no symptoms, other than the absence of the testis from the scrotum; but when it is retained in the inguinal canal it is subjected to pressure and may become inflamed and painful. The retained testis is probably functionally useless; so that a man in whom both testes are retained (*anorchism*) is sterile, though he may not be impotent. The absence of one testis is termed *monorchism*. When a testis is retained in the inguinal canal it is often complicated with a congenital hernia, the funicular process of the peritoneum not being obliterated. In addition to the cases above described, where there is some arrest in the descent of the testis, this organ may descend through the inguinal canal, but may miss the scrotum and assume some abnormal position. The most common form is where the testis, emerging at the subcutaneous inguinal ring, slips down between the scrotum and thigh and comes to rest in the perineum. This is known as *perineal ectopia testis*. With each variety of abnormality in the position of the testis, it is very common to find concurrently a congenital hernia, or, if a hernia be not actually present, the funicular process is usually patent, and almost invariably so if the testis is in the inguinal canal.

The testis, finally reaching the scrotum, may occupy an abnormal position in it. It may be inverted, so that its posterior or attached border is directed forward and the tunica vaginalis is situated behind.

Fluid collections of a serous character are very frequently found in the scrotum. To these the term *hydrocele* is applied. The most common form is the ordinary *vaginal hydrocele,* in which the fluid is contained in the sac of the tunica vaginalis, which is separated, in its normal condition, from the peritoneal cavity by the whole extent of the inguinal canal. In another form, the *congenital hydrocele,* the fluid is in the sac of the tunica vaginalis, but this cavity communicates with the general peritoneal cavity, its tubular process remaining pervious. A third variety, known as an *infantile hydrocele,* occurs in those cases where the tubular process becomes obliterated only at its upper part, at or near the abdominal inguinal ring. It resembles the vaginal hydrocele, except as regards its shape, the collection of fluid extending up the cord into the inguinal canal. Fourthly, the funicular process may become obliterated both at the abdominal inguinal ring and above the epididymis, leaving a central unobliterated portion, which may become distended with fluid, giving rise to a condition known as the *encysted hydrocele of the cord.*

Congenital Hernia.— There are some varieties of oblique inguinal hernia (Fig. 1135) depend-

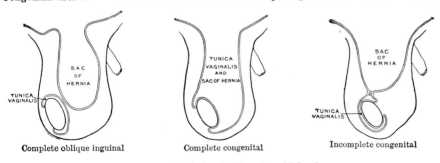

Complete oblique inguinal   Complete congenital   Incomplete congenital

Fig. 1135.— Varieties of oblique ingenial hernia.

ing upon congenital defects in the saccus vaginalis, the pouch of peritoneum which precedes the descent of the testis.

Normally this pouch is closed before birth, closure commencing at two points, viz., at the abdominal inguinal ring and at the top of the epididymis, and gradually extending until the whole of the intervening portion is converted into a fibrous cord. From failure in the completion of this process, variations in the relation of the hernial protrusion to the testis and tunica vaginalis are produced; these constitute distinct varieties of inguinal hernia, viz., the hernia of the funicular process and the complete congenital variety. Mitchell states that of 40 still-born infants examined, 7 showed complete obliteration of the saccus vaginalis on both sides, 12 showed sacs completely patent on both sides, and 21 exhibited all intermediate degrees of obliteration.

Where the saccus vaginalis remains patent throughout, the cavity of the tunica vaginalis communicates directly with that of the peritoneum. The intestine descends along this pouch into the cavity of the tunica vaginalis which constitutes the sac of the hernia, and the gut lies in contact with the testis. Though this form of hernia is termed *complete congenital*, the term does not imply that the hernia existed at birth, but merely that a condition is present which may allow of the descent of the hernia at any moment. As a matter of fact, congenital herniæ frequently do not appear until adult life. Where the processus vaginalis is occluded at the lower point only, *i. e.*, just above the testis, the intestine descends into the pouch of peritoneum as far as the testis, but is prevented from entering the sac of the tunica vaginalis by the septum which has formed between it and the pouch. This is known as *hernia into the funicular process* or *incomplete congenital hernia;* it differs from the former in that instead of enveloping the testis it lies above it.

The Ductus Deferens (Vas Deferens; Seminal Duct).

The **ductus deferens,** the excretory duct of the testis, is the continuation of the canal of the epididymis. Commencing at the lower part of the tail of the epididymis it is at first very tortuous, but gradually becoming less twisted it ascends along the posterior border of the testis and medial side of the epididymis, and, as a constituent of the spermatic cord, traverses the inguinal canal to the abdominal inguinal ring (Fig. 1129). Here it separates from the other structures of the cord, curves around the lateral side of the inferior epigastric artery, and ascends for about 2.5 cm. in front of the external iliac artery (Fig. 1030). It is next directed backward and slightly downward, and, crossing the external iliac vessels obliquely, enters the pelvic cavity, where it lies between the peritoneal membrane and the lateral wall of the pelvis, and descends on the medial side of the obliterated umbilical artery and the obturator nerve and vessels. It then crosses in front of the ureter, and, reaching the medial side of this tube, bends to form an acute angle, and runs medialward and slightly forward between the fundus of the bladder and the upper end of the seminal vesicle (Fig. 1136). Reaching the medial side of the seminal vesicle, it is directed downward and medialward in contact with it, gradually approaching the opposite ductus. Here it lies between the fundus of the bladder and the rectum, where it is enclosed, together with the seminal vesicle, in a sheath derived from the rectovesical portion of the subserous fascia. Lastly, it is directed downward to the base of the prostate, where it becomes greatly narrowed, and is joined at an acute angle by the duct of the seminal vesicle to form the ejaculatory duct, which traverses the prostate behind its middle lobe and opens into the prostatic portion of the urethra, close to the orifice of the prostatic utricle. The ductus deferens presents a hard and cord-like sensation to the fingers, and is of cylindrical form; its walls are dense, and its canal is extremely small. At the fundus of the bladder it becomes enlarged and tortuous, and this portion is termed the **ampulla.** A small triangular area of the fundus of the bladder, between the ductus deferentes laterally and the bottom of the rectovesical excavation of peritoneum above, is in contact with the rectum.

Ductuli Aberrantes.—A long narrow tube, the **ductulus aberrans inferior** (*vas aberrans of Haller*), is occasionally found connected with the lower part of the canal of the epididymis, or with the commencement of the ductus deferens. Its length varies from 3.5 to 35 cm., and it may become dilated toward its extremity; more commonly it retains the same diameter throughout. Its structure is similar to that of the ductus deferens. Occasionally it is found unconnected with the epididymis. A second tube, the **ductulus aberrans superior,** occurs in the head of the epididymis; it is connected with the rete testis.

Paradidymis (*organ of Giraldés*).—This term is applied to a small collection of convoluted tubules, situated in front of the lower part of the cord above the head of the epididymis. These tubes are lined with columnar ciliated epithelium, and probably represent the remains of a part of the Wolffian body.

Structure.—The ductus deferens consists of three coats: (1) an **external** or **areolar coat;** (2) a **muscular coat** which in the greater part of the tube consists of two layers of unstriped muscular fiber: an outer, longitudinal in direction, and an inner, circular; but in addition to these, at the commencement of the ductus, there is a third layer, consisting of longitudinal fibers, placed internal to the circular stratum, between it and the mucous membrane; (3) an **internal** or **mucous coat,** which is pale, and arranged in longitudinal folds. The mucous coat is lined by columnar epithelium which is non-ciliated throughout the greater part of the tube; a variable portion of the testicular end of the tube is lined by two strata of columnar cells and the cells of the superficial layer are ciliated.

The Vesiculæ Seminales (Seminal Vesicales) (Fig. 1136).

The **vesiculæ seminales** are two lobulated membranous pouches, placed between the fundus of the bladder and the rectum, which secrete a fluid to be added to the secretion of the testes. Each sac is somewhat pyramidal in form, the broad end being directed backward, upward and lateralward. It is usually about 7.5 cm. long, but varies in size, not only in different individuals, but also in the same individual on the two sides. The **anterior surface** is in contact with the fundus of the bladder, extending from near the termination of the ureter to the base of the

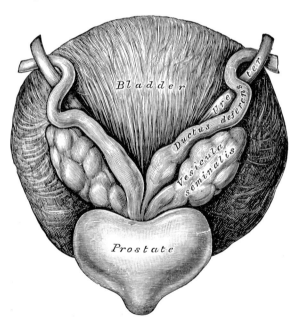

Fɪɢ. 1136.—Fundus of the bladder with the vesiculæ seminales.

prostate. The **posterior surface** rests upon the rectum, from which it is separated by the rectovesical fascia. The **upper extremities** of the two vesicles diverge from each other, and are in relation with the ductus deferentes and the terminations of the ureters, and are partly covered by peritoneum. The **lower extremities** are pointed, and converge toward the base of the prostate, where each joins with the corresponding ductus deferens to form the ejaculatory duct. Along the medial margin of each vesicle runs the ampulla of the ductus deferens.

Each vesicle consists of a single tube, coiled upon itself, and giving off several irregular cecal diverticula; the separate coils, as well as the diverticula, are connected together by fibrous tissue. When uncoiled, the tube is about the diameter of a quill, and varies in length from 10 to 15 cm.; it ends posteriorly in a cul-de-sac; its anterior extremity becomes constricted into a narrow straight duct, which joins with the corresponding ductus deferens to form the ejaculatory duct.

Structure.—The vesiculæ seminales are composed of three coats: an **external** or **areolar coat;** a **middle** or **muscular coat** thinner than in the ductus deferens and arranged in two layers, an outer longitudinal and inner circular; an **internal** or **mucous coat,** which is pale, of a whitish brown color, and presents a delicate reticular structure. The epithelium is columnar, and in the diverticula goblet cells are present, the secretion of which increases the bulk of the seminal fluid.

Vessels and Nerves.—The **arteries** supplying the vesiculæ seminales are derived from the middle and inferior vesical and middle hemorrhoidal. The **veins** and **lymphatics** accompany the arteries. The **nerves** are derived from the pelvic plexuses.

The Ejaculatory Ducts (Ductus Ejaculatorii) (Fig. 1117, 1137).

The **ejaculatory ducts** are two in number, one on either side of the middle line. Each is formed by the union of the duct from the vesicula seminalis with the ductus deferens, and is about 2 cm. long. They commence at the base of the prostate, and run forward and downward between its middle and lateral lobes, and along the sides of the prostatic utricle, to end by separate slit-like orifices close to or just within the margins of the utricle. The ducts diminish in size, and also converge, toward their terminations.

Structure.—The coats of the ejaculatory ducts are extremely thin. They are: an **outer fibrous layer,** which is almost entirely lost after the entrance of the ducts into the prostate; a **layer of muscular fibers** consisting of a thin outer circular, and an inner longitudinal, layer; and **mucous membrane.**

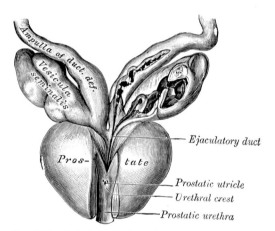

Fig. 1137.—Vesiculæ seminales and ampullæ of ductus deferentes, seen from the front. The anterior walls of the left ampulla, left seminal vesicle, and prostatic urethra have been cut away.

The Penis.

The **penis** is attached to the front and sides of the pubic arch and contains the greater part of the urethra. In the flaccid condition it is cylindrical in shape, but when erect assumes the form of a triangular prism with rounded angles, one side of the prism forming the dorsum. It is composed of three cylindrical masses of cavernous tissue bound together by fibrous tissue and covered with skin. Two of the masses are lateral, and are known as the **corpora cavernosa penis;** the third is median, and is termed the **corpus cavernosum urethræ** (Figs. 1139, 1140).

The integument covering the penis is remarkable for its thinness, its dark color, its looseness of connection with the deeper parts of the organ, and its absence of adipose tissue. At the root of the penis it is continuous with that over the pubis, scrotum, and perineum. At the neck it leaves the surface and becomes folded upon itself to form the **prepuce** or **foreskin.** The internal layer of the prepuce is directly continuous, along the line of the neck, with the integument over the glans. Immediately behind the external urethral orifice it forms a small secondary reduplication, attached along the bottom of a depressed median raphé, which extends from the meatus to the neck; this fold is termed the **frenulum** of the prepuce. The integument covering the glans is continuous with the urethral mucous membrane at the orifice; it is devoid of hairs, but projecting from its free surface are a number of small, highly sensitive papillæ. Scattered glands are present on the neck of the penis and inner layer of the prepuce, the **preputial glands** (Tyson). They secrete a sebaceous material of very peculiar odor, which probably contains casein, and readily undergoes decomposition; when mixed with discarded epithelial cells it is called smegma.

The prepuce covers a variable amount of the glans, and is separated from it by a potential space—the **preputial space**—which presents two shallow fossæ, one on either side of the frenulum.

Fascia.—The **superficial fascia of the penis** is directly continuous with that of the scrotum, and like it, contains a **dartos** tunic with its layer of scattered smooth muscle

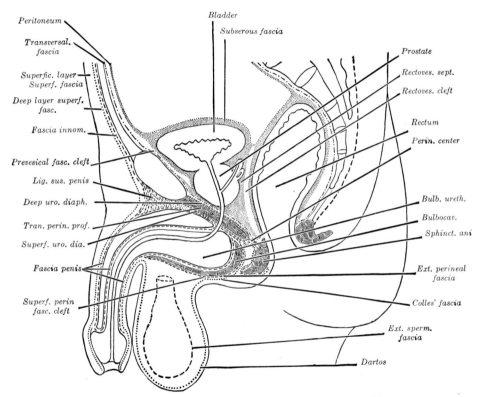

Fig. 1138.—Fasciæ of pelvis and perineum in median sagittal section. Diagram.

cells. It is not divisible into a superficial and deep layer and contains no adipose tissue. A fascial cleft between the superficial and deep fasciæ gives the skin great movability.

The **deep fascia of the penis** (*Buck's fascia*) (Fig. 1138) forms a tubular invest-ment for the shaft of the penis as far anteriorly as the corona glandis. Posteriorly, it invests the crura and bulb and is firmly attached with them to the ischiopubic rami and superficial layer of the urogenital diaphragm. At the anterior or distal extremities of the Bulbocavernosus and Ischiocavernosi, it splits into a superficial and deep lamina; the superficial lamina covers the superficial surface of these muscles as the external perineal fascia of the perineum (page 416); the deep lamina is the continuation of the proper deep fascia of the penis (Buck's fascia). A septum of fascia extends inward between the corpora cavernosa penis and the corpus cavernosum urethræ providing separate tubular investments for these columns of erectile tissue.

Clinical Considerations: The deep fascia of the penis (Buck's fascia) encloses the organ in a strong capsule. An abscess, a hematoma, or an extravasation of urine from rupture of the penile urethra would be confined to the penis by this envelope. A rupture of the urethra in its membranous portion, however, would allow urine to enter the fascial cleft which is between the deep and superficial fasciae and which is continuous with the cleft in the scrotum, under Colles' fascia, and under Scarpa's fascia (see page 417).

Corpora Cavernosa Penis (Fig. 1139).—The anterior three fourths of these two cylindrical masses of erectile tissue are intimately bound together and make up the greater part of the shaft of the penis. At the pubic symphysis, however, their posterior portions diverge from each other as two gradually tapering structures called the **crura**.

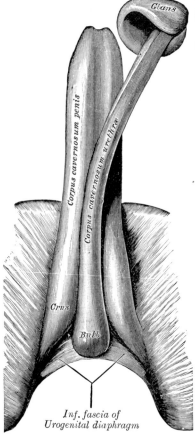

The corpora retain a uniform diameter in the shaft and terminate anteriorly in a bluntly rounded extremity approximately 1 cm. from the end of the penis, being embedded in a cap formed by the glans penis.

The corpora cavernosa penis are surrounded by a strong fibrous envelope consisting of superficial and deep fibers. The superficial fibers are longitudinal in direction, and form a single tube which encloses both corpora; the deep fibers are arranged circularly around each corpus, and form by their junction in the median plane the **septum of the penis**. This is thick and complete behind, but is imperfect in front, where it consists of a series of vertical bands arranged like the teeth

Fig. 1139.—The constituent cavernous cylinders of the penis. The glands and anterior part of the corpus cavernosum urethræ are detached from the corpora cavernosa penis and turned to one side.

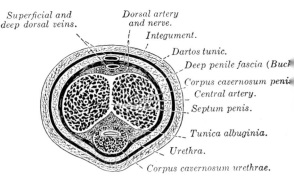

Fig. 1140.—Transverse section of the penis:

of a comb; it is therefore named the **septum pectiniforme**. A shallow groove which marks their junction on the upper surface lodges the deep dorsal vein of the penis, while a deeper and wider groove between them on the under surface contains the corpus cavernosum urethræ.

Each **crus penis**, the tapering posterior portion of a corpus cavernosum penis, terminates just in front of the tuberosity of the ischium in a bluntly pointed process; anteriorly, before it meets its fellow, it presents a slight enlargement, the bulb of the corpus cavernosum penis. The crus is firmly bound to the ramus of the ischium and pubis and is enclosed by the fibers of the Ischiocavernosus muscle.

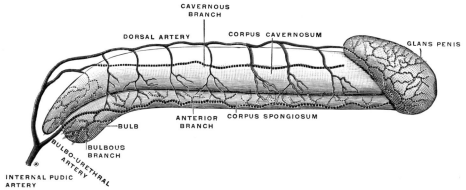

FIG. 1141.—Diagram of the arteries of the penis. (Testut.

The **Corpus Cavernosum Urethræ** (*corpus spongiosum*) (Fig. 1139) is the part of the penis which contains the penile urethra. Its middle portion, in the shaft of the penis, is a uniform cylinder somewhat smaller than a corpus cavernosum penis. At each end it is markedly expanded, the anterior extremity forming the glans penis, the posterior the bulbus urethræ. Between the expansions, it lies in the groove on the under surface of the concorpora cavernosa penis.

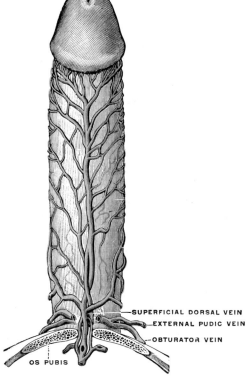

FIG. 1142.—Veins of the penis. (Testut.)

The **glans penis** is the anterior end of the corpus cavernosum urethræ expanded into an obtuse cone very similar to the cap of a mushroom. It is moulded over and securely attached to the blunt extremity of the corpora cavernosa penis, and extends farther over their dorsal than their ventral surfaces. Its periphery is larger in diameter than the shaft, projecting in a rounded border, the **corona glandis**. Proximal to the corona is a constriction forming the **retroglandular sulcus** and the **neck of the penis**. At the summit of the glans is the slit-like external orifice of the urethra.

The **bulbus urethræ** is the conical enlargement of the posterior 4 or 5 cm. of the corpus cavernosum urethræ. It is just superficial to the urogenital diaphragm, the superficial fascia of which is blended with its fibrous capsule and is called the ligament of the bulb.   It is enclosed by the fibers of the Bulbocavernosus.

The urethra enters the corpus cavernosum urethræ 1 or 2 cm. from the posterior extremity of the bulb by piercing the dorsal surface, *i. e.*, the surface which is blended with the urogenital diaphragm.   The posterior most expanded portion of the bulb, accordingly, projects backward toward the anus beyond the entrance of the urethra.

Ligaments.—(See page 393).   The **ligamentum fundiforme penis** is an extensive thickening of the deep layer of superficial fascia (Scarpa's) of the anterior abdominal wall just above the pubis where it is firmly attached to the rectus sheath.   The fibrous bands extend down to the dorsum and sides of the root of the penis.   The **suspensory ligament of the penis**, shorter than the above, is a strong fibrous triangle, derived from the external investing deep fascia, which attaches the dorsum of the root of the penis to the inferior end of the linea alba, the symphysis pubis, and the arcuate pubic ligament.   Serving as ligaments also are the attachments of the crura to the ischiopubic rami and of the bulb to the urogenital diaphragm described above.

Muscles.—The voluntary muscles of the penis are the Bulbocavernosus, Ischiocavernosus, and the Transversus perinei superficialis and are described on page 418.

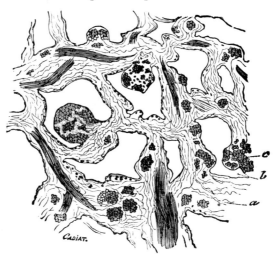

Fig. 1143.—Section of corpus cavernosum penis in a non-distended condition.   (Cadiat.) *a*. Trabeculæ of connective tissue. with many elastic fibers and bundles of plain muscular tissue, some of which are cut across (*c*) *b*. Blood sinuses.

Structure of the Penis.—From the internal surface of the fibrous envelope, tunica albuginia, of the corpora cavernosa penis, as well as from the sides of the septum, numerous bands or cords are given off, which cross the interior of these corpora cavernosa in all directions subdividing them into a number of separate compartments, and giving the entire structure a spongy appearance (Fig. 1143).   These bands and cords are called **trabeculæ**, and consist of white fibrous tissue, elastic fibers, and plain muscular fibers.   In them are contained numerous arteries and nerves.

The component fibers which form the trabeculæ are larger and stronger around the circumference than at the centers of the corpora cavernosa; they are also thicker behind than in front.   The interspaces or cavernous spaces (blood sinuses) on the contrary, are larger at the center than at the circumference, their long diameters being directed transversely.   They are filled with blood, and are lined by a layer of flattened cells similar to the endothelial lining of veins.

The fibrous envelope of the corpus cavernosum urethræ is thinner, whiter in color, and more elastic than that of the corpora cavernosa penis.   The trabeculæ are more delicate, nearly uniform in size, and the meshes between them smaller than in the corpora cavernosa penis: their long diameters, for the most part, corresponding with that of the penis.   The external envelope or outer coat of the corpus cavernosum urethræ is formed partly of unstriped muscular fibers, and a layer of the same tissue immediately surrounds the canal of the urethra.   The corpus cavernosum urethræ with its expanded end the glans penis may be readily dissected free, since it is not so firmly attached to the corpora cavernosa penis as are they to each other.

Under cerebral or spinal stimuli the supply of arterial blood to the blood sinuses or interspaces is increased. This increase in size of sinuses in turn produces compression of the deep veins of the penis due to the elasticity of Buck's fascia. Erection is therefore a mechanical engorgement of the blood sinuses.

Vessels and Nerves.—Most of the blood to the penis is supplied by the internal pudendal artery, a branch of the hypogastric artery. The **arteries** supplying the cavernous spaces are the deep arteries of the penis and branches from the dorsal arteries of the penis, which perforate the fibrous capsule, along the upper surface, especially near the forepart of the organ. On entering the cavernous structure the arteries divide into branches, which are supported and enclosed by the trabeculæ. Some of these arteries end in a capillary net-work, the branches of which open directly into the cavernous spaces; others assume a tendril-like appearance, and form convoluted and somewhat dilated vessels, which were named by Müller **helicine arteries.** They open into the spaces, and from them are also given off small capillary branches to supply the trabecular structure. They are bound down in the spaces by fine fibrous processes, and are most abundant in the back part of the corpora cavernosa (Fig. 1141).

The blood from the cavernous spaces is returned by a series of **veins**, some of which emerge in considerable numbers from the base of the glans penis and converge on the dorsum of the organ to form the deep dorsal vein; others pass out on the upper surface of the coprora cavernosa and join the same vein; some emerge from the under surface of the corpora cavernosa penis and receiving branches from the corpus cavernosum urethræ, wind around the sides of the penis to end in the deep dorsal vein; but the greater number pass out at the root of the penis and join the prostatic plexus. Batson has demonstrated that the deep dorsal vein of the penis has connection with the vertebral veins, hence it is possible to have metastases from cancerous involvement of the pelvic viscera or external genitalia make their way to the vertebræ or even to the skull and brain without going through the heart and lungs. Pyogenic organisms may be transported by the same route. (See page 678).

The **lymphatic vessels of the penis** are described on page 717.

The **nerves** are derived from the pudendal nerve and the pelvic plexuses. On the glans and bulb some filaments of the cutaneous nerves have Pacinian bodies connected with them, and, according to Krause, many of them end in peculiar end-bulbs.

The Prostate (**Prostata; Prostate Gland**). (Figs. 1144, 1117, 1118.)

The **prostate** is a firm, partly glandular and partly muscular body, which is placed immediately below the internal urethral orifice and around the commencement of the urethra. It is situated in the pelvic cavity, below the lower part of the symphysis pubis, above the deep layer of the urogenital diaphragm, and in front of the rectum, through which it may be distinctly felt, especially when enlarged. It is about the size of a chestnut and somewhat conical in shape, and presents for examination a **base**, an **apex**, an **anterior**, a **posterior**, and two **lateral surfaces**.

The **base** (*basis prostatæ*) is directed upward, and is applied to the inferior surface of the bladder. The greater part of this surface is directly continuous with the bladder wall; the urethra penetrates it nearer its anterior than its posterior border.

The **apex** (*apex prostatæ*) is directed downward, and is in contact with the deep layer of the urogenital diaphragm.

Surfaces.—The **posterior surface** (*facies posterior*) is flattened from side to side and slightly convex from above downward; it is separated from the rectum by its sheath and the important Denonvillier's fascia, which corresponds in origin and fate to the processus vaginalis in the inguinal region. It is distant about 4 cm. from the anus. Near its upper border there is a depression through which the two ejaculatory ducts enter the prostate. This depression serves to divide the posterior surface into a lower larger and an upper smaller part. The upper smaller part constitutes the **middle lobe** of the prostate and intervenes between the ejaculatory ducts and the urethra; it varies greatly in size, and in some cases is destitute of glandular tissue. The lower larger portion sometimes presents a shallow median furrow, which imperfectly separates it into a **right** and a **left lateral lobe**: these form the main mass of the gland and are directly continuous with each other behind the urethra. In front of the urethra they are connected by a band which is named the **isthmus**: this consists of the same tissues as the capsule and is devoid of glandular substance.

The **anterior surface** (*facies anterior*) measures about 2.5 cm. from above downward but is narrow and convex from side to side. It is placed about 2 cm. behind the pubic symphysis, from which it is separated by a plexus of veins and a quantity of loose fat. It is connected to the pubic bone on either side by the puboprostatic ligaments. The urethra emerges from this surface a little above and in front of the apex of the gland.

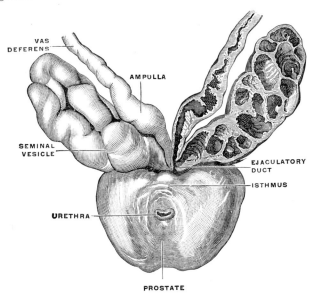

VAS
DEFERENS

AMPULLA

SEMINAL
VESICLE

EJACULATORY
DUCT

ISTHMUS

URETHRA

PROSTATE

Fig. 1144.—Prostate with seminal vesicles and seminal ducts, viewed from in front and above. (Spalteholz.)

The **lateral surfaces** are prominent, and are covered by the anterior portions of the Levatores ani, which are, however, separated from the gland by a plexus of veins.

The prostate measures about 4 cm. transversely at the base, 2 cm. in its anteroposterior diameter, and 3 cm. in its vertical diameter. Its weight is about 20 gm. It is held in its position by the puboprostatic ligaments; by the deep layer of the urogenital diaphragm, which invests the prostate and the commencement of the membranous portion of the urethra; and by the anterior portions of the Levatores ani, which pass backward from the pubis and embrace the sides of the prostate. These portions of the Levatores ani, from the support they afford to the prostate, are named the **Levatores prostatæ**.

The prostate is perforated by the urethra and the ejaculatory ducts (Fig. 1137). The urethra usually lies along the junction of its anterior with its middle third. The ejaculatory ducts pass obliquely downward and forward through the posterior part of the prostate, and open into the prostatic portion of the urethra.

Structure.—The prostate is immediately enveloped by a thin but firm fibrous capsule distinct from that derived from the subserous fascia, and separated from it by a plexus of veins. This capsule is firmly adherent to the prostate and is structurally continuous with the stroma of the gland, being composed of the same tissues, viz.: non-striped muscle and fibrous tissue. The substance of the prostate is of a pale reddish-gray color, of great density, and not easily torn. It consists of glandular substance and muscular tissue.

The **muscular tissue** according to Kölliker, constitutes the proper stroma of the prostate; the connective tissue being very scanty, and simply forming between the muscular fibers, thin trabeculæ, in which the vessels and nerves of the gland ramify. The muscular tissue is arranged as follows: immediately beneath the fibrous capsule is a dense layer, which forms an investing sheath for the gland; secondly, around the urethra, as it lies in the prostate, is another dense layer of circular fibers, continuous above with the internal layer of the muscular coat of the bladder, and blending below with the fibers surrounding the membranous portion of the urethra. Between these two layers strong bands of muscular tissue, which decussate freely, form meshes in which the glandular structure of the organ is imbedded. In that part of the gland which is situated in front of the urethra the muscular tissue is especially dense, and there is here little or no gland tissue; while in that part which is behind the urethra the muscular tissue presents a wide-meshed structure, which is densest at the base of the gland—that is, near the bladder—becoming looser and more sponge-like toward the apex of the organ.

The **glandular substance** is composed of numerous follicular pouches the lining of which frequently shows papillary elevations. The follicles open into elongated canals, which join to form from twelve to twenty small excretory ducts. They are connected together by areolar tissue, supported by prolongations from the fibrous capsule and muscular stroma, and enclosed in a delicate capillary plexus. The epithelium which lines the canals and the terminal vesicles is of the columnar variety. The prostatic ducts open into the floor of the prostatic portion of the urethra, and are lined by two layers of epithelium, the inner layer consisting of columnar and the outer of small cubical cells. Small colloid masses, known as **amyloid bodies** are often found in the gland tubes.

Vessels and Nerves.—The **arteries** supplying the prostate are derived from the internal pudendal, inferior vesical, and middle hemorrhoidal. Its veins form a plexus around the sides and base of the gland; they receive in front the dorsal vein of the penis, and end in the hypogastric veins. The **nerves** are derived from the pelvic plexus.

Bulbourethral Glands (Glandulæ Bulbourethrales; Cowper's Glands). (Fig. 1117).

The **bulbourethral glands** are two small, rounded, and somewhat lobulated bodies, of a yellow color, about the size of peas, placed behind and lateral to the membranous portion of the urethra, between the two layers of the fascia of the urogenital diaphragm. They lie close above the bulb, and are enclosed by the transverse fibers of the Sphincter urethræ membranaceæ.

The excretory duct of each gland, nearly 2.5 cm. long, passes obliquely forward beneath the mucous membrane, and opens by a minute orifice on the floor of the cavernous portion of the urethra about 2.5 cm. in front of the urogenital diaphragm.

Structure.—Each gland is made up of several lobules, held together by a fibrous investment. Each lobule consists of a number of acini, lined by columnar epithelial cells, opening into one duct, which joins with the ducts of other lobules outside the gland to form the single excretory duct.

THE FEMALE GENITAL ORGANS (ORGANA GENITALIA MULIEBRIA).

The female genital organs consist of an internal and an external group. The **internal organs** are situated within the pelvis, and consist of the **ovaries**, the **uterine tubes**, the **uterus**, and the **vagina**. The **external organs** are placed below the urogenital diaphragm and below and in front of the pubic arch. They comprise the **mons pubis**, the **labia majora et minora pudendi**, the **clitoris**, the **bulbus vestibuli**, and the **greater vestibular glands**.

The Ovaries (Ovaria).

The **ovaries** are homologous with the testes in the male. They are two nodular bodies, situated one on either side of the uterus in relation to the lateral wall of the pelvis, and attached to the back of the broad ligament of the uterus, behind and below the uterine tubes (Fig. 1145). The ovaries are of a grayish-pink color, and present either a smooth or a puckered uneven surface. They are each about 4 cm. in length, 2 cm. in width, and about 8 mm. in thickness, and weigh from 2 to 3.5 gm. Each ovary presents a lateral and a medial surface, an upper or tubal and a lower or uterine extremity, and an anterior or mesovarian and a posterior free border. It lies in a shallow depression, named the **ovarian fossa**, on the lateral wall of the pelvis; this fossa is bounded above by the external iliac vessels, in front by the obliterated umbilical artery, and behind by the ureter. The exact position of the ovary has been the subject of considerable difference of opinion, and the description here given applies to the ovary of the nulliparous woman. The ovary becomes displaced during the first pregnancy, and probably never again returns to its original position. In the erect posture the long axis of the ovary is vertical. The *tubal extremity* is near the external iliac vein; to it are attached the ovarian fimbria of the uterine tube and a fold of peritoneum, the **suspensory ligament of the ovary,** which is directed upward over the iliac vessels and contains the ovarian

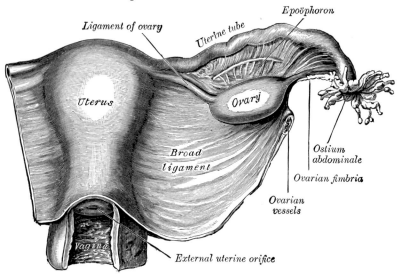

FIG. 1145.—Uterus and right broad ligament, seen from behind. The broad ligament has been spread out and the ovary drawn downward.

vessels. The *uterine end* is directed downward toward the pelvic floor, it is usually narrower than the tubal, and is attached to the lateral angle of the uterus, immediately behind the uterine tube, by a rounded cord termed the **ligament of the ovary,** which lies within the broad ligament and contains some non-striped muscular

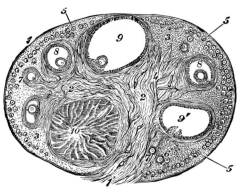

FIG. 1146.—Section of the ovary. (After Schrön.) 1. Outer covering. 1'. Attached border. 2. Central stroma. 3. Peripheral stroma. 4. Bloodvessels. 5. Vesicular follicles in their earliest stage. 6, 7, 8. More advanced follicles. 9. An almost mature follicle. 9'. Follicle from which the ovum has escaped. 10. Corpus luteum.

fibers. The *lateral surface* is in contact with the parietal peritoneum, which lines the ovarian fossa; the *medial surface* is to a large extent covered by the fimbriated extremity of the uterine tube. The *mesovarian border* is straight and is directed toward the obliterated umbilical artery, and is attached to the back of the broad ligament by a short fold named the **mesovarium**. Between the two layers of this fold the bloodvessels and nerves pass to reach the hilum of the ovary. The *free border* is convex, and is directed toward the ureter. The uterine tube arches over the ovary, running upward in relation to its mesovarian border, then curving over its tubal pole, and finally passing downward on its free border and medial surface.

Epoöphoron (*parovarium; organ of Rosenmüller*) (Fig. 1145). — The epoöphoron lies in the mesosalpinx between the ovary and the uterine tube, and consists of a few short tubules (**ductuli transversi**) which converge toward the ovary while their opposite ends open into a rudimentary duct, the **ductus longitudinalis epoöphori**(*duct of Gärtner*).

Paroöphoron. — The paroöphoron consists of a few scattered rudimentary tubules, best seen in the child, situated in the broad ligament between the epoöphoron and the uterus. The ductuli transversi of the epoophoron and the tubules of the paroophoron are remnants of the tubules of the Wolffian body or mesonephros; the ductus longitudinalis epoöphori is a persistent portion of the Wolffian duct. In the fetus the ovaries are situated, like the testes, in the lumbar region, near the kidneys, but they gradually descend into the pelvis (page 1259).

Structure (Fig. 1146).—The surface of the ovary is covered by a layer of columnar cells which constitutes the **germinal epithelium of Waldeyer.** This epithelium which is in linear continuity with the peritoneum gives to the ovary a dull gray color as compared with the shining smoothness of the peritoneum; and the transition between the squamous epithelium of the peritoneum and the columnar cells which cover the ovary is usually marked by a line around the anterior border of the ovary. The ovary consists of a number of vesicular ovarian follicles imbedded in the meshes of a stroma or frame-work.

The **stroma** is a peculiar soft tissue, abundantly supplied with bloodvessels, consisting for the most part of spindle-shaped cells with a small amount of ordinary connective tissue. These cells have been regarded by some anatomists as unstriped muscle cells, which, indeed, they most resemble; by others as connective-tissue cells. On the surface of the organ this tissue is much condensed, and forms a layer (**tunica albuginea**) composed of short connective-tissue fibers, with fusiform cells between them. The stroma of the ovary may contain interstitial cells resembling those of the testis.

Vesicular Ovarian Follicles (*Graafian follicles*).—Upon making a section of an ovary, numerous round transparent vesicles of various sizes are to be seen; they are the follicles, or ovisacs containing the ova. Immediately beneath the superficial covering is a layer of stroma, in which are a large number of minute vesicles, of uniform size, about 0.25 mm. in diameter. These are the follicles in their earliest condition, and the layer where they are found has been termed the **cortical layer.** They are especially numerous in the ovary of the young child. After puberty, and during the whole of the child-bearing period, large and mature, or almost mature follicles are also found in the cortical layer in small numbers, and also "corpora lutea," the remains of follicles which have burst and are undergoing atrophy and absorption. Beneath this superficial stratum, other large and more or less mature follicles are found imbedded in the ovarian stroma. These increase in size as they recede from the surface toward a highly vascular stroma in the center of the organ, termed the **medullary substance** (*zona vasculosa of Waldeyer*). This stroma forms the tissue of the hilum by which the ovary is attached, and through which the bloodvessels enter: it does not contain any follicles.

The larger follicles (Fig. 1147) consist of an external fibrovascular coat, connected with the surrounding stroma of the ovary by a net-work of bloodvessels; and an internal coat, which consists of several layers of nucleated cells, called the **membrana granulosa.** At one part of the mature follicle the cells of the membrana granulosa are collected into a mass which projects into the cavity of the follicle. This is termed the **discus proligerus** or **corona radiata,** and in it the ovum is imbedded. The follicle contains a transparent albuminous fluid.

The development and maturation of the follicles and ova continue uninterruptedly from puberty to the end of the fruitful period of woman's life, while their formation commences before birth. Before puberty the ovaries are small and the follicles contained in them are disposed in a comparatively thick layer in the cortical substance; here they present the appearance of a large number of minute closed vesicles, constituting the early condition of the follicles; many, however, never attain full development, but shrink and disappear. At puberty the ovaries enlarge and become more vascular, the follicles are developed in greater abundance, and their ova are capable of fecundation. The follicles are supposed to secrete hormones necessary for the œstrus cycle and which stimulate the growth of the uterus and mammary glands during pregnancy.

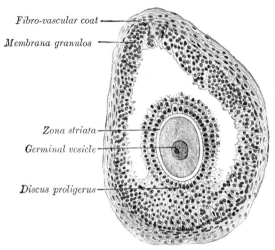

Fibro-vascular coat

Membrana granulos

Zona striata

Germinal vesicle

Discus proligerus

Fig. 1147.—Section of vesicular ovarian follicle of cat. × 50.

Discharge of the Ovum.—The follicles, after attaining a certain stage of development, gradually approach the surface of the ovary and burst; the ovum surrounded by its corona radiata and the fluid contents of the follicle are liberated on the exterior of the ovary, and carried into the uterine tube.

Corpus Luteum. — After the discharge of the ovum the lining of the follicle is thrown into folds, and vascular processes grow inward from the surrounding tissue. In this way the space is filled up and the corpus luteum formed. It consists at first of a radial arrangement of yellow cells with bloodvessels and lymphatic spaces, and later it merges with the surrounding stroma. The corpora lutea give off secretions or hormones: (1) which are necessary for the implantation and normal development of the fertilized egg; (2) which stimulate the growth of the mammary gland and (3) which inhibit ovulation during pregnancy.

Vessels and Nerves.—The **arteries** of the ovaries and uterine tubes are the ovarian from the aorta. Each anastomoses freely in the mesosalpinx, with the uterine artery, giving some branches to the uterine tube, and others which traverse the mesovarium and enter the hilum of the ovary. The **veins** emerge from the hilum in the form of a plexus, the **pampiniform plexus**; the ovarian vein is formed from this plexus, and leaves the pelvis in company with the artery. The **nerves** are derived from the hypogastric or pelvic plexus, and from the ovarian plexus, the uterine tube receiving a branch from one of the uterine nerves.

The Uterine Tube (Tuba Uterina [Fallopii]; Fallopian Tube; Oviduct).
(Figs. 1145, 1148, 1151).

The **uterine tubes** convey the ova from the ovaries to the cavity of the uterus. They are bilateral, extending from the side of the pelvis to the superior lateral angle of the uterus. Each one is suspended by a mesenteric peritoneal fold, called the **mesosalpinx**, which comprises the upper free margin and adjacent movable portion of the broad ligament. Each tube is about 10 cm. long, and consists of three portions: (1) the **isthmus**, or medial constricted third; (2) the **ampulla**, or intermediate dilated portion, which curves over the ovary; and (3) the **infundibulum** with its **abdominal ostium**, surrounded by **fimbriæ**, one of which, the **ovarian fimbria,** is attached to the ovary. The uterine tube is directed lateralward as far as the uterine pole of the ovary, and then ascends along the mesovarian border of the ovary to the tubal pole, over which it arches; finally it turns downward and ends in relation to the free border and medial surface of the ovary. The uterine opening is minute, and will only admit a fine bristle; the abdominal opening is somewhat larger. In connection with the fimbriæ of the uterine tube, or with the broad ligament close to them, there are frequently one or more small pedunculated vesicles. These are termed the **appendices vesiculosæ** (*hydatids of Mórgagni*).

Structure.—The uterine tube consists of three coats: **serous, muscular,** and **mucous.** The **external** or **serous coat** is peritoneal. The **middle** or **muscular coat** consists of an external longitudinal and an internal circular layer of non-striped muscular fibers continuous with those of the uterus. The **internal** or **mucous coat** is continuous with the mucous lining of the uterus, and, at the abdominal ostium of the tube, with the peritoneum. It is thrown into longitudinal folds, which in the ampulla are much more extensive than in the isthmus. The lining epithelium is columnar and ciliated. This form of epithelium is also found on the inner surface of the fimbriæ, while on the outer or serous surfaces of these processes the epithelium gradually merges into the mesothelium of the peritoneum.

Fertilization of the ovum is believed (page 24) to occur in the tube, and the fertilized ovum

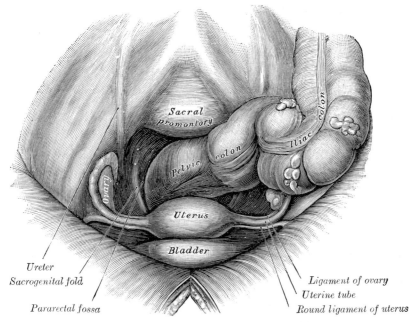

FIG. 1148.—Female pelvis and its contents, seen from above and in front.

is then normally passed on into the uterus; the ovum, however, may adhere to and undergo development in the uterine tube, giving rise to the commonest variety of *ectopic gestation*. In such cases the amnion and chorion are formed, but a true decidua is never present; and the gestation usually

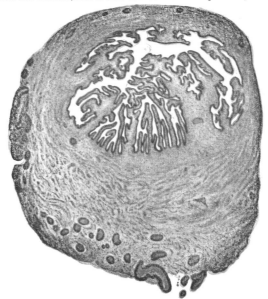

FIG. 1149.—Transverse section of a human uterine tube. Stained with hematoxylin and eosin. × 15.

ends by extrusion of the ovum through the abdominal ostium, although it is not uncommon for the tube to rupture into the peritoneal cavity, this being accompanied by severe hemorrhage, and needing surgical interference.

The Uterus (Womb) (Figs. 1145, 1148, 1150).

The **uterus** is a hollow, thick-walled, muscular organ situated between the bladder and rectum. Into its upper part the uterine tubes open, one on either side, while below, its cavity communicates with that of the vagina. When the ova are discharged from the ovaries they are carried to the uterine cavity through the uterine

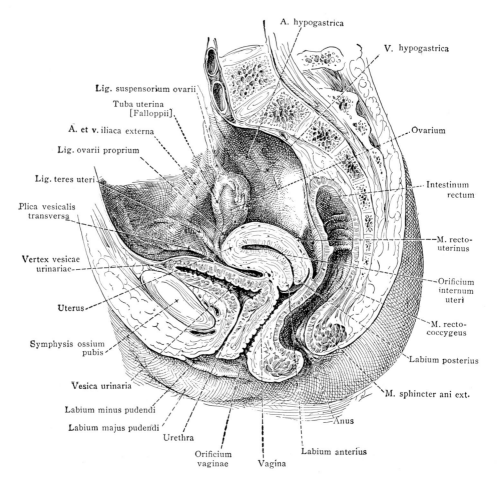

A. hypogastrica

V. hypogastrica

Lig. suspensorium ovarii

Tuba uterina [Falloppii]

A. et v. iliaca externa

Lig. ovarii proprium

Lig. teres uteri

Plica vesicalis transversa

Vertex vesicae urinariae

Uterus

Symphysis ossium pubis

Vesica urinaria

Labium minus pudendi

Labium majus pudendi

Urethra

Orificium vaginae

Vagina

Labium anterius

Anus

M. sphincter ani ext.

Labium posterius

M. recto-coccygeus

Orificium internum uteri

M. recto-uterinus

Intestinum rectum

Ovarium

Fig. 1150.—Median sagittal section of female pelvis. The bladder is empty, the uterus and vagina slightly dilated (Eycleshymer and Jones.)

tubes. If an ovum be fertilized it imbeds itself in the uterine wall and is normally retained in the uterus until prenatal development is completed, the uterus undergoing changes in size and structure to accommodate itself to the needs of the growing embryo (see page 27). After parturition the uterus returns almost to its former condition, but traces of its enlargement remain. It is necessary, therefore, to describe as the type-form the adult virgin uterus, and then to consider the modifications which are effected as a result of pregnancy.

In the virgin state the uterus is flattened antero-posteriorly and is pyriform in shape, with the apex directed downward and backward. It lies between the bladder in front and the pelvic or sigmoid colon and rectum behind, and is completely within the pelvis, so that its base is below the level of the superior pelvic aperture.

The long axis of the uterus usually lies approximately in the axis of the superior pelvic aperture, but as the organ is freely movable its position varies with the state of distention of the bladder and rectum. Except when much displaced by a fully distended bladder, it forms a forward angle with the vagina, since the axis of the vagina corresponds to the axes of the cavity and inferior aperture of the pelvis.

The uterus measures about 7.5 cm. in length, 5 cm. in breadth, at its upper part, and nearly 2.5 cm. in thickness; it weighs from 30 to 40 gm. It is divisible into two portions. On the surface, about midway between the apex and base, is a slight constriction, known as the **isthmus**, and corresponding to this in the interior is a narrowing of the uterine cavity, the **internal orifice** of the uterus. The portion above the isthmus is termed the **body**, and that below, the **cervix**. The part of the body which lies above a plane passing through the points of entrance of the uterine tubes is known as the **fundus**.

Body (*corpus uteri*). — The body gradually narrows from the fundus to the isthmus.

The **vesical** or **anterior surface** (*facies vesicalis*) is flattened and covered by peritoneum, which is reflected on to the bladder to form the vesicouterine excavation. The surface lies in apposition with the bladder.

The **intestinal** or **posterior surface** (*facies intestinalis*) is convex transversely and is covered by peritoneum, which is continued down on to the cervix and vagina. It is in relation with the sigmoid colon, from which it is usually separated by some coils of small intestine.

The **fundus** (*fundus uteri*) is convex in all directions, and covered by peritoneum continuous with that on the vesical and intestinal surfaces. On it rest some coils of small intestine, and occasionally the distended sigmoid colon.

The **lateral margins** (*margo lateralis*) are slightly convex. At the upper end of each the uterine tube pierces the uterine wall. Below and in front of this point the round ligament of the uterus is fixed, while behind it is the attachment of the ligament of the ovary. These three structures lie within a fold of peritoneum which is reflected from the margin of the uterus to the wall of the pelvis, and is named the **broad ligament.**

Cervix (*cervix uteri; neck*).—The cervix is the lower constricted segment of the uterus. It is somewhat conical in shape, with its truncated apex directed downward and backward, but is slightly wider in the middle than either above or below. Owing to its relationships, it is less freely movable than the body, so that the latter may bend on it. The long axis of the cervix is therefore seldom in the same straight line as the long axis of the body. The long axis of the uterus as a whole presents the form of a curved line with its concavity forward, or in extreme cases may present an angular bend at the region of the isthmus.

The cervix is about 1 inch long. The vagina is attached obliquely around the center of the periphery of the cervix. This attachment divides the cervix into two parts, an upper or supravaginal portion and a lower or vaginal portion.

The **supravaginal portion** (*portio supravaginalis* [*cervicis*]) is separated *in front* from the bladder by fibrous tissue (**parametrium**), which extends also on to its *sides* and lateralward between the layers of the broad ligaments. The uterine arteries reach the margins of the cervix in this fibrous tissue, where they cross over the ureters. The ureters, on either side, run downward and forward in the parametrium about 2 cm. from the cervix. *Posteriorly*, the supravaginal cervix is covered by peritoneum, which is prolonged below on to the posterior vaginal wall, when it is reflected on to the rectum, forming the rectouterine excavation. It is in relation with the rectum, from which it may be separated by coils of small intestine.

The **vaginal portion** (*portio vaginalis* [*cervicis*]) of the cervix projects free into the anterior wall of the vagina between the anterior and posterior fornices. On its rounded extremity is a small, depressed, somewhat circular aperture, the **external os** (*orificium externum uteri*), through which the cavity of the cervix communicates with that of the vagina. The external orifice is bounded by two lips, an anterior and a posterior, of which the anterior is the shorter and thicker, although, on account of the slope of the cervix, it projects lower than the posterior. Normally, both lips are in contact with the posterior vaginal wall.

Interior of the Uterus (Fig. 1151).—The cavity of the uterus is small in comparison with the size of the organ.

The **Cavity of the Body** (*cavum uteri*) is a mere slit, flattened antero-posteriorly. It is triangular in shape, the base being formed by the internal surface of the fundus between the orifices of the uterine tubes, the apex by the **internal os** (*orificium internum uteri*) through which the cavity of the body communicates with the canal of the cervix.

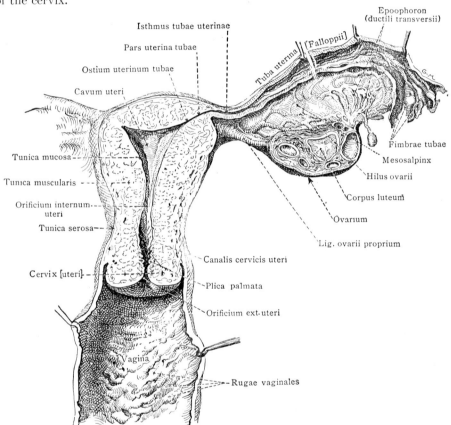

FIG. 1151.—Section through the vagina, uterus, uterine tube and ovary. (Eycleshymer and Jones.)

The **Canal of the Cervix** (*canalis cervicis uteri*) is somewhat fusiform, flattened from before backward, and broader at the middle than at either extremity. It communicates above through the internal orifice with the cavity of the body, and below through the external orifice with the vaginal cavity. The wall of the canal presents an anterior and a posterior longitudinal ridge, from each of which proceed a number of small oblique columns, the **palmate folds**, giving the appearance of branches from the stem of a tree; to this arrangement the name **arbor vitæ uterina** is applied. The folds on the two walls are not exactly opposed, but fit between one another so as to close the cervical canal.

The total length of the uterine cavity from the external orifice to the fundus is about 6.25 cm.

Ligaments.—The principal ligaments of the uterus are the **broad ligaments,** the **round ligaments,** the **uterosacral ligaments,** and the **cardinal ligaments** (*ligamenta transversalia colli*). In addition to these, there are certain peritoneal folds which are called ligaments: the **vesicouterine, rectouterine,** and **sacrogenital ligaments.**

The **broad ligaments** (*ligamentum latum uteri*) are two thin fibrous sheets, covered on both surfaces with peritoneum, which extend from each side of the uterus to the lateral wall of the pelvis. The uterus and these lateral extensions together form a septum across the cavity of the pelvis, dividing it into an anterior or **vesicouterine** and a posterior or **rectouterine fossa.** The broad ligament is thicker at its inferior pelvic attachment than toward its free border. Between the two peritoneal sheets or *leaves of the ligament* are (1) the parametrium, (2) blood vessels and nerves, (3) the uterine tubes, (4) the ureter, (5) the round ligaments, and (6) the vestigial epoophoron and paraoophoron. The ovary might be listed as (7) but it is suspended from rather than contained in the broad ligament.

The **parametrium** is the extension of the subserous connective tissue of the uterus laterally into the broad ligament. The name has been applied also to the whole broad ligament below the attachment of the ovary, but according to the B.N.A. the latter is the **mesometrium.** It contains scattered smooth muscle bundles, is anchored to the lateral pelvic wall, and is continuous with the cardinal ligament of the intrapelvic fascia.

The **uterine artery** of each side enters the base of the broad ligament at the latter's attachment to the lateral wall of the pelvis and traverses the pelvis between the two leaves close to their reflection on to the pelvic floor. It crosses the ureter just before it reaches the cervical portion of the uterus and in the parametrium it follows the lateral border of the uterus up to the isthmus of the uterine tube. It follows the tube laterally and anastomoses with the ovarian artery. The **ovarian artery** crosses the external iliac vessels in a vertical direction and enters the most superior lateral portion of the broad ligament, enclosed in a more or less fibrous cord, the **infundibulopelvic ligament** (*ligamentum suspensorium ovarii*). It follows the attached border of the ovary and anastomoses with the uterine artery.

The superior free border of the broad ligament is occupied by the **uterine tube** except at its lateral extremity where it forms a rounded band, attaching the infundibulum of the tube to the lateral wall of the pelvis. This band, named the infundibulopelvic ligament or suspensory ligament of the ovary, also encloses the ovarian vessels as they enter the broad ligament. The upper portion of the broad ligament, extending down as far as the attachment of the ovary, is called the **mesosalpinx.** It is less fixed than the rest of the ligament and affords a movable mesenteric support for the tube.

The **ureter** crosses the attached inferior border of the broad ligament obliquely, as it courses along the pelvic floor toward the base of the bladder. It comes to within 1 or 2 cm. of the internal os of the uterus at this point and lies close to the uterine artery, between the latter and the pelvic diaphragm.

The round ligaments are described below.

The epoophoron and paraoophoron (page 1307) lie in the mesosalpinx.

The **ovary** is secured to the posterior surface of the broad ligament by a mesenteric attachment, the **mesovarium,** derived from the posterior leaf. It does not lie, therefore, between the leaves of the broad ligament. Folds of the posterior leaf at each end of the ovary cover the infundibulopelvic ligament (*ligamentum suspensorium ovarii*) and the **ligamentum ovarii proprium.**

The **round ligament** (*ligamentum teres uteri*) is a flattened band attached to the superior part of the lateral border of the uterus just below and anterior to the isthmus of the uterine tube. It traverses the pelvis between the leaves of the broad ligament but causes a prominent folding of the anterior leaf only. It reaches the pelvic wall lateral to the lateral vesicoumbilical fold, ascends over the external iliac vessels and inguinal ligament, and penetrates the abdominal wall through the internal inguinal ring. It passes through the inguinal canal and its constituent fibers spread out to help form the substance of the labia majora. In the fetus, the peritoneum is prolonged in the form of a tubular process for a short distance into the inguinal canal beside the ligament. This process is called the **canal of Nuck.** It is generally obliterated in the adult, but sometimes remains pervious even in advanced life. It is analogous to the saccus vaginalis, which precedes the descent of the testis.

The **cardinal ligament** (*ligamentum transversum colli,* Mackenrodt) is a fibrous sheet of the subserous fascia embedded in the adipose tissue on each side of the lower cervix uteri and vagina. To form it, the fasciæ over the anterior and posterior walls of the vagina and cervix come together at the lateral border of these organs, and the resulting sheet extends across the pelvic floor as a deeper continuation of the broad ligament. As the sheet reaches the lateral portion of the pelvic diaphragm, it forms anterior and posterior extensions which are attached to the internal investing layer of deep fascia (supra-anal fascia) on the inner surface of the Levator ani, Coccygeus and Piriformis. This attachment is commonly visible as a white line 2 or 3 cm. below the arcus tendineus of the Levator ani, and is called the **arcus tendineus of the pelvic fascia** (see page 410). The anterior extension is continuous with the tissue supporting the bladder. The posterior extension blends with the uterosacral ligaments. The vaginal arteries cross the pelvis in close association with this ligament, giving it additional substance and support, and bundles of smooth muscle may be imbedded in it.

The **uterosacral ligament** is a prominent fibrous band of subserous fascia which takes a curved course along the lateral wall of the pelvis from the cervix uteri to the sacrum. It is a posterior continuation of the tissue which forms the cardinal ligament. It is attached to the deep fascia and periosteum of the sacrum and contains a bundle of smooth muscle named the **Rectouterinus.** The ligaments on the two sides project out from the wall as crescentic shelves which narrow the diameter of the cavity in front of the lower rectum and mark it off as the cul-de-sac of Douglas.

The **vesicouterine fold** or **anterior ligament** is the reflection of peritoneum from the anterior surface of the uterus, at the junction of the cervix and body, to the posterior surface of the bladder.

The **rectovaginal fold** or **posterior ligament** is the peritoneum reflected from the wall of the posterior fornix of the vagina on to the anterior surface of the rectum.

The **sacrogenital** or **rectouterine folds** (*plica rectouterina* [Douglasi]) are two crescent folds which cover the uterosacral ligaments.

The **rectouterine excavation** (*excavatio rectouterina; cavum Douglasi; pouch or cul-de-sac of Douglas*) is a deep pouch formed by the most inferior or caudal portion of the parietal peritoneum. Its anterior boundary is the supravaginal cervix and posterior fornix of the vagina; posterior, the rectum, and lateral, the sacrogenital folds covering the uterosacral ligaments.

Support of the Uterus.—The principal support of the uterus is the pelvic diaphragm, especially the Levator ani and its investing layers of fascia, and unless it is intact the other structures are unable to carry out their supporting function. The uterus is held in its proper position within the pelvis by its attachment to the vagina and by the cardinal, broad, and uterosacral ligaments. The blood vessels reinforce these ligaments. The round ligaments and the peritoneal folds are of relatively slight importance as mechanical supports. The padding of adipose tissue about the ligaments and organs, in well nourished individuals, is an important element of support also. There is a great variation in the size and development of the supporting structures in different individuals, and they may be thickened or strengthened in response to physiological and pathological changes.

Position of the uterus.—The form, size, and situation of the uterus vary at different periods of life and under different circumstances.

In the fetus and infant the uterus is contained in the abdominal cavity, projecting beyond the superior aperture of the pelvis (Fig. 1152). The cervix is considerably larger than the body.

At puberty the uterus is pyriform in shape, and weighs from 14 to 17 gm. It has descended into the pelvis, the fundus being just below the level of the superior aperture of this cavity. The palmate folds are distinct, and extend to the upper part of the cavity of the organ.

The position of the uterus *in the adult* is liable to considerable variation. With the bladder and rectum empty the body of the uterus is nearly horizontal when the individual is standing. The fundus is about 2 cm. behind the symphysis pubis and slightly cephalic to it. The uterus and vagina are at an angle of about 90° with each other. The external os is half way between the spines of the ischii. As the bladder fills, the uterus is bent back toward the sacrum.

During menstruation the organ is enlarged, more vascular, and its surfaces rounder; the external orifice is rounded, its labia swollen, and the lining membrane of the body thickened, softer, and of a darker color.

During pregnancy the uterus becomes enormously enlarged, and in the eighth month reaches the epigastric region. The increase in size is partly due to growth of preëxisting muscle, and partly to development of new fibers.

After parturition the uterus nearly regains its usual size, weighing about 42 gm.; but its cavity is larger than in the virgin state, its vessels are tortuous, and its muscular layers are more defined; the external orifice is more marked, and its edges present one or more fissures.

In old age the uterus becomes atrophied, and paler and denser in texture; a more distinct constriction separates the body and cervix. The internal orifice is frequently, and the external orifice occasionally, obliterated, while the lips almost entirely disappear.

Structure.—The uterus is composed of three coats: an **external or serous, a middle or muscular,** and an **internal or mucous.**

The **serous coat** (*tunica serosa*) is derived from the peritoneum; it invests the fundus and the whole of the intestinal surface of the uterus; but covers the vesical surface only as far as the junction of the body and cervix. In the lower fourth of the intestinal surface the peritoneum, though covering the uterus, is not closely connected with it, being separated from it by a layer of loose cellular tissue and some large veins.

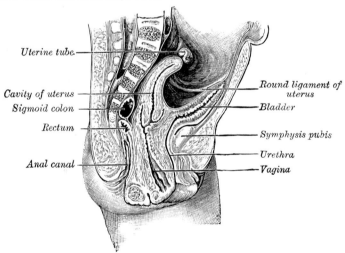

Uterine tube

Cavity of uterus

Sigmoid colon

Rectum

Anal canal

Round ligament of uterus

Bladder

Symphysis pubis

Urethra

Vagina

Fig. 1152.—Sagittal section through the pelvis of a newly born female child.

The **muscular coat** (*tunica muscularis, myometrium*) forms the chief bulk of the substance of the uterus. In the virgin it is dense, firm, and of a grayish color, and cuts almost like cartilage. It is thick opposite the middle of the body and fundus, and thin at the orifices of the uterine tubes. It consists of bundles of unstriped muscular fibers, disposed in a thick, felt-like structure, intermixed with areolar tissue, bloodvessels, lymphatic vessels, and nerves. Muscle fibers are continued on to the uterine tube, the round ligament, and the ligament of the ovary: some passing at each side into the broad ligament, and others running backward from the cervix into the uterosacral ligaments. During pregnancy the muscular tissue becomes more prominently developed, the fibers being greatly enlarged.

The **mucous membrane** (*tunica mucosa,* **endometrium**) (Fig. 1153) is smooth, and closely adherent to the subjacent muscular tissue. It is continuous through the fimbriated extremity of the uterine tubes, with the peritoneum; and, through the external uterine orifice, with the lining of the vagina.

In the body of the uterus the mucous membrane is smooth, soft, of a pale red color, lined by a single layer of high columnar ciliated epithelium, and presents, when viewed with a lens, the orifices of numerous tubular follicles, arranged perpendicularly to the surface. The structure of the corium differs from that of ordinary mucous membranes, and consists of an embryonic nucleated and highly cellular form of connective tissue in which run numerous large lymphatics. In it are the tube-like **uterine glands.**

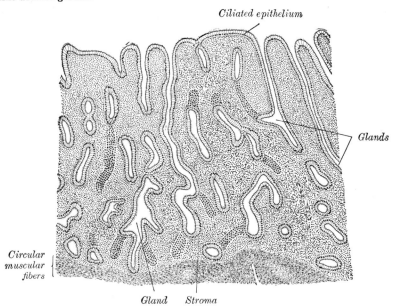

Fig. 1153.—Vertical section of mucous membrane of human uterus. (Sobotta.)

In the cervix the mucous membrane is sharply differentiated from that of the uterine cavity. It is thrown into numerous oblique ridges, which diverge from an anterior and posterior longitudinal raphé. In the upper two-thirds of the canal, the mucous membrane is provided with numerous deep glandular follicles, which secrete a clear viscid alkaline mucus; and, in addition, extending through the whole length of the canal is a variable number of little cysts, which have become occluded and distended with retained secretion. They are called the **ovula Nabothi.** The mucous membrane covering the lower half of the cervical canal presents numerous papillæ. The epithelium of the upper two-thirds is cylindrical and ciliated, but below this it loses its cilia, and gradually changes to stratified squamous epithelium close to the external orifice. On the vaginal surface of the cervix the epithelium is similar to that lining the vagina, viz., stratified squamous.

Vessels and Nerves.—The **arteries** of the uterus are the uterine, from the hypogastric; and the ovarian, from the abdominal aorta (Fig. 532). They are remarkable for their tortuous course in the substance of the organ, and for their frequent anastomoses. The termination of the ovarian artery meets that of the uterine artery, and forms an anastomotic trunk from which branches are given off to supply the uterus, their disposition being circular. The **veins** are of large size, and correspond with the arteries. They end in the uterine plexuses. In the impregnated uterus the arteries carry the blood to, and the veins convey it away from, the intervillous space of the placenta (see page 31). The **lymphatics** are described on page 726. The **nerves** are derived from the hypogastric and ovarian plexuses, and from the third and fourth sacral nerves. Afferent fibers from the uterus enter the spinal cord solely through the eleventh and twelfth thoracic nerves.

The Vagina (Fig. 1150, 1151).

The **vagina** extends from the vestibule to the uterus, and is situated behind the bladder and in front of the rectum; it is directed upward and backward, its axis forming with that of the uterus an angle of over 90°. Its walls are ordinarily in contact, and the usual shape of its lower part on transverse section is that of an H, the transverse limb being slightly curved forward or backward, while the lateral limbs are somewhat convex toward the median line; its middle part has the appearance of a transverse slit.   Its length is 6 to 7.5 cm. along its anterior wall, and 9 cm. along its posterior wall.   It is constricted at its commencement, dilated in the middle, and narrowed near its uterine extremity; it surrounds the vaginal portion of the cervix uteri, its attachment extending higher up on the posterior than on the anterior wall of the uterus.   To the recess behind the cervix the term **posterior fornix** is applied, while the smaller recesses in front and at the sides are called the **anterior** and **lateral fornices.**

Relations.—The **anterior surface** of the vagina is in relation with the fundus of the bladder, and with the urethra.   Its **posterior surface** is separated from the rectum by the rectouterine excavation in its upper fourth, and by the rectovaginal fascia in its middle two-fourths; the lower fourth is separated from the anal canal by the perineal body.   As the terminal portions of the ureters pass forward and medialward to reach the fundus of the bladder, they run close to the lateral fornices of the vagina, and as they enter the bladder are slightly in front of the anterior fornix.

Structure.—The vagina consists of an **internal mucous lining** and a **muscular coat** separated by a layer of erectile tissue.

The **mucous membrane** (*tunica mucosa*) is continuous above with that lining the uterus.   Its inner surface presents two longitudinal ridges, one on its anterior and one on its posterior wall. These ridges are called the **columns of the vagina** and from them numerous transverse ridges or rugæ extend outward on either side.   These rugæ are divided by furrows of variable depth, giving to the mucous membrane the appearance of being studded over with conical projections or papillæ; they are most numerous near the orifice of the vagina, especially before parturition. The epithelium covering the mucous membrane is of the stratified squamous variety.   The submucous tissue is very loose, and contains a plexus of large veins, together with smooth muscular fibers derived from the muscular coat.   It contains a number of mucous crypts, but no true glands.

The **muscular coat** (*tunica muscularis*) consists of two layers: an external longitudinal, which is by far the stronger, and an internal circular layer.   The longitudinal fibers are continuous with the superficial muscular fibers of the uterus.   The strongest fasciculi are those attached to the rectovesical fascia on either side.   The two layers are not distinctly separable from each other, but are connected by oblique decussating fasciculi, which pass from the one layer to the other.   In addition to this, the vagina at its lower end is surrounded by a band of striped muscular fibers, the **Bulbocavernosus** (see page 419).

External to the muscular coat is a layer of connective tissue, containing a large plexus of bloodvessels.

The **erectile tissue** consists of a layer of loose connective tissue, situated between the mucous membrane and the muscular coat; imbedded in it is a plexus of large veins, and numerous bundles of unstriped muscular fibers, derived from the circular muscular layer.   The arrangement of the veins is similar to that found in other erectile tissues.

The External Genital Organs (Partes Genitales Externæ Muliebres)
(Fig. 1154).

The **external genital organs** of the female are: the **mons pubis,** the **labia majora et minora pudendi,** the **clitoris,** the **vestibule of the vagina,** the **bulb of the vestibule,** and the **greater vestibular glands.**   The term **pudendum** or **vulva,** as generally applied, includes all these parts.

The **Mons Pubis** (*commissura labiorum anterior; mons Veneris*), the rounded eminence in front of the pubic symphysis, is formed by a collection of fatty tissue beneath the integument.   It becomes covered with hair at the time of puberty.

The **Labia Majora** (*labia maiora pudendi*) are two prominent longitudinal cutaneous folds which extend downward and backward from the mons pubis and form the lateral boundaries of a fissure or cleft, the **pudendal cleft** or **rima,** into which the vagina and urethra open.   Each labium has two surfaces, an outer, pigmented and covered with strong, crisp hairs; and an inner, smooth and beset with large sebaceous follicles.   Between the two there is a considerable quantity of areolar tissue, fat, and a tissue resembling the dartos tunic of the scrotum, besides vessels, nerves, and glands.   The labia are thicker in front, where they form by their meeting the **anterior labial commissure.**   Posteriorly they are not really joined, but appear to become lost in the neighboring integument, ending close to, and nearly parallel with, each other. Together with the connecting skin between them, they form the **posterior labial commissure** or posterior boundary of the pudendum. The labia majora correspond to the scrotum in the male.

The **Labia Minora** (*labia minora pudendi; nymphæ*) are two small cutaneous folds, situated between the labia majora, and extending from the clitoris obliquely downward, lateralward, and backward for about 4 cm. on either side of the orifice of the vagina, between which and the labia majora they end; in the virgin the posterior ends of the labia minora are usually joined across the middle line by a fold of skin, named the **frenulum of the labia** or **fourchette**. Anteriorly, each labium minus divides into two portions: the upper division passes above the clitoris to meet its fellow of the opposite side, forming a fold which overhangs the glans clitoridis, and is named the **preputium clitoridis**; the lower division passes beneath the clitoris and becomes united to its under surface, forming, with the corresponding structure of the opposite side, the **frenulum of the clitoris**. On the opposed surfaces of the labia minora are numerous sebaceous follicles.

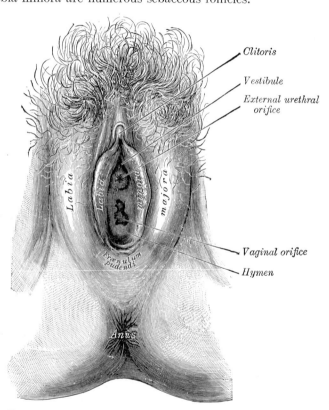

Fig. 1154.—External genital organs of female. The labia minora have been drawn apart.

The **Clitoris** is an erectile structure, homologous with the penis. It is situated beneath the anterior labial commissure, partially hidden between the anterior ends of the labia minora. It consists of two corpora cavernosa, composed of erectile tissue enclosed in a dense layer of fibrous membrane, united together along their medial surfaces by an incomplete fibrous pectiniform septum; each corpus is connected to the rami of the pubis and ischium by a crus; the **free extremity** (*glans clitoridis*) is a small rounded tubercle, consisting of spongy erectile tissue, and highly sensitive. The clitoris is provided like the penis, with a suspensory ligament, and with two small muscles, the Ischiocavernosi, which are inserted into the crura of the clitoris.

The Vestibule (*vestibulum vaginæ*).—The cleft between the labia minora and behind the glans clitoridis is named the **vestibule of the vagina**: in it are seen the urethral and vaginal orifices and the openings of the ducts of the greater vestibular glands.

The **external urethral orifice** (*orificium urethræ externum; urinary meatus*) is placed about 2.5 cm. behind the glans clitoridis and immediately in front of that of the vagina; it usually assumes the form of a short, sagittal cleft with slightly raised margins.

The **vaginal orifice** is a median slit below and behind the opening of the urethra; its size varies inversely with that of the **hymen**.

The **hymen** is a thin fold of mucous membrane situated at the orifice of the vagina; the inner edges of the fold are normally in contact with each other, and the vaginal orifice appears as a cleft between them. The hymen varies much in shape. When stretched, its commonest form is that of a ring, generally broadest posteriorly; sometimes it is represented by a semilunar fold, with its concave margin turned toward the pubes. Occasionally it is cribriform, or its free margin forms a membranous fringe. It may be entirely absent, or may form a complete septum across the lower end of the vagina; the latter condition is known as an **imperforate hymen**. It may persist after copulation, so that its presence cannot be considered a sign of virginity. When the hymen has been ruptured, small rounded elevations known as the **carunculæ hymenales** are found as its remains. Between the hymen and the frenulum of the labia is a shallow depression, named the **navicular fossa**.

The **Bulb of the Vestibule** (*bulbus vestibuli; vaginal bulb*) is the homologue of the bulb and adjoining part of the corpus cavernosum urethræ of the male, and consists of two elongated masses of erectile tissue, placed one on either side of the vaginal orifice and united to each other in front by a narrow median band termed the **pars intermedia**. Each lateral mass measures a little over 2.5 cm. in length. Their posterior ends are expanded and are in contact with the greater vestibular glands; their anterior ends are tapered and joined to one another by the pars intermedia; their deep surfaces are in contact with the superficial layer of the urogenital diaphragm; superficially they are covered by the Bulbocavernosus.

The **Greater Vestibular Glands** (*glandulæ vestibularis majores* [*Bartholini*]; *Bartholin's glands*) are the homologues of the bulbo-urethral glands in the male. They consist of two small, roundish bodies of a reddish-yellow color, situated one on either side of the vaginal orifice in contact with the posterior end of each lateral mass of the bulb of the vestibule. Each gland opens by means of a duct, about 2 cm. long, immediately lateral to the hymen, in the groove between it and the labium minus.

Mamma (Mammary Gland; Breast)

The mammary gland is an accessory of the reproductive system in function, since it secretes milk for nourishment of the infant, but structurally and developmentally it is closely related to the integument. It reaches its typical exquisite development in women during the early childbearing period but is present only in a rudimentary form in infants, children, and men.

In the adult nullipara, each mamma forms a discoidal, hemispherical, or conical eminence on the anterior chest wall, extending from the second to the sixth or seventh rib, and from the lateral border of the sternum into the axilla. It protrudes 3 to 5 cm. from the chest wall, and its cephalocaudal diameter, approximately 10 to 12 cm., is somewhat less than its transverse diameter. Its average weight is 150 to 200 gms., increasing to 400 or 500 gms. during lactation. The left mamma is generally slightly larger than the right.

The glandular tissue forms fifteen or twenty lobes arranged radially about the nipple, each lobe having its own individual excretory duct. The glandular tissue does not occupy the entire eminence called the breast; a variable but considerable amount of adipose tissue fills out the stroma between and around the lobes. The central portion is predominantly glandular, the peripheral predominantly fat. The connective tissue stroma in many places is concentrated into fibrous bands which course vertically through the substance of the breast, attaching the deep layer of the superficial fascia to the corium of the skin. These bands are known as **suspensory ligaments of the breast** or **Cooper's ligaments.** The entire breast is contained within the superficial fascia. The deep surface is separated from the underlying external investing layer of deep fascia by a fascial cleft which allows considerable mobility. The deep surface of the breast is concave, molded over the anterior chest wall mostly in contact with the pectoral fascia, but laterally with the axillary and serratus anterior fascia, and inferiorly it may reach the Obliquus externus and Rectus abdominis.

The **Mammary Papilla** (*papilla mammæ*) or **Nipple** projects as a small cylindrical or conical body, a little below the center of each breast at about the level of the fourth intercostal space. It is perforated at the tip by fifteen or twenty minute openings, the apertures of the lactiferous ducts. The characteristic skin of the nipple, pigmented, wrinkled, and roughened by papillæ, extends outward on the surface of the breast for 1 or 2 cm. to form the **areola.** The color of the nipple and areola in nulliparæ varies from rosy pink to brown, depending on the complexion of the individual. During the second month and progressing through pregnancy, the skin becomes darker and the areola becomes larger. Following lactation the pigmentation diminishes but is never entirely lost and may be used to differentiate nulliparous from parous individuals.

The **areola** (*areola mammæ*) is made rough by the presence of numerous large sebaceous glands which produce small elevations of its surface. These **areolar glands** (*Glands of Montgomery*) secrete a lipoid material which lubricates and protects the nipple during nursing. The subcutaneous tissue of the areola contains circular and radiating smooth muscle bundles which cause the nipple to become erect in response to stimulation.

Development.—The primordium of the mamma is first recognizable during the sixth week of intrauterine life as a bandlike thickening of the ectoderm of the anterolateral body wall. It extends from the axilla to the inguinal region and is called the **milk line.** The thickening of the ectoderm pushes into the subcutaneous mesoderm as it enlarges. After the eighth week, only the portion of the ridge destined to become mamma is identifiable. During the remainder of fetal life the epithelial cells proliferate, gradually forming buds and cords of cells projecting into the subcutaneous tissue, and by birth, in both sexes, little more than the main ducts have formed. The glands remain in this infantile condition in the male.

Adolescent Hypertrophy.—In the female there is but slight change from the infantile condition until the approach of puberty. At this time the mamma enlarges due to an increase in glandular tissue, particularly the ducts, and to a deposit of adipose tissue. The mammary papilla and areola enlarge, increase slightly in pigmentation, acquire smooth muscle and become sensitive. After the onset of the menses, with each period there is a change in the mamma. In the premenstrual phase there is a vascular engorgement, increase in the glands, and enlargement of their lumina. During the postmenstrual phase the gland regresses and then remains in an inactive stage until the next premenstrual phase.

Hypertrophy of Pregnancy.—Visible enlargement of the breast begins after the second month of pregnancy and is accompanied by increased pigmentation and enlargement of the papilla, areola, and areolar glands. The duct system develops first, reaching its completion during the first six months; the acini and secreting portion follow during the last three months. The adipose tissue is almost completely replaced by parenchyma.

The secretion from the mammary gland during the first two or three days after parturition is thin and yellowish and is called **colostrum**. The secretion of true milk begins on the third or fourth day and continues through the nursing period.

Involution after Lactation.—At the termination of nursing, the gland gradually regresses by loss of the glandular tissue; the ducts and acini return to their former size and number, and the interstices are filled with adipose tissue. There is a slight decrease in size of the breast as a whole and it tends to become more flabby and pendulous than the nulliparous breast. The pigmentation of the nipple and areola decrease but do not entirely disappear.

Menopausal Involution.—At the end of the childbearing period, the mammæ regress and the glandular tissue reverts toward the infantile condition. The adipose tissue disappears more slowly, especially in obese individuals, but eventually a senile atrophy occurs which leaves the mamma a shriveled pendulous fold of skin.

Hormonal Relationships.—The hypertrophy of puberty and the cyclic engorgements accompanying menstruation are responses to variations in the concentration of the ovarian sex hormones from the follicles and corpora lutea. The hypertrophy of pregnancy is in response to increase in the corpus luteum hormone. The presence of the ovary is necessary only during the first part of pregnancy; later, the hormones are supplied by the placenta. Lactation is a response to the lactogenic hormone of the hypophysis, but is influenced by the nervous system through the stimulus of suckling. Suppression of the ovarian hormones after the menopause results in the involution. Quite frequently the mammary glands in the newborn of both sexes secrete a fluid called "witches milk", under the influence of the hormones passed through the placenta from the maternal circulation.

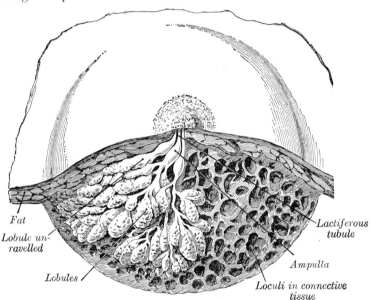

Fat

Lobule un-ravelled

Lobules

Lactiferous tubule

Ampulla

Loculi in connective tissue

Fig. 1155.—Dissection of the lower half of the mamma during the period of lactation. (Luschka.)

Structure (Figs. 1155, 1156).—The mamma consists of gland tissue; of fibrous tissue, connecting its lobes; and of fatty tissue in the intervals between the lobes. The gland tissue, when freed from fibrous tissue and fat, is of a pale reddish color, firm in texture, flattened from before backward and thicker in the center than at the circumference. The subcutaneous surface of the mamma presents numerous irregular processes which project toward the skin and are joined to it by bands of connective tissue. It consists of numerous lobes, and these are composed of lobules, connected together by areolar tissue, bloodvessels, and ducts. The smallest lobules consist of a cluster of rounded alveoli, which open into the smallest branches of the lactiferous ducts; these ducts unite to form larger ducts, and these end in a single canal, corresponding with one of the chief subdivisions of the gland. The number of excretory ducts varies from fifteen to twenty; they are termed the **tubuli lactiferi.** They converge toward the areola, beneath which they form dilatations or **ampullæ,** which serve as reservoirs for the milk, and, at the base of the papillæ, become contracted, and pursue a straight course to its summit, perforating it by separate orifices considerably narrower than the ducts themselves. The ducts are composed of areolar tissue containing longitudinal and transverse elastic fibers; muscular fibers are entirely absent; they are lined by columnar epithelium resting on a basement membrane. The epithelium of the mamma differs according to the state of activity of the organ. In the gland of a woman who is not pregnant or suckling, the alveoli are very small and solid, being filled with a mass of granular polyhedral cells. During pregnancy the alveoli enlarge, and the cells undergo rapid multiplication. At the commencement of lactation, the cells in the center of the alveolus undergo fatty degeneration, and are eliminated in the first milk, as **colostrum corpus-**

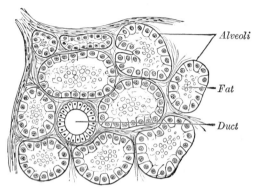

FIG. 1156.—Section of portion of mamma.

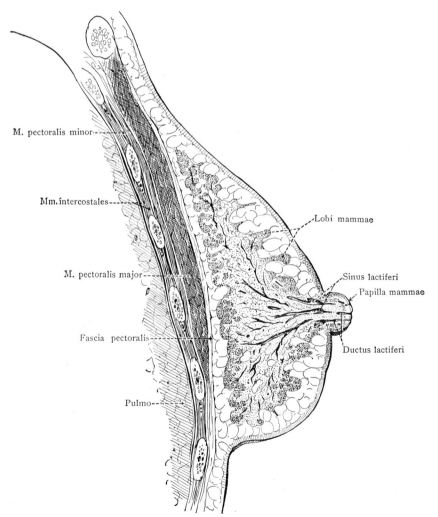

FIG. 1157.—Sagittal section through lactating mammary gland. (Eycleshymer and Jones.)

cles. The peripheral cells of the alveolus remain, and form a single layer of granular, short columnar cells, with spherical nuclei, lining the basement membrane. The cells during the state of activity of the gland, are capable of forming, in their interior, oil globules, which are then ejected into the lumen of the alveolus, and constitute the milk globules. When the acini are distended by the accumulation of the secretion the lining epithelium becomes flattened.

The **fibrous tissue** invests the entire surface of the mamma. Bands of fibrous tissue traverse the gland and connect the overlying skin to the underlying pectoral fascia. These constitute the ligaments of Cooper.

The **fatty tissue** covers the surface of the gland, and occupies the interval between its lobes. It usually exists in considerable abundance, and determines the form and size of the gland. There is no fat immediately beneath the areola and papilla.

Vessels and Nerves.—The **arteries** supplying the mammæ are derived from the thoracic branches of the axillary, the intercostals, and the internal mammary. The **veins** describe an anastomotic circle around the base of the papilla, called by Haller the **circulus venosus.** From this, large branches transmit the blood to the circumference of the gland, and end in the axillary and internal mammary veins. The **lymphatics** are described on page 728. The **nerves** are derived from the anterior and lateral cutaneous branches of the fourth, fifth, and sixth thoracic nerves.

Variations.—Independent of the physiological variations, conditions of underdeveloped breasts (*hypomastia*), *hypertrophy*, and inequality on the two sides are quite common. Variations in position, cephalically or caudally, are not infrequent, as might be expected from the method of embryological development. Absence of the breast, *amastia*, is very rare; an increase in the number of mammæ, **polymastia**, is not as rare. The supernumerary mammæ occur somewhere along the milk line in most instances, but other locations have been reported. Not infrequently they secrete milk during normal periods of lactation. When only the nipples of the supernumerary mammæ are present the condition is **polythelia;** the extra nipples occur along the milk line in the majority of cases and are found in males, though less frequently than in females.

Racial variations may be due to genetic influences which cause the discoidal, hemispherical pear-shaped, or conical forms to predominate. On the other hand, they may be due to intentional practices such as suppressing development by tight bandages at adolescence or tremendously elongating them by manipulation to make nursing convenient for an infant strapped on the back.

Gynecomastia is a condition in which the mammæ of a male are enlarged. In pseudogynecomastia the increase is due to adipose tissue. In the true gynecomastia, to some extent the epithelial tissue but more especially the firmer connective tissue elements are involved. It probably has a background of endocrine dysfunction but this is not clearly understood.

BIBLIOGRAPHY

KIDNEY

The position and mobility of the kidneys in healthy young men and women. MOODY, R. O., and R. G. VAN NUYS: 1940. Anat. Rec., Vol. 76, pp. 111–133.

New directions in renal morphology: a method, its results and its future. OLIVER, J.: 1945. Harvey Lectures, Vol. 40, pp. 102–155.

Lectures on the kidney. SMITH, H. W.: 1943. Univ. Exten. Div.; Univ. Kansas, vi & 134 pp.

HISTOLOGY

Direct evidence of function in kidney of an early human fetus. CAMERON, G., and R. CHAMBERS: 1938. Am. J. Physiol., Vol. 123, pp. 482–485.

The Golgi apparatus in the proximal and distal tubule cells of the perfused frog's kidney. EMMEL, V. M.: 1938. Anat. Rec., Vol. 70, pp. 371–387.

The number and distribution of macrophages and fibroblasts in kidneys of albino rats with emphasis on twenty-five day males. KIRKMAN, H.: 1943. Am. J. Anat., Vol. 73, pp. 451–482.

Fat excretion in the guinea pig kidney. ZWEMER, R. L., and R. M. WOTTON: 1944. Anat. Rec., Vol. 90, pp. 107–114.

DEVELOPMENT AND ANOMALIES

The normal changes in the position of the embryonic kidney. GRUENWALD, P.: 1943. Anat. Rec., Vol. 85, pp. 163–176.

Stimulation of nephrogenic tissue by normal and abnormal inductors. GRUENWALD, P.: 1943. Anat. Rec., Vol. 86, pp. 321–339.

Horseshoe kidney, a study of 32 autopsy and 9 surgical cases. NATION, E. F.: 1945. J. Urol., Vol. 53, pp. 762–768.

The development of the urinogenital system of the albino rat. I. The kidney and its ducts, TORREY, T. W.: 1943. Am. J. Anat., Vol. 72, pp. 113–147.

Growth and differentiation of kidney tissue of the rabbit embryo in omental grafts. WATERMAN. A. J.: 1940. J. Morph., Vol. 67, pp. 369–385.

FASCIA

Développement et anatomie de la loge rénale chez l'homme. BAUMANN, J. A.: 1945. Acta Anat., Vol. 1, pp. 15–65.

The cone of renal fascia in the adult white male. CONGDON, E. D., and J. N. EDSON: 1941. Anat. Rec., Vol. 80, pp. 289–313.

The renal fascia and its relation to the transversalis fascia. TOBIN, C. E.: 1944. Anat. Rec., Vol. 89, pp. 295–311.

BLOOD VESSELS

The blood supply of the kidney, suprarenal gland, and associated structures. ANSON, B. J., E. W. CAULDWELL, J. W. PICK, and L. E. BEATON: 1947. Surg., Gyn. & Obs., Vol. 84, pp. 313–320.

The vascular pole of the glomerulus in the kidney of vertebrates. EDWARDS, J. G.: 1940. Anat. Rec., Vol. 76, pp. 381–389.

Renal lymphatics. PEIRCE, E. C., 2nd,: 1944. Anat. Rec., Vol. 90, pp. 315–335.

Incidence of single and multiple renal arteries in Negroes. RONSTROM, G. N.: 1947. Am. J. Phys. Anthrop., Vol. 5, pp. 485–490.

The arrangement of the capillary tuft of the human glomerulus. WILMER, H. A.: 1941. Anat. Rec., Vol. 80, pp. 507–518.

BLADDER

Nerve endings in the urinary bladder. LANGWORTHY, O. R., and E. L. MURPHY: 1939. J. Comp. Neur., Vol. 71, pp. 487–509.

Normal and abnormal development of the ureter in the human embryo—A mechanistic consideration. MEYER, R.: 1946. Anat. Rec., Vol. 96, pp. 355–371.

Complete unilateral duplication of ureter with analysis of literature. MILLS, J. C.: 1939. Urologic and Cutaneous Rev., Vol. 43, pp. 444–447

Anomalies of urachus: persistent fetal bladder. SIMON, H. E., and N. A. BRANDEBERRY: 1946. J. Urol., Vol. 55, pp. 401–408.

Anatomical and surgical restudy of Denonvilliers' fascia. TOBIN, C. E., and J. A. BENJAMIN: 1945. Surg., Gyn. & Obs., Vol. 80, pp. 373–388.

REPRODUCTIVE SYSTEM
GENERAL

Sex and Internal Secretions. ALLEN, E., C. H. DANFORTH, and E. A. DOISY: 1939. Williams and Wilkins, Baltimore, 2nd Ed., xxxvi + 1346 pp.

The Hormones in Human Reproduction. CORNER, G. W.: 1942. Princeton Univ. Press, xix + 265 pp.

Diagnosis in Sterility. ENGLE, E. T., edit.: 1947. Charles C. Thomas, Springfield, 249 pp.

Reproduction. HOOKER, C. W.: 1946. Ann. Rev. Physiol., Vol. 8, pp. 467–498.

DEVELOPMENT

Sex differentiation during the early pouch stages of the opossum (Didelphys virginiana) and a comparison of the anatomical changes induced by male and female sex hormones. BURNS, R. K., JR.: 1939. J. Morph., Vol. 65, pp. 497–547.

Genital changes in female guinea pigs resulting from destruction of the median eminence. DEY, F. L.: 1943. Anat. Rec., Vol. 87, pp. 85–90.

HERMAPHRODITISM

Hermaphroditism in rodents, with a description of a case in the mouse. HOOKER, C. W., and L. C. STRONG: 1944. Yale J. Biol. & Med., Vol. 16, pp. 341–351.

Genital Abnormalities, Hermaphroditism and Related Adrenal Diseases. YOUNG, H. H.: 1937. Williams & Wilkins, Baltimore, 649 pp.

GERM CELLS

Observational and experimental evidences relating to the origin and differentiation of the definitive germ cells in mice. EVERETT, N. B.: 1943. J. Exp. Zool., Vol. 92, pp. 49–91.

Primordial germ cells in a 4.5-mm. human embryo. HAMLETT, G. W. D.: 1935. Anat. Rec., Vol. 61, pp. 273–279.

MALE REPRODUCTIVE SYSTEM

Bisexual differentiation of the sex ducts in opossums as a result of treatment with androgen. BURNS, R. K.: 1945. J. Exp. Zool., Vol. 100, pp. 119–140.

The effect of male hormone substances upon birth and prenatal development in the rat. HAMILTON, J. B., and J. M. WOLFE: 1938. Anat. Rec., Vol. 70, pp. 433–440.

Reproduction in the Male. HOOKER, C. W.: 1945. Howell, Textbook of Physiology, 15th Ed., Ed. by J. F. Fulton, pp. 1213–1231.

TESTIS

The cytological relationship between the hypophysis and the germinal epithelium of the testis. GATZ, A. J.: 1938. Anat. Rec., Vol. 70, pp. 619–641.

The effect of male hormonal substance upon the testes and upon spermatogenesis. HAMILTON, J. B., and S. L. LEONARD: 1938. Anat. Rec., Vol. 71, pp. 105–117.

The postnatal history and function of the interstitial cells of the testis of the bull. HOOKER, C. W.: 1944. Am. J. Anat., Vol. 74, pp. 1–37.

Components and distribution of the spermatic nerves and the nerves of the vas deferens. KUNTZ, A., and R. E. MORRIS, JR.: 1946. J. Comp. Neur., Vol. 85, pp. 33–44.

Relation of interstitial cell hyperplasia to secretion of male hormone in the sparrow. PFEIFFER, C. A., and A. KIRSCHBAUM: 1943. Anat. Rec., Vol. 85, pp. 211–227.

Magnification of spermatozoa by means of the electron microscope. SEYMOUR, F. I., and M. BENMOSCHE: 1941. J. Am. Med. Assn., Vol. 116, pp. 2489–2490.

Descent of the testis: anatomical and hormonal considerations. WELLS, L. J.: 1943. Surgery, Vol. 14, pp. 436–472.

PENIS

The comparative morphology of the erectile tissue of the penis with especial emphasis on the probable mechanism of erection. DEYSACH, L. J.: 1939. Am. J. Anat., Vol. 64, pp. 111–131.

Congenital absence of the penis. RUKSTINAT, G. J., and R. J. HASTERLIK: 1939. Arch. Path., Vol. 27, pp. 984–993.

Anatomical study and clinical consideration of the fasciæ limiting urinary extravasation from the penile urethra. TOBIN, C. E., and J. A. BENJAMIN: 1944. Surg., Gyn. and Obs., Vol. 79, pp. 195–204.

The value of Buck's and Colles' fasciæ. WESSON, M. B.: 1945. J. Urol., Vol. 53, pp. 365–372.

FEMALE REPRODUCTIVE SYSTEM

OVARY

The fibrous connective tissue of the rabbit ovary from sex differentiation to maturity. DUKE, K. L.: 1947. Anat. Rec., Vol. 98, pp. 507–525.

The changes in the vascular pattern of the ovary of the albino rat during the estrous cycle. BASSETT, D. L.: 1943. Am. J. Anat., Vol. 73, pp. 251–291.

Growth in vitro of ovarian germinal epithelium. LONG, J. H.: 1940. Carnegie Cont. Embryol., Vol. 28, pp. 89–93.

The homology of the vesicular ovarian follicles of the mammalian ovary with the coelom. MOSSMAN, H. W.: 1938. Anat. Rec., Vol. 70, pp. 643–655.

Offspring from unborn mothers. RUSSELL, W. L., and P. M. DOUGLASS: 1945. Proc. Nat. Acad. Sci., Vol. 31, pp. 402–404.

OVA

The first maturation division of the rat ovum. BLANDAU, R. J.: 1945. Anat. Rec., Vol. 92, pp. 449–457.

The origin of ova in the adult opossum. EVERETT, N. B.: 1942. Anat. Rec., Vol. 82, pp. 77–91.

Some observations on the graafian follicles in an adult human ovary. PANKRATZ, D. S.: 1938. Anat. Rec., Vol. 71, pp. 211–219.

The comparative behavior of mammalian eggs in vivo and in vitro. IV. The development of fertilized and artificially activated rabbit eggs. PINCUS, G.: 1939. J. Exp. Zool, Vol. 82, pp. 85–129.

OVULATION

The time of ovulation in the monkey. FARRIS, E. J.: 1946. Anat. Rec., Vol. 95, pp. 337–345.

Cinematographic studies of rabbit ovulation. HILL, R. T., E. ALLEN, and T. C. KRAMER: 1935. Anat. Rec., Vol. 63, pp. 239–245.

Electrometric timing of human ovulation. LANGMAN, L., and H. S. BURR: 1942. Am. J. Obs. & Gyn., Vol. 44, pp. 223–230.

CORPUS LUTEUM

Diestrus and the formation of corpora lutea in rats with persistent estrus, treated with desoxycorticosterone acetate. MARVIN, H. N.: 1947. Anat. Rec., Vol. 98, pp. 383–391.

The microscopically demonstrable lipids of the cylic corpora lutea in the rat. EVERETT, J. W.: 1945. Am. J. Anat., Vol. 77, pp. 293–323.

UTERUS

The distribution of nerves in the adult human myometrium. HIRSCH, E. F., and M. E. MARTIN: 1943. Surg., Gyn. & Obs., Vol. 76, pp. 697–702.

Malformations of uterus; review of subject, including embryology, comparative anatomy, diagnosis and report of cases. JARCHO, J.: 1946. Am. J. Surg., Vol. 71, pp. 106–166.

An electrometric study of uterine activity. LANGMAN, L., and H. S. BURR: 1941. Am. J. Obs. & Gyn., Vol. 42, pp. 59–67.

Physiology of the Uterus, with Clinical Correlations. REYNOLDS, S. R. M.: 1939. Hoeber, New York, xxii & 447 pp.

The relation of hydrostatic conditions in the uterus to the size and shape of the conceptus during pregnancy: a concept of uterine accommodation. REYNOLDS, S. R. M.: 1946. Anat. Rec., Vol. 95, pp. 283–296.

HISTOLOGY

Histological studies of the menstruating mucous membrane of the human uterus. BARTELMEZ, G. W.: 1933. Carnegie, Cont. Embryol., Vol. 24, pp. 141–186.

Histochemical reactions of the endometrium in pregnancy. WISLOCKI, G. B., and E. W. DEMPSEY: 1945. Am. J. Anat., Vol. 77, pp. 365–403.

MENSTRUATION

A study of temperature and electric potentials in the menstrual cycle. BARTON, D. S.: 1940. Yale J. Biol. & Med., Vol. 12, pp. 503–523.

Current views on the causation of menstruation. ENGLE, E. T.: 1939. Am. J. Obs. & Gyn., Vol. 38, pp. 600–608.

Reproduction in American monkeys. I. Estrous cycle, ovulation and menstruation in Cebus. HAMLETT, G. W. D.: 1939. Anat. Rec., Vol. 73, pp. 171–187.

TRANSPORT AND FERTILIZATION OF OVA

The oviduct and egg transport in the albino rat. ALDEN, R. H.: 1942. Anat. Rec., Vol. 84, pp. 137–169.

Implantation of the rat egg. I. Experimental alteration of uterine polarity. ALDEN, R. H.: 1945. J. Exp. Zool., Vol. 100, pp. 229–235.

The duration of the fertilizing capacity of spermatozoa in the female genital tract of the rat. SODERWALL, A. L., and R. J. BLANDAU: 1941. J. Exp. Zool., Vol. 88, pp. 55–64.

HORMONES AND PHYSIOLOGY

Mobilization of alkaline phosphatase in the uterus of the mouse by estrogen. ATKINSON, W. B., and H. ELFTMAN: 1947. Endocrinology, Vol. 40, pp. 30–36.

Evidence in the normal albino rat that progesterone facilitates ovulation and corpus luteum formation. EVERETT, J. W.: 1944. Endocrinology, Vol. 34, pp. 136–137.

Sexual rhythms in the reproductive tract of the adult female opossum and effects of hormonal treatments. MORGAN, C. F.: 1946. Am. J. Anat., Vol. 78, pp. 411–463.

The effect of progesterone on the mouse ovary as influenced by gestation. SELYE, H.: 1939. Anat. Rec., Vol. 75, pp. 59–73.

Local inhibition of hair growth in dogs by percutaneous application of estrone. WILLIAMS, W. L., W. U. GARDNER, and J. DEVITA: 1946. Endocrinology, Vol. 38, pp. 368–375.

FEMALE PELVIS

The blood vessels of the female pelvis in relation to gynecological surgery. CURTIS, A. H., B. J. ANSON, F. L. ASHLEY, and T. JONES: 1942. Surg., Gyn. & Obs., Vol. 75, pp. 421–423.

The more recent conceptions of the pelvic architecture. CALDWELL, W. E., H. C. MOLOY, and D. A. D'ESOPO: 1940. Am. J. Obs. & Gyn., Vol. 40, pp. 558–565.

The growth and development of the pelvis of individual girls before, during, and after puberty. GREULICH, W. W., and H. THOMS: 1944. Yale J. Biol. & Med., Vol. 17, pp. 91–97.

The clinical significance of pelvic variations. THOMS, H., W. R. FOOTE, and I. FRIEDMAN: 1939. Am. J. Obs. & Gyn., Vol. 38, pp. 634–642.

A comparative study of male and female pelvis. THOMS, H., and W. W. GREULICH: 1940. Am. J. Obs. & Gyn., Vol. 39, pp. 56–62.

FASCIA

Further studies in gynecological anatomy and related clinical problems. CURTIS, A. H., B. J. ANSON, and F. L. ASHLEY: 1942. Surg., Gyn. & Obs., Vol. 74, pp. 709–727.

Abdominal and pelvic fascias with surgical applications. DAVIES, J. W.: 1932. Surg., Gyn. & Obs., Vol. 54, pp. 495–504.

The preperitoneal layer—its gynecological application. DAVIES, J. W.: 1935. Surg., Gyn. & Obs., Vol. 60, pp. 941–945.

An histological study of the perivaginal fascia in a nullipara. GOFF, B. H.: 1931. Surg., Gyn. & Obs., Vol. 52, pp. 32–42.

The exact anatomy and development of the ligaments attached to the cervix uteri. POWER, R. M. H.: 1944. Surg., Gyn. & Obs., Vol. 79, pp. 390–396.

The fascia surrounding the vagina, its origin and arrangement. SEARS, N. P.: 1933. Am. J. Obs. & Gyn., Vol. 25, pp. 484–492.

MAMMAE

Supernumerary breast. CHOLNOKY, T. DE.: 1939. Arch. Surg., Vol. 39, pp. 926–941.

Observations on the chemical cytology of the mammary gland. DEMPSEY, E. W., H. BUNTING, and G. B. WISLOCKI: 1947. Am. J. Anat., Vol. 81, pp. 309–341.

Retardation of mammary involution in the mouse by irritation of the nipples. HOOKER, C. W., and W. L. WILLIAMS: 1940. Yale J. Biol. & Med., Vol. 12, pp. 559–564.

Gynecomastia. KARSNER, H. T.: 1946. Am. J. Path., Vol. 22, pp. 235–315.

Arterial blood supply of the breast. MALINIAC, J. W.: 1943. Arch. Surg., Vol. 47, pp. 329–343.

The limitations and dangers of mammography by contrast mediums. ROMANO, S. A., and E. M. McFETRIDGE: 1938. J. Am. Med. Assn., Vol. 110, pp. 1905–1910.

Plastic Surgery of the Breast and Abdominal Wall. THOREK, M.: 1942. Charles C. Thomas, Springfield, xiii & 446 pp.

Normal and experimental mammary involution in the mouse as related to the inception and cessation of lactation. WILLIAMS, W. L.: 1942. Am. J. Anat., Vol. 71, pp. 1–41.

THE DUCTLESS GLANDS
(ENDOCRINE GLANDS.)

THE ductless glands or endocrine glands differ from other glands in that they have no ducts but discharge their secretions into the blood stream. These secretions are chemical substances called hormones. The ductless glands have an extraordinarily rich blood supply.

These glands include the thyroid, the parathyroids, the hypophysis or pituitary body, and the suprarenals. Other organs of unknown or uncertain function or which were formerly believed to be endocrines, are also included in this section. These are the pineal body and the glomus coccygeum. The paraganglia and other bodies of the chromophile system are described.

Other organs with definite endocrine functions, such as the ovaries, the testes, the pancreas, the liver and the mucosa of portions of the gastro-intestinal tract, are described elsewhere.

THE THYROID GLAND (GLANDULA THYREOIDEA; THYROID BODY)
(Fig. 1159).

Development.—The thyroid gland is developed from a median diverticulum of the ventral wall of the pharynx and, according to some authorities, possibly from the ultimobronchial bodies. The median diverticulum appears about the fourth week on the summit of the tuberculum impar, but later is found in the furrow immediately behind the tuberculum (Fig. 973). It grows downward and backward as a tubular duct, which bifurcates and subsequently subdivides into a series of cellular cords, from which the isthmus and lateral lobes of the thyroid gland are developed. The connection of the median diverticulum with the pharynx is termed the **thyroglossal duct**; its continuity is subsequently interrupted, and it undergoes degeneration, its upper end being represented by the foramen cecum of the tongue, and its lower by the pyramidal lobe of the thyroid gland. The ultimobranchial bodies, mentioned above, are considered to be either diverticula of the fourth pouches or representatives of the fifth pouches. They are enveloped by the expanding lateral lobes of the thyroid and, in the human embryo, appear to atrophy without leaving a trace in the adult.

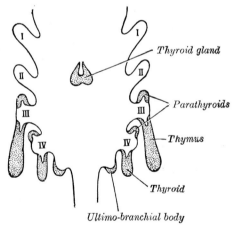

Fig. 1158.—Scheme showing development of branchial epithelial bodies. (Modified from Kohn.) *I, II, III, IV.* Branchial pouches.

Anatomy.—The **thyroid gland** is a highly vascular organ, situated at the front and sides of the neck; it consists of right and left lobes connected across the middle line by a narrow portion, the **isthmus**. Its weight is somewhat variable, but is usually about 30 grams. It is slightly heavier in the female, in whom it becomes enlarged during pregnancy.

The **lobes** (*lobuli gl. thyreoideæ*) are conical in shape, the apex of each being directed upward and lateralward as far as the junction of the middle with the lower third of the thyroid cartilage; the base looks downward, and is on a level with the fifth or sixth tracheal ring. Each lobe is about 5 cm. long; its greatest width is about 3 cm., and its thickness about 2 cm. The **lateral or superficial surface** is convex, and covered by the skin, the superficial and deep fasciæ, the Sternocleidomastoideus, the superior belly of the Omohyoideus, the Sternohyoideus and Sterno-

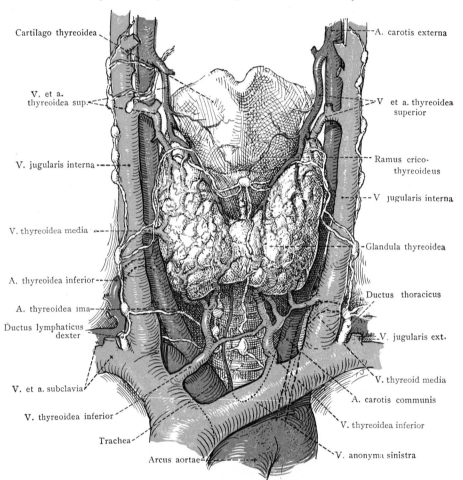

Cartilago thyreoidea

A. carotis externa

V. et a. thyreoidea sup.

V et a. thyreoidea superior

V. jugularis interna

Ramus crico-thyreoideus

V jugularis interna

V. thyreoidea media

Glandula thyreoidea

A. thyreoidea inferior

Ductus thoracicus

A. thyreoidea ima

Ductus lymphaticus dexter

V. jugularis ext.

V. thyreoid media

V. et a. subclavia

A. carotis communis

V. thyreoidea inferior

V. thyreoidea inferior

Trachea

V. anonyma sinistra

Arcus aortae

Fig. 1159.—Blood supply of the thyroid gland, viewed from in front. The thoracic duct and principal lymphatics are also shown. (Eycleshymer and Jones.)

thyreoideus, and beneath the last muscle by the visceral layer of the deep fascia, which forms a capsule for the gland. The **deep or medial surface** is moulded over the underlying structures, viz., the trachea, the Constrictor pharyngis inferior and posterior part of the Cricothyreoideus, the esophagus (particularly on the left side of the neck), the superior and inferior thyroid arteries, and the recurrent nerves. The **anterior border** is thin, and inclines obliquely from above downward toward the middle line of the neck, while the **posterior border** is thick and overlaps the common carotid artery, and, as a rule, the parathyroids.

The **isthmus** (*isthmus gl. thyreoidea*) connects together the lower thirds of the lobes; it measures about 1.25 cm. in breadth, and the same in depth, and usually covers the second and third rings of the trachea. Its situation and size present, however, many variations. In the middle line of the neck it is covered by the skin and fascia, and close to the middle line, on either side, by the Sternothyreoideus. Across its upper border runs an anastomotic branch uniting the two superior thyroid arteries; at its lower border are the inferior thyroid veins. Sometimes the isthmus is altogether wanting.

A third lobe, of conical shape, called the **pyramidal lobe**, frequently *arises* from the upper part of the isthmus, or from the adjacent portion of either lobe, but most commonly the left, and ascends as far as the hyoid bone. It is occasionally quite detached, or may be divided into two or more parts.

A fibrous or muscular band is sometimes found attached, above, to the body of the hyoid bone, and below to the isthmus of the gland, or its pyramidal lobe. When muscular, it is termed the **Levator glandulæ thyreoideæ.**

Small detached portions of thyroid tissue are sometimes found in the vicinity of the lateral lobes or above the isthmus; they are called **accessory thyroid glands** (*glandulæ thyreoideæ accessoriæ*).

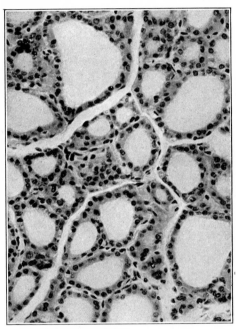

Fig. 1160.—Thyroid gland of a rat. (Kenyon, Am. J. Path.)

Structure.—The thyroid gland is invested by a thin capsule of connective tissue, which projects into its substance and imperfectly divides it into masses of irregular form and size. When the organ is cut into, it is of a brownish-red color, and is seen to be made up of a number of closed vesicles, containing colloid, and separated from each other by intermediate connective tissue (Fig. 1160.)

The thyroid follicles (acini, vesicles) of the adult are closed sacs of inconstant shape and size. They are normally of microscopic dimensions, although macroscopically visible in colloid goiter. The follicles located peripherally may be larger than those centrally placed. The cuboidal epithelium of the normal thyroid rests directly on the delicate connective tissue surrounding the follicle. No basement membrane can be seen. The capillaries and lymphatics are thus in close contact with the secretory epithelium of the gland. The follicle normally is filled with colloid which contains the active principle of the gland, thyroxin. The thyroid epithelium may secrete this hormone directly into the colloid filled lumen of the follicle where it is stored, or the hormone may be secreted directly into the capillaries. The stored colloid may be absorbed and liberated into the capillaries.

The hormone, thyroxin, is characterized by its iodine content. Iodine is essential to the elaboration of the hormone, and is normally obtained in adequate amounts in the diet. Proper functioning of the thyroid gland and normal histological structure is dependent upon the adequacy of available iodine. The thyroid itself is activated or regulated by another hormone, the thyrotropic hormone of the anterior pituitary gland. Removal of the thyroid results in a marked reduction of the oxidative processes of the body. This lowered metabolic rate is characteristic of hypothyroidism. In infancy and childhood the thyroid gland is essential to normal growth of the body.

Vessels and Nerves (Fig. 1161).—The **arteries** supplying the thyroid gland are the superior and inferior thyroids and sometimes an additional branch (thyroidea ima) from the innominate artery or the arch of the aorta, which ascends upon the front of the trachea. The arteries are remarkable for their large size and frequent anastomoses. The **veins** (Fig. 1159) form a plexus on the surface of the gland and on the front of the trachea; from this plexus the superior, middle, and inferior thyroid veins arise; the superior and middle end in the internal jugular, the inferior in the innominate vein. The capillary blood vessels form a dense plexus in the connective tissue around the vesicles, between the epithelium of the vesicles and the endothelium of the lymphatics, which surround a greater or smaller part of the circumference of the vesicle. The **lymphatic vessels** run in the interlobular connective tissue, not uncommonly surrounding the arteries which they accompany, and communicate with a net-work in the capsule of the gland; they may contain colloid material. They end in the thoracic and right lymphatic trunks. The **nerves** are derived from the middle and inferior cervical ganglia of the sympathetic.

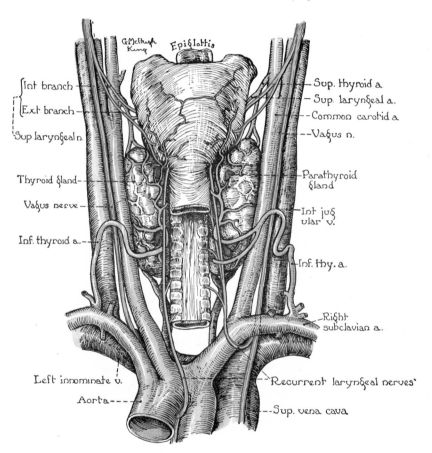

Fig. 1161.—Posterior view of larynx, trachea, thyroid, and parathyroids. Relations of thyroid arteries and laryngeal nerves are shown. (Nordland; Surgery, Gynecology and Obstetrics.)

THE PARATHYROID GLANDS (Fig. 1161).

Development.—The parathyroid bodies are developed as outgrowths from the third and fourth branchial pouches (Fig. 1158).

Anatomy.—The **parathyroid glands** are small brownish-red bodies, situated as a rule between the posterior borders of the lateral lobes of the thyroid gland and its capsule.

They differ from it in structure, being composed of masses of cells arranged in a more or less columnar fashion with numerous intervening capillaries. They measure on an average about 6 mm. in length, and from 3 to 4 mm. in breadth, and usually present the appearance of flattened oval disks. They are divided, according to their situation, into **superior** and **inferior**. The superior, usually two in number, are the more constant in position, and are situated, one on either side, at the level of the lower border of the cricoid cartilage, behind the junction of the pharynx and esophagus. The inferior, also usually two in number, may be applied to the lower edge of the lateral lobes, or placed at some little distance below the thyroid gland, or found in relation to one of the inferior thyroid veins.

In man, they number four as a rule; fewer than four were found in less than 1 per cent. of over a thousand persons (Pepere), but more than four (five or six) in over 33 per cent. of 122 bodies examined by Civalleri. In addition, numerous minute islands of parathyroid tissue may be found scattered in the connective tissue and fat of the neck around the parathyroid glands proper, and quite distinct from them.

Structure.—Microscopically the parathyroids consist of intercommunicating columns of cells supported by connective tissue containing a rich supply of blood capillaries. Most of the cells are clear, but some, larger in size, contain oxyphil granules. Vesicles containing colloid have been described as occurring in the parathyroid

The parathyroids secrete a hormone necessary for calcium metabolism. The tetany which follows parathyroidectomy can be relieved by feeding or injecting calcium salts or parathyroid extracts.

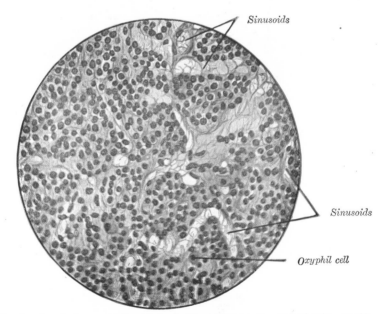

Sinusoids

Sinusoids

Oxyphil cell

FIG. 1162.—A section of a human parathyroid gland. Stained with hematoxylin and eosin. × 400.

THE HYPOPHYSIS CEREBRI.

The **hypophysis cerebri** (*pituitary body, pituitary gland*) (Fig. 1163) is attached to the base of the brain by the pituitary stalk and is situated in the sella turcica (fossa hypophyseos) of the sphenoid bone. The sella turcica is covered by a circular fold of the dura, the diaphragma sellæ. The pituitary stalk passes through the diaphragma.

The hypophysis consists of the pars tuberalis, the anterior hypophysis (pars distalis, pars anterior, anterior lobe, pars glandularis) and the posterior hypophysis (pars posterior, processus infundibuli, posterior lobe). The posterior hypophysis is divided into the small pars intermedia (intermediate lobe) and the neural lobe (pars nervosa, neurohypophysis).

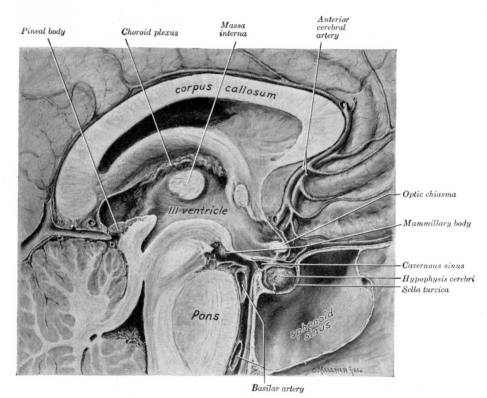

Fig. 1163.—The hypophysis cerebri in position.

The pars tuberalis cups around the hypophyseal stalk at the base of the brain and is partially suprasellar in position. The remainder of the gland occupies the sella and is encapsulated by a dural sheath. The hypophysis is about 1.2 to 1.5 cm. in transverse diameter, 1 cm. in width and 0.5 cm. in depth. The weight of the hypophysis of the adult male is about 0.5 to 0.6 gm. It is always larger in women and in multiparæ may exceed 1 gm. There is a positive correlation between the size of the gland and stature. The gland is largest during the fourth decade of life, and decreases slowly thereafter, the greatest decrease occurring in the anterior lobe. (Rasmussen.)

The anterior lobe is pink or reddish in color, while the posterior lobe is a translucent, pearly grey.

Development of the Hypophysis Cerebri.—The hypophysis (Fig. 1163) is derived from two distinct sources, the **hypophyseal diverticulum** or **Rathke's pouch,** from the ectoderm of the primitive mouth cavity in front of the oral plate and the **infundibular diverticulum** from the floor of the brain. The hypophyseal diverticulum gives rise to three parts, the **pars distalis** (anterior lobe), the **pars intermedia** and the **pars tuberalis** (Figs. 1164 and 1165). The infundibular diverticulum gives rise to the **posterior** or **neural lobe.** The pars distalis constitutes the bulk of the hypophyseal part, and is derived from the anterior wall of the diverticulum. The pars intermedia is derived from the posterior wall of the diverticulum. It comes into close relation with and almost completely surrounds the infundibular diverticulum. It is more or less separated from the pars distalis by the residual lumen of the diverticulum. Thus it seems to be more a part of the posterior lobe than the anterior.

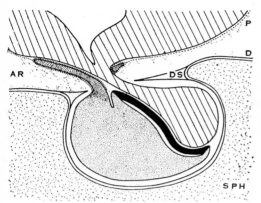

Fig. 1164.—Diagrammatic sagittal section of pituitary, illustrating relation to meninges. Brain floor and pars nervosa are lined; pars distalis, lightly stippled; pars tuberalis, closely stippled; pars intermedia, solid black. *AR*, Arachnoid spaces; *D*, dura; *DS*, diaphragma sellæ; *P*, pia mater; *SPH*, sphenoid bone. (Atwell, Am. J. Anat.; courtesy of Wistar Institute.)

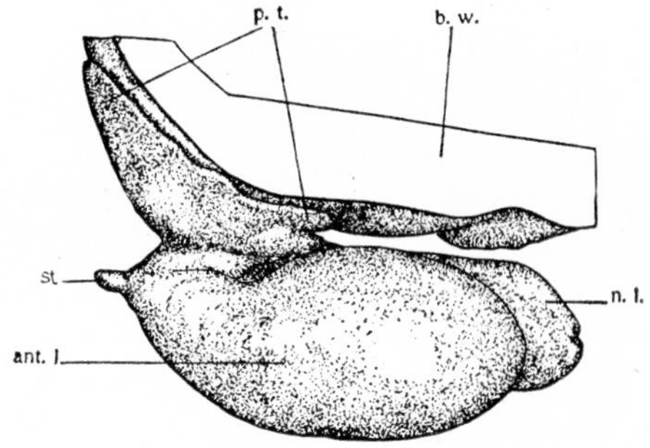

Fig. 1165.—Model of hypophysis and adjacent brain wall from a thirty-day embryo, viewed from the left side. × 25. *b. w.*, brain wall; *p. t.*, pars tuberalis; *st.*, stalk; *ant. l.*, anterior lobe; *n. l.*, neural lobe. (Atwell, Am. J. Anat.; courtesy of Wistar Institute.)

The pars tuberalis arises early as two lateral lobes, from the hypophyseal diverticulum, which extend forward to the under surface of the brain wall and fuse to form a thin plate part of which surrounds the neck of the posterior lobe. The infundibular diverticulum from the floor of the third ventricle lies behind the hypophyseal diverticulum. Its extremity becomes modified to form the posterior lobe while the part attached to the brain is known as the infundibulum. The walls of the posterior lobe become folded, in a very complicated manner so that its cavity is obliterated, and differentiate into a modified ependymal and neuroglia tissue. The epithelium of the pars distalis differentiates into an irregular network of cell-cords between which lie irregular shaped bloodvessels. The pars intermedia remains as a relatively thin sheet of epithelium, poorly vascularized. The pars tuberalis becomes a thin layer lying in the pia mater and exhibits a distinct tubular or alveolar structure. The craniopharyngeal canal extends from the anterior part of the hypophyseal fossa of the sphenoid bone to the apex of the naso-pharynx. It contains the pharyngeal hypophysis. This residual tissue is histologically identical with the anterior lobe and is a vestige from the ectodermal hypophyseal diverticulum (Rathke's pouch).

Structure.—Pars Distalis (anterior lobe). The epithelial cells are arranged in irregular anastomosing cords, in contact with large sinusoids. There are three cell types. The chromophobes are of two types; one type gives origin to the acidophils, and one to the basophils (Severinghaus). The chromophobes constitute about 50 per cent. of the epithelial cells; the acidophils about 40 per cent. of the epithelial cells, and are more numerous in women. The basophils, more numerous in men, form the remaining 10 per cent. An increase in chromophobes and a decrease in acidophils occurs after fifty years of age in both men and women (Rasmussen).

Pars Tuberalis consists of faintly basophilic cells which frequently form vesicles which contain colloid.

Pars Intermedia is rudimentary in man, and increases in size with age (Rasmussen); it is almost avascular.

Circulation.—(Fig. 1166). The superior hypophyseal arteries consist of several branches arising from the internal carotid and the posterior communicating artery. These arteries anastomose with each other on the same side and with those on the opposite side on the infundibular stalk. Branches enter the stalk where they break up into capillaries of a sinusoidal nature. Other branches are distributed to the anterior lobe (pars distalis) where they enter the sinusoids of the anterior lobe. The inferior hypophyseal arteries are two paired branches of the internal carotid artery which traverse the cavernous sinus and after anastomosing on the posterior pole of the infundibular process, which they supply, are distributed to the posterior lobe (pars neuralis).

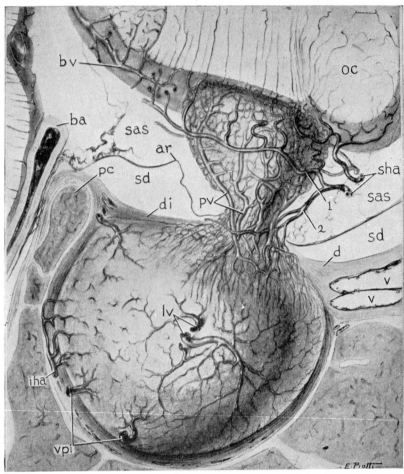

Fig. 1166.—Schematic drawing of the hypophysis of the adult rhesus monkey. *ar*, arachnoid membrane; *ba*, basilar artery; *bv*, basilar vein; *d*, dura; *di*, sellar diaphragm; *iha*, inferior hypophyseal artery; *lv*, lateral hypophyseal veins; *oc*, optic chiasma; *pc*, posterior clinoid process; *pv*, portal venules; *sas*, subarachnoid space; *sd*, subdural space; *sha*, superior hypophyseal arteries (1, branches to hypophyseal stalk; 2, branches to anterior lobe); *v*, dural veins; *vpi*, veins of infundibular process. (Wislocki, Pituitary Gland, Assn. for Research in Nervous and Mental Diseases, Williams and Wilkins.)

The hypophysis has both systemic and portal veins. Portal veins connect the capillaries of the hypophyseal stalk with the sinusoids of the pars distalis. The systemic veins consist of the lateral hypophyseal veins draining from the anterior lobe, and the veins of the infundibular process, all of which enter the cavernous or intercavernous sinus. Wislocki indicates that there are no systemic veins accompanying the superior hypophyseal arteries. Blood from the infundibular stalk, according to Wislocki, is drained through the sinusoids of the anterior lobe and thence to the cavernous sinus by the lateral hypophyseal veins.

Function.—Pars Distalis. The anterior lobe is directly involved in most of the endocrine activities of the body. The ovaries and testes are entirely dependent on the appropriate hormones of the anterior lobe for maturation of germ cells and for the production of the respective hormones of the gonads. (Philip E. Smith.)

The thyroid is activated by a hormone of the anterior lobe. The thyroid and anterior lobe are responsible for the metabolic processes resulting in normal growth of the body. One type of tumor of the pituitary operating in adult life causes overgrowth of terminal appendages, a disease known as acromegaly. Maintenance of the adequacy of the adrenal cortex and the induction of lactation are functions of this gland.

In addition to these important functions, the anterior lobe is important in many aspects of metabolism.

Pars Intermedia of man has no known function.

Pars Nervosa. The physiological rôle of the neurohypophysis cannot yet be stated with any certainty. The oxytocic factor (pitocin) causes contraction of the smooth muscle of the uterus under certain conditions. Pitressin leads to a temporary drop in pulse rate and blood pressure, due largely to coronary constriction. The pars nervosa, alone or in combination with the hypothalamus, has an anti-diuretic effect (Geiling).

THE PINEAL BODY.

The **pineal body** (*epiphysis*) (Fig. 1163) is a small reddish-gray body, about 8 mm. in length which lies in the depression between the superior colliculi. It is attached to the roof of the third ventricle near its junction with the mid-brain. It develops as an outgrowth from the third ventricle of the brain.

In early life it has a glandular structure which reaches its greatest development at about the seventh year. Later, especially after puberty, the glandular tissue gradually disappears and is replaced by connective tissue.

Structure.—The pineal body is destitute of nervous substance, and consists of follicles lined by epithelium and enveloped by connective tissue. These follicles contain a variable quantity of gritty material, composed of phosphate and carbonate of calcium, phosphate of magnesium and ammonia.

Tumors of the pineal body are sometimes associated with hypergenitalism and sexual precocity in boys. Aside from this possible relationship there is no clinical or experimental evidence which would indicate that the pineal is an endocrine gland.

THE CHROMAPHIL AND CORTICAL SYSTEMS.

Chromaphil or chromaffin cells, so-called because they stain yellow or brownish with chromium salts, are associated with the ganglia of the sympathetic nervous system.

Development.—They arise in common with the sympathetic cells from the neural crest, and are therefore ectodermal in origin. The chromaphil and sympathetic cells are indistinguishable from one another at the time of their migration from the spinal ganglia to the regions occupied in the adult. Differentiation of chromaphil cells begins in embryos about 18 mm. in length but is not complete until about birth. The chromaphiloblasts increase in size more than the sympathoblasts and stain less intensely with ordinary dyes. Later the chrome reaction develops. The aortic bodies differentiate first and are prominent in 20 mm. embryos. The paraganglia of the sympathetic plexuses differentiate next and last of all the paraganglia of the sympathetic trunk. After birth the chromaphil organs degenerate but the paraganglia can be recognized with the microscope in sites originally occupied by them.

The **paraganglia** are small groups of chromaphil cells connected with the ganglia of the sympathetic trunk and the ganglia of the celiac, renal, suprarenal, aortic and hypogastric plexuses. They are sometimes found in connection with the ganglia of other sympathetic plexuses. None have been found with the sympathetic ganglia associated with the branches of the trigeminal nerve.

The **aortic glands** or **bodies** are the largest of these groups of chromaphil cells and measure in the newborn about 1 cm. in length. They lie one on either side of the aorta in the region of the inferior mesenteric artery. They decrease in size with age and after puberty are only visible with the microscope. About forty they disappear entirely. Other groups of chromaphil cells have been found associated with the sympathetic plexuses of the abdomen independently of the ganglia.

The medullary portions of the suprarenal glands belong to the chromaphil system.

The Suprarenal Glands (Glandulæ Suprarenalis; Adrenal Capsule)
(Figs. 1167, 1168).

The **suprarenal glands** are two small flattened bodies of a yellowish color, situated at the back part of the abdomen, behind the peritoneum, and immediately above

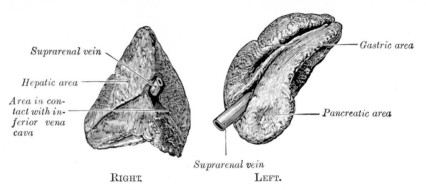

FIG. 1167.—Suprarenal glands viewed from the front.

and in front of the upper end of each kidney (Fig. 1105); hence their name. The right one is somewhat triangular in shape, bearing a resemblance to a cocked hat; the left is more semilunar, usually larger, and placed at a higher level than the right. They vary in size in different individuals, being sometimes so small as to be scarcely detected: their usual size is from 3 to 5 cm. in length, rather less in width, and from 4 to 6 mm. in thickness. Their average weight is from 3.5 to 5.0 gm. each.

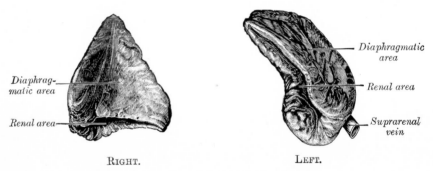

FIG. 1168.—Suprarenal glands viewed from behind.

Development.—Each suprarenal gland consists of a cortical portion derived from the celomic epithelium and a medullary portion originally composed of sympatho-chromaffin tissue. The cortical portion is first recognizable about the beginning of the fourth week as a series of buds from the celomic cells at the root of the mesentery. Later it becomes completely separated from the celomic epithelium and forms a suprarenal ridge projecting into the celom between the mesonephros and the root of the mesentery. Into this cortical portion cells from the neighboring masses of sympatho-chromaffin tissue migrate along the line of its central vein to reach and form the medullary portion of the gland.

Relations.—The relations of the suprarenal glands differ on the two sides of the body.

The **right suprarenal** is situated behind the inferior vena cava and right lobe of the liver, and in front of the diaphragm and upper end of the right kidney. It is roughly triangular in shape; its base, directed downward, is in contact with the medial and anterior aspects of the upper end of the right kidney. It presents two surfaces for examination, an anterior and a posterior. The *anterior surface* looks forward and lateralward, and has two areas: a medial, narrow, and non-peritoneal, which lies behind the inferior vena cava; and a lateral, somewhat triangular, in contact with the liver. The upper part of the latter surface is devoid of peritoneum, and is in relation with the bare area of the liver near its lower and medial angle, while its inferior portion is covered by peritoneum, reflected onto it from the inferior layer of the coronary ligament; occasionally the duodenum overlaps the inferior portion. A little below the apex, and near the anterior border of the gland, is a short furrow termed the **hilum,** from which the suprarenal vein emerges to join the inferior vena cava. The *posterior surface* is divided into upper and lower parts by a curved ridge: the upper, slightly convex, rests upon the diaphragm; the lower, concave, is in contact with the upper end and the adjacent part of the anterior surface of the kidney.

The **left suprarenal,** slightly larger than the right, is crescentic in shape, its concavity being adapted to the medial border of the upper part of the left kidney. It presents a medial border, which is convex, and a lateral, which is concave; its upper end is narrow, and its lower rounded. Its *anterior surface* has two areas: an upper one, covered by the peritoneum of the omental bursa, which separates it from the cardiac end of the stomach, and sometimes from the superior extremity of the spleen; and a lower one, which is in contact with the pancreas and lienal artery, and is therefore not covered by the peritoneum. On the anterior surface, near its lower end, is a furrow or hilum, directed downward and forward, from which the suprarenal vein emerges. Its *posterior surface* presents a vertical ridge, which divides it into two areas; the lateral area rests on the kidney, the medial and smaller on the left crus of the diaphragm.

The surface of the suprarenal gland is surrounded by areolar tissue containing much fat, and closely invested by a thin fibrous capsule, which is difficult to remove on account of the numerous fibrous processes and vessels entering the organ through the furrows on its anterior surface and base.

Small **accessory suprarenals** (*glandulæ suprarenales accessoriæ*) are often to be found in the connective tissue around the suprarenals. The smaller of these, on section, show a uniform surface, but in some of the larger a distinct medulla can be made out.

Structure.—On section, the suprarenal gland is seen to consist of two portions (Fig. 1169): an **external** or **cortical** and an **internal** or **medullary.** The former constitutes the chief part of the organ, and is of a deep yellow color; the medullary substance is soft, pulpy, and of a dark red or brown color.

The **cortical portion** (*substantia corticalis*) consists of a fine connective-tissue net-work, in which is imbedded the glandular epithelium. The epithelial cells are polyhedral in shape and possess rounded nuclei; many of the cells contain coarse granules, others lipoid globules. Owing to differences in the arrangement of the cells, three distinct zones can be made out: (1) the **zona glomerulosa,** situated beneath the capsule, consists of cells arranged in rounded groups, with here and there indications of an alveolar structure; the cells of this zone are very granular, and stain deeply. (2) The **zona fasciculata,** continuous with the zona glomerulosa, is composed of columns of cells arranged in a radial manner; these cells contain finer granules and in many instances globules of lipoid material. (3) The **zona reticularis,** in contact with the medulla, consists of cylindrical masses of cells irregularly arranged; these cells often contain pigment granules which give this zone a darker appearance than the rest of the cortex.

The **medullary portion** (*substantia medullaris*) is extremely vascular, and consists of large chromaphil cells arranged in a network. The irregular polyhedral cells have a finely granular cytoplasm that is probably concerned with the secretion of adrenalin. In the meshes of the cellular network are large anastomosing venous sinuses (sinusoids) which are in close relationship with the chromaphil or medullary cells. In many places the endothelial lining of the blood sinuses is in direct contact with the medullary cells. Some authors consider the endothelium absent in places and here the medullary cells are directly bathed by the blood. This intimate relationship between the chromaphil cells and the blood stream undoubtedly facilitates the discharge of the internal secretion into the blood. There is a loose meshwork of supporting connective tissue containing non-striped muscle fibers. This portion of the gland is richly supplied with non-medullated nerve fibers, and here and there sympathetic ganglia are found.

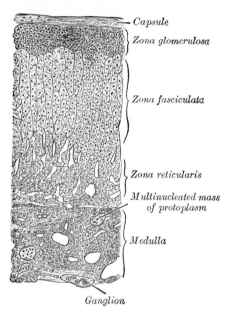

FIG. 1169.—Section of a part of a suprarenal gland. (Magnified.)

Vessels and Nerves.—The suprarenals are highly vascular organs. The arteries are numerous and of comparatively large size. These arteries are derived from the aorta and the inferior phrenic and the renal arteries. Three sets of branches penetrate the capsule, one of which breaks up in capillaries which supply the capsule. The second set breaks up into capillaries which supply the cell cords of the cortex and empty into veins in the medulla. The third set of arteries which enter the cortex traverse the cortex to supply the medulla only and break up in the sinusoids of the medulla. Venous blood from the capsule is collected into veins of the capsule. Blood from the two other sets of arteries is gathered into the central vein in the medulla which emerges at the hilum as the suprarenal vein. On the right side this vein opens into the inferior vena cava, on the left into the left renal vein.

Lymphatics accompany the large bloodvessels and end in the lumbar nodes.

The **nerves** are exceedingly numerous, and are derived from the celiac and renal plexuses. They enter the lower and medial part of the capsule, traverse the cortex, and end around the cells of the medulla. They have numerous small ganglia in the medullary portion of the gland.

Function.—The adrenal medulla gives off an internal secretion, epinephrine, which has definite sympathomimetic actions such as causing a constriction of arterioles, acceleration of the heart rate, contraction of the radial muscle of the iris. In man an injection of the drug epinephrine hydrochloride results in a rise in systolic blood pressure, pulse rate, an increase in the minute volume of the heart and in volume of respiration. These effects are transitory and disappear after one or two hours. A rise in blood sugar, lactic acid and in the basal metabolic rate follows injection of this drug. This is due to an increased enzymatic breakdown of glycogen in liver and in muscle. The action of epinephrine is of brief duration, the hormone being rapidly inactivated in the body (Cori).

The adrenal cortex elaborates one or more hormones essential to maintenance of life. Various fractions serve in the maintenance of physiological "steady states," in regulation of the distribution of water and electrolytes and in many aspects of carbohydrate metabolism, and muscular efficiency. Research in this field is very active.

Glomus Coccygeum (Coccygeal Gland or Body; Luschka's Gland).

The **glomus coccygeum** is placed in front of, or immediately below, the tip of the coccyx. It is about 2.5 mm. in diameter and is irregularly oval in shape; several smaller nodules are found around or near the main mass.

It consists of irregular masses of round or polyhedral cells, the cells of each mass being grouped around a dilated sinusoidal capillary vessel. Each cell contains a large round or oval nucleus, the protoplasm surrounding which is clear, and is not stained by chromic salts.

Glomus caroticum (carotid body) and **glomus aorticum** (aortic body). (See pages 1094 and 1095.)

BIBLIOGRAPHY

DUCTLESS GLANDS

SUPRARENAL GLAND

Volume and cortico-medullary ratio of the adult human suprarenal gland. SWINYARD, C. A.: 1940. Anat. Rec., Vol. 76, pp. 69–79.

DEVELOPMENT

Embryonic and postnatal development of the adrenal cortex, particularly the zona glomerulosa and accessory nodules. GRUENWALD, P.: 1946. Anat. Rec., Vol. 95, pp. 391–421.
Growth of the human suprarenal glands. SWINYARD, C. A.: 1943. Anat. Rec., Vol. 87, pp. 141–150.
The early embryological development of the fetal and permanent adrenal cortex in man. UOTILA, U. U.: 1940. Anat. Rec., Vol. 76, pp. 183–203.
A study of the cytogenesis of cortico-adrenal cells in the cat. WOTTON, R. M., and R. L. ZWEMER: 1943. Anat. Rec., Vol. 86, pp. 409–416.

BLOOD VESSELS

The vascular pattern of the adrenal gland of the mouse and rat and its physiological response to changes in glandular activity. GERSH, I., and A. GROLLMAN: 1941. Carnegie Inst., Cont. Embryol., Vol. 29, pp. 111–125.
The blood vessels of the adrenal gland of the adult cat. BENNETT, H. S., and L. KILHAM: 1940. Anat. Rec., Vol. 77, pp. 447–471.

MEDULLA

Cytological manifestations of secretion in the adrenal medulla of the cat. BENNETT, H. S.: 1941. Am. J. Anat., Vol. 69, pp. 333–381.
The Adrenal Medulla. CORI, C. F., and A. DE M. WELCH: 1941. In: Glandular Physiology and Therapy. Am. Med. Assn., Chicago. pp. 307-326.
Chromaffin tissue and paraganglia. HOLLINSHEAD, W. H.: 1940. Quart. Rev. Biol., Vol. 15, pp. 156–171.

CORTEX

HISTOLOGY

The reduction of osmic acid as an indicator of adrenal cortical activity in the rat. FLEXNER, L. B., and A. GROLLMAN: 1939. Anat. Rec., Vol. 75, pp. 207–221.
Histological studies on lipins. Il. A cytological analysis of the liposomes in the adrenal cortex of the guinea pig. HOERR, N. L.: 1936. Anat. Rec., Vol. 66, pp. 317–342.
The cells of the adrenal cortex of the ewe during the estrual cycle and pregnancy. NAHAM, L. J., and F. F. McKENZIE: 1937. Mo. Agr. Exp. Sta. Research Bull., Vol. 251.
A study of the life history of cortico-adrenal gland cells of the rat by means of trypan blue injections. SALMON, T. N., and R. L. ZWEMER: 1941. Anat. Rec., Vol. 80, pp. 421–429.
Changes in the birefringent material in the adrenal cortex of the rat following administration of adrenotrophic hormone. WEAVER, H. M., and W. O. NELSON: 1943. Anat. Rec., Vol. 85, pp. 51–67.
The characteristics and behavior of living cells in autogenous grafts of adrenal cortex in rabbits. WILLIAMS, R. G.: 1945. Am. J. Anat., Vol. 77, pp. 53–79.
A study of adrenal cortex morphology. ZWEMER, R. L.: 1936. Am. J. Path., Vol. 12, pp. 107–114.

EXPERIMENTAL

Role of capsule in suprarenal regeneration studied with aid of colchicine. BAKER, D. D., and R. N. BAILLIF: 1939. Proc. Soc. Exp. Biol. & Med., Vol. 40, pp. 117–121.

The atrophy of the adrenal cortex following the administration of large amounts of progesterone. CLAUSEN, H. J.: 1940. Endocrinology, Vol. 27, pp. 989–993.

Functional alterations in lymphoid tissue induced by adrenal cortical secretion. DOUGHERTY, T. F., and A. WHITE: 1945. Am. J. Anat., Vol. 77, pp. 81–116.

Response of the alkaline phosphatase of the adrenal cortex of the mouse to androgen. ELFTMAN, H.: 1947. Endocrinology, Vol. 41, pp. 85–91.

Effect of adrenal cortical transplants on life-maintenance and "water-intoxication". EVERSOLE, W. J., A. EDELMANN, and R. GAUNT: 1940. Anat. Rec., Vol. 76, pp. 271–281.

Formation and growth of adrenocortical-like tissue in the ovaries of the adrenalectomized ground squirrel. GROAT, R. A.: 1944. Anat. Rec., Vol. 89, pp. 33–41.

The Function of the Adrenal Cortex, KENDALL, E. C.: 1942. In: Glandular Physiology and Therapy, Am. Med. Assn., Chicago, pp. 273–286.

Relation of adrenal gland and hypophysis to blood sugar levels following administration of alloxan. KIRSCHBAUM, A., L. J. WELLS, and D. MOLANDER: 1945. Proc. Soc. Exp. Biol. & Med., Vol. 58, pp. 294–296.

Correlated chemical and histological studies of the adrenal lipids. I. The effect of extreme muscular activity on the adrenal lipids of the guinea pig. KNOUFF, R. A., J. B. BROWN, and B. M. SCHNEIDER: 1941. Anat. Rec., Vol. 79, pp. 17–38.

The vital necessity of adrenal cortical tissue in a mammal and the effects of proliferation of cortical cells from dormant coelomic mesothelium. MACFARLAND, W. E.: 1945. Anat. Rec., Vol. 93, pp. 233–249.

Homotransplantation of suprarenal glands from prepuberal rats into the eyes of the adult hosts. TURNER, C. D.: 1939. Anat. Rec., Vol. 73, pp. 145–162.

Studies of adrenal cortex: Regeneration of the transplanted gland the vital quality of autogenous grafts. WILLIAMS, R. G.: 1947. Am. J. Anat., Vol. 81, pp. 199–231.

The importance of corticoadrenal regulation of potassium metabolism. ZWEMER, R. L., and R. TRUSZKOWSKI: 1936. Endocrinology, Vol. 21, pp. 40–49.

HYPOPHYSIS

The comparative anatomy and pharmacology of the pituitary gland of unusual "experimental" animals. GEILING, E. M. K.: 1940. Am. J. Obs. & Gyn., Vol. 40, pp. 727–737.

The Neurohypophysis. GEILING, E. M. K., and F. K. OLDHAM: 1942. In: Glandular Physiology and Therapy, Am. Med. Assn., Chicago. pp. 127–141.

DEVELOPMENT

The interrelationship of the parts of the hypophysis in development. BLOUNT, R. F.: 1945. J. Exp. Zool., Vol. 100, pp. 79–101.

The developmental control of pars intermedia by brain. ETKIN, W.: 1943. J. Exp. Zool., Vol. 92, pp. 31–47.

The developmental stage at which the intermediate lobe of the hypophysis becomes determined. Hegre, E. S.: 1946. J. Exp. Zool., Vol. 103, pp. 321–333.

The development of the hypophysis ot the ox. HOUSE, E. L.: 1943. Am. J. Anat., Vol. 73, pp. 1–25.

The development of the hypophysis cerebri of the albino rat. SCHWIND, J. L.: 1928. Am. J. Anat., Vol. 41, pp. 295–319.

HISTOLOGY

Physiological significance and morphology of the carmine cell in the cat's anterior pituitary. FRIEDGOOD, H. B., and A. B. DAWSON: 1940. Endocrinology, Vol. 26, pp. 1022–1031.

The structure and function of the parenchymatous glandular cells in the neurohypophysis of the rat. GERSH, I.: 1939. Am. J. Anat., Vol. 64, pp. 407–443.

A cytological study of the anterior hypophysis of the dog with particular reference to the presence of a fourth cell type. HARTMANN, J. F., W. R. FAIN, and J. M. WOLFE: 1946. Anat. Rec., Vol. 95, pp. 11–27.

The differentiation and significance of argentaffin granules in the hypophysis. POPOFF, A.: 1943. Anat. Rec., Vol. 87, pp. 1–15.

The proportions of the various subdivisions of the normal adult human hypophysis cerebri, etc. RASMUSSEN, A. T.: 1936. Assn. Res. in Nerv. & Ment. Dis., Vol. 17, pp. 118–150.

Cellular changes in the anterior hypophysis with special reference to its secretory activities. SEVERINGHAUS, A. E.: 1937. Physiol. Rev., Vol. 17, pp. 556–588.

On the presence of clefts, fibroid neuroglia, neuroblast-like cells and nerve cells in the human neurohypophysis. SHANKLIN, W. M.: 1946. Anat. Rec., Vol. 96, pp. 143–163.

EXPERIMENTAL

Effects of hypophysectomy, castration, and testosterone propionate on hemopoiesis in the adult male rat. CRAFTS, R. C.: 1946. Endocrinology, Vol. 39, pp. 401–413.

The effects of intra-peritoneal injections of pituitary substances on the rate of tail regeneration in frog tadpoles. PUCKETT, W. O.: 1938. Anat. Rec., Vol. 71, pp. 337–347.

Hypophysectomy and replacement therapy in the rat. SMITH, P. E.: 1930. Am. J. Anat., Vol. 45, pp. 205–273.

Effects of progesterone on the cells of the anterior hypophysis of the rat. WOLFE, J. M.: 1946. Am. J. Anat., Vol. 79, pp. 199–239.

BLOOD VESSELS AND NERVES

Vascular connections of the hypophysis in the leopard frog (Rana Pipiens). CRAIGIE, E. H.: 1939. Anat. Rec., Vol. 74, pp. 61–69.

The nerve supply of the hypophysis of the cat. HAIR, G. W.: 1938. Anat. Rec., Vol. 71, pp. 141–160.

The blood supply of the hypophysis. MORATO, M. J. X.: 1939. Anat. Rec., Vol. 74, pp. 297–320.

The Vascular Supply of the Hypophysis Cerebri of the Rhesus Monkey and Man. WISLOCKI, G. B.: 1938. In: The Pituitary Gland. Assn. Res. in Nerv. & Mental Dis., Williams & Wilkins, Baltimore, Vol. 17, pp. 48–68.

THYROID

Differentiation of chick embryo thyroids in tissue culture. CARPENTER, E.: 1942. J. Exp. Zool., Vol. 89, pp. 407–431.

Mitotic activity in the thyroid gland of female rats. HUNT, T. E.: 1944. Anat. Rec., Vol. 90, pp. 133–138.

The larynx as related to surgery of the thyroid based on an anatomical study. NORDLAND, M.: 1930. Surg., Gyn. & Obs., Vol. 51, pp. 449–459.

Effects of hypotonic solutions upon the living thyroid gland. PLAGGE, J. C.: 1943. Anat. Rec., Vol. 87, pp. 345–353.

Studies on the thyroid gland. I. The structure, extent and drainage of the "lymph-sac" of the thyroid gland (Felis domestica). RAMSAY, A. J., and G. A. BENNETT: 1943. Anat. Rec., Vol. 87, pp. 321–339.

Some new observations bearing on the effect of hyperthyroidism on genital structure and function. RICHTER, K. M.: 1944. J. Morph., Vol. 74, pp. 375–393.

Gross and microscopic structure of thyroid gland in man. RIENHOFF, W. F., JR.: 1930. Carnegie Cont. Emb., Vol. 21, pp. 97–123.

Some properties of living thyroid cells and follicles. WILLIAMS, R. G.: 1944. Am. J. Anat., Vol. 75, pp. 95–119.

DEVELOPMENT

Comments on the origin and growth pattern of thyroid parenchyma. RAMSAY, A. J.: 1938. Anat. Rec., Vol. 70, pp. 287–309.

Development of the thyroid, parathyroid and thymus glands in man. WELLER, G. L., JR.: 1933. Carnegie Cont. Emb., Vol. 24, pp. 93–139.

PARATHYROID

A study of the parathyroid glands of the normal and hypophysectomized monkey (Macaca mulatta). BAKER, B. L.: 1942. Anat. Rec., Vol. 83, pp. 47–73.

Variations produced in bones of growing rats by parathyroid extracts. BURROWS, R. B.: 1938. Am. J. Anat., Vol. 62, pp. 237–290.

The cytology of the parathyroid gland of rats injected with parathyroid extract. DEROBERTIS, E.: 1940. Anat. Rec., Vol. 78, pp. 473–495.

The parathyroid glands and the lateral thyroid in man: their morphogenesis, histogenesis, topographic anatomy and prenatal growth. NORRIS, E. H.: 1937. Carnegie Cont. Emb., Vol. 26, pp. 247–294.

Anatomical evidence of prenatal function of the human parathyroid glands. NORRIS, E. H.: 1946. Anat. Rec., Vol. 96, pp. 129–141.

PINEAL

The pineal eye of the lizard (Anolis carolinensis), a photoreceptor as revealed by oxygen consumption studies. CLAUSEN, H. J., and B. MOFSHIN: 1939. J. Cell. & Comp. Physiol., Vol. 14, pp. 29–41.

Pinealectomy in successive generations of rats. SULLENS, W. E., and M. D. OVERHOLSER: 1941. Endocrinology, Vol. 28, pp. 835–839.

CAROTID BODY

The development of the human carotid body. BOYD, J. D.: 1937. Carnegie Cont. Emb., Vol. 26, pp. 1–31.

A comparative study of the glomus coccygeum and the carotid body. HOLLINSHEAD, W. H.: 1942. Anat. Rec., Vol. 84, pp. 1–16.

A cytological study of the carotid body of the cat. HOLLINSHEAD, W. H.: 1943. Am. J. Anat., Vol. 73, pp. 185–213.

SURFACE AND TOPOGRAPHICAL ANATOMY.

SURFACE ANATOMY OF THE HEAD AND NECK.

Bones (Fig. 1170).—Various bony surfaces and prominences on the skull can be easily identified by palpation. The **external occipital protuberance** is situated behind, in the middle line, at the junction of the skin of the neck with that of the head. The **superior nuchal line** runs lateralward from it on either side, while extending downward from it is the **median nuchal crest,** situated deeply at the bottom of the nuchal furrow. Above the superior nuchal lines the vault of the cranium

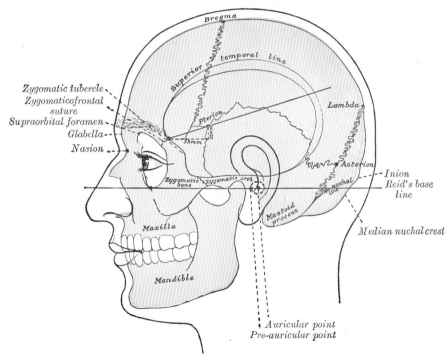

Fig. 1170.—Side view of head, showing surface relations of bones.

is thinly covered with soft structures, so that the form of this part of the head is almost that of the upper portion of the occipital, the parietal, and the frontal bones. The superior nuchal line can be followed lateralward to the mastoid portion of the temporal bone, from which the **mastoid process** projects downward and forward behind the ear. The anterior and posterior borders, the apex, and the external surface of this process are all available for superficial examination. The anterior border lies immediately behind the concha, and the apex is on a level

(1343)

with the lobule of the auricula. About 1 cm. below and in front of the apex of the mastoid process, the **transverse process of the atlas** can be distinguished. In front of the ear the **zygomatic arch** can be felt throughout its entire length; its posterior end is narrow and is situated a little above the level of the tragus; its anterior end is broad and is continued into the zygomatic bone. The lower border of the arch is more distinct than the upper, which is obscured by the attachment of the temporal fascia. In front, and behind, the upper border of the arch can be followed into the **superior temporal line.** In front, this line begins at the zygomatic process of the frontal bone as a curved ridge which runs at first forward and upward on the frontal bone, and then curving backward separates the forehead from the temporal fossa. It can then be traced across the parietal bone, where, though less marked, it can generally be recognized. Finally, it curves downward, and forward, and passing above the external acoustic meatus, ends in the posterior

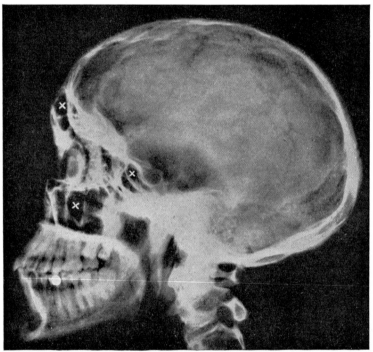

Fig. 1171.—Adult skull. Lateral view. Crosses are placed on the frontal, the maxillary and the sphenoidal sinuses. Behind the last-named, the hypophyseal fossa can be identified. The dense white area below and behind the fossa is due to the petrous part of the temporal bone.

root of the zygomatic arch. Near the line of the greatest transverse diameter of the head are the **parietal eminences,** one on either side of the middle line; further forward, on the forehead, are the **frontal eminences,** which vary in prominence in different individuals and are frequently unsymmetrical. Below the frontal eminences the **superciliary arches,** which indicate the position of the frontal sinuses, can be recognized; as a rule they are small in the female and absent in children. In some cases the prominence of the superciliary arches is related to the size of the frontal sinuses, but frequently there is no such relationship. Situated between, and connecting the superciliary ridges, is a smooth, somewhat triangular area, the **glabella,** below which the **nasion** (*frontonasal suture*) can be felt as a slight depression at the root of the nose.

Below the nasion the **nasal bones,** scantily covered by soft tissues, can be traced to their junction with the nasal cartilages, and on either side of the nasal bone the complete outline of the **orbital margin** can be made out. At the junction of the medial and intermediate thirds of the supraorbital margin the **supraorbital notch,** when present, can be felt; close to the medial end of the infraorbital margin is a little tubercle which serves as a guide to the position of the lacrimal sac. Below and lateral to the orbit, on either side, is the **zygomatic bone** forming the prominence of the cheek; its posterior margin is easily palpable, and on it just above the level of the lateral palpebral commissure is the **zygomatic tubercle.** A slight depression, about 1 cm. above this tubercle, indicates the position of the **zygomaticofrontal suture.** Directly below the orbit a considerable part of the anterior surface of the maxilla and the whole of its alveolar process can be palpated. The outline of the **mandible** can be recognized throughout practically its entire extent; in front of the tragus and below the zygomatic arch is the condyle, and from this the posterior

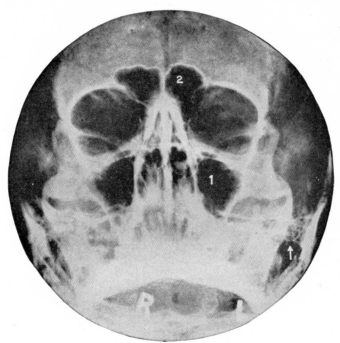

Fɪɢ. 1172.—Adult skull. Frontal view. *1,* Maxillary sinus; *2,* frontal sinus. The arrow is directed towards the mastoid air-cells.

border of the ramus can be followed to the angle; from the angle to the symphysis the lower rounded border of the mandible can be easily traced; the lower part of the anterior border of the ramus and the alveolar process can be made out without difficulty. In the receding angle below the chin is the **hyoid bone,** and the finger can be carried along the bone to the tip of the greater cornu, which is on a level with the angle of the mandible: the greater cornu is most readily appreciated by making pressure on one side, when the cornu of the opposite side will be rendered prominent and can be felt distinctly beneath the skin.

Joints and Muscles.—The **temporomandibular articulation** is quite superficial, and is situated below the posterior end of the zygomatic arch, in front of the external acoustic meatus. Its position can be ascertained by defining the condyle of the mandible; when the mouth opens, the condyle advances out of the mandibular fossa on to the articular tubercle, and a depression is felt in the situation of the joint.

The outlines of the muscles of the head and face cannot be traced on the surface except in the case of the Masseter and Temporalis. The muscles of the scalp are so thin that the outline of the bone is perceptible beneath them. Those of the face are small, covered by soft skin, and often by a considerable layer of fat, and their outlines are therefore concealed; they serve, however, to round off and smooth prominent borders, and to fill up what would otherwise be unsightly angular depressions. Thus the **Orbicularis oculi** rounds off the prominent margin of the orbit, and the **Procerus** fills in the sharp depression below the glabella. In like manner the **labial muscles** converging to the lips, and assisted by the superimposed fat, fill up the sunken hollow of the lower part of the face. When in action the facial muscles produce the various expressions, and in addition throw the skin into numerous folds and wrinkles. The **Masseter** imparts fulness to the hinder part of the cheek; if firmly contracted, as when the teeth are clenched, its quadrilateral outline is plainly visible; the anterior border forms a prominent vertical ridge, behind which is a considerable fulness especially marked at the

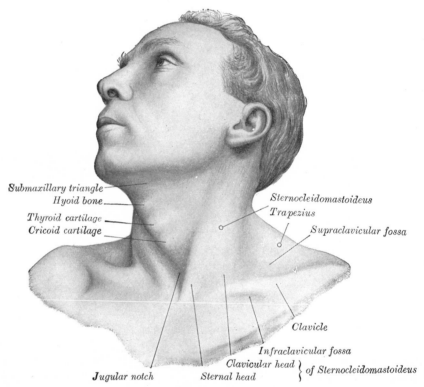

Submaxillary triangle
Hyoid bone
Thyroid cartilage
Cricoid cartilage

Sternocleidomastoideus
Trapezius
Supraclavicular fossa

Clavicle

Infraclavicular fossa
Clavicular head ⎫
Sternal head   ⎬ of Sternocleidomastoideus

Jugular notch

Fig. 1173.—Antero-lateral view of head and neck.

lower part of the muscle. The **Temporalis** is fan-shaped and fills the temporal fossa, substituting for the concavity a somewhat convex swelling, the anterior part of which, on account of the absence of hair on the overlying skin, is more marked than the posterior, and stands out in strong relief when the muscle is in action.

In the neck, the **Platysma** when contracted throws the skin into oblique ridges parallel with the fasciculi of the muscle. The **Sternocleidomastoideus** has the most important influence on the surface form of the neck (Figs. 1173, 1174). When the muscle is at rest its anterior border forms an oblique rounded edge ending below in the sharp outline of the sternal head; the posterior border is only distinct for about 2 or 3 cm. above the middle of the clavicle. During contraction, the sternal head stands out as a sharply defined ridge, while the clavicular head is flatter and less prominent; between the two heads is a slight depression: the fleshy middle portion of the muscle appears as an oblique elevation with a thick, rounded, anterior border, best marked in its lower part. The sternal heads of the two muscles are separated by a V-shaped depression, in which are the **Sternohyoideus** and **Sternothyreoideus,**

Above the hyoid bone, near the middle line, the anterior belly of the **Digastricus** produces a slight convexity.

The anterior border of the **Trapezius** presents as a faint ridge running from the superior nuchal line, downward and forward to the junction of the intermediate and lateral thirds of the clavicle. Between the Sternocleidomastoideus and the Trapezius is the posterior triangle of the neck, the lower part of which appears as a shallow concavity—the **supraclavicular fossa.** In this fossa, the inferior belly of the **Omohyoideus,** when in action, presents as a rounded cord-like elevation a little above, and almost parallel to, the clavicle.

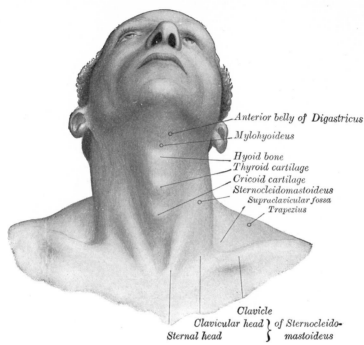

Anterior belly of Digastricus
Mylohyoideus
Hyoid bone
Thyroid cartilage
Cricoid cartilage
Sternocleidomastoideus
Supraclavicular fossa
Trapezius

Clavicle
Clavicular head } *of Sternocleido-*
Sternal head } *mastoideus*

FIG. 1174.—Front view of neck.

Arteries.—The positions of several of the larger arteries can be ascertained from their pulsations.

The **subclavian artery** can be felt by making pressure downward, backward, and medialward behind the clavicular head of the Sternocleidomastoideus; its **transverse cervical** branch may be detected parallel to, and about a finger's breadth above, the clavicle. The **common and external carotid arteries** can be recognized immediately beneath the anterior edge of the Sternocleidomastoideus. The **external maxillary artery** can be traced over the border of the mandible just in front of the anterior border of the Masseter, then about 1 cm. lateral to the angle of the mouth, and finally as it runs up the side of the nose. The pulsation of the **occipital artery** can be distinguished about 3 or 4 cm. lateral to the external occipital protuberance; that of the **posterior auricular** in the groove between the mastoid process and the auricula. The course of the **superficial temporal artery** can be readily followed across the posterior end of the zygomatic arch to a point about 3 to 5 cm. above this, where it divides into its frontal and parietal branches; the pulsation of the frontal branch is frequently visible on the side of the forehead. The **supraorbital artery** can usually be detected immediately above the supraorbital notch or foramen.

SURFACE MARKINGS OF SPECIAL REGIONS OF HEAD AND NECK.

The Cranium.—Scalp.—The soft parts covering the upper surface of the skull form the scalp and comprise the following layers (Fig. 1175): (1) **skin,** (2) **subcutaneous tissue,** (3) **Occipitalis, Frontalis** and **galea aponeurotica,** (4) **subaponeurotic tissue,** (5) **pericranium.** The subcutaneous tissue consists of a close mesh-work of fibers, the meshes of which contain fatty tissue; the fibers bind the skin and galea aponeurotica firmly together, so that when the Occipitalis or the Frontalis is in action the skin moves with the aponeurosis. The subaponeurotic tissue, which intervenes between the galea aponeurotica and the pericranium, is much looser in texture, and permits the movement of the aponeurosis over the underlying bones.

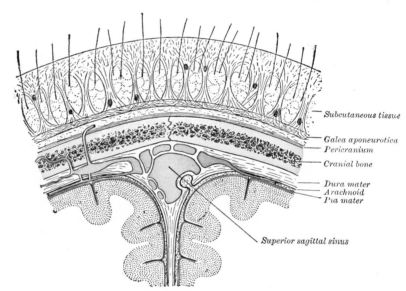

Subcutaneous tissue

Galea aponeurotica
Pericranium

Cranial bone

Dura mater
Arachnoid
Pia mater

Superior sagittal sinus

Fig. 1175.—Diagrammatic section of scalp.

Bony Landmarks (Fig. 1170).—In addition to the bony points already described which can be determined by palpation, the following are utilized for surface markings:

Auricular Point.—The center of the orifice of the external acoustic meatus.

Preauricular Point.—A point on the posterior root of the zygomatic arch immediately in front of the external acoustic meatus.

Asterion.—The point of meeting of the lamboidal, occipitomastoid and parietomastoid sutures; it lies 4 cm. behind and 12 mm. above the level of the auricular point.

Pterion.—The point where the great wing of the sphenoid joins the sphenoidal angle of the parietal; it is situated 35 mm. behind, and 12 mm. above, the level of the zygomaticofrontal suture.

Inion.—The external occipital protuberance.

Lambda.—The point of meeting of the lambdoidal and sagittal sutures; it is in the middle line about 6.5 cm. above the inion.

Bregma.—The meeting-point of the coronal and sagittal sutures; it lies at the point of intersection of the middle line of the scalp with a line drawn vertically upward through the preauricular point.

A line passing through the inferior margin of the orbit and the auricular point is known as **Reid's base line.** The **lambdoidal suture** can be indicated on either side by the upper two-thirds of a line from the lambda to the tip of the mastoid process. The **sagittal suture** is in the line joining the lambda to the bregma. The position of the **coronal suture** on either side is sufficiently represented by a line joining the bregma to the center of the zygomatic arch.

The floor of the middle fossa of the skull is at the level of the posterior three-fourths of the upper border of the zygomatic arch; the articular eminence of the temporal bone is opposite the foramen spinosum and the semilunar ganglion.

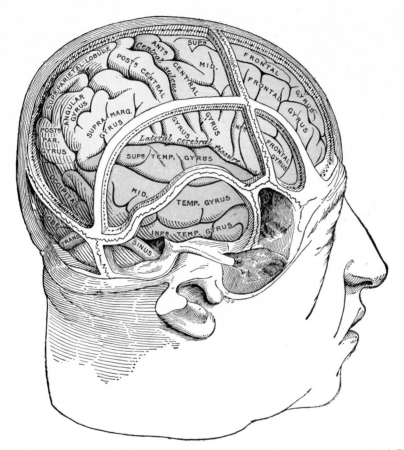

Fig. 1176.—Drawing of a cast by Cunningham to illustrate the relations of the brain to the skull.

Brain (Figs. 1176, 1180).—The general outline of the **cerebral hemisphere,** on either side, may be mapped out on the surface in the following manner. Starting from the nasion, a line drawn along the middle of the scalp to the inion represents the superior border. The line of the lower margin behind is that of the transverse sinus (see page 1353), or more roughly a line convex upward from the inion to the posterior root of the zygomatic process of the temporal bone; thence along the posterior two-thirds of the upper border of the zygomatic arch where the line turns up to the pterion; the front part of the lower margin extends from the pterion to the glabella about 1 cm. above the supraorbital margin. The **cerebellum** is so deeply situated that there is no reliable surface marking for it; a point 4 cm. behind and 1.5 cm. below the level of the auricular point is situated directly over it.

The relations of the principal fissures and gyri of the cerebral hemispheres to the surface of the scalp are of considerable practical importance, and several methods of indicating them have been devised. Necessarily these methods can

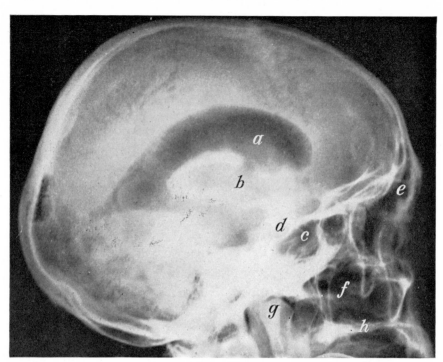

Fig. 1177.—Adult head. a, Lateral ventricle injected with air; b, third ventricle, interventricular foramen mid-way between a and b; c, sphenoidal sinus; d, sella turcica; e, frontal sinus; f, maxillary sinus; g, condyle of mandible; h, hard palate.   (Department of Radiology, University of Pennsylvania.)

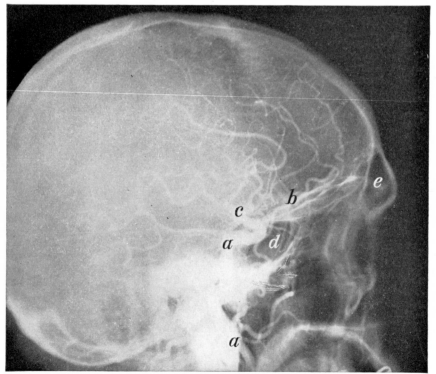

Fig. 1178.—Internal carotid artery. a, After injection of diotrast into the common carotid artery; b, anterior cerebral artery; c, middle cerebral; d, sphenoidal sinus; e, frontal sinus. (Department of Radiology, University of Pennsylvania.)

only be regarded as approximately correct, yet they are all sufficiently accurate for surgical purposes. The **longitudinal fissure** corresponds to the median line of the scalp between the nasion and inion. In order to mark out the **lateral cerebral** (*Sylvian*) **fissure** a point, termed the Sylvian point, which practically corresponds to the pterion, is defined 35 mm. behind and 12 mm. above the level of the fronto-zygomatic suture; this point marks the spot where the lateral fissure divides. Another method of defining the Sylvian point is to divide the distance between the nasion and inion into four equal parts; from the junction of the third and fourth parts (reckoning from the front) draw a line to the zygomaticofrontal suture;

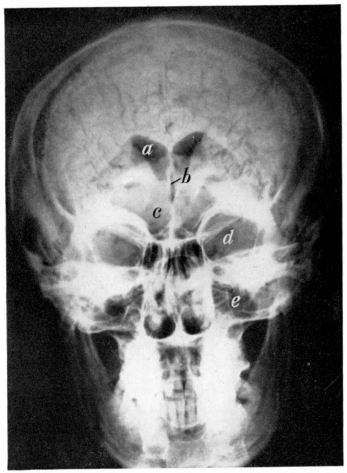

Fig. 1179.—Brain ventricles injected with air. Note extension of air into sulci. *a*, Lateral ventricle; *b*, third ventricle; *c*, frontal sinus; *d*, orbit; *e*, maxillary sinus. (Department of Radiology, University of Pennsylvania.)

from the junction of the first and second parts a line to the auricular point. These two lines intersect at the Sylvian point and the portion of the first line behind this point overlies the posterior ramus of the lateral cerebral fissure. The position of the posterior ramus can otherwise be obtained by joining the Sylvian point to a point 2 cm. below the summit of the parietal eminence. The anterior ascending ramus can be marked out by drawing a line upward at right angles to the line of the posterior ramus for 2 cm. and the anterior horizontal ramus by a line of the same length drawn horizontally forward—both from the Sylvian point. To define the **central sulcus** (*fissure of Rolando*) two points are taken; one is situated 1.25 cm.

behind the center of the line joining the nasion and inion; the second is at the intersection of the line of the posterior ramus of the lateral cerebral fissure with a line through the preauricular point at right angles to Reid's base line. The upper 9 cm. of the line joining these two points overlies the central sulcus and forms an angle, opening forward, of about 70° with the middle line of the scalp. An alternative method is to draw two perpendicular lines from Reid's base line to the top of the head; one from the preauricular point and the other from the posterior border of the mastoid process at its root. A line from the upper end of the posterior line to the point where the anterior intersects the line of the posterior ramus of the lateral fissure indicates the position of the central sulcus. The **precentral** and **postcentral sulci** are practically parallel to the central sulcus; they are situated respectively about 15 mm. in front of, and behind, it. The **superior frontal sulcus** can be mapped out by a line drawn from the junction of the upper and middle

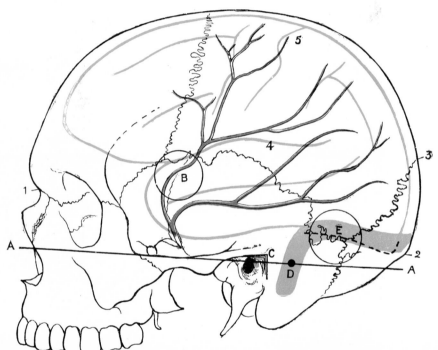

Fig. 1180.—Relations of the brain and middle meningeal artery to the surface of the skull. **1.** Nasion. **2.** Inion. **3.** Lambda. **4.** Lateral cerebral fissure. **5.** Central sulcus. *AA.* Reid's base line. *B.* Point for trephining the anterior branch of the middle meningeal artery. *C.* Suprameatal triangle. *D.* Sigmoid bend of the transverse sinus. *E.* Point for trephining over the straight portion of the transverse sinus, exposing dura mater of both cerebrum and cerebellum. Outline of cerebral hemisphere indicated in blue; course of middle meningeal artery in red.

thirds of the precentral sulcus, in a direction parallel with the longitudinal sulcus, to a point midway between the middle line of the forehead and the temporal line, 4 cm. above the supraorbital notch. The **inferior frontal sulcus** begins at the junction of the middle and lower thirds of the precentral sulcus, and follows the course of the superior temporal line.

The horizontal limb of the **intraparietal sulcus** begins from the junction of the lower with the middle third of the postcentral sulcus and curves backward parallel to the longitudinal fissure, midway between it and the parietal eminence; it then curves downward to end midway between the lambda and the parietal eminence. The external part of the **parietoöccipital fissure** runs lateralward at right angles to the longitudinal fissure for about 2.5 cm. from a point 5 mm. in front of the lambda. If the line of the posterior ramus of the lateral cerebral fissure be continued back to the longitudinal fissure, the last 2.5 cm. of it will indicate the position of the parietoöccipital fissure.

The **lateral ventricle** may be circumscribed by a quadrilateral figure. The upper limit is a horizontal line 5 cm. above the zygomatic arch; this defines the roof of the ventricle. The lower limit is a horizontal line 1 cm. above the zygomatic arch; it indicates the level of the end of the inferior horn. Two vertical lines, one through the junction of the anterior and middle thirds of the zygomatic arch, and the other 5 cm. behind the tip of the mastoid process, indicate the extent of the anterior horn in front and the posterior horn behind.

Vessels.—The line of the anterior division of the **middle meningeal artery** is equidistant from the frontozygomatic suture and the zygomatic arch; it is obtained by joining up the following points: (1) 2.5 cm., (2) 4 cm., and (3) 5 cm. from these two landmarks. The posterior division can be reached 2.5 cm. above the auricular point.

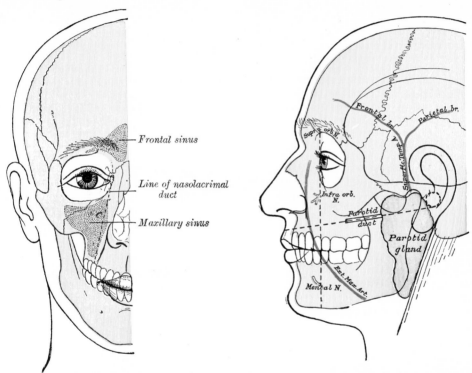

Fig. 1181.—Outline of bones of face, showing position of air sinuses.

Fig. 1182.—Outline of side of face, showing chief surface markings.

The position of the **transverse sinus** is obtained by taking two lines: the first from the inion to a point 2.5 cm. behind the auricular point; the second from the anterior end of the first to the tip of the mastoid process. The second line corresponds roughly to the line of reflection of the skin of the auricula behind, and its upper two-thirds represents the sigmoid part of the sinus. The first part of the sinus has a slight upward convexity, and its highest point is about 4 cm. behind and 1 cm. above the level of the auricular point. The width of the sinus is about 1 cm.

The Face.—**Air Sinuses** (Fig. 1183).—The frontal and maxillary sinuses vary so greatly in form and size that their surface markings must be regarded as only roughly approximate. To mark out the position of the **frontal sinus** three points are taken: (1) the nasion, (2) a point in the middle line 3 cm. above the nasion, (3) a point at the junction of the lateral and intermediate thirds of the supraorbital margin. By joining these a triangular field is described which overlies the greater part of the sinus. The outline of the **maxillary sinus** is irregularly quadrilateral and is obtained by joining up the following points: (1) the lacrimal tubercle, (2) a point on the zygomatic bone at the level of the inferior and lateral margins of the orbit, (3) and (4) points on the alveolar process above the last molar and the second premolar teeth respectively.

External Maxillary Artery.—The course of this artery on the face may be indicated by a line starting from the lower border of the mandible at the anterior margin of the Masseter, and running at first forward and upward to a point 1 cm. lateral to the angle of the mouth, thence to the ala of the nose and upward to the medial commissure of the eye (Fig. 1182).

Trigeminal Nerve.—Terminal branches of this nerve, viz., the supraorbital branch of the ophthalmic, the infraorbital of the maxillary, and the mental of the mandibular emerge from corresponding foramina on the face (Fig. 1182). The supraorbital foramen is situated at the junction of the medial and intermediate thirds of the supraorbital margin. A line drawn from this foramen to the lower border of the mandible, through the interval between the two lower premolar teeth, passes over the infraorbital and mental foramina; the former lies about 1 cm. below the margin of the orbit, while the latter varies in position according to the age of the individual; in the adult it is midway between the upper and lower borders of the mandible, in the child it is nearer the lower border, while in the edentulous jaw of old age it is close to the upper margin.

The position of the sphenopalatine ganglion is indicated from the side by a point on the upper border of the zygomatic arch, 6 mm. from the margin of the zygomatic bone.

Parotid Gland (Fig. 1182).—The upper border of the parotid gland corresponds to the posterior two-thirds of the lower border of the zygomatic arch; the posterior border to the front of the external acoustic meatus, the mastoid process, and the anterior border of Sternocleidomastoideus. The inferior border is indicated by a line from the tip of the mastoid process to the junction of the body and greater cornu of the hyoid bone. In front, the anterior border extends for a variable distance on the superficial surface of the Masseter. The surface marking for the **parotid duct** is a line drawn across the face about a finger's breadth below the zygomatic arch, *i. e.*, from the lower margin of the concha to midway between the red margin of the lip and the ala of the nose; the duct ends opposite the second upper molar tooth and measures about 5 cm. in length.

The Nose.—The outlines of the nasal bones and the cartilages forming the external nose can be easily felt. The mobile portion of the nasal septum, formed by the medial crura of the greater alar cartilages and the skin, is easily distinguished between the nares. When the head is tilted back and a speculum introduced through the naris, the floor of the nasal cavity, the lower part of the nasal septum, and the anterior ends of the middle and inferior nasal conchæ can be examined. The opening of the nasolacrimal duct, which lies under cover of the front of the inferior nasal concha, is situated about 2.5 cm. behind the naris and 2 cm. above the level of the floor of the nasal cavity.

The Mouth.—The orifice of the mouth is bounded by the lips, which are covered externally by the whitish skin and internally by the red mucous membrane. The size of the orifice varies considerably in different individuals, but seems to bear a close relationship to the size and prominence of the teeth; its angles usually correspond to the lateral borders of the canine teeth. Running down the center of the outer surface of the upper lip is a shallow groove—the **philtrum.** If the lips be everted there can be seen, in the middle line of each, a small fold of mucous membrane—the **frenulum**—passing from the lip to the gum. By pulling the angle of the mouth outward the mucous membrane of the cheek can be inspected, and on this, opposite the second molar tooth of the maxilla, is the little papilla which marks the orifice of the parotid duct.

In the floor of the mouth is the **tongue** (Fig. 1007). Its upper surface is convex and is marked along the middle line by a shallow sulcus; the anterior two-thirds are rough and studded with papillæ; the posterior third is smooth and tuberculated. The division between the anterior two-thirds and the posterior third is marked by a V-shaped furrow, the sulcus terminalis, which is situated immediately behind the line of the vallate papillæ.

On the under surface of the tongue (Fig. 1006) the mucous membrane is smooth and devoid of papillæ. In the middle line, the mucous membrane extends to the floor of the mouth as a distinct fold—the frenulum—the free edge of which runs

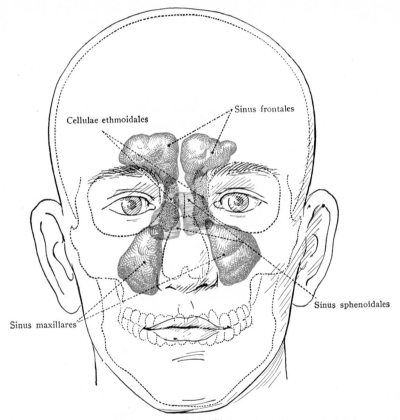

Fig. 1183.—Accessory air sinuses of nose projected on anterior surface of face. (Eycleshymer and Jones.)

forward to the symphysis menti. Sometimes the ranine vein can be seen immediately beneath the mucous membrane, a little lateral to the frenulum. Close to the attachment of the frenulum to the floor of the mouth, the slit-like orifice of the submaxillary duct is visible on either side. Running backward and lateralward from the orifice of the submaxillary duct is the plica sublingualis, produced by the projection of the sublingual gland which lies immediately beneath the mucous membrane. The plica serves also to indicate the line of the submaxillary duct and of the lingual nerve. At the back of the mouth is the isthmus faucium, bounded above by the palatine velum, from the free margin of which the uvula projects downward in the middle line. On either side of the isthmus are the two palatine arches, the anterior formed by the Glossopalatinus and the posterior by the Pharyn-

gopalatinus.   Between the two arches of either side is the palatine **tonsil,** above
which is the small supratonsillar recess; the position of the tonsil corresponds to
the angle of the mandible.   When the mouth is opened widely, a tense band—
the pterygomandibular raphé—can be seen and felt lateral to the glossopalatine
arch.   Its lower end is attached to the mandible behind the last molar tooth,
and immediately below and in front of this the **lingual nerve** can be felt; the upper
end of the ligament can be traced to the pterygoid hamulus.   About 1 cm. in front
of the hamulus and 1 cm. medial to the last molar tooth of the maxilla is the greater
palatine foramen through which the descending palatine vessels and the anterior
palatine nerve emerge.   Behind the last molar tooth of the maxilla the coronoid
process of the mandible is palpable.

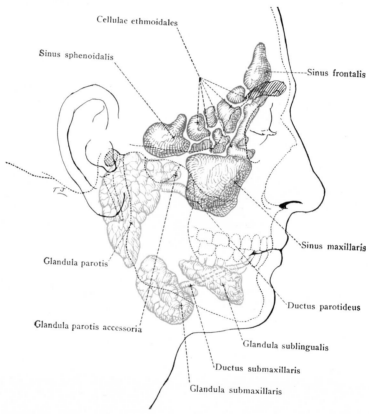

Fig. 1184.—Accessory air sinuses and salivary glands projected on lateral surface of face.   (Eycleshymer and Jones.)

By tilting the head well back a portion of the posterior pharyngeal wall, corresponding to the site of the second and third cervical vertebræ, can be seen through
the isthmus faucium.   On introducing the finger the anterior surfaces of the upper
cervical vertebræ can be felt through the thin muscular wall of the pharynx;
if the finger be hooked round the palatine velum, the choanæ can be distinguished in
front, and the pharyngeal ostium of the auditory tube on either side.   The level
of the choanæ is that of the atlas, while the palatine velum is opposite the body
of the axis.

With the laryngoscope many other structures can be seen.   In the nasal part
of the pharynx (Fig. 1021), the choanæ, the nasal septum, the nasal conchæ, and
the pharyngeal ostia of the auditory tubes can all be examined.   Further down, the
base of the tongue, the anterior surface of the epiglottis with the glossoepiglottic
and pharyngoepiglottic folds bounding the valleculæ, and the piriform sinuses, are

readily distinguished. Beyond these is the entrance to the larynx, bounded on either side by the aryepiglottic folds, in each of which are two rounded eminences corresponding to the corniculate and cuneiform cartilages.

Within the larynx (Fig. 950) on either side are the ventricular and vocal folds (false and true vocal cords) with the ventricle between them. Still deeper are seen the cricoid cartilage and the anterior parts of some of the cartilaginous rings of the trachea, and sometimes, during deep inspiration, the bifurcation of the trachea.

The Eye.—The palpebral fissure is elliptical in shape, and varies in form in different individuals and in different races of mankind; normally it is oblique, in a direction upward and lateralward, so that the lateral commissure is on a slightly higher level than the medial. When the eyes are directed forward as in ordinary vision the upper part of the cornea is covered by the upper eyelid and its lower margin corresponds to the level of the free margin of the lower eyelid, so that usually the lower three-fourths are exposed.

At the medial commissure (Fig. 1185) are the caruncula lacrimalis and the plica semilunaris. When the lids are everted, the tarsal glands appear as a series of nearly straight parallel rows of light yellow granules. On the margins of the lids about 5 mm. from the medial commissure are two small openings—the **lacrimal puncta**; in the natural condition they are in contact with the conjunctiva of the bulb of the eye, so that it is necessary to evert the eyelids to expose them. The position of the lacrimal sac is indicated by a little tubercle which can be plainly felt on the lower margin of the orbit; the sac lies immediately above and medial to the tubercle. If the eyelids be drawn lateralward so as to tighten the skin at the medial commissure a prominent core can be felt be-

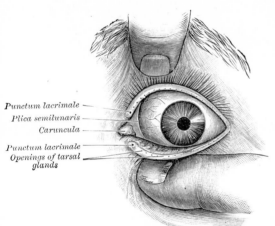

Punctum lacrimale —
Plica semilunaris —
Caruncula —

Punctum lacrimale —
Openings of tarsal glands —

Fig. 1185.—Front of left eye with eyelids separated to show medial canthus.

neath the tightened skin; this is the medial palpebral ligament, which lies over the junction of the upper with the lower two-thirds of the sac, thus forming a useful guide to its situation. The direction of the nasolacrimal duct is indicated by a line from the lacrimal sac to the first molar tooth of the maxilla; the length of the duct is about 12 or 13 mm.

On looking into the eye, the **iris** with its opening, the **pupil**, and the front of the lens can be examined, but for investigation of the **retina** an ophthalmoscope is necessary. With this the **lens**, the vessels of the **retina**, the **optic disk**, and the **macula lutea** can all be inspected (Fig. 870).

On the lateral surface of the nasal part of the frontal bone the pulley of the **Obliquus superior** can be easily reached by pushing the finger backward along the roof of the orbit; the tendon of the muscle can be traced for a short distance backward and lateralward from the pulley.

The Ear.—The various prominences and fossæ of the auricula (see page 1065) are visible (Fig. 895). The opening of the **external acoustic meatus** is exposed by drawing the tragus forward; at the orifice are a few short crisp hairs which serve to prevent the entrance of dust or of small insects; beyond this the secretion of the

ceruminous glands serves to catch any small particles which may find their way into the meatus. The interior of the meatus can be examined through a speculum. At

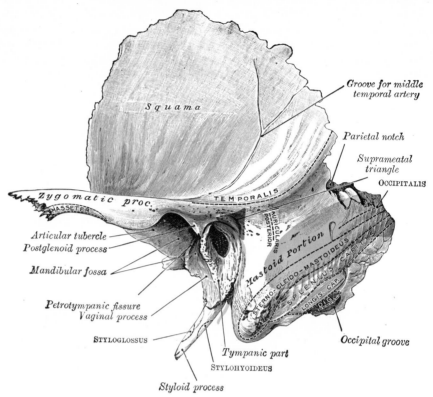

Fig. 1186.—Left temporal bone showing surface markings for the tympanic antrum (red), transverse sinus (blue), and facial nerve (yellow).

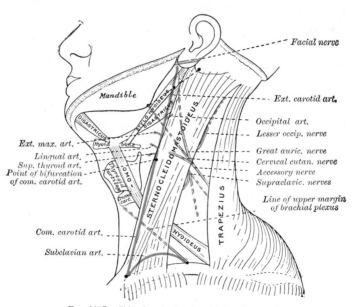

Fig. 1187.—Side of neck, showing chief surface markings.

the line of junction of its bony and cartilaginous portions an obtuse angle is formed which projects into the antero-inferior wall and produces a narrowing of the lumen in this situation. The cartilaginous part, however, is connected to the bony part by fibrinous tissue which renders the outer part of the meatus very movable, and therefore by drawing the auricula upward, backward, and slightly outward, the canal is rendered almost straight. In children the meatus is very short, and this should be remembered in introducing the speculum.

Through the speculum the greater part of the **tympanic membrane** (Fig. 900) is

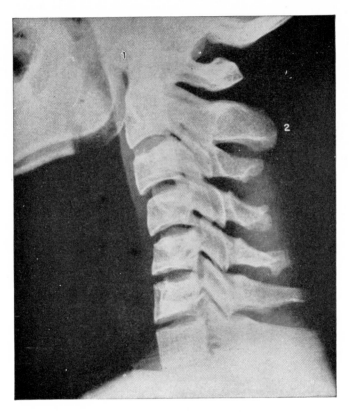

Fig. 1188.—Cervical vertebræ. Lateral view. *1*, Anterior arch of atlas; *2*, spine of axis. The curvature is abnormal.

visible. It is a pearly-gray membrane slightly glistening in the adult, placed obliquely so as to form with the floor of the meatus an angle of about 55 degrees. At birth it is more horizontal and situated in almost the same plane as the base of the skull. The membrane is concave outward, and the point of deepest concavity— the **umbo**—is slightly below the center. Running upward and slightly forward from the umbo is a reddish-yellow streak produced by the manubrium of the malleus. This streak ends above just below the roof of the meatus at a small white rounded prominence which is caused by the lateral process of the malleus projecting against the membrane. The anterior and posterior **malleolar folds** extend from the prominence to the circumference of the membrane and enclose the **pars flaccida.** Behind the streak caused by the manubrium of the malleus a second streak, shorter and very faint, can be distinguished; this is the **long crus of the incus.** A narrow triangular patch extending downward and forward from the umbo reflects the light more brightly than any other part, and is usually described as the **cone of light**.

Tympanic Antrum.—The site of the tympanic antrum is indicated by the **supra-meatal triangle** (Fig. 1186). This triangle is bounded above by the posterior root of the zygomatic arch; behind by a vertical line from the posterior border of the external acoustic meatus; in front and below by the upper margin of the meatus.

The Neck (Fig. 1187).—**Larynx and Trachea.**—In the receding angle below the

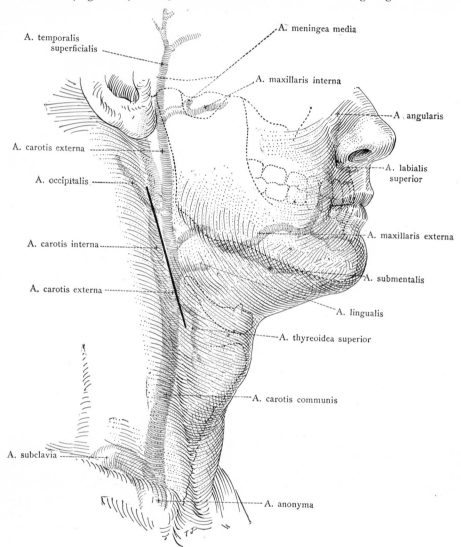

FIG. 1189.—The principal arteries projected on the lateral surface of the neck. (Eycleshymer and Jones.)

chin, the **hyoid bone** (page 1347), situated opposite the fourth cervical vertebra, can easily be made out. A finger's breadth below it is the laryngeal prominence of the **thyroid cartilage**; the space intervening between the hyoid bone and the thyroid cartilage is occupied by the **hyothyroid membrane**. The outlines of the thyroid cartilage are readily palpated; below its lower border is a depression corresponding o the middle **cricothyroid ligament.** The level of the vocal folds corresponds to he middle of the anterior margin of the thyroid cartilage. The anterior part of he cricoid cartilage forms an important landmark on the front of the neck; it ies opposite the sixth cervical vertebra, and indicates the junctions of pharynx vith esophagus, and larynx with trachea. Below the cricoid cartilage the **trachea** :an be felt, though it is only in thin subjects that the separate rings can be distin- quished; as a rule there are seven or eight rings above the jugular notch of the ternum, and of these the second, third, and fourth are covered by the isthmus of the thyroid gland.

Muscles.—The posterior belly of **Digastricus** is marked out by a line from the tip of the mastoid process to the junction of the greater cornu and body of the hyoid one; a line from this latter point to a point just lateral to the symphysis menti ndicates the position of the anterior belly. The line of **Omohyoideus** begins at the lower border of the hyoid bone, curves downward and lateralward to cross Sternocleidomastoideus at the junction of its middle and lower thirds, *i. e.*, opposite the cricoid cartilage, and then runs more horizontally to the acromial end of the clavicle.

Arteries.—The position of the **common carotid** artery in the neck is indicated by a line drawn from the upper part of the sternal end of the clavicle to a point midway between the tip of the mastoid process and the angle of the mandible. From the clavicle to the upper border of the thyroid cartilage this line overlies the common carotid artery, beyond this it is over the external carotid. The **external carotid** artery may otherwise be marked out by the upper part of a line from the side of the cricoid cartilage to the front of the external acoustic meatus, arching the line slightly forward.

The points of origin of the main branches of the external carotid in the neck are all related to the tip of the greater cornu of the hyoid bone as follows: (1) the **superior thyroid,** immediately below it; (2) the **lingual,** on a level with it; (3) the **facial,** and (4) the **occipital** a little above and behind it.

The **subclavian artery** is indicated on the surface by a curved line, convex upward, from the sternoclavicular articulation to the middle of the clavicle. The highest point of the convexity is from 1 to 3 cm. above the clavicle.

Veins.—The surface marking for the **internal jugular** vein is slightly lateral and parallel to that for the common carotid artery. The position of the **external jugular** vein is marked out by a line from the angle of the mandible to the middle of the clavicle. A point on this line about 4 cm. above the clavicle indicates the spot where the vein pierces the deep fascia. The line of the **anterior jugular** vein begins close to the symphysis menti, runs downward parallel with and a little to one side of the middle line and, at a variable distance above the jugular notch, turns lateralward to the external jugular.

Nerves.—The **facial nerve** at its exit from the stylomastoid foramen is situated about 2.5 cm. from the surface, opposite the middle of the anterior border of the mastoid process; a horizontal line from this point to the ramus of the mandible overlies the stem of the nerve. To mark the site of the **accessory nerve** a line is drawn from the angle of the mandible to a point on the anterior border of Sterno- cleidomastoideus about 3 to 4 cm. below the apex of the mastoid process, or to the midpoint of the posterior border of the muscle; the line is continued across the posterior triangle to Trapezius.

The cutaneous branches of the cervical plexus as they emerge from the posterior border of Sternocleidomastoideus may be indicated as follows: the **lesser occipital** begins immediately above the midpoint of the border and runs along the border to the scalp; the **great auricular** and **cervical cutaneous** both start from the middle of the border, the former running upward toward the lobule of the auricula, the latter crossing Sternocleidomastoideus at right angles to its long axis; the **supra-clavicular** nerves emerge from immediately below the middle of the posterior border and run down over the clavicle. The **phrenic** nerve begins at the level of the middle of the thyroid cartilage and runs behind the clavicle about midway between the anterior and posterior borders of Sternocleidomastoideus.

The upper border of the **brachial plexus** is indicated by a line from the side of the cricoid cartilage to the middle of the clavicle.

Submaxillary Gland.—On either side of the neck the superficial portion of the submaxillary gland, as it lies partly under cover of the mandible, can be palpated.

The Triangles of the Neck (Fig. 1190).—The side of the neck presents a somewhat quadrilateral outline, limited, *above,* by the lower border of the body of the mandible, and an imaginary line extending from the angle of the mandible to the mastoid process; *below,* by the upper border of the clavicle; in *front,* by the middle line of the neck; *behind,* by the anterior margin of the Trapezius. This space is subdivided into two large triangles by the Sternocleidomastoideus, which passes obliquely across the neck, from the sternum and clavicle below, to the mastoid process and occipital bone above. The triangular space in front of this muscle is called the **anterior triangle**; and that behind it, the **posterior triangle**.

ANTERIOR TRIANGLE.—The anterior triangle is bounded, in *front,* by the middle line of the neck; *behind,* by the anterior margin of the Sternocleidomastoideus; its *base,* directed upward, is formed by the lower border of the body of the mandible, and a line extending from the angle of the mandible to the mastoid process; its apex is below, at the sternum. This space is subdivided into four smaller triangles by the Digastricus above, and the superior belly of the Omohyoideus below. These smaller triangles are named the **inferior carotid**, the **superior carotid**, the **submaxillary**, and the **suprahyoid**.

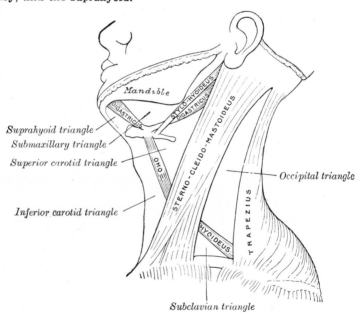

FIG. 1190.—The triangles of the neck.

The **Inferior Carotid,** or **Muscular Triangle,** is bounded, in *front,* by the median line of the neck from the hyoid bone to the sternum; *behind,* by the anterior margin of the Sternocleidomastoideus; *above,* by the superior belly of the Omohyoideus. It is covered by the integument, superficial fascia, Platysma, and deep fascia, ramifying in which are some of the branches of the supraclavicular nerves. Beneath these superficial structures are the Sternohyoideus and Sternothyreoideus, which, together with the anterior margin of the Sternocleidomastoideus, conceal the lower part of the common carotid artery.[1] This vessel is enclosed within its sheath, together with the internal jugular vein and vagus nerve; the vein lies lateral to the artery on the right side of the neck, but overlaps it below on the left side; the nerve lies between the artery and vein, on a plane posterior to both. In front of the sheath are a few descending filaments from the ansa hypoglossi; behind the sheath are the inferior thyroid artery, the recurrent nerve, and the sympathetic trunk; and on its medial side, the esophagus, the trachea, the thyroid gland, and the lower part of the larynx. By cutting into the upper part of this space, and slightly displacing the Sternocleidomastoideus, the common carotid artery may be tied below the Omohyoideus.

The **Superior Carotid, or Carotid Triangle**, is bounded, *behind* by the Sternocleidomastoideus; *below*, by the superior belly of the Omohyoideus; and *above*, by the Stylohyoideus and the posterior belly of the Digastricus. It is covered by the integument, superficial fascia, Platysma and deep fascia; ramifying in which are branches of the facial and cutaneous cervical nerves. Its floor is formed by parts of the Thyrohyoideus, Hyoglossus, and the Constrictores pharyngis medius and inferior. This space when dissected is seen to contain the upper part of the common carotid artery, which bifurcates opposite the upper border of the thyroid cartilage into the external and internal carotid. These vessels are somewhat concealed from view by the anterior margin of the Sternocleidomastoideus, which overlaps them. The external and internal carotids lie side by side, the external being the more anterior of the two. The following branches of the external carotid are also met with in this space: the superior thyroid, running forward and downward; the lingual, directly forward; the external maxillary, forward and upward; the occipital, backward; and the ascending pharyngeal, directly upward on the medial side of the internal carotid. The veins met with are: the internal jugular, which lies on the lateral side of the common and internal carotid arteries; and veins corresponding to the above-mentioned branches of the external carotid—viz., the superior thyroid, the lingual, common facial, ascending pharyngeal, and sometimes the occipital— all of which end in the internal jugular. The nerves in this space are the following. In front of the sheath of the common carotid is the ramus descendens hypoglossi. The hypoglossal nerve crosses both the internal and external carotids above, curving around the origin of the occipital artery. Within the sheath, between the artery and vein, and behind both, is the vagus nerve; behind the sheath, the sympathetic trunk. On the lateral side of the vessels, the accessory nerve runs for a short distance before it pierces the Sternocleidomastoideus; and on the medial side of the external carotid, just below the hyoid bone, may be seen the internal branch of the superior laryngeal nerve; and, still more inferiorly, the external branch of the same nerve. The upper portion of the larynx and lower portion of the pharynx are also found in the front part of this space.

The **Submaxillary or Digastric Triangle** corresponds to the region of the neck immediately beneath the body of the mandible. It is bounded, *above*, by the lower border of the body of the mandible, and a line drawn from its angle to the mastoid process; *below*, by the posterior belly of the Digastricus and the Stylohyoideus; in *front*, by the anterior belly of the Digastricus. It is covered by the integument, superficial fascia, Platysma, and deep fascia, ramifying in which are branches of the facial nerve and ascending filaments of the cutaneous cervical nerve. Its *floor* is formed by the Mylohyoideus, Hyoglossus, and Constrictor pharyngis superior. It is divided into an anterior and a posterior part by the stylomandibular

---

[1] Therefore the common carotid artery and internal jugular vein are not, strictly speaking, contained in this triangle, since they are covered by the Sternocleidomastoideus; that is to say, they lie under that muscle, which forms the posterior border of the triangle. But as they lie very close to the structures which are really contained in the triangle, and whose position it is essential to remember in operating on this part of the artery, it is expedient to study the relations of all these parts together.

ligament. The anterior part contains the submaxillary gland, superficial to which is the anterior facial vein, while imbedded in the gland is the external maxillary artery and its glandular branches; beneath the gland, on the surface of the Mylohyoideus, are the submental artery and the mylohyoid artery and nerve. The posterior part of this triangle contains the external carotid artery, ascending deeply in the substance of the parotid gland; this vessel lies here in front of, and superficial to, the internal carotid, being crossed by the facial nerve, and gives off in its course the posterior auricular, superficial temporal, and internal maxillary branches: more deeply are the internal carotid, the internal jugular vein, and the vagus nerve, separated from the external carotid by the Styloglossus and Stylopharyngeus, and the glossopharyngeal nerve.[1]

The **Suprahyoid Triangle** is limited *behind* by the anterior belly of the Digastricus, in *front* by the middle line of the neck between the mandible and the hyoid bone; *below*, by the body of the hyoid bone; its *floor* is formed by the Mylohyoideus. It contains one or two lymph glands and some small veins; the latter unite to form the anterior jugular vein.

POSTERIOR TRIANGLE.—The posterior triangle is bounded, in *front*, by the Sternocleidomastoideus; *behind*, by the anterior margin of the Trapezius; its *base* is formed by the middle third of the clavicle; its *apex*, by the occipital bone. The space is crossed, about 2.5 cm. above the clavicle, by the inferior belly of the Omohyoideus, which divides it into two triangles, an **upper** or **occipital**, and a **lower or subclavian.**

The **Occipital Triangle,** the larger division of the posterior triangle, is bounded, in *front*, by the Sternocleidomastoideus; *behind*, by the Trapezius; *below*, by the Omohyoideus. Its *floor* is formed from above downward by the Splenius capitis, Levator scapulæ, and the Scaleni medius and posterior. It is covered by the skin, the superficial and deep fasciæ, and by the Platysma below. The accessory nerve is directed obliquely across the space from the Sternocleidomastoideus, which it pierces, to the under surface of the Trapezius; below, the supraclavicular nerves and the transverse cervical vessels and the upper part of the brachial plexus cross the space. A chain of lymph glands is also found running along the posterior border of the Sternocleidomastoideus, from the mastoid process to the root of the neck.

The **Subclavian Triangle,** the smaller division of the posterior triangle, is bounded, *above*, by the inferior belly of the Omohyoideus; *below*, by the clavicle; its *base* is formed by the posterior border of the Sternocleidomastoideus. Its *floor* is formed by the first rib with the first digitation of the Serratus anterior. The size of the subclavian triangle varies with the extent of attachment of the clavicular portions of the Sternocleidomastoideus and Trapezius, and also with the height at which the Omohyoideus crosses the neck. Its height also varies according to the position of the arm, being diminished by raising the limb, on account of the ascent of the clavicle, and increased by drawing the arm downward, when that bone is depressed. This space is covered by the integument, the superficial and deep fasciæ and the Platysma, and crossed by the supraclavicular nerves. Just above the level of the clavicle, the third portion of the subclavian artery curves lateralward and downward from the lateral margin of the Scalenus anterior, across the first rib, to the axilla, and this is the situation most commonly chosen for ligaturing the vessel. Sometimes this vessel rises as high as 4 cm. above the clavicle; occasionally, it passes in front of the Scalenus anterior, or pierces the fibers of that muscle. The subclavian vein lies behind the clavicle, and is not usually seen in this space; but in some cases it rises as high as the artery, and has even been seen to pass with that vessel behind the Scalenus anterior. The brachial plexus of nerves lies above

---

[1] The remark made about the inferior carotid triangle applies also to this one. The structures enumerated as contained in its posterior part lie, strictly speaking, beneath the muscles which form the posterior boundary of the triangle; but as it is very important to bear in mind their close relation to the parotid gland, all these parts are spoken of together.

the artery, and in close contact with it. Passing transversely behind the clavicle are the transverse scapular vessels; and traversing its upper angle in the same direction, the transverse cervical artery and vein. The external jugular vein runs vertically downward behind the posterior border of the Sternocleidomastoideus, to terminate in the subclavian vein; it receives the transverse cervical and transverse scapular veins, which form a plexus in front of the artery, and occasionally a small vein which crosses the clavicle from the cephalic. The small nerve to the Subclavius also crosses this triangle about its middle, and some lymph glands are usually found in the space.

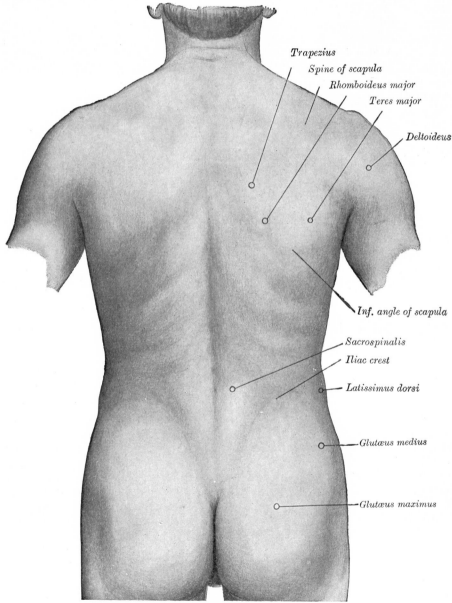

Trapezius
Spine of scapula
Rhomboideus major
Teres major
Deltoideus
Inf. angle of scapula
Sacrospinalis
Iliac crest
Latissimus dorsi
Glutæus medius
Glutæus maximus

FIG. 1191.—Surface anatomy of the back.

SURFACE ANATOMY OF THE BACK.

Bones.—The only subcutaneous parts of the vertebral column are the apices of the spinous processes. These are distinguishable at the bottom of a furrow which runs down the middle line of the back from the external occipital protuberance to the middle of the sacrum. **In the cervical region** the furrow is broad and ends below in a conspicuous projection caused by the spinous processes of the seventh cervical and first thoracic vertebræ. Above this, the spinous process of the sixth cervical vertebra sometimes forms a projection; the other cervical spinous processes are sunken, but that of the axis can be felt. **In the thoracic region** the furrow is shallow and during stooping disappears, and then the spinous processes become more or less visible; the markings produced by them are small and close together. In the **lumbar region** the furrow is deep and the situations of the spinous processes are frequently indicated by little pits or depressions, especially when the muscles in the loins are well-developed. In the **sacral region** the furrow is shallower, presenting a flattened area which ends below at the most prominent part of the dorsal surface of the sacrum, *i. e.*, the spinous process of the third sacral vertebra. At the bottom of the sacral furrow the irregular dorsal surface of the bone may be felt, and below this, in the deep groove running to the anus, the **coccyx.**

The only other portions of the vertebral column which can be felt from the surface are the transverse processes of the first, sixth, and seventh cervical vertebræ.

Muscles. —The muscles proper of the back are so obscured by those of the upper extremity (Fig. 1191) that they have very little influence on surface form. The **Splenii** by their divergence serve to broaden out the upper part of the back of the neck and produce a fulness in this situation. In the loin the **Sacrospinales,** bound down by the lumbodorsal fascia, form rounded

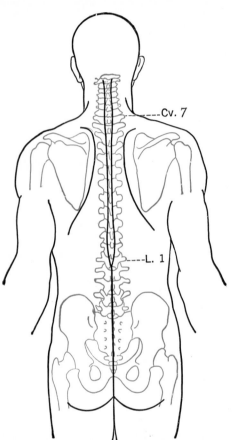

Fig. 1192.—Diagram showing the relation of the medulla spinalis to the dorsal surface of the trunk. The bones are outlined in red.

Level of body of	No. of nerve.	Level of tip of spine of	Level of body of	No of nerve.	Level of tip of spine of
C. 1	C. 1	..	T. 8	T. 9	7 T.
2	{ 2	..	9	10	8
	{ 3	1 C.	10	11	9
3	4	2	..	12	10
4	5	3	11	L. 1	11
5	6	4	..	{ 2	..
6	7	5	12	{ 3	..
..	8	6	..	{ 4	12
.. 7	T. 1	7		{ 5	..
T. 1	2	1 T.		S. 1	
2	3	..	L. 1	2	
3	4	..		3	
4	5	2		4	1 L.
5	6	3		5	
6	7	4		C. 1	
7	8	5	L. 2	..	
		6			

vertical eminences which determine the depth of the spinal furrow and taper below to a point on the dorsal surface of the sacrum. The continuations of the Sacrospinales in the lower thoracic region form flattened planes which are gradually lost on passing upward.

SURFACE MARKINGS OF THE BACK.

Bony Landmarks.—In order to identify any particular spinous process it is customary to count from the prominence caused by the seventh cervical and first thoracic; of these the latter is the more prominent. The root of the spine of the scapula is on a level with the tip of

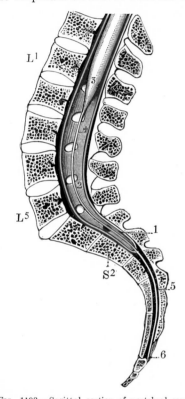

Fig. 1193.—Sagittal section of vertebral canal to show the lower end of the medulla spinalis and the filum terminale. (Testut.) *Li, Lv.* First and fifth lumbar vertebræ. *Sii.* Second sacral vertebra. 1. Dura mater. 2. Lower part of subarachnoid cavity. 3. Lower extremity of medulla spinalis. 4. Filum terminale internum, and 5, Filum terminale externum. 6. Attachment of filum terminale to first segment of coccyx.

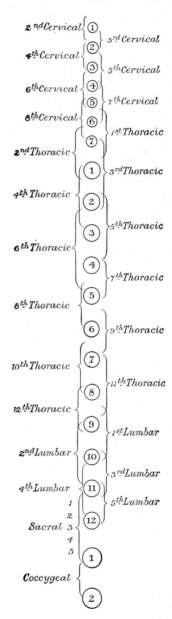

Fig. 1194.—Scheme showing the relations of the regions of attachment of the spinal nerves to the vertebral spinous processes. (After Reid.)

the spinous process of the third thoracic vertebra, and the inferior angle with that of the seventh. The highest point of the iliac crest is on a level with the spinous process of the fourth lumbar, and the posterior superior iliac spine with that of the second sacral.

The transverse process of the atlas is about 1 cm. below and in front of the apex of the mastoid process. The transverse process of the sixth cervical vertebra is opposite the cricoid cartilage; below it is the transverse process of the seventh and occasionally a cervical rib.

Medulla Spinalis.—The position of the lower end of the medulla spinalis varies slightly with the movements of the vertebral column, but, in the adult, in the upright posture it is usually at the level of the spinous process of the second lumbar vertebra (Fig. 1192); at birth it lies at the level of the fourth lumbar.

The **subdural** and **subarachnoid cavities** end below opposite the spinous process of the third sacral vertebra (Fig. 1193).

Spinal Nerves (Fig. 1194).—The table on page 1366, after Macalister, shows the relations which the places of attachment of the nerves to the medulla spinalis present to the bodies and spinous processes of the vertebræ.

SURFACE ANATOMY OF THE THORAX.

Bones.—The skeleton of the thorax is to a very considerable extent covered by muscles, so that in the strongly developed muscular subject it is for the most part concealed. In the emaciated subject, however, the **ribs**, especially in the lower and lateral regions, stand out as prominent ridges with the sunken intercostal spaces between them.

In the middle line, in front, the superficial surface of the **sternum** can be felt throughout its entire length at the bottom of a furrow, the sternal furrow, situated between the Pectorales majores. These muscles overlap the anterior surface somewhat, so that the whole width of the sternum is not subcutaneous, and this overlapping is greatest opposite the middle of the bone; the furrow, therefore, is wide at its upper and lower parts but narrow in the middle. At the upper border of the manubrium sterni is the **jugular notch**: the lateral parts of this notch are obscured by the tendinous origins of the Sternocleidomastoidei, which appear as oblique cords narrowing and deepening the notch. Lower down on the subcutaneous surface is a well-defined transverse ridge, the **sternal angle**; it denotes the junction of the manubrium and body. From the middle of the sternum the sternal furrow spreads out and ends at the junction of the body with the xiphoid process Immediately below this is the **infrasternal notch;** between the sternal ends of the seventh costal cartilages, and below the notch, is a triangular depression, the epigastric fossa, in which the **xiphoid process** can be felt.

On either side of the sternum the costal cartilages and ribs on the front of the thorax are partly obscured by the Pectoralis major, through which, however, they can be felt as ridges with yielding intervals between them corresponding to the intercostal spaces. Of these spaces, that between the second and third ribs is the widest, the next two are somewhat narrower, and the remainder, with the exception of the last two, are comparatively narrow.

Below the lower border of the Pectoralis major on the front of the chest, the broad flat outlines of the ribs as they descend, and the more rounded outlines of the costal cartilages, are often visible. The lower boundary of the front of the thorax which is most plainly seen by bending the body backward, is formed by the xiphoid process, the cartilages of the seventh, eighth, ninth, and tenth ribs, and the ends of the cartilages of the eleventh and twelfth ribs.

On either side of the thorax, from the axilla downward, the flattened external surfaces of the ribs may be defined. Although covered by muscles, all the ribs with the exception of the first, can generally be followed without difficulty over the front and sides of the thorax. The first rib being almost completely covered by the clavicle can only be distinguished in a small portion of its extent.

At the back, the angles of the ribs lie on a slightly marked oblique line on either side of, and some distance from, the spinous processes of the vertebræ. The line diverges somewhat as it descends, and lateral to it is a broad convex surface caused by the projection of the ribs beyond their angles. Over this surface, except where covered by the scapula, the individual ribs can be distinguished.

Muscles.—The surface muscles covering the thorax belong to the musculature of the upper extremity (Figs. 1195, 1205), and will be described in that section (page 1402). There is, however, an area of practical importance bounded by these muscles. It is limited above by the lower border of Trapezius, below by the upper border of Latissimus dorsi, and laterally by the vertebral border of the scapula; the floor is partly formed by Rhomboideus major. If the scapula be drawn forward by folding the arms across the chest, and the trunk bent forward, parts of the sixth and seventh ribs and the interspace between them become subcutaneous and available for auscultation. The space is therefore known as the **triangle of auscultation.**

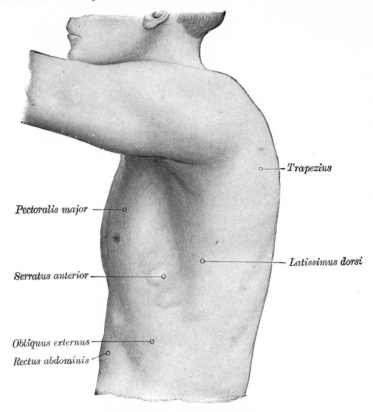

Fig. 1195.—The left side of the thorax.

Mamma.—The size of the mamma is subject to great variations. In the adult nulliparous female, it extends vertically from the second to the sixth rib, and transversely from the side of the sternum to the midaxillary line. In the male and in the nulliparous female the **mammary papilla** is situated in the fourth interspace about 9 or 10 cm. from the middle line, or 2 cm. from the costochondral junction.

SURFACE MARKINGS OF THE THORAX.

Bony Landmarks.—The second costal cartilage corresponding to the sternal angle is so readily found that it is used as a starting-point from which to count the ribs. The lower border of the Pectoralis major at its attachment corresponds to the fifth rib; the uppermost visible digitation of Serratus anterior indicates the sixth rib.

The jugular notch is in the same horizontal plane as the lower border of the body of the second thoracic vertebra; the sternal angle is at the level of the fifth thoracic vertebra, while the junction between the body and xiphoid process of the sternum corresponds to the fibrocartilage between the ninth and tenth thoracic vertebræ.

The influence of the obliquity of the ribs on horizontal levels in the thorax is well shown by the following line. "If a horizontal line be drawn around the body at the level of the inferior angle of the scapula, while the arms are at the sides, the line would cut the sternum in front between the fourth and fifth ribs, the fifth rib in the nipple line, and the ninth rib at the vertebral column." (Treves).

Diaphragm.—The shape and variations of the diaphragm as seen by skiagraphy have already been described (page 391).

Surface Lines.—For clinical purposes, and for convenience of description, the surface of the thorax has been mapped out by arbitrary lines (Fig. 1206). On the front of the thorax the most important vertical lines are the **midsternal**, the middle line of the sternum; and the **mammary**, or, better **midclavicular**, which runs vertically downward from a point midway between the center of the jugular notch and the tip of the acromion. This latter line, if prolonged, is practically continuous with the lateral line on the front of the abdomen. Other vertical lines on the front of the thorax are the **lateral sternal** along the sternal margin, and the **parasternal** midway between the lateral sternal and the mammary.

On either side of the thorax the **anterior** and **posterior axillary lines** are drawn vertically from the corresponding axillary folds; the **midaxillary line** runs downward from the apex of the axilla.

On the posterior surface of the thorax the **scapular line** is drawn vertically through the inferior angle of the scapula.

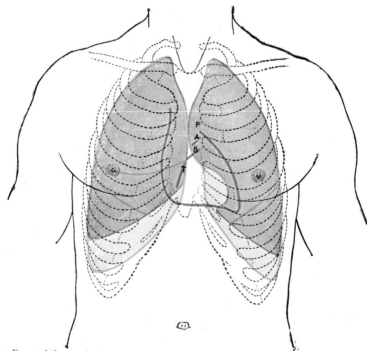

Fig. 1196.—Front of thorax, showing surface relations of bones, lungs (purple), pleura (blue), and heart (red outline). *P.* Pulmonary valve. *A.* Aortic valve. *B.* Bicuspid valve. *T.* Tricuspid valve.

Pleuræ (Figs. 1196, 1197).—The lines of reflection of the pleuræ can be indicated on the surface. On the *right* side the line begins at the sternoclavicular articulation

and runs downward and medialward to the midpoint of the junction between the
manubrium and body of the sternum. It then follows the midsternal line to the
lower end of the body of the sternum or on to the xiphoid process, where it turns
lateralward and downward across the seventh sternocostal articulation. It crosses
the eighth costochondral junction in the mammary line, the tenth rib in the midaxillary line, and is prolonged thence to the spinous process of the twelfth thoracic
vertebra.

On the *left* side, beginning at the sternoclavicular articulation, it reaches the
midpoint of the junction between the manubrium and body of the sternum, and
extends down the midsternal line in contact with that of the opposite side to the
level of the fourth costal cartilage. It then diverges lateralward and is continued
downward slightly lateral to the sternal border, as far as the sixth costal cartilage.
Running downward and lateralward from this point it crosses the seventh costal
cartilage, and from this onward it is similar to the line on the right side, but at a
slightly lower level.

Lungs (Figs. 1196, 1197).—The **apex** of the lung is situated in the neck above the
medial third of the clavicle. The height to which it rises above the clavicle varies
very considerably, but is generally about 2.5 cm. It may, however, extend as
high as 4 or 5 cm., or, on the other hand, may scarcely project above the level
of this bone.

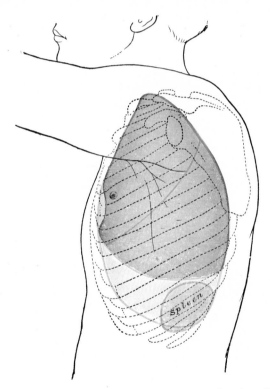

Fig. 1197.—Side of thorax, showing surface markings for bones, lungs (purple), pleura (blue), and spleen (green).

In order to mark out the **anterior borders** of the lungs a line is drawn from each
apex point—2.5 cm. above the clavicle and rather nearer the anterior than the
posterior border of Sternocleidomastoideus—downward and medialward across the
sternoclavicular articulation and manubrium sterni until it meets, or almost meets,
its fellow of the other side at the midpoint of the junction between the manubrium
and body of the sternum. From this point the two lines run downward, prac-

tically along the midsternal line, as far as the level of the fourth costal cartilages. The continuation of the anterior border of the *right* lung is marked by a prolongation of its line vertically downward to the level of the sixth costal cartilage, and then it turns lateralward and downward. The line on the *left* side curves lateralward and downward across the fourth sternocostal articulation to reach the parasternal line at the fifth costal cartilage, and then turns medialward and downward to the sixth sternocostal articulation.

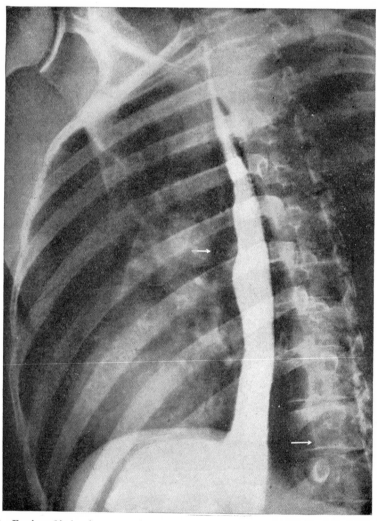

Fig. 1198.—Esophagus during the passage of a barium meal. Note that in the upper part of the esophagus longitudinal folds in the mucous membrane can be identified. The upper arrow points to the shadow of the right bronchus; the lower arrow indicates the tenth thoracic vertebra. Note that the lower part of the esophagus inclines forwards away from the vertebral column.

In the position of expiration the **lower border** of the lung may be marked by a slightly curved line with its convexity downward, from the sixth sternocostal junction to the tenth thoracic spinous process. This line crosses the mid-clavicular line at the sixth, and the midaxillary line at the eighth rib.

The **posterior borders** of the lungs are indicated by lines drawn from the level of the spinous process of the seventh cervical vertebra, down either side of the vertebral column, across the costovertebral joints, as low as the spinous process of the tenth thoracic vertebra.

The position of the **oblique fissure** in either lung can be shown by a line drawn from the spinous process of the second thoracic vertebra around the side of the thorax to the sixth rib in the mid-clavicular line; this line corresponds roughly to the line of the vertebral border of the scapula when the hand is placed on the top of the head. The **horizontal fissure** in the right lung is indicated by a line drawn from the midpoint of the preceding, or from the point where it cuts the midaxillary line, to the midsternal line at the level of the fourth costal cartilage.

Trachea.—This may be marked out on the back by a line from the spinous process of the sixth cervical to that of the fourth thoracic vertebra where it bifur-cates; from its bifurcation the two bronchi are directed downward and lateralward. In front, the point of bifurcation corresponds to the sternal angle.

Esophagus.—The extent of the esophagus may be indicated on the back by a line from the sixth cervical to the level of the ninth thoracic spinous process, 2.5 cm. to the left of the middle line.

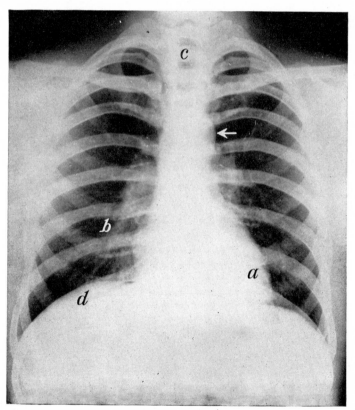

Fig. 1199.—Anterior view, thorax, heart, and diaphragm. *a*, Apex of heart; *b*, bronchi; *c*, trachea; *d*, diaphragm. The arrow points to the arch of the aorta. (Department of Radiology, University of Pennsylvania.)

Heart.—The outline of the heart in relation to the front of the thorax (Figs. 1196, 1200) can be represented by a quadrangular figure. The apex of the heart is first determined, either by its pulsation or as a point in the fifth interspace, 9 cm. to the left of the midsternal line. The other three points are: (*a*) the seventh right sternocostal articulation; (*b*) a point on the upper border of the third right costal cartilage 1 cm. from the right lateral sternal line; (*c*) a point on the lower border of the second left costal cartilage 2.5 cm. from the left lateral sternal line.

A line joining the apex to point (a) and traversing the junction of the body of the sternum with the xiphoid process represents the lowest limit of the heart—its acute margin. The right and left borders are represented respectively by lines joining (a) to (b) and the apex to (c); both lines are convex lateralward, but the convexity is more marked on the right where its summit is 4 cm. distant from the midsternal line opposite the fourth costal cartilage.

A portion of the area of the heart thus mapped out is uncovered by lung, and therefore gives a dull note on percussion; the remainder being overlapped by lung gives a more or less resonant note. The former is known as the area of superficial cardiac dulness, the latter as the area of deep cardiac dulness. The area of super-

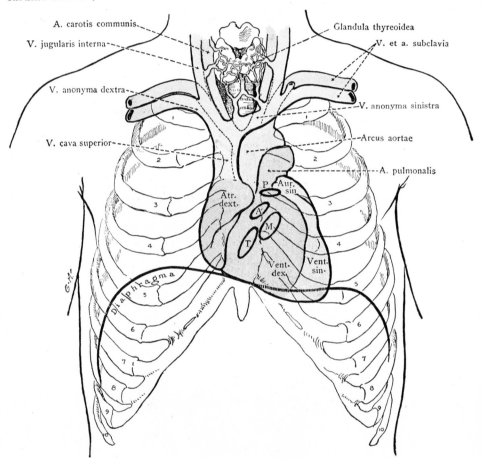

A. carotis communis.
V. jugularis interna
V. anonyma dextra
V. cava superior
Glandula thyreoidea
V. et a. subclavia
V. anonyma sinistra
Arcus aortae
A. pulmonalis
P Aur. sin
Atr. dext.
A
M
T
Vent. dex.
Vent. sin.
Diaphragma

Fig. 1200.—The heart and cardiac valves projected on the anterior chest wall, showing their relation to the ribs, sternum and diaphragm. (Eycleshymer and Jones.)

ficial cardiac dulness is somewhat triangular; from the apex of the heart two lines are drawn to the midsternal line, one to the level of the fourth costal cartilage, the other to the junction between the body and xiphoid process; the portion of the midsternal line between these points is the base of the triangle. Latham lays down the following rule as a sufficient practical guide for the definition of the area of superficial dulness. "Make a circle of two inches in diameter around a point midway between the nipple and the end of the sternum."

The **coronary sulcus** can be indicated by a line from the third left, to the sixth right, sternocostal joint. The **anterior longitudinal sulcus** is a finger's breadth to the right of the left margin of the heart.

The position of the various orifices is as follows: The **pulmonary orifice** is situated in the upper angle of the third left sternocostal articulation; the **aortic** **orifice** is a little below and medial to this, close to the articulation. The **left atrio-**

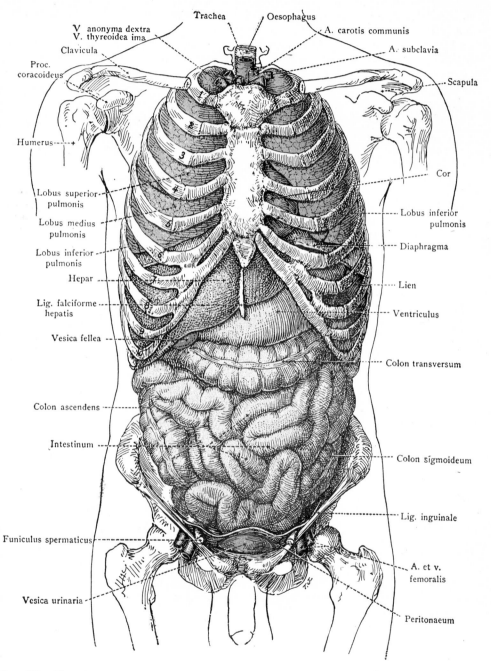

Trachea
Oesophagus
V. anonyma dextra
V. thyreoidea ima
A. carotis communis
Clavicula
A. subclavia
Proc. coracoideus
Scapula
Humerus
Cor
Lobus superior pulmonis
Lobus inferior pulmonis
Lobus medius pulmonis
Diaphragma
Lobus inferior pulmonis
Lien
Hepar
Ventriculus
Lig. falciforme hepatis
Vesica fellea
Colon transversum
Colon ascendens
Intestinum
Colon sigmoideum
Lig. inguinale
Funiculus spermaticus
A. et v. femoralis
Vesica urinaria
Peritonaeum

F\ıg. 1201.—Thoracic and abdominal viscera shown in their norma relations to the skeleton. Anterior view. (Eycleshymer and Jones.)

ventricular opening is opposite the fourth costal cartilage, and rather to the left of the midsternal line; the **right atrioventricular opening** is a little lower, opposite the fourth interspace of the right side. The lines indicating the atrioventricular openings are slightly below and parallel to the line of the coronary sulcus.

Arteries.—The line of the **ascending aorta** begins slightly to the left of the midsternal line opposite the third costal cartilage and extends upward and to the right to the upper border of the second right costal cartilage. The beginning of the **aortic arch** is indicated by a line from this latter point to the midsternal line about 2.5 cm. below the jugular notch. The point on the midsternal line is opposite the summit of the arch, and a line from it to the right sternoclavicular articulation represents the site of the **innominate artery,** while another line from a point slightly to the left of it and passing through the left sternoclavicular articulation indicates the position of the **left common carotid artery** in the thorax.

The **internal mammary artery** descends behind the first six costal cartilages about 1 cm. from the lateral sternal line.

Veins.—The line of the **right innominate vein** crosses the right sternoclavicular joint and the upper border of the first right costal cartilage about 1 cm. from the lateral sternal line; that of the **left innominate vein** extends from the left sternoclavicular articulation to meet the right at the upper border of the first right costal cartilage. The junction of the two lines indicates the origin of the **superior vena cava,** the line of which is continued vertically down to the level of the third right costal cartilage. The end of the **inferior vena cava** is situated opposite the upper margin of the sixth right costal cartilage about 2 cm. from the midsternal line.

SURFACE ANATOMY OF THE ABDOMEN.

Skin.—The skin of the front of the abdomen is thin. In the male it is often thickly hair-clad, especially toward the lower part of the middle line; in the female the hairs are confined to the pubes. Just below the line of the iliac crest, especially marked in fat subjects, is a shallow groove termed the **iliac furrow,** while in the site of the inguinal ligament a sharper fold known as the **fold of the groin** is easily distinguishable.

After distension of the abdomen from pregnancy or other causes the skin commonly presents transverse white lines which are quite smooth, being destitute of papillæ; these are known as **striæ gravidarum** or **striæ albicantes.** The **linea nigra** of pregnancy is often seen as a pigmented brown streak in the middle line between the umbilicus and symphysis pubis.

In the middle line of the front of the abdomen is a shallow furrow which extends from the junction between the body of the sternum with the xiphoid process to a short distance below the umbilicus; it corresponds to the linea alba. The umbilicus is situated in the middle line, but it varies in position as regards its height; in an adult subject it is always placed above the middle point of the body, and in a normal well-nourished subject is from 2 to 2.5 cm. above the level of the tubercles of the iliac crests.

Bones.—The bones in relation with the surface of the abdomen are (1) the lower part of the vertebral column and the lower ribs and (2) the pelvis; the former have already been described (page 1369), the latter will be considered with the lower limb.

Muscles (Fig. 1205).—The only muscles of the abdomen which have any considerable influence on surface form are the Obliquus externus and the Rectus. The upper digitations of origin of **Obliquus externus** are well-marked in a muscular subject, interdigitating with those of Serratus anterior; the lower digitations are covered by the border of Latissimus dorsi and are not visible. The attachment of the Obliqui externus and internus to the crest of the ilium forms a thick oblique roll which determines the iliac furrow. Sometimes on the front of the lateral region of the abdomen an undulating line marks the passing of the muscular fibers of the

Obliquus externus into its aponeurosis. The lateral margin of the Obliquus externus is separated from that of the Latissimus dorsi by a small triangular interval—the **lumbar triangle**—the base of which is formed by the iliac crest, and its floor by Obliquus internus.

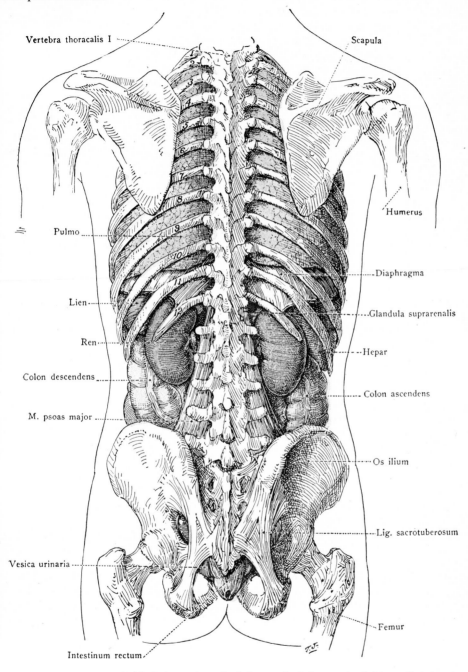

Vertebra thoracalis I

Scapula

Humerus

Pulmo

Diaphragma

Lien

Glandula suprarenalis

Ren

Hepar

Colon descendens

Colon ascendens

M. psoas major

Os ilium

Lig. sacrotuberosum

Vesica urinaria

Femur

Intestinum rectum

FIG. 1202.—Thoracic and abdominal viscera shown in their normal relations to the skeleton. Posterior view. (Eycleshymer and Jones.)

The lateral margin of **Rectus abdominis** is indicated by the **linea semilunaris,** which may be exactly defined by putting the muscle into action. The surface of

87

the Rectus presents three transverse furrows, the **tendinous inscriptions**: the upper two of these, viz., one opposite, or a little below, the tip of the xiphoid process, and the other midway between this point and the umbilicus, are usually well-

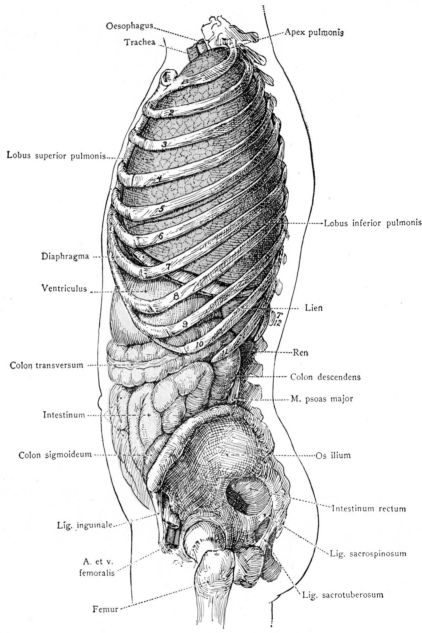

Fig. 1203.—Thoracic and abdominal viscera shown in their normal relations to the skeleton, from the left side. (Eycleshymer and Jones.)

marked; the third, opposite the umbilicus, is not so distinct. Between the two Recti the linea alba can be palpated from the xiphoid process to a point just below the umbilicus; it is represented by a distinct dip between the muscles: beyond this the muscles are in apposition.

Vessels.—In thin subjects the pulsation of the **abdominal aorta** can be readily

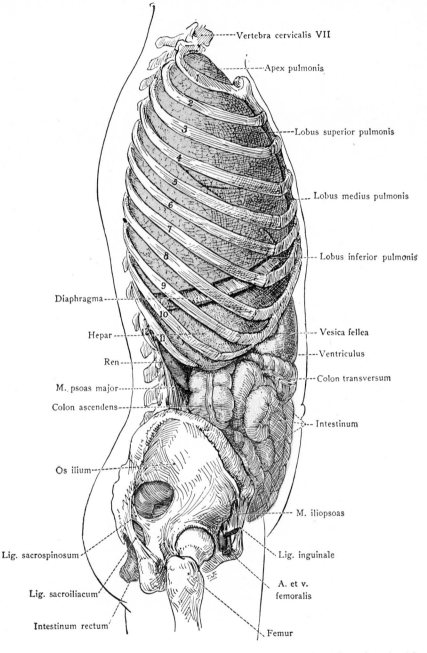

Vertebra cervicalis VII

Apex pulmonis

Lobus superior pulmonis

Lobus medius pulmonis

Lobus inferior pulmonis

Diaphragma

Hepar

Ren

M. psoas major

Colon ascendens

Vesica fellea

Ventriculus

Colon transversum

Intestinum

Os ilium

M. iliopsoas

Lig. sacrospinosum

Lig. inguinale

A. et v. femoralis

Lig. sacroiliacum

Intestinum rectum

Femur

Fig. 1204.—Thoracic and abdominal viscera shown in their normal relations to the skeleton, from the right side. (Eycleshymer and Jones.)

felt by making deep pressure in the middle line above the umbilicus.

Viscera.—Under normal conditions the various portions of the **digestive tube** cannot be identified by simple palpation. Peristalsis of the coils of small intestine

can be observed in some persons with extremely thin abdominal walls when some
degree of constipation exists.   In cases of constipation it is sometimes possible to
trace portions of the great intestine by feeling the fecal masses within the gut.
In thin persons with relaxed abdominal walls the iliac colon can be felt in the left

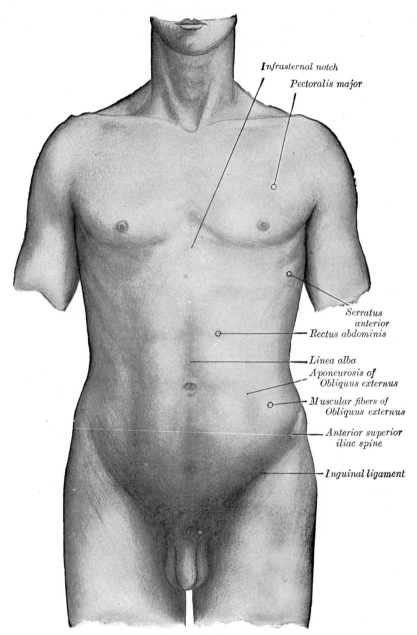

Infrasternal notch

Pectoralis major

*Serratus
anterior*

Rectus abdominis

Linea alba

*Aponeurosis of
Obliquus externus*

*Muscular fibers of
Obliquus externus*

*Anterior superior
iliac spine*

Inguinal ligament

Fig. 1205.—Surface anatomy of the front of the thorax and abdomen.

iliac region—rolling under the fingers when empty and forming a distinct tumor
when distended.
    The greater part of the **liver** lies under cover of the lower ribs and their cartilages,
but in the epigastric fossa it comes in contact with the abdominal wall.   The

position of the liver varies according to the posture of the body. In the erect posture in the adult male the edge of the liver projects about 1 cm. below the lower margin of the right costal cartilages, and its inferior margin can often be felt in this situation if the abdominal wall is thin. In the supine position the liver recedes above the margin of the ribs and cannot then be detected by the finger; in the prone position it falls forward and is then generally palpable in a patient with loose and lax abdominal walls. Its position varies with the respiratory movements; during a deep inspiration it descends below the ribs; in expiration it is raised. Pressure from without, as in tight lacing, by compressing the lower part of the chest, displaces the liver considerably, its anterior edge frequently extending as low as the crest of the ilium. Again its position varies greatly with the state of the stomach and intestines; when these are empty the liver descends, when they are distended it is pushed upward.

The **pancreas** can sometimes be felt, in emaciated subjects, when the stomach and colon are empty, by making deep pressure in the middle line about 7 or 8 cm. above the umbilicus.

The **kidneys** being situated at the back of the abdominal cavity and deeply placed cannot be palpated unless enlarged or misplaced.

SURFACE MARKINGS OF THE ABDOMEN.

Bony Landmarks.—Above, the chief bony markings are the xiphoid process, the lower six costal cartilages, and the anterior ends of the lower six ribs. The junction between the body of the sternum and the xiphoid process is on the level of the tenth thoracic vertebra. Below, the main landmarks are the symphysis pubis and the pubic crest and tubercle, the anterior superior iliac spine, and the iliac crest.

Muscles (Fig. 1205).—The **Rectus** lies between the linea alba and the linea semilunaris; the former is indicated by the middle line, the latter by a curved line, convex lateralward, from the tip of the cartilage of the ninth rib to the pubic tubercle; at the level of the umbilicus the linea semilunaris is about 7 cm. from the middle line. The line indicating the junction of the muscular fibers of **Obliquus externus** with its aponeurosis extends from the tip of the ninth costal cartilage to a point just medial to the anterior superior iliac spine.

The **umbilicus** is at the level of the fibrocartilage between the third and fourth lumbar vertebræ.

The **subcutaneous inguinal ring** is situated 1 cm. above and lateral to the pubic tubercle; the **abdominal inguinal ring** lies 1 to 2 cm. above the middle of the inguinal ligament. The position of the **inguinal canal** is indicated by a line joining these two points.

Surface Lines.—For convenience of description of the viscera and of reference to morbid conditions of the contained parts, the abdomen is divided into nine regions, by imaginary planes, two horizontal and two sagittal, the edges of the planes being indicated by lines drawn on the surface of the body (Fig. 1206). In the older method the upper, or subcostal, horizontal line encircles the body at the level of the lowest points of the tenth costal cartilages; the lower, or intertubercular, is a line carried through the highest points of the iliac crests seen from the front, *i. e.*, through the tubercles on the iliac crests about 5 cm. behind the anterior superior spines. An alternative method is that of Addison, who adopts the following lines: (1) An upper transverse, the **transpyloric**, halfway between the jugular notch and the upper border of the symphysis pubis; this indicates the margin of the transpyloric plane, which in most cases cuts through the pylorus, the tips of the ninth costal cartilages and the lower border of the first lumbar vertebra; (2) a lower transverse line termed the **transtubercular**, since it practically corresponds to that passing through the iliac tubercles; behind, its plane cuts the body of the fifth lumbar vertebra.

By means of these horizontal planes the abdomen is divided into three zones named from above, the **subcostal, umbilical,** and **hypogastric zones.** Each of these is further subdivided into three regions by the two sagittal planes, which are indi-

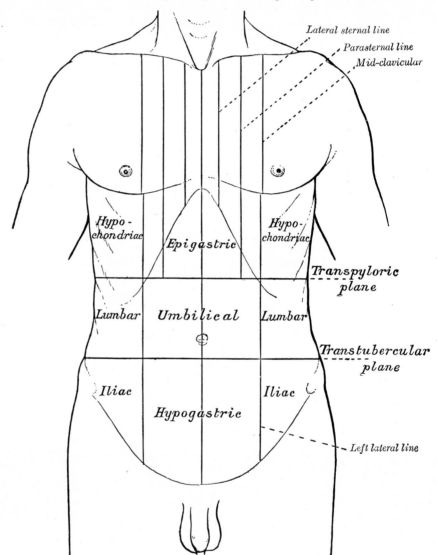

Fig. 1206.—Surface lines of the front of the thorax and abdomen.

cated on the surface by a right and a left lateral line drawn vertically through points halfway between the anterior-superior iliac spines and the middle line. The middle region of the upper zone is called the **epigastric,** and the two lateral regions the **right** and **left hypochondriac.** The central region of the middle zone is the **umbilical,** and the two lateral regions the **right** and **left lumbar.** The middle region of the lower zone is the **hypogastric** or **pubic,** and the lateral are the **right** and **left iliac** or **inguinal.** The middle regions, viz., **epigastric, umbilical,** and **pubic,** can each be divided into right and left portions by the middle line. In the following description of the viscera the regions marked out by Addison's lines are those referred to.

Stomach (Fig. 1207).—The shape of the stomach is constantly undergoing alteration; it is affected by the particular phase of the process of gastric digestion, by the state of the surrounding viscera, and by the amount and character of its contents. Its position also varies with that of the body, so that it is impossible to indicate it on the surface with any degree of accuracy. The measurements given refer to a moderately filled stomach with the body in the supine position. (See page 1209.)

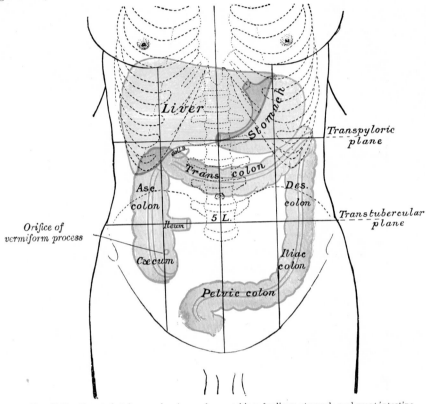

Fig. 1207.—Front of abdomen, showing surface markings for liver, stomach, and great intestine.

The cardiac orifice is opposite the seventh left costal cartilage about 2.5 cm. from the side of the sternum; it corresponds to the level of the tenth thoracic vertebra. The pyloric orifice is on the transpyloric line about 1 cm. to the right of the middle line, or alternately 5 cm. below the seventh right sternocostal articulation; it is at the level of the first lumbar vertebra. A curved line, convex downward and to the left, joining these points indicates the lesser curvature. In the left lateral line the fundus of the stomach reaches as high as the fifth interspace or the sixth costal cartilage, a little below the apex of the heart. To indicate the greater curvature a curved line is drawn from the cardiac orifice to the summit of the fundus, thence downward and to the left, finally turning medialward to the pyloric orifice, but passing, on its way, through the intersection of the left lateral with the transpyloric line. The portion of the stomach which is in contact with the abdominal wall can be represented roughly by a triangular area the base of which is formed by a line drawn from the tip of the tenth left costal cartilage to the tip of the ninth right cartilage, and the sides by two lines drawn from the end of the eighth left costal cartilage to the ends of the base line.

A space of some clinical importance—the **space of Traube**—overlies the stomach and may be thus indicated. It is semilunar in outline and lies within the following boundaries: the lower edge of the left lung, the anterior border of the spleen, the left costal margin and the inferior margin of the left lobe of the liver.

Duodenum (Fig. 1215).—The superior part is horizontal and extends from the pylorus to the right lateral line; the descending part is situated medial to the right lateral line, from the transpyloric line to a point midway between the transpyloric and transtubercular lines. The horizontal part runs with a slight upward slope from the end of the descending part to the left of the middle line; the ascending part is vertical, and reaches the transpyloric line, where it ends in the duodeno-jejunal flexure, about 2.5 cm. to the left of the middle line.

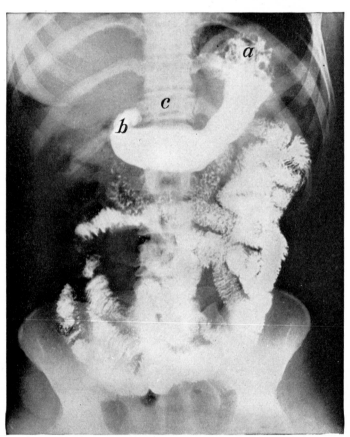

Fig. 1208.—Stomach and small intestines after a barium meal. *a*, Barium has settled out of the fundus of the stomach; *b*, pylorus; *c*, thoracic vertebra XII. (Department of Radiology, University of Pennsylvania.)

Small Intestine.—The coils of small intestine occupy the front of the abdomen. For the most part the coils of the jejunum are situated on the left side, *i. e.*, in the left lumbar and iliac regions, and in the left half of the umbilical region. The coils of the ileum lie toward the right in the right lumbar and iliac regions, in the right half of the umbilical region, and in the hypogastric region; a portion of the ileum is within the pelvis. The end of the ileum, *i. e.*, the **ileocolic junction**, is slightly below and medial to the intersection of the right lateral and transtubercular lines.

Cecum and Vermiform Process.—The **cecum** is in the right iliac and hypogastric regions; its position varies with its degree of distension, but the midpoint

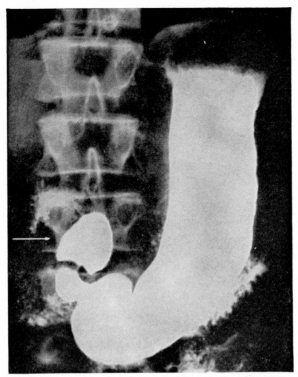

Fig. 1209.—Normal stomach after a barium meal. The tone of the muscular wall is good and supports the weight of the column in the body of the organ. The arrow points to the duodenal cap, below which a gap in the barium indicates the position of the pylorus.

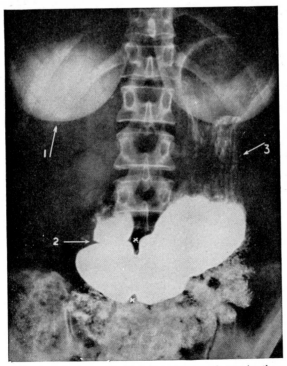

Fig. 1210.—Atonic stomach after a barium meal. Note that this stomach contains the same amount of barium as the stomach in Fig. 1209. Arrow *1* points to the shadow of the right breast; arrow *2*, to the pylorus; arrow *3*, to the upper part of the body of the stomach, where longitudinal folds can be seen in the mucous membrane. ✕✕ marks a wave of peristalsis.

of a line drawn from the right anterior-superior iliac spine to the upper margin of the symphysis pubis will mark approximately the middle of its lower border.

The position of the base of the **vermiform process** is indicated by a point on the lateral line on a level with the anterior superior iliac spine.

Ascending Colon.—The ascending colon passes upward through the right lumbar region, lateral to the right lateral line. The **right colic flexure** is situated in the upper and right angle of intersection of the subcostal and right lateral lines.

Transverse Colon.—The transverse colon crosses the abdomen on the confines of the umbilical and epigastric regions, its lower border being on a level slightly

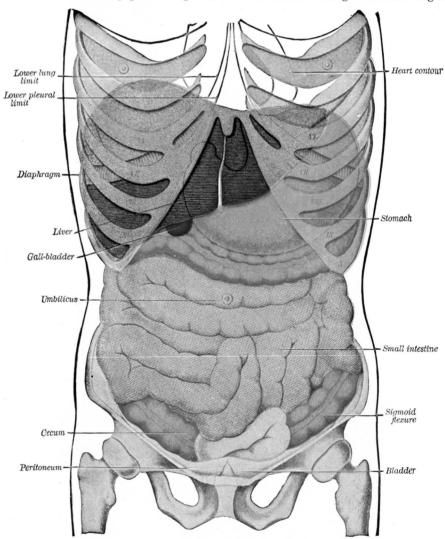

Fig. 1211.—Topography of thoracic and abdominal viscera.

above the umbilicus, its upper border just below the greater curvature of the stomach.

Descending Colon.—The **left colic flexure** is situated in the upper left angle of the intersection between the left lateral and transpyloric lines. The descending colon courses down through the left lumbar region, lateral to the left lateral line, as far as the iliac crest.

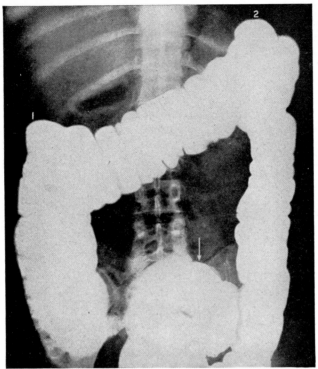

Fig. 1212.—Large intestine after a barium enema. *1,* Right colic flexure; *2,* left colic flexure. The arrow points to the pelvic colon. Note the sacculations of the gut, and the different levels of the two flexures.

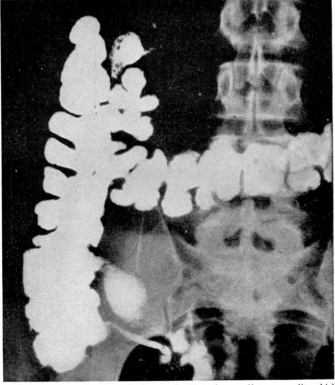

Fig. 1213.—Part of the large intestine after a barium meal. Note the vermiform appendix, which passes from the medial side of the cæcum medially and slightly downwards into the true pelvis. At a slightly higher level the terminal part of the ileum can be recognized. The first part of the transverse colon runs downwards in front of, and slightly medial to, the ascending colon, before it turns to the left.

Iliac Colon.—The line of the iliac colon is from the end of the descending colon to the left lateral line at the level of the anterior-superior iliac spine.

Liver (Fig. 1207).—The upper limit of the right lobe of the liver, in the middle line, is at the level of the junction between the body of the sternum and the xiphoid process; on the right side the line must be carried upward as far as the fifth costal cartilage in the mammary line, and then downward to reach the seventh rib at the side of the thorax. The upper limit of the left lobe can be defined by continuing this line downward and to the left to the sixth costal cartilage, 5 cm. from the middle line. The lower limit can be indicated by a line drawn 1 cm. below the lower margin of the thorax on the right side as far as the ninth costal cartilage, thence obliquely upward to the eighth left costal cartilage, crossing the middle line just above the transpyloric plane and finally, with a slight left convexity, to the end of the line indicating the upper limit.

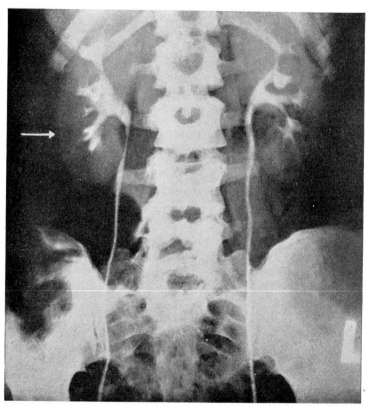

Fig. 1214.—Ureters, pelves and minor calyces after intravenous injection of uroselectan. Note cupping of minor calyces; the relation of the ureter to the transverse processes of the lumbar vertebræ, and the Psoas major. The arrow points to the shadow of the right kidney. Anterior view.

According to Birmingham the limits of the normal liver may be marked out on the surface of the body in the following manner. Take three points: (*a*) 1.25 cm. below the right nipple; (*b*) 1.25 cm. below the tip of the tenth rib; (*c*) 2.5 cm. below the left nipple. Join (*a*) and (*c*) by a line slightly convex upward; (*a*) and (*b*) by a line slightly convex lateralward; and (*b*) and (*c*) by a line slightly convex downward.

The fundus of the **gall-bladder** approaches the surface behind the anterior end of the ninth right costal cartilage close to the lateral margin of the Rectus abdominis.

Pancreas (Fig. 1215).—The pancreas lies in front of the second lumbar vertebra. Its head occupies the curve of the duodenum and is therefore indicated by the same lines as that viscus; its neck corresponds to the pylorus. Its body extends along the transpyloric line, the bulk of it lying above this line to the tail which is in the left hypochondriac region slightly to the left of the lateral line and above the transpyloric.

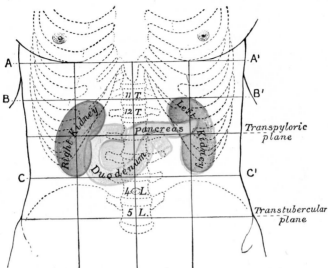

Fig. 1215.—Front of abdomen, showing surface markings for duodenum, pancreas, and kidneys. *A A'*. Plane through joint between body and xiphoid process of sternum. *B B'*. Plane midway between *A A'* and transpyloric plane. *C C'*. Plane midway between transpyloric and transtubercular planes.

Spleen (Figs. 1197, 1216).—To map out the spleen the tenth rib is taken as representing its long axis; vertically it is situated between the upper border of the ninth and the lower border of the eleventh ribs. The highest point is 4 cm. from the middle line of the back at the level of the tip of the ninth thoracic spinous

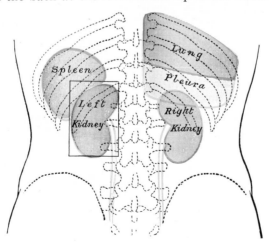

Fig. 1216.—Back of lumbar region, showing surface markings for kidneys, ureters, and spleen. The lower portions of the lung and pleura are shown on the right side.

process; the lowest point is in the midaxillary line at the level of the first lumbar spinous process.

Kidneys (Figs. 1215, 1216).— The right kidney usually lies about 1 cm. lower than the left, but for practical purposes similar surface markings are taken for each.

On the front of the abdomen the upper pole lies midway between the plane of the lower end of the body of the sternum and the transpyloric plane, 5 cm. from the middle line. The lower pole is situated midway between the transpyloric and intertubercular planes, 7 cm. from the middle line. The hilum is on the transpyloric plane, 5 cm. from the middle line. Round these three points a kidney-shaped figure 4 cm. to 5 cm. broad is drawn, two-thirds of which lies medial to the lateral line. To indicate the position of the kidney from the back, the parallelogram of Morris is used; two vertical lines are drawn, the first 2.5 cm.,

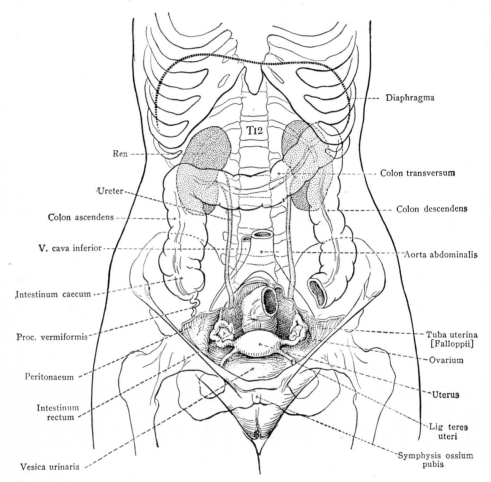

Fig. 1217.—Projection showing the average position of the abdominal and pelvic viscera in the female. Anterior view. (Eycleshymer and Jones.)

the second 9.5 cm. from the middle line; the parallelogram is completed by two horizontal lines drawn respectively at the levels of the tips of the spinous process of the eleventh thoracic and the lower border of the spinous process of the third lumbar vertebra. The hilum is 5 cm. from the middle line at the level of the spinous process of the first lumbar vertebra.

Ureters.—On the front of the abdomen, the line of the ureter runs from the hilum of the kidney to the pubic tubercle; on the back, from the hilum vertically downward, passing practically through the posterior-superior iliac spine (Fig. 1216).

Vessels (Fig. 1219).—The **inferior epigastric artery** can be marked out by a line from a point midway between the anterior-superior iliac spine and the pubic symphysis to the umbilicus. This line also indicates the lateral boundary of **Hesselbach's triangle**—an area of importance in connection with inguinal hernia; the other boundaries are the lateral edge of Rectus abdominis, and the medial half of the inguinal ligament. The line of the **abdominal aorta** begins in the middle line about 4 cm. above the transpyloric line and extends to a point 2 cm. below and

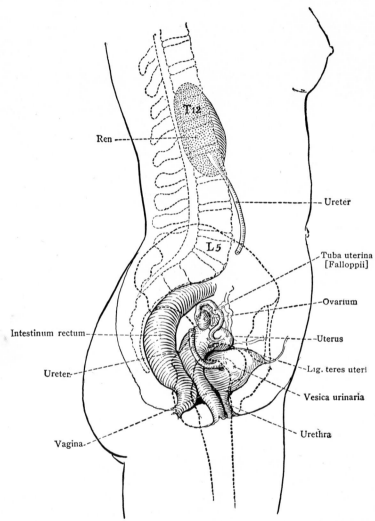

F_{IG}. 1218.—Projection showing the average position of the female pelvic organs. **Lateral view.** (Eycleshymer and Jones.)

to the left of the umbilicus—or more accurately to a point 2 cm. to the left of the middle line on a line which passes through the highest points of the iliac crests (*A A′*, Fig. 1219). The point of termination of the abdominal aorta corresponds to the level of the fourth lumbar vertebra; a line drawn from it to a point midway between the anterior superior iliac spine and the symphysis pubis indicates the common and external iliac arteries. The **common iliac** is represented by the upper third of this line, the **external iliac** by the remaining two-thirds.

Of the larger branches of the abdominal aorta, the **celiac artery is** 4 cm., the **superior mesenteric** 2 cm. above the transpyloric line; the **renal arteries** are 2 cm. below the same line. The **inferior mesenteric** artery is 4 cm. above the bifurcation of the abdominal aorta.

Nerves.—The thoracic nerves on the anterior abdominal wall are represented by lines continuing those of the bony ribs. The termination of the seventh nerve is at the level of the xiphoid process, the tenth reaches the vicinity of the umbilicus, the twelfth ends about midway between the umbilicus and the upper border of the symphysis pubis. The first lumbar is parallel to the thoracic nerves; its iliohypogastric branch becomes cutaneous above the subcutaneous inguinal ring; its ilioinguinal branch at the ring.

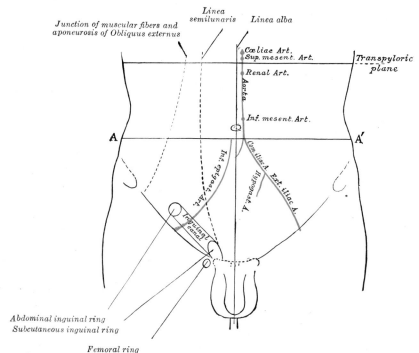

Fig. 1219.—The front of the abdomen, showing the surface markings for the arteries and the inguinal canal. The line A, A' is drawn at the level of the highest points of the iliac crests.

SURFACE ANATOMY OF THE PERINEUM.

Skin.—In the middle line of the posterior part of the perineum and about 4 cm. in front of the tip of the coccyx is the anal orifice. The junction of the mucous membrane of the anal canal with the skin of the perineum is marked by a white line which indicates also the line of contact of the external and internal Sphincters. In the anterior part of the perineum the external genital organs are situated. The skin covering the scrotum is rough and corrugated, but over the penis it is smooth; extending forward from the anus on to the scrotum and penis is a median ridge which indicates the scrotal raphé. In the **female** are seen the skin reduplications forming the labia majora and minora laterally, the frenulum of the labia behind, and the prepuce of the clitoris in front; still more anteriorly is the mons pubis.

Bones.—In the antero-lateral boundaries of the perineum, the whole outline of the pubic arch can be readily traced ending in the ischial tuberosities. Behind in the middle line is the tip of the coccyx.

Muscles and Ligaments.—The margin of the **Glutæus maximus** forms the postero-lateral boundary, and in thin subjects, by pressing deeply, the sacrotuberous ligament can be felt through the muscle. The only other muscles influencing surface form are the **Ischiocavernosus** covering the crus penis, which lies on the side of the pubic arch, and the **Sphincter ani externus**, which, in action, closes the anal orifice and causes a puckering of the skin around it.

SURFACE MARKINGS OF THE PERINEUM.

A line drawn transversely across in front of the ischial tuberosities divides the perineum into a posterior or rectal, and an anterior or urogenital, triangle. This line passes through the central point of the perineum, which is situated about 2.5 cm. in front of the center of the anal aperture or, in the male, midway between the anus and the reflection of the skin on to the scrotum.

Rectum and Anal Canal.—A finger inserted through the anal orifice is grasped by the Sphincter ani externus, passes into the region of the Sphincter ani internus, and higher up encounters the resistance of the Puborectalis; beyond this it may reach the lowest of the transverse rectal folds. In front, the urethral bulb and membranous part of the urethra are first identified, and then about 4 cm. above the anal orifice the prostate is felt; beyond this the vesiculæ seminales, if enlarged, and the fundus of the bladder, when distended, can be recognized. On either side is the ischiorectal fossa. Behind are the anococcygeal body, the pelvic surfaces of the coccyx and lower end of the sacrum, and the sacrospinous ligaments (Fig. 1121).

In the female the posterior wall and fornix of the vagina, and the cervix and body of the uterus can be felt in front, while somewhat laterally the ovaries can just be reached.

Male Urogenital Organs (Fig. 1118).—The **corpora cavernosa penis** can be followed backward to the crura which are attached to the sides of the pubic arch. The **glans penis**, covered by the prepuce, and the external urethral orifice can be examined, and the course of the urethra traced along the under surface of the penis to the bulb which is situated immediately in front of the central point of the perineum. Through the wall of the **scrotum** on either side the **testis** can be palpated; it lies toward the back of the scrotum, and along its posterior border the **epididymis** can be felt; passing upward along the medial side of the epididymis is the **spermatic cord**, which can be traced upward to the subcutaneous inguinal ring.

By means of a sound the general topography of the urethra and bladder can be investigated; with the urethroscope the interior of the urethra can be illuminated and viewed directly; with the cystoscope the interior of the bladder is in a similar manner illuminated for visual examination. In the bladder the main points to which attention is directed are the **trigone**, the **torus uretericus**, the **plicæ uretericæ**, and the openings of the **ureters** and **urethra** (see Fig. 1122).

Female Urogenital Organs.—In the **pudendal cleft** (Fig. 1154) between the labia minora are the openings of the **vagina** and **urethra**. In the virgin the vaginal opening is partly closed by the **hymen**—after coitus the remains of the hymen are represented by the carunculæ hymenales. Between the hymen and the frenulum of the labia is the **fossa navicularis**, while in the groove between the hymen and the labium minus, on either side, the small opening of the **greater vestibular** (*Bartholin's*) **gland** can be seen. These glands when enlarged can be felt on either side of the posterior part of the vaginal orifice. By inserting a finger into the vagina the following structures can be examined through its wall (Fig. 1150). Behind, from below upward, are the **anal canal**, the **rectum**, and the **rectouterine excavation**. Projecting into the roof of the vagina is the vaginal portion of the cervix uteri with the external uterine orifice; in front of and behind the cervix the anterior and posterior **vaginal fornices** respectively can be examined. With the finger in the vagina and the other hand on the abdominal wall the whole of the **cervix** and body of the uterus, the uterine tubes, and the ovaries can be palpated. If a speculum be introduced into the vagina, the walls of the passage, the vaginal portion of the cervix, and the external uterine orifice can all be exposed for visual examination.

The external urethral orifice lies in front of the vaginal opening; the angular gap in which it is situated between the two converging labia minora is termed the vestibule. The urethral canal in the female is very dilatable and can be explored with the finger. About 2.5 cm. in front of the external orifice of the urethra are the glans and prepuce of the clitoris, and still farther forward is the mons pubis.

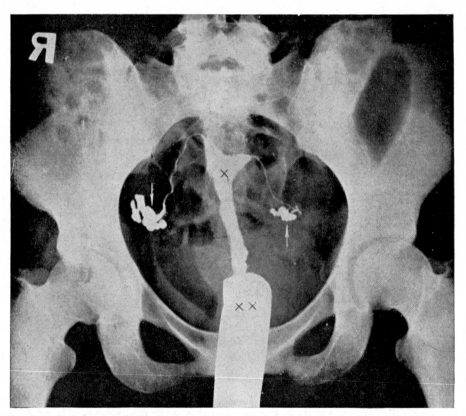

Fig. 1220.—Genital tract in the female, after an injection of barium sulphate into the uterus. ✕, Body of uterus. Note the two cornua leading to the uterine tubes. ✕✕, Speculum in vagina. The arrows indicate the infundibula of the uterine tubes. Some of the barium has passed through the pelvic opening of the tube into the general peritoneal cavity.

SURFACE ANATOMY OF THE UPPER EXTREMITY.

Skin.—The skin covering the shoulder and arm is smooth and very movable on the underlying structures. In the axilla there are numerous hairs and many sudoriferous and sebaceous glands. Over the medial side and front of the forearm the skin is thin and smooth, and contains few hairs but many sudoriferous glands; over the lateral side and back of the arm and forearm it is thicker, denser, and contains more hairs but fewer sudoriferous glands. In the region of the olecranon it is thick and rough, and is very loosely connected to the underlying tissue so that it falls into transverse wrinkles when the forearm is extended. At the front of the wrist there are three transverse furrows in the skin; they correspond respectively from above downward to the positions of the styloid process of the ulna, the wrist-joint, and the midcarpal joint.

The skin of the palm of the hand differs considerably from that of the forearm. At the wrist it suddenly becomes hard and dense and covered with a thick layer of epidermis; on the thenar eminence these characteristics are less marked than elsewhere. In spite of its hardness and density the skin of the palm is exceedingly sensitive and very vascular, but it is destitute of hairs and sebaceous glands. It is tied down by fibrous bands along the lines of flexion of the digits, exhibiting certain furrows of a permanent character. One of these, starting in front of the wrist at the tuberosity of the navicular bone, curves around the thenar eminence and ends on the radial border of the hand a little above the metacarpophalangeal joint of the index finger. A second line begins at the end of the first and extends obliquely across the palm to reach the ulnar border about the middle of the fifth metacarpal bone. A third line begins at the ulnar border about 2.5 cm. distal to the end of the second and extends across the heads of the fifth, fourth, and third

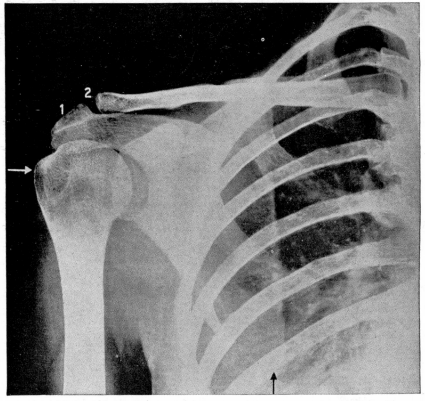

FIG. 1221.—Adult shoulder. *1*, Acromion; *2*, acromio-clavicular joint. The lower arrow indicates the inferior angle of the scapula, the upper arrow the greater tuberosity. Note that the shadow of the head of the humerus overlaps the shadow of the acromial angle and a part of the glenoid cavity.

metacarpal bones. The proximal segments of the fingers are joined to one another on the volar aspect by folds of skin constituting the "web" of the fingers; these folds extend across about the level of the centers of the proximal phalanges and their free margins are continuous with the transverse furrows at the roots of the fingers. Since the web is confined to the volar aspect the fingers appear shorter when viewed from in front than from behind.

Over the fingers and thumb the skin again becomes thinner, especially at the flexures of the joints (where it is crossed by transverse furrows) and over the terminal phalanges; it is disposed on numerous ridges in consequence of the arrangement of the papillæ in it. These ridges form, in different individuals, distinctive and permanent patterns which can be used for purposes of identification. The superficial fascia in the palm of the hand is made up of dense fibro-fatty tissue which binds the skin so firmly to the palmar aponeurosis that very little movement is permitted between the two.

On the back of the hand and fingers the subcutaneous tissue is lax, so that the skin is freely movable on the underlying parts. Over the interphalangeal joints the skin is very loose and is thrown into transverse wrinkles when the fingers are extended.

Bones.—The **clavicle** can be felt throughout its entire length. The enlarged sternal extremity projects above the upper margin of the sternum at the side of the jugular notch, and from this the body of the bone can be traced lateralward immediately under the skin. The medial part is convex forward, but the surface

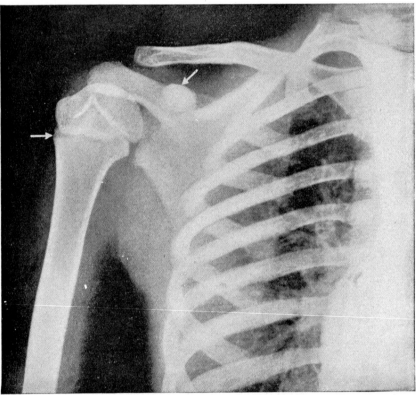

Fig. 1222.—Shoulder of a child aged six years. The upper arrow indicates the coracoid process; the lower arrow indicates the epiphyseal line. Note that the upper end of the diaphysis is conical and projects into the center of the epiphysis. The centers for the head of the humerus and the tuberosities have fused to form a single epiphysis.

is partially obscured by the attachments of Sternocleidomastoideus and Pectoralis major; the lateral third is concave forward and ends at the acromion of the scapula in a slight enlargement. The clavicle is almost horizontal when the arm is lying by the side, although in muscular subjects it may incline a little upward at its acromial end, which is on a plane posterior to the sternal end.

The only parts of the **scapula** that are truly subcutaneous are the spine and acromion, but the coracoid process, the vertebral border, the inferior angle, and to a lesser extent the axillary border can also be readily defined. The acromion and spine are easily recognizable throughout their entire extent, forming with the clavicle the arch of the shoulder. The acromion forms the point of the shoulder; it joins the clavicle at an acute angle—the acromial angle—slightly medial to, and behind the tip of the acromion. The spine can be felt as a distinct ridge, marked on the surface as an oblique depression which becomes less distinct and ends in a slight dimple a little lateral to the spinous processes of the vertebræ. Below this

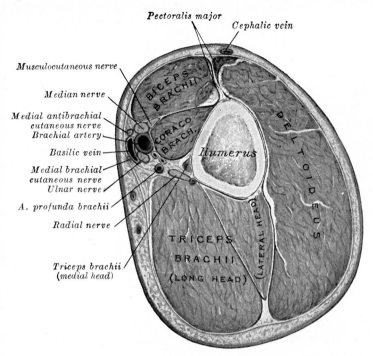

Fig. 1223.—Transverse section through the arm at the junction of the proximal with the intermediate one-third of the humerus.

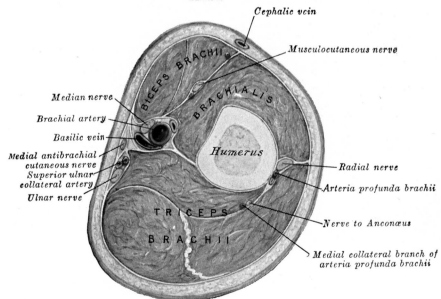

Fig. 1224.—Transverse section through the arm, a little below the middle of the body of the humerus.

point the vertebral border can be traced downward and lateralward to the inferior angle, which can be identified although covered by Latissimus dorsi. From the inferior angle the axillary border can usually be traced upward through its thick muscular covering, forming with its enveloping muscles the posterior fold of the axilla. The coracoid process is situated about 2 cm. below the junction of the intermediate and lateral thirds of the clavicle; it is covered by the anterior border of Deltoideus, and thus lies a little lateral to the infraclavicular fossa or depression which marks the interval between the Pectoralis major and Deltoideus.

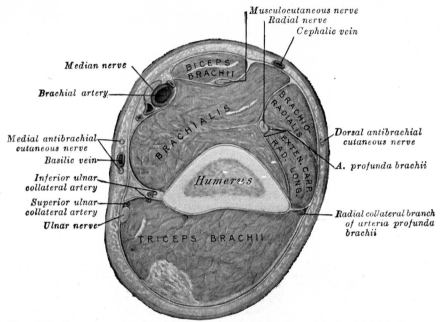

FIG. 1225.—Transverse section through the arm, 2 cm. proximal to the medial epicondyle of the humerus.

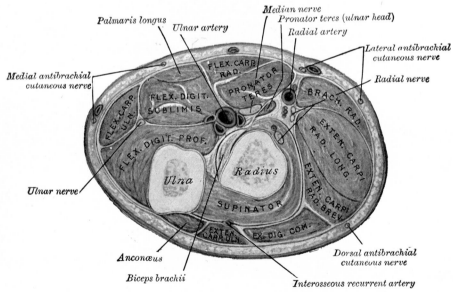

FIG. 1226.—Transverse section through the forearm at the level of the radial (bicipital) tuberosity.

The **humerus** is almost entirely surrounded by muscles, and the only parts which are strictly subcutaneous are small portions of the medial and lateral epicondyles; in addition to these, however, the tubercles and a part of the head of the bone can be felt under the skin and muscles by which they are covered. Of these, the greater tubercle forms the most prominent bony point of the shoulder, extending beyond the acromion; it is best recognized when the arm is lying passive by the side, for if the arm be raised it recedes under the arch of the shoulder. The lesser tubercle, directed forward, is medial to the greater and separated from it by the intertubercular groove, which can be made out by deep pressure. When the arm is abducted the lower part of the head of the humerus can be examined by pressing deeply in the axilla. On either side of the elbow-joint and just above it are the medial and lateral epicondyles. Of these, the former is the more prominent, but the medial supracondylar ridge passing upward from it is much less marked than the lateral, and as a rule is not palpable; occasionally, however, the hook-shaped supra-condylar process (page 189) is found on this border. The position of the lateral epicondyle is best seen during semiflexion of the forearm, and is indicated by a depression; from it the strongly marked lateral supracondylar ridge runs upward.

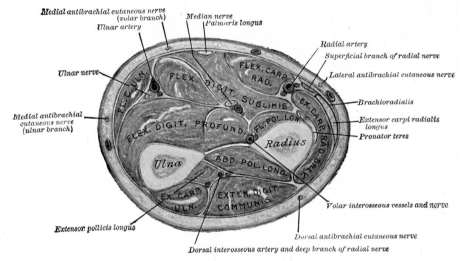

FIG. 1227.—Transverse section through the middle of the forearm.

The most prominent part of the **ulna**, the olecranon, can always be identified at the back of the elbow-joint. When the forearm is flexed the upper quadrilateral surface is palpable, but during extension it recedes into the olecranon fossa. During extension the upper border of the olecranon is slightly above the level of the medial epicondyle and nearer to this than to the lateral; when the forearm is fully flexed the olecranon and the epicondyles form the angles of an equilateral triangle. On the back of the olecranon is a smooth triangular subcutaneous surface, and running down the back of the forearm from the apex of this triangle the prominent dorsal border of the ulna can be felt in its whole length: it has a sinuous outline, and is situated in the middle of the back of the limb above; but below, where it is rounded off, it can be traced to the small subcutaneous surface of the styloid process on the medial side of the wrist. The styloid process forms a prominent tubercle continuous above with the dorsal border and ending below in a blunt apex at the level of the wrist-joint; it is most evident when the hand is in a position midway between supination and pronation. When the forearm is pronated another prominence, the head of the ulna, appears behind and above the styloid process.

Below the lateral epicondyle of the humerus a portion of the head of the **radius** is palpable; its position is indicated on the surface by a little dimple, which is best seen when the arm is extended. If the finger be placed in this dimple and the semiflexed forearm be alternately pronated and supinated the head of the radius will be felt distinctly, rotating in the radial notch. The upper half of the body of the bone is obscured by muscles; the lower half, though not subcutaneous, can be readily examined, and if traced downward is found to end in a lozenge-shaped convex surface on the lateral side of the base of the styloid process; this is the only subcutaneous part of the bone, and from its lower end the apex of the styloid process bends medialward toward the wrist. About the middle of the dorsal surface of the lower end of the radius is the dorsal radial tubercle, best perceived when the wrist is slightly flexed; it forms the lateral boundary of the oblique groove for the tendon of Extensor pollicis longus.

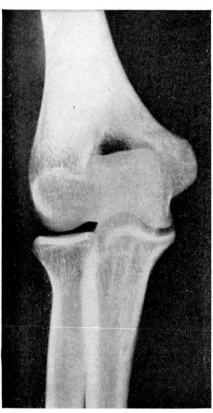 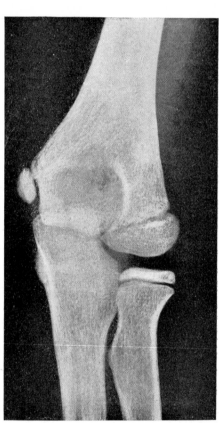

Fig. 1228. — Adult elbow. Frontal view. The shadow of the olecranon extends upwards to the olecranon fossa and obscures the outline of the trochlea. The gap between the humerus and the bones of the forearm is occupied by the articular cartilage of the bones concerned.

Fig. 1229.—Elbow of a child aged eleven years. Frontal view. The upper epiphysis of the radius, the epiphysis for the medial epicondyle, and the center for the capitulum and lateral part of the trochlea can be recognized without difficulty.

On the front of the wrist are two subcutaneous eminences, one, on the radial side, the larger and flatter, produced by the tuberosity of the **navicular** and the ridge on the **greater multangular**; the other, on the ulnar side, by the **pisiform**. The tuberosity of the navicular is distal and medial to the styloid process of the radius, and is most clearly visible when the wrist-joint is extended; the ridge on the greater multangular is about 1 cm. distal to it. The pisiform is about 1 cm. distal to the lower end of the ulna and just distal to the level of the styloid process of the radius; it is crossed by the uppermost crease which separates the front of the forearm from the palm of the hand. The rest of the volar surface of the bony carpus is covered by tendons and the transverse carpal ligament, and is entirely concealed, with the exception of the hamulus of the **hamate bone**, which, however, is difficult to define. On the dorsal surface of the carpus only the **triangular bone** can be clearly made out.

Distal to the carpus the dorsal surfaces of the **metacarpal bones**, covered by the Extensor tendons, except the fifth, are visible only in very thin hands; the dorsal surface of the fifth is, however, subcutaneous throughout almost its whole length. Slightly lateral to the middle line of the hand is a prominence, frequently well-marked, but occasionally indistinct, formed by the styloid process of the third metacarpal bone; it is situated about 4 cm. distal to the dorsal radial tubercle. The heads of the metacarpal bones can be plainly seen and felt, rounded in contour and standing out in bold relief under the skin when the fist is clenched; the head of the third is the most prominent. In the palm of the hand the metacarpal bones are covered by muscles, tendons, and aponeuroses, so that only their heads can be distinguished. The base of the metacarpal bone of the thumb, however, is prominent dorsally, distal to the styloid process of the radius; the body of the bone is easily palpable, ending at the head in a flattened prominence, in front of which are the sesamoid bones.

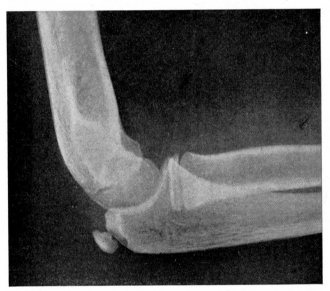

FIG. 1230.—Elbow of a child aged ten years. Lateral view. The upper epiphysis of the radius, the olecranon epiphysis and the center for the capitulum and the lateral part of the trochlea can be recognized without difficulty.

The enlarged ends of the **phalanges** can be easily felt. When the digits are bent the proximal phalanges form prominences, which in the joints between the first and second phalanges are slightly hollow, but flattened and square-shaped in those between the second and third.

Articulations.—The **sternoclavicular joint** is subcutaneous, and its position is indicated by the enlarged sternal extremity of the clavicle, lateral to the long cord-like sternal head of Sternocleidomastoideus. If this muscle be relaxed a depression between the end of the clavicle and the sternum can be felt, defining the exact position of the joint.

The position of the **acromioclavicular joint** can generally be ascertained by determining the slightly enlarged acromial end of the clavicle which projects above the level of the acromion; sometimes this enlargement is so considerable as to form a rounded eminence.

The **shoulder-joint** is deeply seated and cannot be palpated. If the forearm be slightly flexed a curved crease or fold with its convexity downward is seen in front of the elbow, extending from one epicondyle to the other; the **elbow-joint** is slightly distal to the center of the fold. The position of the **radiohumeral joint** can be ascertained by feeling for a slight groove or depression between the head of the radius and the capitulum of the humerus, at the back of the elbow-joint.

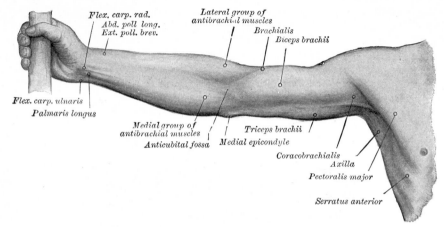

FIG. 1231.—Front of right upper extremity.

The position of the **proximal radioulnar joint** is marked on the surface at the back of the elbow by the dimple which indicates the position of the head of the radius. The site of the **distal radioulnar joint** can be defined by feeling for the slight groove at the back of the wrist between the prominent head of the ulna and the lower end of the radius, when the forearm is in a state of almost complete pronation.

Of the three transverse skin furrows on the front of the wrist, the middle corresponds fairly accurately with the **wrist-joint,** while the most distal indicates the position of the midcarpal articulation.

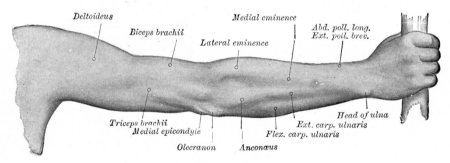

FIG. 1232.—Back of right upper extremity.

The **metacarpophalangeal** and **interphalangeal joints** are readily available for surface examination; the former are situated just distal to the prominences of the knuckles, the latter are sufficiently indicated by the furrows on the volar, and the wrinkles on the dorsal surfaces.

Muscles (Figs. 1173, 1231, 1232).—The anterior border of the **Trapezius** presents as a slight ridge running downward and forward from the superior nuchal line of the occipital bone to the junction of the intermediate and lateral thirds of the clavicle. The inferior border of the muscle forms an undulating ridge passing downward and medialward from the root of the spine of the scapula to the spinous process of the twelfth thoracic vertebra.

The lateral border of the **Latissimus dorsi** (Fig. 1195) may be traced, when the muscle is in action, as a rounded edge starting from the iliac crest and slanting obliquely forward and upward to the axilla, where it takes part with the Teres major in forming the posterior axillary fold.

The **Pectoralis major** (Fig. 1205) conceals a considerable part of the thoracic wall in front. Its sternal origin presents a border which bounds, and determines the width of the sternal furrow. The upper margin is generally well-marked medially and forms the medial boundary of a triangular depression, the infraclavicular fossa, which separates the Pectoralis major from the Deltoideus; it gradually becomes

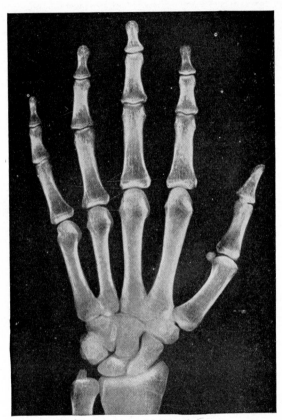

Fig. 1233.—Adult hand.

less marked as it approaches the tendon of insertion and is closely blended with the Deltoideus. The lower border of Pectoralis major forms the rounded anterior axillary fold. Occasionally a gap is visible between the clavicular and sternal parts of the muscle.

When the arm is raised the lowest slip of origin of **Pectoralis minor** produces a fulness just below the anterior axillary fold and serves to break the sharp outline of the lower border of Pectoralis major.

The origin of the **Serratus anterior** (Figs. 1195, 1205) causes a very characteristic surface marking. When the arm is abducted the lower five or six serrations form a zigzag line with a general convexity forward; when the arm is by the side the highest visible serration is that attached to the fifth rib.

The **Deltoideus** with the prominence of the upper end of the humerus produces the rounded contour of the shoulder; it is rounded and fuller in front than behind, where it presents a somewhat flattened form. Above, its anterior border presents a slightly curved eminence which forms the lateral boundary of the infraclavicular fossa; below, it is closely united with the Pectoralis major. Its posterior border is thin, flattened, and scarcely marked above, but is thicker and more prominent below. The insertion of Deltoideus is marked by a depression on the lateral side of the middle of the arm.

Of the scapular muscles the only one which influences surface form is the **Teres major**; it assists the Latissimus dorsi in forming the thick, rounded, posterior axillary fold.

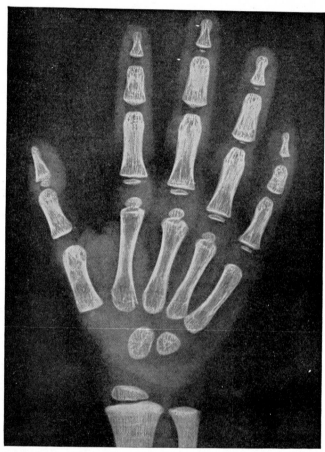

Fig. 1234.—Hand and wrist of a child aged two-and-a-half years. The capitate and hamate bones are in process of ossification, but the other carpal bones are still cartilaginous. The center for the head of the ulna has not yet appeared, but the center for the lower epiphysis of the radius is present. Note the condition of the metacarpal bones and phalanges.

When the arm is raised the **Coracobrachialis** reveals itself as a narrow elevation emerging from under cover of the anterior axillary fold and running medial to the body of the humerus.

On the front and medial aspects of the arm is the prominence of the **Biceps brachii**, bounded on either side by an intermuscular depression. It determines the contour of the front of the arm and extends from the anterior axillary fold to the bend of the elbow; its upper tendons are concealed by the Pectoralis major and Deltoideus, and its lower tendon sinks into the anticubital fossa. When the muscle is fully contracted it presents a globular form, and the lacertus fibrosus attached to its tendon of insertion becomes prominent as a sharp ridge running downward and medialward.

On either side of the Biceps brachii at the lower part of the arm the **Brachialis** is discernible. Laterally it forms a narrow eminence extending some distance up the arm; medially it exhibits only a little fulness above the elbow.

On the back of the arm the long head of the **Triceps brachii** may be seen as a longitudinal eminence, emerging from under cover of Deltoideus and gradually passing into the flattened plane of the tendon of the muscle at the lower part of the back of the arm. When the muscle is in action the medial and lateral heads become prominent.

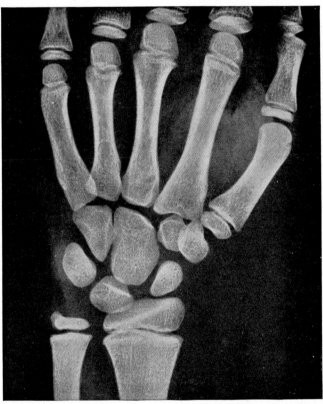

Fig. 1235.—Hand and wrist of a child aged eleven years. All the centers of ossification are present except that for the pisiform bone. Note how the first metacarpal differs from the other metacarpal bones.

On the front of the elbow are two muscular elevations, one on either side, separate above but converging below so as to form the medial and lateral boundaries of the anticubital fossa. The medial elevation consists of the Pronator teres and the Flexors, and forms a fusiform mass, pointed above at the medial epicondyle and gradually tapering off below. The **Pronator teres** is the most lateral of the group, while the **Flexor carpi radialis**, lying to its medial side, is the most prominent and may be traced downward to its tendon, which is situated nearer to the radial than to the ulnar border of the front of the wrist and medial to the radial artery. The **Palmaris longus** presents no surface marking above, but below, its tendon stands out when the muscle is in action as a sharp, tense cord in front of the middle of the wrist. The **Flexor digitorum sublimis** does not directly influence surface form; the position of its four tendons on the front of the lower part of the forearm is indicated by an elongated depression between the tendons of Palmaris longus and Flexor carpi ulnaris. The **Flexor carpi ulnaris** determines the contour of the medial border of the forearm, and is separated from the Extensor group of muscles by the ulnar furrow produced by the subcutaneous dorsal border of the ulna; its tendon is evident along the ulnar border of the lower part of the forearm, and is most marked when the hand is flexed and adducted.

The elevation forming the lateral side of the anticubital fossa consists of the Brachioradialis, the Extensors and the Supinator; it occupies the lateral and a considerable part of the dorsal surface of the forearm in the region of the elbow, and forms a fusiform mass which is altogether on a higher level than that produced by the medial elevation. Its apex is between the Triceps brachii and Brachialis some distance above the elbow-joint; it acquires its greatest breadth opposite the lateral epicondyle, and below this shades off into a flattened surface. About the middle of the forearm it divides into two diverging longitudinal eminences. The lateral eminence consists of the **Brachioradialis** and the **Extensores carpi radiales longus** and **brevis,** and descends from the lateral supracondylar ridge in the direction of the styloid process of the radius. The medial eminence comprises the **Extensor digitorum communis, Extensor digiti quinti proprius,** and the **Extensor carpi ulnaris;** it begins at the lateral epicondyle of the humerus as a tapering mass which is separated above from the Anconæus by a well-marked furrow, and below from the Pronator teres and Flexor group by the ulnar furrow. The medial border of the **Brachioradialis** starts as a rounded elevation above the lateral epicondyle; lower down the muscle forms a prominent mass on the radial side of the upper part of the forearm; below it tapers to its tendon, which may be traced to the styloid process of the radius. The **Anconæus** presents as a triangular slightly elevated area, immediately lateral to the subcutaneous surface of the olecranon and differentiated from the Extensor group by an oblique depression; the upper angle of the triangle is at the dimple over the lateral epicondyle.

At the lower part of the back of the forearm in the interval between the two diverging eminences is an oblique elongated swelling; full above but flattened and partially subdivided below; it is caused by the **Abductor pollicis longus** and the **Extensor pollicis brevis.** It crosses the dorsal and lateral surfaces of the radius to the radial side of the wrist-joint, whence it is continued on to the dorsal surface of the thumb as a ridge best marked when the thumb is extended.

The tendons of most of the Extensor muscles can be seen and felt on the back of the wrist. Laterally is the oblique ridge produced by the Extensor pollicis longus. The Extensor carpi radialis longus is scarcely palpable, but the Extensor carpi radialis brevis can be identified as a vertical ridge emerging from under the ulnar border of the tendon of the Extensor pollicis longus when the wrist is extended. Medial to this the Extensor tendons of the fingers can be felt, the Extensor digiti quinti proprius being separated from the tendons of the Extensor digitorum communis by a slight furrow.

The muscles of the hand are principally concerned, as regards surface form, in producing the thenar and hypothenar eminences, and cannot be individually distinguished; the thenar eminence, on the radial side, is larger and rounder than the hypothenar, which is a long narrow elevation along the ulnar side of the palm. When the **Palmaris brevis** is in action it produces a wrinkling of the skin over the hypothenar eminence and a dimple on the ulnar border. On the back of the hand the **Interossei dorsales** give rise to elongated swellings between the metacarpal bones; the first forms a prominent fusiform bulging when the thumb is adducted, the others are not so marked.

Arteries.—Above the middle of the clavicle the pulsation of the **subclavian artery** can be detected by pressing downward, backward, and medialward against the first rib. The pulsation of the **axillary artery** as it crosses the second rib can be felt below the middle of the clavicle just medial to the coracoid process; along the lateral wall of the axilla the course of the artery can be easily followed close to the medial border of Coracobrachialis. The **brachial artery** can be recognized in practically the whole of its extent, along the medial margin of the Biceps; in the upper two-thirds of the arm it lies medial to the humerus, but in the lower third is more directly on the front of the bone. Over the lower end of the radius, between the styloid process and Flexor carpi radialis, a portion of the **radial artery** is superficial and is used clinically for observations on the pulse.

Veins.—The superficial veins of the upper extremity are easily rendered visible by compressing the proximal trunks; their arrangement is described on pages 668 to 671.

Nerves.—The uppermost trunks of the **brachial plexus** are palpable for a short distance above the clavicle as they emerge from under the lateral border of Sterno-cleidomastoideus; the larger nerves derived from the plexus can be rolled under the finger against the lateral axillary wall but cannot be identified. The **ulnar nerve** can be detected in the groove behind the medial epicondyle of the humerus.

SURFACE MARKINGS OF THE UPPER EXTREMITY.

Bony Landmarks.—The bony landmarks as described above are so readily available for surface recognition that no special measurements are required to indicate them. It may be noted, however, that the medial angle of the scapula is applied to the second rib, while the inferior angle lies against the seventh. The intertubercular groove of the humerus is vertically below the acromioclavicular joint when the arm hangs by the side with the palm of the hand forward.

Articulations.—The **acromioclavicular joint** is situated in a plane passing sagittally through the middle line of the front of the arm. The line of the **elbow-joint** is not straight; the radiohumeral portion is practically at right angles to the long axis of the humerus and is situated about 2 cm. distal to the lateral epicondyle; the ulnohumeral portion is oblique, and its medial end is about 2.5 cm. distal to the medial epicondyle. The position of the **wrist-joint** can be indicated by drawing a curved line, with its convexity upward, between the styloid processes of the radius and ulna; the summit of the convexity is about 1 cm. above the center of a straight line joining the two processes.

Muscles.—The only muscles of the upper extremity which occasionally require definition by surface lines are the Trapezius, the Latissimus dorsi, and the Pectorales major and minor. The antero-superior border of **Trapezius** is indicated by a line from the superior nuchal line about 3 cm. lateral to the external occipital protuberance to the junction of the intermediate and lateral thirds of the clavicle; the line of the lower border extends from the spinous process of the twelfth thoracic vertebra to the vertebral border of the scapula at the root of the spine. The upper border of **Latissimus dorsi** is almost horizontal, running from the spinous process of the seventh thoracic vertebra to the inferior angle of the scapula and thence somewhat obliquely to the intertubercular sulcus of the humerus; the lower border corresponds roughly to a line drawn from the iliac crest about 2 cm. from the lateral margin of the Sacrospinalis to the intertubercular sulcus. The upper margin of **Pectoralis major** extends from the middle of the clavicle to the surgical neck of the humerus; its lower border is practically in the line of the fifth rib and reaches from the fifth costochondral junction to the middle of the anterior border of Deltoideus. The two lines indicating the borders of **Pectoralis minor** begin at the coracoid process of the scapula and extend to the third and fifth ribs respectively, just lateral to the corresponding costal cartilages. On the front of the elbow-joint a triangular space —the **anticubital fossa**—is mapped out for convenience of reference. The base of the triangle is a line joining the medial and lateral epicondyles, while the sides are formed respectively by the salient margins of the Brachioradialis and Pronator teres.

Synovial Sheaths. — On the volar surfaces of the wrist and hand the mucous sheaths of the Flexor tendons (Fig. 404) can be indicated as follows. The sheath for Flexor pollicis longus extends from about 3 cm. above the upper edge of the transverse carpal ligament to the terminal phalanx of the thumb. The common sheath for the Flexores digitorum reaches about 3.5 to 4 cm. above the upper edge of the transverse carpal ligament and extends on the palm of the hand to about the level of the centers of the metacarpal bones. The sheath for the tendons to the little finger is continued from the common sheath to the base of the terminal phalanx

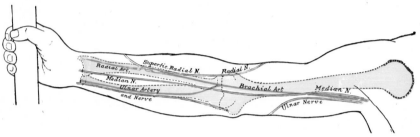

Fig. 1236.—Front of right upper extremity, showing surface markings for bones, arteries, and nerves.

of this finger; the sheaths for the tendons of the other fingers are separated from the common sheath by an interval; they begin opposite the necks of the metacarpal bones and extend to the terminal phalanges. The mucous sheaths of the Extensor tendons are shown in Fig. 405 (see also page 452).

Arteries (Fig. 1236).—The course of the **axillary artery** can be marked out by abducting the arm to a right angle and drawing a line from the middle of the clavicle to the point where the tendon of the Pectoralis major crosses the prominence of the Coracobrachialis. Of the branches of the axillary artery, the origin of the **thoracoacromial** corresponds to the point where the artery crosses the upper border of Pectoralis minor; the **lateral thoracic** takes practically the line of

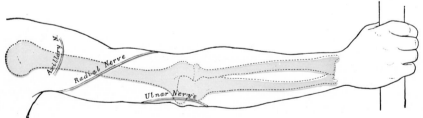

Fig. 1237.—Back of right upper extremity, showing surface markings for bones and nerves.

the lower border of Pectoralis minor; the **subscapular** is sufficiently indicated by the axillary border of the scapula; the **scapular circumflex** is given off the subscapular opposite the midpoint of a line joining the tip of the acromion to the lower edge of the deltoid tuberosity, while the **humeral circumflex** arteries arise from the axillary about 2 cm. above this. The position of the **brachial artery** is marked by a line drawn from the junction of the anterior and middle thirds of the distance between the anterior and posterior axillary folds to a point midway between the epicondyles of the humerus and continued distally for 2.5 cm., at which point the artery bifurcates. With regard to the branches of the brachial artery—the **profunda** crosses the back of the humerus at the level of the insertion of Deltoideus; the **nutrient** is given off opposite the middle of the body of the humerus; a line from this point to the back of the medial condyle represents the **superior ulnar collateral**; the **inferior ulnar collateral** is given off about 5 cm. above the fold of the elbow-joint and runs directly medialward.

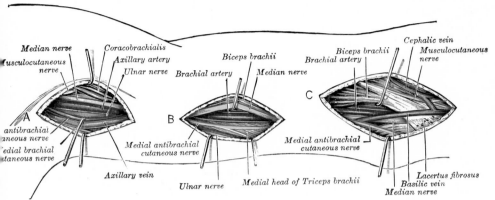

FIG. 1238.—Dissections to show (*A*) the third part of the axillary artery; (*B*) the brachial artery at the middle of the arm, and (*C*) the brachial artery at the lower part of the arm.

The position of the **radial artery** in the forearm is represented by a line from the lateral margin of the Biceps tendon in the center of the anticubital fossa to the medial side of the front of the styloid process of the radius when the limb is in the position of supination. The situation of the distal portion of the artery is indicated by continuing this line around the radial side of the wrist to the proximal end of the first intermetacarpal space.

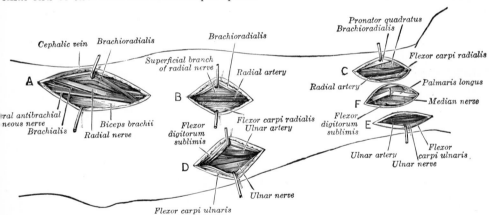

FIG. 1239.—Dissections to show the radial and median nerves, and the radial and ulnar arteries.

On account of the curved direction of the **ulnar artery**, two lines are required to indicate its course; one is drawn from the front of the medial epicondyle to the radial side of the pisiform bone; the lower two-thirds of this line represents two-thirds of the artery; the upper third is represented by a second line from the center of the hollow in front of the elbow-joint to the junction of the upper and middle thirds of the first line.

The **superficial volar arch** (Fig. 1240) can be indicated by a line starting from the radial side of the pisiform bone and curving distalward and lateralward as far as the base of the thumb, with its convexity toward the fingers. The summit of the arch is usually on a level with the ulnar border of the outstretched thumb.

The **deep volar arch** is practically transverse, and is situated about 1 cm. nearer to the carpus.

Nerves (Figs. 1236, 1237).—In the arm the line of the **median nerve** is practically the same as that for the brachial artery; at the bend of the elbow the nerve is medial to the artery. The course of the nerve in the forearm is marked by a line starting from a point just medial to the center of one joining the epicondyles, and extending to the lateral margin of the tendon of Palmaris longus at the wrist.

The **ulnar nerve** follows the line of the brachial artery in the upper half of the arm, but at the middle of the arm it diverges and descends to the back of the medial epicondyle. In the forearm it is represented by a line from the front of the medial epicondyle to the radial side of the pisiform bone.

The course of the **radial nerve** can be indicated by a line from just below the posterior axillary fold, to the lateral side of the humerus at the junction of its middle and lower thirds; thence it passes vertically downward on the front of the arm to the level of the lateral epicondyle. The course of the **superficial radial nerve** is represented by a continuation of this line downward to the junction of the middle and lower thirds of the radial artery; it then crosses the radius and runs distalward to the dorsum of the base of the first metacarpal bone.

The **axillary nerve** crosses the humerus about 2 cm. above the center of a line joining the tip of the acromion to the lower edge of the deltoid tuberosity.

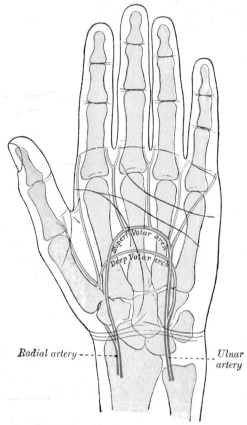

Fig. 1240.—Palm of left hand, showing position of skin creases and bones, and surface markings for the volar arches.

SURFACE ANATOMY OF THE LOWER EXTREMITY.

Skin.—The skin of the thigh, especially in the hollow of the groin and on the medial side, is thin, smooth and elastic, and contains few hairs except on the neighborhood of the pubis. Laterally it is thicker and the hairs are more numerous. The junction of the skin of the thigh with that on the front of the abdomen is marked by a well-defined furrow which indicates the site of the inguinal ligament; the furrow presents a general convexity downward, but its medial half, which is the better marked, is nearly straight. The skin over the buttock is fairly thick and is characterized by its low sensibility and slight vascularity; as a rule it is destitute of conspicuous hairs except toward the post-anal furrow, where in some males they are abundantly developed. An almost transverse fold—the **gluteal fold**—crosses the lower part of the buttock; it practically bisects the lower margin of the Glutæus maximus and is most evident during extension of the hip-joint. The skin over the front of the knee is covered by thickened epidermis; it is loose and thrown into transverse wrinkles when the leg is extended. The skin of the leg is thin, especially on the medial side, and is covered with numerous large hairs. On the dorsum of the foot the skin is thin, loosely connected to subjacent parts, and contains few hairs, on the plantar surface, and especially over the heel, the epidermis is of great thickness, and here, as in the palm of the hand, there are neither hairs nor sebaceous glands.

Bones.—The **hip bones** are largely covered with muscles, so that only at a few points do they approach the surface. In front the anterior superior iliac spine is easily recognized, and in thin subjects stands out as a prominence at the lateral end of the fold of the groin; in fat subjects its position is indicated by an oblique

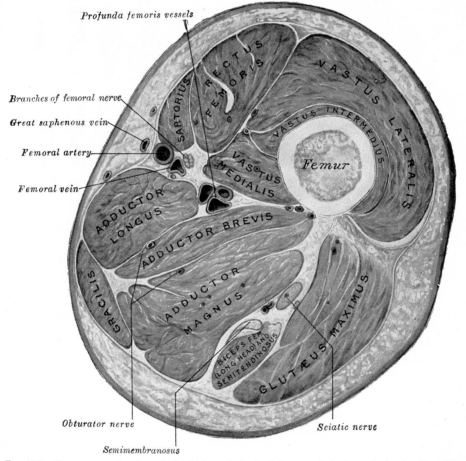

Fig. 1241.—Transverse section through the thigh at the level of the apex of the femoral triangle. Four-fifths of natural size.

depression, at the bottom of which the bony process can be felt. Proceeding upward and backward from this process the sinuously curved iliac crest can be traced to the posterior superior iliac spine, the site of which is indicated by a slight depression; on the outer lip of the crest, about 5 cm. behind the anterior superior spine, is the prominent iliac tubercle. In thin subjects the pubic tubercle is very apparent, but in the obese it is obscured by the pubic fat; it can, however, be detected by following up the tendon of origin of Adductor longus. Another part of the bony pelvis which is accessible to touch is the ischial tuberosity, situated beneath the Glutæus maximus, and, when the hip is flexed, easily felt, as it is then uncovered by muscle.

The **femur** is enveloped by muscles, so that in fairly muscular subjects the only accessible parts are the lateral surface of the greater trochanter and the lower expanded end of the bone. The site of the greater trochanter is generally indicated by a depression, owing to the thickness of the Glutæi medius and minimus which project above it; when, however, the thigh is flexed, and especially if it be crossed over the opposite one, the trochanter produces a blunt eminence on the surface. The lateral condyle is more easily felt than the medial; both epicondyles can be readily identified, and at the upper part of the medial condyle the sharp adductor tubercle can be recognized without difficulty. When the knee is flexed a portion of the patellar surface is uncovered and is palpable.

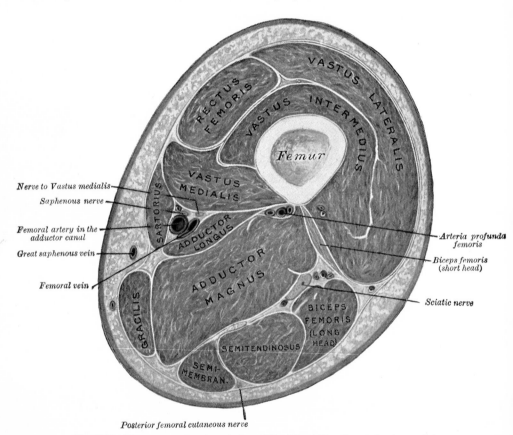

Fig. 1242.—Transverse section through the middle of the thigh. Four-fifths of natural size.

The anterior surface of the **patella** is subcutaneous. When the knee is extended the medial border of the bone is a little more prominent than the lateral, and if the Quadriceps femoris be relaxed the bone can be moved from side to side. When the joint is flexed the patella recedes into the hollow between the condyles of the femur and the upper end of the tibia, and becomes firmly applied to the femur.

A considerable portion of the **tibia** is subcutaneous. At the upper end the condyles can be felt just below the knee; the medial condyle is broad and smooth, and merges into the subcutaneous surface of the body below; the lateral is narrower and more prominent, and on it, about midway between the apex of the patella and the head of the fibula, is the tubercle for the attachment of the iliotibial band. In front of the upper end of the bone, between the condyles, is an oval eminence, the tuberosity, which is continuous below with the anterior crest of the bone. This crest can be identified in the upper two-thirds of its extent as a flexuous ridge, but in the lower third it disappears and the bone is concealed by the tendons of the muscles on the front of the leg. Medial to the anterior crest is the broad surface, slightly encroached on by muscles in front and behind. The medial malleolus forms a broad prominence, situated at a higher level and somewhat farther forward than the lateral malleolus; it overhangs the medial border of the arch of the foot; its anterior border is nearly straight, its posterior presents a sharp edge which forms the medial margin of the groove for the tendon of Tibialis posterior.

The only subcutaneous parts of the **fibula** are the head, the lower part of the body, and the lateral malleolus. The head lies behind and lateral to the lateral condyle of the tibia, and presents as a small prominent pyramidal eminence slightly

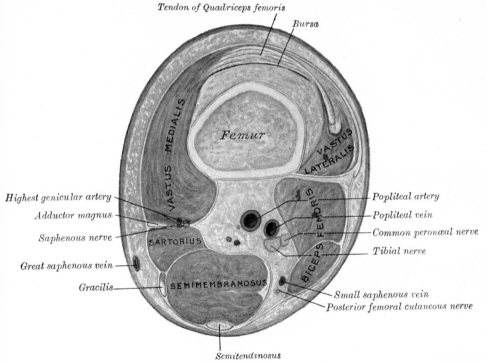

Fig. 1243.—Transverse section through the thigh, 4 cm., proximal to the adductor tubercle of the femur. Four-fifths of natural size.

above the level of the tibial tuberosity; its position can be readily located by following downward the tendon of Biceps femoris. The lateral malleolus is a narrow elongated prominence, from which the lower third or half of the lateral surface of the body of the bone can be traced upward.

On the dorsum of the tarsus the individual bones cannot be distinguished, with the exception of the head of the **talus**, which forms a rounded projection in front of the ankle-joint when the foot is forcibly extended. The whole dorsal surface of the foot has a smooth convex outline, the summit of which is the ridge formed by the head of the talus, the navicular, the second cuneiform, and the second metatarsal bone; from this it inclines gradually lateralward, and rapidly medialward. On the medial side of the foot the medial process of the tuberosity of the **calcaneus** and the ridge separating the posterior from the medial surface of the bone are distinguishable; in front of this, and below the medial malleolus, is the sustentaculum tali. The tuberosity of the **navicular** is palpable about 2.5 to 3 cm. in front of the medial malleolus.

Farther forward, the ridge formed by the base of the **first metatarsal bone** can be obscurely felt, and from this the body of the bone can be traced to the expanded

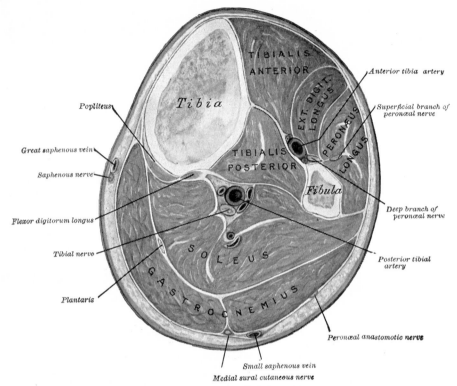

FIG. 1244.—Transverse section through the leg, 9 cm. distal to the knee joint.

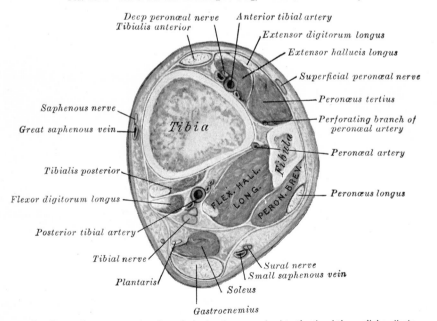

FIG. 1245.—Transverse section through the leg, 6 cm. proximal to the tip of the medial malleolus.

head; beneath the base of the first phalanx is the medial sesamoid bone. On the lateral side of the foot the most posterior bony point is the lateral process of the tuberosity of the calcaneus, with the ridge separating the posterior from the

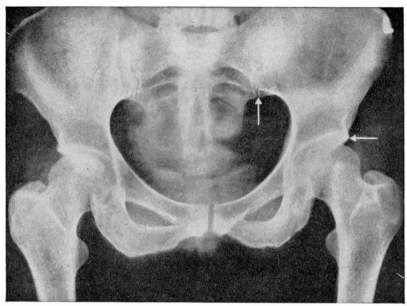

Fig. 1246.—Adult pelvis. The upper arrow indicates the line of the sacro-iliac joint; the lower arrow points to the anterior inferior iliac spine.

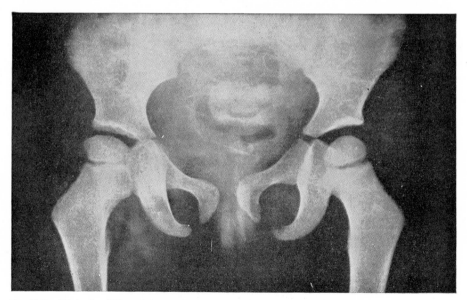

Fig. 1247.—Pelvis of a child aged three-and-a-half years. The epiphysis for the head of the femur is well formed, but the center for the greater trochanter has not yet appeared. The rami of the pubis and ischium are still connected by cartilage and the triradiate cartilage in the acetabulum is wide.

lateral surface of the bone. In front of this the greater part of the lateral surface of the calcaneus is subcutaneous; on it, below and in front of the lateral malleolus, the trochlear process, when present, can be felt. Farther forward the base of the **fifth metatarsal bone** is prominent, and from it the body and expanded head can be traced.

As in the case of the metacarpals, the dorsal surfaces of the **metatarsal bones** are easily defined, although their heads do not form prominences; the plantar

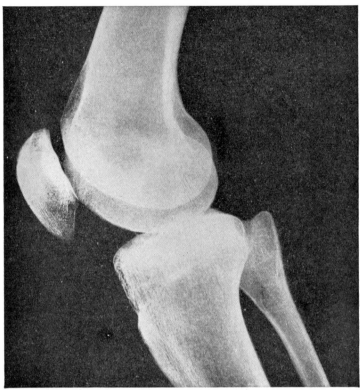

Fig. 1248.—Knee of an adult. Lateral view.

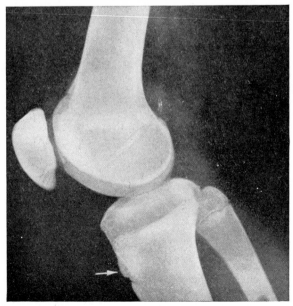

Fig. 1249.—Knee of a boy aged sixteen years. Lateral view. Note that the upper epiphysis of the tibia includes the tibial tubercle, which is indicated by the arrow.

surfaces are obscured by muscles.   The **phalanges** in their whole extent are readily palpable.

Articulations.—The **hip-joint** is deeply seated and cannot be palpated.

The interval between the tibia and femur can always be easily felt; if the **knee-joint** be extended this interval is on a higher level than the apex of the patella, but if the joint be slightly flexed it is directly behind the apex.   When the knee is semiflexed, the medial borders of the patella and of the medial condyle of the femur, and the upper border of the medial condyle of the tibia, bound a triangular depressed area which indicates the position of the joint.

The **ankle-joint** can be felt on either side of the Extensor tendons, and during extension of the joint the superior articular surface of the talus presents below the anterior border of the lower end of the tibia.

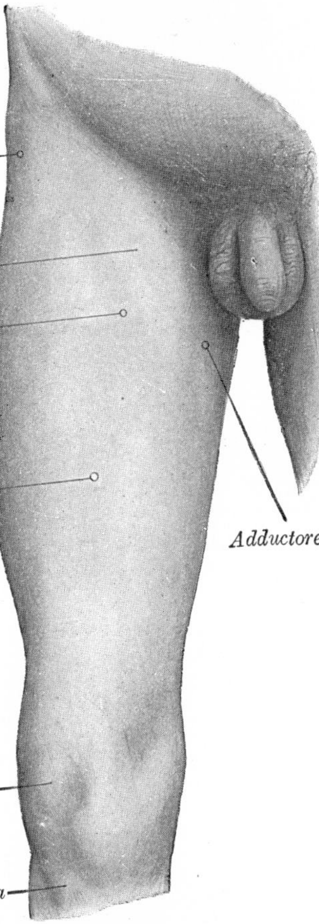

Muscles.—Of the muscles of the thigh, those of the anterior femoral region (Fig. 1250) contribute largely to surface form.   The **Tensor fasciæ latæ** produces a broad elevation immediately below the anterior part of the iliac crest and behind the anterior superior iliac spine; from its lower border a groove caused by the iliotibial band extends downward to the lateral side of the knee-joint.   The upper portion of **Sartorius** constitutes the lateral boundary of the femoral triangle, and, when the muscle is in action, forms a prominent oblique ridge which is continued below into a flattened plane and then gradually merges into a general fulness on the medial side of the knee-joint.   When the Sartorius is not in action, a depression exists between the Quadriceps femoris and the Adductors, and extends obliquely downward and medialward from the apex of the femoral triangle to the side of the knee.   In the angle formed by the divergence of Sartorius and Tensor fasciæ latæ, just below the anterior superior iliac spine, the **Rectus femoris** appears, and in a muscular subject its borders can be clearly defined when the muscle is in action. The **Vastus lateralis** forms a long flattened plane traversed by the groove of the iliotibial band.   The **Vastus medialis** gives rise to a considerable prominence on the medial side of the lower half of the thigh; this prominence increases toward the knee and ends somewhat abruptly with a full curved outline.   The **Vastus intermedius** is completely hidden.   The Adductores cannot be differentiated from one another, with the exception of the upper tendon of Adductor longus and the lower tendon of Adductor magnus.   When the **Adductor longus** is in action its upper tendon stands out as a prominent ridge running obliquely downward and

Tensor fasciæ latæ

Femoral triangle

Sartorius

Quadriceps femoris

Adductores

Patella

Tuberosity of tibia

FIG. 1250.—Front and medial aspect of right thigh.

lateralward from the neighborhood of the pubic tubercle, and forming the medial border of the femoral triangle. The lower tendon of **Adductor magnus** can be distinctly felt as a short ridge extending downward between the Sartorius and Vastus medialis to the adductor tubercle. The adductores fill in the triangular space at the upper part of the thigh, between the femur and the pelvis, and to them is due the contour of the medial border of the thigh, the **Gracilis** contributing largely to the smoothness of the outline.

The **Glutæus maximus** (Fig. 1251) forms the full rounded outline of the buttock; it is more prominent behind, compressed in front, and ends at its tendinous insertion in a depression immediately behind the greater trochanter; its lower border crosses the gluteal fold obliquely downward and lateralward. The upper part of Glutæus medius is visible, but its lower part with Glutæus minimus and the external rotators are completely hidden. From beneath the lower margin of Glutæus maximus the hamstrings appear; at first they are narrow and not well-defined, but as they descend they become more prominent and eventually divide into two well-marked ridges formed by their tendons; these constitute the upper boundaries of the popliteal fossa. The tendon of **Biceps femoris** is a thick cord running to the head of the fibula; the tendons of the **Semimembranosus** and **Semitendinosus** as they run

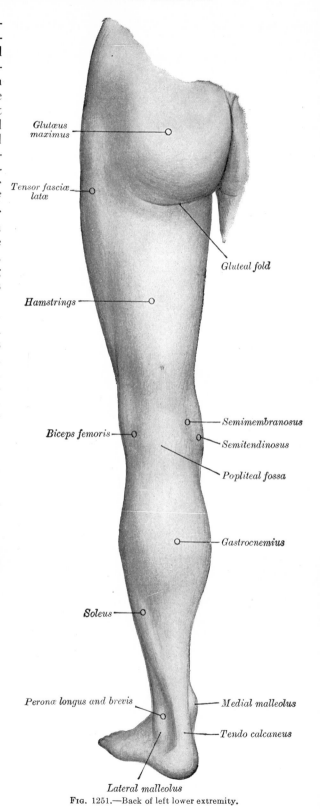

Fig. 1251.—Back of left lower extremity.

medialward to the tibia are separated by a slight furrow; the Semitendinosus is the more medial, and can be felt in certain positions of the limb as a sharp cord, while the Semimembranosus is thick and rounded. The Gracilis is situated a little in front of them.

The **Tibialis anterior** (Fig. 1256) presents a fusiform enlargement at the lateral side of the tibia and projects beyond the anterior crest of the bone; its tendon can be traced on the front of the tibia and ankle-joint and thence along the medial side of the foot to the base of the first metatarsal bone. The fleshy fibers of **Peronæus longus** are strongly marked at the upper part of the lateral side of the leg; it is separated by furrows from Extensor digitorum longus in front and Soleus behind. Below, the fleshy fibers end abruptly in a tendon which overlaps the more flattened

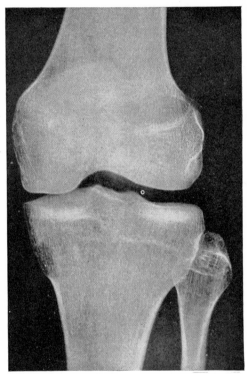

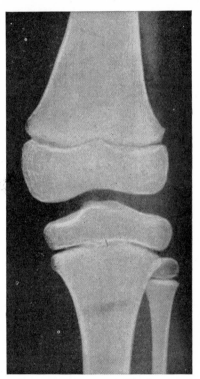

Fig. 1252. — Adult knee. The gap between the lateral condyles of the femur and tibia is occupied by the articular cartilage of the two bones and the lateral semilunar cartilage.

Fig. 1253.—Knee of a child aged seven-and-a-half years. Note that the styloid process of the head of the fibula and the tubercles of the intercondylar eminence of the tibia are still cartilaginous and therefore cannot be recognized.

elevation of **Peronæus brevis**; below the lateral malleolus the tendon of Peronæus brevis is the more marked.

On the dorsum of the foot (Fig. 425) the tendons emerging from beneath the transverse and cruciate crural ligaments spread out and can be distinguished as follows: the most medial and largest is Tibialis anterior, the next is Extensor hallucis proprius, then Extensor digitorum longus dividing into four tendons, to the second, third, fourth, and fifth toes, and lastly Peronæus tertius. The **Extensor digitorum brevis** produces a rounded outline on the dorsum of the foot and a fulness in front of the lateral malleolus. The **Interossei dorsales** bulge between the metatarsal bones.

At the back of the knee is the popliteal fossa, bounded above by the tendons of the hamstrings and below by the Gastrocnemius. Below this fossa is the promi-

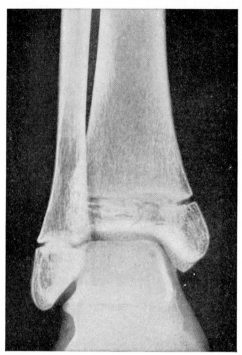

Fig. 1254.—Ankle of a child aged ten years. Note that the inferior epiphyseal line of the fibula is opposite the ankle joint.

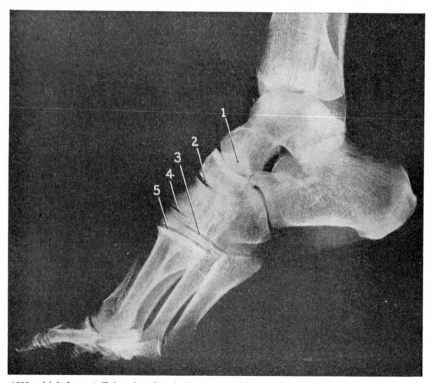

Fig. 1255.—Adult foot. *1*, Tuberosity of navicular bone, partly obscured by the shadow of the head of the talus; *2*, cuneo-navicular joint; *3*, joint between metatarsal III and the lateral cuneiform bone; *4*, joint between metatarsal II and the intermediate cuneiform bone; *5*, joint between metatarsal I and the medial cuneiform bone.

nent fleshy mass of the calf of the leg produced by Gastrocnemius and Soleus (Fig. 1256). When these muscles are in action the borders of **Gastrocnemius** form two well-defined curved lines which converge to the tendocalcaneus; the medial border is the more prominent. At the same time the edges of **Soleus** can be seen forming, on either side of Gastrocnemius, curved eminences, of which the lateral is the longer. The fleshy mass of the calf ends somewhat abruptly in the tendocalcaneus, which tapers in the upper three-fourths of its extent but widens out slightly below. Behind the medial border of the lower part of the tibia (Fig. 426) a well-defined ridge is produced by the tendon of **Tibialis posterior** during contraction of the muscle.

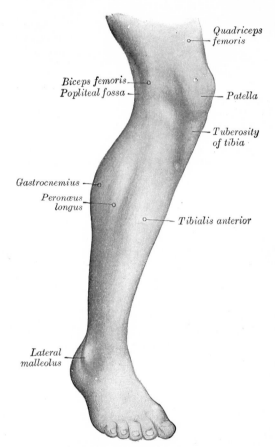

Quadriceps femoris

Biceps femoris
Popliteal fossa

Patella

Tuberosity of tibia

Gastrocnemius
Peronœus longus

Tibialis anterior

Lateral malleolus

Fig. 1256.—Lateral aspect of right leg.

On the sole of the foot the **Abductor digiti quinti** forms a narrow rounded elevation on the lateral side, and the **Abductor hallucis** a lesser elevation on the medial side. The **Flexor digitorum brevis**, bound down by the plantar aponeurosis, is not very apparent; it produces a flattened form, and the thickened skin underlying it is thrown into numerous wrinkles.

Arteries.—The **femoral artery** as it crosses the brim of the pelvis is readily felt; in its course down the thigh its pulsation becomes gradually more difficult of recognition (Fig. 1257). When the knee is flexed the pulsation of the **popliteal artery** can easily be detected in the popliteal fossa.

On the lower part of the front of the tibia the **anterior tibial artery** becomes superficial and can be traced over the ankle into the **dorsalis pedis**; the latter can be followed to the proximal end of the first intermetatarsal space. The pulsation of the **posterior tibial artery** becomes evident near the lower end of the back of the tibia, and is easily detected behind the medial malleolus.

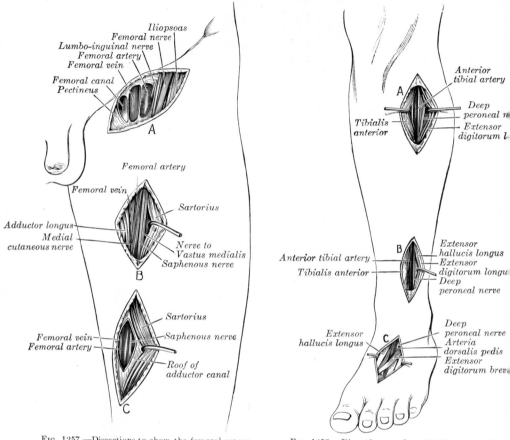

FIG. 1257.—Dissections to show the femoral artery (*A*) at the base of the femoral triangle; (*B*) at the apex of the femoral triangle; and (*C*) in the adductor (Hunter's) canal.

FIG. 1258.—Dissections to show (*A*) the upper: (*B*) the lower, part of the anterior tibial artery; and (*C*) the arteria dorsalis pedis.

Veins.—By compressing the proximal trunks, the venous arch on the dorsum of the foot, together with the great and small saphenous veins leading from it (see page 679), are rendered visible.

Nerves.—The only nerve of the lower extremity which can be located by palpation is the **common peroneal** as it winds around the lateral side of the neck of the fibula.

SURFACE MARKINGS OF THE LOWER EXTREMITY.

Bony Landmarks.—The anterior superior iliac spine is at the level of the sacral promontory—the posterior at the level of the spinous process of the second sacral vertebra. A horizontal line through the highest points of the iliac crests passes also through the spinous process of the fourth lumbar vertebra, while, as already pointed out (page 1382), the transtubercular plane through the tubercles on the iliac crests cuts the body of the fifth lumbar vertebra. The upper margin of the greater sciatic notch is opposite the spinous process of the third sacral vertebra, and slightly below this level is the posterior inferior iliac spine. The surface mark-

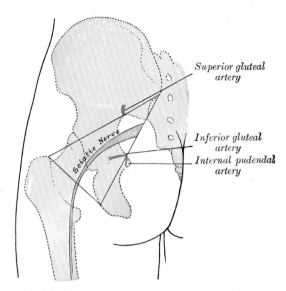

Fig. 1259.—Left gluteal region, showing surface markings for arteries and sciatic nerve.

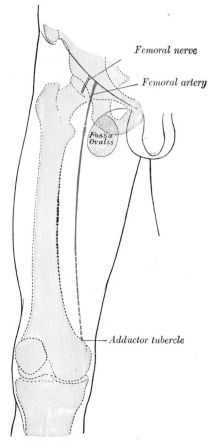

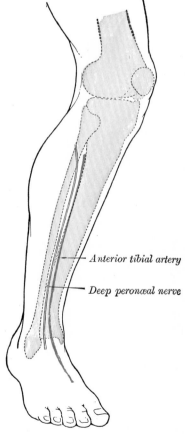

Fig. 1260.—Front of right thigh, showing surface markings for bones, femoral artery and femoral nerve.

Fig. 1261.—Lateral aspect of right leg, showing surface markings for bones, anterior tibial and dorsalis pedis arteries, and deep peroneal nerve.

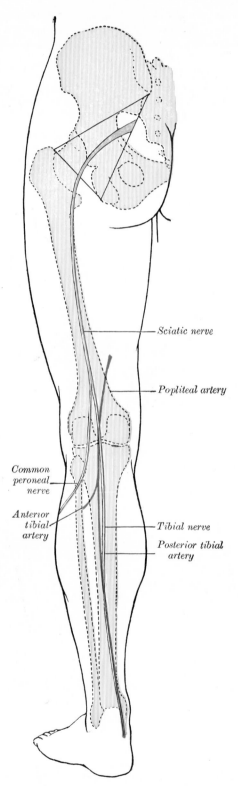

Fig. 1262.—Back of left lower extremity, showing surface markings or bones, vessels, and nerves.

ings of the posterior-inferior iliac spine and the ischial spine are both situated in a line which joins the posterior-superior iliac spine to the outer part of the ischial tuberosity; the posterior inferior spine is 5 cm. and the ischial spine 10 cm. below the posterior-superior spine; the ischial spine is opposite the first piece of the coccyx.

With the body in the erect posture the line joining the pubic tubercle to the top of the greater trochanter is practically horizontal; the middle of this line overlies the acetabulum and the head of the femur.

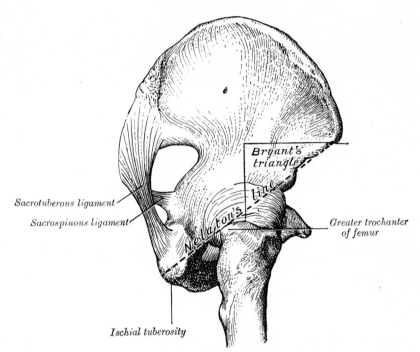

Fig. 1263.—Nélaton's line and Bryant's triangle.

A line used for clinical purposes is that of Nélaton (Fig. 1263), which is drawn from the anterior-superior iliac spine to the most prominent part of the ischial tuberosity; it crosses the center of the acetabulum and the upper border of the greater trochanter. Another surface marking of clinical importance is **Bryant's triangle**, which is mapped out thus: a line from the anterior-superior iliac spine to the top of the greater trochanter forms the base of the triangle; its sides are formed respectively by a horizontal line from the anterior-superior iliac spine and a vertical line from the top of the greater trochanter.

Articulations.—The posterior-superior iliac spine overlies the center of the **sacro-iliac articulations.**

The **hip-joint** may be indicated, as described above, by the center of a horizontal line from the pubic tubercle to the top of the greater trochanter; or more generally, it is below and slightly lateral to the middle of the inguinal ligament. The **knee-joint** is superficial and requires no surface marking. The level of the **ankle-joint** is that of a transverse line about 1 cm. above the level of the tip of the medial malleolus. If the foot be forcibly extended, the head of the talus appears as a rounded prominence on the medial side of the dorsum; just in front of this prominence and behind the tuberosity of the navicular is the **talonavicular joint.** The **calcaneocuboid joint** is situated midway between the lateral malleolus and the prominent base of the fifth metatarsal bone; the line indicating it is parallel to that of the **talonavicular** joint. The line of the **fifth tarsometatarsal joint** is very oblique; it starts from the projection of the base of the fifth metatarsal bone, and if continued would pass through the head of the first metatarsal. The lines of the **fourth** and **third tarsometatarsal joints** are less oblique The **first tarsometatarsal joint** corresponds to a groove which can be felt by making firm pressure on the medial border of the foot 2.5 cm. in front of the tuberosity of the navicular bone; the position of the **second tarsometatarsal joint** is 1.25 cm. behind this. The **metatarsophalangeal joints** are about 2.5 cm. behind the webs of the corresponding toes.

Muscles.—None of the muscles require any special surface lines to indicate them, but there are three intermuscular spaces which occasionally require definition, viz., the femoral triangle, the adductor canal, and the popliteal fossa.

The **femoral triangle** is bounded above by the inguinal ligament, laterally by the medial border of Sartorius, and medially by the medial border of Adductor longus. In the triangle is the fossa ovalis, through which the great saphenous vein dips to join the femoral; the center of this fossa is about 4 cm. below and lateral to the pubic tubercle, its vertical diameter measures about 4 cm. and its transverse about 1.5 cm. The femoral ring is about 1.25 cm. lateral to the pubic tubercle.

The **adductor canal** occupies the medial part of the middle third of the thigh; it begins at the apex of the femoral triangle and lies deep to the vertical part of Sartorius. The **popliteal fossa** is bounded: above and medially by the tendons of Semimembranosus and Semitendinosus; above and laterally by the tendon of Biceps femoris; below and medially by the medial head of Gastrocnemius; below and laterally by the lateral head of Gastrocnemius and the Plantaris.

Synovial Sheaths.—The positions of the synovial sheaths around the tendons about the ankle-joints are sufficiently indicated in Figs. 425, 426 (see also page 489).

Arteries.—The points of emergence of the three main arteries on the buttock, viz., the superior and inferior gluteals and the internal pudendal, may be indicated in the following manner (Fig. 1259). With the femur slightly flexed and rotated inward, a line is drawn from the posterior-superior iliac spine to the posterior-superior angle of the greater trochanter; the point of emergence of the **superior gluteal artery** from the upper part of the greater sciatic foramen corresponds to the junction of the upper and middle thirds of this line. A second line is drawn from the posterior-superior iliac spine to the outer part of the ischial tuberosity; the junction of its lower with its middle third marks the point of emergence of the **inferior gluteal** and **internal pudendal** arteries from the lower part of the greater sciatic foramen. The course of the **femoral artery** (Fig. 1260) is represented by the upper two-thirds of a line from a point midway between the anterior-superior iliac spine and the symphysis pubis to the adductor tubercle, with the thigh abducted and rotated outward; the **profunda femoris** arises from it about 1 to 5 cm. below the inguinal ligament. The course of the upper part of the **popliteal artery** (Fig. 1262) is indicated by a line from the lateral margin of Semimembranosus at the junction of the middle and lower thirds of the thigh, obliquely downward to the middle of the popliteal fossa; from this point it runs vertically downward for about 2.5 cm. or to the level of a line through the lower part of the tibial tuberosity. The line indicating the **anterior tibial artery** (Fig. 1261) is drawn from the medial side of the head of the fibula to a point midway between the malleoli; the artery begins about 3 cm. below the head of the fibula. The **dorsalis pedis artery** is represented on the dorsum of the foot by a line from the center of the interval between the malleoli to the proximal end of the first intermetatarsal space.

The course of the **posterior tibial artery** (Fig. 1262) can be shown by a line from the end of the popliteal artery, *i. e.*, 2.5 cm. below the center of the popliteal fossa, to midway between the tip of the medial malleolus and the center of the convexity of the heel; its main branch, the **peroneal artery,** begins about 7 or 8 cm. below the level of the knee-joint and follows the line of the fibula to the back of the lateral malleolus. The **medial** and **lateral plantar arteries** begin from the end of the posterior tibial; the medial extends to the middle of the plantar surface of the ball of the great toe, the lateral to within a finger's breadth of the tuberosity of the fifth metatarsal bone; from this latter point the **plantar arch** crosses the foot transversely to the proximal end of the first intermetatarsal space.

Veins.—The line of the **great saphenous vein** is from the front of the medial malleolus to the center of the fossa ovalis; the **small saphenous vein** runs from the back of the lateral malleolus to the center of the popliteal fossa.

Nerves.—The course of the **sciatic nerve** (Fig. 1262) can be indicated by a line from a point midway between the outer border of the ischial tuberosity and the posterior superior angle of the greater trochanter to the upper angle of the popliteal fossa. The continuation of this line vertically through the center of the popliteal fossa represents the position of the **tibial nerve,** while the **common peroneal nerve** follows the line of the tendon of Biceps femoris. The lines for the **deep peroneal nerve** and the continuation of the **tibial nerve** correspond respectively to those for the anterior and posterior tibial arteries.

INDEX TO BIBLIOGRAPHIES

A

Abel, S., 1139
Abell, R. G., 549
Abbott, L. C., 339
Adams, W. E., 1022
Adelhelm, E., 497
Adelmann, H. B., 1095
Alden, R. H., 1326
Alexander, W. F., 1250
Allen, E., 1324,
Allen, L., 736
Anderson, C. E., 339
Anderson, R. H., 58
Andrew, N. V., 909
Andrew, W., 909
Angel, J. L., 253
Anson, B. J., 497, 498, 499, 500,
    647, 648, 691, 736, 1020, 1095,
    1250, 1324, 1326
Appleton, M. B., 1139
Arey, L. B., 58
Armstrong, P. B., 550
Ashley, F. L., 499, 647, 648, 1021,
    1326
Ashley, L. M., 58, 549
Ashworth, C. T., 909
Astbury, W. T., 58
Atkinson, W. B., 339, 1326
Atkinson, W. J., Jr., 550

B

Bacon, R. L., 550
Baillif, R. N., 1251, 1339
Baker, B. L., 1341
Baker, D. D., 498, 1339
Baker, R. C., 910, 1021
Barclay, A. E., 549
Barcroft, J., 549
Barnard, J. W., 1021
Barnard, M. C., 58
Baron, M. A., 1251
Barron, D. H., 549
Barry, A., 550
Bartelmez, G. W., 1325
Barton, D. S., 1326
Bassett, D. L., 1325
Bast, T. H., 253, 1095
Batson, O. V., 691
Bauer, W., 338
Baumann, J. A., 1323
Baylin, G. J., 648
Beams, H. W., 1022
Beaton, L. E., 497, 498, 691, 1021,
    1250, 1324
Bélanger, L. F., 1138
Benjamin, J. A., 500, 1324
Benmosche, M., 1325
Bennett, G. A., 338, 499, 1341
Bennett, H. S., 58, 1339
Bergmann, L., 1022
Bevelander, G., 1106
Birch, C., 692
Bishop, G. H., 909
Bishop, W. E., 647
Black, B. M., 340
Blalock, A., 550
Blandau, R. J., 1325, 1326
Block, M., 549
Bloom, W., 253
Blount, R. F., 1340
Blumberg, R., 499
Bodel, J. K., Jr., 253
Bost, F. C., 339
Bowie, D. J., 1250
Boyd, J. D., 58, 1341

Boyden, E. A., 1139, 1250, 1251
Brandeberry, N. A., 1324
Brantigan, O. C., 339
Bremer, J. L., 647, 1139
Brenner, C., 909
Brock, R. C., 1139
Brodie, A. G., 253
Brown, J. B., 1340
Brown, J. O., 908
Brown, S., 691
Browne, E. Z., 647
Bruesch, S. R., 1020
Buchanan, A. R., 339
Bueker, E. D., 909
Buirge, R. E., 1250
Bunting, H., 1326
Burch, G. E., 1095
Burlingame, P. L., 549
Burnett, H. W., Jr., 736
Burns, B. I., 1021, 1022
Burns, R. K., Jr., 1324
Burr, H. S., 1325
Burrows, M. T., 1106
Burrows, R. B., 1341
Butcher, E. O., 1106
Butler, H. W., 648

C

Calder, J., 692
Caldwell, W. E., 1326
Callander, C. L., 1251
Cameron, G., 1323
Campbell, B., 497
Cantor, M. O., 1022
Carey, E. J., 497
Carpenter, E., 1341
Carpenter, W. F., 339
Carr, B. W., 647
Casey, E. J., 1095
Cauldwell, E. W., 647, 1020, 1324
Chambers, R., 549, 1323
Chandler, S. B., 498
Chang, Ch., 499
Charles, C. M., 339
Chase, R. E., 550, 648, 692, 1139
Cholnoky, T. de, 1326
Chouke, K. S., 498, 692
Clark, E. L., 253, 499, 648, 1022
Clark, E. R., 253, 499, 549, 648,
    1022
Clark, S. L., 647
Clausen, H. J., 1340, 1341
Clements, L. P., 1139
Cobb, W. M., 253, 550
Codman, E. A., 339
Coggeshall, H. C., 338
Cohn, R., 1139
Cole, A. E., 498
Coller, F. A., 499
Conel, J. L., 910
Congdon, E. D., 499, 648, 1324
Conn, L. C., 692
Copenhaver, W. M., 549, 550
Corbin, K. B., 338, 1021
Cori, C. F., 1339
Corner, G. W., 58, 1324
Coventry, M. B., 339
Cowdry, E. V., 1106
Cox, H. T., 1106
Cox, P. L., 550
Crafts, R. C., 1340
Craigie, E. H., 1341
Cronkite, A. E., 499
Crosby, E. C., 908
Crouch, R. L., 909
Cuajunco, F., 1022

Cummins, H., 1106
Curtis, A. H., 1326

D

DaFoe, A. R., 58
Danforth, C. H., 1324
Daseler, E. H., 497, 498, 691
Davies, J. W., 500, 1326
Davis, C. L., 549
Davis, J. E., 500
Dawkins, E. A., 1021
Dawson, A. B., 1250, 1340
Dawson, H. L., 1250
De Bruyn, P. P. H., 549
De Garis, C. F., 550, 647, 648, 692
DeRobertis, E. D. P., 1341
D'Esopo, D. A., 1326
Dean, J. L., 550
Deane, H. W., 1250
Dempsey, E. W., 1326
Detwiler, S. R., 910, 1021, 1095
DeVita, J., 1326
Dey, F. L., 1324
Deysach, L. J., 1325
Dixon, F. W., 736, 1095
Doisy, E. A., 1324
Dott, N. M., 1249
Dougherty, T. F., 909, 1340
Douglass, P. M., 1325
Drager, G. A., 1021
Drinker, C. K., 736
DuBois, F. S., 1021
Duke, K. L., 1325
Duncan, D., 1021
Duntley, S. Q., 1106
DuShane, G. P., 910
Dwinnell, L. A., 550
Dykes, J., 497

E

Eastlick, H. L., 58, 498
Edelmann, A., 1340
Edson, J. N., 499, 1324
Edwards, A. E., 692
Edwards, J. E., 692
Edwards, J. G., 1324
Edwards, L. F., 647, 1021, 1095
Elftman, A. G., 1139
Elftman, H., 253, 339, 498, 1326,
    1340
Elliott, H. C., 908
Ellison, F. S., 1095
Emmel, A. F., 497
Emmel, V. M., 1323
Enbom, G., 1249
Enders, R. K., 58
Engle, E. T., 1324, 1326
Etkin, W., 1340
Evans, F. G., 254
Everett, J. W., 1325
Everett, N. B., 1324, 1325
Eversole, W. J., 1340

F

Fain, W. R., 1340
Fales, D. E., 550
Farris, E. J., 1325
Fenton, R. A., 1095
Finley, K. H., 909
Fitzgerald, J. E., 910
Flexner, L. B., 1339
Flynn, J. E., 499
Foerster, O., 1021

Foley, J. O., 1020
Foote, W. R., 1326
Forester, H. B., 1095
Fox, C. A., 909
Francis, C. C., 253
Franklin, K. J., 549, 692
Friedgood, H. B., 1340
Friedman, I., 1326
Friedman, S. M., 692, 1250

G

Gallaudet, B. B., 499
Gardner, E., 339, 909
Gardner, E. D., 339
Gardner, W. U., 1326
Gatz, A. J., 1324
Gaunt, R., 1340
Geiling, E. M. K., 1340
George, W. C., 58
Gersh, I., 1339, 1340
Ghormley, J. W., 339
Ghormley, R. K., 339
Gladstone, S., 1250
Glücksmann, A., 254
Godwin, M. C., 736
Goff, B. H., 500, 1326
Goldsmith, J. B., 648
Goldstein, M. S., 1095
Gomori, G., 1251
Goss, C. M., 58, 497, 549, 550
Goss, L. J., 908
Grafflin, A. L., 1251
Graves, G. O., 910, 1095
Gray, D. J., 253, 254, 339, 497
Gray, H., 549
Grayson, J., 499
Grégoire, C., 736
Grenell, R. G., 910
Greulich, W. W., 1326
Groat, R. A., 1340
Grodinsky, M., 499
Grollman, A., 1339
Gross, L., 550
Gruenwald, P., 1323, 1339
Gushue-Taylor, G., 1251

H

Haines, R. W., 339
Hair, G. W., 1341
Haley, J. C., 1250
Hall, B. V., 58
Hall, C. E., 499
Hall, V. E., 736
Hamilton, J. B., 58, 1106, 1324, 1326
Hamilton, W. J., 58
Hamlett, G. W. D., 58, 1324, 1326
Hammond, G., 500
Hammond, W. S., 1022, 1250
Hansmann, G. H., 1251
Harbin, R. M., 1249
Hard, W. L., 1251
Harman, P. J., 909
Harris, A. J., 1021
Harrison, F., 1021
Harrison, R. G., 58
Hartman, C. G., 58
Hartman, J. F., 1139, 1340
Harvey, H. T., 1251
Harvey, J. C., 647
Hasterlik, R. J., 1325
Haxton, H. A., 339
Hayward, R., 1251
Hegre, E. S., 1340
Henderson, J. M., 1106
Henry, W., 499
Herrnheiser, G., 1138
Hertig, A. T., 58
Hetherington, D. C., 549
Hill, A. H., 253
Hill, H., 498
Hill, R. T., 1325
Hinsey, J. C., 338

Hinton, J. W., 1021
Hirsch, E. F., 1325
Hoerr, N. L., 736, 909, 1095, 1339
Hogg, I. D., 910, 1021
Hollinshead, W. H., 1339, 1341
Holyoke, E. A., 499
Hooker, C. W., 1324, 1326
Hooker, D., 58
Horwitz, M. T., 1021
House, E. L., 1340
Howard, L. M., 647
Howell, A. B., 253, 498
Huber, J. F., 647, 1139
Huggins, C., 253
Hughes, E. S. R., 254
Humphrey, T., 910
Hunt, T. E., 1249, 1341
Huntington, G. S., 1139, 1251
Hutchinson, R. C., 498

I

Ingram, W. R., 1021
Inman, V. T., 339

J

Jackson, C. L., 1139
Jakus, M. A., 499
Janes, R. G., 1251
Janzen, J., 58
Jarcho, J., 1325
Johnson, A. L., 550
Johnson, P. L., 1106
Johnstone, A. S., 1250
Jones, D. S., 1021, 1022
Jones, F. W., 499
Jones, L., 339
Jones, R. L., 340
Jones, T., 1326
Jordan, H. E., 58, 497, 1139
Joy, E. A., 1095

K

Kammeraad, A., 58, 1249
Kampmeier, O. F., 692
Kanavel, A. B., 499
Kaplan, E. B., 339, 499
Karsner, H. T., 1326
Keegan, J. J., 1021
Keen, J. A., 550, 692
Kendall, E. C., 1340
Kennedy, J. A., 647
Kennerdell, E. H., 550
Kernohan, J. W., 339
Kerr, A. T., 1021
Kessler, W. H., 1020
Key, J. A., 338
Keyes, E. L., 498
Keyser, L. L., 1021
Kilham, L., 1339
Kimmel, D. L., 1020
Kindred, J. E., 58, 736
Kirgis, H. D., 1021
Kirkman, H., 1250, 1323
Kirschbaum, A., 1325, 1340
Klemme, R. M., 909
Klumpp, T. G., 550
Knisely, M. H., 736
Knouff, R. A., 1340
Krahl, V. E., 254
Kramer, T. C., 550, 1325
Krogman, W., 254
Kropp, B. N., 339
Krumbhaar, E. B., 736
Kugel, M. A., 550
Kuhlenbeck, H., 908
Kuntz, A., 1022, 1095, 1325

L

Lachmann, E., 339, 1139
Lacroix, P., 253
Lambertsen, C. J., 550

Lander, H. H., 1250
Landis, E. M., 549
Langman, L., 1325
Langworthy, O. R., 1250, 1324
Lanier, R. R., Jr., 254
Lansing, W., 499
Larsell, O., 1095, 1139
Lasker, G. W., 254
Lassek, A. M., 908
Latimer, H. B., 908
Latta, J. S., 1251
Lauer, E. W., 909
Lee, F. C., 499
Leonard, S. L., 1324
Letterman, G. S., 254
Lev, M., 550
Levi, G., 909
Lewis, W. H., 58
Limson, M., 253
Lippincott, S. W., 736
Long, J. A., 549
Long, J. H., 1325
Long, M. E., 497
Lord, J. W., 1021
Lord, F. P., 338
Low, F. N., 647
Lyman, R. Y., 1250

M

MacGregor, J. W., 692
McCarty, R. B., 1251
McCormack, L. J., 1020
McCotter, R. E., 908
McCrady, E., 58
McDonald, J. J., 648
McFarland, W. E., 1340
McFetridge, E. M., 1326
McGregor, A. L., 500
McKenzie, F. F., 1339
McKinniss, M. E., 1022
McLaughlin, H. L., 339
McLean, F. C., 253
McNutt, C. W., 692
McQuitty, J. T., 1106
McVay, C. B., 498, 499, 500
Mackenzie, D. W., Jr., 736
Macklin, C. C., 1138
Mahan, E., 549
Maliniac, J. W., 1326
Mann, F. C., 1250
Mann, I., 1095
Manter, J. T., 340, 498
Marsh, G., 1022
Martin, C. P., 339, 500
Martin, M. E., 1325
Marvin, H. N., 1325
Mason, K. E., 497
Massopust, L., 497
Mayo, C. W., 1251
Menkin, M. F., 58
Mettier, S. R., 550
Mettler, F. A., 908
Meyer, H., 909
Meyer, R., 1324
Michels, N. A., 647, 736
Michelson, M., 253
Miller, J. M., 1251
Miller, R. A., 498, 500, 647, 1021, 1138
Miller, R. N., 908
Miller, W. S., 1139
Mills, J. C., 1324
Minckler, D. B., 909
Minckler, J., 909
Ming-Tzu, P., 648
Mofshin, B., 1341
Molander, D., 1340
Moloy, H. C., 1326
Montagu, M. F. A., 254, 498, 1250
Moody, R. O., 1323
Morato, M. J. X., 1341
Morgan, C. F., 1326
Morgan, E. H., 498
Morris, R. E., Jr., 1325
Morton, D. J., 340

Morton, S. A., 1251
Morton, T. H., 1250
Mossman, H. W., 58, 1329
Mulholland, J. H., 1021
Munger, R. S., 648
Murnaghan, D. P., 1022
Murphy, E. L., 1324
Murray, M. R., 498, 1022
Murray, P. D. F., 253

N

Nachlas, I. W., 1021
Naham, L. J., 1339
Nation, E. F., 1323
Nelson, W. O., 1339
Nemir, A., 1251
Nicholas, J. S., 58
Nicoll, P. A., 736
Noback, C. R., 253
Noback, G. J., 647
Noer, R. J., 1250
Nonidez, J. F., 550, 1022, 1250
Nordland, M., 1341
Norris, E. H., 736, 1341

O

Ohler, E. A., 1021
Oldham, F. K., 1340
O'Leary, J. L., 909
Oliver, J., 1323
Ortega, L., 1250
Overholser, M. D., 1341

P

Paff, G. H., 550
Pankratz, D. C., 1325
Papez, J. W., 909
Park, E. A., 253
Patek, P. R., 736, 909
Patten, B. M., 58, 550
Pearson, A. A., 1020
Pearson, O. P., 58
Peden, J. K., 1250
Peele, T. L., 909
Peirce, E. C., 736, 1324
Pepper, H. R., 1020
Peters, H. C., 1250
Pfeiffer, C. A., 1325
Pheasant, H. C., 254
Pierson, J. M., 1251
Pincus, G., 1325
Pick, J. W., 647, 736, 1324
Plagge, J. C., 1341
Pogogeff, I. A., 498
Popoff, A., 1340
Poynter, C. W. M., 550, 648
Power, R. M. H., 1326
Present, A. J., 1251
Prichard, M. M. L., 549
Pryor, J. W., 253
Puckett, W. O., 1341

R

Ramsay, A. J., 1341
Rasmussen, A. T., 909, 1139, 1340
Rasmussen, G. L., 908
Read, W. T., 647
Reed, A. F., 908, 1021
Reed, S. C., 1106
Reese, J. D., 1022
Rehman, I., 647
Reimann, A. F., 498, 691
Reinhardt, W. O., 736
Reynolds, S. R. M., 1325
Richardson, G. E., 58
Richins, C. A., 1095, 1251
Richter, K. M., 549, 1341
Rienhoff, W. F., 1341
Rioch, D. McK., 909
Rives, J. D., 498
Robinson, B. E., 339
Robuck, J. D., Jr., 692
Rock, J., 58
Rockwell, H., 254
Romano, S. A., 1326

Ronstrom, G. N., 1324
Ropes, M. W., 338
Ross, J. B., 550
Rouvière, H., 736
Rudall, K. M., 58
Rukstinat, G. J., 1325
Rumble, C. T., 1250
Rusk, G. Y., 1251
Russell, W. L., 1325
Ruth, E. B., 338

S

Saccomanno, G., 1021
Salmon, T. N., 1339
Saltzman, A., 339
Sandstrom, C. J., 339
Saphir, O., 550
Sauer, M. E., 1250
Saunders, J. B., 339
Saunders, R. L., 254, 339
Sawin, P. B., 254, 692
Scammon, R. E., 910
Schadewald, M., 498, 909
Schaeffer, J. P., 1095
Scharrer, E., 647
Schmitt, F. O., 499
Schneider, B. M., 1340
Schneider, C. L., 340
Schneider, L. A., 692
Schofield, N. D., 647
Schulze, J. W., 1250
Schunke, G. B., 339
Schwind, J. L., 58, 1340
Sears, N. P., 500, 1326
Seib, G. A., 498
Sellmann, A. H., 1022
Selye, H., 1250, 1326
Senior, H. D., 648
Sensenig, E. C., 253
Severinghaus, A. E., 1340
Seybold, W. D., 909
Seymour, F. I., 1325
Shaft, B., 1021
Shah, M. A., 254, 1250
Shaner, R. F., 58, 549, 692
Shanklin, W. M., 1340
Shapiro, H. H., 338
Sharples, W., 1250
Sheehan, D., 1021
Short, A. R., 1251
Shryock, E. H., 58, 1250
Simer, P. H., 736
Simon, H. E., 1324
Sinclair, J. G., 550, 647
Singer, E., 499
Smith, H. W., 1323
Smith, P. E., 1341
Snook, T., 736
Soderwall, A. L., 1326
Solnitzky, O. C., 909
Specht, N. W., 1250
Spector, B., 1095
Speidel, C. C., 497
Spemann, H., 58
Sperry, R. W., 498
Sprague, J. M., 1022, 1250
Spratt, N. T., Jr., 58, 1095
Stalker, L. K., 1251
Stearns, M. L., 499
Stein, M. R., 338
Stewart, T. D., 339
Stone, L. S., 1095
Stout, A. P., 1022
Straus, W. L., Jr., 254, 498
Strayer, L. M., Jr., 339
Streeter, G. L., 58
Strong, K. C., 648
Strong, L. C., 1324
Strong, L. H., 1138
Sulkin, N. M., 1250
Sullens, W. E., 1341
Sunderland, S., 254, 498, 550, 1021
Swinyard, C. A., 1339
Szepsenwol, J., 498

T

Telford, I. R., 498, 1250
Terry, R. J., 498, 1139
Thomas, T. B., 1251
Thompson, H. C., Jr., 1106
Thoms, H., 1326
Thorek, M., 1326
Tobias, R. J., 736
Tobin, C. E., 500, 1324
Todd, T. W., 253
Torrey, T. W., 1323
Trotter, M., 254, 647, 648, 1106
Truex, R. C., 338, 549, 1022
Truszkowski, R., 1340
Turner, C. D., 1340
Turner, M. L., 736
Turner, R. S., 909

U

Uotila, U. U., 1339

V

Van Cleave, C. D., 692
Van Del, D. T., 498
Van Nuys, R. G., 1323
Vann, H. M., 647
Visscher, M. B., 1250
Von Bonin, G., 1250
Voshell, A. F., 339

W

Waine, H., 338
Waits, W. J., 1106
Wakim, K. G., 1250
Walker, A. E., 909
Waller, W. H., 909
Warner, F. J., 910
Warren, C. F., 338
Warshaw, L. J., 549
Washburn, S. L., 253, 254
Waterman, A. J., 1323
Wearn, J. T., 550
Weatherford, H. L., 1250
Weaver, H. M., 1339
Webb, R. L., 736
Weinstein, B. B., 1021
Welch, A. de M., 1339
Weller, G. L., 1341
Wells, H. G., 499
Wells, J. C., 500
Wells, L. J., 1325, 1340
Wesson, M. B., 500, 1325
Whipple, A. A., 736
White, A., 1340
Williams, R. G., 1339, 1340, 1341
Williams, W. L., 1326
Willis, T. A., 339
Wilmer, H. A., 1324
Windle, W. F., 58, 910, 1139
Wintersteiner, M. P., 736
Wislocki, G. B., 58, 1326
Wolfe, J. M., 58, 499, 1324, 1340, 1341
Wollin, D. G., 550
Woodburne, R. T., 908, 1139
Wotton, R. M., 1323, 1339
Wright, R. R., 497
Wright-Smith, R. J., 550

Y

Yanitelli, S., 499
Yglesias, L., 499, 500
Yntema, C. L., 1022
Yoffey, J. M., 736
Young, E. G., 339
Young, H. H., 1324
Youngstrom, K. A., 908

Z

Zeit, W., 497
Zieman, S. A., 500
Zschiesche, L. J., 550
Zweifach, B. W., 549
Zwemer, R. L., 1323, 1339

SUBJECT INDEX

Italics Indicate Latin Terms

A

ABDOMEN, 1189
 apertures in walls of, 1190
 boundaries of, 1190
 fascia of, 392
  triangular, 396
 lymph nodes of, 714
 muscles of, 392
 regions of, 1190
 surface anatomy of, 1376
  markings of, 1381
Abdominal aorta, 608
 surface markings of, 1391
 aortic plexus, 1017
 muscles, 392
 ring, deep, 405
  external, 395
  inguinal, 405
  internal, 405
 viscera, surface markings of, 1381
 wall, lymphatic vessels of, 717
Abducent nerve, 929
 composition and central connections of, 888
Abduction of joints, 263
Abductor digiti quinti muscle (foot), 493
 (hand), 471
 hallucis muscle, 492
 indicis muscle, 463
 minimi digiti muscle, 461, 493
 pollicis brevis muscle, 459
  longus muscle, 448
  muscle, 459
Abnormalities of urinary bladder, 1283
 of vertebral column, 95
Accelerator urinæ muscle, 418
Accessory hemiazygos vein, 676
 nerve, 942
  composition and central connections of, 882
  cranial part of, 942
  spinal part of, 942
 obturator nerve, 984
 olivary nuclei, 802
 organs of digestive tube, 1141
  of eye, 1051
 pancreatic duct, 1248
 part of parotid gland, 1174
 processes, 85
 pudendal artery, 624
 sinuses of nose, 1030
 spleens, 732
 thyroid glands, 1329
Acetabular fossa, 212
 notch, 212
Acetabulum, 212
Acoustic meatus, external, 112, 150, 1067
  development of, 1061
  internal, 123, 148
 nerve, 935, 1067
  composition and central connections of, 884
  development of, 1062
  nuclei of, 806, 935
Acromioclavicular joint, 291
 movements of, 292
 surface anatomy of, 1401, 1407
Acromion, 180
Acromiothoracic artery, 593
Adam's apple, 1109

Adductor brevis muscle, 472
 canal, 603
  surface anatomy of, 1426
 hallucis muscle, 495
 longus muscle, 472
 magnus muscle, 473
 minimus muscle, 473
 obliquus hallucis muscle, 495
 pollicis muscle, 461
 transversus muscle, 461
 transversus pollicis muscle, 461
 tubercle, 221
Adipose capsule of kidney, 1267
Adminiculum lineæ albæ, 403
Adrenal gland, 1336
 lymphatic capillaries, in,
Afferent nerves, 762
 vessels of kidney, 1272
After-birth, 34
Agger nasi, 166
Aggregated lymphatic nodules, 1221
Agminated follicles, 1221
Air cells, ethmoidal, 159, 1031
  mastoid, 146
 sinuses of nose, 1030
Ala cinerea, 817
 nasi, 1024
 oss. ilii, 207
Alæ of ethmoid, 158
 of sacrum, 89
 of vomer, 174
Alar cartilages of nose, 1024
 lamina, 739
Alcock's canal, 414, 996
Alimentary canal, 1141
 lymphatic capillaries in 696
Allantoic vessels, 35
Allantois, 35
Alveolar arch, 166
 arteries, 569, 570
 border of mandible, 129
 nerves, 920, 926
 point, 166
 process of maxilla, 166
Alveoli, formation of, 1164
Alveus, 876
Amacrine cells of retina, 1047
Ameloblasts, 1162
Amitosis, 19
Amnion, 34
Amniotic cavity, 34
Amphiarthroses, 261
Ampulla of ductus deferens, 1296
 of rectum, 1228
 of semicircular canal, 1079
 of uterine tube, 1308
 of Vater, 1244
Ampullæ of tubuli lactiferi, 1322
Amygdala, 863
Amygdaloid nucleus, 898
Anal canal or anal part of rectum 1229
 development of, 1149
 lymphatic vessels of, 722
 membrane of, 1151
 valves of, 1230
 fascia, 412
Anaphase of karyokinesis, 19
Anastomoses of arteries, 551
 around elbow-joint, 598
  knee-joint, 640
 crucial, 636
Anastomotic branch of inferior gluteal artery, 627

Anastomotica magna of brachial artery, 598
 of femoral artery, 636
Anatomical neck of humerus, 183
Anconæus muscle, 446
Angioblasts, 42, 502
Angiology, 501
Angle of mandible, 130
 of pubis, 211
 of rib, 102
 sacrovertebral, 85
 of sternum, 99
 subscapular, 179
Angular artery, 561
 gyrus, 845
 movement, 262
 vein, 653
Animal cell, 17
Ankle bone, 242
 of child aged ten years, x-ray of, 1420
Ankle-joint, 327
 movements of, 329
 relations of tendons and vessels to, 329
 surface anatomy of, 1417
  markings of, 1425
Annular ligament, 452
 of ankle, 489
 of radius, 301
 of wrist, anterior, 452
  posterior, 452
Annulus fibrosus [of intervertebral fibrocartilage], 266
 inguinalis abdominis, 405
 subcutaneus, 395
 ovalis, 534
 tendineus communis [eye] 1053
Anococcygeal body, 1229
 nerves, 997
 raphè, 407,
Ansa hypoglossi, 958
 subclavia [*Vieussenii*] 1011
Antebrachial cutaneous nerve, dorsal, 973
  lateral, 965
  medial, 966
 fascia, 438
Antecubital fossa, 595
Anterior annular ligament, ankle, 489
  wrist, 452,
 basis bundle, 778
 calcaneoastragaloid ligament, 330
 cerebral artery, 576
 choroidal artery, 578
 circumflex artery, 594
 common ligament, vertebral, 264
 communicating artery, 576
 condyloid foramen, 136
 costotransverse ligament, 277
 costovertebral ligament, 276
 crural nerve, 984
 humeral circumflex artery, 594
 inferior tibiofibular ligament, 326
 intercostal arteries, 589 interosseous artery, 604
  nerve, 967
 jugular vein, surface markings of, 1361
 ligament, knee, 318
  wrist, 303

(1431)

Anterior peroneal artery, 644
  pillar of fauces, 1177
  pulmonary nerves, 941
  radial carpal artery, 600
  radioulnar ligament, 303
  superior dental nerve, 920
    ligament, costotransverse, 277
    tibiofibular, 326
  talotibial ligament, 328
  temporal artery, 566
  tibial nerve, 994
  ulnar carpal artery, 604
    recurrent artery, 602
Antihelix, 1065
Antitragicus muscle, 1066
Antitragus, 1065
Antrum cardiacum, 1207
  of Highmore, 164, 1031
  pyloric, 1208
  tympanic, 147, 1072
    entrance to, 1073
Anus, 1141, 1143
  lymphatic vessels of, 722
Aorta, 553
  abdominal, 608
    branches of, 608
  arch of, 555
    branches of, 556
    peculiarities of, 556
  ascendens, 553
  ascending, 553
  descending, 553, 605
  thoracalis, 605
    rami mediastinales, 606
    pericardiaci, 605
  thoracic, 605
    branches of, 605
  transverse, 555
Aortæ, dorsal, 512
  primitive, 502
  ventral, 511
Aortic arches, 511
  development of, 511
  bodies, 1095, 1335
  cusp, 538
  glands, 1335
  hiatus, 390, 1190
  isthmus, 512, 555
  lymph nodes, 716
  opening of heart, 538
  plexus of sympathetic, 1017
  receptors, 1094
  semilunar valves, 538
  septum, 508
  sinuses, 538, 554
  spindle, 555
  vestibule, 538
Aorticorenal ganglion, 1016
Apertura pelvis [minoris] inferior, 215
    superior, 214
    tympanica canaliculi chordæ, 1069
Aperture, anterior nasal, 115, 125
Apertures in walls of abdomen, 1190
Apex cordis, 532
  of fibula, 235
  of heart, 532
  linguæ, 1165
  of nose, 1024
  oss. sacri, 89
  prostatæ, 1303
  pulmonis, 1130
Aponeurosis, 346
  epicranial, 353
  lumbocostal, 379
  lumbar, 379
  of obliquus externus, 395
  palatine, 1180
  palmar, 453
  palmaris, 453
  pharyngeal, 1187
  plantar, 491
  plantaris, 491
  suprahyoid, 371

Apparatus digestorius, 1141
  juxtaglomerular, 1273
  lacrimalis, 1058
  respiratorius, 1107
  urogenitalis, 1253
Appendages of testis, 1292
Appendices epiploicæ, 1222
  vesiculosæ, 1308
Appendicular artery, 615
  skeleton, 59
Appendix, auricular, left, 537
    right, 533
  ensiform, 100
  of epididymis, 1292
  testis, 1292
  of ventricle of larynx, 1117
  ventriculi larngis, 1117
  vermiform, 1223
  xiphoid, 100
Aquæductus Fallopii, 148
  vestibuli, 148, 1079
Aqueduct, cerebral, 824
  of cochlea, 110, 148
  of Sylvius, 824
Aqueous humor, 1049
Arachnoid, 903
  granulations, 139, 662
  structure of, 904
  villi, 905
Arachnoidea encephali, 903
  spinalis, 903
Arantii, corpus, 536
Arbor vitæ [of cerebellum], 809
  uterina, 1312
Arch or arches, alveolar, 166
  of aorta, 555
  aortic, 511
  of atlas, 78
  axillary, 424
  branchial or visceral, 45
  carotid, 511
  crural, deep 405
  of fauces, 1154, 1176
  of foot, 338
  glossopalatine, 1177
  hyoid, 47
  lumbocostal, lateral, 388
    medial, 388
  mandibular, 46
  palmar, deep, 601
    superficial, 604
  pharyngopalatine, 1177
  plantar, 645
  pubic, 215
  superciliary, 107, 111, 141
  vertebral, 75
    articulations of, 266
  volar, deep, 604
    superficial, 604
  zygomatic, 113
Architecture of femur, 223
Arcuate artery, 643, 1274
  fibers, 803
  ligaments of diaphragm, 388
  line of ilium, 206
  nucleus, 802
  popliteal ligament, 318
Arcus aortæ, 555
  cartilaginis cricoideæ, 1110
  glossopalatinus, 1177
  lumbocostalis lateralis [Halleri], 388
    medialis [Halleri] 388
  parieto-occipitalis, 845
  pharyngopalatinus, 1177
  volaris profundus, 604
    superficialis, 604
Area acoustica, 806
  cribrosa media, 148
    superior, 148
  facialis, 148
  olfactory, 48
  oval, of Flechsig, 782
  parolfactoria, 857
  pericardial, 41
  postrema, 799

Areas of cerebral cortex, 871, 873
Areola of mamma, 1320
Areolæ of bone, 72
Areolar glands, 1320
Arm bone, 183
  fascia of, 434
  muscles of, 434
    development of, 341
Arnold's nerve, 940
Arrectores pilorum muscle, 1104
Arteria alveolaris inferior, 569
    superior posterior, 569
  angularis, 563
  anonyma, 556
  arcuata, 643
  auditiva interna, 584
  auricularis posterior, 565
    profunda, 567
  axillaris, 591
  basilaris, 584
    rami ad pontem, 584
  brachialis, 595
    rami musculares, 598
  buccinatoria, 569
  bulbi urethræ, 625
  canalis pterygoidei, 570, 573
  carotis communis, 557
    externa, 559
    interna, 570
      ramus caroticotympanicus, 572
  centralis retinæ, 575, 1048
  cerebelli inferior anterior, 584
    posterior, 584
    superior, 584
  cerebri anterior, 576
    media, 577
    posterior, 585
  cervicalis ascendens, 586
    profunda, 590
    superficialis, 587
  chorioidea, 578
  circumflexa femoris lateralis, 636
    medialis, 636
    humeri anterior, 594
      posterior, 594
    ilii profunda, 629
      superficialis, 635
    scapulæ, 594
  cœliaca, 608
  colica dextra, 615
    media, 615
    sinistra, 615
  collateralis ulnaris inferior, 598
    superior, 597
  comes nervi phrenici, 588
  comitans nervi ischiadici, 627
  communicans anterior, 576
    posterior, 578
  coronaria [cordis] dextra, 554
    sinistra, 555
  cystica, 612
  dorsalis hallucis, 643
    nasi, 575
    pedis, 642
      ramus plantaris profundus, 643
  penis, 626
  epigastrica inferior, 629
    superficialis, 635
    superior, 589
  femoralis, 630
    rami musculares, 636
  frontalis, 575
  gastrica dextra, 610
    sinistra, 609
  gastroduodenalis, 611
  gastroepiploica dextra, **611**
    sinistra, 612
  genus media, 639
    suprema, 637
  glutæa inferior, 626
    ramus iliacus, 627
      lumbalis, 627
    superior, 628

Arteria hæmorrhoidalis inferior, 625
 media, 622
 superior, 616
hepatica, 610
hypogastrica, 620
ileocolica, 615
iliaca externa, 628
iliolumbalis, 627
infraorbitalis, 569
interossea communis, 603
 dorsalis, 604
 volaris, 604
labialis inferior, 563
 superior, 563
lacrimalis, 573
laryngea inferior, 586
 superior, 560
lienalis, 612
 rami pancreatici, 612
lingualis, 560
 rami dorsales linguæ, 561
 ramus hyoideus, 560
malleolaris anterior lateralis, 642
 medalis, 642
 posterior medialis, 645
mammaria interna, 587
 rami intercostales, 589
 perforantes, 589
 sternales, 589
masseterica, 569
maxillaris externa, 561
 rami glandulares, 562
 ramus tonsillaris, 562
 interna, 566
 rami pterygoidei, 569
 ramus meningeus accessorius, 568
mediana, 604
meningea anterior, 573
 media, 568
mesenterica inferior, 615
 superior, 612
musculophrenica, 589
nutricia fibulæ, 644
 humeri, 597
 tibiæ, 645
obturatoria, 622
occipitalis, 564
 rami musculares, 564
 ramus auricularis, 564
 descendens, 564
 meningeus, 564
ophthalmica, 573
palatina ascendens, 561
 descendens, 570
pancreatica magna, 612
pancreaticoduodenalis inferior, 613
 superior, 611
perforans prima, 637
 secunda, 637
 tertia, 637
pericardiacophrenica, 588
perinei, 625
peronœa, 644
 ramus calcaneus lateralis, 645
 communicans, 645
 perforans, 644
pharyngea ascendens, 565
 rami pharyngei, 565
plantaris lateralis, 645
 medialis, 645
poplitea, 638
princeps cervicis, 564
 hallucis, 647
 pollicis, 601
profunda brachii, 597
 femoris, 636
 linguæ, 561
 penis, 626
pudenda externa profunda, 635
 superficialis, 635
 interna, 623

Arteria pulmonalis, 553
 ramus dexter, 553
 sinister, 553
radialis, 599
 rami musculares, 600
 perforantes, 601
 ramus carpeus dorsalis, 600
 volaris, 600
 volaris superficialis, 600
recurrens radialis, 600
 tibialis anterior, 642
 posterior, 642
 ulnaris anterior, 602
 posterior, 602
sacralis lateralis, 627
 media, 618
sphenopalatina, 570
spinalis anterior, 584
 posterior, 583
sternocleidomastoidea, 564
 stylomastoidea, 565
subclavia, 580
sublingualis, 561
submentalis, 563
subscapularis, 594
supraorbitalis, 573
tarsea lateralis, 643
 mediales, 643
temporalis, media, 566
 superficialis, 566
 rami auriculares anteriores, 566
 ramus frontalis, 566
 parietalis, 566
thoracalis lateralis, 593
 suprema, 592
thoracoacromialis, 593
thoracodorsalis, 594
thyreoidea ima, 556
 inferior, 586
 rami, œsophagei, 586
 tracheales, 586
 superior, 559
 ramus cricothyreoideus, 560
 hyoideus, 560
 sternocleidomastoideus, 560
tibialis anterior, 641
 rami musculares, 642
 posterior, 644
 rami calcanei mediales, 645
 ramus communicans, 645
transversa colli, 590
 ramus ascendens, 590
 descendens, 590
 faciei, 566
 scapulæ, 586
tympanica anterior, 567
 inferior, 565
ulnaris, 601
 rami musculares, 604
 ramus carpeus dorsalis, 604
 volaris, 604
 profundus, 604
urethralis, 626
uterina, 622
vaginalis, 622
vertebralis, 582
 rami spinales, 583
 ramus meningeus, 583
vesicalis inferior, 621
 medialis, 621
 superior, 621
 volaris indicis radialis, 601
Arteriæ bronchiales, 605
 ciliares, 576
 digitales volares communes, 605
 propriæ, 605
 gastricæ breves, 612
 genus inferiores, 640
 superiores, 639
 iliacæ communes, 619
 intercostales, 606
 intestinales, 613
 lumbales, 618

Arteriæ mediastinales anteriores, 589
 metacarpeæ volaris, 601
 metarseæ plantares, 647
 œsophageæ, 606
 ovaricæ, 617
 palpebrales mediales, 574
 phrenicæ inferiores, 618
 rectæ, 1274
 renales, 617
 sacrales laterales, 627
 sigmoideæ, 616
 spermaticæ internæ, 617
 suprarenales mediæ, 617
 surales, 639
 tarseæ laterales, 643
 mediales, 643
 tunica adventitia, 521
 intima, 521
 media, 521
Arterial mesocardium, 529
Arterioles, 501
Artery or Arteries, abdominal aorta, 608
 accessory meningeal, 568
 pudendal, 624
 acromiothoracic, 593
 alveolar, 569
 anastomoses of, 551
 anastomotic branch of inferior gluteal, 627
 anastomotica magna, of brachial, 598
 of femoral, 637
 angular, 563
 anterior cerebral, 576
 choroidal, 578
 ciliary, 576
 communicating, 576
 humeral circumflex, 594
 inferior cerebellar, 584
 meningeal, 573
 spinal, 584
 tibial, 641
 tympanic, 567
 aorta, 553
 abdominal, 608
 arch of, 555
 ascending, 553
 descending, 605
 thoracic, 605
 appendicular, 615
 arcuate, 643, 1274
 articular, of knee, 639
 ascending cervical 586
 palatine, 561
 pharyngeal, 565
 auditory, 584
 internal, 584
 auricular, anterior, 566
 deep, 567
 of occipital, 564
 posterior, 565
 axillary, 591
 azygos, of knee, 639
 of vagina, 622
 basilar, 584
 brachial, 595
 brachiocephalic, 556
 brain, 579
 bronchial, 605, 1137
 buccal, 569
 buccinator, 569
 bulbar, 584
 calcaneal, 645
 calcarine, 585
 capsular, middle, 617
 caroticotympanic, 572
 carotid, common, 557
 external, 559
 internal, 570
 carpal, dorsal, 601
 radial, 600
 ulnar, 604
 volar, 601, 604
 cavernous, 573

Artery or Arteries cecal, ileocolic, 615
central, of retina, 575, 1035, 1048
cerebellar, 584
cerebral, anterior, 576
  hemorrhage, 577
  middle, 577
  posterior, 584
cervical, ascending, 586
  deep, 590
  superficial, 587
  transverse, 590
choroid, 578
choroidal, 578, 585
ciliary, 576
circle of Willis, 579
circumflex, femoral, 636
  humeral, 594
  iliac, 635
coccygeal of inferior gluteal, 626
cochlear, 1090
cœliac, 608
colic, 615
comitans nervi ischiadici, 627
  phrenici, 588
common carotid, 557
  iliac, 619
  interosseous, 603
communicating, anterior, 576
  of dorsalis pedis, 643
  posterior, 578
coronary, of heart, 554
  of stomach, 609
corpus cavernosum, 626
costocervical trunk, 589
cremasteric, 629
cricothyroid, 560
cystic, 612
deep auricular, 567
  brachial, 596
  epigastric, 629
  external pudendal, 635
  femoral, 636
  iliac circumflex, 629
  lingual, 561
  palmar arch, 601
  penis, 624, 626
  plantar, 643
  temporal, 569
  volar branch of ulnar, 604
dental, inferior, 569
  posterior, 569
descending aorta, 605
  branch of occipital, 564
  palatine, 570
digital, foot, 647
  hand, 605
  volar, 605
distribution of, 551
dorsal carpal of radial, 600
  of ulnar, 604
  interosseous, 603
  metacarpal, 601
  nasal, 575
  of penis, 626
dorsales linguæ, 561
dorsalis hallucis, 643
  pedis, 642
  scapulæ, 594
of ductus deferens, 621
epigastric, deep or inferior, 629
  superficial, 635
  superior, 587, 589
esophageal, of aorta, 606
  of inferior thyroid, 586
ethmoidal, 574
external carotid, 559
  iliac, 628
  maxillary, 561
  plantar, 645
  pudendal, 635
  spermatic, 629
facial, 561
  transverse, 566

Artery or Arteries, femoral, 630
  circumflex, 636
fibular, 642
frontal, 575
gastric, 609, 610
gastroduodenal, 611
gastroepiploic, 611
genicular, 637, 639
glandular, submaxillary, 562
gluteal, 626, 628
head and neck, 557
helicine, 1303
hemorrhoidal, inferior, 625
  middle, 622
  superior, 616
hepatic, 610
highest genicular, 637
  intercostal 589
  thoracic, 592
humeral circumflex, 594
hyoid, 560
hypogastric, 620
  obliterated 620
hypophyseal, 573
ileal, of ileocolic, 615
ileocolic, 615
iliac circumflex, 627, 635
  common, 619
  external, 628
  internal, 620
iliolumbar, 627
inferior alveolar, 569
  articular, of knee, 640
  cerebellar, 584
  dental, 569
  epigastric, 629
  genicular, 640
  gluteal, 626
  hemorrhoidal, 625
  labial, 563
  laryngeal, 586
  mesenteric, 615
  pancreaticoduodenal, 613
  phrenic, 618
  profunda, 597
  thyroid, 586
  tympanic, 565
  ulnar collateral, 598
  vesical, 621
infrahyoid, 560
infraorbital, 569
infrascapular, 594
innominate, 556
intercostal, 606, 607
  branches of internal mammary, 589
  superior, 589
interlobular, of kidney, 1275
internal auditory, 584
  carotid, 570
    x-ray of, 1350
  illiac, 620
  mammary, 587
  maxillary, 566
  palpebral, 574
  plantar, 645
  pudendal or pudic, 623, 626
  spermatic, 617
interosseous, anterior, 604
  common, 603
  dorsal, 604
  palmar, 601
  posterior, 604
  volar, 604
intestinal, 613
labial, 563
of labyrinth, 1090
lacrimal, 573
laryngeal, inferior, 586
  superior, 560
lateral calcaneal, 645
  femoral circumflex, 636
  nasal, 563
  palpebral, 567
  sacral, 627
  tarsal, 643

Artery or Arteries, lateral thoracic, 593
left colic, 615
  gastric, 609
  gastroepiploic, 612
lienal, 612
lingual, 560
  deep, 560, 561
  long ciliary, 576
  thoracic, 593
lower extremity, 629
lumbar, 618, 627
malleolar, 642
  internal, 642
mammary, external, 594
  internal, 587
masseteric, 569
maxillary, external, 561
  internal, 566
medial palpebral, 574
  tarsal, 643
mediastinal, from aorta, 606
  from internal mammary, 587
medidural, 560
medullary, 584
meningeal, accessory, 568
  anterior, 573
  of ascending pharyngeal, 565
  middle, 568
  of occipital, 564
  small, 568
  of vertebral, 583
mesenteric, inferior, 615
  superior, 612, 1221
metacarpal, 601
metatarsal, 642
middle capsular, 617
  cerebral, 577
  collateral, 597
  genicular, 639
  hemorrhoidal, 622
  meningeal, 568
  sacral, 618
  suprarenal, 617
  vesical, 621
mode of division of, 551
  of origin of branches, 551
musculophrenic, 587, 589
mylohyoid, 569
nasal, 575
  dorsal, 575
  lateral, 563
nasopalatine, 570
nerves of, 522
nutrient, of femur, 637
  of fibula, 644
  of humerus, 596, 597
  of tibia, 645
obturator, 622
occipital, 564
ophthalmic, 573
ovarian, 617
palatine, ascending 561
  descending, 570
  of ascending pharyngeal, 565
palmar arch, deep, 601
    superficial, 604
palpebral, 573, 574
pancreatic, of lienal, 612
pancreaticoduodenal, 611, 613
perforating, of foot, 647
  of hand, 601
  of internal mammary, 589
  of thigh, 636
pericardiacophrenic, 588
pericardial, 589, 605
perineal, 625
  superficial, 625
peroneal, 644
  anterior, 644
pharyngeal, ascending, 565
  of internal maxillary, 570
phrenic, inferior, 618
  superior, 608
plantar, deep, 643

Artery or Arteries, plantar, lateral (external), 645
medial (internal), 645
metatarsal, 647
pontine, 584
popliteal, 638
posterior alveolar, 569
auricular, 565
cerebral, 584
communicating, 578
dental, 569
humeral circumflex, 594
inferior cerebellar, 584
interosseus, 604
meningeal, from vertebral, 583
scapular, 590
scrotal, 625
spinal, 583
superior alveolar, 569
tibial, 643
prevertebral, 565
princeps cervicis, 564
pollicis, 601
profunda, brachii, 597
cervicalis, 590
femoris, 636
linguæ, 561
of pterygoid canal, 570, 573
pudendal, external, 635
internal, 623, 626
in female, 626
in male, 623
pudic, external, 635
internal, 623
pulmonary, 553
pyloric, 610
radial, 599
collateral, 596
recurrent, 600
radialis indicis, 601
ranine, 561
recurrent, interosseous, 604
of hand, 600
radial, 600
tibial, 642
ulnar, 602
renal, 617
right colic, 615
coronary, 554
gastric, 610
gastroepiploic, 611
sacral, lateral, 627
middle, 618
scapular circumflex, 594
posterior, 590
transverse, 586
sciatic, 626
scrotal, posterior, 625
semilunar ganglion, 573
sheaths of, 522
short ciliary, 576
gastric, 612
sigmoid, 616
spermatic, 617
external, 629
internal, 617
sphenopalatine, 570
spinal, 583
splenic, 612, 733
sternocleidomastoid, 560, 564
sternomastoid, 560, 564
striate, 577
structure of, 521
stylomastoid, 565
subclavian, 580
subcostal, 607
sublingual, 567
submaxillary, 562
submental, 563
subscapular, 594
superficial cervical, 587
epigastric, 635
external pudendal, 635
iliac circumflex, 635
palmar arch, 604

Artery or Arteries, superficial temporal, 566
volar, 600
arch, 600
superior articular, of knee, 639
cerebellar, 584
epigastric, 587, 589
gluteal, 628
hemorrhoidal, 616
intercostal, 589
labial, 563
laryngeal, 560
mesenteric, 612
pancreatico-duodenal, 611
phrenic, 588
profunda, 597
thoracic, 592
thyroid, 559
tympanic, 568
ulnar collateral, 597
vesical, 621
suprahyoid, 560
supraorbital, 573
suprarenal, 617
suprascapular, 586
sural, 639
systemic distribution of, 551
tarsal, 643
temporal, 566
deep, 569
middle, 566
superficial, 566
thoracic, 605
aorta, 605
axis, 593
highest, 592
lateral, 593
superior, 592
thoracoacromial, 593
thoracodorsal, 594
thyrocervical trunk, 585
thyroid axis, 585
ima, 556
inferior, 585
superior, 559
tibial, anterior, 641
posterior, 643
recurrent, 642
tonsillar, 562
tracheal, 586
transverse cervical, 590
facial, 566
perineal, 625
scapular, 585
transversalis colli, 590
trunk, 605
tympanic, 565, 567
ulnar, 601
collateral, 602
recurrent, 602
umbilical, in fetus, 546, 620
upper extremity, 580
urethral, 626
bulb, 625
uterine, 622
vaginal, 622
vasa aberrantia, 597
brevia, 612
intestini tenuis, 613
vertebral, 582
vesical, 621
vestibular, 1090
Vidian, 570, 573
volar arch, deep, 601
superficial, 601
carpal, 600
digital, common, 605
interosseous, 604
metacarpal, 601
proper, 605
volaris indicis radialis, 601
Arthrodia, 262
Articular arteries, 639
capsules, 259, 272
cartilage, 257

Articular, disk of acromioclavicular joint, 291
of distal radioulnar joint, 303
of sternoclavicular joint, 290
of temporomandibular joint, 273
lamella of bone, 256
meniscus, 273
process of vertebræ, 76
tubercle of temporal bone, 108, 144
Articulation or Articulations, 255
acromiclavicular, 291
amphiarthroses, 261
ankle, 327
atlantoöccipital, 272
of atlas with axis or epistropheus, 268
with occipital bone, 272
calcaneocuboid, 332
of calcaneus and astragalus, 330
with the cuboid, 332
carpometacarpal, 308
of cartilages of ribs with each other, 280
classification of, 260
condyloid, 261
costocentral, 275
costochondral, 280
costosternal, 278
costotransverse, 277
costovertebral, 275
coxal, 311
cuboideonavicular, 334
cuneocuboid, 335
cuneonavicular, 334
development, 255
diarthroses, 261
digits, 311, 338
elbow, 290
gomphosis, 260
hip, 311
humeral, 293
immovable, 260
intercarpal, 306
interchondral, 280
intercuneiform, 335
intermetacarpal, 309
intermetatarsal, 336
intertarsal, 330
knee, 317
lower extremity, 311
mandible, 273
metacarpophalangeal, 309
metatarsophalangeal, 337
movable, 261
movements of, 262
of navicular with cuneiform bones, 334
pelvis, 282
with vertebral column, 282
of phalanges of foot, 338
of hand, 311
of pubic bones, 286
symphysis, 286
radiocarpal, 303
radioulnar, 301
by reciprocal reception, 262
sacrococcygeal symphysis, 285
sacroiliac, 282
sacrum and coccyx, 285
scapuloclavicular, 291
schindylesis, 260
shoulder, 293
sternoclavicular, 289
sternocostal, 278
sternum, 280
sutura, 260
symphysis, 261
pubis, 286
synarthroses, 260
synchondrosis, 260
syndesmosis, 261
talocalcaneal, 330
talocalcaneonavicular, 331
talocrural, 327

Articulation or Articulations, tarsometatarsal, 336
  tarsus, 330
  temporomandibular, 273
  tibiofibular, 326
  tibiotarsal, 327
  of trunk, 263
  upper extremity, 289
  of vertebral arches, 266
    bodies, 263
    column, 263
      with cranium, 272
      with pelvis, 282
  wrist, 303
*Articulatio or Articulationes capi-
  tulorum*, 275
  carpometacarpeæ, 308
    pollicis, 308
  costotransversariæ, 277
  costovertebrales, 275
  cubiti, 297
  digitorum manus, 311
    pedis, 338
  ellipsoidea, 262
  genu, 317
  humeri, 293
  intercarpeæ, 306
  interchondrales, 280
  intermetacarpeæ, 309
  intermetatarseæ, 336
  intertarseæ, 330
  metatarsophalangeæ, 337
  ossiculorum auditus, 1074, 1076
  radioulnaris, 301
    distalis, 303
    proximalis, 301
  sellaris, 262
  sternoclavicularis, 289
  sternocostales, 278
  tarsometatarseæ, 336
  trochoidea, 261
Aryepiglottic fold, 1114
Aryepiglotticus muscle, 1118
Arytænoideus muscles, 1118
Arytenoid cartilages, 1111
  glands, 1120
  swellings, 1107
Ascending aorta, 553
  cervical artery, 586
  colon, 1225
  frontal convolution, 843
  lumbar vein, 676
  oblique muscle, 398
  palatine artery, 561
  parietal convolution, 845
  pharyngeal artery, 565
  ramus of ischium, 210
    of os pubis, 211
Association fibers of cerebral
  hemispheres, 865, 867
  neurons, 755
Asterion, 140
Astragalus, 242
Astrocytes, 755
Atavistic epiphyses, 73
Atlantoöccipital articulation, 272
Atlas, 78
Atonic stomach, after a barium
  meal, x-ray of, 1384
Atresia, congenital, of pupil, 1035
Atria of bronchi, 1137
  muscle bundles of, 540
Atrial canal, 505
Atrioventricular bundle of His,
  543
  node, 544
  opening, left, 537
    right, 533
Atrium dextrum, 533
  of heart, left, 536
    primitive, 504
    right, 533
  of nasal fossa, 1026
  sinistrum, 536

Attic or epitympanic recess, 147,
  1069
Attolens aurem muscle, 1066
Attrahens aurem muscle, 1066
Auditory artery, 584
  internal, 584
  canal, external, 1067
  meatus, external, 1067
  nerve, 935
  ossicles, 59, 1074
    development of, 1075
  pit, 1060
  plate, 1060
  teeth of Huschke, 1086
  tube, 1061, 1074
    cartilaginous portion of, 1074
    cushion of, 1074
    isthmus of, 1074
    osseous portion of, 1074
    pharyngeal ostium of, 1184
    tonsil of, 1074
    torus tubarius of, 1074
  veins, 1090
  vesicle, 1061
Auerbach's plexus, 1222
Auricle, left, 537
  right, 533
Auricula dextra, 533
  ear, 1064
    cartilage of, 1065
    development of, 1064
    ligaments of, 1066
    muscles of, 1066
    vessels and nerves of, 1067
  heart, left, 537
    right, 533
  sinistra, 537
Auricular appendix, left, 537
  right, 533
  artery, anterior, 566
    deep, 567
    posterior, 565
  lymph nodes, 702
  nerve, anterior, 925
    great, 955
    posterior, 934
    of vagus, 940
  surface of ilium, 207
    of sacrum, 87
  tubercle of Darwin, 1065
  vein, posterior, 654
Auriculares muscles, 1066
Auriculotemporal nerve, 925
Auriculoventricular groove, 531
Auris interna, 1078
Auscultation, triangle of, 424
Autonomic ganglia of nerves, 764
  nervous system, 997
Axes of pelvis, 215
Axial filament of spermatozoön, 23
  skeleton, 59
Axilla, 590
  fascia of, 428
Axillary arch, 424
  artery, 591
    surface markings of, 1408
  lymph nodes, 711
  nerve, 963
  sheath, 429, 435, 591
  vein, 672
Axis, 79
  celiac, 608
  of lens, 1051
  optic, 1032
  thoracic, 593
  thyroid, 585
  vertebra, 79
Axis-cylinders. 755, 757
  process, 757
Axon of nerve cell, 755, 757
Azygos arteries of vagina, 622
  artery, articular, 639
  uvulæ muscle, 1181
  vein, 676

B

BACK, bones of, surface markings
  of, 1365
  muscles of, 377
    surface markings of, 1366
Baillarger, band of, 863, 868
Ball-and-socket joint, 261
Band of Baillarger, 863, 868
  of Gennari, 868, 873
  of Giacomini, 857
  illiotibial, 468
  moderator, 536
Bare area of liver, 1194
Bartholin, duct of, 1176
  glands of, 1262, 1319
Basal column, posterior, 776
  ganglia, 859
  lamina, 739
  olfactory bundle of Wallenburg,
    896
  plate of placenta, 31
  ridge, or cingulum of teeth, 1156
  vein, 660
Base of cerebral peduncle, 818
  of heart, 531
  of sacrum, 88
  of skull, inferior surface, 107
    upper surface of, 120
Basihyal of hyoid bone, 133
Basilar artery, 584
  crest, 1085
  membrane, 1086
  part of occipital bone, 137
  plexus of veins, 668
  sinus, 668
Basilic vein, 670
  median, 669
Basion, 110
Basis bundle. anterior, 778
  lateral, 781
  cordis, 531
  oss. sacri, 88
  pedunculi, 818
  prostratæ, 1303
  pulmonis, 1130
Basivertebral veins, 677
Basket cells of cerebellum, 811
Bechterew, nucleus of, 806
  pontospinal fasciculis of, 901
Bed of stomach, 1208
Bell, nerve of, 958, 962
Bellini, duct of, 1273
Bertin, ligament of, 313
Betz, giant cells of, 872
Biceps brachii muscle, 435
  femoris muscle, 479
  flexor cubiti muscle, 435
  muscle, 435
Bisipital fascia, 436
  groove, 184
  ridges, 184
Bicuspid teeth, 1157
  valve, 538
Bigelow, Y-shaped ligament of,
  312
Bile capillaries, 1241
  ducts, 1241, 1244
    lymphatic capillaries in 696
  structure of, 1243
Bipolar cells of retina, 1047
Biventer cervicis muscle, 382
Bladder, 1277
  gall, 1243
  urinary, 1277
    abnormalities of, 1283
    development of, 1283
    distended, 1277, 1279
    empty, 1277, 1278
    female, 1280
    in child, 1280
    interior of, 1282
    ligaments of, 1281
    lymphatic vessels of, 723

Bladder, urinary, structure of, 1282
  trigone of, 1282
  vessels and nerves, of, 1283
Blandin, glands of, 1171
Blastocyst, 25
Blastopore, 38
Blood, composition of, 525
  corpuscles, 525
  course of, in adult, 501
   in fetus, 546
  islands, 502
  liquor sanguinis, 525
  plasma, 525
  platelets, 525
Bloodless fold of Treves, 1205
Bloodvessels of bone, 67
  of spleen, 733
Body or Bodies, anococcygeal, 1229
  aortic, 1335
  ciliary, 1041
  coccygeal, 1339
  geniculate, 831
  Malpighian, of kidney, 1272
  olivary, 789
  penis, 1300
  perineal, 416, 1229
  pineal, 822, 832, 1335
  pituitary, 1331
  polar, 22
  quadrigeminal, 823
  restiform, 791, 803, 811
  stomach, 1208
  thyroid, 1327
  trapezoid, 805
  uterus, 1311
  vertebra, 75
Body-stalk, 35, 45
Bone or Bones, ankle, 242
  arm, 183
  astragalus, 242
  atlas, 78
  axis, 79
  bloodvessels of, 67
  breast, 97
  calcaneus, 237
  calf, 235
  canaliculi of, 68, 70
  cancellous tissue of, 66
  capitate, 201
  carpal, 196
  cells, 70
  chemical composition of, 70
  clavicle, 175
  coccyx, 89
  collar, 173
  compact tissue of, 66
  cranial, 134
  cuboid, 244
  cuneiform, of carpus, 197
   of tarsus, 245
  destroyers, 72
  development of, 66
  ear, 1074
  elbow, 189
  epistropheus, 79
  ethmoid, 157
  facial, 160
  femur, 217
  fibula, 235
  fingers, 204
  foot, 237
  frontal, 141
  hamate, 202
  of hand, 196
  Haversian canals of, 68, 69
   systems of, 68
  hip, 206
  humerus, 183
  hyoid, 133
  ilium, 206
  incus, 1075
  inferior maxillary, 127

Bone or Bones, inferior nasal conchæ, 173
  innominate, 206
  ischium, 209
  lacrimal, 168
   lesser, 168
  lacunæ of, 68, 69
  lamellæ of, 68, 69
  lingual, 133
  lower extremity, 206
   jaw, 127
  lunate, 197
  lymphatics of, 68
  malar, 168
  malleus, 1074
  mandible, 127
  marrow of, 67
  maxillæ, 162
  medullary artery of, 67
   membrane of, 66
  metacarpal, 202
  metatarsal, 247
  minute anatomy of, 68
  multangular, greater, 200
   lesser, 201
  nasal, 160
  navicular, of carpus, 197
   of tarsus, 245
  nerves of, 68
  nutrient artery of, 67
  occipital, 134
  os calcis, 237
   coxæ, 206
   magnum, 201
  ossification of, 70
  palate, 170
  palatine, 170
  parietal, 138
  patella, 230
  pelvic, 213
  perforating fibers of, 69
  periosteum of, 66
   lymphatic capillaries in, 693
  phalanges of foot, 250
   of hand, 205
  pisiform, 198
  pubis, 211
  radius, 194
  ribs, 101
  sacrum, 85
  scaphoid, of foot, 245
   of hand, 197
  scapula, 178
  semilunar, 197
  sesamoid, 252
  shin, 231
  sphenoid, 152
  sphenoidal conchæ, 156
  stapes, 1076
  sternum, 97
  strength of, compared with other materials, 66
  structure and physical properties of, 66
  sutural, 160
  talus, 242
  tarsal, 237
  temporal, 143
  thigh, 217
  tibia, 231
  trapezoid, 201
  triangular, 197
  turbinated, 173
  ulna, 189
  unciform, 202
  upper extremity, 175
   jaw, 162
  veins of, 68
  vertebra prominens, 80
  vertebræ, cervical, 76
   coccygeal, 85
   lumbar, 83
   sacral, 85
   thoracic, 81

Bone or Bones, vessels of, 67
  vomer, 174
  Wormian, 160
  zygomatic, 168
Bone-formers, 72
Bony landmarks of abdomen, 1381
  of back, 1367
  of lower extremity, 1422
  of upper extremity, 1407
Bowman, capsule of, 1272, 1273
  glands of, 1029
  membrane of, 1038
Brachia conjunctiva of cerebellum, 809
  of corpora quadrigemina, 823
  pontis, 810
Brachial artery, 595
  surface marking of, 1408
  cutaneous nerve, lateral, 963
   medical, 966
   posterior, 972
  fascia, 434
  plexus, 959
  veins, 671
Brachialis anticus muscle, 436
  muscle, 436
Brachiocephalic artery, 556
  veins, 673
Brachioradialis muscle, 444
Brain, arteries of, 579
  commissures of, 832
  cornu of, anterior, 849
   posterior, 849
  development of, 743
  divisions of, 784
  dura of, 901
  meninges of, 901
  pathways from, to spinal cord, 898
  pia of, 906
  sensory pathways from spinal cord to, 878
  surface markings of, 1349
  veins of, 660
  ventricles injected with air, x-ray of, 1351
Branchial arches, 45
  grooves, 46
Breast bone, 97
Breasts or mammæ, 1319
  development of, 1320
Bregma, 106
Bregmatic fontanelle, 125
Bridge of nose, 1024
Brim of pelvis, 213
Broad ligaments of uterus, 1198, 1311
Broca, cap of, 844
  diagonal band of, 856
  gyrus of, 844
  limbic lobe of, 843
Broedel's line, 1274
Bronchi, 1121
  divisions of, 1133
  eparterial, 1122
  hyparterial, 1123
  intrapulmonary, 1136
  left, 1122, 1135
  lymphatic capillaries in, 696
  right, 1122, 1135
  segmental, 1133
Bronchial arteries, 605, 1137
  nerves, 941
  veins, 676, 1137
Bronchomediastinal lymphatic trunks, 701
Bronchopulmonary segments, 1133
Bronchus dexter, 1122
  sinister, 422, 1122
Brunner's glands, 1221
Bryant's triangle, 1425
Buccæ, 1153

Buccal artery, 569
  branches of facial nerve, 935
  cavity, 1151
  fat pad, 360
  glands, 1153
  nerve, long, 924
Buccinator artery, 569
  muscle, 360
  nerve, 924
Bucco-nasal membrane, 50
Buccopharyngeal fascia, 362, 367
  membrane, 41
Buck's fascia, 1299
Bulb, eye, 1032
  hair, 1102
  olfactory, 854, 875
  of posterior cornu, 851
  spinal, 785
  urethral, 1301
  vaginal, 1319
  of vestibule, 1319
Bulbar arteries, 584
Bulbocavernosus muscle, 418
  actions of, 419
Bulbourethral glands of Cowper,
  1262, 1305
Bulbs of internal jugular vein,
  656
Bulbus cordis, 505
  oculi, 1032
  olfactorius, 854
  urethræ, 1301
  vestibuli, 1319
Bulla ethmoidalis, 125, 1027
Buncle of His, 543
  medial forebrain, 896
  oval, 740
  of Wallenburg, 896
  of Vicq d'Azyr, 828, 835, 898
Burdach, tract of, 770, 781
Burn's space, 367
Bursa, omental, 1201
  development of, 1141
  omentalis, 1201
  pharyngeal, 1185
  prepatellar, 471
Bursæ beneath glutæus maximus, 473
  near knee-joint, 323
  shoulder-joint, 295
  synovial, 259

C

Calamus scriptorius, 816
Calcaneal arteries, 645
  lateral, 645
  medial, 645
  nerve, internal, 992
  medial, 992
  sulcus, 240
  tuberosity, 240
Calcaneo-astragaloid articulation,
  330
  ligaments, 330
Calcaneo-cuboid ligaments, 332
  surface anatomy of, 1425
Calcaneo-navicular ligaments, 333
Calcaneo-tibial ligament, 328
Calcaneus, 237
Calcar avis, 851
Calcarine arteries, 585
  fissure, 842
Calf bone, 235
Calices of kidney, 1272, 1275
Calleja, islands of, 856
Callosal convolution, 844
  fissure, 844
Calloso-marginal fissure, 842
Calyces, renal, 1272, 1275
Camper, fascia of, 392
Canal or Canals, adductor, 630
  Alcock's, 414, 996
  alimentary, 1141
  alveolar, 113, 163
  atrial, 505

Canal or Canals, auditory, external, 1067
  carotid, 110, 148
  central, of spinalis cord, 771
  cervical of uterus, 1312
  condyloid, 123, 136
  craniopharyngeal, 157
  ethmoidal, 143, 159
  femoral, 631
  Haversian, of bone, 68, 69
  of Huguier, 145, 933, 1070
  Hunter's, 630, 633
  hypoglossal, 136
  incisive, 106, 167
  inguinal, 406, 1258
  lacrimal, 1059
  mandibular, 129
  nasolacrimal, 125
  neural, 42
  neurenteric, 42
  of Nuck, 1260, 1314
  of Petit, 1050
  pharyngeal, 107, 114
  pterygoid, 107, 114
  pterygopalatine, 114, 164, 172
  sacral, 89
  of Schlemm, 1035
  semicircular, 1079
    membranous, 1083
  spermatic, 406
  spiral, of modiolus, 1081
  vertebral, 89, 95
Canaliculi of bone, 68, 70
  dental, 1159
Canaliculus, inferior tympanic,
  110, 148
  innominatus of Arnold, 154
    note
  mastoid, 110, 149
Canalis centralis cochleæ, 148
  cervicis uteri, 1312
  reuniens [of Hensen], 1083,
    1085
  semicircularis lateralis, 1080
    posterior, 1080
    superior, 1079
Cancellous tissue of bone, 66
Canine eminence, 162
  fossa, 162
  teeth, 1157
Caninus muscle, 357
Canthi of eyelids, 1055
Cap of Broca, 844
Capillaries, 522
  bile, 1241
  lymphatic, 693
  structure of, 523
Capitate bone, 201
Capitulum fibulæ, 235
  humeri, 187
  mallei, 1075
  stapedis, 1076
Capsula articularis.   See Indi-
    vidual joints.
  externa, 865
  extrema, 863
  interna, 863
  lentis, 1050
  vasculosa lentis, 1035
Capsular artery, middle, 617
Capsule, adipose, of kidney, 1270
  adrenal, 1336
  of Bowman, 1272, 1273
  external, 865
  of Glisson, 1202, 1239
  internal, 863
  lens, 1050
  of Tenon, 1054
Caput cæcum coli, 1222
  femoris, 217
  humeri, 183
  pancreatis, 1245
  tali, 244
Cardiac cycle, 545
  ganglion of Wrisberg, 1015
  glands of stomach, 1212

Cardiac muscular tissue, 540, 544
  nerves, cervical, 941
    great, 1011
    inferior, 941, 1011
    middle, 1011
    superior, 941, 1010
    from sympathetic, 1010
    thoracic, 941
    from vagus, 941
  notch, 1133
  orifice of stomach, 1207
  plexus of nerves, 1015
  veins, 650
Cardinal veins, 516
Carotico-clinoid foramen, 122,
  156
  ligament, 157
Caroticotympanic artery, 572
  nerve, 1008
Carotid arch, 511
  development of, 511
  artery, common, 557
    branches of (occasional),
      surface markings of, 1361
    external, 559
      surface markings, 1361
    internal, 570
      x-ray of, 1350
  body, 1094
  canal, 110, 147
  ganglion, 1007
  groove, 122, 153
  nerve, internal, 1007
  nerves from glossopharyngeal,
    938
  plexus, 1007
    internal, 1007
  sheath, 370
  sinus, 570, 1094
  triangles, 557, 1362
Carpal arteries from radial, 600
  from ulnar, 601
  bones, 196
  net-work, 600
Carpometacarpal   **articulations,**
  308
Carpus, 196
  articulations of, 306
  ossification of, 206
  surface form of, 1399, 1401
Cartilage or Cartilages, articular,
  257
  arytenoid, 111
  auricula, 1065
  corniculate, 1111
  costal, 105, 257
  cricoid, 1110
  cuneiform, 1112
  epiglottic, 1112
  epiphysial, 71
  ethmovomerine, 175
  hyaline, 256
  intrathyroid, 1110
  lacunæ, 256
  laryngeal, 1109
    structure of, 1112
  lateral, 1024
    nasal, 1024
  Meckel's, 46, 130
  of nose, 1024
  permanent, 256
  pinna, 1065
  of Santorini, 1111
  septum of nose, 1024
  sesamoid, 1024
  temporary, 256, 257
  tracheal, 1123
  thyroid, 1109
  vomeronasal, 1028
  white fibro-, 256, 258
  of Wrisberg, 1112
Cartilagines alares minores, 1024
Cartilaginous vertebral column,
  60

Cartilago alaris major, 1024
  crus laterale, 1024
  mediale, 1024
auriculæ, 1065
cricoidea, 1110
epiglottica, 1112
nasi lateralis, 1024
septi nasi, 1024
thyreoidea, 1109
triticea, 1113
Caruncula lacrimalis, 1058
Carunculæ hymenales, 1319
Cauda equina, 697
  helicis, 1065
  pancreatis, 1247
Caudal folds, 45
Caudate lobe of liver, 1235, 1236
  nucleus, 859
  process of liver, 1235
Caudatum, 859
Cavernous arteries, 573
  nerves of penis, 1020
  plexus, 1008, 1009
  portion of urethra, 1285
  sinuses, 665
    nerves in, 929
  spaces of penis, 1300
Cavity or Cavities, body or
    celom, 42
  buccal, 1151
  cotyloid, 212
  glenoid, 182
  of lesser pelvis, 214
  mediastinal, 1127
  nasal, 123, 1026
  mouth proper, 1151
  oral, 1151
  pericardial, 528
  peritoneal, 1194
  pleural, 1124
  of septum pellucidum, 851
  sigmoid, of radius, 195
    of ulna, 192
  subarachnoid, 903, 904
  subdural, 903
  thorax, 527
  tympanic, 1068
    mucous membranes of, 1077
  uterus, 1312
Cavum conchæ, 1065
  laryngis, 1114
  Meckelii, 915
  nasi, 123, 1026
  oris, 1151
    proprium, 1151
  Retzii, 1229, 1279
  septi pellucidi, 851
  subarachnoideale, 904
  tympani, paries carotica, 1073
    labyrinthica, 1071
    mastoidea, 1071
  tympanum, 1068
    paries jugularis, 1069
    membranacea, 1069
    tegmentalis, 1069
  uteri, 1312
Cecal arteries, 615
  fossæ, 1204
Cecum, 1222
  lymphatic vessels of, 722
Celiac artery, 608
  axis, 608
  branches of vagus nerve, 942
  ganglion, 1016
  plexus, 1016
Cell or Cells, animal, 17
  basket, of cerebellum, 811
  Betz, 872
  bone, 70
  centro-aciner, of Langerhans,
    1249
  chromaffin, 1335
  Claudius, 1089
  definition of, 17
  Deiters, 1089
  division of, 17

Cell or Cells, enamel, 1162
  fat, 346
  fundus glands, 1212
  germinal, of medulla spinalis,
    739
  giant, 67
    of Betz, 872
  Golgi, 876
  gustatory, 1023
  Hensen, 1089
  Martinotti, 876
  mass, inner, 37
    intermediate, 41, 44
  membrane, 17
  nerve, 755
  nucleus of, 17
  olfactory, 1029
  Purkinje, 811
  Sertoli, 1293
  spinal ganglion, 767
  reproduction of, 17
  structure of, 17
  vasoformative, 502
Cella, 848
Cellulæ ethmoidales, 1031
Celom, 42
Cement of teeth, 1159
  formation of, 1164
Center of ossification of bone, 71
Centers of ossification, 71
  visual, 838
Central artery of retina, 575, 1035
  canal of medulla spinalis, 771
  cells of fundus glands, 1212
  fissure, 842
  gray stratum of cerebral aque-
    duct, 824
  ligament of medulla spinalis,
    907
  lobe, 847
  nervous system, 737
  sulcus, 842
  tendinous point of perineum,
    416
  tendon of diaphragm, 389
Centrifugal nerve fibers, 762
Centriole, 17
  bodies of ovum, 20
  of spermatozoon, 22
Centripetal nerve fibers, 762
Centroacinar cells of Langerhans,
  1249
Centrosome, 17
Cephalic flexure of embryonic
  brain, 743
  folds, 45
  portion of sympathetic system,
    1007
  vein, 669
    accessory, 670
Ceratohyal of hyoid bone, 134
Cerebellar arteries, 584
  fasciculus, direct, 776
  peduncles, 809
  tract, of Flechsig, 780
  veins, 661
Cerebellum, 807
  brachia conjunctiva, 809
  pontis, 810
  congulate fissures of, 842
  development of, 746
  fibræ propriæ, 809
  gray substance of, 811
  lobes of, 808
  nucleus dentatus, 809
  peduncles of, 809
  structure of, 809
  vermis of, 808
  white substance of, 809
Cerebral aqueduct, 824
  arteries, anterior, 576
    middle, 577
    posterior, 584
  cortex, nerve cells of, 868
    fibers of, 868
    structure of, 868

Cerebral cortex, types of, 871
  fissure, lateral, 841
  hemispheres, 840
    borders of, 841
    cingulum of, 867
    fibers of, association, 867
      commissural, 865
      projection, 865
      transverse, 865
    fissures of, 840
    gray substance of, 868
    gyri of, 841, 843, 845
    lobes of, 843, 844
    poles of, 841
    structure of, 865
    sulci of, 842, 843, 845
    surfaces of, 840
    white substance of, 765
  nerves, 911. *See* Cranial
    nerves.
  peduncles, 817
    structure of, 818
  veins, 660
  ventricles, 814, 838, 848
Cerebrospinal fasciculus, 778, 792
  fibers of internal capsule, 864
  fluid, 907
  nerves, structure of, 760
  spaces, development of, 55
Ceruminous glands, 1068
Cervical artery, ascending, 586
  deep, 590
  superficial, 587
  transverse, 590
  branch of cardiac nerves, 941
    of facial nerve, 935
  enlargement of medulla spina-
    lis, 769
  fascia, 365
  ganglia, 1009, 1011
  lymph nodes, 707
  muscles, lateral, 371
  nerve, cutaneous or transverse,
    955
  nerves, 950, 954
    divisions of, anterior, 954
      posterior, 957
  pleura, 1124
  plexus, 954
    branches of, 955
  portion of sympathetic, 1009
  rib, 81, 106
  veins, 659
  vertebræ, 76
    lateral view, x-ray of, 1359
Cervicalis ascendens muscle, 381
Cervix uteri, 1311
  portio supravaginalis, 1311
  vaginalis, 1311
  of uterus, 1311
Chambers of eye, 1044
Check ligaments, 273
  of eye, 1054
Cheeks, 1151
Chest, 95
Chiasma, optic, 836, 912
  opticum, 836, 912
Chiasmatic groove, 122, 152
Choanæ, 107, 123, 125, 1026
Chondrin, 259
Chondrocranium, 63
Chondro-epitrochearis   muscle,
  430
Chondroglossus muscle, 1170
Chondromucoid, 259
Chondrosternal ligament, 278
  intra-articular, 279
Chondroxiphoid ligaments, 280
Chorda obliqua, 301
  tympani nerve, 933, 1078
Chordæ tendineæ, 535
  Willisi, 661
Chordal furrow, 39
Chorioidea, 1040
  lamina choriocapillaris, 1041
  vasculosa, 1041

Chorion, 27
  frondosum, 31
  læve, 31
Chorionic villi, 29
Choroid artery, 578
  coat of eyeball, 1040
    structure of, 1040
  plexuses of fourth ventricle, 815
  of lateral ventricle, 852
  of third ventricle, 838
Choroidal artery, anterior, 578
  posterior, 585
  fissure, eye, 1033
Chromaffin cells, 1335
Chromaphil and cortical systems, 1335
  development of, 1335
Chromosomes, 18
Chyle, 693
Chyliferous vessels, 693
Cilia, 1055
Ciliaris muscle, 1043
Ciliary arteries, 576
  body, 1041
  ganglion, 918
  glands, 1055
  muscle, 1043
  nerves, 918
  processes, 1042
Cingulate fissures of cerebellum, 843
  gyrus, 844
  sulcus, 842
Cingulum of cerebral hemisphere, 867
  of teeth, 1156
Circle, arterial, of Willis, 579
Circular folds of small intestine, 1219
  sinus, 666
  sulcus, 843, 848
Circulation of blood in adult, 501
  in fetus, 546
Circulus arteriosus major, 576
  minor, 576
  venosus [mammal], 1323
Circumduction, 262
Circumferential fibrocartilage, 258
Circumflex arteries, femoral, 636
  humeral, 594
  nerve, 963
Circuminsular fissure, 843
Circumvallate papillæ, 1167
Cisterna basalis, 905
  cerebellomedullaris, 904
  chiasmatis, 905
  chyli, 701
  fossæ cerebri lateralis, 905
  interpeduncularis, 905
  magna, 904
  pontis, 904
  venæ magnæ cerebri, 905
Cisternæ subarachnoid, 904
  subarachnoidales, 904
Clarke's column, 776, 780
Claudius, cells of, 1089
Claustrum, 873
Clavicle, 175
  ossification of, 177
  pecularities of, in sexes, 177
  structure of, 177
  surface anatomy of, 1396
Clavicula, 175
Clavipectoral fascia, 426
Cleavage lines, skin, 1100
Cleft, fascial, 549
  palate, 127
Cleidohyoideus muscle, 374
Clinging fibers of cerebellum, 813
Clinoid processes, anterior, 122, 155
  middle, 122, 152
  posterior, 122, 152
Clitoris, 1318
  frenulum of, 1318

Clitoris, glans of, 1318
  nerves of, 996
  prepuce of, 1318
Clivus of sphenoid, 153
Cloaca, ectodermal, 1150
  entodermal, 1150
  pelvic portion of, 1261
  phallic portion of, 1261
  vesico-urethral portion of, 1261
Cloacal duct, 1150
  membrane, 41, 1150
  tubercle, 1262
Cloquet, lymph nodes of, 713
Closing membranes, branchial, 46
Coccygeal arteries, 626
  body, 1339
  cornua, 90
  gland, 1339
  nerve, division, of anterior, 896
    posterior, 954
  plexus, 996
  vertebræ, 75
Coccygeus muscle, 407
Coccyx, 75, 89
  ossification of, 93
Cochlea, 1080
  aqueduct of, 148
  cupula of, 1081
  hamulus laminæ spiralis, 1082
  helicotrema of, 1081, 1082
  lamina spiralis ossea, 1082
  modiolus of, 1080
  scalæ of, 1082
  spiral canal of, 1081
    lamina of, 1081
  vessels of, 1090
Cochlear artery, 1090
  nerve, 935, 1090
    composition and central connections of, 884
  nuclei, 806, 935
  root of acoustic nerve, 935
Cochleariform process, 150, 1074
Cog-tooth of malleus, 1075
Colic arteries of ileocolic, 615
  left, 615
  middle, 615
  right, 615
  flexures, right and left, 1222
  impression, 1234
  valve, 1224
Collar bone, 175
Collateral circulation, 551
  fissure, 843
  ganglia, 1007
Collecting tubes of kidney, 1273
Colles, fascia of, 210, 393, 417, 1300
Colliculi, inferior, 822, 823
  superior, 822, 823
Colliculus of arytenoid cartilage, 111
  facialis, 816
  inferior, 823
  nervi optici, 1046
  superior, 823
Collum anatomicum humeri, 184
  femoris, 218
  mallei, 1075
  tali, 244
Coloboma, 1034
Colon, 1225
  ascending, 1225
  descending, 1226
  iliac, 1226
  left or splenic flexure of, 1226
  pelvic, 1227
  right or hepatic flexure of, 1226
  sigmoid, 1227
  structure of, 1230
  transverse, 1226
  tunica mucosa, 1232
    muscularis, 1230
    serosa, 1230
  vessels and nerves of, 1232

Colored lines of Retzius, 1160
  or red corpuscles, 525
Colorless corpuscles, 525
Colostrum, 1321
  corpuscles, 1322
Columella, 50
Columna anterior [medulla spinalis], 770
  lateralis [medulla spinalis], 771
  nasi, 1024
  posterior [medulla spinalis], 771
  vertebralis, 75
Columnæ carneæ, 535
Columns of Clarke, 776
  of fornix, 859
  of medulla spinalis, 773, 774, 776
  rectal, of Morgagni, 1229
  renal, 1272
  of vagina, 1317
  vertebral, 75
Comes nervi phrenici, 588
Comitans nervi ischiadici, 627
Comma-shaped fasciculus, 782
Commissura labiorum anterior, 1317
  palpebrarum lateralis, 1055
    medialis, 1055
Commissural fibers of cerebral hemispheres, 865
Commissure of brain, anterior, 752, 859
  posterior, 832
  of corpus callosum, 752
  of Gudden, 837, 912
  habenular, 832
  hippocampal, 859, 897
  of labia majora, 1317
  of medulla spinalis, anterior and posterior gray, 772
    anterior white, 769
  optic, 836
Commissures, palpebral, 1055
Common bile duct, 1242, 1244
  lymphatics of, 723
  carotid artery, 557
  dental germ, 1161
  iliac arteries, 619
  lymph nodes, 715
  veins, 685
  integument, 1096
  interosseous artery, 603
  ligament, 264
  peroneal nerve, 993
Communicans fibularis nerve, 993
  tibialis nerve, 991
Communicantes cervicales nerves, 957
Communicating artery, anterior, 576
  from dorsalis pedis, 643
  posterior, 578
Compact tissue of bone, 66
Comparison of bones of hand and foot, 251
Complexus muscle, 382
Composition and central connections of cranial nerves, 881
  of spinal nerves, 876
Compressor naris muscle, 356
Concha of auricula, 1065
  nasal, inferior, 173
    middle, 160
    superior, 160
  nasalis inferior, 173
Conchæ, sphenoidal, 156
  sphenoidales, 156
Conchal crest, 164, 171
Condyle of mandible, 130
Condyles of femur, 222
  occipital, 136
  of tibia, 231, 232
Condyloid articulation, 262
  canal, 136
  foramen, anterior, 136
  fossa, 110, 136

Condyloid, process of mandible, 130
Cone bipolars of retina, 1047
  granules of retina, 1048
  of origin, of axon, 756
Cones of retina, 1048
Confluence of sinuses, 136, 665
Coni vasculosi, 1295
Conical papillæ, 1168
Conjoined tendon of internal oblique and transversalis muscles, 399
Conjugate diameter of pelvis, 214
Conjunctiva, 1056
  bulbar portion, 1057
  caruncle lacrimalis, 1058
  fornix, 1057
  lacus lacrimli, 1058
  palpebral portion, 1057
  plica semilunaris, 1058
Connecting fibrocartilages, 258
Connective tissues, 345
  extraperitoneal, 406
Conoid ligament, 291
  tubercle, 176
Constriction, duodenopyloric, 1207
Constrictor, pharyngis inferior muscle, 1185
  medius muscle, 1185
  superior muscle, 1185
  urethræ muscles, 419, 421
Conus arteriosus, 535
  elasticus [larynx], 1113
  medullaris, 767
Convoluted tubes of kidney, 1273
Convolution, callosal, 844
  frontal, ascending, 843
  occipitotemporal, 846
  parietal, ascending, 845
Cooper, ligament of, 397, 1320
Copula, 1143
Cor, 530
Coracoacromial ligament, 292
Coracobrachialis muscle, 435
Corococlavicular fascia, 427
  ligament, 291
Coracohumeral ligament, 295
Coracoid process, 182
  tuberosity, 176
Cord, gangliated, 1006
  spermatic, 1289
  spinal, 767
  umbilical, 35
  vocal, false, 1116
    inferior, 1116
    superior, 1116
    true, 1116
Corium or cutis vera, 1098
  layers of, 1099
  stratum papillare, 1099
    reticulare, 1100
Cornea, 1035, 1038
  structure of, 1038
Corneal corpuscles, 1038
  endothelium, 1038
  epithelium, 1038
  spaces, 1038
Corniculate cartilages, 1111
Cornu anterius, 849
  inferior, 851
  of medulla spinalis, 771
  posterius, 849
Cornua, of coccyx, 89
  of hyoid bone, 134
  of lateral ventricles, 848, 852
  majora [*os hyoidei*], 133
  minora [*os hyoidei*], 134
  of sacrum, 87
  of thyroid cartilage, 1109, 1110
Corona glandis, 1301
  radiata [brain], 865
    [ovum], 20
Coronal suture, 106, 111
91

Coronary arteries, 554
  of stomach, 609
  artery of heart, 554
    peculiarities of, 555
  ligament of liver, 1237
  ligaments of knee, 321
  plexuses, 1016
  sinus, 650
    opening of, 534
  of stomach, 691
  sulcus of heart, 531
  veins of heart, 650
Coronoid fossa, 187
  process of mandible, 130
  of ulna, 189
Corpora cavernosa, penis, 1262, 1300
  bulbs of, 1301
  crura of, 1300
  mammillaria, 833
  quadrigemina, 822
    brachia of, 823
    structure of, 823
Corpus Arantii, 536
  callosum, 866
    development of, 752
    genu of, 866
    rostrum of, 866
    splenium of, 866
  cavernosum, artery to, 626
    urethræ, 1300, 1301
  ciliare, 1041
  femoris, 221
  fibulæ, 235
  geniculatum laterale, 831
    mediale, 831
  Highmori, 1292
  humeri, 184
  incudis, 1075
  luteum, 1308
  maxillæ, 162
  oss. hyoidei, 133
    ilii, 206
    ischii, 209
    pubis, 211
  pancreatis, 1245
  papillare [corium], 1099
  penis, 1300
  pineale, 832
  radii, 194
  sphenoidale, 152
  spongiosum, 1301
  sterni, 99
  striatum, 749, 750, 859
  tali, 243
  tibiæ, 232
  ulnæ, 192
  uteri, 1311
  vertebræ, 76
  vitreum, 1049
Corpuscles, blood, 525
  genital, 1091
  Golgi and Mazzoni, 1092
  Grandry, 1091
  granular, 67
  Hassall, 735
  Herbst, 1092
  Pacinian, 1091
  renal, 1272
  Ruffini, 1092
  Wagner and Meissner, 1092
Corrugator cutis ani muscle, 421
  muscle, 356
  supercilii muscle, 356
Cortex of cerebellum, 811
  of cerebrum 868
  of kidney, 1272
  of lymph nodes, 699
  of suprarenal, 1337
Corti, ganglion of, 1081, 1090
Cortical arches of kidney, 1272
  arterial system of brain, 579
  portion of suprarenal gland, 1336
  substance of kidney, 1272
    of lens, 1051

Costæ, 101
Costal cartilages, 105, 257
  element or process, 77
  groove, 102
  pleura, 1124
  tuberosity, 177
Costocentral articulation, 275
Costocervical trunk, 589
Costochondral articulations, 280
Costocoracoid ligament, 430
  membrane, 430
Costocoracoideus muscle, 430
Costomediastinal sinus, 1126
Costosternal articulations, 278
Costotransverse articulations, 277
  ligaments, 277
Costovertebral articulations, 275
  ligament, anterior, 276
Costoxiphoid ligament, 280
Cotyledons, 33
Cotyloid cavity, 212
  ligament, 212
Coverings of ovum, 20
Cowper's glands, 1262, 1305
Coxal articulation, 311
  movements of, 316
  muscles in relation to, 316
Cranial arachnoid, 903
  bones, 134
  dura mater, 901
  fossa, anterior, 120
    middle, 121
    posterior, 123
  nerves, 911
    abducent, 929
    accessory, 942
    acoustic, 935
    composition and central connections of, 881
    development of, 753
    eighth, 935
    eleventh, 942
    facial, 930
    fifth, 915
    first, 911
    fourth, 914
    glossopharyngeal, 936
    hypoglossal, 943
    ninth, 936
    oculomotor, 913
    olfactory, 911
    optic, 912
    second, 912
    seventh, 930
    sixth, 929
    tenth, 938
    third, 913
    trigeminal, 915
    trochlear, 914
    twelfth, 943
    vagus, 938
  parasympathic nerves, 1001
  pia mater, 907
  sympathetics, 1001
Cranium, 106
  bones of, 134
  development of, 63
  membranous, 63
Cremaster muscle, 398, 1289
Cremasteric artery, 629
  fascia, 399, 1289
Crescents of Gianuzzi, 1176
Crest or Crests, basilar, 1085
  conchal, 164, 171
  ethmoidal, 165, 172
  frontal, 142
  iliac, 207
  incisor, 167
  infratemporal, 111, 154
  internal occipital, 123, 136
  intertrochanteric, 219
  lacrimal, 166, 168
  nasal, 167, 171
  neural, 42, 741
  obturator, 211
  pubic, 211

Crest or Crests, right atrial, 533
　sphenoidal, 153
　supramastoid, 144
　tibial 232
　of tubercles of humerus, 184
　urethral, in female, 1285
　　in male, 1284
Cribriform fascia, 467
　plate of ethmoid, 157
Cricoarytænoideus lateralis muscle, 1118
　posterior muscle, 1118
Cricoarytenoid ligament, 1114
　muscles, 1118
Cricoid cartilage, 1110
Cricothyreoideus muscle, 1118
Cricothyroid artery, 560
　ligament, middle, 1113
　membrane, 1113
　muscle, 1118
Cricotracheal ligament, 1113
Crista arcuata [arytenoid cartilage], 1111
　colli costæ, 101
　falciformis, 148
　galli, 158
　terminalis [of His], 505
　vestibuli, 1079
Crossed commissural fibers, 773
　pyramidal tract, 779
Crown of a tooth, 1155
Crucial anastomosis, 636
　ligaments, 320
Cruciate crural ligament, 489
　eminence of occipital bone, 136
　ligament of atlas, 271
　ligaments of knee, 320
Crura of diaphragm, 388
　of fornix, 857
　of penis, 1300
　of stapes, 1076
　of subcutaneous inguinal ring, 395
Crural arch, deep, 405, 630
　facia, 480
　ligament, transverse, 489
　nerve, anterior, 984
　septum, 632
　sheath, 630
Crureus muscle, 471
Crus commune [semicircular canals], 1079
　fornicis, 857
Crusta or pes of cerebral peduncle, 818
　petrosa of teeth, 1157
　　formation of, 1160
Cruveilhier, glenoid ligaments of, 310, 337
　fascia, 411
Crypts of Lieberkühn, 1221
Crystalline lens, 1050
　cortical substance of, 1051
　development of, 1034
　nucleus of, 1051
Cuboid bone, 244
Cuboideonavicular articulation, 334
Cul de sac of Douglas, 1197, 1314
Cuneate nucleus, 791
　tubercle, 791
Cuneiform bone of carpus, 197
　of tarsus, first, 245
　　second, 246
　　third, 246
　cartilages, 1112
　tubercle, 1116
Cuneocuboid articulation, 335
Cuneonavicular articulation, 334
Cuneus, 846
Cup, optic, 1033
Cupula of cochlea, 1081
　of pleura, 1124
Curvatura ventriculi major, 1208
　minor, 1207

Curvatures of stomach, 1207
Curved lines of ilium, 207
Curves of vertebral column, 93
Cushion of auditory tube, 1184
　of epiglottis, 1112
Cushions, endocardial, 506
Cusp, aortic, 538
Cusps of bicuspid valve, 538
　of tricuspid valve, 535
Cutaneous cervical nerve, 955
　nerve, external, 982
　　internal, 966, 984
　　lesser, 966
　　middle, 984
　nerves, 946
　　of abdomen, 977
　　of back, 952
　　of face, 928
　　of foot, 993
　　of lower limb, 981
　　of neck, 955
　　of thorax, 974
　　of upper limb, 964
Cuticle, 1096, 1104
Cuticula dentis, 1163
Cutis plate, 59
　vera or corium, 1098
Cutting teeth, 1156
Cuvier, ducts of, 516
Cycle, cardiac, 545
Cymba conchæ, 1065
Cystic artery, 612
　duct, 1243
　vein, 691
Cytoplasm, 17, 344
Cytotrophoblast, 27

D

Dacryon, 118
Dartos tunic, 1287
Darwin, auricular tubercle of, 1065
Decidua, 29
　basalis, 30
　capsularis, 30
　development of, 29
　parietalis, 30
　placentalis, 30
　stratum compactum of, 30
　　spongiosum of, 30
　unaltered or boundary layer of, 30
　vera, 30
Decidual cells, 30
Deciduous teeth, 1158
Decussation of lemniscus, 794
　of optic nerves, 912
　pyramidal, 788
　sensory, 794
Deep abdominal ring, 405
　artery of penis, 624, 626
　auricular artery, 567
　cerebral veins, 660
　cervical artery, 590
　　fascia, 365
　　lymph nodes, 707
　　vein, 659
　crural arch, 405, 630
　epigastric artery, 629, 630
　　vein, 682
　external pudic artery, 635
　fascia, 348
　femoral artery, 636
　iliac circumflex artery, 637,
　　vein, 682
　lingual artery, 561
　muscles of back, 377
　palmar arch, 601
　peroneal nerve, 993
　petrosal nerve, 922
　plantar artery, 643
　Sylvian vein, 660
　temporal arteries, 569
　　nerves, 924
　transverse fascia of leg, 481, 484

Degeneration, Wallerian, 765
Degenerative changes in nerve tissue, 765
Deglutition, 1182
Deiters, cells of, 1089
　nucleus of, 806, 887
Deltoid ligament, 328
　tuberosity, 185
Deltoideus muscle, 432
Demilunes of Heidenhain, 1176
Demours, membrane of, 1038
Dendrites, 756, 757
Dendrons, 756, 757
　of nerve cells, 756
Dens, or odontoid process of axis, 79
　serotinus, 1157
Dental artery, inferior, 569
　　posterior, 569
　canaliculi, 1159
　formulæ, 1155
　furrow, 1161
　germs, 1161
　lamina, 1161
　nerve, inferior, 926
　pulp, 1158
　sac, 1163
Dentate fissure, 846
　gyrus, 856, 897
　ligament, 907
Dentes, 1155
　canini, 1157
　decidui, 1158
　incisivi, 1156
　molares, 1157
　permanentes, 1156
　præmolares, 1157
Dentin, 1159
　formation of, 1163
　intertubular, 1159
　secondary, 1160
Dentinal canaliculi, 1159
　fibers, 1159
　matrix, 1159
　sheath of Neumann, 1159
　tubules, 1159
Depressions for arachnoid granulations, 139
Depressor alæ nasi muscle, 356
　anguli oris muscle, 358
　labii inferioris muscle, 358
　septi muscle, 356
Dermic coat of hair follicle, 1103
Dermis, 1098
Descemet, membrane of, 1038
Descendens cervicalis nerve, 958
　hypoglossi nerve, 945
Descending aorta, 605
　colon, 1225
　comma-shaped fasciculus, 782
　oblique muscle, 393
　palatine artery, 570
　process of lacrimal bone, 168
　ramus of hypoglossal nerve, 945
　of ischium, 210
　of os pubis, 212
Descent of testis, 1258
Detrusor urinæ muscle, 1283
Development of allantois, 36
　of amnion, 34
　of anal canal, 1149
　of aortic arches, 511
　of arteries, 509
　of body cavities, 52
　of bone, 66
　of brain, 743
　of branchial or visceral arches, 45
　of carotid arch, 511
　of cerebrospinal spaces, 55
　of chorion, 27
　of chromaphil and cortical systems, 1335
　of corpus callosum, 752
　of cranial nerves, 753

Development of decidua, 29
  of deciduous teeth, 1160
  of diencephalon, 747
  of digestive tube, 1141, 1142
  of ear, 1060
  of embryo, 37
  of external organs of genera-
    tion, 1262
  of eye, 1033
  of face, 48
  of fetal membranes, 27
  of fore-brain, 747
  of heart, 504
  of hind-brain, 744
  of hypophysis cerebri, 1331
  of joints, 255
  of kidney, 1260
  of limbs, 51
  of liver, 1237
  of lymphatic system, 693
  of mammæ, 1320
  of medulla spinalis, 767
  of mid-brain, 746
  of mouth, 1141
  of muscles, 341
  of nervous system, 737
  of neural groove and tube, 42
  of nose, 48
  of notochord, 39
  of ovaries, 1257
  of palate, 50
  of palatine tonsils, 1143
  of pancreas, 1248
  of parathyroid glands, 1330
  of permanent teeth, 1164
  of pharyngeal pouches, 45
  of placenta, 27, 31
  of primitive segments, 43
  of prostate, 1261
  of rectum, 1149
  of respiratory organs, 1107
  of rhinencephalon, 749
  of rhombencephalon, 744
  of ribs, 61
  of salivary glands, 1142
  of skeleton, 59
  of skin, 1096
  of skull, 63
  of spinal nerves, 741
  of spleen, 730
  of sternum, 62
  of streak, 38
  of suprarenal glands, 1336
  of sympathetic nervous system,
    754
  of teeth, 1160
  of testis, 1258
  of thymus, 734
  of thyroid gland, 1327
  of tongue, 1143
  of umbilical cord, 35
  of urethra, 1263
  of urinary bladder, 1261
    and generative organs, 1253
  of valves of heart, 508
  of vascular system, 502
  of veins, 515
  of venous sinuses of dura mater,
    519
  of ventral aorta, 511
  of vertebral column, 59
  of visceral arches, 45
  of yolk-sac, 35
Diagonal band of Broca, 856
Diameters of pelvis, 214, 215
Diaphragm, 388
  lymphatic vessels of, 728
  muscles of, 388
  pelvic, 407, 1189
  urogenital, 418
Diaphragma sellæ, 902
Diaphragmatic lymph nodes, 726
  pleura, 1124
Diaphysis, 73
Diarthroses, 261

Diencephalon, 825
  development of, 747
Digastric fossa, 146
  muscle, 371
  nerve from facial, 934
  triangle, 1363
Digastricus muscle, 371
Digestion, organs of, 1141
Digestive apparatus, 1141
  development of, 1141, 1144
  tube, 1141
    surface markings of, 1379
Digital arteries of foot, 647
  of hand, 605
  from superficial volar arch,
    605
  fossa of epididymis, 1292
  of femur, 218
  nerves of lateral plantar, 992
  of medial plantar, 992
  of median, 967
  of musculocutaneous, 972
  radial, 972
  of ulnar, 968
  veins of foot, 681
  of hand, 668
Digits, articulations of, 311
Dilatator naris anterior muscle,
    357
  posterior muscle, 356
  pupillæ muscle, 1044
  tubæ muscle, 1074
Diploic veins, 659
Direct cerebellar fasciculus, 776
  tract, 795
    of Flechsig, 780
  pyramidal tract, 778
Discus articularis, 273
Disk, interpubic, 287
  optic, 1046
Disks, tactile, of Merkel, 1090
Diverticulum ilei, 1217
  Meckel's, 35, 1217
Divisions of bronchi, 1133
  of cells, 17
Dorsal aortæ, 512
  artery of penis, 626
  carpal artery, of radial, 600
    of ulnar, 604 ·
  ligament, 452
  cutaneous nerves, 992, 995
  fissure of medulla oblongata,
    786
  interossei muscles, 462, 496
  interosseous artery, 603
    nerve, 973
  lamina, 739
  mesogastrium, 1146
  metacarpal arteries, 601
    veins, 668
  nasal artery, 575
  nerve of penis, 997
  peripheral band, 782
  pulmonary nerves, 941
  scapular nerve, 961
  spinal artery, 583
  veins of penis, 684
  venous arch of foot, 679
    net-work of hand, 668
  vestibular nucleus, 806
Dorsalis hallucis artery, 643
  pedis artery, 642
    branches of 643
    surface markings of, 1426
  scapulæ artery, 594
Dorsoepitrochlearis brachii mus-
    cle, 424
Dorsomedian fissure of medulla
    oblongata, 786
Dorsum ilii, 207
  linguæ, 1166
  nasi, 1024
  sellæ, 122, 152
  of tongue, 1166
Douglas, pouch or Cul de sac of,
    1197

Drum, ear, 1068
Duct or Ducts, accessory pan-
    creatic, 1248
  of Bartholin, 1176
  of Bellini, 1273
  of bulbourethral glands, 1305
  cloacal, 1150
  common bile, 1242, 1244
  of Cuvier, 516
  cystic, 1242, 1243
  ejaculatory, 1286, 1298
  frontonasal, 125, 143
  of Gärtner, 1307
  hepatic, 1242
  lacrimal, 1058, 1059
  lactiferous, 1322
  liver, 1242
  lymphatic right, 702
  Müllerian, 1255
  nasolacrimal or nasal, 1060
  pancreatic, 1247
  parotid, 1174
  pronephric, 1253
  prostatic, 1284
    orifices of, 1284
  of Rivinus, 1176
  of Santorini, 1248
  semicircular, 1083
  seminal, 1297
  Skene's 1262
  Stensen's 1174
  sublingual, 1175
  submaxillary, 1175
  thoracic, 700
  thyroglossal, 1166, 1327
  vitelline, 35
  Wharton's, 1175
  of Wirsung, 1247
  Wolffian, 1253
Ductless glands, 1327
  chromophil and cortical sys-
    tems, 1335
  parathyroid, 1330
  pineal body, 1335
  suprarenals, 1336
  thyroid, 1327
Ductuli aberrantes [testis], 1296
  efferentes [testis], 1294
  transversi [epoöphoron], 1307
Ductus arteriosus, 546
  choledochus, 1244
  cochlearis, 1083
  deferens, 1296
    ampulla of, 1296
  endolymphaticus, 1079, 1083
  longitudinalis epoöphori, 1307
  pancreaticus [*Wirsungi*], 1247
  utriculosaccularis, 1083
  venosus, 547
    development of, 516
    fossa for, 1236
    obliterated, 690
Duodenal fossæ, 1204
  glands, 1221
  impression, 1234
Duodenojejunal flexure, 1216
  fold, 1204
  fossa, 1204
Duodenomesocolic fold, 1204
Duodenopyloric constriction,
    1207
Duodenum, 1213
  lymphatic vessels of, 721
  suspensory ligament, 1216
  muscle of, 1216
  vessels and nerves of, 1216
Dura mater, cranial, 901
  arteries of, 902
  endosteal layer of, 902
  meningeal layer of, 902
  nerves of, 902
  processes of, 901
  structure of, 902
  veins of, 902
  encephali, 901

Dura mater, spinal, 903
structure of, 903
spinalis, 903
venous sinuses of, 661
development of, 519
Dural sinuses, 661

E

EAR, 1060
auricula of, 1064
cochlea, 1080
development of, 1060
external, 1064
muscles of, 1066
internal, or labyrinth, 1078
meatus acusticus externus, 1067
membranous labyrinth, 1082
middle, 1061, 1068
osseous labyrinth, 1078
pinna of, 1061, 1064
semicircular canals of, 1079
tympanic cavity of, 1068
mucous membrane of, 1077
muscles of, 1077
ossicles of, 1074
vessels and nerves of, 1077
vestibule of, 1078
Eberstaller, medial frontal sulcus of, 844
Ectoderm, 41
Ectodermal cloaca, 1150
Ectoplasm, 17
Edinger-Westphal nucleus of mid-brain, 821
Efferent nerves, 762
Eighth nerve, 935
Ejaculator urinæ muscle, 418
Ejaculatory ducts, 1286, 1298
Elastic fibrocartilage, 259
laminæ of cornea, 1038
membrane of larynx, 1113
Elbow, adult, frontal view, *x*-ray of, 1400
bone, 189
of child aged eleven years, frontal view, *x*-ray of, 1400
ten years, lateral view, *x*-ray of, 1401
Elbow-joint, 297
anastomoses around, 598
movements of, 300
surface anatomy of, 1402, 1405
markings of, 1402, 1405
vessels and nerves of, 300
Eleventh nerve, 942
Ellipsoidea, 262
Embryo, development of, 37
growth of, 44, 56
Embryology, 17, *See* also Development
Embryonic disk, 37
Eminence, canine, 162
cruciate, occipital bone, 136
frontal, 107, 111, 141
hypothenar, 449
iliopectineal, 208
intercondyloid, of tibia, 231
medial, of rhomboid fossa, 816
parietal, 106, 111, 140
pyramidal, of tympanic cavity, 1073
thenar, 449
Eminentia arcuata, 147
articularis, 144
pyramidalis, 1073
Emissary veins, 668
Enamel cells, 1162
droplet, 1163
epithelium, 1162
fibers or prisms, 1159
organ, 1162
of teeth, 1159
formation of, 1163
Enarthrosis, 262

Encephalon, 784
End-bulbs of Krause, 1091
End-plates, motor, of Kühne, 763
Endocardial cushions, 506
Endocardium, 539
Endocrine glands, 1327
Endoplasm, 17
Endolymph, 1082
Endomysium, 344
Endosteal layer of dura mater, 902
Endothelium of blood vessels, 521
corneal, 1038
of lymphatic vessels, 608
Enlargements of medulla spinalis, 769
Ensiform appendix, 100
Entoderm, 41
Entodermal cloaca, 1150
Eosinophil corpuscles, 526
Eparterial branch of right bronchus, 1122, 1133
Ependymal layer, 738
Epicardium, 539
Epicondyles of femur, 222
of humerus, 187
Epicranial aponeurosis, 353
Epicranius muscle, 353
Epidermic coat of hair follicle, 1103
Epidermis, development of, 1096
structure of, 1096
Epididymis, 1291
appendix of, 1292
Epidural space, 903
Epigastric artery, deep or inferior, 629
surface markings of, 1391
superficial, 635
superior, 589
lymph nodes, 715
region, 1190
vein, deep, 682
inferior, 682
Epiglottis, 1112
tubercle or cushion of, 1112
Epineurium, 760
Epiotic center of temporal bone, 151
Epiphyses. See Individual bones
Epiphysial cartilage, 71
Epiphysis, 832, 1335
Epiploic foramen, 1195, 1201
Epistropheus, 79, 91
Epithalamus, 748, 831
fasciculus retroflexus [of Meynert], 832
ganglion habenulæ, 832
pineal body, 832
structure of, 832
posterior commissure, 832
nucleus of, 832
trigonum habenulæ, 832
Epithelium, enamel, 1163
germinal, 1257, 1307
stratified of cornea, 1036
Epitrochleo-anconæus muscle, 440
Epitympanic recess, 1069
Eponychium, 1101
Epoöphoron, 1255, 1307
Equator of lens, 1051
Erector clitoridis muscle, 420
penis muscle, 419
spinæ or sacrospinalis muscle 379
Eruption of teeth, 1164
Esophageal arteries, 586, 606
glands, 1189
hiatus in diaphragm, 390
nerves, 939
plexus, 939
Esophagus, 1187
abdominal portion of, 1188
cervical portion of, 1187
lymphatic vessels of, 730

Esophagus, nerves of, 1189
structure of, 1188
tela submucosa, 1189
thoracic portion of, 1187
tunica mucosa, 1189
muscularis, 1188
vessels of, 1189
x-ray of, during passage of a barium meal, 1372
Ethmoid bone, 157
articulations of, 160
crest, 165, 172
cribriform plate of, 157
foramina, 118
horizontal lamina of, 158
labyrinth of lateral mass of, 159
lamina papyracea of, 159
os planum of, 159
perpendicular plate of, 158
uncinate process of, 159
vertical plate, 158
Ethmoidal arteries, 574
canals, 142
cells, 159, 1031
notch, 142
process of inferior nasal concha. 172,
sinuses, 159, 1027
spine, 121, 152
Ethmovomerine cartilage, 175
Eustachian tube, 1074
valve, 533, 534
Excavation, rectouterine, 1197
retrovesical, 1196
vesicouterine. 1197
Extensor carpi radialis accessorius muscle, 445
brevis muscle, 445
intermedius muscle, 445
longus muscle, 444
ulnaris muscle, 446
coccygis muscle, 383
digiti quinti proprius muscle, 445
digitorum brevis muscle, 491
communis muscle, 445
longus muscle, 482
hallucis brevis muscle, 491
longus muscle, 481
indicis proprius muscle, 449
minimi digiti muscle, 445
ossis metacarpi pollicis muscle, 448
metatarsi hallucis muscle, 481
pollicis brevis muscle, 448
longus muscle, 448
primi internodii pollicis muscle, 448
proprius hallucis muscle, 481
secundi internodii pollicis muscle, 448
Exterior of skull, 106
External acoustic meatus, 112, 1061, 1067
arcuate ligament, 388
auditory canal, 1067
meatus, 1067
calcaneal artery, 645
calcaneo-astragaloid ligament, 330
canthus of eyelids, 1055
circumflex artery, thigh, 636
cutaneous nerve, thigh, 982
geniculate body, 831
inguinal ring, 396
intercostal muscles, 386
jugular vein, surface markings of, 1361
lateral ligament, 273, 299, 306
ligament of malleus, 1076
malleolar artery, 642
mammary artery, 594
oblique muscle, 393
organs of generation, 1286, 1317
development of, 1262

External plantar artery, 645
  nerve, 992
  popliteal nerve, 993
  pterygoid muscle, 364
    nerve, 924
  pudic arteries, 635
  respiratory nerve of Bell, 962
  saphenous vein, 679
  semilunar fibrocartilage, 321
  spermatic artery, 629
    fascia, 1288
    nerve 982
  sphincter ani muscle, 421
Extraspinal veins, 676
Extremitas acromialis [clavicula],
    177
  sternalis [clavicula], 177
Extrinsic muscles of tongue, 1168
Eye, 1032
  accessory organs of, 1032
  bulb of, 1032
    anterior chamber, 1036, 1044
      pole, 1032
    aqueous humor, 1049
    canal of Schlemm, 1035
    chambers of, 1044
    choroid, 1035, 1040
    ciliary body, 1041
      muscle, 1036, 1043
      processes, 1042
    cornea, 1035, 1038
    crystalline lens, 1034, 1050
      spatia zonularis, 1050
      suspensory ligament,
        1050
    development of, 1033
    iris, 1043
    optic axis, 1032
    orbiculus ciliaris, 1041
    posterior chamber, 1044
      pole, 1032
    pupil, 1043
    pupillary membrane, 1035
    refracting media, 1049
    retina, 1034, 1045
      central artery, 1048
      fovea centralis, 1048
      layers of, 1048
      macula lutea, 1048
      optic disc, 1046
      ora serrata, 1046
      par ciliaris, 1046, 1048
        iridica, 1046, 1048
      pigmented layer, 1046
      proper, 1046
      rods and cones, 1048
      supporting frame-work of,
        of, 1048
    sclera, 1035, 1037
    tapetum, 1041
    tunic, fibrous, 1037
      nervous, 1045
      uvea, 1040
      vascular, 1040
    vascular tunic of, 1040
    vessels and nerves of, 1051
    vitreous body, 1035, 1049
    zonula ciliaris, 1035, 1050
  capsule of Tenon, 1054
  conjunctiva, 1056
  development of, 1033
    central artery of retina, 1035
    choroidal fissure, 1033
    hyaloid artery, 1035
    lens vesicle, 1033
    optic cup, 1033
      nerve, 1034
      stalk, 1033
      vesicle, 1033
    pupillary membrane, 1035,
      1044
  fascia bulbi, 1054
  surface anatomy, 1351
  tarsal glands of, 1056
  tunics of, 1037
Eyeball. *See* Eye, bulb of.

Eyebrows, 1055
Eyelashes, 1055
Eyelids, 1055
  canthus of, 1055
  development of, 1036
  muscles of, 355
  structure of, 1055
  surface anatomy of, 1357
  tarsi of, 1055
Eye-teeth, 1157

F

FACE, bones of, 160
  development of, 48
  lymphatics of, 702
  surface anatomy of, 1353
Facial artery, 561
  surface markings of, 1361
  transverse, 566
  bones, 160
  canal, hiatus of, 147
    prominence of, 1071
  lymph nodes, 703
  nerve, 930
    composition and central con-
      nections of, 887
    sympathetic efferent fibers
      of, 1002
  vein, anterior, 653
    common, 653
    deep, 653
    posterior, 653
    transverse, 653
Falciform ligament of liver, 1196,
    1237
  margin of fossa ovalis, 468
  process of sacrotuberous liga-
    ment, 285
Fallopian tubes, 1308
Fallopius, aqueduct of, promi-
    nence of, 1071
False ligaments of bladder, 1281
  pelvis, 213
  ribs, 102
  vocal cords, 1116
Falx aponeurotica inguinalis, 399
  cerebelli, 902
  cerebri, 751, 902
Fascia or Fasciæ, 347
  of abdomen, 392
    triangular, 396
  anal, 410
  ankle, 489
  antebrachial, 438
  antebrachii, 438
  arm, 434
  axillary, 427
  bicipital, 436
  brachial, 434
  brachii, 434
  buccopharyngeal, 362, 367
  Buck's, 1299, 1300, 1303
  Camper's, 392
  cervical, 365
  clavipectoral, 426
  Colles', 210, 393, 417, 1300
  colli, 365
  coracoclavicular, 427
  coracoclavicularis, 427
  cremasteric, 398
  cribrosa, 467
  cruris, 480
  dartos, 1299
  deep, 348
    of penis, 1299
    of deltoideus, 431
  dorsal, of foot, 491
  external spermatic, 1288
  forearm, 438
  hand, 449
  iliaca, 464
  iliopectineal, 465
  infraspinata, 433
  infundibuliform, 404, 1289
  innermost spermatic, 1289

Fascia or Fasciæ, innomata, 393,
    1288
  intercolumnar, 1288
  intercostal, 386
  intercrural, 397, 1288
  internal spermatic, 1289
  lata, 467
    falciform margin of, 468
    fossa ovalis of, 468
    iliotibial tract or band of, 468
  leg, 480
    deep transverse, 481
  lumbar, 379
  lumbodorsal, 378
  masseteric, 361
  middle spermatic, 1289
  of abdomen, 392
    triangular, 396
  obturator, 409
  orbital, 1055
  palmar, 453
  parotideomasseteric, 361
  pectoral, 426
  pelvic, 407
  penile, 1299
  perineal, 411
  piriformis, 409
  plantar, 491
  pretracheal, 370
  prevertebral, 368
  psoas and iliacus, 465, 466
  rectovesical, 1297
  renalis, 1267
  Scarpa's, 392
  Sibson's, 368, 1125
  spermatic, external, 397, 1288
    innermost, 1289
    internal, 1289
    middle, 1289
  subscapular, 432
  subscapularis, 432
  superficial, 347, 364
    of penis, 1209
  supraspinata, 432
  supraspinatous, 432
  temporal, 361
  thigh, 466
  thoracic region, 386, 426
  transversalis, 403, 1190, 1267
  triangular, of abdomen, 396
  upper extremity, 422
  urogenital diaphragm, 419, 420,
    1284
    region, 417
  vertebral, 368
Fasciculi, intrafusal, 1092
Fasciculus, cerebrospinal, 778, 899
  cerebrospinalis anterior, 778
    lateralis, 779
  comma-shaped, 782
  cuneatus, 781, 792
  gracilis, 781, 792, 899
  lateral cerebrospinal, 779
    proper, 771
    spinothalamic, 780
  lateralis proprius, 781
  of Lissauer, 780
  longitudinal inferior, 867
    medial, 778, 788, 796, 819
    posterior, 808
    superior, 867
  mammillo-tegmentalis, 896
  mammillo-thalamic, 828
  occipitofrontal, 867
  olfactory, 859
  olivospinal, 780
  perpendicular, 867
  pontospinal, 901
  posterior proper, 781
  retroflexus of Meynert, 832, 896
  rubrospinal, 779, 900
  secondary sensory, 780
  spinocerebellar, dorsal, 776, 780
    795
    ventral, 780
  spinoölivary, 881

Fasciculus, spinotectal, 780, 881
  spinothalamic, 819
  tectospinal, 778, 823, 895
  uncinate, 867
  ventral spinothalamic, 778, 795
  vestibulospinal, 778, 901
Facies dorsalis sacri, 86
  pelvina sacri, 85
Fasciola cinerea, 856
Fauces, arches or pillars of, 1154, 1177
  isthmus of, 1177
  muscles of, actions of, 1180
Female genital organs, 1305
  bulb of vestibule, 1319
  carunculæ hymenales, 1319
  clitoris, 1318
  development of, 1253
  epoöphoron, 1307
  fourchette, 1318
  glands of Bartholin, 1319
  hymen, 1319
  labia majora, 1317
    minora, 1318
  mons pubis, 1317
  navicular fossa, 1319
  ovaries, 1305
  uterine tubes, 1308
  uterus or womb, 1310
  vagina, 1316
  vestibule, 1319
    greater vestibular glands, 1319
  x-ray of, 1394
  urethra, 1286
Femoral artery, 630
  surface marking of, 1426
  canal, 631
  circumflex arteries, 636
  cutaneous nerve, anterior, 984
    lateral, 982
    posterior, 988
  fossa, 633
  nerve, 984
  ring, 631
  septum, 632
  sheath, 630
  triangle, 630, 633
  vein, 681
Femur, 217
  architecture of, 223
  of distal portion, 228
  inner, of upper, 223
  ossification of, 230
  surface anatomy of, 1414
Fenestra cochleæ, 1071
  ovalis, 1071
  rotunda, 1071
  vestibuli, 1071, 1078
Fertilization of ovum, 24
Fertilized ovum, segmentation of, 25
Fetal membranes, development of, 27
Fetus, circulation in, 546
  foramen ovale in, 546
  valve of inferior vena cava in, 546
  vascular system in, peculiarities of, 546
Fibers, arcuate, 794, 803
  dentinal, 1159
  intercolumnar, 395,
  intercrural, 395
  intrafusal, 1092
  of muscle, 343
  nerve, 757
    non-medullated, 757
  olfactory projection, 897
  olivocerebellar, 802
  of Purkinje, 545
  preganglionic, 881
  reticular, 346
  sustentacular, of Müller, 1048
  of tactile discrimination, 880
  taste, 887

Fibers, of Tomes, 1159
  touch, 880
Fibræ pontis profundæ, 804
  superficiales, 804
  propriæ [cerebellum], 809, 811
Fibrocartilage, 258
  circumferential, 258
  connecting, 258
  interarticular, 258
  intervetebral, 265
  semilunar, of knee, 320, 321
  stratiform, 258
  yellow or elastic, 259
  white, 258
Fibrocartilaginous lamina, interpubic, 287
Fibrous capsule of Glisson, 1239
  rings of heart, 539
  sheaths of flexor tendons of fingers, 442
    of toes, 493
  tunic of kidney, 1270
Fibula, 235
  nutrient artery of, 644
  ossification of, 237
  surface form of, 1413
Fibular artery, 642
  collateral ligament of knee-joint, 319
Fifth metacarpal bone, 204
  metatarsal bone, 249
  nerve, 915
Filiform papillæ of tongue, 1168
Filum terminale, 741, 767, 769
Fimbria, ovarian, 1308
Fimbriæ of uterine tube, 1308
Fingers, bones of, 202
First cuneiform bone, 245
  dorsal metacarpal artery, 601
    bone, 263
  metatarsal artery, 642
    bone, 247
  nerve, 911
Fissura antitragohelicina, 1066
  calcarina, 842
  cerebri lateralis [*Sylvii*], 842
    longitudinalis, 840
  collateralis, 843
  hippocampi, 846
  mediana anterior [medullæ oblongatæ], 786
    [*spinalis*], 769
  parietooccipitalis, 842
  petrotympanica, 1069
  posterior [medullæ oblongatæ], 786
  prima [cerebellum], 746, 808
  secunda [cerebellum], 746
Fissure or Fissures, anterior median of medulla spinalis, 769
  callosomarginal, 842
  cerebellar, 808
    cingulate, 842
    development of, 746
    floccular, 746
  cerebral, 753, 795, 840, 841
    calcarine, 753, 842
    callosal, 844
    central, 842
    collateral, 753, 843
    development of, 753
    external rhinal, 750
    hippocampal, 751, 846
    interlobular, 841
    lateral, 751, 841
    longitudinal, 840
    parietoöccipital, 842
    transverse, 853
  choroidal, 852, 1033
  circuminsular, 843
  dentate, 846
  Glaserian, 145, 1069
  of liver, 1236
  longitudinal, 840
  of lungs, 1133
  of medulla oblongata, 786

Fissure or Fissures, orbital, inferior, 111, 117
  superior, 118, 122, 155
  petroöccipital, 110, 123
  petrosphenoidal, 110
  petrotympanic, 108, 145, 1069
  pterygoid, 156
  pterygomaxillary, 113
  of Rolando, 753, 842
  sphenomaxillary, 111, 113
  of Sylvius, 753, 841
  tympanomastoid, 109
  vestibular, 1082
Fixation of kidney, 1269
  muscles, 351
Flechsig, cerebellar tract of, 780, 878
  oval area of, 782
Flexor accessorius, muscle, 494
  brevis minimi digiti muscle, 462, 496
  carpi radialis muscle, 439
    ulnaris muscle, 440
  digiti quinti brevis muscle of foot, 496
    of hand, 462
  digitorum brevis muscle, 492
    longus muscle, 486
    profundus muscle, 441
    sublimis muscle, 440
  hallucis brevis muscle, 494
    longus muscle, 484
  longus digitorum muscle, 486
  pollicis brevis muscle, 460
    longus muscle, 443
Flexure, cervical, 743
  colic, left, 1222
    right, 1222
  hepatic, 1226
  pontine, 743
  sigmoid, 1222, 1227
  splenic, 1226
  ventral cephalic, 743
Floating ribs, 101
Floccular fissure, 746
Floor of fourth ventricle, 815
Floor-plate of medulla spinalis, 738
Fluid, cerebrospinal, 907
  vitelline, 35
Fold or Folds, aryepiglottic, 1114, 1116
  caudal, 45
  cephalic, 45
  duodenojejunal, 1204
  duodenomesocolic, 1204
  gastropancreatic, 1201
  glossoepiglottic, 1112
  ileocecal, 1205
  malleolar, 1071, 1359
  rectouterine, 1313
  rectovesical, 1198
  sacrogenital, 1198, 1313
  salpingopalatine, 1184
  salpingopharyngeal, 1184
  transverse, of rectum, 1228
  Treves, 1205
  umbilical, 1281
  uterus, palmate of, 1312
  ventricular, of larynx, 1116
  vestigial of Marshall, 519, 530
  vocal, of larynx, 1116
Follicle of hair, 1102
Follicles, agminated, 1221
  Graafian, or vesicular ovarian, 1307
Fontana, spaces of, 1038
Fontanelles, 125
Foot, adult, x-ray of, 1420
  arches of, 338
  fascia of, 491
  muscles of, 491
  ossification of bones of, 250
  phalanges of, articulations of, 338
  skeleton of, 238, 239
  surface anatomy of, 1419

Foramen or foramina, caroticoclinoid, 122, 156
cecum of frontal bone, 142
 of medulla oblongata, 776
 of tongue, 1143, 1165
condyloid, anterior, 136
epiploicum, 1147, 1195, 1201
ethmoidal, 118
Huschke, 150
incisive, 107, 167
infraorbital, 116, 162
interventricular, 839, 851
intervertebral, 76
jugular, 110, 123
lacerum, 110, 122
Luschka, 815, 905
magnum, 110, 123, 134, 137
Majendii, 815, 905
mandibular, 129
mastoid, 111, 114, 146
mental, 117, 128
of Monro, 839, 852
obturator, 212
optic, 122, 152, 156
ovale of heart, 506, 546
 of sphenoid, 108, 113, 122, 154
palatine, 107
parietal, 106, 139
rotundum, 114, 122, 154
sacral, 85, 87
Scarpa, 106, 167
sciatic, 285
singulare, 148
sphenopalatine, 114, 172
spinosum, 108, 122, 154
Stenson, 107, 167
sternal, 99
stylomastoid, 109, 149
supraorbital, 115, 119, 142
supratrochlear, 187
Thebesii, 533
thyroid, 212
transversarium, 75
vena-caval, 309
venarum minimarum, 533
vertebral, 75
Vesalii, 122, 154
of Winslow, 610, 1147, 1195, 1201
zygomaticofacial, 116, 168
zygomaticoörbital, 170
zygomaticotemporal, 111, 169
Forceps, anterior, 867
 posterior, 867
Forearm, fascia of, 438
 muscles of, 438
Fore-brain, 42, 824
 development of, 747
Foregut, 1141
Forel, tegmental field of, 832
Foreskin, 1298
Formatio reticularis, 771, 807
 of medulla spinalis, 771, 807
Fornix of brain, 857
 body of, 858
 columns of, 859
 crura of, 857
 development of, 752
 of conjunctiva, 1057
 ventricles of, 858
Fossa or Fossæ, acetabular, 212
 antecubital, 595
 canine, 162
 cecal, 1204
 cochlearis, 1079
 condyloid, 110, 136
 coronoid, 187
 cranii anterior, 120
  media, 121
  posterior, 123
 digastric, 146
 digital, of epidermis, 1292
  of femur, 218
 duodenal, 1204
 duodenojejunal, 1204

Fossa or Fossæ, femoral, 633
 for ductus venosus, 1236
 for gall-bladder, 1236
 for inferior vena cava, 1236
 for umbilical vein, 1236
 glenoid, 145
 hypophyseos, 122, 152
 ileocecal, 1205
 iliac, 207
 incisive, 117, 128, 162
 incudis, 1073
 infraspinatous, 180
 infratemporal, 112
 intercondyloid, of femur, 222
  of tibia, 231
 interpeduncular, 817, 839
 intersigmoid, 1206
 ischiorectal, 412
 ischiorectalis, 412
 jugular, 148
 lacrimal, 117, 142
 of liver, 1236
 mandibular, 108, 112, 145
 mastoid, 145
 nasal, 1026
 navicularis [uretha], 1285
  [vulva], 1319
 occipital, inferior, 123
 olecranon, 187
 ovalis of fascia lata, 468
  of heart, 534
 ovarian, 1198, 1305
 pararectal, 1198
 paravesical, 1198
 pericecal, 1204
 peritoneal, 1204
 popliteal, 638
 pterygoid, 156
 pterygopalatine, 114
 radial, 187
 retrocecal, 1206
 retroperitoneal, 1204
 rhomboid, 815
 rhomboidea, 815
 of Rosenmüller, 1183, 1185
 sagittal, of liver, 1236
 sagittalis sinistra [liver], 1236
 scaphoid, 107, 156
 of skull, anterior, 119
  middle, 121
  posterior, 123
 sphenomaxillary, 114
 subarcuate, 148
 subscapular, 178
 supraspinatous, 179
 supratonsillar, 1177
 Sylvian, 753
 temporal, 111
 trochanteric, 218
 vermian, 136
 vesicæ felleæ, 1236
Fountain decussation of Meynert, 823
Fourchette, 1318
Fourth metacarpal bone, 203
 metatarsal bone, 249
 nerve, 914
 ventricle, 814
  floor of, 814
Fovea capitis femoris, 217
 centralis retinæ, 1046, 1048
  structure of, 1048
 dentis, 78
 inguinal, lateral, 405
  medial, 405
 of rhomboid fossa, 816
 trochlear, 117, 142
Free nerve-endings, 1090
Frenula of colic valve, 1225
Frenulum of clitoris, 1318
 of labia minora, 1318
 linguæ, 1166
 of lips, 1152
 of prepuce, 1297
 veli, 822

Frontal air sinuses, 142, 1030
 artery, 575
 bone, 141
  articulations of, 143
  orbital or horizontal part of, 142
  ossification of, 143
  squama of, 141
  structure of, 143
 convolution, ascending, 843
 crest, 121, 142
 eminences, 107, 111, 141
 gyri, 843, 844
 lobe, 843
 nerve, 916
 operculum, 847
 process of maxilla, 165
 sulci, 843
 suture, 107, 115, 141
 vein, 652
Frontalis muscle, actions of, 353
Fronto-ethmoidal suture, 121
Fronto-nasal duct, 143
 process, 48
Fronto-pontile fibers, 804, 816
Fronto-sphenoidal process of zygomatic bone, 169
Fundiform ligament of penis, 1301
Fundus, oculi, 1045
 stomach, 1212
  glands,1212
 tympani, 1069
 uteri, 1311
Fungiform papillæ of tongue, 1167
Funiculus separans, 817
 spermaticus, 1289
Funiculi of medulla spinalis, 776
Furcal nerve, 978
Furrow, chordal, 39
 dental, 1161
 naso-optic, 50, 1036
Fusiform gyrus, 846

G

Galea aponeurotica, 353
Galen, veins of, 660
Gall-bladder, 1243
 fossa for, 1236
 lymphatic capillaries in, 697
 vessels of, 723
 structure of, 1243
Ganglia of nerves, autonomic, 764
  sensory, 764
Gangliated cord, 1006
Ganglion or Ganglia, 764
 aorticorenal, 1016
 basal, 859
 cardiac, of Wrisberg, 1015
 carotid, 1007
 celiac, 1013
 central, 1006
 cervical, 1009, 1011
 cervicale inferius, 1011
  medius, 1011
  superius, 1009
 ciliary, 918
 collateral, 1006, 1007
 Corti, 1081, 1090
 Gasserian, 915
 genicular, 932
 habenulæ, 832
 impar, 1006, 1013
 inferior, of glossopharyngeal 937
 interpeduncular, 817, 897
 jugular, 937, 939
 Langley's, 1177
 lenticular, 918
 Meckel's, 921
 nodosum, 939, 940
 ophthalmic, 918
 otic, 926

Ganglion or Ganglia, petrous, 937
　phrenicum, 1017
　ridge or neural crest, 42, 741
　Scarpa, 935, 1089
　semilunar, of abdomen, 1016
　　of trigeminal nerve, 915
　semilunare [Gasseri], 915
　sphenopalatine, 921
　　rami nasales posteriores supe-
　　　riores, 923
　　orbitales, 922
　spinal, 948
　spiral, of cochlea, 1081, 1090
　splanchnicum, 1013
　submaxillary, 927
　superior, of glossopharyngeal,
　　937
　　mesenteric, 1017
　vagus, 939
　Wrisberg, 1015
Ganglionic layer of retina, 1046
Gärtner, duct of, 1255, 1307
Gasserian ganglion, 915
Gaster, 1207
Gastric arteries, short, 612
　artery, left, 609
　　right, 610
　glands, 1212
　impression, 1234
　lymph nodes, 717
　nerves from vagus, 942
　plexuses from sympathetic,
　　1019
　　from vagus, 942
　veins, short, 690
Gastrocnemius muscle, 483
Gastrocolic ligament, 1196, 1197
　omentum, 1202
Gastroduodenal artery, 611
Gastroepiploic arteries, 611, 612
　lymph node, right, 717
　veins, 690, 691
Gastrohepatic omentum, 1202
Gastrolienal ligament, 732, 1200
Gastropancreatic fold, 1201
Gastrophrenic ligament, 1208
Gemellus inferior muscle, 477
　superior muscle, 477
Gemmules of nerves, 757
General sensations, peripheral
　terminations of nerve of, 1090
Generation, development of ex-
　ternal organs of, 1262
Genicular arteries, 637, 639
　ganglion of facial nerve, 932
Geniculate bodies, 831
Geniculum of facial nerve, 932
Genioglossus muscle, 1168
Geniohyoglossus muscle, 1168
Geniohyoid muscle, 373
Geniohyoideus muscle, 373
Genital cord, 1255, 1258
　corpuscles, 1091
　glands, development, 1255
　organs of female, 1305
　　external, 1317
　　of male, 1286
　ridge, 1255
　swellings, 1262
　tract in female, x-ray of, 1394
　tubercle, 1262
Genitocrural nerve, 982
Genitofemoral nerve, 982
Gennari, band of, 868, 873
Genu of corpus callosum, 840, 865
　of facial nerve, 919
　of internal capsule, 864
Gerlach, tube tonsil of, 1074
Germ centers of lymph nodule,
　699
　dental, 1161
Germinal epithelium, 1256, 1307
Giacomini, band of, 857
Giant cells, 67
　of Betz, 872
Gianuzzi, crescents of, 1176

Gimbernat's ligament, 395
Gingivæ, 1153
Ginglymus, 261
Giraldes, organ of, 1297
Girdle of inferior extremity, 175
　pelvic, 175
　shoulder, 175
　superior extremity, 175
Glabella, 107, 115
Gladiolus, 99
Gland or Glands, accessory, of
　　mouth, 1177
　part of parotid, 1174
　aortic, 1335
　areolar, mammæ, 1320
　arytenoid, 1120
　Bartholin, 1262, 1319
　Blandin, 1171
　Bowman, 1028
　Brunner's, 1221
　buccal, 1153
　bulbourethral, 1305
　cardiac, 1212
　ceruminous, 1068
　ciliary, 1055
　coccygeal, 1339
　Cowper's, 1262, 1305
　ductless, 1327
　duodenal, 1221
　endocrine, 1327
　esophageal, 1188
　of eye, 1056
　fundus, 1212
　gastric, 1212
　genital, 1255
　intestinal, 1221
　labial, 1152
　lacrimal, 1058
　larynx, 1120
　lenticular, of stomach, 1213
　lingual, 1171
　Littré, 1285
　Luschka's, 1339
　mammary, 1319
　Meibomian, 1056
　molar, 1153
　of Montgomery, 1320
　mucous, of tongue, 1171
　of Nuhn, 1171
　oxyntic, 1212
　Pacchioni, 905
　parathyroid, 1330
　parotid, 1173
　Peyer's, 1221
　pituitary, 1331
　preputial, 1299
　prostate, 1303
　pyloric, 1212
　salivary, 1173
　sebaceous, 1104
　serous, of tongue, 1171
　sublingual, 1175
　submaxillary, 1175
　sudoriferous, 1104
　suprarenal, 1336
　sweat, 1104
　tarsal, 1056
　thymus, 734
　thyroid, 1327
　tongue, 1171
　trachoma, 1058
　urethral, 1285
　uterine, 1316
　vestibular, greater, 1262, 1319
Glans clitoridis, 1318
　penis, 1301
Glaserian fissure, 145, 1069
Glenohumeral ligaments, 295
Glenoid cavity, 182
　fossa, 145
　ligament of Cruveilhier, 310,
　　337
　　of shoulder, 295
Glenoidal labrum of hip-joint, 314
　of shoulder-joint, 295
Gliding joints, 261

Glisson's capsule, 1202, 1239
Globular processes of His, 49
Globus major [epididymis], 1291
　minor [epididymis], 1291
　pallidus, 860
Glomus aorticum, 1095, 1339
　caroticum, 1094, 1339
　coccygeum, 1014, 1339
Glossoepiglottic folds, 1112, 1165
Glossopalatine arch, 1177
Glossopalatinus muscle, 1168
Glossopharyngeal nerve, 936
　composition and central con-
　　nections of, 883
　sympathetic afferent fibers
　　of, 1002
Glottis respiratoria, 1117
　vocalis, 1117
　rima of, 1117
Glutæus maximus muscle, 473
　medius muscle, 474
　minimus muscle, 475
Gluteal artery, inferior, 626
　superior, 628
　lines of ilium, 207
　muscles, 473
　nerves, 988
　tuberosity, 221
　veins, 683
Golgi, cells of 876
　organs of, 347, 1092
Golgi and Mazzoni, corpuscles of,
　1092
Goll, tract of, 776, 781
Gomphosis, 260
Gowers, tract of, 780, 858
Graafian follicles, 1307
　structure of, 1307
Gracile nucleus, 791
Gracilis muscle, 471
Grandry, tactile corpuscles of,
　1091
Granular corpuscles, 67
　layer of dentin, 1159
Granulations, arachnoid, 905
Gray commissures of medulla
　spinalis, 771
　nerve fibers, 757
　substance of cerebellum, 811
　　of cerebral hemispheres, 868
　　of cortex, 874
　　of medulla oblongata, 796
　　spinalis, 770
Great auricular nerve, 955
　cardiac nerve, 1011
　　vein, 650
　cerebral vein, 660, 853
　longitudinal fissure, 840
　omentum, 1202
　sacrosciatic ligament, 285
　saphenous vein, 679
　splanchnic nerve, 1012
　transverse fissure of brain, 853
　wings of sphenoid, 154
Greater cavernous nerve, 1020
　curvature of stomach, 1207
　multangular bone, 200
　occipital nerve, 951
　omentum, 1190, 1202
　palatine foramen, 107
　pelvis, 213
　peritoneal sac, 1194
　sciatic foramen, 285
　　notch, 210
　sigmoid cavity, 192
　splanchnic nerve, 1012, 1013
　superficial petrosal nerve, 921
　trochanter, 218
　vestibular glands, 1262, 1319
Groove, auriculoventricular, 531
　bicipital, 184
　carotid, 122, 153
　chiasmatic, 122, 152
　costal, 102
　infraorbital, 118, 163
　interatrial, 531

Groove, intertubercular, of humerus, 184
  lacrimal, 118, 164
  musculospiral, 185
  mylohyoid, 129
  neural, 42
  obturator, 212
  occipital, 109, 146
  olfactory, 121
  optic, 152
  primitive, 38
  pterygopalatine, 156
  vertebral, 94
Growth of embryo, 56
Gubernaculum dentis, 1164
  testis, 1258
Gudden, commissure of, 837, 912
  mammillo-tegmental bundle of, 896
Gullet, 1187
Gums, 1153
Gustatory calyculi, 1023
  cells, 1023
  hair, 1023
  pore, 1023
Gynecomastia, 1323
Gyre, medifrontal, 844
  precentral, 843
  subfrontal, 844
  superfrontal, 844
Gyrus or Gyri, of brain, 841
  Medius, 844
    superior, 844
  angular, 845
  of Broca, 844
  central anterior, 843
    posterior, 845
  cingulate, 844
  dentate, 856, 867
  frontal, 844
  frontalis inferior, 844
  fusiform, 846
  hippocampal, 846, 857
  of insula, 847
  lingual, 846
  marginal, 844
  occipital, 845
  olfactory, 855
  orbital, 844
  precuneus, 845
  quadrate, 845
  straight, 844
  subcallosal, 856, 897
  superior parietal lobule, 845
  supracallosal, 856
  supramarginal, 845
  temporal, 846
  transverse, of Heschl, 846
  uncus, 846

H

Habenular commissure, 832
Hair bulb, 1102
  cells of spiral organ of Corti, 1088
Hairs, 1102
  cuticle of, 1096
  follicle of, 1102
  gustatory, 1023
  olfactory, 1029
  root of, 1102
  scapus or shaft of, 1104
  structure of, 1104
Haller, vas aberrans of, 1296
Hamate bone, 202
Hamstring muscles, 479
Hamulus of hammate bone, 202
  lacrimal, 168
  laminæ spiralis, 1082
  pterygoid, 107
Hand, adult, x-ray of, 1403
  and wrist of child aged eleven
        years, x-ray of, 1405
    two-and-a-half years, x-
        ray of, 1404

Hand, fascia of, 453
  muscles of, 449
  phalanges of, articulations of, 311
  skeleton of, 196
  surface anatomy of, 1394
  markings of, 1407
Hard palate, 1153
Hare-lip, 127
Harrison's sulcus, 106
Hassall, corpuscles of 735
Haustra, 1231
Haversian canals of bone, 68, 69
  systems of bone, 68
Head, adult, x-ray of, 1350
  arteries of, 557
  lymphatics of, 702
  muscles of, 352
    development of, 342
  veins of, 651
Hearing, organ of, 1060
Heart, 530
  apex of, 532
  arteries of, 545
  atrioventricular bundle of His, 543
    node, 544
  atrium, left, 536
    right, 533
  base of, 531
  component parts of, 531
  development of, 504
  endocardium, 539
  fibers of ventricles, 545
  fibrous rings of, 539
  lymphatic capillaries of, 697
    vessels of, 730
  marginal veins of, 650
  muscular structure of, 540
  nerves of, 545
  size and weight of, 530
  structure of, 540
  surface marking of, 1373
  trigonum fibrosum, 539
  valves of, 528
    development of, 508
  veins of, 650
  ventricle, left, 537
    right, 535
  ventricular septum of, 539
Heart-wall, 539
Heidenhain, demilunes of, 1176
Helicine arteries, 1303
Helicis major muscle, 1066
  minor muscle, 1066
Helicotrema, 1081
Helix, 1065
Hemal nodes, 700
Hemiazygos vein, 676
  accessory, 676
Hemispheres, cerebellar, 808
  cerebral, 749, 840
Hemolymph nodes, 700
Hemorrhoidal artery, inferior, 625
  middle, 622
  superior, 616
  nerve, inferior, 996
  plexuses of nerves, 1019
  vein, inferior, 684
    middle, 684
    superior, 690
  venous plexus, 684
Henle, loop of, 1273
Henle's layer of hair follicle, 1104
Hensen, canalis reuniens of, 1083, 1085
  stripe of, 1089
  supporting cells of, 1089
Hepar, 1233
  capsula fibrosa [Glissoni], 1239
  facies inferior, 1233
    posterior, 1234
    superior, 1233
  margo anterior, 1235
  tunica serosa, 1239

Hepatic artery 610, 1241
  branches of vagus nerve, 942
  cells, 1241
  cylinders, 1238
  duct, 1242
  flexure of colon, 1226
  lymph nodes, 717
  plexus, 1017
  sinusoids, 1238, 1241
  veins, 688, 1239, 1241
Hepatoduodenal ligament, 1196, 1202
Hepatogastric ligament, 1196, 1202
Hepatorenal ligament, 1196
Herbst, corpuscles of, 1092
Hernia, congenital, complete, 1296
  incomplete, 1296
  into funicular process, 1296
Herophilus, torcular of, 659
Heschl, gyri of, 846
Hesselbach, interfoveolar ligament, of, 404
  triangle of, 1391
Hiatus, aortic, 390
  esophageal, 390
  of facial canal, 147
  semilunaris, 125, 1027
Higher or cortical visual centers, 838
Highest intercostal artery, 589
  veins, 674
  nuchal line, 135
  thoracic artery, 592
Highmore, antrum of, 164, 1031
Hilum of kidney, 1266
  of lung, 1131
  of suprarenal, 1337
Hind-brain, development of, 42, 744
Hind-gut, 45, 1141
Hinge-joint, 261
Hip bone, 206
  articulations of, 213
  ossification of, 212
  structure of, 212
  surface anatomy of, 1411
Hip-joint, 311
  movements of, 316
  muscles in relation with, 316
  surface marking of, 1411
Hippocampal commissure, 859, 897
  fissure, 751, 846
  gyrus, 846
Hippocampus, 752, 857
His, atrioventricular bundle of, 543
  globular processes of, 49
Hook bundle of Risien Russell, 810
Horizontal cells of retina, 1047
  part of palatine bone, 170
  semicircular canal, 1080
Houston's valves of rectum, 1228
Howship's lacunæ, 67
Huguier, canal of, 145, 933, 1070
Humeral articulation, 293
  bursæ in relation to, 295
  movements of, 296
  vessels and nerves of, 296
  circumflex arteries, 594
Humerus, 183
  ossification of, 188
  structure of, 187
  surface anatomy of, 1398
Humor, aqueous, 1049
Hunter's canal, 630, 633
Huschke, auditory teeth of, 1086
  foramen of, 150
Huxley's layer of hair follicle, 1104
Hydatid of Morgagni, 1255, 1292, 1308
  pedunculated, of epididymis, 1292

Hymen, 1319
Hyoepiglottic ligament, 1113
Hyoglossal membrane, 1171
Hyoglossus muscle, 1170
Hyoid arch, 47
  arteries, 560
  bone, 133
    body of, 133
    cornua of, 133
    ossification of, 134
Hyothyroid ligaments, 1112
  membrane, 1112
Hyparterial bronchi, 1123, 1133
Hypochondriac regions, 1190
Hypochordal bar or brace, 60
Hypogastric artery, 620
  branches of, 621
  in fetus, 546, 620
  obliterated, 620
  variations in, 620
  lymph nodes, 617
  plexus, sympathetic, 1015, 1019
  region, 1190
  vein, 683
  zone, 1190
Hypoglossal canal, 136
  nerve, 943
    composition and central con-
      nections of, 881
    nucleus of, 796
Hypophyseal artery, 573
  fossa, 152
Hypophysis cerebri, 1331
  development of, 1332
  function of, 1334
  named parts, 1332, 1333
  structure of, 1333
Hypothalamus, 748, 833
  corpora mammillaria, 833
  hypophysis or pituitary body.
    833, 1331
  infundibulum, 833
  optic chiasma, 833
  subthalamic tegmental region,
    832
  tuber cinerum, 833
Hypothenar eminence, 449
  facial compartment, 456
  muscles, 461

                    I

Ileocecal fold, 1205
  fossæ, 1205
  valve, 1225
Ileocolic artery, 615
  lymph nodes, 720
Ileum, 1216
  lymphatic vessels of, 721
Iliac arteries, common, 619
    surface markings of, 1391
  external, 619, 628
    surface markings of, 1391
  internal, 620
  circumflex artery, deep, 629
    superficial, 635
    vein, deep, 682
    superficial, 680
  colon, 1226
  fascia, 464
  fossa, 207
  furrow, 1376
  lymph nodes, 715
  spines, 208
  tuberosity, 207
  vein, common, 685
    external, 682
    internal, 683
Iliacus muscle, 466
  fascia of, 464
Iliocapsularis muscle, 466
Iliococcygeus muscle, 408
Iliocostalis cervicis muscle, 381
  dorsi muscle, 381
  lumborum muscle, 381

Iliofemoral ligament, 312
Iliohypogastric nerve, 979
Ilioinguinal nerve, 980
Iliolumbar artery, 627
  ligament, 282
  vein, 686
Iliopectineal eminence, 208
  fascia, 465
Iliosacralis muscle, 409
Iliotibial band or tract, 468
Iliotrochanteric ligament, 313
Ilium, 206
  ala of, 207
  body of, 206
  crest of, 207
  dorsum of, 207
  gluteal lines of, 207
  spines of, 207
Imbedding or implantation of
  ovum, 26
Immovable articulations, 260
Impression, colic, 1234
  duodenal, 1234
  gastric, 1234
  renal, 1234
  rhomboid, 177
  suprarenal, 1234
  trigeminal, 147
Incisive bone, 167
  canals, 107, 167
  foramen, 107, 167
  fossa, 117, 162
  teeth, 1155
Incisor crest, 167
  teeth, 1155
Incisura angularis, 1208
  apicis cordis, 531
  cardiaca, 1207
  fastigii, 746
  radialis, 192
  semilunaris, 192
  temporalis, 846
  tentorii, 902
Incremental lines of Salter, 1159
Incus, 1075
  crus breve, 1075
    longum, 1076
  development of, 1061
  ligaments of, 1076
Inferior alveolar artery, 563
  articular arteries, knee, 640
  calcaneonavicular ligament, 333
  cerebellar peduncles, 811
  constrictor muscle, 1185
  dental artery, 569
    nerve, 926
  epigastric vein, 682
  fascia of urogenital diaphragm,
    414
  ganglion, 937, 940
  labial artery, 563
  laryngeal nerve, 941
  longitudinal sinus, 662
  maxillary nerve, 923
  oblique muscle, 1054
  profunda artery, 597
  pubic ligament, 286
  quadrigeminal body, 823
  sagittal sinus, 662
  striate veins, 660
  tarsal plate, 1055
  thyroarytenoid ligaments, 1116
  turbinated bone, 173
  vesical artery, 621
  vocal cords, 1116
Infraclavicular branches of brachial plexus, 961
Infracostales muscles, 387
Infraglenoid tuberosity, 181
Infrahyoid artery, 560
  muscles, 374
Infraorbital artery, 569
  canal, 163
  foramen, 116, 162
  groove, 118, 163
  plexus of nerves, 921

Infrapatellar pad of fat, 322
Infrascapular artery, 594
Infraspinatous fascia, 433
  fossa, 180
  muscle, 374
Infrasternal notch, 1368
Infratemporal crest, 111, 154
  fossa, 112
  surface of maxilla, 162
Infratrochlear nerve, 918
Infundibuliform fascia, 404, 1289
Infundibulopelvic ligament, 1313
Infundibulum of brain, 833
  of ethmoid bone, 125, 160,
    1027
Inguinal aponeurotic falx, 399
  canal, 406, 1289
  ligament, 395
    reflected, 396
  lymph nodes, 712
  regions, 1190
  ring, abdominal, 405
    subcutaneous, 395
Inion, 114
Inlet of pelvis, 214
Innominate artery, 556
  bone, 206
  fascia, 393, 1288
  veins, 673
    peculiarities of, 674
Inscriptions, tendinous, of rectus
  abdominis, 400
Insertion of muscles, 345
Insula, 847
  circular sulcus of, 848
  development of, 848
  gyri of, 848
  opercula of, 847
Integument, common, 1096
Interalveolar cell-islets, 1249
Interarticular chondrosternal lig-
  ament, 279
  costocentral ligaments, 277
  fibrocartilages, 258
  sternocostal ligaments, 279
Interatrial groove, 531
Intercalatum, 819
Intercapitular veins, 669, 681
Intercarpal articulations, 306
  movements of, 307
Intercavernous sinuses, 666
Intercellular biliary passages,
  1241
Intercentral ligaments, 263
Interchondral ligaments, 280
Interclavicular ligament, 290
Interclinoid ligament, 157
Intercolumnar fascia, 1288
  fibers, 395
Intercondyloid eminence of tibia,
  231
  fossa of femur, 222
  of tibia, posterior, 231
Intercostal arteries from aorta,
  606
  highest, 589
  from internal mammary, 589
    superior, 589
  fasciæ, 386
  lymph nodes, 726
  membranes, 386, 387
  muscles, 386
  nerves, 947
  spaces, 101
  veins, 674
Intercostales externi muscles, 386
  interni muscles, 387
Intercostobrachial nerve, 975
Intercrural fascia, 397, 1288
  fibers, 395
Intercuneiform articulations, 335
Interfoveolar ligament of Hesselbach, 404
Interglobular spaces, 1159
Interior of bladder, 1282
  of larynx, 1114

Interior of skull, 119
of uterus, 1312
Interlobular arteries of kidney, 1274
Intermetacarpal articulations, 309
Intermetatarsal articularions, 336
Internal abdominal ring, 405
acoustic meatus, 148
arcuate ligament, 388
calcaneal arteries, 645
nerves, 992
calcaneo-astragaloid ligament, 331
calcaneo-navicular ligament, 333
canthus of eyelids, 1055
capsule of brain, 863
carotid artery, x-ray of, 1350
circumflex artery, 636
cutaneous nerve, arm, 966
lesser, 966
geniculate body, 831
iliac artery, 620
lymph nodes, 716
vein, 683
intercostals muscle, 387
jugular vein, surface markings of, 1361
lateral ligament, elbow, 299
mandible, 273
wrist, 305
malleolar artery, 642
mammary artery, 587
lymph nodes, 726
maxillary lymph nodes, 704
oblique muscle, 398
palpebral arteries, 574
plantar artery, 645
nerve, 992
popliteal nerve, 989
pterygoid muscle, 363
pudenal artery, 623
veins, 684
pudic artery, 623
nerve, 996
veins, 684
respiratory nerve of Bell, 958
saphenous nerve, 985
vein, 679
semilunar fibrocartilage, 321
sphincter ani muscle, 421
Interossei muscles of foot, 496
of hand, 462
Interosseous arteries, 603, 604
ligament, 278
membrane of forearm, 301
of leg, 326
nerve, dorsal or posterior, 973
volar or anterior, 967
volaris primus muscle, 463
Interparietal bone, 138
Interpeduncular fossa, 817, 839
ganglion, 817, 836
Interphalangeal articulations, 311, 338
Interpleural space, 1128
Interpubic disk, 287
fibrocartilaginous lamina, 287
Intersegmental neurons, 772
septa, 59
Intersigmoid fossa, 1206
Interspinal ligaments, 267
Interspinales muscles, 383
Interspinous ligament, 267
Intertarsal articulations, 330
Intertragic notch, 1065
Intertransversales muscle, 383
Intertransverse ligaments, 267
Intertrochanteric crest, 219
line, 219
Intertubercular plane, 1190
Intertubular dentin, 1159
Intervenous tubercle, 534
Interventricular foramen, 839, 851
septum, 539

Intervertebral fibrocartilages, 265
foramina, 76
veins, 678
Intervillous space, 27
Intestinal arteries, 613
glands, 1221
villi, 1219
Intestine, development of, 1144
large, 1222
x-ray of, after barium enema, 1387
lymphatic nodules of, 1221
lymphatics of, 723
small, 1213
lymphatic vessels of, 723
structure of, 1218
vessels and nerves of, 1221
surface markings of, 1384
Intestinum cædum, 1222
crassum, 1222
ileum, 1216
jejunum, 1216
rectum, 1227
tenue, 1213
tela submucosa, 1219
tunica mucosa, 1219
muscularis, 1219
serosa, 1219
Intra-articular ligament, 277
Intracartilaginous ossification, 71
Intracellar bodies, 19
Intra-epithelial plexus of cornea, 1039
Intrafusal fasciculi, 1092
fibers, 1092
Intrajugular process, 136
Intralobular veins, 1241
Intramembranous ossification, 70
Intraparietal sulcus, 845
Intrapulmonary bronchi, 1136
Intraspinal veins, 677
Intrathyroid cartilage, 1110
Intrinsic muscles of tongue, 1170
spinal reflex paths, 877
Iris, 1043
Ischiocapsular ligament, 313
Ischiocavernosus muscle, 419, 420
Ischiorectal fossa, 412
Ischium, 209
body of, 209
rami of, 210
spine of, 210
tuberosity of, 210
Island of Reil, 847
Islands, blood, 502
of Calleja, 856
of Langerhans, 1249
Isthmus, aortic, 512, 555
faucium, 1151, 1177
of external acoustic meatus, 1067
glandula thyreoidea, 1328
of limbic lobe, 844
rhombencephali, 744
of thyroid gland, 1327
of uterine tube, 1308
Iter chordæ anterius, 1069, 1070
posterius, 1069
Ivory of teeth, 1159

J

JACOB's membrane, 1048
Jacobson, nerve of, 938, 1077
vomeronasal organs of, 51, 1028
Jejunum, 1216
lymphatic vessels of, 721
Jelly of Wharton, 35
Joints. *See* Articulations.
development of, 255
Jugular foramen, 110, 123
fossa, 148
ganglion of glossopharyngeal nerve, 937
of vagus nerve, 939

Jugular nerve, 1010
notch, 99, 136
process, 110, 136
surface of temporal bone, 149
tubercle, 137
vein, anterior, 655
external, 654
internal, 656
bulb of, 656
posterior external, 655, 1361
surface markings of, 1361
Jugum sphenoidale, 157
Juxtaglomerular apparatus, 1273

K

KARYOKINESIS, 19
Kerkring, valves of, 1219
Kidneys, 1264
artery of, 612
calyces of, 1272
development of, 1264
fascia of, 1267
fixation of, 1269
hilum of, 1266
lymphatic capillaries in, 697
vessels of, 723
Malpighian corpuscle, 1272
medullary substance of, 1272
minute anatomy of, 1272
nerves of, 1274
paranephric body, 1269
relations of, 1264
renal artery, 617
structure of, 1270
surface marking of, 1390
tubules of, 1273
veins of, 687, 1274
weight and dimensions of, 1264
Knee-cap, 230
x-ray of an adult, 1416, 1419
of child aged seven-and-a-half years, 1419
Knee-joint, 317
bursæ of, 323
movements of, 324
surface anatomy of, 1417
Krause, end-bulbs of, 1091
Kühne, motor end-plates of, 763

L

LABBÉ, posterior anastomotic vein of, 660
Labia majora, 1317
minora, 1318
oris, 1151
Labial arteries, 563
commissures, 1317, 1318
glands, 1153
grooves, 1142
Labiodental lamina, 1161
Labrum glenoidale, 295, 314
Labyrinth, membranous, 1082
vessels of, 1090
osseous, 1078
Labyrinthus ethmoidalis, 159
Lacertus fibrosus, 436, 438
Lacinate ligament, 489
Lacrimal apparatus, 1058
artery, 573
bone, 168
canals, 1059
caruncula, 1058
crest, anterior, 166
posterior, 118
ducts or canals, 1058
ampullæ of, 1060
fossa, 117, 142, 166
gland, 1058
groove, 118, 164
hamulus, 168
nerve, 916
notch, 163

Lacrimal papilla, 1055
process of inferior nasal concha, 173
punctum, 1055
sac, 1036, 1058, 1060
tubercle, 166
Lacteals, 693
Lactiferous ducts, 1322
Lacuna magna [of urethra], 1285
Lacunæ of bone, 68
of cartilage, 256
of urethra, 1285
venous, 662
Lacunar ligament, 395
Lacus lacrimalis, 1055, 1058
Lagena, 1085
Lambda, 106
Lambdoidal suture, 106, 114, 137
Lamellæ of bone, 68
articular, 256
Lamina basalis, 1041
cartilaginis cricoideæ, 1110
choriocapillaris, 1041
cribrosa ethmoidalis, 158
scleræ, 1037
dental, 1161
dorsal or alar, 739
elastic, of cornea, 1038
elastica anterior, 1038
posterior, 1038
fibrocartilaginea interpubica, 287
labiodental, 1161
lingual, 1161
medullary, 827
nasal, 49
perpendicularis, 158
reticular, 1089
spiral, of cochlea, 1082
spiralis ossea, 1082
terminalis, 747, 838, 1009
vasculosa, 1040
ventral or basal, 739
of vertebræ, 76, 77
Lancisi, nerves of, 897
Langerhans, centro-acinar cells of, 1249
islands of, 1249
Langer's lines, 1100
Langley's ganglion, 1177
Large deep petrosal nerve, 922
intestine, 1222
cecum, 1222
colic valve, 1224
colon, 1225
ascending, 1225
descending, 1226
iliac, 1226
sigmoid or pelvic, 1227
transverse, 1226
rectum, 1227
superficial petrosal nerve, 921
x-ray of after barium enema, 1387
Laryngeal artery, inferior, 586
superior, 560
nerves, 940
inferior, 941
recurrent, 941
superior, 940
part of pharynx, 1183
prominence, 1109
saccule, 1117
sinus, 1116
Larynx, 1108
cartilages of, 1109
conus elasticus of, 1113
elastic membrane of, 1113
glands of, 1120
interior of, 1114
ligaments of, 1112
lymphatic vessels of, 707, 1120
mucous membrane of, 1120
muscles of, 1118
actions of, 1120
nerves of, 1120
rima glottidis of, 1117

Larynx, surface marking of, 1359
ventricle of, 1116
ventricular folds of, 1116
vessels of, 1120
vestibule of, 1114
vocal cords of, 1116
folds of, 1116
Lateral cartilages, nose, 1024
cerebrospinal fasciculus, 779
crioarytenoid muscle, 1118
hyothyroid ligament, 1112
mesoderm, 41
nasal cartilage, 1024
olfactory gyrus, 851
stria, 854
sinuses of dura, 664
spinothalamic fasciculus, 780
thyrohyoid ligament, 1112
vertebral muscles, 376
Latissimus dorsi muscle, 423
Layer of rods and cones, 1048
Layers of cerebral cortex, 868
Least splanchnic nerve, 1013
Left atrium, 536
auricle, 536
auricular appendix, 537
coronary plexus, 1016
vein, 650
lobe of liver, 1237
ventricle, 537
Leg, fascia of, 480
deep transverse, 484
muscles of, 480
development of, 341
Lemniscus, lateral, 819
lateralis, 819
medial, 819
spinal, 780
Lens, capsule of, 1050
vascular, 1035
changes produced in, by age, 1051
crystalline, 1034, 1050
development of, 1034
equator of, 1051
poles of, 1051
structure of, 1051
suspensory ligament of, 1050
vesicle, 1033
Lenticular ganglion, 918
glands of stomach, 1213
process of incus, 1076
Lentiform nucleus, 861
Lesser cavernous nerve, 1020
curvature of stomach, 1207
lacrimal bone, 168
multangular bone, 201
omentum, 1202
pelvis, 214
peritoneal sac, 1197, 1201
sac or omental bursa of peritoneum, 1194
boundaries of, 1201
sciatic foramen, 285
notch, 210
sigmoid cavity, 192
splanchnic nerve, 1013
trochanter, 219
tubercle, 185
tuberosity, 185
Leucocytes, 525
Levator anguli oris muscle, 357
scapulæ muscle, 426
ani muscle, 407
claviculæ muscle, 426
glandulæ thyreoideæ muscle, 1329
menti muscle, 358
palati muscle, 1180
palpebræ superioris muscle, 1051
prostatæ muscle, 408
scapulæ muscle, 426
veli palatini muscle, 1180
Levatores costarum muscle, 387
Lieberkühn, crypts of, 1221

Lien, 730
accessorius, 732
extremitas inferior, 731
superior, 731
facies diaphragmatica, 731
gastrica, 731
renalis, 731
margo anterior, 731
posterior, 731
Lienal artery, 612
plexus of nerves, 1017
vein, 690
Ligament or Ligaments, acromio-clavicular, 291
alar, 273
ankle, 327
annular of ankle, 489
of radius, 301
of stapes, 1077
of wrist, 452
anterior, ankle, 326
inferior, 326
longitudinal, 264
superior, costotransverse, 277
tibiofibular, 326
wrist, 303
apical odontoid, 273
arcuate, 388
popliteal, 318
gastrolienal, 732
phrenicolienal, 732
atlantoaxial, 270
atlantoöccipital, 272
of auricula or pinna, 1066
of Bertin, 313
bifurcated, 332
of Bigelow, 312
bladder, 1281
broad, of uterus, 1313
calcaneo-astragaloid, 330
calcaneo-cuboid, 332
calcaneo-fibular, 329
calcaneo-navicular, plantar, 333
calcaneo-tibial, 328
capsular. *See* Individual joints
cardinal, 1313, 1314
carotico-clinoid, 157
carpo-metacarpal, 308
carpus, 306, 307
central, of medulla spinalis, 907
check of atlas, 273
of eye, 1054
chondrosternal, 278
intra-articular, 279
chondroxiphoid, 280
common, anterior, 264
posterior, 264
conoid, 291
Cooper's, 397, 426, 1320
coracoacromial, 292
coracoclavicular, 291
coracohumeral, 295
coronary, of knee, 321
of liver, 1196, 1237
costocoracoid, 430
costotransverse, 277, 278
costovertebral, anterior, 276
costoxiphoid, 280
cotyloid, 212
cricoarytenoid, posterior, 1114
cricotracheal, 1113
crucial, knee, 320
cruciate, crural, 489
of atlas, 271
of knee, 320
cuboideonavicular, 335
deltoid, of ankle-joint, 328
dentate, 907
dorsal carpal, 452
radiocarpal, 304
radioulnar, 303
elbow, 297
falciform, of liver, 1196, 1237
fibular collateral, of knee-joint, 319
fundiform, of penis, 1301

Ligament or Ligaments, gastrocolic, 1196, 1197
gastrolienal, 1200
gastrophrenic, 1208
Gimbernat's, 395
glenohumeral, 295
glenoid, 295
of Cruveilhier, 310, 337
of shoulder-joint, 295
glenoidal labrum of hip-joint,
314
of shoulder-joint, 295
hepatoduodenal, 1196, 1202
hepatogastric, 1196, 1202
hepatorenal, 1196, 1237
Hesselbach's, 404
hip-joint, 311
hyoepiglottic, 1113
hyothyroid, 1112
iliofemoral, 312
iliolumbar, 282
iliotrochanteric, 313
of incus, 1062
inferior transverse of scapula,
293
infundibulopelvic, 1313
inguinal, 395
reflected, 396
interarticular, of ribs, 277
sternocostal, 279
intercarpal, 306
intercentral, 263
interchondral, 280
interclavicular, 290
interclinoid, 157
intercuneiform, 335
interfoveolar, 404
intermetacarpal, 309
intermetatarsal, 336
interosseous, ankle, 236
rib, 378
interphalangeal, foot, 338
hand, 311
wrist, 306
interpubic fibrocartilaginous
lamina, 287
interspinal, 267
interspinous, 267
intertarsal, 330
intertransverse, 267, 286
intra-articular, 277
ischiocapsular, 313
knee-joint, 317
laciniate, 489
lacunar, 395
of larynx, 1112
lateral atlantoäccipital, 272
external, ankle, 329
elbow, 299
mandible, 273
wrist, 306
internal, 273, 299, 305
of uterus, 1313
left triangular, of liver, 1196
vena caval, 530
long plantar, 332
of Mackenrodt, 1314
of malleus, 1076
medial palpebral, 355
metacarpophalangeal, 309
metatarsophalangeal, 337
middle cricothyroid, 1113
mucosum of knee, 322
of neck of rib, 278
nuchæ, 267
oblique cord, 301
popliteal, 318
occipitoaxial, 272
odontoid, 273
orbicular, 301
of ossicles, 1076
ovarian, 1206
palmar, 306, 309
palpebral, 1056
pectinate, of iris, 1039
pelvic, 282

Ligament or Ligaments, phrenicocolic, 1204
phrenicopericardiac, right, 686
of pinna or auricula, 1066
plantar, long, 332
posterior, tibiofibular, 326
cricoarytenoid, 1114
inferior, 326
longitudinal, 264
of knee, 318
sacroiliac, 284
superior, tibiofibular, 326
Poupart's, 395
pterygomandibular, 360
pterygospinous, 157, 361
pubic, 286
pubocapsular, 313
pubofemoral, 313
pulmonary, 1126
quadrate, 301
radial collateral, of elbow-joint,
299
of wrist-joint, 306
radiate, 276
sternocostal, 278
radiocarpal-joint, 303
radioulnar, 303
reflected inguinal, 396
rhomboid, 290
right triangular of liver, 1196
round, hip-joint, 314
of liver, 1237
of uterus, 1314
sacrococcygeal, 286
sacroiliac, 283, 284
sacrosciatic, 285
sacrospinous, 285
sacrotuberous, 285
scapular, 292
shoulder-joint, 293
sphenomandibular, 273, 363
spinoglenoid, 293
spiral, of ductus cochlearis,
1085
stellate, 276
sternoclavicular, 289
sternocostal, 278
sternopericardiac, 529
sternal, 280
structure of, 259
stylohyoid, 372
stylomandibular, 275, 367
stylomaxillary, 275
subpubic, 286
superficial transverse of fingers,
453
superior transverse of scapula,
293
suprascapular, 293
supraspinal, 267
supraspinous, 267
suspensory, of axilla, 428
of eye, 1054
of lens, 1050
of mamma, 426
of ovary, 1306
of penis, 1301
sutural, 255
talocalcaneal, 330, 331
talofibular, 329
talonavicular, dorsal, 332
talotibial, 328
tarsometatarsal, 336
tarsus, 330
temporomandibular, 273
tendo oculi, 356
teres, of hip, 313
of liver, 1237
of uterus, 1314
thyroarytenoid, inferior, 1116
thyroepiglottic, 1114
thyrohyoid, 1112
tibial collateral, of knee-joint,
319
tibiofibular, 326

Ligament or Ligaments, tibionavicular, 328
transversalis colli uteri, 1313
transverse acetabular, 314
of atlas, 270
carpal, 452
crural, 489
humeral, 295
inferior, tibiofibular, 326
of knee, 321
metacarpal, 309
metatarsal, 337
pelvic, 416
scapula, 293
trapezoid, 291
triangular, of liver, 1196, 1237
of tubercle of rib, 278
of urethra, 416₄
ulnar collateral of elbow-joint,
299
of wrist-joint, 205
uterine, 1313
utero-sacral, 1314
ventricular, of larynx, 1116
vertebral, 263
volar carpal, 450
metacarpophalangeal, 309
radiocarpal, 303
radioulnar, 303
of Wrisberg, 312
Y-shaped, of Bigelow, 312
of Zinn, 1053
Ligamenta accessoria plantaria,
337
auricularia [*Valsalva*], 1066
basium [*oss. metacarp.*]
dorsalia, 309
interossea, 309
[*oss. metatars.*] *dorsalia,* 336
interossea, 337
plantaria, 336
carpometacarpeæ dorsalia, 308
volaria, 309
collateralia metatarsophalangea,
337
cuneometatarsea interossea, 336
flava (*ligmenta subflava*), 266
intercarpea dorsalia, 306
interossea, 306
volaria, 306
intercuneiformia dorsalia, 335
interossea, 335
plantaria, 335
navicularicuneiformia dorsalia,
334
plantaria, 334
ossiculorum auditus, 1076
sternocostalia radiata, 278
suspensoria [of mammal], 426
tarsometatarsea dorsalia, 336
plantaria, 336
vocales, 1116
Ligamentous action of muscles,
263
Ligamentum acromioclaviculare,
291
annulare baseos stapedis, 1077
radii, 301
arcuatum pubis, 286
arteriosum, 548
calcaneocuboideum dorsale, 332
plantare, 332
calcaneonaviculare plantare, 333
capituli costæ interarticulare, 277
radiatum, 276
capitulorum [*oss. metacarpal-
ium*] *transversum,* 309
carpi dorsale, 452
transversum, 452
volare, 450
collaterale carpi radiale, 306
ulnare, 305
fibulare, 319
radiale, 299
tibiale, 319
ulnare, 299

Ligamentum, colli costæ, 278
  coronarium hepatis, 1237
  costoclaviculare, 290
  costotransversariumanterius, 277
    posterius, 278
  cricoarytænoideum posterius,
    1114
  cricothyreoideum medium, 1113
  cruciatum anterius, 320
    posterius, 320
  cuboideonaviculare dorsale, 335
    plantare, 335
  hyothyreoideum laterale, 1112
    medium, 1112
  incudis posterius, 1076
    superius, 1076
  inguinale [Pourparti] 395
    reflexum [Collesi], 396
  lacunare [Gimbernati], 395
  latum pulmonis, 1126
    uteri, 1313
  longitudinale anterius, 264
    posterius, 264
  mallei anterius, 1076
    laterale, 1076
    superius, 1076
  malleoli lateralis anterius, 326
    posterius, 326
  nuchæ, 267
  patellæ, 318
  popliteum obliquum, 318
  pubicum superius, 286
  pubocapsulare, 313
  radiocarpeum dorsale, 304
    volare, 303
  sacrococcygeum anterius, 286
    laterale, 286
    posterius, 286
  sacroiliacum anterius, 283
    interoseum, 285
    posterius, 284
  talocalcaneum anterius, 330
    interosseum, 331
    laterale, 330
    mediale, 331
    posterius, 330
  talofibulare anterius, 329
    posterius, 329
  talonaviculare dorsale, 332
  teres femoris, 313
    hepatis, 1196, 1237
    uteri, 1313
  transversum acetabuli, 314
    atlantis, 270
      crus, inferius, 271
        superius, 271
    cruris, 489
    genu, 321
    scapulæ inferius, 293
      superius, 293
  triangulare dextrum, 1237
    sinistrum, 1237
  tuberculi, costæ, 278
  venosum, 1236
Ligature of arteries.   *See each*
  Artery.
Limbs, development of, 51
Limiting membranes of retina,
  1048
Line or Lines, arcuate, of ilium,
  207
  cleavage, 1100
  colored, of Retzius, 1160
  curved, of ilium, 207
  gluteal, of ilium, 207
  iliopectineal, 207, 211
  incremental, of Salter, 1159
  intercondyloid, 222
  intertrochanteric, 219
  Langer's, 1100
  mylohyoid, 128
  nuchal, 110, 135
  oblique, of fibula, 236
    of mandible, 128
    of radius, 195
  pectineal, femur, 221
    ilium, 207, 211

Line or Lines, popliteal, of tibia,
  233
  spiral, of femur, 219
  of Schreger, 1159
  temporal, 107, 111, 139
  tension, 1100
Linea alba, 402
  aspera, 221
  nigra, 1376
  quadrata, 221
  semicircularis, 403
  splendens, 907
Lineæ semilunares, 403
Lingua, 1165
  apex, 1165
  dorsum, 1166
  facies inferior, 1166
  musculi, 1168
  papillæ, 1167
  radix, 1165
  tunica mucosa, 1171
Lingual artery, 560
  deep, 561
    surface markings of, 1361
  bone, 133
  branches of glossopharyngeal
    nerve, 938
  gyrus, 846
  lamina, 1161
  lymph nodes, **704**
  nerve, 926
  papillæ, 1167
  tonsil, 1166, 1171
  veins, 656
Lingula of mandibulæ, 129
  of sphenoid, 122, 153
Lip, hare, 127
  tympanic, 1086
  vestibular, 1086
Lips, 1152
Liquor sanguinis, 525
Lissauer, fasciculus of, 780
  tract of, 771
Littré, urethral glands of, 1285
Liver, 1233
  arteries of, 1239
  bare area of, 1194
  bile ducts of, 1241
    common, 1242
    cystic, 1243
  development of, 1238
  excretory apparatus of, 1242
  fixation of, 1237
  fossæ of, 1236
  function of, 1238
  gall-bladder, 1243
  hepatic artery, 610, 1241
    cells, 1241
    duct, 1241, 1242
    veins, 688, 1241
  ligaments of, 1234
  lobes of, 1236
  lobules of, 1240
  longitudinal fissures of, 1236
  lymphatic capillaries in, 696
    vessels of, 722
  nerves of, 1239
  portal vein, 689, 1239, 1241
  structure of, 1239
  surface markings of, 1388
  surfaces of, 1233, 1234
  vessels of, 1239
Lobe or Lobes of cerebellum,
  809
  of cerebral hemisphere, 843
    frontal, 843
    insula, 847
    occipital, 845
    parietal, 844
    precuneus, 845
    quadrate, 845
    temporal, 846
  of liver, 1236
  of lung, 1133
  Spigelian, 1236
  of thyroid gland, 1328

Lobule of auricula, 1065
  paracentral, 844
  parietal, 844
Lobules of liver, 1240
  of testes, 1293
Lobuli glandulæ thyreodeæ, 1328
  hepatis, 1240
Lobulus parietalis inferior, 845
  superior, 845
Lobus caudatus, 1236
  frontalis, 843
  hepatis dexter, 1236
    sinister, 1237
  occipitalis, 846
  parietalis, 845
  quadratus, 1236
  temporalis, 846
Lockwood, tendon of, 1053
Locus cæruleus, 807
Loewenthal's tract, 901
Long buccal nerve, 924
  calcaneocuboid ligament, 332
  ciliary nerves, 918
  external lateral ligament, knee,
    319
  or internal saphenous nerve,
    985
  plantar ligament, 332
  saphenous nerve, 985
    vein, 679
  subscapular nerve, 962
  thoracic artery, 593
    nerve, 962
Longissimus capitis muscle, 381
  cervicis muscle, 381
  dorsi muscle, 381
Longitudinal fasciculus, inferior,
  867
    superior, 867
  fissure, cerebral, 840
    great, 840
    of liver, 1236
  sinuses, 661, 662
  striæ, lateral and medial, 857
  sulci of heart, 531
Longitudinalis linguæ inferior
  muscle, 1170
    superior muscle, 1170
Longus capitis muscle, 375
  colli muscle, 375
Loop of Henle, 1273
Lower extremity, arteries of, 629
  articulations of, 311
  bones of, 206
  lymphatic nodes of, 712
    vessels of, 713
  muscles of, 464
  surface anatomy of, 1410
    markings of, 1422
  veins of, 678
  jaws, bones of, 127
  lateral cartilage, nose, 1024
  visual centers, 819
Lower, tubercle of, 534
Lumbar aponeurosis, 379
  arteries, 618
  enlargement of medulla spina-
    lis, 769
  lymph nodes, 716
  nerves, anterior, 977
    posterior, 953
  plexus of nerves, 978
  regions of abdomen, 1190
  triangle, 424
  vein, ascending, 676, 686
  veins, 686
  vertebræ, 75, 83, 92
    variations of, 85
Lumbocostal aponeurosis, 379
  arch, 388
  ligament of rib, 277
Lumbodorsal fascia, 378
Lumboinguinal nerve, 982
Lumbosacral plexus, 977
  trunk, 977
Lumbricales muscles of foot, 494
  of hand, 462

Lunate bone, 197
surface of acetabulum, 212
Lung-buds, 1107
Lungs, 1129
development of, 1107
fissures and lobes of, 1133
nerves of, 1137
root of, 1135
structure of, 1136
surface markings of, 1371
vessels of, 1137
Lunulæ of nails, 1101
of semilunar valves, 536
Luschka, formina of, 815, 905
gland of, 1339
Luys, nucleus of, 829
Lymph Node or Nodes, abdominal, 714
aortic, 716
auricular, 702
axillary, 711
buccinator, 703
cervical, 707
capsule, 699
of Cloquet, 713
cortex of, 699
deltoideopectoral, 710
diaphragmatic, 726
epigastric, 715
facial, 702, 703
gastric, 717
gastroepiploic, right, 917
of head, 702
hepatic, 717
hilum of, 699
hypogastric, 716
ileocolic, 710
iliac, 715
infraorbital, 703
inguinal, 712, 713
intercostal, 726
internal mammary, 726
lingual, 704
of lower extremity, 712
lumbar, 716
mastoid, 702
maxillary, 703
mediastinal, 728
medulla, 699
mesenteric, 717, 720
mesocolic, 721
of neck, 702, 707
obturator, 716
occipital, 702
pancreaticoduodenal, 720
pancreaticolienal, 720
pararectal, 721
paratracheal, 708
parietal, 714, 715
parotid, 703
pelvic, 714
popliteal, 712
preauricular, 702
retropharyngeal, 704
of Rosenmüller, 713
sacral, 716
sinuses, 699
splenic, 720
Stahr, middle gland of, 707
sternal, 726
structure of, 698
subinguinal, 713
submaxillary, 707
submental, 707
suprahyoid, 707
supramandibular, 703
supratrochlear, 710
of thorax, 726
tibial, anterior, 712
of tongue, 705
tracheobronchial, 729
of upper extremity, 711
visceral, of abdomen and pelvis, 714, 717
Lymphatic capillaries, 693
distribution of, 693
duct, right, 702

Lymphatic nodules, aggregated, 1221
solitary, 1221
of spleen, 732
system, 693
trunks, bronchomediastinal, 701, 729
intestinal, 701
jugular, 702
lumbar, 701
subclavian, 701
vessels, 697
of abdominal viscera, 721
wall, 714
of anal canal and anus, 722
of auricula and external acoustic meatus, 704
of bladder, 723
of cecum, 722
of colon, 722
of common bile-duct, 723
development of, 693
of diaphragm, 728
of ductus deferens, 725
of duodenum, 721
of esophagus, 730
of external genitals, 717
of face, 704
of gall-bladder, 723
of gluteal region, 722
of heart, 730
of ileum, 721
of jejunum, 721
of kidney, 723
lacteals, 693
of larynx, 707
of liver, 722
of lower extremity, 712
of lungs, 730
of mamma, 728
of mouth, 705
of nasal cavities, 705
of neck, 707
of ovary, 725
of palatine tonsil, 705
of pancreas, 723
of pelvic viscera, 721
of pelvis, 714
of penis, 724
of perineum, 717
of pharynx, 707, 709
of pleura, 730
of prostate, 724
of rectum, 722
of reproductive organs, 725
of scalp, 704
of small intestine, 721
of spleen, 723
of stomach, 721
structure of, 698
of suprarenal glands, 723
of testes, 725
of thoracic viscera, 730
wall, 728
of thymus, 734
of thyroid gland, 709
of tongue, 705
of upper extremity, 710
of ureter, 724
of urethra, 725
of urinary organs, 723
of uterine tube, 725
of uterus, 726
of vagina, 726
of vermiform process, 722
of vesculæ seminales, 725
Lymphocyte, 526
Lymphoglandulæ, 698
auriculares, 702
axillares, 711
cervicales, 707
epigastricæ, 715
faciales profundæ, 704
gastricæ, 717
hepaticæ, 717
hypogastricæ, 716
inguinales, 712

Lymphoglandulæ, intercostales, 726
linguales, 704
lumbales, 716
mediastinales, 728
mesentericæ, 720
mesocolicæ, 721
occipitales, 702
pancreaticolienales, 720
parotideæ, 703
popliteæ, 712
sternales, 726
subinguinales, 713
submaxillares, 707
tibialis, anterior, 712
Lyra of fornix, 857, 897

M

MACEWEN, suprameatal triangle of, 145
Mackenrodt, ligament of, 1314
Macrophages, 67, 526
Macula acustica sacculi, 1083
utriculi, 1083
cribrosa media, 1079
superior, 1079
lutea, 1046, 1048
structure of, 1048
Majendie, foramen of, 815, 905
Malar bone, 168
process of maxilla, 165
Male genital organs, 1286
bulbourethral glands, 1305
ductus deferens, 1296
ejaculatory duct, 1298
penis, 1298
prostate, 1303
testes and their coverings, 1286
vesculæ seminales, 1297
pronucleus, 25
urethra, 1284
Malleolar arteries, 642
folds, 1071, 1359
sulcus, 235
Malleolus, lateral, 237
medial, 234
Malleus, 1074
development of, 1061
ligaments of, 1076
Malpighian bodies of spleen, 734
corpuscles of kidney, 1273
Mammæ, 1319
development of, 1320
hypertrophy of, 1320
lymphatic vessels of, 728
nerves of, 1323
papilla or nipple of, 1320
structure of, 1321
vessels of, 1323
Mammary arteries, external, 593
internal, 587
gland, 1319
internal lymph node, 726
veins, internal, 674
Mammillary process, 85
Mandible, 127
angle of, 130
articulations of, 131, 273
body of, 127
changes in, due to age, 131
condyloid process of, 130
coronoid process of, 130
ossification of, 130
ramus of, 129
symphysis of, 128
Mandibular arch, 46
branches of facial nerve, 935
canal, 129
foramen, 129
fossa, 112, 145
nerve, 923
notch, 130
Manubrium of malleus, 1075
of sternum, 98
Margin, supraorbital, 141

Marginal artery, heart, 549
  gyrus, 844
  veins of foot, 679
    of heart, 650
Marrow of bone, 67
Marshall, oblique vein of, 519, 530, 651
  vestigial fold of, 519, 530, 651
Massa intermedia, 826, 839
Masses, lateral, of atlas, 78
Masseter muscle, 362
Masseteric artery, 569
  fascia, 361
  nerve, 923
Mastication, muscles of, 361
Mastoid canaliculus, 110, 149
  cells, 147
  foramen, 111, 114, 146
  fossa, 145
  lymph nodes, 702
  notch, 109, 146
  portion of temporal bone, 151
  process, 146
Matrix of nail, 1101
Maturation of ovum, 20
Maxilla, 162
  articulations of, 167
  changes in, due to age, 167
  ossification of, 163
Maxillary antrum artery, external, 164, 561, 1031
  internal, 566
  lymph nodes, internal, 704
  nerve, 918
    inferior, 923
  process of inferior nasal concha, 173
    of palatine bone, 172
    of zygomatic bone, 170
  processes of fetus, 47
  sinus, 162, 164, 1031
  tuberosity, 163
  vein, internal, 654
Meatus or meatuses, acusticus externus, 1067
  cartilagineus, 1067
  osseus, 1068
  auditory, external, 112, 150, 1067
    internal acoustic, 123, 932, 935, 1089
  of ear, 1067
  external acoustic, 112, 150, 1067
  internal acoustic, 123, 932, 935, 1089
  of nose, 125, 1026
  urinarius, 1285
  urinary, 1319
Mechanism of pelvis, 287
  of respiration, 391
  of thorax, 280
Meckel's cartilages, 46, 130
  diverticulum, 35, 1217
  ganglion, 921
Media, refracting, of eye, 1049
Medial geniculate body, 831
  lemniscus, 819
  longitudinal fasciculus, 819
  tarsal arteries, 643
  wall of nasal cavity, 1027
Median antebrachial vein, 670
  basilic vein, 670
  nerve, 967
  olfactory gyrus, 855
  stria, 855
Mediastinal arteries from aorta, 606
    from internal mammary, 589
  lymph nodes, 728, 729
  pleura, 1124
Mediastinum, 1127
  testis, 1292
Medicornu, 851
Medidural artery, 568
Medifrontal gyre, 844
Medullated nerve fibers, 757

Medulla, adrenal, 1337
  of hair, 1104
  oblongata, 785
    anterior district of, 787
    arcuate fibers of, 794
    development of, 745
    fasciculus cuneatus, 790
      gracilis, 790
    fissures and sulci of, 786, 787
    formatio reticularis, 807
    gray substance of, 796
    lateral district of, 788
    olive of, 789
    posterior district of, 790
    pyramid of, 787
    restiform bodies of, 791
    structure of, 792
  spinalis, 43, 767
    central canal of, 771
    columns of, 770
    development of, 738
    enlargements of, 769
    fissures of, 769
    gray commissures of, 771
      substance of, 770
    ligamentum denticulatum, 905
    meninges of, 901
    neuroglia of, 773, 777
    posterior column of, 771
      substance of, 776
    sulci of, 767
    suprarenal, 1337
    veins of, 678
    white commissure of, 769
Medullary artery of bone, 67
  lamina, 827
  membrane of bone, 66
  portion of suprarenal gland, 1337
  segments of nerves, 757
  sheath of nerve-fibers, 757
  spaces of bone, 72
  substance of kidney, 1272
    of lymph node, 699
    of ovaries, 1307
    of suprarenal, 1337
  velum, 815
Medullated nerve-fibers, 757
Megakaryocytes, 67
Meibomian glands, 1056
Meiosis, 20
Meissner's plexus, 1222
  tactile corpuscles, 1092
Membrana allantöoccipitalis, anterior, 272
  posterior, 272
  granulosa [of Graafian follicle]. 1307
  tectoria [of atlas and occipital bone], 272
Membrane or membranes, anal, 1151
  arachnoid, 906
  atlantoöccipital, 272
  basilar, 1086
  bones, 66
  of brain and spinal cord, 902
  Bowman's, 1038
  buccopharyngeal, 41
  cell, 17
  cloacal, 41, 1150
  costocoracoid, 430
  criothyroid, 1113
  Demours', 1038
  Descemet's, 1038
  elastic, of larynx, 1113
  fenestrated, 521
  fetal, development of, 27
  hyaloid, 1035
  hyoglossal, 1171
  hyothyroid, 1112
  intercostal, 386
  interosseous, of forearm, 301
    of leg, 326
  Jacob's, 1048
  limiting, retina, 1048

Membrane or membranes, medullary, of bone, 66
  Nasmyth's, 1163
  nuclear, 18
  obturator, 476
  pharyngeal, 1141
  pupillary, 1035, 1044
  Reissner's, 1085
  synovial, 259
  tectorial, of ductus cochlearis, 1089
  thyrohyoid, 1112
  tympanic, 1070
  vestibular, 1085
  vitelline, 25
Membranous cochlea, 1083
  cranium, 63
  labyrinth, 1082
  portion of urethra, 1285
  semicircular canals, 1083
  vertebral column, 60
Meningeal artery, accessory, 568
  anterior, 568
    from ascending pharyngeal, 566
  middle, 568
    surface marking of, 1353
    from occipital, 564
  posterior 566
    from vertebral, 583
  branch of spinal nerve, 950
  layer of dura matter, 902
  nerve from hypoglossal, 945
    from maxillary, 923
Meninges of brain and medulla spinalis, 901
Menisci, 320
  of knee-joint, 320
Meniscus, articular, 273
Menstrual age of fetus, 55
Mental foramen, 117, 128
  nerve, 926
  protuberance, 128
  spines, 128
  tubercle, 128
Mentalis muscle, 358
Mentohyoideus muscle, 372
Merkel, tactile disks of, 1090
Mesencephalon, 42, 746, 817
  lymph nodes, 720, 721
  plexuses of nerves, 1017
  veins, 690
Mesenteries, 1198, 1202
  mesentery proper, 1202
  sigmoid mesocolon, 1196, 1202
  transverse mesocolon, 1202
Mesenteriole of vermiform process, 1223
Mesenterium, 1202
Mesocardium, arterial, 529
  venous, 529
Mesocolic lymph nodes, 721
Mesocolon, sigmoid, 1198, 1202
  transverse, 1202
Mesoderm, 41
  formation of, 41
Mesogastrium, 1145
Mesometrium, 1313
Mesonephros, 1254
Mesorchium, 1255, 1258
Mesosalpinx, 1313
Mesothelium, 528
Mesovarium, 1255, 1306, 1307
Metacarpal arteries, 601
  bones, 202
    articulations of, 204
    characteristics of, 203
    ossification of, 206
Metacarpophalangeal articulations, 309
Metacarpus, 202
Metaphase of karyokinesis, 19
Metatarsal arteries, 643
  bones, 247
    characteristics of, 247

Metatarsal bones, surface anatomy of, 1365
veins, 681
Metatarsophalangeal articulations, 337
surface anatomy of, 1426
Metatarsus, 247
ossification of, 250
Metathalamus, 748, 831
Metencephalon, 744
Metopic suture, 141
Meynert, fasciculus retroflexus of, 832, 876
fountain decussation of, 823
Microcytes, 525
Microgliocytes, 755
Mid-brain, 42, 817
development of, 746
Mid-carpal joint, 307
Middle capsular artery, 617
cerebellar peduncles, 810
constrictor muscle, 1185
costotransverse ligament, 278
cutaneous nerve, thigh, 984
dental nerve, 920
subscapular nerve, 963
superior alveolar nerve, 920
suprarenal artery, 617
thyrohyoid ligament, 1112
tibiofibular ligament, 326
vesical artery, 621
Milk line, 1320
teeth, 1158
Mitochondria sheath, 23
Mitosis, 19
Mitral orifice, 538
valve, 538
Moderator band, 536
Modiolus of cochlea, 1080
Molar glands, 1153
teeth, 1157
Molecular layer of cortex of cerebellum, 811
of cerebrum, 871
Monakow, rubrospinal fasciculus of, 779
Monro, foramen of, 839, 852
sulcus of, 839
Mons pubis, 1305, 1317
Veneris, 1317
Morgagni, hydatid of, 1255, 1292, 1308
rectal columns of, 1229
sinus of, 1185
Morula, 25
Moss fibers, 813
Motor areas of cerebral cortex, 872
Motor end-plates, 763
nerves, 762
neurons, lower and upper, 779, 900
tract, 898
Mouth, 1151
development of, 1141
lymphatics of, 705
mucous membrane of, 1151
muscles of, 357
Movable articulations, 261
Movements admitted in joints, 262
Mucous glands of tongue, 1171
sheaths. *See* Synovial
Müller, orbitals muscle of, 1054
sustentacular fibers of, 1048
Müllerian duct, 1254
eminence, 1255
Multangular bones, 200
Multicuspid teeth, 1157
Multifidus muscle, 383
spinæ muscle, 383
Muscle or Muscles, abdominal, 392
action of, 351
anal region, 411
anterior crural, 480
femoral, 466
vertebral, 375
anterolateral, of abdomen, 392

Muscle or Muscles, arm, 434
development of, 342
of auricula or pinna, 354, 1066
axillary arch, 424
back, 377
surface markings of, 1366
bundles of atria, 540
of ventricles, 541
cardiac, 544
cervical, 365
constrictors of pharynx, 1185
urethræ, 419, 421
development of, 341
diaphragm, 388
digastric, 371
dorsal antebrachial, 444
external sphincter ani, 421
eyelid, 355
fasciculi of, 344
fibers of, 343
fixation, 351
foot, 491
forearm, 438
form of, 341
gluteal region, **473**
hamstring, 479
hand, 449
head, 342, 352
development of, **342**
hypothenar, 461
iliac region, 464
infracostal, 387
insertion of, 345
intercostal, 386
intermediate volar, 462
internal sphincter ani, 421
interosseous, dorsal, 496
of foot, 496
of hand, 462
plantar, 497
volar, 461
laryngeal, 1118
lateral cervical, 371
crural, 487
vertebral, 376
leg, 480
development of, 342
lower extremity, 464
lumbrical of foot, 494
of hand, 462
lymphatics of, 345
mastication, 361
medial femoral, 471
mouth, 357
neck, 364
nerves and vessels of, 345
nose, 356
oblique of abdomen, 493, 498
inferior of eye, 1054
superior of eye, 1052
ocular, 1051
omohyoid, 374
orbitals of H. Müller, 1054
origin of, 345
palate, 1180
pelvic, 407
perineal, deep transverse, 421
superficial transverse, 419
of perineum, 411
pharynx, 1183
of pinna or auricula, 1066
plantar, first layer, 492
fourth layer, 490
second layer, 494
third layer, 494
plate, 59
posterior crural, 483
femoral, 479
pterygoid, 364
scalp, 352
sense, impulse of, 877
shoulder-girdle, development of, 342
striped, 343
structure of, 343
suboccipital, 384

Muscle or Muscles, superficial cervical, 364
suprahyoid, 371
suspensory, of duodenum, 1215
synergetic, 351
temporal, 362
tendons of, 346
thenar, 459
thigh, 466
thoracic, 386
surface anatomy of, 1369
tongue, 1168
trachelomastoid, 381
trunk, 377
tympanic cavity, 1077
upper extremity, 422
ureters, 1282
urogenital region (female), 419
(male), 417
uvula, 1181
ventrolateral, of neck, development of, 342
volar antebrachial, 438
Musculus or Musculi, abductor, hallucis, 492
digiti quinti (pedis), 493
manus, 461
indicis, 462
minimi digiti, 461
pollicis, 459
brevis, 459
longus, 448
accelerator urinæ, 418
accessorius, 381
of foot, 494
adductor brevis, 472
hallucis, 495
longus, 472
magnus, 473
minimus, 473
obliquus hallucis, 495
pollicis, 461
pollicis obliquus, 461
transversus, 461
anconæus, 446
antitragicus, 1066
arrectores pilorum, 1104
articularis genu or *subcrureus*, 471
aryepiglotticus, 1118
arytænoideus, 1118
attollens aurem, 1066
attrahens aurem, 1066
auricularis, 1066
azygos uvulæ, 1181
biceps, 435
brachii, 435
femoris, 479
flexor cubiti, 435
biventer cervicis, 382
brachialis, 436
anticus, 436
brachioradialis, 444
buccinator, 360
bulbocavernosus, 418, 419
caninus, 357
cervicalis ascendens, 381
chondro-epitrochlearis, 430
chondroglossus, 1168
ciliaris, 1029
cleidohyoideus, 374
coccygeus, 409
complexus, 382
compressor naris, 356
constrictor phargynis inferior, 1185
medius, 1185
superior, 1185
urethræ, 419, 421
coracobrachialis, 435
corrugator, 356
cutis ani, 421
supercilii, 356
costocoracoideus, 430
cremaster, 398
cricoarytænoideus, 1118

92

Musculus or *Musculi*, cricothyroideus, 1118
  crureus, 471
  deltoideus, 432
  depressor alæ nasi, 356
    anguli oris, 358
    labii inferioris, 358
    septi, 356
  detrusor urinæ, 1283
  digastricus, 371
  dilator naris, 356
    pupillæ, 1044
  dorsoepitrochlearis brachii, 424
  ejaculator urinæ, 418
  epicranius, 353
  epitrochleo-anconæus, 440
  erector clitoridis, 420
    penis, 419
    spinæ, 379
  extensor carpi radialis accessorius, 444
      brevior, 445
      brevis, 445
      intermedius, 445
      longior, 444
      longus, 444
      ulnaris, 446
    hallucis brevis, 491
    coccygis, 383
    digiti quinti proprius, 445
    digitorum brevis, 491
      communis, 445
      longus, 482
    hallucis longus, 481
    indicis, 449
      proprius, 449
    minimi digiti, 445
    ossis metacarpi hallucis, 481
      pollicis, 448
    pollicis brevis, 448
      longus, 448
    primi internodii pollicis, 448
    proprius hallucis, 481
    secundi internodii pollicis, 448
  flexor accessorius, 494
    brevis minimi digiti, 462, 496
    carpi radialis, 439
      ulnaris, 440
    digiti quinti brevis [pedis], 496
      [manus], 462
    digitorum brevis, 492
      longus, 486
      profundus, 441
      sublimis, 440
    hallucis brevis, 494
      longus, 486
      pollicis brevis, 460
      longus, 443
  frontalis, 353
  gastrocnemius, 483
  gemellus, 477
    inferior, 477
    superior, 477
  genioglossus, 1168
  geniohyoglossus, 1168
  geniohyoideus, 373
  glossopalatinus, 1168, note, 1177 1181
  glutæus maximus, 473
    medius, 474
    minimus, 475
  gracilis, 471
  helicis major, 1066
    minor, 1066
  hyoglossus, 1168
  iliacus, 466
    minor, 466
  iliocapsularis, 466
  iliococcygeus, 408
  iliocostalis, 381
    cervicis, 381
    dorsi, 381
    lumborum, 381
  iliosacralis, 409
  incisivus labii, 359, 360

Musculus or *Musculi*, infrahyoid, 374
  infraspinatus. 433
  intercostales, **386**
    externi, 376
    interni, 376
  interossei dorsales manus, 462
    pedis, 476
    plantares, 497
    volares, 463
  interosseus volaris primus, 463
  interspinales, 383
  intertransversales, 383
  ischiocavernosus, 419, 420
  latissimus dorsi, 423
  levator anguli oris, 357
      scapulæ, 426
    ani, 407
    claviculæ, 426
    glandulæ thyreoideæ, 1329
    menti, 358
    palati, 1180
    palpebræ superioris, 1051
    prostatæ, 408
    scapulæ, 426
    veli palantini, 1180
  levatores costarum, 387
  lingualis, 1170
  longissimus capitis, 381
    cervicis, 381
    dorsi, 381
  longitudinalis linguæ, 1170
  longus capitis, 375
    colli, 375
  lumbricales [manus], 494, 462
    [pedis], 494
  masseter, 362
  mentalis, 358
  mentohyoideus, 372
  multifidus spinæ, 383
  mylohyoideus, 373
  nasalis, 356
  nasolabialis, 360
  obliquus auriculæ, 1066
    capitis, 384
    externus abdominis, 393
      inferior, 384
      oculi, 1040
    internus abdominis, 397
      superior, 384
      oculi, 1053, 1054
  obturator externus, 478
    internus, 476
  occipitalis, 353
  occipitofrontalis, 353
  omohyoideus, 374
  opponens digiti quinti [manus], 496, 462
    [pedis], 462, 496
    minimi digiti, 462
    pollicis, 459
  orbicularis oculi, 356
    oris, 360
    palpebrarum, 355
  ossiculorum auditus, 1077
  palatoglossus, note, 1168, note, 1181
  palatopharyngeus, 1182
  palmaris brevis, 461
    longus, 439
  pectineus, 471
  pectoralis major, 429
    minimus, 430
    minor, 430
  peronæus accessorius, 488
    brevis, 488
    longus, 487
    quartus, 488
    quinti digiti, 488
    tertius, 482
  peroneocalcaneus externus, 488
    internus, 486
  peroneocuboideus, 488
  peroneotibialis, 484
  pharyngopalatinus, 1182
  piriformis, 476

Musculus or *Musculi*, pisiannularis, 462
  pisimetacarpus, 462
  pisiuncinatus, 462
  plantaris, 484
  platysma, 364
  popliteus, 484
    minor, 484
  procerus, 356
  pronator quadratus, **443**
    teres, 439
  psoas, major, 466
    minor, 466
    parvus, 466
  pterygoideus externus, 364
    internus, 363
  pubococcygeus, 409
  puborectalis, 408
  pubovesicales, 1281
  pyramidalis abdominis, 402
    nasi, 356
  quadratus femoris, 478
    labii, 357
    lumborum, 406
    menti, 358
    plantæ, 494
  quadriceps extensor femoris, 470
  recti [of eyeball], 1053
  rectococcygeal, 1231
  rectovesicales, 1281
  rectus abdominis, 400
    capitus anterior, 375
      lateralis, 376
      posterior, 384
    anticus, 375
    posticus, 384
    femoris, 470
  retrahens aurem, 1066
  rhomboideus major, 424
    minor, 424
    occipitalis, 424
  risorius, 357
  rotatores, 383
    spinæ, 383
  sacrospinalis, 379
  salpingopharyngeus, 1186
  sartorius, 469
  scalenus anterior, 376
    anticus, 376
    medius, 376
    pleuralis, 377
    posterior, 377
    posticus, 377
  semimembranosus, 480
  semispinalis capitis, 382
    cervicis, 382
    colli, 382
    dorsi, 382
  semitendinosus, 479
  serratus anterior, 431
    magnus, 431
    posterior, inferior, 388
      superior, 388
    posticus, 387
  soleus, 483
  sphincter ani, externus, 421
    internus, 421
    pupillæ, 1044
    recti, 421
    urethræ membranaceæ, 419
    vaginæ, 419
    vesicæ, 1283
  spinalis capitis, 382
    cervicis, 382
    colli, 381
    dorsi, 382
  splenius capitis, 379
    cervicis, 379
    colli, 379
  stapedius, 1074
  sternalis, 430
  sternoclavicularis, 431
  sternocleidomastoideus, 371
  sternohyoideus, 374
  sternomastoideus, 371
  sternothyroideus, 374

Musculus or Musculi, styloglossus,
  1170
  stylohyoideus, 372
  stylopharyngeus, 1186
  subanconæus, 437
  subclavius, 431
  subcostales, 387
  subcrureus, 471
  subcapularis, 432
  supinator, 447
    brevis, 447
    longus, 444
  supraclavicularis, 371
  supracostalis, 386
  supraspinatus, 433
  temporalis, 362
  tensor faciæ latæ, 476
    palati, 1180
    tarsi, 355
    tympani, 1077
    veli palatini, 1180
  teres major, 434
    minor, 434
  tibiofacialis anterior, 481
  thyreoarytænoideus, 1119
  thyreoepiglotticus, 1191
  thyroarytenoideus, 1119
  thyrohyoideus, 374
  tibialis anterior, 481
    anticus, 481
    posterior, 486
  trachealis, 1124
  tragicus, 1066
  transversalis, 398
    cervicis, 381
  transversus abdominis, 398
    auriculæ, 1066
    linguæ, 1170
    menti, 358
    nuchæ, 354
    pedis, 495
    perinæi, 417, 419
      profundus, 419, 421
      superficialis [in female], 419
        [in male], 417
    thoracis, 387
  trapezius, 423
  triangularis, 358
    sterni, 387
  triceps, brachii, 437
    extensor cubiti, 437
    suræ, 483
  uvulæ, 1180
  vastus externus, 470
    intermedius, 471
    internus, 471
    lateralis, 470
    medialis, 471
  ventricularis, 1119
  verticalis linguæ, 1170
  vocalis, 1119
  zygomaticus, 357
    major, 357
Muscular fibers of heart, 540
  process of arytenoid cartilage,
    1111
  tissue, cardiac, 544
  triangle, 375, 1362
Muscularis mucosæ, 1219
Musculi oculi, 1051
  ossiculorum auditus, 1077
  papillares [of left ventricle], 538
    [of right ventricle], 535, 536
  pectinati [of left auricle], 537
    [of right auricle], 533
  pubovesicales, 1283
Musculocutaneous nerve of arm,
  964
  of leg, 995
Musculophrenic artery, 587
Musculospiral groove, 185
  nerve, 972
Myelencephalon, 744
Myelinated nerve fibers, 757
Mylohyoid artery, 569
  groove, 129

Mylohyoid line, 128
  muscle, 373
  nerve, 926
Myocæl, 44, 59
Myocardium, 539
Myology, 341
Myometrium, 1315

N

NAILS, 1101
Nares, 1024, 1026
Nasal aperture, anterior, 123, 125
  artery, 575
  lateral, 563
  bones, 160
    articulations of, 162
    ossification of, 162
  cartilages, 1024
  cavities, 123, 1026
    arteries of, 1030
    lymphatic capillaries in, 705
    vessels of, 605
    mucous membrane of, 1028
    nerves of, 1030
    veins of, 605
    vestibule of, 1026
  concha, inferior, 173
    middle, 160
    superior, 160
  crest, 167, 171
  duct, 1060
  fossa, 123, 1026
  laminæ, 49
  meatus, 1026
  mucous membrane, 1028
  nerve from ophthalmic, 917
  nerves from nasopalatine gan-
    glion, 922
  notch of frontal bone, 142
    of maxilla, 162
  part of frontal bone, 142
    of pharynx, 1183
  process of frontal bone, 142
    of maxilla, 165
  processes of fetus, 48
  septum, 124
  sinuses, 1030
  spine, anterior, 116, 162, 167
    of frontal bone, 142
    posterior, 107, 170
Nasalis muscle, 356
Nasion, 115, 142
Nasmyth's membrane, 1163
Nasociliary nerve, 917
Nasofrontal vein, 665
Nasolabialis muscle, 360
Nasolacrimal canal, 125
  duct, 1036, 1060
Naso-optic furrow, 50, 1036
Nasopalatine nerve, 923
  recess, 1029
Nasopharynx, 1183
Nasus externus, 1024
Navicular bone of carpus, 197
  of tarsus, 245
  fossa, 1319
Neck, lymph nodes of, 702, 707
  vessels of, 709
  muscles of, 364
    development of, 341
  triangles of, 1362
  veins of, 651
Nélaton's line, 1425
Neopallium, 749, 750
Nerve cells, 755
  of cerebellar cortex, 811
  of cerebral cortex, 868
  of spinal cord, 773
  endings, 1090
  fasciculi of medulla spinalis,
    777
  fibers of cerebral cortex, 871
    medullated, 757
    non-medullated, 757
  roots, 948

Nerve or Nerves, abducent, 929
  accessory, 942
  acoustic, 935, 1089
  alveolar, 920, 926
  anococcygeal, 997
  anterior crural, 984
    interosseous, 967
    superior alveolar, 920
    thoracic, 962
    tibial, 994
  antebrachial cutaneous, 965
  Arnold's, 940
  auditory, 935
  auricular, 955
    great, of auriculotemporal,
      925
    posterior, 934
    of vagus, 940
  auriculotemporal, 925
  axillary, 963
  brachial cutaneous, lateral, 963
    medial, 966
    posterior, 972
  bronchial, 941
  buccal, of facial, 935
    long, 924
  buccinator, 924
  calcaneal, medial, 992
  cardiac, cervical, vagus, 941
    great, sympathetic, 1011
    of sympathetic, 1011
    thoracic, 941
    of vagus, 941
  caroticotympanic, 1009, 1077
  carotid of glossopharyngeal,
    938
  cavernous, of penis, 1020
  celiac, of vagus, 942
  cell, 755
  cerebral, 911. See Cranial.
  cerebrospinal, structure of, 760
  cervical, 950, 954
    cutaneous, 955
    divisions of, 950, 951
    of facial, 935
    transverse, 955
  chorda tympani, 933, 1078
  ciliary, 918
  circumflex, 963
  of clitoris, 996
  coccygeal, division of, 955,
    986
  cochlear, 935, 1090
  cone of, origin of, 756
  cranial, 753, 881, 911
    abducent, [sixth], 929
    accessory, [eleventh], 942
    acoustic, [eighth], 935
    composition and central con-
      nections of, 981
    facial, [seventh], 930
    glossopharyngeal, [ninth],
      936
    hypoglossal, [twelfth], 943
    oculomotor, [third], 919
    olfactory, [first], 911
    optic, [second], 912
    trigeminal, [fifth], 915
    trochlear, [fourth], 914
    vagus, [tenth], 938
  crural, anterior, 984
  cutaneous cervical, 955
    external, thigh, 982
    internal, forearm, 966
    lesser, thigh, 984
    middle, thigh, 984
  deep branch of radial, 973
    of ulnar, 972
  peroneal, 994
  petrosal, 922
  temporal, 924
  descending ramus of hypo-
    glossal, 945
  development of, 737
  digastric, form facial, 934
  digital, of lateral plantar, 993

Nerve or Nerves, digital, of medial plantar, 992
of median, 967
of radial, 972
of superficial peroneal, 995
of ulnar, 968
dorsal antebrachial cutaneous, 973
branch of ulnar, 971
cutaneous, foot, 992, 995
digital, 994
of penis, 997
scapular, 961
of dura mater, 902
dural, 940
eighth, 935
eleventh, 943
endings, 1090
end-organs of, 1090
epineurium of, 760
esophageal, 942
external nasal, 920
plantar, 992
popliteal, 993
pterygoid, 924
saphenous, 992
spermatic, 982
facial, 930
femoral, 984
cutaneous, anterior, 984
lateral, 982
posterior, 988
fasciculi, 777
fibers, 757
gray, 757
medullary sheath, 757
medullated, 757
myelin, 757
mylinated, 757
neurolemma, 757
non-medullated, 757
primitive sheath, 757
white, 757
fifth, 914
first, 911
fourth, 914
frontal, 916
ganglia of, 764
autonomic, 764
sensory, 764
gastric branches of vagus, 942
gemmula of, 757
genitocrural, 982
genitofemoral, 982
glossopharyngeal, 936
gluteal, 988
great auricular, 955
greater occipital, 951
splanchnic, 1013
superficial petrosal, 921, 932
hemorrhoidal, inferior, 996
hepatic branches of vagus, 942
hypoglossal, 881, 943
iliohypogastric, 979
ilioinguinal, 980
incisive, 926
inferior dental, 926
infrapatellar, 985
infratrochlear, 918
intercostal, 974
intercostobrachial, 975
intermedius of Wrisberg, 930
internal calcaneal, 992
carotid, 1007
cutaneous of arm, 966
plantar, 992
popliteal, 990
saphenous, 985
interosseous, dorsal, 973
volar, 967
Jacobson's, 938, 1077
jugular, 1010
labial posterior, 996
superior, 921
lacrimal, 916
of Lancisi, 897

Nerve or Nerves, laryngeal, 940
laryngopharyngeal of sympathetic, 1010
lateral antebrachial cutaneous, 965
brachial cutaneous, 963
femoral cutaneous, 982
plantar, 992
sural cutaneous, 993
lesser splanchnic, 1013
lingual, 926
of glossopharyngeal, 938
long ciliary, 918
saphenous, 985
subscapular, 963
thoracic, 962
lowest splanchnic, 1013
lumbar, divisions of, 953, 977
lumboinguinal, 982
lumbosacral trunk, 977
mandibular, 923
of facial, 935
masseteric, 923
maxillary, 918
inferior, 923
medial antebrachial cutaneous 966
brachial cutaneous. 966
plantar, 992
sural cutaneous, 991
median, 967
meningeal, of hypoglossal, 945
of maxillary, 923
middle, 920
of vagus, 940
mental, 926
middle superior alveolar, 920
motor, 762
musculocutaneous of arm, 964
of leg, 995
musculospiral, 972
mylohyoid, 926
nasal, of ophthalmic, 917
from sphenopalarine, ganglion, 922
nasociliary, 917
nasopalatine, 923
ninth, 936
obturator, 982
accessory, 984
occipital, greater, 951
smaller, 955
third, 951
oculomotor, 913
olfactory, 911
ophthalmic, 916
optic, 912
orbital, 920
origins of, 753
palatine, 922
palamar cutaneous, of median, 967
of ulnar, 969
palpebral, inferior, 920
parasympathetic, cranial, 1001
sacral, 1004
perforating cutaneous, 995
perineal, 996
perineurium of, 760
peroneal, 993
deep, 994
superficial, 995
petrosal, deep, 922, 1008
external, 1011
greater superficial, 921
large, deep, 922
superficial, 921, 922
smaller superficial, 1077
pharyngeal, of glossopharyngeal, 938
of sphenopalatine ganglion, 923
of vagus, 940
phrenic, 958
plantar, 992
plexus of, 760

Nerve or Nerves, plexus of, annular, 1039
aortic abdominal, 1017
Auerbach's, 1222
brachial, 954
cardiac, 1014, 1016
carotid, 1007
cavernous, 1020
celiac, 1016
cervical, 954
posterior, 950, 951, 953, 955
coccygeal, 997
corneal, 1038
coronary, 1015
esophageal, 939, 942
formation of, 760
gastric, 942, 1017
hemorrhoidal, 1020
hepatic, 1017
hypogastric, 1019
infraorbital, 921
lienal, 1017
lumbar, 953, 977
lumbosacral, 977
Meissner's, 1222
mesenteric, 1019
myenteric, 1221
ovarian, 1017
parotid, 932
patellar, 982, 985
pelvic, 1020
pharyngeal, 938, 940, 1010
phrenic, 1017
prostatic, 1020
pudendal, 996
pulmonary, 939, 941, 942
renal, 1017
sacral, 953, 986
solar, 1016
spermatic, 1017
splenic, 1017
subsartorial, 984
submucosal, intestine, 1222
suprarenal, 1017
tonsillar, 938
tympanic, 938, 1077
uterine, 1020
vaginal, 1020
vesical, 1020
pneumogastric, 938
popliteal, 989, 993
posterior scrotal, 996
of pterygoid canal, 922
to pterygoidens externus, 924
internus, 923
pterygopalatine, 923
pudendal, 996
inferior, 989
pudic, internal, 996
pulmonary, 941
radial, 972
rami communicantes, gray and white, 1006
recurrent, laryngeal, 941
reflexes, spinal, 877
respiratory, of Bell, 958, 962
to rhomboids, 961
roots, 782, 948
sacral, 953, 986
saphenous, 985, 993
sciatic, 986, 990
scrotal, posterior, 996
second, 912
seventh, 930
short ciliary, 918
sixth, 929
smaller occipital, 955
spermatic, external, 982
sphenopalatine branches of maxillary, 920
spinal, 946
composition and central connections of, 876
development of, 741
divisions of, 950, 957
roots of, 782, 948

Nerve or Nerves, spinal, structure of, 949
  accessory, 942
  splanchnic, 1011
  of spleen, 734
  to stapedius, 933
  stylohyoid, 934
  subscapular, 963
  to subclavius, 961
  superficial branch of radial, 973
    of ulnar, 972
  superior labial, 921
  supra-acromial, 957
  supraclavicular, 956
  supraorbital, 917
  suprascapular, 961
  suprasternal, 956
  supratrochlear, 917
  sural, 992
    cutaneous, lateral, 993
  sympathetic, 997
    cranial, 1001
    sacral, 1004
    thoracolumbar, 1006
  of taste, 1024
  temporal, deep, 924
    of facial, 934
  temporomalar, 920
  tenth, 938
  terminations of, 762
  third, 913
  thoracic, divisions of, 952, 962, 973
  thoracodorsal, 963
  thyrohyoid, 945
  tibial, 990
    anterior, 994
  tissue, degenerative changes in, 765
  of tongue, 1170
  tonsillar, 938
  transverse cervical, 955
  trifacial, 915
  trigeminal, 915
  trochlear, 914
  twelfth, 943
  tympanic of glossopharyngeal, 938
  ulnar, 968, 982
    collateral, 972
  of urethral bulb, 996
  vagus, 938
  vestibular, 935, 1089
  Vidian, 923
  volar digital, 967
    interosseous, 967
  of Wrisberg, 966
  zygomatic, 920
    of facial, 911
  zygomaticofacial, 920
  zygomaticotemporal, 920
Nervi auriculares anteriores, 925
  cavernosi penis minores, 1029
  clunium inferiores, 989
  coccygei, 986
  communicantes cervicales, 957
    hypoglossi, 957
  digitales dorsales hallucis, 994
    plantares communes, 992
      proprii, 992
  ethmoidales, 918
  lumbales, 953
    anteriores, 977
    posteriores, 953
  magnocellulares of von Monakow, 794
  nervorum, 760
  olfactorii, 911
  spinales, 946
    rami anteriores, 954
      posteriores, 950
  supraclaviculares, 956
  temporales profundi, 924
  terminales, 911
  thoracales, 952
    anteriores, 962, **973**

Nervous system, 737
  autonomic, 754, 997
  central, 737
  development of, 737
  histology of, 755
  parasympathetic, 1001
  peripheral, 911
  sympathetic, 997
Nervus abducens, 929
  accessorius, 942
    ramus externus, 942
      internus, 942
  acusticus, 1089
  alveolaris inferior, 926
  auricularis magnus, 955
    posterior, 934
  auriculotemporalis, 925
  axillaris, 963
  canalis pterygoidei, 922
  cardiacus inferior, 1011
    medius, 1011
    superior, 1010
  caroticotympanicus inferior, 938
    superior, 938
  cavernosus penis major, 1020
  coccygeus, 954
  cochlearis, 1090
  clunium inferior medialis, 995
  communicans fibularis, 993
    tibialis, 991
  cutaneus antebrachii dorsalis, 973
    lateralis, 965
    medialis, 966
    brachii medialis, 966
      posterior, 972
    colli, 955
    dorsalis intermedius, 995
      medialis, 995
    femoralis lateralis, 982
      posterior, 988
  descendens cervicalis, 958
    hypoglossi, 945
  dorsalis clitoridis, 997
    penis, 997
    scapulæ, 961
  facialis, 930
    rami buccales, 935
      temporales, 934
      zygomatici, 935
    ramus colli, 935
      digastricus, 935
      marginalis mandibulæ, 935
      stylohyoideus, 935
  femoralis, 984
  frontalis, 916
  furcalis, 978
  glossopharyngeus, 936
    ganglion petrosum, 937
      superius, 937
    rami linguales, 938
      pharyngei, 938
      tonsillares, 938
    ramus stylopharyngeus, 938
  glutæus inferior, 988
    superior, 988
  hæmorrhoidalis inferior, 996
  hypoglossus, 943
    ramus descendens, 945
      thyreohyoideus, 945
  iliohypogastricus, 979
  ilioinguinalis, 980
  infratrochlearis, 918
  intermedius [of Wrisberg], 930
  interosseus dorsalis, 973
    volaris, 967
  ischiadicus, 990
  laryngeus superior, 940
  maxillaris, 918
    labialis superiores, 921
    nasales externi, 920
    palpebrales inferiores, 920
    ramus alveolaris superior anteriores, 920
      medius, 920
  meatus auditorii externi, 925

Nervus peronæus communis, 993
  profundus, 994
  superficialis, 995
  petrosus profundus, 922
    superficialis major, 921
      minor, 1077
  plantaris lateralis, 992
    medialis, 992
  pterygoideus externus, 924
    internus, 923
  spinosus, 923
  stapedius, 933
  subclavius, 961
  suralis, 992
    lateralis, 993
    medialis, 991
  thoracalis longus, 962
  thoracodorsalis, 963
  ulnaris, 968
    rami musculares, 972
    ramus cutaneus palmaris, 971
      dorsalis manus, 971
      profundus, 972
      superficialis, 972
      volaris manus, 971
  vagus, 938
    rami bronchiales, 941
    cardiaci, 941
    cæliaci, 942
    gastrici, 942
    hepatica, 942
    œsophagei, 942
    ramus auricularis, 940
    laryngeus, 940
      inferior, 941
      superior, 940
    meningeus, 940
    pharyngdus, 940
  Vidii, 922
  zygomaticus, 920
Net-work, carpal, 600
  malleolar, 642
Neumann, dentinal sheath of, 1159
Neural arch, 75
  canal, 42
  crest, 42, **741**
  folds, 42
  groove, 42
  tube, 42
Neurenteric canal, **42**
Neuroblasts, **741**
Neurocentral synchondrosis, 90
Neuroglia, 755
Neurolemma, 757
Neurology, 737
Neuromeres, 768
Neuromuscular spindles, 1092
Neuron theory, 764
Neurons, 755
  motor, 900
Neurotendinous spindles, 1092
Neutrophil colorless corpuscles, 526
Ninth nerve, 936
Nipple or papilla of mamma, 1320
Nissl's granules, 756
Node or nodes, atrioventricular, 544
  hemal, 700
  hemolymph, 700
  lymph, 698
    primitive, 39
  of Ranvier, 757
  sinoatrial, 540
Noduli lymphatici aggregati, 1221
  solitarii, 1221, 1232
Non-medullated nerve fibers, 757
Norma basalis, of skull, 107
  frontalis, 115
  lateralis, 110
  occipitalis, 114
  verticalis, 106
Normal stomach x-ray of after a barium meal, 1384

Nose, 1024
  accessory sinuses of, 1030
  alar cartilages of, 1024
  arteries of, 1025
  cartilage of septum of, 1024
  cartilaginous frame-work of, 1024
  cavities of, 1026
  development of, 48
  external, 1024
  lateral cartilage of, 1024
  lymphatics of, 703
  mucous membrane of, 1028
  muscles of, 356, 1025
  nerves of, 1025
  veins of, 1025
Notch, acetabular, 212
  cardiac, 1133
  ethmoidal, 142
  intertragic, 1065
  jugular, 136
  lacrimal, 163
  mandibular, 130
  mastoid, 109, 146
  nasal, of frontal, 142
    of maxilla, 162
  parietal, 146
  presternal, 99
  of Rivinus, 1069
  scapular, 180
  sciatic, 209, 210, 215
  semilunar, of ulna, 192
  sphenopalatine, 173
  superior thyroid, 1109
  supraorbital, 115, 119, 141
  ulnar, of radius, 195
  umbilical, of liver, 1235
  vertebral, 76
Notochord, 39
Nuchal fascia, 377
  ligament, 267
  line, 110, 135
Nuck, canal of, 1260, 1314
Nuclear layer of cerebellar cortex, 813
  layers of retina, 1046, 1047
  membrane, 18
Nucleated sheath of Schwann, 757
Nuclei of cochlear nerve, 806, 935
  of glossopharyngeal and vagus nerves, 797
  of oculomotor nerve, 914
  olivary, 800
  of origin of motor nerves, 915
  pontis, 805
  of trigeminal nerve, 805
  of vestibular nerve, 806, 935
Nucleoli, 18
Nucleoplasm, 18
Nucleus, 17
  abducent nerve, 942
  accessory cuneate, 794
    nerve, 942
  accumbens, 856
  ambiguus, 797
  amygdalæ, 863
  amygdaloid, 898
  arcuatus, 802
  autonomic, 797
  of Bechterew, 806
  caudate, 859
  cell, 17
  cochlear nerve, 798
  cuneatus, 791
  of Darkscheivitsch, 816
  of Deiter's, 806
  dentatus [of cerebellum], 809, 813, 814
  dorsalis, 776
  emboliformis, 813, 814
  facial nerve, 805, 931
  fastigii, 813, 814
  globosus, 815
  gracilis, 792
  hypoglossal nerve, 796

Nucleus, hypothalmic, 834
  intercalatus, 806, 835
  lacrimalis, 798
  lentiform, 861
  of lens, 1051
  of Luys, 829
  of medial longitudinal fasciculus, 818
  nervus abducentis, 805
    facialis, 805
    trigemini, 805
  olivaris superior, 802
  olivary, 800, 802
  of Perlia, 821
  of posterior commissure, 831, 832
  pulposus, 61
  red, 822
  salivatorius, 798
  of Schwalbe, 806
  sensory, 803, 931
  tractus solitarius, 798
  trapezoid, 805
  vagus nerve, 797
  vestibular nerve, 806
  Von Monakow, 794
Nuel, space of, 1089
Nuhn, glands of, 1171
Nutrient artery of bone, 67
  of femur, 637
  of fibula, 644
  of humerus, 596, 597
  of tibia, 645
  foramen of fibula, 234
Nymphæ, 1318

O

Obelion, 107
Obex, 815
Oblique cord, 301
  ligament, 301
  line of fibula, 236
    of mandible, 128
    of radius, 195
  muscle of abdomen, 393, 398
    of eye, inferior, 1054
      superior, 1053
  popliteal ligament, 318
  ridge of clavicle, 176
  sinus of pericardium, 529
  vein of left atrium, 530, 651
    of Marshall, 519, 530, 651
Obliquus auriculæ muscle, 1066
  capitis inferior muscle, 384
    superior muscle, 384
  externus abdominis muscle, 393
  inferior muscle, 384
  internus abdominis muscle, 398
  oculi inferior muscle, 1054
    superior muscle, 1053
  superior muscle, 384
Obliterated ductus anteriosus, 548
  venosus, 690
  hypogastric artery, 620
  umbilical vein, 690, 1195
Obturator artery, 622
  crest, 211
  externus muscle, 478
  fascia, 409
  foramen, 212
  groove, 212
  internus muscle, 476
  lymph node, 716
  membrane, 476
  nerve, 982
    accessory, 984
  tubercle, 212
  vein, 683, 684
Occipital artery, 564
  surface marking of, 1361
  bone, 134
    articulations of, 138
    basilar part of, 137
    lateral parts of, 136

Occipital bone, ossification of, 138
  squama of, 135
  structure of, 138
    condyles, 136
  crest, internal, 123, 136
  fossæ, 123
  groove, 109, 146
  lobe, 845
  lymph nodes, 702
  nerve, 951, 957
  protuberance, 110, 111, 135, 136
  sinus, 665
  sulcus, 845
  triangle, 375, 1364
  vein, 654
Occipitalis muscle, 353
Occipitoaxial ligaments, 272
Occipitofrontal fasciculus, 867
Occipitofrontalis muscle, 353
Occipitomastoid suture, 111, 114, 123
Occipitotemporal convolution 846
Ocular bulb, 1032
  muscles, 1051
Oculomotor nerve, 913
  composition and central connections of, 890
  sulcus, 817
Odontoblasts, 1158, 1163
Odontoid ligaments, 273
  process of axis, 79
Olecranon, 189
  fossa, 187
  process, 189
Olfactory areas, 48
  bulb, 854, 875
    structure of, 875
  cells, 1024
  fasciculus, 859
  groove, 121
  gyrus, 854
  hair, 1029
  nerves, 911
    composition and central connections of, 895
    development of, 1030
  pits, 48
  projection fibers, 897
  stria, 854, 896
  sulcus, 844
  tract, 854
  trigone, 854
  tubercle, 854
Oligodendrocytes, 755
Oliva, 788
Olive, 788
  peduncle, of, 802
Olivary body, 788
  nucleus, 800, 802
Olivocerebellar fibers, 802
Olivospinal fasciculus, 780
Omental bursa, 1197, 1201
  recess, 1201
Omentum, gastrocolic, 1202
  gastrohepatic, 1202
  greater, 1202
  lesser, 1201
  small, 1202
Omohyoid muscle, 374
Opening of aorta in left ventricle, 538
  aortic, in diaphragm, 390
  caval, in diaphragm, 390
  of coronary sinus, 534
  esophageal, in diaphragm, 390
  of inferior vena cava, 534
  of pulmonary artery, 535
    veins, 537
  saphenous, 467, 468
  of superior cava, 533
  thoracic, 528
Openings, atrioventricular, 535, 537
  in roof of fourth ventricle, 815
Opercula of insula, 847

Ophthalmic artery, 573
  ganglion, 918
  nerve, 916
  veins, 665
Opisthion, 110
Opisthotic center of temporal
  bone, 150
Opponens digiti quinti muscle,
  462
  minimi digiti muscle, 462
  pollicis muscle, 459
Optic axis, 1032
  chiasma, 836, 912, 1034
  commissure, 836
  cup, 1033
  disk, 1046
  foramen, 122, 152
  groove, 152
  nerve, 912, 1034
    composition and central con-
      nections of, 893
  radiations, 838
  recess, 838
  stalk, 747, 1033
  thalamus, 825
  tracts, 837, 913
  vesicle, 747, 1033
Ora serrata, 1046, 1048
Oral cavity, 1151
  part of pharynx, 1183
Orbicular ligament, 301
Orbicularis oculi muscle, 355
  lacrimal part, 355
  orbital part, 355
  palpebral part, 355
  oris muscle, 358
  palpebrarum muscle, 355
Orbiculus ciliaris muscle, 1041
  relation of nerves in 930
Orbital fascia, 1055
  fissures, 111, 119, 122, 155, 170
  gyri, 844
  nerve, 920
  operculum, 847
  plates, 142
  process of palatine bone, 172
    of zygomatic bone, 169
  septum, 1056, 1069
  sulcus, 844
  vein, 652
Orbitosphenoids, 155
Orbits, 117
Organ, of Corti, 1087
  enamel, 1057
  of Giraldes, 1297
  of hearing, 1060
  of Rosenmüller, 1255, 1307
  of sight, 1032
  of smell, 1024
  spiral, of Corti, 1087
Organa genitalia muliebria, 1305
  virilia, 1286
  oculi accessoria, 1051
Organon auditus, 1060
  gustus, 1023
  olfactorius, 1024
  spirale [Corti], 1087
  visus, 1032
Organs, of digestion, 1141
  genital, of female, 1305
    of male, 1286
  of Golgi, 347, 1092
  of taste, 1023
  of the senses, 1023
  urinary, 1264
  urogenital, 1253
  vomero-nasal, of Jacobson, 51,
    1028
Orifice, atrioventricular, 535,
  537
  cardiac, of stomach, 1207
  mitral, 538
  of mouth, 1151
  pyloric, of stomach, 1207
  urethral, 1282, 1285, 1319
  of uterus, 1312

Orifice, vaginal, 1319
Orifices of ureters, 1282
Orificium externum uteri, 1312
  internum uteri, 1312
Origin of muscles, 341
Os acetabuli, 213
  calcis, 237
  capitatum, 201
  coccygis, 89
  coxæ, 206
    articulations of, 213
    ossification of, 212
    structure of, 212
  cuboideum, 244
  cuneiforme primum, 245
    secundum, 246
    tertium, 246
  ethmoidale, 157
  external of uterus, 1312
  frontale, 141
  hamatum, 202
  hyoideum, 133
  ilii, 206
  incisivum, 167
  innominatum, 206
  internal of uterus, 1312
  ischii, 209
  lacrimale, 168
  lunatum, 197
  magnum, 201
  multangulum, 201
  naviculare manus, 197
    pedis, 245
  occipitale, 134
  palatinum, 170
  parietale, 138
  pisiforme, 198
  planum, 159
  pubis, 211
  sacrum, 85
  sphenoidale, 152
    alæ magna, 154
    parva, 155
  temporale, 143
  trigonum, 244
  triquetrum, 197
  zygomaticum, 168
Ossa carpi, 196
  cranii, 134
  extremitatis superioris, 175
  faciei, 160
  metacarpalia, 202
  metatarsalia, 247
  nasalia, 160
  sesamoidea, 252
  tarsi, 237
Ossicles, auditory, 1074
  ligaments of, 1076
Ossicula auditus, 1074
Ossification of atlas, 91
  of axis, 91
  of bone, center of, **71**
  of clavicle, 177
  of coccyx, 93
  of ethmoid, 160
  of femur, 230
  of fibula, 237
  of foot, 250
  of frontal, 143
  of hand, 206
  of hip bone, 212
  of humerus, 188
  of hyoid, 134
  of inferior nasal concha, 174
  intracartilaginous, 71
  intramembranous, 70
  of lacrimal, 168
  of lumbar vertebræ, 92
  of mandible, 130
  of maxilla, 167
  of nasal, 162
  of occipital, 138
  of os coxæ or innominatum, 212
  of palatine, 173
  of parietal, 140
  of patella, 231

Ossification of radius, 196
  of ribs, 105
  of sacrum, 92
  of scapula, 183
  of seventh cervical vertebra, 92
  of sphenoid, 157
  of sternum, 100
  subperiosteal, 72
  of temporal, 150
  of tibia, 235
  of ulna, 194
  of vertebral column, 90
  of vomer, 175
  of zygomatic, 170
Osteoblasts, 67, 70, 72
Osteoclasts, 67, 72, 1164
Osteodentin, 1160
Osteogenetic fibers, 71
Osteology, 59
Ostium, abdominal, of uterine
  tube, 1308
  of eustachian tube, 1175
  maxillare, 125, 1027
  pharyngeal, of auditory tube,
    1184
  primitive urogenital, 1263
  primum [heart], 506
  secundum [heart], 506
Otic ganglion, 926
Otoconia, 1083
Outlet of pelvis, 214
Ova, primitive, 1257
Oval area of Flechsig, 782
  bundle, 740
Ovarian arteries, 617
  fossa, 1198, 1305
  plexus of nerves, 1017
  veins, 687
Ovaries, 1305
  descent of, 1260
  development of 1257
  ligaments of, 1306
  lymphatic capillaries of, 697
    vessels of, 725
  medullary substance of, 1307
  nerves of, 1308
  structure of, 1307
  vesicular or Graafian follicles
    of, 1307
  vessels of, 1308
Oviduct, 1308
Ovula Nabothi, 1316
Ovum, 20
  corona radiata of, 20
  discharge of, 1308
  fertilization of, 24
  germinal spot of, 20
    vesicle of, 20
  imbedding of, 26
  implantation of, 26
  maturation of, 20
  segmentation of, 25
  size of, 20
  zona pellucida of, 20
Oxyntic cells, 1212
  glands, 1212
Oxyphil white blood corpuscles,
  525

P

PACCHIONIAN bodies, 905
Pacinian corpuscles, 1091
Pain, impuses of, 880
Palatal process of maxilla, 166
Palate, 1153
  arches of, 1154
  bone, 170
  cleft, 127
  development of, **50**
  hard, 1154
  soft, 1154
Palatine aponeurosis, 1180
  artery, ascending, 561
    pharyngeal, 565
    descending, 570

Palatine bone, 170
  articulations of, 173
  horizontal part of, 170
  orbital process of, 172
  ossification of, 173
  pyramidal process or tuber-
    osity of, 172
  sphenoidal process of, 173
  vertical part of, 171
  foramen, 107
  muscles, 1180
  nerves, 922
  process of maxilla, 166
  processes of fetus, 50
  tonsils, 1177
  uvula, 1154
  velum, 1154
Palatoglossus muscle, 1168, *note,*
  1181
Palatopharyngeus muscle, 1182
Palatum, 1153
  durum, 1153
  molle, 1154
Palmar aponeurosis, 453
  arch, deep, 601
    superficial, 604
  cutaneous branch of median
    nerve, 967
    of ulnar nerve, 971
  fascia, 453
  interossei muscles, 463
  interosseous arteries, 604
  ligaments, 306, 309
  nerves of ulnar, 971
Palmaris brevis muscle, 461
  longus muscle, 439
Palmate folds of uterus, 1312
Palpebræ, 1055
Palpebral arteries, 573, 574
  commissures or canthi, 1055
  fissure, 1055
  ligament, 1056
    medial, 355
  nerves from maxillary, 920
  raphe, lateral, 355
Pampiniform plexus of spermatic
  veins, 686
Pancreas, 1244
  accessory duct of, 1248
  body of, 1246
  development of, 1248
  duct of, 1247
  head of, 1244, 1245
  lymphatic vessels of, 723
  neck of, 1246
  nerves of, 1249
  structure of, 1248
  surface marking of, 1389
  tail of, 1247
  uncinate process of, 1245
  vessels of, 1249
Pancreatic arteries, 612
  duct, 1247
    accessory, 1248
  veins, 690
Pancreatica magna artery, 612
Pancreaticoduodenal arteries, 611
  613
  lymph nodes, 722
  veins, 691
Pancreaticolienal lymph nodes,
  720
Papilla, lacrimal, 1055
  mammæ, 1320
Papillæ, circumvallate, 1167
  conial, 1168
  filiform, 1168
  fungiform, 1167
  of skin, 1099
  of tongue, 1167
  vallatæ, 1167
Papillary layer of skin, 1099
  process, 1235
Paracentral lobule, 844
Paradidymis, 1297
Parallel striæ of Retzius, 1159

Paramastoid process, 137
Paramedial sulcus, 844
Parametrium, 1311
Paranephric body, 1269
Paranucleus, 1249
Paraplexus, 852
Pararectal fossa, 1198
  lymph nodes, 722
Pararenal fat, 1269
Parasympathetic nerves, cranial,
  1001
  sacral, 1004
Parathyroid glands, 1330
  development of, 1330
  structure of, 1331
Paravesical fossa, 1198
Paraxial mesoderm, 41
Parietal bone, 138
  cells of fundic glands, 1212
  convolution, ascending, 845
  eminence, 106, 111, 139
  foramen, 106, 139
  lobe, 844
  gyri of, 845
  notch, 146
  operculum, 848
  pleura, 1124
  pericardium, 528
  peritoneum, 1194
  veins, 515, 516
Parietomastoid suture, 114, 123
Parietoöccipital fissure, 842
Parietotemporal artery, 578
Parolfactory area, 857
Paroöphoron, 1255, 1307
Parotid duct, 1174
  gland, 1173
    accessory part of, 1174
    nerves of, 1175
    of, 1174, 1175
    structure of, 1174, 1175
    surface marking of, 1354
    vessels of, 1175
  lymph nodes, 703
  plexus, 932
Paratideomasseteric fascia, 361
Parovarium, 1307
Pars ciliaris retinæ, 1043, 1046,
  1048
  iridica retinæ, 1044, 1046, 1048
Partes genitales externæ muliebres,
  1305
Parumbilical veins, 691
Patella, 230
  articulation of, 231
  movements of, 324
  ossification of, 231
  structure of, 230
  surface anatomy of, 1412
Patellar plexus, 982, 985
  retinacula, 318
  surface of femur, 223
Pathways from brain to spinal
  cord, 898
Pectinate ligament of iris, 1039
Pectineal line, 221
Pectineus muscle, 471
Pectiniforme septum, 1300
Pectoralis major muscle, 429
  minimus muscle, 430
  minor muscle, 430
Pedicles of a vertebra, 76, 77
Peduncle or peduncles, cerebellar,
  809
  cerebral, 818
  olivary, 802
Pelvic colon, 1227
  diaphragm, 407
    fascia of, 410, 414
  girdle, 175
  muscles, 407
  plexuses, 1020
  portion of sympathetic system,
    1013
Pelvis, 213, 1189
  adult, x-ray of, 1415

Pelvis, articulations of, 282
  axes of, 215
  boundaries of, 213, 215
  brim of, 213
  cavity of lesser, 214
  diameters, 214, 215
  greater or false, 213
  in fetus, 217
  inferior aperture, 215
  inlet of, 214
  lesser or true, 214
  ligaments of, 283, 284
  linea terminalis of, 213
  lymph nodes of, 714
  major, 213
  male and female, differences
    between, 216
  mechanism of, 287
  minor, 214
  outlet of, 215
  position of, 216
  renal, 1272
  superior aperture, 214
  x-ray of, child aged three-an-a-
    half years, 1415
Penis, 1298
  body of, 1301
  bulb, 1301
  corona glandis, 1301
  corpora cavernosa, 1298, 1300
  corpus cavernosum urethræ, or
    corpus spongiosum, 1298,
    1301
  crura of, 1300
  deep artery of, 624, 626
  dorsal artery of, 624, 626
    veins of, 684
  fascia, 1299, 1300
  fundiform ligament of, 1301
  glands, 1299
  glans, 1301
  foreskin of, 1298
  lymphatic vessels of, 724
  muscles of, 417
  neck of, 1301
  nerves of, 1303
  prepuce of, 1298
  septum pectiniforme, 1300
  structure of, 1302
  suspensory ligament of, 1301
Perforated substance, 817
Perforating arteries from internal
    mammary, 589
  from plantar, 647
  from profunda femoris, 637
  of hand, 601
  cutaneous nerve, gluteal, 995
  fibers of Sharpey, 69
Pericardiacophrenic artery, 588
Pericardial area, 41
  arteries, 589, 605
  pleura, 1125
Pericardium, 528
  fibrous, 529
  nerves of, 530
  oblique sinus of, 529
  relations of, 529
  serous, 528
  structure of, 528
  transverse sinus of, 529
  vessels of, 530
  vestigial fold of, 530
Pericecal folds, 1204
  fossæ, 1204
Perichondrium, 72, 256
Perikaryon, 755
Perilymph, 1078, 1082
Perineal artery, 625
  body, 1229
  branch of fourth sacral nerve,
    989
  fat, 1267
  muscle, superficial deep trans-
    verse, 417, 419
  nerve, 996

Perineum, boundaries of, 411
central tendinous point of, 416
fascia of, 411
lymphatic vessels of, 717
muscles of, 417
Perineurium, 752, 760
Periorbita, 1055
Periosteum, 67
Peripheral end-organs, 1090
nervous system, 911
organs of special senses, 1023
terminations of nerves of general sensations, 1090
Periscleral lymph space, 1054
Peritoneal cavity, 1194
fossæ or recesses, 1204
sacs, 1195, 1197, 1200
Peritoneum, 1194
epiploic foramen of, 1201
greater sac of, 1194
ligaments of, 1202
lymphatic capillaries in, 697
main cavity or greater sac of, 1195
horizontal disposition of, 1198, 1200
vertical disposition of, 1195
mesenteries, 1202
omenta, 1201
omental bursa of, 1201
vertical disposition of, 1197
parietal portion of, 1194
visceral portion of, 1194
Perlia, nucleus of, 821
Permanent teeth, 1155
development of, 1164
Peronæus accessorius muscle, 488
brevis muscle, 488
longus muscle, 487
quartus muscle, 488
quinti digiti muscle, 488
tertius muscle, 482
Peroneal artery, 644
muscles, 487
nerves, 986, 993, 994, 995
retinacula, 489
septa, 481
Peroneocalcaneus externus muscle, 488
internus muscle, 486
Peroneocuboideus muscle, 488
Peroneotibialis muscle, 484
Perpendicular fasciculus, 867
line of ulna, 193
plate of ethmoid, 158
Pes or base of cerebral peduncle, 818
Petit, canal of, 1050
triangle of, 424
Petroöccipital fissure, 110
Petrosal nerve, deep, 922
external, 1011
large deep, 922
superficial, 921
superficial, greater, 921, 932
smaller, 1077
process, 153
sinuses, 656, 660
Petrosphenoidal fissure, 110
Petrosquamous sinus, 665
suture, 147, 149
Petrotympanic fissure, 108, 145, 1069
Petrous ganglion, 937
portion of temporal bone, 147
Peyer's glands, 1221
patches, 1221
Phalangeal processes of Corti's rods, 1089
Phalanges digitorum manus, 205
pedis, 250
of foot, 250
of hand, 205
ungual, 250

Pharyngeal aponeurosis, 1187
artery, ascending, 565
bursa, 1185
grooves, 46
membrane, 1141
nerve from glossopharyngeal, 938
from sphenopalatine ganglion, 923
from vagus, 940
ostium of auditory tube, 1184
plexus of nerves, 938, 940, 1010
pouches, 45
recess, 1183
tonsil, 1185
tubercle, 108, 137
veins, 657
Pharyngopalatine arch, 1177
Pharyngopalatinus muscle, 1182
Pharynx, 1182
apeneurosis of, 1187
development of, 1187
laryngeal part of, 1185
mucous coat of, 1187
muscles of, 1185
nasal part of, 1183
oral part of, 1185
structure of, 1187
Philtrum, 359
Phrenic arteries, 608, 618
nerve, 958
plexus of nerves, 1017
veins, 674, 688
Phrenicocolic ligament, 1204
Phrenicocostal sinus, 1126
Phrenicolienal ligament, 732
Phrenicopericardiac ligament, 686
Pia of brain, 906
of cord, 906
mater, cranial, 906
encephali, 906
spinal, 907
spinalis, 907
Pigment of iris, 1044
of skin, 1098
Pigmented layer of retina, 1046
Pili, 1102
Pillars of Corti, 1087
of external abdominal ring, 397
of fauces, 1159 1177
Pineal body, 832, 1335
structure of, 832, 1335
recess, 839
Pinna, 1064
cartilage of, 1065
ligaments of, 1066
fascia of, 409
Piriformis muscle, 476
Pisiannularis muscle, 462
Pisiform bone, 198
Pisimetacarpus muscle, 462
Pisiuncinatus muscle, 462
Pisohamate ligament, 306
Pisometacarpal ligament, 306
Pits, olfactory, 48
Pituitary body, 1331
gland, 1331
Pivot-joint, 261
Placenta, 31
circulation through, 546
cotyledons of, 34
Placenta, development of, 27
fetal portion of, 31
maternal portion of, 31
previa, 34
separation of, 34
Plane, intertubercular, 1190
subcostal, 1190
transpyloric, 1190
Plantar aponeurosis, 491
arch, 645
arteries, 645
cutaneous venous arch, 679
digital veins, 681
fascia, 491
interossei muscles, 497

Plantar ligament, long, 332
metatarsal arteries, 645
nerves, 992
Plantaris muscle, 484
Planum nuchale, 114, 135
occipitale, 114, 135
Plasmagel, 17
Plate or Plates, cribriform of ethmoid, 157
orbital, or frontal, 142
perpendicular, of ethmoid, 158
pterygoid, of sphenoid, 150
tarsal, 1055
Platelets of blood, 525
Platysma muscle, 364, 1346
Pleura, 1124
cavity of, 1124
cervical, 1124
costal, 1124
cupula of, 1124
diaphragmatic, 1124
lymphatic vessels of, 730
mediastinal, 1124
nerves of, 1127
parietal, 1124
pericardial, 1125
pulmonary, 1124
reflections of, 1124
structure of, 1127
surface markings of, 1370
vessels of, 1127
Plexiform layers of retina, 1037
Plexus, choroid, of fourth ventricle, 815
of lateral ventricle, 852
of third ventricle, 838
of nerves, annular, 1039
aortic abdominal, 1017
Auerbach's 1222
brachial, 954, 959
cardiac, 1015
cavernous, 1009
celiac, 1016
cervical, 954, 957, 959
posterior, 950, 951, 955
coccygeal, 997
corneal, 1039
coronary, 1016
esophageal, 939, 942
formation of, 760
gastric, 942, 1017
hemorrhoidal, 1019, 1233
hepatic, 1017
hypogastric, 1019
infraorbital, 921
internal carotid, 1007
lienal, 1017
lumbar, 977
lumbosacral, 977
Meissner's, 1222
mesenteric, 1017
myenteric, 1222
ovarian, 1017
parotid, 932
patellar, 982, 985
pelvic, 1019, 1020
pharyngeal, 938, 940, 1010
phrenic, 1017
prostatic, 1020
pudendal, 996
pulmonary, 939, 941, 942
renal, 1017
sacral, 986
solar, 1016
spermatic, 1017
splenic, 1017
submucosal, 1222
subsartorial, 984
suprarenal, 1017
tympanic, 1077
uterine, 1020
vaginal, 1020
vesical, 1020
of veins, basilar 668
hemorrhoidal, 684
pterygoid, 653

Plexus, of veins, pudendal, 684
  uterine, 685
  vertebral, 677
  vesical, 684
  vesicoprostatic, 684
Plica or plicæ, circulars [*Ker-kringi*], 1219
  fimbriata [tongue], 1166
  gubernatrix, 1259
  lacrimalis [*Hasneri*], 1060
  semilunaris [conjunctiva], 1057, 1058
  [tonsil], 1177
  sublingualis, 1175
  triangularis [tonsil], 1177
  uretericæ, 1282
  vascularis, 1259
  ventriculares [larynx], 1116
  vesicalis transversa, 1198
  vocales, 1116
Pneumogastric nerve, 938
Polar bodies or polocytes, 22
Poles of cerebral hemispheres, 841
  of eyeball, 1032
  of lens, 1051
Polkissen, 1273
Polymorphonuclear, leucocytes, 526
Pons, 803
  development of, 746
  hepatis, 1236
  structure of, 803
  Varolii, 803
Ponticulus [auricula], 1066
Pontine arteries, 584
Pontospinal fasciculus, 901
Popliteal artery, 638
    surface marking of, 1426
  fossa or space, 638
  line of tibia, 233
  lymph nodes, 712
  nerves, 989, 993
  surface of femur, 221
  vein, 681
Popliteus muscle, 484
  minor, 484
Pore, gustatory, 1023
Porta hepatis, 1236
Portal vein, 689
Postanal gut, 1151
Postaxial borders of limbs, 51
Postcentral sulcus, 845
Postcornu, 849
Posterior alveolar artery, 569
  annular ligament, 452
  basis bundle, 781
  calcaneo-astragaloid ligament, 330
  circumflex numeral artery, 594
  column of medulla spinalis, 771
  common ligament, 264
  cornu of brain, 849
    of medulla spinalis, 771
  costotransverse ligament, 278
  cricoarytenoid muscle, 1118
  deep cervical vein, 659
  dental artery, 569
  ground bundle, 781
  humeral circumflex artery, 594
  inferior tibiofibular ligament, 326
  interosseous artery, 604
    nerve, 973
  pillar of fauces, 1177
  proper fasciculus, 781
  pulmonary nerves, 941
  radial carpal artery, 600
  radioulnar ligament, 303
  root of spiral nerves, 783
  sacrosciatic ligament, 285
  scapular artery, 590
    nerve, 961
  scrotal nerves, 996
  spinal artery, 583
  superior alveolar artery, 569
  tolotibical ligament, 328

Posterior temporal artery, 566
  tibiofibular ligament, 304, 318
  ulnar carpal artery, 604
    recurrent artery, 602
  vertebral vein, 659
Postero-lateral ganglionic arteries, 585
Postero-medial ganglionic arteries, 585
Postgemina, 823
Postnodular fissure, 797
Postpyramidal fissure, 797
Postsphenoid part of sphenoid, 157
Pouch of Douglas, 1197, 1314
  of Prussak, 1077
  Rathke's, 1332
Pouches, pharyngeal, 45
Poupart's ligament, 395
Præputium clitoridis, 1318
  penis, 1298
Preaortic portion of duodenum, 1215
Preauricular lymph nodes, 702
  point, 1348
  sulcus of ilium, 207
Preaxial borders of limbs, 51
Precentral gyre, 843
  sulcus, 843
Precornu, 849
Precuneus, 845
Preganglionic fibers, 881
Pregemina, 823
Premolar teeth, 1157
Prepatellar bursa, 471
Prepuce of clitoris, 1318
  of penis, 1298
  development of, 1262
Preputial glands, 1299
  space, 1299
Prepyramidal tract, 781
Presphenoid, 157
Presternal notch, 99
Pretracheal fascia, 370
Prevertebral artery, 565
  fascia, 368
Prevesical facial cleft, 1279
Primary areolæ of bone, 72
  spermatocytes, 23
Primitive aortæ, 509
  atrium, 504, 506
  choanæ, 50
  costal arches, 61
  groove, 38
  jugular veins, 517
  node, 39
  ova, 1257
  palate, 50
  segments, 43, 59
  sheath of nerve fiber, 757
  streak, 38
  urogenital ostium, 1263
  ventricle of heart, 506
Princeps cervicis artery, 564
  pollicis artery, 601
Prismata adamantina, 1159
Procerus muscle, 356, 1346
Process or Processes, alveolar, 166
  articular, of vertebræ, 76
  axis-cylinder, 757
  ciliary, 1042
  clinoid, 122, 152, 155
  condyloid, of mandible, 130
  coracoid, 182
  coronoid, of mandible, 130
    of ulna, 189
  costal, 77
  descending, of lacrimal, 168
  dura mater, 901
  frontal, of maxilla, 165
  fronto-nasal, 48
  fronto-sphenoidal, of zygomatic, 169
  globular, of His, 49
  inferior nasal concha, 173
  intrajugular, 136

Process or Processes, jugular, 110, 136
  lateral nasal, 49
  lenticular, of incus, 1076
  malar, of maxilla, 165
  mastoid, 146
  maxillary, of inferior nasal concha, 174
    of palatine bone, 172
    of zygomatic bone, 170
  muscular, or arytenoid, 1111
  nasal, of frontal bone, 142
    of maxilla, 165
  odontoid, of axis or epistropheus, 79
  orbital, of palatine bone, 172
    of zygomatic bone, 169
  palatal, of maxilla, 166
  palatine, of maxilla, 166
  papillary, of liver, 1235
  paramastoid, 137
  petrosal, 153
  phalangeal, of Corti's rods, 1089
  protoplasmic, 756
  pterygoid, of sphenoidal bone, 156
  pyramidal, of palatine bone, 108, 172
  septal cartilage of nose, 1024
  turbinated, 156
  sphenoidal, of palatine bone, 173
  spinous, of ilium, 208
    of vertebræ, 76
  styloid, of fibula, 235
    of radius, 196
    of temporal bone, 109, 150
    of ulna, 194
  temporal, of zygomatic, 170
  transverse, of vertebræ, 77, 79
  trochlear, of calcaneus, 241
  uncinate, of ethmoid, 159
  vaginal, of sphenoid, 156
    of temporal, 149, 150
  vermiform, 1223
  vertebræ, 83, 85
  vocal, of arytenoid, 1111
  xiphoid, 100
  zygomatic, of frontal, 142
    of maxilla, 165
    of temporal bone, 144
Processus styloideus, 150
Prochordal plate, 41
Proctodeum, 1151
Prodentin, 1164
Profunda arteries, 597
  brachii artery, 597
  cervicalis artery, 590
  femoris artery, 636
    surface markings of, 1426
  vein, 681
  linguæ artery, 561
Projection fibers of cerebral hemispheres, 865
Prominence of aqueduct of Fallopius, 1171
  of facial canal, 1071
  laryngeal, 1109
Promontorium, 1071
Promontory of tympanic cavity, 1071
Pronator quadratus muscle, 443
  teres muscle, 439
Pronephric duct, 1253
Pronephros, 1253
Proötic center of temporal bone, 150
Prophase of karyokinesis, 19
Prosencephalon, 42, 747, 824
Prostate, 1303
  development of, 1261
  gland, 1303
  lobes of, 1303
  lymphatic vessels of, 724
  nerves of, 1305

Prostate, structure of, 1304
vessels of, 1305
Prostatic ducts, orifices of, 1285
plexus of nerves, 1020
portion of urethra, 1284
sinus, 1284
utricle, 1284
Protoplasm, 17
Protoplasmic process of nerve cells, 756
Protuberance, mental, 128
occipital, 110, 111, 135, 136
Prussak, pouch of, 1077
Psalterium, 857
Psoas magnus muscle, 466
major muscle, 466
fascia covering, 465
minor muscle, 466
parvus muscle, 466
Pterion, 111
ossicle, 160
Pterotic center of temporal bone, 141
Pterygoid canal, 107, 114
fissure, 156
fossa of sphenoid, 156
hamulus, 107, 156
muscles, 364
nerve, external, 924
plates, 156
plexus of veins, 653
processes of sphenoid, 156
tubercle, 156
Pterygoideus externus muscle, 364
internus muscle, 364
Pterygomandibular ligament, 360
raphé, 360
Pterygomaxillary fissure, 113
Pterygopalatine canal, 164
fossa, 114, 160
groove, 156
nerve, 923
Pterygospinous ligament, 157, 361
Pubic arch, 215
bones, articulation of, 286
ligaments, 286
region, 1190
tubercle or spine, 211
vein, 682
Pubis, 211
angle of, 211
body of, 211
crest of, 211
iliopectineal eminence of, 211
obturator crest of, 211
rami of, 211
symphysis of, 286
tubercle or spine of, 211
Pubocapsular ligament, 312, 313
Pubococcygeus muscle, 409
Pubofemoral ligament, 313
Puboprostatic ligament, 415, 1281
Puborectalis muscle, 408
Pubovesical ligaments, 1281
Pubovesicales muscles, 1281
Pudendal artery, accessory, 624
internal, in female, 623
in male, 623
cleft or rima, 1317
nerve, 996
inferior, 989
plexus, nervous, 996
venous, 684
veins, internal, 684
Pudendum, 1317
Pudic arteries, 623, 635
nerve, internal, 996
veins, internal, 684
Pulmonary artery, 553
opening in right ventricle, 535
ligaments, 1126
nerves, 942
pleura, 1124

Pulmonary semilunar valves, 536
veins, 650
openings of, in left atrium, 537
Pulmones, 1129
facies costalis, 1131
mediastinalis, 1131
margo anterior, 1132
inferior, 1132
posterior, 1132
Pulp cavity of teeth, 1158
dental, 1158
of spleen, 733
Pulpa lienis, 733
Pulvinar, 825, 830
Puncta lacrimalia, 1055, 1059
Pupil, 1040
congenital atresia of, 1035
Pupillary membrane, 1035
Purkinje, cells of, 811
fibers of, 545
Putamen, 750, 860
Pyloric antrum, 1208
artery, 610
glands, 1212
orifice of stomach, 1201
part of stomach, 1207, 1208
valve, 1209
veins, 671
Pyramid or pyramids, 1073
of medulla oblongata, 787
renal, 1272
of temporal bone, 147
of vestibule, 1079
Pyramidal cells of cerebral cortex, 868
decussation, 786
eminence of tympanic cavity, 1073
lobe of thyroid gland, 1328
process of palatine bone, 172
tracts, 778
Pyramidalis muscle, 402
nasi muscle, 356
Pyramis medullæ oblongatæ, 787

Q

QUADRATE lobe of liver, 1236
Quadratus femoris muscle, 478
labii inferioris muscle, 358
superioris muscle, 357
lumborum muscle, 406
fascia covering, 406
menti muscle, 358
plantæ muscle, 494
Quadriceps extensor muscle, 470
femoris muscle, 470
Quadrigeminal bodies, 822, 823

R

RADIAL artery, 599
branches of, 600
peculiarities of, 600
recurrent, 600
surface marking of, 1407
fibers of cerebral cortex, 865
fossa, 187
nerve, 972
surface markings of, 1411
sulcus, 185
tuberosity, 194
Radialis indicis artery, 601
Radiate ligament, 276
sternocostal ligaments, 278
Radices arci vertebræ, 76
Radiocarpal articulation 303
movements of, 306
Radiohumeral joint, surface anatomy of, 1402
Radioulnar articulations, 301
ligaments, 301
union, middle, 301

Radius, 194
ossification of, 196
structure of, 196
surface anatomy of, 1399
Radix linguæ, 1165
pili, 1102
pulmonis, 1135
Rami of ischium, 210
of pubis, 211
Ramus of mandible, 129
Ranine artery, 561
vein, 656
Ranvier, nodes of, 757
Raphé, anococcygeal, 421
lateral palpebral, 356
of palate, 1154
pterygomandibular, 360
of scrotum, 1287
Rathke's pouch, 1332
Receptaculum chyli, 701
Recess or recesses, epitympanic, 1069
lateral, of fourth ventricle, 815
nasopalatine, 1028
omental, 1201
optic, 838
peritoneal, 1204
pharyngeal, 1183, 1185
pineal, 839
sphenoethmoidal, 125, 1026
of Tröltsch, 1077
Recessus ellipticus, 1079
infundibuli, 838
intersigmoideus, 1206
pinealis, 839
sacciformis, 303
sphæricus, 1078, 1079
suprapinealis, 839
Rectal ampulla, 1228
columns of Morgagni, 1229
Rectococcygeal muscles, 1231
Rectouterine excavation, 1197, 1314
folds, 1314
Rectovesical excavation, 1197
folds, 1198
layer of pelvic fascia, 1297
Rectovesicles muscles, 1281
Rectum, 1227
ampulla of, 1228
anal part of, 1229
development of, 1149
Houston's valves of, 1228
lymphatic vessels of, 722
relations of, 1229
Rectus abdominis muscle, 400
sheath of, 400
capitis anterior muscle, 375
anticus major muscle, 375
minor muscle, 375
capitis lateralis muscle, 376
posterior major muscle, 384
minor muscle, 384
femoris muscle, 470
muscles of eyeball, 1053
Recurrent artery, interosseous, 604
radial, 600
tibial, 642
ulnar, 602
branches from deep volar arch, 601
laryngeal nerve, 941
nerve, 941
Red corpuscles, 525
nucleus, 822
Reflected inguinal ligament, 396
Reflections of pleuræ, 1124
Reflex paths, spinal intrinsic, 877
Refracting media of eye, 1049
Regions of abdomen, 1189
Reil, island of, 847
Reissner, vestibular membrane of, 1085
Renal arteries, 617
calyces, 1272

Renal columns, 1272
  corpuscles, 1272
  fascia, 1267
  impression, 1234
  pelvis, 1275
  plexus, 1017
  pyramids, 1272
  sinus, 1272
  tubules, 1272, 1273
  veins, 687
  vessels, afferent and efferent, 1272
Renes, 1264
Reproduction of cells, 19
Reproductive system, female, 1305
  male, 1286
Respiration, mechanism of, 391
Respiratory apparatus, 1107
  development of, 1107
  nerve of Bell, 958, 962
  system, 1107
Restiform bodies of medulla, 791, 803
Rete canalis hypoglossi, 668
  foraminis ovalis, 668
  testis, 1294
Retia venosa vertebrarum, 677
Reticular lamina, 1089
  layer of skin, 1098
Retina, 1045
  central artery of, 575
  development of, 1035
  fovea centralis, 1046
  layers of, 1046
  macula lutea, 1046
  membrana limitans, 1048
  ora serrata, 1046
  structure of, 1046
  supporting frame-work of, 1048
Retinacula of hip-joint, 312
  patellar, 318
  peroneal, 489
Retrahens aurem muscle, 1066
Retroglandular sulcus of penis, 1301
Retroperitoneal fossæ, 1204
Retropharyngeal lymph nodes, 704
  space, 369
Retzius, colored lines of, 1160
  space of, 1279
Rhinal fissure, external, 750
Rhinencephalon, 854
  development of, 749
Rhodopsin, 1046
Rhombencephalon, 42, 744
  development of, 744
Rhombic grooves, 746
  lip, 745
Rhomboid fossa, 815
  impression, 177
  ligament, 290
Rhomboideus major muscles, 424
  minor muscle, 424
  occipitalis muscle, 424
Ribs, 101
  common characteristics of, 101
  development of, 61
  false, 101
  floating or vertebral, 101
  ossification of, 105
  peculiar, 104
  structure of, 105
  true, 101
  vertebrochondral, 101
  vertebrosternal, 101
Ridge, ganglion, 42, 741
  supracondylar, 185
  trapezoid or oblique, 176
Ridges, bicipital, 184
Right atrium, 533
  auricle, 533
  auricular appendix, 533
  coronary artery, 554

Right coronary plexus, 986
  veins, 650
  gastroepiploic lymph nodes, 717
  ventricle, 535
Rima glottidis, 1114, 1117
  of mouth, 1151
  palpebrarum, 1055
  pudendal, 1317
Ring or rings, abdominal, 396, 405
  femoral, 631
  fibrous, of heart, 539
  subcutaneous inguinal, 395
  tympanic, 151
Risorius muscle, 357
Rivinus, ducts of, 1176
  notch of, 1069
Rod-bipolars of retina, 1047
Rod-granules of retina, 1047
Rods and cones, layer of, 1048
  of Corti, 1087
  of retina, 1048
Rolando, fissure of, 753, 842
  substantia gelatinosa of, 771
  tubercle of, 791
Root of lung, 1135
  of penis, 1298
Root-sheaths of hair, 1103
Roots of spinal nerves, 782, 948
  of teeth, 1155
Rosenmüller, fossa of, 1183, 1185
  lymph node of, 713
  organ of, 1255, 1307
Rostrum of corpus callosum, 866
  sphenoidal, 154
Rotary joint, 261
Rotation, movement of, 262
Rotatores muscles, 383
  spinæ muscle, 383
Round ligament of hip-joint, 313
  of liver, 1237
  of uterus, 1313
Rubrospinal fasciculus, 900
Ruffini, corpuscles of, 1092
Russell, Risen, hook bundle of, 810
Rust-colored layer of cerebellar cortex, 813

S

Sac, dental, 1162
  lacrimal, 1060
  of peritoneum, 1195, 1197
Saccule, laryngeal, 1117
  of vestibule, 1083
Sacculus, 1083
Saccus lacrimalis, 1060
  vaginalis, 1259
Sacral arteries, lateral, 627
  artery, middle, 618
  canal, 89
  cornua, 87
  crest, 86, 87
  foramina, 85, 87
  groove, 86
  lymph nodes, 716
  nerves, division of, 953, 986
  nucleus of medulla spinalis, 776
  parasympathetic nerves, 1004
  plexus, 986
  sympathetics, 1004
  tuberosity, 87
  veins, 684, 685
Sacrococcygeal ligaments, 286
Sacrogenital folds, 1198, 1313
Sacroiliac articulation, 282
  ligaments, 283, 284
Sacrosciatic ligaments, 285
Sacrospinalis muscle, 379
Sacrovertebral angle, 85
Sacrum, 75, 85
  ala of, 89
  apex, of, 89
  articulations of, 89

Sacrum, auricular surface of, 87
  base of, 88
  ossification of, 92
  structure of, 89
  variations of, 89
Saddle-joint, 262
Sagittal fossa of liver, 1236
  sinuses, 661, 662
  sulcus, 136, 139, 142
  suture, 106, 114
Salivary glands, 1173
  development of, 1142
  parotid, 1173
  structure of, 1176
  sublingual, 1175
  submaxillary, 1175
Salpingopalatine fold, 1184
Salpingopharyngeal fold, 1185
Salpingopharyngeus muscle, 1185
Salter, incremental lines of, 1159
Santorini, cartilages of, 1111
  duct of, 1248
Saphenous nerves, 965, 985
  opening, 468
  veins, 678, 679, 680
Sarcolemma, 343
Sarcoplasm, 344
Sartorius muscle, 469
Scala media [cochlea], 1083
  tympani, 1082
  vestibuli, 1082
Scalene tubercle, 104
Scalenus anterior muscle, 376
  anticus muscle, 376
  medius muscle, 376
  pleuralis muscle, 377
  posterior muscle, 377
  posticus muscle, 377
Scalp, lymphatic vessels of, 704
  muscle of, 352
  skin of, 352
Scapha, 1065
Scaphoid bone, ankle, 245
  wrist, 197
  fossa of sphenoid, 107, 156
Scapula, 178
  acromion of, 180
  coracoid process of, 182
  glenoid cavity of, 182
  ligaments of, 292
  ossification of, 183
  spine of, 180
  structure of, 192
  surface anatomy of, 1396
Scapular arteries, 586
  circumflex artery, 594
  nerve, posterior, 961
  notch, 180
Scapuloclavicular articulatio, 291
Scapus or shaft of hair, 1104
  pili, 1104
Scarpa, fascia of, 392
  foramina of, 107, 167
  ganglion of, 935, 1089
  triangle of, 633
Schwalbe, nucleus of, 806
Schindylesis, 260
Schlemm, canal of, 1035
Schreger, lines of, 1159
Schwann, sheath of, 757
Sciatic artery, 626
  foramen, 285
  nerves, 986, 990
  notch, 210
  veins, 684
Sclera, 1037
Sclero-corneal junction, 1038
Sclerotogenous layer, 59
Sclerotome, 59
Scrotal arteries, posterior, 625
  nerves, posterior, 996
Scrotum, 1287
  dartos tunic of, 1287
  integument of, 1287
  nerves of, 1289

Scrotum, raphé of, 1287
  vessels of, 1289
Sebaceous glands, 1104
Sebum cutaneum, 1104
Second cuneiform bone, 246
  metacarpal bone, 203
  metatarsal bone, 248
  nerve, 912
Secondary areolæ of bone, 72
  dentin, 1159
  oöcytes, 22
  sensory fasciculus, 780
  spermatocytes, 24
  tympanic membrane, 1071
Segment, medullary, 757
Segmentation, nucleus, 25
  of fertilized ovum, 25
Segments, primitive, 43
  spinal, 768
Sella turcica, 122, 152
Semicanalis m. tensoris tympani,
  150, 1074
  tubæ auditivæ, 150, 1074
Semicircular canals, 1079, 1080
  ducts, 1083
Semilunar artery, 573
  bone, 197
  fibrocartilages of knee, 321
  ganglion of abdomen, 1016
  of trigeminal nerve, 915
  notch of ulna, 192
Semimembranosus muscle, 480
Seminal duct, 1296
  vesicles, 1297
Semispinalis capitis muscle, 382
  cervicis muscle, 382
  colli muscle, 382
  dorsi muscle, 382
Semitendinosus muscle, 479
Sensations, peripheral terminations of nerves of, 1090
Senses, organs of, 1023
  special, organs of, 1023
Sensory decussation, 794
  ganglia of nerves, 764
  pathways from spinal cord to
  brain, 878
Septum, aortic, 508
  canalis musculotubarii, 150,
  1074
  crural, 632
  femorale, 632
  inferius of heart, 506
  intermedium, 506
  interventricular, 539
  lucidum, 852
  mobile nasi, 1024
  nasal, 123, 124
  orbital, 1056
  pectiniforme penis, 1300
  pellucidum, 852
  primum, 506
  secundum, 506
  spurium, 505
  subarachnoid, 905
  tongue, 1171
  transversum, 53
  of semicircular ducts, 1083
  urorectal, 1150
  ventricular, 506, 539
  ventriculorum, 539
Serous glands of tongue, 1171
  membrane, pericardium, 528
  peritoneum, 1194
  pleura, 1134
Serratus anterior muscle, 431
  magnus muscle, 431
  posterior inferior muscle, 388
  superior muscle, 387
  posticus muscles, 387
Sertoli, cells of, 1293
Sesamoid bones, 252
  cartilages, 1024
Seventh nerve, 928
Shaft of hair, 1104

Sheath or Sheaths of arteries, 522
  carotid, 370
  crural, 630
  dentinal, of Neumann, 1159
  femoral, 630
  flexor tendons of fingers, 442
  of toes, 493
  rectus abdominis muscle, 400
  of Schwann, 757
  synovial of tendons around ankle, 489
  in front of wrist, 452
  on back of wrist, 452
  tendon, fibrous, 454
  synovial, 452
Shin bone, 231
Short calcaneocuboid ligament,
  332
  gastric veins, 690
  plantar ligament, 332
  saphenous nerve, 993
  vein, 680
Shoulder, adult, x-ray of, 1395
  blade, 178
  of child aged six years, x-ray
  of, 1396
  girdle, 175
  muscles of, 431
  development of, 342
Shoulder-joint, 293
  bursæ near, 295
  movements of, 296
  vessels and nerves of, 296
Sibson's fascia, 368, 1125
Sight, organ of, 1032
Sigmoid arteries, 616
  cavity of radius, 195
  of ulna, 192
  colon, 1227
  flexure of colon, 1225, 1227
  mesocolon, 1196, 1198, 1203,
  1227
  sinus, 664
  sulcus, 146
Sinoatrial node, 540, 543
Sinus or Sinuses, air, 1030
  aortic, 538
  basilar, 668
  carotid, 570, 1094
  cavernous, 665
  cervicalis, 47
  circular, 666
  confluence of, 136, 665
  coronary, 650
  costomediastinal, 1126
  dura mater, 661
  epididymis, 1292
  external jugular vein, 656
  frontal, 142, 1030
  intercavernous, 666
  laryngeal, 1116
  lateral, 664
  longitudinal, 661, 662
  maxillary, 164, 1031
  of Morgagni, 1185
  oblique, 529
  occipital, 665
  of nose, 1030
  paranasal, 1030
  pericardial, 529
  petrosal, 666
  petrosquamous, 665
  phrenicocostal, 1126
  pocularis, 1284
  prostatic, 1284
  pyriformis, 1185
  renal, 1267, 1272
  rhomboidalis, 42
  sagittal, 661, 662
  sclerae, 1035
  septum, 505
  sigmoid, 664
  sphenoidal, 153, 1031
  sphenoparietal, 665
  straight, 662
  tentorial, 662

Sinus or Sinuses, *tonsillaris*, 47,
  1177
  transverse, 529, 664, 668
  urogenital, 1261
  Valsalva, 536, 538
  venarum, 533
  venosus, 504, 505, 533
Sinusoids of Minot, 515, 1238
Sixth nerve, 929
Skeleton, development of, 59
Skene's duct, 1262
Skin, 1096
  appendages of, 1101
  hairs, 1102
  nails, 1101
  sebaceous glands, 1104
  sudoriferous glands, 1105
  sweat glands, 1105
  arteries of, 1101
  cleavage lines, 1099, 1100
  corium or cutis vera, 1098
  development of, 1096
  epidermis or cuticle, 1096
  furrows of, 1096
  Langer's lines, 1100
  lymphatic capillaries in, 695
  nerves of, 1101
  papillary layer of, 1099
  reticular layer of, 1100
  stratum corneum, 1098
  mucosum, 1098
  true, 1098
Skull, 106
  adult, frontal view, x-ray of,
  1345
  lateral view, x-ray of, 1344
  development of, 63
  differences in, due to age, 125
  exterior of, 106
  fossa of, 120-123
  interior of, 119
  norma basalis, 107
  frontalis, 115
  lateralis, 110
  occipitalis, 114
  verticalis, 106
  sexual differences in, 127
  surface anatomy of, 1343
  upper surface of base of, 120
Skull-cap, inner surface of, 119
Small cardiac vein, 650
  cavenous nerves, 1020
  intestine, 1213
  and stomach, x-ray of, 1384
  circular folds of, 1219
  duodenum, 1216
  glands of, 1221
  ileum, 1216
  jejunum, 1216
  lymphatic nodules of, 1221
  vessels of 721
  Meckel's, diverticulum of,
  1217
  mucous membrane of, 1219
  muscular coat of, 1219
  nerves of, 1221
  Peyer's patches of, 1221
  serous coat of, 1219
  submucous coat of, 1219
  valvulæ conniventes of, 1219
  vessels of, 1221
  villi of, 1219
  occipital nerve, 955
  saphenous vein, 680
  sciatic nerve, 986
  wings of sphenoid, 155
Smaller occipital nerve, 955
Smallest cardiac veins, 651
Smell, organ of, 1024
Soft palate, 1153
  aponeurosis of, 1180
  arches or pillars of, 1154
  muscles of, 1180
Solar plexus, 1016
Sole of foot, muscles of, first layer,
  492

Sole of foot, muscles of, fourth layer, 496
  second layer, 494
  third layer, 494
Soleus muscle, 483
Solitary cells of medulla spinalis, 776
  lymph nodules, 1221
Somatic fibers of spinal nerves, 948
  layer of mesoderm, 41
Somatopleure, 42
Somites, 43
Space or spaces, Burns, 367
  corneal, 1038
  Fontana, 1038
  intercostal, 101
  interglobular, of teeth, 1159
  interpleural, 1127
  middle palmar, 457
  Nuel's, 1089
  popliteal, 638
  preputial, 1299
  prevesical, 1279
  retropharyngeal, 369
  retropubic, 1279
  Retzius', 1279
  subarachnoid, 904
  suprasternal, 367
  Tenon's, 1037
  thenar, 458
  Traube's, 1384
Spatia zonularia, 1050
Spermatic artery, internal, 617
  canal, 406
  cord, 1289
    structure of, 1289
  fascia, external, 397, 1288
    middle, 398, 1289
    innermost, 1289
    internal, 405, 1289
  nerve, 982
  plexus of nerves, 1017
  veins, 686, 1290
Spermatids, 24, 1293
Spermatoblasts, 1292
Spermatocytes, 24, 1293
Spermatogonia, 23, 1293
Spermatozoön, 22, 1293
  formation of, 1293
Sphenoethmoidal recess, 125, 1 26
  suture, 121
Sphenofrontal suture, 111, 121
Sphenoid bone, 152
  body of, 152
  pterygoid processes of, 156
  wings of, 154, 155
Sphenoidal air sinuses, 153, 1031
  conchæ, 156
  crest, 153
  process of palatine bone, 173
    of septal cartilage of nose, 1024
  rostrum, 154
  spine, 108, 154
  turbinated processes, 156
Sphenomandibular ligament, 273, 363
Sphenomaxillary fissure, 113
  fossa, 114
Sphenopalatine artery, 570
  foramen, 114, 125, 172
  ganglion, 921
  nerves, 920
  notch, 172, 173
Sphenoparietal sinus, 665
  suture, 111
Sphenosquamosal suture, 111
Sphenozygomatic suture, 111
Sphincter ani externus muscle, 421
  internus muscle, 421
  pupillæ muscle, 1044
  recti muscle, 421
  urethræ membranaceæ muscle, 419, 421

Sphincter vaginæ muscle, 419
  vesicæ, 1283
Spigelian lobe of liver, 1236
Spina angularis, 108, 154
  helicis, 1065
  scapulæ, 180
  vestibuli, 505
Spinal accessory nerve, **942**
  arteries, 583
  bulb, 785
  column, 75
  cord, 767
    dura of, 903
    pathways from brain to, 898
    pia of, 907
    sensory pathways from, to brain, 878
  ganglia, 948
  lemniscus, 780
  nerves, 946
    afferent (sensory) fibers of, 949
    autonomic fibers of, 949
    composition and central connections of, 876
    connections with sympathetic, 949
    development of, 743
    divisions of, 950, 954
    fibers of, 950
    parasympathetic fibers of, 950
    points of emergence of, 948
    roots of, 782, 948
    size and direction of, 948
    somatic efferent fibers of, 949
    structure of, 949
    sympathetic fibers of, 949
  reflex paths, intrinsic, 877
  segments, 768
Spinalis capitis muscle, 382
  cervicis muscle, 382
  colli muscle, 382
  dorsi muscle, 382
Spindle, aortic, 555
  neuromuscular, 1092
  neurotendinous, 1092
Spine or Spines, ethmoidal, 121, 152
  frontal bone, 142
  iliac, 208, 209
  ischial, 210
  mental, 128
  nasal, 107, 116, 162, 167, 170
  pubic, 211
  scapular, 180
  sphenoidal, 108, 154
  suprameatal, 112, 150
  tibial, 231
  trochlear, 142
Spinoglenoid ligament, 293
Spinoölivary fasciculus, 881
Spinotectal fasciculus, 780, 881
Spinothalamic fasciculus, 780
Spinous process, vertebra, 76
Spiral canal of modiolus, 1081
  ligament, 1085
  line of femur, 219
  organ of Corti, 1087
  thread of spermatozoön, 23
Splanchnic fibers of spinal nerves, 950
  layer of mesoderm, 41
  nerves, 1012
Splanchnopleure, 42
Spleen, 730
  accessory, 732
  bloodvessels of, 733
  development of, 731
  lymphatic nodules of, 734
    vessels, of, 723
  Malpighian bodies of, 734
  nerves of, 734
  relations of, 731
  size and weight of, 734

Spleen, structure of, 732
  supernumerary, 734
  surface marking of, 1389
  surfaces of, 731
  trabeculæ of, 732
Splenial center of ossification, **131**
Splenic artery, 612, 734
  distribution of, 732
  cells, 733
  flexure of colon, 1225
  lymph nodes, 720
  plexus, 1017
  pulp, 733
  vein, 690
Splenium of corpus callosum, 866
Splenius capitis muscle, 379
  cervicis muscle, 379
  colli muscle, 379
Spongioblasts, 741
Spring ligament, 334
Spur of malleus, 1075
Squama, frontal, 141
  occipital, 135
  temporal, 143
Squamosal suture, 111
Stahr, middle gland of, 707
Stalks, optic, 747, 1033
Stapedius muscle, 1077
Stapes, 1076
  annular ligament of, 1077
  development of, 1061
Stellate ligament, 276
  veins of kidney, 1274
Stensen, duct of, 1174
  foramina of, 107, 167
Stephanion, 111
Sternal angle, 99, 1368
  end of clavicle, 177
  foramen, 99
  lymph nodes, 726
  plate, 62
Sternalis muscle, 430
Sternebræ, 98
Sternoclavicular articulation, 289
  surface anatomy of, 1401
Sternoclavicularis muscle, 431
Sternocleidomastoid artery, 560, 564
Sternocleidomastoideus muscle, 371, 1346
Sternocostal articulations, 278
  ligaments, 278
  surface of heart, 532
Sternohyoideus muscle, 374
Sternomastoid artery, 560, 564
  muscle, 371
Sternopericardiac ligaments, 529
Sternothyroideus muscle, 374
Sternum, 97
  articulations of, 101, 280
  development of, 62
  ossification of, 100
Stomach, 1207
  and small intestines, x-ray of, 1384
  atonic, after a barium meal, x-ray of, 1385
  bed, 1208
  body of, 1208
  cardiac glands of, 1212
    orifice of, 1207
  component parts of, 1208
  curvatures of, 1207
  development of, 1144
  duodenopyloric constriction of, 1207
  fundus of, 1208
    glands of, 1212
  incisura angularis, 1208
  interior of, 1209
  lymphatic vessels of, 721
  mucous membrane of, 1210
  muscular coat of, 1209
  nerves of, 1213
  normal, x-ray of, after a barium meal, 1385

Stomach, openings of, 1207
  position of, 1208
  pyloric antrum, 1208
    glands, 1212
    orifice, 1207
    valve, 1209
  serous coat of, 1209
  shape and position of, 1207
  structure of, 1209
  subdivisions of, 1208
  sulcus intermedius, 1208
  surface marking of, 1382
  surfaces of, 1208
  teeth, 1157
  vessels of, 1213
Stomodeum, 1141
Stratiform fibrocartilage, 259
Stratum cinereum, 823
  compactum [decidua], 30
  corneum, 1098
  germinativum, 1098
  granulosum, 1098
  intermedium [choroid], 1041
  lemnisci, 823
  lucidum, 1098
  mucosum, 1098
  opticum [retina], 1046
    [superior colliculus], 823
  papillare, 1099
  reticulare, 1100
  spongiosum [decidua], 30
  zonale, 823
Streak, primitive, 38
Stria, longitudinal, 857
Striate arteries, 577
  veins, inferior, 660
Striated muscle, 343
  lymphatic capillaries in, 697
Stripe of Hensen, 1089
Striped muscle, 345
Stroma of iris, 1044
  of kidney, 1275
  of ovary, 1307
Styloglossus muscle, 1170
Stylohyal part of styloid process, 150
Stylohyoid ligament, 372
  nerve, from facial, 934
Stylohyoideus muscle, 372
Styloid process of fibula, 235
  of radius, 196
  of temporal bone, 109, 150
  of ulna, 194
Stylomandibular ligament, 275, 367
Stylomastoid artery, 565
  foramen, 109, 149
Stylomaxillary ligament, 275
Stylopharyngeus muscle, 1186
Subanconeus muscle, 437
Subarachnoid cavity, 904
  cisternæ, 904
  septum, 905
  space, 904
Subarcuate fossa, 148
Subcallosal gyrus, 856, 897
Subcardinal veins, 517
Subclavian arteries, 580
  first part of left, 580
  first part of right, 580
  second portion of, 581
  surface anatomy of, 1347
    marking of, 1361
  third portion of, 581
  triangle, 375, 1364
  vein, 672
Subclavius muscle, 431
Subcostal arteries, 607
  zone, 1190
Subcostales muscles, 387
Subcrureus or articularis genu muscle, 471
Subcutaneous inguinal ring, 395
Subdural cavity, 904
Subepithelial plexus of cornea, 1039

Subfrontal gyre, 844
Subinguinal lymph nodes, 713
Sublingual artery, 561
  gland, 1175
Sublobular veins, 1240
Submaxillary artery, 562
  duct, 1175
  ganglion, 927
  gland, 1175
    surface markings of, 1362
  lymph nodes, 707
  triangle, 372, 1363
Submental artery, 563
  lymph nodes, 707
  triangle, 372
Submucosa, plexus of, 1222
Suboccipital muscles, 384
  triangle, 384, 583
Subparietal sulcus, 845
Subperiosteal ossification, 72
Subperitoneal connective tissue, 406
Subpleural mediastinal plexus, 589
Subpubic ligament, 286
Subsartorial plexus, 984
Subscapular angle, 179
  artery, 594
  fascia, 432
  fossa, 178
  nerves, 962
Subscapularis muscle, 432
Subserous fascia, 347, 1194
Substantia adamantina, 1159
  alba, 776
  eburnea, 1159
  ferruginea, 816
  gelatinosa centralis, 771
    of Rolando, 771
    nerve cells in, 776
  grisea centralis, 770
  nigra, 818
  ossea, 1160
  propria (cornea), 1038
Subthalamic tegmental region, 832
Suctorial pad, 360
Sudoriferous glands, 1104
Sulci and fissures of cerebral hemisphere, 842
  development of, 752
  of medulla oblongata, 786, 787
  spinalis, 769
Sulcus, anterior longitudinal, of heart, 531
  antihelicis transversus, 1066
  arteriæ vertebralis, 78
  basilaris, 803
  calcaneal, 240
  central, 842
  centralis [*Rolandi*], 842
  cingulate, 842
  cinguli, 842
  circular, 843, 848
  circularis, 843
  coronary, of heart, 531
  frontal, 843, 844
  intermedius [stomach], 1208
  intraparietal, 845
  lateral cerebral, 817
  limitans [rhomboid fossa], 816
  lunatus, 845
  malleolar, 237
  medial frontal, of Eberstaller, 844
  median, of rhomboid fossa, 816
    of tongue, 1166
  medianus posterior, 769
  Munro, 839
  occipital, 845
  oculomotor, 817
  olfactory, 844
  orbital, 844
  paramedial, 844
  postcentral, 845

Sulcus, posterior longitudinal, of heart, 531
  preauricular, of ilium, 207
  precentral, 843
  radial, 185
  retroglandular, 1301
  sagittalis, 136, 139, 142
  sigmoid, 146
  spirales, 1085
  subparietal, 845
  tali, 243
  temporal, 846
  terminal, or right atrium, 533
    of tongue, 1166
  tubæ auditivæ, 110, 155
  tympanic, 150, 1068, 1071
Supercilia, 1055
Superciliary arches, 107, 111, 115, 141
Superficial cervical artery, 587
  lymph nodes, 707
  muscle, 364
  nerve, 955
  epigastric artery, 635
  external pudendal artery, 635
    pudic artery, 635
  iliac circumflex artery, 635
  long plantar ligament, 332
  palmar arch, 604
  perineal artery, 625
  peroneal nerve, 995
  Sylvian vein, 660
  temporal artery, 566
    vein, 653
  transverse ligament of fingers, 453
    perineal muscle, 417, 419
  volar artery, 604
Superficialis volæ artery, 600
Superfrontal gyre, 844
Superior articular arteries, 639
  calcaneocuboid ligament, 332
  cerebellar peduncles, 809
  constrictor muscle, 1185
  dental nerve, 920
  epigastric artery, 589
  intercostal artery, 589
  lingualis muscle, 1170
  longitudinal sinus, 661
  maxillary nerve, 918
  medullary velum, 815
  nasal concha, 160
  nuchal line, 135
  oblique muscle, 1053
  orbital fissure, 118, 122, 155
  pancreaticoduodenal artery, 611
  petrosal sinus, 666
  profunda artery, 597
  sagittal sinus, 661
  semicircular canal, 1079
  tarsal plate, 1055
  thoracic artery, 592
  thyroid artery, surface markings of, 1361
  tibiofibular articulation, 326
  tympanic artery, 568
  ulnar collateral artery, 597
  vesical artery, 621
  vocal cords, 1116
Supernumerary spleen, 732
Supinator brevis muscle, 447
  longus muscle, 444
  muscle, 447
Supporting cells of Hensen, 1089
  of Sertoli, 1293
  frame-work of retina, 1048
Supra-acromial nerves, 957
Supracallosal gyrus, 856
Supraclavicular branches of brachial plexus, 961
  nerves, 956
Supraclavicularis muscle, 371
Supracondylar process, 189
Supracostalis muscle, 386
Supraglenoid tuberosity, 182

Suprahyoid aponeurosis, 371
  artery, 560
  lymph nodes, 707
  muscles, 371
  triangle, 372, 1364
Supramarginal gyrus, 845
Supramastoid crest, 144
Suprameatal spine, 112, 150
  triangle, 112
Supraorbital artery, 573
  foramen, 115, 119, 142
  margin, 141
  nerve, 917
  notch, 115, 119, 141
  vein, 653
Suprarenal arteries, 617, 618
  glands, 1336
    development of, 1336
    functions of, 1338
    lymphatic vessels of, 723
    nerves of, 1338
    relations of, 1336
    structure of, 1337
    vessels of, 1338
  impression, 1234
  plexus, 1017
  veins, 688
Suprascapular artery, 586
  ligament, 293
  nerve, 961
Supraspinal ligament, 267
Supraspinatous fascia, 432
  fossa, 179
  muscle, 433
Supraspinous ligament, 267
Suprasternal nerves, 956
  space, 367
Supratonsillar fossa, 1177
Supratroclear foramen, 187
  nerve, 917
Sural arteries, 639
  cutaneous nerve, lateral, 993
    medial, 991
  nerve, 992
Surface anatomy and surface
    markings of abdomen,
    1376, 1381
  accessory nerve, 1361
  acromioclavicular joint, 1401,
    1407
  adductor canal, 1426
  ankle-joint, 1417, 1425
  anterior jugular vein, 1361
    tibial artery, 1421, 1426
  aorta, abdominal, 1379, 1391
    ascending, 1376
  aortic arch, 1376
  appendix vermiformis, 1384
  axillary artery, 1406, 1408
    nerve, 1410
  back, 1365, 1367
  bones of abdomen, 1378
    of back, 1365
    of cranium, 1348
    of lower extremity, 1422
    of thorax, 1368, 1369
    of upper extremity, 1394
    1407
  brachial artery, 1407, 1408
    plexus, 1362, 1407
  brain, 1349
  Bryant's triangle, 1425
  calcaneus, 1413
  calcaneo-cuboid joint, 1425
  carpal bones, 1401
  caruncula lacrimalis, 1357
  cecum, 1384
  celiac artery, 1392
  cerebellum, 1349
  cerebral hemisphere, 1349
  cervical cutaneous nerve,
    1361
  clavicle, 1396
  colon, ascending, 1386
    descending, 1386
    iliac, 1388

Surface anatomy and surface
    markings of colon, trans-
    verse, 1386
  common carotid artery, 1361
    iliac artery, 1391
    peroneal nerve, 1422, 1427
  deep peroneal nerve, 1427
  deltoideus muscle, 1403
  diaphragm, 1370
  digestive tube, 1379
  dorsalis pedis artery, 1421
    1426
  duodenum, 1384
  ear, 1357
  elbow-joint, 1402, 1405
  esophagus, 1373
  external carotid artery, 1361
    iliac artery, 1391
    jugular vein, 1361
    maxillary artery, 1354
  eye, 1357
  facial artery, 1361
    nerve, 1361
  femoral artery, 1421, 1426
    triangle, 1426
  femur, 1412
  fibula, 1413
  fissures of brain, 1351
  fold of groin, 1379
  frontal sinus, 1353
  gall-bladder, 1388
  gluteal arteries, 1426
    fold, 1410
  great auricular nerve, 1361
  head and neck, 1343, 1348
  heart, 1373
    coronary sulcus, 1374
    longitudinal sulcus, 1374
    orifices of, 1375
  Hesselbach's triangle, 1391
  hip-bones, 1411
  hip-joint, 1417, 1425
  humeral circumflex artery,
    1408
  humerus, 1398
  hyoid bone, 1360
  ileocolic junction, 1384
  iliac arteries, 1391
    furrow, 1376
  inferior, epigastric artery,
    1391
    vena cava, 1376
  infrasternal notch, 1368
  inguinal rings and canal,
    1381
  innominate artery, 1376
    veins, 1376
  internal jugular vein, 1361
    mammary artery, 1376
    pudendal artery, 1426
  intestines, 1384
  joints of fingers, 1401
    foot, 1426
  jugular notch, 1368
    veins, 1361
  kidneys, 1381, 1389
  knee-joint, 1417, 1425
  lacrimal puncta, 1357
    sac, 1357
  larynx, 1360
  lateral plantar artery, 1427
    thoracic artery, 1408
    ventricle of brain, 1353
  latissimus dorsi, 1403, 1407
  left common carotid artery
    in thorax, 1376
  lesser occipital nerve, 1361
  lingual artery, 1361
  liver, 1380, 1388
  lower extremity, 1410, 1422
  lungs, 1371
  mamma, 1369
  maxillary sinus 1354
  medial plantar artery, 1427

Surface anatomy and surface
    markings of median nerve,
    1410
  medulla spinalis, 1368
  mesenteric arteries, 1392
  metacarpal bones, 1401
  metatarsal bones, 1416
  metatarso-phalangeal joint,
    1426
  middle meningeal artery,
    1353
  mouth, 1354
  muscles of abdomen, 1376,
    1381
    of arm, 1403, 1404, 1405
    of back, 1366
    of buttock, 1418
    of foot, 1419
    of forearm, 1405, 1406
    of hand, 1406
    of head and neck, 1343,
      1348, 1361
    of leg, 1419, 1426
    of thigh, 1417
    of thorax, 1369
  nasal part of pharynx, 1356
  nasolacrimal duct, 1354
  neck, 1360
  Nélaton's line, 1425
  nose, 1354
  nutrient artery, humerus,
    1409
  occipital artery, 1361
  palatine arches, 1355
  palmar or volar arches, 1409
  palpebral fissure, 1357
  pancreas, 1381, 1389
  parotid duct, 1354
    gland, 1354
  patella, 1412
  pectorales muscles, 1403,
    1407
  pelvis, 1411
  perineum, 1392, 1393
  peroneal artery, 1427
    nerves, 1427
  phalanges of foot, 1417
    of hand, 1401
  phrenic nerve, 1362
  plantar arch, 1427
    arteries, 1427
  pleuræ, 1370
  plica semilunaris, eye, 1357
  popliteal artery, 1421, 1426
    fossa, 1426
  posterior tibial artery, 1422,
    1426
  profunda brachii artery, 1408
    femoris artery, 1426
  pupil, 1357
  radial artery, 1407, 1409
    nerve, 1410
  radiohumeral joint, 1402
  radioulnar joints, 1402
  radius, 1399
  rectum and anal canal, 1393
  Reid's base line, 1348
  renal arteries, 1392
  sacroiliac joint, 1425
  saphenous veins, 1427
  scapula, 1396
  scapular circumflex artery,
    1408
  sciatic nerve, 1427
  serratus anterior muscle, 1403
  shoulder-joint, 1401
  space of Traube, 1384
  spinal nerves, 1368
  spleen, 1389
  sternal angle, 1368
  sternoclavicular joint, 1401
  sternocleidomastoideus mus-
    cle, 1346
  stomach, 1383
  striæ gravidarum or albi-
    cantes, 1376

Surface anatomy and surface markings of subclavian artery, 1347, 1361
subdural and subarachnoid cavities, 1368
submaxillary gland, 1362
subscapular artery, 1408
superior thyroid artery, 1361
vena cava, 1376
supraclavicular nerves. 1362
synovial sheaths around ankle, 1426
of wrist and hand, 1408
talus, 1413
tarsometatarsal joint, 1426
tarsus and foot, 1366, 1368
temporomandibular joint, 1345
tendinous inscriptions of rectus abdominis, 400, 1378
thoracoacromial artery, 1408
thorax, 1368, 1369
tibia, 1412
tibial artery, 1424
nerve, 1427
tongue, 1355
tonsil, 1356
trachea, 1360, 1373
transverse sinus, 1353
trapezius, 1402
triangles of neck, 1362
trigeminal nerve, 1354
tympanic antrum, 1360
membrane, 1359
ulna, 1399
ulnar artery, 1409
collateral arteries, 1409
nerve, 1407, 1410
umbilicus, 1381, 1382
upper extremity, 1394, 1407
ureters, 1391
urogenital organs, female, 1393
male, 1393
vermiform process, 1384
vertebral column, 1365
volar or palmar arches, 1409, 1410
wrist and hand, 1402
wrist-joint, 1402, 1406
Suspensory ligament, axilla, 428
breast, 426, 1320
eye, 1054
lens, 1050
ovary, 1306
penis, 1301
Sustentacular fibers of Müller, 1048
Sustentaculum lienis, 1204
tali, 240, 241
Sutura dentata, 260
harmonia, 260
limbosa, 260
notha, 260
serrata, 260
squamosa, 260
vera, 260
Sutural bones, 160
ligament, 255
Suture, coronal, 106, 111
frontal, 107, 141
frontoethmoidal, 121
lambdoidal, 106, 111, 137, 140
metopic, 141
occipitomastoid, 111
parietomastoid, 111
petroöccipital, 110
petrosquamous, 147, 149
sagittal, 106
sphenoethmoidal, 121
sphenofrontal, 111, 121
sphenoparietal, 111, 122
sphenopetrosal, 122
sphenosquamosal, 111, 122
sphenozygomatic, 111
squamosal, 111, 122

Suture, zygomaticofrontal, 111
zygomaticotemporal, 111
Sweat glands, 1104
Sylvian fissure, 753
fossa, 753
veins, 660
Sylvius, aqueduct of, 824
fissure of 841
Sympathetic fibers of spinal nerves, 948
nerves, 997
connections with spinal nerves, 948, 1006
nervous system, development of, 755
plexuses. 1013
system, cephalic portion of, 1007
cervical portion of, 1008
pelvic portion of, 1013
thoracic portion of, 1012
trunks, 1006
Symphysis of mandible, 128
ossium pubis, 286
pubis, 286
sacrococcygea, 285
Synarthroses, 260
Synchondrosis, 260
neurocentral, 90
Syncytial layer, 27
Syncytiotrophoblast, 27
Syndesmology, 255. See Joints and Ligaments.
Syndesmosis, 261
tibiofibularis, 326
Synovia, 259
Synovial bursæ, 259, 349
membrane, 259. See also Individual Joints.
sheaths, 259
of tendons around ankle, 489
on back of wrist, 450
on front of wrist, 452
Systemic circulation, 501
veins, 649

T

TACTILE corpuscles of Golgi and Mazzoni, 1092
of Grandry, 1091
of Pacini, 1091
of Ruffini, 1092
of Wagner and Meissner, 1092
discrimination, fibers of, 880
Tænia coli, 1222
pontis, 803
semicircularis, 862, 898
thalami, 826
ventriculi quarti, 815
Tæniæ of fourth ventricle, 815
of muscular coat of large intestine, 1222
Talocalcaneal articulation, 330
Talocalcaneonavicular articulation, 331
Talocrural articulation, 327
Talofibular ligaments, 329
Talonavicular joint, surface anatomy of, 1425
Talotibial ligaments, 328
Talus, 242
ossification of, 250
Tapetum of choroid of eye, 1041
of corpus callosum, 867
Tarsal arteries, 643
bones, 237
glands, 1056
plates, 1055
Tarsi of eyelids, 1055
Tarsometatarsal articulations, 336
surface anatomy of, 1426
Tarsus, 237
articulations of, 330
inferior, eye, 1055

Tarsus, ossification of,250
superior, eye, 1055
surface markings of, 1426
synovial membranes of, 336
Taste fibers, 887, 939
nerves of, 1024
organ of, 1023
Taste-buds, 1023, 1172
Tectorial membrane of ductus cochlearis, 1089
Tectospinal fasciculus, 900
Teeth, 1155
bicuspid, 1157
canine, 1157
cement or crusta petrosa of, 1160
crown of, 1156, 1157
cutting, 1156
deciduous, 1158
dental canaliculi of, 1159
dentin of, 1159
development of, 1160
enamel of, 1159
eruption of, 1164
eye, 1157
general characters of, 1155
incisive, 1156
incisors, 1156
ivory of, 1159
milk, 1158
molar, 1157
multicuspid. 1157
necks of, 1155, 1156
permanent, 1156
successional, 1164
superadded, 1164
premolar, 1157
pulp cavity of, 1158
roots of, 1155, 1156
stomach, 1157
structure of, 1158
substantia adamantina of, 1159
eburnea of, 1159
ossea of, 1160
temporary, 1158
wisdom, 1157
Tegmen tympani, 147, 1069
Tegmental part of pons, 805
Tegmentum, 818
Tela chorioidea [fourth ventricle], 815
[third ventricle], 852
Telencephalon, 747, 749, 840
Telophase of karyokinesis, 19
Temperature, impulses of, 880
Temporal arteries, 566, 569
bone, 143
articulations of, 152
mastoid portion of, 146
ossification of, 150
petrous portion of, 147
pyramid of, 147
squama of, 143
structure of, 150
tympanic part of, 150
fascia, 361
fossa, 111
gyri, 846
lines, 107, 111, 142
lobe, 846
muscle, 362
nerves of auriculotemporal, 925
of facial, 934
operculum, 848
process of zygomatic bone, 169
veins, 653
Temporalis muscle, 362, 1346
Temporary teeth, 1158
Temporomalar nerve, 920
Temporomandibular articulation, 273
surface anatomy of, 1345
Temporomaxillary vein, 654
Tedinous arch of pelvic fascia, 407
inscriptions of rectus abdominis muscle, 400
levator ani muscle. 407

Tendo Achillis, 384
　calcaneus, 483
　oculi, 356
Tendon or tendons, 346
　back of wrist, relations of, 452
　central, of diaphragm, 389
　conjoined, of internal oblique
　　and transversalis muscles,
　　399
　of conus arteriosus, 535
　front of wrist, 452
　superior, of Lockwood, 1053
　of Zinn, 1053
Tendril fibers of cerebellum, 813
Tenon, capsule of, 1054
Tension lines, 1100
Tensor fasciæ latæ muscles, 479
　palati muscle, 1180
　tarsi muscle, 355
　tympani muscle, 1077
　　semicanal for, 150, 1073
　veli palatini muscle, 1180
Tenth nerve, 938
Tentorial sinus, 662
Tentorium cerebelli, 902
Teres major muscle, 434
　minor muscle, 434
Terminal crest of right atrium,
　533
　sulcus of right atrium, 533
　vein, 660
　ventricle, 739, 771
Testis or Testes, 1286
　appendages of, 1292
　appendix of, 1292
　coni vasculosi of, 1295
　coverings of, 1286
　descent of, 1258
　development of, 1258
　ductuli efferentes, 1294
　ductus deferens, 1296
　gubernaculum 1258
　lobules of, 1293
　lymphatic capillaries of, 697'
　　vessels of, 725
　mediastinum, 1292
　rete 1294
　structure of, 1293
　tubuli recti, 1294
　　seminiferi, 1293
　tunica albuginea, 1292
　　vaginalis, 1292
　　vasculosa, 1292, 1293
Thalami, 825
　development of, 747
　intermediate mass of, 748, 827
　structure of, 827
　surfaces of, 826, 827
Thebesius, foramina of, 533
　valve of, 534, 650
　veins of, 651
Thenar eminence, 449
　facial cleft, 458
　　compartment, 456
　muscles, 459
　space, 458
Thigh bone, 217
　fascia lata of, 467
　　superficial, 466
　muscles of, 466
Third cuneiform bone, 246
　metacarpal bone, 203
　metatarsal bone, 249
　nerve, 913
　trochanter, 221
　ventricle of brain, 838
Thoracic aorta, 605
　arteries, 592, 593
　axis, 593
　cardiac nerves, 941
　duct, 700
　nerves, divisions of, 952, 962,
　　973
　portion of gangliated cord, 1012
　vertebræ, 75, 81
Thoracoacromial artery, 599

Thoracodorsal artery, 594
　nerve, 963
Thoracoepigastric vein, 680
Thoracolumbar sympathetics,
　1004
Thorax, 95
　boundaries of, 96
　cavity of, 527
　lymph nodes, 726
　lymphatic vessels of, 728
　mechanism of, 280
　muscles of, 386
　　surface anatomy of, 1369
　openings of, 96, 97, 528
　　parts passing through, 528
　skeleton of, 95
　surface anatomy of, 1369
　　markings of, 1369
　x-ray of heart and diaphragm,
　　anterior view, 1373
Thumb, carpometacarpal articu-
　lation of, 308
Thymus, 734
　development of, 734
　glands, 734
　lymphatic vessels of, 730
　nerves of, 735
　structure of, 735
　vessels of, 735
Thyreoarytænoideus muscle, 1119
Thyreohyoideus muscle, 374
Thyreoidea ima artery, 556
Thyroarytenoid ligaments, 1116
　muscle, 1119
Thyrocervical trunk, 585
Thyroepiglottic ligament, 1112
　muscle, 1119
Thyroglossal duct, 1166, 1327
Thyrohyals of hyoid bone, 133
Thyrohyoid ligaments, 1112
　membrane, 1112
　muscle, 374
Thyroid arteries, 559, 586
　axis, 585
　body, 1327
　cartilage, 1109
　foramen, 212
　gland, 1327
　　development of, 1327
　　isthmus of, 1327, 1328
　　lobes of, 1328
　　lymphatic vessels of, 708
　　nerves of, 1330
　　pyramidal lobe of, 1329
　　structure of, 1329
　　vessels of, 1330
　notch, superior, 1109
　veins, 657, 1330
Thyroids, accessory, 1329
Tibia, 231
　nutrient artery of, 645
　ossification of, 235
　surface anatomy of, 1412
Tibial artery, anterior, 641
　　surface marking of, 1426
　posterior, 643
　　surface marking of, 1422,
　　1426
　recurrent, 642
　collateral ligament of knee-
　　joint, 319
　nerve, 994
　　anterior, 994
　surfaces of femur, 223
　veins, 681
Tibialis anterior muscle, 481
　anticus muscle, 481
　posterior muscle, 486
Tibiofascialis muscle, 481
Tibiofibular articulation, 326
　ligament, middle, 326
　syndesmosis, 326
Tibionavicular ligament, 328
Tibiotarsal articulation, 327
Tissues, connective, 345
Tomes' fibers, 1159

Tongue, 1165
　development of, 1143
　dorsum of, 1166
　frenulum of, 1166
　glands of 1171
　lymph node of, 705
　lymphatic vessels of, 705
　mucous membrane of, 1171
　muscles of, 1168
　　actions of, 1170
　nerves of, 1170
　papillæ of, 1167
　septum of, 1171
　structure of, 1171
　vessels of, 1172
Tonsil, 1177
　lingual, 1166, 1179
　palatine, 1177
　　development of, 1143
　　lymphatic vessels of, 705
　　nerves of, 1179, 1180
　　structure of, 1179
　　vessels of, 1179
　pharyngeal, 1185
　tubal, 1074
Tonsillæ intestinales, 1221
　palatinæ, 1177
Tonsillar artery, 562
　nerves from glossopharyngeal,
　　938
　sinus, 1177
Torcular Herophili, 136, 665
Torus of auditory tube, 1184
　uretericus, 1282
　uterinus, 1198
Touch fibers, 878
Trabeculæ carneæ, 535, 538
　of penis, 1302
　of spleen, 732
　of testis, 1292
Trachea, 1121
　lymphatic capillaries in, 696
　nerves of, 1124
　relations of, 1121
　structure of, 1123
　vessels of, 1124
Tracheal artery, 586
Trachealis muscle, 1124
Trachelomastoid muscle, 381
Tracheobronchial lymph nodes,
　729
Trachoma glands, 1058
Tract or Tracts, anterior basis
　　bundle, 778
　of Burdach, 781
　cerebellar, of Flechsig, 780, 878
　comma, 782
　dorsal peripheral band, 782
　of Goll, 770, 781
　of Gowers, 780, 879
　lateral basis bundle, 781
　of Lissauer, 771, 777
　olfactory, 854
　optic, 837, 893, 913
　prepyramidal, 779
　pyramidal, 778
Tractus iliotibialis, 468
　olfactorius, 854
　spiralis foraminosus, 148
Tragicus muscle, 1066
Tragus, 1065
Transpyloric plane, 1190
Transversa colli artery, 590
Transversalis cervicis muscle, 381
　colli artery, 590
　fascia, 403
　muscle, 398
Transverse acetabular ligament
　　of hip-joint, 314
　aorta, 555
　carpal ligament, 452
　cervical artery, 590
　　nerve, 955
　colon, 1226
　crural ligament, 489
　facial artery, 566

Transverse facial vein, 653
fibers of cerebral hemispheres, 865
fissure of brain, 853
of liver, 547, 1236
folds of rectum, 1230
ligament, atlas, 271
humeral, 295
fingers, 460
knee, 321
metacarpal, 309
metatarsal, 337
pelvis, 416
ligaments of scapula, 293
lingualis muscle, 1170
mesocolon, 1196, 1202, 1226
occipital sulcus, 845
portion of duodenum, 1215
process of a vertebra, 76
scapular artery, 586
sinus, 123, 668
of pericardium, 529
temporal gyri, 846
Transversus abdominis muscle, 398
auriculæ muscle, 1066
linguæ muscle, 1170
menti muscle, 358
nuchæ muscle, 353
pedis muscle, 495
perinæi muscles, 417
profundus muscle in female, 421
in male, 419
superficialis muscle, 418, 419
in female, 419
in male, 417
thoracis muscle, 387
Trapezium, 200
Trapezius muscle, 423
Trapezoid body, 805, 885
bone, 201
ligament, 291
nucleus, 805, 885
ridge, 176
Traube, space of, 1402
Treves, bloodless fold of, 1205
Triangle or triangles, of auscultation, 424
Bryant's, 1425
carotid, 372, 1362, 1363
cervical, 365, 372, 1362
digastric, 372, 1363
femoral, 633
Hesselbach's, 1391
lumbar, 424
muscular, 375, 1362
neck, 365, 372, 1362
occipital, 375, 1364
of Petit, 424
Scarpa's, 633
subclavian, 375, 1363
submaxillary, 372, 1361
submental, 372
suboccipital, 384, 583
suprahyoid, 372, 1363
suprameatal, 112, 145
Triangular articular disk, 303
bone, 197
fascia of abdomen, 396
ligament, 416
of liver, 1196
Triangularis muscle, 358
sterni muscle, 387
Triceps brachii muscle, 437
extensor cubiti muscle, 437
muscle, 437
suræ muscle, 483
Tricuspid valve, 535
Trifacial nerve, 915
Trigeminal nerve, 915
ciliary ganglion, 918
composition and central connections of, 887
impression for, 147
mandibular division, 923

Trigeminal nerve, maxillary division, 918
ophthalmic division, 916
otic ganglion, 926
referred pain in, 928
semilunar ganglion, 915
sphenopalatine ganglion, 921
submaxillary ganglion, 927
surface marking of, 1354
Trigone, olfactory, 855
Trigonum femorale, 633
fibrosum, 539
habenulæ, 832
hypoglossi, 816, 943
olfactorium, 855
vesicæ, 1282
Trochanter, greater, 218
lesser, 219
third, 221
Trochanteric fossa, 218
Trochlea of humerus, 187
Trochlear fovea, 117, 142
nerve, 914
composition and central connections of, 890
process of calcaneus, 241
spine, 142
Trochoid joint, 261
Trolard, anastomotic vein of, 660
Troltsch, recess of, 1077
Trophoblast, 27
True pelvis, 214
skin, 1098
vocal cords, 1116
Truncus arteriosus, 508
costocervicalis, 589
sympathicus, 1006
thyreocervicalis, 585
Trunk, arteries of, 605
articulations of, 263
costocervical, 589
muscles of, 377
thyrocervical, 585
Tuba auditiva [Eustachii], 1074
uterina [Fallopii], 1308
Tube, auditory, 1074
digestive, 1141
Eustachian, 1074
Fallopian, 1308
neural, 42
uterine, 1308
Tuber cinereum, 791
frontale, 141
omentale [liver], 1234
[pancreas], 1246
parietale, 139
Tubercle, adductor, 221
anterior, 78
articular, of temporal bone, 108, 144
auricular, of Darwin, 1065
conoid, 176
cuneate, 791
cuneiform, 1116
of epiglottis, 1112
of femur, 219
greater, 184
of humerus, 183
lesser, 184
intervenous, 534
jugular, 137
lacrimal, 166
of Lower, 534
mental, 128
obturator, 212
olfactory, 855
peroneal, 241
pharyngeal, 108, 137
posterior, 78
pubic, 211
pyterygoid, 156
of rib, 102
of Rolando, 791
scalene, 104
Tuberculum acusticum, 817, 935
impar, 1143

Tuberculum intervenosum, 534
majur [*humeri*], 184
minus [*humeri*], 184
sellæ, 122, 152
Tuberosity, calcaneal, 240
coracoid, 176
costal, 177
of cuboid, 244
deltoid, 185
of fifth metatarsal bone, 249
gluteal, 221
greater, 184
iliac, 207
infraglenoid, 181
ischial, 210
lesser, 184
maxillary, 163
of navicular bone, 245
of palatine bone, 172
radial, 194
supraglenoid, 182
tibial 231
ulna, 192
Tubuli lactiferi, 1322
recti [testis], 1294
seminiferi, 1293
Tubulus, renal, 1272, 1273
Tunic, dartos, 1287
fibrous, of kidney, 1268
Tunica adventitia, 512
albuginea [ovary], 1307
[testis], 1292
conjunctiva bulbi, 1057
dartos, 1287
elastica externa, 521
fibrosa oculi, 1037
fibrosa oculi, 1037
intima, 521
media, 521
serosa, 1194, 1209
vaginalis, 1288, 1292
communis [*testis et funiculi spermatici*,] 1289
propria testis, 1292
vasculosa [testis], 1293
oculi, 1040
Tunics of eyeball, 1037, 1040
Tunnel of Corti, 1088
Turbinated bone, 173
processes, sphenoidal, 156
Turner, intraparietal sulcus, 845
Twelfth nerve, 943
Tympanic antrum, 147
artery, 567
from ascending pharyngeal, 565
from internal maxillary, 567
canaliculus, inferior, 110, 148
cavity, 1068
arteries of, 1077
attic or epitympanic recess of, 1069
carotid or anterior wall of, 1073
jugular wall or floor of, 1069
labyrinthic or median wall of, 1071
mastoid or posterior wall of, 1071
membranous or lateral wall of, 1069
mucous membrane of, 1077
muscles of, 1077
nerves of, 1077
ossicles of, 1074
tegmental wall or roof of, 1069
vessels of, 1077
lip, 1086
membrane, 1070
nerve (Jacobson's), 938, 1077
plexus, 938, 1077
ring, 151
sulcus, 150, 1068, 1071
Tympanohuyal part of temporal bone, 150
Tympanomastoid fissure, 109
Tympanum, 1068

U

ULNA, 189
ossification of, 194
structure of, 194
surface anatomy of, 1399
Ulnar artery, 601
surface marking of, 1409
collateral artery, 597
recurrent artery, 602
nerve, 968
notch of radius, 195
Ultimo-branchial bodies, 1327
Umbilical arteries in fetus, 546
cord, 35
folds, 1281
fossa of liver, 1236
notch of liver, 1235
veins, 35, 515, 549
obliterated, 690, 1195
vesicle, 45
zone, 1190
Umbilicus, 1376, 1381
Umbo of membrana tympani, 1071
Unciform bone, 202
Uncinate fasciculus, 867
Uncus, 846
Ungual phalanges, 205, 250
Ungues, 1101
Upper extremity, bones of, 175
jaw, 162
Urachus, 1261
Ureter, 1275
arteries of, 1277
lymphatic vessels of, 724
muscles of, 1283
nerves of, 1277
orifices of, 1282
Ureters, x-ray of, pelves and
minor calyces after intravenous
injection of uroselectan, 1388
Urethra, development of, 1263
female, 1286
male, 1284
crest or verumontanum of,
1284, 1286
lymphatic vessels of, 725
muliebris, 1286
virilis, 184
Urethral artery, 626
bulb, 1285
crest, in female, 1286
in male, 1284
glands, 1285
orifices, 1282, 1285, 1319
plate, 1263
Urinary bladder, 1277
abnormalities of, 1283
female, 1280
ligaments of, 1281
lymphatic capillaries in, 697
male, 1277
meatus, 1319
organs, 1264
Urogenital apparatus, 1253
diaphragm, 416
fold, 1254
organs, 1253
ostium, primitive, 1263
sinus, 1261
Urorectal septum, 1150
Uterine artery, 622
glands, 1316
plexus of nerves, 1020
plexuses of veins, 685
Uterosacral ligaments, 1313
Uterus, 1310
in adult, 1315
cervix of, 1311
development of, 1255
during menstruation, 1315
pregnancy, 1315
in fetus, 1315
form, size and situation of, 1315
fundus of, 1311
interior of, 1312

Uterus, isthmus of, 1311
ligaments of, 1313
lymphatic capillaries of, 697
vessels of, 726
masculinus, or prostatic utricle,
1284
nerves of, 1316
in old age, 1315
palmate folds of, 1312
after parturition, 1315
position of, 1314
at puberty, 1315
virgin state of, 1310
Utricle, prostatic, 1284
of vestibule, 1082, 1083
Utriculus, 1083
Uvea, 1040
Uvula of cerebellum, 797
palatine, 1154
vesicæ, 1282

V

VAGINA, 1316
lymphatic vessels of, 726
relations of, 1317
structure, 1317
Vaginæ mucosæ, 259
Vaginal artery, 622
bulb, 1319
orifice, 1319
plexus of nerves, 1020
plexuses of veins, 685
process of sphenoid bone, 156
of temporal bone, 149
Vagus nerve, 938
cardiac nerves, 941
composition and central connections of, 882
jugular ganglion, 939
laryngeal nerves, 940
nodosa ganglion, 940
sympathetic afferent fibers,
1003
efferent fibers of, 1003
Valleculæ of tongue, 1112
Valve or valves, anal, 1230
bicuspid, 538
colic, 1224
or coronary sinus, 534, 650
Eustachian, 534
heart, development of, 508
Houston's, 1228
ileocecal, 1224
of inferior vena cava, 534, 686
Kerkring's, 1219
lymphatics, 698
mitral, 538
pulmonary, 536
pyloric, 1209
right and left venous, 505
semilunar aortic, 538
Thebesian, 534, 650
triscupid, 535
of veins, 524
of Vieussens, 814
Valvula sinus coronarii [Thebesii],
534
tricuspidalis, 535
venæ cavæ inferioris, 534
Valvulæ conniventes, 1219
Vas aberrans of Haller, 1296
deferens, 1296
spirale, 1087
Vas aberrantia [from brachial
artery], 597
gastrica brevia, 612
intestini tenuis, 613
vasorum [arteries], 522
[veins], 524
Vascular capsule of lens, 1035
system, changes in, at birth, 548
development of, 502
peculiarities in fetus, 546
tunics of eye, 1040

Vasoformative cells, 502
Vastus externus muscle, 470
intermedius muscle, 470, 471
internus muscle, 471
lateralis muscle, 470
medialis muscle, 471
Vater, ampulla of, 1244
Vein or Veins, of abdomen, 678
accessory hemiazygos, 676
anastomotic, of Labbé, 660
angular, 653
auditory, 1090
auricular, 654
axillary, 672
azygos, 676
basal, 660
basilic, 670
median, 669
basivertebral, 677
brachial, 671
brachiocephalic, 673
brain, 660
bronchial, 676, 1137
cardiac, 650, 651
cardinal, 516
cephalic, 668
accessory, 670
cerebellar, 660
cerebral, 660, 853
choroid, 660
coats of, 524
common facial, 653
iliac, 685
coronary, 650
of stomach, 691
of corpus striatum, 862
cystic, 691
deep cerebral, 660
cervical, 659
epigastric, 682
facial, 653
femoral, 681
forearm, 671
hand, 671
lower extremity, 681
upper extremity, 671
development of, 515
digital, of foot, 668
of hand, 668
diploic, 659
dorsal digital, 668
metacarpal, 668, 671
of penis, 684
emissary, 661, 668
epigastric, 682
extraspinal, 676
facial, 652, 653,
femoral, 681
frontal, 652
of Galen, 660
gastroepiploic, 690, 691
gluteal, 683
hand, 669, 671
head and neck, 651
of heart, 650
hemiazygos, 676
hemorrhoidal, 684, 690
hepatic, 688
hypogastric, 683
iliac, 682, 685
inferior vena cava, 685
innominate, 673
intercapitular, 669, 681
intercostal, highest, 674
interlobular, of kidney, 1274
interlobular, of liver, 1241
intervertebral, 678
intralobular, of liver, 1241
intraspinal, 677
jugular, 654, 655, 656
anterior, 655
external, 654
internal, 656
posterior, 655
primitive, 517
labial, 652
lateral sacral, 684

Vein or Veins of Labbé, posterior anastomotic, 660
of left atrium, 530
lineal or splenic, 690
lingual, 656
of lower extremity, 678
lumbar, 686
ascending, 676
mammary, internal, 674
marginal, of foot, 679
of heart, 650
maxillary, internal, 654
median antebrachial, 670
basilic, 669
of medulla spinalis, 678
mesenteric, 690
metatarsal, 681
nasofrontal, 665
neck, 651, 654
oblique, of left atrium [Marshalli], 519, 530, 651
obturator, 683, 684
occipital, 654
ophthalmic, 661, 665
orbital, 652
ovarian, 687
palpebral, 653
pancreatic, 689
pancreaticodudodenal, 691
parumbilical, 691
of pelvis, 678
penis, dorsal of, 684
peroneal, 681
pharyngeal, 657
phrenic, inferior, 688
superior, 674
plantar, 681
plexus of, basilar, 668
hemorrhoidal, 684
prostatic, 684
pterygoid, 653
pudendal, 684
uterine, 685
vaginal, 686
vertebral, 676
vesical, 684
vesicoprostatic, 684
popliteal, 681
portal, 649, 688, 689
posterior of left ventricle, 651
primitive jugular, 517
profunda femoris, 681
pubic, 682
pudendal, internal, 684
pudic, 684
pulmonary, 537, 649
pyloric, 691
ranine, 656
renal, 687, 1283
sacral, 684, 685
saphenous, 679, 680
sciatic, 684
short gastric, 690
spermatic, 686
of spinal cord, 678
splenic or lineal, 690
striate, inferior, 660
structure of, 524
subcardinal, 517
subclavian, 672
sublobular, of liver, 1240
superficial, 649
of lower extremity, 678
of upper extremity, 668
superior cerebral, 660
mesenteric, 690
phrenic, 674
vena cava, 674
supraorbital, 653
suprarenal, 688
Sylvian, 660
systemic, 649, 650
temporal, 653
temporomaxillary, 654
terminal, 660
Thebesian, 651

Vein or Veins, thoraco-epigastric, 680
of thorax, 668
thyroid, inferior, 674
middle, 657
superior, 657
tibial, 681
transverse facial, 653
Trolard, great anastomotic of, 660
umbilical, 35, 503, 515
obliterated, 690, 1195
of upper extremity, 668
valves of, 524
vena azygos major, 676
minor, 767
cava, inferior, 685
superior, 674
vertebral, 659
column 676
visceral, 515
vitelline, 502, 515
volar, 669, 671
Velamentous insertion of umbilical cord, 34
Velum interpositum, 853
medullaræ, 814
medullary, 814
palatine, 1154
Vena angularis, 653
anonyma dextra, 674
sinistra, 674
auricularis posterior, 654
cava inferior, 517, 685
superior, 674
surface making of, 1376
caval foramen in diaphragm, 390
cephalica accessoria, 670
cerebri magna, 660
media, 660
cervicalis profunda, 659
circumflexa ilii profunda, 682
cordis, 650, 651
coronaria ventriculi, 691
corporis striati, 660
epigastrica inferior, 682
facialis anterior, 653
posterior, 654
gastroepiploica, 690, 691
hæmorrhoidalis media, 684
iliaca externa, 682
jugularis anterior, 655
externa, 654
interna, 656
posterior, 655
linealis, 690
magna [Galeni], 660, 853
maxillaris interna, 654
mediana antebrachii, 670
cubiti, 669
mesenterica inferior, 690
superior, 690
obliqua atrii sinistri [Marshalli], 651
occipitalis, 654
ophthalmica, 665, 666
poplitea, 681
portæ, 689
posterior ventriculi sinistri, 651
profunda femoris, 681
saphena magna, 679
parva, 680
temporalis superficialis, 653
Venæ advehentes, 515
anonymæ, 672
basivertebrales, 677
brachiales, 671
bronchiales, 676
cerebelli, 661
cerebri, 660
internæ [Galeni], 853
comitantes, 649
cordis, 650
minimæ, 533
digitales plantares, 681

Venæ diploicæ, 659
dorsales penis, 684
gastricæ breves, 690
glutaeæ, 683
iliacæ communes, 685
intercostales suprema, 674
intervetebrales, 678
mammariæ internæ, 674
pancreaticoduodenales, 691
parumbilicales, 691
phrenicæ inferiores, 688
revehentes, 515
spinales, 678
stellatæ [kidney], 1274
vorticosæ, 1038, 1051
Venous arches, 679
lacunæ of dura mater, 662
mesocardium, 529
plexus, hemorrhoidal, 684
ovarian, 687, 1308
pampiniform, 686, 1290, 1308
pharyngeal, 657
pterygoid, 653
pudendal, 684
spermatic, 686, 1290
uterine, 685
vaginal, 685
vesical, 684
sinuses, 649
of dura mater, 661
development of, 519
valves, right and left, 505
Ventral aorta, development of, 511
cochlear nucleus, 806
fissure of medulla oblongata, 786
lamina, 739
mesogastrium, 1145, 1149
psalterium, 897
pulmonary nerves, 941
spinal artery, 584
spinothalamic fasciculus, 778, 795
Ventricle of fornix, 858
of mid-brain, 824
terminal, of medulla spinalis, 739, 771
Ventricles, of brain, 814, 815, 838, 848
x-ray of, injected with air, 1351
of fornix, 858
of heart, 505, 535, 537
of larynx, 1114, 1116
muscle bundles of, 541
Ventricular folds of larynx, 1116
ligament of larynx, 1116
septum, 506, 539
Ventricularis muscle, 1119
Ventriculus, 1207
dexter, 535
laryngis [Morgagni,] 1116
lateralis, 848
quartus, 814
sinister, 537
tertius, 838
Ventromedian fissure of medulla oblongata, 786
Vermian fossa, 136
Vermiform process or appendix, 1223
Vermis of cerebellum, 808
Vertebra prominens, 80
Vertebræ, 75
cervical, 75, 76
lateral view, x-ray of, 1359
coccygeal, 75, 85
ligaments of, 263, 267
lumbar, 83
muscles, lateral, 376
sacral, 85
thoracic, 81
Vertebral arch, 75
arches, articulations of, 266

Vertebral artery, 582
  canal, 89, 95
  column, 75, 93
    articulations of, 263
    surface form of, 1367
    veins of, 676
  fascia, 368
  foramen, 75, 81
  groove, 94
  notches, 76
  ribs, 101
  veins, 659
  venous plexuses, 676
Vertical lingualis muscle, 1170
  part of palatine bone, 171
Verticalis linguæ muscle, 1170
Vesica fellea, 1243
  urinaria, 1277
Vesical artery, 621
  plexus of nerves, 1020
  of veins, 684
Vesicle, auditory, 1061
  germinal, 20
  lens, 1033
  optic, 747, 1033
  umbilical, 45
Vesicoprostatic plexus of veins,
  684
Vesicouterine excavation, 1197
Vesiculæ seminales, 1279
Vesicular ovarian follicles, 1307
Vestibular arteries, 1090
  bulb, 1319
  fissure, 1082
  ganglion, 1089
  glands, greater, 1319
  lip, 1086
  membrane, 1085
  nerve, 935, 1089
    composition and central con-
      nections of, 884, 886
    nuclei of, 806
Vestibule, aortic, 538
  of internal ear, 1078
  of larynx, 1114
  of mouth, 1151
  of nasal cavity, 1026
  of omental bursa, 1201
  of vagina, 1319
Vestibulospinal fasciculus, 778,
  901
Vestibulum, 1078
Vestigal fold of Marshall, 519,
  530, 651
  of pericardium, 530
Vicq d'Azyr, bundle of, 828, 835,
  898
Vidian artery, 570, 573
  canal, 107,114
  nerve, 922
Vieussens, valve of, 814
Villi, arachnoid, 905
  of chorion, 27, 29, 30
  of intestine, 1219

Visceral arches, 45
  nervous system, 1001
  receptors, 1093
  veins, 515
Visual area of cortex, 873
  centers, 838
  purple, 1046
Visuopsychic, area, 873
Visuosensory area, 873
Vitelline circulation, 35, 502
  duct, 35, 45, 1145
  fluid, 35
  membrane, 25
  veins, 502, 515
Vitellus, 20, 502
Vitreous body of eye, 1035, 1049
Vocal cords, 1116
  folds, 1116
  process of arytenoid cartilage,
    1111
Vocalis muscle, 1119
Voice, organ of, 1108
Volar arches, 600, 604
    surface markings of, 1409
  branch of ulnar verve, 971
  carpal artery, 600
    ligament, 450
    net-work, 600
  digital arteries, 605
    nerves, 967
  interosseous artery, 604
    nerve, 967
  metacarpal arteries, 601
    veins, 671
  venous arches, 671
Volaris indicis radialis artery, 601
Vomer, 174
Vomeronasal cartilage, 1028
  organs, 51, 1028
Vulva, 1317

W

WAGNER and Meissner, corpus-
  cles of, 1092
Waldeyer, germinal epithelium
  of, 1307
  odontoblasts of, 1158
  zona vasculosa of, 1307
Wallenburg, basal olfactory bun-
  dle of, 896
Wallerian degeneration, 765, 777
Wharton's, duct, 1175
  jelly, 35
White fibrocartilage, 258
  nerve-fibers, 757
Willis, circle of, 579
Windpipe, 1121
Winslow, foramen of, 610, 1147
  1195, 1201
Wirsung, duct of, 1247
Wisdom teeth, 1157

Wolffian body, 1254
  duct, 1253
  tubules, 1254
Womb, 1310
Wormian bones, 160
Wrisberg, cardiac ganglion of,
    1015
  cartilages of, 1112
  ligament of, 321
  nerve of, 966
  nervus intermedius of, 930
Wrist and hand of child aged
    eleven years, x-ray of,
      1405
    two-and-a-half years,
      x-ray of, 1404
Wrist-joint, 303
  surface anatomy of, 1402
  tendons in back of, 452
    in front of, 452

X

XIPHOID appendix, 100
  process, 100

Y

Y-SHAPED cartilage of acetabulum, 212
  ligament of Bigelow, 312
Yolk-sac, 35
Yolk-stalk, 1145

Z

ZINN, ligament or tendon of, 1053
  zonule of, 1050
Zona pellucida, 20
  vasculosa of Waldeyer, 1307
Zones of abdomen, 1190
Zonula ciliaris, 1035, 1050
Zonule of Zinn, 1050
Zygomatic arch, 113
  bone, 168
  branch of facial nerve, 935
  nerve, 920
  process of frontal bone, 142
    of maxilla, 165
    of temporal bone, 144
Zygomaticofacial foramen, 116,
    169
  nerve, 920
Zygomaticofrontal stuture, 111
Zygomaticoörbital foramina, 170
Zygomaticotemporal foramen,
    111, 169
  nerve, 920
  suture, 111
Zygomaticus muscle, **357**